MYB
MUNICIPAL YEAR BOOK

EDITOR Dean Wanless
ASSISTANT EDITOR Ali O'Gorman
EDITORIAL DIRECTOR Michael Burton
MANAGING DIRECTOR Graham Bond
MARKETING MANAGER Mustak Kothia

PUBLISHED BY: Hemming Media
A DIVISION OF HEMMING GROUP LTD
32 Vauxhall Bridge Road
t +44 (0)20 7973 6400
f +44 (0)20 7973 4794
e myb@hgluk.com

ISBN 978-0-7079-7149-0

Hemming Media is a division of Hemming Group Ltd.

Founded in 1893 with the launch of The MJ magazine, Hemming Group Ltd is a family owned company, specialising in the provision of business to business information.

Hemming Media deliver several print and online titles in the local government marketplace including: The Municipal Year Book, LocalGov.co.uk, The MJ, Surveyor, the Surveyor Highway Maintenance Yearbook, LAPV and TEC. Hemming Information Services also publishes a selection of private sector directories and magazines including the Retail Directory, Bridge Design and Engineering and Lingerie Buyer.

Other divisions of the Hemming Group include Hemming Conferences, which specialises in organising public sector conferences, and Brintex, the organisers of leading trade fairs such as the LGA Annual Conference and The London International Wine Trade Fair.

The Municipal Year Book was founded in 1897 by Sir Robert Donald, GBE, LLD

A member of the Professional Publishers Association

Letter from the editor

As I sit down to write this letter the news has just been released that the government is blaming under-performing local authorities for the looming care crisis. Unfortunately, local government bashing has become a real theme for the government and the popular press in recent years, unaware of the exceptional amount of work that has gone into retaining a strong standard of services in the face of devastating budget cuts.

The current situation in care is indicative of the agility that we've shown in recent years. Increasingly, local authorities are working more closely with other organisations to ensure that as a high a standard as is possible is achieved for all citizens. This often means working closely with other councils, with other public sector organisations and also with partners in the private and third sectors.

This agility shows that the people in our sector as able to come up with innovative solutions to the many crises that we have faced.

While some may be slow to adopt these new working practises, the potential that digital and smart technologies allow us will make their adoption inevitable over the course of the next decade.

A large part of this potential will be delivered by working more closely with other organisations. This has been a real strength of the Municipal Year Book since its first edition over 100 years ago. We aim to help you to find the details of other local government professionals who are facing the same challenges as you are. By working together, we will find the best solutions to the many obstacles that we face today.

The compilation of a reference book as big as The Municipal Year Book is a long and complicated process and would be impossible without the local government professionals that take the time to ensure that we have the most up-to-date information available. As ever, I must extend my thanks to them.

Thanks also to Ali O'Gorman who has worked tirelessly to finesse the data into our systems and has the unenviable job of proof reading the whole book once it's ready to go to press. Sylke Elder also does invaluable work once the AGMs have been held and the race begins to update councillor information.

Our website, www.municipalyearbook.co.uk, is kept in order by Barry Halper who also steps in to administer the database as required.

Kothia Mustak makes the job of getting Municipal Year Book onto the desks of the right people in the sector look easy. I'm sure it isn't!

I trust that you will find The Municipal Year Book a useful resource and, as ever, we welcome any feedback that you may have.

Dean Wanless
Managing Editor – Municipal Year Book
d.wanless@hgluk.com

Foreword
By Jo Miller -
Chief Executive - Doncaster Metropolitan Borough
Council & President of SOLACE

Happy new year. I hope you, like me will face 2017 with optimistic realism. I find the end of one year and start of another a time to reflect and refocus. I'm looking forward to starting my fifth year as Doncaster's chief executive - one half of a female elected mayor /chief executive duo leading this fantastic place. I have the job of my life and one which I'm excited to do almost every day.

The year ahead is exciting and daunting in equal measure. Daunting because of the very significant challenges of managing ever decreasing resources in an area that has been hardest hit in the nation's unequal and unfair response to austerity. Daunting because 2017 sees all out council elections and elections for an elected mayor of Doncaster. Quite a time too to be President of Solace, speaking out and up for public services and the places we lead.

Whenever I find the daunting bit rising up to equal the exciting bit, I remember how far we have come as a place , and how far we can go, no matter what. Because political and economic cycles come and go, but places and people always prevail. And as Margaret Mead said " Never doubt that a small group of thoughtful, committed citizens can change the world; indeed, it's the only thing that ever has ". That's in our DNA here.

I first came to Doncaster in 2010 on secondment from the LGA when the council was deemed the worst in Britain and was significantly failing its people. My secondment only lasted a few months and at the end of it,I knew I wanted to return because I could see the endless sense of possibility the place presented if only everyone could work together and crack on. So I hot footed it back as soon as possible, taking the chief executive role.

Well, crack on we have, with shoulders to the wheel, grit, determination, hard work and a deep desire to serve our people and serve them well. Looking out rather than looking in, focussing on what we can do rather than what we can't, being clear about what we are fighting for as well as standing against - we've made real, tangible progress. From toxic partner to partner of choice, from lagging behind the sector to help lead it, Doncaster is playing its part.

Doncaster is a city in all but name. We account for 22 per cent of the Sheffield City Region economy though we share no boundary with Sheffield itself. Our economy looks to the rest of South Yorkshire, to Leeds, Wakefield and York, to Scunthorpe, Selby and Goole, and to North Nottinghamshire at the southern end.

The Mayor and I have a relentless focus on growing the economy and the ability of our population to participate in it. We say to businesses we want you to come here and be successful, but we want you to share your success with your workers as progressive employers. We know that as a place we compete with many others for inward investment and growth, so we have to make sure our offer and delivery are pin sharp. The educational attainment and skills base in Yorkshire and the Humber is below the UK average, and in Doncaster it is below even that. Improving education and skills is critical to achieving the inclusive growth we desire.

All of this is about place. We understand this place, its psyche, characteristics, strengths, assets, threats and weaknesses to formulate our response as an organisation to the operating conditions we face. Knowing our place doesn't just impact on what we do and say, but how we say and do it and with/to whom. So, because Doncaster isn't a city, despite its size and characteristics, we know from work with business and local communities that it feels like a somewhat chippy underdog. We've tried to harness that psyche as we pitch for opportunities, like the National High Speed Rail College, currently being built and opening in September 2017

Like many other metropolitan areas, Doncaster has seen a massive reduction in budget in recent times and is set for the same over the next few years, as revenue support grant goes 60 per cent of our income to zero. Alongside efficiency and protecting vital services, our priorities for investment have focussed on growing the economy, and the ability of Doncaster people to participate in it. Place impacts on what we do and how we do it.

It's a strategy that's proving successful. Housebuilding has tripled since 2010 and is at a 12 year high. The number of businesses is growing and we've experienced the second highest growth in business stock in the UK last year. The employment rate is at an 11 year high, with triple the growth rate in Yorkshire and the UK, and NEET levels are reducing - there are more and better jobs. Apprenticeship starts are more than the regional and national average. We are reducing the skills gap and closing the GCSE attainment gap. A great story, but still 75 per cent of businesses employ four people or less, and productivity and wages are low. In the EU referendum, seven out of 10 voters opted to leave the EU.

So good growth is happening, and local people are benefitting, but in the current 'post-fact' society, metrics don't necessarily cut it - which is why our partnership, Team Doncaster, is focussing on telling the human stories that residents and businesses can connect to, to raise their ambition, aspiration and participation.

Despite good progress made, our ambition is high and we know what we need to do to serve our place and people well over these next few years.

Top of the page is Doncaster learning. By 2021 the focus of Doncaster's Education and Skills and support for children and young people will be geared towards skills for life, creativity, employment, and careers alongside academic achievement.

With this, we will reset the bar for attainment and aspiration, so all young people expect to work and pursue fulfilling jobs, careers and live. Without it, our young people will be at risk of underachieving, with consequences for them, their families, the local economy and for public services.

Next, we focus on Doncaster earning. By 2021 our economic growth will be more inclusive. The local economy will continue to grow through inward investment and growth of existing firms. Citizens and businesses of Doncaster will directly benefit by accessing necessary skills, jobs and supply chains, and increasing their incomes.

With this, we will go faster in breaking the cycle of unemployment, low incomes and poverty that has held back generations and driven demand for public services. Without it, we will miss our economic opportunity, and risk social polarisation and loss of hope.

We also need to focus on Doncaster caring. Doncaster's model of adults and children's health and social care, and how we support our most at risk and vulnerable people will be focused on prevention, early intervention and enabling people to be safe, healthy and independent at home and in their communities. We will use the strengths and caring power of our people and communities, working with services as the front line of local, joined up delivery.

With this, our at risk, older, ill and vulnerable citizens will enjoy better lives, and be healthy and independent for longer. Without it, our health & social care system will be unable to cope - limiting access and quality of care and support.

Last but by no means least we focus on Doncaster as a vibrant place of choice to live and work. Citizens will have access to a full range of housing options. Our culture offer and in and out of town centre shopping and relaxation will be at modern city standard. Better quality opportunities for leisure and sports activities and green spaces will enable healthy and fun lifestyles and good transport links across Doncaster will enable access for all.

With this, Doncaster citizens will enjoy a better quality of life, and more money earned in Doncaster will being spent in the local economy, reducing pressure on public services. Without it, other areas will reap the benefits of our growth and Doncaster will not fulfil its potential to be a modern thriving place.

Team Doncaster - the borough's partnership across all sectors with a unifying purpose of ensuring that this place and its people thrive, is at the heart of Doncaster's renaissance and these future plans. Rightly it's a large call on civic leadership, both political and managerial, as we act as first amongst equals to bring together the resources of our place to achieve progress. It's an energising relationship where we focus on what we can do together to achieve progress, rather than what we can't do. At its core, this civic leadership of place is about distributed leadership, collaboration and networks, as we know that we achieve more by loosening power and control whilst maintaining accountability.

I love my job.

Jo Miller - Chief Executive; Doncaster Metropolitan Borough Council & President of SOLACE

local
government
insight from
the people
in the
know...

...from **38p**
per day

For nearly 125 years, **The MJ** has provided the latest news, views and analysis on the issues that matter to you. It is the leading local government publication in the UK and a crucial source of information for the sector.

At a time of unprecedented change within the sector, with huge cuts to budgets, the impact of Brexit, an end to grant funding, devolution, a change in regional economic policy, rising demand and the need to transform services for the future, **The MJ** and themj.co.uk are a vital source of information and best practice to help keep you up to speed with a fast-moving agenda.

A subscription to The MJ cost just 38p per day, **to subscribe simply:**

visit themj.co.uk
call +44 (0)20 7973 6694
customer@hgluk.com

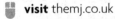

www.themj.co.uk

Contents

User Guide

MAIN COUNCIL CONTACT DETAILS

Under the council heading you will find the full council name followed by its main contact address. For Wales, Scotland and Northern Ireland the council's local language name is listed in brackets after the full council name.

The council type is indicated to the right of the council name.

ELECTION FREQUENCY

This shows the type and frequency of elections held by each local authority. If elections are "of whole council" this means elections are held every four years. If elections are "held by thirds" then one third of the seats are elected for each year for three years out of four.

MEMBERS OF THE COUNCIL

The Municipal Year Book asks local authorities to indicate the Leader and Deputy Leader of the council, the Chair / Mayor / Sheriff / Provost and their deputies and the Group Leaders of the political parties represented on their council.

A full political breakdown can be found in each council entry at the end of the "members of the council" section.

INDICES

An index for local authorities by type can be found at the end of the local authorities listings.

KEY TO POLITICAL PARTIES

ALL	Alliance Party
C	Conservative
CAP	Community Action Party
DUP	Democratic Unionist Party
GRN	Green
IND	Independent
INDNA	Independent (Non-Alligned)
INDU	Independent Unionists
LAB	Labour
LIB	Liberal
LD	Liberal Democrats
NILAB	Northern Ireland Labour Party
O	Other
OFF	Official Unionist
PC	Plaid Cymru
PUP	Progressive Unionist Party
R	Ratepayer or Residents Association
RSP	Respect the Unity Coalition
SD	Social Democrat Party
SF	Sinn Fein
SNP	Scottish National Party
UKIP	UK Independence Party
UU	Ulster Unionists
VCNY	Vacancy
WP	Workers Party

User Guide - Sample Entry

Below is an example of an entry from the Municipal Year Book. This page provides a brief explanation of all of the information contained within the local authority entry.

Council name and type (ie. Unitary, district etc)	**York, City of** U
Main Contact details for the local authority	City of York Council, West Offices, Station Rise, York YO1 6GA ☎ 01904 551550 📠 01904 553560 🖥 www.york.gov.uk
Useful information relating to the council	**FACTS AND FIGURES** **Parliamentary Constituencies:** York Central, York Outer **EU Constituencies:** Yorkshire and the Humber **Election Frequency:** Elections are of whole council
Details of decision making officers	**PRINCIPAL OFFICERS** **Chief Executive:** Mr Steve Stewart, Chief Executive, West Offices, Station Rise, York YO1 6GA ☎ 01904 552000 ✆ steve.stewart@york.gov.uk
Full list of council members	**COUNCILLORS** *Leader of the Council* **Steward**, Chris (CON - Rural West York) cllr.csteward@york.gov.uk
Overall political composition of the council	**POLITICAL COMPOSITION** LAB: 15, CON: 14, LD: 12, GRN: 4, IND: 2
Details of committee chairs.	**COMMITTEE CHAIRS** **Licensing:** Ms Helen Douglas

Local Government in Figures

Types of local authority

County	27	Unitary	55
District	201	Scottish Unitary	32
London	33	Welsh Unitary	22
Metropolitan	36	Northern Ireland	11
		TOTAL	**417**

Most populous authorities

Kent	1427.4	Hertfordshire	1107.5
Essex	1413	Birmingham City	1036.9
Hampshire	1296.8	Norfolk	862.3
Lancashire	1169.3	Staffordshire	831.3
Surrey	1127.3	West Sussex	799.7

Average population of local authorities by type ('000s) - 2011

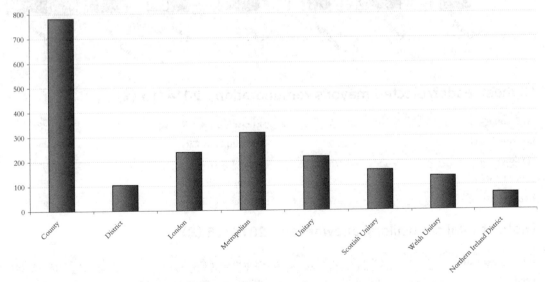

Highest gross budgets - 2014/15 (£'000s)

Birmingham City	3,008,400,000	Hampshire	1,933,610,000
Glasgow, City of	2,230,781,000	Essex	1,868,879,000
Lancashire	2,213,800,000	Surrey	1,785,434,000
Kent	2,201,666,000	Edinburgh, City of	1,783,115,000
Leeds City	2,028,187,000	Hertfordshire	1,626,340,000

Highest net budgets - 2014/15 (£'000s)

Glasgow, City of	1,449,577,000	Edinburgh, City of	925,098,000
Kent	960,005,000	Birmingham City	881,300,000
Surrey	952,010,000	Hampshire	858,144,000
Essex	947,083,000	Fife	763,436,000
Lancashire	932,100,000	Hertfordshire	747,979,000

Average gross & net budgets by local authority type - 2014/15 (£'000s)

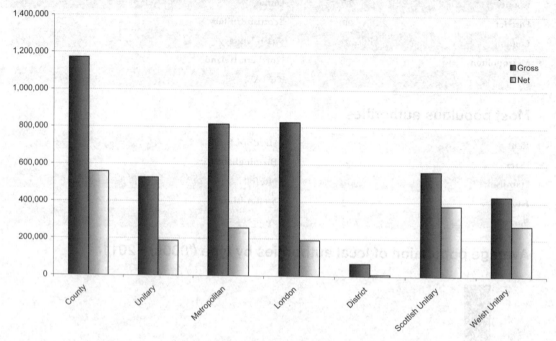

Highest leader/elected mayor's remuneration - 2014/15 (£)

Newham	81,029	Kensington & Chelsea	66,788
Liverpool City	79,500	Birmingham City	66,619
Hackney	79,073	Bristol City	66,396
Salford City	69,000	Wandsworth	65,366
Lewisham	67,909	Wiltshire Unitary	63,820

Highest total councillors' allowances - 2014/15 (£)

Birmingham City	2,700,000	Manchester City	1,957,000
Leeds City	2,138,984	Wiltshire Unitary	1,938,000
Durham	2,038,000	Surrey	1,926,000
Bradford City	2,002,940	Kent	1,768,000
Cornwall	1,980,000	Highland	1,764,000

Highest chief executive salaries - 2014/15 (£)

Wandsworth	219,089	Hampshire	208,513
Surrey	216,242	Essex	205,972
Southwark	216,236	Coventry City	205,675
Buckinghamshire	216,175	Manchester City	203,934
Sunderland	209,468	Westminster City	203,387

Average chief executive salaries by local authority type - 2014/15 (£)

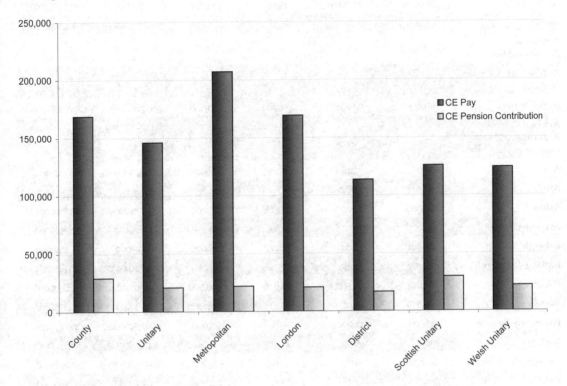

Remuneration & budget data - 2014/15

Council	Chief Executive Salary 2014/15 (£)	Chief Executive Pension 2014/15 (£)	Leaders' Allowance 2014/15 (£)	Total Members' Allowances 2014/15 (£)	Gross Budget 2014/15 (£'000)	Net Budget 2014/15 (£'000)
Aberdeen City	144,686	27,648	37,477	540,439	711,133,000	461,085,000
Aberdeenshire	134,540	17,353	38,642	1,665,000	805,035,000	600,833,000
Adur	104,283	19,501	13,050	161,634	47,417,000	7,132,000
Allerdale	100,000	12,600	23,967	265,733	53,215,000	15,010,000
Amber Valley	81,000	10,000	15,190	232,000	58,514,000	17,408,000
Angus	130,421	22,343	33,123	362,528	348,272,000	243,053,000
Antrim & Newtownabbey						
Ards & North Down Borough						
Argyll & Bute	121,817	23,038	32,960	820,000	310,966,000	239,388,000
Armagh City, Banbridge & Craigavon						
Arun	102,944	19,480	19,279	472,000	81,954,000	874,000
Ashfield	106,012	12,608,000		390,457	77,479,000	9,045,000
Ashford	129,000	17,000	25,568	327,000	63,590,000	-14,374,000
Aylesbury Vale	148,000	34,000	21,888	457,000	93,785,000	23,356,000
Babergh	120,901	20,847	11,927	228,000	38,195,000	-4,242,000
Barking & Dagenham	123,197	6,188	45,028	816,000	856,840,000	146,687,000
Barnet	187,613	48,592	38,026	1,206,000	930,307,000	258,155,000
Barnsley	170,000	36,000	36,346	912,000	582,340,000	134,541,000
Barrow-in-Furness	93,000	12,000		125,000	48,635,000	7,865,000
Basildon	118,417		22,445	390,000	164,954,000	19,132,000
Basingstoke & Deane	85,630	10,753	23,619	589,431	89,690,000	31,296,000
Bassetlaw	100,741	13,485	17,777	328,000	63,562,000	-2,259,000
Bath & North East Somerset	150,000	31,500	38,367	796,394	404,689,000	155,618,000
Bedford	170,000	23,877	60,933	634,000	351,410,000	149,475,000
Belfast City						
Bexley	185,397	41,262	45,809	833,000	495,246,000	210,877,000
Birmingham City	182,500	38,872	66,619	2,700,000	3,008,400,000	881,300,000
Blaby	100,000	17,100	14,973	238,241	31,666,667	10,608,754
Blackburn with Darwen	141,000	17,000	22,701	528,000	438,357,000	158,355,000
Blackpool	98,593	12,127	26,351	517,000	397,715,000	149,062,000
Blaenau Gwent	114,566	24,632	42,300	776,000	219,026,000	139,817,000
Bolsover	115,000	14,835	24,118	454,000	50,151,000	783,000
Bolton	176,530	31,021	40,864	866,000	697,569,000	229,936,000
Boston	87,850		12,470	194,000	37,407,000	8,264,000
Bournemouth	125,000	23,000	26,943	768,000	468,522,000	181,421,000

Council	Chief Executive Salary 2014/15 (£)	Chief Executive Pension 2014/15 (£)	Leaders' Allowance 2014/15 (£)	Total Members' Allowances 2014/15 (£)	Gross Budget 2014/15 (£'000)	Net Budget 2014/15 (£'000)
Bracknell Forest	159,600	20,000	37,641	583,000	288,069,000	128,815,000
Bradford City	178,476	16,730	49,432	2,002,940	1,304,297,000	438,842,000
Braintree	130,000	20,000	32,162	428,000	74,813,000	19,653,000
Breckland	108,611	15,205		452,000	65,147,000	13,048,000
Brent	193,698	0		1,035,694	1,075,495,000	134,398,000
Brentwood	102,000	3,912	19,036	281,000	41,813,000	2,194,000
Bridgend	128,169	26,051	48,000	1,079,000	466,020,000	318,614,000
Brighton & Hove	160,099	29,618	26,856	856,000	750,241,000	197,689,000
Bristol City	180,617	31,839	66,396	1,059,000	1,035,601,000	297,872,000
Broadland	108,093	14,921	13,940	237,525	42,937,000	11,313,000
Bromley	180,061	0		1,013,000	561,997,000	203,781,000
Bromsgrove	127,500	13,897	16,933	258,000	44,772,000	18,620,000
Broxbourne	98,017	18,129	18,267	247,000	69,021,000	18,918,000
Broxtowe	105,757	21,725	19,332	312,000	56,865,000	7,754,000
Buckinghamshire	216,175	48,860	50,931	983,000	760,296,000	366,336,000
Burnley	80,305	10,681	13,500	176,761	73,070,000	20,438,000
Bury					498,864,000	157,986,000
Caerphilly	137,000	28,496	45,600	1,211,214	521,860,000	297,679,000
Calderdale	146,000	21,000	33,814	699,000	483,173,000	209,293,000
Cambridge City	117,859	20,961	18,245	244,295	105,429,000	-629,000
Cambridgeshire	190,383	37,794	29,856	810,577	777,327,000	341,275,000
Camden	160,567	28,238	38,370	865,000	956,304,000	207,281,000
Cannock Chase	112,890	19,496	23,489	376,628	67,945,000	10,361,000
Canterbury City	110,000	16,000		386,029	112,015,000	15,841,000
Cardiff	166,937	38,228	52,662	1,289,268	1,049,558,000	573,228,000
Carlisle City	97,000	13,000	14,490	343,000	64,063,000	18,849,000
Carmarthenshire	168,938	0	48,000	1,284,569	616,962,000	394,461,000
Castle Point	133,000	0	20,093	242,000	45,419,000	4,023,000
Causeway Coast & Glens						
Central Bedfordshire	181,300	44,237	42,333	1,233,000	489,403,000	189,177,000
Ceredigion	108,226	16,421	42,300	806,000	211,554,000	142,096,000
Charnwood	115,631	29,609	16,700	371,000	66,075,000	-550,000
Chelmsford	131,851	17,463	27,282	502,000	117,477,000	34,085,000
Cheltenham	109,764	17,641	21,494	319,472	82,243,000	13,268,000
Cherwell	127,512	18,655	17,664	314,000	73,747,000	21,937,000
Cheshire East	173,682	38,070	38,318	1,447,000	673,994,000	306,658,000
Cheshire West & Chester	180,000	10,000	40,103	1,391,000	694,481,000	257,954,000
Chesterfield	104,626	13,794	32,206	349,000	107,151,000	3,165,000
Chichester	114,690	19,841	18,112	311,000	744,448,000	14,508,000

Council	Chief Executive Salary 2014/15 (£)	Chief Executive Pension 2014/15 (£)	Leaders' Allowance 2014/15 (£)	Total Members' Allowances 2014/15 (£)	Gross Budget 2014/15 (£'000)	Net Budget 2014/15 (£'000)
Chiltern	128,000	13,605	17,940	278,000	38,213,000	9,841,000
Chorley	108,000	12,000	21,616	296,000	50,795,000	13,746,000
Christchurch	136,742		14,252	152,000	30,877,000	7,894,000
City of London	122,000	11,000			315,600,000	142,800,000
Clackmannanshire	96,990	19,883	18,244	403,454	179,957,000	110,902,000
Colchester	121,144	16,643	26,292	550,000	111,139,000	-3,102,000
Conwy	111,573	21,310	47,500	1,064,000	318,184,000	200,625,000
Copeland						
Corby	94,000	30,000	17,971	172,000	54,685,000	3,284,000
Cornwall	162,000	26,730	32,450	1,980,000	1,200,275,000	534,704,000
Cotswold	117,200	12,603	16,000	262,873	44,120,854	-761,533
Coventry City	205,675	38,878	36,602	971,000	820,138,000	345,887,000
Craven	95,475	14,067	12,470	158,000	23,009,000	5,487,000
Crawley	121,753	19,731	18,614	326,000	129,123,000	14,005,000
Croydon	180,000	23,580	62,352	1,580,000	1,071,829,000	283,392,000
Cumbria	140,000	18,200	31,107	1,058,000	851,281,000	442,993,000
Dacorum	128,443	19,783	19,804	381,000	111,734,000	-10,993,000
Darlington	151,220	27,976	31,792	629,172	237,672,000	76,244,000
Dartford	107,506	0	39,661	342,000	59,897,000	331,000
Daventry	119,732	13,881	15,262	261,437	31,376,000	10,662,000
Denbighshire	132,144	16,583	42,770	843,000	316,722,000	193,521,000
Derby City	133,333	25,680	40,305	810,000	684,569,000	225,343,000
Derbyshire	140,749	27,488	42,816	1,019,000	1,253,016,000	572,610,000
Derbyshire Dales	100,000	13,000	14,660	210,000	35,512,000	9,299,000
Derry City & Strabane						
Devon	149,995	28,199	35,970	1,028,869	1,142,815,000	601,380,000
Doncaster	149,000	19,221	30,000	987,786	639,920,000	212,184,000
Dorset	146,000	30,000	31,778	735,000	746,735,000	380,035,000
Dover	115,000	17,000	18,812	270,000	71,949,000	-3,540,000
Dudley	129,000	0	27,474	867,000	719,948,000	206,559,000
Dumfries & Galloway	135,380	29,107	33,123	972,000	451,842,000	356,960,000
Dundee City	97,789	55,000	33,123	613,979	569,405,000	375,474,000
Durham	200,000	0	49,875	2,038,000	1,576,250,000	728,377,000
Ealing	170,631	0	41,808	1,001,000	1,110,440,000	244,897,000
East Ayrshire	127,054	23,946	33,434	363,691	430,767,000	291,508,000
East Cambridgeshire	126,642	27,228	11,185	207,013	37,964,760	10,162,403
East Devon	128,000	18,000	18,781	397,000	92,031,000	17,148,000
East Dorset	115,000	16,215	16,452	197,000	38,279,000	10,627,000
East Dunbartonshire	119,223	23,589	32,123	284,582	296,086,000	233,036,000
East Hampshire	95,227	12,462		305,000	50,214,000	14,970,000

Council	Chief Executive Salary 2014/15 (£)	Chief Executive Pension 2014/15 (£)	Leaders' Allowance 2014/15 (£)	Total Members' Allowances 2014/15 (£)	Gross Budget 2014/15 (£'000)	Net Budget 2014/15 (£'000)
East Hertfordshire	115,150	19,090	24,395	389,000	69,871,000	18,887,000
East Lindsey	105,000	16,800	19,446	366,000	86,680,000	19,104,000
East Lothian	110,551	23,401	27,329	450,586	287,206,000	209,386,000
East Northamptonshire	104,000	31,000	11,945	240,000	36,411,000	9,764,000
East Renfrewshire	115,678	21,348	27,602	384,698	279,974,000	202,513,000
East Riding of Yorkshire	170,000	26,000	46,741	46,741	676,022,000	244,000,000
East Staffordshire	120,000	18,240		258,795	55,352,000	15,624,000
East Sussex	184,738	37,502	35,698	894,000	818,143,000	391,266,000
Eastbourne	113,330	22,849		137,000	90,172,000	5,486,000
Eastleigh	99,434	12,956	25,939	382,000	80,091,000	18,113,000
Eden			8,568	203,000	22,983,000	8,770,000
Edinburgh, City of	161,741	34,450	49,683	1,298,098	1,783,115,000	925,098,000
Elmbridge	127,011	19,664	16,635	373,898	79,812,000	15,851,000
Enfield	188,955	0	35,774	900,000	1,186,200,000	312,700,000
Epping Forest	112,000	17,808	15,050	316,000	96,733,000	-243,000
Epsom & Ewell	106,000	16,000	5,624	157,000	45,537,000	9,052,000
Erewash	110,234	28,534	16,602	276,161	55,461,000	14,535,000
Essex	205,972	25,830	63,395	1,556,000	1,868,879,000	947,083,000
Exeter City	110,000	25,190	21,250	264,000	96,154,000	11,240,000
Falkirk	129,141	58,000	33,123	378,625	520,087,000	357,790,000
Fareham	131,741	15,540	26,266	412,000	45,218,000	2,830,000
Fenland					53,957,000	14,500,000
Fermanagh & Omagh						
Fife	144,981	31,606	38,520	498,877	1,097,058,000	763,436,000
Flintshire	131,233	32,967	47,933	1,366,000	419,057,000	266,904,000
Forest Heath	148,734		14,889	205,000	30,522,000	7,677,000
Forest of Dean	84,640	12,104	14,090	290,355	40,505,000	10,290,000
Fylde	92,000	11,000		242,000	36,775,000	8,431,000
Gateshead	158,307	24,854	31,030	1,052,000	573,924,000	174,405,000
Gedling	98,334	12,095	17,683	284,000	49,899,000	13,951,000
Glasgow, City of			49,536	1,725,000	2,230,781,000	1,449,577,000
Gloucester City			22,803	291,000	78,187,000	19,652,000
Gloucestershire	161,235	16,768	36,000	768,000	826,217,000	414,689,000
Gosport	101,034	13,213	19,482	89,000	57,408,000	6,201,000
Gravesham	114,800	0	23,707	220,000	63,638,000	-29,251,000
Great Yarmouth	154,225	0	12,943	208,409	83,509,000	9,096,000
Greenwich	110,833	20,504	55,795	931,487	736,101,000	79,706,000
Guildford	127,951	18,213	8,800	302,631	108,814,000	9,147,000
Gwynedd	103,805	23,252	48,000	1,327,000	341,252,000	221,345,000

Council	Chief Executive Salary 2014/15 (£)	Chief Executive Pension 2014/15 (£)	Leaders' Allowance 2014/15 (£)	Total Members' Allowances 2014/15 (£)	Gross Budget 2014/15 (£'000)	Net Budget 2014/15 (£'000)
Hackney	177,725	34,600	79,073	1,164,000	1,031,407,000	62,255,000
Halton	168,900	35,100	29,568	748,232	345,106,000	126,819,000
Hambleton	100,980	1,288	25,887	239,061	38,816,688	52,114
Hammersmith & Fulham	185,000	27,270	41,126	816,000	644,687,000	140,814,000
Hampshire	208,513	23,340	40,970	1,414,000	1,933,610,000	858,144,000
Harborough						
Haringey	200,313	48,874	41,997	1,105,000	1,065,177,000	189,501,000
Harlow	105,705	15,433	11,110	181,000	146,894,000	38,686,000
Harrogate	116,130	17,728	15,506	365,000	90,072,000	11,999,000
Harrow	171,894	0	39,740	846,000	525,527,000	117,840,000
Hart	93,363	12,110	15,977	209,000	40,036,000	9,440,000
Hartlepool	116,667	16,567	24,757	270,528	257,523,000	95,522,000
Hastings	86,663	20,503	21,783	273,000	85,424,000	17,921,000
Havant	130,066	17,019	19,112	3,335,000	62,283,000	14,968,000
Havering	88,517	0	55,256	928,553	516,570,000	151,204,000
Herefordshire	144,006	21,169		600,000	368,700,000	168,700,000
Hertfordshire	173,760	35,795	49,395	1,441,000	1,626,340,000	747,979,000
Hertsmere	139,000	24,000		332,000	67,557,000	15,377,000
High Peak	120,798	20,052	12,907	188,011	43,220,000	-5,541,000
Highland	155,878	26,838	39,028	1,764,000	808,893,000	561,034,000
Hillingdon	198,571	43,874	56,163	1,342,000	630,335,000	150,347,000
Hinckley & Bosworth	136,712	22,421	16,213	207,299	46,022,000	3,082,000
Horsham	123,781	21,649	15,237	343,000	74,259,000	23,232,000
Hounslow	179,828	40,572	36,476	806,000	716,600,000	175,400,000
Huntingdonshire	125,955	22,250	18,245	397,000	79,268,000	19,330,000
Hyndburn	116,144	32,805		277,441	48,536,000	13,071,000
Inverclyde	116,949	62,548	385,327	27,602	263,250,000	192,292,000
Ipswich	99,225	16,968		287,000	133,018,000	19,482,000
Isle of Anglesey	92,000	4,000	43,000	677,000	201,436,000	127,119,000
Isle of Wight	102,638	0	23,102	485,000	334,384,000	145,837,000
Islington	160,000	20,000	47,214	835,000	977,660,000	215,864,000
Kensington & Chelsea	186,000	17,401	66,788	1,129,000	610,534,000	153,274,000
Kent	200,950	42,199	54,914	1,768,000	2,201,666,000	960,005,000
Kettering	98,000	12,000	18,401	296,000	45,806,000	-4,479,000
King's Lynn & West Norfolk	129,470	18,126	19,900	444,000	81,024,000	20,365,000
Kingston upon Hull City	129,543	19,172	29,943	1,026,000	708,779,000	181,031,000
Kingston upon Thames	119,000	0	40,294	670,155	385,229,000	128,314,000
Kirklees	156,907	21,653		37,721	977,313,000	165,391,000

Council	Chief Executive Salary 2014/15 (£)	Chief Executive Pension 2014/15 (£)	Leaders' Allowance 2014/15 (£)	Total Members' Allowances 2014/15 (£)	Gross Budget 2014/15 (£'000)	Net Budget 2014/15 (£'000)
Knowsley	160,000	40,800	35,653	882,000	559,088,000	136,487,000
Lambeth	190,000	0		1,266,000	1,132,778,000	241,469,000
Lancashire	170,000	21,420	39,952	1,300,000	2,213,800,000	932,100,000
Lancaster City	107,000	14,000	14,360	283,000	113,517,000	22,253,000
Leeds City	176,645	25,573	50,577	2,138,984	2,028,187,000	701,692,000
Leicester City	127,485	25,128	57,710	981,694	1,045,960,000	301,245,000
Leicestershire	187,000	40,000	46,380	1,100,000	750,500,000	361,800,000
Lewes	100,000	21,000	17,036	193,000	54,450,000	-6,968,000
Lewisham	115,432	29,211	67,909	997,000	1,241,773,000	437,906,000
Lichfield	100,283	22,418	15,157	275,000	43,935,000	11,525,000
Lincoln City	109,294	18,471	14,450	224,465	88,805,000	10,908,000
Lincolnshire	173,392	34,125	31,100	1,347,000	1,042,507,000	547,657,000
Lisburn City & Castlereagh						
Liverpool City	199,500	26,949	79,500	1,267,000	1,297,155,000	435,010,000
Luton	193,148	24,418		446,000	587,058,000	182,722,000
Maidstone	114,000	17,000	21,956	340,867	89,699,000	23,865,000
Maldon	104,000	14,000		232,000	30,135,000	8,656,000
Malvern Hills	102,211	10,408	16,800	242,143	34,425,000	8,602,000
Manchester City	203,934	0	57,032	1,957,000	1,480,336,000	484,791,000
Mansfield	46,000	6,000	53,682	463,095	95,854,000	17,269,000
Medway	155,967	27,124	34,374	762,000	610,853,000	212,296,000
Melton	93,696	13,485	16,900	188,000	26,880,000	3,622,000
Mendip	91,853	11,815	14,315	254,000	55,827,000	14,222,000
Merthyr Tydfil	115,192	27,877	42,140	721,000	175,444,000	113,568,000
Merton	185,000	25,715	43,470	730,000	529,209,000	192,699,000
Mid & East Antrim						
Mid Devon	82,183	15,214	18,580	298,000	49,236,000	7,408,000
Mid Suffolk	175,377		14,678	246,000	43,590,000	4,351,000
Mid Sussex	110,000	18,454	25,097	381,792	59,921,389	13,877,313
Mid Ulster District						
Middlesbrough	140,000	20,160	61,300	569,000	390,617,000	144,748,000
Midlothian	111,461	22,274	27,602	176,743	302,375,000	219,654,000
Milton Keynes	160,873	27,944	40,000	784,000	523,856,000	64,983,000
Mole Valley	91,498	15,011	7,690	213,000	48,217,000	13,596,000
Monmouthshire	110,000	23,210	56,300	806,000	216,783,000	142,986,000
Moray	105,803	20,417	27,878	526,010	275,566,000	208,768,000
Neath Port Talbot	134,253	21,749	33,460	1,211,000	421,012,000	275,273,000
New Forest	104,721	0	25,226	477,740	100,856,000	9,263,000
Newark & Sherwood	113,490	14,186	13,829	231,330	63,524,000	1,483,000
Newcastle upon Tyne City	155,395	0	25,325	928,000	865,772,000	177,685,000

Council	Chief Executive Salary 2014/15 (£)	Chief Executive Pension 2014/15 (£)	Leaders' Allowance 2014/15 (£)	Total Members' Allowances 2014/15 (£)	Gross Budget 2014/15 (£'000)	Net Budget 2014/15 (£'000)
Newcastle-under-Lyme	113,139	19,368		323,126	60,459,000	17,460,000
Newham	195,000	51,784	81,029	1,237,000	1,133,133,000	91,145,000
Newport City			48,000	915,862		
Newry City, Mourne & Down						
Norfolk	180,000	27,900	35,657	1,061,000	1,326,199,000	698,849,000
North Ayrshire	131,078	25,298	33,454	605,650	522,196,000	330,534,000
North Devon	105,912	14,828	19,128	305,391	52,395,000	14,095,000
North Dorset	130,000	16,120	14,674	238,000	32,049,000	10,605,000
North East Derbyshire			22,232	390,000	80,971,000	10,935,000
North East Lincolnshire	135,000	20,250		489,000	285,508,000	128,893,000
North Hertfordshire	117,205	17,547	17,100	332,000	70,109,000	20,469,000
North Kesteven	110,352	20,070	17,708	317,000	53,023,000	6,318,000
North Lanarkshire	162,362	48,551	36,462	1,488,679	1,049,337,000	747,301,000
North Lincolnshire	129,699	28,923		568,000	339,178,000	152,619,000
North Norfolk	108,358	15,712	16,220	298,943	50,373,000	11,934,000
North Somerset	147,000	34,178		661,794	434,445,000	167,242,000
North Tyneside	144,625	23,454	61,734	731,000	562,131,000	146,733,000
North Warwickshire	103,036	14,940		230,000	42,256,000	6,332,000
North West Leicestershire	120,651	21,717	18,900	221,884	50,336,000	3,288,000
North Yorkshire	168,691	24,414	33,698	969,000	983,918,000	417,342,000
Northampton	138,000	20,000		427,000	182,609,000	9,320,000
Northamptonshire	184,000	24,000		910,000	909,233,000	453,301,000
Northumberland	143,937	22,643	31,940	1,528,000	761,533,000	286,084,000
Norwich City	132,997	18,543	16,515	350,804	111,536,000	-50,697,000
Nottingham City	160,000	0	46,326	1,093,000	1,017,411,000	313,666,000
Nottinghamshire	169,499	33,137	45,098	1,443,060	1,123,292,000	513,645,000
Nuneaton & Bedworth	82,248			274,000	77,193,000	1,632,000
Oadby & Wigston	97,000	24,000	11,270	153,441	27,580,000	10,730,000
Oldham	166,000	29,000	36,956	990,000	554,245,000	167,719,000
Orkney	102,417	39,067	27,878	433,000	125,680,000	93,722,000
Oxford City	144,232	29,712	26,449	329,000	173,242	28,105,000
Oxfordshire	75,600	15,044	39,390	887,000	876,455,000	481,435,000
Pembrokeshire	87,342	13,451		1,100,250	525,036,000	387,348,000
Pendle			7,000	173,828	53,631,000	17,356,000
Perth & Kinross	129,941	22,103	33,454	785,210	430,562,000	321,985,000
Peterborough City	169,106	27,514	29,460	667,000	472,784,000	163,500,000
Plymouth City	150,000	20,550	41,472	983,000	593,908,000	225,644,000
Poole	114,711	21,777	30,589	547,000	266,185,000	83,919,000

Council	Chief Executive Salary 2014/15 (£)	Chief Executive Pension 2014/15 (£)	Leaders' Allowance 2014/15 (£)	Total Members' Allowances 2014/15 (£)	Gross Budget 2014/15 (£'000)	Net Budget 2014/15 (£'000)
Portsmouth City	148,885	19,504	29,481	600,000	534,485,000	143,007,000
Powys	138,000	32,000	40,000	1,236,000	441,548,000	308,092,000
Preston	122,000	14,000	13,826	286,000	87,226,000	21,522,000
Purbeck	87,000	12,000	13,848	171,000	24,350,000	6,521,000
Reading	135,000	22,545	23,446	449,922	384,051,000	74,301,000
Redbridge	95,567	0	42,138	910,000	817,358,000	203,547,000
Redcar & Cleveland	145,239	21,931	22,440	770,000	312,289,000	114,079,000
Redditch	127,500	14,408	11,607	150,000	64,733,000	1,027,000
Reigate & Banstead	146,000	26,000	18,764	416,379	92,597,000	23,684,000
Renfrewshire	137,400	62,000	33,117	805,818	591,608,000	365,438,000
Rhondda Cynon Taff	142,000	30,000	53,000	1,447,300	686,300,000	452,955,000
Ribble Valley	108,735	9,663		211,152	20,703,405	7,121,919
Richmond upon Thames	147,162	39,439	35,650	684,000	439,838,000	171,747,000
Richmondshire	95,325	13,822	7,920	133,722	25,220,825	3,421,033
Rochdale	129,000	24,000	26,520	731,000	552,657,000	203,044,000
Rochford	109,164	15,064	25,500	284,000	33,737,000	9,289,000
Rossendale						
Rother	90,000	18,000	16,613	222,000	49,733,000	12,556,000
Rotherham	160,000	0	37,217	1,103,000	609,295,000	187,034,000
Rugby			23,957	363,638	62,611,000	3,715,000
Runnymede	121,561	0	11,476	193,000	30,499,000	-19,695,000
Rushcliffe	120,809	15,340	19,328	317,000	36,641,000	12,571,000
Rushmoor	125,219	0	19,366	294,066	67,169,000	19,343,000
Rutland	116,981	23,045		181,000	61,238,000	35,632,000
Ryedale	104,460	15,042	10,595	132,000	25,461,000	8,188,000
Salford City	155,450	28,206	69,000	963,000	694,145,000	238,631,000
Sandwell	138,733	18,209	25,500	1,231,000	825,465,000	172,049,000
Scarborough	106,370	17,346	19,808	266,000	81,934,000	20,530,000
Scottish Borders	128,617	21,746	33,123	758,000	321,892,000	252,522,000
Sedgemoor	132,282	15,899	23,435	357,000	72,134,000	9,527,000
Sefton	135,059	34,018	29,905	770,000	614,510,000	209,973,000
Selby	95,000	12,000	14,404	197,000	38,751,000	3,949,000
Sevenoaks	141,447	4,358	20,964	378,000	52,129,000	14,360,000
Sheffield City	184,588	35,072	7,477	1,245,000	1,274,062,000	390,900,000
Shepway	134,492	15,632	25,537	324,000	67,979,000	-2,377,000
Shetland	101,033	19,000	27,933	496,000	183,916,000	121,300,000
Shropshire Unitary	101,466	13,698	34,542	1,205,000	594,823,000	225,582,000
Slough	157,479	18,425	26,384	472,000	348,645,000	100,467,000
Solihull	132,271	8,214	26,888	543,000	486,387,000	155,714,000
Somerset	151,400	20,400	39,250	860,000	808,832,000	379,393,000

Council	Chief Executive Salary 2014/15 (£)	Chief Executive Pension 2014/15 (£)	Leaders' Allowance 2014/15 (£)	Total Members' Allowances 2014/15 (£)	Gross Budget 2014/15 (£'000)	Net Budget 2014/15 (£'000)
South Ayrshire	128,517	24,563	33,447	606,834	490,557,000	298,567,000
South Bucks	93,750	12,487	14,637	171,000	35,012,000	9,908,000
South Cambridgeshire	123,636	23,931	15,379	381,354	69,912,000	2,471,000
South Derbyshire	121,000	15,488	24,693	351,000	46,048,000	7,793,000
South Gloucestershire	155,724	30,055	32,433	1,077,000	620,662,000	254,553,000
South Hams	94,000	13,900	19,679	251,000	49,453,000	12,531,000
South Holland			24,279	361,000	45,902,000	3,446,000
South Kesteven	120,000	21,000	19,311	368,231	71,244,000	2,455,000
South Lakeland	104,984	14,908		277,000	46,750,000	14,023,000
South Lanarkshire	167,380	31,736	39,028	420,129	985,389,000	667,324,000
South Norfolk	127,126	21,506	14,632	305,216	57,124,000	16,055,000
South Northamptonshire	129,744	20,302	14,048	310,000	38,365,000	20,222,000
South Oxfordshire	134,919	16,595	23,067	254,000	61,223,000	18,059,000
South Ribble	106,662	13,546	18,277	322,000	44,416,000	15,570,000
South Somerset	61,000	22,000		546,000	81,034,000	21,359,000
South Staffordshire	97,075	15,762	15,000	304,343	43,157,000	12,054,000
South Tyneside	152,813	24,204	33,722	839,000	521,391,000	179,569,000
Southampton City	166,786	21,849	33,064	654,000	626,364,000	185,873,000
Southend-on-Sea	120,296	0	34,020	625,000	433,132,000	138,397,000
Southwark	216,236	30,465	60,664	1,246,075	1,201,172,000	319,568,000
Spelthorne	114,688	19,250		259,000	60,982,000	16,723,000
St. Albans City	100,900	30,200	19,110	421,000	79,592,000	5,437,000
St. Edmundsbury	111,050	26,338	15,794	327,000	63,474,000	13,875,000
St. Helens	140,000	18,000		575,000	420,504,000	141,929,000
Stafford	88,293	14,775	11,114	254,248	58,366,000	15,414,000
Staffordshire	103,551	20,343	44,265	1,000,000	1,202,900,000	454,900,000
Staffordshire Moorlands	157,775	26,191	12,467	253,664	33,983,000	11,491,000
Stevenage	101,600	8,026	28,277	447,314	48,093,000	-49,176,000
Stirling	107,478	23,283	27,043	428,300	284,138,000	205,757,000
Stockport	180,584	0		905,000	674,122,000	235,219,000
Stockton-on-Tees	165,191	23,622	34,300	698,323	458,469,000	144,448,000
Stoke-on-Trent City	195,000	23,449	43,790	777,000	643,008,000	219,127,000
Stratford-upon-Avon	115,581	14,656	15,275	325,000	53,114,000	17,534,000
Stroud	110,569	32,257	14,451	329,000	72,297,000	7,237,000
Suffolk	155,000	40,300	35,599	1,181,000	1,060,036,000	551,102,000
Suffolk Coastal	172,987		19,772	253,000	73,975,000	362,000
Sunderland	209,468	33,300	46,036	1,152,000	642,569,000	261,433,000
Surrey	216,242	32,004	30,400	1,926,000	1,785,434,000	952,010,000
Surrey Heath	115,000	11,000	18,386	281,000	39,652,000	13,974,000
Sutton	167,355	29,120	51,379	897,000	451,530,000	156,840,000

Council	Chief Executive Salary 2014/15 (£)	Chief Executive Pension 2014/15 (£)	Leaders' Allowance 2014/15 (£)	Total Members' Allowances 2014/15 (£)	Gross Budget 2014/15 (£'000)	Net Budget 2014/15 (£'000)
Swale	149,000	46,000		380,000	85,882,000	14,558,000
Swansea, City of	140,000	0		1,287,000	761,339,000	438,482,000
Swindon	145,668	25,056		630,000	533,294,000	180,134,000
Tameside	1,666,929	32,718	47,676	1,197,000	491,492,000	143,391,000
Tamworth	112,987	17,773	18,239	238,000	54,026,000	4,741,000
Tandridge	127,321	21,008		218,000	67,055,000	15,198,000
Taunton Deane	120,000	0		330,000	80,500,000	9,540,000
Teignbridge	118,860	22,345	23,358	355,748	77,009,000	24,823,000
Telford & Wrekin	137,000	16,619	31,638	618,000	438,033,000	124,981,000
Tendring	121,670	17,881	23,550	469,000	105,134,000	13,061,000
Test Valley	136,000	18,000	18,871	442,000	61,844,000	20,270,000
Tewkesbury	111,239	16,170	15,600	337,904	34,881,303	9,432,382
Thanet	116,500	15,123		369,000	133,310,000	21,543,000
Three Rivers	121,515	19,018	13,161	253,000	46,671,000	14,296,000
Thurrock	170,000	11,628	38,040	671,000	316,351,000	81,242,000
Tonbridge & Malling	112,000	17,000	23,196	405,000	61,780,000	16,117,000
Torbay	137,000	13,000	35,467	432,000	283,300,000	122,500,000
Torfaen	114,212	25,149	42,300	957,000	280,397,000	177,663,000
Torridge	83,474	15,693		227,000	32,900,000	7,721,000
Tower Hamlets	181,043	27,160	24,222	788,000	1,250,192,000	260,661,000
Trafford	163,389	27,263	41,708	703,000	398,125,000	132,690,000
Tunbridge Wells	118,335	14,472	24,750	363,973	66,211,000	12,906,000
Uttlesford	105,000	14,199	14,371	275,000	40,149,000	198,000
Vale of Glamorgan	109,094	24,764	47,940	847,000	351,015,000	219,809,000
Vale of White Horse	134,919	16,595		281,000	53,671,000	15,971,000
Wakefield City	184,410	28,897	45,938	1,049,000	640,681,000	257,939,000
Walsall	194,271	0	28,079	739,000	643,215,000	235,565,000
Waltham Forest	195,000	0	51,100	1,022,000	842,151,000	187,207,000
Wandsworth	219,089	45,030	65,366	996,249	835,723,000	117,892,000
Warrington	123,300	0	27,926	694,000	467,247,000	173,146,000
Warwick	126,995	18,033	12,822	293,000	62,922,000	-12,428,000
Warwickshire	172,866	30,252	32,142	815,000	772,600,000	382,200,000
Watford	136,456	21,696	20,072	452,000	78,160,000	28,903,000
Waveney	108,738	17,941	18,186	374,000	73,975,000	362,000
Waverley	125,475	22,905	16,880	327,000	53,446,000	-23,252,000
Wealden	108,084	0	9,481	178,000	55,278,000	2,084,000
Wellingborough	125,000	21,000	14,417	341,000	40,665,000	12,974,000
Welwyn Hatfield	138,418	21,480	25,634	527,000	86,603,000	-20,499,000
West Berkshire	96,900	11,822	12,600	191,000	352,825,000	159,296,000
West Devon	130,000	16,120	13,626	352,000	27,840,000	8,760,000
West Dorset	124,615	23,893	33,454	463,204	56,969,000	14,868,000

Council	Chief Executive Salary 2014/15 (£)	Chief Executive Pension 2014/15 (£)	Leaders' Allowance 2014/15 (£)	Total Members' Allowances 2014/15 (£)	Gross Budget 2014/15 (£'000)	Net Budget 2014/15 (£'000)
West Dunbartonshire	92,015	12,360	15,287	344,000	404,225,000	227,479,000
West Lancashire					78,964,000	13,002,000
West Lindsey	105,000	26,999	16,975	270,000	39,656,000	10,841,000
West Lothian	141,821	28,933	33,454	705,000	517,907,000	403,645,000
West Oxfordshire	112,590	17,512	23,925	337,416	48,268,000	13,369,000
West Somerset	110,000	20,240		147,000	22,759,000	5,713,000
West Sussex	176,008	31,594	42,613	1,262,000	1,225,140,000	570,814,000
Western Isles	102,417	18,947	27,878	655,220	133,344,000	105,750,000
Westminster City	203,387	0	44,000	928,000	1,022,956,000	283,563,000
Weymouth & Portland	130,000	16,120	11,009	253,611	49,139,000	7,698,000
Wigan	165,000	32,752	48,719	1,143,000	760,352,000	215,636,000
Wiltshire Unitary	148,271	25,206	63,820	1,938,000	919,549,000	398,740,000
Winchester City	98,000	13,000	22,314	428,546	555,914,000	-12,916,000
Windsor & Maidenhead	125,571	16,073	25,776	665,000	279,291,000	100,665,000
Wirral	159,798	22,066	31,639	762,000	726,477,000	254,701,000
Woking	128,553	17,815	20,800	282,502	74,275,000	3,621,000
Wokingham	132,331	25,736	27,552	588,000	319,576,000	123,456,000
Wolverhampton	140,000	7,140		927,000	763,400,000	252,500,000
Worcester City	88,010	20,972		209,226	55,798,000	11,314,000
Worcestershire	155,523	19,352	33,412	900,000	774,900,000	351,800,000
Worthing	104,283	19,501	16,566	228,534	68,987,000	14,410,000
Wrexham	121,000	33,263	61,300	957,000	512,264,000	341,569,000
Wychavon	110,979	15,272	17,000	291,125	56,275,000	12,659,000
Wycombe	140,487	20,669	16,684	435,457	92,485,000	31,231,000
Wyre	103,076	13,589	23,364	312,710	57,107,677	15,700,484
Wyre Forest	108,640	14,340	17,550	215,835	55,849,000	11,383,000
York, City of	86,667	0	24,017	593,000	369,596,000	90,280,000

Aberdeen City   S

Aberdeen City Council, Ground Floor, Marischall College, Broad Street, Aberdeen AB10 1AB

☎ 03000 200292 📠 01224 636181 🖥 www.aberdeencity.gov.uk

FACTS AND FIGURES
Parliamentary Constituencies: Aberdeen North, Aberdeen South, Gordon
EU Constituencies: Scotland
Election Frequency: Elections are of whole council

PRINCIPAL OFFICERS

Chief Executive: Mrs Angela Scott, Chief Executive, Business Hub 12, Level 2 West, Marischal College, Broad Street, Aberdeen AB10 1AB ☎ 01224 522500 ⁀ anscott@aberdeencity.gov.uk

Senior Management: Mr Marc Cole, City Centre Director, Business Hub 12, 2nd Floor West, Marischal College, Broad Street, Aberdeen AB10 1AB ☎ 01224 522441 ⁀ macole@aberdeencity.gov.uk

Senior Management: Mr Richard Ellis, Interim Deputy Chief Executive & Director - Corporate Governance, Business Hub 12, 2nd Floor West, Marischal College, Broad Street, Aberdeen AB10 1AB ☎ 01224 522550 ⁀ rellis@aberdeencity.gov.uk

Senior Management: Ms Gayle Gorman, Director - Education & Children's Services, Business Hub 12, 2nd Floor West, Marischal College, Broad Street, Aberdeen AB10 1AB ☎ 01224 523458 ⁀ ggorman@aberdeencity.gov.uk

Senior Management: Mr Pete Leonard, Director - Communities, Housing & Infrastructure, Business Hub 12, 2nd Floor West, Marischal College, Broad Street, Aberdeen AB10 1AB ☎ 01224 523899 ⁀ pleonard@aberdeencity.gov.uk

Senior Management: Ms Judith Proctor, Chief Officer - Aberdeen City Health & Social Care Partnership, Business Hub 12, 2nd Floor West, Marischal College, Broad Street, Aberdeen AB10 1AB ☎ 01224 655725 ⁀ judith.proctor@aberdeencity.gov.uk

Architect, Building / Property Services: Mr Hugh Murdoch, Transportation Manager, Business Hub 4, Ground Floor North, Marischal College, Broad Street, Aberdeen AB10 1AB ☎ 01224 523965 ⁀ hughm@aberdeencity.gov.uk

Architect, Building / Property Services: Mr William Watson, Principal Architect, Business Hub 10, Level 2 South, Marischall College, Broad Street, Aberdeen AB10 1AB ☎ 01224 346265 ⁀ williamwatson@aberdeencity.gov.uk

Best Value: Mr Ciaran Monaghan, Head of Service, Business Hub 12, 2nd Floor West, Marischal College, Broad Street, Aberdeen AB10 1AB ☎ 01224 522293 ⁀ cmonaghan@aberdeencity.gov.uk

Building Control: Ms Gale Beattie, Acting Head of Planning & Sustainable Development, Business Hub 4, Ground Floor North, Marischal College, Broad Street, Aberdeen AB10 1AB ☎ 01224 523330 ⁀ galeb@aberdeencity.gov.uk

Building Control: Mr Gordon Spence, Building Standards Manager, Business Hub 4, Ground Floor North, Marischal College, Broad Street, Aberdeen AB10 1AB ☎ 01224 522436 ⁀ gspence@aberdeencity.gov.uk

Catering Services: Mr John Landragon, Catering Manager, Business Hub 10, 2nd Floor South, Marischal College, Broad Street, Aberdeen AB10 1AB ☎ 07801 129544 ⁀ jlandragon@aberdeencity.gov.uk

Children / Youth Services: Mr Euan Couperwhite, Head of Policy, Performance & Resources, Business Hub 13, 2nd Floor North, Marischal College, Broad Street, Aberdeen AB10 1AB ☎ 01224 522073 ⁀ ecouperwhite@aberdeencity.gov.uk

Children / Youth Services: Mr Andrew Griffiths, Interim Head of Education Services, Business Hub 13, 2nd Floor North, Marischal College, Broad Street, Aberdeen AB10 1AB ☎ 01224 522375 ⁀ andgriffiths@aberdeencity.gov.uk

Children / Youth Services: Ms Bernadette Oxley, Head of Children's Social Work, Business Hub 13, 2nd Floor North, Marischal College, Broad Street, Aberdeen AB10 1AB ☎ 01224 522110 ⁀ boxley@aberdeencity.gov.uk

Children / Youth Services: Ms Helen Shanks, Head of Inclusion, Business Hub 13, 2nd Floor North, Marischal College, Broad Street, Aberdeen AB10 1AB ☎ 01224 522473 ⁀ hshanks@aberdeencity.gov.uk

Civil Registration: Ms Carol Mair, Senior Registrar, Business Hub 3, Ground Floor South, Marischal College, Broad Street, Aberdeen AB10 1AB ☎ 01224 523369 ⁀ camair@aberdeencity.gov.uk

Civil Registration: Ms Marion Philip, Senior Registrar, Business Hub 3, Ground Floor South, Marischal College, Broad Street, Aberdeen AB10 1AB ☎ 01224 522331 ⁀ mphilip@aberdeencity.gov.uk

PR / Communications: Ms Dawn Schultz, City Promotions & Events Manager, 1st Floor, Old Town House, Broad Street, Aberdeen AB10 1FY ☎ 01224 522767 ⁀ dschultz@aberdeencity.gov.uk

Community Safety: Ms Nicola Murray, ASBIT Manager, Community Safety Hub, 1st Floor, Frederick Street Centre, Frederick Street, Aberdeen AB24 5HY ☎ 01224 219462 ⁀ nmurray@aberdeencity.gov.uk

Community Safety: Mr Rob Simpson, Interim Head of Communities & Housing, Business Hub 11, 2nd Floor West, Marischal College, Broad Street, Aberdeen AB10 1AB ☎ 01224 522540 ⁀ robsimpson@aberdeencity.gov.uk

Computer Management: Mr Paul Alexander, IT & Customer Services Manager, Business Hub 17, 3rd Floor North, Marischal College, Broad Street, Aberdeen AB10 1AB ☎ 01224 522606 ⁀ paalexander@aberdeencity.gov.uk

Computer Management: Mr Simon Haston, Head of IT & Transformation, Business Hub 17, 3rd Floor West, Marischal College, Broad Street, Aberdeen AB10 1AB ☎ 01224 523366 ⁀ shaston@aberdeencity.gov.uk

ABERDEEN CITY

Computer Management: Ms Sandra Massey, IT Manager, Business Hub 17, 3rd Floor North, Marischal College, Broad Street, Aberdeen AB10 1AB ☎ 01224 522778 ⌨ smassey@aberdeencity.gov.uk

Consumer Protection and Trading Standards: Ms Carole Jackson, Protective Services Manager, Business Hub 15, 3rd Floor South, Marischal College, Broad Street, Aberdeen AB10 1AB ☎ 01224 522057 ⌨ cjackson@aberdeencity.gov.uk

Contracts: Mr Craig Innes, Head of Procurement ☎ 01224 665650 ⌨ cinnes@aberdeencity.gov.uk

Corporate Services: Ms Gayle Gorman, Director - Education & Children's Services, Business Hub 12, 2nd Floor West, Marischal College, Broad Street, Aberdeen AB10 1AB ☎ 01224 523458 ⌨ ggorman@aberdeencity.gov.uk

Corporate Services: Mr Pete Leonard, Director - Communities, Housing & Infrastructure, Business Hub 12, 2nd Floor West, Marischal College, Broad Street, Aberdeen AB10 1AB ☎ 01224 523899 ⌨ pleonard@aberdeencity.gov.uk

Corporate Services: Mrs Angela Scott, Chief Executive, Business Hub 12, Level 2 West, Marischal College, Broad Street, Aberdeen AB10 1AB ☎ 01224 522500 ⌨ anscott@aberdeencity.gov.uk

Customer Service: Mr Ewan Sutherland, Head of HR, Business Hub 18, 38 Powis Terrace, Marischal College, Broad Street, Aberdeen AB10 1AB ☎ 01224 522192 ⌨ esutherland@aberdeencity.gov.uk

Economic Development: Mr Richard Sweetnam, Head of Economic Development, Business Hub 4, Ground Floor North, Marischal College, Broad Street, Aberdeen AB10 1AB ☎ 01224 522662 ⌨ rsweetnam@aberdeencity.gov.uk

Education: Mr Andrew Griffiths, Interim Head of Education Services, Business Hub 13, 2nd Floor North, Marischal College, Broad Street, Aberdeen AB10 1AB ☎ 01224 522375 ⌨ andgriffiths@aberdeencity.gov.uk

E-Government: Mr Ian Watt, E-Government Manager, Business Hub 17, 3rd Floor North, Marischal College, Broad Street, Aberdeen AB10 1AB ☎ 01224 522830 ⌨ ianw@aberdeencity.gov.uk

Electoral Registration: Mr Ian Milton, Assessor & Electoral Registration Officer, Grampian Valuation Joint Board, Woodhill House, Westburn Road, Aberdeen AB16 5GA ☎ 01224 664360 ⌨ assessor@grampian-vjb.gov.uk

Emergency Planning: Mr David McIntosh, Emergency Planning Manager, Business Hub 15, 3rd Floor South, Marischal College, Broad Street, Aberdeen AB10 1AB ☎ 01224 522261 ⌨ dmcintosh@aberdeencity.gov.uk

Energy Management: Ms Mai Muhammad, Energy Manager, Business Hub 10, 2nd Floor South, Marischal College, Broad Street, Aberdeen AB10 1AB ☎ 01224 522383 ⌨ mmuhammad@aberdeencity.gov.uk

Environmental / Technical Services: Mr Mark Reilly, Head of Public Infrastructure & Environment, Kittybrewster Depot, 38 Powis Terrace, Aberdeen AB25 3RF ☎ 01224 523096 ⌨ mareilly@aberdeencity.gov.uk

Environmental Health: Ms Carole Jackson, Protective Services Manager, Business Hub 15, 3rd Floor South, Marischal College, Broad Street, Aberdeen AB10 1AB ☎ 01224 522057 ⌨ cjackson@aberdeencity.gov.uk

Estates, Property & Valuation: Mr Stephen Booth, Senior Services Manager - Asset Management, Business Hub 10, 2nd Floor South, Marischal College, Broad Street, Aberdeen AB10 1AB ☎ 01224 522675 ⌨ stbooth@aberdeencity.gov.uk

European Liaison: Mr Yasa Ratnayeke, Senior Partnership, Performance & Funding Officer, Business Hub 4, Ground Floor North, Marischal College, Broad Street, Aberdeen AB10 1AB ☎ 01224 523807 ⌨ yratnayeke@aberdeencity.gov.uk

Events Manager: Ms Dawn Schultz, City Promotions & Events Manager, 1st Floor, Old Town House, Broad Street, Aberdeen AB10 1FY ☎ 01224 522767 ⌨ dschultz@aberdeencity.gov.uk

Facilities: Mr Andy Campbell, Facilities Manager, Business Hub 11, 2nd Floor West, Marischal College, Broad Street, Aberdeen AB10 1AB ☎ 01224 523494 ⌨ ancampbell@aberdeencity.gov.uk

Finance: Mr Steven Whyte, Head of Finance, Business Hub 7, 1st Floor West, Marischal College, Broad Street, Aberdeen AB10 1AB ☎ 01224 523566 ⌨ swhyte@aberdeencity.gov.uk

Pensions: Ms Laura Colliss, Pensions Manager, Business Hub 16, 3rd Floor West, Marischal College, Broad Street, Aberdeen AB10 1AB ☎ 01224 264158 ⌨ lcolliss@nespf.org.uk

Pensions: Mr Gary Gray, Benefit Admin & Technical Manager, Business Hub 16, 3rd Floor West, Marischal College, Broad Street, Aberdeen AB10 1AB ☎ 01224 264159 ⌨ gagray@nespf.org.uk

Pensions: Ms Caroline Mann, Senior Pensions Officer - Investments, Business Hub 16, 3rd Floor West, Marischal College, Broad Street, Aberdeen AB10 1AB ☎ 01224 264168 ⌨ camann@nespf.org.uk

Pensions: Mr Michael Scroggie, Accounting Manager, Business Hub 16, 3rd Floor West, Marischal College, Broad Street, Aberdeen AB10 1AB ☎ 01224 264178 ⌨ mscroggie@nespf.org.uk

Fleet Management: Mr Paul Reid, Fleet Compliance Manager, Kittybrewster Depot, 38 Powis Terrace, Aberdeen AB25 3RF ☎ 01224 489164 ⌨ paureid@aberdeencity.gov.uk

Grounds Maintenance: Mr Steven Shaw, Environment Manager, Kittybrewster Depot, 38 Powis Terrace, Aberdeen AB25 3RF ☎ 01224 489273 ⌨ stevens@aberdeencity.gov.uk

Health and Safety: Mrs Mary Agnew, Health, Safety & Wellbeing Manager, Business Hub 18, 38 Powis Terrace, Marischal College, Broad Street, Aberdeen AB10 1AB ☎ 01224 523088 ⌨ magnew@aberdeencity.gov.uk

Highways: Mr Richard Blain, Roads Operations Manager, West Tullos Roads Depot, Craigshaw Drive, Aberdeen AB12 3AL
☎ 01224 241525 ⌁ rblain@aberdeencity.gov.uk

Housing: Ms Wendy Carle, Housing Manager, Tillydrone Housing Office, Formartin Road, Aberdeen AB24 2UY ☎ 01224 489526
⌁ wcarle@aberdeencity.gov.uk

Housing: Mr John Quinn, Head of Land & Property Assets, Business Hub 10, 2nd Floor South, Marischal College, Broad Street, Aberdeen AB10 1AB ☎ 01224 523363
⌁ jquinn@aberdeencity.gov.uk

Housing: Mr Martin Smith, Area Housing Manager, Mastrick Customer Access Point, Spey Road, Aberdeen AB16 6SH
☎ 01224 788538 ⌁ martinsmith@aberdeencity.gov.uk

Housing: Mr Graham Souter, Housing Manager, Business Hub 1, Lower Ground Floor West, Marischal College, Broad Street, Aberdeen AB10 1AB ☎ 01224 522135
⌁ gsouter@aberdeencity.gov.uk

Legal: Mr Fraser Bell, Head of Legal & Democratic Services, Business Hub 6, 1St Floor South, Marischal College, Broad Street, Aberdeen AB10 1AB ☎ 01224 522084 ⌁ frbell@aberdeencity.gov.uk

Leisure and Cultural Services: Mr Neil Bruce, Service Manager - Culture, Business Hub 13, 2nd Floor North, Marischal College, Broad Street, Aberdeen AB10 1AB ☎ 01224 523144
⌁ neilbr@aberdeencity.gov.uk

Licensing: Mr Fraser Bell, Head of Legal & Democratic Services, Business Hub 6, 1St Floor South, Marischal College, Broad Street, Aberdeen AB10 1AB ☎ 01224 522084
⌁ frbell@aberdeencity.gov.uk

Lifelong Learning: Ms Jo Mackie, Service Manager - Communities & Partnerships, Business Hub 18, Level 4 West, Marischal College, Broad Street, Aberdeen AB10 1AB
☎ 01224 522732 ⌁ jomackie@aberdeencity.gov.uk

Lighting: Mr Richard Blain, Roads Operations Manager, West Tullos Roads Depot, Craigshaw Drive, Aberdeen AB12 3AL
☎ 01224 241525 ⌁ rblain@aberdeencity.gov.uk

Member Services: Mr Roderick MacBeath, Head of Democratic Services, 1st Floor, Town House, Broad Street, Aberdeen AB10 1AQ
☎ 01224 523054 ⌁ rmacbeath@aberdeencity.gov.uk

Parking: Mr Robin Donald, City Warden Officer, Community Safety Hub, 1st Floor, Frederick Street Centre, Frederick Street, Aberdeen AB24 5HY ☎ 01224 219454 ⌁ rdonald@aberdeencity.gov.uk

Parking: Mr Doug Ritchie, Traffic Engineering Manager, Business Hub 11, 2nd Floor West, Marischal College, Broad Street, Aberdeen AB10 1AB ☎ 01244 522325 ⌁ dritchie@aberdeencity.gov.uk

Partnerships: Ms Judith Proctor, Chief Officer - Aberdeen City Health & Social Care Partnership, Business Hub 12, 2nd Floor West, Marischal College, Broad Street, Aberdeen AB10 1AB
☎ 01224 655725 ⌁ judith.proctor@aberdeencity.gov.uk

Partnerships: Mr Yasa Ratnayeke, Senior Partnership, Performance & Funding Officer, Business Hub 4, Ground Floor North, Marischal College, Broad Street, Aberdeen AB10 1AB
☎ 01224 523807 ⌁ yratnayeke@aberdeencity.gov.uk

Personnel / HR: Mr Ewan Sutherland, Head of HR, Business Hub 18, 38 Powis Terrace, Marischal College, Broad Street, Aberdeen AB10 1AB ☎ 01224 522192 ⌁ esutherland@aberdeencity.gov.uk

Planning: Ms Gale Beattie, Acting Head of Planning & Sustainable Development, Business Hub 4, Ground Floor North, Marischal College, Broad Street, Aberdeen AB10 1AB
☎ 01224 523330 ⌁ galeb@aberdeencity.gov.uk

Procurement: Mr Craig Innes, Head of Procurement, Woodhill House, Ashgrove Road, Aberdeen AB16 5GA ☎ 01224 665650
⌁ cinnes@aberdeencity.gov.uk

Public Libraries: Mr Neil Bruce, Service Manager - Culture, Business Hub 13, 2nd Floor North, Marischal College, Broad Street, Aberdeen AB10 1AB ☎ 01224 523144 ⌁ neilbr@aberdeencity.gov.uk

Recycling & Waste Minimisation: Mr Peter Lawrence, Waste & Recycling Manager, Kittybrewster Depot, 38 Powis Terrace, Aberdeen AB25 3RF ☎ 01224 489331
⌁ plawrence@aberdeencity.gov.uk

Regeneration: Mr John Quinn, Head of Land & Property Assets, Business Hub 10, 2nd Floor South, Marischal College, Broad Street, Aberdeen AB10 1AB ☎ 01224 523363 ⌁ jquinn@aberdeencity.gov.uk

Road Safety: Mr Doug Ritchie, Traffic Engineering Manager, Business Hub 11, 2nd Floor West, Marischal College, Broad Street, Aberdeen AB10 1AB ☎ 01244 522325
⌁ dritchie@aberdeencity.gov.uk

Social Services: Ms Anne Donaldson, Service Manager - Family & Community Support, Business Hub 13, 2nd Floor North, Marischal College, Broad Street, Aberdeen AB10 1AB ☎ 01224 523019
⌁ adonaldson@aberdeencity.gov.uk

Social Services: Ms Judith Proctor, Chief Officer - Aberdeen City Health & Social Care Partnership, Business Hub 12, 2nd Floor West, Marischal College, Broad Street, Aberdeen AB10 1AB ☎ 01224 655725 ⌁ judith.proctor@aberdeencity.gov.uk

Social Services: Mr Graeme Simpson, Children's Services Manager, Business Hub 13, 2nd Floor North, Marischal College, Broad Street, Aberdeen AB10 1AB ☎ 01224 523496
⌁ gsimpson@aberdeencity.gov.uk

Social Services: Ms Sally Wilkins, Lead Service Manager, Business Hub 8, 1st Floor North, Marischal College, Broad Street, Aberdeen AB10 1AB ☎ 01224 522860
⌁ sawilkins@aberdeencity.gov.uk

Social Services (Adult): Mr Tom Cowan, Head of Operations, Business Hub 8, 1st Floor North, Marischal College, Broad Street, Aberdeen AB10 1AB ☎ 01224 655727
⌁ tcowan@aberdencity.gov.uk

ABERDEEN CITY

Social Services (Children): Ms Bernadette Oxley, Head of Children's Social Work, Business Hub 13, 2nd Floor North, Marischal College, Broad Street, Aberdeen AB10 1AB ☎ 01224 522110 ✆ boxley@aberdeencity.gov.uk

Staff Training: Mr Ewan Sutherland, Head of HR, Business Hub 18, 38 Powis Terrace, Marischal College, Broad Street, Aberdeen AB10 1AB ☎ 01224 522192 ✆ esutherland@aberdeencity.gov.uk

Street Scene: Mr Steven Shaw, Environment Manager, Kittybrewster Depot, Powis Terrace, Aberdeen AB25 2RF ☎ 01224 489273 ✆ stevens@aberdeencity.gov.uk

Sustainable Development: Ms Gale Beattie, Acting Head of Planning & Sustainable Development, Business Hub 4, Ground Floor North, Marischal College, Broad Street, Aberdeen AB10 1AB ☎ 01224 523330 ✆ galeb@aberdeencity.gov.uk

Tourism: Ms Dawn Schultz, City Promotions & Events Manager, 1st Floor, Old Town House, Broad Street, Aberdeen AB10 1FY ☎ 01224 522767 ✆ dschultz@aberdeencity.gov.uk

Town Centre: Mr Andrew Win, Programmes & Projects Manager, Business Hub 4, Ground Floor North, Marischal College, Broad Street, Aberdeen AB10 1AB ☎ 01224 523060 ✆ andrewwin@aberdeencity.gov.uk

Traffic Management: Mr Doug Ritchie, Traffic Engineering Manager, Business Hub 11, 2nd Floor West, Marischal College, Broad Street, Aberdeen AB10 1AB ☎ 01244 522325 ✆ dritchie@aberdeencity.gov.uk

Transport: Ms Gale Beattie, Acting Head of Planning & Sustainable Development, Business Hub 4, Ground Floor North, Marischal College, Broad Street, Aberdeen AB10 1AB ☎ 01224 523330 ✆ galeb@aberdeencity.gov.uk

Transport Planner: Ms Gale Beattie, Acting Head of Planning & Sustainable Development, Business Hub 4, Ground Floor North, Marischal College, Broad Street, Aberdeen AB10 1AB ☎ 01224 523330 ✆ galeb@aberdeencity.gov.uk

Waste Collection and Disposal: Mr Peter Lawrence, Waste & Recycling Manager, 1st Floor, Kittybrewster Depot, Powis Terrace, Aberdeen AB25 3RF ☎ 01224 489331 ✆ plawrence@aberdeencity.gov.uk

Waste Management: Mr Peter Lawrence, Waste & Recycling Manager, 1st Floor, Kittybrewster Depot, Powis Terrace, Aberdeen AB25 3RF ☎ 01224 489331 ✆ plawrence@aberdeencity.gov.uk

Children's Play Areas: Mr Steven Shaw, Environment Manager, Kittybrewster Depot, 38 Powis Terrace, Aberdeen AB25 3RF ☎ 01224 489273 ✆ stevens@aberdeencity.gov.uk

COUNCILLORS

Lord Provost: Adam, George (LAB - Hilton / Woodside / Stockethill)
gadam@aberdeencity.gov.uk

Deputy Provost: Reynolds, John (IND - Bridge of Don)
jreynolds@aberdeencity.gov.uk

Leader of the Council: Laing, Jenny (LAB - Midstocket / Rosemount)
jelaing@aberdeencity.gov.uk

Deputy Leader of the Council: Boulton, Marie (IND - Lower Deeside)
mboulton@aberdeencity.gov.uk

Allan, Yvonne (LAB - Torry / Ferryhill)
yallan@aberdeencity.gov.uk

Cameron, David (SNP - Kingswell / Sheddocksley / Summerhill)
dacameron@aberdeencity.gov.uk

Carle, Scott (LAB - Northfield / Mastrick North)
sccarle@aberdeencity.gov.uk

Cooney, Neil (LAB - Kincorth / Nigg / Cove)
ncooney@aberdeencity.gov.uk

Copeland, Neil (SNP - Hilton / Woodside / Stockethill)
neilcopeland@aberdeencity.gov.uk

Corall, John (SNP - Hazlehead / Ashley / Queens Cross)
jcorall@aberdeencity.gov.uk

Cormie, Bill (SNP - Midstocket / Rosemount)
bcormie@aberdeencity.gov.uk

Crockett, Barney (LAB - Dyce / Bucksburn / Danestone)
bcrockett@aberdeencity.gov.uk

Delaney, Steve (LD - Kingswell / Sheddocksley / Summerhill)
sdelaney@aberdeencity.gov.uk

Dickson, Graham (SNP - Torry / Ferryhill)
gdickson@aberdeencity.gov.uk

Donelly, Alan (CON - Torry / Ferryhill)
adonnelly@aberdeencity.gov.uk

Dunbar, Jackie (SNP - Northfield / Mastrick North)
jdunbar@aberdeencity.gov.uk

Dunbar, Lesley (LAB - Hilton / Woodside / Stockethill)
lesdunbar@aberdeencity.gov.uk

Finlayson, Andrew (IND - Kincorth / Nigg / Cove)
afinlayson@aberdeencity.gov.uk

Flynn, Stephen (SNP - Kincorth / Nigg / Cove)
sflynn@aberdeencity.gov.uk

Graham, Gordon (LAB - Northfield / Mastrick North)
ggraham@aberdeencity.gov.uk

Grant, Ross (LAB - Tillydrone / Seaton / Old Aberdeen)
rossgrant@aberdeencity.gov.uk

Greig, Martin (LD - Hazlehead / Ashley / Queens Cross)
mgreig@aberdeencity.gov.uk

Hutchinson, Michael (LAB - George Street / Harbour)
mihutchinson@aberdeencity.gov.uk

Ironside, Len (LAB - Kingswell / Sheddocksley / Summerhill)
lironside@aberdeencity.gov.uk

Jaffrey, Muriel (SNP - Bridge of Don)
mjaffrey@aberdeencity.gov.uk

Kiddie, James (SNP - Torry / Ferryhill)
jkiddie@aberdeencity.gov.uk

Lawrence, Graeme (LAB - Dyce / Bucksburn / Danestone)
glawrence@aberdeencity.gov.uk

MacGregor, Neil (SNP - Dyce / Bucksburn / Danestone)
nmacgregor@aberdeencity.gov.uk

Malik, M. Tauqeer (LAB - Lower Deeside)
mmalik@aberdeencity.gov.uk

Malone, Aileen (LD - Lower Deeside)
amalone@aberdeencity.gov.uk

Milne, Ramsay (LAB - Tillydrone / Seaton / Old Aberdeen)
rmilne@aberdeencity.gov.uk

Morrison, Nathan (LAB - George Street / Harbour)
namorrison@aberdeencity.gov.uk

Morrison, Jean (LAB - George Street / Harbour)
jemorrison@aberdeencity.gov.uk

Nicoll, Alex (SNP - Midstocket / Rosemount)
anicoll@aberdeencity.gov.uk

Noble, Jim (SNP - Tillydrone / Seaton / Old Aberdeen)
jimnoble@aberdeencity.gov.uk

Samarai, Gill (SNP - Dyce / Bucksburn / Danestone)
gsamarai@aberdeencity.gov.uk

Stewart, Jennifer (LD - Hazlehead / Ashley / Queens Cross)
jastewart@aberdeencity.gov.uk

Stuart, Sandy (SNP - Bridge of Don)
sandystuart@aberdeencity.gov.uk

Taylor, Angela (LAB - Airyhall / Broomhill / Garthdee)
angelataylor@aberdeencity.gov.uk

Thomson, Ross (O - Hazlehead / Ashley / Queens Cross)
rossthomson@aberdeencity.gov.uk

Townson, Gordon (SNP - Airyhall / Broomhill / Garthdee)
gtownson@aberdeencity.gov.uk

Young, Willie (LAB - Bridge of Don)
wyoung@aberdeencity.gov.uk

Yuill, Ian (LD - Airyhall / Broomhill / Garthdee)
iyuill@aberdeencity.gov.uk

POLITICAL COMPOSITION

LAB: 18, SNP: 15, LD: 5, IND: 3, CON: 1, O: 1

COMMITTEE CHAIRS

Audit, Risk & Scrutiny: Mr Stephen Flynn

Communities, Housing & Infrastructure: Mr Neil Cooney

Education & Children's Services: Ms Angela Taylor

Finance, Policy & Resources: Mr Willie Young

Licensing: Ms Marie Boulton

Pensions: Mr Barney Crockett

Planning: Mr Ramsay Milne

Aberdeenshire S

Aberdeenshire Council, Woodhill House, Westburn Road, Aberdeen AB16 5GB
☎ 03456 081208 💻 www.aberdeenshire.gov.uk

FACTS AND FIGURES

Parliamentary Constituencies: Aberdeenshire West and Kincardine, Banff and Buchan, Gordon
EU Constituencies: Scotland
Election Frequency: Elections are of whole council

PRINCIPAL OFFICERS

Chief Executive: Mr Jim Savege, Chief Executive, Woodhill House, Westburn Road, Aberdeen AB16 5GB ☎ 01224 665400 🖰 jim.savege@aberdeenshire.gov.uk

Senior Management: Mr Stephen Archer, Director - Infrastructure Services, Woodhill House, Westburn Road, Aberdeen AB16 5GB ☎ 01224 664520 🖰 stephen.archer@aberdeenshire.gov.uk

Senior Management: Mr Adam Coldwells, Chief Officer - Aberdeenshire Health & Social Care Partnership, Woodhill House, Westburn Road, Aberdeen AB16 5GB 🖰 adam.coldwells@aberdeenshire.gov.uk

Senior Management: Mr Ritchie Johnson, Director - Business Services, Woodhill House, Westburn Road, Aberdeen AB16 5GB ☎ 01224 665444 🖰 ritchie.johnson@aberdeenshire.gov.uk

Senior Management: Ms Maria Walker, Director - Education & Children's Services, Woodhill House, Westburn Road, Aberdeen AB16 5GB ☎ 01224 665420 🖰 maria.walker@aberdeenshire.gov.uk

Architect, Building / Property Services: Mr Allan Whyte, Head of Property & Facilities Management, Woodhill House, Westburn Road, Aberdeen AB16 5GB ☎ 01224 664500 🖰 allan.whyte@aberdeenshire.gov.uk

Building Control: Mr Robert Gray, Head of Planning & Building Standards, Woodhill House, Westburn Road, Aberdeen AB16 5GB ☎ 01224 664728 🖰 robert.gray@aberdeenshire.gov.uk

Civil Registration: Ms Karen Wiles, Head of Legal & Governance, Woodhill House, Westburn Road, Aberdeen AB16 5GB ☎ 01467 536160 🖰 karen.wiles@aberdeenshire.gov.uk

PR / Communications: Ms Kate Bond, Head of Customer Communication & Improvement, Woodhill House, Westburn Road, Aberdeen AB16 5GB ☎ 01224 664405 🖰 kate.bond@aberdeenshire.gov.uk

Community Planning: Ms Amanda Roe, Policy, Performance & Improvement Manager, Woodhill House, Westburn Road, Aberdeen AB16 5GB ☎ 01467 536139 🖰 amanda.roe@aberdeenshire.gov.uk

Computer Management: Ms Nicola Graham, Head of ICT, Woodhill House, Westburn Road, Aberdeen AB16 5GB ☎ 01467 536101 🖰 nicola.graham@aberdeenshire.gov.uk

Contracts: Mr Craig Innes, Head of Central Procurement Services, Woodhill House, Westburn Road, Aberdeen AB16 5GB ☎ 01224 665650 🖰 craig.innes@aberdeenshire.gov.uk

Corporate Services: Mr Alan Wood, Head of Finance, Woodhill House, Westburn Road, Aberdeen AB16 5GB ☎ 01224 664202 🖰 alan.wood@aberdeenshire.gov.uk

Customer Service: Ms Morag Esson, Customer Services Manager, Woodhill House, Westburn Road, Aberdeen AB16 5GB ☎ 01467 536135 🖰 morag.esson@aberdeenshire.gov.uk

ABERDEENSHIRE

Economic Development: Ms Belinda Miller, Head of Economic Development & Protective Services, Woodhill House, Westburn Road, Aberdeen AB16 5GB ☎ 01467 536144 ✆ belinda.miller@aberdeenshire.gov.uk

Education: Mr Vincent Docherty, Head of Service - Inclusion & Integration, Woodhill House, Westburn Road, Aberdeen AB16 5GB ☎ 01224 664397 ✆ vincent.docherty@aberdeenshire.gov.uk

Education: Mr Andrew Griffiths, Head of Service - Education & Staff Development, Woodhill House, Westburn Road, Aberdeen AB16 5GB ☎ 01224 664142 ✆ andrew.griffiths@aberdeenshire.gov.uk

Education: Ms Maria Walker, Director - Education & Children's Services, Woodhill House, Westburn Road, Aberdeen AB16 5GB ☎ 01224 665420 ✆ maria.walker@aberdeenshire.gov.uk

E-Government: Ms Nicola Graham, Head of ICT, Woodhill House, Westburn Road, Aberdeen AB16 5GB ☎ 01467 536101 ✆ nicola.graham@aberdeenshire.gov.uk

Electoral Registration: Mr Allan Bell, Senior Committee Officer / Elections Organiser, Woodhill House, Westburn Road, Aberdeen AB16 5GB ☎ 01224 665119 ✆ allan.bell@aberdeenshire.gov.uk

Emergency Planning: Mr David McIntosh, Emergency Planning Manager, 1 Queen's Gardens, Aberdeen AB15 4YD ☎ 01224 633030 ✆ david@grampian.epu.co.uk

Energy Management: Mr Brian Smith, Engineering Services Manager, Woodhill House, Westburn Road, Aberdeen AB16 5GB ☎ 01224 664510 ✆ brian.smith@aberdeenshire.gov.uk

Environmental / Technical Services: Mr David Cooper, Environmental Health Officer, Gordon House, Blackhall Road, Inverurie AB51 3WA ☎ 01467 628159 ✆ david.cooper@aberdeenshire.gov.uk

Environmental Health: Mr David Cooper, Environmental Health Officer, Gordon House, Blackhall Road, Inverurie AB51 3WA ☎ 01467 628159 ✆ david.cooper@aberdeenshire.gov.uk

Estates, Property & Valuation: Mr John Gahagan, Estates Manager, Woodhill House, Westburn Road, Aberdeen AB16 5GB ☎ 01224 664778 ✆ john.gahagan@aberdeenshire.gov.uk

European Liaison: Mr Martin Brebner, European Programmes Executive, Woodhill House, Westburn Road, Aberdeen AB16 5GB ☎ 01224 665225 ✆ martin.brebner@aberdeenshire.gov.uk

Facilities: Mr Tom Buchan, Facilities Manager, Woodhill House, Westburn Road, Aberdeen AB16 5GB ☎ 01224 664496 ✆ tom.buchan@aberdeenshire.gov.uk

Finance: Mr Alan Wood, Head of Finance, Woodhill House, Westburn Road, Aberdeen AB16 5GB ☎ 01224 664202 ✆ alan.wood@aberdeenshire.gov.uk

Fleet Management: Mr Ian Paisley, Fleet Manager, Inverurie Repair Depot, Harlaw Way, Inverurie AB51 4TE ☎ 01467 627530 ✆ ian.paisley@aberdeenshire.gov.uk

Grounds Maintenance: Mr Philip McKay, Head of Roads, Landscape Services & Waste Mangement, T & I Operations, Harlaw Way, Inverurie AB51 4SG ☎ 01467 536279 ✆ philip.mckay@aberdeenshire.gov.uk

Health and Safety: Ms Pamela Bruce, Principal Health & Safety Adviser, Woodhill House, Westburn Road, Aberdeen AB16 5GB ☎ 01224 664067 ✆ pamela.bruce@aberdeenshire.gov.uk

Highways: Mr Philip McKay, Head of Roads, Landscape Services & Waste Mangement, Harlaw Way, Inverurie AB51 4SG ☎ 01467 536279 ✆ philip.mckay@aberdeenshire.gov.uk

Legal: Ms Karen Wiles, Head of Legal & Governance, Woodhill House, Westburn Road, Aberdeen AB16 5GB ☎ 01467 536160 ✆ karen.wiles@aberdeenshire.gov.uk

Leisure and Cultural Services: Mr John Harding, Head of Service - Lifelong Learning & Leisure, Woodhill House, Westburn Road, Aberdeen AB16 5GB ☎ 01224 664653 ✆ john.harding@aberdeenshire.gov.uk

Licensing: Ms Karen Wiles, Head of Legal & Governance, Woodhill House, Westburn Road, Aberdeen AB16 5GB ☎ 01467 536160 ✆ karen.wiles@aberdeenshire.gov.uk

Lifelong Learning: Mr John Harding, Head of Service - Lifelong Learning & Leisure, Woodhill House, Westburn Road, Aberdeen AB16 5GB ☎ 01224 664653 ✆ john.harding@aberdeenshire.gov.uk

Lighting: Mr Keith Melvin, Strategy / Lighting Engineer, Gordon House, Blackhall Road, Inverurie AB51 3WA ☎ 01467 628014 ✆ keith.melvin@aberdeenshire.gov.uk

Parking: Mr Mark Skilling, Strategy Manager, Woodhill House, Westburn Road, Aberdeen AB16 5GB ☎ 01467 536165 ✆ mark.skilling@aberdeenshire.gov.uk

Personnel / HR: Ms Laura Simpson, Head of HR & OD, Woodhill House, Westburn Road, Aberdeen AB16 5GB ☎ 01467 536164 ✆ laura.simpson@aberdeenshire.gov.uk

Planning: Mr Robert Gray, Head of Planning & Building Standards, Woodhill House, Westburn Road, Aberdeen AB16 5GB ☎ 01224 664728 ✆ robert.gray@aberdeenshire.gov.uk

Procurement: Mr Craig Innes, Head of Central Procurement Services, Woodhill House, Westburn Road, Aberdeen AB16 5GB ☎ 01224 665650 ✆ craig.innes@aberdeenshire.gov.uk

Public Libraries: Ms Sharon Jamieson, Library & Information Services Manager, Meldrum Meg Way, Olmeldron, Inverurie AB51 0GN ☎ 01651 871210 ✆ sharon.jamieson@aberdeenshire.gov.uk

Recycling & Waste Minimisation: Mr Philip McKay, Head of Roads, Landscape Services & Waste Mangement, Harlaw Way, Inverurie AB51 4SG ☎ 01467 536279 ✆ philip.mckay@aberdeenshire.gov.uk

Regeneration: Ms Christine Webster, Regeneration & Town Centre Manager, Banff Town House, Low Street, Banff AB45 1AU ☎ 07785 730652 ✆ christine.webster@aberdeenshire.gov.uk

Road Safety: Mr Mark Skilling, Strategy Manager, Woodhill House, Westburn Road, Aberdeen AB16 5GB ☎ 01467 536165
⌨ mark.skilling@aberdeenshire.gov.uk

Social Services (Adult): Mr Philip English, Partnership Manager, Woodhill House, Westburn Road, Aberdeen AB16 5GB
☎ 01224 664940 ⌨ philip.english@aberdeenshire.gov.uk

Social Services (Children): Mr Robert Driscoll, Head of Children's Services / CSWO, Woodhill House, Westburn Road, Aberdeen AB16 5GB ☎ 01467 536177
⌨ robert.driscoll@aberdeenshire.gov.uk

Staff Training: Ms Laura Simpson, Head of HR & OD, Woodhill House, Westburn Road, Aberdeen AB16 5GB ☎ 01467 536164
⌨ laura.simpson@aberdeenshire.gov.uk

Street Scene: Mr Philip McKay, Head of Roads, Landscape Services & Waste Mangement, Harlaw Way, Inverurie AB51 4SG
☎ 01467 536279 ⌨ philip.mckay@aberdeenshire.gov.uk

Sustainable Development: Mr Barry Simons, Sustainability & Climate Change Co-ordinator, Woodhill House, Westburn Road, Aberdeen AB16 5GB ☎ 01224 664719
⌨ barry.simons@aberdeenshire.gov.uk

Tourism: Mr David Wright, Industry Support Executive - Tourism, Woodhill House, Westburn Road, Aberdeen AB16 5GB
☎ 01224 664574 ⌨ david.wright@aberdeenshire.gov.uk

Town Centre: Ms Audrey Michie, Strategic Town Centres Executive, Woodhill House, Westburn Road, Aberdeen AB16 5GB
☎ 01467 628278 ⌨ audrey.michie@aberdeenshire.gov.uk

Traffic Management: Mr Philip McKay, Head of Roads, Landscape Services & Waste Mangement, Harlaw Way, Inverurie AB51 4SG ☎ 01467 536279 ⌨ philip.mckay@aberdeenshire.gov.uk

Transport: Mr Richard McKenzie, Public Transport Manager, Woodhill House, Westburn Road, Aberdeen AB16 5GB
☎ 01224 664580 ⌨ richard.mckenzie@aberdeenshire.gov.uk

Transport Planner: Mr Richard McKenzie, Public Transport Manager, Woodhill House, Westburn Road, Aberdeen AB16 5GB
☎ 01224 664580 ⌨ richard.mckenzie@aberdeenshire.gov.uk

Total Place: Mr Alexander MacLeod, Housing Manager - Strategy, Gordon House, Blackhall Road, Inverurie AB51 3WA
☎ 01467 628445 ⌨ alexander.macleod@aberdeenshire.gov.uk

Waste Collection and Disposal: Mr Philip McKay, Head of Roads, Landscape Services & Waste Mangement, Harlaw Way, Inverurie AB51 4SG ☎ 01467 536279
⌨ philip.mckay@aberdeenshire.gov.uk

Waste Management: Mr Philip McKay, Head of Roads, Landscape Services & Waste Mangement, Harlaw Way, Inverurie AB51 4SG ☎ 01467 536279 ⌨ philip.mckay@aberdeenshire.gov.uk

Children's Play Areas: Mr Philip McKay, Head of Roads, Landscape Services & Waste Mangement, Harlaw Way, Inverurie AB51 4SG ☎ 01467 536279 ⌨ philip.mckay@aberdeenshire.gov.uk

COUNCILLORS

Provost: Vernal, Hamish (SNP - Inverurie & District)
cllr.h.vernal@aberdeenshire.gov.uk

Deputy Provost: Grant, Allison (SNP - West Garioch)
cllr.a.grant@aberdeenshire.gov.uk

Group LeaderEvison, Alison (LAB - North Kincardine)
cllr.a.evison@aberdeenshire.gov.uk

Group LeaderFord, Martin (SGP - East Garioch)
cllr.m.ford@aberdeenshire.gov.uk

Group LeaderGifford, Jim (CON - Mid-Formartine)
cllr.j.gifford@aberdeenshire.gov.uk

Group LeaderJohnston, Paul (IND - Mid-Formartine)
cllr.p.johnston@aberdeenshire.gov.uk

Group LeaderKitts-Hayes, Martine (LD - Inverurie & District)
cllr.m.kitts-hayes@aberdeenshire.gov.uk

Agnew, Wendy (CON - Stonehaven & Lower Deeside)
cllr.w.agnew@aberdeenshire.gov.uk

Aitchison, David (SNP - Westhill & District)
cllr.d.aitchison@aberdeenshire.gov.uk

Allan, Amanda (SNP - Westhill & District)
cllr.a.j.allan@aberdeenshire.gov.uk

Allan, Anne (SNP - Peterhead North & Rattray)
cllr.a.m.allan@aberdeenshire.gov.uk

Argyle, Peter (LD - Aboyne, Upper Deeside & Donside)
cllr.p.argyle@aberdeenshire.gov.uk

Bellarby, Peter (LD - Stonehaven & Lower Deeside)
cllr.p.bellarby@aberdeenshire.gov.uk

Bews, Alistair (SNP - North Kincardine)
cllr.a.bews@aberdeenshire.gov.uk

Blackett, Geva (SNP - Aboyne, Upper Deeside & Donside)
cllr.g.blackett@aberdeenshire.gov.uk

Buchan, Charles (SNP - Fraserburgh & District)
cllr.c.buchan@aberdeenshire.gov.uk

Buchan, Alan (IND - Peterhead North & Rattray)
cllr.a.buchan@aberdeenshire.gov.uk

Carr, George (CON - Mearns)
cllr.g.carr@aberdeenshire.gov.uk

Cassie, Ross (SNP - Troup)
cllr.r.cassie@aberdeenshire.gov.uk

Chapman, Edie (CON - Central Buchan)
cllr.e.chapman@aberdeenshire.gov.uk

Christie, Raymond (LAB - Stonehaven & Lower Deeside)
cllr.r.christie@aberdeenshire.gov.uk

Clark, Graeme (SNP - Stonehaven & Lower Deeside)
cllr.g.clark@aberdeenshire.gov.uk

Clark, Karen (LD - Banchory & Mid-Deeside)
cllr.k.clark@aberdeenshire.gov.uk

Clark, Linda (SNP - Banchory & Mid-Deeside)
cllr.l.clark@aberdeenshire.gov.uk

Cowling, Richard (CON - Inverurie & District)
cllr.r.cowling@aberdeenshire.gov.uk

Cox, John (IND - Banff & District)
cllr.j.cox@aberdeenshire.gov.uk

Cullinane, Nan (LD - East Garioch)
cllr.n.cullinane@aberdeenshire.gov.uk

ABERDEENSHIRE

Davidson, Isobel (LD - Ellon & District)
cllr.i.davidson@aberdeenshire.gov.uk

Dick, Jean (SNP - Mearns)
cllr.j.dick@aberdeenshire.gov.uk

Duncan, Sandy (SNP - Turriff & District)
cllr.a.duncan@aberdeenshire.gov.uk

Farquhar, Katrina (CON - Aboyne, Upper Deeside & Donside)
cllr.k.farquhar@aberdeenshire.gov.uk

Findlater, Mark (IND - Troup)
cllr.m.findlater@aberdeenshire.gov.uk

Gardiner, Alan (IND - Peterhead North & Rattray)
cllr.a.gardiner@aberdeenshire.gov.uk

Gray, Ian (SNP - Banff & District)
cllr.i.gray@aberdeenshire.gov.uk

Hendry, Allan (SNP - Mid-Formartine)
cllr.a.hendry@aberdeenshire.gov.uk

Hood, Fergus (SNP - East Garioch)
cllr.f.hood@aberdeenshire.gov.uk

Howatson, Bill (LD - Mearns)
cllr.w.howatson@aberdeenshire.gov.uk

Ingleby, Moira (CON - Huntly, Strathbogie & Howe of Alford)
cllr.m.ingleby@aberdeenshire.gov.uk

Ingram, Jim (SNP - Central Buchan)
cllr.j.ingram@aberdeenshire.gov.uk

Latham, John (IND - Huntly, Strathbogie & Howe of Alford)
cllr.j.latham@aberdeenshire.gov.uk

Lonchay, Sheena (LD - West Garioch)
cllr.s.lonchay@aberdeenshire.gov.uk

Malone, Tom (IND - Peterhead South & Cruden)
cllr.t.malone@aberdeenshire.gov.uk

McKail, Ron (CON - Westhill & District)
cllr.r.mckail@aberdeenshire.gov.uk

McRae, Fiona (SNP - Peterhead North & Rattray)
cllr.f.mcrae@aberdeenshire.gov.uk

Merson, Rob (SNP - Ellon & District)
cllr.r.merson@aberdeenshire.gov.uk

Mollison, Ian (LD - North Kincardine)
cllr.i.mollison@aberdeenshire.gov.uk

Nelson, Carl (CON - North Kincardine)
cllr.c.nelson@aberdeenshire.gov.uk

Norrie, Alisan (IND - Turriff & District)
cllr.a.norrie@aberdeenshire.gov.uk

Oddie, Patricia (CON - West Garioch)
cllr.p.oddie@aberdeenshire.gov.uk

Owen, Gillian (CON - Ellon & District)
cllr.g.owen@aberdeenshire.gov.uk

Partridge, Hamish (SNP - Troup)
cllr.h.partridge@aberdeenshire.gov.uk

Petrie, Gwyneth (SNP - Huntly, Strathbogie & Howe of Alford)
cllr.g.petrie@aberdeenshire.gov.uk

Pirie, Lenny (SNP - Central Buchan)
cllr.l.pirie@aberdeenshire.gov.uk

Pratt, Stuart (SNP - Peterhead South & Cruden)
cllr.s.pratt@aberdeenshire.gov.uk

Robertson, Anne (LD - Turriff & District)
cllr.a.robertson@aberdeenshire.gov.uk

Roy, Mike (CON - Banff & District)
cllr.m.roy@aberdeenshire.gov.uk

Shand, Cryle (SNP - Mid-Formartine)
cllr.c.shand@aberdeenshire.gov.uk

Smith, Norman (IND - Central Buchan)
cllr.n.smith@aberdeenshire.gov.uk

Smith, Stephen (SNP - Peterhead South & Cruden)
cllr.s.smith@aberdeenshire.gov.uk

Stewart, Margo (CON - Huntly, Strathbogie & Howe of Alford)
cllr.m.stewart@aberdeenshire.gov.uk

Stewart, Dave (INDNA - Mearns)
cllr.d.stewart@aberdeenshire.gov.uk

Stuart, Bryan (SNP - Inverurie & District)
cllr.b.stuart@aberdeenshire.gov.uk

Tait, Ian (IND - Fraserburgh & District)
cllr.i.tait@aberdeenshire.gov.uk

Thomson, Richard (SNP - Ellon & District)
cllr.r.thomson@aberdeenshire.gov.uk

Topping, Brian (SNP - Fraserburgh & District)
cllr.b.topping@aberdeenshire.gov.uk

Walker, Iris (LD - Westhill & District)
cllr.i.walker@aberdeenshire.gov.uk

Watt, Michael (IND - Fraserburgh & District)
cllr.m.watt@aberdeenshire.gov.uk

Webster, Jill (CON - Banchory & Mid-Deeside)
cllr.j.webster@aberdeenshire.gov.uk

POLITICAL COMPOSITION
SNP: 28, CON: 14, IND: 11, LD: 11, LAB: 2, SGP: 1, INDNA: 1

COMMITTEE CHAIRS
Audit & Scrutiny: Ms Gillian Owen

Education, Learning & Leisure: Ms Alison Evison

Policy & Resources: Mr Martine Kitts-Hayes

Social Work & Housing: Ms Anne Allan

Adur   D

Adur District Council, Civic Centre, Ham Road, Shoreham-by-Sea BN43 6PR
☎ 01273 263000 ✆ info@adur.gov.uk 🖳 www.adur.gov.uk

FACTS AND FIGURES
Parliamentary Constituencies:
EU Constituencies: South East
Election Frequency: Elections are biennial

PRINCIPAL OFFICERS
Chief Executive: Mr Alex Bailey, Chief Executive, Civic Centre, Ham Road, Shoreham-by-Sea BN43 6PR ☎ 01903 221001 ✆ alex.bailey@adur-worthing.gov.uk

Senior Management: Mr Paul Brewer, Director - Digital & Resources, Worthing Town Hall, Chapel Road, Worthing BN11 1HA ☎ 01903 221302 ✆ paul.brewer@adur-worthing.gov.uk

Senior Management: Ms Mary D'Arcy, Director - Communities, Worthing Town Hall, Chapel Road, Worthing BN11 1HA ☎ 01903 221300 ✆ mary.d'arcy@adur-worthing.gov.uk

Senior Management: Ms Jane Eckford, Director - Customer Service, Worthing Town Hall, Chapel Road, Worthing BN11 1HA ☎ 01903 221059 ✆ jane.eckford@adur-worthing.gov.uk

Senior Management: Mr Martin Randall, Director - Economy, Civic Centre, Ham Road, Shoreham-by-Sea BN43 6PR ☎ 01903 221209 ✆ martin.randall@adur-worthing.gov.uk

Architect, Building / Property Services: Mr Steve Spinner, Head of Business & Technical Services, Portland House, Richmond Road, Worthing BN11 1LF ☎ 01903 221019 ✆ steve.spinner@adur-worthing.gov.uk

Building Control: Mr James Appleton, Head of Growth, Portland House, Richmond Road, Worthing BN11 1HS ☎ 01903 221333 ✆ james.appleton@adur-worthing.gov.uk

PR / Communications: Mr Neil Hopkins, Head of Communications, Worthing Town Hall, Chapel Road, Worthing BN11 1HA ✆ neil.hopkins@adur-worthing.gov.uk

Community Planning: Mr Paul Pennicott, Strategic Projects Officer, Worthing Town Hall, Chapel Road, Worthing BN11 1HA ☎ 01903 221347 ✆ paul.pennicott@adur-worthing.gov.uk

Community Safety: Mrs Jacqui Cooke, Safer Communities Manager, Worthing Town Hall, Chapel Road, Worthing BN11 1HA ☎ 08456 070999 ✆ jacqui.cooke@adur-worthing.gov.uk

Computer Management: Mr Simon Taylor, CenSus IT Operations Manager, Worthing Town Hall, Chapel Road, Worthing BN11 1HA ☎ 01903 221197 ✆ simon.taylor@adur-worthing.gov.uk

Contracts: Mr Steve Spinner, Head of Business & Technical Services, Portland House, Richmond Road, Worthing BN11 1LF ☎ 01903 221019 ✆ steve.spinner@adur-worthing.gov.uk

Corporate Services: Mr Paul Brewer, Director - Digital & Resources, Worthing Town Hall, Chapel Road, Worthing BN11 1HA ☎ 01903 221302 ✆ paul.brewer@adur-worthing.gov.uk

Customer Service: Ms Jane Eckford, Director - Customer Service, Worthing Town Hall, Chapel Road, Worthing BN11 1HA ☎ 01903 221059 ✆ jane.eckford@adur-worthing.gov.uk

Direct Labour: Mr Paul Brewer, Director - Digital & Resources, Worthing Town Hall, Chapel Road, Worthing BN11 1HA ☎ 01903 221302 ✆ paul.brewer@adur-worthing.gov.uk

Economic Development: Ms Tina Barker, Economic Development Officer, Commerce Way, Lancing BN15 8TA ☎ 01273 263206 ✆ tina.barker@adur-worthing.gov.uk

E-Government: Mr Paul Brewer, Director - Digital & Resources, Worthing Town Hall, Chapel Road, Worthing BN11 1HA ☎ 01903 221302 ✆ paul.brewer@adur-worthing.gov.uk

Electoral Registration: Ms Teresa Bryant, Electoral Services Manager, Worthing Town Hall, Chapel Road, Worthing BH11 1HA ☎ 01903 221474 ✆ teresa.bryant@adur-worthing.gov.uk

Emergency Planning: Mr Lloyd Harris, Emergency Planning Officer, Worthing Town Hall, Chapel Road, Worthing BN11 1HA ☎ 01903 221025 ✆ lloyd.harris@adur-worthing.gov.uk

Energy Management: Mr Paul Brewer, Director - Digital & Resources, Worthing Town Hall, Chapel Road, Worthing BN11 1HA ☎ 01903 221302 ✆ paul.brewer@adur-worthing.gov.uk

Environmental / Technical Services: Mr Paul Brewer, Director - Digital & Resources, Worthing Town Hall, Chapel Road, Worthing BN11 1HA ☎ 01903 221302 ✆ paul.brewer@adur-worthing.gov.uk

Environmental Health: Mr James Elliot, Senior Environmental Health Officer, Portland House, Richmond Road, Worthing BN11 1HS ☎ 01273 263032 ✆ james.elliot@adur-worthing.gov.uk

Estates, Property & Valuation: Mr James Appleton, Head of Growth, Worthing Town Hall, Chapel Road, Worthing BN11 1HA ☎ 01903 221333 ✆ james.appleton@adur-worthing.gov.uk

Facilities: Mr Steve Spinner, Head of Business & Technical Services, Portland House, Richmond Road, Worthing BN11 1LF ☎ 01903 221019 ✆ steve.spinner@adur-worthing.gov.uk

Finance: Mrs Sarah Gobey, Executive Head of Financial Services, Worthing Town Hall, Chapel Road, Worthing BN11 1HA ☎ 01903 221221 ✆ sarah.gobey@adur-worthing.gov.uk

Fleet Management: Ms Jane Eckford, Director - Customer Service, Worthing Town Hall, Chapel Road, Worthing BN11 1HA ☎ 01903 221059 ✆ jane.eckford@adur-worthing.gov.uk

Grounds Maintenance: Mr Andy Edwards, Head of Environment, Commerce Way, Lancing BN15 8TA ☎ 01273 263137 ✆ andy.edwards@adur-worthing.gov.uk

Health and Safety: Mrs Lesley Dexter, Senior Corporate Safety Officer, Portland House, Richmond Road, Worthing BN11 1LF ☎ 01273 263430 ✆ lesley.dexter@adur-worthing.gov.uk

Housing: Mr Paul Cooper, Head of Housing, Portland House, Richmond Road, Worthing BN11 1LF ☎ 01903 221190 ✆ paul.cooper@adur-worthing.gov.uk

Housing Maintenance: Mr Paul Cooper, Head of Housing, Portland House, Richmond Road, Worthing BN11 1LF ☎ 01903 221190 ✆ paul.cooper@adur-worthing.gov.uk

Legal: Ms Susan Sale, Solicitor to the Council, Worthing Town Hall, Chapel Road, Worthing BN11 1HA ☎ 01903 221119 ✆ susan.sale@adur-worthing.gov.uk

ADUR

Leisure and Cultural Services: Ms Amanda O'Reilly, Head of Culture, Worthing Town Hall, Chapel Road, Worthing BN11 1HA ☎ 01903 221142 ✆ amanda.o'reilly@adur-worthing.gov.uk

Licensing: Mr Simon Jones, Licensing Officer, Commerce Way, Lancing BN15 8TA ☎ 01273 263191 ✆ simon.jones@adur-worthing.gov.uk

Member Services: Mrs Julia Smith, Democratic Services Manager, Worthing Town Hall, Chapel Road, Worthing BN11 1HA ☎ 01903 221150 ✆ julia.smith@adur-worthing.gov.uk

Parking: Mr Ashley Miles, Technical Assistant, Worthing Town Hall, Chapel Road, Worthing BN11 1HA ☎ 01903 221022 ✆ ashley.miles@adur-worthing.gov.uk

Partnerships: Mr Alex Bailey, Chief Executive, Civic Centre, Ham Road, Shoreham-by-Sea BN43 6PR ☎ 01903 221001 ✆ alex.bailey@adur-worthing.gov.uk

Personnel / HR: Mr Paul Brewer, Director - Digital & Resources, Worthing Town Hall, Chapel Road, Worthing BN11 1HA ☎ 01903 221302 ✆ paul.brewer@adur-worthing.gov.uk

Personnel / HR: Ms Heidi Christmas, Human Resources Manager, Worthing Town Hall, Chapel Road, Worthing BN11 1HA ✆ heidi.christmas@adur-worthing.gov.uk

Planning: Mr James Appleton, Head of Growth, Portland House, Richmond Road, Worthing BN11 1HS ☎ 01903 221333 ✆ james.appleton@adur-worthing.gov.uk

Procurement: Mr Bill Williamson, Procurement Officer, Worthing Town Hall, Chapel Road, Worthing BN11 1HA ☎ 01903 221056 ✆ bill.williamson@adur-worthing.gov.uk

Recycling & Waste Minimisation: Ms Jane Eckford, Director - Customer Service, Worthing Town Hall, Chapel Road, Worthing BN11 1HA ☎ 01903 221059 ✆ jane.eckford@adur-worthing.gov.uk

Regeneration: Mr James Appleton, Head of Growth, Portland House, Richmond Road, Worthing BN11 1HS ☎ 01903 221333 ✆ james.appleton@adur-worthing.gov.uk

Staff Training: Ms Lois Ford, Learning & Development Co-ordinator, Worthing Town Hall, Chapel Road, Worthing BN11 1HA ☎ 01903 221043 ✆ lois.ford@adur-worthing.gov.uk

Street Scene: Mr David Steadman, Adur Town Centre & Street Scene Co-ordinator, Civic Centre, Ham Road, Shoreham-by-Sea BN43 6PR ☎ 01273 263152 ✆ david.steadman@adur-worthing.gov.uk

Sustainable Communities: Mr James Appleton, Head of Growth, Portland House, Richmond Road, Worthing BN11 1HS ☎ 01903 221333 ✆ james.appleton@adur-worthing.gov.uk

Sustainable Development: Mr James Appleton, Head of Growth, Portland House, Richmond Road, Worthing BN11 1HS ☎ 01903 221333 ✆ james.appleton@adur-worthing.gov.uk

Tourism: Ms Amanda O'Reilly, Head of Culture, Worthing Town Hall, Chapel Road, Worthing BN11 1HA ☎ 01903 221142 ✆ amanda.o'reilly@adur-worthing.gov.uk

Town Centre: Mr David Steadman, Adur Town Centre & Street Scene Co-ordinator, Civic Centre, Ham Road, Shoreham-by-Sea BN43 6PR ☎ 01273 263152 ✆ david.steadman@adur-worthing.gov.uk

Waste Collection and Disposal: Mr Tony Patching, Head of Waste & Cleansing, Worthing Town Hall, Chapel Road, Worthing BN11 1HA ☎ 01273 263049 ✆ tony.patching@adur-worthing.gov.uk

Waste Management: Mr Tony Patching, Head of Waste & Cleansing, Worthing Town Hall, Chapel Road, Worthing BN11 1HA ☎ 01273 263049 ✆ tony.patching@adur-worthing.gov.uk

COUNCILLORS

ChairBridges, Ann (CON - Widewater) ann.bridges@adur.gov.uk

Deputy ChairButcher, James (CON - Churchill) james.butcher@adur.gov.uk

Leader of the Council: Parkin, Neil (CON - St Nicolas) neil.parkin@adur.gov.uk

Deputy Leader of the Council: Dunn, Angus (CON - Hillside) angus.dunn@adur.gov.uk

Albury, Carol (CON - Manor) carol.albury@adur.gov.uk

Albury, Carson (CON - Manor) carson.albury@adur.gov.uk

Alden, Les (LAB - Eastbrook) les.alden@adur.gov.uk

Barton, George (CON - Peverel) george.barton@adur.gov.uk

Bishop, Ken (UKIP - Southlands) ken.bishop@adur.gov.uk

Boggis, Brian (CON - Peverel) brian.boggis@adur.gov.uk

Boram, Kevin (CON - Buckingham) kevin.boram@adur.gov.uk

Burghard, Clive (UKIP - Widewater) clive.burghard@adur.gov.uk

Chipp, Stephen (CON - St Mary's) stephen.chipp@adur.gov.uk

Coomber, Brian (CON - St Nicolas) brian.coomber@adur.gov.uk

Evans, Emma (CON - Buckingham) emma.evans@adur.gov.uk

Funnell, Jim (CON - Eastbrook) jim.funnell@adur.gov.uk

Graysmark, Paul (CON - Southlands) paul.graysmark@adur.gov.uk

Haywood, Liz (UKIP - Mash Barn) liz.haywood@adur.gov.uk

Hilditch, Emily (CON - Southwick Green) emily.hilditch@adur.gov.uk

Lambourne, David (UKIP - Mash Barn)
david.lambourne@adur.gov.uk

Loader, Joss (R - Marine)
joss.loader@adur.gov.uk

Mear, Barry (LAB - Cokeham)
barry.mear@adur-worthing.gov.uk

Metcalfe, Peter (CON - Southwick Green)
peter.metcalfe@adur.gov.uk

Monk, Robin (UKIP - Churchill)
robin.monk@adur.gov.uk

Patmore, Geoff (UKIP - Widewater)
geoff.patmore@adur.gov.uk

Phillips, Lyn (UKIP - Cokeham)
lyn.phillips@adur.gov.uk

Simmons, David (CON - Hillside)
david.simmons@adur.gov.uk

Stride, Ben (IND - Marine)
ben.stride@adur.gov.uk

Zeglam, Sami (LAB - St Mary's)
sami.zeglam@adur.gov.uk

POLITICAL COMPOSITION
CON: 17, UKIP: 7, LAB: 3, R: 1, IND: 1

COMMITTEE CHAIRS

Licensing: Mr Brian Coomber

Planning: Mr Peter Metcalfe

Allerdale   D

Allerdale Borough Council, Allerdale House, Workington
CA14 3YJ
☎ 01900 702702 🖷 01900 702507 ⌁ enquiries@allerdale.gov.uk
🖳 www.allerdale.gov.uk

FACTS AND FIGURES
Parliamentary Constituencies: Penrith and The Border,
Workington
EU Constituencies: North West
Election Frequency: Elections are of whole council

PRINCIPAL OFFICERS

Chief Executive: Mr Ian Frost, Chief Executive, Allerdale House,
Workington CA14 3YJ ☎ 01900 702975 ⌁ ian.frost@allerdale.gov.uk

Senior Management: Mr Andrew Seekings, Corporate Director,
Allerdale House, Workington CA14 3YJ ☎ 01900 702528
⌁ andrew.seekings@allerdale.gov.uk

Architect, Building / Property Services: Mr David Bryden,
Construction Services Manager - Property Services, Allerdale
House, Workington CA14 3YJ ☎ 01900 702753
⌁ david.bryden@allerdale.gov.uk

Building Control: Mr Kevin Kerrigan, Head of Development
Services, Allerdale House, Workington CA14 3YJ ☎ 01900 702799
⌁ kevin.kerrigan@allerdale.gov.uk

PR / Communications: Mr Andrew Gilbert, Communications &
Marketing Manager, Allerdale House, Workington CA14 3YJ
☎ 01900 702701 ⌁ andrew.gilbert@allerdale.gov.uk

Community Safety: Mr Charles Holmes, Head of Community
Services, Allerdale House, Workington CA14 3YJ ☎ 01900 702959
⌁ charles.holmes@allerdale.gov.uk

Computer Management: Mr Paul Wood, Head of Customer &
Commissioning, OD & Transformation, Allerdale House, Workington
CA14 3YJ ☎ 01900 702889 ⌁ paul.wood@allerdale.gov.uk

Customer Service: Ms Colette Symes, Customer Services Team
Leader, Allerdale House, Workington CA14 3YJ ☎ 01900 702702
⌁ colette.eymes@allerdale.gov.uk

Electoral Registration: Mr Andrew Seekings, Corporate Director,
Allerdale House, Workington CA14 3YJ ☎ 01900 702528
⌁ andrew.seekings@allerdale.gov.uk

Emergency Planning: Mr Graeme Wilson, Head of Housing &
Health, Allerdale House, Workington CA14 3YJ ☎ 01900 702661
⌁ graeme.wilson@allerdale.gov.uk

Environmental Health: Mr Graeme Wilson, Head of Housing &
Health, Allerdale House, Workington CA14 3YJ ☎ 01900 702661
⌁ graeme.wilson@allerdale.gov.uk

Finance: Ms Catherine Nicholson, Head of Finance, Allerdale
House, Workington CA14 3YJ ☎ 01900 702503
⌁ catherine.nicholson@allerdale.gov.uk

Treasury: Mr Barry Lennox, Treasurer, Allerdale House,
Workington CA14 3YJ ☎ 01900 702586
⌁ barry.lennox@allerdale.gov.uk

Health and Safety: Mr Barry Chambers, Corporate Health &
Safety Advisor, Allerdale House, Workington CA14 3YJ
☎ 01900 702599 ⌁ barry.chambers@allerdale.gov.uk

Housing: Mr Graeme Wilson, Head of Housing & Health, Allerdale
House, Workington CA14 3YJ ☎ 01900 702661
⌁ graeme.wilson@allerdale.gov.uk

Legal: Ms Sharon Sewell, Head of Governance, Allerdale House,
Workington CA14 3YJ ☎ 01900 702887
⌁ sharon.sewell@allerdale.gov.uk

Leisure and Cultural Services: Ms Rebecca Stamper, Sport
Development Officer, Allerdale House, Workington CA14 3YJ
☎ 01900 702711 ⌁ rebecca.stamper@allerdale.gov.uk

Licensing: Ms Gillian Collinson, Senior Land Charges & Licensing
Officer, Allerdale House, Workington CA14 3YJ ☎ 01900 702692
⌁ gillian.collinson@allerdale.gov.uk

Member Services: Ms Gayle Roach, Democratic Services Co-
ordinator, Allerdale House, Workington CA14 3YJ ☎ 01900 702817
⌁ gayle.roach@allerdale.gov.uk

ALLERDALE

Parking: Mr Mike Rollo, Parking Operations Manager, Allerdale House, Workington CA14 3YJ ☎ 01900 702859
✆ mike.rollo@allerdale.gov.uk

Personnel / HR: Ms Zoe Pluckrose, Head of People Resources, Allerdale House, Workington CA14 3YJ ☎ 01900 702725
✆ zoe.pluckrose@allerdale.gov.uk

Planning: Mr Kevin Kerrigan, Head of Development Services, Allerdale House, Workington CA14 3YJ ☎ 01900 702799
✆ kevin.kerrigan@allerdale.gov.uk

Regeneration: Mr Nik Hardy, Head of Economic Growth, Allerdale House, Workington CA14 3YJ ☎ 01900 702778
✆ nik.hardy@allerdale.gov.uk

Street Scene: Mr Robert Henderson, Locality Officer, Allerdale House, Workington CA14 3YJ ☎ 01900 702819
✆ robert.henderson@allerdale.gov.uk

Town Centre: Mr Joe Broomfield, Joint Town Centre Manager, Allerdale House, Workington CA14 3YJ ☎ 01900 702766
✆ joe.broomfield@allerdale.gov.uk

Town Centre: Ms Toni Magean, Town Centre Manager, Allerdale House, Workington CA14 3YJ ☎ 01900 702568
✆ toni.magean@allerdale.gov.uk

Waste Management: Mr Charles Holmes, Head of Community Services, Allerdale House, Workington CA14 3YJ ☎ 01900 702959
✆ charles.holmes@allerdale.gov.uk

COUNCILLORS

Mayor: Tibble, Celia (LAB - Seaton)
celia.tibble@allerdale.gov.uk

Deputy Mayor: Bainbridge, Mary (LAB - St Michaels Workington)
mary.bainbridge@allerdale.gov.uk

Leader of the Council: Smith, Alan (LAB - All Saints Cockermouth)
alan.smith@allerdale.gov.uk

Deputy Leader of the Council: Fryer, Mark (LAB - Stainburn Workington)
mark.fryer@allerdale.gov.uk

Group LeaderFinlay, Bill (IND - Aspatria)
bill.finlay@allerdale.gov.uk

Group LeaderMarkley, Anthony (CON - Holme)
anthony.markley@allerdale.gov.uk

Group LeaderWilson, David (UKIP - Aspatria)
david.wilson@allerdale.gov.uk

Annison, Tony (CON - Crummock)
anthony.annison@allerdale.gov.uk

Armstrong, Carole (LAB - Moss Bay Workington)
carole.armstrong@allerdale.gov.uk

Bales, Peter (LAB - Moorclose Workington)
peter.bales@allerdale.gov.uk

Cannon, Barbara (LAB - Moss Bay Workington)
barbara.cannon@allerdale.gov.uk

Cockburn, Nicky (IND - Broughton St Bridgets)
nicky.cockburn@allerdale.gov.uk

Colhoun, John (LAB - Ellen)
john.colhoun@allerdale.gov.uk

Cook, John (CON - Silloth)
john.cook@allerdale.gov.uk

Cowell, Joseph (CON - Wigton)
joe.cowell@allerdale.gove uk

Crouch, John (LAB - Wigton)
john.crouch@allerdale.gov.uk

Davies, Len (LAB - All Saints Cockermouth)
len.davies@allerdale.gov.uk

Davis-Johnston, Adrian (CON - Derwent Valley)
adrian.davis-johnston@allerdale.gov.uk

Fairbairn, Duncan (CON - Warnell)
duncan.fairbairn@allerdale.gov.uk

Farebrother, Janet (LAB - Broughton St Bridgets)
janet.farebrother@allerdale.gov.uk

Fitzgerald, Marion (IND - Dalton)
marion.fitzgerald@allerdale.gov.uk

Grainger, Malcolm (CON - Boltons)
malcolm.grainger@allerdale.gov.uk

Hansen, Konrad (LAB - St Johns Workington)
konrad.hansen@allerdale.gov.uk

Harrington, Hilary (IND - Harrington Workington)
hilary.harrington@allerdale.gov.uk

Heaslip, Michael (LAB - St Johns Workington)
michael.heaslip@allerdale.gov.uk

Hedworth, Alan (CON - Waver)
alan.hedworth@allerdale.gov.uk

Hodgson, Vaughan (CON - Marsh)
vaughan.hodgson@allerdale.gov.uk

Holliday, Joe (INDNA - St Johns Workington)
joe.holliday@allerdale.gov.uk

Jackson, Margaret (CON - Christchurch Cockermouth)
margaret.jackson@allerdale.gov.uk

Jefferson, William (INDNA - Silloth)
william.jefferson@allerdale.gov.uk

Jenkinson, Mark (UKIP - Seaton)
mark.jenkinson@allerdale.gov.uk

Johnston, Frank (LAB - Moss Bay Workington)

Kendall, Peter (LAB - Flimby)
peter.kendall@allerdale.gov.uk

Kendall, Angela (LAB - Netherhall Maryport)
angela.kendall@allerdale.gov.uk

Lister, Jim (CON - Solway)
jim.lister@allerdale.gov.uk

Lywood, Tony (LAB - Keswick)
tony.lywood@allerdale.gov.uk

Macdonald, Patricia (CON - Wampool)
patricia.macdonald@allerdale.gov.uk

Maguire, Lousie (LAB - Ellen)
louise.maguire@allerdale.gov.uk

McCarron-Holmes, Carni (LAB - Ewanrigg Maryport)
carni.mccarron-holmes@allerdale.gov.uk

Miskelly, Billy (LAB - St Michaels Workington)
billy.miskelly@allerdale.gov.uk

Mounsey, Jacqueline (CON - Wharrels)
jacqueline.mounsey@allerdale.gov.uk

Munby, Ronald (CON - Keswick)
ron.munby@allerdale.gov.uk

Nicholson, Eric (CON - Christchurch Cockermouth)
eric.nicholson@allerdale.gov.uk

Osborn, Jim (LAB - Harrington Workington)
jim.osborn@allerdale.gove.uk

Pegram, Bill (LAB - Netherhall Maryport)
bill.pegram@allerdale.gov.uk

Pitcher, Alan (CON - Wigton)
alan.pitcher@allerdale.gov.uk

Pugmire, Martin (IND - Keswick)
martin.pugmire@allerdale.gov.uk

Robertson, Denis (INDNA - Moorclose Workington)
denis.robertson@allerdale.gov.uk

Sandwith, Joe (UKIP - Seaton)
joe.sandwith@allerdale.gov.uk

Scholfield, Neil (LAB - St Michaels Workington)
neil.scholfield@llerdale.gov.uk

Smith, Christine (LAB - All Saints Cockermouth)
christine.smith@allerdale.gov.uk

Stoddart, Stephen (INDNA - Moorclose Workington)
stephen.stoddart@allerdale.gov.uk

Tibble, Philip (LAB - Clifton)
philip.tibble@allerdale.gov.uk

Williamson, Lee (LAB - Ewanrigg Maryport)
lee.williamson@allerdale.gov.uk

Wood, Janice (LAB - Ellenborough Maryport)
janice.wood@allerdale.gov.uk

Wood, Martin (LAB - Ellenborough Maryport)
martin.wood@allerdale.gov.uk

POLITICAL COMPOSITION
LAB: 28, CON: 16, IND: 5, INDNA: 4, UKIP: 3

COMMITTEE CHAIRS

Audit: Ms Mary Bainbridge

Development: Mr Peter Bales

Licensing: Mrs Angela Kendall

Amber Valley   D

Amber Valley Borough Council, Po Box 17, Town Hall, Ripley
DE5 3BT
☎ 01773 570222 🖷 01773 841616 🖉 enquiry@ambervalley.gov.uk
🖳 www.ambervalley.gov.uk

FACTS AND FIGURES
Parliamentary Constituencies: Amber Valley
EU Constituencies: East Midlands
Election Frequency: Elections are by thirds

PRINCIPAL OFFICERS

Senior Management: Ms Sylvia Delahay, Executive Director -
Resources, PO Box 1, Town Hall, Market Place, Ripley DE5 3BT
☎ 01773 841610 🖉 sylvia.delahay@ambervalley.gov.uk

Senior Management: Mr Julian Townsend, Executive Director -
Operations, Town Hall, Market Place, Ripley DE5 3BT
☎ 01773 841316 🖉 julian.townsend@ambervalley.gov.uk

Architect, Building / Property Services: Mr Simon Gladwin,
Assistant Director - Landscapes, Growth & Community Safety,
Town Hall, Market Place, Ripley DE5 3BT ☎ 01773 841415
🖉 simon.gladwin@ambervalley.gov.uk

Best Value: Ms Sylvia Delahay, Executive Director - Resources,
PO Box 1, Town Hall, Market Place, Ripley DE5 3BT
☎ 01773 841610 🖉 sylvia.delahay@ambervalley.gov.uk

Building Control: Mr Dave Chard, Building Control Manager,
Town Hall, Market Place, Ripley DE5 3BT ☎ 01773 841513
🖉 dave.chard@ambervalley.gov.uk

Community Planning: Mr Derek Stafford, Assistant Director -
Planning & Regeneration, Town Hall, Market Place, Ripley DE5 3BT
☎ 01773 841581 🖉 derek.stafford@ambervalley.gov.uk

Community Safety: Ms Sally Price, Community Safety Officer,
Town Hall, Market Place, Ripley DE5 3BT ☎ 01773 841652
🖉 sally.price@ambervalley.gov.uk

Computer Management: Mr Carl Marples, IT Operations &
Support Manager, PO Box 1, Town Hall, Market Place, Ripley
DE5 3BT ☎ 01773 841347 🖉 carl.marples@ambervalley.gov.uk

Corporate Services: Ms Sylvia Delahay, Executive Director -
Resources, PO Box 1, Town Hall, Market Place, Ripley DE5 3BT
☎ 01773 841610 🖉 sylvia.delahay@ambervalley.gov.uk

Economic Development: Mr Simon Gladwin, Assistant Director -
Landscapes, Growth & Community Safety, Town Hall, Market Place,
Ripley DE5 3BT ☎ 01773 841415
🖉 simon.gladwin@ambervalley.gov.uk

E-Government: Mr Andy Wilde, Information Development
Manager, PO Box 1, Town Hall, Market Place, Ripley DE5 3BT
☎ 01773 570222 🖉 andy.wilde@ambervalley.gov.uk

Electoral Registration: Ms Jill Harris, Democratic Services
Officer - Elections, Po Box 17, Town Hall, Ripley DE5 3BT
☎ 01773 841634 🖉 jill.harris@ambervalley.gov.uk

Emergency Planning: Ms Helen Holmes, Emergency Planning
Officer, Town Hall, Market Place, Ripley DE5 3BT ☎ 01773 570222
🖉 helen.holmes@ambervalley.gov.uk

Energy Management: Mrs Sharon Hampson, Facilities & Energy
Co-ordinator, Town Hall, Market Place, Ripley DE5 3BT ☎ 01773
841563 🖉 sharon.hampson@ambervalley.gov.uk

Environmental / Technical Services: Mr Julian Townsend,
Executive Director - Operations, Town Hall, Market Place, Ripley
DE5 3BT ☎ 01773 841316 🖉 julian.townsend@ambervalley.gov.uk

AMBER VALLEY

Environmental Health: Mr Julian Townsend, Executive Director - Operations, Town Hall, Market Place, Ripley DE5 3BT
☎ 01773 841316 ⌂ julian.townsend@ambervalley.gov.uk

Estates, Property & Valuation: Ms Marie Winter, Legal Executive - Property & Contracts, Town Hall, Market Place, Ripley DE5 3BT ☎ 01773 841643 ⌂ marie.winter@ambervalley.gov.uk

Events Manager: Mrs Joanne Bamford, Town Centres Development Officer, Town Hall, Market Place, Ripley DE5 3BT
☎ 01773 841485 ⌂ joanne.bamford@ambervalley.gov.uk

Facilities: Mrs Sharon Hampson, Facilities & Energy Co-ordinator, Town Hall, Market Place, Ripley DE5 3BT ☎ 01773 841563
⌂ sharon.hampson@ambervalley.gov.uk

Finance: Ms Sylvia Delahay, Executive Director - Resources, PO Box 1, Town Hall, Market Place, Ripley DE5 3BT ☎ 01773 841610
⌂ sylvia.delahay@ambervalley.gov.uk

Treasury: Ms Sylvia Delahay, Executive Director - Resources, PO Box 1, Town Hall, Market Place, Ripley DE5 3BT ☎ 01773 841610
⌂ sylvia.delahay@ambervalley.gov.uk

Grounds Maintenance: Mr Simon Gladwin, Assistant Director - Landscapes, Growth & Community Safety, Town Hall, Market Place, Ripley DE5 3BT ☎ 01773 841415
⌂ simon.gladwin@ambervalley.gov.uk

Health and Safety: Mr Brian Shore, Safety & Resilience Advisor, Town Hall, Market Place, Ripley DE5 3BT ☎ 01773 841668
⌂ brian.shore@ambervalley.gov.uk

Home Energy Conservation: Ms Joanne Walker, Housing Officer, Town Hall, Market Place, Ripley DE5 3BT ☎ 01773 841332
⌂ joanne.walker@ambervalley.gov.uk

Housing: Mr David Arkle, Housing Manager, Town Hall, Market Place, Ripley DE5 3BT ☎ 01773 841334
⌂ david.arkle@ambervalley.gov.uk

Legal: Mr Chris Potter, Assistant Director - Legal & Democratic Services, Town Hall, Market Place, Ripley DE5 3BT
☎ 01773 841397 ⌂ chris.potter@ambervalley.gov.uk

Leisure and Cultural Services: Mr Kirk Monk, Assistant Director - Wellbeing, Town Hall, Market Place, Ripley DE5 3BT
☎ 01773 841646 ⌂ kirk.monk@ambervalley.gov.uk

Licensing: Ms Heather Adams, Licensing Manager, Town Hall, Market Place, Ripley DE5 3BT ☎ 01773 841602
⌂ heather.adams@ambervalley.gov.uk

Member Services: Mr Paul Benski, Democratic Services Manager, Town Hall, Market Place, Ripley DE5 3BT
☎ 01773 841641 ⌂ paul.benski@ambervalley.gov.uk

Parking: Ms Pam Leigh, Central Operations Team Leader, Town Hall, Market Place, Ripley DE5 3BT ☎ 01773 841437
⌂ pam.leigh@ambervalley.gov.uk

Partnerships: Mr Julian Townsend, Executive Director - Operations, Town Hall, Market Place, Ripley DE5 3BT
☎ 01773 841316 ⌂ julian.townsend@ambervalley.gov.uk

Personnel / HR: Ms Sylvia Delahay, Executive Director - Resources, PO Box 1, Town Hall, Market Place, Ripley DE5 3BT
☎ 01773 841610 ⌂ sylvia.delahay@ambervalley.gov.uk

Planning: Mrs Sarah Johnson, Planning Manager, Town Hall, Market Place, Ripley DE5 3BT ☎ 01773 841511
⌂ sarah.johnson@ambervalley.gov.uk

Procurement: Ms Sylvia Delahay, Executive Director - Resources, PO Box 1, Town Hall, Market Place, Ripley DE5 3BT
☎ 01773 841610 ⌂ sylvia.delahay@ambervalley.gov.uk

Recycling & Waste Minimisation: Ms Theresa Barnes, Principal Waste Performance & Recycling Officer, Town Hall, Market Place, Ripley DE5 3BT ☎ 01773 841323
⌂ theresa.barnes@ambervalley.gov.uk

Regeneration: Mr Simon Gladwin, Assistant Director - Landscapes, Growth & Community Safety, Town Hall, Market Place, Ripley DE5 3BT ☎ 01773 841415
⌂ simon.gladwin@ambervalley.gov.uk

Street Scene: Mrs Sharon Sutton, Landscape Development Manager, Town Hall, Market Place, Ripley DE5 3BT
☎ 01773 841570 ⌂ sharon.sutton@ambervalley.gov.uk

Sustainable Communities: Mr Derek Stafford, Assistant Director - Planning & Regeneration, Town Hall, Market Place, Ripley DE5 3BT ☎ 01773 841581 ⌂ derek.stafford@ambervalley.gov.uk

Sustainable Development: Mr Derek Stafford, Assistant Director - Planning & Regeneration, Town Hall, Market Place, Ripley DE5 3BT ☎ 01773 841581
⌂ derek.stafford@ambervalley.gov.uk

Tourism: Mrs Joanne Bamford, Town Centres Development Officer, Town Hall, Market Place, Ripley DE5 3BT ☎ 01773 841485
⌂ joanne.bamford@ambervalley.gov.uk

Town Centre: Mr Simon Gladwin, Assistant Director - Landscapes, Growth & Community Safety, Town Hall, Market Place, Ripley DE5 3BT ☎ 01773 841415 ⌂ simon.gladwin@ambervalley.gov.uk

Waste Collection and Disposal: Mr Ian Shaw, Environment Manager, Town Hall, Market Place, Ripley DE5 3BT
☎ 01773 841324 ⌂ ian.shaw@ambervalley.gov.uk

Waste Management: Mr Ian Shaw, Environment Manager, Town Hall, Market Place, Ripley DE5 3BT ☎ 01773 841324
⌂ ian.shaw@ambervalley.gov.uk

Children's Play Areas: Mr Simon Gladwin, Assistant Director - Landscapes, Growth & Community Safety, Town Hall, Market Place, Ripley DE5 3BT ☎ 01773 841415
⌂ simon.gladwin@ambervalley.gov.uk

COUNCILLORS

Mayor: Iliffe, Richard (CON - Shipley Park, Horsley & Horsley Woodhouse)
richard.iliffe@ambervalley.gov.uk

Deputy Mayor: Wilson, David (CON - Swanwick)
david.wilson@ambervalley.gov.uk

Leader of the Council: Buttery, Kevin (CON - Kilburn, Denby & Holbrook)
kevin.buttery@ambervalley.gov.uk

Deputy Leader of the Council: Ainsworth, Trevor (CON - Kilburn, Denby & Holbrook)
trevor.ainsworth@ambervalley.gov.uk

Ainstrop, Barrie (LAB - Heanor East)
barrie.aistrop@ambervalley.gov.uk

Ashton, Ron (CON - Ripley & Marehay)
ron.ashton@ambervalley.gov.uk

Bellamy, Ben (LAB - Belper North)
ben.bellamy@ambervalley.gov.uk

Bennett, Marlene (LAB - Alfreton)
marlene.bennett@ambervalley.gov.uk

Booth, Dan (CON - Belper Central)
daniel.booth@ambervalley.gov.uk

Booth, Joseph (CON - Belper North)
joseph.booth@ambervalley.gov.uk

Brown, Jack (CON - Ironville & Riddings)
jack.brown@ambervalley.gov.uk

Bull, Norman (CON - Kilburn, Denby & Holbrook)
norman.bull@ambervalley.gov.uk

Cox, Jackie (CON - Belper East)
jackie.cox@ambervalley.gov.uk

Curran, Teresa (LAB - Heanor West)
teresa.curran@ambervalley.gov.uk

Dolman, Gail (LAB - Alfreton)
gail.dolman@ambervalley.gov.uk

Emmas-Williams, Christopher (LAB - Codnor & Waingroves)
chris.emmas-williams@ambervalley.gov.uk

Emmas-Williams, Roland (LAB - Ripley)
roland.emmas-williams@ambervalley.gov.uk

Evanson, Steven (CON - Duffield)
steven.evanson@ambervalley.gov.uk

Gee, Gareth (CON - Crich)
gareth.gee@ambervalley.gov.uk

Gration, Brian (LAB - Langley Mill & Aldercar)
brian.gration@ambervalley.gov.uk

Hamilton, Eileen (LAB - Langley Mill & Aldercar)
eileen.hamilton@ambervalley.gov.uk

Harry, Isobel (LAB - Codnor & Waingroves)
isobel.harry@ambervalley.gov.uk

Hayes, Stephen (CON - Swanwick)
stephen.hayes@ambervalley.gov.uk

Hill, Kieran (LAB - Heanor & Loscoe)
kieran.hill@ambervalley.gov.uk

Hillier, Paul (CON - Belper South)
paul.hillier@ambervalley.gov.uk

Holmes, Tony (LAB - Ripley)
tony.holmes@ambervalley.gov.uk

Johnsen, Erik (LAB - Belper South)
erik.johnsen@ambervalley.gov.uk

Jones, Paul (LAB - Heanor West)
paul.jones@ambervalley.gov.uk

Longden, Heather (LAB - Heanor & Loscoe)
heather.longden@ambervalley.gov.uk

Lyttle, Brian (LAB - Somercotes)
brian.lyttle@ambervalley.gov.uk

McCabe, John (LAB - Somercotes)
john.mccabe@ambervalley.gov.uk

Moss, Paul (CON - Ripley)
paul.moss@ambervalley.gov.uk

Neville, Maurice (LAB - Belper Central)
maurice.neville@ambervalley.gov.uk

Oakes, Sheila (LAB - Heanor East)
sheila.oakes@ambervalley.gov.uk

Orton, Jane (CON - South West Parishes)
jane.orton@ambervalley.gov.uk

Short, Christopher (CON - Duffield)
chris.short@ambervalley.gov.uk

Smith, Paul (LAB - Ironville & Riddings)
paul.smith@ambervalley.gov.uk

Stevenson, Alex (CON - Shipley Park, Horsley & Horsley Woodhouse)
alex.stevenson@ambervalley.gov.uk

Taylor, Valerie (CON - Heage & Ambergate)
valerie.taylor@ambervalley.gov.uk

Taylor, David (CON - Alport)
david.taylor@ambervalley.gov.uk

Thorpe, Valerie (CON - Wingfield)
valerie.thorpe@ambervalley.gov.uk

Tomlinson, Martin (CON - Belper East)
martin.tomlinson@ambervalley.gov.uk

Walker, John (LAB - Alfreton)
john.walker@ambervalley.gov.uk

Ward, Angela (CON - Heage & Ambergate)
angela.ward@ambervalley.gov.uk

Wilson, Mick (LAB - Ripley & Marehay)
mick.wilson@ambervalley.gov.uk

POLITICAL COMPOSITION
CON: 23, LAB: 22

COMMITTEE CHAIRS

Audit & Governance: Mr Christopher Short

Licensing: Ms Jackie Cox

Planning: Mr Jack Brown

Angus   S

Angus Council, Angus House, Orchardbank Business Park, Forfar DD8 1AX

☎ 03452 777778 ✆ chiefexec@angus.gov.uk 🖳 www.angus.gov.uk

FACTS AND FIGURES
Parliamentary Constituencies: Angus, Dundee West

ANGUS

EU Constituencies: Scotland
Election Frequency: Elections are of whole council

PRINCIPAL OFFICERS

Chief Executive: Mr Richard Stiff, Chief Executive, Angus House, Orchardbank Business Park, Forfar DD8 1AX ☎ 01307 476101 ⌂ chiefexec@angus.gov.uk

Deputy Chief Executive: Mr Mark Armstrong, Strategic Director - Resources, Angus House, Orchardbank Business Park, Forfar DD8 1AX ☎ 01307 476469 ⌂ armstrongm@angus.gov.uk

Senior Management: Mr Mark Armstrong, Strategic Director - Resources, Angus House, Orchardbank Business Park, Forfar DD8 1AX ☎ 01307 476469 ⌂ armstrongm@angus.gov.uk

Senior Management: Mr Alan McKeown, Strategic Director - Communities, Angus House, Orchardbank Business Park, Forfar DD8 1AX ☎ 01307 474711 ⌂ mckeowna@angus.gov.uk

Senior Management: Mrs Margo Williamson, Strategic Director - Children & Learning, Angus House, Orchardbank Business Park, Forfar DD8 1AX ☎ 01307 476468 ⌂ williamsonm@angus.gov.uk

Access Officer / Social Services (Disability): Ms Fiona Rennie, Senior Planning Officer, Ravenswood, Forfar DD8 2ZG ☎ 01307 473130 ⌂ rennief@angus.gov.uk

Architect, Building / Property Services: Mr Ken Brown, Service Manager - Property & Communities Directorate, Bruce House, Wellgate, Arbroath DD11 3TP ☎ 03452 777778 ⌂ brownka@angus.gov.uk

Building Control: Ms Kate Cowey, Service Manager - Planning, Angus House, Orchardbank Business Park, Forfar DD8 1AX ☎ 03452 777778 ⌂ coweyk@angus.gov.uk

Catering Services: Ms Fiona Dawson, Catering Advisor, Angus House, Orchardbank Business Park, Forfar DD8 1AE ☎ 01307 461460 ⌂ dawsonf@angus.gov.uk

Children / Youth Services: Mr Tim Armstrong, Head of Children & Young People's Services, Ravenswood, New Road, Forfar DD8 2ZG ☎ 03452 777778 ⌂ armstrongt@angus.gov.uk

Civil Registration: Ms Sandra Pattie, Chief Registrar - Resources Directorate, 9 West High Street, Forfar DD8 1BD ☎ 01307 464973 ⌂ patties@angus.gov.uk

PR / Communications: Ms Moira Naulty, Communications Manager, Angus House, Orchardbank Business Park, Forfar DD8 1AX ☎ 01307 476090 ⌂ naultym@angus.gov.uk

Community Planning: Ms Vivien Smith, Head of Planning & Place - Communities Directorate, William Wallace House, Orchardbank Business Park, Forfar DD8 1WH ☎ 01307 476105 ⌂ smithv@angus.gov.uk

Community Safety: Mr Bob Myles, Service Manager - Community Safety, The Mart, 13 Market Street, Forfar DD8 3EY ☎ 03452 777778 ⌂ mylesb@angus.gov.uk

Computer Management: Mr Steve Roud, Service Manager - Resources, Angus House, Orchardbank Business Park, Forfar DD8 1AX ☎ 01307 476406 ⌂ rouds@angus.gov.uk

Consumer Protection and Trading Standards: Mr Stewart Ball, Service Manager - Regulatory & Protective Services, County Buildings, Market Street, Forfar DD8 3WR ☎ 01307 473213 ⌂ ballsl@angus.gov.uk

Economic Development: Ms Alison Smith, Service Manager - Economic Development, County Buildings, Market Street, Forfar DD8 3WD ☎ 01307 473222 ⌂ smithaj@angus.gov.uk

Education: Ms Pauline Stephen, Head of Schools & Learning, Angus House, Orchardbank Business Park, Forfar DD8 1AX ☎ 01307 467347 ⌂ stephenp@angus.gov.uk

Electoral Registration: Mrs Shona Cameron, Elections & Business Support Manager, Angus House, Orchardbank Business Park, Forfar DD8 1AN ☎ 01307 476226 ⌂ cameronsd@angus.gov.uk

Emergency Planning: Ms Jacqui Semple, Resilience Manager, Angus House, Orchardbank Business Park, Forfar DD8 1AX ☎ 01307 476123 ⌂ semplej@angus.gov.uk

Energy Management: Mr Ken Brown, Service Manager - Property & Communities Directorate, Bruce House, Wellgate, Arbroath DD11 3TP ☎ 03452 777778 ⌂ brownka@angus.gov.uk

Environmental Health: Mr Stewart Ball, Service Manager - Regulatory & Protective Services, County Buildings, Market Street, Forfar DD8 3WR ☎ 01307 473213 ⌂ ballsl@angus.gov.uk

Estates, Property & Valuation: Mr Neil MacKenzie, Principal Estates Manager, Bruce House, Wellgate, Arbroath DD11 3TP ☎ 03452 777778 ⌂ mackenzien@angus.gov.uk

European Liaison: Ms Shelley Hague, Senior External Funding Officer, Angus House, Orchardbank Business Park, Forfar DD8 1AX ☎ 01307 473222 ⌂ hagues@angus.gov.uk

Events Manager: Ms Jacqui Semple, Resilience Manager, Angus House, Orchardbank Business Park, Forfar DD8 1AX ☎ 01307 476123 ⌂ semplej@angus.gov.uk

Finance: Mr Ian Lorimer, Head of Finance, Angus House, Orchardbank Business Park, Forfar DD8 1AF ☎ 01307 476222 ⌂ lorimeri@angus.gov.uk

Fleet Management: Mr Graham Robertson, Fleet Manager, Burgh Yard, Cairnie Loan, Arbroath DD11 4DS ☎ 01241 876736 ⌂ robertsong@angus.gov.uk

Grounds Maintenance: Mr Kevin Robertson, Service Manager - Parks & Burial Grounds, The Mart, 13 Market Street, Forfar DD8 3EY ☎ 03452 777778 ⌂ robertsonk@angus.gov.uk

Health and Safety: Mrs Susan Bruce, Safety Manager, Angus House, Orchardbank Business Park, Forfar DD8 1AP ☎ 01307 476120 ⌂ bruces@angus.gov.uk

Highways: Mr Ian Cochrane, Head of Technical & Property Services, County Buildings, Market Street, Forfar DD8 1BX ☎ 01307 473278 ✆ cochraneia@angus.gov.uk

Home Energy Conservation: Mr Gareth Boswere, Service Manager - Technical, Angus House, Orchardbank Business Park, Forfar DD8 1AX ✆ boswereg@angus.gov.uk

Housing: Mr John Morrow, Service Manager - Housing, William Wallace House, Orchard Loan, Forfar DD8 1WH ☎ 01307 474786 ✆ morrowj@angus.gov.uk

Housing Maintenance: Mr Alan McKeown, Strategic Director - Communities, Angus House, Orchardbank Business Park, Forfar DD8 1AX ☎ 01307 474711 ✆ mckeowna@angus.gov.uk

Legal: Mrs Sheona Hunter, Head of Legal & Democratic Services, Angus House, Orchardbank Business Park, Forfar DD8 1AN ☎ 01307 476262 ✆ hunters@angus.gov.uk

Licensing: Mrs Sheona Hunter, Head of Legal & Democratic Services, Angus House, Orchardbank Business Park, Forfar DD8 1AN ☎ 01307 476262 ✆ hunters@angus.gov.uk

Lifelong Learning: Mrs Margo Williamson, Strategic Director - Children & Learning, Angus House, Orchardbank Business Park, Forfar DD8 1AX ☎ 01307 476468 ✆ williamsonm@angus.gov.uk

Lighting: Mr John Shand, Lighting Partnership Manager, Tayside Contracts Area Office, Kirriemuir Road, Forfar DD8 3TH ☎ 01307 473932 ✆ shandj@angus.gov.uk

Lottery Funding, Charity and Voluntary: Ms Shelley Hague, Senior External Funding Officer, Angus House, Orchardbank Business Park, Forfar DD8 1AX ☎ 01307 473222 ✆ hagues@angus.gov.uk

Member Services: Mrs Elaine Whittet, Manager - Executive Support, Angus House, Orchardbank Business Park, Forfar DD8 1AX ☎ 01307 476099 ✆ whittete@angus.gcsx.gov.uk

Parking: Mr Ian Cochrane, Head of Technical & Property Services, County Buildings, Market Street, Forfar DD8 1BX ☎ 01307 473278 ✆ cochraneia@angus.gov.uk

Personnel / HR: Mrs Sharon Faulkner, Head of HR, IT & Organisational Development, Angus House, Orchardbank Business Park, Forfar DD8 1AP ☎ 01307 476091 ✆ personnel@angus.gov.uk

Planning: Ms Kate Cowey, Service Manager - Planning, Angus House, Orchardbank Business Park, Forfar DD8 1AX ☎ 03452 777778 ✆ coweyk@angus.gov.uk

Procurement: Mr Mark Allan, Procurement Manager, Angus House, Orchardbank Business Park, Forfar DD8 1AF ☎ 01307 476195 ✆ allanm@angus.gov.uk

Recycling & Waste Minimisation: Mr Graeme Dailly, Service Manager - Environmental Management & Waste, Dewar House, Hill Terrace, Arbroath DD11 1AH ☎ 01241 435602 ✆ daillyg@angus.gov.uk

Regeneration: Ms Debbie Gowans, Community Regeneration Officer, William Wallace House, Orchardbank Business Park, Forfar DD8 1WH ☎ 01307 474153 ✆ gowansd@angus.gov.uk

Road Safety: Mr Ian Cochrane, Head of Technical & Property Services, County Buildings, Market Street, Forfar DD8 1BX ☎ 01307 473278 ✆ cochraneia@angus.gov.uk

Social Services: Mrs Margo Williamson, Strategic Director - Children & Learning, Angus House, Orchardbank Business Park, Forfar DD8 1AX ☎ 01307 476468 ✆ williamsonm@angus.gov.uk

Social Services (Children): Mr Tim Armstrong, Head of Children & Young People's Services, Ravenswood, New Road, Forfar DD8 2ZG ☎ 03452 777778 ✆ armstrongt@angus.gov.uk

Staff Training: Mr Ken Ritchie, Senior Service Manager - Human Resources, Angus House, Orchardbank Business Park, Forfar DD8 1AP ☎ 01307 476091 ✆ personnel@angus.gov.uk

Street Scene: Mr Ian Cochrane, Head of Technical & Property Services, County Buildings, Market Street, Forfar DD8 1BX ☎ 01307 473278 ✆ cochraneia@angus.gov.uk

Sustainable Development: Ms Kate Cowey, Service Manager - Planning, Angus House, Orchardbank Business Park, Forfar DD8 1AX ☎ 03452 777778 ✆ coweyk@angus.gov.uk

Tourism: Ms Alison Smith, Service Manager - Economic Development, County Buildings, Market Street, Forfar DD8 3WD ☎ 01307 473222 ✆ smithaj@angus.gov.uk

Traffic Management: Mr Graham Harris, Traffic Manager, County Buildings, Market Street, Forfar DD8 3WR ☎ 01307 473283

Transport: Ms Kate Cowey, Service Manager - Planning, Angus House, Orchardbank Business Park, Forfar DD8 1AX ☎ 03452 777778 ✆ coweyk@angus.gov.uk

Transport Planner: Ms Kate Cowey, Service Manager - Planning, Angus House, Orchardbank Business Park, Forfar DD8 1AX ☎ 03452 777778 ✆ coweyk@angus.gov.uk

Waste Collection and Disposal: Mr Graeme Dailly, Service Manager - Environmental Management & Waste, Dewar House, Hill Terrace, Arbroath DD11 1AH ☎ 01241 435602 ✆ daillyg@angus.gov.uk

Waste Management: Mr Graeme Dailly, Service Manager - Environmental Management & Waste, Dewar House, Hill Terrace, Arbroath DD11 1AH ☎ 01241 435602 ✆ daillyg@angus.gov.uk

COUNCILLORS

Leader of the Council: Gaul, Iain (SNP - Kirriemuir & Dean) cllrgaul@angus.gov.uk

Bowles, Bill (IND - Carnoustie & District) cllrbowles@angus.gov.uk

Boyd, Brian (IND - Carnoustie & District) cllrboyd@angus.gov.uk

Brown, Colin (IND - Forfar & District) cllrbrown@angus.gov.uk

ANGUS

Devine, Lynne (SNP - Forfar & District)
cllrdevine@angus.gov.uk

Duff, Bill (SNP - Montrose & District)
cllrduff@angus.gov.uk

Evans, Mairi (SNP - Brechin & Edzell)
cllrevans@angus.gov.uk

Fairweather, David (IND - Arbroath West & Letham)
cllrfairweather@angus.gov.uk

Fotheringham, Craig (CON - Monifieth & Sidlaw)
cllrfotheringham@angus.gov.uk

Gaul, Jeanette (SNP - Kirriemuir & Dean)
cllrgaulje@angus.gov.uk

Geddes, Martyn (CON - Arbroath East & Lunan)
cllrgeddes@angus.gov.uk

Hands, Sheila (SNP - Monifieth & Sidlaw)
cllrhands@angus.gov.uk

Houston, Jim (SNP - Brechin & Edzell)
cllrhouston@angus.gov.uk

King, Alex (SNP - Arbroath West & Letham)
cllrking@angus.gov.uk

Lumgair, David (CON - Arbroath West & Letham)
cllrlumgair@angus.gov.uk

May, David (LD - Montrose & District)
cllrmay@angus.gov.uk

McLaren, Ian (IND - Forfar & District)
cllrmclaren@angus.gov.uk

Middleton, Glennis (SNP - Forfar & District)
cllrmiddletong@angus.gov.uk

Morrison, Donald (SNP - Arbroath East & Lunan)
cllrmorrison@angus.gov.uk

Murray, Rob (SNP - Monifieth & Sidlaw)
cllrmurray@angus.gov.uk

Myles, Bob (IND - Brechin & Edzell)
cllrmyles@angus.gov.uk

Oswald, Helen (SNP - Carnoustie & District)
cllroswald@angus.gov.uk

Proctor, Ronnie (CON - Kirriemuir & Dean)
cllrproctor@angus.gov.uk

Salmond, Mark (IND - Montrose & District)
cllrsalmond@angus.gov.uk

Smith, Ewan (IND - Arbroath West & Letham)
cllrsmith@angus.gov.uk

Spink, Bob (IND - Arbroath East & Lunan)
cllrspink@angus.gov.uk

Thomson, Margaret (LAB - Monifieth & Sidlaw)
cllrthomson@angus.gov.uk

Valentine, Paul (SNP - Montrose & District)
cllrvalentine@angus.gov.uk

Welsh, Sheena (SNP - Arbroath East & Lunan)
cllrwelsh@angus.gov.uk

POLITICAL COMPOSITION
SNP: 14, IND: 9, CON: 4, LAB: 1, LD: 1

Antrim & Newtownabbey, Antrim and Newtownabbey Borough Council, Mossley Mill, Carnmoney Road North, Newtownabbey BT36 5QA
☎ 028 9446 3113 ▯ wwwantrimandnewtownabbey.gov.uk

PRINCIPAL OFFICERS

Chief Executive: Ms Jacqui Dixon, Chief Executive, Antrim and Newtownabbey Borough Council, Mossley Mill, Carnmoney Road North, Newtownabbey BT36 5QA ☎ 028 9034 0003
✆ jacqui.dixon@antrimandnewtownabbey.gov.uk

Senior Management: Mrs Geraldine Girvan, Director - Operations, Antrim Civic Centre, 50 Stiles Way, Antrim BT41 2UB
☎ 028 9446 3113
✆ geraldine.girvan@antrimandnewtownabbey.gov.uk

Senior Management: Ms Majella McAlister, Director - Community Planning & Regeneration, Antrim and Newtownabbey Borough Council, Mossley Mill, Carnmoney Road North, Newtownabbey BT36 5QA ☎ 028 9034 0000
✆ majella.mcalister@antrimandnewtownabbey.gov.uk

Senior Management: Mrs Andrea McCooke, Director - Organisation Development, Antrim Civic Centre, 50 Stiles Way, Antrim BT41 2UB ☎ 028 9446 3113 ✆ andrea.mccooke@antrimandnewtownabbey.gov.uk

Access Officer / Social Services (Disability): Mr Jason Douglas, Corporate Health & Safety Officer, Antrim Civic Centre, 50 Stiles Way, Antrim BT41 2UB ☎ 028 9034 0000
✆ jason.douglas@antrimandnewtownabbey.gov.uk

Architect, Building / Property Services: Mr Reggie Hillen, Head of Capital Development, Antrim and Newtownabbey Borough Council, Mossley Mill, Carnmoney Road North, Newtownabbey BT36 5QA ☎ 028 9034 0000
✆ reggie.hillen@antrimandnewtownabbey.gov.uk

Building Control: Ms Bronagh Doonan, Head of Property & Building Services, Antrim and Newtownabbey Borough Council, Mossley Mill, Carnmoney Road North, Newtownabbey BT36 5QA ☎ 028 9034 0000
✆ brongah.doonan@antrimandnewtownabbey.gov.uk

Civil Registration: Mrs Tracey White, Head of Communication & Customer Services, Antrim and Newtownabbey Borough Council, Mossley Mill, Carnmoney Road North, Newtownabbey BT36 5QA
☎ 028 9446 3113 ✆ tracey.white@antrimandnewtownabbey.gov.uk

PR / Communications: Mrs Tracey White, Head of Communication & Customer Services, Antrim and Newtownabbey Borough Council, Mossley Mill, Carnmoney Road North, Newtownabbey BT36 5QA ☎ 028 9446 3113
✆ tracey.white@antrimandnewtownabbey.gov.uk

Community Planning: Mrs Louise Moore, Head of Community Planning, Antrim and Newtownabbey Borough Council, Mossley Mill, Carnmoney Road North, Newtownabbey BT36 5QA
☎ 028 9034 0000 ✆ louise.moore@antrimandnewtownabbey.gov.uk

Community Safety: Mrs Louise Moore, Head of Community Planning, Antrim and Newtownabbey Borough Council, Mossley Mill, Carnmoney Road North, Newtownabbey BT36 5QA ☎ 028 9034 0000 ┐ louise.moore@antrimandnewtownabbey.gov.uk

Computer Management: Mr Graham Smyth, ICT Manager, Antrim and Newtownabbey Borough Council, Mossley Mill, Carnmoney Road North, Newtownabbey BT36 5QA ☎ 028 9446 3113 ┐ graham.smyth@antrimandnewtownabbey.gov.uk

Consumer Protection and Trading Standards: Mr Clifford Todd, Head of Environmental Health, Antrim and Newtownabbey Borough Council, Mossley Mill, Carnmoney Road North, Newtownabbey BT36 5QA ☎ 028 9034 0000 ┐ clifford.todd@antrimandnewtownabbey.gov.uk

Contracts: Mr John Balmer, Head of Finance, Antrim Civic Centre, 50 Stiles Way, Antrim BT41 2UB ☎ 028 9446 3113 ┐ john.balmer@antrimandnewtownabbey.gov.uk

Customer Service: Mrs Tracey White, Head of Communication & Customer Services, Antrim and Newtownabbey Borough Council, Mossley Mill, Carnmoney Road North, Newtownabbey BT36 5QA ☎ 028 9446 3113 ┐ tracey.white@antrimandnewtownabbey.gov.uk

Economic Development: Mr Paul Kelly, Head of Economic Development, Antrim and Newtownabbey Borough Council, Mossley Mill, Carnmoney Road North, Newtownabbey BT36 5QA ☎ 028 9034 0000 ┐ paul.kelly@antrimandnewtownabbey.gov.uk

Emergency Planning: Mrs Laura Boyle, Emergency Planning Officer, Antrim Civic Centre, 50 Stiles Way, Antrim BT41 2UB ☎ 028 9446 3113

Energy Management: Ms Bronagh Doonan, Head of Property & Building Services, Antrim and Newtownabbey Borough Council, Mossley Mill, Carnmoney Road North, Newtownabbey BT36 5QA ☎ 028 9034 0000 ┐ brongah.doonan@antrimandnewtownabbey.gov.uk

Environmental / Technical Services: Mr Jim Gurney, Head of Waste Management, Antrim Civic Centre, 50 Stiles Way, Antrim BT41 2UB ☎ 028 9446 3113 ┐ jim.gurney@antrimandnewtownabbey.gov.uk

Environmental Health: Mr Clifford Todd, Head of Environmental Health, Antrim and Newtownabbey Borough Council, Mossley Mill, Carnmoney Road North, Newtownabbey BT36 5QA ☎ 028 9034 0000 ┐ clifford.todd@antrimandnewtownabbey.gov.uk

Events Manager: Mrs Ursula Fay, Head of Arts & Culture, Antrim Civic Centre, 50 Stiles Way, Antrim BT41 2UB ☎ 028 9446 3113 ┐ ursula.fay@antrimandnewtownabbey.gov.uk

Facilities: Ms Bronagh Doonan, Head of Property & Building Services, Antrim and Newtownabbey Borough Council, Mossley Mill, Carnmoney Road North, Newtownabbey BT36 5QA ☎ 028 9034 0000 ┐ brongah.doonan@antrimandnewtownabbey.gov.uk

Finance: Mr John Balmer, Head of Finance, Antrim Civic Centre, 50 Stiles Way, Antrim BT41 2UB ☎ 028 9446 3113 ┐ john.balmer@antrimandnewtownabbey.gov.uk

Fleet Management: Ms Lynda Gregg, Fleet Management Supervisor, Antrim Civic Centre, 50 Stiles Way, Antrim BT41 2UB ☎ 028 9446 3113 ┐ lynda.gregg@antrimandnewtownabbey.gov.uk

Grounds Maintenance: Mr Ivor McMullen, Head of Leisure, Antrim Civic Centre, 50 Stiles Way, Antrim BT41 2UB ☎ 028 9446 3113 ┐ ivor.mcmullen@antrimandnewtownabbey.gov.uk

Health and Safety: Mr Jason Douglas, Corporate Health & Safety Officer, Antrim Civic Centre, 50 Stiles Way, Antrim BT41 2UB ☎ 028 9034 0000 ┐ jason.douglas@antrimandnewtownabbey.gov.uk

Legal: Mr Paul Casey, Legal Services Manager, Antrim Civic Centre, 50 Stiles Way, Antrim BT41 2UB ☎ 028 9446 3113 ┐ paul.casey@antrimandnewtownabbey.gov.uk

Leisure and Cultural Services: Mrs Geraldine Girvan, Director - Operations, Antrim Civic Centre, 50 Stiles Way, Antrim BT41 2UB ☎ 028 9446 3113 ┐ geraldine.girvan@antrimandnewtownabbey.gov.uk

Licensing: Mr Clifford Todd, Head of Environmental Health, Antrim and Newtownabbey Borough Council, Mossley Mill, Carnmoney Road North, Newtownabbey BT36 5QA ☎ 028 9034 0000 ┐ clifford.todd@antrimandnewtownabbey.gov.uk

Lottery Funding, Charity and Voluntary: Mrs Louise Moore, Head of Community Planning, Antrim and Newtownabbey Borough Council, Mossley Mill, Carnmoney Road North, Newtownabbey BT36 5QA ☎ 028 9034 0000 ┐ louise.moore@antrimandnewtownabbey.gov.uk

Member Services: Mrs Liz Johnston, Head of Governance, Antrim Civic Centre, 50 Stiles Way, Antrim BT41 2UB ☎ 028 9446 3113 ┐ liz.johnston@antrimandnewtownabbey.gov.uk

Parking: Mrs Geraldine Girvan, Director - Operations, Antrim Civic Centre, 50 Stiles Way, Antrim BT41 2UB ☎ 028 9446 3113 ┐ geraldine.girvan@antrimandnewtownabbey.gov.uk

Partnerships: Ms Majella McAlister, Director - Community Planning & Regeneration, Antrim and Newtownabbey Borough Council, Mossley Mill, Carnmoney Road North, Newtownabbey BT36 5QA ☎ 028 9034 0000 ┐ majella.mcalister@antrimandnewtownabbey.gov.uk

Personnel / HR: Mrs Andrea McCooke, Director - Organisation Development, Antrim Civic Centre, 50 Stiles Way, Antrim BT41 2UB ☎ 028 9446 3113 ┐ andrea.mccooke@antrimandnewtownabbey.gov.uk

Planning: Ms Majella McAlister, Director - Community Planning & Regeneration, Antrim and Newtownabbey Borough Council, Mossley Mill, Carnmoney Road North, Newtownabbey BT36 5QA ☎ 028 9034 0000 ┐ majella.mcalister@antrimandnewtownabbey.gov.uk

Procurement: Mr John Balmer, Head of Finance, Antrim Civic Centre, 50 Stiles Way, Antrim BT41 2UB ☎ 028 9446 3113 ┐ john.balmer@antrimandnewtownabbey.gov.uk

ANTRIM & NEWTOWNABBEY

Recycling & Waste Minimisation: Mr Jim Gurney, Head of Waste Management, Antrim Civic Centre, 50 Stiles Way, Antrim BT41 2UB ☎ 028 9446 3113
✆ jim.gurney@antrimandnewtownabbey.gov.uk

Regeneration: Ms Majella McAlister, Director - Community Planning & Regeneration, Antrim and Newtownabbey Borough Council, Mossley Mill, Carnmoney Road North, Newtownabbey BT36 5QA ☎ 028 9034 0000
✆ majella.mcalister@antrimandnewtownabbey.gov.uk

Staff Training: Mrs Joan Cowan, People Development Manager, Antrim Civic Centre, 50 Stiles Way, Antrim BT41 2UB
☎ 028 9446 3113 ✆ joan.cowan@antrimandnewtownabbey.gov.uk

Sustainable Communities: Mrs Louise Moore, Head of Community Planning, Antrim and Newtownabbey Borough Council, Mossley Mill, Carnmoney Road North, Newtownabbey BT36 5QA
☎ 028 9034 0000 ✆ louise.moore@antrimandnewtownabbey.gov.uk

Sustainable Development: Ms Majella McAlister, Director - Community Planning & Regeneration, Antrim and Newtownabbey Borough Council, Mossley Mill, Carnmoney Road North, Newtownabbey BT36 5QA ☎ 028 9034 0000
✆ majella.mcalister@antrimandnewtownabbey.gov.uk

Tourism: Mr Paul Kelly, Head of Economic Development, Antrim and Newtownabbey Borough Council, Mossley Mill, Carnmoney Road North, Newtownabbey BT36 5QA ☎ 028 9034 0000
✆ paul.kelly@antrimandnewtownabbey.gov.uk

Town Centre: Mr Paul Kelly, Head of Economic Development, Antrim and Newtownabbey Borough Council, Mossley Mill, Carnmoney Road North, Newtownabbey BT36 5QA ☎ 028 9034 0000 ✆ paul.kelly@antrimandnewtownabbey.gov.uk

Waste Collection and Disposal: Mr Jim Gurney, Head of Waste Management, Antrim Civic Centre, 50 Stiles Way, Antrim BT41 2UB
☎ 028 9446 3113 ✆ jim.gurney@antrimandnewtownabbey.gov.uk

Waste Management: Mr Jim Gurney, Head of Waste Management, Antrim Civic Centre, 50 Stiles Way, Antrim BT41 2UB
☎ 028 9446 3113 ✆ jim.gurney@antrimandnewtownabbey.gov.uk

COUNCILLORS

Mayor: Hogg, Thomas (DUP - Macedon)
thomas.hogg@antrimandnewtownabbey.gov.uk

Deputy Mayor: Blair, John (ALL - Glengormley Urban)
john.blair@antrimandnewtownabbey.gov.uk

Alderman: Agnew, Fraser (UUP - Threemilewater)
fraser.agnew@antrimandnewtownabbey.gov.uk

Alderman: Ball, William (DUP - Threemilewater)
william.ball@antrimandnewtownabbey.gov.uk

Alderman: Barr, Pamela (DUP - Threemilewater)
pamela.barr@antrimandnewtownabbey.gov.uk

Alderman: Burns, Thomas (SDLP - Airport)
thomas.burns@antrimandnewtownabbey.gov.uk

Alderman: Campbell, Tom (ALL - Threemilewater)
tom.campbell@antrimandnewtownabbey.gov.uk

Alderman: Cosgrove, Mark (UUP - Glengormley Urban)
mark.cosgrove@antrimandnewtownabbey.gov.uk

Alderman: DeCourcy, William (DUP - Macedon)
william.decourcy@antrimandnewtownabbey.gov.uk

Alderman: Girvan, Mandy (DUP - Ballyclare)
mandy.girvan@antrimandnewtownabbey.gov.uk

Alderman: Montgomery, Jim (UUP - Antrim)
jim.montgomery@antrimandnewtownabbey.gov.uk

Alderman: Smyth, John (DUP - Antrim)
john.smyth@antrimandnewtownabbey.gov.uk

Arthurs, David (O - Ballyclare)
david.arthurs@antrimandnewtownabbey.gov.uk

Ball, Audrey (DUP - Glengormley Urban)
audrey.ball@antrimandnewtownabbey.gov.uk

Beatty, Trevor (DUP - Dunsilly)
trevor.beatty@antrimandnewtownabbey.gov.uk

Bingham, Jim (UUP - Ballyclare)
jim.bingham@antrimandnewtownabbey.gov.uk

Brett, Phillip (DUP - Glengormley Urban)
phillip.brett@antrimandnewtownabbey.gov.uk

Clarke, Linda (DUP - Dunsilly)
linda.clarke@antrimandnewtownabbey.gov.uk

Cushinan, Henry (SF - Dunsilly)
henry.cushinan@antrimandnewtownabbey.gov.uk

Duffin, Brian (SDLP - Dunsilly)
brian.duffin@antrimandnewtownabbey.gov.uk

Girvan, Tim (DUP - Ballyclare)
tim.girvan@antrimandnewtownabbey.gov.uk

Goodman, Michael (SF - Glengormley Urban)
michael.goodman@antrimandnewtownabbey.gov.uk

Hamill, Paul (DUP - Macedon)
paul.hamill@antrimandnewtownabbey.gov.uk

Hollis, David (O - Macedon)
david.hollis@antrimandnewtownabbey.gov.uk

Kells, Nigel (DUP - Antrim)
nigel.kells@antrimandnewtownabbey.gov.uk

Kelly, Neil (ALL - Antrim)
neil.kelly@antrimandnewtownabbey.gov.uk

Kelso, Ben (UUP - Threemilewater)
ben.kelso@antrimandnewtownabbey.gov.uk

Logue, Annemarie (SF - Airport)
annemarie.logue@antrimandnewtownabbey.gov.uk

Lynch, Roisin (SDLP - Antrim)
roisin.lynch@antrimandnewtownabbey.gov.uk

Magill, Matthew (DUP - Airport)
matthew.magill@antrimandnewtownabbey.gov.uk

Maguire, Michael (UUP - Glengormley Urban)
michael.maguire@antrimandnewtownabbey.gov.uk

McClelland, Noreen (SDLP - Glengormley Urban)
noreen.mcclelland@antrimandnewtownabbey.gov.uk

McWilliam, Vera (UUP - Ballyclare)
vera.mcwilliam@antrimandnewtownabbey.gov.uk

Michael, Paul (UUP - Airport)
paul.michael@antrimandnewtownabbey.gov.uk

Rea, Mervyn (UUP - Airport)
mervyn.rea@antrimandnewtownabbey.gov.uk

Ritchie, Drew (UUP - Antrim)
drew.ritchie@antrimandnewtownabbey.gov.uk

Ross, Stephen (DUP - Threemilewater)
stephen.ross@antrimandnewtownabbey.gov.uk

Scott, John (UUP - Macedon)
john.scott@antrimandnewtownabbey.gov.uk

Swann, Roderick (UUP - Dunsilly)
roderick.swann@antrimandnewtownabbey.gov.uk

Webb, William (ALL - Macedon)
billy.webb@antrimandnewtownabbey.gov.uk

POLITICAL COMPOSITION
DUP: 15, UUP: 12, SDLP: 4, ALL: 4, SF: 3, O: 2

Ards & North Down Borough Council   N

Ards & North Down Borough Council, Ards & North Down Borough Council, Town Hall, The Castle, Bangor BT20 4BT
☎ 0300 013 3333 ⌨ www.ardsandnorthdown.gov.uk

PRINCIPAL OFFICERS

Chief Executive: Mr Stephen Reid, Chief Executive, Ards & North Down Borough Council, Town Hall, The Castle, Bangor BT20 4BT
☎ 0300 013 3333 ⌨ stephen.reid@ardsandnorthdown.gov.uk

Deputy Chief Executive: Mr David Anderson, Executive Assistant, Ards & North Down Borough Council, Town Hall, The Castle, Bangor BT20 4BT ☎ 0300 013 3333
⌨ david.anderson@ardsandnorthdown.gov.uk

Senior Management: Mr Graeme Bannister, Director - Community & Wellbeing, Ards & North Down Borough Council, Town Hall, The Castle, Bangor BT20 4BT ☎ 028 9182 4058
⌨ graeme.bannister@ardsandnorthdown.gov.uk

Senior Management: Mr Dave Clarke, Director - Finance & Performance, Ards & North Down Borough Council, Town Hall, The Castle, Bangor BT20 4BT ☎ 028 9127 8026
⌨ dave.clarke@ardsandnorthdown.gov.uk

Senior Management: Mr David Lindsay, Director - Environment, Waste Recycling Centre, Balloo Road, Bangor BT19 7QY
☎ 0300 013 3333 ⌨ david.lindsay@ardsandnorthdown.gov.uk

Senior Management: Mrs Christine Mahon, Director - Regeneration, Development & Planning, Signal Centre, 2 Innotec Drive, Balloo Road, Bangor BT19 7BD ☎ 028 9127 8030
⌨ christine.mahon@ardsandnorthdown.gov.uk

Senior Management: Mrs Wendy Monson, Director - Organisational Development & Administration, Ards & North Down Borough Council, Town Hall, The Castle, Bangor BT20 4BT
☎ 0300 013 3333 ⌨ wendy.monson@ardsandnorthdown.gov.uk

Access Officer / Social Services (Disability): Mrs Shirley Poxon, Policy Officer, Ards & North Down Borough Council, Town Hall, The Castle, Bangor BT20 4BT ☎ 0300 013 3333
⌨ shirley.poxon@ardsandnorthdown.gov.uk

Architect, Building / Property Services: Mr David Lindsay, Director - Environment, Waste Recycling Centre, Balloo Road, Bangor BT19 7QY ☎ 0300 013 3333
⌨ david.lindsay@ardsandnorthdown.gov.uk

Best Value: Mrs Debbie Bolton, Procurement Manager, Ards & North Down Borough Council, Town Hall, The Castle, Bangor BT20 4BT ☎ 0300 013 3333 ⌨ debbie.bolton@ardsandnorthdown.gov.uk

Building Control: Mr David Lindsay, Director - Environment, Waste Recycling Centre, Balloo Road, Bangor BT19 7QY ☎ 0300 013 3333 ⌨ david.lindsay@ardsandnorthdown.gov.uk

Civil Registration: Mrs Heather Cannavan, Registrar, Ards & North Down Borough Council, Town Hall, The Castle, Bangor BT20 4BT ☎ 0300 013 3333
⌨ heather.cannavan@ardsandnorthdown.gov.uk

Civil Registration: Mrs Pauline Mossey, Registrar, Ards & North Down Borough Council, Town Hall, The Castle, Bangor BT20 4BT
☎ 0300 013 3333 ⌨ pauline.mossey@ardsandnorthdown.gov.uk

PR / Communications: Ms Claire Jackson, Corporate Communications Manager, Ards & North Down Borough Council, Town Hall, The Castle, Bangor BT20 4BT ☎ 028 9127 8052
⌨ claire.jackson@ardsandnorthdown.gov.uk

Community Planning: Ms Patricia Mackey, Community Planning Manager, Ards & North Down Borough Council, Town Hall, The Castle, Bangor BT20 4BT ☎ 0300 013 3333
⌨ patricia.mackey@ardsandnorthdown.gov.uk

Community Safety: Mr Alan McCay, PCSP Manager, Ards & North Down Borough Council, Town Hall, The Castle, Bangor BT20 4BT ☎ 0300 013 3333 ⌨ alan.mccay@ardsandnorthdown.gov.uk

Computer Management: Mr Dave Clarke, Director - Finance & Performance, Ards & North Down Borough Council, Town Hall, The Castle, Bangor BT20 4BT ☎ 028 9127 8026
⌨ dave.clarke@ardsandnorthdown.gov.uk

Corporate Services: Ms Claire Jackson, Corporate Communications Manager, Ards & North Down Borough Council, Town Hall, The Castle, Bangor BT20 4BT ☎ 028 9127 8052
⌨ claire.jackson@ardsandnorthdown.gov.uk

Customer Service: Mrs Wendy Monson, Director - Organisational Development & Administration, Ards & North Down Borough Council, Town Hall, The Castle, Bangor BT20 4BT ☎ 0300 013 3333 ⌨ wendy.monson@ardsandnorthdown.gov.uk

Economic Development: Mrs Christine Mahon, Director - Regeneration, Development & Planning, Signal Centre, 2 Innotec Drive, Balloo Road, Bangor BT19 7BD ☎ 028 9127 8030
⌨ christine.mahon@ardsandnorthdown.gov.uk

E-Government: Mr Andrew Scott, Head of Performance & Projects, Ards & North Down Borough Council, Town Hall, The Castle, Bangor BT20 4BT ☎ 0300 013 3333
⌨ andrew.scott@ardsandnorthdown.gov.uk

ARDS & NORTH DOWN BOROUGH COUNCIL

Emergency Planning: Mrs Jill Hunter, Risk Manager, Ards & North Down Borough Council, Town Hall, The Castle, Bangor BT20 4BT ☎ 0300 013 3333 ⏚ jill.hunter@ardsandnorthdown.gov.uk

Environmental / Technical Services: Mr David Lindsay, Director - Environment, Ards & North Down Borough Council, Town Hall, The Castle, Bangor BT20 4BT ☎ 0300 013 3333 ⏚ david.lindsay@ardsandnorthdown.gov.uk

Environmental Health: Mr Marcus Potts, Head of Environmental Health Protection & Development, Ards & North Down Borough Council, Town Hall, The Castle, Bangor BT20 4BT ☎ 0300 013 3333 ⏚ marcus.potts@ardsandnorthdown.gov.uk

Events Manager: Mrs Christine Mahon, Director - Regeneration, Development & Planning, Signal Centre, 2 Innotec Drive, Balloo Road, Bangor BT19 7BD ☎ 028 9127 8030 ⏚ christine.mahon@ardsandnorthdown.gov.uk

Finance: Mr Dave Clarke, Director - Finance & Performance, Ards & North Down Borough Council, Town Hall, The Castle, Bangor BT20 4BT ☎ 028 9127 8026 ⏚ dave.clarke@ardsandnorthdown.gov.uk

Fleet Management: Mr David Lindsay, Director - Environment, Waste Recycling Centre, Balloo Road, Bangor BT19 7QY ☎ 0300 013 3333 ⏚ david.lindsay@ardsandnorthdown.gov.uk

Grounds Maintenance: Mr Ian Beaney, Grounds Maintenance Manager, Ards & North Down Borough Council, Town Hall, The Castle, Bangor BT20 4BT ☎ 0300 013 3333 ⏚ ian.beaney@ardsandnorthdown.gov.uk

Health and Safety: Ms Amanda Martin, Head of Administration, Ards & North Down Borough Council, Town Hall, The Castle, Bangor BT20 4BT ☎ 028 9182 4190 ⏚ amanda.martin@ardsandnorthdown.gov.uk

Leisure and Cultural Services: Ms Jan Nixey, Head of Community & Culture, Ards & North Down Borough Council, Town Hall, The Castle, Bangor BT20 4BT ☎ 0300 013 3333 ⏚ jan.nixey@ardsandnorthdown.gov.uk

Licensing: Mr David Brown, Licensing & Regulatory Services Manager, Ards & North Down Borough Council, Town Hall, The Castle, Bangor BT20 4BT ☎ 0300 013 3333 ⏚ david.brown@ardsandnorthdown.gov.uk

Lighting: Mr Peter Caldwell, Head of Assets & Property Services, North Road Depot, Quarry Heights, Newtownards BT23 7SZ ☎ 0300 013 3333 ⏚ peter.caldwell@ardsandnorthdown.gov.uk

Member Services: Mrs Jeanette Wilson, Democratic Services Manager, Ards & North Down Borough Council, Town Hall, The Castle, Bangor BT20 4BT ☎ 028 9182 4069 ⏚ jeanette.wilson@ardsandnorthdown.gov.uk

Parking: Mr Peter Caldwell, Head of Assets & Property Services, North Road Depot, Quarry Heights, Newtownards BT23 7SZ ☎ 0300 013 3333 ⏚ peter.caldwell@ardsandnorthdown.gov.uk

Personnel / HR: Mrs Wendy Monson, Director - Organisational Development & Administration, Ards & North Down Borough Council, Town Hall, The Castle, Bangor BT20 4BT ☎ 0300 013 3333 ⏚ wendy.monson@ardsandnorthdown.gov.uk

Planning: Mrs Ann McCullough, Head of Planning, 2 Church Street, Newtownards BT23 4AP ☎ 028 9127 8008 ⏚ ann.mccullough@ardsandnorthdown.gov.uk

Procurement: Mr Dave Clarke, Director - Finance & Performance, Ards & North Down Borough Council, Town Hall, The Castle, Bangor BT20 4BT ☎ 028 9127 8026 ⏚ dave.clarke@ardsandnorthdown.gov.uk

Recycling & Waste Minimisation: Mr David Lindsay, Director - Environment, Waste Recycling Centre, Balloo Road, Bangor BT19 7QY ☎ 0300 013 3333 ⏚ david.lindsay@ardsandnorthdown.gov.uk

Regeneration: Mr Brian Dorrian, Head of Regeneration, Signal Centre, 2 Innotec Drive, Bangor BT19 7PD ☎ 028 9182 4020 ⏚ brian.dorrian@ardsandnorthdown.gov.uk

Staff Training: Ms Rosemary McCullough, Lead Officer - Human Resources & Organisational Development, Ards & North Down Borough Council, Town Hall, The Castle, Bangor BT20 4BT ☎ 028 9127 8040 ⏚ rosemary.mccullough@ardsandnorthdown.gov.uk

Sustainable Development: Ms Amanda Martin, Head of Administration, Ards & North Down Borough Council, Town Hall, The Castle, Bangor BT20 4BT ☎ 028 9182 4190 ⏚ amanda.martin@ardsandnorthdown.gov.uk

Tourism: Mrs Christine Mahon, Director - Regeneration, Development & Planning, Signal Centre, 2 Innotec Drive, Balloo Road, Bangor BT19 7BD ☎ 028 9127 8030 ⏚ christine.mahon@ardsandnorthdown.gov.uk

Waste Collection and Disposal: Mr David Lindsay, Director - Environment, Waste Recycling Centre, Balloo Road, Bangor BT19 7QY ☎ 0300 013 3333 ⏚ david.lindsay@ardsandnorthdown.gov.uk

Waste Management: Mr David Lindsay, Director - Environment, Waste Recycling Centre, Balloo Road, Bangor BT19 7QY ☎ 0300 013 3333 ⏚ david.lindsay@ardsandnorthdown.gov.uk

COUNCILLORS

Mayor: Graham, Alan (DUP - Bangor West)
alan.graham@northdownandards.gov.uk

Deputy Mayor: McClean, Carl (UUP - Bangor Central)
carl.mcclean@northdownandards.gov.uk

Alderman: Carson, Angus (UUP - Ards Peninsula)
angus.carson@northdownandards.gov.uk

Alderman: Gibson, Robert (DUP - Comber)
robert.gibson@northdownandards.gov.uk

Alderman: Henry, Ian (UUP - Bangor Central)
ian.henry@northdownandards.gov.uk

Alderman: Irvine, Wesley (DUP - Bangor Central)
wesley.irvine@northdownandards.gov.uk

Alderman: Keery, Bill (DUP - Bangor East & Donaghadee)
bill.keery@northdownandards.gov.uk

Alderman: McDowell, Alan (ALL - Newtownards)
alan.mcdowell@northdownandards.gov.uk

Alderman: Smith, Marion (UUP - Bangor West)
marion.smith@northdownandards.gov.uk

Adair, Robert (DUP - Ards Peninsula)
robert.adair@northdownandards.gov.uk

Allen, Daniel (IND - Holywood & Clandeboye)
daniel.allen@northdownandards.gov.uk

Anderson, Stuart (ALL - Bangor Central)
stuart.anderson@northdownandards.gov.uk

Armstrong-Cotter, Naomi (DUP - Newtownards)
naomi.armstrong@northdownandards.gov.uk

Barry, John (GRN - Holywood & Clandeboye)
john.barry@northdownandards.gov.uk

Boyle, Joe (SDLP - Ards Peninsula)
joe.boyle@northdownandards.gov.uk

Brooks, Mark (UUP - Bangor East & Donaghadee)
mark.brooks@northdownandards.gov.uk

Cathcart, Alistair (DUP - Bangor Central)
alistair.cathcart@northdownandards.gov.uk

Chambers, David (UUP - Bangor East & Donaghadee)
david.chambers@ardsandnorthdown.gov.uk

Comber, Stephen (O - Comber)
stephen.coopers@northdownandards.gov.uk

Cummings, Trevor (DUP - Comber)
trevor.cummings@northdownandards.gov.uk

Dunne, Stephen (DUP - Holywood & Clandeboye)
stephen.dunne@northdownandards.gov.uk

Edmund, Nigel (DUP - Ards Peninsula)
nigel.edmund@northdownandards.gov.uk

Ferguson, Katherine (UUP - Newtownards)
katherine.ferguson@northdownandards.gov.uk

Fletcher, James (UUP - Comber)
james.fletcher@northdownandards.gov.uk

Gilmour, Jennifer (DUP - Holywood & Clandeboye)
jennifer.gilmour@northdownandards.gov.uk

Girvan, Deborah (ALL - Comber)
deborah.given@northdownandards.gov.uk

Kennedy, Colin (DUP - Newtownards)
colin.kennedy@northdownandards.gov.uk

Leslie, Alan (DUP - Bangor West)
alan.leslie@northdownandards.gov.uk

Martin, Peter (DUP - Bangor East & Donaghadee)
peter.martin@northdownandards.gov.uk

McAlpine, Lorna (ALL - Ards Peninsula)

McIlveen, Stephen (DUP - Newtownards)
stephen.mcilveen@northdownandards.gov.uk

Menagh, Jimmy (IND - Newtownards)
jimmy.menagh@northdownandards.gov.uk

Muir, Andrew (ALL - Holywood & Clandeboye)
andrew.muir@northdownandards.gov.uk

Roberts, Paul (GRN - Bangor West)
paul.roberts@northdownandards.gov.uk

Robinson, Noelle (IND - Bangor Central)
noelle.robinson@northdownandards.gov.uk

Smart, Richard (UUP - Newtownards)
richard.smart@northdownandards.gov.uk

Smith, Tom (DUP - Bangor East & Donaghadee)
tom.smith@northdownandards.gov.uk

Thompson, Eddie (DUP - Ards Peninsula)
eddie.thompson@northdownandards.gov.uk

Walker, Gavin (ALL - Bangor East & Donaghadee)
gavin.walker@northdownandards.gov.uk

Wilson, Scott (ALL - Bangor West)
scott.wilson@northdownandards.gov.uk

POLITICAL COMPOSITION
DUP: 17, UUP: 9, ALL: 7, IND: 3, GRN: 2, O: 1, SDLP: 1

COMMITTEE CHAIRS

Environment: Mr Joe Boyle

Regeneration & Development: Mr Tom Smith

Argyll & Bute   S

Argyll & Bute Council, Kilmory, Lochgilphead PA31 8RT
☎ 01546 605522 ⌁ enquiries@argyll-bute.gov.uk
🖥 www.argyll-bute.gov.uk

FACTS AND FIGURES
Parliamentary Constituencies: Argyll and Bute
EU Constituencies: Scotland
Election Frequency: Elections are of whole council

PRINCIPAL OFFICERS

Chief Executive: Mr Cleland Sneddon, Chief Executive, Kilmory, Lochgilphead PA31 8RT ☎ 01546 604112 ⌁ cleland.sneddon@argyll-bute.gov.uk

Senior Management: Ms Kirsty Flanagan, Head of Strategic Finance, Kilmory, Lochgilphead PA31 8RT ☎ 01546 604268 ⌁ kirsty.flanagan@argyll-bute.gov.uk

Senior Management: Mr Douglas Hendry, Executive Director - Customer Services, Kilmory, Lochgilphead PA31 8RT ☎ 01546 604244 ⌁ douglas.hendry@argyll-bute.gov.uk

Senior Management: Ms Ann Marie Knowles, Acting Executive Director - Community Services, Kilmory, Lochgilphead PA31 8RT

Senior Management: Ms Pippa Milne, Executive Director - Development & Infrastructure, Kilmory, Lochgilphead PA31 8RT ☎ 01546 604076 ⌁ pippa.milne@argyll-bute.gov.uk

Architect, Building / Property Services: Mr Angus Gilmour, Head of Planning & Regulatory Services, Kilmory, Lochgilphead PA31 8RT ☎ 01546 604288 ⌁ angus.gilmour@argyll-bute.gov.uk

Best Value: Ms Jane Fowler, Head of Improvement & HR, Kilmory, Lochgilphead PA31 8RT ☎ 01546 604466 ⌁ jane.fowler@argyll-bute.gov.uk

ARGYLL & BUTE

Building Control: Mr Martin Matheson, Building Standards Manager, Blairbadach House, Helensburgh G84 8ND ☎ 01436 658881 ⏻ martin.matheson@argyll-bute.gov.uk

Catering Services: Mr Malcolm MacFadyen, Head of Facility Services, Kilmory, Lochgilphead PA31 8RT ☎ 01546 604412 ⏻ malcolm.macfadyen@argyll-bute.gov.uk

Children / Youth Services: Ms Louise Long, Head of Children & Families, Kilmory, Lochgilphead PA31 8RT ☎ 01546 604256 ⏻ louise.long@argyll-bute.gov.uk

Civil Registration: Ms Shona Brechin, Area Registrar, Dalriada House, Lochgilphead PA31 8ST ☎ 01546 604515 ⏻ shona.brechin@argyll-bute.gov.uk

Community Planning: Ms Eileen Wilson, Community Planning Manager, 25 West King Street, Helensburgh G84 8UW ☎ 01436 658726 ⏻ eileen.wilson@argyll-bute.gov.uk

Community Safety: Mr Charles Reppke, Head of Governance & Law, Kilmory, Lochgilphead PA31 8RT ☎ 01546 604192 ⏻ charles.reppke@argyll-bute.gov.uk

Computer Management: Ms Judy Orr, Head of Support & Customer Services, Witchburn Road, Campbeltown PA28 6JX ☎ 01586 555280 ⏻ judy.orr@argyll-bute.gov.uk

Consumer Protection and Trading Standards: Mr Angus Gilmour, Head of Planning & Regulatory Services, Kilmory, Lochgilphead PA31 8RT ☎ 01546 604288 ⏻ angus.gilmour@argyll-bute.gov.uk

Contracts: Ms Anne MacColl-Smith, Service Commissioning Manager, Kilmory, Lochgilphead PA31 8RT ☎ 01546 604194 ⏻ anne.maccoll-smith@argyll-bute.gov.uk

Customer Service: Mr Douglas Hendry, Executive Director - Customer Services, Kilmory, Lochgilphead PA31 8RT ☎ 01546 604244 ⏻ douglas.hendry@argyll-bute.gov.uk

Customer Service: Mrs Judy Orr, Head of Customer & Support Services, Witchburn Road, Campbeltown PA28 6JU ☎ 01586 555280 ⏻ judy.orr@argyll-bute.gov.uk

Economic Development: Mr Fergus Murray, Head of Economic Development & Strategic Transport, Kilmory, Lochgilphead PA31 8RT ☎ 01546 604293 ⏻ fergus.murray@argyll-bute.gov.uk

Education: Ms Ann Marie Knowles, Acting Executive Director - Community Services, Kilmory, Lochgilphead PA31 8RT

E-Government: Ms Judy Orr, Head of Support & Customer Services, Witchburn Road, Campbeltown PA28 6JX ☎ 01586 555280 ⏻ judy.orr@argyll-bute.gov.uk

Electoral Registration: Mr Charles Reppke, Head of Governance & Law, Kilmory, Lochgilphead PA31 8RT ☎ 01546 604192 ⏻ charles.reppke@argyll-bute.gov.uk

Emergency Planning: Ms Carol Keeley, Emergency Planning Officer, 25 West King Street, Helensburgh G84 8UW ☎ 01436 677819 ⏻ carol.keeley@argyll-bute.gov.uk

Energy Management: Mr Paul Gillies, Energy Manager, Argyll House, Alexandra Parade, Dunoon PA23 8AJ ☎ 01369 708573 ⏻ paul.gillies@argyll-bute.gov.uk

Environmental / Technical Services: Mr Angus Gilmour, Head of Planning & Regulatory Services, Kilmory, Lochgilphead PA31 8RT ☎ 01546 604288 ⏻ angus.gilmour@argyll-bute.gov.uk

Environmental Health: Mr Angus Gilmour, Head of Planning & Regulatory Services, Kilmory, Lochgilphead PA31 8RT ☎ 01546 604288 ⏻ angus.gilmour@argyll-bute.gov.uk

Estates, Property & Valuation: Mr Malcolm MacFadyen, Head of Facility Services, Kilmory, Lochgilphead PA31 8RT ☎ 01546 604412 ⏻ malcolm.macfadyen@argyll-bute.gov.uk

European Liaison: Mr Fergus Murray, Head of Economic Development & Strategic Transport, Kilmory, Lochgilphead PA31 8RT ☎ 01546 604293 ⏻ fergus.murray@argyll-bute.gov.uk

Facilities: Mr Malcolm MacFadyen, Head of Facility Services, Kilmory, Lochgilphead PA31 8RT ☎ 01546 604412 ⏻ malcolm.macfadyen@argyll-bute.gov.uk

Finance: Ms Kirsty Flanagan, Head of Strategic Finance, Kilmory, Lochgilphead PA31 8RT ☎ 01546 604268 ⏻ kirsty.flanagan@argyll-bute.gov.uk

Fleet Management: Mr Walter MacArthur, Fleet & Waste Manager, Manse Brae, Lochgilphead PA31 8RD ☎ 01546 604190 ⏻ walter.macarthur@argyll-bute.gov.uk

Grounds Maintenance: Mr Tom Murphy, Assistant Operations Manager - Roads & Grounds, Blairvedach House, Helensburgh G84 8ND ☎ 01436 658908 ⏻ tom.murphy@argyll-bute.gov.uk

Health and Safety: Mr Andrew MacKrell, Health & Safety Manager, Whitegate Offices, Lochgilphead PA31 8SY ☎ 01546 604133 ⏻ andrew.mackrell@argyll-bute.gov.uk

Highways: Mr Jim Smith, Head of Roads & Amenity Services, Kilmory, Lochgilphead PA31 8RT ☎ 01546 604324 ⏻ jim.smith@argyll-bute.gov.uk

Housing: Mr Donald MacVicar, Head of Community & Culture, Kilmory, Lochgilphead PA31 8RT ☎ 01546 604364 ⏻ donald.macvicar@argyll-bute.gov.uk

Housing Maintenance: Mr Donald MacVicar, Head of Community & Culture, Kilmory, Lochgilphead PA31 8RT ☎ 01546 604364 ⏻ donald.macvicar@argyll-bute.gov.uk

Legal: Mr Charles Reppke, Head of Governance & Law, Kilmory, Lochgilphead PA31 8RT ☎ 01546 604192 ⏻ charles.reppke@argyll-bute.gov.uk

Leisure and Cultural Services: Mr Donald MacVicar, Head of Community & Culture, Kilmory, Lochgilphead PA31 8RT ☎ 01546 604364 ⌨ donald.macvicar@argyll-bute.gov.uk

Licensing: Mr Charles Reppke, Head of Governance & Law, Kilmory, Lochgilphead PA31 8RT ☎ 01546 604192 ⌨ charles.reppke@argyll-bute.gov.uk

Lighting: Mr Ryan McGlynn, Technical Officer - Street Lighting, Manse Brae, Lochgilphead PA31 8RD ☎ 01546 604646 ⌨ ryan.mcglynn@argyll-bute.gov.uk

Lottery Funding, Charity and Voluntary: Ms Arlene Cullum, Funding Officer, 25 West King Street, Helensburgh G84 8UW ☎ 07979 214501 ⌨ arlene.cullum@argyll-bute.gov.uk

Member Services: Mr Charles Reppke, Head of Governance & Law, Kilmory, Lochgilphead PA31 8RT ☎ 01546 604192 ⌨ charles.reppke@argyll-bute.gov.uk

Partnerships: Ms Eileen Wilson, Community Planning Manager, 25 West King Street, Helensburgh G84 8UW ☎ 01436 658726 ⌨ eileen.wilson@argyll-bute.gov.uk

Personnel / HR: Ms Jane Fowler, Head of Improvement & HR, Kilmory, Lochgilphead PA31 8RT ☎ 01546 604466 ⌨ jane.fowler@argyll-bute.gov.uk

Planning: Mr Angus Gilmour, Head of Planning & Regulatory Services, Kilmory, Lochgilphead PA31 8RT ☎ 01546 604288 ⌨ angus.gilmour@argyll-bute.gov.uk

Procurement: Ms Anne MacColl-Smith, Service Commissioning Manager, Kilmory, Lochgilphead PA31 8RT ☎ 01546 604194 ⌨ anne.maccoll-smith@argyll-bute.gov.uk

Public Libraries: Ms Pat McCann, Culture & Libraries Manager, West King Street Library, West King Street, Helensburgh G84 8GB ☎ 01436 658811 ⌨ pat.mccann@argyll-bute.gov.uk

Recycling & Waste Minimisation: Mr Alan Millar, Performance Manager - Waste Management, Manse Brae, Lochgilphead PA31 8RD ☎ 01546 604628 ⌨ alan.millar@argyll-bute.gov.uk

Regeneration: Mr Donald MacVicar, Head of Community & Culture, Kilmory, Lochgilphead PA31 8RT ☎ 01546 604364 ⌨ donald.macvicar@argyll-bute.gov.uk

Road Safety: Mrs June Graham, Road Safety Officer, Kilmory, Lochgilphead PA31 8RT ☎ 01546 604182 ⌨ june.graham@argyll-bute.gov.uk

Social Services: Ms Louise Long, Head of Children & Families, Kilmory, Lochgilphead PA31 8RT ☎ 01546 604256 ⌨ louise.long@argyll-bute.gov.uk

Social Services: Mr Allen Stevenson, Head of Adult Services, H&L Civic Centre, 38 Clyde Street, Helensburgh G84 7PG ☎ 01369 708513 ⌨ allen.stevenson@argyll-bute.gov.uk

Social Services (Adult): Mr Allen Stevenson, Head of Adult Services, H&L Civic Centre, 38 Clyde Street, Helensburgh G84 7PG ☎ 01369 708513 ⌨ allen.stevenson@argyll-bute.gov.uk

Social Services (Children): Ms Louise Long, Head of Children & Families, Kilmory, Lochgilphead PA31 8RT ☎ 01546 604256 ⌨ louise.long@argyll-bute.gov.uk

Staff Training: Ms Jane Fowler, Head of Improvement & HR, Kilmory, Lochgilphead PA31 8RT ☎ 01546 604466 ⌨ jane.fowler@argyll-bute.gov.uk

Street Scene: Mr Tom Murphy, Assistant Operations Manager - Roads & Grounds, Blairvedach House, Helensburgh G84 8ND ☎ 01436 658908 ⌨ tom.murphy@argyll-bute.gov.uk

Sustainable Communities: Mr Fergus Murray, Head of Economic Development & Strategic Transport, Kilmory, Lochgilphead PA31 8RT ☎ 01546 604293 ⌨ fergus.murray@argyll-bute.gov.uk

Sustainable Development: Mr Angus Gilmour, Head of Planning & Regulatory Services, Kilmory, Lochgilphead PA31 8RT ☎ 01546 604288 ⌨ angus.gilmour@argyll-bute.gov.uk

Tourism: Mr Fergus Murray, Head of Economic Development & Strategic Transport, Kilmory, Lochgilphead PA31 8RT ☎ 01546 604293 ⌨ fergus.murray@argyll-bute.gov.uk

Town Centre: Mr Fergus Murray, Head of Economic Development & Strategic Transport, Kilmory, Lochgilphead PA31 8RT ☎ 01546 604293 ⌨ fergus.murray@argyll-bute.gov.uk

Traffic Management: Mr Jim Smith, Head of Roads & Amenity Services, Kilmory, Lochgilphead PA31 8RT ☎ 01546 604324 ⌨ jim.smith@argyll-bute.gov.uk

Transport: Ms Moya Ingram, Strategic Transportation Manager, Whitegates Office, Whitegates Road, Lochgilphead PA31 8RD ☎ 01546 604190 ⌨ moya.ingram@argyll-bute.gov.uk

Waste Collection and Disposal: Mr Tom Murphy, Assistant Operations Manager - Roads & Grounds, Blairvedach House, Helensburgh G84 8ND ☎ 01436 658908 ⌨ tom.murphy@argyll-bute.gov.uk

Waste Management: Mr Alan Millar, Performance Manager - Waste Management, Manse Brae, Lochgilphead PA31 8RD ☎ 01546 604628 ⌨ alan.millar@argyll-bute.gov.uk

COUNCILLORS

Provost: Scoullar, Len (IND - Isle of Bute) len.scoullar@argyll-bute.gov.uk

Deputy Provost: Kinniburgh, David (CON - Helensburgh & Lomond South) david.kinniburgh@argyll-bute.gov.uk

Leader of the Council: Walsh, Dick (IND - Dunoon) dick.walsh@argyll-bute.gov.uk

Deputy Leader of the Council: Morton, Ellen (LD - Helensburgh & Lomond South) ellen.morton@argyll-bute.gov.uk

ARGYLL & BUTE

Armour, John (SNP - South Kintyre)
john.armour@argyll-bute.gov.uk

Blair, William Gordon (SNP - Cowal)
gordon.blair@argyll-bute.gov.uk

Breslin, Michael (INDNA - Dunoon)
michael.breslin@argyll-bute.gov.uk

Colville, Rory (LD - South Kintyre)
rory.colville@argyll-bute.gov.uk

Corry, Maurice (CON - Lomond North)
maurice.corry@argyll-bute.gov.uk

Currie, Robin (LD - Kintyre & the Islands)
robin.currie@argyll-bute.gov.uk

Dance, Vivien (INDNA - Helensburgh Central)
vivien.dance@argyll-bute.gov.uk

Devon, Mary-Jean (IND - Oban South & Isles)
mary-jean.devon@argyll-bute.gov.uk

Freeman, George (IND - Lomond North)
george.freeman@argyll-bute.gov.uk

Horn, Anne (SNP - Kintyre & the Islands)
anne.horn@argyll-bute.gov.uk

Kelly, Donald (IND - South Kintyre)
donald.kelly2@argyll-bute.gov.uk

MacDougall, Alistair (IND - Oban South & Isles)
alistair.macdougall@argyll-bute.gov.uk

MacIntyre, Robert (IND - Isle of Bute)
robert.macintyre@argyll-bute.gov.uk

MacIntyre, Robert (IND - Lomond North)
robertgraham.macintyre@argyll-bute.gov.uk

MacIntyre, Neil (LAB - Oban South & Isles)
neil.macintyre@argyll-bute.gov.uk

MacLean, Iain Stewart (IND - Oban North & Lorn)
iainstewart.MacLean@argyll-bute.gov.uk

MacMillan, Donald (IND - Mid Argyll)
donald.macmillan@argyll-bute.gov.uk

Marshall, Bruce (IND - Cowal)
bruce.marshall@argyll-bute.gov.uk

McAlpine, John (IND - Kintyre & the Islands)
john.mcalpine@argyll-bute.gov.uk

McCuish, Roddy (IND - Oban South & Isles)
roderick.mccuish@argyll-bute.gov.uk

McKenzie, Julie (SNP - Oban North & Lorn)
julie.mckenzie@argyll-bute.gov.uk

McNaughton, Alex (IND - Cowal)
alex.mcnaughton@argyll-bute.gov.uk

McQueen, James (IND - Dunoon)
james.mcqueen@argyll-bute.gov.uk

Morton, Aileen (LD - Helensburgh Central)
aileen.morton@argyll-bute.gov.uk

Mulvaney, Gary (CON - Helensburgh Central)
gary.mulvaney@argyll-bute.gov.uk

Philand, Douglas (IND - Mid Argyll)
dougie.philand@argyll-bute.gov.uk

Robb, James (SNP - Helensburgh Central)
james.robb@argyll-bute.gov.uk

Robertson, Elaine (IND - Oban North & Lorn)
elaine.robertson@argyll-bute.gov.uk

Strong, Isobel (SNP - Isle of Bute)
isobel.strong@argyll-bute.gov.uk

Taylor, Sandy (SNP - Mid Argyll)
sandy.taylor@argyll-bute.gov.uk

Trail, Richard (SNP - Helensburgh & Lomond South)
richard.trail@argyll-bute.gov.uk

POLITICAL COMPOSITION

IND: 17, SNP: 8, LD: 4, CON: 3, INDNA: 2, LAB: 1, Vacant: 1

Armagh City, Banbridge & Craigavon District   N

Armagh City, Banbridge & Craigavon District, Council Offices,
The Palace Demesne, Armagh BT60 4EL
☎ 0300 030 0900 info@armaghbanbridgecraigavon.gov.uk
💻 www.armaghbanbridgecraigavon.gov.uk

PRINCIPAL OFFICERS

Chief Executive: Mr Roger Wilson, Chief Executive, Council
Offices, The Palace Demesne, Armagh BT60 4EL

Senior Management: Ms Olga Murtagh, Strategic Director -
Place, Council Offices, The Palace Demesne, Armagh BT60 4EL
 olga.murtagh@armaghbanbridgecraigavon.gov.uk

Senior Management: Ms Sharon O'Gorman, Strategic Director -
Position, Council Offices, The Palace Demesne, Armagh BT60 4EL
 sharon.o'gorman@armaghbanbridgecraigavon.gov.uk

Senior Management: Mr Mike Reardon, Interim Strategic
Director - People, Council Offices, The Palace Demesne, Armagh
BT60 4EL mike.reardon@armaghbanbridgecraigavon.gov.uk

Building Control: Mr Jonathan Hayes, Head of Building Control,
Council Offices, The Palace Demesne, Armagh BT60 4EL
 jonathan.hayes@armaghbanbridgecraigavon.gov.uk

Community Planning: Mrs Elaine Gillespie, Head of Community
Planning, Council Offices, The Palace Demesne, Armagh BT60 4EL
 elaine.gillespie@armaghbanbridgecraigavon.gov.uk

Economic Development: Ms Nicola Wilson, Head of Economic
Development, Council Offices, The Palace Demesne, Armagh BT60
4EL nicola.wilson@armaghbanbridgecraigavon.gov.uk

Finance: Mr Graham Coulter, Head of Finance, Council Offices,
The Palace Demesne, Armagh BT60 4EL

Leisure and Cultural Services: Ms Catriona Regan, Head
of Health & Recreation, Council Offices, The Palace Demesne,
Armagh BT60 4EL
 catriona.regan@armaghbanbridgecraigavon.gov.uk

Member Services: Mrs Marrie Mallon, Democratic Services
Officer, Council Offices, The Palace Demesne, Armagh BT60 4EL
 marrie.mallon@armaghbanbridgecraigavon.gov.uk

Personnel / HR: Ms Sharon Currans, Head of HR, Council Offices, The Palace Demesne, Armagh BT60 4EL

Regeneration: Ms Therese Rafferty, Head of Regeneration, Council Offices, The Palace Demesne, Armagh BT60 4EL ✏ therese.rafferty@armaghbanbridgecraigavon.gov.uk

COUNCILLORS

The Lord Mayor: Causby, Darryn (DUP - Portadown)

Barr, Glenn (UUP - Banbridge)

Baxter, Mark (DUP - Lagan River)

Beattie, Doug (UUP - Portadown)

Berry, Paul (O - Cusher)

Black, Carol (UUP - Lagan River)

Buckley, Jonathan (DUP - Portadown)

Burns, Ian (UUP - Banbridge)

Cairns, Maire (SF - Lurgan)

Campbell, Mealla (SDLP - Armagh)

Curran, Brendan (SF - Banbridge)

Donnelly, Freda (DUP - Armagh)

Doyle, Seamus (SDLP - Banbridge)

Gamble, Hazel (DUP - Lagan River)

Greenfield, Paul (DUP - Banbridge)

Hatch, Arnold (UUP - Portadown)

Haughey, Sharon (SDLP - Cusher)

Haughian, Keith (SF - Lurgan)

Ingram, Elizabeth (UUP - Banbridge)

Jones, David (UKIP - Portadown)

Keating, Garath (SF - Armagh)

Kennedy, Gordon (UUP - Cusher)

Lennon, Fergal (SF - Craigavon)

Lockhart, Carla (DUP - Lurgan)

McAlinden, Declan (SDLP - Craigavon)

McCrum, Junior (DUP - Banbridge)

McCusker, Colin (UUP - Lurgan)

McKenna, Gemma (SF - Portadown)

McNally, Darren (SF - Armagh)

Moutray, Philip (UUP - Lurgan)

Nelson, Joe (SDLP - Lurgan)

Nicholson, Sam (UUP - Armagh)

O'Hanlon, Thomas (SDLP - Armagh)

Rankin, Paul (DUP - Lagan River)

Seeley, Catherine (SF - Lurgan)

Smith, Robert (DUP - Craigavon)

Speers, Jim (UUP - Cusher)

Tinsley, Margaret (DUP - Craigavon)

Twyble, Kenneth (UUP - Craigavon)

Wilson, Gareth (DUP - Cusher)

Woods, Marc (UUP - Lagan River)

POLITICAL COMPOSITION
UUP: 13, DUP: 12, SF: 8, SDLP: 6, UKIP: 1, O: 1

Arun   D

Arun District Council, Arun Civic Centre, Maltravers Road, Littlehampton BN17 5LF
☎ 01903 737500 📠 01903 730442 ✏ info@arun.gov.uk
💻 www.arun.gov.uk

FACTS AND FIGURES
Parliamentary Constituencies: Arundel and South Downs, Bognor Regis and Littlehampton, Worthing West
EU Constituencies: South East
Election Frequency: Elections are of whole council

PRINCIPAL OFFICERS

Chief Executive: Mr Nigel Lynn, Chief Executive, Arun Civic Centre, Maltravers Road, Littlehampton BN17 5LF
☎ 01903 737600 ✏ nigel.lynn@arun.gov.uk

Deputy Chief Executive: Mr Nigel Croad, Resources Director & Deputy Chief Executive, Arun Civic Centre, Maltravers Road, Littlehampton BN17 5LF ☎ 01903 737810
✏ nigel.croad@arun.gov.uk

Senior Management: Mrs Philippa Dart, Director - Environmental Services, Town Hall, Clarence Road, Bognor Regis PO21 1LD
☎ 01903 737811 ✏ philippa.dart@arun.gov.uk

Senior Management: Mr Karl Roberts, Director - Planning & Economic Regeneration, Arun Civic Centre, Maltravers Road, Littlehampton BN17 5LF ☎ 01903 737760
✏ karl.roberts@arun.gov.uk

Senior Management: Mr Paul Warters, Director - Customer Services, Arun Civic Centre, Maltravers Road, Littlehampton BN17 5LF ☎ 01903 737510 ✏ paul.warters@arun.gov.uk

Best Value: Mr Paul Askew, Head of Policy & Partnerships, Arun Civic Centre, Maltravers Road, Littlehampton BN17 5LF
☎ 01903 737515 ✏ paul.askew@arun.gov.uk

Building Control: Mr James Henn, Building Control Manager, Arun Civic Centre, Maltravers Road, Littlehampton BN17 5LF
☎ 01903 737596 ✏ jim.henn@arun.gov.uk

PR / Communications: Ms Justine Vincent, Communications Manager, Arun Civic Centre, Maltravers Road, Littlehampton BN17 5LF ☎ 01903 737606 ✏ justine.vincent@arun.gov.uk

Community Safety: Ms Georgina Bouette, Community Safety Manager, Arun Civic Centre, Maltravers Road, Littlehampton BN17 5LF ☎ 01903 737605 ✏ georgina.bouette@arun.gov.uk

Computer Management: Mr Chris Lawrence, ICT Manager, Arun Civic Centre, Maltravers Road, Littlehampton BN17 5LF
☎ 01903 737803 ⏴ chris.lawrence@arun.gov.uk

Contracts: Mr Philip Pickard, Procurement Officer, Arun Civic Centre, Maltravers Road, Littlehampton BN17 5LF ☎ 01903 737677 ⏴ philip.pickard@arun.gov.uk

Customer Service: Mrs Jackie Follis, Head of HR & Customer Services, Arun Civic Centre, Maltravers Road, Littlehampton BN17 5LF ☎ 01903 737580 ⏴ jackie.follis@arun.gov.uk

Economic Development: Ms Denise Vine, Head of Economic Regeneration, Arun Civic Centre, Maltravers Road, Littlehampton BN17 5LF ☎ 01903 737846 ⏴ denise.vine@arun.gov.uk

Electoral Registration: Mrs Liz Futcher, Head of Democratic Services, Arun Civic Centre, Maltravers Road, Littlehampton BN17 5LF ☎ 01903 737610 ⏴ liz.futcher@arun.gov.uk

Emergency Planning: Mr Guy Edwards, Emergency Planning Officer, Town Hall, Clarence Road, Bognor Regis PO21 1LD
☎ 01903 737953 ⏴ guy.edwards@arun.gov.uk

Energy Management: Ms Helen Cooper, Energy Efficiency Officer, Arun Civic Centre, Maltravers Road, Littlehampton BN17 5LF ☎ 01903 737743 ⏴ helen.cooper@arun.gov.uk

Environmental Health: Mr Nat Slade, Environmental Health Manager, Arun Civic Centre, Maltravers Road, Littlehampton BN17 5LF ☎ 01903 737683 ⏴ nat.slade@arun.gov.uk

Estates, Property & Valuation: Mr Alan Peach, Head of Finance & Property, Arun Civic Centre, Maltravers Road, Littlehampton BN17 5LF ☎ 01903 737558 ⏴ alan.peach@arun.gov.uk

Events Manager: Ms Jasmine Ede, Marketing & Events Assistant, Arun Civic Centre, Maltravers Road, Littlehampton BN17 5LF
☎ 01903 737920 ⏴ jasmine.ede@arun.gov.uk

Facilities: Ms Kim Breden, Facilities Team Leader, Arun Civic Centre, Maltravers Road, Littlehampton BN17 5LF ☎ 01903 737964 ⏴ kim.breden@arun.gov.uk

Finance: Mr Nigel Croad, Resources Director & Deputy Chief Executive, Arun Civic Centre, Maltravers Road, Littlehampton BN17 5LF ☎ 01903 737810 ⏴ nigel.croad@arun.gov.uk

Treasury: Ms Sian Southerton, Senior Accountant / Treasury & Investment Officer, Arun Civic Centre, Maltravers Road, Littlehampton BN17 5LF ☎ 01903 737861 ⏴ sian.southerton@arun.gov.uk

Grounds Maintenance: Mrs Philippa Dart, Director - Environmental Services, Town Hall, Clarence Road, Bognor Regis PO21 1LD ☎ 01903 737811 ⏴ philippa.dart@arun.gov.uk

Health and Safety: Mr Colin Combes, Corporate Health & Safety Officer, Arun Civic Centre, Maltravers Road, Littlehampton BN17 5LF ☎ 01903 737682 ⏴ colin.combes@arun.gov.uk

Home Energy Conservation: Mr Brian Pople, Head of Housing, Arun Civic Centre, Maltravers Road, Littlehampton BN17 5LF
☎ 01903 737718 ⏴ brian.pople@arun.gov.uk

Housing: Mr Brian Pople, Head of Housing, Arun Civic Centre, Maltravers Road, Littlehampton BN17 5LF ☎ 01903 737718 ⏴ brian.pople@arun.gov.uk

Housing Maintenance: Ms Elaine Gray, Housing Customer Services Manager, Arun Civic Centre, Maltravers Road, Littlehampton BN17 5LF ☎ 01903 737823 ⏴ elaine.gray@arun.gov.uk

Legal: Mrs Wendy Ashenden-Bax, Head of Legal & Administration, Arun Civic Centre, Maltravers Road, Littlehampton BN17 5LF
☎ 01903 737589 ⏴ wendy.ashenden-bax@arun.gov.uk

Leisure and Cultural Services: Mrs Philippa Dart, Director - Environmental Services, Town Hall, Clarence Road, Bognor Regis PO21 1LD ☎ 01903 737811 ⏴ philippa.dart@arun.gov.uk

Licensing: Mrs Sarah Meeting, Licensing Team Manager, Arun Civic Centre, Maltravers Road, Littlehampton BN17 5LF
☎ 01903 737681 ⏴ sarah.meeting@arun.gov.uk

Member Services: Mrs Liz Futcher, Head of Democratic Services, Arun Civic Centre, Maltravers Road, Littlehampton BN17 5LF
☎ 01903 737610 ⏴ liz.futcher@arun.gov.uk

Parking: Mr Calvin Baylis, Outdoor Services Manager, Arun Civic Centre, Maltravers Road, Littlehampton BN17 5LF ☎ 01903 737649 ⏴ calvin.baylis@arun.gov.uk

Partnerships: Mr Roger Wood, Head of Neighbourhoods, Arun Civic Centre, Maltravers Road, Littlehampton BN17 5LF
☎ 01903 737671 ⏴ roger.wood@arun.gov.uk

Personnel / HR: Mrs Jackie Follis, Head of HR & Customer Services, Arun Civic Centre, Maltravers Road, Littlehampton BN17 5LF ☎ 01903 737580 ⏴ jackie.follis@arun.gov.uk

Planning: Mr Karl Roberts, Director - Planning & Economic Regeneration, Arun Civic Centre, Maltravers Road, Littlehampton BN17 5LF ☎ 01903 737760 ⏴ karl.roberts@arun.gov.uk

Procurement: Mr Philip Pickard, Procurement Officer, Arun Civic Centre, Maltravers Road, Littlehampton BN17 5LF ☎ 01903 737677 ⏴ philip.pickard@arun.gov.uk

Recycling & Waste Minimisation: Mrs Philippa Dart, Director - Environmental Services, Town Hall, Clarence Road, Bognor Regis PO21 1LD ☎ 01903 737811 ⏴ philippa.dart@arun.gov.uk

Regeneration: Mr Karl Roberts, Director - Planning & Economic Regeneration, Arun Civic Centre, Maltravers Road, Littlehampton BN17 5LF ☎ 01903 737760 ⏴ karl.roberts@arun.gov.uk

Regeneration: Ms Denise Vine, Head of Economic Regeneration, Arun Civic Centre, Maltravers Road, Littlehampton BN17 5LF
☎ 01903 737846 ⏴ denise.vine@arun.gov.uk

Staff Training: Mrs Jackie Follis, Head of HR & Customer Services, Arun Civic Centre, Maltravers Road, Littlehampton BN17 5LF ☎ 01903 737580 ✆ jackie.follis@arun.gov.uk

Sustainable Communities: Mr Karl Roberts, Assistant Director of Planning & Housing Strategy, Arun Civic Centre, Maltravers Road, Littlehampton BN17 5LF ☎ 01903 737760 ✆ karl.roberts@arun.gov.uk

Sustainable Development: Mr Roger Wood, Head of Neighbourhoods, Arun Civic Centre, Maltravers Road, Littlehampton BN17 5LF ☎ 01903 737671 ✆ roger.wood@arun.gov.uk

Town Centre: Mr John Edgvet, Littlehampton Town Centre Regeneration Officer, Arun Civic Centre, Maltravers Road, Littlehampton BN17 5LF ☎ 01903 737856 ✆ john.edgvet@arun.gov.uk

Waste Collection and Disposal: Mr Gareth Rollings, Cleansing Operations Manager, Arun Civic Centre, Maltravers Road, Littlehampton BN17 5LF ☎ 01903 737659 ✆ gareth.rollings@arun.gov.uk

Children's Play Areas: Mr Oliver Handson, Greenspace Contract & Development Manager, Town Hall, Clarence Road, Bognor Regis PO21 1LD ☎ 01903 737955 ✆ oliver.handson@arun.gov.uk

COUNCILLORS

ChairHaymes, Stephen (CON - Yapton)
cllr.stephen.haymes@arun.gov.uk

Vice-ChairPendleton, Jacky (CON - Bersted)
cllr.jacky.pendleton@arun.gov.uk

Leader of the Council: Brown, Gillian (CON - Aldwick East)
gilliannanbrown@aol.com

Deputy Leader of the Council: Wensley, Dudley (CON - Angmering & Findon)
cllr.dudley.wensley@arun.gov.uk

Ambler, Derek (UKIP - Yapton)
cllr.derek.ambler@arun.gov.uk

Ayres, Marian (CON - Courtwick with Toddington)
cllr.marian.ayres@arun.gov.uk

Ballard, Keith (CON - Barnham)
cllr.keith.ballard@arun.gov.uk

Bence, Susan (CON - Bersted)
cllr.susan.bence@arun.gov.uk

Bence, Trevor (CON - Pevensey (Bognor Regis))
cllr.trevor.bence@arun.gov.uk

Bicknell, Paul (CON - Angmering & Findon)
paul@bicknells.f2s.com

Blampied, George (CON - River)
cllr.george.blampied@arun.gov.uk

Bower, Richard (CON - East Preston)
r.bower@btconnect.com

Bower, Philipa (CON - Rustington West)
philippa.bower@btconnect.com

Brooks, James (IND - Marine)
cllr.jim.brooks@arun.gov.uk

Brown, Leonard (CON - Orchard)

Buckland, Ian (LD - River)
cllr.ian.buckland@arun.gov.uk

Cates, Colin (UKIP - River)
cllr.colin.cates@arun.gov.uk

Chapman, Terence (CON - East Preston)
cllr.terence.chapman@arun.gov.uk

Charles, John (CON - Barnham)
cllr.john.charles@arun.gov.uk

Clayden, Mike (CON - East Preston)
cllr.mike.clayden@arun.gov.uk

Cooper, Andy (CON - Angmering & Findon)
cllr.andy.cooper@arun.gov.uk

Daniells, Sandra (CON - Pevensey)
cllr.sandra.daniells@arun.gov.uk

Dendle, Paul (CON - Arundel & Walberton)
cllr.paul.dendle@arun.gov.uk

Dillon, Pat (CON - Pevensey)
cllr.pat.dillon@arun.gov.uk

Dingemans, Norman (CON - Arundel & Walberton)
cllr.norman.dingemans@arun.gov.uk

Edwards, David (CON - Felpham East)
cllr.david.edwards@arun.gov.uk

Elkins, Roger (CON - Ferring)
cllr.roger.elkins@arun.gov.uk

English, Paul (CON - Felpham East)
cllr.paul.english@arun.gov.uk

Gammon, Alan (CON - Brookfield)
cllr.alan.gammon@arun.gov.uk

Hall, Dawn (CON - Pagham)
cllr.dawn.hall@arun.gov.uk

Harrison-Horn, Pauline (CON - Rustington West)
cllr.pauline.harrison-horn@arun.gov.uk

Hitchins, Phil (CON - Aldwick West)
cllr.phil.hitchins@arun.gov.uk

Hughes, Christopher (CON - Barnham)
cllr.christopher.hughes@arun.gov.uk

Maconachie, Dougal (CON - Marine)
cllr.dougal.maconachie@arun.gov.uk

Maconachie, Jacqui (CON - Aldwick West)

Madeley, Gill (CON - Felpham West)
cllr.gill.madeley@arun.gov.uk

Neno, Emma (CON - Rustington East)
cllr.emma.neno@arun.gov.uk

Northeast, Michael (LAB - Courtwick with Toddington)
cllr.mike.northeast@arun.gov.uk

Oakley, Barbara (CON - Middleton-on-Sea)
cllr.barbara.oakley@arun.gov.uk

Oliver-Redgate, Colin (CON - Ferring)
cllr.colin.oliver-redgate@arun.gov.uk

Oppler, Francis (LD - Orchard)
cllr.francis.oppler@arun.gov.uk

Patel, Ashvin (CON - Pagham)
ashvinpatel@hotmail.co.uk

Porter, Stella (CON - Rustington West)
cllr.stella.porter@arun.gov.uk

Purchese, Daniel (LD - Beach)
cllr.dan.purchese@arun.gov.uk

Rapnik, Ann (UKIP - Bersted)
cllr.ann.rapnik@arun.gov.uk

Reynolds, Stephen (CON - Hotham)
cllr.steve.reynolds@arun.gov.uk

Rhodes, Vicky (UKIP - Courtwick with Toddington)
cllr.vicky.rhodes@arun.gov.uk

Stainton, Elaine (CON - Felpham West)
cllr.elaine.stainton@arun.gov.uk

Tyler, Graham (CON - Rustington East)
cllr.graham.tyler@arun.gov.uk

Walsh, James (LD - Beach)
cllr.james.walsh@arun.gov.uk

Warren, Mick (CON - Brookfield)
cllr.mick.warren@arun.gov.uk

Wells, Paul (LD - Hotham)
cllr.paul.wells@arun.gov.uk

Wheal, Robert (CON - Arundel & Walberton)
cllr.robert.wheal@arun.gov.uk

Wotherspoon, Paul (CON - Middleton-on-Sea)
cllr.paul.wotherspoon@arun.gov.uk

POLITICAL COMPOSITION
CON: 43, LD: 5, UKIP: 4, IND: 1, LAB: 1

COMMITTEE CHAIRS

Audit & Governance: Mr Mike Clayden

Development Control: Mrs Jacqui Maconachie

Licensing: Mr Norman Dingemans

Ashfield   D

Ashfield District Council, Council Offices, Urban Road, Kirkby-in-Ashfield NG17 8DA
☎ 01623 450000 🖷 01623 457585 📧 info@ashfield-dc.gov.uk
🖥 www.ashfield-dc.gov.uk

FACTS AND FIGURES
Parliamentary Constituencies: Ashfield, Newark
EU Constituencies: East Midlands
Election Frequency: Elections are of whole council

PRINCIPAL OFFICERS

Chief Executive: Mr Robert Mitchell, Chief Executive, Council Offices, Urban Road, Kirkby-in-Ashfield NG17 8DA ☎ 01623 457251 📧 r.mitchell@ashfield-dc.gov.uk

Deputy Chief Executive: Mr David Greenwood, Deputy Chief Executive - Resources, Council Offices, Urban Road, Kirkby-in-Ashfield NG17 8DA ☎ 01623 457201 📧 d.greenwood@ashfield-dc.gov.uk

Assistant Chief Executive: Mrs Ruth Dennis, Assistant Chief Executive - Governance, Council Offices, Urban Road, Kirkby-in-Ashfield NG17 8DA ☎ 01623 457009 📧 r.dennis@ashfield-dc.gov.uk

Access Officer / Social Services (Disability): Ms Sharon Allman, Equality & Diversity Research Officer, Mansfield District Council, Civic Centre, Chesterfield Road South, Mansfield NG19 7BH ☎ 01623 463042 📧 sallman@mansfield.gov.uk

Architect, Building / Property Services: Ms Elaine Saxton, Asset Manager, Council Offices, Urban Road, Kirkby-in-Ashfield NG17 8DA ☎ 01623 457360 📧 e.p.saxton@ashfield-dc.gov.uk

Best Value: Mrs Joanne Wright, Corporate Performance & Improvement Manager, Council Offices, Urban Road, Kirkby-in-Ashfield NG17 8DA ☎ 01623 457328 📧 j.wright@ashfield-dc.gov.uk

Building Control: Mr Richard Scott, Building Control Manager, Council Offices, Urban Road, Kirkby-in-Ashfield NG17 8DA ☎ 01623 457387 📧 r.j.scott@ashfield-dc.gov.uk

Catering Services: Ms Elaine Saxton, Asset Manager, Council Offices, Urban Road, Kirkby-in-Ashfield NG17 8DA ☎ 01623 457360 📧 e.p.saxton@ashfield-dc.gov.uk

PR / Communications: Ms Carys Turner-Jones, Corporate Communications Manager, Ashfield District Council, Urban Road, Kirkby-in-Ashfield NG17 8DA ☎ 01623 457004 📧 c.turner-jones@ashfield-dc.gov.uk

Community Planning: Mr Stuart Wiltshire, Interim Forward Planning Team Manager, Council Offices, Urban Road, Kirkby-in-Ashfield NG17 8DA ☎ 01623 457383 📧 s.wiltshire@ashfield-dc.gov.uk

Community Safety: Mr Carl Holland, Interim Community Protection Manager, Council Offices, Urban Road, Kirkby-in-Ashfield NG17 8DA ☎ 01623 457349 📧 c.holland@ashfield-dc.gov.uk

Computer Management: Mr Andy Slate, ICT Manager, Council Offices, Urban Road, Kirkby-in-Ashfield NG17 8DA ☎ 01623 457555 📧 a.slate@ashfield-dc.gov.uk

Corporate Services: Mr Craig Bonar, Service Director - Corporate Services, Council Offices, Urban Road, Kirkby-in-Ashfield NG17 8DA ☎ 01623 457203 📧 c.bonar@ashfield-dc.gov.uk

Customer Service: Mr Craig Scott, Revenues & Customer Services Manager, Council Offices, Urban Road, Kirkby-in-Ashfield NG17 8DA ☎ 01623 457263 📧 c.scott@ashfield-dc.gov.uk

Economic Development: Mr Paul Thomas, Regeneration Manager, Civic Centre, Chesterfield Road South, Mansfield NG19 7BH ☎ 01623 463369 📧 pthomas@mansfield.gov.uk

Emergency Planning: Ms Jenni French, Business Contingency & Sustainability Manager, Ashfield District Council, Urban Road, Kirkby-in-Ashfield NG17 8DA ☎ 01623 457370 📧 j.french@ashfield-dc.gov.uk

Energy Management: Ms Jenni French, Business Contingency & Sustainability Manager, Ashfield District Council, Urban Road, Kirkby-in-Ashfield NG17 8DA ☎ 01623 457370 ⌂ j.french@ashfield-dc.gov.uk

Environmental Health: Mr Chris Booth, Environmental Health Manager, Council Offices, Urban Road, Kirkby-in-Ashfield NG17 8DA ☎ 01623 457228 ⌂ c.booth@ashfield-dc.gov.uk

Estates, Property & Valuation: Mr Matthew Kirk, Estates Manager, Council Offices, Urban Road, Kirkby-in-Ashfield NG17 8DA ☎ 01623 457277 ⌂ m.kirk@ashfield-dc.gov.uk

Facilities: Mr Neil Cotterill, Facilities Manager, Council Offices, Urban Road, Kirkby-in-Ashfield NG17 8DA ☎ 01623 457257 ⌂ n.cotterill@ashfield-dc.gov.uk

Finance: Mr David Greenwood, Deputy Chief Executive - Resources, Council Offices, Urban Road, Kirkby-in-Ashfield NG17 8DA ☎ 01623 457201 ⌂ d.greenwood@ashfield-dc.gov.uk

Fleet Management: Mr David White, Transport Services Manager, Northern Depot, Station Road, Sutton-in-Ashfield NG17 5HB ☎ 01623 457883 ⌂ d.c.white@ashfield-dc.gov.uk

Grounds Maintenance: Mrs Sam Dennis, Service Lead - Waste & Environment, Northern Depot, Station Road, Sutton-in-Ashfield NG17 5HB ☎ 01623 457873 ⌂ s.dennis@ashfield-dc.gov.uk

Health and Safety: Mr Patrick Godsall, Health & Safety Officer, Council Offices, Urban Road, Kirkby-in-Ashfield NG17 8DA ☎ 01623 457282 ⌂ p.godsall@ashfield-dc.gov.uk

Home Energy Conservation: Mr Martin Trouse, Energy Co-ordinator, Council Offices, Urban Road, Kirkby-in-Ashfield NG17 8DA ☎ 01623 457034 ⌂ m.trouse@ashfield-dc.gov.uk

Housing: Mr Peter Kandola, Strategic Housing & Development Manager, Council Offices, Urban Road, Kirkby-in-Ashfield NG17 8DA ☎ 01623 457351 ⌂ p.kandola@ashfield-dc.gov.uk

Housing Maintenance: Mr Paul Bingham, Director - Asset Management, Ashfield Homes Ltd, Broadway, Brook Street, Sutton-in-Ashfield NG17 1AL ☎ 01623 608877 ⌂ p.bingham@ashfield-dc.gov.uk

Legal: Ms Beth Brown, Principal Solicitor, Council Offices, Urban Road, Kirkby-in-Ashfield NG17 8DA ☎ 01623 457339 ⌂ principalsolicitor@ashfield-dc.gov.uk

Leisure and Cultural Services: Mrs Theresa Hodgkinson, Locality & Community Empowerment Manager, Council Offices, Urban Road, Kirkby-in-Ashfield NG17 8DA ☎ 01623 457588 ⌂ t.hodgkinson@ashfield-dc.gov.uk

Licensing: Mr Chris Booth, Environmental Health Manager, Council Offices, Urban Road, Kirkby-in-Ashfield NG17 8DA ☎ 01623 457228 ⌂ c.booth@ashfield-dc.gov.uk

Member Services: Mr David Dalby, Democracy Manager, Council Offices, Urban Road, Kirkby-in-Ashfield NG17 8DA ☎ 01623 457314 ⌂ d.dalby@ashfield-dc.gov.uk

Parking: Mr Neil Cotterill, Facilities Manager, Council Offices, Urban Road, Kirkby-in-Ashfield NG17 8DA ☎ 01623 457257 ⌂ n.cotterill@ashfield-dc.gov.uk

Personnel / HR: Mrs Mariam Amos, HR Manager, Civic Centre, Chesterfield Road South, Mansfield NG19 7BH ☎ 01623 663032 ⌂ mamos@mansfield.gov.uk

Planning: Mrs Christine Sarris, Corporate Planning & Building Control Manager, Council Offices, Urban Road, Kirkby-in-Ashfield NG17 8DA ☎ 01623 457375 ⌂ c.m.sarris@ashfield-dc.gov.uk

Procurement: Ms Sharon Lynch, Corporate Finance Manager, Council Offices, Urban Road, Kirkby-in-Ashfield NG17 8DA ☎ 01623 457202 ⌂ s.lynch@ashfield-dc.gov.uk

Recycling & Waste Minimisation: Mrs Sam Dennis, Service Lead - Waste & Environment, Council Offices, Urban Road, Kirkby-in-Ashfield NG17 8DA ☎ 01623 457873 ⌂ s.dennis@ashfield-dc.gov.uk

Regeneration: Mr Paul Thomas, Regeneration Manager, Civic Centre, Chesterfield Road South, Mansfield NG19 7BH ☎ 01623 463369 ⌂ pthomas@mansfield.gov.uk

Staff Training: Mrs Lorraine Powney, Principal Learning & Development Adviser, Civic Centre, Chesterfield Road South, Mansfield NG19 7BH ☎ 01623 463250 ⌂ lpowney@mansfield.gov.uk

Street Scene: Mr Carl Holland, Interim Community Protection Manager, Council Offices, Urban Road, Kirkby-in-Ashfield NG17 8DA ☎ 01623 457349 ⌂ c.holland@ashfield-dc.gov.uk

Sustainable Development: Ms Jenni French, Business Contingency & Sustainability Manager, Ashfield District Council, Urban Road, Kirkby-in-Ashfield NG17 8DA ☎ 01623 457370 ⌂ j.french@ashfield-dc.gov.uk

Town Centre: Mr Trevor Watson, Service Director - Economy, Council Offices, Urban Road, Kirkby-in-Ashfield NG17 8DA ☎ 01623 457374 ⌂ t.watson@ashfield-dc.gov.uk

Transport: Mr David White, Transport Services Manager, Northern Depot, Station Road, Sutton-in-Ashfield NG17 5HB ☎ 01623 457883 ⌂ d.c.white@ashfield-dc.gov.uk

Waste Collection and Disposal: Mr Paul Rowbotham, Waste Operations Officer, Northern Depot, Station Road, Sutton-in-Ashfield NG17 5HB ☎ 01623 457860 ⌂ p.rowbotham@ashfield-dc.gov.uk

Waste Management: Mr Paul Rowbotham, Waste Operations Officer, Northern Depot, Station Road, Sutton-in-Ashfield NG17 5HB ☎ 01623 457860 ⌂ p.rowbotham@ashfield-dc.gov.uk

COUNCILLORS

ChairGriffiths, David (LAB - Leamington) cllr.d.griffiths@ashfield-dc.gov.uk

Vice-ChairMorrison, Lachlan (LAB - Hucknall Central) cllr.l.s.morrison@ashfield-dc.gov.uk

ASHFIELD

Leader of the Council: Butler, Cheryl (LAB - Kirkby Cross & Portland)
cllr.c.butler@ashfield-dc.gov.uk

Deputy Leader of the Council: Davis, Don (LAB - Annesley & Kirkby Woodhouse)
cllr.d.davis@ashfield-dc.gov.uk

Anderson, Lee (LAB - Huthwaite & Brierley)
cllr.l.anderson@ashfield-dc.gov.uk

Aspinall, James (LAB - St Mary's)
cllr.j.aspinall@ashfield-dc.gov.uk

Baron, Christopher (LAB - Hucknall West)
cllr.c.baron@ashfield-dc.gov.uk

Bissett, Rachel (LAB - Hucknall North)
cllr.r.bissett@ashfield-dc.gov.uk

Bradley, Benjamin (CON - Hucknall North)
cllr.b.bradley@ashfield-dc.gov.uk

Brewer, Anthony (LD - Skegby)
cllr.a.brewer@ashfield-dc.gov.uk

Brown, Amanda (LAB - Central & New Cross)
cllr.a.brown@ashfield-dc.gov.uk

Brown, Tim (LAB - Central & New Cross)
cllr.t.brown@ashfield-dc.gov.uk

Carroll, Steven (LAB - Sutton Junction & Harlow Wood)
cllr.s.t.carroll@ashfield-dc.gov.uk

Chapman, Christian (LD - Jacksdale)
cllr.c.chapman@ashfield-dc.gov.uk

Donnelly, Joanne (LAB - Abbey Hill)
cllr.j.donnelly@ashfield-dc.gov.uk

Hollis, Helen (LAB - The Dales)
cllr.h.hollis@ashfield-dc.gov.uk

Hollis, Tom (LD - Ashfields)
cllr.t.j.hollis@ashfield-dc.gov.uk

James, Jacqueline (LAB - Summit)
cllr.j.james@ashfield-dc.gov.uk

Knight, John (LAB - Summit)
cllr.j.knight@ashfield-dc.gov.uk

Madden, Rachel (LD - Annesley & Kirkby Woodhouse)
cllr.r.e.madden@ashfield-dc.gov.uk

Mason, Catherine Ann (LAB - Carsic)
cllr.c.mason@ashfield-dc.gov.uk

Maxwell, Glenys (LAB - Huthwaite & Brierley)
cllr.g.c.maxwell@ashfield-dc.gov.uk

Mitchell, Lauren (LAB - Hucknall South)
cllr.l.mitchell@ashfield-dc.gov.uk

Morrison, Keir (LAB - Hucknall South)
cllr.k.a.morrison@ashfield-dc.gov.uk

Murphy, Michael (CON - Hucknall North)
cllr.m.murphy@ashfield-dc.gov.uk

Ndiweni, Nicolle (LAB - Hucknall Central)
cllr.n.ndiweni@ashfield-dc.gov.uk

Quinn-Wilcox, Christine (IND - Selston)
cllr.c.l.quinn-wilcox@ashfield-dc.gov.uk

Roberts, Paul (LAB - Skegby)
cllr.p.roberts@ashfield-dc.gov.uk

Rostance, Kevin (CON - Hucknall West)
cllr.k.rostance@ashfield-dc.gov.uk

Rostance, Philip (CON - Hucknall West)
cllr.p.rostance@ashfield-dc.gov.uk

Sears-Piccavey, Robert (IND - Underwood)
cllr.sears-piccavey@ashfield-dc.gov.uk

Smith, Helen (LD - Stanton Hill & Teversal)
cllr.h.smith@ashfield-dc.gov.uk

Smith, Michael (LAB - Kingsway)
cllr.m.smith@ashfield-dc.gov.uk

Wilson, Samuel (IND - Selston)
cllr.s.wilson@ashfield-dc.gov.uk

Zadrozny, Jason (IND - Larwood)
cllr.j.zadrozny@ashfield-dc.gov.uk

POLITICAL COMPOSITION
LAB: 22, LD: 5, CON: 4, IND: 4

COMMITTEE CHAIRS

Audit: Mr Kevin Rostance

Licensing: Mr Michael Smith

Planning: Mr John Knight

Ashford   D

Ashford Borough Council, Civic Centre, Tannery Lane, Ashford TN23 1PL
☎ 01233 331111 🖷 01233 645654 💻 www.ashford.gov.uk

FACTS AND FIGURES
Parliamentary Constituencies: Ashford
EU Constituencies: South East
Election Frequency: Elections are of whole council

PRINCIPAL OFFICERS

Chief Executive: Mrs Tracey Kerly, Chief Executive, Civic Centre, Tannery Lane, Ashford TN23 1PL ☎ 01233 330607
🖑 tracey.kerly@ashford.gov.uk

Deputy Chief Executive: Mr Paul Naylor, Deputy Chief Executive, Civic Centre, Tannery Lane, Ashford TN23 1PL ☎ 01233 330436
🖑 paul.naylor@ashford.gov.uk

Architect, Building / Property Services: Mr Paul McKenner, Head of Corporate Property & Projects, Civic Centre, Tannery Lane, Ashford TN23 1PL ☎ 01233 330419
🖑 paul.mckenner@ashford.gov.uk

Building Control: Mr Tim Parrett, Head of Development Delivery, Civic Centre, Tannery Lane, Ashford TN23 1PL ☎ 01233 330275
🖑 tim.parrett@ashford.gov.uk

Children / Youth Services: Mr Simon Harris, Sports Projects Manager, Civic Centre, Tannery Lane, Ashford TN23 1PL
☎ 01233 330232 🖑 simon.harris@ashford.gov.uk

PR / Communications: Mr Dean Spurrell, Communications & Marketing Manager, Civic Centre, Tannery Lane, Ashford TN23 1PL
☎ 01233 330647 🖑 dean.spurrell@ashford.gov.uk

Community Safety: Mr Gareth Recht, Community Safety Operations Manager, Ashford Community Safety Unit, Tufton Street, Ashford TN23 1BT ☎ 01233 330652 ◌ gareth.recht@ashford.gov.uk

Computer Management: Ms Michelle Pecci, Head of HR, Communications & Technology, Civic Centre, Tannery Lane, Ashford TN23 1PL ☎ 01233 330602 ◌ michelle.pecci@ashford.gov.uk

Contracts: Mrs Christina Fuller, Head of Cultural & Project Services, Civic Centre, Tannery Lane, Ashford TN23 1PL ☎ 01233 330477 ◌ christina.fuller@ashford.gov.uk

Customer Service: Mrs Julie Rogers, Head of Environmental & Customer Service, Civic Centre, Tannery Lane, Ashford TN23 1PL ☎ 01233 330856 ◌ julie.rogers@ashford.gov.uk

Economic Development: Mr Andrew Osborne, Economic Development Manager, Civic Centre, Tannery Lane, Ashford TN23 1PL ☎ 01233 330310 ◌ andrew.osborne@ashford.gov.uk

E-Government: Ms Michelle Pecci, Head of HR, Communications & Technology, Civic Centre, Tannery Lane, Ashford TN23 1PL ☎ 01233 330602 ◌ michelle.pecci@ashford.gov.uk

Electoral Registration: Mrs Valma Page, Electoral Services Manager, Civic Centre, Tannery Lane, Ashford TN23 1PL ☎ 01233 330462 ◌ valma.page@ashford.gov.uk

Emergency Planning: Ms Laurel Niven, Team Leader - Resilience & Events Safety, Civic Centre, Tannery Lane, Ashford TN23 1PL ☎ 01233 330271 ◌ lauren.niven@ashford.gov.uk

Environmental Health: Mrs Sheila Davison, Head of Health, Parking & Community Safety, Civic Centre, Tannery Lane, Ashford TN23 1PL ☎ 01233 330224 ◌ sheila.davison@ashford.gov.uk

Estates, Property & Valuation: Mr Paul McKenner, Head of Corporate Property & Projects, Civic Centre, Tannery Lane, Ashford TN23 1PL ☎ 01233 330419 ◌ paul.mckenner@ashford.gov.uk

Facilities: Mr John Young, Customer, Property & Technology Manager, Civic Centre, Tannery Lane, Ashford TN23 1PL ☎ 01233 330865 ◌ john.young@ashford.gov.uk

Finance: Mr Ben Lockwood, Head of Finance, Civic Centre, Tannery Lane, Ashford TN23 1PL ☎ 01233 330540 ◌ ben.lockwood@ashford.gov.uk

Treasury: Mr Ben Lockwood, Head of Finance, Civic Centre, Tannery Lane, Ashford TN23 1PL ☎ 01233 330540 ◌ ben.lockwood@ashford.gov.uk

Fleet Management: Ms Joy Cross, Human Resources Manager, Civic Centre, Tannery Lane, Ashford TN23 1PL ☎ 01233 330400 ◌ joy.cross@ashford.gov.uk

Grounds Maintenance: Mrs Julie Rogers, Head of Environmental & Customer Service, Civic Centre, Tannery Lane, Ashford TN23 1PL ☎ 01233 330856 ◌ julie.rogers@ashford.gov.uk

Health and Safety: Mrs Sheila Davison, Head of Health, Parking & Community Safety, Civic Centre, Tannery Lane, Ashford TN23 1PL ☎ 01233 330224 ◌ sheila.davison@ashford.gov.uk

Housing: Ms Sharon Williams, Head of Housing, Civic Centre, Tannery Lane, Ashford TN23 1PL ☎ 01233 330803 ◌ sharon.williams@ashford.gov.uk

Housing Maintenance: Mr Chris Tillin, Planned Maintenance Manager, Civic Centre, Tannery Lane, Ashford TN23 1PL ☎ 01233 330483 ◌ chris.tillin@ashford.gov.uk

Legal: Mr Terry Mortimer, Head of Legal & Democratic Services, Civic Centre, Tannery Lane, Ashford TN23 1PL ☎ 01233 330210 ◌ terry.mortimer@ashford.gov.uk

Leisure and Cultural Services: Mrs Christina Fuller, Head of Cultural & Project Services, Civic Centre, Tannery Lane, Ashford TN23 1PL ☎ 01233 330477 ◌ christina.fuller@ashford.gov.uk

Licensing: Mrs Jo Fox, Health, Parking & Community Safety Manager, Civic Centre, Tannery Lane, Ashford TN23 1PL ☎ 01233 330641 ◌ jo.fox@ashford.gov.uk

Lottery Funding, Charity and Voluntary: Mrs Christina Fuller, Head of Cultural & Project Services, Civic Centre, Tannery Lane, Ashford TN23 1PL ☎ 01233 330477 ◌ christina.fuller@ashford.gov.uk

Member Services: Mr Keith Fearon, Member Services & Scrutiny Manager, Civic Centre, Tannery Lane, Ashford TN23 1PL ☎ 01233 330564 ◌ keith.fearon@ashford.gov.uk

Parking: Mrs Jo Fox, Health, Parking & Community Safety Manager, Civic Centre, Tannery Lane, Ashford TN23 1PL ☎ 01233 330641 ◌ jo.fox@ashford.gov.uk

Personnel / HR: Ms Michelle Pecci, Head of HR, Communications & Technology, Civic Centre, Tannery Lane, Ashford TN23 1PL ☎ 01233 330602 ◌ michelle.pecci@ashford.gov.uk

Planning: Mr Richard Alderton, Head of Planning & Development, Civic Centre, Tannery Lane, Ashford TN23 1PL ☎ 01233 330239 ◌ richard.alderton@ashford.gov.uk

Procurement: Mr Paul McKenner, Head of Corporate Property & Projects, Civic Centre, Tannery Lane, Ashford TN23 1PL ☎ 01233 330419 ◌ paul.mckenner@ashford.gov.uk

Recycling & Waste Minimisation: Mrs Julie Rogers, Head of Environmental & Customer Service, Civic Centre, Tannery Lane, Ashford TN23 1PL ☎ 01233 330856 ◌ julie.rogers@ashford.gov.uk

Regeneration: Mr Giles Holloway, Development & Regeneration Manager, Civic Centre, Tannery Lane, Ashford TN23 1PL ☎ 01233 330427 ◌ giles.holloway@ashford.gov.uk

Staff Training: Ms Joy Cross, Human Resources Manager, Civic Centre, Tannery Lane, Ashford TN23 1PL ☎ 01233 330400 ◌ joy.cross@ashford.gov.uk

ASHFORD

Street Scene: Mrs Julie Rogers, Head of Environmental & Customer Service, Civic Centre, Tannery Lane, Ashford TN23 1PL ☎ 01233 330856 ⏚ julie.rogers@ashford.gov.uk

Sustainable Communities: Mr Richard Alderton, Head of Planning & Development, Civic Centre, Tannery Lane, Ashford TN23 1PL ☎ 01233 330239 ⏚ richard.alderton@ashford.gov.uk

Sustainable Development: Mr Richard Alderton, Head of Planning & Development, Civic Centre, Tannery Lane, Ashford TN23 1PL ☎ 01233 330239 ⏚ richard.alderton@ashford.gov.uk

Tourism: Miss Sarah Barber, Tourism & Nature Conservation Manager, Civic Centre, Tannery Lane, Ashford TN23 1PL ☎ 01233 330345 ⏚ sarah.barber@ashford.gov.uk

Town Centre: Miss Jo Wynn-Carter, Regeneration Manager, Civic Centre, Tannery Lane, Ashford TN23 1PL ☎ 01233 330326 ⏚ jo.wynn-carter@ashford.gov.uk

Waste Collection and Disposal: Mrs Julie Rogers, Head of Environmental & Customer Service, Civic Centre, Tannery Lane, Ashford TN23 1PL ☎ 01233 330856 ⏚ julie.rogers@ashford.gov.uk

Waste Management: Mrs Julie Rogers, Head of Environmental & Customer Service, Civic Centre, Tannery Lane, Ashford TN23 1PL ☎ 01233 330856 ⏚ julie.rogers@ashford.gov.uk

Children's Play Areas: Mrs Christina Fuller, Head of Cultural & Project Services, Civic Centre, Tannery Lane, Ashford TN23 1PL ☎ 01233 330477 ⏚ christina.fuller@ashford.gov.uk

COUNCILLORS

Mayor: Dyer, Geraldine (CON - Weald North) geraldine.dyer@ashford.gov.uk

Deputy Mayor: Koowaree, George (LD - North Willesborough (Ashford))

Leader of the Council: Clarkson, Gerry (CON - Charing) gerrydclarkson@aol.com

Deputy Leader of the Council: Bell, Neil (CON - Biddenden) neilbell@solutionprovider.co.uk

Group LeaderChilton, Brendan (LAB - Stanhope (Ashford)) brendan.chilton@ashford.gov.uk

Group LeaderOvenden, Noel (IND - Wye with Hinxhill) noel.ovenden@ashford.gov.uk

Adby, Jeremy (LD - North Willesborough (Ashford)) jeremy.adby@btinternet.com

Apps, Harold (CON - Victoria (Ashford))

Barrett, Bill (CON - Singleton South) barrettwbarrett@aol.com

Bartlett, Paul (CON - Weald East) paul.bartlett@ashford.gov.uk

Bell, Clair (CON - Weald Central) clairbell@solutionprovider.co.uk

Bennett, Mike (CON - Rolvenden & Tenterden West) mikebennettkm@tiscali.co.uk

Blanford, Jessamy (CON - Great Chart with Singleton North) jessamy.blandford@ashford.gov.uk

Bradford, Brad (CON - Weald South) brad.bradford@ashford.gov.uk

Britcher, Jill (LAB - Beaver (Ashford)) jill.britcher@ashford.gov.uk

Buchanan, Andrew (CON - Bybrook (Ashford)) andrewjohnbuchanan@hotmail.com

Burgess, Michael (CON - Isle of Oxney) michael.burgess@ashford.gov.uk

Clokie, Paul (CON - Tenterden North) paul.clokie@ashford.gov.uk

Dehnel, Stephen (CON - Downs North) stephen.dehnel@ashford.gov.uk

Farrell, Dara (LAB - Victoria (Ashford)) dara.farrell@ashford.gov.uk

Feacey, Peter (CON - Godinton (Ashford)) peterfeacey@talktalk.net

Galpin, Graham (CON - Stour (Ashford)) graham.galpin@ashford.gov.uk

Heyes, Bernard (CON - Godinton (Ashford)) bernardjdheys@talktalk.net

Heyes, Tina (CON - Park Farm North) tinaheyes@btinternet.com

Hicks, Aline (CON - Weald South) aline.hicks@ashford.gov.uk

Hooker, Kate (LAB - Aylesford Green (Ashford)) katehooker12@yahoo.co.uk

Howard, William (CON - Saxon Shore) william.howard@ashford.gov.uk

Knowles, Callum (CON - Tenterden) callum@tenterden.co.uk

Krause, Larry (CON - Downs West) larry.krause@btinternet.com

Link, John (CON - St. Michaels)

Martin, Marion (CON - Little Burton Farm (Ashford)) marionmartino6@btinternet.com

Martin, Jane (CON - Saxon Shore) jane.martin@ashford.gov.uk

Michael, Winston (IND - Boughton Aluph & Eastwell) winston.michael@ashford.gov.uk

Murphy, Beverley (UKIP - Beaver (Ashford))

Pickering, Alan (CON - Weald Central) alan@ampickering.com

Powell, Luke (CON - Bockhanger (Ashford)) lukejpowell1@gmail.com

Shorter, Neil (CON - Washford) njshorter@btinternet.com

Sims, Philip (IND - Kennington (Ashford)) philip.sims@ashford.gov.uk

Smith, David (IND - South Willesborough (Ashford)) david.smith@ashford.gov.uk

Waters, Chris (CON - Stour (Ashford)) chris.waters@ashford.gov.uk

Webb, Jenny (CON - Norman (Ashford))
jennywebb@live.co.uk

Wedgbury, Jim (CON - Park Farm South)
jimwedgbury@aol.com

White, Gerald (CON - Highfield (Ashford))
gerald.white@ashford.gov.uk

POLITICAL COMPOSITION
CON: 32, IND: 4, LAB: 4, LD: 2, UKIP: 1

Aylesbury Vale   D

Aylesbury Vale District Council, Council Offices, The Gateway, Gatehouse Road, Aylesbury HP19 8FF
☎ 01296 585858 🖷 01296 336977
🖑 customerfulfilment@aylesburyvaledc.gov.uk
🖳 www.aylesburyvaledc.gov.uk

FACTS AND FIGURES
Parliamentary Constituencies: Aylesbury, Buckingham
EU Constituencies: South East
Election Frequency: Elections are of whole council

PRINCIPAL OFFICERS

Chief Executive: Mr Andrew Grant, Chief Executive, The Gateway, Gatehouse Road, Aylesbury HP19 8FF ☎ 01296 585001
🖑 agrant@aylesburyvaledc.gov.uk

Senior Management: Ms Tracey Aldworth, Director, The Gateway, Gatehouse Road, Aylesbury HP19 8FF ☎ 01296 585003
🖑 taldworth@aylesburyvaledc.gov.uk

Senior Management: Mr Andrew Small, Director, The Gateway, Gatehouse Road, Aylesbury HP19 8FF ☎ 01296 585507
🖑 asmall@aylesburyvaledc.gov.uk

Building Control: Mr Adam Heeley, Building Control & Access Manager, The Gateway, Gatehouse Road, Aylesbury HP19 8FF
☎ 01296 585459 🖑 aheely@aylesburyvaledc.gov.uk

PR / Communications: Miss Teresa Lane, Head of Communications, Marketing & Town Centre Management, The Gateway, Gatehouse Road, Aylesbury HP19 8FF ☎ 01296 585006
🖑 tlane@aylesburyvaledc.gov.uk

Community Safety: Ms Kay Aitken, Community Safety Officer, The Gateway, Gatehouse Road, Aylesbury HP19 8FF ☎ 01296 585005 🖑 kaitken@aylesburyvaledc.gov.uk

Computer Management: Mr Alan Evans, Head of IT Services, The Gateway, Gatehouse, Aylesbury HP19 8FF ☎ 01296 585767
🖑 aevans@aylesburyvaledc.gov.uk

Contracts: Ms Sarah Deyes, Procurement Strategy Officer, The Gateway, Gatehouse Road, Aylesbury HP19 8FF ☎ 01296 585871
🖑 sdeyes@aylesburyvaledc.gov.uk

Customer Service: Ms Janet Forsdike, Service Improvement Manager, Council Offices, The Gateway, Gatehouse Road, Aylesbury HP19 8FF ☎ 01296 585083
🖑 jforsdike@aylesburyvaledc.gov.uk

Direct Labour: Mr Andy Wilkins, Operations Manager, Pembroke Road, Aylesbury HP20 1DG ☎ 01296 585303
🖑 awilkins@aylesburyvaledc.gov.uk

Economic Development: Mr Steve McAteer, Interim Economy Partnership Manager, Council Offices, The Gateway, Gatehouse Road, Aylesbury HP19 8FF ☎ 01296 585657
🖑 smcateer@aylesburyvaledc.gov.uk

E-Government: Mr Alan Evans, Head of IT Services, The Gateway, Gatehouse Road, Aylesbury HP19 8FF ☎ 01296 585767
🖑 aevans@aylesburyvaledc.gov.uk

Electoral Registration: Mr Chris Sheard, Electoral Registration Officer, The Gateway, Gatehouse Road, Aylesbury HP19 8FF
☎ 01296 585050

Emergency Planning: Mr David Thomas, Corporate Health & Safety Advisor, The Gateway, Gatehouse Road, Aylesbury HP19 8FF
☎ 01296 585158 🖑 dthomas@aylesburyvaledc.gov.uk

Energy Management: Mr Alan Asbury, Sustainability Team Leader, The Gateway, Gatehouse Road, Aylesbury HP19 8FF
☎ 01296 585112 🖑 aasbury@aylesburyvaledc.gov.uk

Environmental / Technical Services: Mr Robert Smart, Environment Officer, The Gateway, Gatehouse Road, Aylesbury HP19 8FF ☎ 01296 585147 🖑 rsmart@aylesburyvaledc.gov.uk

Environmental Health: Mr Richard Hiscock, Environmental Support Manager, The Gateway, Gatehouse Road, Aylesbury HP19 8FF ☎ 01296 585156 🖑 rhiscock@aylesburyvaledc.gov.uk

Events Manager: Ms Sophia Fulchini, Conference Centre Manager, The Gateway, Gatehouse Road, Aylesbury HP19 8FF
☎ 01296 585969 🖑 sfulchini@aylesburyvaledc.gov.uk

Facilities: Ms Jane Heywood, Facilities Manager, The Gateway, Gatehouse Road, Aylesbury HP19 8FF ☎ 01296 585191
🖑 sfulchini@aylesburyvaledc.gov.uk

Finance: Mr Andrew Small, Director, The Gateway, Gatehouse Road, Aylesbury HP19 8FF ☎ 01296 585507
🖑 asmall@aylesburyvaledc.gov.uk

Treasury: Mr Andrew Small, Director, The Gateway, Gatehouse Road, Aylesbury HP19 8FF ☎ 01296 585507
🖑 asmall@aylesburyvaledc.gov.uk

Grounds Maintenance: Mr Gareth Bird, Community Spaces Manager, Council Offices, The Gateway, Gatehouse Road, Aylesbury HP19 8FF ☎ 01296 585228 🖑 gbird@aylesburyvaledc.gov.uk

Health and Safety: Mr David Thomas, Corporate Health & Safety Advisor, The Gateway, Gatehouse Road, Aylesbury HP19 8FF
☎ 01296 585158 🖑 dthomas@aylesburyvaledc.gov.uk

Home Energy Conservation: Mr Robert Smart, Environment Officer, The Gateway, Gatehouse Road, Aylesbury HP19 8FF
☎ 01296 585147 🖑 rsmart@aylesburyvaledc.gov.uk

AYLESBURY VALE

Housing: Mr Will Rysdale, Housing Development & Strategy Manager, Council Offices, The Gateway, Gatehouse Road, Aylesbury HP19 8FF ☎ 01296 585561
✆ housingneeds@aylesburyvaledc.gov.uk

Licensing: Mr Peter Seal, Licensing Officer, The Gateway, Gatehouse Road, Aylesbury HP19 8FF ☎ 01296 585083
✆ pseal@aylesburyvaledc.gov.uk

Lottery Funding, Charity and Voluntary: Ms Sarah Rothwell, Community Chest Grants Officer, Council Offices, The Gateway, Gatehouse Road, Aylesbury HP19 8FF ☎ 01296 585634
✆ srothwell@aylesburyvaledc.gov.uk

Member Services: Mr Bill Ashton, Democratic Services Manager, Council Offices, The Gateway, Gatehouse Road, Aylesbury HP19 8FF ☎ 01296 585040 ✆ washton@aylesburyvaledc.gov.uk

Parking: Mr Stephen Harding, Parking Manager, The Gateway, Gatehouse Road, Aylesbury HP19 8FF ☎ 01296 585381
✆ sharding@aylesburyvaledc.gov.uk

Planning: Ms Susan Kitchen, Manager - Development Management, Council Offices, The Gateway, Gatehouse Road, Aylesbury HP19 8FF ☎ 01296 585436
✆ skitchen@aylesburyvaledc.gov.uk

Procurement: Ms Sarah Deyes, Procurement Strategy Officer, The Gateway, Gatehouse Road, Aylesbury HP19 8FF
☎ 01296 585871 ✆ sdeyes@aylesburyvaledc.gov.uk

Recycling & Waste Minimisation: Mr Alan Asbury, Sustainability Team Leader, The Gateway, Gatehouse Road, Aylesbury HP19 8FF
☎ 01296 585112 ✆ aasbury@aylesburyvaledc.gov.uk

Staff Training: Ms Sarah Rodda, Training Administrator, Council Offices, The Gateway, Gatehouse Road, Aylesbury HP19 8FF
☎ 01296 585015 ✆ srodda@aylesburyvaledc.gov.uk

Sustainable Communities: Mrs Stephanie Moffat, Community Engagement Manager, The Gateway, Gatehouse Road, Aylesbury HP19 8FF ☎ 01296 585295 ✆ smoffat@aylesburyvaledc.gov.uk

Town Centre: Ms Diana Fawcett, Town Centre Manager, The Gateway, Gatehouse Road, Aylesbury HP19 8FF ☎ 01296 396370
✆ dfawcett@aylesburyvaledc.gov.uk

Transport: Mr Barry Waters, Transport Manager, New Century House, 18 Pembroke Road, Stocklake Industrial Estate, Aylesbury HP20 1DG ☎ 01296 585514 ✆ bwaters@aylesburyvaledc.gov.uk

Waste Collection and Disposal: Mr Andy Wilkins, Operations Manager, Pembroke Road, Aylesbury HP20 1DG ☎ 01296 585303
✆ awilkins@aylesburyvaledc.gov.uk

Waste Management: Mr Pete Randall, Refuse Manager, Pembroke Road, Aylesbury HP20 1DG ☎ 01296 585858

COUNCILLORS

ChairBloom, Jenny (CON - Mandeville & Elm Farm)
jbloom@aylesburyvaledc.gov.uk

Vice-ChairRenshell, Susan (CON - Winslow)
srenshaell@aylesburyvaledc.gov.uk

Leader of the Council: Blake, Neil (CON - Great Brickhill & Newton Longville)
nblake@aylesburyvaledc.gov.uk

Deputy Leader of the Council: Bowles, Steve (CON - Wendover & Halton)
sbowles@aylesburyvaledc.gov.uk

Adams, Chris (UKIP - Riverside)
chris.adams@ukip.org

Adams, Brian (UKIP - Walton Court & Hawkslade)
badams@aylesburyvaledc.gov.uk

Agoro, Peter (LD - Southcourt)
pagoro9@gmail.com

Bateman, Mark (LAB - Southcourt)
mbateman@aylesburyvaledc.gov.uk

Blake, Janet (CON - Stewkley)
jblake@aylesburyvaledc.gov.uk

Bond, Ashley (CON - Watermead)
abond@aylesburyvaledc.gov.uk

Brandis, Judy (CON - Haddenham & Stone)
jbrandis@aylesburyvaledc.gov.uk

Branston, Cameron (CON - Grendon Underwood & Brill)
cbrantson@aylesburyvaledc.gov.uk

Chapple, Sue (CON - Mandeville & Elm Farm)
schapple@aylesburyvaledc.gov.uk

Chapple, Bill (CON - Aston Clinton & Stoke Mandeville)
bchapple@aylesburyvaledc.gov.uk

Chilver, John (CON - Steeple Claydon)
jchilver@aylesburyvaledc.gov.uk

Christensen, Anders (LD - Gatehouse)
achristensen@aylesburyvaledc.gov.uk

Cole, Simon (CON - Buckingham North)
scole@aylesburyvaledc.gov.uk

Cole, Andrew (CON - Coldharbour)
acole@aylesburyvaledc.gov.uk

Collins, Michael (CON - Aston Clinton & Stoke Mandeville)
mcollins@aylesburyvaledc.gov.uk

Cooper, Peter (IND - Wingrave)
pcooper@aylesburyvaledc.gov.uk

Edmonds, Michael (CON - Haddenham & Stone)
medmonds@aylesburyvaledc.gov.uk

Everitt, Ben (CON - Great Brickhill & Newton Longville)
beveritt@aylesburyvaledc.gov.uk

Fealey, Patrick (CON - Tingewick)
pfealey@aylesburyvaledc.gov.uk

Foster, Brian (CON - Haddenham & Stone)
bfoster@aylesburyvaledc.gov.uk

Glover, Netta (CON - Wing)
nglover@aylesburyvaledc.gov.uk

Harrison, Allison (LD - Oakfield & Bierton)
aharrison@aylesburyvaledc.gov.uk

Hawkett, Mike (CON - Long Crendon)
mhawkett@aylesburyvaledc.gov.uk

Hetherington, Andy (UKIP - Elmhurst)
ahetherington@aylesburyvaledc.gov.uk

Hewson, Kevin (CON - Quainton)
khewson@aylesburyvaledc.gov.uk

Hunter-Watts, Tom (IND - Bedgrove)
tom.hunterwatts@gmail.com

Hussain, Tuffail (LD - Gatehouse)
thussain@aylesburyvaledc.gov.uk

Huxley, Andy (UKIP - Riverside)
ahuxley@aylesburyvaledc.gov.uk

Irwin, Paul (CON - Waddesdon)
pirwin@aylesburyvaledc.gov.uk

Jenkins, Sandra (CON - Pitstone & Cheddington)
sjenkins@aylesburyvaledc.gov.uk

Khan, Raj (LD - Elmhurst)
rkhan@buckscc.gov.uk

King, Roger (CON - Mandeville & Elm Farm)
rking@aylesburyvaledc.gov.uk

Lambert, Steven (LD - Coldharbour)
slambert@aylesburyvaledc.gov.uk

Lewis, Nick (CON - Riverside)
nelewis@aylesburyvaledc.gov.uk

Macpherson, Angela (CON - Marsh Gibbon)
amacpherson@aylesburyvaledc.gov.uk

Mills, Timothy (CON - Buckingham North)
tmills@aylesburyvaledc.gov.uk

Monger, Llew (LD - Winslow)
lmonger@aylesburyvaledc.gov.uk

Moore, Graham (CON - Gatehouse)
gmoore@aylesburyvaledc.gov.uk

Mordue, Howard (CON - Buckingham South)
hmordue@aylesburyvaledc.gov.uk

Paternoster, Carole (CON - Aston Clinton & Stoke Mandeville)
cpaternoster@aylesburyvaledc.gov.uk

Poll, Chris (CON - Edlesborough)
cpoll@aylesburyvaledc.gov.uk

Powell, Gary (CON - Walton Court & Hawkslade)
gpowell@aylesburyvaledc.gov.uk

Rand, Michael (CON - Oakley)
mrand@aylesburyvaledc.gov.uk

Russel, Barbara (CON - Central & Walton)
brussel@aylesburyvaledc.gov.uk

Sims, Edward (CON - Central & Walton)

Smith, Mike (LD - Coldharbour)
msmith2@aylesburyvaledc.gov.uk

Southam, Andrew (CON - Wendover & Halton)
asoutham@aylesburyvaledc.gov.uk

Stamp, Mary (CON - Oakfield & Bierton)

Stanier Bt, Beville (CON - Great Horwood)
bstanier@aylesburyvaledc.gov.uk

Strachan, Peter (CON - Wendover & Halton)
pstrachan@aylesburyvaledc.gov.uk

Stuchbury, Robin (LAB - Buckingham South)
stuchbury@dsl.pipex.com

Town, Derek (CON - Pitstone & Cheddington)
dtown@aylesburyvaledc.gov.uk

Ward, Julie (CON - Oakfield & Bierton)
jward@aylesburyvaledc.gov.uk

Whyte, Warren (CON - Luffield Abbey)
wwhyte@aylesburyvaledc.gov.uk

Winn, Mark (CON - Bedgrove)
mwinn@aylesburyvaledc.gov.uk

POLITICAL COMPOSITION
CON: 43, LD: 8, UKIP: 4, IND: 2, LAB: 2

COMMITTEE CHAIRS

Audit: Mr Kevin Hewson

Development Management: Mr Patrick Fealey

Finance & Scrutiny: Mr Michael Rand

Licensing: Mrs Judy Brandis

Babergh   D

Babergh District Council, Council Offices, Corks Lane, Hadleigh, Ipswich IP7 6SJ
☎ 01473 826622 ✆ customer.services@baberghmidsuffolk.gov.uk
🖥 www.babergh.gov.uk

FACTS AND FIGURES
Parliamentary Constituencies:
EU Constituencies: Eastern
Election Frequency: Elections are of whole council

PRINCIPAL OFFICERS

Deputy Chief Executive: Ms Lindsay Barker, Deputy Chief Executive, Council Offices, Corks Lane, Hadleigh, Ipswich IP7 6SJ
☎ 01473 825844 ✆ lindsay.barker@midsuffolk.gov.uk; lindsay.barker@baberghmidsuffolk.gov.uk

Senior Management: Mr Tom Barker, Assistant Director - Planning for Growth, Council Offices, Corks Lane, Ipswich IP7 6SJ ☎ 01449 724647 ✆ tom.barker@midsuffolk.gov.uk

Senior Management: Ms Suki Binjal, Interim Assistant Director - Law & Governance, Council Offices, Corks Lane, Hadleigh, Ipswich IP7 6SJ ☎ 01473 825811 ✆ suki.binjal@baberghmidsuffolk.gov.uk

Senior Management: Mr Paul Doe, ICT Strategic Lead, Council Offices, Corks Lane, Hadleigh, Ipswich IP7 6SJ ☎ 01473 825746 ✆ michael.evans@baberghmidsuffolk.gov.uk

Senior Management: Mr Mike Evans, Strategic Director, Council Offices, Corks Lane, Hadleigh, Ipswich IP7 6SJ ☎ 01473 825746 ✆ michael.evans@baberghmidsuffolk.gov.uk

Senior Management: Mr Jonathan Free, Assistant Director - Communities & Public Access, Council Offices, Corks Lane, Hadleigh, Ipswich IP7 6SJ ☎ 01449 724859 ✆ jonathan.free@baberghmidsuffolk.gov.uk

BABERGH

Senior Management: Mr Chris Fry, Assistant Director - Environment & Projects, Council Offices, Corks Lane, Hadleigh, Ipswich IP7 6SJ ☎ 01449 724805 ✆ chris.fry@baberghmidsuffolk.gov.uk

Senior Management: Mr Martin King, Assistant Director - Supported Living, Council Offices, 131 High Street, Needham Market IP6 8DL ☎ 01473 826649 ✆ martin.king@midsuffolk.gov.uk; martin.king@baberghmidsuffolk.gov.uk

Senior Management: Ms Lou Rawsthorne, Assistant Director - Investment & Commercial Delivery, Council Offices, Corks Lane, Hadleigh, Ipswich IP7 6SJ ☎ 01449 724772 ✆ lou.rawsthorne@baberghmidsuffolk.gov.uk

Senior Management: Ms Katherine Steel, Assistant Director - Corporate Resources, Council Offices, Corks Lane, Hadleigh, Ipswich IP7 6SJ ☎ 01449 724772 ✆ katherine.steel@baberghmidsuffolk.gov.uk

Architect, Building / Property Services: Mr Steve Clarke, Senior Surveyor - Building Services, Council Offices, 131 High Street, Needham Market IP6 8DL ☎ 01473 825774 ✆ stephen.clarke@baberghmidsuffolk.gov.uk

Best Value: Ms Karen Coll, Corporate Manager - Business Improvement, Council Offices, 131 High Street, Needham Market IP6 8DL ☎ 01449 724566 ✆ karen.coll@baberghmidsuffolk.gov.uk

Building Control: Mr Gary Starling, Corporate Manager - Building Control, Council Offices, Corks Lane, Hadleigh, Ipswich IP7 6SJ ☎ 01449 724502 ✆ gary.starling@baberghmidsuffolk.gov.uk

Community Planning: Mr Bill Newman, Corporate Manager - Strategic Planning, Council Offices, Corks Lane, Hadleigh, Ipswich IP7 6SJ ☎ 01473 825712 ✆ bill.newman@baberghmidsuffolk.gov.uk

Community Safety: Ms Sue Clements, Corporate Manager - Strong & Safe Communities, Council Offices, Corks Lane, Hadleigh, Ipswich IP7 6SJ ☎ 01449 724657 ✆ sue.clemments@baberghmidsuffolk.gov.uk

Computer Management: Mr Kevin Peck, Information & Technology Architect, Council Offices, Corks Lane, Hadleigh, Ipswich IP7 6SJ ☎ 01473 825824 ✆ kevin.peck@baberghmidsuffolk.gov.uk

Computer Management: Mr Carl Reeder, Corporate Manager - Information Management & ICT, Council Offices, Corks Lane, Hadleigh, Ipswich IP7 6SJ ☎ 01449 724862 ✆ carl.reeder@baberghmidsuffolk.gov.uk

Contracts: Ms Tracey Farthing, Senior Commissioning & Procurement Officer, Council Offices, Corks Lane, Hadleigh, Ipswich IP7 6SJ ☎ 01473 825715 ✆ tracey.farthing@baberghmidsuffolk.gov.uk

Contracts: Mrs Rachel Hodson-Gibbons, Corporate Manager - Commissioning, Council Offices, 131 High Street, Needham Market IP6 8DL ☎ 01449 724587 ✆ rachel.hodson-gibbons@baberghmidsuffolk.gov.uk

Corporate Services: Ms Suki Binjal, Interim Assistant Director - Law & Governance, Council Offices, Corks Lane, Hadleigh, Ipswich IP7 6SJ ☎ 01473 825811 ✆ suki.binjal@baberghmidsuffolk.gov.uk

Corporate Services: Ms Katherine Steel, Assistant Director - Corporate Resources, Council Offices, Corks Lane, Hadleigh, Ipswich IP7 6SJ ☎ 01449 724772 ✆ katherine.steel@baberghmidsuffolk.gov.uk

Customer Service: Mr Jonathan Free, Assistant Director - Communities & Public Access, Council Offices, Corks Lane, Hadleigh, Ipswich IP7 6SJ ☎ 01449 724859 ✆ jonathan.free@baberghmidsuffolk.gov.uk

Direct Labour: Mr Martin King, Assistant Director - Supported Living, Council Offices, 131 High Street, Needham Market IP6 8DL ☎ 01473 826649 ✆ martin.king@midsuffolk.gov.uk; martin.king@baberghmidsuffolk.gov.uk

Economic Development: Mr Lee Carvell, Corporate Manager - Open for Business, Council Offices, Corks Lane, Hadleigh, Ipswich IP7 6SJ ☎ 01473 825719 ✆ lee.carvell@baberghmidsuffolk.gov.uk

Economic Development: Ms Lou Rawsthorne, Assistant Director - Investment & Commercial Delivery, Council Offices, Corks Lane, Hadleigh, Ipswich IP7 6SJ ☎ 01449 724772 ✆ lou.rawsthorne@baberghmidsuffolk.gov.uk

E-Government: Mr Carl Reeder, Corporate Manager - Information Management & ICT, Council Offices, Corks Lane, Hadleigh, Ipswich IP7 6SJ ☎ 01449 724862 ✆ carl.reeder@baberghmidsuffolk.gov.uk

Electoral Registration: Mrs Emily Yule, Corporate Manager - Elections & Electoral Management, Council Offices, Corks Lane, Hadleigh, Ipswich IP7 6SJ ☎ 01473 825891 ✆ emily.yule@baberghmidsuffolk.gov.uk

Emergency Planning: Ms Sue Herne, Emergency Planning Responsive Officer, Council Offices, 131 High Street, Needham Market, Ipswich IP6 8DL ☎ 01449 724851 ✆ sue.herne@baberghmidsuffolk.gov.uk

Energy Management: Mr Steve Clarke, Senior Surveyor - Building Services, Council Offices, 131 High Street, Needham Market IP6 8DL ☎ 01473 825774 ✆ stephen.clarke@baberghmidsuffolk.gov.uk

Energy Management: Mr Iain Farquharson, Environmental Management Officer, Council Offices, 131 High Street, Needham Market IP6 8DL ☎ 01449 724878 ✆ iain.farquharson@baberghmidsuffolk.gov.uk

Environmental / Technical Services: Mr Martin King, Assistant Director - Supported Living, Council Offices, 131 High Street, Needham Market IP6 8DL ☎ 01473 826649 ✆ martin.king@midsuffolk.gov.uk;

Environmental Health: Mr Chris Fry, Head - Environment, Council Offices, Corks Lane, Hadleigh, Ipswich IP7 6SJ ☎ 01473 826649 ✆ chris.fry@baberghmidsuffolk.gov.uk

Estates, Property & Valuation: Mr Steve Clarke, Senior Surveyor - Building Services, Council Offices, 131 High Street, Needham Market IP6 8DL ☎ 01473 825774 ✆ stephen.clarke@baberghmidsuffolk.gov.uk

European Liaison: Mr Lee Carvell, Corporate Manager - Open for Business, Council Offices, Corks Lane, Hadleigh, Ipswich IP7 6SJ ☎ 01473 825719 ✆ lee.carvell@baberghmidsuffolk.gov.uk

Facilities: Ms Heather Worton, Corporate Manager, Council Offices, Corks Lane, Hadleigh, Ipswich IP7 6SJ ☎ 01473 825702 ✆ heather.worton@baberghmidsuffolk.gov.uk

Finance: Ms Katherine Steel, Assistant Director - Corporate Resources, Council Offices, Corks Lane, Hadleigh, Ipswich IP7 6SJ ☎ 01449 724772 ✆ katherine.steel@baberghmidsuffolk.gov.uk

Grounds Maintenance: Mr Peter Garrett, Corporate Manager - Countryside & Public Realm, Council Offices, Corks Lane, Hadleigh, Ipswich IP7 6SJ ☎ 01449 724944 ✆ peter.garrett@baberghmidsuffolk.gov.uk

Health and Safety: Mr John Grayling, Corporate Manager - Food & Safety, Council Offices, 131 High Street, Needham Market, Ipswich IP6 8DL ☎ 01449 724722 ✆ john.grayling@baberghmidsuffolk.gov.uk

Health and Safety: Ms Eira Trafford, Health & Safety Business Partner, Council Offices, 131 High Street, Needham Market IP6 8DL ☎ 01473 825752 ✆ eira.trafford@baberghmidsuffolk.gov.uk

Home Energy Conservation: Ms Heather Worton, Corporate Manager, Council Offices, Corks Lane, Hadleigh, Ipswich IP7 6SJ ☎ 01473 825702 ✆ heather.worton@baberghmidsuffolk.gov.uk

Housing: Mr Martin King, Assistant Director - Supported Living, Council Offices, 131 High Street, Needham Market IP6 8DL ☎ 01473 826649 ✆ martin.king@midsuffolk.gov.uk; martin.king@baberghmidsuffolk.gov.uk

Housing Maintenance: Mr Gavin Fisk, Interim Corporate Manager - Responsive Repairs, Council Offices, Corks Lane, Hadleigh, Ipswich IP7 6SJ ☎ 01449 724969 ✆ gavin.fisk@baberghmidsuffolk.gov.uk

Legal: Ms Suki Binjal, Interim Assistant Director - Law & Governance, Council Offices, Corks Lane, Hadleigh, Ipswich IP7 6SJ ☎ 01473 825811 ✆ suki.binjal@baberghmidsuffolk.gov.uk

Leisure and Cultural Services: Mr Jonathan Free, Assistant Director - Communities & Public Access, Council Offices, Corks Lane, Hadleigh, Ipswich IP7 6SJ ☎ 01449 724859 ✆ jonathan.free@baberghmidsuffolk.gov.uk

Leisure and Cultural Services: Mr Jonathan Seed, Corporate Manager - Health & Wellbeing, Council Offices, 131 High Street, Needham Market IP6 8DL ☎ 01449 724857 ✆ jonathan.seed@baberghmidsuffolk.gov.uk

Licensing: Mr Lee Carvell, Corporate Manager - Open for Business, Council Offices, Corks Lane, Hadleigh, Ipswich IP7 6SJ ☎ 01473 825719 ✆ lee.carvell@baberghmidsuffolk.gov.uk

Lottery Funding, Charity and Voluntary: Ms Sue Clements, Corporate Manager - Strong & Safe Communities, Council Offices, Corks Lane, Hadleigh, Ipswich IP7 6SJ ☎ 01449 724657 ✆ sue.clemments@baberghmidsuffolk.gov.uk

Member Services: Ms Jeanette McGarry, Interim Head of Democratic Services, Council Offices, Corks Lane, Hadleigh, Ipswich IP7 6SJ ☎ 01473 825891 ✆ jeanette.mcgarry@baberghmidsuffolk.gov.uk

Parking: Mr Jonathan Free, Assistant Director - Communities & Public Access, Council Offices, Corks Lane, Hadleigh, Ipswich IP7 6SJ ☎ 01449 724859 ✆ jonathan.free@baberghmidsuffolk.gov.uk

Partnerships: Ms Sue Clements, Corporate Manager - Strong & Safe Communities, Council Offices, Corks Lane, Hadleigh, Ipswich IP7 6SJ ☎ 01449 724657 ✆ sue.clemments@baberghmidsuffolk.gov.uk

Personnel / HR: Ms Jackie Foglietta, Corporate Manager - Organisational Development, Council Offices, Corks Lane, Hadleigh, Ipswich IP7 6SJ ☎ 01449 724803 ✆ jackie.foglietta@baberghmidsuffolk.gov.uk

Planning: Mr Tom Barker, Assistant Director - Planning for Growth, Council Offices, Corks Lane, Hadleigh, Ipswich IP7 6SJ ☎ 01449 724647 ✆ tom.barker@midsuffolk.gov.uk

Planning: Mr Philip Isbel, Professional Lead - Growth & Sustainable Planning, Council Offices, 131 High Street, Needham Market IP6 8DL ☎ 01449 724537 ✆ philip.isbel@baberghmidsuffolk.gov.uk

Procurement: Ms Tracey Farthing, Senior Commissioning & Procurement Officer, Council Offices, Corks Lane, Hadleigh, Ipswich IP7 6SJ ☎ 01473 825715 ✆ tracey.farthing@baberghmidsuffolk.gov.uk

Procurement: Mrs Rachel Hodson-Gibbons, Corporate Manager - Commissioning, Council Offices, 131 High Street, Needham Market IP6 8DL ☎ 01449 724587 ✆ rachel.hodson-gibbons@baberghmidsuffolk.gov.uk

Recycling & Waste Minimisation: Mr Oliver Faiers, Corporate Manager - Waste, Council Offices, Corks Lane, Hadleigh, Ipswich IP7 6SJ ☎ 01449 778621 ✆ oliver.faiers@baberghmidsuffolk.gov.uk

Recycling & Waste Minimisation: Mr Chris Fry, Head - Environment, Council Offices, Corks Lane, Hadleigh, Ipswich IP7 6SJ ☎ 01473 826649 ✆ chris.fry@baberghmidsuffolk.gov.uk

Regeneration: Mr Lee Carvell, Corporate Manager - Open for Business, Council Offices, Corks Lane, Hadleigh, Ipswich IP7 6SJ ☎ 01473 825719 ✆ lee.carvell@baberghmidsuffolk.gov.uk

Staff Training: Mrs Jo Knight, Leadership & OD Business Partner, Council Offices, Corks Lane, Hadleigh, Ipswich IP7 6SJ ☎ 01473 825804 ✆ jo.knight@baberghmidsuffolk.gov.uk

Sustainable Communities: Mr Jonathan Free, Assistant Director - Communities & Public Access, Council Offices, Corks Lane, Hadleigh, Ipswich IP7 6SJ ☎ 01449 724859 ✆ jonathan.free@baberghmidsuffolk.gov.uk

BABERGH

Sustainable Development: Mr Chris Fry, Assistant Director - Environment & Projects, Council Offices, Corks Lane, Hadleigh, Ipswich IP7 6SJ ☎ 01449 724805 ⌁ chris.fry@baberghmidsuffolk.gov.uk

Tourism: Mr Lee Carvell, Corporate Manager - Open for Business, Council Offices, Corks Lane, Hadleigh, Ipswich IP7 6SJ ☎ 01473 825719 ⌁ lee.carvell@baberghmidsuffolk.gov.uk

Waste Collection and Disposal: Mr Oliver Faiers, Corporate Manager - Waste, Council Offices, Corks Lane, Hadleigh, Ipswich IP7 6SJ ☎ 01449 778621 ⌁ oliver.faiers@baberghmidsuffolk.gov.uk

Waste Collection and Disposal: Mr Chris Fry, Assistant Director - Environment & Projects, Council Offices, Corks Lane, Hadleigh, Ipswich IP7 6SJ ☎ 01449 724805 ⌁ chris.fry@baberghmidsuffolk.gov.uk

Waste Management: Mr Oliver Faiers, Corporate Manager - Waste, Council Offices, Corks Lane, Hadleigh, Ipswich IP7 6SJ ☎ 01449 778621 ⌁ oliver.faiers@baberghmidsuffolk.gov.uk

Waste Management: Mr Chris Fry, Head - Environment, Council Offices, Corks Lane, Hadleigh, Ipswich IP7 6SJ ☎ 01473 826649 ⌁ chris.fry@baberghmidsuffolk.gov.uk

Children's Play Areas: Mr Jonathan Free, Assistant Director - Communities & Public Access, Council Offices, Corks Lane, Hadleigh, Ipswich IP7 6SJ ☎ 01449 724859 ⌁ jonathan.free@baberghmidsuffolk.gov.uk

COUNCILLORS

ChairBurgoyne, Peter (CON - Pinewood)
peter.burgoyne@babergh.gov.uk

Vice-ChairBeer, Peter (CON - Great Cornard (South))
peter.beer@babergh.gov.uk

Leader of the Council: Jenkins, Jennifer (CON - Leavenheath)
jennifer.jenkins@babergh.gov.uk

Deputy Leader of the Council: Barrett, Simon (CON - Sudbury South)
simon.barrett@babergh.gov.uk

Group LeaderArthey, Clive (IND - North Cosford)
clive.arthey@babergh.gov.uk

Group LeaderCarpendale, Sue (LD - Mid Samford)
sue.carpendale@babergh.gov.uk

Ayres, Sue (CON - Sudbury (North))
sue.ayres@babergh.gov.uk

Barrett, Melanie (CON - Nayland)
melanie.barrett@babergh.gov.uk

Bavington, Tony (LAB - Great Cornard (North))
tony.bavington@babergh.gov.uk

Burgoyne, Sue (CON - Hadleigh (South))
sue.burgoyne@babergh.gov.uk

Burrows, Tom (CON - Great Conrad (North))
tom.burrows@babergh.gov.uk

Busby, David (LD - Pinewood)
david.busby@babergh.gov.uk

Campbell, Tina (CON - Hadleigh (North))
tina.campbell@babergh.gov.uk

Creffield, Michael (CON - Brett Vale)
michael.creffield.gov.uk

Davis, Derek (IND - Berners)
derek.davis@babergh.gov.uk

Dawson, Sian (CON - Hadliegh (North))
sian.dawson@babergh.gov.uk

Ferguson, Alan (CON - South Cosford)
alan.ferguson@babergh.gov.uk

Gasper, Barry (CON - Brook)
barry.gasper@babergh.gov.uk

Grandon, Kathryn (CON - Hadleigh South)
kathryn.grandon@babergh.gov.uk

Hinton, John (CON - Dodnash)
john.hinton@babergh.gov.uk

Holland, David (CON - Sudbury (South))
david.holland@babergh.gov.uk

Holt, Michael (CON - Glemsford & Stanstead)
michael.holt@babergh.go.uk

Hurren, Bryn (LD - Boxford)
bryn.hurrren@babergh.gov.uk

Kemp, Richard (IND - Long Melford)
richard.kemp@babergh.gov.uk

Lawrenson, Frank (CON - Waldingfield)
frank.lawrenson@babergh.gov.uk

Long, James (IND - Chadacre)
james.long@babergh.gov.uk

Maybury, Margaret (CON - Waldingfield)
margaret.maybury@babergh.gov.uk

McCraw, Alistair (IND - Alton)
alastair.mccraw@babergh.gov.uk

Newman, Mark (CON - Great Cornard (South))
mark.newman@babergh.gov.uk

Nunn, John (IND - Long Melford)
john.nunn@babergh.gov.uk

Osborne, Adrian (CON - Sudbury (East))
adrian.osborne@babergh.gov.uk

Osborne, Jan (CON - Sudbury (East))
jan.osborne@babergh.gov.uk

Parker, Lee (CON - Bures St Mary)
lee.parker@babergh.gov.uk

Patrick, Peter (CON - Berners)
peter.patrick@babergh.gov.uk

Plumb, Stephen (IND - Glemsford & Stanstead)
stephen.plumb@babergh.gov.uk

Ridley, Nick (CON - Brook)
nick.ridley@babergh.gov.uk

Rose, David (IND - Holbrook)
david.rose@babergh.gov.uk

Shropshire, William (CON - Lavenham)
william.shropshire@babergh.gov.uk

Smith, Ray (CON - Sudbury (North))
ray.smith@babergh.gov.uk

Steer, Harriet (CON - Alton)
harriet.steet@babergh.gov.uk

Swan, Fenella (CON - Mid Samford)
fenella.swan@babergh.gov.uk

Ward, John (CON - Lower Brett)
john.ward@babergh.gov.uk

Williams, Stephen (CON - Dodnash)
stephen.williams@babergh.gov.uk

POLITICAL COMPOSITION
CON: 31, IND: 8, LD: 3, LAB: 1

COMMITTEE CHAIRS

Audit & Standards: Mr William Shropshire

Planning: Mr Peter Beer

Barking & Dagenham   L

Barking & Dagenham London Borough Council, Civic Centre, Dagenham RM10 7BN
☎ 020 8215 3000 ⌁ 3000direct@lbbd.gov.uk 🖳 www.lbbd.gov.uk

FACTS AND FIGURES
Parliamentary Constituencies: Barking, Dagenham and Rainham
EU Constituencies: London
Election Frequency: Elections are of whole council

PRINCIPAL OFFICERS

Chief Executive: Mr Chris Naylor, Chief Executive, Town Hall, Barking IG11 7LU ☎ 020 8227 2789 ⌁ chris.naylor@lbbd.gov.uk

Senior Management: Ms Anne Bristow, Strategic Director - Service Development & Integration, Town Hall, 1 Town Square, Barking IG11 7LU ☎ 020 8227 2300 ⌁ anne.bristow@lbbd.gov.uk

Senior Management: Mr Jonathan Bunt, Strategic Director - Finance & Investment, Civic Centre, Dagenham RM10 7BN
☎ 020 8724 8427 ⌁ jonathan.bunt@lbbd.gov.uk

Senior Management: Mr John East, Strategic Director - Growth & Homes, Civic Centre, Dagenham RM10 7BN
⌁ john.east@lbbd.gov.uk

Senior Management: Ms Meena Kishinani, Ambition 2020 Transformation Programme Director, Town Hall, 1 Town Square, Barking IG11 7LU ☎ 020 8227 3507
⌁ meena.kishinani@lbbd.gov.uk

Senior Management: Ms Claire Symonds, Strategic Director - Customer, Commercial & Service Delivery, Civic Centre, Dagenham RM10 7BN ⌁ claire.symonds@lbbd.gov.uk

Senior Management: Mrs Fiona Taylor, Director - Law & Governance, Civic Centre, Dagenham RM10 7BN ☎ 020 8227 2114 ⌁ fiona.taylor@bdtlegal.org.uk

Architect, Building / Property Services: Mr Richard Zurawik, Land Data Manager, Civic Centre, Dagenham RM10 7BN
☎ 020 8227 3954 ⌁ richard.zurawik@lbbd.gov.uk

Building Control: Mr Daniel Pope, Group Manager - Development & Planning, Town Hall, 1 Town Square, Barking IG11 7LU
☎ 020 8227 3929 ⌁ daniel.pope@lbbd.gov.uk

Catering Services: Ms Maureen Lowes, Catering Services Manager, Town Hall, 1 Town Square, Barking IG11 7LU
☎ 020 8227 5505 ⌁ maureen.lowes@lbbd.gov.uk

Children / Youth Services: Ms Meena Kishinani, Ambition 2020 Transformation Programme Director, Town Hall, 1 Town Square, Barking IG11 7LU ☎ 020 8227 3507 ⌁ meena.kishinani@lbbd.gov.uk

Civil Registration: Ms Cheryl Davis, Registration & Citizenship Manager, Arden House, 198 Long Bridge Road, Barking IG11 8SY
☎ 020 8270 4744 ⌁ cheryl.davis@lbbd.gov.uk

PR / Communications: Ms Sal Asghar, Interim Strategy & Performance Manager, Town Hall, Barking IG11 7LU
☎ 020 8227 3734 ⌁ salauoddin.asghar@lbbd.gov.uk

Community Planning: Ms Sal Asghar, Interim Strategy & Performance Manager, Town Hall, Barking IG11 7LU
☎ 020 8227 3734 ⌁ salauoddin.asghar@lbbd.gov.uk

Community Safety: Ms Glynis Rogers, Divisional Director - Community Safety & Public Protection, Town Hall, 1 Town Square, Barking IG11 7LU ☎ 020 8227 2827 ⌁ glynis.rogers@lbbd.gov.uk

Consumer Protection and Trading Standards: Mr Robin Payne, Divisional Director - Environment, Frizlands Municipal Offices, Dagenham RM10 7HX ☎ 020 8227 5660
⌁ robin.payne@lbbd.gov.uk

Economic Development: Mr David Harley, Group Manager - Economic Development, Town Hall, 1 Town Square, Barking IG11 7LU ☎ 020 8227 5316 ⌁ david.harley@lbbd.gov.uk

Education: Ms Jane Hargreaves, Divisional Director - Education, Roycraft House, 15 Linton Road, Barking IG11 7LU
☎ 020 8227 2686 ⌁ jane.hargreaves@lbbd.gov.uk

Education: Mrs Helen Jenner, Corporate Director - Children's Services, Town Hall, 1 Town Square, Barking IG11 7LU
☎ 020 8227 5800 ⌁ helen.jenner@lbbd.gov.uk

Electoral Registration: Mr John Dawe, Group Manager - Democratic Services, Civic Centre, Dagenham RM10 7BN
☎ 020 8227 2135 ⌁ john.dawe@lbbd.gov.uk

Emergency Planning: Mr David McClory, Civil Protection Manager, Town Hall, 1 Town Square, Barking IG11 7LU
☎ 020 8227 3588 ⌁ david.mcclory@lbbd.gov.uk

Energy Management: Ms Sandra Joseph, Manager - Energy, Town Hall, 1 Town Square, Barking IG11 7LU ☎ 020 8227 3385
⌁ sandra.joseph@lbbd.gov.uk

Environmental Health: Mr Robin Payne, Divisional Director - Environment, Frizlands Municipal Offices, Dagenham RM10 7HX
☎ 020 8227 5660 ⌁ robin.payne@lbbd.gov.uk

BARKING & DAGENHAM

Estates, Property & Valuation: Mr Andy Bere, Strategy Manager, Town Hall, Barking IG11 7LU ☎ 020 8227 3047 ⏻ andy.bere@lbbd.gov.uk

Facilities: Mr Clive Bennett, Facilities Manager, Town Hall, Barking IG11 7LU ☎ 020 8227 3669 ⏻ clive.bennett@lbbd.gov.uk

Finance: Mr Jonathan Bunt, Strategic Director - Finance & Investment, Civic Centre, Dagenham RM10 7BN ☎ 020 8724 8427 ⏻ jonathan.bunt@lbbd.gov.uk

Pensions: Mr David Dickinson, Group Manager - Treasury & Pensions, Civic Centre, Dagenham RM10 7BN ☎ 020 8227 2722 ⏻ david.dickinson@lbbd.gov.uk

Pensions: Ms Justine Springfield, Pensions Manager, Civic Centre, Dagenham RM10 7BN ☎ 020 8227 2607 ⏻ justine.spring@lbbd.gov.uk

Fleet Management: Mr Mark Fransener, Group Manager - Transport & Asset Management, Frizland Depot, Frizlands Lane, Dagenham RM10 7HX ☎ 020 8724 2834 ⏻ mark.fransener@lbbd.gov.uk

Grounds Maintenance: Mr Tony Ralph, Group Manager - Direct Services, Frizland Depot, Frizlands Lane, Dagenham RM10 7HX ☎ 020 8227 2974 ⏻ tony.ralph@lbbd.gov.uk

Health and Safety: Ms Gail Clark, Group Manager - HR Strategy, Civic Centre, Dagenham RM10 7BN ☎ 020 8227 3543 ⏻ gail.clark@lbbd.gov.uk

Highways: Mr Robert Curtis, Service Manager - Networks & Street Enforcement, Frizlands Depot, Frizlands Lane, Dagenham RM10 7BN ☎ 020 8227 2122 ⏻ robert.curtis@lbbd.gov.uk

Home Energy Conservation: Ms Sandra Joseph, Manager - Energy, Town Hall, 1 Town Square, Barking IG11 7LU ☎ 020 8227 3385 ⏻ sandra.joseph@lbbd.gov.uk

Housing: Mr Steven Tucker, Director - Housing, Town Hall, 1 Town Square, Barking IG11 7LU ☎ 020 8227 5700 ⏻ steven.tucker@lbbd.gov.uk

Housing Maintenance: Mr Rob Wood, Head of Housing, Pondfield House, Wantz Road, Dagenham RM10 8PP ☎ 020 8724 8831 ⏻ robert.wood@lbbd.gov.uk

Legal: Mr David Lawson, Head of Legal Services & Monitoring Officer, c/o The Town Hall, Ingrave Road, Brentwood CM15 8AY ☎ 01277 312860 ⏻ david.lawson@brentwood.gov.uk

Legal: Mrs Fiona Taylor, Director - Law & Governance, Civic Centre, Dagenham RM10 7BN ☎ 020 8227 2114 ⏻ fiona.taylor@bdtlegal.org.uk

Leisure and Cultural Services: Mr Paul Hogan, Divisional Director - Culture & Sport, Town Hall, 1 Town Square, Barking IG11 7LU ☎ 020 8227 3576 ⏻ paul.hogan@lbbd.gov.uk

Licensing: Mr Theo Lamptey, Team Leader - Trading Standards & Licensing Officer, Roycraft House, Linton Road, Barking IG11 8HE ☎ 020 8227 5655 ⏻ theo.lamptey@lbbd.gov.uk

Lottery Funding, Charity and Voluntary: Ms Monica Needs, Market Development Manager, Integration & Commissioning, Town Hall, Barking IG11 7LU ☎ 020 8227 2936 ⏻ monica.needs@lbbd.gov.uk

Member Services: Ms Belinda Lee, PA to the Leader, Town Hall, 1 Town Square, Barking IG11 7LU ☎ 020 8724 8448 ⏻ belinda.lee@lbbd.gov.uk

Parking: Ms Sharon Harrington, Group Manager - Parking, Town Hall, 1 Town Square, Barking IG11 7LU ☎ 020 8227 2952 ⏻ sharon.harrington@lbbd.gov.uk

Personnel / HR: Mr Martin Rayson, Divisional Director - Human Resources & OD, Town Hall, 1 Town Square, Barking IG11 7LU ☎ 020 8227 3113 ⏻ martin.rayson@lbbd.gov.uk

Planning: Mr Jeremy Grint, Divisional Director - Regeneration, Barking Town Hall, Barking IG11 7LU ☎ 020 8227 2443 ⏻ jeremy.grint@lbbd.gov.uk

Public Libraries: Mr Zoinul Abidin, Group Manager - Libraries, Barking Town Hall, Barking RM10 7HX ☎ 020 8724 8533 ⏻ zoinul.abidin@lbbd.gov.uk

Recycling & Waste Minimisation: Mr Tony Ralph, Group Manager - Direct Services, Frizland Depot, Frizlands Lane, Dagenham RM10 7HX ☎ 020 8227 2974 ⏻ tony.ralph@lbbd.gov.uk

Regeneration: Mr Jeremy Grint, Divisional Director - Regeneration, Barking Town Hall, 1 Town Square, Barking IG11 7LU ☎ 020 8227 2443 ⏻ jeremy.grint@lbbd.gov.uk

Road Safety: Mr Daniel Connelly, Highways Traffic & Parking Officer, Frizlands Depot, Frizlands Lane, Dagenham RM10 7HX ☎ 020 8227 2465 ⏻ daniel.connelly@lbbd.gov.uk

Social Services (Adult): Mr Bruce Morris, Divisional Director - Adult Social Care, Town Hall, 1 Town Square, Barking IG11 7LU ☎ 020 8227 2749 ⏻ bruce.morris@lbbd.gov.uk

Social Services (Children): Mrs Helen Jenner, Corporate Director - Children's Services, Town Hall, 1 Town Square, Barking IG11 7LU ☎ 020 8227 5800 ⏻ helen.jenner@lbbd.gov.uk

Safeguarding: Ms Meena Kishinani, Ambition 2020 Transformation Programme Director, Town Hall, 1 Town Square, Barking IG11 7LU ☎ 020 8227 3507 ⏻ meena.kishinani@lbbd.gov.uk

Childrens Social Care: Ms Ann Graham, Divisional Director - Complex Needs & Social Care, Town Hall, 1 Town Square, Barking IG11 7LU ☎ 020 8227 2233 ⏻ ann.graham@lbbd.gov.uk

Public Health: Mr Matthew Cole, Director - Public Health, Civic Centre, Dagenham RM10 7BN ☎ 020 8227 3657 ⏻ matthew.cole@lbbd.gov.uk

Staff Training: Ms Gail Clark, Group Manager - HR Strategy, Civic Centre, Dagenham RM10 7BN ☎ 020 8227 3543
✆ gail.clark@lbbd.gov.uk

Sustainable Communities: Mr Jeremy Grint, Divisional Director - Regeneration, Barking Town Hall, 1 Town Square, Barking IG11 7LU
☎ 020 8227 2443 ✆ jeremy.grint@lbbd.gov.uk

Sustainable Development: Mr Jeremy Grint, Divisional Director - Regeneration, Barking Town Hall, 1 Town Square, Barking IG11 7LU
☎ 020 8227 2443 ✆ jeremy.grint@lbbd.gov.uk

Town Centre: Mr Ralph Cook, Manager - Market Contracts, Roycroft House, Linton Road, Barking IG11 8HE ☎ 020 8227 6015
✆ ralph.cook@lbbd.gov.uk

Traffic Management: Mr Blane Parker, Traffic Officer, Frizlands Depot, Frizlands Lane, Dagenham RM10 7HX ☎ 020 8227 3489
✆ blane.parker@lbbd.gov.uk

Transport Planner: Mr Jeremy Grint, Divisional Director - Regeneration, Barking Town Hall, 1 Town Square, Barking IG11 7LU
☎ 020 8227 2443 ✆ jeremy.grint@lbbd.gov.uk

Waste Collection and Disposal: Mr Tony Ralph, Group Manager - Direct Services, Frizland Depot, Frizlands Lane, Dagenham RM10 7HX ☎ 020 8227 2974 ✆ tony.ralph@lbbd.gov.uk

Waste Management: Mr Tony Ralph, Group Manager - Direct Services, Frizland Depot, Frizlands Lane, Dagenham RM10 7HX
☎ 020 8227 2974 ✆ tony.ralph@lbbd.gov.uk

COUNCILLORS

Leader of the Council: Rodwell, Darren (LAB - Alibon)
darren.rodwell@lbbd.gov.uk

Deputy Leader of the Council: Ashraf, Saima (LAB - Gascoigne)
saima.ashraf@lbbd.gov.uk

Deputy Leader of the Council: Twomey, Dominic (LAB - Gascoigne)
dominic.twomey@lbbd.gov.uk

Ahammad, Syed (LAB - Longbridge)
syed.ahammad@lbbd.gov.uk

Alasia, Sanchia (LAB - Alibon)
sanchia.alasia@lbbd.gov.uk

Alexander, Jeannette (LAB - Eastbury)
jeannette.alexander@lbbd.gov.uk

Bartlett, Melanie (LAB - Whalebone)
melanine.bartlett2@lbbd.gov.uk

Bremmer, Simon (LAB - Goresbrook)

Bright, Sade (LAB - Chadwell Heath)
sade.bright@lbbd.gov.uk

Butt, Laila (LAB - Abbey)
laila.butt@lbbd.gov.uk

Carpenter, Evelyn (LAB - Becontree)
evelyn.carpenter@lbbd.gov.uk

Chand, Peter (LAB - River)
peter.chand@lbbd.gov.uk

Channer, Josephine (LAB - Thames)
josephine.channer@lbbd.gov.uk

Choudhury, Faruk (LAB - Becontree)
faruk.choudhury@lbbd.gov.uk

Fergus, Edna (LAB - Eastbrook)
edna.fergus@lbbd.gov.uk

Freeborn, Irma (LAB - Goresbrook)
irma.freeborn@lbbd.gov.uk

Gafoor Aziz, Abdul (LAB - Gascoigne)
abdul.gafooraziz@lbbd.gov.uk

Geddes, Cameron (LAB - Thames)
cameron.geddes2@lbbd.gov.uk

Ghani, Syed (LAB - Valence)
syed.ghani@lbbd.gov.uk

Gill, Rocky (LAB - Longbridge)
rocky.gill@lbbd.gov.uk

Haroon, Kashif (LAB - Mayesbrook)
kashif.haroom@lbbd.gov.uk

Hughes, Chris (LAB - Alibon)
christopher.hughes@lbbd.gov.uk

Jamu, Amardeep (LAB - River)
amardeep.jamu@lbbd.gov.uk

Jones, Jane (LAB - Valence)
jane.jones@lbbd.gov.uk

Kangethe, Elizabeth (LAB - Parsloes)
elizabeth.kangethe@lbbd.gov.uk

Keller, Eileen (LAB - River)
eileen.keller2@lbbd.gov.uk

Lawrence, Danielle (LAB - Abbey)
danielle.lawrence@lbbd.gov.uk

McCarthy, Mick (LAB - Eastbrook)
mick.mccarthy@lbbd.gov.uk

Miah, Giasuddin (LAB - Abbey)
miah.giasuddin@lbbd.gov.uk

Miles, Dave (LAB - Heath)
dave.miles2@lbbd.gov.uk

Mullane, Margaret (LAB - Village)
margaret.mullane@lbbd.gov.uk

Ogungbose, James (LAB - Becontree)
james.ogungbose@lbbd.gov.uk

Oluwole, Adegboyega (LAB - Mayesbrook)
adeboyega.oluwole@lbbd.gov.uk

Quadri, Moin (LAB - Goresbrook)
moin.quadri@lbbd.gov.uk

Rai, Hardial (LAB - Eastbury)
hardialsingh.rai@lbbd.gov.uk

Ramsay, Tony (LAB - Eastbrook)
tony.ramsay@lbbd.gov.uk

Reason, Linda (LAB - Heath)
linda.reason2@lbbd.gov.uk

Rice, Chris (LAB - Parsloes)
chris.rice@lbbd.gov.uk

Rice, Lynda (LAB - Longbridge)
lynda.rice@lbbd.gov.uk

BARKING & DAGENHAM

Shaukat, Faraaz (LAB - Eastbury)
faraaz.shaukut@lbbd.gov.uk

Smith, Danielle (LAB - Mayesbrook)
daniellej.smith@lbbd.gov.uk

Smith, Liam (LAB - Whalebone)
liam.smith@lbbd.gov.uk

Tarry, Sam (LAB - Chadwell Heath)
sam.tarry@lbbd.gov.uk

Turner, Bill (LAB - Thames)
bill.turner@lbbd.gov.uk

Wade, Jeff (LAB - Chadwell Heath)
jeff.wade@lbbd.gov.uk

Waker, Lee (LAB - Village)
lee.waker@lbbd.gov.uk

Waker, Philip (LAB - Village)
philip.waker@lbbd.gov.uk

White, John (LAB - Whalebone)
john.white@lbbd.gov.uk

Worby, Maureen (LAB - Valence)
maureen.worby@lbbd.gov.uk

Young, Dan (IND - Heath)
daniel.young@lbbd.gov.uk

Zanitchkhah, Linda (LAB - Parsloes)
linda.zanitchkhah2@lbbd.gov.uk

POLITICAL COMPOSITION
LAB: 50, IND: 1

COMMITTEE CHAIRS

Audit & Public Accounts: Mr Dave Miles

Children's Services: Ms Elizabeth Kangethe

Development Control: Ms Sanchia Alasia

Health & Adult Services: Mr Peter Chand

Health & Wellbeing: Ms Maureen Worby

Licensing: Ms Josephine Channer

Pensions: Mr Dominic Twomey

Barnet   L

London Borough of Barnet, Building 2, North London
Business Park, Oakleigh Road South, New Southgate,
London N11 1NP
☎ 020 8359 2000 🖨 0871 911 6188 🖥 first.contact@barnet.gov.uk
🖳 www.barnet.gov.uk

FACTS AND FIGURES
Parliamentary Constituencies: Chipping Barnet, Finchley and
Golders Green, Hendon
EU Constituencies: London
Election Frequency: Elections are of whole council

PRINCIPAL OFFICERS

Chief Executive: Mr John Hooton, Interim Chief Executive,
Building 2, North London Business Park, Oakleigh Road South,
New Southgate, London N11 1NP ☎ 020 8359 2000
🖥 john.hooton@barnet.gov.uk

Deputy Chief Executive: Ms Cath Shaw, Deputy Chief Executive
& Commissioning Director - Growth & Development, Building
2, North London Business Park, Oakleigh Road South, New
Southgate, London N11 1NP ☎ 020 8539 2000
🖥 cath.shaw@barnet.gov.uk

Senior Management: Mr Jamie Blake, Commissioning Director
- Environment, Building 2, North London Business Park, Oakleigh
Road South, New Southgate, London N11 1NP ☎ 020 8359 2000
🖥 jamie.blake@barnet.gov.uk

Senior Management: Ms Anisa Darr, Director - Resources,
Building 2, North London Business Park, Oakleigh Road South,
New Southgate, London N11 1NP ☎ 020 8359 2000
🖥 anisa.darr@barnet.gov.uk

Senior Management: Mr Stephen Evans, Interim Chief Operating
Officer, Building 2, North London Business Park, Oakleigh Road
South, London N11 1NP ☎ 020 8359 2000
🖥 stephen.evans@barnet.gov.uk

Senior Management: Ms Davina Fiore, Director - Assurance,
Building 2, North London Business Park, Oakleigh Road South,
New Southgate, London N11 1NP ☎ 020 8359 2000
🖥 maryellen.salter@barnet.gov.uk

Senior Management: Dr Andrew Howe, Director - Public Health,
Building 2, North London Business Park, Oakleigh Road South,
New Southgate, London N11 1NP ☎ 020 8359 3970
🖥 andrew.howe@harrow.gov.uk

Senior Management: Ms Susie Kemp, Interim Director -
Strategy, Building 2, North London Business Park, Oakleigh Road
South, New Southgate, London N11 1NP ☎ 020 8359 2000
🖥 susie.kemp@barnet.gov.uk

Senior Management: Mr Mathew Kendall, Director - Adults &
Communities, Building 2, North London Business Park, Oakleigh
Road South, New Southgate, London N11 1NP ☎ 020 8359 2000
🖥 mathew.kendall@barnet.gov.uk

Senior Management: Ms Katie Mayers, Head of
Communications, Marketing & Engagement, Building 2, North
London Business Park, Oakleigh Road South, New Southgate,
London N11 1NP 🖥 katie.mayers@barnet.gov.uk

Senior Management: Mr Chris Munday, Commissioning Director
- Children & Young People / Family Services Director, Building
2, North London Business Park, Oakleigh Road South, New
Southgate, London N11 1NP ☎ 020 8359 2000
🖥 chris.munday@barnet.gov.uk

Senior Management: Ms Dawn Wakeling, Director - Adults &
Health, Building 2, North London Business Park, Oakleigh Road
South, New Southgate, London N11 1NP ☎ 020 8359 2000
🖥 dawn.wakeling@barnet.gov.uk

Senior Management: Ms Caroline Woolf, Interim Commercial
Director, Building 2, North London Business Park, Oakleigh Road
South, New Southgate, London N11 1NP ☎ 020 8539 2000
🖥 caroline.woolf@barnet.gov.uk

Access Officer / Social Services (Disability): Mr Jon Dickinson, Assistant Director - Adult Social Care, Building 2, North London Business Park, Oakleigh Road South, New Southgate, London N11 1NP ☎ 020 8359 2000 ⌨ jon.dickinson@barnet.gov.uk

Architect, Building / Property Services: Mr Chris Smith, Head of Estates Management, Building 2, North London Business Park, Oakleigh Road South, New Southgate, London N11 1NP ☎ 020 8359 2000 ⌨ chris.smith@barnet.gov.uk

Building Control: Mr Nick Lennox, Area Manager for Building Control, Building 2, North London Business Park, Oakleigh Road South, New Southgate, London N11 1NP ☎ 020 8359 2000 ⌨ nick.lennox@barnet.gov.uk

Building Control: Mr Steve Snell, Area Manager For Building Control, Building 2, North London Business Park, Oakleigh Road South, New Southgate, London N11 1NP ☎ 020 8359 2000 ⌨ steve.snell@barnet.gov.uk

Catering Services: Ms Teresa Goodall, Catering Services Manager, Building 4, North London Business Patk, Oakleigh Road South, New Southgate, London N11 1NP ☎ 020 8359 2000 ⌨ teresa.goodall@barnet.gov.uk

Children / Youth Services: Ms Flo Armstrong, Head of Youth & Communities, Building 2, North London Business Park, Oakleigh Road South, New Southgate, London N11 1NP ☎ 020 8359 2000 ⌨ flo.armstrong@barnet.gov.uk

Children / Youth Services: Mr Ian Harrison, Education & Skills Director, Building 2, North London Business Park, Oakleigh Road South, New Southgate, London N11 1NP ☎ 020 8359 2000 ⌨ ian.harrison@barnet.gov.uk

Children / Youth Services: Ms Jo Pymont, Assistant Director - Children's Social Care, Building 2, North London Business Park, Oakleigh Road South, New Southgate, London N11 1NP ☎ 020 8359 5734 ⌨ jo.pymont@barnet.gov.uk

Children / Youth Services: Mr Duncan Tessier, Early Intervention & Prevention Assistant Director, Building 2, North London Business Park, Oakleigh Road South, New Southgate, London N11 1NP ☎ 020 8359 2000 ⌨ duncan.tessier@barnet.gov.uk

PR / Communications: Ms Katie Mayers, Head of Communications, Marketing & Engagement, Building 2, North London Business Park, Oakleigh Road South, New Southgate, London N11 1NP ⌨ katie.mayers@barnet.gov.uk

Community Planning: Mr John Allen, Assistant Director - Planning, Building 2, North London Business Park, Oakleigh Road South, New Southgate, London N11 1NP ☎ 020 8359 2000 ⌨ john.allen@barnet.gov.uk

Community Safety: Ms Kiran Vagarwal, Head of Community Safety, Building 2, North London Business Park, Oakleigh Road South, New Southgate, London N11 1NP ☎ 020 8359 2000 ⌨ kiran.vagarwal@barnet.gov.uk

Consumer Protection and Trading Standards: Ms Emma Phasey, Trading Standards Licensing Manager, Building 4, North London Business Park, Oakleigh Road South, New Southgate, London N11 1NP ☎ 020 8359 2000 ⌨ emma.phasey@barnet.gov.uk

Corporate Services: Mr Jamie Masraff, Head of Programme & Resources, Building 2, North London Business Park, Oakleigh Road South, New Southgate, London N11 1NP ☎ 020 8359 2000 ⌨ jamie.masraff@barnet.gov.uk

Customer Service: Ms Kari Manovitch, Head of Customer Strategy & Programmes, Building 2, North London Business Park, Oakleigh Road South, New Southgate, London N11 1NP ☎ 020 8359 2000 ⌨ kari.manovitch@barnet.gov.uk

Education: Mr Ian Harrison, Education & Skills Director, Building 2, North London Business Park, Oakleigh Road South, New Southgate, London N11 1NP ☎ 020 8359 2000 ⌨ ian.harrison@barnet.gov.uk

Electoral Registration: Ms Davina Fiore, Director - Assurance, Building 2, North London Business Park, Oakleigh Road South, New Southgate, London N11 1NP ☎ 020 8359 2000 ⌨ maryellen.salter@barnet.gov.uk

Emergency Planning: Ms Kate Solomon, Emergency Planning Manager, Building 2, North London Business Park, Oakleigh Road South, New Southgate, London N11 1NP ☎ 020 8359 2000 ⌨ kate.solomon@barnet.gov.uk

Environmental Health: Mr Rick Mason, Assistant Director - Environmental Health, Building 2, North London Business Park, Oakleigh Road South, New Southgate, London N11 1NP ⌨ rick.mason@barnet.gov.uk

Estates, Property & Valuation: Mr Chris Smith, Head of Estates Management, Building 2, North London Business Park, Oakleigh Road South, New Southgate, London N11 1NP ☎ 020 8359 2000 ⌨ chris.smith@barnet.gov.uk

Facilities: Mr Sean Patten, Facilities Manager, Building 2, North London Business Park, Oakleigh Road South, New Southgate, London N11 1NP ☎ 020 8359 2000 ⌨ sean.patten@barnet.gov.uk

Finance: Mr John Hooton, Interim Chief Executive, Building 2, North London Business Park, Oakleigh Road South, New Southgate, London N11 1NP ☎ 020 8359 2000 ⌨ john.hooton@barnet.gov.uk

Finance: Ms Patricia Phillipson, Head of Finance, Building 2, North London Business Park, Oakleigh Road South, New Southgate, London N11 1NP ☎ 020 8359 2000 ⌨ patricia.phillipson@barnet.gov.uk

Fleet Management: Mr Bernard McGreevy, Environment Transport Service Manager, Building 2, North London Business Park, Oakleigh Road South, New Southgate, London N11 1NP ☎ 020 8359 2000 ⌨ bernard.mcgreevy@barnet.gov.uk

Grounds Maintenance: Ms Jenny Warren, Head of Parks, Street Cleansing & Grounds Maintenance, Building 2, North London Business Park, North London Business Park, Oakleigh, London N11 1NP ☎ 020 8359 2000 ⌨ jenny.warren@barnet.gov.uk

Health and Safety: Mr Mike Koumi, Head of Health, Safety & Wellbeing, Building 2, North London Business Park, Oakleigh Road South, New Southgate, London N11 1NP ☎ 020 8359 2000 ⌨ mike.houmi@barnet.gov.uk

BARNET

Highways: Mr Richard Chalmers, Associate Director - Highways, Building 2, North London Business Park, Oakleigh Road South, New Southgate, London N11 1NP ☎ 020 8359 2000
🖰 richard.chalmers@capita.gov.uk

Highways: Mr Dean Cronk, Assistant Director - Highways, Building 2, North London Business Park, Oakleigh Road South, New Southgate, London N11 1NP ☎ 020 8359 2000
🖰 dean.cronk@capita.gov.uk

Highways: Mr Michael Hitchings, Regulation Services Manager - Highways, Building 2, North London Business Park, Oakleigh Road, New Southgate, London N11 1NP ☎ 020 8359 2000
🖰 michael.hitchings@capita.gov.uk

Housing: Ms Cath Shaw, Deputy Chief Executive & Commissioning Director - Growth & Development, Building 2, North London Business Park, Oakleigh Road South, New Southgate, London N11 1NP ☎ 020 8539 2000 🖰 cath.shaw@barnet.gov.uk

Housing: Mr Paul Shipway, Head of Strategy & Performance, Building 2, North London Business Park, Oakleigh Road South, New Southgate, London N11 1NP ☎ 020 8359 2000
🖰 paul.shipway@barnet.gov.uk

Legal: Ms Jennifer Farmer, Head of Joint Legal Services, Building 2, North London Business Park, Oakleigh Road South, New Southgate, London N11 1NP ☎ 020 8359 2000
🖰 jennifer.farmer@barnet.gov.uk

Licensing: Ms Emma Phasey, Trading Standards Licensing Manager, Building 4, North London Business Park, Oakleigh Road South, New Southgate, London N11 1NP ☎ 020 8359 2000
🖰 emma.phasey@barnet.gov.uk

Lighting: Mr Roger Gilbert, Street Lighting Project Manager, Building 2, North London Business Park, Oakleigh Road South, New Southgate, London N11 1NP ☎ 020 8359 2000
🖰 roger.gilbert@barnet.gov.uk

Lottery Funding, Charity and Voluntary: Mr Ken Argent, Grants Manager, Building 4, North London Business Park, Oakleigh Road South, New Southgate, London N11 1NP ☎ 020 8359 2000
🖰 ken.argent@barnet.gov.uk

Member Services: Mr Andrew Charlwood, Head of Governance, Building 2, North London Business Park, Oakleigh Road South, New Southgate, London N11 1NP ☎ 020 8359 2000
🖰 andrew.charlwood@barnet.gov.uk

Parking: Mr Paul Bragg, Head of Parking, Building 2, North London Business Park, Oakleigh Road South, New Southgate, London N11 1NP ☎ 020 8359 2000 🖰 paul.bragg@barnet.gov.uk

Personnel / HR: Mr Graeme Lennon, Human Resources Director, Building 2, North London Business Park, Oakleigh Road South, New Southgate, London N11 1NP ☎ 020 8359 2000
🖰 graeme.lennon@barnet.gov.uk

Planning: Mr John Allen, Assistant Director - Planning, Building 2, North London Business Park, Oakleigh Road South, New Southgate, London N11 1NP ☎ 020 8359 2000
🖰 john.allen@barnet.gov.uk

Procurement: Ms Elizabeth Stavreski, Head of Procurement, Building 2, North London Business Park, Oakleigh Road South, New Southgate, London N11 1NP ☎ 020 8359 2000
🖰 elizabeth.stavreski@barnet.gov.uk

Recycling & Waste Minimisation: Mr Graeme Laws, Joint Street Scene Director, North London Business Park, Oakleigh Road South, New Southgate, London N11 1NP ☎ 020 8359 2000
🖰 graeme.laws@barnet.gov.uk

Recycling & Waste Minimisation: Mr Shaun Morley, Joint Street Scene Director, North London Business Park, Oakleigh Road South, New Southgate, London N11 1NP ☎ 020 8359 2000
🖰 shaun.morley@barnet.gov.uk

Regeneration: Ms Cath Shaw, Deputy Chief Executive & Commissioning Director - Growth & Development, Building 2, North London Business Park, Oakleigh Road South, New Southgate, London N11 1NP ☎ 020 8539 2000 🖰 cath.shaw@barnet.gov.uk

Road Safety: Ms Lisa Wright, Principal Engineer of Traffic Management & Schools, Building 4, North London Business Park, Oakleigh Road South, New Southgate, London N11 1NP
☎ 020 8359 2000 🖰 lisa.wright@barnet.gov.uk

Social Services: Ms Jo Pymont, Assistant Director - Children's Social Care, Building 2, North London Business Park, Oakleigh Road South, New Southgate, London N11 1NP ☎ 020 8359 5734
🖰 jo.pymont@barnet.gov.uk

Social Services (Adult): Mr Jon Dickinson, Assistant Director - Adult Social Care, Building 2, North London Business Park, Oakleigh Road South, New Southgate, London N11 1NP
☎ 020 8359 2000 🖰 jon.dickinson@barnet.gov.uk

Social Services (Adult): Mr Mathew Kendall, Director - Adults & Communities, Building 2, North London Business Park, Oakleigh Road South, New Southgate, London N11 1NP ☎ 020 8359 2000
🖰 mathew.kendall@barnet.gov.uk

Social Services (Adult): Ms Dawn Wakeling, Director - Adults & Health, Building 2, North London Business Park, Oakleigh Road South, New Southgate, London N11 1NP ☎ 020 8359 2000
🖰 dawn.wakeling@barnet.gov.uk

Safeguarding: Ms Elaine Atkinson, Head of Safeguarding, North London Business Park, Oakleigh Road South, New Southgate, London N11 1NP ☎ 020 8359 2000 🖰 elaine.atkinson@barnet.gov.uk

Families: Mr Duncan Tessier, Early Intervention & Prevention Assistant Director, Building 2, North London Business Park, Oakleigh Road South, New Southgate, London N11 1NP
☎ 020 8359 2000 🖰 duncan.tessier@barnet.gov.uk

Looked after Children: Ms Jo Pymont, Assistant Director - Children's Social Care, Building 2, North London Business Park, Oakleigh Road South, New Southgate, London N11 1NP
☎ 020 8359 5734 🖰 jo.pymont@barnet.gov.uk

Looked after Children: Ms Siobhan Williams, Head of Intervention & Planning, North London Business Park, Oakleigh Road South, New Southgate, London N11 1NP ☎ 020 8359 2000
🖰 siobhan.williams@barnet.gov.uk

Childrens Social Care: Ms Kate Malleson, Head of Youth & Family Support, North London Business Park, Oakleigh Road South, New Southgate, London N11 1NP ☎ 020 8359 5734
⌕ kate.malleson@barnet.gov.uk

Public Health: Dr Andrew Howe, Director - Public Health, Building 2, North London Business Park, Oakleigh Road South, New Southgate, London N11 1NP ☎ 020 8359 3970
⌕ andrew.howe@harrow.gov.uk

Street Scene: Mr Nick Patterson, Interim Head of Recycling & Waste, North London Business Park, Oakleigh Road South, New Southgate, London N11 1NP ☎ 020 8359 2000
⌕ nick.patterson@barnet.gov.uk

Sustainable Development: Mr Michael Lai, Waste Strategy Group Manager, Building 4, North London Business Park, Oakleigh Road South, New Southgate, London N11 1NP ☎ 020 8359 2000
⌕ michael.lai@barnet.gov.uk

Traffic Management: Mr Richard Chalmers, Associate Director - Highways, Building 2, North London Business Park, Oakleigh Road South, New Southgate, London N11 1NP ☎ 020 8359 2000
⌕ richard.chalmers@capita.gov.uk

Transport: Mr Bernard McGreevy, Environment Transport Service Manager, Building 2, North London Business Park, Oakleigh Road South, New Southgate, London N11 1NP ☎ 020 8359 2000
⌕ bernard.mcgreevy@barnet.gov.uk

Waste Management: Mrs Nicola Cross, Waste Strategy Manager, Building 4, North London Business Park, Oakleigh Road South, New Southgate, London N11 1NP ☎ 020 8359 2000
⌕ nicola.cross@barnet.gov.uk

COUNCILLORS

Mayor: Longstaff, David (CON - High Barnet)
cllr.d.longstaff@barnet.gov.uk

Deputy Mayor: Khatri, Sury (CON - Mill Hill)
cllr.s.khatri@barnet.gov.uk

Leader of the Council: Cornelius, Richard (CON - Totteridge)
cllr.r.cornelius@barnet.gov.uk

Deputy Leader of the Council: Thomas, Daniel (CON - Finchley Church End)
cllr.d.thomas@barnet.gov.uk

Braun, Maureen (CON - Hendon)
cllr.m.braun@barnet.gov.uk

Brayne, Jess (LAB - Underhill)
cllr.j.brayne@barnet.gov.uk

Challice, Rebecca (LAB - East Barnet)
cllr.r.challice@barnet.gov.uk

Coakley Webb, Pauline (LAB - Coppetts)
cllr.p.coakleywebb@barnet.gov.uk

Cohen, Philip (LAB - East Barnet)
cllr.p.cohen@barnet.gov.uk

Cohen, Dean (CON - Golders Green)
cllr.d.cohen@barnet.gov.uk

Cohen, Jack (LD - Childs Hill)
cllr.j.cohen@barnet.gov.uk

Cohen, Melvin (CON - Golders Green)
cllr.m.cohen@barnet.gov.uk

Cooke, Geof (LAB - Woodhouse)
cllr.g.cooke@barnet.gov.uk

Cornelius, Alison (CON - Totteridge)
cllr.a.cornelius@barnet.gov.uk

Davey, Tom (CON - Hale)
cllr.t.davey@barnet.gov.uk

Duschinksy, Val (CON - Mill Hill)
cllr.v.duschinskly@barnet.gov.uk

Edwards, Paul (LAB - Underhill)
cllr.p.edwards@barnet.gov.uk

Farrier, Claire (LAB - Burnt Oak)
cllr.c.farrier@barnet.gov.uk

Finn, Anthony (CON - Hendon)
cllr.a.finn@barnet.gov.uk

Gordon, Brian (CON - Edgware)
cllr.b.gordon@barnet.gov.uk

Greenspan, Eva (CON - Finchley Church End)
cllr.e.greenspan@barnet.gov.uk

Grover, Rohit (CON - Gardem Sibirb)
cllr.R.Grover@barnet.gov.uk

Hart, John (CON - Mill Hill)
cllr.j.hart@barnet.gov.uk

Hart, Helena (CON - Edgware)
cllr.h.hart@barnet.gov.uk

Houston, Ross (LAB - West Finchley)
cllr.r.houston@barnet.gov.uk

Hutton, Anne (LAB - Woodhouse)
cllr.a.hutton@barnet.gov.uk

Ioannidis, Andreas (LAB - Brunswick Park)
cllr.a.ioannidis@barnet.gov.uk

Kay, Devra (LAB - West Hendon)
cllr.d.kay@barnet.gov.uk

Langleben, Adam (LAB - West Hendon)
cllr.a.langleben@barnet.gov.uk

Levine, Kathy (LAB - Brunswick Park)
cllr.k.levine@barnet.gov.uk

Lyons, Kitty (LAB - Hale)

Marshall, John (CON - Garden Suburb)
cllr.j.marshall@barnet.gov.uk|

McGuirk, Kathy (LAB - West Finchley)
cllr.k.mcguirk@barnet.gov.uk

Mittra, Arjun (LAB - East Finchley)
cllr.a.mittra@barnet.gov.uk

Moore, Alison (LAB - East Finchley)
cllr.a.moore@barnet.gov.uk

Naqvi, Ammar (LAB - Burnt Oak)
cllr.A.Naqvi@Barnet.gov.uk

Narenthira, Nagus (LAB - Colindale)
cllr.n.narenthira@Barnet.gov.uk

Old, Graham (CON - Finchley Church End)
cllr.g.old@barnet.gov.uk

O-Macauley, Charlie (LAB - Burnt Oak)
cllr.c.omacauley@barnet.gov.uk

BARNET

Or-Bach, Alon (LAB - East Finchley)

Patel, Reema (LAB - Coppetts)
cllr.r.patel@barnet.gov.uk

Perry, Bridget (CON - High Barnet)
cllr.b.perry@barnet.gov.uk

Prentice, Wendy (CON - High Barnet)
cllr.w.prentice@barnet.gov.uk

Rajput, Sachin (CON - Oakleigh)
cllr.s.rajput@barnet.gov.uk

Rawlings, Barry (LAB - Coppetts)
cllr.b.rawlings@barnet.gov.uk

Rayner, Hugh (CON - Hale)
cllr.h.rayner@barnet.gov.uk

Roberts, Tim (LAB - Underhill)
cllr.T.Roberts@barnet.gov.uk

Rozenberg, Gabriel (CON - Garden Suburb)
cllr.g.rozenberg@barnet.gov.uk

Rutter, Lisa (CON - Brunswick Park)
cllr.l.rutter@barnet.gov.uk

Ryde, Shimon (CON - Childs Hill)
cllr.s.ryde@barnet.gov.uk

Salinger, Brian (CON - Oakleigh)
cllr.b.salinger@barnet.gov.uk

Sargeant, Gill (LAB - Colindale)
cllr.g.sargeant@barnet.gov.uk

Scannell, Joan (CON - Edgware)
cllr.j.scannell@barnet.gov.uk

Schneiderman, Alan (LAB - Woodhouse)
cllr.a.schneiderman@barnet.gov.uk

Shooter, Mark (CON - Hendon)
cllr.m.shooter@barnet.gov.uk

Slocombe, Agnes (LAB - West Hendon)
cllr.a.slocombe@barnet.gov.uk

Sowerby, Stephen (CON - Oakleigh)
cllr.s.sowerby@barnet.gov.uk

Stock, Caroline (CON - Totteridge)
caroline.stock9@gmail.com

Thompstone, Reuben (CON - Golders Green)
cllr.r.thompstone@barnet.gov.uk

Tierney, Jim (LAB - West Finchley)
cllr.j.tierney@barnet.gov.uk

Williams, Laurie (LAB - East Barnet)
cllr.l.williams@barnet.gov.uk

Zinkin, Peter (CON - Childs Hill)
cllr.p.zinkin@barnet.gov.uk

Zubairi, Zakia (LAB - Colindale)
cllr.z.zubairi@barnet.gov.uk

POLITICAL COMPOSITION
CON: 32, LAB: 30, LD: 1

COMMITTEE CHAIRS

Adults & Safeguarding: Mr Sachin Rajput

Children, Education, Libraries & Safeguarding: Mr Reuben Thompstone

Health & Wellbeing: Ms Helena Hart

Licensing: Mr John Hart

Pensions: TBA

Pensions: Mr Mark Shooter

Planning: Mr Melvin Cohen

Barnsley   M

Barnsley Metropolitan Borough Council, Town Hall, Church Street, Barnsley S70 2TA
☎ 01226 770770 🖷 01226 773099 ✆ online@barnsley.gov.uk
🖳 www.barnsley.gov.uk

FACTS AND FIGURES
Parliamentary Constituencies: Barnsley Central, Barnsley East
EU Constituencies: Yorkshire and the Humber
Election Frequency: Elections are by thirds

PRINCIPAL OFFICERS

Chief Executive: Ms Diana Terris, Chief Executive, Westgate Plaza One, PO Box 609, Barnsley S70 9FH ☎ 01226 773301 ✆ dianaterris@barnsley.gov.uk

Senior Management: Ms Julia Bell, Director - Human Resources, Performance & Communications, Westgate Plaza One, PO Box 634, Barnsley S70 9GG ☎ 01226 773304 ✆ juliabell@barnsley.gov.uk

Senior Management: Ms Julia Burrows, Director - Public Health, Westgate Plaza One, PO Box 609, Barnsley S70 9FH ☎ 01226 773477 ✆ juliaburrows@barnsley.gov.uk

Senior Management: Ms Rachel Dickinson, Executive Director - People, Westgate Plaza One, PO Box 609, Barnsley S70 9FH ☎ 01226 773602 ✆ judithharwood@barnsley.gov.uk

Senior Management: Ms Frances Foster, Director - Finance, Assets & Information Services, Westgate Plaza One, PO Box 609, Barnsley S70 9FH ☎ 01226 773163 ✆ francesfoster@barnsley.gov.uk

Senior Management: Mr Andrew Frosdick, Director - Legal & Governance, Westgate Plaza One, PO Box 609, Barnsley S70 9FH ☎ 01226 773001 ✆ andrewfrosdick@barnsley.gov.uk

Senior Management: Mr Matt Gladstone, Executive Director - Place, Westgate Plaza One, PO Box 602, Barnsley S70 9FB ☎ 01226 772001 ✆ mattgladstone@barnsley.gov.uk

Senior Management: Mrs Wendy Lowder, Acting Executive Director - Communities, Westgate Plaze One, PO Box 609, Barnsley S70 9FH ☎ 01226 772301 ✆ wendylowder@barnsley.gov.uk

Architect, Building / Property Services: Mr Jeremy Sykes, Service Director - Assets, Gateway Plaza, PO Box 634, Barnsley S70 9GG ☎ 01226 774607 ✆ jeremysykes@barnsley.gov.uk

Building Control: Mr Tim Cliffe, Group Leader - Building Control, Westgate Plaza One, PO Box 609, Barnsley S70 9FH ☎ 01226 772660 ✆ timcliffe@barnsley.gov.uk

Children / Youth Services: Ms Margaret Libreri, Service Director - Education, Early Start & Prevention, Gateway Plaza, Sackville Street, Barnsley S70 9JF ☎ 01226 773598 ⌂ margaretlibreri@barnsley.gov.uk

Civil Registration: Ms Kathryn Green, Head of Customer Service Operations, Gateway Plaza, PO Box 609, Barnsley S70 9FH ☎ 01226 773144 ⌂ kathryngreen@barnsley.gov.uk

PR / Communications: Ms Rachel King, Head of Communications & Marketing, Town Hall, Church Street, Barnsley S70 2TA ⌂ rachelking@barnsley.gov.uk

Community Planning: Mrs Wendy Lowder, Acting Executive Director - Communities, Gateway Plaza, Sackville Street, Barnsley S70 9JE ☎ 01226 772301 ⌂ wendylowder@barnsley.gov.uk

Community Safety: Mr Paul Brannan, Head of Service - Safer Barnsley, Beevor Court 2, PO Box 609, Barnsley S71 1 ☎ 01226 770770 ⌂ paulbrannan@barnsley.gov.uk

Community Safety: Mr Paul Hussey, Interim Service Director - Stronger, Safer, Healthier Communities, Town Hall, Church Street, Barnsley S70 2TA ⌂ paulhussey@barnsley.gov.uk

Computer Management: Mr Luke Sayers, Service Director - Information Services, Gateway Plaza, PO Box 609, Barnsley S70 9FH ☎ 01226 775702 ⌂ lukesayers@barnsley.gov.uk

Consumer Protection and Trading Standards: Mr Simon Frow, Head of Service - Regulatory Services, Westgate Plaza One, PO Box 609, Barnsley S70 9FH ☎ 01226 772541 ⌂ simonfrow@barnsley.gov.uk

Contracts: Ms Karen Temple, Managing Director - NPS Barnsley Ltd, Gateway Plaza, Sackville Street, Barnsley S70 2RD ☎ 01226 774392 ⌂ karen.temple@nps.co.uk

Customer Service: Ms Ann O'Flynn, Service Director - Customer Services, Gateway Plaza, PO Box 634, Barnsley S70 9GG ☎ 01226 772080 ⌂ annoflynn@barnsley.gov.uk

Economic Development: Mr David Shepherd, Service Director - Economic Regeneration, Westgate Plaza One, PO Box 609, Barnsley S70 9FH ☎ 01226 772621 ⌂ davidshepherd@barnsley.gov.uk

Education: Ms Margaret Libreri, Service Director - Education, Early Start & Prevention, Gateway Plaza, Sackville Street, Barnsley S70 9JF ☎ 01226 773598 ⌂ margaretlibreri@barnsley.gov.uk

E-Government: Mr Luke Sayers, Service Director - Information Services, Gateway Plaza, PO Box 609, Barnsley S70 9FH ☎ 01226 775702 ⌂ lukesayers@barnsley.gov.uk

Electoral Registration: Ms Debra Buckingham, Elections & Local Land Charges Manager, Town Hall, Church Street, Barnsley S70 2TA ☎ 01226 772343 ⌂ debrabuckingham@barnsley.gov.uk

Emergency Planning: Mr Simon Dobby, Head of Health, Safety & Emergency Resilience, Westgate Plaza One, PO Box 634, Barnsley S70 9GG ☎ 01226 772289 ⌂ simondobby@barnsley.gov.uk

Estates, Property & Valuation: Mr Tim Hartley, Corporate Asset Management Manager, Westgate Plaza One, PO Box 609, Barnsley S70 9FH ☎ 01226 774615 ⌂ timhartley@barnsley.gov.uk

Finance: Ms Frances Foster, Director - Finance, Assets & Information Services, Westgate Plaza One, PO Box 609, Barnsley S70 9FH ☎ 01226 773163 ⌂ francesfoster@barnsley.gov.uk

Health and Safety: Mr Simon Dobby, Head of Health, Safety & Emergency Resilience, Westgate Plaza One, PO Box 634, Barnsley S70 9GG ☎ 01226 772289 ⌂ simondobby@barnsley.gov.uk

Legal: Mr Andrew Frosdick, Director - Legal & Governance, Westgate Plaza One, PO Box 609, Barnsley S70 9FH ☎ 01226 773001 ⌂ andrewfrosdick@barnsley.gov.uk

Licensing: Mr Simon Frow, Head of Service - Regulatory Services, Westgate Plaza One, PO Box 609, Barnsley S70 9FH ☎ 01226 772541 ⌂ simonfrow@barnsley.gov.uk

Lifelong Learning: Mr Tom Smith, Head of Service - Employment & Skills, Gateway Plaza, PO Box 634, Barnsley S70 9GG ☎ 01226 773830 ⌂ tomsmith@barnsley.gov.uk

Member Services: Mr Ian Turner, Service Director - Governance & Member Support, Gateway Plaza, PO Box 634, Barnsley S70 9GG ☎ 01226 773421 ⌂ ianturner@barnsley.gov.uk

Personnel / HR: Ms Julia Bell, Director - Human Resources, Performance & Communications, Westgate Plaza One, PO Box 634, Barnsley S70 9GG ☎ 01226 773304 ⌂ juliabell@barnsley.gov.uk

Planning: Mr Joe Jenkinson, Head of Service - Planning & Building Control, Westgate Plaza One, PO Box 609, Barnsley S70 9FH ☎ 01226 772588 ⌂ joejenkinson@barnsley.gov.uk

Procurement: Ms Karen Temple, Managing Director - NPS Barnsley Ltd, Gateway Plaza, Sackville Street, Barnsley S70 2RD ☎ 01226 774392 ⌂ karen.temple@nps.co.uk

Public Libraries: Ms Kathryn Green, Head of Customer Service Operations, Gateway Plaza, PO Box 609, Barnsley S70 9FH ☎ 01226 773144 ⌂ kathryngreen@barnsley.gov.uk

Regeneration: Mr David Shepherd, Service Director - Economic Regeneration, Westgate Plaza One, PO Box 609, Barnsley S70 9FH ☎ 01226 772621 ⌂ davidshepherd@barnsley.gov.uk

Social Services (Adult): Mr Lennie Sahota, Interim Service Director - Adult Social Care & Health, Town Hall, Church Street, Barnsley S70 2TA ⌂ lenniesahota@barnsley.gov.uk

Social Services (Children): Ms Mel John-Ross, Service Director - Children's Social Care & Safeguarding, Gateway Plaza, Sackville Street, Barnsley S70 9JF ☎ 01226 773665 ⌂ melaniejohn-ross@barnsley.gov.uk

Safeguarding: Ms Mel John-Ross, Service Director - Children's Social Care & Safeguarding, Gateway Plaza, Sackville Street, Barnsley S70 9JF ☎ 01226 773665 ⌂ melaniejohn-ross@barnsley.gov.uk

BARNSLEY

Childrens Social Care: Ms Mel John-Ross, Service Director - Children's Social Care & Safeguarding, Gateway Plaza, Sackville Street, Barnsley S70 9JF ☎ 01226 773665
⌖ melaniejohn-ross@barnsley.gov.uk

Public Health: Ms Julia Burrows, Director - Public Health, Westgate Plaza One, PO Box 609, Barnsley S70 9FH
☎ 01226 773477 ⌖ juliaburrows@barnsley.gov.uk

Staff Training: Mr Michael Potter, Service Director - Organisation & Workforce Improvement, Westgate Plaza One, PO Box 634, Barnsley S70 9GG ☎ 01226 774594
⌖ michaelpotter@barnsley.gov.uk

Transport: Mr Paul Castle, Service Director - Environment & Transport, Westgate Plaze One, PO Box 609, Barnsley S70 9FH
☎ 01226 774369 ⌖ paulcastle@barnsley.gov.uk

Transport Planner: Mr Paul Castle, Service Director - Environment & Transport, Westgate Plaze One, PO Box 609, Barnsley S70 9FH ☎ 01226 774369 ⌖ paulcastle@barnsley.gov.uk

COUNCILLORS

Mayor: Burgess, Linda (LAB - Darton West)
cllrlindaburgess@barnsley.gov.uk

Leader of the Council: Houghton, Stephen (LAB - Cudworth)
cllrstephenhoughton@barnsley.gov.uk

Deputy Leader of the Council: Andrews, Jim (LAB - Rockingham)
cllrjamesandrews@barnsley.gov.uk

Group LeaderBirkinshaw, Phillip (IND - Dodworth)
cllrphillipbirkinshaw@barnsley.gov.uk

Group LeaderWilson, John (CON - Penistone East)
cllrjohnwilson@barnsley.gov.uk

Barnard, Robert (CON - Penistone East)
cllrrobertbarnard@barnsley.gov.uk

Birkinshaw, Doug (LAB - Central)
cllrdougbirkinshaw@barnsley.gov.uk

Bruff, Margaret (LAB - Central)
cllrmargaretbruff@barnsley.gov.uk

Carr, Gill (IND - Worsbrough)
cllrgillcarr@barnsley.gov.uk

Carr, Jack (IND - Dodworth)
cllrjackcarr@barnsley.gov.uk

Cave, Alice (LAB - Darton West)
cllralicecave@barnsley.gov.uk

Charlesworth, Gail (LAB - Darton East)
cllrgailcharlesworth@barnsley.gov.uk

Cheetham, Tim (LAB - Royston)
cllrtimcheetham@barnsley.gov.uk

Cherryholme, Anita (LAB - Old Town)
cllranitacherryholme@barnsley.gov.uk

Clarke, John (LAB - Worsbrough)
cllrjohnclarke@barnsley.gov.uk

Clements, Malcolm (LAB - Royston)
cllrmalcolmclements@barnsley.gov.uk

Coates, Dorothy (LAB - Darfield)
cllrdorothycoates@barnsley.gov.uk

Dures, Emma (LAB - Rockingham)
cllremmadures@barnsley.gov.uk

Dyson, Martin (LAB - Central)
cllrmartindyson@barnsley.gov.uk

Dyson, Karen (LAB - Stairfoot)
cllrkarendyson@barnsley.gov.uk

Ennis, Jeff (LAB - North East)
cllrjeffennis@barnsley.gov.uk

Franklin, Robin (LAB - Hoyland Milton)
cllrrobinfranklin@barnsley.gov.uk

Frost, Robert (LAB - Wombwell)
cllrrobertfrost@barnsley.gov.uk

Gardiner, Alan (LAB - Dearne North)
cllralangardiner@barnsley.gov.uk

Gollick, Annette (LAB - Dearne North)
cllrannettegollick@barnsley.gov.uk

Green, Donna (LAB - Kingstone)
cllrdonnagreen@barnsley.gov.uk

Green, Steve (LAB - Monk Bretton)
cllrstevegreen@barnsley.gov.uk

Griffin, Dave (LAB - Penistone West)
cllrdavidgriffin@barnsley.gov.uk

Griffin, Daniel (LAB - Wombwell)
cllrdanielgriffin@barnsley.gov.uk

Grundy, Liz (IND - Old Town)
cllrlizgrundy@barnsley.gov.uk

Hampson, Allan (LAB - North East)
cllrallanhampson@barnsley.gov.uk

Hand-Davis, Paul (CON - Penistone East)
cllrpaulhand-davis@barnsley.gov.uk

Hayward, Joseph (LAB - Cudworth)
cllrjoehayward@barnsley.gov.uk

Higginbottom, Dorothy (LAB - North East)
cllrdorothyhigginbottom@barnsley.gov.uk

Howard, Sharon (LAB - Darton West)
cllrsharonhoward@barnsley.gov.uk

Johnson, Charlotte (LAB - Dearne South)
cllrcharlottejohnson@barnsley.gov.uk

Johnson, Wayne (LAB - Stairfoot)
cllrwaynejohnson@barnsley.gov.uk

Lamb, Chris (LAB - Rockingham)
cllrchrislamb@barnsley.gov.uk

Leech, David (LAB - St. Helen's)
cllrdavidleech@barnsley.gov.uk

Lofts, Phillip (LAB - Old Town)
cllrphilliplofts@barnsley.gov.uk

Makinson, Caroline (LAB - Royston)
cllrcarolinemakinson@barnsley.gov.uk

Markham, Pauline (LAB - Darfield)
cllrpaulinemarkham@barnsley.gov.uk

Mathers, Brian (LAB - Stairfoot)
cllrbrianmathers@barnsley.gov.uk

Miller, Roy (LAB - Darton East)
cllrroymiller@barnsley.gov.uk

Millner, Andrew (CON - Penistone West)
cllrandrewmillner@barnsley.gov.uk

Mitchell, Kath (LAB - Kingstone)
cllrkathmitchell@barnsley.gov.uk

Noble, May (LAB - Dearne South)
cllrmaynoble@barnsley.gov.uk

Platts, Jenny (LAB - St. Helen's)
cllrjennyplatts@barnsley.gov.uk

Pourali, Roya (LAB - Worsbrough)
cllrroyapourali@barnsley.gov.uk

Richardson, Kenneth (LAB - Monk Bretton)
cllrkenrichardson@barnsley.gov.uk

Riggs, Richard (LAB - Dodworth)
cllrrichardriggs@barnsley.gov.uk

Saunders, Caroline (LAB - Darfield)
cllrcarolinesaunders@barnsley.gov.uk

Sheard, Margaret (LAB - Monk Bretton)
cllrmargaretsheard@barnsley.gov.uk

Shepherd, Tim (LAB - Hoyland Milton)
cllrtimshepherd@barnsley.gov.uk

Sixsmith, Ralph (LAB - Dearne South)
cllrralphsixsmith@barnsley.gov.uk

Spence, Harry (NP - Darton East)
cllrharryspence@barnsley.gov.uk

Stowe, Mick (LAB - Hoyland Milton)
cllrmickstowe@barnsely.gov.uk

Tattersall, Sarah (LAB - St. Helen's)
cllrsarahjanetattersall@barnsley.gov.uk

Unsworth, Joe (LAB - Penistone West)
cllrjoeunsworth@barnsley.gov.uk

Williams, Kevin (LAB - Kingstone)
cllrkevinwilliams@barnsley.gov.uk

Worton, Jennifer (LAB - Dearne North)
cllrjenniferworton@barnsley.gov.uk

Wraith, Richard (LAB - Wombwell)
cllrrichardwraith@barnsley.gov.uk

Wraith, Charlie (LAB - Cudworth)
cllrcharleswraith@barnsley.gov.uk

POLITICAL COMPOSITION
LAB: 54, CON: 4, IND: 4, NP: 1

COMMITTEE CHAIRS

Audit: Mr Kenneth Richardson

Health & Wellbeing: Sir Stephen Houghton

Licensing: Mr Charlie Wraith

Planning: Mr Doug Birkinshaw

Barrow-in-Furness   D

Barrow-in-Furness Borough Council, Town Hall, Duke Street, Barrow-in-Furness LA14 2LD
☎ 01229 876543 ✆ customerservices@barrowbc.gov.uk
🖥 www.barrowbc.gov.uk

BARROW-IN-FURNESS

FACTS AND FIGURES
Parliamentary Constituencies: Barrow and Furness
EU Constituencies: North West
Election Frequency: Elections are by thirds

PRINCIPAL OFFICERS

Chief Executive: Mr Phil Huck, Executive Director, Town Hall, Duke Street, Barrow-in-Furness LA14 2LD ☎ 01229 876543 ✆ philhuck@barrowbc.gov.uk

Senior Management: Ms Susan Roberts, Director - Resources, Town Hall, Duke Street, Barrow-in-Furness LA14 2LD ☎ 01229 876543 ✆ smroberts@barrowbc.gov.uk

Access Officer / Social Services (Disability): Mr Kevin Morrison, Development Services Manager, Town Hall, Duke Street, Barrow-in-Furness LA14 2LD ☎ 01229 876543 ✆ kcmorrison@barrowbc.gov.uk

Architect, Building / Property Services: Mr Brian Vickers, Building Surveyor, Town Hall, Duke Street, Barrow-in-Furness LA14 2LD ☎ 01229 876543 ✆ bvickers@barrowbc.gov.uk

Best Value: Mr John Penfold, Corporate Support Manager, Town Hall, Duke Street, Barrow-in-Furness LA14 2LD ☎ 01229 876543 ✆ jpenfold@barrowbc.gov.uk

Building Control: Mr Kevin Morrison, Development Services Manager, Town Hall, Duke Street, Barrow-in-Furness LA14 2LD ☎ 01229 876543 ✆ kcmorrison@barrowbc.gov.uk

Community Planning: Mr Steve Solsby, Assistant Director - Regeneration & Built Environment, Town Hall, Duke Street, Barrow-in-Furness LA14 2LD ☎ 01229 876543 ✆ ssolsby@barrowbc.gov.uk

Computer Management: Mr Graham Fraser, IT Manager, Town Hall, Duke Street, Barrow-in-Furness LA14 2LD ☎ 01229 876543 ✆ gfraser@barrowbc.gov.uk

Contracts: Mr Chris Jones, Property Services Group Manager, Town Hall, Duke Street, Barrow-in-Furness LA14 2LD ☎ 01229 876543 ✆ cwjones@barrowbc.gov.uk

Contracts: Mrs Margaret Wilson, Leisure Centre Manager, Parks Leisure Centre, Greengate Street, Barrow-in-Furness LA13 9DT ☎ 01229 871146 ✆ mwilson@barrowbc.gov.uk

Corporate Services: Mr John Penfold, Corporate Support Manager, Town Hall, Duke Street, Barrow-in-Furness LA14 2LD ☎ 01229 876543 ✆ jpenfold@barrowbc.gov.uk

Customer Service: Mr John Penfold, Corporate Support Manager, Town Hall, Duke Street, Barrow-in-Furness LA14 2LD ☎ 01229 876543 ✆ jpenfold@barrowbc.gov.uk

Economic Development: Mr Steve Solsby, Assistant Director - Regeneration & Built Environment, Town Hall, Duke Street, Barrow-in-Furness LA14 2LD ☎ 01229 876543 ✆ ssolsby@barrowbc.gov.uk

Electoral Registration: Mr Jon Huck, Democratic Services Manager, Town Hall, Duke Street, Barrow-in-Furness LA14 2LD ☎ 01229 876543 ✆ jwhuck@barrowbc.gov.uk

BARROW-IN-FURNESS

Electoral Registration: Mrs Judith Swarbrick, Electoral Services Co-ordinator, Town Hall, Duke Street, Barrow-in-Furness LA14 2LD ☎ 01229 876543 ⌂ jswarbrick@barrowbc.gov.uk

Emergency Planning: Mr Andy Buck, Health & Safety Advisor, Town Hall, Duke Street, Barrow-in-Furness LA14 2LD ☎ 01229 876543 ⌂ abuck@barrowbc.gov.uk

Energy Management: Mr Chris Jones, Property Services Group Manager, Town Hall, Duke Street, Barrow-in-Furness LA14 2LD ☎ 01229 876543 ⌂ cwjones@barrowbc.gov.uk

Environmental / Technical Services: Mr Alan Barker, Streetcare Manager, Town Hall, Duke Street, Barrow-in-Furness LA14 2LD ☎ 01229 876543 ⌂ abarker@barrowbc.gov.uk

Environmental Health: Mrs Anne Pearson, Environmental Health Manager, Town Hall, Duke Street, Barrow-in-Furness LA14 2LD ☎ 01229 876543 ⌂ apearson@barrowbc.gov.uk

Estates, Property & Valuation: Mr David Joyce, Commercial Estates Manager, Town Hall, Duke Street, Barrow-in-Furness LA14 2LD ☎ 01229 876543 ⌂ djjoyce@barrowbc.gov.uk

European Liaison: Mr Steve Solsby, Assistant Director - Regeneration & Built Environment, Town Hall, Duke Street, Barrow-in-Furness LA14 2LD ☎ 01229 876543 ⌂ ssolsby@barrowbc.gov.uk

Events Manager: Mrs Sandra Baines, Forum Venue Manager, The Forum, Duke Street, Barrow-in-Furness LA14 1HH ☎ 01229 876484 ⌂ sbaines@barrowbc.gov.uk

Facilities: Mr Chris Jones, Property Services Group Manager, Town Hall, Duke Street, Barrow-in-Furness LA14 2LD ☎ 01229 876543 ⌂ cwjones@barrowbc.gov.uk

Treasury: Ms Gill Punton, Accountancy Services Manager, Town Hall, Duke Street, Barrow-in-Furness LA14 2LD ☎ 01229 876543 ⌂ smroberts@barrowbc.gov.uk

Grounds Maintenance: Mr Alan Barker, Streetcare Manager, Town Hall, Duke Street, Barrow-in-Furness LA14 2LD ☎ 01229 876543 ⌂ abarker@barrowbc.gov.uk

Health and Safety: Mr Andy Buck, Health & Safety Advisor, Town Hall, Duke Street, Barrow-in-Furness LA14 2LD ☎ 01229 876543 ⌂ abuck@barrowbc.gov.uk

Home Energy Conservation: Mr Chris Jones, Property Services Group Manager, Town Hall, Duke Street, Barrow-in-Furness LA14 2LD ☎ 01229 876543 ⌂ cwjones@barrowbc.gov.uk

Housing: Mr Colin Garnett, Assistant Director - Housing, Town Hall, Duke Street, Barrow-in-Furness LA14 2LD ☎ 01229 876462 ⌂ cgarnett@barrowbc.gov.uk

Housing Maintenance: Mr Les Davies, Maintenance & Asset Manager, Housing Department, Cavendish House, 78 Duke Street, Barrow-in-Furness LA14 1RR ☎ 01229 876540 ⌂ ldavies@barrowbc.gov.uk

Legal: Mrs Jane Holden, Acting Principal Legal Officer, Town Hall, Duke Street, Barrow-in-Furness LA14 2LD ☎ 01229 876543 ⌂ jmholden@barrowbc.gov.uk

Leisure and Cultural Services: Mrs Sandra Baines, Venue Manager, The Forum, Duke Street, Barrow-in-Furness LA14 1HH ☎ 01229 876482 ⌂ sbaines@barrowbc.gov.uk

Leisure and Cultural Services: Mr Keith Johnson, Assistant Director - Community Services, Town Hall, Duke Street, Barrow-in-Furness LA14 2LD ☎ 01229 876543 ⌂ kjohnson@barrowbc.gov.uk

Leisure and Cultural Services: Ms Sabine Skae, Collections & Exhibitions Manager, The Dock Museum, North Road, Barrow-in-Furness LA14 2PW ☎ 01229 876401 ⌂ sskae@barrowbc.gov.uk

Leisure and Cultural Services: Mrs Margaret Wilson, Leisure Centre Manager, Parks Leisure Centre, Greengate Street, Barrow-in-Furness LA13 9DT ☎ 01229 871146 ⌂ mwilson@barrowbc.gov.uk

Licensing: Mrs Anne Pearson, Environmental Health Manager, Town Hall, Duke Street, Barrow-in-Furness LA14 2LD ☎ 01229 876543 ⌂ apearson@barrowbc.gov.uk

Lottery Funding, Charity and Voluntary: Mr Keith Johnson, Assistant Director - Community Services, Town Hall, Duke Street, Barrow-in-Furness LA14 2LD ☎ 01229 876543 ⌂ kjohnson@barrowbc.gov.uk

Member Services: Mr Jon Huck, Democratic Services Manager, Town Hall, Duke Street, Barrow-in-Furness LA14 2LD ☎ 01229 876543 ⌂ jwhuck@barrowbc.gov.uk

Parking: Mr Mike Otto, Car Parks & Admin Manager, Town Hall, Duke Street, Barrow-in-Furness LA14 2LD ☎ 01229 876543 ⌂ mwotto@barrowbc.gov.uk

Personnel / HR: Ms Cathy Hornby, HR Manager, Town Hall, Duke Street, Barrow-in-Furness LA14 2LD ☎ 01229 876543 ⌂ chornby@barrowbc.gov.uk

Planning: Mr Jason Hipkiss, Development Services Manager, Town Hall, Duke Street, Barrow-in-Furness LA14 2LD ☎ 01229 876543 ⌂ jhipkiss@barrowbc.gov.uk

Procurement: Mrs Kimberley Fisher, Procurement Officer, Town Hall, Duke Street, Barrow-in-Furness LA14 2LD ☎ 01229 876543 ⌂ kfisher@barrowbc.gov.uk

Recycling & Waste Minimisation: Mr Peter Buckley, Recycling Officer, Town Hall, Duke Street, Barrow-in-Furness LA14 2LD ☎ 01229 876543 ⌂ pbuckley@barrowbc.gov.uk

Regeneration: Mr Steve Solsby, Assistant Director - Regeneration & Built Environment, Town Hall, Duke Street, Barrow-in-Furness LA14 2LD ☎ 01229 876543 ⌂ ssolsby@barrowbc.gov.uk

Staff Training: Ms Cathy Hornby, HR Manager, Town Hall, Duke Street, Barrow-in-Furness LA14 2LD ☎ 01229 876543 ⌂ chornby@barrowbc.gov.uk

Street Scene: Mr Alan Barker, Streetcare Manager, Town Hall, Duke Street, Barrow-in-Furness LA14 2LD ☎ 01229 876543 ⌨ abarker@barrowbc.gov.uk

Sustainable Communities: Mr Steve Solsby, Assistant Director - Regeneration & Built Environment, Town Hall, Duke Street, Barrow-in-Furness LA14 2LD ☎ 01229 876543 ⌨ ssolsby@barrowbc.gov.uk

Sustainable Development: Mr Steve Solsby, Assistant Director - Regeneration & Built Environment, Town Hall, Duke Street, Barrow-in-Furness LA14 2LD ☎ 01229 876543 ⌨ ssolsby@barrowbc.gov.uk

Waste Collection and Disposal: Mr Alan Barker, Streetcare Manager, Town Hall, Duke Street, Barrow-in-Furness LA14 2LD ☎ 01229 876543 ⌨ abarker@barrowbc.gov.uk

Waste Management: Mr Alan Barker, Streetcare Manager, Town Hall, Duke Street, Barrow-in-Furness LA14 2LD ☎ 01229 876543 ⌨ abarker@barrowbc.gov.uk

Children's Play Areas: Mr Alan Barker, Streetcare Manager, Town Hall, Duke Street, Barrow-in-Furness LA14 2LD ☎ 01229 876543 ⌨ abarker@barrowbc.gov.uk

COUNCILLORS

Leader of the Council: Pidduck, David (LAB - Hindpool)
dpidduck@barrowbc.gov.uk

Deputy Leader of the Council: Sweeney, M B (LAB - Parkside)
mbsweeney@barrowbc.gov.uk

Barlow, Desmond (LAB - Walney North)
dbarlow@barrowbc.gov.uk

Biggins, Trevor (LAB - Central)
tabiggins@barrowbc.gov.uk

Blezard, (LAB - Dalton South)

Brook, (LAB - Ormsgill)
dbrook@barrowbc.gov.uk

Burns, A (LAB - Hindpool)
aburns@barrowbc.gov.uk

Callister, Anthony (LAB - Walney North)
acallister@barrowbc.gov.uk

Cassells, (LAB - Risedale)

Cassidy, F (LAB - Walney South)
fcassidy@barrowbc.gov.uk

Derbyshire, Marie (LAB - Newbarns)
mderbyshire@barrowbc.gov.uk

Gawne, (CON - Roosecote)
dgawne@barrowbc.gov.uk

Gill, (CON - Hawcoat)
lgill@barrowbc.gov.uk

Hamilton, K (LAB - Risedale)
krhamilton@barrowbc.gov.uk

Harkin, (LAB - Dalton North)
sharkin@barrowbc.gov.uk

Heath, (CON - Dalton North)
jdheath@barrowbc.gov.uk

Husband, A G (LAB - Walney North)
aghusband@barrowbc.gov.uk

Johnston, A (LAB - Barrow Island)
ajohnston@barrowbc.gov.uk

Maddox, Wendy (LAB - Dalton South)
wemaddox@barrowbc.gov.uk

McClure, Rory (CON - Roosecote)
rmcclure@barrowbc.gov.uk

McClure, W (CON - Newbarns)
wmcclure@barrowbc.gov.uk

McEwan, (LAB - Ormsgill)
wmcewan@barrowbc.gov.uk

McLeavey, (CON - Roosecote)
mmcleavy@barrowbc.gov.uk

Murphy, John (LAB - Newbarns)
jdmurphey@barrowdc.gov.uk

Murray, F (LAB - Dalton South)
fgmurray@barrowbc.gov.uk

Opie, S (LAB - Parkside)
sopie@barrowdc.gov.uk

Pemberton, A (CON - Hawcoat)
aipemberton@barrowbc.gov.uk

Preston, (LAB - Risedale)
hpreston@barrowbc.gov.uk

Proffitt, (LAB - Central)
aproffitt@barrowbc.gov.uk

Roberts, David (CON - Hawcoat)
droberts@barrowbc.gov.uk

Seward, D (LAB - Parkside)
dmseward@barrowbc.gov.uk

Thomson, Ann (LAB - Hindpool)
mathomson@barrowbc.gov.uk

Thomson, Colin (LAB - Walney South)
cthomson@barrowbc.gov.uk

Thurlow, A (LAB - Dalton North)
athurlow@barrowbc.gov.uk

Wall, H (LAB - Walney South)
hwall@barrowbc.gov.uk

Williams, (LAB - Ormsgill)
lwilliams@barrowbc.gov.uk

POLITICAL COMPOSITION
LAB: 28, CON: 8

COMMITTEE CHAIRS

Audit: Mrs A Burns

Licensing: Mr Anthony Callister

Planning: Ms Ann Thomson

Basildon   D

Basildon Borough Council, The Basildon Centre, St. Martin's Square, Basildon SS14 1DL
☎ 01268 533333 📠 01268 294350
⌨ customerservices@basildon.gov.uk
💻 www.basildon.gov.uk

BASILDON

FACTS AND FIGURES

Parliamentary Constituencies: Basildon and Billericay, Basildon South and Thurrock East
EU Constituencies: Eastern
Election Frequency: Elections are by thirds

PRINCIPAL OFFICERS

Chief Executive: Mr Bala Mahendran, Chief Executive, The Basildon Centre, St. Martins Square, Basildon SS14 1DL ☎ 01268 208252 ⁸ bala.mahendran@basildon.gov.uk

Senior Management: Mr Kieran Carrigan, Commissioning Director - Resourcing & Place Shaping, The Basildon Centre, St. Martin's Square, Basildon SS14 1DL ☎ 01268 208182 ⁸ kieran.carrigan@basildon.gov.uk

Senior Management: Mr Scott Logan, Commissioning Director - People & Place, The Basildon Centre, St. Martin's Square, Basildon SS14 1DL ☎ 01268 208244 ⁸ scott.logan@basildon.gov.uk

Architect, Building / Property Services: Mr Phil Jones, Manager - Building Control, The Basildon Centre, St. Martin's Square, Basildon SS14 1DL ☎ 01268 206738 ⁸ phil.jones@basildon@gov.uk

Best Value: Mr Paul Burkinshaw, Group Manager - Corporate Governance & Support, The Basildon Centre, St. Martin's Square, Basildon SS14 1DL ☎ 01268 207972 ⁸ paul.burkinshaw@basildon.gov.uk

Building Control: Mr Phil Jones, Manager - Building Control, The Basildon Centre, St. Martin's Square, Basildon SS14 1DL ☎ 01268 206738 ⁸ phil.jones@basildon@gov.uk

Catering Services: Mr Paul Brace, Manager - Leisure, Open Space & Community Facilities, The Basildon Centre, St. Martin's Square, Basildon SS14 1DL ☎ 01268 208063 ⁸ paul.brace@basildon.gov.uk

PR / Communications: Mr Adrian Wardle, Communications Manager, The Basildon Centre, St. Martin's Square, Basildon SS14 1DL ☎ 01268 206719 ⁸ adrian.wardle@basildon.gov.uk

Community Safety: Ms Paula Mason, Community Safety Manager, The Basildon Centre, St. Martin's Square, Basildon SS14 1DL ☎ 01268 206833 ⁸ paula.mason@basildon.gov.uk

Computer Management: Mr Lee Hession, Manager - Information & Communication Technology, The Basildon Centre, St. Martin's Square, Basildon SS14 1DL ☎ 01268 207785 ⁸ lee.hession@basildon.gov.uk

Contracts: Mrs Lorraine Browne, Group Manager - Legal & Procurement, The Basildon Centre, St. Martin's Square, Basildon SS14 1DL ☎ 01268 207850 ⁸ lorraine.browne@basildon.gov.uk

Corporate Services: Mr Paul Burkinshaw, Group Manager - Corporate Governance & Support, The Basildon Centre, St. Martin's Square, Basildon SS14 1DL ☎ 01268 207972 ⁸ paul.burkinshaw@basildon.gov.uk

Customer Service: Mr Tom Walker, Manager - Customer Services, The Basildon Centre, St. Martin's Square, Basildon SS14 1DL ☎ 01268 206689 ⁸ tom.walker@basildon.gov.uk

Economic Development: Ms Gunilla Edwards, Team Manager - Economic Development, The Basildon Centre, St. Martin's Square, Basildon SS14 1DL ☎ 01268 207846 ⁸ gunilla.edwards@basildon.gov.uk

Electoral Registration: Mr Paul Burkinshaw, Group Manager - Corporate Governance & Support, The Basildon Centre, St. Martin's Square, Basildon SS14 1DL ☎ 01268 207972 ⁸ paul.burkinshaw@basildon.gov.uk

Emergency Planning: Mr Lee Hession, Manager - Information & Communication Technology, The Basildon Centre, St. Martin's Square, Basildon SS14 1DL ☎ 01268 207785 ⁸ lee.hession@basildon.gov.uk

Emergency Planning: Mr Scott Logan, Commissioning Director - People & Place, The Basildon Centre, St. Martin's Square, Basildon SS14 1DL ☎ 01268 208244 ⁸ scott.logan@basildon.gov.uk

Environmental Health: Mr Phil Easteal, Group Manager - Regulation, The Basildon Centre, St. Martin's Square, Basildon SS14 1DL ☎ 01268 208243 ⁸ phil.easteal@basildon.gov.uk

Estates, Property & Valuation: Ms Elaine Parry, Manager - Corporate Property, The Basildon Centre, St. Martin's Square, Basildon SS14 1DL ☎ 01268 207796 ⁸ elaine.parry@basildon.gov.uk

European Liaison: Ms Gunilla Edwards, Team Manager - Economic Development, The Basildon Centre, St. Martin's Square, Basildon SS14 1DL ☎ 01268 207846 ⁸ gunilla.edwards@basildon.gov.uk

Facilities: Mr Paul Humphreys, Service Manager - Corporate Property, The Basildon Centre, St. Martin's Square, Basildon SS14 1DL ☎ 01268 207897 ⁸ paul.humphreys@basildon.gov.uk

Finance: Mr Kieran Carrigan, Commissioning Director - Resourcing & Place Shaping, The Basildon Centre, St Martin's Square, Basildon SS14 1DL ☎ 01268 208182 ⁸ kieran.carrigan@basildon.gov.uk

Pensions: Mr Stuart Brian, Group Manager - HR & OD, The Basildon Centre, St. Martin's Square, Basildon SS14 1DL ☎ 01268 207994 ⁸ stuart.brian@basildon.gov.uk

Fleet Management: Mr Hugh Reynolds, Manager - Street Scene & Technical Services, Central Depot, Barleylands Road, Billericay CM11 2UF ☎ 01268 206784 ⁸ hugh.reynolds@basildon.gov.uk

Grounds Maintenance: Mr Hugh Reynolds, Manager - Street Scene & Technical Services, Central Depot, Barleylands Road, Billericay CM11 2UF ☎ 01268 206784 ⁸ hugh.reynolds@basildon.gov.uk

Home Energy Conservation: Mr Phil Easteal, Group Manager - Regulation, The Basildon Centre, St. Martin's Square, Basildon SS14 1DL ☎ 01268 208243 ⁸ phil.easteal@basildon.gov.uk

Housing: Ms Mandie Skeat, Head - Housing Services, The Basildon Centre, St. Martin's Square, Basildon SS14 1DL ☎ 01268 208163 ⌁ mandi.skeat@basildon.gov.uk

Housing Maintenance: Mr James Henderson, Property Services Business Manager, The Basildon Centre, St. Martin's Square, Basildon SS14 1DL ☎ 01268 206788 ⌁ james.henderson@basildon.gov.uk

Legal: Mrs Lorraine Browne, Group Manager - Legal & Procurement, The Basildon Centre, St. Martin's Square, Basildon SS14 1DL ☎ 01268 207850 ⌁ lorraine.browne@basildon.gov.uk

Leisure and Cultural Services: Mr Paul Brace, Manager - Leisure, Open Space & Community Facilities, Towngate Theatre, St Martin's Square, Basildon SS14 1DL ☎ 01268 208063 ⌁ paul.brace@basildon.gov.uk

Leisure and Cultural Services: Mr Gary Edwards, Head of Street Scene & Leisure Services, Central Depot, Barleylands Road, Billericay CM11 2UF ☎ 01268 206783 ⌁ gary.edwards@basildon.gov.uk

Lottery Funding, Charity and Voluntary: Ms Leah Douglas, Community Involvement Manager, The Basildon Centre, St. Martin's Square, Basildon SS14 1DL ☎ 01268 208074 ⌁ leah.douglas@basildon.gov.uk

Member Services: Mr Paul Burkinshaw, Group Manager - Corporate Governance & Support, The Basildon Centre, St. Martin's Square, Basildon SS14 1DL ☎ 01268 207972 ⌁ paul.burkinshaw@basildon.gov.uk

Parking: Mr Hugh Reynolds, Manager - Street Scene & Technical Services, Central Depot, Barleylands Road, Billericay CM11 2UF ☎ 01268 206784 ⌁ hugh.reynolds@basildon.gov.uk

Partnerships: Mr Paul Burkinshaw, Group Manager - Corporate Governance & Support, The Basildon Centre, St. Martin's Square, Basildon SS14 1DL ☎ 01268 207972 ⌁ paul.burkinshaw@basildon.gov.uk

Personnel / HR: Mr Stuart Brian, Group Manager - HR & OD, The Basildon Centre, St. Martin's Square, Basildon SS14 1DL ☎ 01268 207994 ⌁ stuart.brian@basildon.gov.uk

Planning: Mr Phil Easteal, Group Manager - Regulation, The Basildon Centre, St. Martin's Square, Basildon SS14 1DL ☎ 01268 208243 ⌁ phil.easteal@basildon.gov.uk

Procurement: Mrs Lorraine Browne, Group Manager - Legal & Procurement, The Basildon Centre, St. Martin's Square, Basildon SS14 1DL ☎ 01268 207850 ⌁ lorraine.browne@basildon.gov.uk

Recycling & Waste Minimisation: Mr Gary Edwards, Head of Street Scene & Leisure Services, Central Depot, Barleylands Road, Billericay CM11 2UF ☎ 01268 206783 ⌁ gary.edwards@basildon.gov.uk

Regeneration: Ms Claire Hamilton, Head of Regeneration & Economic Development, The Basildon Centre, St. Martin's Square, Basildon SS14 1DL ☎ 01268 207914 ⌁ claire.hamilton@basildon.gov.uk

Staff Training: Mr Stuart Brian, Group Manager - HR & OD, The Basildon Centre, St. Martin's Square, Basildon SS14 1DL ☎ 01268 207994 ⌁ stuart.brian@basildon.gov.uk

Street Scene: Mr Hugh Reynolds, Manager - Street Scene & Technical Services, Central Depot, Barleylands Road, Billericay CM11 2UF ☎ 01268 206784 ⌁ hugh.reynolds@basildon.gov.uk

Sustainable Communities: Ms Leah Douglas, Community Involvement Manager, The Basildon Centre, St. Martin's Square, Basildon SS14 1DL ☎ 01268 208074 ⌁ leah.douglas@basildon.gov.uk

Sustainable Development: Ms Mandie Skeat, Head - Housing Services, The Basildon Centre, St. Martin's Square, Basildon SS14 1DL ☎ 01268 208163 ⌁ mandi.skeat@basildon.gov.uk

Transport: Mr Hugh Reynolds, Manager - Street Scene & Technical Services, Central Depot, Barleylands Road, Billericay CM11 2UF ☎ 01268 206784 ⌁ hugh.reynolds@basildon.gov.uk

Total Place: Mr Kieran Carrigan, Commissioning Director - Resourcing & Place Shaping, The Basildon Centre, St. Martin's Square, Basildon SS14 1DL ☎ 01268 208182 ⌁ kieran.carrigan@basildon.gov.uk

Waste Collection and Disposal: Mr Gary Edwards, Head of Street Scene & Leisure Services, Central Depot, Barleylands Road, Billericay CM11 2UF ☎ 01268 206783 ⌁ gary.edwards@basildon.gov.uk

Waste Management: Mr Gary Edwards, Head of Street Scene & Leisure Services, Central Depot, Barleylands Road, Billericay CM11 2UF ☎ 01268 206783 ⌁ gary.edwards@basildon.gov.uk

Children's Play Areas: Mr Paul Brace, Manager - Leisure, Open Space & Community Facilities, Towngate Theatre, St Martin's Square, Basildon SS14 1DL ☎ 01268 208063 ⌁ paul.brace@basildon.gov.uk

COUNCILLORS

Mayor: Harrison, David (IND - Wickford Park) david.harrison@members.basildon.gov.uk

Deputy Mayor: Ward, Stephen (UKIP - Pitsea South East) stephen.ward@members.basildon.gov.uk

Leader of the Council: Turner, Philip (CON - Billericay West) phil.turner@members.basildon.gov.uk

Deputy Leader of the Council: Blake, Kevin (CON - Burstead) kevin.blake@members.basildon.gov.uk

Group Leader Allport-Hodge, Linda (UKIP - Langdon Hills) linda.allport-hodge@members.basildon.gov.uk

Group Leader Callaghan, Gavin (LAB - Pitsea North West) gavin.callaghan@members.basildon.gov.uk

Group Leader Smith, Kerry (IND - Nethermayne) kerry.smith@members.basildon.gov.uk

Allen, Stuart (CON - Crouch) stuart.allen@members.basildon.gov.uk

Arnold, Amanda (CON - Pitsea South East) amanda.arnold@members.basildon.gov.uk

BASILDON

Baggott, Andrew (CON - Burstead)
andrew.baggott@members.basildon.gov.uk

Ball, Alan (IND - Wickford Castledon)
alan.ball@members.basildon.gov.uk

Barnes, Andrew (CON - Laindon Park)
andrew.barnes@members.basildon.gov.uk

Bennett, Alan (LAB - Lee Chapel North)
alan.bennett@members.basildon.gov.uk

Block, (LAB - Vange)

Brown, Adele (LAB - Fryerns)
adele.brown@members.basildon.gov.uk

Burton-Sampson, (LAB - St Martin's)

Buxton, Andrew (LAB - St Martin's)
andrew.buxton@members.basildon.gov.uk

Canham, Gary (UKIP - Pitsea North West)
gary.canham@members.basildon.gov.uk

Carrion, (UKIP - Pitsea South East)

Clancy, Imelda (IND - Pitsea North West)
imelda.clancy@members.basildon.gov.uk

Dadds, David (CON - Billericay East)
david.dadds@members.basildon.gov.uk

Davies, Allan (LAB - Fryerns)
allan.davies@members.basildon.gov.uk

Ellis, Mark (UKIP - Laindon Park)
mark.ellis@members.basildon.gov.uk

Fellowes, (UKIP - Nethermayne)

Ferguson, Frank (UKIP - Lee Chapel North)
frank.ferguson@members.basildon.gov.uk

Gordon, (LAB - Lee Chapel North)

Green, (UKIP - Laindon Park)

Hedley, Anthony (CON - Billericay West)
anthony.hedley@members.basildon.gov.uk

Hillier, Stephen (CON - Langdon Hills)
stephen.hillier@members.basildon.gov.uk

Hodge, Stephen (UKIP - Nethermayne)
stephen.hodge@members.basildon.gov.uk

Holliman, Peter (UKIP - Wickford North)
peter.holliman@members.basildon.gov.uk

Jackman, Christopher (CON - Wickford Park)
chris.jackman@members.basildon.gov.uk

Lawrence, Daniel (CON - Billericay West)
daniel.lawrence@members.basildon.gov.uk

McGeorge, Melissa (LAB - Vange)
melissa.mcgeorge@members.basildon.gov.uk

Moore, Richard (CON - Burstead)
richard.moore@members.basildon.gov.uk

Morris, Carole (CON - Wickford North)
carole.morris@members.basildon.gov.uk

Morris, Don (CON - Wickford Castledon)
don.morris@members.basildon.gov.uk

Mowe, Michael (CON - Wickford North)
michael.mowe@members.basildon.gov.uk

Sargent, Terri (CON - Crouch)
terri.sargent@members.basildon.gov.uk

Schrader, Andrew (CON - Billericay East)
andrew.schrader@members.basildon.gov.uk

Sheppard, David (UKIP - Fryerns)
david.sheppard@members.basildon.gov.uk

Sullivan, Stuart (CON - Billericay East)
stuart.sullivan@members.basildon.gov.uk

POLITICAL COMPOSITION
CON: 18, UKIP: 11, LAB: 9, IND: 4

COMMITTEE CHAIRS

Audit & Risk: Mr Gary Canham

Licensing: Mr Peter Holliman

Planning: Ms Adele Brown

Regeneration & Environment: Mr Alan Ball

Basingstoke & Deane   D

Basingstoke & Deane Borough Council, Civic Offices, London Road, Basingstoke RG21 4AH
☎ 01256 844844 🖶 01256 845200 🖳 www.basingstoke.gov.uk

FACTS AND FIGURES
Parliamentary Constituencies: Basingstoke, Hampshire North West
EU Constituencies: South East
Election Frequency: Elections are by thirds

PRINCIPAL OFFICERS

Chief Executive: Mr Melbourne Barrett, Chief Executive, Civic Offices, London Road, Basingstoke RG21 4AH ☎ 01256 844844
🖰 melbourne.barrett@basingstoke.gov.uk

Senior Management: Ms Rebecca Emmett, Executive Director - Borough Services, Civic Offices, London Road, Basingstoke RG21 4AH ☎ 01256 844844 🖰 rebecca.emmett@basingstoke.gov.uk

Senior Management: Mr Kevin Jaquest, Executive Director - Finance & Resources (S151 Officer), Civic Offices, London Road, Basingstoke RG21 4AH ☎ 01256 844844
🖰 kevin.jaquest@basingstoke.gov.uk

Senior Management: Mrs Laura Taylor, Executive Director - Borough Development, Civic Offices, London Road, Basingstoke RG21 4AH ☎ 01256 844844 🖰 laura.taylor@basingstoke.gov.uk

Best Value: Mr Kevin Jaquest, Executive Director - Finance & Resources (S151 Officer), Civic Offices, London Road, Basingstoke RG21 4AH ☎ 01256 844844 🖰 kevin.jaquest@basingstoke.gov.uk

PR / Communications: Mrs Sara Shepherd, Communications & Media Manager, Civic Offices, London Road, Basingstoke RG21 4AH ☎ 01256 844844 🖰 sara.shepherd@basingstoke.gov.uk

Community Planning: Mrs June Balcombe, Community Development Manager, Civic Offices, London Road, Basingstoke RG21 4AH ☎ 01256 844844 🖰 june.balcombe@basingstoke.gov.uk

Community Safety: Ms Caroline Ryan, Shared Service Community Manager, Civic Offices, London Road, Basingstoke RG21 4AH ☎ 01256 844844 ⊙ caroline.ryan@basingstoke.gov.uk

Community Safety: Ms Marion Short, Wellbeing & Community Manager, Civic Offices, London Road, Basingstoke RG21 4AH ☎ 01256 844844 ⊙ marion.short@basingstoke.gov.uk

Computer Management: Mr Paul Tatam, IT Manager, Civic Offices, London Road, Basingstoke RG21 4AH ☎ 01256 844844 ⊙ paul.tatam@basingstoke.gov.uk

Contracts: Mrs Laura Taylor, Executive Director - Borough Development, Civic Offices, London Road, Basingstoke RG21 4AH ☎ 01256 844844 ⊙ laura.taylor@basingstoke.gov.uk

Customer Service: Mrs Katy Sallis, Customer Services Manager, Civic Offices, London Road, Basingstoke RG21 4AH ☎ 01256 844844 ⊙ katy.sallis@basingstoke.gov.uk

Economic Development: Ms Di Hayward, Economy, Culture & Borough Promotion Manager, Civic Offices, London Road, Basingstoke RG21 4AH ☎ 01256 844844 ⊙ di.hayward@basingstoke.gov.uk

Electoral Registration: Ms Karen Widdowson, Senior Electoral Services Manager, Civic Offices, London Road, Basingstoke RG21 4AH ☎ 01256 844844 ⊙ karen.widdowson@basingstoke.gov.uk

Environmental Health: Mr Tom Payne, Regulatory Services Manager, Civic Offices, London Road, Basingstoke RG21 4AH ☎ 01256 844844 ⊙ tom.payne@basingstoke.gov.uk

European Liaison: Mr Daniel Garnier, Economic Development Manager, Civic Offices, London Road, Basingstoke RG21 4AH ☎ 01256 844844 ⊙ daniel.garnier@basingstoke.gov.uk

Facilities: Ms Sheila Smith, Head of HR & Organisational Development, Civic Offices, London Road, Basingstoke RG21 4AH ☎ 01256 844844 ⊙ sheila.smith@basingstoke.gov.uk

Finance: Mr Kevin Jaquest, Executive Director - Finance & Resources (S151 Officer), Civic Offices, London Road, Basingstoke RG21 4AH ☎ 01256 844844 ⊙ kevin.jaquest@basingstoke.gov.uk

Finance: Mr Dean Pletts, Accountancy Manager, Civic Offices, London Road, Basingstoke RG21 4AH ☎ 01256 844844 ⊙ dean.pletts@basingstoke.gov.uk

Grounds Maintenance: Mr Colin Rowland, Head of Street Scene, Parks & Regulatory Services, Civic Offices, London Road, Basingstoke RG21 4AH ☎ 01256 844844 ⊙ colin.rowland@basingstoke.gov.uk

Health and Safety: Mr Paul Beaumont, Corporate Health & Safety Advisor, Civic Offices, London Road, Basingstoke RG21 4AH ☎ 01256 844844 ⊙ paulk.beaumont@basingstoke.gov.uk

Highways: Mr Richard Wareham, Community Design & Regeneration Manager, Civic Offices, London Road, Basingstoke RG21 4AH ☎ 01256 844844 ⊙ richard.wareham@basingstoke.gov.uk

Home Energy Conservation: Ms Lucy Martins, Climate Change Officer, Civic Offices, London Road, Basingstoke RG21 4AH ☎ 01256 844844 ⊙ lucy.martins@basingstoke.gov.uk

Legal: Ms Lisa Kirkman, Head of Law & Governance / Monitoring Officer, Civic Offices, London Road, Basingstoke RG21 4AH ☎ 01256 844844 ⊙ lisa.kirkman@basingstoke.gov.uk

Leisure and Cultural Services: Ms Di Hayward, Economy, Culture & Borough Promotion Manager, Civic Offices, London Road, Basingstoke RG21 4AH ☎ 01256 844844 ⊙ di.hayward@basingstoke.gov.uk

Licensing: Mrs Linda Cannon, Licensing Manager, Civic Offices, London Road, Basingstoke RG21 4AH ☎ 01256 844844 ⊙ linda.cannon@basingstoke.gov.uk

Member Services: Ms Karen Widdowson, Senior Electoral Services Manager, Civic Offices, London Road, Basingstoke RG21 4AH ☎ 01256 844844 ⊙ karen.widdowson@basingstoke.gov.uk

Parking: Mr Geoff Hislop, Engineering & Parking Team Leader, Civic Offices, London Road, Basingstoke RG21 4AH ☎ 01256 844844 ⊙ geoff.hisop@basingstoke.gov.uk

Partnerships: Ms Di Hayward, Economy, Culture & Borough Promotion Manager, Civic Offices, London Road, Basingstoke RG21 4AH ☎ 01256 844844 ⊙ di.hayward@basingstoke.gov.uk

Personnel / HR: Ms Sheila Smith, Head of HR & Organisational Development, Civic Offices, London Road, Basingstoke RG21 4AH ☎ 01256 844844 ⊙ sheila.smith@basingstoke.gov.uk

Planning: Mr Mike Townsend, Planning & Development Manager, Civic Offices, London Road, Basingstoke RG21 4AH ☎ 01256 844844 ⊙ mike.townsend@basingstoke.gov.uk

Procurement: Mr Kevin Jaquest, Executive Director - Finance & Resources (S151 Officer), Civic Offices, London Road, Basingstoke RG21 4AH ☎ 01256 844844 ⊙ kevin.jaquest@basingstoke.gov.uk

Recycling & Waste Minimisation: Ms Sarah Incher, Waste & Recycling Manager, Civic Offices, London Road, Basingstoke RG21 4AH ☎ 01252 774173 ⊙ sarah.incher@hart.gov.uk

Staff Training: Ms Sheila Smith, Head of HR & Organisational Development, Civic Offices, London Road, Basingstoke RG21 4AH ☎ 01256 844844 ⊙ sheila.smith@basingstoke.gov.uk

Street Scene: Mr Colin Rowland, Head of Street Scene, Parks & Regulatory Services, Civic Offices, London Road, Basingstoke RG21 4AH ☎ 01256 844844 ⊙ colin.rowland@basingstoke.gov.uk

Tourism: Mr Daniel Garnier, Economic Development Manager, Civic Offices, London Road, Basingstoke RG21 4AH ☎ 01256 844844 ⊙ daniel.garnier@basingstoke.gov.uk

Town Centre: Mr Daniel Garnier, Economic Development Manager, Civic Offices, London Road, Basingstoke RG21 4AH ☎ 01256 844844 ⊙ daniel.garnier@basingstoke.gov.uk

BASINGSTOKE & DEANE

Transport: Mr Richard Wareham, Community Design & Regeneration Manager, Civic Offices, London Road, Basingstoke RG21 4AH ☎ 01256 844844 ✆ richard.wareham@basingstoke.gov.uk

Waste Collection and Disposal: Ms Sarah Incher, Waste & Recycling Manager, Civic Offices, London Road, Basingstoke RG21 4AH ☎ 01252 774173 ✆ sarah.incher@hart.gov.uk

Waste Management: Ms Sarah Incher, Waste & Recycling Manager, Civic Offices, London Road, Basingstoke RG21 4AH ☎ 01252 774173 ✆ sarah.incher@hart.gov.uk

Children's Play Areas: Mr David Perkins, Operations Manager, Civic Offices, London Road, Basingstoke RG21 4AH ☎ 01256 844844 ✆ david.perkins@basingstoke.gov.uk

COUNCILLORS

Mayor: Frankum, Jane (LAB - Popley West)
cllr.jane.frankum@basingstoke.gov.uk

Deputy Mayor: Frankum, Paul (LAB - Popley West)
cllr.paul.frankum@basingstoke.gov.uk

Leader of the Council: Sanders, Clive (CON - East Woodhay)
cllr.clive.sanders@basingstoke.gov.uk

Deputy Leader of the Council: Reid, Terri (CON - Hatch Warren & Beggarwood)
cllr.terri.reid@basingstoke.gov.uk

Ashfield, Chloe (LAB - Whitchurch)
cllr.chloe.ashfield@basingstoke.gov.uk

Bean, Rebecca (CON - Hatch Warren & Beggarwood)
cllr.rebecca.bean@basingstoke.gov.uk

Bound, Simon (CON - Rooksdown)
cllr.simon.bound@basingstoke.gov.uk

Bound, Michael (LD - Baughurst & Tadley North)
cllr.michael.bound@basingstoke.gov.uk

Bower, Joyce (CON - Chineham)
cllr.joyce.bower@basingstoke.gov.uk

Burgess, Rita (CON - Kempshott)
cllr.rita.burgess@basingstoke.gov.uk

Court, Anne (CON - Kempshott)
cllr.anne.court@basingstoke.gov.uk

Cousens, Jack (LAB - Brookvale & Kings Furlong)
cllr.jack.cousens@basingstoke.gov.uk

Cubit, Onnalee (IND - Basing)
cllr.onnalee.cubitt@basingstoke.gov.uk

Day, Stephen (LD - Grove)
cllr.stephen.day@basingstoke.gov.uk

Eachus, Hayley (CON - Kempshott)
cllr.hayley.eachus@basingstoke.gov.uk

Edwards, Laura (CON - Winklebury)
cllr.laura.edwards@basingstoke.gov.uk

Falconer, Graham (CON - Burghclere, Highclere & St Mary Bourne)
cllr.graham.falconer@basingstoke.gov.uk

Frost, Stuart (CON - Oakley & North Waltham)
cllr.stuart.frost@basingstoke.gov.uk

Gardiner, Roger (CON - Pamber & Silchester)
cllr.roger.gardiner@basingstoke.gov.uk

Godesen, Sven (CON - Basing)
cllr.sven.godesen@basingstoke.gov.uk

Golding, Hannah (CON - Brighton Hill North)
cllr.hannah.golding@basingstoke.gov.uk

Golding, Rob (CON - Oakley & North Waltham)
cllr.rob.goulding@basingstoke.gov.uk

Harvey, Paul (LAB - Norden)
cllr.paul.harvey@basingstoke.gov.uk

Hood, George (LAB - Norden)
cllr.george.hood@basingstoke.gov.uk

Hussey, Ronald (LD - Grove)
cllr.ron.hussey@basingstoke.gov.uk

Izett, John (CON - Burghclere, Highclere & St Mary Bourne)
cllr.john.izett@basingstoke.gov.uk

James, Gavin (LD - Eastrop)
cllr.gavin.james@basingstoke.gov.uk

James, Laura (LAB - Norden)
cllr.laura.james@basingstoke.gov.uk

Jones, Tony (LAB - Buckskin)
cllr.tony.jones@basingstoke.gov.uk

Keating, Sean (LAB - South Ham)
cllr.sean.keating@basingstoke.gov.uk

Leeks, David (CON - Tadley South)
cllr.david.leeks@basingstoke.gov.uk

Lonie, Pamela (LAB - Brighton Hill South)
cllr.pamela.lonie@basingstoke.gov.uk

McCormick, Andrew (LAB - Brighton Hill South)
cllr.andrew.mccormick@basingstoke.gov.uk

Miller, Paul (CON - Chineham)
cllr.paul.miller@basingstoke.gov.uk

Musson, Robert (CON - Tadley South)
cllr.robert.musson@basingstoke.gov.uk

Parker, Stuart (LD - Eastrop)
cllr.stuart.parker@basingstoke.gov.uk

Phillimore, Colin (LAB - Overton, Laverstoke & Steventon)
cllr.colin.phillimore@basingstoke.gov.uk

Pierce, Nigel (LAB - Buckskin)
cllr.nigel.pierce@basingstoke.gov.uk

Pinder, Clive (CON - Basing)
cllr.clive.pinder@basingstoke.gov.uk

Potter, David (LAB - Popley East)
cllr.david.potter@basingstoke.gov.uk

Putty, Dan (CON - Hatch Warren & Beggarwood)
cllr.dan.putty@basingstoke.gov.uk

Regan, Colin (LAB - South Ham)
cllr.colin.regan@basingstoke.gov.uk

Rhatigan, Ken (CON - Kingsclere)
cllr.ken.rhatigan@basingstoke.gov.uk

Richards, Jonathan (CON - Tadley Central)
cllr.jonathan.richards@basingstoke.gov.uk

Robinson, Nicholas (CON - Bramley & Sherfield)
cllr.nick.robinson@basingstoke.gov.uk

Robinson, Tristan (CON - Sherborne St John)
cllr.tristan.robinson@basingstoke.gov.uk

Rowland, Venetia (CON - Bramley & Sherfield)
cllr.venetia.rowland@basingstoke.gov.uk

Ruffell, Mark (CON - Upton Grey & The Candovers)
cllr.mark.ruffell@basingstoke.gov.uk

Sherlock, Donald (CON - Kingsclere)
cllr.donald.sherlock@basingstoke.gov.uk

Smith, Joseph (CON - Winklebury)
cllr.joe.smith@basingstoke.gov.uk

Still, Elaine (CON - Chineham)
cllr.elaine.still@basingstoke.gov.uk

Tate, Robert (CON - Baughurst & Tadley North)
cllr.robert.tate@basingstoke.gov.uk

Taylor, Diane (CON - Oakley & North Waltham)
cllr.diane.taylor@basingstoke.gov.uk

Taylor, Mark (LAB - Brighton Hill North)
cllr.mark.taylor@basingstoke.gov.uk

Tilbury, Ian (IND - Overton, Laverstoke & Steventon)
cllr.ian.tilbury@basingstoke.gov.uk

Tucker, Marilyn (CON - Pamber & Silchester)
cllr.marilyn.tucker@basingstoke.gov.uk

Watts, Gary (LAB - South Ham)
cllr.gary.watts@basingstoke.gov.uk

Watts, Keith (LD - Whitchurch)
cllr.keith.watts@basingstoke.gov.uk

Westbrook, Michael (LAB - Brookvale & Kings Furlong)
cllr.michael.westbrook@basingstoke.gov.uk

Westbrook, Janet (LAB - Popley East)
cllr.janet.westbrook@basingstoke.gov.uk

POLITICAL COMPOSITION
CON: 33, LAB: 19, LD: 6, IND: 2

COMMITTEE CHAIRS

Audit & Accounts: Mr Roger Gardiner

Community, Environment & Partnerships: Mr Rob Golding

Development Control: Mr Paul Miller

Licensing: Ms Diane Taylor

Bassetlaw   D

Bassetlaw District Council, Queen's Buildings, Potter Street, Worksop S80 2AH
☎ 01909 533533 📠 01909 501758 🖥 www.bassetlaw.gov.uk

FACTS AND FIGURES
Parliamentary Constituencies: Bassetlaw
EU Constituencies: East Midlands
Election Frequency: Elections are by thirds

PRINCIPAL OFFICERS

Chief Executive: Mr Neil Taylor, Chief Executive, Queen's Buildings, Potter Street, Worksop S80 2AH ☎ 01909 533221 ✆ neil.taylor@bassetlaw.gov.uk

Senior Management: Mrs Beverley Alderton-Sambrook, Head - Regeneration, Queen's Buildings, Potter Street, Worksop S80 2AH ☎ 01909 533187 ✆ beverley.alderton-sambrook@bassetlaw.gov.uk

Senior Management: Mr David Armiger, Director - Regeneration & Neighbourhoods, Queen's Buildings, Potter Street, Worksop S80 2AH ☎ 01909 533187 ✆ david.armiger@bassetlaw.gov.uk

Senior Management: Mr Stephen Brown, Head - Corporate Services, Queen's Buildings, Potter Street, Worksop S80 2AH ☎ 01909 533767 ✆ steve.brown@bassetlaw.gov.uk

Senior Management: Mr Mike Hill, Head - Finance & Property, Queen's Buildings, Potter Street, Worksop S80 2AH ☎ 01909 533174 ✆ mike.hill@bassetlaw.gov.uk

Senior Management: Mrs Elizabeth Prime, Head - Neighbourhoods, Queen's Buildings, Potter Street, Worksop S80 2AH ☎ 01909 533219 ✆ liz.prime@bassetlaw.gov.uk

Senior Management: Ms Ros Theakstone, Director - Corporate Resources, Queen's Buildings, Potter Street, Worksop S80 2AH ☎ 01909 533160 ✆ ros.theakstone@bassetlaw.gov.uk

Access Officer / Social Services (Disability): Mr Malcolm Robson, Access Officer, Queen's Buildings, Potter Street, Worksop S80 2AH ☎ 01909 533195 ✆ malcolm.robson@bassetlaw.gov.uk

Architect, Building / Property Services: Mr John Unstead, Property Manager, Queen's Buildings, Worksop S80 2AH ☎ 01909 533706 ✆ john.unstead@bassetlaw.gov.uk

Building Control: Mrs Angela Edwards, Building Control Manager, Queen's Buildings, Potter Street, Worksop S80 2AH ☎ 01909 533130 ✆ angela.edwards@bassetlaw.gov.uk

Building Control: Mr Robert Whatley, Principal Building Control Officer, Queen's Buildings, Potter Street, Worksop S80 2AH ☎ 01909 533130 ✆ bob.whatley@bassetlaw.gov.uk

PR / Communications: Mr Jonathan Brassington, Communications Manager, Queen's Buildings, Potter Street, Worksop S80 2AH ☎ 01909 533726 ✆ jonathan.brassington@bassetlaw.gov.uk

Community Safety: Mr Gerald Connor, Community Safety Co-ordinator, Queen's Buildings, Potter Street, Worksop S80 2AH ☎ 01909 533153 ✆ gerald.connor@bassetlaw.gov.uk

Computer Management: Mr David Harwood, Strategic ICT Manager, Queen's Buildings, Potter Street, Worksop S80 2AH ☎ 01909 533122 ✆ david.harwood@bassetlaw.gov.uk

Contracts: Mr Howard Lane, Lead Service Procurement Manager, Bassetlaw District Council, Queens Building, Potter Street, Worksop S80 2AH ☎ 01909 533449 ✆ howard.lane@bassetlaw.gov.uk

Corporate Services: Ms Ros Theakstone, Director - Corporate Resources, Queen's Buildings, Potter Street, Worksop S80 2AH ☎ 01909 533160 ✆ ros.theakstone@bassetlaw.gov.uk

BASSETLAW

Customer Service: Mr Stephen Brown, Head - Corporate Services, Queen's Buildings, Potter Street, Worksop S80 2AH
☎ 01909 533767 ⏚ steve.brown@bassetlaw.gov.uk

Economic Development: Mr Robert Wilkinson, Economic Development Team Manager, Queen's Buildings, Potter Street, Worksop S80 2AH ☎ 01909 533230 ⏚ robert.wilkinson@bassetlaw.gov.uk

E-Government: Mr Stephen Brown, Head - Corporate Services, Queen's Buildings, Potter Street, Worksop S80 2AH
☎ 01909 533767 ⏚ steve.brown@bassetlaw.gov.uk

Electoral Registration: Mrs Julie Briggs, Electoral Services Manager, Queen's Buildings, Potter Street, Worksop S80 2AH
☎ 01909 533464 ⏚ julie.briggs@bassetlaw.gov.uk

Emergency Planning: Mr Jim Moran, Principal Safety Officer, Carlton Forest House, Hundred Acre Lane, Carlton Forest, Worksop S81 0TS ☎ 01909 534337 ⏚ jim.moran@bassetlaw.gov.uk

Environmental / Technical Services: Mr David Armiger, Director - Regeneration & Neighbourhoods, Queen's Buildings, Potter Street, Worksop S80 2AH ☎ 01909 533187 ⏚ david.armiger@bassetlaw.gov.uk

Environmental Health: Mrs Elizabeth Prime, Head - Neighbourhoods, Queen's Buildings, Potter Street, Worksop S80 2AH ☎ 01909 533219 ⏚ liz.prime@bassetlaw.gov.uk

Environmental Health: Mr Julian Proudman, Environmental Health Team Manager, Queen's Buildings, Potter Street, Worksop S80 2AH ☎ 01909 533219 ⏚ julian.proudman@bassetlaw.gov.uk

Estates, Property & Valuation: Mr John Unstead, Property Manager, Queen's Buildings, Worksop S80 2AH ☎ 01909 533706 ⏚ john.unstead@bassetlaw.gov.uk

Finance: Mr Mike Hill, Head - Finance & Property, Queen's Buildings, Potter Street, Worksop S80 2AH ☎ 01909 533174 ⏚ mike.hill@bassetlaw.gov.uk

Fleet Management: Mr Peter Jones, Operational Services Manager - Fleet & Admin Services, Hundred Acre Lane, Carlton Forest, Worksop S81 0TS ☎ 01909 534487 ⏚ peter.jones@bassetlaw.gov.uk

Grounds Maintenance: Mr Keith Somers, Operational Services Manager - Parks, Open Spaces & Cemeteries, West House, Hundred Acre Lane, Carlton Forest, Worksop S81 0TS
☎ 01919 534420 ⏚ keith.somers@bassetlaw.gov.uk

Health and Safety: Mr Jim Moran, Principal Safety Officer, Carlton Forest House, Hundred Acre Lane, Carlton Forest, Worksop S81 0TS ☎ 01909 534337 ⏚ jim.moran@bassetlaw.gov.uk

Legal: Mr Stephen Brown, Head - Corporate Services, Queen's Buildings, Potter Street, Worksop S80 2AH ☎ 01909 533767 ⏚ steve.brown@bassetlaw.gov.uk

Leisure and Cultural Services: Mr Peter Clark, Leisure & Cultural Services Manager, 17b The Square, Retford DN22 6DB
☎ 01909 534507 ⏚ peter.clark@bassetlaw.gov.uk

Licensing: Mr Stephen Wormald, Senior Solicitor, Queen's Buildings, Potter Street, Worksop S80 2AH ☎ 01909 533456 ⏚ stephen.wormald@bassetlaw.gov.uk

Lottery Funding, Charity and Voluntary: Mr Mike Hill, Head - Finance & Property, Queen's Buildings, Potter Street, Worksop S80 2AH ☎ 01909 533174 ⏚ mike.hill@bassetlaw.gov.uk

Member Services: Ms Ros Theakstone, Director - Corporate Resources, Queen's Buildings, Potter Street, Worksop S80 2AH
☎ 01909 533160 ⏚ ros.theakstone@bassetlaw.gov.uk

Parking: Mr Richard Blagg, Town Centre Manager - Operational, Queen's Buildings, Potter Street, Worksop S80 2AH
☎ 01909 535104 ⏚ richard.blagg@bassetlaw.gov.uk

Partnerships: Ms Ros Theakstone, Director - Corporate Resources, Queen's Buildings, Potter Street, Worksop S80 2AH
☎ 01909 533160 ⏚ ros.theakstone@bassetlaw.gov.uk

Personnel / HR: Mrs Karen Childs, HR Service Manager, Queen's Buildings, Potter Street, Worksop S80 2AH ☎ 01909 534123 ⏚ karen.childs@bassetlaw.gov.uk

Planning: Mrs Beverley Alderton-Sambrook, Head - Regeneration, Queen's Buildings, Potter Street, Worksop S80 2AH
☎ 01909 533187 ⏚ beverley.alderton-sambrook@bassetlaw.gov.uk

Procurement: Mr Mike Hill, Head - Finance & Property, Queen's Buildings, Potter Street, Worksop S80 2AH ☎ 01909 533174 ⏚ mike.hill@bassetlaw.gov.uk

Recycling & Waste Minimisation: Mr Tim Andrew, Operational Services Manager - Waste & Recyling, Hundred Acre Lane, Carlton Forest, Worksop S81 0TS ☎ 01909 534422 ⏚ tim.andrew@bassetlaw.gov.uk

Recycling & Waste Minimisation: Mr David Armiger, Director - Regeneration & Neighbourhoods, Queen's Buildings, Potter Street, Worksop S80 2AH ☎ 01909 533187 ⏚ david.armiger@bassetlaw.gov.uk

Regeneration: Mr Robert Wilkinson, Economic Development Team Manager, Queen's Buildings, Potter Street, Worksop S80 2AH ☎ 01909 533230 ⏚ robert.wilkinson@bassetlaw.gov.uk

Staff Training: Mrs Jenny Rodriguez, HR Business Partner - Learning & Development, Queen's Buildings, Potter Street, Worksop S80 2AH ☎ 01909 534134 ⏚ jenny.rodriguez@bassetlaw.gov.uk

Street Scene: Mr Tim Andrew, Operational Services Manager - Waste & Recyling, Hundred Acre Lane, Carlton Forest, Worksop S81 0TS ☎ 01909 534422 ⏚ tim.andrew@bassetlaw.gov.uk

Sustainable Communities: Mr David Armiger, Director - Regeneration & Neighbourhoods, Queen's Buildings, Potter Street, Worksop S80 2AH ☎ 01909 533187 ⏚ david.armiger@bassetlaw.gov.uk

Sustainable Communities: Ms Ros Theakstone, Director - Corporate Resources, Queen's Buildings, Potter Street, Worksop S80 2AH ☎ 01909 533160 ✐ ros.theakstone@bassetlaw.gov.uk

Sustainable Development: Mr David Armiger, Director - Regeneration & Neighbourhoods, Queen's Buildings, Potter Street, Worksop S80 2AH ☎ 01909 533187 ✐ david.armiger@bassetlaw.gov.uk

Tourism: Ms Sandra Withington, Development & Marketing Officer, Queen's Buildings, Potter Street, Worksop S80 2AH ☎ 01909 533533 ✐ sandra.withington@bassetlaw.gov.uk

Town Centre: Mr Richard Blagg, Town Centre Manager - Operational, Queen's Buildings, Potter Street, Worksop S80 2AH ☎ 01909 535104 ✐ richard.blagg@bassetlaw.gov.uk

Transport: Mr Peter Jones, Operational Services Manager - Fleet & Admin Services, Hundred Acre Lane, Carlton Forest, Worksop S81 0TS ☎ 01909 534487 ✐ peter.jones@bassetlaw.gov.uk

Waste Collection and Disposal: Mr Tim Andrew, Operational Services Manager - Waste & Recyling, Hundred Acre Lane, Carlton Forest, Worksop S81 0TS ☎ 01909 534422 ✐ tim.andrew@bassetlaw.gov.uk

Waste Collection and Disposal: Mr David Armiger, Director - Regeneration & Neighbourhoods, Queen's Buildings, Potter Street, Worksop S80 2AH ☎ 01909 533187 ✐ david.armiger@bassetlaw.gov.uk

Waste Management: Mr Tim Andrew, Operational Services Manager - Waste & Recyling, Hundred Acre Lane, Carlton Forest, Worksop S81 0TS ☎ 01909 534422 ✐ tim.andrew@bassetlaw.gov.uk

Waste Management: Mr David Armiger, Director - Regeneration & Neighbourhoods, Queen's Buildings, Potter Street, Worksop S80 2AH ☎ 01909 533187 ✐ david.armiger@bassetlaw.gov.uk

Children's Play Areas: Mr Peter Clark, Leisure & Cultural Services Manager, 17b The Square, Retford DN22 6DB ☎ 01909 534507 ✐ peter.clark@bassetlaw.gov.uk

COUNCILLORS

ChairAnderson, James (LAB - East Retford West)
jim.anderson@bassetlaw.gov.uk

Vice-ChairRichardson, Madelaine (LAB - Worksop North East)
madelaine.richardson@bassetlaw.gov.uk

Leader of the Council: Greaves, Simon (LAB - Worksop North East)
simon.greaves@bassetlaw.gov.uk

Deputy Leader of the Council: White, Jo (LAB - Worksop East)
jo.white@bassetlaw.gov.uk

Bowles, Barry (CON - Blyth)
barry.bowles@bassetlaw.gov.uk

Brand, Hazel (IND - Misterton)
hazel.brand@bassetlaw.gov.uk

Brett, Dean (LAB - Worksop North West)
dean.brett@bassetlaw.gov.uk

Burton, Hugh (IND - Sturton)
hugh.burton@bassetlaw.gov.uk

Carrington-Wilde, Robin Brian (LAB - Carlton)
robin.carrington-wilde@bassetlaw.gov.uk

Challinor, David (LAB - Harworth)
david.challinor@bassetlaw.gov.uk

Chambers, Alan (LAB - East Retford West)
alan.chambers@bassetlaw.gov.uk

Clarkson, Garry (LAB - East Retford North)
garry.clarkson@bassetlaw.gov.uk

Critchley, Teresa (CON - Rampton)
teresa.critchley@bassetlaw.gov.uk

Dukes, Kevin (LAB - Welbeck)
kevin.dukes@bassetlaw.gov.uk

Entwistle, Clifford (LAB - Worksop East)
cliff.entwistle@bassetlaw.gov.uk

Evans, June (LAB - Harworth)
june.evans@bassetlaw.gov.uk

Farncombe, Sarah (LAB - Worksop North)
sarah.farncombe@bassetlaw.gov.uk

Fielding, Sybil (LAB - Worksop North West)
sybil.fielding@bassetlaw.gov.uk

Foley, Deidre (LAB - Worksop South East)
deidre.foley@bassetlaw.gov.uk

Freeman, Gillian (LAB - Langold)
gillian.freeman@bassetlaw.gov.uk

Gray, Michael (CON - Ranskill)
michael.gray@bassetlaw.gov.uk

Greaves, Kevin (LAB - Worksop South)
kevin.greaves@bassetlaw.gov.uk

Hare, Dianne (CON - Worksop South)
dianne.hare@bassetlaw.gov.uk

Isard, Shirley (CON - Tuxford & Trent)
shirley.isard@bassetlaw.gov.uk

Isard, Keith (CON - Tuxford & Trent)
keith.isard@bassetlaw.gov.uk

Jones, Gwynneth (LAB - Worksop North)
gwynneth.jones@bassetlaw.gov.uk

Leigh, Julie (LAB - Worksop South)
julie.leigh@bassetlaw.gov.uk

Merryweather, Deborah (LAB - Worksop East)
deborah.merryweather@bassetlaw.gov.uk

Ogle, John (CON - East Markham)
john.ogle@bassetlaw.gov.uk

Oxby, Graham (LAB - East Retford North)
graham.oxby@bassetlaw.gov.uk

Pidwell, David George (LAB - Carlton)
david.pidwell@bassetlaw.gov.uk

Potts, David (LAB - Worksop North)
david.potts@bassetlaw.gov.uk

Potts, Josie (LAB - Worksop South East)
josie.potts@bassetlaw.gov.uk

Pressley, David (LAB - Worksop North West)
david.pressley@bassetlaw.gov.uk

BASSETLAW

Quigley, Michael (CON - East Retford East)
michael.quigley@bassetlaw.gov.uk

Rhodes, Alan (LAB - Worksop North East)
alan.rhodes@bassetlaw.gov.uk

Richards, Helen (LAB - East Retford South)
helen.richards@bassetlaw.gov.uk

Sanger, Joan (IND - Beckingham)
joan.sanger@bassetlaw.gov.uk

Scottorne, Steve (LAB - Carlton)
steve.scotthorne@bassetlaw.gov.uk

Shaw, Susan (LAB - East Retford East)
susan.shaw@bassetlaw.gov.uk

Shephard, John (LAB - Worksop South East)
john.shephard@bassetlaw.gov.uk

Simpson, Annette (CON - Everton)
annette.simpson@bassetlaw.gov.uk

Smith, Anita (LAB - Harworth)
anita.smith@bassetlaw.gov.uk

Storey, Michael (LAB - East Retford East)
michael.storey@bassetlaw.gov.uk

Sutton, Kathleen (CON - Clayworth)
kath.sutton@bassetlaw.gov.uk

Taylor, Tracey (CON - Sutton)
tracey.taylor@bassetlaw.gov.uk

Tromans, Anthony (CON - East Retford North)
anthony.tromans@bassetlaw.gov.uk

Troop, Carolyn (LAB - East Retford South)
carolyn.troop@bassetlaw.gov.uk

POLITICAL COMPOSITION
LAB: 33, CON: 12, IND: 3

Bath & North East Somerset   U

Bath & North East Somerset Council, Lewis House, Manvers
Street, Bath BA1 1JG
☎ 01225 477000 🖷 01225 477499 ⁂ enquiries@bathnes.gov.uk
🖳 www.bathnes.gov.uk

FACTS AND FIGURES
Parliamentary Constituencies: Bath
EU Constituencies: South West
Election Frequency: Elections are of whole council

PRINCIPAL OFFICERS

Chief Executive: Mr Ashley Ayre, Chief Executive, Guildhall, High
Street, Bath BA1 1LA ☎ 01225 394200
⁂ ashley_ayre@bathnes.gov.uk

Senior Management: Mr Mike Bowden, Strategic Director -
People & Communities, Guildhall, High Street, Bath BA1 5AW
☎ 01225 396289 ⁂ mike_bowden@bathnes.gov.uk

Senior Management: Ms Louise Fradd, Strategic Director -
Place, Guildhall, High Street, Bath BA1 5AW ☎ 01225 394567
⁂ louise_fradd@bathnes.gov.uk

Senior Management: Dr Bruce Lawrence, Director - Public
Health, Guildhall, High Street, Bath BA1 5AW
⁂ bruce_lawrence@bathnes.gov.uk

Senior Management: Ms Maria Lucas, Divisional Director - Legal
& Democratic Services (Monitoring Officer), Riverside, Temple
Street, Keynsham, Bristol BS31 1LA ☎ 01225 395171
⁂ maria_lucas@bathnes.gov.uk

Senior Management: Mr Andrew Pate, Strategic Director -
Resources, Guildhall, High Street, Bath BA1 5AW ☎ 01225 477300
⁂ andrew_pate@bathnes.gov.uk

Architect, Building / Property Services: Mr Derek Quilter,
Divisional Director - Project Delivery, 10 Palace Mews, Bath BA1
2NH ☎ 01225 477739 ⁂ derek_quilter@bathnes.gov.uk

Building Control: Mr David Trigwell, Divisional Director - Planning
& Transport Development, Riverside, Temple Street, Keynsham
BS31 1LA ☎ 01225 477702 ⁂ david_trigwell@bathnes.gov.uk

Catering Services: Mr Derek Quilter, Divisional Director - Project
Delivery, 10 Palace Mews, Bath BA1 2NH ☎ 01225 477739
⁂ derek_quilter@bathnes.gov.uk

Children / Youth Services: Mr Richard Baldwin, Divisional
Director - CYP Specialist Services, Guildhall, High Street, Bath BA1
5AW ☎ 01225 396289 ⁂ richard_baldwin@bathnes.gov.uk

Civil Registration: Ms Maria Lucas, Divisional Director - Legal &
Democratic Services (Monitoring Officer), Riverside, Temple Street,
Keynsham, Bristol BS31 1LA ☎ 01225 395171
⁂ maria_lucas@bathnes.gov.uk

PR / Communications: Mr David Thompson, Divisional Director -
Organisational Development, Guildhall, High Street, Bath BA1 5AW
☎ 01225 394368 ⁂ dave_thompson@bathnes.gov.uk

Community Planning: Mr David Trethewey, Divisional Director -
Strategy & Performance, Guildhall, High Street, Bath BA1 5AW
☎ 01225 477300 ⁂ david_trethewey@bathnes.gov.uk

Community Safety: Mr David Trethewey, Divisional Director -
Strategy & Performance, Guildhall, High Street, Bath BA1 5AW
☎ 01225 477300 ⁂ david_trethewey@bathnes.gov.uk

Computer Management: Mrs Angela Parratt, Head -
Transformation, Guildhall, High Street, Bath BA1 5AW
☎ 01225 476576 ⁂ angela_parratt@bathnes.gov.uk

Consumer Protection and Trading Standards: Mr Matthew
Smith, Divisional Director - Environmental Services, Royal Victoria
Park Nursery, Marlborough Lane, Bath BA1 2LZ ☎ 01225 396888
⁂ matthew_smith@bathnes.gov.uk

Contracts: Mr Jeff Wring, Head - Audit West, Guildhall, High
Street, Bath BA1 5AW ☎ 01225 477323
⁂ jeff_wring@bathnes.gov.uk

Corporate Services: Mr Tim Richens, Divisional Director -
Business Support, Guildhall, High Street, Bath BA1 5AW
☎ 01225 477468 ⁂ tim_richens@bathnes.gov.uk

Customer Service: Mr Ian Savigar, Divisional Director - Customer Services, Lewis House, Manvers Street, Bath BA1 1JG ☎ 01225 477327 ⊕ ian_savigar@bathnes.gov.uk

Direct Labour: Mr Matthew Smith, Divisional Director - Environmental Services, Royal Victoria Park Nursery, Marlborough Lane, Bath BA1 2LZ ☎ 01225 396888 ⊕ matthew_smith@bathnes.gov.uk

Economic Development: Mr John Wilkinson, Divisional Director - Community Regeneration, 10 Palace Mews, Bath BA1 2NH ☎ 01225 396593 ⊕ john_wilkinson@bathnes.gov.uk

Education: Mr Richard Baldwin, Divisional Director - CYP Specialist Services, Guildhall, High Street, Bath BA1 5AW ☎ 01225 396289 ⊕ richard_baldwin@bathnes.gov.uk

Electoral Registration: Ms Maria Lucas, Divisional Director - Legal & Democratic Services (Monitoring Officer), Riverside, Temple Street, Keynsham, Bristol BS31 1LA ☎ 01225 395171 ⊕ maria_lucas@bathnes.gov.uk

Emergency Planning: Mr Jeff Wring, Head - Audit West, Guildhall, High Street, Bath BA1 5AW ☎ 01225 477323 ⊕ jeff_wring@bathnes.gov.uk

Energy Management: Mr Derek Quilter, Divisional Director - Project Delivery, 10 Palace Mews, Bath BA1 2NH ☎ 01225 477739 ⊕ derek_quilter@bathnes.gov.uk

Environmental / Technical Services: Mr Matthew Smith, Divisional Director - Environmental Services, Royal Victoria Park Nursery, Marlborough Lane, Bath BA1 2LZ ☎ 01225 396888 ⊕ matthew_smith@bathnes.gov.uk

Environmental Health: Mr Matthew Smith, Divisional Director - Environmental Services, Royal Victoria Park Nursery, Marlborough Lane, Bath BA1 2LZ ☎ 01225 396888 ⊕ matthew_smith@bathnes.gov.uk

Estates, Property & Valuation: Mr Derek Quilter, Divisional Director - Project Delivery, 10 Palace Mews, Bath BA1 2NH ☎ 01225 477739 ⊕ derek_quilter@bathnes.gov.uk

Events Manager: Mr Mike Butler, Interim Divisional Director - Tourism, Leisure & Culture, Guildhall, High Street, Bath BA1 5AW ☎ 01225 395385 ⊕ michael_butler@bathnes.gov.uk

Facilities: Mr Derek Quilter, Divisional Director - Project Delivery, 10 Palace Mews, Bath BA1 2NH ☎ 01225 477739 ⊕ derek_quilter@bathnes.gov.uk

Finance: Mr Tim Richens, Divisional Director - Business Support, Guildhall, High Street, Bath BA1 5AW ☎ 01225 477468 ⊕ tim_richens@bathnes.gov.uk

Pensions: Ms Liz Woodyard, Pensions Investments Manager, Riverside, Temple Street, Keynsham BS31 1LA ☎ 01225 395306 ⊕ liz_woodyard@bathnes.gov.uk

Fleet Management: Mr Matthew Smith, Divisional Director - Environmental Services, Royal Victoria Park Nursery, Marlborough Lane, Bath BA1 2LZ ☎ 01225 396888 ⊕ matthew_smith@bathnes.gov.uk

Grounds Maintenance: Mr Matthew Smith, Divisional Director - Environmental Services, Royal Victoria Park Nursery, Marlborough Lane, Bath BA1 2LZ ☎ 01225 396888 ⊕ matthew_smith@bathnes.gov.uk

Health and Safety: Mr William Harding, Head - Human Resources, Riverside, Temple Street, Keynsham, Bristol BS31 1LA ☎ 01225 477203 ⊕ william_harding@bathnes.gov.uk

Highways: Mr David Trigwell, Divisional Director - Planning & Transport Development, Lewis House, PO BOX 5006, Bath BA1 1JG ☎ 01225 477702 ⊕ david_trigwell@bathnes.gov.uk

Home Energy Conservation: Mrs Jane Shayler, Divisional Director - Adult Care, Health & Housing Strategy & Commissioning, St Martin's Hospital, Clara Cross Lane, Midford Road, Bath BA2 5RP ☎ 01225 396120 ⊕ jane_shayler@bathnes.gov.uk

Housing: Mrs Jane Shayler, Divisional Director - Adult Care, Health & Housing Strategy & Commissioning, St Martin's Hospital, Clara Cross Lane, Midford Road, Bath BA2 5RP ☎ 01225 396120 ⊕ jane_shayler@bathnes.gov.uk

Local Area Agreement: Mr David Trethewey, Divisional Director - Strategy & Performance, Lewis House, Manvers Street, Bath BA11 1JG ☎ 01225 396353 ⊕ david_trethewey@bathnes.gov.uk

Legal: Ms Maria Lucas, Divisional Director - Legal & Democratic Services (Monitoring Officer), Riverside, Temple Street, Keynsham, Bristol BS31 1LA ☎ 01225 395171 ⊕ maria_lucas@bathnes.gov.uk

Leisure and Cultural Services: Mr Mike Butler, Interim Divisional Director - Tourism, Leisure & Culture, Guildhall, High Street, Bath BA1 5AW ☎ 01225 395385 ⊕ michael_butler@bathnes.gov.uk

Licensing: Mr Matthew Smith, Divisional Director - Environmental Services, Royal Victoria Park Nursery, Marlborough Lane, Bath BA1 2LZ ☎ 01225 396888 ⊕ matthew_smith@bathnes.gov.uk

Lifelong Learning: Mr Jeremy Smalley, Divisional Director - Development & Regeneration, Riverside, Temple Street, Keynsham, Bristol BS31 1LA ☎ 01225 477822 ⊕ jeremy_smalley@bathnes.gov.uk

Lighting: Mr Matthew Smith, Divisional Director - Environmental Services, Royal Victoria Park Nursery, Marlborough Lane, Bath BA1 2LZ ☎ 01225 396888 ⊕ matthew_smith@bathnes.gov.uk

Lottery Funding, Charity and Voluntary: Mr David Trethewey, Divisional Director - Strategy & Performance, Lewis House, Manvers Street, Bath BA11 1JG ☎ 01225 396353 ⊕ david_trethewey@bathnes.gov.uk

Member Services: Ms Maria Lucas, Divisional Director - Legal & Democratic Services (Monitoring Officer), Riverside, Temple Street, Keynsham, Bristol BS31 1LA ☎ 01225 395171 ⊕ maria_lucas@bathnes.gov.uk

BATH & NORTH EAST SOMERSET

Parking: Mr Matthew Smith, Divisional Director - Environmental Services, Royal Victoria Park Nursery, Marlborough Lane, Bath BA1 2LZ ☎ 01225 396888 ⏚ matthew_smith@bathnes.gov.uk

Partnerships: Mr David Tretheway, Divisional Director - Strategy & Performance, Lewis House, Manvers Street, Bath BA11 1JG ☎ 01225 396353 ⏚ david_trethewey@bathnes.gov.uk

Personnel / HR: Mr William Harding, Head - Human Resources, Riverside, Temple Street, Keynsham, Bristol BS31 1LA ☎ 01225 477203 ⏚ william_harding@bathnes.gov.uk

Planning: Ms Lisa Bartlett, Divisional Director - Development, Guildhall, High Street, Bath BA1 5AW ⏚ lisa_bartlett@bathnes.gov.uk

Procurement: Mr Jeff Wring, Head - Audit West, Guildhall, High Street, Bath BA1 5AW ☎ 01225 477323 ⏚ jeff_wring@bathnes.gov.uk

Public Libraries: Mr Mike Butler, Interim Divisional Director - Tourism, Leisure & Culture, Guildhall, High Street, Bath BA1 5AW ☎ 01225 395385 ⏚ michael_butler@bathnes.gov.uk

Recycling & Waste Minimisation: Mr Matthew Smith, Divisional Director - Environmental Services, Royal Victoria Park Nursery, Marlborough Lane, Bath BA1 2LZ ☎ 01225 396888 ⏚ matthew_smith@bathnes.gov.uk

Regeneration: Mr Derek Quilter, Divisional Director - Project Delivery, 10 Palace Mews, Bath BA1 2NH ☎ 01225 477739 ⏚ derek_quilter@bathnes.gov.uk

Road Safety: Mr David Trigwell, Divisional Director - Planning & Transport Development, Riverside, Temple Street, Keynsham BS31 1LA ☎ 01225 477702 ⏚ david_trigwell@bathnes.gov.uk

Social Services: Mr Richard Baldwin, Divisional Director - CYP Specialist Services, Guildhall, High Street, Bath BA1 5AW ☎ 01225 396289 ⏚ richard_baldwin@bathnes.gov.uk

Social Services (Adult): Mrs Jane Shayler, Divisional Director - Adult Care, Health & Housing Strategy & Commissioning, St Martin's Hospital, Clara Cross Lane, Midford Road, Bath BA2 5RP ☎ 01225 396120 ⏚ jane_shayler@bathnes.gov.uk

Social Services (Children): Mr Maurice Lindsay, Divisional Director - Children, YP & Family Support Services, Riverside, Temple Street, Keynsham, Bristol BS31 1LA ☎ 01225 396289 ⏚ maurice_lindsay@bathnes.gov.uk

Fostering & Adoption: Mr Richard Baldwin, Divisional Director - CYP Specialist Services, Guildhall, High Street, Bath BA1 5AW ☎ 01225 396289 ⏚ richard_baldwin@bathnes.gov.uk

Safeguarding: Mr Mike Bowden, Strategic Director - People & Communities, Guildhall, High Street, Bath BA1 5AW ☎ 01225 396289 ⏚ mike_bowden@bathnes.gov.uk

Families: Mr Richard Baldwin, Divisional Director - CYP Specialist Services, Guildhall, High Street, Bath BA1 5AW ☎ 01225 396289 ⏚ richard_baldwin@bathnes.gov.uk

Childrens Social Care: Mr Richard Baldwin, Divisional Director - CYP Specialist Services, Guildhall, High Street, Bath BA1 5AW ☎ 01225 396289 ⏚ richard_baldwin@bathnes.gov.uk

Public Health: Dr Bruce Lawrence, Director - Public Health, Guildhall, High Street, Bath BA1 5AW ⏚ bruce_lawrence@bathnes.gov.uk

Staff Training: Mr William Harding, Head - Human Resources, Riverside, Temple Street, Keynsham, Bristol BS31 1LA ☎ 01225 477203 ⏚ william_harding@bathnes.gov.uk

Street Scene: Mr Matthew Smith, Divisional Director - Environmental Services, Royal Victoria Park Nursery, Marlborough Lane, Bath BA1 2LZ ☎ 01225 396888 ⏚ matthew_smith@bathnes.gov.uk

Sustainable Communities: Mr David Tretheway, Divisional Director - Strategy & Performance, Lewis House, Manvers Street, Bath BA11 1JG ☎ 01225 396353 ⏚ david_trethewey@bathnes.gov.uk

Sustainable Development: Mr David Tretheway, Divisional Director - Strategy & Performance, Lewis House, Manvers Street, Bath BA11 1JG ☎ 01225 396353 ⏚ david_trethewey@bathnes.gov.uk

Tourism: Mr Mike Butler, Interim Divisional Director - Tourism, Leisure & Culture, Guildhall, High Street, Bath BA1 5AW ☎ 01225 395385 ⏚ michael_butler@bathnes.gov.uk

Town Centre: Mr Matthew Smith, Divisional Director - Environmental Services, Royal Victoria Park Nursery, Marlborough Lane, Bath BA1 2LZ ☎ 01225 396888 ⏚ matthew_smith@bathnes.gov.uk

Traffic Management: Mr David Trigwell, Divisional Director - Planning & Transport Development, Trimbridge House, Trim Street, Bath BA1 2DP ☎ 01225 477702 ⏚ david_trigwell@bathnes.gov.uk

Transport: Mr David Trigwell, Divisional Director - Planning & Transport Development, Trimbridge House, Trim Street, Bath BA1 2DP ☎ 01225 477702 ⏚ david_trigwell@bathnes.gov.uk

Transport Planner: Mr David Trigwell, Divisional Director - Planning & Transport Development, Trimbridge House, Trim Street, Bath BA1 2DP ☎ 01225 477702 ⏚ david_trigwell@bathnes.gov.uk

Total Place: Mr David Tretheway, Divisional Director - Strategy & Performance, Lewis House, Manvers Street, Bath BA11 1JG ☎ 01225 396353 ⏚ david_trethewey@bathnes.gov.uk

Waste Collection and Disposal: Mr Matthew Smith, Divisional Director - Environmental Services, Royal Victoria Park Nursery, Marlborough Lane, Bath BA1 2LZ ☎ 01225 396888 ⏚ matthew_smith@bathnes.gov.uk

Children's Play Areas: Mr Matthew Smith, Divisional Director - Environmental Services, Royal Victoria Park Nursery, Marlborough Lane, Bath BA1 2LZ ☎ 01225 396888 ⏚ matthew_smith@bathnes.gov.uk

COUNCILLORS

Chair: Hale, Alan (CON - Keynsham South) alan_hale@bathnes.gov.uk

Vice-Chair: Beath, Cherry (LD - Combe Down)
cherry_beath@bathnes.gov.uk

Leader of the Council: Warren, Tim (CON - Mendip)
tim@warrenequestrian.co.uk

Group LeaderCarr, Jonathan (GRN - Abbey)
jonathan.carr@bathnesgreens.org.uk

Group LeaderMoss, Robin (LAB - Westfield)
robin_moss@bathnes.gov.uk

Group LeaderRayment, Joe (LAB - Twerton)
joe_rayment@bathnes.gov.uk

Anketell-Jones, Patrick (CON - Lansdown)
patrick_aneketell-jones@bathnes.gov.uk

Appleyard, Rob (LD - Lambridge)
rob_appleyard@bathnes.gov.uk

Ball, Timothy (LD - Twerton)
tim_ball@bathnes.gov.uk

Barrett, Colin (CON - Weston)
barrettsofbath@yahoo.co.uk

Becker, Jasper (CON - Widcombe)
jasper_becker@bathnes.gov.uk

Bevan, Sarah (IND - Peasedown)
sarah_bevan@bathnes.gov.uk

Blackburn, Colin (IND - Westmoreland)
colin_blackburn@bathnes.gov.uk

Brett, Lisa (LD - Walcot)
lisa_brett@bathnes.gov.uk

Bull, John (LAB - Paulton)
john_bull@bathnes.gov.uk

Butters, Neil (LD - Bathavon South)
cllrneilbutters@aol.com

Clarke, Anthony (CON - Lansdown)
anthony_clarke@bathnes.gov.uk

Cochrane, Matt (CON - Bathwick)
matt_cochrane@bathnes.gov.uk

Crossley, Paul (LD - Southdown)
paul_crossley@bathnes.gov.uk

Dando, Chris (LAB - Radstock)
christopher_dando@bathnes.gov.uk

Darey, Fiona (CON - Walcot)
fiona_darey@bathnes.gov.uk

Davies, Matthew (CON - Weston)
matthew_davies@bathnes.gov.uk

Davis, Sally (CON - Farmborough)
sally_davis@bathnes.gov.uk

Deacon, Douglas (IND - Timsbury)
douglas_deacon@bathnes.gov.uk

Dixon, Emma (CON - Saltford)
emma_dixon@bathnes.gov.uk

Evans, Michael (CON - Midsomer Norton North)
michael_evans@bathnes.gov.uk

Furse, Andrew (LD - Kingsmead)
andrew_furse@bathnes.gov.uk

Gerrish, Charles (CON - Keynsham North)
charles_gerrish@bathnes.gov.uk

Gilchrist, Ian (LD - Widcombe)
ian_gilchrist@bathnes.gov.uk

Goodman, Bob (CON - Combe Down)
bob_goodman@bathnes.gov.uk

Haeberling, Francine (CON - Saltford)
francine_haeberling@bathnes.gov.uk

Hardman, Liz (LAB - Paulton)
liz_hardman@bathnes.gov.uk

Hassett, Donal (CON - Newbridge)
donal_hassett@bathnes.gov.uk

Hedges, Stephen (LD - Odd Down)
steve_hedges@bathnes.gov.uk

Horstmann, Deirdre (CON - Radstock)
deirdre_horstmann@bathnes.gov.uk

Jackson, Eleanor (LAB - Westfield)
eleanor_jackson@bathnes.gov.uk

Jeffries, Steve (CON - Bathwick)
steve_jeffries@bathnes.gov.uk

Kew, Les (CON - High Littleton)
les_kew@bathnes.gov.uk

Longstaff, Marie (CON - Keynsham East)
marie_brewer@bathnes.gov.uk

Macrae, Barry (CON - Midsomer Norton North)
barry_macrae@bathnes.gov.uk

May, Paul (CON - Publow & Whitchurch)
paul_may@bathnes.gov.uk

Millar, Alison (LD - Bathavon North)
alison_millar@bathnes.gov.uk

Myers, Paul (CON - Midsomer Norton Redfield)
paul_myers@bathnes.gov.uk

Norton, Michael (CON - Lyncombe)
michael_norton@bathnes.gov.uk

O'Brien, Lisa (CON - Keynsham South)
lisa_o'brien@bathnes.gov.uk

Organ, Bryan (CON - Keynsham East)
bryan_organ@bathnes.gov.uk

Patterson, Lin (GRN - Lambridge)
lin_patterson@bathnes.gov.uk

Pearce, Christopher (CON - Kingsmead)
chris_pearce@bathnes.gov.uk

Player, June (IND - Westmoreland)
june_player@bathnes.gov.uk

Pritchard, Victor (CON - Chew Valley South)
vic_pritchard@bathnes.gov.uk

Richardson, Liz (CON - Chew Valley North)
liz_richardson@bathnes.gov.uk

Roberts, Nigel (LD - Odd Down)
nigelroberts@clara.co.uk

Roberts, Caroline (LD - Newbridge)
cmroberts@clara.co.uk

Romero, Dine (LD - Southdown)
dine_romero@bathnes.gov.uk

Sandry, Will (LD - Oldfield)
willsandry@blueyonder.co.uk

BATH & NORTH EAST SOMERSET

Shelford, Mark (CON - Lyncombe)
mark_shelford@bathnes.gov.uk

Simmons, Brian (CON - Keynsham North)
brian_simmons@bathnes.gov.uk

Stephenson-McGall, Shaun (LD - Oldfield)
shaun_mcgall@bathnes.gov.uk

Turner, Peter (CON - Abbey)
peter_turner@bathnes.gov.uk

Veal, Martin (CON - Bathavon North)
martin_veal@bathnes.gov.uk

Veale, David (CON - Bathavon West)
david_veale@bathnes.gov.uk

Walker, Karen (IND - Peasedown)
karen_walker@bathnes.gov.uk

Ward, Geoff (CON - Bathavon North)
geoff_ward@bathnes.gov.uk

Warrington, Karen (CON - Clutton)
karen_warrington@bathnes.gov.uk

Watt, Christopher (CON - Midsomer Norton Redfield)
chris.watt@cognisantresearch.com

POLITICAL COMPOSITION
CON: 37, LD: 15, LAB: 6, IND: 5, GRN: 2

COMMITTEE CHAIRS

Communities, Transport & Environment: Mr John Bull

Health & Wellbeing: Mrs Francine Haeberling

Licensing: Mr Les Kew

Pensions: Mr David Veale

Planning, Housing & Economic Development: Mr Rob Appleyard

Bedford   U

Bedford Borough Council, Borough Hall, Cauldwell Street, Bedford MK42 9AP
☎ 01234 267422 🖶 01234 221606 ✆ customerservices@bedford.gov.uk
🖥 www.bedford.gov.uk

FACTS AND FIGURES
Parliamentary Constituencies: Bedford
EU Constituencies: Eastern
Election Frequency: Elections are by thirds

PRINCIPAL OFFICERS

Chief Executive: Mr Philip Simpkins, Chief Executive, Borough Hall, Cauldwell Street, Bedford MK42 9AP ☎ 01234 718202 ✆ philip.simpkins@bedford.gov.uk

Senior Management: Mr Kevin Crompton, Director - Children's & Adults' Services, Borough Hall, Cauldwell Street, Bedford MK42 9AP ☎ 01234 228620 ✆ kevin.crompton@bedford.gov.uk

Senior Management: Mr Mark Minion, Head of Corporate Policy & Programme Management, Borough Hall, Cauldwell Street, Bedford MK42 9AP ☎ 01234 228078 ✆ mark.minion@bedford.gov.uk

Senior Management: Ms Muriel Scott, Director - Public Health, Borough Hall, Cauldwell Street, Bedford MK42 9AP ☎ 0300 300 5616 ✆ muriel.scott@centralbedfordshire.gov.uk

Access Officer / Social Services (Disability): Mr Stuart O'Dell, Access Officer, Borough Hall, Cauldwell Street, Bedford MK42 9AP ☎ 01234 221762 ✆ stuart.odell@bedford.gov.uk

Architect, Building / Property Services: Mr Malcolm Parker, Business Manager (Consultancy), Borough Hall, Cauldwell Street, Bedford MK42 9AP ☎ 01234 718662 ✆ malcolm.parker@bedford.gov.uk

Best Value: Mr Jashpal Mann, Corporate Performance & Policy Manager, Borough Hall, Cauldwell Street, Bedford MK42 9AP ☎ 01234 228380 ✆ jashpal.mann@bedford.gov.uk

Building Control: Mr Steven Eyre, Building Control Manager, Borough Hall, Cauldwell Street, Bedford MK42 9AP ☎ 01234 221759 ✆ steven.eyre@bedford.gov.uk

Catering Services: Mr Adrian Piper, Head of Property Services, Borough Hall, Cauldwell Street, Bedford MK42 9AP ☎ 01234 718248 ✆ adrian.piper@bedford.gov.uk

Children / Youth Services: Mr Kevin Crompton, Director - Children's & Adults' Services, Borough Hall, Cauldwell Street, Bedford MK42 9AP ☎ 01234 228620 ✆ kevin.crompton@bedford.gov.uk

Civil Registration: Mr Keith Simmons, Head of Member & Election Services, Borough Hall, Cauldwell Street, Bedford MK42 9AP ☎ 01234 221676 ✆ keith.simmons@bedford.gov.uk

PR / Communications: Mr Keiron Fletcher, Senior Communications Officer, Borough Hall, Cauldwell Street, Bedford MK42 9AP ☎ 01234 276277 ✆ keiron.fletcher@bedford.gov.uk

Community Planning: Mr Stewart Briggs, Executive Director - Environment & Sustainable Communities, Borough Hall, Cauldwell Street, Bedford MK42 9AP ☎ 01234 228283 ✆ stewart.briggs@bedford.gov.uk

Community Safety: Mr Craig Austin, Assistant Director - Regulatory Services, Borough Hall, Cauldwell Street, Bedford MK42 9AP ☎ 01234 276774 ✆ craig.austin@bedford.gov.uk

Computer Management: Mr Raghbir Singh, Senior IT Manager, Borough Hall, Cauldwell Street, Bedford MK42 9AP ☎ 01234 276221 ✆ raghbir.singh@bedford.gov.uk

Consumer Protection and Trading Standards: Mr Craig Austin, Assistant Director - Regulatory Services, Borough Hall, Cauldwell Street, Bedford MK42 9AP ☎ 01234 276774 ✆ craig.austin@bedford.gov.uk

Contracts: Mr Mark Stephens, Assistant Chief Executive - Business Transformation, Borough Hall, Cauldwell Street, Bedford MK42 9AP ☎ 01234 228150 ✆ mark.stephens@bedford.gov.uk

Corporate Services: Mr Andy Watkins, Assistant Chief Executive & Chief Finance Officer, Borough Hall, Cauldwell Street, Bedford MK42 9AP ☎ 01234 718208 ✆ andy.watkins@bedford.gov.uk

Customer Service: Mr Lee Phanco, Assistant Chief Financial Officer & Head of Revenues & Benefits, Borough Hall, Cauldwell Street, Bedford MK40 1SJ ☎ 01234 718358 ⌕ lee.phanco@bedford.gov.uk

Economic Development: Mr Mark Oakley, Head of Economic Development, Borough Hall, Cauldwell Street, Bedford MK42 9AP ☎ 01234 221730 ⌕ mark.oakley@bedford.gov.uk

Education: Mr Colin Foster, Chief Education Officer, Borough Hall, Cauldwell Street, Bedford MK42 9AP ☎ 01234 228311 ⌕ colin.foster@bedford.gov.uk

E-Government: Mr Lawrence McArdle, Head of IT Services, Borough Hall, Cauldwell Street, Bedford MK42 9AP ☎ 01234 276221 ⌕ lawrence.mcardle@bedford.gov.uk

Electoral Registration: Mr Keith Simmons, Head of Member & Election Services, Borough Hall, Cauldwell Street, Bedford MK42 9AP ☎ 01234 221676 ⌕ keith.simmons@bedford.gov.uk

Emergency Planning: Mr Craig Austin, Assistant Director - Regulatory Services, Borough Hall, Cauldwell Street, Bedford MK42 9AP ☎ 01234 276774 ⌕ craig.austin@bedford.gov.uk

Energy Management: Mr Craig Austin, Assistant Director - Regulatory Services, Borough Hall, Cauldwell Street, Bedford MK42 9AP ☎ 01234 276774 ⌕ craig.austin@bedford.gov.uk

Environmental / Technical Services: Mr Craig Austin, Assistant Director - Regulatory Services, Borough Hall, Cauldwell Street, Bedford MK42 9AP ☎ 01234 276774 ⌕ craig.austin@bedford.gov.uk

Environmental Health: Mr Craig Austin, Assistant Director - Regulatory Services, Borough Hall, Cauldwell Street, Bedford MK42 9AP ☎ 01234 276774 ⌕ craig.austin@bedford.gov.uk

Estates, Property & Valuation: Mr Adrian Piper, Head of Property Services, Borough Hall, Cauldwell Street, Bedford MK42 9AP ☎ 01234 718248 ⌕ adrian.piper@bedford.gov.uk

Events Manager: Mr Andy Pidgen, Events & Marketing Manager, Corn Exchange, St Paul's Square, Bedford MK40 1SL ☎ 01234 227392 ⌕ andy.pidgen@bedford.gov.uk

Facilities: Mr Adrian Piper, Head of Property Services, Borough Hall, Cauldwell Street, Bedford MK42 9AP ☎ 01234 718248 ⌕ adrian.piper@bedford.gov.uk

Finance: Mr Andy Watkins, Assistant Chief Executive & Chief Finance Officer, Borough Hall, Cauldwell Street, Bedford MK42 9AP ☎ 01234 718208 ⌕ andy.watkins@bedford.gov.uk

Treasury: Mr Geoff Reader, Head of Pensions & Treasury, Borough Hall, Cauldwell Street, Bedford MK42 9AP ☎ 01234 228562 ⌕ geoff.reader@bedford.gov.uk

Pensions: Mr Geoff Reader, Head of Pensions & Treasury, Borough Hall, Cauldwell Street, Bedford MK42 9AP ☎ 01234 228562 ⌕ geoff.reader@bedford.gov.uk

Fleet Management: Mr Chris Pettifer, Head of Transport Operations, Borough Hall, Cauldwell Street, Bedford MK42 9AP ☎ 01234 228881 ⌕ chris.pettifer@bedford.gov.uk

Grounds Maintenance: Mr Craig Austin, Assistant Director - Regulatory Services, Borough Hall, Cauldwell Street, Bedford MK42 9AP ☎ 01234 276774 ⌕ craig.austin@bedford.gov.uk

Health and Safety: Mr Craig Austin, Assistant Director - Regulatory Services, Borough Hall, Cauldwell Street, Bedford MK42 9AP ☎ 01234 276774 ⌕ craig.austin@bedford.gov.uk

Highways: Mr Glenn Barcham, Assistant Director - Highways & Transport, Borough Hall, Cauldwell Street, Bedford MK42 9AP ☎ 01234 228075 ⌕ glenn.barcham@bedford.gov.uk

Highways: Mr Brian Hayward, Head of Highways, Borough Hall, Cauldwell Street, Bedford MK42 9AP ☎ 01234 228012 ⌕ brian.hayward@bedford.gov.uk

Home Energy Conservation: Mr James Shearman, Corporate Carbon & Energy Manager, Borough Hall, Cauldwell Street, Bedford MK42 9AP ☎ 01234 718286 ⌕ james.shearman@bedford.gov.uk

Housing: Mr Paul Rowland, Assistant Director - Planning, Borough Hall, Cauldwell Street, Bedford MK42 9AP ☎ 01234 221720 ⌕ paul.rowland@bedford.gov.uk

Housing: Mr Simon White, Assistant Director of Commissioning & Business Support, Borough Hall, Cauldwell Street, Bedford MK42 9AP ☎ 01234 276097 ⌕ simon.white@bedford.gov.uk

Local Area Agreement: Mr Mark Minion, Head of Corporate Policy & Programme Management, Borough Hall, Cauldwell Street, Bedford MK42 9AP ☎ 01234 228078 ⌕ mark.minion@bedford.gov.uk

Legal: Mrs Barbara Morris, Assistant Chief Executive - Governance & Human Resources, Borough Hall, Cauldwell Street, Bedford MK42 9AP ☎ 01234 228434 ⌕ barbara.morris@bedford.gov.uk

Leisure and Cultural Services: Mr Craig Austin, Assistant Director - Regulatory Services, Borough Hall, Cauldwell Street, Bedford MK42 9AP ☎ 01234 276774 ⌕ craig.austin@bedford.gov.uk

Licensing: Mr Keith Simmons, Head of Member & Election Services, Borough Hall, Cauldwell Street, Bedford MK42 9AP ☎ 01234 221676 ⌕ keith.simmons@bedford.gov.uk

Lifelong Learning: Mr Kevin Crompton, Director - Children's & Adults' Services, Borough Hall, Cauldwell Street, Bedford MK42 9AP ☎ 01234 228620 ⌕ kevin.crompton@bedford.gov.uk

Lighting: Mr Darryl Hall, Project Engineer (Electrical), Borough Hall, Cauldwell Street, Bedford MK42 9AP ☎ 01234 221702 ⌕ darryl.hall@bedford.gov.uk

Lottery Funding, Charity and Voluntary: Mr Lee Phanco, Assistant Chief Financial Officer & Head of Revenues & Benefits, Borough Hall, Cauldwell Street, Bedford MK40 1SJ ☎ 01234 718358 ⌕ lee.phanco@bedford.gov.uk

BEDFORD

Member Services: Mr Keith Simmons, Head of Member & Election Services, Borough Hall, Cauldwell Street, Bedford MK42 9AP ☎ 01234 221676 ⏚ keith.simmons@bedford.gov.uk

Parking: Mr Stewart Briggs, Executive Director - Environment & Sustainable Communities, Borough Hall, Cauldwell Street, Bedford MK42 9AP ☎ 01234 228283 ⏚ stewart.briggs@bedford.gov.uk

Partnerships: Mr Mark Minion, Head of Corporate Policy & Programme Management, Borough Hall, Cauldwell Street, Bedford MK42 9AP ☎ 01234 228078 ⏚ mark.minion@bedford.gov.uk

Personnel / HR: Mrs Barbara Morris, Assistant Chief Executive - Governance & Human Resources, Borough Hall, Cauldwell Street, Bedford MK42 9AP ☎ 01234 228434 ⏚ barbara.morris@bedford.gov.uk

Planning: Mr Paul Rowland, Assistant Director - Planning, Borough Hall, Cauldwell Street, Bedford MK42 9AP ☎ 01234 221720 ⏚ paul.rowland@bedford.gov.uk

Procurement: Mr Mark Stephens, Assistant Chief Executive - Business Transformation, Borough Hall, Cauldwell Street, Bedford MK42 9AP ☎ 01234 228150 ⏚ mark.stephens@bedford.gov.uk

Public Libraries: Mrs Jenny Poad, Head of Libraries, Bedford Central Library, Harpur Street, Bedford MK40 1PG ☎ 01234 718158 ⏚ jenny.poad@bedford.gov.uk

Recycling & Waste Minimisation: Mr Stewart Briggs, Executive Director - Environment & Sustainable Communities, Borough Hall, Cauldwell Street, Bedford MK42 9AP ☎ 01234 228283 ⏚ stewart.briggs@bedford.gov.uk

Regeneration: Mr Mark Oakley, Head of Economic Development, Borough Hall, Cauldwell Street, Bedford MK42 9AP ☎ 01234 221730 ⏚ mark.oakley@bedford.gov.uk

Road Safety: Mr Glenn Barcham, Assistant Director - Highways & Transport, Borough Hall, Cauldwell Street, Bedford MK42 9AP ☎ 01234 228075 ⏚ glenn.barcham@bedford.gov.uk

Social Services (Adult): Mr Kevin Crompton, Director - Children's & Adults' Services, Borough Hall, Cauldwell Street, Bedford MK42 9AP ☎ 01234 228620 ⏚ kevin.crompton@bedford.gov.uk

Public Health: Ms Muriel Scott, Director - Public Health, Borough Hall, Cauldwell Street, Bedford MK42 9AP ☎ 0300 300 5616 ⏚ muriel.scott@centralbedfordshire.gov.uk

Staff Training: Mr John McCann, Head of Learning & Development, Borough Hall, Cauldwell Street, Bedford MK42 9AP ☎ 01234 228358 ⏚ john.mccann@bedford.gov.uk

Street Scene: Mr Stewart Briggs, Executive Director - Environment & Sustainable Communities, Borough Hall, Cauldwell Street, Bedford MK42 9AP ☎ 01234 228283 ⏚ stewart.briggs@bedford.gov.uk

Sustainable Development: Mr Craig Austin, Assistant Director - Regulatory Services, Borough Hall, Cauldwell Street, Bedford MK42 9AP ☎ 01234 276774 ⏚ craig.austin@bedford.gov.uk

Tourism: Mr Mark Oakley, Head of Economic Development, Borough Hall, Cauldwell Street, Bedford MK42 9AP ☎ 01234 221730 ⏚ mark.oakley@bedford.gov.uk

Town Centre: Mr Mark Oakley, Head of Economic Development, Borough Hall, Cauldwell Street, Bedford MK42 9AP ☎ 01234 221730 ⏚ mark.oakley@bedford.gov.uk

Traffic Management: Mr Glenn Barcham, Assistant Director - Highways & Transport, Borough Hall, Cauldwell Street, Bedford MK42 9AP ☎ 01234 228075 ⏚ glenn.barcham@bedford.gov.uk

Traffic Management: Mr Brian Hayward, Head of Highways, Borough Hall, Cauldwell Street, Bedford MK42 9AP ☎ 01234 228012 ⏚ brian.hayward@bedford.gov.uk

Transport: Mr Glenn Barcham, Assistant Director - Highways & Transport, Borough Hall, Cauldwell Street, Bedford MK42 9AP ☎ 01234 228075 ⏚ glenn.barcham@bedford.gov.uk

Transport: Mr Chris Pettifer, Head of Transport Operations, Borough Hall, Cauldwell Street, Bedford MK42 9AP ☎ 01234 228881 ⏚ chris.pettifer@bedford.gov.uk

Transport Planner: Mr Glenn Barcham, Assistant Director - Highways & Transport, Borough Hall, Cauldwell Street, Bedford MK42 9AP ☎ 01234 228075 ⏚ glenn.barcham@bedford.gov.uk

Waste Collection and Disposal: Mr Stewart Briggs, Executive Director - Environment & Sustainable Communities, Borough Hall, Cauldwell Street, Bedford MK42 9AP ☎ 01234 228283 ⏚ stewart.briggs@bedford.gov.uk

Waste Management: Mr Stewart Briggs, Executive Director - Environment & Sustainable Communities, Borough Hall, Cauldwell Street, Bedford MK42 9AP ☎ 01234 228283 ⏚ stewart.briggs@bedford.gov.uk

Children's Play Areas: Mr Stewart Briggs, Executive Director - Environment & Sustainable Communities, Borough Hall, Cauldwell Street, Bedford MK42 9AP ☎ 01234 228283 ⏚ stewart.briggs@bedford.gov.uk

COUNCILLORS

Mayor: Hodgson, Dave (LD - No Ward) dave.hodgson@bedford.gov.uk

Deputy Mayor: Royden, Charles (LD - Brickhill) charlesroyden@gmail.com

Deputy Leader of the Council: Vann, Henry (LD - De Parys) henry.vann@bedford.gov.uk

Group Leader: Meader, Carl (LAB - Kempston South) carl.meader@bedford.gov.uk

Group Leader: Moon, Stephen (CON - Great Barford) shmoon@tiscali.co.uk

Group Leader: Oliver, Susan (LAB - Cauldwell) s.j.oliver@ntlworld.com

Group Leader: Olney, Patricia (IND - Oakley) pat.olney@btopenworld.com

Group Leader: Rider, Wendy (LD - Brickhill)
wendyrider41@gmail.com

Atkins, Colleen (LAB - Harpur)
colleenatkins@ntlworld.com

Bootiman, Rosemary (LD - Putnoe)

Boutall, Anthony (CON - Kempston Central & East)
anthony.boutall@bedford.gov.uk

Carofano, Giovanni (CON - Newnham)
giovanni.carofano@bedford.gov.uk

Charles, Randolph (LAB - Cauldwell)
randolph.charles@bedford.gov.uk

Coombes, Graeme (CON - Wilshamstead)
wilhamstead.ward@yahoo.co.uk

Corp, Sheryl (CON - Great Barford)
sheryl.corp@bedford.gov.uk

Fletcher, David (CON - Castle)
david.fletcher@bedford.gv.uk

Forth, Anthony (LAB - Goldington)
anthony.forth@bedford@bedofrd.gov.uk

Foster, Alison (CON - Harrold)
afield_foster@btinternet.com

Gam, Jon (CON - Bromham & Biddenham)
jonathan.gam@btinternet.com

Gerard, Anita (LD - Kingsbrook)
anitagerard.kb@gmail.com

Headley, Michael (LD - Putnoe)
michael@mheadley.co.uk

Hill, Tim (LD - Elstow & Stewartby)
tim.hill@bedford.gov.uk

Holland, Sarah-Jayne (LD - Eastcotts)
sarahjayne.holland@bedford.gov.uk

Hunt, Shan (LAB - Kempston North)
shanhunt@ntlworld.com

Hunt, Will (LAB - Kempston West)
willhunt@ntlworld.com

Jackson, Louise (LAB - Harpur)
louise.king@bedford.gov.uk

Masud, Mohammed (LAB - Queens Park)
mohammed.masud@bedford.gov.uk

McMurdo, Doug (IND - Sharnbrook)
doug.mcmurdo@bedford.gov.uk

Mingay, John (CON - Newnham)
john.mingay@bedford.gov.uk

Nawaz, Mohammed (LAB - Kempston Central & East)
mohammed.nawaz@bedford.gov.uk

Reale, Luigi (LAB - Castle)
luigi.reale@bedford.gov.uk

Rigby, Roger (CON - Bromham & Biddenham)
roger.rigby110@googlemail.com

Saunders, James (LAB - Kingsbrook)
james.saunders@bedford.gov.uk

Sawyer, David (LD - De Parys)
sawyerbedford@hotmail.com

Smith, Mark (CON - Kempston Rural)
mark.smith792@googlemail.com

Towler, Martin (CON - Riseley)
martin.towler@bedford.gov.uk

Uko, Jade (LAB - Goldington)
jadeluko@bedford.gov.uk

Walker, Jane (CON - Clapham)
jane@janewalker.co.uk

Wooton, John (CON - Wooton)
joh.wheeler@bedford.gov.uk

Wootton, Tom (CON - Wyboston)
tom.wootton@bedford.gov.uk

Yasin, Mohammad (LAB - Queens Park)
mohammad.yasin@bedford.gov.uk

POLITICAL COMPOSITION
CON: 15, LAB: 14, LD: 10, IND: 2

COMMITTEE CHAIRS

Adult Services & Health: Mr John Mingay

Licensing: Mr Will Hunt

Planning: Mrs Anita Gerard

Belfast City   N

Belfast City, Belfast City Hall, Belfast BT1 5GS
☎ 028 9032 0202 ✆ generalenquiries@belfastcity.gov.uk
🖥 www.belfastcity.gov.uk

FACTS AND FIGURES
Parliamentary Constituencies:
EU Constituencies:
Election Frequency:

PRINCIPAL OFFICERS

Chief Executive: Ms Suzanne Wylie, Chief Executive, Belfast City Hall, Belfast BT1 5GS ☎ 028 9027 0201 ✆ wylies@belfastcity.gov.uk

Deputy Chief Executive: Mr Ronan Cregan, Deputy Chief Executive & Director - Finance & Resources, Belfast City Hall, Belfast BT1 5GS ☎ 028 9050 0532 ✆ creganr@belfastcity.gov.uk

Senior Management: Mr John Walsh, Town Solicitor, Belfast City Hall, Belfast BT1 5GS ☎ 028 9027 0239 ✆ walshj@belfastcity.gov.uk

Architect, Building / Property Services: Mr George Wright, Head - Facilities Management, Duncrue Complex, Duncrue Road, Belfast BT3 9BP ☎ 028 9037 3034 ✆ wrightg@belfastcity.gov.uk

Building Control: Mr Trevor Martin, Head - Building Control, 5th Floor, 9 Lanyon Place, Belfast BT1 3LP ☎ 028 9027 0283 ✆ martint@belfastcity.gov.uk

Catering Services: Ms Gail Maguire, Restaurant & Catering Manager, Cecil Ward Building, 4 - 10 Linenhall Street, Belfast BT2 8BP ☎ 028 9027 0326 ✆ maguireg@belfastcity.gov.uk

BELFAST CITY

Children / Youth Services: Ms Aine Hargey, Young People Co-ordinator, Cecil Ward Building, 4 - 10 Linenhall Street, Belfast BT2 8BP ☎ 028 9032 0202 Ext 3595 ⌁ hargeya@belfastcity.gov.uk

Civil Registration: Ms Vivienne Fullerton, Registrar, Belfast City Hall, Belfast BT1 5GS ☎ 028 9027 0274 ⌁ fullertonv@belfastcity.gov.uk

Civil Registration: Miss Aileen Tyney, Registrar, Belfast City Hall, Belfast BT1 5GS ☎ 028 9027 0274 ⌁ tyneya@belfast.gov.uk

PR / Communications: Mr Eamon Deeny, Head - Corporate Communications, Belfast City Hall, Belfast BT1 5GS ☎ 028 9027 0664 ⌁ deenye@belfastcity.gov.uk

Community Planning: Mr David Cuthbert, Community Planning Project Officer, Belfast City Hall, Belfast BT1 5GS ☎ 028 9032 0202 Ext 3320 ⌁ cuthebertd@belfastcity.gov.uk

Community Planning: Ms Kim Walsh, Community Planning Project Officer, Belfast City Hall, Belfast BT1 5GS ☎ 028 9032 0202 Ext 3640 ⌁ walshk@belfastcity.gov.uk

Community Safety: Ms Alison Allen, Safer City Manager, Cecil Ward Building, 4 - 10 Linenhall Street, Belfast BT2 8BP ☎ 028 9032 0202 Ext 3780 ⌁ allena@belfastcity.gov.uk

Computer Management: Mr Paul Gribben, Head - Digital Services, 22 - 38 Gloucester Street, Belfast BT1 4LS ☎ 028 9024 4832 ⌁ gribbenp@belfastcity.gov.uk

Consumer Protection and Trading Standards: Mrs Siobhan Toland, Head - Environmental Health Service, Cecil Ward Building, 4 - 10 Linenhall Street, Belfast BT2 8BP ☎ 028 9027 0304 ⌁ tolands@belfastcity.gov.uk

Contracts: Mr Donal Rogan, Head - Contracts, 24 - 26 Adelaide Street, Belfast BT2 8GD ☎ 028 9027 0289 ⌁ rogand@belfastcity.gov.uk

Corporate Services: Mr Andrew Harrison, Head - Audit, Governance & Risk, 24 - 26 Adelaide Street, Belfast BT2 8GD ☎ 028 9027 0513 ⌁ harrisona@belfastcity.gov.uk

Economic Development: Ms Lisa Toland, Head - Economic & International Development, Cecil Ward Building, 4 - 10 Linenhall Street, Belfast BT2 8BP ☎ 028 9027 0529 ⌁ tolandl@belfastcity.gov.uk

E-Government: Mr Paul Gribben, Head - Digital Services, 22 - 38 Gloucester Street, Belfast BT1 4LS ☎ 028 9024 4832 ⌁ gribbenp@belfastcity.gov.uk

Emergency Planning: Mr David Neill, Emergency Co-ordination Officer, Cecil Ward Building, 4 - 10 Linenhall Street, Belfast BT2 8BP ☎ 028 9027 0734 ⌁ neilld@belfastcity.gov.uk

Energy Management: Mr Ciaran McGrath, Energy Manager, Duncrue Complex, Duncrue Road, Belfast BT3 9BP ☎ 028 9027 0383 ⌁ mcgrathc@belfastcity.gov.uk

Environmental / Technical Services: Mrs Siobhan Toland, Head - Environmental Health Service, Cecil Ward Building, 4 - 10 Linenhall Street, Belfast BT2 8BP ☎ 028 9027 0304 ⌁ tolands@belfastcity.gov.uk

Environmental Health: Mrs Siobhan Toland, Head - Environmental Health Service, Cecil Ward Building, 4 - 10 Linenhall Street, Belfast BT2 8BP ☎ 028 9027 0304 ⌁ tolands@belfastcity.gov.uk

Estates, Property & Valuation: Ms Cathy Reynolds, Estates Manager, Adelaide Exchange, 24 - 26 Adelaide Street, Belfast BT2 8GD ☎ 028 9027 0386 ⌁ reynoldsc@belfastcity.gov.uk

European Liaison: Ms Laura Leonard, European Manager, Cecil Ward Building, 4 - 10 Linenhall Street, Belfast BT2 8BP ☎ 028 9027 0317 ⌁ leonardl@belfastcity.gov.uk

Events Manager: Mr Gerry Copeland, City Events Manager, Cecil Ward Building, 4 - 10 Linenhall Street, Belfast BT2 8BP ☎ 028 9027 0341 ⌁ copelandg@belfastcity.gov.uk

Facilities: Mr George Wright, Head - Facilities Management, Duncrue Complex, Duncrue Road, Belfast BT3 9BP ☎ 028 9037 3034 ⌁ wrightg@belfastcity.gov.uk

Finance: Mr Ronan Cregan, Deputy Chief Executive & Director - Finance & Resources, Belfast City Hall, Belfast BT1 5GS ☎ 028 9050 0532 ⌁ creganr@belfastcity.gov.uk

Fleet Management: Mr Gerry Millar, Director - Property & Projects, Adelaide Exchange, 24 - 26 Adelaide Street, Belfast BT2 8GD ☎ 028 9032 0202 Ext 6239 ⌁ millarg@belfastcity.gov.uk

Grounds Maintenance: Ms Rose Crozier, Assistant Director - Parks & Leisure Services, Adelaide Exchange, 24 - 26 Adelaide Street, Belfast BT2 8GD ☎ 028 9032 0202 Ext 3460 ⌁ crozierr@belfastcity.gov.uk

Health and Safety: Ms Emma Eaton, Corporate Health & Safety Manager, Adelaide Exchange, 24 - 26 Adelaide Street, Belfast BT2 8GD ☎ 028 9027 0581 ⌁ eatone@belfastcity.gov.uk

Legal: Mr John Walsh, Town Solicitor, Belfast City Hall, Belfast BT1 5GS ☎ 028 9027 0239 ⌁ walshj@belfastcity.gov.uk

Licensing: Mr Stephen Hewitt, Building Control Manager, 9 Lanyon Place, Belfast BT1 3LP ☎ 028 9027 0287 ⌁ hewitts@belfastcity.gov.uk

Member Services: Mr Stephen McCrory, Democratic Services Manager, Belfast City Hall, Belfast BT1 5GS ☎ 028 9027 0382 ⌁ mccrorys@belfastcity.gov.uk

Parking: Mr George Doherty, Project Officer - Off Street Parking, Cecil Ward Building, 4 - 10 Linenhall Street, Belfast BT2 8BP ☎ 028 9032 0202 Ext 3676 ⌁ dohertyg@belfastcity.gov.uk

Personnel / HR: Ms Jill Minne, Director - HR & Organisational Development, Belfast City Hall, Belfast BT1 5GS ☎ 028 9027 0395 ⌁ minnej@belfastcity.gov.uk

Planning: Mr Phil Williams, Director - Planning & Place, Cecil Ward Building, 4 - 10 Linenhall Street, Belfast BT2 8BP
☎ 028 9032 0202 Ext 2300 ✆ williamsp@belfastcity.gov.uk

Procurement: Mr Donal Rogan, Head - Contracts, 24 - 26 Adelaide Street, Belfast BT2 8GD ☎ 028 9027 0289
✆ rogand@belfastcity.gov.uk

Recycling & Waste Minimisation: Mr Tim Walker, Head - Waste Management Service, Cecil Ward Building, 4 - 10 Linenhall Street, Belfast BT2 8BP ☎ 028 9032 0202 ✆ walkert@belfastcity.gov.uk

Regeneration: Ms Lisa Toland, Head - Economic & International Development, Cecil Ward Building, 4 - 10 Linenhall Street, Belfast BT2 8BP ☎ 028 9027 0529 ✆ tolandl@belfastcity.gov.uk

Staff Training: Ms Catherine Christy, Human Resources Manager, 21 Linenhall Street, Belfast BT2 8AB ☎ 028 9037 3021
✆ christyc@belfastcity.gov.uk

Street Scene: Mr Sam Skimin, Head - Cleansing Services, 5th Floor, 9 Lanyon Place, Belfast BT7 3LP ☎ 028 9037 3021
✆ skimins@belfastcity.gov.uk

Sustainable Development: Ms Clare McKeown, Sustainable Development Manager, 21 Linenhall Street, Belfast BT2 8AB
☎ 028 9027 0492 ✆ mckeownc@belfastcity.gov.uk

Tourism: Mr Brian Johnston, Tourism, Culture & Arts Manager, Cecil Ward Building, 4 - 10 Linenhall Street, Belfast BT2 8BP
☎ 028 9027 0228 ✆ johnstonbrian@belfastcity.gov.uk

Town Centre: Ms Nuala Gallagher, Director - City Centre Development, 21 Linenhall Street, Belfast BT2 8AB
☎ 028 9032 0202 ✆ gallaghern@belfastcity.gov.uk

Transport Planner: Mr Keith Sutherland, Development Planning & Policy Manager, Cecil Ward Building, 4 - 10 Linenhall Street, Belfast BT2 8BP ☎ 028 9032 0202 Ext 3578
✆ sutherlandk@belfastcity.gov.uk

Waste Collection and Disposal: Mr Jim Ferguson, Operations Manager, 5th Floor, 9 Lanyon Place, Belfast BT1 3LP
☎ 028 9032 0202 ✆ fergusonj@belfastcity.gov.uk

Waste Management: Mr Tim Walker, Head - Waste Management Service, Cecil Ward Building, 4 - 10 Linenhall Street, Belfast BT2 8BP ☎ 028 9032 0202 ✆ walkert@belfastcity.gov.uk

COUNCILLORS

The Lord Mayor: Kingston, Brian (DUP - Court)
kingstonb@belfastcity.gov.uk

Deputy Lord Mayor: Campbell, Mary Ellen (SF - Castle)
maryellencampbell@hotmail.com

High SheriffRodgers, Jim (UUP - Ormiston)
rodgersj@belfastcity.gov.uk

Alderman: Browne, David (UUP - Castle)
d.browne@ntlworld.com

Alderman: Convery, Patrick (SDLP - Castle)
converyp@belfastcity.gov.uk

Alderman: Haire, Tom (DUP - Ormiston)
hairet@belfastcity.gov.uk

Alderman: McCoubrey, Frank (DUP - Court)
frankmccoubrey1@hotmail.co.uk

Alderman: McGimpsey, Chris (UUP - Lisnasharragh)
drcdmcgimpsey@live.co.uk

Alderman: McKee, Gareth (DUP - Oldpark)
gareth@dup-belfast.co.uk

Alderman: Patterson, Lydia (DUP - Castle)
lydia@dup-belfast.co.uk

Alderman: Patterson, Ruth (IND - Botanic)
dup_patterson@yahoo.co.uk

Alderman: Reynolds, Lee (DUP - Balmoral)

Alderman: Sandford, Tommy (DUP - Lisnasharragh)
tommy.sandford@belfastcity.gov.uk

Armitage, David (ALL - Titanic)
armitaged@belfastcity.gov.uk

Attwood, Tim (SDLP - Black Mountain)
attwoodt@belfastcity.gov.uk

Austin, Janice (SF - Black Mountain)

Beattie, Ciaran (SF - Black Mountain)
ciaranbeattie@aol.com

Bell, David (SF - Collin)
daithi2@hotmail.com

Boyle, Declan (SDLP - Botanic)
declan.boyle@belfastcity.gov.uk

Brown, Ross (GRN - Ormiston)
brownr@belfastcity.gov.uk

Bunting, Jolene (O - Court)
jolene.bunting@belfastcity.gov.uk

Carson, Arder (SF - Black Mountain)
ardercarson@yahoo.co.uk

Clarke, Mary (SF - Oldpark)
maryclarke111@hotmail.com

Collins, Matthew (O - Black Mountain)

Copeland, Sonia (UUP - Titanic)
sonia.copeland@belfastcity.gov.uk

Corr, Steven (SF - Black Mountain)
steviecorr@gmail.com

Corr Johnston, Julie-Anne (O - Oldpark)
julieacorr@pupni.co.uk

Craig, Graham (UUP - Botanic)
craiggraham@belfastcity.gov.uk

Dudgeon, Jeffrey (UUP - Balmoral)
jeffreydudgeon@hotmail.com

Garrett, Matt (SF - Collin)
garrettm@belfastcity.gov.uk

Graham, Aileen (DUP - Lisnasharragh)
aileen.graham@belfastcity.gov.uk

Groves, Emma (SF - Black Mountain)
empgroves@msn.com

Hargey, Deirdre (SF - Botanic)
deirdrehargey@hotmail.com

BELFAST CITY

Heading, Brian (SDLP - Collin)
headingb@belfastcity.gov.uk

Howard, Carole (ALL - Lisnasharragh)
carole.howard@belfastcity.gov.uk

Hussey, John (DUP - Ormiston)
john.hussey@belfastcity.gov.uk

Hutchinson, Billy (O - Court)
hutchinsonb@belfastcity.gov.uk

Johnston, Peter (UUP - Ormiston)
peter.johnston@belfastcity.gov.uk

Jones, Mervyn (ALL - Ormiston)
mervynjones54@yahoo.co.uk

Kennedy, Brian (DUP - Titanic)
kennedyb@belfastcity.gov.uk

Kyle, John (O - Titanic)
kylej@belfastcity.gov.uk

Long, Michael (ALL - Lisnasharragh)
long_m_a@hotmail.com

Lyons, Donal (SDLP - Balmoral)

Magee, JJ (SF - Oldpark)
jj@sinnfein.ie

Magennis, Stephen (SF - Collin)
magennis@belfastcity.gov.uk

McAllister, Nuala (ALL - Castle)
nuala.mcallister@belfastcity.gov.uk

McAteer, Geraldine (SF - Balmoral)
mcateer@belfastcity.gov.uk

McCabe, Gerry (SF - Oldpark)
mccabeg@belfastcity.gov.uk

McConville, Mary (SF - Court)
mcconville@belfastcity.gov.uk

McCusker, Paul (SDLP - Oldpark)

McDonough-Brown, Emmet (ALL - Botanic)
mcdonough-brown@belfastcity.gov.uk

McVeigh, Jim (SF - Court)
mcveighjames@belfastcity.gov.uk

Mullan, Kate (SDLP - Lisnasharragh)
mullankate@belfastcity.gov.uk

Newton, Adam (DUP - Titanic)
adam.newton@live.co.uk

O'Donnell, Margaret (SF - Titanic)

O'Hara, Charlene (SF - Collin)
charlene.ohara@belfastcity.gov.uk

O'Neill, Sian (ALL - Ormiston)
oneills@belfastcity.gov.uk

Spence, Guy (DUP - Castle)
speceg@belfastcity.gov.uk

Walsh, Séanna (SF - Collin)
seannawalsh@yahoo.com

POLITICAL COMPOSITION
SF: 19, DUP: 12, ALL: 7, SDLP: 7, UUP: 7, O: 5, IND: 1, GRN: 1

COMMITTEE CHAIRS

Licensing: Mr David Armitage

People & Communities: Mr Matt Garrett

Planning: Mr Peter Johnston

Bexley   L

London Borough of Bexley, Bexley Civic Offices, 2 Watling Street, Bexleyheath DA6 7AT
☎ 020 8303 7777 🖷 020 8301 2661 ✆ customer.services@bexley.gov.uk
🖳 www.bexley.gov.uk

FACTS AND FIGURES
Parliamentary Constituencies: Bexleyheath & Crayford, Erith and Thamesmead, Old Bexley and Sidcup
EU Constituencies: South East
Election Frequency: Elections are of whole council

PRINCIPAL OFFICERS

Chief Executive: Ms Gill Steward, Chief Executive, Bexley Civic Offices, 2 Watling Street, Bexleyheath DA6 7AT ☎ 020 3045 3232 ✆ gill.steward@bexley.gov.uk

Senior Management: Mr Tom Brown, Deputy Director - Adult Care, Bexley Civic Offices, 2 Watling Street, Bexleyheath DA6 7AT ☎ 020 3045 4318 ✆ tom.brown@bexley.gov.uk

Senior Management: Ms Alison Griffin, Director - Finance & Resources, Bexley Civic Offices, 2 Watling Street, Bexleyheath DA6 7AT ☎ 020 3045 4955 ✆ alison.griffin@bexley.gov.uk

Senior Management: Dr Nada Lemic, Director - Public Health, Bexley Civic Offices, 2 Watling Street, Bexleyheath DA6 7AT ☎ 020 8303 7777 ✆ nada.lemic@bromley.gov.uk

Senior Management: Mr Paul Moore, Director - Regeneration, Communities & Customer Services, Bexley Civic Offices, 2 Watling Street, Bexleyheath DA6 7AT ☎ 020 3045 4901 ✆ paul.moore@bexley.gov.uk

Senior Management: Ms Jackie Tiotto, Director - Children's Services, Bexley Civic Offices, 2 Watling Street, Bexleyheath DA6 7AT ☎ 020 3045 4090 ✆ jackie.tiotto@bexley.gov.uk

Access Officer / Social Services (Disability): Prof Vinod Kumar Khanna, Chief Executive - Inspire Community Trust, 20 Whitehall Lane, Erith DA8 2DH ☎ 020 3045 5312 ✆ vinod.kumar@bexley.gov.uk

Best Value: Mr Trevor Wentworth, Programme Manager, Bexley Civic Offices, 2 Watling Street, Bexleyheath DA6 7AT ☎ 020 3045 5757 ✆ trevor.wentworth@bexley.gov.uk

Children / Youth Services: Ms Jackie Tiotto, Director - Children's Services, Bexley Civic Offices, 2 Watling Street, Bexleyheath DA6 7AT ☎ 020 3045 4090 ✆ jackie.tiotto@bexley.gov.uk

PR / Communications: Mr John Ferry, Head of Communications, Bexley Civic Offices, 2 Watling Street, Bexleyheath DA6 7AT ☎ 020 3045 4867 ✆ john.ferry@bexley.gov.uk

Community Safety: Ms Emma Leathers, Community Safety Manager, Footscray Offices, Maidstone road, Sidcup DA14 5HS ☎ 020 3045 3992 ⏪ emma.leathers@bexley.gov.uk

Computer Management: Mr James Scott, Head of ICT (Systems & Security), Bexley Civic Offices, 2 Watling Street, Bexleyheath DA6 7AT ☎ 020 3045 4350 ⏪ james.scott@bexley.gov.uk

Consumer Protection and Trading Standards: Mr David Bryce-Smith, Deputy Director - Public Protection, Housing & Public Realm, Bexley Civic Offices, 2 Watling Street, Bexleyheath DA6 7AT ☎ 020 3045 5718 ⏪ david.brycesmith@bexley.gov.uk

Corporate Services: Mr Steve Hobdell, Development Control Admin & Systems Manager, Bexley Civic Offices, 2 Watling Street, Bexleyheath DA6 7AT ☎ 020 3045 5740 ⏪ steve.hobdell@bexley.gov.uk

Customer Service: Mr Graham Ward, Deputy Director - Customer Relations & Corporate Services, Bexley Civic Offices, 2 Watling Street, Bexleyheath DA6 7AT ☎ 020 3045 4622 ⏪ graham.ward@bexley.gov.uk

Electoral Registration: Mr David Easton, Head of Electoral & Members' Services, Bexley Civic Offices, 2 Watling Street, Bexleyheath DA6 7AT ☎ 020 3045 3675 ⏪ david.easton@bexley.gov.uk

Emergency Planning: Mr Tony Plowright, Emergency Planning & Business Continuity Manager, Bexley Civic Offices, 2 Watling Street, Bexleyheath DA6 7AT ☎ 020 3045 4623 ⏪ tony.plowright@bexley.gov.uk

Energy Management: Mr Kevin Murphy, Head of Housing Services, Bexley Civic Offices, 2 Watling Street, Bexleyheath DA6 7AT ☎ 020 3045 5623 ⏪ kevin.murphy@bexley.gov.uk

Environmental Health: Mr David Bryce-Smith, Deputy Director - Public Protection, Housing & Public Realm, Bexley Civic Offices, 2 Watling Street, Bexleyheath DA6 7AT ☎ 020 3045 5718 ⏪ david.brycesmith@bexley.gov.uk

Estates, Property & Valuation: Ms Suzanne Jackson, Head of Regeneration & Assets, Bexley Civic Offices, 2 Watling Street, Bexleyheath DA6 7AT ☎ 020 3045 4830 ⏪ suzanne.jackson@bexley.gov.uk

Finance: Ms Alison Griffin, Director - Finance & Resources, Bexley Civic Offices, 2 Watling Street, Bexleyheath DA6 7AT ☎ 020 3045 4955 ⏪ alison.griffin@bexley.gov.uk

Home Energy Conservation: Mr Kevin Murphy, Head of Housing Services, Bexley Civic Offices, 2 Watling Street, Bexleyheath DA6 7AT ☎ 020 3045 5623 ⏪ kevin.murphy@bexley.gov.uk

Legal: Mr Akin Alabi, Head of Legal Services & Monitoring Officer, Bexley Civic Offices, 2 Watling Street, Bexleyheath DA6 7AT ☎ 020 3045 3922 ⏪ akin.alabi@bexley.gov.uk

Leisure and Cultural Services: Ms Toni Ainge, Deputy Director - Communities, Libraries, Leisure & Parks, Bexley Civic Offices, 2 Watling Street, Bexleyheath DA6 7AT ☎ 020 3045 4879 ⏪ antonia.ainge@bexley.gov.uk

Licensing: Mr David Bryce-Smith, Deputy Director - Public Protection, Housing & Public Realm, Bexley Civic Offices, 2 Watling Street, Bexleyheath DA6 7AT ☎ 020 3045 5718 ⏪ david.brycesmith@bexley.gov.uk

Parking: Mr Benjamin Stephens, Head of Parking Shared Services, Bexley Civic Offices, 2 Watling Street, Bexleyheath DA6 7AT ☎ 020 8313 4514 ⏪ benjamin.stephens@bexley.gov.uk

Personnel / HR: Mr Nick Hollier, Deputy Director - HR & Corporate Support, Bexley Civic Offices, 2 Watling Street, Bexleyheath DA6 7AT ☎ 020 3045 4091 ⏪ nick.hollier@bexley.gov.uk

Public Libraries: Ms Judith Mitlin, Head of Libraries, Heritage & Archives, Footscray Offices, Maidstone road, Sidcup DA14 5HS ☎ 020 3045 4531 ⏪ judith.mitlin@bexley, gov, uk

Regeneration: Mr Paul Moore, Director - Regeneration, Communities & Customer Services, Bexley Civic Offices, 2 Watling Street, Bexleyheath DA6 7AT ☎ 020 3045 4901 ⏪ paul.moore@bexley.gov.uk

Road Safety: Mr Mark Bunting, Team Leader - Road Safety, Bexley Civic Offices, 2 Watling Street, Bexleyheath DA6 7AT ☎ 020 3045 5875 ⏪ mark.bunting@bexley.gov.uk

Social Services (Adult): Mr Tom Brown, Deputy Director - Adult Care, Bexley Civic Offices, 2 Watling Street, Bexleyheath DA6 7AT ☎ 020 3045 4318 ⏪ tom.brown@bexley.gov.uk

Social Services (Children): Ms Sheila Murphy, Deputy Director - Social Care, Safeguarding & SEN, Bexley Civic Offices, 2 Watling Street, Bexleyheath DA6 7AT ☎ 020 3045 4128 ⏪ sheila.murphy@bexley.gov.uk

Public Health: Dr Nada Lemic, Director - Public Health, Bexley Civic Offices, 2 Watling Street, Bexleyheath DA6 7AT ☎ 020 8303 7777 ⏪ nada.lemic@bromley.gov.uk

Staff Training: Mr Nick Hollier, Deputy Director - HR & Corporate Support, Bexley Civic Offices, 2 Watling Street, Bexleyheath DA6 7AT ☎ 020 3045 4091 ⏪ nick.hollier@bexley.gov.uk

Sustainable Communities: Ms Susan Clark, Head of Development Control, Bexley Civic Offices, 2 Watling Street, Bexleyheath DA6 7AT ☎ 020 3045 5761 ⏪ susan.clark@bexley.gov.uk

Tourism: Ms Toni Ainge, Deputy Director - Communities, Libraries, Leisure & Parks, Bexley Civic Offices, 2 Watling Street, Bexleyheath DA6 7AT ☎ 020 3045 4879 ⏪ antonia.ainge@bexley.gov.uk

Children's Play Areas: Mr Colin Rowland, Head of Parks & Open Spaces, Bexley Civic Offices, 2 Watling Street, Bexleyheath DA6 7AT ☎ 020 3045 3686 ⏪ colin.rowland@bexley.gov.uk

COUNCILLORS

Mayor: Pallen, Eileen (CON - Barnehurst) councillor.eileen.pallen@bexley.gov.uk

BEXLEY

Deputy Mayor: Clark, Val (CON - Falconwood & Welling)
councillor.val.clark@bexley.gov.uk

Leader of the Council: O'Neill, Teresa (CON - Brampton)
councillor.teresa.o'neill@bexley.gov.uk

Deputy Leader of the Council: Leitch, Rob (CON - Sidcup)
rob.leitch@bexley.gov.uk

Group LeaderBeazley, Chris (UKIP - St Michael's)
chris.beazley@bexley.gov.uk

Group LeaderDeadman, Alan (LAB - North End)
christina.ford@bexley.gov.uk

Amaning, Esther (LAB - Lesnes Abbey)
esther.amaning@bexley.gov.uk

Ashmole, Roy (CON - Christchurch)
councillor.roy.ashmole@bexley.gov.uk

Bacon, Gareth (CON - Longlands)
councillor.gareth.bacon@bexley.gov.uk

Bacon, Cheryl (CON - Cray Meadows)
councillor.cheryl.bacon@bexley.gov.uk

Bailey, Linda (CON - Danson Park)
councillor.linda.bailey@bexley.gov.uk

Beckwith, Brian (CON - Blackfen & Lamorbey)
councillor.brian.beckwith@bexley.gov.uk

Beckwith, Aileen (CON - Sidcup)
councillor.aileen.beckwith@bexley.gov.uk

Begho, Derry (LAB - Thamesmead East)
derry.begho@bexley.gov.uk

Betts, Nigel (CON - Falconwood & Welling)
councillor.nigel.betts@bexley.gov.uk

Bishop, Christine (CON - Crayford)
christine.bishop@bexley.gov.uk

Bishop, Brian (CON - Colyers)
councillor.brian.bishop@bexley.gov.uk

Boateng, Edward (LAB - Erith)
councillor.edward.boateng@bexley.gov.uk

Borella, Stefano (LAB - North End)
councillor.stefano.borella@bexley.gov.uk

Camsey, Sybil (CON - Brampton)
councillor.sybil.camsey@bexley.gov.uk

Catterall, Christine (CON - East Wickham)
christine.catterall@bexley.gov.uk

Craske, Peter (CON - Blackfen & Lamorbey)
councillor.peter.craske@bexley.gov.uk

D'Amiral, Graham (CON - Blendon & Penhill)
councillor.graham.d'amiral@bexley.gov.uk

Davey, John (CON - Crayford)
councillor.john.davey@bexley.gov.uk

Dourmoush, Andy (CON - Longlands)
andy.dourmoush@bexley.gov.uk

Downing, Alan (CON - St Mary's)
councillor.alan.downing@bexley.gov.uk

Downing, Ross (CON - Cray Meadows)
councillor.ross.downing@bexley.gov.uk

Ezenwata, Endy (LAB - Thamesmead East)
endy.exenwata@bexley.gov.uk

Ferreira, Joe (LAB - Erith)
joe.ferreira@bexley.gov.uk

Fothergill, Maxine (CON - Colyers)
councillor.maxine.fothergill@bexley.gov.uk

Francis, Daniel (LAB - Belvedere)
daniel.francis@bexley.gov.uk

French, Louie (CON - Falconwood & Welling)
louie.french@bexley.gov.uk

Fuller, John (CON - Christchurch)
councillor.john.fuller@bexley.gov.uk

Hackett, Danny (LAB - Lesnes Abbey)
danny.hackett@bexley.gov.uk

Hall, Steven (CON - Blendon & Penhill)
councillor.steven.hall@bexley.gov.uk

Hunt, James (CON - East Wickham)
councillor.james.hunt@bexley.gov.uk

Hurt, David (CON - Barnehurst)
councillor.david.hurt@bexley.gov.uk

Husband, John (LAB - Lesnes Abbey)
john.husband@bexley.gov.uk

Langstead, Brenda (LAB - North End)
councillor.brenda.langstead@bexley.gov.uk

Leaf, David (CON - Longlands)
david.leaf@bexley.gov.uk

Lucia-Hennis, Geraldene (CON - Crayford)
councillor.geraldene.lucia-hennis@bexley.gov.uk

MacDonald, Gill (LAB - Belvedere)
councillor.gill.macdonald@bexley.gov.uk

Marriner, Howard (CON - Barnehurst)
councillor.howard.marriner@bexley.gov.uk

Massey, Sharon (CON - Danson Park)
councillor.sharon.massey@bexley.gov.uk

Massey, Donald (CON - Cray Meadows)
councillor.donald.massey@bexley.gov.uk

McGannon, Colin (UKIP - Colyers)
mac.mcgannon@bexley.gov.uk

Munur, Cafer (CON - East Wickham)
cafer@munur@bexley.gov.uk

Newman, Sean (LAB - Belvedere)
councillor.sean.newman@bexley.gov.uk

Newton, Caroline (CON - St Michael's)
councillor.caroline.newton@bexley.gov.uk

Ogundayo, Mabel (LAB - Thamesmead East)
mabel.ogundayo@bexley.gov.uk

O'Hare, Nick (CON - Blendon & Penhill)
councillor.nick.o'hare@bexley.gov.uk

Oppong-Asare, Abena (LAB - Erith)
abena.oppong-asare@bexley.gov.uk

Read, Philip (CON - Northumberland Heath)
councillor.philip.read@bexley.gov.uk

Reader, Peter (CON - Northumberland Heath)
councillor.peter.reader@bexley.gov.uk

Sawyer, Alex (CON - St Mary's)
councillor.alex.sawyer@bexley.gov.uk

Seymour, Melvin (CON - Northumberland Heath)
councillor.melvin.seymour@bexley.gov.uk

Slaughter, June (CON - Sidcup)
councillor.june.slaughter@bexley.gov.uk

Smith, Lynn (UKIP - Blackfen & Lamorbey)
lynn.smith@bexley.gov.uk

Smith, Brad (CON - Christchurch)
councillor.brad.smith@bexley.gov.uk

Tandy, Colin (CON - St Mary's)
councillor.colin.tandy@bexley.gov.uk

Waters, John (CON - Danson Park)
councillor.john.waters@bexley.gov.uk

Wilkinson, John (CON - Brampton)
john.wilkinson@bexley.gov.uk

POLITICAL COMPOSITION
CON: 44, LAB: 15, UKIP: 3

COMMITTEE CHAIRS

Audit: Mr David Leaf

Licensing: Mr John Fuller

Pensions: Mr Louie French

Planning: Mr Peter Reader

Birmingham City   M

Birmingham City Council, The Council House, Victoria Square, Birmingham B1 1BB
☎ 0121 303 9944 ◌ contact@birmingham.gov.uk
💻 www.birmingham.gov.uk

FACTS AND FIGURES
Parliamentary Constituencies: Birmingham, Edgbaston, Birmingham, Erdington, Birmingham, Hall Green, Birmingham, Hodge Hill, Birmingham, Ladywood, Birmingham, Northfield, Birmingham, Perry Bar, Birmingham, Selly Oak, Birmingham, Yardley, Sutton Coldfield
EU Constituencies: West Midlands
Election Frequency: Elections are by thirds

PRINCIPAL OFFICERS

Chief Executive: Mr Mark Rogers, Chief Executive, The Council House, Victoria Square, Birmingham B1 1BB ☎ 0121 303 2000 ◌ mark.rogers@birmingham.gov.uk

Assistant Chief Executive: Ms Piali DasGupta, Assistant Chief Executive, The Council House, Victoria Square, Birmingham B1 1BB ◌ piali.dasgupta@birmingham.gov.uk

Senior Management: Mr Paul Dransfield, Strategic Director - Programmes & Projects, The Council House, Victoria Square, Birmingham B1 1BB ☎ 0121 303 3803 ◌ paul.dransfield@birmingham.gov.uk

Senior Management: Mr Peter Hay, Strategic Director - People, Louisa Ryland House, 44 Newhall Street, Birmingham B3 3PL
☎ 0121 303 2992 ◌ peter.hay@birmingham.gov.uk

Senior Management: Ms Jacqui Kennedy, Strategic Director - Place, Louisa Ryland House, 44 Newhall Street, Birmingham B3 3PL ☎ 0121 303 6121 ◌ jacqui.kennedy@birmingham.gov.uk

Senior Management: Mr Waheed Nazir, Strategic Director - Economy, Birmingham City Council, Baskerville House, Broad Street, Birmingham B1 2ND ☎ 0121 464 7735
◌ waheed.nazir@birmingham.gov.uk

Senior Management: Ms Angela Probert, Strategic Director - Change & Support Services, The Council House, Victoria Square, Birmingham B1 1BB ◌ angela.probert@birmingham.gov.uk

Senior Management: Mr Jon Warlow, Strategic Director - Finance & Legal, Birmingham City Coucil, PO Box 16306, Woodstock Street, Aston, Birmingham B7 4BL ☎ 0121 303 2950 ◌ jon.warlow@birmingham.gov.uk

Access Officer / Social Services (Disability): Ms Jill Crosbie, Head of Access to Education, 10 Woodcock Street, Aston, Birmingham B7 3BU ☎ 0121 303 1795 ◌ jill.crosbie@birmingham.gov.uk

Access Officer / Social Services (Disability): Ms Gillian King, Inclusion Support Manager, 10 Woodcock Street, Aston, Birmingham B7 3BU ☎ 07968 117438 ◌ gillian.king@birmingham.gov.uk

Architect, Building / Property Services: Mr Mark Bieganski, Head of Property Strategy & Information, The Council House, Victoria Square, Birmingham B1 1BB ☎ 0121 303 3645 ◌ mark.bieganski@birmingham.gov.uk

Architect, Building / Property Services: Mr Peter Jones, Director - Property, The Council House, Victoria Square, Birmingham B1 1BB ☎ 0121 303 3844 ◌ peter.jones@birmingham.gov.uk

Best Value: Mr Phil Andrews, Head of Asset Management, The Council House, Victoria Square, Birmingham B1 1BB ☎ 0121 303 3696 ◌ phil.andrews@birmingham.gov.uk

Building Control: Mr Richard Culliford, Head of Building Consultancy, Acivico Ltd, 3rd Floor, 1 Lancaster Circus Queensway, Birmingham B4 7DJ ☎ 0121 303 4096 ◌ richard.culliford@acivico.co.uk

Catering Services: Mr Muir Wilson, Head of Civic Catering, Acivivo Ltd, 3rd Floor, 1 Lancaster Circus Queensway, Birmingham B4 7DJ ☎ 0121 303 4987 ◌ muir.wilson@brimingham.gov.uk

Children / Youth Services: Mr Trevor Brown, Head of Service - Youth Offending, 10 Woodcock Street, Aston, Birmingham B7 3BU ☎ 0121 464 0600 ◌ trevor.brown@birmingham.gov.uk

Children / Youth Services: Mr Ian Burgess, Head of Children's Services & Education, The Council House, Victoria Square, Birmingham B1 1BB ☎ 0121 303 4643 ◌ ian.burgess@birmingham.gov.uk

Children / Youth Services: Ms Dawn Roberts, Assistant Director - Children's Services Early Help, 10 Woodcock Street, Aston, Birmingham B7 3BU ☎ 0121 464 4400 ◌ dawn.roberts@birmingham.gov.uk

BIRMINGHAM CITY

Children / Youth Services: Mr Sukhwinder Singh, Head of Children's Services (Safeguarding), The Council House, Victoria Square, Birmingham B1 1BB ☎ 0121 303 7812 🖷 sukhwinder.singh@birmingham.gov.uk

Civil Registration: Ms Andrea Haines, Acting Head of Operations - Bereavement Services, Coronors, Mortuary & Registration Services, PO Box 2122, Margaret Street, Birmingham B3 3BU ☎ 0121 303 0200 🖷 andrea.haines@birmingham.gov.uk

PR / Communications: Mr Stephen Arnold, Head of Marketing, The Council House, Victoria Square, Birmingham B1 1BB ☎ 0121 303 2923 🖷 stephen.arnold@birmingham.gov.uk

PR / Communications: Ms Deborah Harries, Head of Public Affairs, The Council House, Victoria Square, Birmingham B1 1BB ☎ 0121 303 4777 🖷 deborah.harries@birmingham.gov.uk

PR / Communications: Ms Eleri Roberts, Assistant Director - Communications, The Council House, Victoria Square, Birmingham B1 1BB ☎ 0121 303 4302 🖷 eleri.roberts@birmingham.gov.uk

Computer Management: Mr Anthony Elliott, Head of Directorate ICT - Business Change, 10 Woodcock Street, Aston, Birmingham B7 3BU ☎ 07730 281736 🖷 anthony.elliott@birmingham.gov.uk

Consumer Protection and Trading Standards: Ms Alison Harwood, Head of Operations - Bereavement Services, Coroners & Mortuary and Registration Services, PO Box 2122, Margaret Street, Birmingham B3 3BU ☎ 0121 303 0201 🖷 alison.harwood@birmingham.gov.uk

Consumer Protection and Trading Standards: Sajeela Naseer, Head of Trading Standards, PO Box 2122, Margaret Street, Birmingham B3 3BU ☎ 0121 303 6112 🖷 sajeela.naseer@birmingham.gov.uk

Contracts: Mr Richard Tibbatts, Head of Category - Contract Management, The Council House, Victoria Square, Birmingham B1 1BB ☎ 0121 303 0015 🖷 richard.tibbatts@birmingham.gov.uk

Corporate Services: Mr Lloyd Broad, Head of European & International Affairs, The Council House, Victoria Square, Birmingham B1 1BB ☎ 0121 303 2377 🖷 lloyd.broad@birmingham.gov.uk

Corporate Services: Ms Helen Burnett, Head of Business & Commercial Development, The Council House, Victoria Square, Birmingham B1 1BB ☎ 07867 469883 🖷 helen.burnett@birmingham.gov.uk

Corporate Services: Mr Paul Dransfield, Strategic Director - Programmes & Projects, The Council House, Victoria Square, Birmingham B1 1BB ☎ 0121 303 3803 🖷 paul.dransfield@birmingham.gov.uk

Corporate Services: Mr Kevin Hubery, Head of Strategic Policy & Leadership Support, The Council House, Victoria Square, Birmingham B1 1BB ☎ 0121 303 4821 🖷 kevin.hubery@birmingham.gov.uk

Corporate Services: Mr Nigel Kletz, Assistant Director - Corporate Procurement, The Council House, Victoria Square, Birmingham B1 1BB ☎ 0121 303 6610 🖷 nigel.kletz@birmingham.gov.uk

Corporate Services: Ms Angela Probert, Strategic Director - Change & Support Services, The Council House, Victoria Square, Birmingham B1 1BB 🖷 angela.probert@birmingham.gov.uk

Corporate Services: Mr Richard Tibbatts, Head of Category - Contract Management, The Council House, Victoria Square, Birmingham B1 1BB ☎ 0121 303 0015 🖷 richard.tibbatts@birmingham.gov.uk

Customer Service: Ms Shipli Akbar, Assistant Director - Employment, The Council House, Victoria Square, Birmingham B1 1BB ☎ 0121 303 4571 🖷 shilpi.akbar@birmingham.gov.uk

Customer Service: Ms Paula Buckley, Assistant Director - Customer Services, The Council House, Victoria Square, Birmingham B1 1BB ☎ 0121 464 8298 🖷 paul.buckley@birmingham.gov.uk

Customer Service: Mr Phil Docherty, Head of Revenues Client Services, The Council House, Victoria Square, Birmingham B1 1BB ☎ 07920 275505 🖷 phil.docherty@birmingham.gov.uk

Customer Service: Mr Chris Gibbs, Service Director - Customer Services, The Council House, Victoria Square, Birmingham B1 1BB ☎ 0121 464 6387 🖷 chris.gibbs@birmingham.gov.uk

Customer Service: Ms Tracy Holsey, Head of Rent Service, The Council House, Victoria Square, Birmingham B1 1BB ☎ 0121 675 4286 🖷 tracy.holsey@birmingham.gov.uk

Customer Service: Ms Sue Jones, Revenues Director, The Council House, Victoria Square, Birmingham B1 1BB ☎ 07808 585389 🖷 sue.jones@birmingham.gov.uk

Customer Service: Mr David Kinnair, Head of Benefits, The Council House, Victoria Square, Birmingham B1 1BB ☎ 0121 464 7844 🖷 david.kinnair@birmingham.gov.uk

Economic Development: Mr Waheed Nazir, Strategic Director - Economy, Birmingham City Council, Baskerville House, Broad Street, Birmingham B1 2ND ☎ 0121 464 7735 🖷 waheed.nazir@birmingham.gov.uk

Economic Development: Mr Clive Skidmore, Head of Investment & Development, The Council House, Victoria Square, Birmingham B1 1BB ☎ 0121 303 1667 🖷 clive.skidmore@birmingham.gov.uk

Education: Mr Ian Burgess, Head of Children's Services & Education, The Council House, Victoria Square, Birmingham B1 1BB ☎ 0121 303 4643 🖷 ian.burgess@birmingham.gov.uk

Education: Mr Colin Diamond, Interim Executive Director - Education, 10 Woodcock Street, Aston, Birmingham B7 3BU ☎ 0121 464 2808 🖷 colin.diamond@birmingham.gov.uk

Education: Ms Emma Leaman, Assistant Director - Education Infrastructure, 10 Woodcock Street, Aston, Birmingham B7 3BU
☎ 0121 675 8784 ◌ emma.leaman@birmingham.gov.uk

Education: Ms Julie Newbold, Head of Schools Admissions & Pupil Placements Service, 10 Woodcock Street, Aston, Birmingham B7 3BU, Tel: 0121 303 2268 ◌ julie.newbold@birmingham.gov.uk

Education: Mr Simon Wellman, Head of Service - SENAR (Special Education Needs, Assessment & Review), 10 Woodcock Street, Aston, Birmingham B7 3BU ☎ 0121 303 0112
◌ simon.wellman@birmingham.gov.uk

Electoral Registration: Mr Robert Connelly, Head of Electoral Services, The Council House, Victoria Square, Birmingham B1 1BB
☎ 0121 303 2443 ◌ robert.connelly@birmingham.gov.uk

Environmental Health: Mr Mark Croxford, Head of Environmental Health & Markets Service, PO Box 2122, Margaret Street, Birmingham B3 3BU ☎ 0121 303 6350
◌ mark.croxford@birmingham.gov.uk

Environmental Health: Ms Amanda Prosser-Davies, Operations Manager - Markets, PO Box 2122, Margaret Street, Birmingham B3 3BU ☎ 0121 303 7788
◌ amanda.prosser-davies@birmingham.gov.uk

European Liaison: Mr Lloyd Broad, Head of European & International Affairs, The Council House, Victoria Square, Birmingham B1 1BB ☎ 0121 303 2377
◌ lloyd.broad@birmingham.gov.uk

Events Manager: Mr Steve Hollingworth, Assistant Director - Sport, Events & Parks, PO Box 2122, Margaret Street, Birmingham B3 3BU ☎ 0121 464 2024 ◌ steve.hollingworth@birmingham.gov.uk

Facilities: Mr Leo McMulkin, Head of Total Facilities Management, Acivico Ltd, 3rd Floor, 1 Lancaster Circus Queensway, Birmingham B4 7DJ ☎ 0121 303 6633 ◌ leo.mcmulkin@acivico.co.uk

Finance: Ms Sarah Dunlavey, Assistant Director - Financial Services, The Council House, Victoria Square, Birmingham B1 1BB
☎ 0121 675 8714 ◌ sarah.dunlavey@birmingham.gov.uk

Finance: Mr Steve Powell, Assistant Director - Financial Strategy, The Council House, Victoria Square, Birmingham B1 1BB ☎ 0121 303 4087 ◌ steve.powell@birmingham.gov.uk

Finance: Ms Kay Reid, Assistant Director - Audit & Risk Management, The Council House, Victoria Square, Birmingham B1 1BB ☎ 0121 464 3396 ◌ kay.reid@birmingham.gov.uk

Finance: Mr Jon Warlow, Strategic Director - Finance & Legal, Birmingham City Coucil, PO Box 16306, Woodstock Street, Aston, Birmingham B7 4BL ☎ 0121 303 2950
◌ jon.warlow@birmingham.gov.uk

Pensions: Ms Sally Plant, Pensions Manager, 10 Woodcock Street, Aston, Birmingham B7 3BU ☎ 07823 534910
◌ sally.plant@birmingham.gov.uk

Grounds Maintenance: Mr Robin Bryan, Acting Head of Parks, PO Box 2122, Margaret Street, Birmingham B3 3BU
☎ 0121 464 0448 ◌ robin.bryan@birmingham.gov.uk

Grounds Maintenance: Mr Bob Churn, Acting Head - Landscape & Contract Developments, PO Box 2122, Margaret Street, Birmingham B3 3BU ☎ 0121 303 3536 ◌ bob.churn@birmingham.gov.uk

Health and Safety: Mr Kevin Coley, Health & Safety Manager, The Council House, Victoria Square, Birmingham B1 1BB
☎ 0121 303 2420 ◌ kevin.coley@birmingham.gov.uk

Highways: Mr Kevin Hicks, Assistant Director - Highways & Infrastructure, 1 Lancaster Circus, Queensway, Birmingham B4 7DQ
☎ 0121 303 7693 ◌ kevin.hicks@birmingham.gov.uk

Housing: Mr Jonthan Antill, Senior Service Manager - South Quadrant Housing Services, PO Box 2122, Margaret Street, Birmingham B7 3BU ☎ 07825 052148
◌ jonthan.antill@birmingham.gov.uk

Housing: Mr Jim Crawshaw, Integrated Service Head - Homeless & Pre-tenancy Services, 10 Woodcock Street, Aston, Birmingham B7 3BU ☎ 0121 675 2154 ◌ jim.crawhaw@birmingham.gov.uk

Housing: Ms Carol Dawson, Senior Service Manager - North Quadrant Housing Services, PO Box 2122, Margaret Street, Birmingham B7 3BU ☎ 0121 464 1898
◌ carol.dawson@birmingham.gov.uk

Housing: Ms Brenda Gallagher, Senior Service Manager - Central & West Quadrant Housing Services, PO Box 2122, Margaret Street, Birmingham B7 3BU ☎ 07766 924195
◌ brenda.gallagher@birmingham.gov.uk

Housing: Mr Carl Hides, Senior Service Manager - East Quadrant Housing Services, PO Box 2122, Margaret Street, Birmingham B3 3BU ☎ 07766 924195 ◌ carl.hides@birmingham.gov.uk

Housing: Mr Rob James, Service Director - Housing Transformation, PO Box 2122, Margaret Street, Birmingham B3 3BU
☎ 0121 464 9819 ◌ rob.james@birmingham.gov.uk

Housing: Mr Alan Lotinga, Service Director - Adult Care & Housing Options, 10 Woodcock Street, Aston, Birmingham B7 3BU
☎ 0121 303 6694 ◌ alan.lotinga@birmingham.gov.uk

Legal: Ms Kate Charlton, Acitng City Solicitor, The Council House, Victoria Square, Birmingham B1 1BB ☎ 0121 464 1173
◌ kate_charlton@birmingham.gov.uk

Legal: Ms Charmaine Murray, Head of Adult Services & Human Rights Law, The Council House, Victoria Square, Birmingham B1 1BB ☎ 0121 303 2857 ◌ charmaine_murray@birmingham.gov.uk

Legal: Mr Jon Warlow, Strategic Director - Finance & Legal, Birmingham City Coucil, PO Box 16306, Woodstock Street, Aston, Birmingham B7 4BL ☎ 0121 303 2950
◌ jon.warlow@birmingham.gov.uk

BIRMINGHAM CITY

Leisure and Cultural Services: Ms Val Birchall, Assistant Director - Culture & Visitor Economy, PO Box 2122, Margaret Street, Birmingham B3 3BU ☎ 0121 303 2919 ⌁ val.birchall@birmingham.gov.uk

Leisure and Cultural Services: Mr Symon Easton, Head of Cultural Development, PO Box 2122, Margaret Street, Birmingham B3 3BU ☎ 0121 303 1301 ⌁ symon.easton@birmingham.gov.uk

Leisure and Cultural Services: Mr Steve Hollingworth, Assistant Director - Sport, Events & Parks, PO Box 2122, Margaret Street, Birmingham B3 3BU ☎ 0121 464 2024 ⌁ steve.hollingworth@birmingham.gov.uk

Licensing: Mr Chris Neville, Head of Licensing, PO Box 2122, Margaret Street, Birmingham B3 3BU ☎ 0121303 6103 ⌁ chris.neville@birmingham.gov.uk

Member Services: Mr Robert Connelly, Head of Electoral Services, The Council House, Victoria Square, Birmingham B1 1BB ☎ 0121 303 2443 ⌁ robert.connelly@birmingham.gov.uk

Member Services: Ms Rose Horsfall, PA to Leader of the Council: , The Council House, Victoria Square, Birmingham B1 1BB ☎ 0121 303 5147 ⌁ rose.horsfall@birmingham.gov.uk

Member Services: Mr Prakash Patel, Head of Committee & Member Services, The Council House, Victoria Square, Birmingham B1 1BB ☎ 0121 303 2018 ⌁ prakash.patel@birmingham.gov.uk

Personnel / HR: Ms Dawn Hewins, Director - Human Resources, The Council House, Victoria Square, Birmingham B1 1BB ☎ 0121 303 2120 ⌁ dawn.hewins@birmingham.gov.uk

Personnel / HR: Ms Shauna Posaner, Assistant Director - Organisational Development & Change, The Council House, Victoria Square, Birmingham B1 1BB ☎ 0121 675 6368 ⌁ shauna.posaner@birmingham.gov.uk

Personnel / HR: Ms Mandy Quayle, Assistant Director - HR Services, The Council House, Victoria Square, Birmingham B1 1BB ☎ 07813 188319 ⌁ mandy.quayle@birmingham.gov.uk

Planning: Mr Richard Cowell, Assistant Director - Development, The Council House, Victoria Square, Birmingham B1 1BB ☎ 0121 303 9880 ⌁ richard.cowell@birmingham.gov.uk

Planning: Mr Simon Hodge, Area Planning Manager - North, The Council House, Victoria Square, Birmingham B1 1BB ☎ 0121 464 7958 ⌁ simon.hodge@birmingham.gov.uk

Planning: Ms Tracy Humphreys, Area Planning Manager - East, The Council House, Victoria Square, Birmingham B1 1BB ☎ 0121 464 7951 ⌁ tracy.humphreys@birmingham.gov.uk

Planning: Mr Ghaz Hussain, Area Planning & Regeneration Manager, The Council House, Victoria Square, Birmingham B1 1BB ☎ 0121 464 7738 ⌁ ghaz.hussain@birmingham.gov.uk

Planning: Ms Louise Robinson, Area Planning Manager - City Centre, The Council House, Victoria Square, Birmingham B1 1BB ☎ 0121 303 5929 ⌁ louise.robinson@birmingham.gov.uk

Planning: Mr Simon Turner, Area Planning Manager - South, The Council House, Victoria Square, Birmingham B1 1BB ☎ 0121 464 7955 ⌁ simon.turner@birmingham.gov.uk

Procurement: Ms Debbie Husler, Head of Category - Procurement, The Council House, Victoria Square, Birmingham B1 1BB ☎ 0121 303 0017 ⌁ debbie.husler@birmingham.gov.uk

Procurement: Mr Nigel Kletz, Assistant Director - Corporate Procurement, The Council House, Victoria Square, Birmingham B1 1BB ☎ 0121 303 6610 ⌁ nigel.kletz@birmingham.gov.uk

Procurement: Mr Mike Smith, Head of Category - Commissioning, The Council House, Victoria Square, Birmingham B1 1BB ☎ 07827 367139 ⌁ mike.smith@birmingham.gov.uk

Procurement: Mr Richard Tibbatts, Head of Category - Contract Management, The Council House, Victoria Square, Birmingham B1 1BB ☎ 0121 303 0015 ⌁ richard.tibbatts@birmingham.gov.uk

Public Libraries: Ms Dawn Beaumont, Head of Library Services, PO Box 2122, Margaret Street, Birmingham B3 3BU ☎ 0121 303 6884 ⌁ dawn.beaumont@birmingham.gov.uk

Regeneration: Mr James Betjemann, Regeneration Manager - East / South, The Council House, Victoria Square, Birmingham B1 1BB ☎ 0121 303 4174 ⌁ john.betjemann@birmingham.gov.uk

Regeneration: Mr Ghaz Hussain, Area Planning & Regeneration Manager, The Council House, Victoria Square, Birmingham B1 1BB ☎ 0121 464 7738 ⌁ ghaz.hussain@birmingham.gov.uk

Regeneration: Mr Ian MacLeod, Assistant Director - Regeneration, The Council House, Victoria Square, Birmingham B1 1BB ☎ 0121 675 7244 ⌁ ian.macleod@birmingham.gov.uk

Regeneration: Mr Russell Poulton, Regeneration Manager - City Centre / North, The Council House, Victoria Square, Birmingham B1 1BB ☎ 0121 464 9841 ⌁ russell.d.poulton@birmingham.gov.uk

Social Services (Adult): Mr Alan Lotinga, Service Director - Adult Care & Housing Options, 10 Woodcock Street, Aston, Birmingham B7 3BU ☎ 0121 303 6694 ⌁ alan.lotinga@birmingham.gov.uk

Social Services (Adult): Ms Diana Morgan, Assistant Director - Specialist Care Services, 10 Woodcock Street, Aston, Birmingham B7 3BU ☎ 0121 303 4061 ⌁ diana.morgan@birmingham.gov.uk

Social Services (Adult): Mr Afsaneh Sabouri, Head of Enablement, 10 Woodcock Street, Aston, Birmingham B7 3BU ☎ 0121 675 5175 ⌁ afsaneh.sabouri@birmingham.gov.uk

Social Services (Children): Mr Chris Atkinson, Assistant Director - Children with Complex Needs, 10 Woodcock Street, Aston, Birmingham B7 3BU ☎ 0121 303 2573 ⌁ chris.atkinson@birmingham.gov.uk

Social Services (Children): Mr Chris Bush, Head of Disabled Children's Social Care, 10 Woodcock Street, Aston, Birmingham B7 3BU ☎ 0121 675 0463 ⌁ chris.bush@birmingham.gov.uk

Social Services (Children): Ms Kay Child, Assistant Director - Children's Services East, 10 Woodcock Street, Aston, Birmingham B7 3BU ☎ 0121 303 0626 ✆ kay.child@birmingham.gov.uk

Social Services (Children): Ms Debbie Currie, Assistant Director - Child Protection, Performance & Partnership, 10 Woodcock Street, Aston, Birmingham B7 3BU ☎ 0121 303 2468 ✆ debbie.currie@birmingham.gov.uk

Social Services (Children): Mr Alastair Gibbons, Executive Director - Children's Services, 10 Woodcock Street, Aston, Birmingham B7 3BU ☎ 0121 675 3892 ✆ alastair.gibbons@birmingham.gov.uk

Social Services (Children): Mr Andy Pepper, Assistant Director - Children in Care Provider Services, 10 Woodcock Street, Aston, Birmingham B7 3BU ☎ 0121 675 7742 ✆ andy.pepper@birmingham.gov.uk

Social Services (Children): Ms Lorna Scarlett, Assistant Director - Children's Services North, West & Central, 10 Woodcock Street, Aston, Birmingham B7 3BU ☎ 0121 303 0807 ✆ lorna.scarlett@birmingham.gov.uk

Social Services (Children): Ms Yvette Waide, Assistant Director - Children's Services South, 10 Woodcock Street, Aston, Birmingham B7 3BU ☎ 0121 303 8252 ✆ yvette.waide@birmingham.gov.uk

Social Services (Children): Ms Julie Young, Assistant Director - Safeguarding, 10 Woodcock Street, Aston, Birmingham B7 3BU ☎ 0121 675 8521 ✆ julie.young@birmingham.gov.uk

Fostering & Adoption: Ms Theresa Kane, Head of Service - Fostering & Adoption, 10 Woodcock Street, Aston, Birmingham B7 3BU ☎ 0121 303 9762 ✆ theresa.kane@birmingham.gov.uk

Public Health: Mr Wayne Harrison, Assistant Director - Public Health - Intelligence & Strategy, 10 Woodcock Street, Aston, Birmingham B7 3BU ☎ 0121 303 5622 ✆ wayne.harrison@birmingham.gov.uk

Public Health: Dr Adrian Phillips, Director - Public Health, 10 Woodcock Street, Aston, Birmingham B7 3BU ☎ 0121 303 4909 ✆ adrian.x.phillips@birmingham.gov.uk

Public Health: Dr Dennis Wilkes, Assistant Director - Public Health - Population Health & Care, 10 Woodcock Street, Aston, Birmingham B7 3BU ☎ 0121 303 4959 ✆ dennis.wilkes@birmingham.gov.uk

Traffic Management: Mr Kevin Hicks, Assistant Director - Highways & Infrastructure, 1 Lancaster Circus, Queensway, Birmingham B4 7DQ ☎ 0121 303 7693 ✆ kevin.hicks@birmingham.gov.uk

Transport: Mr Phil Edwards, Head of Growth & Transportation, The Council House, Victoria Square, Birmingham B1 1BB ☎ 0121 303 7409 ✆ phil.edwards@birmingham.gov.uk

Transport: Mr Raj Mack, Head of Digital Birmingham, The Council House, Victoria Square, Birmingham B1 1BB ☎ 0121 464 5792 ✆ raj.s.mack@birmingham.gov.uk

Transport: Mr Varinder Raulia, Head of Infrastructure Projects, The Council House, Victoria Square, Birmingham B1 1BB ☎ 020 303 7363 ✆ varinder.raulia@birmingham.gov.uk

Transport: Ms Anne Shaw, Assistant Director - Transport & Connectivity, The Council House, Victoria Square, Birmingham B1 1BB ☎ 0121 303 6467 ✆ anne.shaw@birmingham.gov.uk

Transport Planner: Ms Anne Shaw, Assistant Director - Transport & Connectivity, The Council House, Victoria Square, Birmingham B1 1BB ☎ 0121 303 6467 ✆ anne.shaw@birmingham.gov.uk

Waste Management: Mr Anthony Greener, Director - Waste Management, PO Box 2122, Margaret Street, Birmingham B3 3BU ☎ 0121 675 0648 ✆ anthony.greener@birmingham.gov.uk

Waste Management: Mr Darren Share, Acting Assistant Director - Waste Management, PO Box 2122, Margaret Street, Birmingham B3 3BU ☎ 0121 303 4477 ✆ darren.share@birmingham.gov.uk

COUNCILLORS

The Lord Mayor: Rice, Carl (LAB - Ladywood) carl.rice@birmingham.gov.uk

Deputy Lord Mayor: Hassall, Ray (LD - Perry Barr) ray.hassall@birmingham.gov.uk

Leader of the Council: Clancy, John (LAB - Quinton) john.clancy@birmingham.gov.uk

Deputy Leader of the Council: Ward, Ian (LAB - Shard End) ian.ward@birmingham.gov.uk

Group LeaderAlden, Robert (CON - Erdington) robert.alden@birmingham.gov.uk

Group LeaderHunt, Jon (LD - Perry Barr) jon.hunt@birmingham.gov.uk

Afzal, Muhammad (LAB - Aston) muhammad.afzal@birmingham.gov.uk

Ahmed, Uzma (LAB - Bordesley Green) uzma.ahmed@birmingham.gov.uk

Aikhlaq, Mohammed (LAB - Bordesley Green) mohammed.aikhlaq@birmingham.gov.uk

Alden, Deirdre (CON - Edgbaston) deirdre.alden@birmingham.gov.uk

Alden, John (CON - Harborne) john.alden@birmingham.gov.uk

Ali, Tahir (LAB - Nechells) tahir.ali@birmingham.gov.uk

Ali, Nawaz (LAB - South Yardley) nawaz.ali@birmingham.gov.uk

Anderson, Sue (LD - Sheldon) sue.anderson@birmingham.gov.uk

Atwal, Gurdial Singh (LAB - Handsworth Wood) gurdialsingh.atwal@birmingham.gov.uk

Azim, Mohammed (LAB - Sparkbrook) mohammed.azim@birmingham.gov.uk

Barnett, Susan (LAB - Billesley) susan.barnett@birmingham.gov.uk

Barrie, David (CON - Sutton New Hall) david.barrie@birmingham.gov.uk

BIRMINGHAM CITY

Beauchamp, Bob (CON - Erdington)
bob.beauchamp@birmingham.gov.uk

Bennett, Matt (CON - Edgbaston)
matt.s.bennett@birmingham.gov.uk

Booth, Kate (LAB - Quinton)
kate.booth@birmingham.gov.uk

Booton, Steve (LAB - Weoley)
Steve.Booton@birmingham.gov.uk

Bore, Albert (LAB - Ladywood)
albert.bore@birmingham.gov.uk

Bowles, Barry (LAB - Hall Green)
barry.bowles@birmingham.gov.uk

Brew, Randal (CON - Northfield)
randal.brew@birmingham.gov.uk

Bridle, Marje (LAB - Shard End)
marje.bridle@birmingham.gov.uk

Brown, Mick (LAB - Tyburn)
mick.brown@birmingham.gov.uk

Buchanan, Alex (LAB - Billesley)
alex.buchanan@birmingham.gov.uk

Burden, Sam (LAB - Hall Green)
samburden1@gmail.com

Cartwright, Andy (LAB - Longbridge)
andy.cartwright@birmingham.gov.uk

Chatfield, Tristan (LAB - Oscott)
tristan.chatfield@birmingham.gov.uk

Choudhry, Zaker (LD - South Yardley)
zaker.choudhry@birmingham.gov.uk

Clancy, Debbie (CON - Northfield)
Debbie.Clancy@birmingham.gov.uk

Clinton, Lynda (LAB - Tyburn)
lynda.clinton@birmingham.gov.uk

Collin, Lyn (CON - Sutton Vesey)
lyn.collin@birmingham.gov.uk

Cornish, Maureen (CON - Sutton Four Oaks)
maureen.cornish@birmingham.gov.uk

Cotton, John (LAB - Shard End)
john.cotton@birmingham.gov.uk

Cruise, Ian (IND - Longbridge)
ian.cruise@birmingham.gov.uk

Dad, Basharat (LAB - Stechford & Yardley North)
basharat.dad@birmingham.gov.uk

Davis, Philip (LAB - Billesley)
phil.davis@birmingham.gov.uk

Donaldson, Diane (LAB - Hodge Hill)
diane.donaldson@birmingham.gov.uk

Douglas Osborn, Peter (CON - Weoley)
peter.douglasosborn@birmingham.gov.uk

Dring, Barbara (LAB - Oscott)
barbara.dring@birmingham.gov.uk

Eustace, Neil (LD - Stechford & Yardley North)
neil.eustace@birmingham.gov.uk

Fazal, Mohammed (LAB - Springfield)
mohammed.fazal@birmingham.gov.uk

Finnegan, Mick (LAB - Stockland Green)
mick.finnegan@birmingham.gov.uk

Flood, Des (CON - Bartley Green)
des.flood@birmingham.gov.uk

Francis, Jayne (LAB - Harborne)
jayne.francis@birmingham.gov.uk

Gregson, Matthew (LAB - Quinton)
matthew.gregson@birmingham.gov.uk

Griffiths, Peter (LAB - Kings Norton)
peter.griffiths@birmingham.gov.uk

Griffiths, Carole (LAB - Longbridge)
carole.griffiths@birmingham.gov.uk

Hamilton, Paulette (LAB - Handsworth Wood)
paulette.hamilton@birmingham.gov.uk

Hardie, Andrew (CON - Sutton Vesey)
andrew.hardie@birmingham.gov.uk

Harmer, Roger (LD - Acocks Green)
roger.harmer@birmingham.gov.uk

Hartley, Kath (LAB - Ladywood)
kath.hartley@birmingham.gov.uk

Henley, Barry (LAB - Brandwood)
barry.henley@birmingham.gov.uk

Holbrook, Penny (LAB - Stockland Green)
penny.holbrook@birmingham.gov.uk

Hughes, Des (LAB - Kingstanding)
Des.S.Hughes@birmingham.gov.uk

Hussain, Shabrana (LAB - Springfield)
shabrana.hussain@birmingham.gov.uk

Hussain, Mahmood (LAB - Lozells & East Handsworth)
mahmood.hussain@birmingham.gov.uk

Huxtable, Timothy (CON - Bournville)
timothy.huxtable@birmingham.gov.uk

Idrees, Mohammed (LAB - Washwood Heath)
mohammed.idrees@birmingham.gov.uk

Iqbal, Zafar (LAB - South Yardley)
zafar@southyardley.co.uk

Islam, Ziaul (LAB - Aston)
ziaul.islam@birmingham.gov.uk

Jenkins, Meirion (CON - Sutton Four Oaks)
m.jenkins@rapidcomputing.co.uk

Jenkins, Kerry (LAB - Hall Green)
kerry.jenkins@birmingham.gov.uk

Jevon, Simon (CON - Kings Norton)
simon.jevon@conservatives.com

Johnson, Julie (LAB - Weoley)
julie.johnson@birmingham.gov.uk

Jones, Carol (LD - Stechford & Yardley North)
carol.jones@birmingham.gov.uk

Jones, Brigid (LAB - Selly Oak)
brigid.jones@birmingham.gov.uk

Jones, Josh (LAB - Stockland Green)
josh.jones@birmingham.gov.uk

Kauser, Nagina (LAB - Aston)
nagina.kauser@birmingham.gov.uk

Kennedy, Tony (LAB - Sparkbrook)
tony.kennedy@birmingham.gov.uk

Khan, Ansar Ali (LAB - Washwood Heath)
ansar.ali.khan@birmingham.gov.uk

Khan, Mariam (LAB - Washwood Heath)
mariam.khan@birmingham.gov.uk

Khan, Changese (LAB - Selly Oak)
changese.khan@birmingham.gov.uk

Kooner, Narinder Kaur (LAB - Handsworth Wood)
narinderkaur.kooner@birmingham.gov.uk

Lal, Chaman (LAB - Soho)
chaman.lal@birmingham.gov.uk

Leddy, Mike (LAB - Brandwood)
mike.leddy@birmingham.gov.uk

Lines, John (CON - Bartley Green)
john.lines@birmingham.gov.uk

Lines, Bruce (CON - Bartley Green)
bruce.lines@birmingham.gov.uk

Linnecor, Keith (LAB - Oscott)
keith.linnecor@birmingham.gov.uk

Locke, Mary (LAB - Bournville)
mary.locke@birmingham.gov.uk

Mackey, Ewan (CON - Sutton Trinity)
ewan.mackey@suttontrinityconservatives.co.uk

Mahmood, Majid (LAB - Hodge Hill)
majid.mahmood@birmingham.gov.uk

McCarthy, Karen (LAB - Selly Oak)
karen.mccarthy@birmingham.gov.uk

McKay, James (LAB - Harborne)
james.mckay@birmingham.gov.uk

Moore, Gareth (CON - Erdington)
gareth.moore@birmingham.gov.uk

Mosquito, Yvonne (LAB - Nechells)
yvonne.mosquito@birmingham.gov.uk

O'Reilly, Brett (LAB - Northfield)
brett.o'reilly@birmingham.gov.uk

O'Shea, John (LAB - Acocks Green)
john.o'shea@birmingham.gov.uk

Pears, David (CON - Sutton Trinity)
david.pears@birmingham.gov.uk

Phillips, Eva (LAB - Brandwood)
eva.phillips@birmingham.gov.uk

Pocock, Rob (LAB - Sutton Vesey)
rob.pocock@birmingham.gov.uk

Quinn, Victoria (LAB - Sparkbrook)
victoria.quinn@birmingham.gov.uk

Quinnen, Hendrina (LAB - Lozells & East Handsworth)
hendrina.quinnen@birmingham.gov.uk

Rashid, Chauhdry (LAB - Nechells)
chauhdry.rashid@birmingham.gov.uk

Rehman, Habib (LAB - Springfield)
habib.ul.rehman@birmingham.gov.uk

Robinson, Fergus (CON - Edgbaston)
fergus.robinson@birmingham.gov.uk

Sambrook, Gary (CON - Kingstanding)
gary.sambrook@birmingham.gov.uk

Seabright, Valerie (LAB - Kings Norton)
valerie.seabright@birmingham.gov.uk

Sealey, Rob (CON - Bournville)
robert.sealey@birmingham.gov.uk

Shah, Shafique (LAB - Bordesley Green)
shafique.shah@birmingham.gov.uk

Sharpe, Mike (LAB - Tyburn)
mike.sharpe@birmingham.gov.uk

Spence, Sybil (LAB - Soho)
sybil.spence@birmingham.gov.uk

Spencer, Claire (LAB - Moseley & Kings Heath)
claire.spencer@birmingham.gov.uk

Stacey, Stewart (LAB - Acocks Green)
stewart.stacey@birmingham.gov.uk

Storer, Ron (CON - Kingstanding)
ron.storer@birmingham.gov.uk

Straker-Welds, Martin (LAB - Moseley & Kings Heath)
martin.straker.welds@birmingham.gov.uk

Thompson, Sharon (LAB - Soho)
sharon.thompson@birmingham.gov.uk

Tilsley, Paul (LD - Sheldon)
paul.tilsley@birmingham.gov.uk

Trench, Karen (LD - Perry Barr)
karen.trench@birmingham.gov.uk

Trickett, Lisa (LAB - Moseley & Kings Heath)
lisa.trickett@birmingham.gov.uk

Underwood, Anne (CON - Sutton Four Oaks)
anne.underwood@birmingham.gov.uk

Waddington, Margaret (CON - Sutton Trinity)
margaret.waddington@birmingham.gov.uk

Ward, Mike (LD - Sheldon)
mike.ward@birmingham.gov.uk

Williams, Fiona (LAB - Hodge Hill)
fiona.williams@birmingham.gov.uk

Wood, Ken (CON - Sutton New Hall)
ken.wood@birmingham.gov.uk

Yip, Alex (CON - Sutton New Hall)
Alex.Yip@birmingham.gov.uk

Zaffar, Waseem (LAB - Lozells & East Handsworth)
waseem.zaffar@birmingham.gov.uk

POLITICAL COMPOSITION
LAB: 80, CON: 29, LD: 10, IND: 1

COMMITTEE CHAIRS

Audit: Mr Sam Burden

Economy, Skills & Sustainability: Ms Victoria Quinn

Education & Vulnerable Children: Ms Susan Barnett

Health & Social Care: Mr Majid Mahmood

Licensing: Ms Barbara Dring

BLABY

Blaby   D

Blaby District Council, Council Offices, Desford Road,
Narborough LE19 2EP
☎ 0116 275 0555 🖷 0116 275 0368 ✆ customer.services@blaby.gov.uk
🖳 www.blaby.gov.uk

FACTS AND FIGURES
Parliamentary Constituencies: Charnwood, Leicestershire South
EU Constituencies: East Midlands
Election Frequency: Elections are of whole council

PRINCIPAL OFFICERS

Chief Executive: Mrs Jane Toman, Chief Executive, Council
Offices, Desford Road, Narborough LE19 2EP ☎ 0116 272 7576
✆ jane.toman@blaby.gov.uk

Senior Management: Mr Mark Alflat, Director - Place, Council
Offices, Desford Road, Narborough LE19 2EP ☎ 0116 272 7504
✆ mark.alflat@blaby.gov.uk

Senior Management: Ms Sarah Pennelli, Director - People &
Finance, Council Offices, Desford Road, Narborough LE19 2EP
☎ 0116 272 7650 ✆ sarah.pennelli@blaby.gov.uk

Best Value: Mrs Alison Moran, Performance & Audit Manager,
Council Offices, Desford Road, Narborough LE19 2EP
☎ 0116 272 7732 ✆ alison.moran@blaby.gov.uk

Building Control: Mr Jon Wells, Regulatory & Leisure Services
Group Manager, Council Offices, Desford Road, Narborough LE19
2EP ☎ 0116 272 7545 ✆ jon.wells@blaby.gov.uk

PR / Communications: Ms Julie Hutchinson, Communications
Manager, Council Offices, Desford Road, Narborough LE19 2EP
☎ 0116 272 7648 ✆ julie.hutchinson@blaby.gov.uk

Community Safety: Ms Quin Quinney, Community Services
Group Manager, Council Offices, Desford Road, Narborough LE19
2EP ☎ 0116 272 7595 ✆ quin.quinney@blaby.gov.uk

Computer Management: Mr Colin Jones, Corporate Services
Group Manager, Council Offices, Desford Road, Narborough LE19
2EP ☎ 0116 272 7569 ✆ colin.jones@blaby.gov.uk

Contracts: Mr Colin Jones, Corporate Services Group Manager,
Council Offices, Desford Road, Narborough LE19 2EP ☎ 0116 272
7569 ✆ colin.jones@blaby.gov.uk

Corporate Services: Mr Colin Jones, Corporate Services Group
Manager, Council Offices, Desford Road, Narborough LE19 2EP
☎ 0116 272 7569 ✆ colin.jones@blaby.gov.uk

Customer Service: Mr Colin Jones, Corporate Services Group
Manager, Council Offices, Desford Road, Narborough LE19 2EP
☎ 0116 272 7569 ✆ colin.jones@blaby.gov.uk

Economic Development: Ms Catherine Hartley, Planning &
Economic Development Group Manager, Council Offices, Desford
Road, Narborough LE19 2EP ☎ 0116 272 7727
✆ catherine.hartley@blaby.gov.uk

E-Government: Ms Julie Hutchinson, Communications Manager,
Council Offices, Desford Road, Narborough LE19 2EP
☎ 0116 272 7648 ✆ julie.hutchinson@blaby.gov.uk

Electoral Registration: Mr Neil Briggs, Customer Services
& Electoral Services Manager, Council Offices, Desford Road,
Narborough LE19 2EP ☎ 0116 272 7667 ✆ neil.briggs@blaby.gov.uk

Emergency Planning: Mr Jon Wells, Regulatory & Leisure
Services Group Manager, Council Offices, Desford Road,
Narborough LE19 2EP ☎ 0116 272 7545 ✆ jon.wells@blaby.gov.uk

Energy Management: Mr Jon Wells, Regulatory & Leisure
Services Group Manager, Council Offices, Desford Road,
Narborough LE19 2EP ☎ 0116 272 7545 ✆ jon.wells@blaby.gov.uk

Environmental / Technical Services: Mr Kevin Pegg,
Neighbourhood Services Group Manager, Council Offices, Desford
Road, Narborough LE19 2EP ☎ 0116 272 7615
✆ kevin.pegg@blaby.gov.uk

Environmental Health: Mr Jon Wells, Regulatory & Leisure
Services Group Manager, Council Offices, Desford Road,
Narborough LE19 2EP ☎ 0116 272 7545 ✆ jon.wells@blaby.gov.uk

Estates, Property & Valuation: Ms Sarah Pennelli, Director -
People & Finance, Council Offices, Desford Road, Narborough LE19
2EP ☎ 0116 272 7650 ✆ sarah.pennelli@blaby.gov.uk

Finance: Ms Sarah Pennelli, Financial Services Group Manager,
Council Offices, Desford Road, Narborough LE19 2EP
☎ 0116 272 7650 ✆ sarah.pennelli@blaby.gov.uk

Fleet Management: Mr Kevin Pegg, Neighbourhood Services
Group Manager, Council Offices, Desford Road, Narborough LE19
2EP ☎ 0161 272 7615 ✆ kevin.pegg@blaby.gov.uk

Grounds Maintenance: Mr Kevin Pegg, Neighbourhood Services
Group Manager, Council Offices, Desford Road, Narborough LE19
2EP ☎ 0161 272 7615 ✆ kevin.pegg@blaby.gov.uk

Health and Safety: Mr Jon Thorpe, Corporate Health & Safety
Advisor, Council Offices, Desford Road, Narborough LE19 2EP
☎ 0116 272 7571 ✆ jon.thorpe@blaby.gov.uk

Home Energy Conservation: Ms Quin Quinney, Community
Services Group Manager, Council Offices, Desford Road,
Narborough LE19 2EP ☎ 0116 272 7595 ✆ quin.quinney@blaby.
gov.uk

Housing: Ms Quin Quinney, Community Services Group Manager,
Council Offices, Desford Road, Narborough LE19 2EP
☎ 0116 272 7595 ✆ quin.quinney@blaby.gov.uk

Legal: Mr Colin Jones, Corporate Services Group Manager, Council
Offices, Desford Road, Narborough LE19 2EP ☎ 0116 272 7569
✆ colin.jones@blaby.gov.uk

Leisure and Cultural Services: Mr Jon Wells, Regulatory &
Leisure Services Group Manager, Council Offices, Desford Road,
Narborough LE19 2EP ☎ 0116 272 7545 ✆ jon.wells@blaby.gov.uk

Licensing: Mr Jon Wells, Regulatory & Leisure Services Group Manager, Council Offices, Desford Road, Narborough LE19 2EP
☎ 0116 272 7545 ⌘ jon.wells@blaby.gov.uk

Lottery Funding, Charity and Voluntary: Ms Jill Stevenson, Domestic Violence Co-ordinator Outreach, Council Offices, Desford Road, Narborough LE19 2EP ☎ 0116 272 7582
⌘ jill.stevenson@blaby.gov.uk

Member Services: Mrs Sandeep Tiensa, Democratic Services Officer, Council Offices, Desford Road, Narborough LE19 2EP
☎ 0116 272 7640 ⌘ sandeep.tiensa@blaby.gov.uk

Parking: Mr Jon Wells, Regulatory & Leisure Services Group Manager, Council Offices, Desford Road, Narborough LE19 2EP
☎ 0116 272 7545 ⌘ jon.wells@blaby.gov.uk

Partnerships: Ms Jill Stevenson, Domestic Violence Co-ordinator Outreach, Council Offices, Desford Road, Narborough LE19 2EP
☎ 0116 272 7582 ⌘ jill.stevenson@blaby.gov.uk

Personnel / HR: Mr Mark Foote, Strategic Manager - People & Performance, Council Offices, Desford Road, Narborough LE19 2EP
☎ 0116 272 7570 ⌘ mark.foote@blaby.gov.uk

Planning: Ms Catherine Hartley, Planning & Economic Development Group Manager, Council Offices, Desford Road, Narborough LE19 2EP ☎ 0116 272 7727
⌘ catherine.hartley@blaby.gov.uk

Procurement: Ms Sarah Pennelli, Director - People & Finance, Council Offices, Desford Road, Narborough LE19 2EP
☎ 0116 272 7650 ⌘ sarah.pennelli@blaby.gov.uk

Recycling & Waste Minimisation: Mr Kevin Pegg, Neighbourhood Services Group Manager, Council Offices, Desford Road, Narborough LE19 2EP ☎ 0161 272 7615
⌘ kevin.pegg@blaby.gov.uk

Sustainable Communities: Mrs Jane Toman, Chief Executive, Council Offices, Desford Road, Narborough LE19 2EP
☎ 0116 272 7576 ⌘ jane.toman@blaby.gov.uk

Sustainable Development: Ms Catherine Hartley, Planning & Economic Development Group Manager, Council Offices, Desford Road, Narborough LE19 2EP ☎ 0116 272 7727
⌘ catherine.hartley@blaby.gov.uk

Town Centre: Mr Jon Wells, Regulatory & Leisure Services Group Manager, Council Offices, Desford Road, Narborough LE19 2EP
☎ 0116 272 7545 ⌘ jon.wells@blaby.gov.uk

Waste Collection and Disposal: Mr Kevin Pegg, Neighbourhood Services Group Manager, Council Offices, Desford Road, Narborough LE19 2EP ☎ 0161 272 7615 ⌘ kevin.pegg@blaby.gov.uk

Waste Management: Mr Kevin Pegg, Neighbourhood Services Group Manager, Council Offices, Desford Road, Narborough LE19 2EP ☎ 0161 272 7615 ⌘ kevin.pegg@blaby.gov.uk

Children's Play Areas: Mr Jon Wells, Regulatory & Leisure Services Group Manager, Council Offices, Desford Road, Narborough LE19 2EP ☎ 0116 272 7545 ⌘ jon.wells@blaby.gov.uk

COUNCILLORS

ChairMerrill, Christine (LD - Saxondale)
cllr.chris.merrill@blaby.gov.uk

Vice-ChairClements, David (CON - Forest)
cllr.david.clements@blaby.gov.uk

Leader of the Council: Richardson, Terry (CON - Pastures)
cllr.terry.richardson@blaby.gov.uk

Deputy Leader of the Council: Wright, Maggie (CON - Normanton)
cllr.maggie.wright@blaby.gov.uk

Aslam, Shabbir (LAB - Ravenhurst & Fosse)
cllr.shabbir.aslam@blaby.gov.uk

Breckon, Lee (CON - Fairstone)
cllr.lee.breckon@blaby.gov.uk

Breckon, Scarlet (CON - Ellis)
cllr.scarlet.breckon@blaby.gov.uk

Broomhead, Marian (CON - Blaby South)
cllr.marian.broomhead@blaby.gov.uk

Cashmore, Cheryl (CON - Enderby & St John's)
cllr.cheryl.cashmore@blaby.gov.uk

Clifford, Adrian (CON - Countesthorpe)
cllr.adrian.clifford@blaby.gov.uk

Coar, Stuart (CON - Forest)
cllr.stuart.coar@blaby.gov.uk

Coe, Sharon (CON - North Whetstone)
cllr.sharon.coe@blaby.gov.uk

Denney, Roy (CON - Fairstone)
cllr.roy.denney@blaby.goiv.uk

DeWinter, Alex (LAB - Winstanley)
cllr.alex.dewinter@blaby.gov.uk

Dracup, Lindsay (CON - Forest)
cllr.lindsay.dracup@blaby.gov.uk

Findlay, David (CON - Countesthorpe)
cllr.david.findlay@blaby.gov.uk

Freer, David (CON - Croft Hill)
cllr.david.freer@blaby.gov.uk

Frost, Chris (CON - Muxloe)
cllr.chris.frost@blaby.gov.uk

Garner, Barry (CON - Narborough & Littlethorpe)
cllr.barry.garner@blaby.gov.uk

Greenwood, Tony (CON - Muxloe)
cllr.tony.greenwood@blaby.gov.uk

Hewson, Iain (CON - Stanton & Flamville)
cllr.iain.hewson@blaby.gov.uk

Huss, Graham (CON - Ellis)
cllr.graham.huss@blaby.gov.uk

Jackson, Mark (CON - North Whetstone)
cllr.mark.jackson@blaby.gov.uk

Jackson, Guy (CON - Pastures)
cllr.guy.jackson@blaby.gov.uk

BLABY

Jennings, David (CON - Countesthorpe)
cllr.david.jennings@blaby.gov.uk

Matthews, Trevor (CON - Narborough & Littlethorpe)
cllr.trevor.matthews@blaby.gov.uk

Maxwell, Sam (LAB - Ravenhurst & Fosse)
cllr.sam.maxwell@blaby.gov.uk

Moitt, Phil (LAB - Ravenhurst & Fosse)
cllr.phil.moitt@blaby.gov.uk

Moseley, Antony (LD - Blaby South)
cllr.antony.moseley@blaby.gov.uk

Phillimore, Les (CON - Cosby with South Whetstone)
cllt.les.phillimore@blaby.gov.uk

Richardson, Louise (CON - Enderby & St John's)
cllr.louis.richardson@blaby.gov.uk

Sanders, Gary (LAB - Winstanley)
cllr.gary.sanders@blaby.gov.uk

Scott, Sheila (CON - Stanton & Flamville)
cllr.sheila.scott@blaby.gov.uk

Tanner, Alan (CON - Cosby with South Whetstone)
cllr.alan.tanner@blaby.gov.uk

Taylor, Ben (CON - Winstanley)
cllr.ben.taylor@blaby.gov.uk

Welsh, Bev (LD - Saxondale)
cllr.bev.welsh@blaby.gov.uk

Welsh, Geoff (LD - Saxondale)
cllr.chris.welsh@blaby.gov.uk

Woods, Deanne (DUP - Stanton & Flamville)
cllr.deanne.woods@blaby.gov.uk

Wright, Bill (LAB - Millfield)
cllr.bill.wright@blaby.gov.uk

POLITICAL COMPOSITION
CON: 28, LAB: 6, LD: 4, DUP: 1

COMMITTEE CHAIRS

Audit: Ms Sharon Coe

Licensing: Mr Roy Denney

Planning: Mr David Findlay

Blackburn with Darwen   U

Blackburn with Darwen Borough Council, King William Street, Blackburn BB1 7DY
☎ 01254 585585 🖷 01254 682201 ✆ info@blackburn.gov.uk
🖳 www.blackburn.gov.uk

FACTS AND FIGURES
Parliamentary Constituencies: Blackburn, Rossendale and Darwen
EU Constituencies: North West
Election Frequency: Elections are by thirds

PRINCIPAL OFFICERS

Chief Executive: Mr Harry Catherall, Chief Executive, Town Hall, Blackburn BB1 7DY ☎ 01254 585370
✆ harry.catherall@blackburn.gov.uk

Deputy Chief Executive: Ms Denise Park, Executive Director - Resources, Town Hall, Blackburn BB1 7DY ☎ 01254 585655
✆ denise.park@blackburn.gov.uk

Senior Management: Mr Tom Flanagan, Executive Director - Place, Town Hall, Blackburn BB1 7DY ☎ 01254 585504
✆ tom.flanagan@blackburn.gov.uk

Senior Management: Mr Dominic Harrison, Director - Public Health, 10 Duke Street, Blackburn BB2 1DH ☎ 01254 666933
✆ dominic.harrison@blackburn.gov.uk

Senior Management: Ms Sally McIvor, Executive Director - People, Town Hall, Blackburn BB1 7DY ☎ 01254 585299
✆ sally.mcivor@blackburn.gov.uk

Architect, Building / Property Services: Mr Stuart Davey, Building Services Manager, Capita Symonds, Castleway House, 17 Preston New Road, Blackburn BB2 1AU ☎ 01254 273342
✆ stuart.davey@capita.co.uk

Building Control: Mr Brian Bailey, Director - Growth & Prosperity, Town Hall, Blackburn BB1 7DY ☎ 01254 585360
✆ brian.bailey@blackburn.gov.uk

Catering Services: Mr Neil Dagnall, Bar & Catering Manager, King Georges Hall, Northgate, Blackburn BB2 1AA
☎ 01254 582579 ✆ neil.dagnall@blackburn.gov.uk

Children / Youth Services: Ms Linda Clegg, Director - Children's Services, 10 Duke Street, Blackburn BB2 1DH ☎ 01254 666762
✆ linda.clegg@blackburn.gov.uk

PR / Communications: Mr Marc Schmid, Head of Corporate Services, Town Hall, Blackburn BB1 7DY ☎ 01254 585480
✆ marc.schmid@blackburn.gov.uk

Community Safety: Mr Mark Aspin, Community Safety Manager, Town Hall, Blackburn BB1 7DY ☎ 01254 585512
✆ mark.aspin@blackburn.gov.uk

Computer Management: Mr Shane Agnew, Head of IT, Strategy & Operations, Town Hall, Blackburn BB1 7DY ☎ 01254 588808
✆ shane.agnew@blackburn.gov.uk

Consumer Protection and Trading Standards: Mr Tony Watson, Head of Environment & Public Protection Services, Davyfield Road, Davyfield, Blackburn BB1 2QY ☎ 01254 266362
✆ tony.watson@blackburn.gov.uk

Corporate Services: Mr Marc Schmid, Head of Corporate Services, Town Hall, Blackburn BB1 7DY ☎ 01254 585480
✆ marc.schmid@blackburn.gov.uk

Customer Service: Mr Andy Ormerod, Head of Revenues, Benefits & Customer Services, Town Hall, Blackburn BB1 7DY
☎ 01254 585773 ✆ andy.ormerod@blackburn.gov.uk

Economic Development: Mr Brian Bailey, Director - Growth & Prosperity, Town Hall, Blackburn BB1 7DY ☎ 01254 585360
✆ brian.bailey@blackburn.gov.uk

Education: Mr Mebz Bobat, Head of Education, Partnership Services, 10 Duke Street, Blackburn BB2 1DH ☎ 01254 666510 ✆ mebz.bobat@blackburn.gov.uk

E-Government: Ms Denise Park, Executive Director - Resources, Town Hall, Blackburn BB1 7DY ☎ 01254 585655 ✆ denise.park@blackburn.gov.uk

Electoral Registration: Mr Ben Aspinall, Scrutiny Elections & School Appeals Manager, Town Hall, Blackburn BB1 7DY ☎ 01254 585191 ✆ ben.aspinall@blackburn.gov.uk

Emergency Planning: Ms Rachel Hutchinson, Civil Contingencies Manager, Town Hall, Blackburn BB1 7DY ✆ rachel.hutchinson@blackburn.gov.uk

Energy Management: Ms Gwen Kinloch, Environmental Strategy & Projects Manager, Town Hall, Blackburn BB1 7DY ✆ gwen.kinloch@blackburn.gov.uk

Environmental / Technical Services: Mr Martin Eden, Director - Environment & Leisure, Town Hall, Blackburn BB1 7DY ☎ 01254 585102 ✆ martin.eden@blackburn.gov.uk

Environmental Health: Mr Gary Johnston, Service Manager - Environmental Health, Town Hall, Blackburn BB1 7DY ☎ 01254 266375 ✆ gary.johnston@blackburn.gov.uk

European Liaison: Mr Sayyed Osman, Director - Housing & Localities, Town Hall, Blackburn BB1 7DY ☎ 01254 585340 ✆ sayyed.osman@blackburn.gov.uk

Events Manager: Mr Steve Burch, Events & Promotion Manager, King George's Hall, Northgate, Blackburn BB2 1AA ☎ 01254 582579 ✆ steve.burch@blackburn.gov.uk

Facilities: Mr Steve Cox, Facilities Manager, C Floor, Tower Block, Town Hall, Blackburn BB1 7DY ☎ 01254 585497 ✆ steve.cox@blackburn.gov.uk

Finance: Ms Louise Mattinson, Director - Finance & IT, Town Hall, Blackburn BB1 7DY ☎ 01254 585600 ✆ louise.mattinson@blackburn.gov.uk

Fleet Management: Mr Neil Bolton, Head of Fleet Management, Davyfield Road, Davyfield, Blackburn BB1 2QY ☎ 01254 585095 ✆ neil.bolton@blackburn.gov.uk

Grounds Maintenance: Mr Gary Blackshaw, Assistant Manager - Green Spaces, Town Hall, Blackburn BB1 7DY ☎ 01254 666350 ✆ garry.blackshaw@blackburn.gov.uk

Health and Safety: Mr David Almond, Health & Safety & Wellbeing Manager, Town Hall, Blackburn BB1 7DY ☎ 01254 585873 ✆ david.almond@blackburn.gov.uk

Highways: Mr Brian Bailey, Director - Growth & Prosperity, Town Hall, Blackburn BB1 7DY ☎ 01254 585360 ✆ brian.bailey@blackburn.gov.uk

Home Energy Conservation: Mr Stuart Pye, Home Improvement & Energy Solutions Manager, Town Hall, Blackburn BB1 7DY ☎ 01254 588890 ✆ stuart.pye@blackburn.gov.uk

Housing: Mr Stephen Richards, Housing Needs & Support Manager, Town Hall, Blackburn BB1 7DY ☎ 01254 585132 ✆ stephen.richards@blackburn.gov.uk

Local Area Agreement: Ms Philippa Cross, Policy & Performance Manager, Town Hall, Blackburn BB1 7DY ☎ 01254 585245 ✆ philippa.cross@blackburn.gov.uk

Legal: Ms Sian Roxborough, Head of Legal / Council Solicitor, Town Hall, Blackburn BB1 7DY ☎ 01254 585252 ✆ sian.roxborough@blackburn.gov.uk

Leisure and Cultural Services: Mr Martin Eden, Director - Environment & Leisure, Town Hall, Blackburn BB1 7DY ☎ 01254 585102 ✆ martin.eden@blackburn.gov.uk

Leisure and Cultural Services: Ms Claire Ramwell, Head of Service, Town Hall, Blackburn BB1 7DY ☎ 01254 585201 ✆ claire.ramwell@blackburn.gov.uk

Licensing: Ms Janet White, Senior Public Protection Officer, Town Hall, Blackburn BB1 7DY ☎ 01254 585007 ✆ janet.white@blackburn.gov.uk

Member Services: Mr Phil Llewllyn, Executive & Councillor Support Manager, Town Hall, Blackburn BB1 7DY ☎ 01254 585369 ✆ phil.llewellyn@blackburn.gov.uk

Parking: Mr George Bell, Associate Director - Highways & Transportation, Capita, Castleway House, 17 Preston New Road, Blackburn BB2 1AU ☎ 01254 273454

Personnel / HR: Ms Mandy Singh, Head of HR, Town Hall, Blackburn BB1 7DY ☎ 01254 585612 ✆ mandy.singh@blackburn.gov.uk

Planning: Mr David Proctor, Head of Regeneration (Planning & Transport), Town Hall, Blackburn BB1 7DY ☎ 01254 585521 ✆ david.proctor@blackburn.gov.uk

Procurement: Mr Chris Bradley, Strategic Procurement Manager, Town Hall, Blackburn BB1 7DY ☎ 01254 585296 ✆ christopher.bradley@blackburn.gov.uk

Public Libraries: Ms Kath Sutton, Service Manager, Blackburn Library, Blackburn BB2 1AG ☎ 01254 587907 ✆ kath.sutton@blackburn.gov.uk

Recycling & Waste Minimisation: Mr Stuart Hammond, Environmental Sustainability & Enforcement Manager, Davyfield Road, Blackburn BB1 2LX ☎ 01254 585863 ✆ stuart.hammond@blackburn.gov.uk

Regeneration: Mr Brian Bailey, Director - Growth & Prosperity, Town Hall, Blackburn BB1 7DY ☎ 01254 585360 ✆ brian.bailey@blackburn.gov.uk

Road Safety: Ms Lisa Heywood, Road Safety Officer, Capita, Castleway House, 17 Preston New Road, Blackburn BB2 1AU ☎ 01254 273223 ✉ lisa.heywood@capita.gov.uk

Social Services: Mr Steve Tingle, Director - Adult Services (DASS), 10 Duke Street, Blackburn BB2 1DH ☎ 01254 585349 ✉ stephen.tingle@blackburn.gov.uk

Social Services (Adult): Mr Steve Tingle, Director - Adult Services (DASS), 10 Duke Street, Blackburn BB2 1DH ☎ 01254 585349 ✉ stephen.tingle@blackburn.gov.uk

Social Services (Children): Ms Linda Clegg, Director - Children's Services, 10 Duke Street, Blackburn BB2 1DH ☎ 01254 666762 ✉ linda.clegg@blackburn.gov.uk

Childrens Social Care: Ms Linda Clegg, Director - Children's Services, 10 Duke Street, Blackburn BB2 1DH ☎ 01254 666762 ✉ linda.clegg@blackburn.gov.uk

Street Scene: Mr Brian Bailey, Director - Growth & Prosperity, Town Hall, Blackburn BB1 7DY ☎ 01254 585360 ✉ brian.bailey@blackburn.gov.uk

Tourism: Ms Susan Walmsley, Visitor Services Manager, Town Hall, Blackburn BB1 7DY ☎ 01254 588923 ✉ susan.walmsley@blackburn.gov.uk

Town Centre: Ms Julia Simpson, Town Centre Projects Manager, Town Hall, Blackburn BB1 7DY ☎ 01254 588958 ✉ julie.simpson@blackburn.gov.uk

Transport: Mr Mike Cliffe, Strategic Transport Manager, Town Hall, Blackburn BB1 7DY ☎ 01254 585310 ✉ mike.cliffe@blackburn.gov.uk

Waste Collection and Disposal: Mr Tony Watson, Head of Environment & Public Protection Services, Davyfield Road, Davyfield, Blackburn BB1 2QY ☎ 01254 266362 ✉ tony.watson@blackburn.gov.uk

Waste Management: Mr Tony Watson, Head of Environment & Public Protection Services, Davyfield Road, Davyfield, Blackburn BB1 2QY ☎ 01254 266362 ✉ tony.watson@blackburn.gov.uk

COUNCILLORS

Mayor: Akhtar, Hussain (LAB - Shear Brow)
hussain.akhtar@blackburn.gov.uk

Deputy Mayor: Rigby, Colin (CON - North Turton with Tockholes)
colin.rigby@blackburn.gov.uk

Leader of the Council: Khan, Mohammed (LAB - Wensley Fold)
mohammed.khan@blackburn.gov.uk

Deputy Leader of the Council: Kay, Andy (LAB - Higher Croft)
andy.kay@blackburn.gov.uk

Group LeaderFoster, David (LD - Whitehall)
david.foster@blackburn.gov.uk

Group LeaderLee, Michael (CON - Beardwood with Lammack)
michael.lee@blackburn.gov.uk

Akhtar, Parwaiz (LAB - Bastwell)
parwaiz.akhtar@blackburn.gov.uk

Ali, Imtiaz (CON - Beardwood with Lammack)
imitaz.ali@blackburn.gov.uk

Bateson, Maureen (LAB - Ewood)
maureen.bateson@blackburn.gov.uk

Brookfield, Stephanie (LAB - Ewood)
stephanie.brookfield@blackburn.gov.uk

Casey, Jim (LAB - Ewood)
jim.casey@blackburn.gov.uk

Connor, Kevin (CON - Marsh House)
kevin.connor@blackburn.gov.uk

Daley, Julie (CON - Beardwood with Lammack)
julie.daley@blackburn.gov.uk

Davies, Roy (LD - Sudell)
roy.davies@blackburn.gov.uk

Desai, Mustafa (LAB - Queen's Park)
mustafa.desai@blackburn.gov.uk

Entwistle, Eileen (LAB - Sudell)
eileen.entwhistle@blackburn.gov.uk

Fazal, Tasleem (LAB - Corporation Park)
tasleem.fazal@blackburn.gov.uk

Foster, Karimeh (LD - Whitehall)
karimeh.foster@blackburn.gov.uk

Gee, Denise (CON - Fernhurst)
denise.gee@blackburn.gov.uk

Groves, Jamie (LAB - Ewood)
jamie.groves@blackburn.gov.uk

Gunn, Julie (LAB - Meadowhead)
julie.gunn@gov.uk

Hardman, Derek (CON - Livesey with Pleasington)
derek.hardman@blackburn.gov.uk

Harling, Dave (LAB - Wensley Fold)
dave.harling@blackburn.gov.uk

Hollings, Pete (LAB - Sunnyhurst)
peter.hollings@blackburn.gov.uk

Humphrys, Tony (LAB - Shadsworth with Whitebirk)
anthony.humphrys@blackburn.gov.uk

Hussain, Faryad (LAB - Queen's Park)
faryad.hussain@blackburn.gov.uk

Hussain, Iftakhar (LAB - Bastwell)
iftakhar.hussain@blackburn.gov.uk

Hussain, Shaukat (LAB - Bastwell)
shaukat.hussain@blackburn.gov.uk

Jan-Virmani, Yusuf (LAB - Audley)
yusuf.jan-virmani@blackburn.gov.uk

Johnson, Mike (LAB - Higher Croft)
m.johnson@blackburn.gov.uk

Khan, Zamir (LAB - Audley)
zamir.khan@blackburn.gov.uk

Khonat, Suleman (LAB - Shear Brow)
suleman.khonat@blackburn.gov.uk

Liddle, Sylvia (LAB - Roe Lee)
sylvia.liddle@blackburn.gov.uk

Mahmood, Arshid (LAB - Corporation Park)
arshid.mahmood@blackburn.gov.uk

Mahmood, Quesir (LAB - Wensley Fold)
quesir.mahmood@blackburn.gov.uk

Marrow, Paul (CON - Livesey with Pleasington)
paul.marrow@blackburn.gov.uk

Maxfield, Trevor (LAB - Earcroft)
trevor.maxfield@blackburn.gov.uk

McFall, Pat (LAB - Little Harwood)
pat.mcfall@blackburn.gov.uk

McGurk, Vicky (LAB - Shadsworth with Whitebirk)
vicky.mcgurk@blackburn.gov.uk

McKinlay, Don (LAB - Higher Croft)
don.mckinlay@blackburn.gov.uk

Mulla, Salim (LAB - Queen's Park)
salim.mulla@blackburn.gov.uk

Murray, Keith (CON - Meadowhead)
keith.v.murray@blackburn.gov.uk

Nuttall, Carl (LAB - Mill Hill)
carl.nuttall@blackburn.gov.uk

Oates, Jane Margaret (LAB - Sudell)
jane.oates@blackburn.gov.uk

Patel, Abdul (LAB - Little Harwood)
abdul.patel@blackburn.gov.uk

Pearson, John (CON - Livesey with Pleasington)
john.pearson@blackburn.gov.uk

Rigby, Jean (CON - North Turton with Tockholes)
jean.rigby@blackburn.gov.uk

Riley, Phil (LAB - Roe Lee)
phil.riley@blackburn.gov.uk

Roberts, John (LAB - Marsh House)
john.roberts@blackburn.gov.uk

Shorrock, James (LAB - Shadsworth with Whitebirk)
james.shorrock@blackburn.gov.uk

Sidat, Salim (LAB - Audley)
salim.sidat@blackburn.gov.uk

Slater, Julie (CON - East Rural)
julie.slater@blackburn.gov.uk

Slater, Jacqueline (CON - Fernhurst)
jacqueline.slater@blackburn.gov.uk

Slater, John (CON - Fernhurst)
john.slater@blackburn.gov.uk

Slater, Neil (CON - Marsh House)
neil.slater@blackburn.gov.uk

Smith, Jim (LAB - Mill Hill)
jim.smith@blackburn.gov.uk

Smith, Dave (LAB - Sunnyhurst)
david.smith@blackburn.gov.uk

Surve, Naushad (LAB - Little Harwood)
naushad.surve@blackburn.gov.uk

Talbot, Damian (LAB - Mill Hill)
damian.talbot@blackburn.gov.uk

Tapp, Konrad (CON - Meadowhead)
konrad.tapp@blackburn.gov.uk

Taylor, Brian (LAB - Sunnyhurst)
brian.taylor@blackburn.gov.uk

Vali, Shiraj Adam (LAB - Shear Brow)
shiraj.vali@blackburn.gov.uk

Whittle, Ron (LAB - Roe Lee)
ron.whittle@blackburn.gov.uk

Wright, John (LAB - Corporation Park)
john.wright@blackburn.gov.uk

POLITICAL COMPOSITION
LAB: 45, CON: 16, LD: 3

COMMITTEE CHAIRS

Audit: Mr Salim Sidat

Children's Services: Ms Sylvia Liddle

Health & Wellbeing: Mr Mohammed Khan

Licensing: Mr John Wright

Planning & Highways: Mr Dave Smith

Regeneration & Neighbourhoods: Mr Naushad Surve

Blackpool   U

Blackpool Borough Council, Number One Bickerstaffe Square, Talbot Road, Blackpool FY1 3AH
☎ 01253 477477 🖷 01253 477101 ⌁ webmaster@blackpool.gov.uk
💻 www.blackpool.gov.uk

FACTS AND FIGURES
Parliamentary Constituencies: Blackpool North and Cleveleys, Blackpool South
EU Constituencies: North West
Election Frequency: Elections are of whole council

PRINCIPAL OFFICERS

Chief Executive: Mr Neil Jack, Chief Executive, Number One Bickerstaffe Square, Talbot Road, Blackpool FY1 3AH
☎ 01253 477000 ⌁ chief.executive@blackpool.gov.uk

Deputy Chief Executive: Ms Carmel McKeogh, Deputy Chief Executive, Number One Bickerstaffe Square, Talbot Road, Blackpool FY1 3AH ☎ 01253 477247
⌁ carmel.mckeogh@blackpool.gov.uk

Senior Management: Mr Carl Baker, Deputy Director - People (Children's Services), Number One Bickerstaffe Square, Talbot Road, Blackpool FY1 3AH ☎ 01253 478972
⌁ carl.baker@blackpool.gov.uk

Senior Management: Mr John Blackledge, Director - Community & Environmental Services, Number One Bickerstaffe Square, Talbot Road, Blackpool FY1 3AH ☎ 01253 478400
⌁ john.blackledge@blackpool.gov.uk

Senior Management: Mr Alan Cavill, Director - Place, Number One Bickerstaffe Square, Talbot Road, Blackpool FY1 3AH
☎ 01253 477006 ⌁ alan.cavill@blackpool.gov.uk

BLACKPOOL

Senior Management: Ms Delyth Curtis, Director - People (Statutory Director - Children's Services), Number One Bickerstaffe Square, Talbot Road, Blackpool FY1 3AH ☎ 01253 476558 ✆ delyth.curtis@blackpool.gov.uk

Senior Management: Dr Arif Rajpura, Director - Public Health, Number One Bickerstaffe Square, Talbot Road, Blackpool FY1 3AH ☎ 01253 476367 ✆ arif.rajpura@blackpool.gov.uk

Senior Management: Ms Karen Smith, Deputy Director - People - (Statutory Director - Adult Services), Number One Bickerstaffe Square, Talbot Road, Blackpool FY1 3AH ☎ 01253 477502 ✆ karen.smith@blackpool.gov.uk

Senior Management: Mr Steve Thompson, Director - Resources, Number One Bickerstaffe Square, Talbot Road, Blackpool FY1 3AH ☎ 01253 478505 ✆ steve.thompson@blackpool.gov.uk

Senior Management: Mr Mark Towers, Director - Governance & Regulatory Services, Number One Bickerstaffe Square, Talbot Road, Blackpool FY1 3AH ☎ 01253 477007 ✆ mark.towers@blackpool.gov.uk

Architect, Building / Property Services: Mr Stephen Waterfield, Head of Property & Asset Management, Number One Bickerstaffe Square, Talbot Road, Blackpool FY1 3AH ☎ 01253 476069 ✆ stephen.waterfield@blackpool.gov.uk

Building Control: Mr Steve Matthews, Head of Housing, Planning & Transport, The Enterprise Centre, Lytham Road, Blackpool FY1 6DU ☎ 01253 476122 ✆ steve.matthews@blackpool.gov.uk

Children / Youth Services: Mr Carl Baker, Deputy Director - People (Children's Services), Number One Bickerstaffe Square, Talbot Road, Blackpool FY1 3AH ☎ 01253 478972 ✆ carl.baker@blackpool.gov.uk

Children / Youth Services: Ms Delyth Curtis, Director - People (Statutory Director - Children's Services), Number One Bickerstaffe Square, Talbot Road, Blackpool FY1 3AH ☎ 01253 476558 ✆ delyth.curtis@blackpool.gov.uk

Civil Registration: Ms Joceline Greenaway, Head of Registration & Bereavement Services, Number One Bickerstaffe Square, Talbot Road, Blackpool FY1 3AH ☎ 01253 477173 ✆ joceline.greenaway@blackpool.gov.uk

PR / Communications: Mr Jenny Bollington, Media Manager, Number One Bickerstaffe Square, Talbot Road, Blackpool FY1 3AH ☎ 01253 477192 ✆ jenny.bollington@blackpool.gov.uk

Computer Management: Mr Tony Doyle, Head of ICT Services, Number One Bickerstaffe Square, Talbot Road, Blackpool FY1 3AH ☎ 01253 478834 ✆ tony.doyle@blackpool.gov.uk

Corporate Services: Mr Trevor Rayner, Head of Corporate Procurement & Development, Number One Bickerstaffe Square, Talbot Road, Blackpool FY1 3AH ☎ 01253 478531 ✆ trevor.raynor@blackpool.gov.uk

Customer Service: Ms Marie McRoberts, Assistant Treasurer - Revenues, Benefits & Customer Services, Number One Bickerstaffe Square, Talbot Road, Blackpool FY1 3AH ☎ 01253 478910 ✆ marie.mcroberts@blackpool.gov.uk

Economic Development: Mr Peter Legg, Head of Economic Development, FYCreatives, 154-158 Church Street, Blackpool FY1 3PS ☎ 01253 477320 ✆ peter.legg@blackpool.gov.uk

Environmental Health: Mr Tim Coglan, Service Manager - Public Protection, Number One Bickerstaffe Square, Talbot Road, Blackpool FY1 3AH ☎ 01253 478367 ✆ tim.coglen@blackpool.gov.uk

Estates, Property & Valuation: Mr Stephen Waterfield, Head of Property & Asset Management, Number One Bickerstaffe Square, Talbot Road, Blackpool FY1 3AH ☎ 01253 476069 ✆ stephen.waterfield@blackpool.gov.uk

Treasury: Ms Marie McRoberts, Assistant Treasurer - Revenues, Benefits & Customer Services, Number One Bickerstaffe Square, Talbot Road, Blackpool FY1 3AH ☎ 01253 478910 ✆ marie.mcroberts@blackpool.gov.uk

Grounds Maintenance: Mr John Hawkin, Head of Leisure, Catering Services & Illuminations, Number One Bickerstaffe Square, Talbot Road, Blackpool FY1 3AH ☎ 01253 478169 ✆ john.hawkin@blackpool.gov.uk

Health and Safety: Mr Terry Hall, Health & Safety Manager, Number One Bickerstaffe Square, Talbot Road, Blackpool FY1 3AH ☎ 01253 477264 ✆ terry.hall@blackpool.gov.uk

Housing: Mr Steve Matthews, Head of Housing, Planning & Transport, Number One Bickerstaffe Square, Talbot Road, Blackpool FY1 3AH ☎ 01253 476200 ✆ steve.matthews@blackpool.gov.uk

Legal: Mrs Carmel White, Chief Corporate Solicitor, Number One Bickerstaffe Square, Talbot Road, Blackpool FY1 3AH ☎ 01253 477477 ✆ carmel.white@blackpool.gov.uk

Leisure and Cultural Services: Ms Polly Hamilton, Head of Cultural Services, Number One Bickerstaffe Square, Talbot Road, Blackpool FY1 3AH ☎ 01253 476155 ✆ polly.hamilton@blackpool.gov.uk

Licensing: Ms Sharon Davies, Head of Licensing Services, Number One Bickerstaffe Square, Talbot Road, Blackpool FY1 3AH ☎ 01253 478518 ✆ sharon.davies@blackpool.gov.uk

Member Services: Ms Lorraine Hurst, Head of Democratic Governance (Deputy Monitoring Officer), Number One Bickerstaffe Square, Talbot Road, Blackpool FY1 3AH ☎ 01253 477127 ✆ lorraine.hurst@blackpool.gov.uk

Personnel / HR: Ms Linda Dutton, Head of Human Resources, Organisation & Workplace Development, Number One Bickerstaffe Square, Talbot Road, Blackpool FY1 3AH ☎ 07584 606831 ✆ linda.dutton@blackpool.gov.uk

Planning: Mr Steve Matthews, Head of Housing, Planning & Transport, Number One Bickerstaffe Square, Talbot Road, Blackpool FY1 3AH ☎ 01253 476200
✆ steve.matthews@blackpool.gov.uk

Procurement: Mr Trevor Rayner, Head of Corporate Procurement & Development, Number One Bickerstaffe Square, Talbot Road, Blackpool FY1 3AH ☎ 01253 478531
✆ trevor.raynor@blackpool.gov.uk

Regeneration: Mr Peter Legg, Head of Economic Development, Number One Bickerstaffe Square, Talbot Road, Blackpool FY1 3AH ☎ 01253 477320 ✆ peter.legg@blackpool.gov.uk

Social Services (Adult): Ms Lynn Gornall, Principal Social Worker & Head of Safeguarding (Adults), Number One Bickerstaffe Square, Talbot Road, Blackpool FY1 3AH ☎ 01253 477477
✆ lynn.gornell@blackpool.gov.uk

Social Services (Adult): Mr Les Marshall, Head of Adult Social Care, Number One Bickerstaffe Square, Talbot Road, Blackpool FY1 3AH ☎ 01253 476782 ✆ les.marshall@blackpool.gov.uk

Social Services (Adult): Ms Karen Smith, Deputy Director - People - (Statutory Director - Adult Services), Number One Bickerstaffe Square, Talbot Road, Blackpool FY1 3AH ☎ 01253 477502 ✆ karen.smith@blackpool.gov.uk

Social Services (Children): Ms Amanda Hatton, Deputy Director - People, Number One Bickerstaffe Square, Talbot Road, Blackpool FY1 3AH ☎ 01253 477477 ✆ amanda.hatton@blackpool.gov.uk

Fostering & Adoption: Ms Amanda Hatton, Deputy Director - People, Number One Bickerstaffe Square, Talbot Road, Blackpool FY1 3AH ☎ 01253 477477 ✆ amanda.hatton@blackpool.gov.uk

Safeguarding: Ms Josephine Lee, Principal Social Worker, Number One Bickerstaffe Square, Talbot Road, Blackpool FY1 3AH ☎ 01253 476827 ✆ josephine.lee@blackpool.gov.uk

Families: Ms Merle Davies, Head of Early Help for Children & Families, Number One Bickerstaffe Square, Talbot Road, Blackpool FY1 3AH ☎ 01253 476168 ✆ merle.davies@blackpool.gov.uk

Public Health: Dr Arif Rajpura, Director - Public Health, Number One Bickerstaffe Square, Talbot Road, Blackpool FY1 3AH ☎ 01253 476367 ✆ arif.rajpura@blackpool.gov.uk

Tourism: Mr Philip Welsh, Head of Visitor Economy, Number One Bickerstaff Square, Talbot Road, Blackpool FY1 3AH ☎ 01253 477312 ✆ philip.welsh@blackpool.gov.uk

COUNCILLORS

Leader of the Council: Blackburn, Simon (LAB - Brunswick)
cllr.simon.blackburn@blackpool.gov.uk

Deputy Leader of the Council: Campbell, Gillian (LAB - Park)
cllr.gillian.campbell@blackpool.gov.uk

Benson, Kath (LAB - Layton)
cllr.kathryn.benson@blackpool.gov.uk

Brown, Tony (CON - Warbreck)
cllr.tony.brown@blackpool.gov.uk

Cain, Graham (LAB - Bloomfield)
cllr.graham.cain@blackpool.gov.uk

Callow, Maxine (CON - Norbreck)
cllr.maxine.callow@blackpool.gov.uk

Callow, Peter (CON - Norbreck)
cllr.peter.callow@blackpool.gov.uk

Clapham, Donald (CON - Bispham)
cllr.don.clapham@blackpool.gov.uk

Coleman, Debbie (CON - Hawes Side)
cllr.debbie.coleman@blackpool.gov.uk

Coleman, Ian (LAB - Talbot)
cllr.ian.coleman@blackpool.gov.uk

Coleman, Gary (LAB - Brunswick)
cllr.gary.coleman@blackpool.gov.uk

Collett, Eddie (LAB - Tyldesley)
cllr.eddie.collett@blackpool.gov.uk

Cox, Christian (CON - Squires Gate)
cllr.christian.cox@blackpool.gov.uk

Critchley, Kim (LAB - Hawes Side)
cllt.kim.critchley@blackpool.gov.uk

Cross, Amy (LAB - Ingthorpe)
cllr.amy.cross@blackpool.gov.uk

Elmes, Jim (LAB - Marton)
cllr.jim.elmes@blackpool.gov.uk

Galley, Paul (CON - Anchorsholme)
cllr.paul.galley@blackpool.gov.uk

Henderson, Lily (CON - Highfield)
cllr.lily.henderson@blackpool.gov.uk

Humphreys, Alistair (LAB - Squires Gate)
cllr.alistaire.humphreys@blackpool.gov.uk

Hunter, Peter (LAB - Highfield)
cllr.peter.hunter@blackpool.gov.uk

Hutton, Adrian (LAB - Clifton)
cllr.adrian.hutton@blackpool.gov.uk

Jackson, Fred (LAB - Victoria)
cllr.fred.jackson@blackpool.gov.uk

Jones, John (LAB - Bloomfield)
cllr.john.jones@blackpool.gov.uk

Kirkwood, Maria (LAB - Park)
cllr.maria.kirkwood@blackpool.gov.uk

Matthews, Allan (LAB - Tyldesley)
cllr.allan.matthews@blackpool.gov.uk

Maycock, Colin (CON - Bispham)
cllr.colinlmaycock@blackpool.gov.uk

Mitchell, Martin (LAB - Layton)
cllr.martin.mitchell@blackpool.gov.uk

O'Hara, David (LAB - Waterloo)
cllr.david.ohara@blackpool.gov.uk

Owen, David (LAB - Victoria)
cllr.david.owen@blackpool.gov.uk

Roberts, Jason (CON - Stanley)
cllr.jason.roberts@blackpool.gov.uk

BLACKPOOL

Robertson, Derek (CON - Waterloo)
cllr.derek.robertson@blackpool.gov.uk

Rowson, Kath (LAB - Ingthorpe)
cllr.kath.rowson@blackpool.gov.uk

Ryan, Chris (LAB - Greenlands)
cllr.chris.ryan@blackpool.gov.uk

Scott, Danny (CON - Warbreck)
cllr.danny.scott@blackpool.gov.uk

Singleton, Vikki (LAB - Marton)
cllr.vikki.singleton@blackpool.gov.uk

Smith, Mark (LAB - Talbot)
cllr.mark.smith@blackpool.gov.uk

Stansfield, Andrew (CON - Stanley)
cllr.andrew.stansfield@blackpool.gov.uk

Taylor, Ivan (LAB - Claremont)
cllr.ivan.taylor@blackpool.gov.uk

Taylor, Luke (LAB - Clifton)
cllr.luke.taylor@blackpool.gov.uk

Williams, Lynn (LAB - Claremont)
cllr.lynn.williams@blackpool.gov.uk

Williams, Tony (CON - Anchorsholme)
cllr.tony.williams@blackpool.gov.uk

Wright, Christine (LAB - Greenlands)
cllr.christine.wright@blackpool.gov.uk

POLITICAL COMPOSITION
LAB: 28, CON: 14

COMMITTEE CHAIRS

Licensing: Mr Adrian Hutton

Blaenau Gwent   W

Blaenau Gwent County Borough Council, Municipal Offices,
Civic Centre, Ebbw Vale NP23 6XB
☎ 01495 311556 ✆ info@blaenau-gwent.gov.uk
🖥 www.blaenau-gwent.gov.uk

FACTS AND FIGURES
Parliamentary Constituencies: Blaenau Gwent
EU Constituencies: Wales
Election Frequency: Elections are of whole council

PRINCIPAL OFFICERS

Chief Executive: Mr Stephen Gillingham, Lead Corporate Director
/ Head of Paid Service, Municipal Offices, Civic Centre, Ebbw Vale
NP23 6XB ☎ 01495 356088
✆ stephen.gillingham@blaenau-gwent.gov.uk

Senior Management: Mr Richard Crook, Corporate Director -
Environment & Regeneration, Municipal Offices, Civic Centre, Ebbw
Vale NP23 6XB ☎ 01495 355530
✆ richard.crook@blaenau-gwent.gov.uk

Senior Management: Ms Liz Majer, Corporate Director - Social
Services, Anvil Court, Church Street, Abertillery NP13 1DB
☎ 01495 355261 ✆ liz.majer@blaenau-gwent.gov.uk

Senior Management: Mr Dave McAuliffe, Chief Finance Officer,
Anvil Court, Church Street, Abertillery NP13 1DB ☎ 01495 355005
✆ dave.mcauliffe@blaenau-gwent.gov.uk

Access Officer / Social Services (Disability): Mr Huw Lewis,
Equalities Officer, Municipal Offices, Civic Centre, Ebbw Vale NP23
6XB ☎ 01495 355108 ✆ huw.lewis@blaenau-gwent.gov.uk

Architect, Building / Property Services: Mr Clive Rogers, Head
of Technical Services, Municipal Offices, Civic Centre, Ebbw Vale
NP23 6XB ☎ 01495 355384

Best Value: Mrs Bernadette Elias, Head of Policy & Performance,
Municipal Offices, Civic Centre, Ebbw Vale NP23 6XB
☎ 01495 355016 ✆ bernadette.elias@blaenau-gwent.gov.uk

Building Control: Mr Steve Smith, Service Manager -
Development, Municipal Offices, Civic Centre, Ebbw Vale NP23
6XB ☎ 01495 355510 ✆ steve.smith@blaenau-gwent.gov.uk

Catering Services: Mr Matthew Perry, Service Manager -
Community Services, Central Depot, Barleyfield Industrial Estate,
Brynmawr NP23 4YF ☎ 01495 355955
✆ matthew.perry@blaenau-gwent.gov.uk

Children / Youth Services: Mrs Joanne Sims, Youth Services
Manager, Ebbw Vale Institute, Ebbw Vale, Blaenau NP23 6BE
☎ 01495 357866 ✆ joanne.sims@blaenau-gwent.gov.uk

Civil Registration: Mrs Sue Mitchell, Superintendent Registrar,
Blaenau Gwent Register Office, Registration Suite, Bedwellty
House, Morgan Street, Tredegar NP22 3XN ☎ 01495 353370
✆ sue.mitchell@blaenau-gwent.gov.uk

PR / Communications: Mr Sean Scannell, Corporate
Communications, Marketing & Customer Access Manager,
Municipal Offices, Civic Centre, Ebbw Vale NP23 6XB
☎ 01495 355113 ✆ sean.scannell@blaenau-gwent.gov.uk

Community Planning: Mrs Bernadette Elias, Head of Policy &
Performance, Municipal Offices, Civic Centre, Ebbw Vale NP23 6XB
☎ 01495 355016 ✆ bernadette.elias@blaenau-gwent.gov.uk

Community Safety: Mrs Helena Hunt, Policy Team Leader,
Municipal Offices, Civic Centre, Ebbw Vale NP23 6XB
☎ 01495 356145 ✆ helena.hunt@blaenau-gwent.co.uk

Computer Management: Mrs Linda Squire, Assistant Director
- Revenues, Benefits & ICT, Municipal Offices, Civic Centre, Ebbw
Vale NP23 6XB ☎ 01495 355176
✆ linda.squire@blaenau-gwent.gov.uk

Consumer Protection and Trading Standards: Mr Dave
Thompson, Service Manager - Public Protection, Municipal Offices,
Civic Centre, Ebbw Vale NP23 6XB ☎ 01495 355067
✆ dave.thompson@blaenau-gwent.gov.uk

Contracts: Mr Richard Crook, Corporate Director - Environment
& Regeneration, Municipal Offices, Civic Centre, Ebbw Vale NP23
6XB ☎ 01495 355530 ✆ richard.crook@blaenau-gwent.gov.uk

Corporate Services: Mrs Angela O'Leary, Corporate Support Manager, Municipal Offices, Civic Centre, Ebbw Vale NP23 6XB
☎ 01495 355090 ◌ angela.oleary@blaenau-gwent.gov.uk

Customer Service: Mr Sean Scannell, Corporate Communications, Marketing & Customer Access Manager, Municipal Offices, Civic Centre, Ebbw Vale NP23 6XB
☎ 01495 355113 ◌ sean.scannell@blaenau-gwent.gov.uk

Direct Labour: Mr Richard Crook, Corporate Director - Environment & Regeneration, Municipal Offices, Civic Centre, Ebbw Vale NP23 6XB ☎ 01495 355530 ◌ richard.crook@blaenau-gwent.gov.uk

Economic Development: Mrs Frances Williams, Service Manager - Regeneration, Municipal Offices, Civic Centre, Ebbw Vale NP23 6XB ☎ 01495 355616 ◌ frances.williams@blaenau-gwent.gov.uk

Education: Ms Lynette Jones, Corporate Director - Education, Municipal Offices, Civic Centre, Ebbw Vale NP23 6XB
◌ lynette.jones@blaenau-gwent.gov.uk

Electoral Registration: Mrs Angela O'Leary, Corporate Support Manager, Municipal Offices, Civic Centre, Ebbw Vale NP23 6XB
☎ 01495 355090 ◌ angela.oleary@blaenau-gwent.gov.uk

Emergency Planning: Mrs Deanne Griffiths, Principal Civil Contingencies Officer, Municipal Offices, Civic Centre, Ebbw Vale NP23 6XB ☎ 01495 355568 ◌ deanne.griffiths@blaenau-gwent.gov.uk

Energy Management: Mr Peter Morgan, Senior Energy Officer, Municipal Offices, Civic Centre, Ebbw Vale NP23 6XB
☎ 01495 355562 ◌ peter.morgan@blaenau-gwent.gov.uk

Environmental / Technical Services: Mr Alan Reed, Head of Public Services, Municipal Offices, Civic Centre, Ebbw Vale NP23 6XB ☎ 01495 355612 ◌ alan.reed@blaenau-gwent.gov.uk

Environmental Health: Mr Dave Thompson, Service Manager - Public Protection, Municipal Offices, Civic Centre, Ebbw Vale NP23 6XB ☎ 01495 355067 ◌ dave.thompson@blaenau-gwent.gov.uk

Estates, Property & Valuation: Mr Paul Miles, Valuation & Estates Officer, Municipal Offices, Civic Centre, Ebbw Vale NP23 6XB ☎ 01495 355030 ◌ paul.miles@blaenau-gwent.gov.uk

European Liaison: Mrs Frances Williams, Service Manager - Regeneration, Municipal Offices, Civic Centre, Ebbw Vale NP23 6XB ☎ 01495 355616 ◌ frances.williams@blaenau-gwent.gov.uk

Facilities: Mr Richard Crook, Corporate Director - Environment & Regeneration, Municipal Offices, Civic Centre, Ebbw Vale NP23 6XB ☎ 01495 355530 ◌ richard.crook@blaenau-gwent.gov.uk

Finance: Mr Dave McAuliffe, Chief Finance Officer, Anvil Court, Church Street, Abertillery NP13 1DB ☎ 01495 355005
◌ dave.mcauliffe@blaenau-gwent.gov.uk

Fleet Management: Mr Neil Hughes, Transport & Highways Principal Officer, Central Depot, Barleyfield Industrial Estate, Brynmawr NP23 4YF ☎ 01495 355629
◌ neil.hughes@blaenau-gwent.gov.uk

Health and Safety: Mr Jim Thomas, Health & Safety Manager, Municipal Offices, Civic Centre, Ebbw Vale NP23 6XB
☎ 01495 355035 ◌ jim.thomas@blaenau-gwent.gov.uk

Highways: Mr Alan Reed, Head of Public Services, Municipal Offices, Civic Centre, Ebbw Vale NP23 6XB ☎ 01495 355612
◌ alan.reed@blaenau-gwent.gov.uk

Home Energy Conservation: Mr Richard Crook, Corporate Director - Environment & Regeneration, Municipal Offices, Civic Centre, Ebbw Vale NP23 6XB ☎ 01495 355530
◌ richard.crook@blaenau-gwent.gov.uk

Housing: Mr Dave Thompson, Service Manager - Public Protection, Municipal Offices, Civic Centre, Ebbw Vale NP23 6XB
☎ 01495 355067 ◌ dave.thompson@blaenau-gwent.gov.uk

Legal: Mrs Andrea Jones, Head of Legal & Corp Compliance, Municipal Offices, Civic Centre, Ebbw Vale NP23 6XB
☎ 01495 355024 ◌ andrea.jones@blaenau-gwent.gov.uk

Leisure and Cultural Services: Mr Lynn Phillips, Assistant Director - Leisure Services & School Transformation, Leisure Services & School Transformation, Anvil Court, Church Street, Abertillery NP13 1DB ☎ 01495 355603
◌ lynn.phillips@blaenau-gwent.gov.uk

Licensing: Mr Dave Thompson, Service Manager - Public Protection, Municipal Offices, Civic Centre, Ebbw Vale NP23 6XB ☎ 01495 355067 ◌ dave.thompson@blaenau-gwent.gov.uk

Lifelong Learning: Ms Lynette Jones, Corporate Director - Education, Municipal Offices, Civic Centre, Ebbw Vale NP23 6XB
◌ lynette.jones@blaenau-gwent.gov.uk

Member Services: Mrs Ceri Edwards Brown, Member Development Co-ordinator, Municipal Offices, Civic Centre, Ebbw Vale NP23 6XB ☎ 01495 356139
◌ ceri.edwardsbrown@blaenau-gwent.gov.uk

Partnerships: Ms Ceri Bird, Integrated Services Team Manager - Children & Families, Heart of the Valleys Children's Centre, High Street, Blaenau NP13 3BN ☎ 01495 354719
◌ ceri.bird@blaunau-gwent.gov.uk

Personnel / HR: Ms Andrea Prosser, Head of Organisational Development, Municipal Offices, Civic Centre, Ebbw Vale NP23 6XB ☎ 01495 355041 ◌ andrea.prosser@blaenau-gwent.gov.uk

Planning: Mr Steve Smith, Service Manager - Development, Municipal Offices, Civic Centre, Ebbw Vale NP23 6XB
☎ 01495 355510 ◌ steve.smith@blaenau-gwent.gov.uk

Procurement: Mr Lee Williams, Corporate Procurement Manager, Municipal Offices, Civic Centre, Ebbw Vale NP23 6XB
☎ 01495 355686 ◌ lee.williams@blaenau-gwent.gov.uk

Public Libraries: Mr Lynn Phillips, Assistant Director - Leisure Services & School Transformation, Leisure Services & School Transformation, Anvil Court, Church Street, Abertillery NP13 1DB ☎ 01495 355603 ◌ lynn.phillips@blaenau-gwent.gov.uk

BLAENAU GWENT

Recycling & Waste Minimisation: Mr Matthew Perry, Service Manager - Community Services, Central Depot, Barleyfield Industrial Estate, Brynmawr NP23 4YF ☎ 01495 355955 ✆ matthew.perry@blaenau-gwent.gov.uk

Regeneration: Mr Alan Reed, Head of Public Services, Municipal Offices, Civic Centre, Ebbw Vale NP23 6XB ☎ 01495 355612 ✆ alan.reed@blaenau-gwent.gov.uk

Social Services: Ms Liz Majer, Corporate Director - Social Services, Anvil Court, Church Street, Abertillery NP13 1DB ☎ 01495 355261 ✆ liz.majer@blaenau-gwent.gov.uk

Social Services (Adult): Mr Damien McCann, Head of Adult Services, Anvil Court, Church Street, Abertillery NP13 1DB ☎ 01495 355383 ✆ damien.mccann@blaenau-gwent.gov.uk

Social Services (Children): Mrs Tanya Evans, Head of Children's Services, Anvil Court, Church Street, Abertillery NP13 1DB ☎ 01495 356067 ✆ tanya.evans@blaenau-gwent.gov.uk

Staff Training: Mr Simon Green, Organisational Development Officer, Municipal Offices, Civic Centre, Ebbw Vale NP23 6XB ☎ 01495 355040 ✆ simon.green@blaenau-gwent.gov.uk

Street Scene: Mr Matthew Perry, Service Manager - Community Services, Central Depot, Barleyfield Industrial Estate, Brynmawr NP23 4YF ☎ 01495 355955 ✆ matthew.perry@blaenau-gwent.gov.uk

Tourism: Mr Lynn Phillips, Assistant Director - Leisure Services & School Transformation, Leisure Services & School Transformation, Anvil Court, Church Street, Abertillery NP13 1DB ☎ 01495 355603 ✆ lynn.phillips@blaenau-gwent.gov.uk

Town Centre: Mrs Beth McPherson, Town Centre Manager, Municipal Offices, Civic Centre, Ebbw Vale NP23 6XB ☎ 01495 355539 ✆ beth.mcpherson@blaenau-gwent.gov.uk

Transport: Mr Richard Crook, Corporate Director - Environment & Regeneration, Municipal Offices, Civic Centre, Ebbw Vale NP23 6XB ☎ 01495 355530 ✆ richard.crook@blaenau-gwent.gov.uk

Transport Planner: Ms Sharn Annett, Assistant Director - Department Business Management & Support (S.M.S.), Catering & Partnerships, Heart of the Valleys Children's Centre, High Street, Blaenau NP13 3BN ☎ 01495 354719 ✆ sharn.annett@blaenau-gwent.gov.uk

Waste Collection and Disposal: Mr Matthew Perry, Service Manager - Community Services, Central Depot, Barleyfield Industrial Estate, Brynmawr NP23 4YF ☎ 01495 355955 ✆ matthew.perry@blaenau-gwent.gov.uk

Children's Play Areas: Mr Alun Watkins, Team Leader - Grounds Maintenance & Bereavement Services, Central Depot, Barleyfield Industrial Estate, Brynmawr NP23 4YF ☎ 01495 355603 ✆ alun.watkins@blaenau-gwent.gov.uk

COUNCILLORS

Mayor: Sutton, Barrie (LAB - Brynmawr)
barrie.sutton@blaenau.gwent.gov.uk

Deputy Mayor: Willis, Bernard (LAB - Tredegar Central & West)
bernard.willis@blaenau-gwent.gov.uk

Leader of the Council: Thomas, Stephen (LAB - Tredegar Central & West)
stephen.thomas@blaenau-gwent.gov.uk

Baldwin, Peter (LAB - Nantyglo)
peter.baldwin@blaenau-gwent.gov.uk

Bartlett, Graham (LAB - Cwmtillery)
graham.bartlett@blaenau-gwent.gov.uk

Bartlett, Mike (LAB - Llanhilleth)
mike.bartlett@blaenau-gwent.gov.uk

Bender, Keren (LAB - Cwm)
keren.bender@blaenau-gwent.gov.uk

Bevan, Derrick (LAB - Cwm)
derrick.bevan@blaenau-gwent.gov.uk

Brown, Kevin (IND - Brynmawr)
kevin.brown@blaenau-gwent.gov.uk

Chaplin, Keith (LAB - Abertillery)
keith.chaplin@blaenau-gwent.gov.uk

Clements, Brian (LAB - Ebbw Vale South)
brian.clements@blaenau-gwent.gov.uk

Collier, Garth (IND - Blaina)
garth.collier@blaenau-gwent.gov.uk

Coughlin, Derek (LAB - Ebbw Vale North)
derek.coughlin@blaenau-gwent.gov.uk

Cross, Malcom (LAB - Sirhowy)
malcolm.cross@blaenau-gwent.gov.uk

Daniels, Nigel (INDNA - Abertillery)
nigel.daniels@blaenau-gwent.gov.uk

Hancock, Denzil (IND - Six Bells)
denzil.hancock@blaenau-gwent.gov.uk

Hayden, Keith (LAB - Georgetown)
keith.hayden@blaenau-gwent.gov.uk

Hobbs, Anita (LAB - Tredegar Central & West)
nita.hobbs@blaenau-gwent.gov.uk

Holland, Mark (LAB - Six Bells)
mark.holland@blaenau-gwent.gov.uk

Jones, Richard (LAB - Abertillery)
richard.jones@blaenau-gwent.gov.uk

Lewis, Ann (LAB - Ebbw Vale North)
ann.lewis@blaenau-gwent.gov.uk

Lewis, Mostyn (LAB - Ebbw Vale South)
mostyn.lewis@blaenau-gwent.gov.uk

Mason, John (IND - Nantyglo)
john.mason@blaenau-gwent.gov.uk

McCarthy, Hedley (LAB - Llanhilleth)
hedley.mccarthy@blaenau-gwent.gov.uk

McIlwee, Jim (LAB - Llanhilleth)
jim.mcilwee@blaenua-gwent.gov.uk

Meredith, Clive (IND - Badminton)
clive.meredith@blaenau-gwent.gov.uk

Morgan, Jennifer (LAB - Ebbw Vale North)
jennifer.morgan@blaenau-gwent.gov.uk

Morgan, John (LAB - Georgetown)
john.morgan@blaenau-gwent.gov.uk

Owens, Dennis (LAB - Sirhowy)
dennis.owens@blaenau-gwent.gov.uk

Pagett, Bob (LAB - Blaina)
bob.pagett@blaenau-gwent.gov.uk

Rowberry, Diane (LAB - Sirhowy)
diane.rowberry@blaenau-gwent.gov.uk

Scully, Brian (LAB - Badminton)
brian.scully@blaenau-gwent.gov.uk

Sharrem, Tim (LAB - Cwmtillery)
tim.sharrem@blaenau-gwent.gov.uk

Thomas, Godfrey (IND - Beaufort)
godfrey.thomas@blaenua-gwent.gov.uk

Tidey, Christine (LAB - Cwmtillery)
christine.tidey@blaenau-gwent.gov.uk

Trollope, Haydn (LAB - Tredegar Central & West)
hayden.trollope@blaenau-gwent.gov.uk

Wilkshire, David (LAB - Rassau)
david.wilkshire@blaenau-gwent.gov.uk

Winnett, Lisa (LAB - Blaina)
lisa.winnett@blaenau-gwent.gov.uk

POLITICAL COMPOSITION
LAB: 31, IND: 6, INDNA: 1

Bolsover   D

Bolsover District Council, The Arc, High Street, Clowne, Staveley S43 4JY
☎ 01246 242424; 🖨 01246 242423;
✆ enquiries@bolsover.gov.uk 🖳 www.bolsover.gov.uk

FACTS AND FIGURES
Parliamentary Constituencies: Bolsover
EU Constituencies: East Midlands
Election Frequency: Elections are of whole council

PRINCIPAL OFFICERS

Chief Executive: Mr Dan Swaine, Chief Executive, The Arc, High Street, Clowne, Staveley S43 4JY ☎ 01246 242401
✆ dan.swaine@ne-derbyshire.gov.uk

Senior Management: Mr Paul Hackett, Joint Executive Director - Transformation, The Arc, High Street, Clowne, Staveley S43 4JY
☎ 01246 242566 ✆ paul.hackett@ne-derbyshire.gov.uk

Senior Management: Mr Bryan Mason, Joint Executive Director - Operations, The Arc, High Street, Clowne, Staveley S43 4JY
☎ 01246 242431 ✆ bryan.mason@ne-derbyshire.gov.uk

Architect, Building / Property Services: Mr Grant Galloway, Assistant Director - Property & Estates, The Arc, High Street, Clowne, Staveley S43 4JY ☎ 01246 242284
✆ grant.galloway@bolsover.gov.uk

Building Control: Mr Malcolm Clinton, Business Manager, Unit 2, Dunston Technology Park, Millennium Way, Dunston Road, Chesterfield S41 8ND ☎ 01246 345817
✆ malcolm.clinton@ne-derbyshire.gov.uk

PR / Communications: Mr Scott Chambers, Communications, Marketing & Design Manager, The Arc, High Street, Clowne, Staveley S43 4JY ☎ 01246 242323
✆ scott.chambers@bolsover.gov.uk

Community Planning: Mrs Pam Brown, Chief Executive's & Partnership Manager, The Arc, High Street, Clowne, Staveley S43 4JY ☎ 01246 242499 ✆ pam.brown@bolsover.gov.uk

Community Safety: Mr Peter Campbell, Assistant Director - Community Safety & Head of Housing, The Arc, High Street, Clowne, Staveley S43 4JY ☎ 01246 593038
✆ peter.campbell@bolsover.gov.uk

Computer Management: Mr Nick Blaney, Joint IT Services Manager, The Arc, High Street, Clowne, Staveley S43 4JY ☎ 01246 217103; 01246 217103; 01246 717097
✆ nick.blaney@ne-derbyshire.gov.uk

Customer Service: Mrs Jane Foley, Joint Assistant Director - Customer Service & Improvement, The Arc, High Street, Clowne, Staveley S43 4JY ☎ 01246 242343 ✆ jane.foley@bolsover.gov.uk

Economic Development: Mrs Allison Westray-Chapman, Joint Assistant Director - Economic Growth, The Arc, High Street, Clowne, Staveley S43 4JY ☎ 01246 217199
✆ allison.westray-chapman@ne-derbyshire.gov.uk

Electoral Registration: Miss Kath Whittingham, Head of Elections, The Arc, High Street, Clowne, Staveley S43 4JY
✆ kath.whittingham@bolsover.gov.uk

Emergency Planning: Mr Paul Hackett, Joint Executive Director - Transformation, The Arc, High Street, Clowne, Staveley S43 4JY
☎ 01246 242566 ✆ paul.hackett@ne-derbyshire.gov.uk

Energy Management: Mr Edward Owen, Energy Officer, The Arc, High Street, Clowne, Staveley S43 4JY ☎ 01246 217847
✆ edward.owen@ne-derbyshire.gov.uk

Environmental / Technical Services: Mr James Arnold, Joint Assistant Director - Planning & Environmental Health, The Arc, High Street, Clowne, Staveley S43 4JY ☎ 01246 217436
✆ james.arnold@bolsover.gov.uk

Environmental Health: Ms Sharon Gillott, Environmental Health Commercial Manager, District Council Offices, 2013 Mill Lane, Wingerworth, Chesterfield S42 6NG ☎ 01246 237848
✆ sharon.gillott@bolsover.gov.uk

Estates, Property & Valuation: Mr Grant Galloway, Assistant Director - Property & Estates, The Arc, High Street, Clowne, Staveley S43 4JY ☎ 01246 242284
✆ grant.galloway@bolsover.gov.uk

European Liaison: Mr Dan Swaine, Chief Executive, The Arc, High Street, Clowne, Staveley S43 4JY ☎ 01246 242401
✆ dan.swaine@ne-derbyshire.gov.uk

Facilities: Mr Matthew Cooper, Property & Estates Manager, The Arc, High Street, Clowne, Staveley S43 4JY
✆ matthew.cooper@bolsover.gov.uk

BOLSOVER

Finance: Ms Dawn Clarke, Joint Assistant Director - Finance, Revenues & Benefits, The Arc, High Street, Clowne, Staveley S43 4JY ☎ 01246 217658 ✆ dawn.clarke@ne-derbyshire.gov.uk

Fleet Management: Ms Pam Burrows, Joint Fleet & Transport Manager, Riverside Depot, Doe Lea, Bolsover S44 5NY ☎ 01246 593043 ✆ pam.burrows@bolsover.gov.uk

Grounds Maintenance: Mr Steve Jowett, Joint Street Services Manager, Riverside Depot, Doe Lea, Bolsover S44 5NY ☎ 01246 593044 ✆ steve.jowett@ne-derbyshire.gov.uk

Health and Safety: Mr Mark Spotswood, Health & Safety Officer, Riverside Depot, Doe Lea, Bolsover S44 5NY ☎ 01246 242403 ✆ mark.spotswood@bolsover.gov.uk

Housing: Mr Peter Campbell, Assistant Director - Community Safety & Head of Housing, The Arc, High Street, Clowne, Staveley S43 4JY ☎ 01246 593038 ✆ peter.campbell@bolsover.gov.uk

Housing Maintenance: Mr Peter Campbell, Assistant Director - Community Safety & Head of Housing, The Arc, High Street, Clowne, Staveley S43 4JY ☎ 01246 593038 ✆ peter.campbell@bolsover.gov.uk

Legal: Mrs Sarah Sternberg, Joint Assistant Director - Governance, The Arc, High Street, Clowne, Staveley S43 4JY ☎ 01246 242414 ✆ sarah.sternberg@bolsover.gov.uk

Leisure and Cultural Services: Mr Lee Hickin, Joint Assistant Director - Leisure, The Arc, High Street, Clowne, Staveley S43 4JY ☎ 01246 217218 ✆ lee.hickin@bolsover.gov.uk

Licensing: Mr John Chambers, Licensing Co-ordinator, 2013 Mill Lane, Wingerworth, Chesterfield S42 6NG ☎ 01246 217216 ✆ john.chambers@ne-derbyshire.gov.uk

Member Services: Mr Matthew Kane, Democratic Services Manager, The Arc, High Street, Clowne, Staveley S43 4JY ☎ 01246 242505 ✆ matthew.kane@ne-derbyshire.gov.uk

Partnerships: Mrs Pam Brown, Chief Executive's & Partnership Manager, The Arc, High Street, Clowne, Staveley S43 4JY ☎ 01246 242499 ✆ pam.brown@bolsover.gov.uk

Personnel / HR: Ms Stephanie Barker, Assistant Director - Human Resources & Payroll, The Arc, High Street, Clowne, Staveley S43 4JY ☎ 01246 242237 ✆ stephanie.barker@ne-derbyshire.gov.uk

Planning: Mr James Arnold, Joint Assistant Director - Planning & Environmental Health, The Arc, High Street, Clowne, Staveley S43 4JY ☎ 01246 217436 ✆ james.arnold@bolsover.gov.uk

Recycling & Waste Minimisation: Mr Steve Brunt, Joint Assistant Director - Street Scene, Riverside Depot, Doe Lea, Bolsover S44 5NY ☎ 01246 593044 ✆ steve.brunt@bolsover.gov.uk

Street Scene: Mr Steve Brunt, Joint Assistant Director - Street Scene, Riverside Depot, Doe Lea, Bolsover S44 5NY ☎ 01246 593044 ✆ steve.brunt@bolsover.gov.uk

Waste Collection and Disposal: Mr Steve Brunt, Joint Assistant Director - Street Scene, Riverside Depot, Doe Lea, Bolsover S44 5NY ☎ 01246 593044 ✆ steve.brunt@bolsover.gov.uk

Waste Management: Mr Steve Brunt, Joint Assistant Director - Street Scene, Riverside Depot, Doe Lea, Bolsover S44 5NY ☎ 01246 593044 ✆ steve.brunt@bolsover.gov.uk

COUNCILLORS

ChairWalker, Kenneth (LAB - Shirebrook Langwith)
ken.walker@bolsover.gov.uk

Leader of the Council: Syrett, Ann (LAB - Pleasley)
ann.syrett@bolsover.gov.uk

Deputy Leader of the Council: Dooley, Mary (LAB - Pinxton)
mary.dooley@bolsover.gov.uk

Alexander, Tom (LAB - Pinxton)
tom.alexander@bolsover.gov.uk

Anderson, Andrew (LAB - Shirebrook South East)
andrew@shirebrooktowncouncil.co.uk

Barnes, Paul (LAB - South Normanton West)
paul.barnes@bolsover.gov.uk

Bennett, Toni (LAB - Bolsover South)
toni.bennet@bolsover.gov.uk

Bowler, Rosemary (LAB - Bolsover West)
rose.bowler@bolsover.gov.uk

Bowmer, Pauline (LAB - Pleasley)
pauline.bowmer@bolsover.gov.uk

Bulolock, Dextor (IND - Blackwell)
dexter.bullock@bolsover.gov.uk

Buxton, Gwyneth (LAB - Clowne North)
gwyneth.buston@bolsover.gov.uk

Cannon, Tracey (LAB - South Normanton East)
tracey.cannon@bolsover.gov.uk

Clifton, James (IND - Elmton with Creswell)
jim.clifton@bolsover.gov.uk

Connerton, Terry (LAB - Clowne North)
terry.connerton@bolsover.gov.uk

Cooper, Paul (LAB - Bolsover North West)
paul.cooper@bolsover.gov.uk

Cooper, Pat (LAB - Bolsover South)
pat.cooper@bolsover.gov.uk

Crane, Malcolm (LAB - Scarcliffe)
malc.crane@bolsover.gov.uk

Dixey, Mark (LAB - Bolsover West)
mark.dixey@bolsover.gov.uk

Fritchley, Stephen (LAB - Shirebrook North West)
steve.fritchley@bolsover.gov.uk

Gilmour, Hilary (LAB - Barlborough)
hilary.gilmour@bolsover.gov.uk

Heffer, Ray (IND - Tibshelf)
ray.heffer@bolsover.gov.uk

Joesbury, Andrew (IND - South Normanton East)
andrew.joesbury@bolsover.gov.uk

McGregor, Duncan (LAB - Elmton with Creswell)
duncan.mcgregor@bolsover.gov.uk

Moesby, Clive (LAB - Blackwell)
clive-moesby@bolsover.gov.uk

Munro, Tom (LAB - Whitwell)
tom.munro@bolsover.gov.uk

Murray-Carr, Brian (LAB - Shirebrook East)
brian.murray-carr@bolsover.gov.uk

Peake, Sandra (LAB - Shirebrook South West)
sandra.peake@bolsover.gov.uk

Reid, Karl (LAB - Clowne South)
karl.reid@bolsover.gov.uk

Ritchie, John (LAB - Whitwell)
john.ritchie@bolsolver.gov.uk

Smith, Paul (LAB - South Normanton West)
phil.smith@bolsover.gov.uk

Smith, Jim (LAB - Clowne South)
jim.smith@bolsover.gov.ukl

Statter, Sue (LAB - Bolsover North West)
sue.statter@bolsover.gov.uk

Stevenson, Emma (LAB - South Normanton West)
emma.stevenson@bolsover.gov.uk

Turner, Rita (LAB - Elmton with Creswell)
rita.turner@bolsover.gov.uk

Watson, Deborah (IND - Tibshelf)
deborah.watson@bolsover.gov.uk

Watson, Brian (LAB - Barlborough)
brian.watson@bolsover.gov.uk

Wilson, Jen (LAB - Scarcliffe)
jennifer.wilson@bolsover.gov.uk

POLITICAL COMPOSITION
LAB: 32, IND: 5

COMMITTEE CHAIRS

Licensing: Mr Kenneth Walker

Planning: Mr Duncan McGregor

Bolton   M

Bolton Metropolitan Borough Council, Town Hall, Bolton
BL1 1RU
☎ 01204 333333 🖶 01204 331042 ✆ firstname.surname@bolton.gov.uk
🖳 www.bolton.gov.uk

FACTS AND FIGURES
Parliamentary Constituencies: Bolton North East, Bolton South
East, Bolton West
EU Constituencies: North West
Election Frequency: Elections are by thirds

PRINCIPAL OFFICERS

Chief Executive: Mrs Margaret Asquith, (Acting Chief Executive)
Deputy Chief Executive, Town Hall, Bolton BL1 1RU ☎ 01204
332010 ✆ margaret.asquith@bolton.gov.uk

Senior Management: Mr John Daly, Acting Director - People, 1st
Floor, Town Hall, Bolton BL1 1RU ☎ 01204 332130
✆ john.daly@bolton.gov.uk

Senior Management: Mr David Herne, Director - Public Health,
1st Floor, Town Hall, Bolton BL1 1RU ✆ david.herne@bolton.gov.uk

Senior Management: Mr Stephen Young, Director - Place, 3rd
Floor, Town Hall, Bolton BL1 1RU ☎ 01204 336490
✆ stephen.young@bolton.gov.uk

Architect, Building / Property Services: Mr Stephen Young,
Director - Place, 3rd Floor, Town Hall, Bolton BL1 1RU
☎ 01204 336490 ✆ stephen.young@bolton.gov.uk

Building Control: Mr Stephen Young, Director - Place, 3rd Floor,
Town Hall, Bolton BL1 1RU ☎ 01204 336490
✆ stephen.young@bolton.gov.uk

Catering Services: Ms Donna Ball, Assistant Director - Place, 3rd
Floor, Town Hall, Bolton BL1 1RU ☎ 01204 336713
✆ donna.ball@bolton.gov.uk

Children / Youth Services: Mr John Daly, Acting Director -
People, 1st Floor, Town Hall, Bolton BL1 1RU ☎ 01204 332130
✆ john.daly@bolton.gov.uk

Civil Registration: Mrs Helen Gorman, Borough Solicitor, 2nd
Floor, Town Hall, Bolton BL1 1RU ☎ 01204 331001
✆ helen.gorman@bolton.gov.uk

PR / Communications: Mrs Helen Gorman, Borough Solicitor,
2nd Floor, Town Hall, Bolton BL1 1RU ☎ 01204 331001
✆ helen.gorman@bolton.gov.uk

Community Safety: Ms Sarah Schofield, Assistant Director -
Neighbourhood & Regulatory Services, 3rd Floor, Town Hall, Bolton
BL1 1RU ☎ 01204 336718 ✆ sarah.schofield@bolton.gov.uk

Computer Management: Ms Sue Johnson, Borough Treasurer,
2nd Floor, Town Hall, Bolton BL1 1RU ☎ 01204 331504
✆ sue.johnson@bolton.gov.uk

Consumer Protection and Trading Standards: Ms Sarah
Schofield, Assistant Director - Neighbourhood & Regulatory
Services, 3rd Floor, Town Hall, Bolton BL1 1RU ☎ 01204 336718
✆ sarah.schofield@bolton.gov.uk

Direct Labour: Ms Donna Ball, Assistant Director - Place, 3rd
Floor, Town Hall, Bolton BL1 1RU ☎ 01204 336713
✆ donna.ball@bolton.gov.uk

Economic Development: Mr Phil Green, Assistant Director -
Economic, 3rd Floor, Town Hall, Bolton BL1 1RU ☎ 01204 334187
✆ phil.green@bolton.gov.uk

Education: Mr John Daly, Acting Director - People, 1st Floor, Town
Hall, Bolton BL1 1RU ☎ 01204 332130 ✆ john.daly@bolton.gov.uk

E-Government: Mrs Helen Gorman, Borough Solicitor, 2nd Floor,
Town Hall, Bolton BL1 1RU ☎ 01204 331001
✆ helen.gorman@bolton.gov.uk

BOLTON

Electoral Registration: Mrs Helen Gorman, Borough Solicitor, Town Hall, Bolton BL1 1RU ☎ 01204 331001
✆ helen.gorman@bolton.gov.uk

Emergency Planning: Mr Stephen Young, Director - Place, 3rd Floor, Town Hall, Bolton BL1 1RU ☎ 01204 336490
✆ stephen.young@bolton.gov.uk

Environmental / Technical Services: Mr Stephen Young, Director - Place, 3rd Floor, Town Hall, Bolton BL1 1RU
☎ 01204 336490 ✆ stephen.young@bolton.gov.uk

Environmental Health: Ms Sarah Schofield, Assistant Director - Neighbourhood & Regulatory Services, 3rd Floor, Town Hall, Bolton BL1 1RU ☎ 01204 336718 ✆ sarah.schofield@bolton.gov.uk

Estates, Property & Valuation: Mr Stephen Young, Director - Place, 3rd Floor, Town Hall, Bolton BL1 1RU ☎ 01204 336490
✆ stephen.young@bolton.gov.uk

Events Manager: Mrs Nicola Littlewood, Marketing Manager, 2nd Floor, Town Hall, Bolton BL1 1RU ☎ 01204 334072
✆ nicola.littlewood@bolton.gov.uk

Facilities: Mr Stephen Young, Director - Place, 3rd Floor, Town Hall, Bolton BL1 1RU ☎ 01204 336490
✆ stephen.young@bolton.gov.uk

Finance: Ms Sue Johnson, Borough Treasurer, 2nd Floor, Town Hall, Bolton BL1 1RU ☎ 01204 331504 ✆ sue.johnson@bolton.gov.uk

Fleet Management: Ms Donna Ball, Assistant Director - Place, 3rd Floor, Town Hall, Bolton BL1 1RU ☎ 01204 336713
✆ donna.ball@bolton.gov.uk

Grounds Maintenance: Ms Sarah Schofield, Assistant Director - Neighbourhood & Regulatory Services, 3rd Floor, Town Hall, Bolton BL1 1RU ☎ 01204 336718 ✆ sarah.schofield@bolton.gov.uk

Health and Safety: Mr Shaun Wheeler, Head of Human Resources, 2nd Floor, Town Hall, Bolton BL1 1RU ☎ 01204 331209
✆ shaun.wheeler@bolton.gov.uk

Highways: Mr Stephen Young, Director - Place, 3rd Floor, Town Hall, Bolton BL1 1RU ☎ 01204 336490
✆ stephen.young@bolton.gov.uk

Housing: Mr Stephen Young, Director - Place, 3rd Floor, Town Hall, Bolton BL1 1RU ☎ 01204 336490
✆ stephen.young@bolton.gov.uk

Legal: Mrs Helen Gorman, Borough Solicitor, 2nd Floor, Town Hall, Bolton BL1 1RU ☎ 01204 331001 ✆ helen.gorman@bolton.gov.uk

Leisure and Cultural Services: Mr Stephen Young, Director - Place, 3rd Floor, Town Hall, Bolton BL1 1RU ☎ 01204 336490
✆ stephen.young@bolton.gov.uk

Licensing: Ms Sarah Schofield, Assistant Director - Neighbourhood & Regulatory Services, 3rd Floor, Town Hall, Bolton BL1 1RU ☎ 01204 336718 ✆ sarah.schofield@bolton.gov.uk

Lifelong Learning: Mr Phil Green, Assistant Director - Economic, 3rd Floor, Town Hall, Bolton BL1 1RU ☎ 01204 334187
✆ phil.green@bolton.gov.uk

Lighting: Mr Stephen Young, Director - Place, 3rd Floor, Town Hall, Bolton BL1 1RU ☎ 01204 336490
✆ stephen.young@bolton.gov.uk

Lottery Funding, Charity and Voluntary: Mr Michael Kane, Corporate Policy & Partnerships Manager, 2nd Floor, Town Hall, Bolton BL1 1RU ☎ 01204 333333 ✆ michael.kane@bolton.gov.uk

Member Services: Mrs Helen Gorman, Borough Solicitor, 2nd Floor, Town Hall, Bolton BL1 1RU ☎ 01204 331001
✆ helen.gorman@bolton.gov.uk

Parking: Mr Stephen Young, Director - Place, 3rd Floor, Town Hall, Bolton BL1 1RU ☎ 01204 336490 ✆ stephen.young@bolton.gov.uk

Personnel / HR: Ms Sue Johnson, Borough Treasurer, 2nd Floor, Town Hall, Bolton BL1 1RU ☎ 01204 331504
✆ sue.johnson@bolton.gov.uk

Planning: Mr John Berry, Head of Development Management, 3rd Floor, Town Hall, Bolton BL1 1RU ☎ 01204 336004
✆ john.berry@bolton.gov.uk

Procurement: Ms Sue Johnson, Borough Treasurer, 2nd Floor, Town Hall, Bolton BL1 1RU ☎ 01204 331504
✆ sue.johnson@bolton.gov.uk

Public Libraries: Mrs Julie Spencer, Head of Libraries, Museums & Archives, Central Library, Le Mans Crescent, Bolton BL1 1SA
☎ 01204 332276 ✆ julie.spencer@bolton.gov.uk

Recycling & Waste Minimisation: Ms Donna Ball, Assistant Director - Place, 3rd Floor, Town Hall, Bolton BL1 1RU
☎ 01204 336713 ✆ donna.ball@bolton.gov.uk

Regeneration: Mr Stephen Young, Director - Place, 3rd Floor, Town Hall, Bolton BL1 1RU ☎ 01204 336490
✆ stephen.young@bolton.gov.uk

Road Safety: Mr Stephen Young, Director - Place, 3rd Floor, Town Hall, Bolton BL1 1RU ☎ 01204 336490
✆ stephen.young@bolton.gov.uk

Social Services: Mr John Daly, Acting Director - People, 1st Floor, Town Hall, Bolton BL1 1RU ☎ 01204 332130
✆ john.daly@bolton.gov.uk

Social Services (Adult): Mr John Daly, Acting Director - People, 1st Floor, Town Hall, Bolton BL1 1RU ☎ 01204 332130
✆ john.daly@bolton.gov.uk

Social Services (Children): Mr John Daly, Acting Director - People, 1st Floor, Town Hall, Bolton BL1 1RU ☎ 01204 332130
✆ john.daly@bolton.gov.uk

Public Health: Mr David Herne, Director - Public Health, 1st Floor, Town Hall, Bolton BL1 1RU ✆ david.herne@bolton.gov.uk

Staff Training: Mr Shaun Wheeler, Head of Human Resources, 2nd Floor, Town Hall, Bolton BL1 1RU ☎ 01204 331209 ✆ shaun.wheeler@bolton.gov.uk

Street Scene: Ms Sarah Schofield, Assistant Director - Neighbourhood & Regulatory Services, 3rd Floor, Town Hall, Bolton BL1 1RU ☎ 01204 336718 ✆ sarah.schofield@bolton.gov.uk

Sustainable Development: Mr Stephen Young, Director - Place, 3rd Floor, Town Hall, Bolton BL1 1RU ☎ 01204 336490 ✆ stephen.young@bolton.gov.uk

Tourism: Mr Keith Davies, Director - Development & Regeneration, 3rd Floor, Town Hall, Bolton BL1 1RU ☎ 01204 334002 ✆ keith.davies@bolton.gov.uk

Town Centre: Mr Stephen Young, Director - Place, 3rd Floor, Town Hall, Bolton BL1 1RU ☎ 01204 336490 ✆ stephen.young@bolton.gov.uk

Traffic Management: Mr Stephen Young, Director - Place, The Wellsprings, Civic Centre, Bolton BL1 1US ☎ 01204 336490 ✆ stephen.young@bolton.gov.uk

Transport Planner: Mr Stephen Young, Director - Place, 3rd Floor, Town Hall, Bolton BL1 1RU ☎ 01204 336490 ✆ stephen.young@bolton.gov.uk

Waste Collection and Disposal: Ms Donna Ball, Assistant Director - Place, 3rd Floor, Town Hall, Bolton BL1 1RU ☎ 01204 336713 ✆ donna.ball@bolton.gov.uk

Waste Management: Ms Donna Ball, Assistant Director - Place, 3rd Floor, Town Hall, Bolton BL1 1RU ☎ 01204 336713 ✆ donna.ball@bolton.gov.uk

Children's Play Areas: Ms Sarah Schofield, Assistant Director - Neighbourhood & Regulatory Services, 3rd Floor, Town Hall, Bolton BL1 1RU ☎ 01204 336718 ✆ sarah.schofield@bolton.gov.uk

COUNCILLORS

Mayor: Byrne, Lynda (LAB - Breightmet)
lynda.byrne@bolton.gov.uk

Deputy Mayor: Donaghy, Martin (LAB - Tonge with the Haulgh)
martin.donaghy@bolton.gov.uk

Leader of the Council: Morris, Cliff (LAB - Halliwell)
cliff.morris@bolton.gov.uk

Deputy Leader of the Council: Thomas, Linda (LAB - Halliwell)
linda.thomas@bolton.gov.uk

Group LeaderGreenhalgh, David (CON - Bromley Cross)
david.greenhalgh@bolton.gov.uk

Group LeaderHayes, Roger (LD - Smithills)
roger.hayes@bolton.gov.uk

Group LeaderHornby, Sean (UKIP - Little Lever & Darcy Lever)
sean.hornby@bolton.gov.uk

Adia, Ebrahim (LAB - Rumworth)
ebrahim.adia@bolton.gov.uk

Allen, Robert (CON - Heaton & Lostock)
robert.allen@bolton.gov.uk

Ayub, Mohammed (LAB - Great Lever)
mohammed.ayub@bolton.gov.uk

Burrows, Derek (LAB - Kearsley)
derek.burrows@bolton.gov.uk

Bury, Alan (LAB - Horwich & Blackrod)
alan.bury@bolton.gov.uk

Byrne, John (LAB - Breightmet)
john.bynre@bolton.gov.uk

Chadwick, David (LAB - Westhoughton South)
david.chadwick@bolton.gov.uk

Cox, Martyn (CON - Westhoughton North & Chew Moor)
martyn.cox@bolton.gov.uk

Critchley, Norman (CON - Bromley Cross)
norman.critchley@bolton.gov.uk

Cunliffe, Ann (LAB - Horwich & Blackrod)
ann.cunliffe@bolton.gov.uk

Cunningham, Mark (UKIP - Kearsley)
mark.cunningham@bolton.gov.uk

Darvesh, Hanif (LAB - Crompton)
hanif.darvesh@bolton.gov.uk

Dean, Mudasir (CON - Bradshaw)
mudasir.dean@bolton.gov.uk

Fairclough, Hilary (CON - Astley Bridge)
hilary.fairclough@bolton.gov.uk

Francis, Mike (LAB - Harper Green)
michael.francis@bolton.gov.uk

Gibbon, Rees (UKIP - Little Lever & Darcy Lever)
rees.gibbon@bolton.gov.uk

Gillies, Jean (LAB - Farnworth)
jean.gillies@bolton.gov.uk

Harkin, Guy (LAB - Crompton)
guy.harkin@bolton.gov.uk

Haslam, Stuart (CON - Bradshaw)
stuart.haslam@bolton.gov.uk

Haworth, Susan (LAB - Harper Green)
susan.haworth@bolton.gov.uk

Ibrahim, Ismail (LAB - Rumworth)
ismail.ibrahim@bolton.gov.uk

Ibrahim, Asif (LAB - Farnworth)
asif.ibrahim@bolton.gov.uk

Iqbal, Mohammed (LAB - Great Lever)
mohammed.igbal@botlon.gov.uk

Irving, Liam (LAB - Kearsley)
liam.irving@bolton.gov.uk

Ismail, Bilkis (LAB - Crompton)
bilkis.ismail@bolton.gov.uk

Jones, Kevan (LAB - Westhoughton South)
kevan.jones@bolton.gov.uk

Kay, Rosa (LAB - Rumworth)
rosa.kay@bolton.gov.uk

Kellett, Joyce (LAB - Horwich North East)
joyce.kellett@bolton.gov.uk

BOLTON

Kirk-Robinson, Zoe (CON - Westhoughton North & Chew Moor)
zoe.kirk-robinson@bolton.gov.uk

Martin, Andrew (LD - Smithills)
andrew.martin@bolton.gov.uk

McKeon, Kevin (LAB - Horwich North East)
kevin.mckeon@bolton.gov.uk

Mistry, Champak (LAB - Harper Green)
champak.mistry@bolton.gov.uk

Morgan, Andrew (CON - Heaton & Lostock)
andrew.morgan@bolton.gov.uk

Murray, Madeline (LAB - Great Lever)
madeline.murray@bolton.gov.uk

Newall, Debbie (LAB - Breightmet)
debbie.newall@bolton.gov.uk

Parkinson, Diane (UKIP - Hulton)
diane.parkinson@bolton.gov.uk

Peel, Nicholas (LAB - Tonge with the Haulgh)
nicholas.peel@bolton.gov.uk

Pickup, Stephen (LAB - Horwich & Blackrod)
stephen.pickup@bolton.gov.uk

Radcliffe, Jacqueline (CON - Bradshaw)
jacqueline.radcliffe@bolton.gov.uk

Richardson, Paul (UKIP - Little Lever & Darcy Lever)
paul.richardson@bolton.gov.uk

Shaikh, Shafaqat (LAB - Hulton)
shafaqat.shaikh@bolton.gov.uk

Shaw, Colin (CON - Heaton & Lostock)
colin.shaw@bolton.gov.uk

Sherrington, Elaine (LAB - Tonge with the Haulgh)
elaine.sherrington@bolton.gov.uk

Silvester, Richard (LAB - Horwich North East)
richard.silvester@bolton.gov.uk

Spencer, Noel (LAB - Farnworth)
noel.spencer@bolton.gov.uk

Swarbrick, Carole (LD - Smithills)
carole.swarbrick@bolton.gov.uk

Walsh, John (CON - Astley Bridge)
john.walsh@bolton.gov.uk

Watters, Anna-Marie (LAB - Westhoughton South)
anna-marie.watters@bolton.gov.uk

Whitehead, Darren (LAB - Hulton)
darren.whitehead@bolton.gov.uk

Wild, Paul (CON - Astley Bridge)
paul.wild@bolton.gov.uk

Wild, Christine (CON - Westhoughton North & Chew Moor)
christine.wild@bolton.gov.uk

Wilkinson, Alan (CON - Bromley Cross)
alan.wilkinson@bolton.gov.uk

Zaman, Akhtar (LAB - Halliwell)
akhtar.zaman@bolton.gov.uk

POLITICAL COMPOSITION
LAB: 37, CON: 15, UKIP: 5, LD: 3

COMMITTEE CHAIRS
Audit: Mr David Greenhalgh

Children's Services & Safeguarding: Ms Jean Gillies

Health & Adult Social Care: Mr Champak Mistry

Health & Wellbeing: Mrs Linda Thomas

Licensing & Environmental Regulation: Mr Martin Donaghy

Planning: Mr Hanif Darvesh

Boston   D

Boston Borough Council, Municipal Buildings, West Street, Boston PE21 8QR
☎ 01205 314200 🖷 01205 364604 ⏚ info@boston.gov.uk
🖳 www.boston.gov.uk

FACTS AND FIGURES
Parliamentary Constituencies: Boston and Skegness
EU Constituencies: East Midlands
Election Frequency: Elections are of whole council

PRINCIPAL OFFICERS
Chief Executive: Mr Phil Drury, Chief Executive, Municipal Buildings, West Street, Boston PE21 8QR ☎ 01205 314200
⏚ phil.drury@boston.gov.uk

Senior Management: Mr Robert Barlow, Deputy Chief Executive & Strategic Director - Resources / S151 Officer, Municipal Buildings, West Street, Boston PE21 8QR ☎ 01507 613411
⏚ robert.barlow@boston.gov.uk

Architect, Building / Property Services: Mr Steve Lumb, Head of Built Environment & Development, Municipal Buildings, West Street, Boston PE21 8QR ☎ 01205 314200
⏚ steve.lumb@boston.gov.uk

Architect, Building / Property Services: Mr Gary Sargeant, Corporate Asset Manager, Tedder Hall, Manby Park, Louth LN11 8UP ☎ 01507 613020 ⏚ gary.sargeant@e-lindsey.gov.uk

Building Control: Mr Steve Lumb, Head of Built Environment & Development, Municipal Buildings, West Street, Boston PE21 8QR ☎ 01205 314200 ⏚ steve.lumb@boston.gov.uk

PR / Communications: Mr Andrew Malkin, Communications Manager, Municipal Buildings, West Street, Boston PE21 8QR ☎ 01205 314308 ⏚ andrew.malkin@boston.gov.uk

Community Safety: Mr Andy Fisher, Head of Housing, Health & Communities, Municipal Buildings, West Street, Boston PE21 8QR ☎ 01205 314200 ⏚ andy.fisher@boston.gov.uk

Customer Service: Ms Michelle Sacks, Head of Customer & Democratic Services, Municipal Buildings, West Street, Boston PE21 8QR ⏚ michelle.sacks@boston.gov.uk

Direct Labour: Mr George Bernard, Head of Operations, Fen Road, Frampton Fen, Boston PE20 1RZ ☎ 01205 311112
⏚ george.bernard@boston.gov.uk

Economic Development: Mr Steve Lumb, Head of Built Environment & Development, Municipal Buildings, West Street, Boston PE21 8QR ☎ 01205 314200 🖰 steve.lumb@boston.gov.uk

Electoral Registration: Mrs Lorraine Bush, Democratic Services Manager, Municipal Buildings, West Street, Boston PE21 8QR ☎ 01205 314224 🖰 lorraine.bush@boston.gov.uk

Emergency Planning: Mr Andy Fisher, Head of Housing, Health & Communities, Municipal Buildings, West Street, Boston PE21 8QR ☎ 01205 314200 🖰 andy.fisher@boston.gov.uk

Energy Management: Mr Ian Farmer, Partnerships & Sustainability Manager, Municipal Buildings, West Street, Boston PE21 8QR ☎ 01205 314200 🖰 ian.farmer@boston.gov.uk

Environmental Health: Mr Andy Fisher, Head of Housing, Health & Communities, Municipal Buildings, West Street, Boston PE21 8QR ☎ 01205 314200 🖰 andy.fisher@boston.gov.uk

Estates, Property & Valuation: Mr Andy Fisher, Head of Housing, Health & Communities, Municipal Buildings, West Street, Boston PE21 8QR ☎ 01205 314200 🖰 andy.fisher@boston.gov.uk

Finance: Mr Robert Barlow, Deputy Chief Executive & Strategic Director - Resources / S151 Officer, Municipal Buildings, West Street, Boston PE21 8QR ☎ 01507 613411 🖰 robert.barlow@boston.gov.uk

Finance: Mr Paul Julian, Head of Finance, Municipal Buildings, West Street, Boston PE21 8QR 🖰 paul.julian@boston.gov.uk

Grounds Maintenance: Mr George Bernard, Head of Operations, Fen Road, Frampton Fen, Boston PE20 1RZ ☎ 01205 311112 🖰 george.bernard@boston.gov.uk

Health and Safety: Ms Katharine Nundy, Head of HR & Transformation, Municipal Buildings, West Street, Boston PE21 8QR ☎ 01205 314274 🖰 katharine.nundy@boston.gov.uk

Housing: Mr Andy Fisher, Head of Housing, Health & Communities, Municipal Buildings, West Street, Boston PE21 8QR ☎ 01205 314200 🖰 andy.fisher@boston.gov.uk

Legal: Ms Michelle Sacks, Head of Customer & Democratic Services, Municipal Buildings, West Street, Boston PE21 8QR 🖰 michelle.sacks@boston.gov.uk

Leisure and Cultural Services: Mr Phil Perry, Head of Service, Municipal Buildings, West Street, Boston PE21 8QR ☎ 01205 341200 🖰 phil.perry@boston.gov.uk

Licensing: Ms Fiona White, Principal Licensing & Land Charges Officer, Municipal Buildings, West Street, Boston PE21 8QR ☎ 01205 314242 🖰 fiona.white@boston.gov.uk

Lottery Funding, Charity and Voluntary: Mr Andy Fisher, Head of Housing, Health & Communities, Municipal Buildings, West Street, Boston PE21 8QR ☎ 01205 314200 🖰 andy.fisher@boston.gov.uk

Member Services: Mrs Lorraine Bush, Democratic Services Manager, Municipal Buildings, West Street, Boston PE21 8QR ☎ 01205 314224 🖰 lorraine.bush@boston.gov.uk

Parking: Mr Steve Lumb, Head of Built Environment & Development, Municipal Buildings, West Street, Boston PE21 8QR ☎ 01205 314200 🖰 steve.lumb@boston.gov.uk

Partnerships: Mr Steve Lumb, Head of Built Environment & Development, Municipal Buildings, West Street, Boston PE21 8QR ☎ 01205 314200 🖰 steve.lumb@boston.gov.uk

Personnel / HR: Ms Katharine Nundy, Head of HR & Transformation, Municipal Buildings, West Street, Boston PE21 8QR ☎ 01205 314274 🖰 katharine.nundy@boston.gov.uk

Planning: Mr Steve Lumb, Head of Built Environment & Development, Municipal Buildings, West Street, Boston PE21 8QR ☎ 01205 314200 🖰 steve.lumb@boston.gov.uk

Recycling & Waste Minimisation: Mr George Bernard, Head of Operations, Fen Road, Frampton Fen, Boston PE20 1RZ ☎ 01205 311112 🖰 george.bernard@boston.gov.uk

Staff Training: Ms Katharine Nundy, Head of HR & Transformation, Municipal Buildings, West Street, Boston PE21 8QR ☎ 01205 314274 🖰 katharine.nundy@boston.gov.uk

Sustainable Communities: Mr Andy Fisher, Head of Housing, Health & Communities, Municipal Buildings, West Street, Boston PE21 8QR ☎ 01205 314200 🖰 andy.fisher@boston.gov.uk

Sustainable Development: Mr Steve Lumb, Head of Built Environment & Development, Municipal Buildings, West Street, Boston PE21 8QR ☎ 01205 314200 🖰 steve.lumb@boston.gov.uk

Tourism: Mr Phil Perry, Head of Service, Municipal Buildings, West Street, Boston PE21 8QR ☎ 01205 341200 🖰 phil.perry@boston.gov.uk

Town Centre: Mr Steve Lumb, Head of Built Environment & Development, Municipal Buildings, West Street, Boston PE21 8QR ☎ 01205 314200 🖰 steve.lumb@boston.gov.uk

Waste Collection and Disposal: Mr George Bernard, Head of Operations, Fen Road, Frampton Fen, Boston PE20 1RZ ☎ 01205 311112 🖰 george.bernard@boston.gov.uk

Waste Management: Mr George Bernard, Head of Operations, Fen Road, Frampton Fen, Boston PE20 1RZ ☎ 01205 311112 🖰 george.bernard@boston.gov.uk

COUNCILLORS

Mayor: Woodliffe, Stephen (CON - West) stephen.woodliffe@boston.gov.uk

Deputy Mayor: Dennis, Maureen (CON - Old Leake & Wrangle) maureen.dennis@boston.gov.uk

Leader of the Council: Bedford, Peter (CON - Coastal) peter.bedford@boston.gov.uk

Deputy Leader of the Council: Brookes, Michael (CON - Swineshead & Holland Fen) michael.brookes@boston.gov.uk

BOSTON

Austin, Richard (IND - Wyberton)
richard.austin@boston.gov.uk

Austin, Alison (IND - South)
alison.austin@boston.gov.uk

Ball, Stephen (UKIP - Skirbeck)
stephen.ball@boston.gov.uk

Brotherton, Colin (CON - Kirton & Frampton)
colin.brotherton@boston.gov.uk

Brown, David (UKIP - Wyberton)
david.brown@boston.gov.uk

Cooper, Mike (CON - Five Villages)
michael.cooper@boston.gov.uk

Dani, Anton (UKIP - Fenside)
anton.dani@boston.gov.uk

Edge, Viven (UKIP - Witham)
viven.edge@boston.gov.uk

Edwards, James (UKIP - Kirton & Frampton)
james.edwards@boston.gov.uk

Evans, Ben (CON - Staniland)
ben.evans@boston.gov.uk

Gleeson, Paul (LAB - Skirbeck)
paul.gleeson@boston.gov.uk

Gregory, Gordon (CON - Trinity)
gordon.gregory@boston.gov.uk

Griggs, Martin (CON - Skirbeck)
martin.griggs@boston.gov.uk

Noble, Jonathan (UKIP - Fishtoft)
jonathan.noble@boston.gov.uk

Pierpoint, Barrie (INDNA - Old Leake & Wrangle)
barrie.pierpoint@boston.gov.uk

Ransome, Felicity (UKIP - Costal)
felicity.ransome@boston.gov.uk

Ransome, Elizabeth (UKIP - Swineshead & Holland Fen)
elizabeth.ransome@boston.gov.uk

Ransome, Sue (UKIP - Station)
sue.ransome@boston.gov.uk

Raven, Stephen (UKIP - Witham)
stephen.raven@boston.gov.uk

Rush, Brian (UKIP - Staniland)
brian.rush@boston.gov.uk

Rylott, Claire (CON - Kirton & Frampton)
claire.rylott@boston.gov.uk

Skinner, Judith Ann (CON - Fishtoft)
judith.skinner@boston.gov.uk

Skinner, Paul (CON - Fishtoft)
paul.skinner@boston.gov.uk

Spencer, Aaron (CON - Five Villages)
aaron.spencer@boston.gov.uk

Stevens, Yvonne (UKIP - Trinity)
yvonne.stevens@boston.gov.uk

Welton, Nigel (LAB - Fenside)
nigel.welton@boston.gov.uk

POLITICAL COMPOSITION
CON: 13, UKIP: 12, LAB: 2, IND: 2, INDNA: 1

COMMITTEE CHAIRS

Audit & Governance: Mr Gordon Gregory

Licensing: Mr Colin Brotherton

Planning: Mrs Alison Austin

Bournemouth   U

Bournemouth Council, Town Hall, Bourne Avenue,
Bournemouth BH2 6DY
☎ 01202 451451 🖷 01202 451000
🖐 firstname.surname@bournemouth.gov.uk
🖳 www.bournemouth.gov.uk

FACTS AND FIGURES
Parliamentary Constituencies: Bournemouth East, Bournemouth
West
EU Constituencies: South West
Election Frequency: Elections are of whole council

PRINCIPAL OFFICERS

Chief Executive: Mr Tony Williams, Chief Executive, Town Hall,
Bourne Avenue, Bournemouth BH2 6DY ☎ 01202 451130
🖐 tony.williams@bournemouth.gov.uk

Deputy Chief Executive: Ms Jane Portman, Deputy Chief
Executive & Executive Director - Adult & Children, Town Hall,
Bourne Avenue, Bournemouth BH2 6DY ☎ 01202 456104
🖐 jane.portman@bournemouth.gov.uk

Senior Management: Mrs Carole Aspden, Service Director -
Children & Young People's Services, Town Hall, Bourne Avenue,
Bournemouth BH2 6DY ☎ 01202 456118
🖐 carole.aspden@bournemouth.gov.uk

Senior Management: Mr Larry Austin, Service Director -
Environment, Southcote Road Depot, 103 Southcote Road,
Bournemouth BH1 3SW ☎ 01202 451690
🖐 larry.austin@bournemouth.gov.uk

Senior Management: Mr Roger Ball, Service Director -
Development Services, Town Hall Annexe, St. Stephen's Road,
Bournemouth BH2 6EA ☎ 01202 451340
🖐 roger.ball@bournemouth.gov.uk

Senior Management: Ms Sue Bickler, Head of Community
Regeneration, Town Hall, Bourne Avenue, Bournemouth BH2 6DY
☎ 01202 454966 🖐 sue.bickler@bournemouth.gov.uk

Senior Management: Ms Ivor Cawthorn, Strategic
Commissioning Manager, Town Hall, Bourne Avenue, Bournemouth
BH2 6DY ☎ 01202 458703 🖐 ivor.cawthorn@bournemouth.gov.uk

Senior Management: Ms Tanya Coulter, Service Director - Legal
& Democratic Services, Town Hall, Bourne Avenue, Bournemouth
BH2 6DY ☎ 01202 451172 🖐 tanya.coulter@bournemouth.gov.uk

Senior Management: Mr Neil Goddard, Service Director -
Community Learning & Commissioning, Town Hall, Bourne Avenue,
Bournemouth BH2 6DY ☎ 01202 456136
🖐 neil.goddard@bournemouth.gov.uk

Senior Management: Dr David Phillips, Director - Public Health, Civic Centre, Poole BH15 2RU ☎ 01305 225868 ⊕ d.phillips@poole.gov.uk

Senior Management: Mr Mark Smith, Director - Tourism, Visitor Information Bureau, Westover Road, Bournemouth BH1 2BU ☎ 01202 451706 ⊕ mark.smith@bournemouth.gov.uk

Architect, Building / Property Services: Mr Roger Ball, Service Director - Development Services, Town Hall Annexe, St. Stephen's Road, Bournemouth BH2 6EA ☎ 01202 451340 ⊕ roger.ball@bournemouth.gov.uk

Best Value: Ms Clare Matthews, Policy, Strategy & Performance Officer, Town Hall, Bourne Avenue, Bournemouth BH2 6DY ☎ 01202 454958 ⊕ clare.matthews@bournemouth.gov.uk

Building Control: Mr Roger Ball, Service Director - Development Services, Town Hall Annexe, St. Stephen's Road, Bournemouth BH2 6EA ☎ 01202 451340 ⊕ roger.ball@bournemouth.gov.uk

Catering Services: Mr Graham Twigg, Facilities Management Service Delivery Manager, Town Hall, Bourne Avenue, Bournemouth BH2 6DY ⊕ graham.twigg@bournemouth.gov.uk

Children / Youth Services: Mrs Carole Aspden, Service Director - Children & Young People's Services, Town Hall, Bourne Avenue, Bournemouth BH2 6DY ☎ 01202 456118 ⊕ carole.aspden@bournemouth.gov.uk

Civil Registration: Ms Helen Rigg, Registration & Coroners Services Manager, Town Hall, Bourne Avenue, Bournemouth BH2 6DY ☎ 01202 454629 ⊕ helen.rigg@bournemouth.gov.uk

PR / Communications: Mrs Georgia Turner, Corporate Communications Manager, Town Hall, Bournemouth BH2 6DY ☎ 01202 451039 ⊕ georgia.turner@bournemouth.gov.uk

Community Safety: Mr Andrew Williams, Team Manager - Safer & Stronger Communities, Town Hall, Bourne Avenue, Bournemouth BH2 6DY ☎ 01202 458240 ⊕ andrew.williams@bournemouth.gov.uk

Computer Management: Mr Nick Palmer, Head of Strategic ICT, Town Hall, Bourne Avenue, Bournemouth BH2 6DY ☎ 01202 451312 ⊕ nick.palmer@bournemouth.gov.uk

Consumer Protection and Trading Standards: Mr Andy Sherriff, Principal Trading Standards Officer, Town Hall, Bourne Avenue, Bournemouth BH2 6DY ☎ 01202 541440 ⊕ andy.sherriff@bournemouth.gov.uk

Contracts: Mr Jeremy Richardson, Head of Strategic Procurement & Commissioning, Town Hall, Bourne Avenue, Bournemouth BH2 6DY ☎ 01202 458233 ⊕ jeremy.richardson@bournemouth.gov.uk

Customer Service: Ms Maria O'Reilly, Head of Customer Services, Town Hall, Bourne Avenue, Bournemouth BH2 6DY ☎ 01202 454953 ⊕ maria.o'reilly@bournemouth.gov.uk

Customer Service: Mr Stuart Walters, Customer Services Manager, Town Hall, Bourne Avenue, Bournemouth BH2 6DY ☎ 01202 454711 ⊕ stuart.walters@bournemouth.gov.uk

Economic Development: Mr Christopher Shephard, Head of Economic Development & Sustainability, Town Hall, Bourne Avenue, Bournemouth BH2 6DY ☎ 01202 454643 ⊕ chris.shephard@bournemouth.gov.uk

Education: Ms Jane Portman, Deputy Chief Executive & Executive Director - Adult & Children, Town Hall, Bourne Avenue, Bournemouth BH2 6DY ☎ 01202 456104 ⊕ jane.portman@bournemouth.gov.uk

Electoral Registration: Mr Matt Pitcher, Electoral Services Officer, Room 40, Town Hall, Bourne Avenue, Bournemouth BH2 6DY ☎ 01202 451122 ⊕ matt.pitcher@bournemouth.gov.uk

Emergency Planning: Ms Alyson Whitley, Resilience & Safety Manager, Town Hall, Bourne Avenue, Bournemouth BH2 6DY ☎ 01202 451281 ⊕ alyson.whitley@bournemouth.gov.uk

Energy Management: Mr Roger Ball, Service Director - Development Services, Town Hall Annexe, St. Stephen's Road, Bournemouth BH2 6EA ☎ 01202 451340 ⊕ roger.ball@bournemouth.gov.uk

Environmental / Technical Services: Mr Roger Ball, Service Director - Development Services, Town Hall Annexe, St. Stephen's Road, Bournemouth BH2 6EA ☎ 01202 451340 ⊕ roger.ball@bournemouth.gov.uk

Environmental Health: Mr Roger Ball, Service Director - Development Services, Town Hall Annexe, St. Stephen's Road, Bournemouth BH2 6EA ☎ 01202 451340 ⊕ roger.ball@bournemouth.gov.uk

Estates, Property & Valuation: Mr Gary Platt, Property Services Manager, Town Hall Annexe, St. Stephen's Road, Bournemouth BH2 6EA ☎ 01202 451477 ⊕ gary.platt@bournemouth.gov.uk

European Liaison: Mr Christopher Kelu, Business Support Officer, Town Hall, Bourne Avenue, Bournemouth BH2 6DY ☎ 01202 545630 ⊕ christopher.kelu@bournemouth.gov.uk

Events Manager: Mr Jon Weaver, Marketing & Events Manager, Visitor Information Bureau, Westover Road, Bournemouth BH1 2BU ☎ 01202 451737 ⊕ jon.weaver@bournemouth.gov.uk

Facilities: Mr Graham Twigg, Facilities Management Service Delivery Manager, Town Hall, Bourne Avenue, Bournemouth BH2 6DY ⊕ graham.twigg@bournemouth.gov.uk

Fleet Management: Mr Larry Austin, Service Director - Environment, Southcote Road Depot, 103 Southcote Road, Bournemouth BH1 3SW ☎ 01202 451690 ⊕ larry.austin@bournemouth.gov.uk

Grounds Maintenance: Mr Michael Rowland, Green Spaces Project Officer, Queens Park Pavilion, Queens Park West Drive, Bournemouth BH8 9BY ☎ 01202 451632 ⊕ michael.rowlands@bournemouth.gov.uk

Health and Safety: Mr John Towner, Corporate Health & Safety Officer, Town Hall, Bourne Avenue, Bournemouth BH2 6DY ☎ 01202 451484 ⊕ john.towner@bournemouth.gov.uk

BOURNEMOUTH

Highways: Mr Ken Hobbs, Principal Traffic Engineer, Town Hall Annexe, St. Stephen's Road, Bournemouth BH2 6EA ☎ 01202 451388 ✆ ken.hobbs@bournemouth.gov.uk

Home Energy Conservation: Mr Roger Ball, Service Director - Development Services, Town Hall Annexe, St. Stephen's Road, Bournemouth BH2 6EA ☎ 01202 451340 ✆ roger.ball@bournemouth.gov.uk

Housing: Ms Lorraine Mealings, Strategic Housing Services Manager, Town Hall, Bourne Avenue, Bournemouth BH2 6DY ☎ 01202 458226 ✆ lorraine.mealings@bournemouth.gov.uk

Housing Maintenance: Mr Gary Josey, Service Director - Housing & Communities, Housing Technical Services, Unit 4, Dalling Road, Poole BH12 6DJ ☎ 01202 458301 ✆ gary.josey@bournemouth.gov.uk

Legal: Ms Sian Ballingall, Legal & Democratic Services Manager, Town Hall, Bourne Avenue, Bournemouth BH2 6DY ☎ 01202 454648 ✆ sian.ballingall@bournemouth.gov.uk

Leisure and Cultural Services: Mr Neil Goddard, Service Director - Community Learning & Commissioning, Town Hall, Bourne Avenue, Bournemouth BH2 6DY ☎ 01202 456136 ✆ neil.goddard@bournemouth.gov.uk

Licensing: Mr Roger Ball, Service Director - Development Services, Town Hall Annexe, St. Stephen's Road, Bournemouth BH2 6EA ☎ 01202 451340 ✆ roger.ball@bournemouth.gov.uk

Lighting: Mr Roger Ball, Service Director - Development Services, Technical Services, Town Hall Annexe, St Stephen's Road, Bournemouth BH2 6EA ☎ 01202 451340 ✆ roger.ball@bournemouth.gov.uk

Lottery Funding, Charity and Voluntary: Mr Gary Bentham, Community Liaison Officer, Town Hall, Bourne Avenue, Bournemouth BH2 6DY ☎ 01202 451165 ✆ gary.bentham@bournemouth.gov.uk

Member Services: Mrs Karen Tompkins, Democratic & Member Support Services Manager, Town Hall, Bourne Avenue, Bournemouth BH2 6DY ☎ 01202 454689 ✆ karen.tompkins@bournemouth.gov.uk

Parking: Mr Gary Powell, Enforcement & Parking Manager, Enforcement & Parking Centre, Town Hall Annexe, St Stephen's Road, Bournemouth BH2 6DY ☎ 01202 451456 ✆ gary.powell@bournemouth.gov.uk

Personnel / HR: Ms Saskia DeVries, Interim Head of Strategic PR, Town Hall, Bourne Avenue, Bournemouth BH2 6DY ☎ 01202 451134 ✆ saskia.devries@bournemouth.gov.uk

Planning: Mr Larry Austin, Service Director - Environment, Southcote Road Depot, 103 Southcote Road, Bournemouth BH1 3SW ☎ 01202 451690 ✆ larry.austin@bournemouth.gov.uk

Procurement: Mr Jeremy Richardson, Head of Strategic Procurement & Commissioning, Town Hall, Bourne Avenue, Bournemouth BH2 6DY ☎ 01202 458233 ✆ jeremy.richardson@bournemouth.gov.uk

Public Libraries: Mr Neil Goddard, Service Director - Community Learning & Commissioning, Town Hall, Bourne Avenue, Bournemouth BH2 6DY ☎ 01202 456136 ✆ neil.goddard@bournemouth.gov.uk

Recycling & Waste Minimisation: Mr Roger Ball, Service Director - Development Services, Town Hall Annexe, St. Stephen's Road, Bournemouth BH2 6EA ☎ 01202 451340 ✆ roger.ball@bournemouth.gov.uk

Road Safety: Mr John Satchwell, Road Safety Manager, Town Hall Annexe, St. Stephen's Road, Bournemouth BH2 6EA ☎ 01202 451461 ✆ john.satchwell@bournemouth.gov.uk

Social Services: Ms Sue Ross, Interim Service Director - Children's Social Care, Town Hall, Bourne Avenue, Bournemouth BH2 6DY ☎ 01202 458721 ✆ sue.ross@bournemouth.gov.uk

Social Services (Adult): Mr Andy Sharp, Service Director - Adult Social Care, Town Hall, Bourne Avenue, Bournemouth BH2 6DY ✆ andy.sharp@bournemouth.gov.uk

Social Services (Children): Ms Sue Ross, Interim Service Director - Children's Social Care, Town Hall, Bourne Avenue, Bournemouth BH2 6DY ☎ 01202 458721 ✆ sue.ross@bournemouth.gov.uk

Public Health: Dr David Phillips, Director - Public Health, Civic Centre, Poole BH15 2RU ☎ 01305 225868 ✆ d.phillips@poole.gov.uk

Street Scene: Mr Stuart Best, Street Services Manager, Southcote Road Depot, 103 Southcote Road, Bournemouth BH1 3SW ☎ 01202 451423 ✆ stuart.best@bournemouth.gov.uk

Sustainable Development: Mr Bill Cotton, Executive Director - Environment & Economy, Town Hall, Bourne Avenue, Bournemouth BH2 6DY ☎ 01202 458702 ✆ bill.cotton@bournemouth.gov.uk

Tourism: Mr Mark Smith, Director - Tourism, Visitor Information Bureau, Westover Road, Bournemouth BH1 2BU ☎ 01202 451706 ✆ mark.smith@bournemouth.gov.uk

Traffic Management: Mr Ken Hobbs, Principal Traffic Engineer, Town Hall Annexe, St. Stephen's Road, Bournemouth BH2 6EA ☎ 01202 451388 ✆ ken.hobbs@bournemouth.gov.uk

Transport: Mr Larry Austin, Service Director - Environment, Southcote Road Depot, 103 Southcote Road, Bournemouth BH1 3SW ☎ 01202 451690 ✆ larry.austin@bournemouth.gov.uk

Transport Planner: Mr Ian Kalra, Transportation Services Manager, Town Hall, Bourne Avenue, Bournemouth BH2 6DY ☎ 01202 451447 ✆ ian.kalra@bournemouth.gov.uk

Waste Management: Mr Roger Ball, Service Director - Development Services, Town Hall Annexe, St. Stephen's Road, Bournemouth BH2 6EA ☎ 01202 451340 ✆ roger.ball@bournemouth.gov.uk

Children's Play Areas: Mr Andy McDonald, Parks Manager - Operations, Town Hall, Bourne Avenue, Bournemouth BH2 6DY ☎ 01202 451695 ✆ andy.mcdonald@bournemouth.gov.uk

COUNCILLORS

Mayor: Coope, Eddie (CON - East Southbourne & Tuckton)
eddie.coope@bournemouth.gov.uk

Deputy Mayor: Adams, John (CON - Strouden Park)
john.adams@bournemouth.gov.uk

Leader of the Council: Beesley, John (CON - Westbourne & West Cliff)
john.beesley@bournemouth.gov.uk

Deputy Leader of the Council: Greene, Nicola (CON - Wallisdown & Winton West)
nicola.greene@bournemouth.gov.uk

Anderson, Sue (CON - Moordown)
sue.anderson@bournemouth.gov.uk

Anderson, Mark (CON - Queens Park)
mark.anderson@bournemouth.gov.uk

Angiolini, Amedeo (CON - Kinson North)
amedeo.angiolini@bournemouth.gov.uk

Bartlett, Stephen (CON - Redhill & Northbourne)
stephen.bartlett@bournmouth.gov.uk

Battistini, Mark (CON - Kinson North)
mark.battistini@bournemouth.gov.uk

Borthwick, Derek (CON - Throop & Muscliff)
derek.borthwich@bournemouth.gov.uk

Broadhead, Philip (CON - Talbot & Branksome Woods)
philip.boradhead@bournemouth@gov.uk

Bull, Simon (GRN - Winton East)
simon.bull@bournemouth.gov.uk

Chapman, Robert (CON - Central)
robert.chapman@bournemouth.gov.uk

Clark, Ian (CON - Throop & Muscliff)
ian.clark@bournemouth.gov.uk

Crawford, Blair (CON - West Southbourne)
blair.crawford@bouremouth.gov.uk

Davies, Malcolm (CON - East Southbourne & Tuckton)
malcolm.davies@bournemouth.gov.uk

Decent, Norman (CON - Kinson South)
norman.decent@bournmout.gov.uk

D'Orton-Gibson, David (CON - Redhill & Northbourne)
david.dorton-gibson@bournemouth.gov.uk

Dove, Bobbie (CON - Littledown & Ilford)
bobbi.dove@bournemouth.gov.k

Dunlop, Beverley (CON - Moordown)
beverley.dunlop@bournemouth.gov.uk

Edwards, Jackie (CON - Redhill & Northbuorne)
jacki.edwards@bournmouth.gov.uk

Fear, Laurence (UKIP - Kinson South)
laurence.fear@bournmouth.gov.uk

Filer, Anne (CON - East Cliff & Springbourne)
anne.filer@bournemouth.gov.uk

Filer, Michael (CON - East Cliff & Springbourne)
michael.filer@bournemouth.gov.uk

Greene, Mike (CON - Central)
mike.greene@bournemouth.gov.uk

Hedges, Nigel (CON - Wallisdown & Winton West)
nigel.hedges@bournemouth.gov.uk

Johnson, Cheryl (CON - Queens Park)
cheryl.johnson@bournemouth.gov.uk

Jones, Andy (CON - Boscombe East)
andy.jones@bournemouth@gov.uk

Kelly, Jane (CON - Boscombe West)
jane.kelly@bournemouth.gov.uk

Kelsey, David (CON - East Cliff & Springbourne)
david.kelsey@bournemouth.gov.uk

Lancashire, Ian (CON - Moordown)
ian.lancashire@bournemouth.gov.uk

Lawton, Robert (CON - East Southbourne & Tuckton)

MacLoughlin, Stephen (CON - Queens Park)
stephen.macloughlin@bournemouth.gov.uk

Marley, Roger (CON - Kinson South)
roger.marley@bournemouth.gov.uk

Mayne, Chris (CON - West Southbourne)
chris.mayne@bournemouth.gov.uk

McQueen, Donald (CON - Winton East)
donald.mcqueen@bournemouth.gov.uk

Morgan, Andrew (CON - Talbot & Branksome Woods)
andrew.morgan@bournemouth.gov.uk

Oakley, Patrick (CON - Winton East)
patrick.oakley@bournemouth.gov.uk

Pacifico-Mackin, Gina (CON - Boscombe East)
gina.pacificomakin@bournmouth.gov.uk

Phillips, Susan (CON - Wallisdown & Winton West)
susan.phillips@bournemouth.gov.uk

Price, Lynda (CON - Talbot & Branksome Woods)
lynda.price@bournemouth.gov.uk

Rey, Anne (IND - Throop & Muscliff)
anne.rey@bournemouth.gov.uk

Rochester, Christopher (CON - Boscombe East)
christopher.rochester@bournemouth.gov.uk

Ross, Nick (CON - Westbourne & West Cliff)
ncik.ross@bournemouth.gov.uk

Russell, Allister (CON - West Southbourne)
allister.russell@bournemouth.gov.uk

Seymour, Gill (CON - Littledown & Iford)
gill.seymour@bournemouth.gov.uk

Smith, David (CON - Central)
david.smith@bournemouth.gov.uk

Stanley-Watts, Philip (CON - Boscombe West)
philip.stanley-watts@bournemouth.gov.uk

Stollard, Rae (CON - Westbourne & West Cliff)
rae.stollard@bournemouth.gov.uk

Trickett, John (CON - Strouden Park)
john.trickett@bournemouth.gov.uk

Turtle, David (CON - Kinson North)
david.turtle@bournemouth.gov.uk

Wakefield, Christopher (CON - Boscombe West)
christopher.wakefield@bournemouth.gov.uk

Weinhonig, Michael (CON - Strouden Park)
michael.weinhonig@bournemouth.gov.uk

Williams, Lawrence (CON - Littledown & Iford)

BOURNEMOUTH

POLITICAL COMPOSITION
CON: 51, IND: 1, GRN: 1, UKIP: 1

COMMITTEE CHAIRS

Children's Services: Mr Christopher Wakefield

Environment & Transport: Mr Mark Anderson

Health & Adult Social Care: Mr David D'Orton-Gibson

Licensing: Mr Andrew Morgan

Planning: Mr David Kelsey

Bracknell Forest   U

Bracknell Forest Borough Council, Easthampstead House, Town Square, Bracknell RG12 1AQ
☎ 01344 352000 🖷 01344 411875
✆ customer.services@bracknell-forest.gov.uk
🖳 www.bracknell-forest.gov.uk

FACTS AND FIGURES
Parliamentary Constituencies: Bracknell
EU Constituencies: South East
Election Frequency: Elections are of whole council

PRINCIPAL OFFICERS

Chief Executive: Mr Timothy Wheadon, Chief Executive, Easthampstead House, Town Square, Bracknell RG12 1AQ
☎ 01344 352000 ✆ timothy.wheadon@bracknell-forest.gov.uk

Deputy Chief Executive: Mrs Alison Sanders, Deputy Chief Executive & Director - Corporate Services, Easthampstead House, Town Square, Bracknell RG12 1AQ ☎ 01344 352000
✆ alison.sanders@bracknell-forest.gov.uk

Assistant Chief Executive: Mr Victor Nicholls, Assistant Chief Executive, Easthampstead House, Town Square, Bracknell RG12 1AQ ☎ 01344 352000 ✆ victor.nicholls@bracknell-forest.gov.uk

Senior Management: Ms Nikki Edwards, Director - Children, Young People & Learning, Easthampstead House, Town Square, Bracknell RG12 1AQ ☎ 01344 352000
✆ nikki.edwards@bracknell-forest.gov.uk

Senior Management: Dr Lise Llewellyn, Director - Public Health, Time Square, Market Street, Bracknell RG12 1JD ☎ 01344 352000
✆ lise.llewellyn@bracknell-forest.gov.uk

Senior Management: Mr Vincent Paliczka, Director - Environment, Culture & Communities, Time Square, 4th Floor Time Square South, Market Street, Bracknell RG12 1AU ☎ 01344 352000
✆ vincent.paliczka@bracknell-forest.gov.uk

Senior Management: Mrs Alison Sanders, Deputy Chief Executive & Director - Corporate Services, Easthampstead House, Town Square, Bracknell RG12 1AQ ☎ 01344 352000
✆ alison.sanders@bracknell-forest.gov.uk

Senior Management: Mrs Gillian Vickers, Director - Adult Social Care, Health & Housing, Time Square, Market Street, Bracknell RG12 1JD ☎ 01344 352000 ✆ gill.vickers@bracknell-forest.gov.uk

Access Officer / Social Services (Disability): Mrs Ann Groves, Urban Design Officer, Time Square, Market Street, Bracknell RG12 1JD ☎ 01344 352000 ✆ ann.groves@bracknell-forest.gov.uk

Architect, Building / Property Services: Mr Steven Caplan, Chief Officer - Property, Easthampstead House, Town Square, Bracknell RG12 1AQ ☎ 01344 352000
✆ steven.caplan@bracknell-forest.gov.uk

Best Value: Mr Richard Beaumont, Head - Overview & Scrutiny, Easthampstead House, Town Square, Bracknell RG12 1AQ
☎ 01344 352000 ✆ richard.beaumont@bracknell-forest.gov.uk

Building Control: Mr David Constable, Senior Building Control Surveyor, Time Square, Market Street, Bracknell RG12 1JD
☎ 01344 352000 ✆ david.constable@bracknell-forest.gov.uk

Catering Services: Mr David Eagle, Contracts Monitoring Officer, Time Square, Market Street, Bracknell RG12 1JD ☎ 01344 352000
✆ david.eagle@bracknell-forest.gov.uk

Children / Youth Services: Ms Nikki Edwards, Director - Children, Young People & Learning, Easthampstead House, Town Square, Bracknell RG12 1AQ ☎ 01344 352000
✆ nikki.edwards@bracknell-forest.gov.uk

Children / Youth Services: Mrs Lorna Hunt, Chief Officer - Children's Social Care, Time Square, Market Street, Bracknell RG12 1JD ☎ 01344 352000 ✆ lorna.hunt@bracknell-forest.gov.uk

Civil Registration: Mrs Ann Moore, Head - Democratic & Registration Services, Easthampstead House, Town Square, Bracknell RG12 1AQ ☎ 01344 352000
✆ ann.moore@bracknell-forest.gov.uk

PR / Communications: Miss Melinda Brown, Head - Communications & Marketing, Easthampstead House, Town Square, Bracknell RG12 1AQ ☎ 01344 352000
✆ melinda.brown@bracknell-forest.gov.uk

Community Planning: Mr Victor Nicholls, Assistant Chief Executive, Easthampstead House, Town Square, Bracknell RG12 1AQ ☎ 01344 352000 ✆ victor.nicholls@bracknell-forest.gov.uk

Community Safety: Mrs Kellie Williams, Safer Communities Manager, Easthampstead House, Town Square, Bracknell RG12 1AQ
☎ 01344 352000 ✆ kellie.williams@bracknell-forest.gov.uk

Computer Management: Mr Pat Keane, Chief Officer - Information Services, Easthampstead House, Town Square, Bracknell RG12 1AQ ☎ 01344 352000
✆ pat.keane@bracknell-forest.gov.uk

Consumer Protection and Trading Standards: Mr Robert Sexton, Trading Standards & Services Manager, Time Square, Market Street, Bracknell RG12 1JD ☎ 01344 352000
✆ robert.sexton@bracknell-forest.gov.uk

Contracts: Mr Timothy Wheadon, Chief Executive, Easthampstead House, Town Square, Bracknell RG12 1AQ ☎ 01344 352000
✆ timothy.wheadon@bracknell-forest.gov.uk

Corporate Services: Mrs Alison Sanders, Deputy Chief Executive & Director - Corporate Services, Easthampstead House, Town Square, Bracknell RG12 1AQ ☎ 01344 352000 ⌁ alison.sanders@bracknell-forest.gov.uk

Customer Service: Mrs Bobby Mulheir, Chief Officer - Customer Services, Time Square, Market Street, Bracknell RG12 1JD ☎ 01344 352000 ⌁ bobby.mulheir@bracknell-forest.gov.uk

Economic Development: Mr Victor Nicholls, Assistant Chief Executive, Easthampstead House, Town Square, Bracknell RG12 1AQ ☎ 01344 352000 ⌁ victor.nicholls@bracknell-forest.gov.uk

Education: Ms Nikki Edwards, Director - Children, Young People & Learning, Easthampstead House, Town Square, Bracknell RG12 1AQ ☎ 01344 352000 ⌁ nikki.edwards@bracknell-forest.gov.uk

E-Government: Mr Pat Keane, Chief Officer - Information Services, Easthampstead House, Town Square, Bracknell RG12 1AQ ☎ 01344 352000 ⌁ pat.keane@bracknell-forest.gov.uk

Electoral Registration: Ms Glenda Favor-Anderson, Registration Services Manager, Easthampstead House, Town Square, Bracknell RG12 1AQ ☎ 01344 352000 ⌁ glenda.favor-anderson@bracknell-forest.gov.uk

Emergency Planning: Mrs Louise Osborn, Emergency Planning Officer, The Central Depot, Old Bracknell Lane West, Bracknell Forest Borough Council, Bracknell RG12 7QT ☎ 01344 352000 ⌁ louise.osborn@bracknell-forest.gov.uk

Energy Management: Mr Steven Milne, Energy Manager, Time Square, Market Street, Bracknell RG12 1JD ☎ 01344 352000 ⌁ steven.milne@bracknell-forest.gov.uk

Environmental / Technical Services: Mr Vincent Paliczka, Director - Environment, Culture & Communities, Time Square, Market Street, Bracknell RG12 1JD ☎ 01344 352000 ⌁ vincent.paliczka@bracknell-forest.gov.uk

Environmental Health: Mr Steve Loudoun, Chief Officer - Environment & Public Protection, Time Square, Market Street, Bracknell RG12 1JD ☎ 01344 352000 ⌁ steve.loudoun@bracknell-forest.gov.uk

Estates, Property & Valuation: Mr Steven Caplan, Chief Officer - Property, Easthampstead House, Town Square, Bracknell RG12 1AQ ☎ 01344 352000 ⌁ steven.caplan@bracknell-forest.gov.uk

Facilities: Mr Steve Booth, Head of Property & Facilities, Easthampstead House, Town Square, Bracknell RG12 1AQ ☎ 01344 352000 ⌁ steve.booth@bracknell-forest.gov.uk

Finance: Mr Alan Nash, Borough Treasurer, Easthampstead House, Town Square, Bracknell RG12 1AQ ☎ 01344 352000 ⌁ alan.nash@bracknell-forest.gov.uk

Health and Safety: Mr Andy Anderson, Senior Health & Safety Advisor, Easthampstead House, Town Square, Bracknell RG12 1AQ ☎ 01344 352000 ⌁ andy.anderson@bracknell-forest.gov.uk

Highways: Mr Steve Loudoun, Chief Officer - Environment & Public Protection, Time Square, Market Street, Bracknell RG12 1JD ☎ 01344 352000 ⌁ steve.loudoun@bracknell-forest.gov.uk

Home Energy Conservation: Mrs Hazel Hill, Sustainable Energy Officer, Time Square, Market Street, Bracknell RG12 1JD ☎ 01344 352000 ⌁ hazel.hill@bracknell-forest.gov.uk

Housing: Mr Simon Hendey, Chief Officer - Housing, Time Square, Market Street, Bracknell RG12 1JD ☎ 01344 352000 ⌁ simon.hendey@bracknell-forest.gov.uk

Local Area Agreement: Mr Victor Nicholls, Assistant Chief Executive, Easthampstead House, Town Square, Bracknell RG12 1AQ ☎ 01344 352000 ⌁ victor.nicholls@bracknell-forest.gov.uk

Legal: Mr Sanjay Prashar, Borough Solicitor, Easthampstead House, Town Square, Bracknell RG12 1AQ ☎ 01344 352000 ⌁ sanjay.prashar@bracknell-forest.gov.uk

Leisure and Cultural Services: Mr Vincent Paliczka, Director - Environment, Culture & Communities, Time Square, Market Street, Bracknell RG12 1JD ☎ 01344 352000 ⌁ vincent.paliczka@bracknell-forest.gov.uk

Licensing: Ms Laura Driscoll, Licensing Team Leader, Easthampstead House, Town Square, Bracknell RG12 1AQ ☎ 01344 352517 ⌁ laura.driscoll@bracknell-forest.gov.uk

Lighting: Mr Steve Loudoun, Chief Officer - Environment & Public Protection, Time Square, Market Street, Bracknell RG12 1JD ☎ 01344 352000 ⌁ steve.loudoun@bracknell-forest.gov.uk

Lottery Funding, Charity and Voluntary: Mr Victor Nicholls, Assistant Chief Executive, Easthampstead House, Town Square, Bracknell RG12 1AQ ☎ 01344 352000 ⌁ victor.nicholls@bracknell-forest.gov.uk

Member Services: Mrs Kirsty Hunt, Senior Democratic Services Officer, Easthampstead House, Town Square, Bracknell RG12 1AQ ☎ 01344 352000 ⌁ kirsty.hunt@bracknell-forest.gov.uk

Parking: Mr Andrew Hunter, Chief Officer - Planning & Transport, Time Square, Market Street, Bracknell RG12 1JD ☎ 01344 352000 ⌁ andrew.hunter@bracknell-forest.gov.uk

Partnerships: Ms Abby Thomas, Head - Performance & Partnerships, Easthampstead House, Town Square, Bracknell RG12 1AQ ☎ 01344 352000 ⌁ abby.thomas@bracknell-forest.gov.uk

Personnel / HR: Mrs Nikki Gibbons, Chief Officer - Human Resources, Easthampstead House, Town Square, Bracknell RG12 1AQ ☎ 01344 352000 ⌁ nikki.gibbons@bracknell-forest.gov.uk

Planning: Mr Andrew Hunter, Chief Officer - Planning & Transport, Time Square, Market Street, Bracknell RG12 1JD ☎ 01344 352000 ⌁ andrew.hunter@bracknell-forest.gov.uk

Procurement: Mr Geoff Reynolds, Head - Procurement, Easthampstead House, Town Square, Bracknell RG12 1AQ ☎ 01344 352000 ⌁ geoff.reynolds@bracknell-forest.gov.uk

BRACKNELL FOREST

Public Libraries: Ms Ruth Burgess, Head - Libraries, Time Square, Market Street, Bracknell RG12 1JD ☎ 01344 352000 ᐃ ruth.burgess@bracknell-forest.gov.uk

Recycling & Waste Minimisation: Mrs Janet Dowlman, Waste & Recycling Manager, Time Square, Market Street, Bracknell RG12 1JD ☎ 01344 352000 ᐃ janet.dowlman@bracknell-forest.gov.uk

Regeneration: Mr Victor Nicholls, Assistant Chief Executive, Easthampstead House, Town Square, Bracknell RG12 1AQ ☎ 01344 352000 ᐃ victor.nicholls@bracknell-forest.gov.uk

Social Services: Mrs Gillian Vickers, Director - Adult Social Care, Health & Housing, Time Square, Market Street, Bracknell RG12 1JD ☎ 01344 352000 ᐃ gill.vickers@bracknell-forest.gov.uk

Social Services (Adult): Mrs Gillian Vickers, Director - Adult Social Care, Health & Housing, Time Square, Market Street, Bracknell RG12 1JD ☎ 01344 352000 ᐃ gill.vickers@bracknell-forest.gov.uk

Social Services (Children): Mrs Lorna Hunt, Chief Officer - Children's Social Care, Time Square, Market Street, Bracknell RG12 1JD ☎ 01344 352000 ᐃ lorna.hunt@bracknell-forest.gov.uk

Childrens Social Care: Mrs Lorna Hunt, Chief Officer - Children's Social Care, Time Square, Market Street, Bracknell RG12 1JD ☎ 01344 352000 ᐃ lorna.hunt@bracknell-forest.gov.uk

Public Health: Dr Lise Llewellyn, Director - Public Health, Time Square, Market Street, Bracknell RG12 1JD ☎ 01344 352000 ᐃ lise.llewellyn@bracknell-forest.gov.uk

Staff Training: Mrs Nikki Gibbons, Chief Officer - Human Resources, Easthampstead House, Town Square, Bracknell RG12 1AQ ☎ 01344 352000 ᐃ nikki.gibbons@bracknell-forest.gov.uk

Street Scene: Mr Steve Loudoun, Chief Officer - Environment & Public Protection, Time Square, Market Street, Bracknell RG12 1JD ☎ 01344 352000 ᐃ steve.loudoun@bracknell-forest.gov.uk

Sustainable Communities: Mr Simon Hendey, Chief Officer - Housing, Time Square, Market Street, Bracknell RG12 1JD ☎ 01344 352000 ᐃ simon.hendey@bracknell-forest.gov.uk

Tourism: Mr Vincent Paliczka, Director - Environment, Culture & Communities, Time Square, Market Street, Bracknell RG12 1JD ☎ 01344 352000 ᐃ vincent.paliczka@bracknell-forest.gov.uk

Waste Collection and Disposal: Mrs Janet Dowlman, Waste & Recycling Manager, Time Square, Market Street, Bracknell RG12 1JD ☎ 01344 352000 ᐃ janet.dowlman@bracknell-forest.gov.uk

Waste Collection and Disposal: Mr Vincent Paliczka, Director - Environment, Culture & Communities, Time Square, Market Street, Bracknell RG12 1JD ☎ 01344 352000 ᐃ vincent.paliczka@bracknell-forest.gov.uk

Waste Management: Mr Vincent Paliczka, Director - Environment, Culture & Communities, Time Square, Market Street, Bracknell RG12 1JD ☎ 01344 352000 ᐃ vincent.paliczka@bracknell-forest.gov.uk

COUNCILLORS

Mayor: Virgo, Tony (CON - Ascot)
tony.virgo@bracknell-forest.gov.uk

Deputy Mayor: McKenzie-Boyle, Tina (CON - Priestwood & Garth)
tina.mckenzie-boyle@bracknell-forest.gov.uk

Leader of the Council: Bettison, Paul (CON - Little Sandhurst & Wellington)
paul.bettison@bracknell-forest.gov.uk

Deputy Leader of the Council: Birch, Dale (CON - Little Sandhurst & Wellington)
dale.birch@bracknell-forest.gov.uk

Allen, Nick (CON - College Town)
nick.allen@bracknell-forest.gov.uk

Angell, Bob (CON - Bullbrook)
robert.angell@bracknell-forest.gov.uk

Angell, Jan (CON - Great Hollands South)
jan.angell@bracknell-forest.gov.uk

Barnard, Gareth (CON - Warfield Harvest Ride)
gareth.barnard@bracknell-forest.gov.uk

Birch, Gill (CON - Hanworth)
gill.birch@bracknell-forest.gov.uk

Birch, Graham (CON - Priestwood & Garth)
graham.birch@bracknell-forest.gov.uk

Brossard, Michael (CON - Central Sandhurst)
michael.brossard@bracknell-forest.gov.uk

Brunel-Walker, Marc (CON - Crown Wood)
marc.brunel-walker@bracknell-forest.gov.uk

Dudley, Colin (CON - Crown Wood)
colin.dudley@bracknell-forest.gov.uk

Finch, Alvin (CON - Priestwood & Garth)
alvin.finch@bracknell-forest.gov.uk

Finnie, Jim (CON - Crowthorne)
jim.finnie@bracknell-forest.gov.uk

Gaw, Moira (CON - Winkfield & Cranbourne)
moira.gaw@bracknell-forest.gov.uk

Hamilton, Dee (CON - Wildridings & Central)
dee.hamilton@bracknell-forest.gov.uk

Harrison, John (CON - Binfield with Warfield)
john.harrison@bracknell-forest.gov.uk

Hayes, Suki (CON - Crown Wood)
suki.hayes@bracknell-forest.gov.uk

Hayes, Dorothy (CON - Ascot)
dorothy.hayes@bracknell-forest.gov.uk

Heydon, Peter (CON - Old Bracknell)
peter.heydon@bracknell-forest.gov.uk

Hill, Peter (CON - Great Hollands North)
peter.hill@bracknell-Forest.gov.uk

Ingham, Sandra (CON - Hanworth)
sandra.ingham@bracknell-froest.gov.uk

King, Phillip (CON - Central Sandhurst)
phillip.king@bracknell.gov.uk

Leake, Ian (CON - Binfield with Warfield)
ian.leake@bracknell-forest.gov.uk

Mattick, Isabel (CON - Harmans Water)
isabel.mattick@bracknell-forest@gov.uk

McCracken, Jennifer (CON - Great Hollands South)
jennie.mccracken@bracknell-forest.gov.uk

McCracken, Iain (CON - Old Bracknell)
iain.mccracken@bracknell-forest.gov.uk

McKenzie, Pauline (CON - College Town)
pauline.mckenzie@bracknell-forest.gov.uk

McLean, Robert (CON - Warfield Harvest Ride)
robert.mclean@bracknell-forest.gov.uk

Merry, Ash (CON - Harmans Water)
ash.merry@bracknell-forest.gov.uk

Miller, Kirsten (CON - Bullbrook)
kirsten.miller@bracknell-forest.gov.uk

Peacey, Sarah (CON - Binfield with Warfield)
sara.peacey@bracknell-forest.gov.uk

Phillips, Susie (CON - Winkfield & Cranbourne)
susie.phillips@bracknell-forest.gov.uk

Porter, John (CON - Owlsmoor)
john.porter@bracknell-forest.gov.uk

Skinner, Michael (CON - Wildridings & Central)
michael.skinner@bracknell-forest.gov.uk

Temperton, Mary (LAB - Great Hollands North)
mary.temperton@bracknell-forest.gov.uk

Thompson, Clifton (CON - Warfield Harvest Ride)
cliff.thompson@bracknell-forest.gov.uk

Tullett, Malcolm (CON - Hanworth)
malcolm.tullett@bracknell-forest.gov.uk

Turrell, Chris (CON - Harmans Water)
chris.turrell@bracknell-forest.gov.uk

Wade, Bob (CON - Crowthorne)
bob.wade@bracknell-forest.gov.uk

Worrall, David (CON - Owlsmoor)
david.worrall@bracknell-forest.gov.uk

POLITICAL COMPOSITION
CON: 41, LAB: 1

COMMITTEE CHAIRS

Adult Social Care & Housing: Mr John Harrison

Audit & Governance: Mr Nick Allen

Children, Young People & Learning: Ms Gill Birch

Environment, Culture & Communities: Mr Bob Angell

Planning: Mr Colin Dudley

Bradford City   M

Bradford City Council, City Hall, Channing Way, Bradford
BD1 1HY
☎ 01274 432111
🖥 www.bradford.gov.uk

FACTS AND FIGURES
Parliamentary Constituencies: Bradford East, Bradford South,
Bradford West, Keighley, Shipley
EU Constituencies: Yorkshire and the Humber
Election Frequency: Elections are by thirds

PRINCIPAL OFFICERS

Chief Executive: Ms Kersten England, Chief Executive, City Hall,
Channing Way, Bradford BD1 1HY
🖰 kersten.england@bradford.gov.uk

Senior Management: Mr Parveen Akhtar, City Solicitor, City Hall,
Channing Way, Bradford BD1 1HY
🖰 parveen.akhtar@bradford.gov.uk

Senior Management: Mr Rodney Barton, Director - West
Yorkshire Pension Fund, City Hall, Channing Way, Bradford BD1
1HY ☎ 01274 434999 🖰 rodney.barton@bradford.gov.uk

Senior Management: Mr Mike Cowlam, Strategic Director -
Regeneration, Olicana House, 35 Chapel Street, Little Germany,
Bradford BD1 5RE ☎ 01274 433761
🖰 mike.cowlam@bradford.gov.uk

Senior Management: Ms Sue Dunkley, Director - Human
Resources, City Hall, Channing Way, Bradford BD1 1HY
🖰 sue.dunkley@bradford.gov.uk

Senior Management: Mr Steve Hartley, Strategic Director -
Environment & Sport, City Hall, Channing Way, Bradford BD1 1HY
☎ 01274 434748 🖰 steve.hartley@bradford.gov.uk

Senior Management: Mr Michael Jameson, Strategic Director -
Children's Services, City Hall, Channing Way, Bradford BD1 1HY
🖰 michael.jameson@bradford.gov.uk

Senior Management: Ms Bev Maybury, Strategic Director -
Health & Wellbeing, City Hall, Channing Way, Bradford BD1 1HY
🖰 bev.maybury@bradford.gov.uk

Senior Management: Mr Stuart McKinnon-Evans, Director -
Finance, City Hall, Channing Way, Bradford BD1 1HY
🖰 stuart.mckinnon-evans@bradford.gov.uk

Senior Management: Ms Anita Parkin, Director - Public Health,
City Hall, Channing Way, Bradford BD1 1HY
🖰 anita.parkin@bradford.gov.uk

Access Officer / Social Services (Disability): Ms Linda Mason,
Interim Assistant Director - Access & Inclusion, City Hall, Channing
Way, Bradford BD1 1HY 🖰 linda.mason@bradford.gov.uk

Building Control: Mr Chris Eaton, Head - Building Control, City
Hall, Channing Way, Bradford BD1 1HY ☎ 01274 431000
🖰 chris.eaton@bradford.gov.uk

Children / Youth Services: Mr Michael Jameson, Strategic
Director - Children's Services, City Hall, Channing Way, Bradford
BD1 1HY 🖰 michael.jameson@bradford.gov.uk

Children / Youth Services: Ms Cindy Peek, Deputy Director -
Children's Services, City Hall, Channing Way, Bradford BD1 1HY
🖰 cindy.peek@bradford.gov.uk

Civil Registration: Ms Christina Smith, Superintendent Registrar,
City Hall, Channing Way, Bradford BD1 1HY ☎ 01274 432151
🖰 christina.smith@bradford.gov.uk

BRADFORD CITY

PR / Communications: Ms Alison Milner, Assistant Director - Communications, City Hall, Channing Way, Bradford BD1 1HY ☎ 01274 432131 ◦ᵖ alison.milner@bradford.gov.uk

Computer Management: Mr James Drury, Assistant Director - Council Change Program, City Hall, Channing Way, Bradford BD1 1HY ☎ 01274 432850 ◦ᵖ james.drury@bradford.gov.uk

Corporate Services: Mr Stuart McKinnon-Evans, Director - Finance, City Hall, Channing Way, Bradford BD1 1HY ◦ᵖ stuart.mckinnon-evans@bradford.gov.uk

Economic Development: Mr Mike Cowlam, Strategic Director - Regeneration, Jacob's Well, Nelson Street, Bradford BD1 5RW ☎ 01274 433761 ◦ᵖ mike.cowlam@bradford.gov.uk

Education: Mr Michael Jameson, Strategic Director - Children's Services, City Hall, Channing Way, Bradford BD1 1HY ◦ᵖ michael.jameson@bradford.gov.uk

E-Government: Mr Stuart McKinnon-Evans, Director - Finance, City Hall, Channing Way, Bradford BD1 1HY ◦ᵖ stuart.mckinnon-evans@bradford.gov.uk

Electoral Registration: Ms Susan Saunders, Electoral Services Manager, Ground Floor, City Hall, Channing Way, Bradford BD1 1HY ☎ 01274 432285 ◦ᵖ susan.saunders@bradford.gov.uk

Emergency Planning: Mr Mike Powell, Emergency Planning Manager, City Hall, Channing Way, Bradford BD1 1HY ☎ 01274 432011 ◦ᵖ mike.powell@bradford.gov.uk

Energy Management: Mr Steve Hartley, Strategic Director - Environment & Sport, City Hall, Channing Way, Bradford BD1 1HY ☎ 01274 434748 ◦ᵖ steve.hartley@bradford.gov.uk

Environmental / Technical Services: Mr Steve Hartley, Strategic Director - Environment & Sport, City Hall, Channing Way, Bradford BD1 1HY ☎ 01274 434748 ◦ᵖ steve.hartley@bradford.gov.uk

Environmental Health: Mr Steve Hartley, Strategic Director - Environment & Sport, City Hall, Channing Way, Bradford BD1 1HY ☎ 01274 434748 ◦ᵖ steve.hartley@bradford.gov.uk

Estates, Property & Valuation: Mr Mike Cowlam, Strategic Director - Regeneration, Olicana House, 35 Chapel Street, Little Germany, Bradford BD1 5RE ☎ 01274 433761 ◦ᵖ mike.cowlam@bradford.gov.uk

Events Manager: Ms Vanessa Mitchell, Manager - Major Programmes, Jacobs Well, Bradford BD1 5RW ☎ 01274 434783 ◦ᵖ vanessa.mitchell@bradford.gov.uk

Finance: Mr Stuart McKinnon-Evans, Director - Finance, City Hall, Channing Way, Bradford BD1 1HY ◦ᵖ stuart.mckinnon-evans@bradford.gov.uk

Pensions: Mr Rodney Barton, Director - West Yorkshire Pension Fund, City Hall, Channing Way, Bradford BD1 1HY ☎ 01274 434999 ◦ᵖ rodney.barton@bradford.gov.uk

Health and Safety: Ms Susan Ingham, Senior Occupational Safety Officer, City Hall, Channing Way, Bradford BD1 1HY ☎ 01274 434246 ◦ᵖ susan.ingham@bradford.gov.uk

Highways: Mr Julian Jackson, Assistant Director - Planning, Transportation & Highways, City Hall, Channing Way, Bradford BD1 1HY ☎ 01274 437419 ◦ᵖ julian.jackson@bradford.gov.uk

Housing: Ms Sheila O'Neill, Interim Assitant Director - Housing, Employment & Skills, City Hall, Channing Way, Bradford BD1 1HY ◦ᵖ shelia.o'neill@bradford.gov.uk

Local Area Agreement: Ms Roz Hall, Assistant Director - Strategic Support, Argus Chambers, Britannia House, Bradford BD1 1HX ☎ 01274 431000 ◦ᵖ roz.hall@bradford.gov.uk

Legal: Ms Suzan Hemingway, Acting Chief Executive (City Solicitor), City Hall, Channing Way, Bradford BD1 1HY ☎ 01274 432496 ◦ᵖ suzan.hemingway@bradford.gov.uk

Leisure and Cultural Services: Mr Mike Cowlam, Strategic Director - Regeneration, Olicana House, 35 Chapel Street, Little Germany, Bradford BD1 5RE ☎ 01274 433761 ◦ᵖ mike.cowlam@bradford.gov.uk

Licensing: Ms Tracy McLuckie, Manager - Local Land Charges & Licensing, City Hall, Channing Way, Bradford BD1 1HY ☎ 01274 432209 ◦ᵖ tracy.mcluckie@bradford.gov.uk

Lifelong Learning: Mr Michael Jameson, Strategic Director - Children's Services, City Hall, Channing Way, Bradford BD1 1HY ◦ᵖ michael.jameson@bradford.gov.uk

Lighting: Mr Allun Preece, Principal Engineer, Flockton House, Flockton Road, Bradford BD4 7RY ☎ 01274 434019 ◦ᵖ allun.preece@bradford.gov.uk

Member Services: Ms Suzan Hemingway, Acting Chief Executive (City Solicitor), City Hall, Channing Way, Bradford BD1 1HY ☎ 01274 432496 ◦ᵖ suzan.hemingway@bradford.gov.uk

Parking: Mr Paul Ratcliffe, Parking Services Manager, City Hall, Channing Way, Bradford BD1 1HY ◦ᵖ paul.ratcliffe@bradford.gov.uk

Personnel / HR: Mr Matt Burghardt, Assistant Director - Human Resources, City Exchange, 61 Hall Ings, Bradford BD1 5SG ☎ 01274 436135 ◦ᵖ matt.burghardt@bradford.gov.uk

Procurement: Ms Jill Cambell, Assistant Director, Procurement, City Hall, Channing Way, Bradford BD1 1HY ☎ 01274 431000 ◦ᵖ jill.cambell@bradford.gov.uk

Procurement: Mr Shahid Nazir, Interim Assistant Director - Commissioning & Procurement, City Hall, Channing Way, Bradford BD1 1HY ◦ᵖ shahid.nazir@bradford.gov.uk

Public Libraries: Ms Christine Dyson, Principal Head of Libraries, Archives & Information Service, City Hall, Channing Way, Bradford BD1 1HY ☎ 01274 431000 ◦ᵖ christine.dyson@bradford.gov.uk

Public Libraries: Ms Jackie Kitwood, Principal Head - Libraries, Archives & Information Service, City Hall, Channing Way, Bradford BD1 1HY ☎ 01274 431000 🖰 jackie.knitwood@bradford.gov.uk

Recycling & Waste Minimisation: Ms Edith Grooby, Recycling Officer & Waste Minimisation, City Hall, Channing Way, Bradford BD1 1HY ☎ 01274 432854 🖰 edith.grooby@bradford.gov.uk

Regeneration: Mr Mike Cowlam, Strategic Director - Regeneration, Olicana House, 35 Chapel Street, Little Germany, Bradford BD1 5RE ☎ 01274 433761 🖰 mike.cowlam@bradford.gov.uk

Social Services (Adult): Mr Bernard Lanigan, Interim Strategic Director - Adult & Community Services, City Hall, Channing Way, Bradford BD1 1HY ☎ 01274 432900 🖰 bernard.lanigan@bradford.gov.uk

Social Services (Children): Mr Michael Jameson, Strategic Director - Children's Services, City Hall, Channing Way, Bradford BD1 1HY 🖰 michael.jameson@bradford.gov.uk

Safeguarding: Mr George McQueen, Assistant Director - Access & Inclusion, City Hall, Channing Way, Bradford BD1 1HY 🖰 george.mcqueen@bradford.gov.uk

Childrens Social Care: Ms Julie Jenkins, Assistant Director - Children's Specialist Services, City Hall, Channing Way, Bradford BD1 1HY 🖰 julie.jenkins@bradford.gov.uk

Public Health: Ms Anita Parkin, Director - Public Health, City Hall, Channing Way, Bradford BD1 1HY 🖰 anita.parkin@bradford.gov.uk

Street Scene: Mr Steve Hartley, Strategic Director - Environment & Sport, City Hall, Channing Way, Bradford BD1 1HY ☎ 01274 434748 🖰 steve.hartley@bradford.gov.uk

Tourism: Ms Jackie Bennett, Senior Marketing Officer - Tourism, City Hall, Channing Way, Bradford BD1 1HY ☎ 01274 431847 🖰 jackie.bennett@bradford.gov.uk

Town Centre: Ms Yvonne Crossley, Town Centre Manager, Shipley Town Hall, Shipley BD18 3EJ ☎ 01274 437136 🖰 yvonne.crossley@bradford.gov.uk

Traffic Management: Mr Julian Jackson, Assistant Director - Planning, Transportation & Highways, City Hall, Channing Way, Bradford BD1 1HY ☎ 01274 437419 🖰 julian.jackson@bradford.gov.uk

Transport: Mr Julian Jackson, Assistant Director - Planning, Transportation & Highways, City Hall, Channing Way, Bradford BD1 1HY ☎ 01274 437419 🖰 julian.jackson@bradford.gov.uk

Transport Planner: Mr Julian Jackson, Assistant Director - Planning, Transportation & Highways, City Hall, Channing Way, Bradford BD1 1HY ☎ 01274 433766 🖰 julian.jackson@bradford.gov.uk

Total Place: Mr Stuart McKinnon-Evans, Director - Finance, City Hall, Channing Way, Bradford BD1 1HY 🖰 stuart.mckinnon-evans@bradford.gov.uk

Waste Collection and Disposal: Mr Steve Hartley, Strategic Director - Environment & Sport, City Hall, Channing Way, Bradford BD1 1HY ☎ 01274 434748 🖰 steve.hartley@bradford.gov.uk

Waste Management: Mr Steve Hartley, Strategic Director - Environment & Sport, City Hall, Channing Way, Bradford BD1 1HY ☎ 01274 434748 🖰 steve.hartley@bradford.gov.uk

COUNCILLORS

The Lord Mayor: Reid, Geoff (LD - Eccleshill)
geoff.reid@bradford.gov.uk

Deputy Lord Mayor: Griffiths, Alun (LD - Idle & Thackley)
alun.griffiths@bradford.gov.uk

Leader of the Council: Hinchcliffe, Susan (LAB - Windhill & Wrose)
susan.hinchcliffe@bradford.gov.uk

Deputy Leader of the Council: Slater, Val (LAB - Royds)
val.slater@bradford.gov.uk

Group LeaderCooke, Simon (CON - Bingley Rural)
simon.cooke@bradford.gov.uk

Group LeaderSunderland, Jeanette (LD - Idle & Thackley)
jeanette.sunderland@bradford.gov.uk

Ahmed, Riaz (LD - Bradford Moor)
cllr.riazahmed@bradford.gov.uk

Ahmed, Aneela (LAB - City)
aneela.ahmed@bradford.gov.uk

Akhtar, Sameena (LAB - Manningham)
sameena.akhtar@bradford.gov.uk

Ali, Zafar (CON - Keighley Central)
zafar.ali@bradford.gov.uk

Amran, Mohammed (LAB - Heaton)
mohammed.amran@bradford.gov.uk

Azam, Nazam (LAB - City)
nazam.azam@bradford.gov.uk

Bacon, Cath (LAB - Keighley West)
cath.bacon@bradford.gov.uk

Barker, Gerry (CON - Wharfedale)
gerry.barker@bradford.gov.uk

Berry, Ralph (LAB - Wibsey)
ralph.berry@bradford.gov.uk

Brown, Russell (CON - Worth Valley)
russell.brown@bradford.gov.uk

Carmody, Lisa (CON - Queensbury)
lisa.carmody@bradford.gov.uk

Cromie, Lynda (IND - Queensbury)
lynda.cromie@bradford.gov.uk

Cromie, Paul (IND - Queensbury)
paul.cromie@bradford.gov.uk

Davies, Debbie (CON - Baildon)
debbie.davies@bradford.gov.uk

Dodds, Joanne (LAB - Great Horton)
joanne.dodds@bradford.gov.uk

Duffy, Sue (LAB - Thornton & Allerton)
sue.duffy@bradford.gov.uk

BRADFORD CITY

Dunbar, Richard (LAB - Thornton & Allerton)
richard.dunbar@bradford.gov.uk

Ellis, Michael (CON - Bingley Rural)
michael.ellis@bradford.gov.uk

Engel, Sinead (LAB - Clayton & Fairweather Green)
sinead.engel@bradford.gov.uk

Farley, Adrian (LAB - Keighley West)
adrian.farley@bradford.gov.uk

Fear, Dominic (LD - Idle & Thackley)
dominic.fear@bradford.gov.uk

Ferriby, Sarah (LAB - Wyke)
sarah.ferriby@bradford.gov.uk

Gibbons, Mike (CON - Ilkley)
mike.gibbons@bradford.gov.uk

Green, David (LAB - Wibsey)
david.green@bradford.gov.uk

Greenwood, Vanda (LAB - Windhill & Wrose)
vanda.greenwood@bradford.gov.uk

Hawkesworth, Anne (IND - Ilkley)
anne.hawkesworth@bradford.gov.uk

Heseltine, David (CON - Bingley)
david.heseltine@bradford.gov.uk

Hussain, Abid (LAB - Keighley Central)
cllr.abidhussain@bradford.gov.uk

Hussain, Imran (LAB - Toller)
cllr.imranhussain@bradford.gov.uk

Hussain, Tariq (LAB - Great Horton)
cllr.tariqhussain@bradford.gov.uk

Hussain, Hawarun (GRN - Shipley)
hawarun.hussain@bradford.gov.uk

Hussain, Arshad (LAB - Toller)
arshad.hussain@bradford.gov.uk

Hussain, Khadim (IND - Keighley Central)
khadim.hussain@bradford.gov.uk

Hussain, Shabir (LAB - Manningham)
shabir.hussain@bradford.gov.uk

Ikram, Naveeda (LAB - Little Horton)
naveeda.ikram@bradford.gov.uk

Iqbal, Zafar (LAB - Bradford Moor)
zafar.iqbal@bradford.gov.uk

Jabar, Abdul (LAB - Great Horton)
abdul.jabar@bradford.gov.uk

Jamil, Rizwana (LAB - Bowling & Barkerend)
rizwana.jamil@bradford.gov.uk

Johnson, Michael (LAB - Tong)
michael.johnson@bradford.gov.uk

Khan, Imran (LAB - Bowling & Barkerend)
cllr.imrankhan@bradford.gov.uk

Khan, Hassan (LAB - Bowling & Barkerend)
hassan.khan@bradford.gov.uk

Lal, Shakeela (LAB - City)
shakeela.lal@bradfod.gov.uk

Lee, Doreen (LAB - Keighley East)
doreen.lee@bradford.gov.uk

Love, Martin (GRN - Shipley)
martin.love@bradford.gov.uk

Mallinson, Andrew (CON - Craven)
andrew.mallinson@bradford.gov.uk

Miller, Glen (CON - Worth Valley)
glen.miller@bradford.gov.uk

Mohammed, Nussrat (LAB - Heaton)
nussrat.mohammed@bradford.gov.uk

Morries, Brian (UKIP - Keighley West)
brian.morris@bradford.gov.uk

Mullaney, Beverley (LAB - Thornton & Allerton)
beverley.mullaney@bradford.gov.uk

Naylor, Adrian (IND - Craven)
adrian.naylor@bradford.gov.uk

Nazir, Sarfraz (LAB - Manningham)
sarfraz.nazir@bradford.gov.uk

Peart, Tess (LAB - Tong)
tess.peart@bradford.gov.uk

Pennignton, John (CON - Bingley)
john.pennington@bradford.gov.uk

Pollard, Nicola (LD - Eccleshill)
nicola.pollard@bradford.gov.uk

Pollard, Mike (CON - Balidon)
mike.pollard@bradford.gov.uk

Poulsen, Rebecca (CON - Worth Valley)
rebecca.poulsen@bradford.gov.uk

Pullen, Steve (LAB - Keighley East)
steve.pullen@bradford.gov.uk

Riaz, Naveed (CON - Bingley Rural)
naveed.riaz@bradford.gov.uk

Rickard, Jack (CON - Craven)
jack.rickard@bradford.gov.uk

Ross-Shaw, Alexander (LAB - Windhill & Wrose)
alex.ross-shaw@bradford.gov.uk

Sajawal, Talat (IND - Little Horton)
talat.sajawal@bradford.gov.uk

Salam, Taj (LAB - Little Horton)
taj.salam@bradford.gov.uk

Shabbir, Mohammad (IND - Heaton)
mohammad.shabbir@bradford.gov.uk

Shafiq, Mohammed (LAB - Bradford Moor)
mohammed.shafiq@bradford.gov.uk

Shaheen, Fozia (LAB - Toller)
fozia.shaheen@bradford.gov.uk

Shaw, Mark (CON - Bingley)
mark.shaw@bradford.gov.uk

Slater, Malcolm (LAB - Keighley East)
malcolm.slater@bradford.gov.uk

Smith, Brian (CON - Ilkley)
martin.smith@bradford.gov.uk

Smith, Dale (CON - Wharfedale)
dale.smith@bradford.gov.uk

Stelling, Michael (LD - Bolton & Undercliffe)
michael.stelling@bradford.gov.uk

Stubbs, Brendan (LD - Eccleshill)
brendan.stubbs@bradford.gov.uk

Sunderland, Rachel (LD - Bolton & Undercliffe)
rachel.sunderland@bradford.gov.uk

Swallow, Michelle (LAB - Clayton & Fairweather Green)
michelle.swallow@bradford.gov.uk

Tait, Angela (LAB - Royds)
angela.tait@bradford.gov.uk

Thirkill, Carol (LAB - Clayton & Fairweather Green)
carol.thirkill@bradford.gov.uk

Thornton, Andrew (LAB - Royds)
andrew.thornton@bradford.gov.uk

Townend, Valerie (CON - Balidon)
val.townend@bradford.gov.uk

Wainwright, Alan (LAB - Tong)
alan.wainwright@bradford.gov.uk

Warburton, David (LAB - Wyke)
david.warburton@bradford.gov.uk

Ward, David (LD - Bolton & Undercliffe)
david.ward@bradford.gov.uk

Warnes, Kevin (GRN - Shipley)
kevin.warnes@bradford.gov.uk

Watson, Rosie (LAB - Wyke)
rosie.watson@bradford.gov.uk

Whiteley, Jackie (CON - Wharfedale)
jackie.whiteley@bradford.gov.uk

POLITICAL COMPOSITION
LAB: 47, CON: 21, LD: 10, IND: 7, GRN: 3, UKIP: 1, Vacant: 1

COMMITTEE CHAIRS

Audit & Governance: Mr Michael Johnson

Children's Services: Mr Dale Smith

Environment & Waste Management: Mr Martin Love

Health & Social Care: Ms Vanda Greenwood

Licensing: Mr Malcolm Slater

Regeneration & Economy: Mr Adrian Farley

Braintree   D

Braintree District Council, Causeway House, Braintree CM7 9HB
☎ 01376 552525 🖷 01376 552626 ✆ csc@braintree.gov.uk
🖥 www.braintree.gov.uk

FACTS AND FIGURES
Parliamentary Constituencies: Braintree, Witham
EU Constituencies: Eastern
Election Frequency: Elections are of whole council

PRINCIPAL OFFICERS

Chief Executive: Ms Nicola Beach, Chief Executive, Causeway House, Braintree CM7 9HB ☎ 01376 552525 ✆ nicola.beach@braintree.gov.uk

Senior Management: Ms Joanne Albini, Head of Housing & Community, Causeway House, Braintree CM7 9HB ☎ 01376 557753 ✆ joanne.albini@braintree.gov.uk

Senior Management: Mr Lee Crabb, Head of Environment & Leisure, Causeway House, Braintree CM7 9HB ☎ 01376 552525 ✆ lee.crabb@braintree.gov.uk

Senior Management: Mr Chris Fleetham, Corporate Director, Causeway House, Bocking End, Braintree CM7 9HB ☎ 01376 552525 ✆ chris.fleetham@braintree.gov.uk

Senior Management: Mr Jon Hayden, Corporate Director, Causeway House, Braintree CM7 9HB ☎ 01376 552525 ✆ jon.hayden@braintree.gov.uk

Senior Management: Mr Ian Hunt, Head of Governance, Causeway House, Braintree CM7 9HB ☎ 01376 552525 ✆ ian.hunt@braintree.gov.uk

Senior Management: Mr Paul Partridge, Head of Operations, Causeway House, Bocking End, Braintree CM7 9HB ☎ 01376 552525 ✆ paul.partridge@braintree.gov.uk

Senior Management: Ms Cherie Root, Head of Business Solutions, Causeway House, Bocking End, Braintree CM7 9HB ☎ 01376 552525 ✆ cherie.root@braintree.gov.uk

Senior Management: Mr Trevor Wilson, Head of Finance, Causeway House, Braintree CM7 9HB ☎ 01376 552525 ✆ trevor.wilson@braintree.gov.uk

Senior Management: Mr Andy Wright, Corporate Director, Causeway House, Braintree CM7 9HB ☎ 01376 552525 ✆ andy.wright@braintree.gov.uk

Architect, Building / Property Services: Mr Trevor Wilson, Head of Finance, Causeway House, Braintree CM7 9HB ☎ 01376 552525 ✆ trevor.wilson@braintree.gov.uk

Building Control: Mr Lee Crabb, Head of Environment & Leisure, Causeway House, Braintree CM7 9HB ☎ 01376 552525 ✆ lee.crabb@braintree.gov.uk

PR / Communications: Ms Tania Roberge, Marketing & Communications Manager, Causeway House, Braintree CM7 9HB ☎ 01376 552525 ✆ tania.roberge@braintree.gov.uk

Community Safety: Ms Joanne Albini, Head of Housing & Community, Causeway House, Braintree CM7 9HB ☎ 01376 557753 ✆ joanne.albini@braintree.gov.uk

Computer Management: Ms Cherie Root, Head of Business Solutions, Causeway House, Bocking End, Braintree CM7 9HB ☎ 01376 552525 ✆ cherie.root@braintree.gov.uk

Corporate Services: Mr Ian Hunt, Head of Governance, Causeway House, Braintree CM7 9HB ☎ 01376 552525 ✆ ian.hunt@braintree.gov.uk

BRAINTREE

Customer Service: Ms Cherie Root, Head of Business Solutions, Causeway House, Bocking End, Braintree CM7 9HB ☎ 01376 552525 ◌ cherie.root@braintree.gov.uk

Electoral Registration: Mr Steve Daynes, Electoral Registration Manager, Causeway House, Braintree CM7 9HB ☎ 01376 552525 ◌ steve.daynes@braintree.gov.uk

Emergency Planning: Ms Kathy Brown, Health, Safety & Emergency Manager, Causeway House, Bocking End, Braintree CM7 9BR ☎ 01376 557753 ◌ kathy.brown@braintree.gov.uk

Energy Management: Mr Mark Wilson, Health, Safety & Emergency Manager, Causeway House, Braintree CM7 9HB ☎ 01376 552525 ◌ mark.wilson@braintree.gov.uk

Environmental Health: Mr Lee Crabb, Head of Environment & Leisure, Causeway House, Braintree CM7 9HB ☎ 01376 552525 ◌ lee.crabb@braintree.gov.uk

Estates, Property & Valuation: Mr Andrew Epsom, Asset & Property Manager, Causeway House, Bocking End, Braintree CM7 9HB ☎ 01376 552525 ◌ andrew.epsom@braintree.gov.uk

Facilities: Mr Andrew Epsom, Asset & Property Manager, Causeway House, Bocking End, Braintree CM7 9HB ☎ 01376 552525 ◌ andrew.epsom@braintree.gov.uk

Finance: Mr Chris Fleetham, Corporate Director, Causeway House, Bocking End, Braintree CM7 9HB ☎ 01376 552525 ◌ chris.fleetham@braintree.gov.uk

Fleet Management: Ms Hayley Goodard, Waste & Transport Manager, Unit 4, Lakes Industrial Park, Lower Chapel Hill, Braintree CM7 3RU ☎ 01376 332300 ◌ hayley.goodard@braintree.gov.uk

Grounds Maintenance: Mr Paul Partridge, Head of Operations, Causeway House, Bocking End, Braintree CM7 9HB ☎ 01376 552525 ◌ paul.partridge@braintree.gov.uk

Health and Safety: Mr Mark Wilson, Health, Safety & Emergency Manager, Causeway House, Braintree CM7 9HB ☎ 01376 552525 ◌ mark.wilson@braintree.gov.uk

Home Energy Conservation: Mr Mark Wilson, Health, Safety & Emergency Manager, Causeway House, Braintree CM7 9HB ☎ 01376 552525 ◌ mark.wilson@braintree.gov.uk

Housing: Ms Joanne Albini, Head of Housing & Community, Causeway House, Braintree CM7 9HB ☎ 01376 557753 ◌ joanne.albini@braintree.gov.uk

Legal: Ms Sarah Stockings, Property Law Solicitor, Causeway House, Braintree CM7 9HB ☎ 01376 552525 ◌ sara.stockings@braintree.gov.uk

Leisure and Cultural Services: Mr Robert Rose, Museum Services Manager, Town Hall Centre, Market Place, Braintree CM7 3YG ☎ 01376 325266 ◌ robert.rose@braintree.gov.uk

Licensing: Mr Lee Crabb, Head of Environment & Leisure, Causeway House, Braintree CM7 9HB ☎ 01376 552525 ◌ lee.crabb@braintree.gov.uk

Lifelong Learning: Ms Sam Jenkins, Learning & Development Consultant, Causeway House, Bocking End, Braintree CM7 9HB ☎ 01376 552525 ◌ sam.jenkins@braintree.gov.uk

Member Services: Ms Emma Wisbey, Member Services Manager, Causeway House, Braintree CM7 9HB ☎ 01376 552525 ◌ emma.wisbey@braintree.gov.uk

Parking: Mr Paul Partridge, Head of Operations, Causeway House, Bocking End, Braintree CM7 9HB ☎ 01376 552525 ◌ paul.partridge@braintree.gov.uk

Personnel / HR: Ms Helen Krischock, HR Manager, Causeway House, Braintree CM7 9HB ☎ 01376 552525 ◌ helen.krischock@braintree.gov.uk

Planning: Mr Jon Hayden, Corporate Director, Causeway House, Braintree CM7 9HB ☎ 01376 552525 ◌ jon.hayden@braintree.gov.uk

Planning: Ms Tessa Lambert, Development Control Manager, Causeway House, Braintree CM7 9HB ☎ 01376 552525 ◌ tessa.lambert@braintree.gov.uk

Procurement: Mr James Sinclair, Procurement Manager, Causeway House, Braintree CM7 9HB ☎ 01376 552525 ◌ james.sinclair@braintree.gov.uk

Recycling & Waste Minimisation: Mr Samir Pandya, Waste Manager, Unit 4, Lakes Industrial Park, Lower Chapel Hill, Braintree CM7 3RU ☎ 01376 332300 ◌ samir.pandya@braintree.gov.uk

Staff Training: Ms Sam Jenkins, Learning & Development Consultant, Causeway House, Bocking End, Braintree CM7 9HB ☎ 01376 552525 ◌ sam.jenkins@braintree.gov.uk

Street Scene: Mr Paul Partridge, Head of Operations, Causeway House, Bocking End, Braintree CM7 9HB ☎ 01376 552525 ◌ paul.partridge@braintree.gov.uk

Sustainable Communities: Mr Jon Hayden, Corporate Director, Causeway House, Braintree CM7 9HB ☎ 01376 552525 ◌ jon.hayden@braintree.gov.uk

Sustainable Development: Mr Jon Hayden, Corporate Director, Causeway House, Braintree CM7 9HB ☎ 01376 552525 ◌ jon.hayden@braintree.gov.uk

Town Centre: Mr Jon Hayden, Corporate Director, Causeway House, Braintree CM7 9HB ☎ 01376 552525 ◌ jon.hayden@braintree.gov.uk

Transport: Mr Jon Hayden, Corporate Director, Causeway House, Braintree CM7 9HB ☎ 01376 552525 ◌ jon.hayden@braintree.gov.uk

Transport Planner: Mr Jon Hayden, Corporate Director, Causeway House, Braintree CM7 9HB ☎ 01376 552525
✆ jon.hayden@braintree.gov.uk

Waste Collection and Disposal: Ms Hayley Goodard, Waste & Transport Manager, Unit 4, Lakes Industrial Park, Lower Chapel Hill, Braintree CM7 3RU ☎ 01376 332300
✆ hayley.goodard@braintree.gov.uk

Waste Management: Mr Paul Partridge, Head of Operations, Causeway House, Bocking End, Braintree CM7 9HB
☎ 01376 552525 ✆ paul.partridge@braintree.gov.uk

Children's Play Areas: Mr Paul Partridge, Head of Operations, Causeway House, Bocking End, Braintree CM7 9HB
☎ 01376 552525 ✆ paul.partridge@braintree.gov.uk

COUNCILLORS

Leader of the Council: Butland, Graham (CON - Great Notley & Black Notley)
cllr.gbutland@braintree.gov.uk

Deputy Leader of the Council: Schmidt, Wendy (CON - Bocking Blackwater)
cllr.wschmidt@braintree.gov.uk

Abbott, James (GRN - Silver End & Cressing)
cllr.jabbott@braintree.gov.uk

Allen, Julia (CON - Halstead Trinity)
cllr.jallen@braintree.gov.uk

Bailey, Christopher (CON - Witham North)
cllr.cbailey@braintree.gov.uk

Banthorpe, Michael (CON - Rayne)
cllr.mbanthorpe@braintree.gov.uk

Baugh, John (CON - Bocking South)
cllr.jbaugh@braintree.gov.uk

Beavis, Joanne (CON - Hedingham)
cllr.jbeavis@braintree.gov.uk

Bebb, David (CON - Hatfield Peverel & Terling)
cllr.dbebb@braintree.gov.uk

Bolton, Robert (CON - Bumpstead)
cllr.rbolton@braintree.gov.uk

Bowers, Kevin (CON - Silver End & Cressing)
cllr.kbowers@braintree.gov.uk

Bowers-Flint, Lynette (CON - Coggeshall)
cllr.lflint@braintree.gov.uk

Canning, Stephen (CON - Bocking Blackwater)
cllr.scanning@braintree.gov.uk

Cunningham, John (CON - Braintree Central & Beckers Green)
cllr.jcunningham@braintree.gov.uk

Cunningham, Mary (CON - Braintree Central & Beckers Green)
cllr.mcunningham@braintree.gov.uk

Cunningham, Tom (CON - Great Notley & Black Notley)
cllr.tcunningham@braintree.gov.uk

Dunn, Malcolm (CON - Braintree South)
cllr.mdunn@braintree.gov.uk

Elliott, John (CON - Kelvedon & Feering)
cllr.jelliott@braintree.gov.uk

Goodman, John (CON - Witham North)
cllr.jgoodman@braintree.gov.uk

Hensman, Andrew (CON - Braintree Central & Beckers Green)
cllr.ahensman@braintree.gov.uk

Horner, Patrick (CON - Witham West)
cllr.phorner@braintree.gov.uk

Hufton-Rees, Daryn (CON - Hatfield Peverel & Terling)
cllr.dhufton-rees@braintree.gov.uk

Hume, David (R - Halstead St Andrews)
cllr.dhume@braintree.gov.uk

Johnson, Hylton (CON - Hedingham)
cllr.hjohnson@braintree.gov.uk

Kilmartin, Angela (CON - Witham Central)
cllr.akilmartin@braintree.gov.uk

Kirby, Stephen (CON - Halstead St Andrews)
cllr.skirby@braintree.gov.uk

Mann, David (LAB - Bocking North)
cllr.dmann@braintree.gov.uk

McKee, John (CON - Braintree West)
cllr.jmckee@braintree.gov.uk

Mitchell, Robert (CON - Kelvedon & Feering)
cllr.rmitchell@braintree.gov.uk

Money, Janet (CON - Witham South)
cllr.jmoney@braintree.gov.uk

Newton, Patricia (CON - Coggeshall)
cllr.ladynewton@braintree.gov.uk

O'Reilly-Cicconi, John (CON - Gosfield & Greenstead Green)
cllr.jo'reilly-cicconi@braintree.gov.uk

Parker, Iona (CON - Stour Valley North)
cllr.iparker@braintree.gov.uk

Paul, Stephanie (CON - Bocking North)
cllr.spaul@braintree.gov.uk

Pell, Jacqueline (R - Halstead Trinity)
cllr.jpell@braintree.gov.uk

Ramage, Ron (CON - Braintree West)
cllr.rramage@braintree.gov.uk

Ricci, Frankie (CON - Great Notley & Black Notley)
cllr.fricci@braintree.gov.uk

Rose, Bill (CON - Witham West)
cllr.wrose@braintree.gov.uk

Santomauro, Vanessa (CON - Braintree South)
cllr.vsantomauro@braintree.gov.uk

Scattergood, Wendy (CON - Stour Valley South)
cllr.wscattergood@braintree.gov.uk

Schwier, Peter (CON - Three Fields)
cllr.pschwier@braintree.gov.uk

Siddall, Chris (CON - The Colnes)
cllr.csiddall@braintree.gov.uk

Spray, Gabrielle (CON - The Colnes)
cllr.gspray@braintree.gov.uk

Tattersley, Peter (CON - Three Fields)
cllr.ptattersley@braintree.gov.uk

Thompson, Corinne (CON - Witham South)
cllr.cthompson@braintree.gov.uk

BRAINTREE

Thorogood, Moia (LAB - Bocking South)
cllr.mthorogood@braintree.gov.uk

van Dulken, Richard (CON - Yeldham)
cllr.rvandulken@braintree.gov.uk

Walters, Lyn (CON - Bocking Blackwater)
cllr.lwaters@braintree.gov.uk

Wilson, Sue (CON - Witham Central)
cllr.swilson@braintree.gov.uk

POLITICAL COMPOSITION
CON: 44, LAB: 2, R: 2, GRN: 1

Breckland   D

Breckland District Council, Elizabeth House, Walpole Loke,
Dereham NR19 1EE
☎ 01362 656870 📧 contactus@breckland.gov.uk
🖥 www.breckland.gov.uk

FACTS AND FIGURES
Parliamentary Constituencies:
EU Constituencies: Eastern
Election Frequency: Elections are of whole council

PRINCIPAL OFFICERS

Chief Executive: Ms Anna Graves, Chief Executive, Elizabeth
House, Walpole Loke, Dereham NR19 1EE ☎ 07833 503139
📧 chief.executive@breckland-sholland.go.uk

Senior Management: Mr Mark Finch, Finance Manager, Elizabeth
House, Walpole Loke, Dereham NR19 1EE ☎ 07917 587078
📧 mark.finch@breckland-sholland.gov.uk

Senior Management: Mr Duncan Hall, Housing Manager,
Elizabeth House, Walpole Loke, Dereham NR19 1EE
☎ 07500 915488 📧 duncan.hall@west-norfolk.gov.uk

Senior Management: Ms Julie Kennealy, Executive Director -
Commercialisation, Elizabeth House, Walpole Loke, Dereham NR19
1EE ☎ 01775 764567 📧 julie.kennealy@breckland-sholland.gov.uk

Senior Management: Mrs Maxine O'Mahony, Executive Director
- Strategy & Governance, Elizabeth House, Walpole Loke, Dereham
NR19 1EE ☎ 01775 764603
📧 maxine.omahony@breckland-sholland.gov.uk

Senior Management: Mrs Vicky Thomson, Democratic Services
& Legal Manager, Elizabeth House, Walpole Loke, Dereham NR19
1EE ☎ 07827 843173 📧 vicky.thomson@breckland-sholland.gov.uk

Senior Management: Mr Robert Walker, Executive Director -
Place, Elizabeth House, Walpole Loke, Dereham NR19 1EE
☎ 07867 988826 📧 robert.walker@breckland-sholland.gov.uk

Architect, Building / Property Services: Mr Stephen Udberg,
Asset & Property Manager, Elizabeth House, Walpole Loke,
Dereham NR19 1EE ☎ 07827 843157
📧 steve.udberg@breckland-sholland.gov.uk

PR / Communications: Mr Rob Leigh, Shared Executive
Manager - People & Information, Elizabeth House, Walpole Loke,
Dereham NR19 1EE ☎ 01775 761161
📧 rob.leigh@breckland-sholland.gov.uk

Community Safety: Ms Riana Rudland, Community Development
& Health Manager, Elizabeth House, Walpole Loke, Dereham NR19
1EE ☎ 07823 553988 📧 riana.rutland@breckland-sholland.gov.uk

Computer Management: Mr Rob Leigh, Shared Executive
Manager - People & Information, Elizabeth House, Walpole Loke,
Dereham NR19 1EE ☎ 01775 761161
📧 rob.leigh@breckland-sholland.gov.uk

Contracts: Mr Greg Pearson, Corporate Improvement &
Performance Manager, Elizabeth House, Walpole Loke, Dereham
NR19 1EE ☎ 01775 761161
📧 greg.pearson@breckland-sholland.gov.uk

Customer Service: Mr Rob Leigh, Shared Executive Manager -
People & Information, Elizabeth House, Walpole Loke, Dereham
NR19 1EE ☎ 01775 761161 📧 rob.leigh@breckland-sholland.gov.uk

E-Government: Mr Rob Leigh, Shared Executive Manager -
People & Information, Elizabeth House, Walpole Loke, Dereham
NR19 1EE ☎ 01775 761161 📧 rob.leigh@breckland-sholland.gov.uk

Electoral Registration: Mr Rory Ringer, Democratic Services
Manager, Elizabeth House, Walpole Loke, Dereham NR19 1EE
☎ 01362 656870 📧 rory.ringer@breckland.gov.uk

Emergency Planning: Mr David Rimmer, Emergency Planning
Officer, Elizabeth House, Walpole Loke, Dereham NR19 1EE
☎ 01362 656870 📧 david.rimmer@breckland.gov.uk

Environmental Health: Mr Phil Adams, Shared Executive
Manager - Public Protection, Elizabeth House, Walpole Loke,
Dereham NR19 1EE ☎ 01775 764657
📧 phillip.adams@breckland-sholland.gov.uk

Estates, Property & Valuation: Ms Zoe Footer, Commercial
Property Manager, Elizabeth House, Walpole Loke, Dereham NR19
1EE ☎ 01362 656870 📧 zoe.footer@breckland.gov.uk

Finance: Mr Mark Finch, Finance Manager, Elizabeth House,
Walpole Loke, Dereham NR19 1EE ☎ 07917 587078
📧 mark.finch@breckland-sholland.gov.uk

Treasury: Mr Mark Finch, Finance Manager, Elizabeth House,
Walpole Loke, Dereham NR19 1EE ☎ 07917 587078
📧 mark.finch@breckland-sholland.gov.uk

Home Energy Conservation: Mr Gordon Partridge, Principal
Housing Officer, Elizabeth House, Walpole Loke, Dereham NR19
1EE ☎ 01362 656275 📧 gordon.partridge@breckland.gov.uk

Housing: Mr Duncan Hall, Housing Manager, Elizabeth House,
Walpole Loke, Dereham NR19 1EE ☎ 07500 915488
📧 duncan.hall@west-norfolk.gov.uk

Legal: Mr Michael Horn, Solicitor to the Council, Elizabeth House, Walpole Loke, Dereham NR19 1EE ☎ 01362 656870 ✆ mike.horn@breckland.gov.uk

Leisure and Cultural Services: Ms Riana Rudland, Community Development & Health Manager, Elizabeth House, Walpole Loke, Dereham NR19 1EE ☎ 07823 553988 ✆ riana.rutland@breckland-sholland.gov.uk

Licensing: Ms Donna Hall, Licensing & Business Support Manager, Council Offices, Priory Road, Spalding PE11 2XE ☎ 01775 761161

Member Services: Mrs Vicky Thomson, Democratic Services & Legal Manager, Elizabeth House, Walpole Loke, Dereham NR19 1EE ☎ 07827 843173 ✆ vicky.thomson@breckland-sholland.gov.uk

Planning: Mr Paul Jackson, South Holland Place Manager, Elizabeth House, Walpole Loke, Dereham NR19 1EE ☎ 01775 764402 ✆ paul.jackson@breckland-sholland.gov.uk

Procurement: Mr Greg Pearson, Corporate Improvement & Performance Manager, Elizabeth House, Walpole Loke, Dereham NR19 1EE ☎ 01775 761161 ✆ greg.pearson@breckland-sholland.gov.uk

Recycling & Waste Minimisation: Ms Emily Spicer, Environmental Services Manager, Elizabeth House, Walpole Loke, Dereham NR19 1EE ☎ 07900 168280 ✆ emily.spicer@breckland-sholland.gov.uk

Staff Training: Mrs Julia Perry, Training & Development Manager, Elizabeth House, Walpole Loke, Dereham NR19 1EE ☎ 01362 656896 ✆ julia.perry@breckland.gov.uk

Street Scene: Ms Emily Spicer, Environmental Services Manager, Elizabeth House, Walpole Loke, Dereham NR19 1EE ☎ 07900 168280 ✆ emily.spicer@breckland-sholland.gov.uk

Sustainable Communities: Ms Riana Rudland, Community Development & Health Manager, Elizabeth House, Walpole Loke, Dereham NR19 1EE ☎ 07823 553988 ✆ riana.rutland@breckland-sholland.gov.uk

Waste Collection and Disposal: Ms Emily Spicer, Environmental Services Manager, Elizabeth House, Walpole Loke, Dereham NR19 1EE ☎ 07900 168280 ✆ emily.spicer@breckland-sholland.gov.uk

Waste Management: Ms Emily Spicer, Environmental Services Manager, Elizabeth House, Walpole Loke, Dereham NR19 1EE ☎ 07900 168280 ✆ emily.spicer@breckland-sholland.gov.uk

COUNCILLORS

ChairBorrett, Bill (CON - Upper Wensum)
bill.borrett@breckland.gov.uk

Vice-ChairMillbank, Kate (CON - Dereham Toftwood)
kate.millbank@breckland.gov.uk

Leader of the Council: Nunn, William (CON - Forest)
william.nunn@breckland.gov.uk

Deputy Leader of the Council: Chapman-Allen, Sam (CON - Forest) sam.chapman-allen@breckland.gov.uk

Group LeaderJermy, Terry (LAB - Thetford Burrell)
terry.jermy@breckland.gov.uk

Ashby, Tristan (CON - Attleborough Queens & Besthorpe)
tristan.ashby@breckland.gov.uk

Askew, Stephen (CON - Attleborough Queens & Besthorpe)
steveaskew79@yahoo.com

Bambridge, Gordon (CON - Upper Wensum)
gordon.bambridge@breckland.gov.uk

Bishop, Jane (CON - Thetford Priory)
jane.bishop@breckland.gov.uk

Bowes, Claire (CON - Watton)
claire.bowes@breckland.gov.uk

Brame, Roy (CON - Thetford Castle)
roy.brame@breckland.gov.uk

Carter, Trevor (CON - Hermitage)
trevor.carter@breckland.gov.uk

Carter, Charles (CON - Saham Toney)
charles.carter@breckland.gov.uk

Chapman-Allen, Marion (CON - Guiltcross)
marion.chapman-allen@breckland.gov.uk

Clarke, Harry (LAB - Dereham Withburga)
harry.clarke@breckland.gov.uk

Claussen, Paul (CON - Mattishall)
paul.claussen@breckland.gov.uk

Cowen, Phillip (CON - All Saints & Wayland)
phillip.cowen@breckland.gov.uk

Crawford, Denis (UKIP - Thetford Burrell)
denis.crawford@breckland.gov.uk

Darby, Paul (CON - Swaffham)
paul.darby@breckland.gov.uk

Dimoglou, Pablo (CON - Mattishall)
pablo.dimoglou@breckland.gov.uk

Duffield, Richard (CON - Lincoln)
richard.duffield@breckland.gov.uk

Duigan, Phillip (CON - Dereham Toftwood)
phillip.duigan@breckland.gov.uk

Gilbert, Keith (IND - Watton)
keith.gilbert@breckland.gov.uk

Gould, Elizabeth (CON - Launditch)
elizabeth.gould@breckland.gov.uk

Hewett, Paul (CON - Shipdham with Scarning)
paul.hewett@breckland.gov.uk

Hollis, Jennifer (UKIP - Thetford Boudica)
jennifer.hollis@breckland.gov.uk

Joel, Adrian (CON - The Buckenhams & Banham)
adrian.joel@breckland.gov.uk

Jolly, Ellen (CON - Harling & Heathlands)
ellen.jolly@breckland.gov.uk

Martin, Keith (CON - Attleborough Burgh & Haverscroft)
keith.martin@breckland.gov.uk

Matthews, Shirley (CON - Swaffham)
shirley.matthews@breckland.gov.uk

Monument, Thomas (CON - Dereham Withburga)
thomas.monument@breckland.gov.uk

BRECKLAND

Monument, Linda (CON - Dereham Neatherd)
linda.monument@breckland.gov.uk

Nairn, Mike (CON - Bedingfield)
mike.nairn@breckland.gov.uk

Newton, John (UKIP - Thetford Castle)
john.newton@breckland.gov.uk

Oliver, Rhodri (CON - Attleborough Queens & Besthorpe)
rhodri.oliver@breckland.gov.uk

Richmond, William (CON - Dereham Neatherd)
william.richmond@breckland.gov.uk

Richmond, Robert (CON - Lincoln)
robert.richmond@breckland.gov.uk

Robinson, Mark (CON - Thetford Boudica)
mark.robinson@breckland.gov.uk

Rogers, John (CON - Saham Toney)
john.rogers@breckland.gov.uk

Sharpe, Frank (CON - Ashill)
frank.sharpe@breckland.gov.uk

Sherwood, Ian (CON - Swaffham)
ian.sherwood@breckland.gov.uk

Smith, William (CON - All Saints & Wayland)
william.smith@breckland.gov.uk

Stasiak, Adrian (CON - Attleborough Burgh & Haverscroft)
adrian.stasiak@breckland.gov.uk

Taylor, Mark (UKIP - Thetford Priory)
mark.taylor@breckland.gov.uk

Turner, Lynda (CON - Shipdham with Scarning)
lynda.turner@breckland.gov.uk

Wassell, Michael (CON - Watton)
michael.wassell@breckland.gov.uk

Webb, Alison (CON - Dereham Neatherd)
alison.webb@breckland.gov.uk

Wilkin, Nigel (CON - Necton)
nigel.wilkin@breckland.gov.uk

Wilkinson, Peter (CON - Nar Valley)
peter.wilkinson@breckland.gov.uk

POLITICAL COMPOSITION
CON: 42, UKIP: 4, LAB: 2, IND: 1

COMMITTEE CHAIRS

Audit: Mr Bill Borrett

Licensing: Ms Marion Chapman-Allen

Planning: Mr Nigel Wilkin

Brent   L

Brent London Borough Council, Brent Civic Centre, Engineers Way, Wembley HA9 0FJ
☎ 020 8937 1234 ⁸ customer.services@brent.gov.uk
🖥 www.brent.gov.uk

FACTS AND FIGURES
Parliamentary Constituencies: Brent Central, Brent North, Hampstead and Kilburn
EU Constituencies: London

Election Frequency: Elections are of whole council

PRINCIPAL OFFICERS

Chief Executive: Ms Carolyn Downs, Chief Executive, Brent Civic Centre, Engineers Way, Wembley HA9 0FJ ☎ 020 8937 1007
⁸ carolyn.downs@brent.gov.uk

Senior Management: Mr Amar Dave, Strategic Director - Regeneration & Environment, Brent Civic Centre, Engineers Way, Wembley HA9 0FJ ⁸ amar.dave@brent.gov.uk

Senior Management: Ms Althea Loderick, Strategic Director - Resources, Brent Civic Centre, Engineers Way, Wembley HA9 0FJ ☎ 020 8937 1529 ⁸ althea.loderick@brent.gov.uk

Senior Management: Mr Philip Porter, Strategic Director - Community Wellbeing, Brent Civic Centre, Engineers Way, Wembley HA9 0FJ ☎ 020 8937 5937 ⁸ phil.porter@brent.gov.uk

Senior Management: Ms Gail Tolley, Strategic Director - Children & Young People, Brent Civic Centre, Engineers Way, Wembley HA9 0FJ ☎ 020 8937 6422 ⁸ gail.tolley@brent.gov.uk

Access Officer / Social Services (Disability): Mr David Dunkley, Director- Rehabilitation, 15 Brondesbury Road, Kilburn, London NW6 6BX ☎ 020 8937 4297 ⁸ d.dunkley@nhs.net

Architect, Building / Property Services: Mr Richard Barrett, Operational Director - Property & Projects, Brent Civic Centre, Engineers Way, Wembley HA9 0FJ ☎ 020 8937 1330
⁸ richard.barrett@brent.gov.uk

Children / Youth Services: Ms Angela Chiswell, Head of Youth Support Services, Brent Civic Centre, Engineers Way, Wembley HA9 0FJ ☎ 020 8937 3667 ⁸ angela.chiswell@brent.go.uk

Children / Youth Services: Ms Cate Duffy, Interim Operational Director - Safeguarding, Performance & Strategy, Brent Civic Centre, Engineers Way, Wembley HA9 0FJ ☎ 020 8937 3510 ⁸ cate.duffy@brent.gov.uk

Civil Registration: Mr Mark Rimmer, Head - Registration & Nationality Service, Brent Civic Centre, Engineers Way, Wembley HA9 0FJ ☎ 020 8937 1011 ⁸ mark.rimmer@brent.gov.uk

PR / Communications: Mr Robert Mansfield, Head of Communications, Brent Civic Centre, Engineers Way, Wembley HA9 0FJ ☎ 020 8937 4229 ⁸ robert.mansfield@brent.gov.uk

Computer Management: Mr Prod Sarigianis, Head of Digital Services (Acting), Brent Civic Centre, Engineers Way, Wembley HA9 0FJ ☎ 020 8937 6080 ⁸ prod.sarigianis@brent.gov.uk

Consumer Protection and Trading Standards: Mr Simon Legg, Senior Regulatory Services Manager, Brent Civic Centre, Engineers Way, Wembley HA9 0FJ ☎ 020 8937 5522 ⁸ simon.legg@brent.gov.uk

Contracts: Mr Jonathan Treherne, Senior Contract Lawyer, Brent Civic Centre, Engineers Way, Wembley HA9 0FJ ☎ 020 8937 1542 ⁸ jonathan.treherne@brent.gov.uk

Customer Service: Ms Margaret Read, Director - Customer Services, Brent Civic Centre, Engineers Way, Wembley HA9 0FJ ☎ 020 8937 1521 ⌂ margaret.read@brent.gov.uk

Education: Ms Sue Gates, Head - Early Help, Brent Civic Centre, Engineers Way, Wembley HA9 0FJ ☎ 020 8937 2710 ⌂ sue.gates@brent.gov.uk

Electoral Registration: Mr Sean O'Sullivan, Electoral Services Manager, Brent Civic Centre, Engineers Way, Wembley HA9 0FJ ☎ 020 8937 1370 ⌂ s.osullivan@brent.gov.uk

Events Manager: Ms Kat Parker, Head - Conference & Event Sales, Brent Civic Centre, Engineers Way, Wembley HA9 0FJ ☎ 020 8937 4344 ⌂ kat.parker@brent.gov.uk

Finance: Mr Conrad Hall, Chief Finance Officer, Brent Civic Centre, Engineers Way, Wembley HA9 0FJ ☎ 020 8937 6528 ⌂ conrad.hall@brent.gov.uk

Pensions: Ms Anna McCormack, Principal Consultant, Brent Civic Centre, Engineers Way, Wembley HA9 0FJ ☎ 020 8937 3936 ⌂ anna.mccormack@brent.gov.uk

Fleet Management: Mr Simon Finney, Interim Head - Passenger Transport, Hirst Hall, Lower Lane, GEC Estate, East Lane, Wembley HA9 0FJ ☎ 020 8937 5072 ⌂ simon.finney@brent.gov.uk

Highways: Mr Tony Kennedy, Head of Highways & Infrastructure, Brent Civic Centre, Engineers Way, Wembley HA9 0FJ ☎ 020 8937 5151 ⌂ tony.kennedy@brent.gov.uk

Housing: Mr Jon Lloyd-Owen, Operational Director - Housing & Employment, Brent Civic Centre, Engineers Way, Wembley HA9 0FJ ☎ 020 8937 5199 ⌂ jon.lloyd-owen@brent.gov.uk

Housing Maintenance: Mr Tom Bremner, Chief Executive - BHP, Brent Civic Centre, Engineers Way, Wembley HA9 0FJ ☎ 020 8937 2200 ⌂ tom.bremner@bhphousing.co.uk

Legal: Ms Fiona Alderman, Chief Legal Officer, Brent Civic Centre, Engineers Way, Wembley HA9 0FJ ☎ 020 8937 4104 ⌂ fiona.alderman@brent.gov.uk

Licensing: Ms Yogini Patel, Senior Regulatory Service Manager, Brent Civic Centre, Engineers Way, Wembley HA9 0FJ ☎ 020 8937 5262 ⌂ yogini.patel@brent.gov.uk

Lifelong Learning: Ms Rashmi Agarwal, Head of Culture, Brent Civic Centre, Engineers Way, Wembley HA9 0FJ ☎ 020 8937 3143 ⌂ rashmi.agarwal@brent.gov.uk

Lighting: Mr Gavin Moore, Head of Parking & Lighting, Brent Civic Centre, Engineers Way, Wembley HA9 0FJ ☎ 020 8937 2979 ⌂ gavin.f.moore@brent.gov.uk

Member Services: Mr Thomas Cattermole, Head - Executive & Member Services, Brent Civic Centre, Engineers Way, Wembley HA9 0FJ ☎ 020 8937 5446 ⌂ thomas.cattermole@brent.gov.uk

Parking: Mr Gavin Moore, Head of Parking & Lighting, Brent Civic Centre, Engineers Way, Wembley HA9 0FJ ☎ 020 8937 2979 ⌂ gavin.f.moore@brent.gov.uk

Planning: Mr Mike Kiely, Head of Planning, Transportation & Licensing, Brent Civic Centre, Engineers Way, Wembley HA9 0FJ ⌂ mike.kiely@brent.gov.uk

Procurement: Mr Terry Brewer, Head of Procurement, Brent Civic Centre, Engineers Way, Wembley HA9 0FJ ☎ 020 8937 1625 ⌂ terry.brewer@brent.gov.uk

Public Libraries: Ms Rashmi Agarwal, Head of Culture, Brent Civic Centre, Engineers Way, Wembley HA9 0FJ ☎ 020 8937 3143 ⌂ rashmi.agarwal@brent.gov.uk

Recycling & Waste Minimisation: Mr Robert Anderton, Head of Environmental Improvement, Brent Civic Centre, Engineers Way, Wembley HA9 0FJ ☎ 020 8937 5001 ⌂ robert.anderton@brent.gov.uk

Road Safety: Ms Debbie Huckle, Safety & Travel Planning, Brent Civic Centre, Engineers Way, Wembley HA9 0FJ ☎ 020 8903 5570 ⌂ debbie.huckle@brent.gov.uk

Social Services: Mr Kevin Jones, Interim Operational Director - Integration & Improved Outcomes, Brent Civic Centre, Engineers Way, Wembley HA9 0FJ ☎ 020 8937 4183 ⌂ kevin.jones@brent.gov.uk

Social Services (Adult): Mr Philip Porter, Strategic Director - Community Wellbeing, Brent Civic Centre, Engineers Way, Wembley HA9 0FJ ☎ 020 8937 5937 ⌂ phil.porter@brent.gov.uk

Public Health: Dr Melanie Smith, Director - Public Health, Brent Civic Centre, Engineers Way, Wembley HA9 0FJ ☎ 020 8937 6227 ⌂ melanie.smith@brent.gov.uk

Staff Training: Mr Sanmi Akinlab, HR Manager, Brent Civic Centre, Engineers Way, Wembley HA9 0FJ ☎ 020 8937 3245 ⌂ sanmi.akinlab@brent.gov.uk

Staff Training: Mr Afzal Ghany, HR Manager, Brent Civic Centre, Engineers Way, Wembley HA9 0FJ ☎ 020 8937 1082 ⌂ afzal.ghany@brent.gov.uk

Street Scene: Mr Robert Anderton, Head of Environmental Improvement, Brent Civic Centre, Engineers Way, Wembley HA9 0FJ ☎ 020 8937 5001 ⌂ robert.anderton@brent.gov.uk

Traffic Management: Mr Tony Kennedy, Head of Highways & Infrastructure, Brent Civic Centre, Engineers Way, Wembley HA9 0FJ ☎ 020 8937 5151 ⌂ tony.kennedy@brent.gov.uk

Waste Collection and Disposal: Mr Robert Anderton, Head of Environmental Improvement, Brent Civic Centre, Engineers Way, Wembley HA9 0FJ ☎ 020 8937 5001 ⌂ robert.anderton@brent.gov.uk

Waste Management: Mr Robert Anderton, Head of Environmental Improvement, Brent Civic Centre, Engineers Way, Wembley HA9 0FJ ☎ 020 8937 5001 ⌂ robert.anderton@brent.gov.uk

BRENT

COUNCILLORS

Mayor: Ahmed, Parvez (LAB - Dollis Hill)
cllr.parvez.ahmed@brent.gov.uk

Deputy Mayor: Chohan, Bhagwanji (LAB - Alperton)
cllr.bhagwanji.chohan@brent.gov.uk

Leader of the Council: Butt, Muhammed (LAB - Tokyngton)
cllr.muhammed.butt@brent.gov.uk

Deputy Leader of the Council: McLennan, Margaret (LAB - Northwick Park)
cllr.margaret.mclennan@brent.gov.uk

Group LeaderKansagra, Suresh (CON - Kenton)
cllr.suresh.kansagra@brent.gov.uk

Group LeaderWarren, John (CON - Brondesbury Park)
cllr.john.warren@brent.gov.uk

Aden, Abdi (LAB - Sudbury)
cllr.abdifatah.aden@brent.gov.uk

Agha, Amer (LAB - Welsh Harp)
cllr.amer.agha@brent.gov.uk

Allie, James (LAB - Alperton)
cllr.james.allie@brent.gov.uk

Bradley, Matt (LAB - Preston)
cllr.matthew.bradley@brent.gov.uk

Carr, Helen (LD - Mapesbury)
cllr.helen.carr@brent.gov.uk

Chan, Jumbo (LAB - Kensal Green)
cllr.jumbo.chan@brent.gov.uk

Choudhary, Shafique (LAB - Barnhill)
cllr.shafique.choudhary@brent.gov.uk

Choudry, Aslam (LAB - Dudden Hill)
cllr.aslam.choudry@brent.gov.uk

Colacicco, Lia (LAB - Mapesbury)
cllr.lia.colacicco@brent.gov.uk

Collier, Bernard (LAB - Willesden Green)
cllr.bernard.collier@brent.gov.uk

Colwill, Reg (CON - Kenton)
cllr.reg.colwill@brent.gov.uk

Conneely, Rita (LAB - Kilburn)
cllr.rita.conneely@brent.gov.uk

Crane, George (LAB - Fryent)
cllr.george.crane@brent.gov.uk

Daly, Mary (LAB - Sudbury)
cllr.mary.daly@brent.gov.uk

Davidson, Joel (CON - Brondesbury Park)
cllr.joel.davidson@brent.gov.uk

Denselow, James (LAB - Queen's Park)
cllr.james.denselow@brent.gov.uk

Dixon, Liz (LAB - Dollis Hill)
cllr.liz.dixon@brent.gov.uk

Duffy, John (LAB - Kilburn)
cllr.john.duffy@brent.gov.uk

Eniola, Aisha (LAB - Harlesden)
cllr.aisha.eniola@brent.gov.uk

Ezeajughi, Ernest (LAB - Stonebridge)
cllr.ernest.ezeajughi@brent.gov.uk

Farah, Harbi (LAB - Welsh Harp)
cllr.harbi.farah@brent.gov.uk

Harrison, Patricia (LAB - Preston)
cllr.patricia.harrison@brent.gov.uk

Hector, Claudia (LAB - Kensal Green)
cllr.claudia.hector@brent.gov.uk

Hirani, Krupesh (LAB - Dudden Hill)
cllr.krupesh.hirani@brent.gov.uk

Hoda-Benn, Aisha (LAB - Sudbury)
cllr.aisha.hoda-benn@brent.gov.uk

Hossain, Jean (LAB - Preston)
cllr.jean.hossain@brent.gov.uk

Hylton, Orleen (LAB - Tokyngton)
cllr.orleen.hylton@brent.gov.uk

Jones, Lesley (LAB - Willesden Green)
cllr.lesley.jones@brent.gov.uk

Kabir, Sandra (LAB - Queensbury)
cllr.sandra.kabir@brent.gov.uk

Kelcher, Matt (LAB - Kensal Green)
cllr.matt.kelcher@brent.gov.uk

Khan, Sabina (LAB - Stonebridge)
cllr.sabina.khan@brent.gov.uk

Long, Janice (LAB - Dudden Hill)
cllr.janice.long@brent.gov.uk

Mahmood, Arshad (LAB - Dollis Hill)
cllr.arshad.mahmood@brent.gov.uk

Marquis, Sarah (LAB - Barnhill)
cllr.sarah.marquis@brent.gov.uk

Mashari, Roxanne (LAB - Welsh Harp)
cllr.roxanne.mashari@brent.gov.uk

Maurice, Michael (CON - Kenton)
cllr.michael.maurice@brent.gov.uk

McLeish, Lloyd (LAB - Harlesden)
cllr.lloyd.mcleish@brent.gov.uk

Miller, Tom (LAB - Willesden Green)
cllr.tom.miller@brent.gov.uk

Mitchell Murray, Wilhelmina (LAB - Wembley Central)
cllr.wilhelmina.mitchellmurray@brent.gov.uk

Mitchell Murray, Joshua (LAB - Northwick Park)
cllr.joshua.murray@brent.gov.uk

Moher, Ruth (LAB - Fryent)
cllr.ruth.moher@brent.gov.uk

Naheerathan, Kana (LAB - Queensbury)
cllr.kana.naheerathan@brent.gov.uk

Nerva, Neil (LAB - Queen's Park)
cllr.neil.nerva@brent.gov.uk

Patel, Mili (LAB - Alperton)
cllr.mili.patel@brent.gov.uk

Patel, Ramesh (LAB - Queensbury)
cllr.ramesh.patel@brent.gov.uk

Pavey, Michael (LAB - Barnhill)
cllr.michael.pavey@brent.gov.uk

Perrin, Keith (LAB - Northwick Park)
cllr.keith.perrin@brent.gov.uk

Pitruzzella, Barbara (LAB - Kilburn)
cllr.barbara.pitruzzella@brent.gov.uk

Shahzad, Ahmad (LAB - Mapesbury)
cllr.ahmad.shahzad@brent.gov.uk

Shaw, Carol (LD - Brondesbury Park)
cllr.carol.shaw@brent.gov.uk

Sheth, Krupa (LAB - Wembley Central)
cllr.krupa.sheth@brent.gov.uk

Sheth, Ketan (LAB - Tokyngton)
cllr.ketan.sheth@brent.gov.uk

Southwood, Eleanor (LAB - Queen's Park)
cllr.eleanor.southwood@brent.gov.uk

Stopp, Sam (LAB - Wembley Central)
cllr.sam.stopp@brent.gov.uk

Tatler, Shama (LAB - Fryent)
cllr.shama.tatler@brent.gov.uk

Thomas, Bobby (LAB - Harlesden)
cllr.bobby.thomas@brent.gov.uk

Van Kalwala, Zaffar (LAB - Stonebridge)
cllr.zaffar.vankalwala@brent.gov.uk

POLITICAL COMPOSITION
LAB: 56, CON: 5, LD: 2

COMMITTEE CHAIRS

Health & Wellbeing: Mr Krupesh Hirani

Licensing: Mr Arshad Mahmood

Planning: Ms Sarah Marquis

Brentwood   D

Brentwood Borough Council, c/o The Town Hall, Ingrave Road, Brentwood CM15 8AY
☎ 01277 312500 🖷 01277 312743 ◌ enquiries@brentwood.gov.uk
🖳 www.brentwood.gov.uk

FACTS AND FIGURES
Parliamentary Constituencies: Brentwood and Ongar
EU Constituencies: Eastern
Election Frequency: Elections are by thirds

PRINCIPAL OFFICERS

Chief Executive: Mr Philip Ruck, Head of Paid Service, c/o The Town Hall, Ingrave Road, Brentwood CM15 8AY ☎ 01277 312712
◌ philip.ruck@brentwood.gov.uk

Senior Management: Ms Helen Gregory, Interim Head of Housing & Benefits, c/o The Town Hall, Ingrave Road, Brentwood CM15 8AY ☎ 01277 312586 ◌ helen.gregory@brentwood.gov.uk

Senior Management: Mr Chris Leslie, Finance Director & S151 Officer, c/o The Town Hall, Ingrave Road, Brentwood CM15 8AY ☎ 01277 312542 ◌ chris.leslie@brentwood.gov.uk

Senior Management: Mr Roy Ormsby, Head of Streetscene & Community, c/o The Town Hall, Ingrave Road, Brentwood CM15 8AY ☎ 01277 312554 ◌ roy.ormsby@brentwood.gov.uk

Senior Management: Mr Steve Summers, Group Manager - In-House Services, c/o The Town Hall, Ingrave Road, Brentwood CM15 8AY ☎ 01277 312749 ◌ steve.summers@brentwood.gov.uk

Senior Management: Mr Daniel Toohey, Head of Legal (Monitoring Officer), c/o The Town Hall, Ingrave Road, Brentwood CM15 8AY ☎ 01277 312554 ◌ daniel.toohey@brentwood.gov.uk

Building Control: Mr Gary Price, Building Control Team Leader, c/o The Town Hall, Ingrave Road, Brentwood CM15 8AY
☎ 01277 312534 ◌ gary.price@brentwood.gov.uk

Children / Youth Services: Ms Kim Anderson, Partnerships, Leisure & Funding Manager, c/o The Town Hall, Ingrave Road, Brentwood CM15 8AY ☎ 01277 312634
◌ kim.anderson@brentwood.gov.uk

PR / Communications: Mrs Leona Murray-Green, Business Development & Communications Manager, c/o The Town Hall, Ingrave Road, Brentwood CM15 8AY ☎ 01277 312630
◌ leona.murraygreen@brentwood.gov.uk

Community Planning: Mr Philip Drane, Planning Policy Team Leader, c/o The Town Hall, Ingrave Road, Brentwood CM15 8AY
☎ 01277 312609 ◌ philipdrane@brentwood.gov.uk

Community Safety: Ms Tracey Lilley, Anti-Social Behaviour Co-ordinator, c/o The Town Hall, Ingrave Road, Brentwood CM15 8AY
☎ 01277 312644 ◌ tracey.lilley@brentwood.gov.uk

Computer Management: Mr Tim Huggins, ICT Manager, Town Hall, Ingrave Road, Brentwood CM15 8AY ☎ 01277 312719
◌ tim.huggins@brentwood.gov.uk

Corporate Services: Mrs Zoe Borman, Corporate Support Officer, c/o The Town Hall, Ingrave Road, Brentwood CM15 8AY
☎ 01277 312736 ◌ zoe.borman@brentwood.gov.uk

Customer Service: Ms Samantha Stow, Revenues & Benefits Manager, c/o The Town Hall, Ingrave Road, Brentwood CM15 8AY
☎ 01277 312855 ◌ samantha.stow@brentwood.gov.uk

Direct Labour: Mr Darren Laver, Waste & Grounds Manager, c/o The Town Hall, Ingrave Road, Brentwood CM15 8AY
☎ 01277 312779 ◌ darren.laver@brentwood.gov.uk

Economic Development: Ms Anne Knight, Economic Development Officer, c/o The Town Hall, Ingrave Road, Brentwood CM15 8AY ☎ 01277 312607 ◌ anne.knight@brentwood.gov.uk

E-Government: Mr Tim Huggins, ICT Manager, Town Hall, Ingrave Road, Brentwood CM15 8AY ☎ 01277 312719
◌ tim.huggins@brentwood.gov.uk

Electoral Registration: Mrs Carole Tatton-Bennett, Electoral Services Manager, c/o The Town Hall, Ingrave Road, Brentwood CM15 8AY ☎ 01277 312709
◌ carole.tatton-bennett@brentwood.gov.uk

Emergency Planning: Ms Sue White, Emergency Planning Officer, c/o The Town Hall, Ingrave Road, Brentwood CM15 8AY
☎ 01277 312821 ◌ sue.white@brentwood.gov.uk

BRENTWOOD

Estates, Property & Valuation: Mr Russell Clinker, Senior Asset Manager, c/o The Town Hall, Ingrave Road, Brentwood CM15 8AY ☎ 01277 312931 ✆ russell.clinker@brentwood.gov.uk

Events Manager: Ms Kim Anderson, Partnerships, Leisure & Funding Manager, c/o The Town Hall, Ingrave Road, Brentwood CM15 8AY ☎ 01277 312634 ✆ kim.anderson@brentwood.gov.uk

Finance: Mr John Chance, Finance Director & S151 Officer, c/o The Town Hall, Ingrave Road, Brentwood CM15 8AY ☎ 01277 312542 ✆ john.chance@brentwood.gov.uk

Grounds Maintenance: Mr Stuart Anderson, Open Space Strategy Co-ordinator, c/o The Town Hall, Ingrave Road, Brentwood CM15 8AY ☎ 01277 312654 ✆ stuart.anderson@brentwood.gov.uk

Health and Safety: Mr Mark Stanbury, Senior Environmental Health Officer, c/o The Town Hall, Ingrave Road, Brentwood CM15 8AY ☎ 01277 312510 ✆ mark.stanbury@brentwood.gov.uk

Housing: Ms Helen Gregory, Interim Head of Housing & Benefits, c/o The Town Hall, Ingrave Road, Brentwood CM15 8AY ☎ 01277 312586 ✆ helen.gregory@brentwood.gov.uk

Housing Maintenance: Ms Helen Gregory, Interim Head of Housing & Benefits, c/o The Town Hall, Ingrave Road, Brentwood CM15 8AY ☎ 01277 312586 ✆ helen.gregory@brentwood.gov.uk

Legal: Mr David Lawson, Head of Legal Services & Monitoring Officer, c/o The Town Hall, Ingrave Road, Brentwood CM15 8AY ☎ 01277 312860 ✆ david.lawson@brentwood.gov.uk

Leisure and Cultural Services: Ms Kim Anderson, Partnerships, Leisure & Funding Manager, c/o The Town Hall, Ingrave Road, Brentwood CM15 8AY ☎ 01277 312634 ✆ kim.anderson@brentwood.gov.uk

Licensing: Mr Paul Adams, Principal Licensing Officer, c/o The Town Hall, Ingrave Road, Brentwood CM15 8AY ☎ 01277 312503 ✆ paul.adams@brentwood.gov.uk

Member Services: Mr Daniel Toohey, Head of Legal (Monitoring Officer), c/o The Town Hall, Ingrave Road, Brentwood CM15 8AY ☎ 01277 312554 ✆ daniel.toohey@brentwood.gov.uk

Parking: Mr Alan McBean, Parking Manager, c/o The Town Hall, Ingrave Road, Brentwood CM15 8AY ☎ 01277 312583 ✆ alan.mcbean@brentwood.gov.uk

Procurement: Ms Jane Mitchell, Payments & Procurement Officer, c/o The Town Hall, Ingrave Road, Brentwood CM15 8AY ☎ 01277 312853 ✆ jane.mitchell@brentwood.gov.uk

Recycling & Waste Minimisation: Mr Darren Laver, Waste & Grounds Manager, c/o The Town Hall, Ingrave Road, Brentwood CM15 8AY ☎ 01277 312779 ✆ darren.laver@brentwood.gov.uk

Town Centre: Ms Elaine Richardson, Town Centre Development Co-ordinator, c/o The Town Hall, Ingrave Road, Brentwood CM15 8AY ☎ 01277 312515 ✆ elaine.richardson@brentwood.gov.uk

Waste Collection and Disposal: Mr Darren Laver, Waste & Grounds Manager, c/o The Town Hall, Ingrave Road, Brentwood CM15 8AY ☎ 01277 312779 ✆ darren.laver@brentwood.gov.uk

Waste Management: Mr Darren Laver, Waste & Grounds Manager, c/o The Town Hall, Ingrave Road, Brentwood CM15 8AY ☎ 01277 312779 ✆ darren.laver@brentwood.gov.uk

Children's Play Areas: Mr Stuart Anderson, Open Space Strategy Co-ordinator, c/o The Town Hall, Ingrave Road, Brentwood CM15 8AY ☎ 01277 312654 ✆ stuart.anderson@brentwood.gov.uk

COUNCILLORS

Mayor: Hones, Noelle (CON - Ingatestone, Fryerning & Mountnessing)
noelle.hones@brentwood.gov.uk

Deputy Mayor: Russell, Will (CON - Brentwood West)
will.russell@brentwood.gov.uk

Leader of the Council: McKinlay, Louise (CON - Hutton North)
louise.mckinlay@brentwood.gov.uk

Deputy Leader of the Council: Kerslake, John (CON - Hutton Central)
john.kerslake@brentwood.gov.uk

Group LeaderAspinell, Barry (LD - Pilgrims Hatch)
barry.aspinell@brentwood.gov.uk

Group LeaderBarrett, Gareth (LAB - Brentwood South)
gareth.barrett@brentwood.gov.uk

Barrell, Paul (CON - Warley)
paul.barrell@brentwood.gov.uk

Bridge, Thomas (CON - Ingatestone, Fryerning & Mountnessing)
thomas.bridge@brentwood.gov.uk

Chilvers, Karen (LD - Brentwood West)
karen.chilvers@brentwood.gov.uk

Clarke, Nigel (LD - Warley)
nigel.clarke@brentwood.gov.uk

Cloke, Jon (CON - Ingatestone, Fryerning & Mountnessing)
jon.cloke@brentwood.gov.uk

Coe, Ann (CON - South Weald)
ann.coe@brentwood.gov.uk

Davies, Vicky (LD - Pilgrims Hatch)
vicky.davies@brentwood.gov.uk

Faragher, Paul (CON - Hutton Central)
paul.faragher@brentwood.gov.uk

Fulcher, Alison (LD - Brentwood North)
alison.fulcher@brentwood.gov.uk

Hirst, Roger (CON - Hutton South)
roger.hirst@brentwood.gov.uk

Hossack, Chris (CON - Hutton East)
chris.hossack@brentwood.gov.uk

Hubbard, Jill (LD - Warley)
jill.hubbard@brentwood.gov.uk

Keeble, Roger (IND - Tipps Cross)
roger.keeble@brentwood.gov.uk

Kendall, David (LD - Pilgrims Hatch)
david.kendall@brentwood.gov.uk

McCheyne, Roger (CON - Brizes & Doddinghurst)
roger.mccheyne@brentwood.gov.uk

Middlehurst, Aimi (CON - Tipps Cross)
aimi.middlehurst@brentwood.gov.uk

Morrissey, Julie (LAB - Brentwood South)
julie.morrissey@brentwood.gov.uk

Murphy, Sheila (CON - Herongate, Ingrave & West Horndon)
sheilah.murphy@brentwood.gov.uk

Mynott, Philip (LD - Brentwood North)
philip.mynott@brentwood.gov.uk

Newberry, John (LD - Brentwood West)
john.newberry@brentwood.gov.uk

Parker, Keith (CON - Brizes & Doddinghurst)
keith.parker@brentwood.gov.uk

Poppy, Cliff (CON - Brizes & Doddinghurst)
cliff.poppy@breentwood.gov.uk

Pound, Jan (CON - Shenfield)
jan.pound@brentwood.gov.uk

Reed, Mark (CON - Hutton South)
mark.reed@brentwood.gov.uk

Rowlands, Louise (CON - Shenfield)
louise.rowlland@brenford.gov.uk

Salde, Melissa (CON - Brentwood North)
melissa.slade@brentwood.gov.uk

Sanders, Olivia (CON - Hutton East)
olivia.sanders@brentwood.gov.uk

Squirrell, Jo (LD - Herongate, Ingrave & West Horndon)
joanne.squirrell@brentwood.gov.uk

Trump, William (CON - Hutton North)
william.trump@brentwood.gov.uk

Tumbridge, James (CON - Shenfield)
james.tumbridge@brentwood.gov.uk

Wiles, Andrew (CON - Brentwood South)
andrew.wiles@brentwood.gov.uk

POLITICAL COMPOSITION
CON: 24, LD: 10, LAB: 2, IND: 1

COMMITTEE CHAIRS

Audit: Mrs Jan Pound

Community, Health & Leisure: Mr Keith Parker

Environment & Housing Management: Mr Chris Hossack

Planning & Licensing: Mr Roger McCheyne

Policy, Finance & Resources: Mrs Louise McKinlay

Bridgend   W

Bridgend County Borough Council, Civic Offices, Angel
Street, Bridgend CF31 4WB
☎ 01656 643643 📠 01656 668126 ✆ talktous@bridgend.gov.uk
💻 www.bridgend.gov.uk

FACTS AND FIGURES
Parliamentary Constituencies: Bridgend, Ogmore
EU Constituencies: Wales

Election Frequency: Elections are of whole council

PRINCIPAL OFFICERS

Chief Executive: Mr Darren Mepham, Chief Executive, Civic
Offices, Angel Street, Bridgend CF31 4WB ☎ 01656 643227
✆ darren.mepham@bridgend.gov.uk

Senior Management: Mrs Susan Cooper, Corporate Director -
Social Services & Wellbeing, Civic Offices, Angel Street, Bridgend
CF31 4WB ☎ 01656 642251 ✆ susan.cooper@bridgend.gov.uk

Senior Management: Mr Andrew Jolley, Corporate Director -
Operational & Partnership Services, Civic Offices, Angel Street,
Bridgend CF31 4WB ☎ 01656 643106
✆ andrew.jolley@bridgend.gov.uk

Senior Management: Ms Deborah McMillan, Corporate Director
- Education & Family Support, Civic Offices, Angel Street, Bridgend
CF31 4WB ☎ 01656 642617 ✆ deborah.mcmillan@bridgend.gov.uk

Senior Management: Mr Mark Shephard, Corporate Director -
Communities, Civic Offices, Angel Street, Bridgend CF31 4WB
☎ 01656 643227 ✆ mark.shephard@bridgend.gov.uk

Architect, Building / Property Services: Mr Mark Evans, Group
Manager - Built Environment, Waterton Lane Depot, Bridgend CF31
3YP ☎ 01656 642827 ✆ mark.evans@bridgend.gov.uk

Best Value: Ms Yuan Shen, Corporate Improvement Manager
& Integrated Partnerships Manager, Civic Offices, Angel Street,
Bridgend CF31 4WB ☎ 01656 643224
✆ yuan.shen@bridgend.gov.uk

Building Control: Mr Mark Evans, Group Manager - Built
Environment, Waterton Lane Depot, Bridgend CF31 3YP
☎ 01656 642827 ✆ mark.evans@bridgend.gov.uk

Catering Services: Ms Louise Kerton, Team Manager - Catering
Services, Supplies Building, Waterton, Bridgend CF31 7YR
☎ 01656 664527 ✆ louise.kerton@bridgend.gov.uk

Children / Youth Services: Ms Nicola Echanis, Head of
Education & Early Help, Civic Offices, Angel Street, Bridgend CF31
4WB ☎ 01656 642611 ✆ nicola.echanis@bridgend.gov.uk

Children / Youth Services: Ms Laura Kinsey, Head of Children's
Social Care, Civic Offices, Angel Street, Bridgend CF31 4WB
☎ 0166 642314 ✆ laura.kinsey@bridgend.gov.uk

Civil Registration: Ms Lucy Bratcher, Superintendent Registrar,
Register Office, Ty'r Ardd, Sunnyside, Bridgend CF31 4AR
☎ 01656 642391 ✆ lucy.bratcher@bridgend.gov.uk

Community Safety: Mr John Davies, Community Safety Team
Leader, Bridgend Police Station, Brackla Street, Bridgend CF31 1BZ
☎ 01656 815918 ✆ john.davies@bridgend.gov.uk

Computer Management: Mr Martin Morgans, Group Manager -
ICT Services, Sunnyside House, Sunnyside, Bridgend CF31 4AR
☎ 01656 642110 ✆ martin.morgans@bridgend.gov.uk

BRIDGEND

Consumer Protection and Trading Standards: Mr Lee Jones, Head of Regulatory, Partnerships & Transformation, Civic Offices, Angel Street, Bridgend CF31 4WB ☎ 01656 643259 ⏚ lee.jones@bridgend.gov.uk

Customer Service: Ms Beverley Davies, Customer Service Manager, Civic Offices, Angel Street, Bridgend CF31 4WB ☎ 01656 643333 ⏚ beverley.davies@bridgend.gov.uk

Economic Development: Ms Satwant Pryce, Head of Regeneration & Development, Civic Offices, Angel Street, Bridgend CF31 4WB ☎ 01656 643151 ⏚ satwant.pryce@bridgend.gov.uk

Education: Ms Deborah McMillan, Corporate Director - Education & Family Support, Civic Offices, Angel Street, Bridgend CF31 4WB ☎ 01656 642617 ⏚ deborah.mcmillan@bridgend.gov.uk

E-Government: Mr Martin Morgans, Group Manager - ICT Services, Sunnyside House, Sunnyside, Bridgend CF31 4AR ☎ 01656 642110 ⏚ martin.morgans@bridgend.gov.uk

Electoral Registration: Mr Gary Ennis, Electoral Services Manager, Civic Offices, Angel Street, Bridgend CF31 4WB ☎ 01656 643609 ⏚ gary.ennis@bridgend.gov.uk

Emergency Planning: Mrs Julie Cooper, Principal Emergency Planning Officer, Civic Offices, Angel Street, Bridgend CF31 4WB ☎ 01656 643300 ⏚ julie.cooper@bridgend.gov.uk

Energy Management: Ms Satwant Pryce, Head of Regeneration & Development, Civic Offices, Angel Street, Bridgend CF31 4WB ☎ 01656 643151 ⏚ satwant.pryce@bridgend.gov.uk

Environmental / Technical Services: Mr Zak Shell, Head of Neighbourhood Services, Civic Offices, Angel Street, Bridgend CF31 4WB ☎ 01656 643151 ⏚ zak.shell@bridgend.gov.uk

Environmental Health: Mr Philip Stanton, Service Manager - Environmental Health, Raven's Court, Brewery Lane, Bridgend CF31 4AP ☎ 01656 643141 ⏚ philip.stanton@bridgend.gov.uk

Estates, Property & Valuation: Ms Fiona Blick, Group Manager - Property Services, Raven's Court, Brewery Lane, Bridgend CF31 4AP ☎ 01656 642702 ⏚ fiona.blick@bridgend.gov.uk

European Liaison: Mr Mark Halliwell, Manager - Regeneration Funding, Innovation Centre, Bridgend Science Park, Bridgend CF31 3NA ☎ 01656 815329 ⏚ mark.halliwell@bridgend.gov.uk

Events Manager: Ms Emma Blandon, Marketing & Engagement Manager, Raven's Court, Brewery Lane, Bridgend CF31 4AP ☎ 01656 642047 ⏚ emma.blandon@bridgend.gov.uk

Facilities: Mr Paul Thomas, Principal Surveyor - Property & Facilities Management, Raven's Court, Brewery Lane, Bridgend CF31 4AP ☎ 01656 642704 ⏚ paul.thomas@bridgend.gov.uk

Finance: Mr Randal Hemmingway, Head of Finance, Civic Offices, Angel Street, Bridgend CF31 4WB ☎ 01656 643307 ⏚ randal.hemmingway@bridgend.gov.uk

Fleet Management: Mr Trevor Lloyd, Joint Fleet Services Manager, Ty Thomas JVM, Newlands Avenue, Brackla Industrial Estate, Bridgend CF31 4WB ☎ 01656 642874 ⏚ trevor.lloyd@bridgend.gov.uk

Grounds Maintenance: Mr Gareth Evans, Parks & Playing Fields Manager, Civic Offices, Angel Street, Bridgend CF31 4WB ☎ 01656 642720 ⏚ gareth.evans@bridgend.gov.uk

Health and Safety: Ms Claire Howells, Heath & Safety Manager, Waterton Lane Depot, Bridgend CF31 3YP ☎ 01656 642872 ⏚ claire.howells@bridgend.gov.uk

Highways: Mr Kevin Mulcahy, Group Manager - Highways Services, Civic Offices, Angel Street, Bridgend CF31 4WB ☎ 01656 642535 ⏚ kevin.mulcahy@bridgend.gov.uk

Home Energy Conservation: Mr Mark Shephard, Corporate Director - Communities, Civic Offices, Angel Street, Bridgend CF31 4WB ☎ 01656 643227 ⏚ mark.shephard@bridgend.gov.uk

Housing: Ms Satwant Pryce, Head of Regeneration & Development, Civic Offices, Angel Street, Bridgend CF31 4WB ☎ 01656 643151 ⏚ satwant.pryce@bridgend.gov.uk

Legal: Ms Kelly Watson, Head of Legal, Civic Offices, Angel Street, Bridgend CF31 4WB ☎ 01656 643248 ⏚ kelly.watson@bridgend.gov.uk

Licensing: Ms Yvonne Witchell, Licensing Team Leader, Civic Offices, Angel Street, Bridgend CF31 4WB ☎ 01656 643105 ⏚ yvonne.witchell@bridgend.gov.uk

Member Services: Mr Gary Jones, Head of Democratic Services, Civic Offices, Angel Street, Bridgend CF31 4WB ☎ 01656 643385 ⏚ gary.jones@bridgend.gov.uk

Parking: Mr John Duddridge, Collaboration Manager, Morien House, Bennett Street, Bridgend Industrial Estate, Bridgend CF31 4WB ☎ 01656 642535 ⏚ john.duddridge@bridgend.gov.uk

Partnerships: Mr Lee Jones, Head of Regulatory, Partnerships & Transformation, Civic Offices, Angel Street, Bridgend CF31 4WB ☎ 01656 643259 ⏚ lee.jones@bridgend.gov.uk

Partnerships: Ms Yuan Shen, Corporate Improvement Manager & Integrated Partnerships Manager, Civic Offices, Angel Street, Bridgend CF31 4WB ☎ 01656 643224 ⏚ yuan.shen@bridgend.gov.uk

Personnel / HR: Ms Sarah Kingsbury, Head of Human Resources & Organisational Development, Raven's Court, Brewery Lane, Bridgend CF31 4AP ☎ 01656 643209 ⏚ sarah.kingsbury@bridgend.gov.uk

Planning: Ms Satwant Pryce, Head of Regeneration & Development, Civic Offices, Angel Street, Bridgend CF31 4WB ☎ 01656 643151 ⏚ satwant.pryce@bridgend.gov.uk

Recycling & Waste Minimisation: Mr Andrew Hobbs, Group Manager - Street Works, Civic Offices, Angel Street, Bridgend CF31 4WB ☎ 01656 643416 ⏚ andrew.hobbs@bridgend.gov.uk

Regeneration: Ms Satwant Pryce, Head of Regeneration & Development, Civic Offices, Angel Street, Bridgend CF31 4WB
☎ 01656 643151 ⌨ satwant.pryce@bridgend.gov.uk

Regeneration: Mr Mark Shephard, Corporate Director - Communities, Civic Offices, Angel Street, Bridgend CF31 4WB
☎ 01656 643227 ⌨ mark.shephard@bridgend.gov.uk

Road Safety: Mr Zak Shell, Head of Neighbourhood Services, Civic Offices, Angel Street, Bridgend CF31 4WB ☎ 01656 643151
⌨ zak.shell@bridgend.gov.uk

Social Services: Mrs Susan Cooper, Corporate Director - Social Services & Wellbeing, Civic Offices, Angel Street, Bridgend CF31 4WB ☎ 01656 642251 ⌨ susan.cooper@bridgend.gov.uk

Social Services (Adult): Ms Jackie Davies, Head of Adult Social Care, Civic Offices, Angel Street, Bridgend CF31 4WB
☎ 01656 642121 ⌨ jacqueline.davies@bridgend.gov.uk

Social Services (Children): Ms Laura Kinsey, Head of Children's Social Care, Civic Offices, Angel Street, Bridgend CF31 4WB
☎ 0166 642314 ⌨ laura.kinsey@bridgend.gov.uk

Street Scene: Mr Zak Shell, Head of Neighbourhood Services, Civic Offices, Angel Street, Bridgend CF31 4WB ☎ 01656 643151
⌨ zak.shell@bridgend.gov.uk

Sustainable Communities: Mr Michael Jenkins, Principal Sustainable Development Officer, Civic Offices, Angel Street, Bridgend CF31 4WB ☎ 01656 643179
⌨ michael.jenkins@bridgend.gov.uk

Sustainable Development: Mr Michael Jenkins, Principal Sustainable Development Officer, Civic Offices, Angel Street, Bridgend CF31 4WB ☎ 01656 643179
⌨ michael.jenkins@bridgend.gov.uk

Tourism: Ms Satwant Pryce, Head of Regeneration & Development, Civic Offices, Angel Street, Bridgend CF31 4WB
☎ 01656 643151 ⌨ satwant.pryce@bridgend.gov.uk

Town Centre: Ms Rhiannon Kingsley, Town Centre Manager, Civic Offices, Angel Street, Bridgend CF31 4WB ☎ 01656 815225
⌨ rhiannon.kingsley@bridgend.gov.uk

Traffic Management: Mr Anthony Godsall, Traffic & Transportation Manager, Civic Offices, Angel Street, Bridgend CF31 4WB ☎ 01656 642523 ⌨ Tony.Godsall@bridgend.gov.uk

Transport: Mr John Duddridge, Collaboration Manager, Civic Offices, Angel Street, Bridgend CF31 4WB ☎ 01656 642535
⌨ john.duddridge@bridgend.gov.uk

Transport: Mr Anthony Godsall, Traffic & Transportation Manager, Civic Offices, Angel Street, Bridgend CF31 4WB ☎ 01656 642523
⌨ Tony.Godsall@bridgend.gov.uk

Waste Collection and Disposal: Mr Andrew Hobbs, Group Manager - Street Works, Civic Offices, Angel Street, Bridgend CF31 4WB ☎ 01656 643416 ⌨ andrew.hobbs@bridgend.gov.uk

Waste Management: Mr Andrew Hobbs, Group Manager - Street Works, Civic Offices, Angel Street, Bridgend CF31 4WB
☎ 01656 643416 ⌨ andrew.hobbs@bridgend.gov.uk

COUNCILLORS

Mayor: Jenkins, Reg (LAB - No Ward)
mayor@bridgend.gov.uk

Deputy Mayor: Jones, Cherie (LAB - Litchard)
cllr.cherie.jones@bridgend.gov.uk

Leader of the Council: Nott, Melvyn (LAB - Sarn)
cllr.meg.nott@bridgend.gov.uk

Deputy Leader of the Council: David, Huw (LAB - Cefn Cribwr)
cllr.huw.david@bridgend.gov.uk

Group LeaderGreen, Cheryl (LD - Bryntirion, Laleston & Merthyr Mawr)
cllr.cheryl.green@bridgend.gov.uk

Group LeaderTildesley, Jeff (IND - Cornelly)
cllr.jeff.tildesley@bridgend.gov.uk

Aspey, Sean (IND - Porthcawl West Central)
cllr.sean.aspey@bridgend.gov.uk

Butcher, Megan (IND - Cornelly)
cllr.megan.butcher@bridgend.gov.uk

Clarke, Norah (LD - Nottage)
cllr.norah.clarke@bridgend.gov.uk

Davies, Gerald (LD - Rest Bay)
cllr.gerald.davies@bridgend.gov.uk

Davies, Pamela (LAB - Bryntirion, Laleston & Merthyr Mawr)
cllr.pam.davies@bridgend.gov.uk

Davies, Wyn (CON - Caerau)
cllr.wyn.davies@Bridgend.gov.uk

Dodd, Ella (IND - Coity)
cllr.ella.dodd@bridgend.gv.uk

Edwards, Keith (LAB - Maesteg East)
cllr.keith.edwards@bridgend.gov.uk

Ellis, Luke (LAB - Pyle)
cllr.luke.ellis@bridgend.gov.uk

Farr, Neelo (LAB - Newcastle)
cllr.neelo.farr@Bridgend.gov.uk

Foley, Peter (IND - Morfa)
cllr.peter.foley@bridgend.gov.uk

Gregory, Michael (LAB - Felindre)
cllr.mike.gregory@bridgend.gov.uk

Hughes, Edith (LAB - Oldcastle)
cllr.edith.m.hughes@bridgend.gov.uk

James, Malcolm (PC - Llangynwyd)
cllr.malcolm.james@bridgend.gov.uk

James, Clive (LAB - Pyle)
cllr.clive.james@bridgend.gov.uk

James, Pauline (LAB - Pyle)
cllr.pauline.james@bridgend.gov.uk

John, Phil (LAB - Caerau)
cllr.phil.john@bridgend.gov.uk

Jones, Brian (IND - Porthcawl East Central)
cllr.brian.jones@bridgend.gov.uk

BRIDGEND

Jones, Martyn (LAB - Bettws)
cllr.martyn.jones@bridgend.gov.uk

Jones, Craig (LAB - Brackla)
cllr.craig.l.jones@bridgend.gov.uk

Lewis, David (LAB - Pen-Y-Fai)
cllr.david.lewis@bridgend.gov.uk

Lewis, Janice (LAB - Bryncoch)
cllr.janice.lewis@bridgend.gov.uk

McCarthy, John (LAB - Hendre)
cllr.john.mccarthy@bridgend.gov.uk

Morgan, Lyn (LAB - Ynysawdre)
cllr.lyn.morgan@bridgend.gov.uk

Morgan, Haydn (LAB - Morfa)
cllr.haydn.morgan@bridgend.gov.uk

Owen, David (IND - Nant-y-Moel)
cllr.david.owen@bridgend.gov.uk

Owen, Alexander (LAB - Penprysg)
cllr.alex.owen@bridgend.gov.uk

Patel, Dhanisha (LAB - Ogmore Vale)
cllr.dhanisha.patel@bridgend.gov.uk

Phillips, Gareth (LAB - Oldcastle)
cllr.gareth.phillips@bridgend.gov.uk

Pugh, David (LAB - Blaengarw)
membersbcbc@bridgend.gov.uk

Reeves, Mal (LAB - Maesteg East)
cllr.mal.reeves@bridgend.gov.uk

Reeves, Ceri (LAB - Maesteg West)
cllr.ceri.reeves@bridgend.gov.uk

Sage, David (LAB - Brackla)
cllr.david.sage@bridgend.gov.uk

Smith, Charles (LAB - Llangewydd & Brynhyfryd)
cllr.charles.smith@bridgend.gov.uk

Spanswick, John (LAB - Brackla)
cllr.john.spanswick@bridgend.gov.uk

Thomas, Ross (LAB - Maesteg West)
cllr.ross.thomas@bridgend.gov.uk

Thomas, Gary (LAB - Bryncethin)
cllr.gary.thomas@bridgend.gov.uk

Thomas, Marlene (LAB - Llangeinor)
cllr.marlene.thomas@bridgend.gov.uk

Townsend, Hailey (LAB - Brackla)
cllr.hailey.j.townsend@bridgend.gov.uk

Venables, Elaine (IND - Coychurch Lower)
cllr.elaine.venables@bridgend.gov.uk

Watts, Kenneth (CON - Newton)
cllr.ken.watts@bridgend.gov.uk

Westwood, Cleone (LAB - Cefn Glas)
cllr.cleone.westwood@bridgend.gov.uk

White, Phillip (LAB - Caerau)
cllr.phil.white@bridgend.gov.uk

White, David (LAB - Newcastle)
cllr.david.white@bridgend.gov.uk

Williams, Richard (LAB - Hendre)
cllr.richard.williams@bridgend.gov.uk

Williams, Hywel (LAB - Blackmill)
cllr.hywel.williams@bridgend.gov.uk

Winter, Mel (IND - Aberkenfig)
membersbcbc@bridgend.gov.uk

Young, Richard (LAB - Pendre)
cllr.richard.young@bridgend.gov.uk

POLITICAL COMPOSITION
LAB: 39, IND: 9, LD: 3, CON: 2, PC: 1

COMMITTEE CHAIRS

Adult Social Care: Mr David Sage

Audit: Ms Ella Dodd

Children & Young People: Mr Peter Foley

Community, Environment & Leisure: Mr John Spanswick

Development Control: Ms Marlene Thomas

Licensing: Mr Richard Williams

Brighton & Hove   U

Brighton & Hove City Council, Kings House, Grand Avenue,
Hove BN3 2LS
☎ 01273 290000 ☐ www.brighton-hove.gov.uk

FACTS AND FIGURES
Parliamentary Constituencies: Brighton, Kemptown, Brighton,
Pavilion, Hove
EU Constituencies: South East
Election Frequency: Elections are of whole council

PRINCIPAL OFFICERS

Chief Executive: Mr Geoff Raw, Chief Executive, Kings House,
Grand Avenue, Hove BN3 2LS ☎ 01273 290453
✉ geoff.raw@brighton-hove.gov.uk

Assistant Chief Executive: Ms Paula Murray, Assistant Chief
Executive, Kings House, Grand Avenue, Hove BN3 2LS
☎ 01273 292534 ✉ paula.murray@brighton-hove.gov.uk

Senior Management: Mr Brian Doughty, Interim Executive
Director - Adult Services, Kings House, Grand Avenue, Hove BN3
2LS ☎ 01273 290000 ✉ brian.doughty@brighton-hove.gov.uk

Senior Management: Mr Abraham Ghebre-Ghiorghis, Executive
Lead Officer - Strategy, Governance & Law, Kings House, Grand
Avenue, Hove BN3 2LS ☎ 01273 291500
✉ abraham.ghebre-ghiorghis@brighton-hove.gov.uk

Senior Management: Mr Pinaki Ghoshal, Executive Director -
Families, Children & Learning, Kings House, Grand Avenue, Hove
BN3 2LS ✉ pinaki.ghoshal@brighton-hove.gov.uk

Senior Management: Mr Nick Hibberd, Executive Director -
Economy, Environment & Culture, Kings House, Grand Avenue,
Hove BN3 2LS ☎ 01273 293020
✉ nick.hibberd@brighton-hove.gov.uk

Senior Management: Mr David Kuenssberg, Executive Director - Finance & Resources, Kings House, Grand Avenue, Hove BN3 2LS ✆ david.kuenssberg@brighton-hove.gov.uk

Senior Management: Mr Rob Persey, Executive Director - Health & Social Care, Kings House, Grand Avenue, Hove BN3 2LS ✆ rob.persey@brighton-hove.gov.uk

Senior Management: Ms Larissa Reed, Executive Director - Neighbourhoods, Communities & Housing, Kings House, Grand Avenue, Hove BN3 2LS ✆ larissa.reed@brighton-hove.gov.uk

Senior Management: Dr Tom Scanlon, Director - Public Health, Kings House, Grand Avenue, Hove BN3 2LS ☎ 01273 291480 ✆ tom.scanlon@brighton-hove.gov.uk

Access Officer / Social Services (Disability): Mr Brian Doughty, Interim Executive Director - Adult Services, Kings House, Grand Avenue, Hove BN3 2LS ☎ 01273 290000 ✆ brian.doughty@brighton-hove.gov.uk

Architect, Building / Property Services: Mrs Angela Dymott, Head of Property & Design, King's House, Grand Avenue, Hove BN3 2LS ☎ 01273 291450 ✆ angela.dymott@brighton-hove.gov.uk

Building Control: Mr Mike Sansom, Head of Building Control, Hove Town Hall, Norton Road, Hove BN3 3BE ☎ 01273 292188 ✆ mike.sansom@brighton-hove.gov.uk

Catering Services: Mrs Angela Dymott, Head of Property & Design, King's House, Grand Avenue, Hove BN3 2LS ☎ 01273 291450 ✆ angela.dymott@brighton-hove.gov.uk

Children / Youth Services: Mr Pinaki Ghoshal, Executive Director - Families, Children & Learning, Kings House, Grand Avenue, Hove BN3 2LS ✆ pinaki.ghoshal@brighton-hove.gov.uk

Civil Registration: Ms Valerie Pearce, Head of City Services, 2nd Floor, Priory House, Bartholemew Square, Brighton BN1 1JR ☎ 01273 290000 ✆ valerie.pearce@brighton-hove.gov.uk

PR / Communications: Ms Claire Saul, Head of Communications, Kings House, Grand Avenue, Hove BN3 2LS ☎ 01273 290000 ✆ claire.saul@brighton-hove.gov.uk

Community Planning: Mr Andrew Ashcroft, Interim Head of Planning, Kings House, Grand Avenue, Hove BN3 2LS ☎ 01273 290000 ✆ andrew.ashcroft@brighton-hove.gov.uk

Community Planning: Mr Rob Dumbrill, Parks Development Manager, Kings House, Grand Avenue, Hove BN3 2LS ☎ 01273 292929 ✆ rob.dumbrill@brighton-hove.gov.uk

Community Safety: Ms Linda Beanlands, Commissoner - Community Safety, 162 North Street, Brighton BN1 2LS ☎ 01273 291115 ✆ linda.beanlands@brighton-hove.gov.uk

Computer Management: Mr Mark Watson, Head of ICT, Kings House, Grand Avenue, Hove BN3 2LS ☎ 01273 290283 ✆ mark.watson@brighton-hove.gov.uk

Consumer Protection and Trading Standards: Mr John Peerless-Mountford, Principal Trading Standards Officer, 2nd Floor, Bartholemew House, Bartholemew Square, Brighton BN1 1JA ☎ 01273 292486 ✆ john.peerless@brighton-hove.gov.uk

Contracts: Ms Rachel Musson, Executive Director - Finance & Resources, Kings House, Grand Avenue, Hove BN3 2LS ☎ 01273 291333 ✆ rachel.musson@brighton-hove.gov.uk

Corporate Services: Mr Graham Liddell, Head of Internal Audit, Kings House, Grand Avenue, Hove BN3 2LS ☎ 01273 290000 ✆ graham.liddell@brighton-hove.gov.uk

Corporate Services: Mr Richard Tuset, Head of Policy & Performance, Kings House, Grand Avenue, Hove BN3 2LS ☎ 01273 295514 ✆ richard.tuset@brighton-hove.gov.uk

Customer Service: Ms Valerie Pearce, Head of City Services, 4th Floor, Priory House, Bartholomew Square, Brighton BN1 1JR ☎ 01273 290000 ✆ valerie.pearce@brighton-hove.gov.uk

Economic Development: Ms Cheryl Finella, Economic Development Manager, Kings House, Grand Avenue, Hove BN3 2LS ☎ 01273 291095 ✆ cheryl.finella@brighton-hove.gov.uk

Economic Development: Mr Nick Hibberd, Executive Director - Economy, Environment & Culture, Kings House, Grand Avenue, Hove BN3 2LS ☎ 01273 293020 ✆ nick.hibberd@brighton-hove.gov.uk

Education: Ms Jo Lyons, Assistant Director - Families, Children & Learning, Kings House, Grand Avenue, Hove BN3 2LS ☎ 01273 293514 ✆ jo.lyons@brighton-hove.gov.uk

E-Government: Mr Mark Watson, Head of ICT, Kings House, Grand Avenue, Hove BN3 2LS ☎ 01273 290283 ✆ mark.watson@brighton-hove.gov.uk

Electoral Registration: Mr Paul Holloway, Head of Life Events & ES, Town Hall, Bartholomew Square, Brighton BN1 1JA ☎ 01273 292005 ✆ paul.holloway@brighton-hove.gov.uk

Emergency Planning: Mr Robin Humphries, Civil Contingencies Manager, Kings House, Grand Avenue, Hove BN3 2LS ☎ 01273 291313 ✆ robin.humphries@brighton-hove.gov.uk

Energy Management: Mrs Angela Dymott, Head of Property & Design, King's House, Grand Avenue, Hove BN3 2LS ☎ 01273 291450 ✆ angela.dymott@brighton-hove.gov.uk

Environmental / Technical Services: Mr Geoff Raw, Chief Executive, Kings House, Grand Avenue, Hove BN3 2LS ☎ 01273 290453 ✆ geoff.raw@brighton-hove.gov.uk

Estates, Property & Valuation: Mrs Angela Dymott, Head of Property & Design, King's House, Grand Avenue, Hove BN3 2LS ☎ 01273 291450 ✆ angela.dymott@brighton-hove.gov.uk

Events Manager: Mr Ian Shurrock, Commissioner - Sports & Leisure, Kings House, Grand Avenue, Hove BN3 2LS ☎ 01273 292084 ✆ ian.shurrock@brighton-hove.gov.uk

BRIGHTON & HOVE

Facilities: Mrs Angela Dymott, Head of Property & Design, King's House, Grand Avenue, Hove BN3 2LS ☎ 01273 291450 ⏚ angela.dymott@brighton-hove.gov.uk

Finance: Mr David Kuenssberg, Executive Director - Finance & Resources, Kings House, Grand Avenue, Hove BN3 2LS ⏚ david.kuenssberg@brighton-hove.gov.uk

Finance: Ms Rachel Musson, Executive Director - Finance & Resources, Kings House, Grand Avenue, Hove BN3 2LS ☎ 01273 291333 ⏚ rachel.musson@brighton-hove.gov.uk

Fleet Management: Mr Richard Bradley, Interim Joint Executive Director - Environment, Development & Housing, Kings House, Grand Avenue, Hove BN3 2LS ☎ 01273 290000 ⏚ richard.bradley@brighton-hove.gov.uk

Grounds Maintenance: Mr Richard Bradley, Interim Joint Executive Director - Environment, Development & Housing, Kings House, Grand Avenue, Hove BN3 2LS ☎ 01273 290000 ⏚ richard.bradley@brighton-hove.gov.uk

Health and Safety: Ms Hilary Ellis, Head of Health & Safety, King's House, Grand Avenue, Hove BN3 2LS ☎ 01273 291305 ⏚ hilary.ellis@brighton-hove.gov.uk

Highways: Mr Jeff Elliott, Highway & Traffic Manager, Kings House, Grand Avenue, Hove BN3 2LS ☎ 01273 292468 ⏚ jeff.elliott@brighton-hove.gov.uk

Highways: Mr Mark Prior, Head of Transport, Kings House, Grand Avenue, Hove BN3 2LS ☎ 01273 292095 ⏚ mark.prior@brighton-hove.gov.uk

Home Energy Conservation: Mr Geoff Raw, Chief Executive, Kings House, Grand Avenue, Hove BN3 2LS ☎ 01273 290453 ⏚ geoff.raw@brighton-hove.gov.uk

Local Area Agreement: Mr Richard Tuset, Head of Policy & Performance, Kings House, Grand Avenue, Hove BN3 2LS ☎ 01273 295514 ⏚ richard.tuset@brighton-hove.gov.uk

Legal: Mr Abraham Ghebre-Ghiorghis, Executive Lead Officer - Strategy, Governance & Law, Kings House, Grand Avenue, Hove BN3 2LS ☎ 01273 291500 ⏚ abraham.ghebre-ghiorghis@brighton-hove.gov.uk

Leisure and Cultural Services: Mr Toby Kingsbury, Sports Facilities Manager, Kings House, Grand Avenue, Hove BN3 2LS ☎ 01273 292701 ⏚ toby.kingsbury@brighton-hove.gov.uk

Leisure and Cultural Services: Mr Geoff Raw, Chief Executive, Kings House, Grand Avenue, Hove BN3 2LS ☎ 01273 290453 ⏚ geoff.raw@brighton-hove.gov.uk

Leisure and Cultural Services: Mr Ian Shurrock, Commissioner - Sports & Leisure, Kings House, Grand Avenue, Hove BN3 2LS ☎ 01273 292084 ⏚ ian.shurrock@brighton-hove.gov.uk

Lifelong Learning: Ms Jo Lyons, Assistant Director - Families, Children & Learning, Kings House, Grand Avenue, Hove BN3 2LS ☎ 01273 293514 ⏚ jo.lyons@brighton-hove.gov.uk

Lighting: Mr Geoff Raw, Chief Executive, Kings House, Grand Avenue, Hove BN3 2LS ☎ 01273 290453 ⏚ geoff.raw@brighton-hove.gov.uk

Member Services: Mr Mark Wall, Head of Democratic Services, King's House, Grand Avenue, Hove BN3 2LS ☎ 01273 291006 ⏚ mark.wall@brighton-hove.gov.uk

Parking: Mr Mark Prior, Head of Transport, Kings House, Grand Avenue, Hove BN3 2LS ☎ 01273 292095 ⏚ mark.prior@brighton-hove.gov.uk

Partnerships: Mr Simon Newell, Head of Partnerships & External Relationships, Kings House, Grand Avenue, Hove BN3 2LS ☎ 01273 291128 ⏚ simon.newell@brighton-hove.gov.uk

Partnerships: Mr Richard Tuset, Head of Policy & Performance, Kings House, Grand Avenue, Hove BN3 2LS ☎ 01273 295514 ⏚ richard.tuset@brighton-hove.gov.uk

Personnel / HR: Ms Sue Moorman, Head of Resources & Organisational Development, Kings House, Grand Avenue, Hove BN3 2LS ☎ 01273 293629 ⏚ sue.moorman@brighton-hove.gov.uk

Planning: Mr Andrew Ashcroft, Interim Head of Planning, Kings House, Grand Avenue, Hove BN3 2LS ☎ 01273 290000 ⏚ andrew.ashcroft@brighton-hove.gov.uk

Procurement: Mr David Kuenssberg, Executive Director - Finance & Resources, Kings House, Grand Avenue, Hove BN3 2LS ⏚ david.kuenssberg@brighton-hove.gov.uk

Public Libraries: Ms Sally McMahon, Head of Libraries & Information Services, Jubilee Library, Jubilee Street, Brighton BN1 1GE ☎ 01273 296933 ⏚ sally.mcmahon@brighton-hove.gov.uk

Recycling & Waste Minimisation: Ms Gillian Marston, Head of City Infrastructure, Hollingdean Depot, Upper Hollingdean Road, Brighton BN1 7GA ☎ 01273 274701 ⏚ gillian.marston@brighton-hove.gov.uk

Regeneration: Ms Gillian Marston, Head of City Infrastructure, Hollingdean Depot, Upper Hollingdean Road, Brighton BN1 7GA ☎ 01273 274701 ⏚ gillian.marston@brighton-hove.gov.uk

Road Safety: Mr Dave Parker, Head of Transport Planning, Hove Town Hall, Hove BN3 4AH ☎ 01273 292474 ⏚ david.parker@brighton-hove.gov.uk

Social Services: Mr Brian Doughty, Interim Executive Director - Adult Services, Kings House, Grand Avenue, Hove BN3 2LS ☎ 01273 290000 ⏚ brian.doughty@brighton-hove.gov.uk

Social Services (Adult): Mr Brian Doughty, Interim Executive Director - Adult Services, Kings House, Grand Avenue, Hove BN3 2LS ☎ 01273 290000 ⏚ brian.doughty@brighton-hove.gov.uk

Social Services (Children): Mr Steve Barton, Lead Commissioner - Integrated Families, Kings House, Grand Avenue, Hove BN3 2LS ☎ 01273 296105 ⏚ steve.barton@brighton-hove.gov.uk

Social Services (Children): Ms Jo Lyons, Assistant Director - Families, Children & Learning, Kings House, Grand Avenue, Hove BN3 2LS ☎ 01273 293514 ✆ jo.lyons@brighton-hove.gov.uk

Families: Mr Steve Barton, Lead Commissioner - Integrated Families, Kings House, Grand Avenue, Hove BN3 2LS ☎ 01273 296105 ✆ steve.barton@brighton-hove.gov.uk

Childrens Social Care: Mr James Dougan, Head of Children & Families, Kings House, Grand Avenue, Hove BN3 2LS ✆ james.dougan@brighton-hove.gov.uk

Public Health: Dr Tom Scanlon, Director - Public Health, Kings House, Grand Avenue, Hove BN3 2LS ☎ 01273 291480 ✆ tom.scanlon@brighton-hove.gov.uk

Sustainable Communities: Mr Thurstan Crockett, Head of Sustainability & Environmental Policy, King's House, Grand Avenue, Hove BN3 2LS ☎ 01273 292503 ✆ thurstan.crockett@brighton-hove.gov.uk

Sustainable Development: Mr Martin Randall, Head of Planning & Public Protection, Kings House, Grand Avenue, Hove BN3 2LS ☎ 01273 292257 ✆ martin.randall@brighton-hove.gov.uk

Tourism: Mr Adam Bates, Head of Tourism & Leisure, Brighton Town Hall, Brighton BN1 1JR ☎ 01273 292633 ✆ adam.bates@brighton-hove.gov.uk

Traffic Management: Mr Mark Prior, Head of Transport, Kings House, Grand Avenue, Hove BN3 2LS ☎ 01273 292095 ✆ mark.prior@brighton-hove.gov.uk

Transport Planner: Mr Austen Hunter, Head of Transport Operations, 6a Pavilion Buildings, Brighton BN1 1EE ☎ 01273 292245 ✆ austen.hunter@brighton-hove.gov.uk

Waste Collection and Disposal: Ms Gillian Marston, Head of City Infrastructure, Hollingdean Depot, Upper Hollingdean Road, Brighton BN1 7GA ☎ 01273 274701 ✆ gillian.marston@brighton-hove.gov.uk

Waste Management: Ms Gillian Marston, Head of City Infrastructure, Hollingdean Depot, Upper Hollingdean Road, Brighton BN1 7GA ☎ 01273 274701 ✆ gillian.marston@brighton-hove.gov.uk

COUNCILLORS

Mayor: Hyde, Lynda (CON - Rottingdean Coastal)
lynda.hyde@brighton-hove.gcsx.gov.uk

Deputy Mayor: West, Pete (GRN - St. Peter's & North Laine)
pete.west@brighton-hove.gcsx.gov.uk

Leader of the Council: Morgan, Warren (LAB - East Brighton)
warren.morgan@brighton-hove.gcsx.gov.uk

Deputy Leader of the Council: Mitchell, Gill (LAB - East Brighton)
gill.mitchell@brighton-hove.gcsx.gov.uk

Group LeaderMacCafferty, Phelim (GRN - Brunswick & Adelaide)
phelim.maccafferty@brighton-hove.gcsx.gov.uk

Group LeaderTheobald, Geoffrey (CON - Patcham)
geoffrey.theobald@brighton-hove.gcsx.gov.uk

Allen, Kevin (LAB - Preston Park)
kevin.allen@brighton-hove.gov.uk

Atkinson, Peter (LAB - North Portslade)
peter.atkinson@brighton-hove.gov.uk

Barford, Karen (LAB - Queen's Park)
karen.barford@brighton-hove.gov.uk

Barnett, Dawn (CON - Hangleton & Knoll)
dawn.barnett@brighton-hove.gcsx.gov.uk

Barradell, Maggie (LAB - East Brighton)
maggie.barradell@brighton-hove.gov.uk

Bell, Steve (CON - Woodingdean)
steve.bell@brighton-hove.gov.uk

Bennett, Jayne (CON - Hove Park)
jayne.bennett@brighton-hove.gcsx.gov.uk

Bewick, Tom (LAB - Westbourne)
tom.bewick@brighton-hove.gov.uk

Brown, Vanessa (CON - Hove Park)
vanessa.brown@brighton-hove.gcsx.gov.uk

Cattell, Julie (LAB - Preston Park)
julie.cattell@brighton-hove.gov.uk

Chapman, Daniel (LAB - Queen's Park)
daniel.chapman@brighton-hove.gov.uk

Cobb, Denise (CON - Westbourne)
denise.cobb@brighton-hove.gcsx.gov.uk

Daniel, Emma (LAB - Hanover & Elm Grove)
emma.daniel@brighton-hove.gcsx.gov.uk

Deane, Lizzie (GRN - St. Peter's & North Laine)
lizzie.deane@brighton-hove.gcsx.gov.uk

Druitt, Tom (GRN - Regency)
tom.druitt@brighton-hove.gov.uk

Gibson, David (GRN - Hanover & Elm Grove)
david.gibson@brighton-hove.gov.uk

Gilbey, Penny (LAB - North Portslade)
penny.gilbey@brighton-hove.gcsx.gov.uk

Greenbaum, Louisa (GRN - St. Peter's & North Laine)
louisa.greenbaum@brighton-hove.gov.uk

Hamilton, Les (LAB - South Portslade)
leslie.hamilton@brighton-hove.gcsx.gov.uk

Hill, Tracey (LAB - Hollingbury & Stanmer)
tracey.hill@brighton-hove.gov.uk

Horan, Saoirse (LAB - Goldsmid)
saoirse.horan@brighton-hove.gov.uk

Inkpin-Leissner, Michael (LAB - Hollingbury & Stanmer)
michael.inkpin-leissner@brighton-hove.gov.uk

Janio, Tony (CON - Hangleton & Knoll)
tony.janio@brighton-hove.gcsx.gov.uk

Knight, Amanda (GRN - Goldsmid)
amanda.knight@brighton-hove.gov.uk

Lewry, Nick (CON - Hangleton & Knoll)
nick.lewry@brighton-hove.gov.uk

Littman, Leo (GRN - Preston Park)
leo.littman@brighton-hove.gcsx.gov.uk

Marsh, Mo (LAB - Moulsecoomb & Bevendean)
mo.marsh@brighton-hove.gcsx.gov.uk

BRIGHTON & HOVE

Meadows, Anne (LAB - Moulsecoomb & Bevendean)
anne.meadows@brighton-hove.gcsx.gov.uk

Mears, Mary (CON - Rottingdean Coastal)
mary.mears@brighton-hove.gcsx.gov.uk

Miller, Joe (CON - Rottingdean Coastal)
joe.miller@brighton-hove.gov.uk

Moonan, Clare (LAB - Central Hove)
clare.moonan@brighton-hove.gov.uk

Morris, Adrian (LAB - Queen's Park)
adrian.morris@brighton-hove.gov.uk

Nemeth, Robert (CON - Wish)
robert.nemeth@brighton-hove.gov.uk

Norman, Ken (CON - Withdean)
ken.norman@brighton-hove.gcsx.gov.uk

Norman, Ann (CON - Withdean)
ann.norman@brighton-hove.gcsx.gov.uk

O'Quinn, Jackie (LAB - Goldsmid)
Jackie.o'quinn@brighton-hove.gov.uk

Page, Dick (GRN - Hanover & Elm Grove)
dick.page@brighton-hove.gov.uk

Peltzer Dunn, Garry (CON - Wish)
garry.peltzerdunn@brighton-hove.gcsx.gov.uk

Penn, Caroline (LAB - Hollingbury & Stanmer)
caroline.penn@brighton-hove.gov.uk

Phillips, Alex (GRN - Regency)
alex.phillips@brighton-hove.gov.uk

Robins, Alan (LAB - South Portslade)
alan.robins@brighton-hove.gcsx.gov.uk

Simson, Dee (CON - Woodingdean)
dee.simson@brighton-hove.gcsx.gov.uk

Sykes, Ollie (GRN - Brunswick & Adelaide)
ollie.sykes@brighton-hove.gcsx.gov.uk

Taylor, Nick (CON - Withdean)
nick.taylor@brighton-hove.gov.uk

Theobald, Carol (CON - Patcham)
carol.theobald@brighton-hove.gcsx.gov.uk

Wares, Lee (CON - Patcham)
lee.wares@brighton-hove.gov.uk

Wealls, Andrew (CON - Central Hove)
andrew.wealls@brighton-hove.gov.uk

Yates, Daniel (LAB - Moulsecoomb & Bevendean)
daniel.yates@brighton-hove.gov.uk

POLITICAL COMPOSITION
LAB: 23, CON: 20, GRN: 11

COMMITTEE CHAIRS

Audit: Mrs Ann Norman

Children, Young People & Skills: Mr Tom Bewick

Economic Development & Culture: Mr Alan Robins

Environment, Transport & Sustainability: Ms Gill Mitchell

Health & Wellbeing: Mr Daniel Yates

Housing: Ms Anne Meadows

Licensing: Ms Jackie O'Quinn

Neighbourhoods, Communities & Equalities: Ms Emma Daniel

Planning: Ms Julie Cattell

Policy, Resources & Growth: Mr Warren Morgan

Bristol City   U

Bristol City Council, City Hall, College Green, Bristol BS1 5TR
☎ 0117 922 2000 🖷 0117 922 2024 🖳 www.bristol.gov.uk

FACTS AND FIGURES
Parliamentary Constituencies: Bristol East, Bristol North West, Bristol South, Bristol West
EU Constituencies: South West
Election Frequency: Elections are by thirds

PRINCIPAL OFFICERS

Chief Executive: Mr Stephen Hughes, Interim Chief Executive, City Hall, PO Box 3176, Bristol BS3 9FS ☎ 0117 922 2341 ⬧ stephen.hughes@bristol.gov.uk

Senior Management: Ms Alison Comley, Strategic Director - Neighbourhoods, City Hall, PO Box 3176, Bristol BS3 9FS ☎ 0117 903 7860 ⬧ alison.comley@bristol.gov.uk

Senior Management: Mrs Anna Klonowski, Interim Strategic Director - Business Change, City Hall, PO Box 3176, Bristol BS3 9FS ☎ 0117 357 4451 ⬧ anna.klonowski@bristol.gov.uk

Senior Management: Ms Becky Pollard, Director - Public Health, Avon Quay, Cumberland Basin Road, Bristol BS1 6XL ☎ 0117 922 2874 ⬧ becky.pollard@bristol.gov.uk

Senior Management: Mr John Readman, Strategic Director - People, City Hall, PO Box 3176, Bristol BS3 9FS ☎ 0117 903 7960 ⬧ john.readman@bristol.gov.uk

Senior Management: Mr Barra Mac Ruairi, Strategic Director - Place, City Hall, PO Box 3176, Bristol BS3 9FS ☎ 0117 352 5558 ⬧ barra@bristol.gov.uk

Access Officer / Social Services (Disability): Mr Tom Gilchrist, Service Manager - Private Housing & Accessible Homes, City Hall, PO Box 3176, Bristol BS3 9FS ☎ 0117 352 1975 ⬧ tom.gilchrist@bristol.gov.uk

Architect, Building / Property Services: Mr Robert Orrett, Service Director - Property, City Hall, PO Box 3176, Bristol BS3 9FS ☎ 0117 922 4086 ⬧ robert.orrett@bristol.gov.uk

Best Value: Ms Netta Meadow, Service Director - Strategic Commissioning & Commercial Relations, City Hall, PO Box 3176, Bristol BS3 9FS ☎ 0117 923 7744 ⬧ netta.meadow@bristol.gov.uk

Building Control: Mr Steve Pearce, Building Control Manager, City Hall, PO Box 3176, Bristol BS3 9FS ☎ 0117 922 3770 ⬧ steve.pearce@bristol.gov.uk

Catering Services: Mr Simon Westbrook, Interim Service Manager - Traded Services, St Anne's House, 1st Floor, St Anne's Road, Bristol BS4 4AB ☎ 0117 352 5957
⌖ simon.westbrook@bristol.gov.uk

Civil Registration: Ms Yvonne Dawes, Electoral Services Manager, B Bond Floor 5, Smeaton Road, Bristol BS1 6XN
☎ 0117 922 3488 ⌖ yvonne.dawes@bristol.gov.uk

PR / Communications: Mr Tim Borrett, Service Manager - Public Relations, City Hall, PO Box 3176, Bristol BS3 9FS ☎ 0117 922 3332
⌖ tim.borrett@bristol.gov.uk

PR / Communications: Ms Zoe Willcox, Service Director - Planning & Sustainable Development, City Hall, PO Box 3176, Bristol BS3 9FS ☎ 0117 922 2942 ⌖ zoe.willcox@bristol.gov.uk

Community Planning: Ms Di Robinson, Service Director - Neighbourhoods & Communities, City Hall, PO Box 3176, Bristol BS3 9FS ☎ 0117 352 1036 ⌖ di.robinson@bristol.gov.uk

Community Safety: Mr Peter Anderson, Manager - Safer Bristol, St Anne's House, St Anne's Road, Bristol BS4 4AB
☎ 0117 922 2309 ⌖ peter.anderson@bristol.gov.uk

Community Safety: Mr Nick Hooper, Service Director - Housing Solutions, City Hall, PO Box 3176, Bristol BS3 9FS ☎ 0117 922 4681
⌖ nick.hooper@bristol.gov.uk

Computer Management: Mr Dominic Mason, Interim Service Director - Change, City Hall, PO Box 3176, Bristol BS3 9FS
☎ 0117 903 7371 ⌖ dominic.mason@bristol.gov.uk

Consumer Protection and Trading Standards: Mr Jonathan Martin, Trading Standards & Licensing Manager, City Hall, PO Box 3176, Bristol BS3 9FS ☎ 07710 397039
⌖ jonathan.martin@bristol.gov.uk

Corporate Services: Ms Cathy Mullins, Interim Service Director - Policy, Strategy & Communications, City Hall, PO Box 3176, Bristol BS3 9FS ☎ 0117 352 1403 ⌖ cathy.mullins@bristol.gov.uk

Customer Service: Ms Patsy Mellor, Service Director - Citizen Services, City Hall, PO Box 3176, Bristol BS3 9FS ☎ 0117 352 6218
⌖ patsy.mellor@bristol.gov.uk

Economic Development: Mr Alistair Reid, Service Director - Economy, City Hall, PO Box 3176, Bristol BS3 9FS ☎ 0117 903 7481
⌖ alistair.reid@bristol.gov.uk

Education: Mr Paul Jacobs, Service Director - Education & Skills, City Hall, PO Box 3176, Bristol BS3 9FS ☎ 0117 922 4836
⌖ paul.jacobs@bristol.gov.uk

Electoral Registration: Mr Gareth Cook, Electoral Services Manager, c/o 9 Willway Street, Bedminster, Bristol BS3 4SP
☎ 0117 922 3451 ⌖ gareth.cook@bristol.gov.uk

Electoral Registration: Ms Yvonne Dawes, Electoral Services Manager, B Bond Floor 5, Smeaton Road, Bristol BS1 6XN
☎ 0117 922 3488 ⌖ yvonne.dawes@bristol.gov.uk

Emergency Planning: Mr Simon Creed, Civil Protection Manager, The Create Centre, Smeaton Road, Bristol BS1 6XN
☎ 0117 922 3233 ⌖ simon.creed@bristol.gov.uk

Energy Management: Mr Bill Edrich, Service Director - Energy, City Hall, PO Box 3176, Bristol BS3 9FS ☎ 0117 922 4991
⌖ bill.edrich@bristol.gov.uk

Environmental / Technical Services: Ms Gillian Douglas, Interim Service Director - Clean & Green, City Hall, PO Box 3176, Bristol BS3 9FS ☎ 0117 357 4185 ⌖ gillian.douglas@bristol.gov.uk

Estates, Property & Valuation: Mr Robert Orrett, Service Director - Property, City Hall, PO Box 3176, Bristol BS3 9FS
☎ 0117 922 4086 ⌖ robert.orrett@bristol.gov.uk

European Liaison: Ms Shelley Nania, European & International Manager, Engine Shed, Station Approach, Temple Meads, Bristol BS1 6QH ☎ 0117 922 3229 ⌖ shelley.nania@bristol.gov.uk

Events Manager: Ms Melissa Inman, Head of Arts & Events, City Hall, PO Box 3176, Bristol BS3 9FS ☎ 0117 922 2653
⌖ melissa.inman@bristol.gov.uk

Finance: Ms Annabel Scholes, Interim Service Director - Finance, City Hall, PO Box 3176, Bristol BS3 9FS ☎ 0117 922 2419
⌖ annabel.scholes@bristol.gov.uk

Fleet Management: Mr Nick Gingell, Fleet Services Manager, Brislington Depot, Sandy Park, Bristol BS4 3NZ ☎ 0117 352 5611
⌖ nick.gingell@bristol.gov.uk

Grounds Maintenance: Ms Gemma Dando, Head of Neighbourhood Management, City Hall, PO Box 3176, Bristol BS3 9FS ☎ 0117 352 1090 ⌖ gemma.dando@bristol.gov.uk

Highways: Mr Gareth Vaughn-Williams, Head of Highways, Wilder House, Wilder Street, Bristol BS2 8HP ☎ 0117 903 6833
⌖ gareth.vaughn-williams@bristol.gov.uk

Housing: Mr Steve Barrett, Service Director - Housing Services, 1st Floor St Anne's House, St Anne's Road, Bristol BS4 4AB
☎ 0117 922 4082 ⌖ steve.barrett@bristol.gov.uk

Housing: Mr Nick Hooper, Service Director - Housing Solutions, City Hall, PO Box 3176, Bristol BS3 9FS ☎ 0117 922 4681
⌖ nick.hooper@bristol.gov.uk

Housing: Ms Mary Ryan, Service Director - Housing Services, 1st Floor St Anne's House, St Anne's Road, Bristol BS4 4AB
☎ 0117 922 4589 ⌖ mary.ryan@bristol.gov.uk

Housing Maintenance: Ms Zara Naylor, Head of Responsive Maintenance, The A Shed, Sandy Park Depot, Bristol BS4 3NZ
☎ 0117 922 4129 ⌖ zara.naylor@bristol.gov.uk

Legal: Ms Shahzia Daya, Interim Service Manager - Legal, City Hall, PO Box 3176, Bristol BS3 9FS ☎ 0117 922 2413
⌖ shahzia.daya@bristol.gov.uk

BRISTOL CITY

Leisure and Cultural Services: Ms Gillian Douglas, Interim Service Director - Clean & Green, City Hall, PO Box 3176, Bristol BS3 9FS ☎ 0117 357 4185 ✉ gillian.douglas@bristol.gov.uk

Licensing: Mr Jonathan Martin, Trading Standards & Licensing Manager, City Hall, PO Box 3176, Bristol BS3 9FS ☎ 07710 397039 ✉ jonathan.martin@bristol.gov.uk

Lifelong Learning: Ms Jane Taylor, Head of Employment, Learning & Skills, The Park, Daventry Road, Knowle, Bristol BS3 9FS ☎ 0117 922 4570 ✉ jane.taylor@bristol.gov.uk

Lighting: Mr David Bunting, Head of Traffic, Wilder House, Wilder Street, Bristol BS2 8PH ☎ 0117 922 3085 ✉ david.bunting@bristol.gov.uk

Member Services: Ms Caroline Elwood, Interim Service Manager - Legal (Place), City Hall, PO Box 3176, Bristol BS3 9FS ☎ 0117 922 2908 ✉ caroline.elwood@bristol.gov.uk

Parking: Mr David Bunting, Head of Traffic, Wilder House, Wilder Street, Bristol BS2 8PH ☎ 0117 922 3085 ✉ david.bunting@bristol.gov.uk

Partnerships: Ms Suzanne Wilson, City Innovation Manager, City Hall, PO Box 3176, Bristol BS3 9FS ☎ 0117 357 4717 ✉ suzanne.wilson@bristol.gov.uk

Personnel / HR: Mr Richard Billingham, Service Director - HR & Workplace Section, City Hall, PO Box 3176, Bristol BS3 9FS ☎ 0117 922 2670 ✉ richard.billingham@bristol.gov.uk

Planning: Ms Zoe Willcox, Service Director - Planning & Sustainable Development, City Hall, PO Box 3176, Bristol BS3 9FS ☎ 0117 922 2942 ✉ zoe.willcox@bristol.gov.uk

Public Libraries: Ms Kate Murray, Libraries Manager, Bristol Central Library, College Green, Bristol BS1 5TL ☎ 0117 352 1264 ✉ k.murray@bristol.gov.uk

Recycling & Waste Minimisation: Ms Gillian Douglas, Interim Service Director - Clean & Green, City Hall, PO Box 3176, Bristol BS3 9FS ☎ 0117 357 4185 ✉ gillian.douglas@bristol.gov.uk

Regeneration: Mr Alistair Reid, Service Director - Economy, City Hall, PO Box 3176, Bristol BS3 9FS ☎ 0117 903 7481 ✉ alistair.reid@bristol.gov.uk

Road Safety: Mr Ed Plowden, Head of Sustainable Transport, City Hall, PO Box 3176, Bristol BS3 9FS ☎ 0117 922 2357 ✉ ed.plowden@bristol.gov.uk

Social Services: Mr John Readman, Strategic Director - People, City Hall, PO Box 3176, Bristol BS3 9FS ☎ 0117 903 7960 ✉ john.readman@bristol.gov.uk

Social Services (Adult): Mr Mike Hennessey, Service Director - Care & Support (Adults), City Hall, PO Box 3176, Bristol BS3 9FS ☎ 0117 903 7951 ✉ mike.hennessey@bristol.gov.uk

Social Services (Children): Ms Hilary Brooks, Interim Service Director - Care & Support (Children & Families), City Hall, PO Box 3176, Bristol BS1 9FS ✉ hilary.brooks@bristol.gov.uk

Families: Ms Hilary Brooks, Interim Service Director - Care & Support (Children & Families), City Hall, PO Box 3176, Bristol BS1 9FS ✉ hilary.brooks@bristol.gov.uk

Public Health: Ms Becky Pollard, Director - Public Health, Avon Quay, Cumberland Basin Road, Bristol BS1 6XL ☎ 0117 922 2874 ✉ becky.pollard@bristol.gov.uk

Street Scene: Ms Gillian Douglas, Interim Service Director - Clean & Green, City Hall, PO Box 3176, Bristol BS3 9FS ☎ 0117 357 4185 ✉ gillian.douglas@bristol.gov.uk

Sustainable Communities: Ms Zoe Willcox, Service Director - Planning & Sustainable Development, City Hall, PO Box 3176, Bristol BS3 9FS ☎ 0117 922 2942 ✉ zoe.willcox@bristol.gov.uk

Sustainable Development: Ms Zoe Willcox, Service Director - Planning & Sustainable Development, City Hall, PO Box 3176, Bristol BS3 9FS ☎ 0117 922 2942 ✉ zoe.willcox@bristol.gov.uk

Traffic Management: Mr David Bunting, Head of Traffic, Wilder House, Wilder Street, Bristol BS2 8PH ☎ 0117 922 3085 ✉ david.bunting@bristol.gov.uk

Transport: Mr Peter Mann, Service Director - Transport, City Hall, PO Box 3176, Bristol BS3 9FS ☎ 0117 922 2943 ✉ peter.mann@bristol.gov.uk

Transport Planner: Mr Adam Crowther, Head of Strategic City Transport, Wilder House, Wilder Street, Bristol BS2 8PH ☎ 0117 903 6854 ✉ adam.crowther@bristol.gov.uk

Total Place: Mr Barra Mac Ruairi, Strategic Director - Place, City Hall, PO Box 3176, Bristol BS3 9FS ☎ 0117 352 5558 ✉ barra@bristol.gov.uk

Waste Collection and Disposal: Ms Gillian Douglas, Interim Service Director - Clean & Green, City Hall, PO Box 3176, Bristol BS3 9FS ☎ 0117 357 4185 ✉ gillian.douglas@bristol.gov.uk

Waste Management: Ms Gillian Douglas, Interim Service Director - Clean & Green, City Hall, PO Box 3176, Bristol BS3 9FS ☎ 0117 357 4185 ✉ gillian.douglas@bristol.gov.uk

Children's Play Areas: Ms Gillian Douglas, Interim Service Director - Clean & Green, City Hall, PO Box 3176, Bristol BS3 9FS ☎ 0117 357 4185 ✉ gillian.douglas@bristol.gov.uk

COUNCILLORS

The Lord Mayor: Lovell, Jeff (LAB - Filwood)
cllr.jeff.lovell@bristol.gov.uk

Deputy Lord Mayor: Davies, Christopher (LD - Knowle)
cllr.christopher.davies@bristol.gov.uk

Group Leader: Bolton, Charlie (GRN - Southville)
cllr.charlie.bolton@bristol.gov.uk

Group Leader: Hopkins, Gary (LD - Knowle)

Group Leader: Weston, Mark (CON - Henbury & Brentry)
cllr.mark.weston@bristol.gov.uk

Abraham, Peter (CON - Stoke Bishop)
cllr.peter.abraham@bristol.gov.uk

Alexander, Donald (LAB - Avonmouth & Lawrence Weston)
cllr.donald.alexander@bristol.gov.uk

Alexander, Lesley (CON - Frome Vale)
lesley.alexander@bristol.gov.uk

Beech, Nicola (LAB - St George Central)
cllr.nicola.beech@bristol.gov.uk

Bowden-Jones, Nicola (LAB - Frome Vale)
cllr.nicola.bowden-jones@bristol.gov.uk

Bradley, Harriet (LAB - Brislington West)
cllr.harriet.bradley@bristol.gov.uk

Bradshaw, Mark (LAB - Bedminster)
cllr.mark.bradshaw@bristol.gov.uk

Brain, Mark (LAB - Hartcliffe & Withywood)
cllr.mark.brain@bristol.gov.uk

Breckels, Fabian (LAB - St George Troopers Hill)
cllr.fabian.breckels@bristol.gov.uk

Brook, Tom (LAB - Bishopston & Ashley Down)
cllr.tom.brook@bristol.gov.uk

Campion-Smith, Clare (LD - Westbury-on-Trym & Henleaze)
cllr.clare.campion-smith@bristol.gov.uk

Carey, Tony (CON - Brislington East)
cllr.tony.carey@bristol.gov.uk

Cheney, Craig (LAB - Hillfields)
cllr.craig.cheney@bristol.gov.uk

Clark, Barry (LAB - Hengrove & Whitchurch Park)
cllr.barry.clark@bristol.gov.uk

Clark, Jos (LD - Brislington West)
cllr.jos.clark@bristol.gov.uk

Clarke, Stephen (GRN - Southville)
cllr.stephen.clarke@bristol.gov.uk

Clough, Harriet (LD - Hengrove & Whitchurch Park)
cllr.harriet.clough@bristol.gov.uk

Combley, Eleanor (GRN - Bishopston & Ashley Down)
cllr.eleanor.combley@bristol.gov.uk

Craig, Asher (LAB - St George West)
cllr.asher.craig@bristol.gov.uk

Davies, Mike (LAB - Ashley)
cllr.mike.davies@bristol.gov.uk

Denyer, Carla (GRN - Clifton Down)
cllr.carla.denyer@bristol.gov.uk

Dudd, Kye (LAB - Central)
cllr.kye.dudd@bristol.gov.uk

Eddy, Richard (CON - Bishopsworth)
cllr.richard.eddy@bristol.gov.uk

English, Jude (GRN - Ashley)
cllr.jude.english@bristol.gov.uk

Fodor, Martin (GRN - Redland)
cllr.martin.fodor@bristol.gov.uk

Godwin, Helen (LAB - Southmead)
cllr.helen.godwin-teige@bristol.gov.uk

Goggin, Paul (LAB - Hartcliffe & Withywood)
cllr.paul.goggin@bristol.gov.uk

Gollop, Geoffrey (CON - Westbury-on-Trym & Henleaze)
cllr.geoffrey.gollop@bristol.gov.uk

Goulandris, John (CON - Stoke Bishop)
cllr.john.goulandris@bristol.gov.uk

Hance, Fi (GRN - Redland)
cllr.fi.hance@bristol.gov.uk

Hickman, Margaret (LAB - Lawrence Hill)
cllr.marg.hickman@bristol.gov.uk

Hiscott, Claire (CON - Horfield)
cllr.claire.hiscott@bristol.gov.uk

Holland, Helen (LAB - Hartcliffe & Withywood)
cllr.helen.holland@bristol.gov.uk

Jackson, Christopher (LAB - Filwood)
cllr.christopher.jackson@bristol.gov.uk

Jama, Hibaq (LAB - Lawrence Hill)
cllr.hibaq.jama@bristol.gov.uk

Johnson, Carole (LAB - Ashley)
cllr.carole.johnson@bristol.gov.uk

Jones, Steve (CON - Stockwood)
cllr.steve.jones@bristol.gov.uk

Keen, Anna (LAB - Hillfields)
cllr.anna.keen@bristol.gov.uk

Kent, Tim (LD - Hengrove & Whitchurch Park)
cllr.tim.kent@bristol.gov.uk

Khan, Mahmadur (LAB - Eastville)
cllr.mahmadur.khan@bristol.gov.uk

Kirk, Gill (LAB - Lockleaze)
cllr.gill.kirk@bristol.gov.uk

Lake, Cleo (GRN - Cotham)
cllr.cleo.lake@bristol.gov.uk

Langley, Mike (CON - Brislington East)
cllr.mike.langley@bristol.gov.uk

Massey, Brenda (LAB - Southmead)
cllr.brenda.massey@bristol.gov.uk

Mead, Olly (LAB - Horfield)
cllr.olly.mead@bristol.gov.uk

Melias, Matthew (CON - Avonmouth & Lawrence Weston)
cllr.matthew.melias@bristol.gov.uk

Morris, Graham (CON - Stockwood)
cllr.graham.morris@bristol.gov.uk

Negus, Anthony (LD - Cotham)
cllr.anthony.negus@bristol.gov.uk

O'Rourke, Paula (GRN - Clifton)
cllr.paula.o'rourke@bristol.gov.uk

Pearce, Steve (LAB - St George Central)
cllr.s.pearce@bristol.gov.uk

Phipps, Celia (LAB - Bedminster)
cllr.celia.phipps@bristol.gov.uk

Pickersgill, Ruth (LAB - Easton)
cllr.ruth.pickersgill@bristol.gov.uk

Quartley, Kevin (CON - Bishopsworth)
cllr.kevin.quartley@bristol.gov.uk

BRISTOL CITY

Radford, Liz (CON - Westbury-on-Trym & Henleaze)
cllr.liz.radford@bristol.gov.uk

Sergeant, Jo (LAB - Avonmouth & Lawrence Weston)
cllr.jo.sergeant@bristol.gov.uk

Shah, Afzal (LAB - Easton)
cllr.afzal.shah@bristol.gov.uk

Smith, Paul (LAB - Central)
cllr.paul.smith@bristol.gov.uk

Stevens, Clive (GRN - Clifton Down)
cllr.clive.stevens@bristol.gov.uk

Thomas, Jerome (GRN - Clifton)
cllr.jerome.thomas@bristol.gov.uk

Threlfall, Mhairi (LAB - Eastville)
cllr.mhairi.threlfall@bristol.gov.uk

Tincknell, Estella (LAB - Lockleaze)
cllr.estella.tincknell@bristol.gov.uk

Wellington, Jon (LAB - Windmill Hill)
cllr.jon.wellington@bristol.gov.uk

Whittle, Lucy (LAB - Windmill Hill)
cllr.lucy.whittle@bristol.gov.uk

Windows, Chris (CON - Henbury & Brentry)
cllr.chris.windows@bristol.gov.uk

Wright, Mark (LD - Hotwells & Harbourside)
cllr.mark.wright@bristol.gov.uk

POLITICAL COMPOSITION
LAB: 36, CON: 15, GRN: 11, LD: 8

Broadland   D

Broadland District Council, Thorpe Lodge, 1 Yarmouth Road,
Thorpe St. Andrew, Norwich NR7 0DU
☎ 01603 431133 🖨 01603 300087 ⌨ reception@broadland.gov.uk
🖥 www.broadland.gov.uk

FACTS AND FIGURES
Parliamentary Constituencies: Norwich North
EU Constituencies: Eastern
Election Frequency: Elections are of whole council

PRINCIPAL OFFICERS

Chief Executive: Mr Phil Kirby, Chief Executive, Thorpe Lodge, 1
Yarmouth Road, Thorpe St. Andrew, Norwich NR7 0DU
☎ 01603 430521 ⌨ phil.kirby@broadland.gov.uk

Deputy Chief Executive: Mr Matthew Cross, Deputy Chief
Executive, Thorpe Lodge, 1 Yarmouth Road, Thorpe St. Andrew,
Norwich NR7 0DU ☎ 01603 430588
⌨ matthew.cross@broadland.gov.uk

Senior Management: Mr Richard Block, Head of Environmental
Services, Thorpe Lodge, 1 Yarmouth Road, Thorpe St. Andrew,
Norwich NR7 0DU ☎ 01603 430535
⌨ richard.block@broadland.gov.uk

Senior Management: Mr Phil Courtier, Head of Planning, Thorpe
Lodge, 1 Yarmouth Road, Thorpe St. Andrew, Norwich NR7 0DU
☎ 01603 430566 ⌨ phil.courtier@broadland.gov.uk

Senior Management: Mr Stephen Fennell, Head of Corporate
Resources, Thorpe Lodge, 1 Yarmouth Road, Thorpe St. Andrew,
Norwich NR7 0DU ☎ 01603 430524
⌨ stephen.fennell@broadland.gov.uk

Senior Management: Mr Hamish Melville, Head of Economic
Development, Thorpe Lodge, 1 Yarmouth Road, Thorpe St. Andrew,
Norwich NR7 0DU ☎ 01603 430611
⌨ hamish.melville@broadland.gov.uk

Senior Management: Mrs Jill Penn, Head of Finance, Revenues
Services & S151 Officer, Thorpe Lodge, 1 Yarmouth Road, Thorpe St.
Andrew, Norwich NR7 0DU ☎ 01603 430589
⌨ jill.penn@broadland.gov.uk

Senior Management: Mr Martin Thrower, Head of Democratic
Services & Monitoring Officer, Thorpe Lodge, 1 Yarmouth Road,
Thorpe St. Andrew, Norwich NR7 0DU ☎ 01603 430546
⌨ martin.thrower@broadland.gov.uk

Access Officer / Social Services (Disability): Mr Kevin
Philcox, Divisional Environmental Health Officer - Housing, Thorpe
Lodge, 1 Yarmouth Road, Thorpe St. Andrew, Norwich NR7 0DU
☎ 01603 430552 ⌨ kevin.philcox@broadland.gov.uk

Architect, Building / Property Services: Mr John Frary,
Facilities Manager, Thorpe Lodge, 1 Yarmouth Road, Thorpe St.
Andrew, Norwich NR7 0DU ☎ 01603 430416
⌨ john.frary@broadland.gov.uk

Building Control: Mr Alan Osborne, Director - CNC Building
Control Services, South Norfolk Council, Swan Lane, Long Stratton
NR15 2XE ☎ 01508 533633

PR / Communications: Mr James Dunne, Marketing &
Communications Manager, Thorpe Lodge, 1 Yarmouth Road, Thorpe
St. Andrew, Norwich NR7 0DU ☎ 01603 430523
⌨ james.dunne@broadland.gov.uk

Computer Management: Mr Stephen Fennell, Head of
Corporate Resources, Thorpe Lodge, 1 Yarmouth Road, Thorpe St.
Andrew, Norwich NR7 0DU ☎ 01603 430524
⌨ stephen.fennell@broadland.gov.uk

Corporate Services: Mr Martin Thrower, Head of Democratic
Services & Monitoring Officer, Thorpe Lodge, 1 Yarmouth Road,
Thorpe St. Andrew, Norwich NR7 0DU ☎ 01603 430546
⌨ martin.thrower@broadland.gov.uk

Customer Service: Ms Dee Young, Personnel & Customer
Services Manager, Thorpe Lodge, 1 Yarmouth Road, Thorpe St.
Andrew, Norwich NR7 0DU ☎ 01603 430526
⌨ dee.young@broadland.gov.uk

Economic Development: Mr Hamish Melville, Head of Economic
Development, Thorpe Lodge, 1 Yarmouth Road, Thorpe St. Andrew,
Norwich NR7 0DU ☎ 01603 430611
⌨ hamish.melville@broadland.gov.uk

Economic Development: Mr Kevin Philcox, Divisional
Environmental Health Officer - Housing, Thorpe Lodge, 1 Yarmouth
Road, Thorpe St. Andrew, Norwich NR7 0DU ☎ 01603 430552
⌨ kevin.philcox@broadland.gov.uk

E-Government: Mr Matthew Cross, Deputy Chief Executive, Thorpe Lodge, 1 Yarmouth Road, Thorpe St. Andrew, Norwich NR7 0DU ☎ 01603 430588 ✆ matthew.cross@broadland.gov.uk

Electoral Registration: Mrs Linda Mockford, Electoral Services Manager, Thorpe Lodge, 1 Yarmouth Road, Thorpe St. Andrew, Norwich NR7 0DU ☎ 01603 430424 ✆ linda.mockford@broadland.gov.uk

Emergency Planning: Mr Simon Faraday Drake, Emergency Planning Manager, Thorpe Lodge, 1 Yarmouth Road, Thorpe St. Andrew, Norwich NR7 0DU ☎ 01603 430643 ✆ simon.faraday.drake@broadland.gov.uk

Energy Management: Ms Deborah Baillie-Murden, Climate Change Officer, Thorpe Lodge, 1 Yarmouth Road, Thorpe St. Andrew, Norwich NR7 0DU ☎ 01603 430629 ✆ debra.baillie-murden@broadland.gov.uk

Environmental / Technical Services: Mr Richard Block, Head of Environmental Services, Thorpe Lodge, 1 Yarmouth Road, Thorpe St. Andrew, Norwich NR7 0DU ☎ 01603 430535 ✆ richard.block@broadland.gov.uk

Environmental Health: Mr Richard Block, Head of Environmental Services, Thorpe Lodge, 1 Yarmouth Road, Thorpe St. Andrew, Norwich NR7 0DU ☎ 01603 430535 ✆ richard.block@broadland.gov.uk

Facilities: Mr John Frary, Facilities Manager, Thorpe Lodge, 1 Yarmouth Road, Thorpe St. Andrew, Norwich NR7 0DU ☎ 01603 430416 ✆ john.frary@broadland.gov.uk

Finance: Mrs Jill Penn, Head of Finance, Revenues Services & S151 Officer, Thorpe Lodge, 1 Yarmouth Road, Thorpe St. Andrew, Norwich NR7 0DU ☎ 01603 430589 ✆ jill.penn@broadland.gov.uk

Treasury: Mrs Jill Penn, Head of Finance, Revenues Services & S151 Officer, Thorpe Lodge, 1 Yarmouth Road, Thorpe St. Andrew, Norwich NR7 0DU ☎ 01603 430589 ✆ jill.penn@broadland.gov.uk

Health and Safety: Mr John Frary, Facilities Manager, Thorpe Lodge, 1 Yarmouth Road, Thorpe St. Andrew, Norwich NR7 0DU ☎ 01603 430416 ✆ john.frary@broadland.gov.uk

Housing: Mrs Leigh Booth, Strategic Housing Manager, Thorpe Lodge, 1 Yarmouth Road, Thorpe St. Andrew, Norwich NR7 0DU ☎ 01603 430566 ✆ leigh.booth@broadland.gov.uk

Legal: Mr Martin Thrower, Head of Democratic Services & Monitoring Officer, Thorpe Lodge, 1 Yarmouth Road, Thorpe St. Andrew, Norwich NR7 0DU ☎ 01603 430546 ✆ martin.thrower@broadland.gov.uk

Licensing: Mr Paul Hemnell, Environmental Enforcement Manager, Thorpe Lodge, 1 Yarmouth Road, Thorpe St. Andrew, Norwich NR7 0DU ☎ 01603 430577 ✆ paul.hemnell@broadland.gov.uk

Lifelong Learning: Mrs Sharon Tapp, Economic Development Training Manager, 9 Hellesdon Park Road, Norwich NR6 5DR ☎ 01603 788950 ✆ sharon.tapp@broadland.gov.uk

Lighting: Mr Richard Block, Head of Environmental Services, Thorpe Lodge, 1 Yarmouth Road, Thorpe St. Andrew, Norwich NR7 0DU ☎ 01603 430535 ✆ richard.block@broadland.gov.uk

Lottery Funding, Charity and Voluntary: Ms Sally Hoare, Partnership & Funding Officer, Thorpe Lodge, 1 Yarmouth Road, Thorpe St. Andrew, Norwich NR7 0DU ☎ 01603 430620 ✆ sally.hoare@broadland.gov.uk

Member Services: Mr Martin Thrower, Head of Democratic Services & Monitoring Officer, Thorpe Lodge, 1 Yarmouth Road, Thorpe St. Andrew, Norwich NR7 0DU ☎ 01603 430546 ✆ martin.thrower@broadland.gov.uk

Personnel / HR: Mr Stephen Fennell, Head of Corporate Resources, Thorpe Lodge, 1 Yarmouth Road, Thorpe St. Andrew, Norwich NR7 0DU ☎ 01603 430524 ✆ stephen.fennell@broadland.gov.uk

Planning: Mr Phil Courtier, Head of Planning, Thorpe Lodge, 1 Yarmouth Road, Thorpe St. Andrew, Norwich NR7 0DU ☎ 01603 430566 ✆ phil.courtier@broadland.gov.uk

Procurement: Mr Stephen Fennell, Head of Corporate Resources, Thorpe Lodge, 1 Yarmouth Road, Thorpe St. Andrew, Norwich NR7 0DU ☎ 01603 430524 ✆ stephen.fennell@broadland.gov.uk

Recycling & Waste Minimisation: Mr Richard Block, Head of Environmental Services, Thorpe Lodge, 1 Yarmouth Road, Thorpe St. Andrew, Norwich NR7 0DU ☎ 01603 430535 ✆ richard.block@broadland.gov.uk

Staff Training: Ms Dee Young, Personnel & Customer Services Manager, Thorpe Lodge, 1 Yarmouth Road, Thorpe St. Andrew, Norwich NR7 0DU ☎ 01603 430526 ✆ dee.young@broadland.gov.uk

Street Scene: Mr Peter Leggett, Street Scene Officer, Thorpe Lodge, 1 Yarmouth Road, Thorpe St. Andrew, Norwich NR7 0DU ☎ 01603 431133 ✆ peter.leggett@broadland.gov.uk

Sustainable Communities: Mr Phil Courtier, Head of Planning, Thorpe Lodge, 1 Yarmouth Road, Thorpe St. Andrew, Norwich NR7 0DU ☎ 01603 430566 ✆ phil.courtier@broadland.gov.uk

Sustainable Communities: Mr Phil Kirby, Chief Executive, Thorpe Lodge, 1 Yarmouth Road, Thorpe St. Andrew, Norwich NR7 0DU ☎ 01603 430521 ✆ phil.kirby@broadland.gov.uk

Tourism: Ms Kirstin Hughes, Economic Development Manager, Thorpe Lodge, 1 Yarmouth Road, Thorpe St. Andrew, Norwich NR7 0DU ☎ 01603 430563 ✆ kirstin.hughes@broadland.gov.uk

Waste Collection and Disposal: Mr Richard Block, Head of Environmental Services, Thorpe Lodge, 1 Yarmouth Road, Thorpe St. Andrew, Norwich NR7 0DU ☎ 01603 430535 ✆ richard.block@broadland.gov.uk

Waste Management: Mr Richard Block, Head of Environmental Services, Thorpe Lodge, 1 Yarmouth Road, Thorpe St. Andrew, Norwich NR7 0DU ☎ 01603 430535 ✆ richard.block@broadland.gov.uk

BROADLAND

COUNCILLORS

ChairWard, John (CON - Sprowston East)
cllr.john.ward@broadland.gov.uk

Leader of the Council: Proctor, Andrew (CON - Brundall)
cllr.andrew.proctor@broadland.gov.uk

Deputy Leader of the Council: Clancy, Stuart (CON - Taverham South)
cllr.stuart.clancy@broadland.gov.uk

Group LeaderHarrison, David (LD - Aylsham)
cllr.david.harrison@broadland.gov.uk

Group LeaderRoper, Dan (LD - Spixworth with St Faiths)
cllr.dan.roper@broadland.gov.uk

Adams, Tony (CON - Hellesdon South East)
cllr.tony.adams@broadland.gov.uk

Bannock, Claudette (CON - Taverham South)
cllr.claudette.bannock@broadland.gov.uk

Buck, Danny (CON - Hellesdon North West)
cllr.danny.buck@broadland.gov.uk

Carrick, Paul (CON - Hevingham)
cllr.paul.carrick@broadland.gov.uk

Dunn, Stuart (CON - Old Catton & Sprowston West)
cllr.stuart.dunn@broadland.gov.uk

Emsell, Jonathan (CON - Thorpe St Andrew South East)
cllr.jonathan.emsell@broadland.gov.uk

Everett, Graham (CON - Reepham)
cllr.graham.everett@broadland.gov.uk

Fisher, John (CON - Thorpe St Andrew North West)
cllr.john.fisher@broadland.gov.uk

Foulger, Roger (CON - Drayton South)
cllr.roger.foulger@broadland.gov.uk

Grady, Richard (CON - Hellesdon South East)
cllr.richard.grady@broadland.gov.uk

Graham, Ian (CON - Aylsham)
cllr.ian.graham@broadland.gov.uk

Gurney, Shelagh (CON - Hellesdon North West)
cllr.shelagh.gurney@broadland.gov.uk

Harrison, Chris (CON - Blofield with South Walsham)
cllr.chris.harrison@broadland.gov.uk

Hempsall, Lana (CON - Acle)
cllr.lana.hempsall@broadland.gov.uk

Keeler, Joanne (CON - Horsford & Felthorpe)
cllr.joanne.keeler@broadland.gov.uk

Knowles, Robin (CON - Sprowston Central)
cllr.robin.knowles@broadland.gov.uk

Kular, Balvinder (LD - Spixworth with St Faiths)
cllr.balvinder.kular@broadland.gov.uk

Landamore, Tony (CON - Sprowston Central)
cllr.tony.landamore@broadland.gov.uk

Lawn, Sue (CON - Thorpe St Andrew South East)
cllr.susan.lawn@broadland.gov.uk

Leggett, Judy (CON - Sprowston East)
cllr.judy.leggett@broadland.gov.uk

Leggett, Kenneth (CON - Old Catton & Sprowston West)
cllr.ken.leggett@broadland.gov.uk

Lodge, Tamsin (CON - Horsford & Felthorpe)
cllr.tamsin.lodge@broadland.gov.uk

Mackie, Ian (CON - Thorpe St Andrew North West)
cllr.ian.mackie@broadland.gov.uk

Mallett, Andrew (CON - Taverham North)
cllr.andrew.mallett@broadland.gov.uk

Mallett, Alan (CON - Coltishall)
cllr.alan.mallett@broadland.gov.uk

Mancini-Boyle, Trudy (CON - Thorpe St Andrew South East)
cllr.trudy.mancini-boyle@broadland.gov.uk

Moncur, Ian (CON - Sprowston East)
cllr.ian.moncur@broadland.gov.uk

Nurden, Grant (CON - Marshes)
cllr.grant.nurden@broadland.gov.uk

O'Neill, Frank (CON - Blofield with South Walsham)
cllr.frank.oneill@broadland.gov.uk

Peck, Greg (CON - Eynesford)
cllr.greg.peck@broadland.gov.uk

Ray-Mortlock, Victor (CON - Drayton North)
cllr.victor.ray-mortlock@broadland.gov.uk

Riley, Steve (LD - Aylsham)
cllr.steve.riley@broadland.gov.uk

Rix, Barbara (LD - Buxton)
cllr.barbara.rix@broadland.gov.uk

Shaw, Nigel (CON - Thorpe St Andrew North West)
cllr.nigel.shaw@broadland.gov.uk

Snowling, Michael (CON - Brundall)
cllr.michael.snowling@broadland.gov.uk

Tapp, Vincent (CON - Wroxham)
cllr.vincent.tapp@broadland.gov.uk

Vincent, Shaun (CON - Plumstead)
cllr.shaun.vincent@broadland.gov.uk

Vincent, Karen (CON - Old Catton & Sprowston West)
cllr.karen.vincent@broadland.gov.uk

Ward, David (CON - Burlingham)
cllr.david.ward@broadland.gov.uk

Whymark, Fran (CON - Wroxham)
cllr.fran.whymark@broadland.gov.uk

Willmott, David (CON - Taverham North)
cllr.david.willmott@broadland.gov.uk

Woodbridge, Simon (CON - Great Witchingham)
cllr.simon.woodbridge@broadland.gov.uk

POLITICAL COMPOSITION
CON: 42, LD: 5

COMMITTEE CHAIRS

Audit: Mr Nigel Shaw

Licensing: Mr Stuart Dunn

Planning: Mr Ian Moncur

Bromley   L

Bromley London Borough Council, Civic Centre, Stockwell Close, Bromley BR1 3UH

☎ 020 8464 3333 ▣ www.bromley.gov.uk

FACTS AND FIGURES
Parliamentary Constituencies: Beckenham, Bromley and Chislehurst, Orpington
EU Constituencies: London
Election Frequency: Elections are of whole council

PRINCIPAL OFFICERS

Chief Executive: Mr Doug Patterson, Chief Executive, Civic Centre, Stockwell Close, Bromley BR1 3UH ☎ 020 8313 4354 ✆ doug.patterson@bromley.gov.uk

Senior Management: Ms Jane Bailey, Statutory Lead - Education, Civic Centre, Stockwell Close, Bromley BR1 3UH ☎ 020 8313 4146 ✆ jane.bailey@bromley.gov.uk

Senior Management: Mr Mark Bowen, Director - Corporate Services & Monitoring Officer, Civic Centre, Stockwell Close, Bromley BR1 3UH ☎ 020 8313 4355 ✆ mark.bowen@bromley.gov.uk

Senior Management: Mr Nigel Davies, Executive Director - Environment & Community Services, Civic Centre, Stockwell Close, Bromley BR1 3UH ☎ 020 8313 4443 ✆ nigel.davies@bromley.gov.uk

Senior Management: Mr Marc Hume, Director - Regeneration & Transformation, Civic Centre, Stockwell Close, Bromley BR1 3UH ☎ 020 8461 7557 ✆ marc.hume@bromley.gov.uk

Senior Management: Mr Stephen John, Statutory Lead - Adult Services, Civic Centre, Stockwell Close, Bromley BR1 3UH ☎ 020 8313 4197 ✆ stephen.john@bromley.gov.uk

Senior Management: Dr Nada Lemic, Director - Public Health, Bexley Civic Offices, 2 Watling Street, Bexleyheath DA6 7AT ☎ 020 8303 7777 ✆ nada.lemic@bromley.gov.uk

Senior Management: Mr Peter Turner, Director - Finance, Civic Centre, Stockwell Close, Bromley BR1 3UH ☎ 020 8313 4338 ✆ peter.turner@bromley.gov.uk

Senior Management: Ms Kay Weiss, Statutory Lead - Children's Services, Civic Centre, Stockwell Close, Bromley BR1 3UH ☎ 020 8313 4062 ✆ kay.weiss@bromley.gov.uk

Building Control: Mr Steve Moore, Head of Building Control, Building Control, Civic Centre, Stockwell Close, Bromley BR1 3UH ☎ 020 8313 4315 ✆ steve.moore@bromley.gov.uk

Civil Registration: Ms Carol Tyson, Superintendent Registrar, Civic Centre, Stockwell Close, Bromley BR1 3UH ☎ 020 8313 7957 ✆ carol.tyson@bromley.gov.uk

PR / Communications: Ms Susie Clark, Communications Analyst, Civic Centre, Stockwell Close, Bromley BR1 3UH ☎ 020 8461 7790 ✆ susie.clark@bromley.gov.uk

PR / Communications: Ms Amanda Day, Communications Analyst, Civic Centre, Stockwell Close, Bromley BR1 3UH ☎ 020 8313 4390 ✆ amanda.day@bromley.gov.uk

Computer Management: Mr Stuart Elsey, Acting Head of IT, Civic Centre, Stockwell Close, Bromley BR1 3UH ✆ stuart.elsey@bromley.gov.uk

Consumer Protection and Trading Standards: Mr Rob Vale, Head of Trading Standards & Community Protection, Civic Centre, Stockwell Close, Bromley BR1 3UH ☎ 020 8313 4785 ✆ robert.vale@bromley.gov.uk

Contracts: Mr Dave Starling, Head of Corporate Procurement, Civic Centre, Stockwell Close, Bromley BR1 3UH ☎ 020 8313 4639 ✆ dave.starling@bromley.gov.uk

Customer Service: Mr Duncan Bridgewater, Head of Customer Services, Civic Centre, Stockwell Close, Bromley BR1 3UH ☎ 020 8313 7676 ✆ duncan.bridgewater@bromely.gov.uk

Education: Ms Jane Bailey, Statutory Lead - Education, Civic Centre, Stockwell Close, Bromley BR1 3UH ☎ 020 8313 4146 ✆ jane.bailey@bromley.gov.uk

Electoral Registration: Mrs Carol Ling, Electoral Services Manager, Civic Centre, Stockwell Close, Bromley BR1 3UH ☎ 020 8313 4367 ✆ carol.ling@bromley.gov.uk

Energy Management: Mr Gerry Kelly, Property Energy Manager, Civic Centre, Stockwell Close, Bromley BR1 3UH ☎ 020 8313 4570 ✆ gerry.kelly@bromley.gov.uk

Environmental Health: Mr Jim McGowan, Head of Environmental Protection, Civic Centre, Stockwell Close, Bromley BR1 3UH ☎ 020 8313 4651 ✆ jim.mcgowan@bromley.gov.uk

Estates, Property & Valuation: Ms Heather Hosking, Head of Strategic Property, Civic Centre, Stockwell Close, Bromley BR1 3UH ☎ 020 8313 4421 ✆ heather.hosking@bromley.gov.uk

Events Manager: Mr Toby Smith, Ranger Services Manager, Civic Centre, Stockwell Close, Bromley BR1 3UH ☎ 020 8658 1593 ✆ toby.smith@bromley.gov.uk

Facilities: Mr Andrew Champion, Facilities & Support Services Manager, Civic Centre, Stockwell Close, Bromley BR1 3UH ☎ 020 8313 4394 ✆ andrew.champion@bromley.gov.uk

Finance: Mr Peter Turner, Director - Finance, Civic Centre, Stockwell Close, Bromley BR1 3UH ☎ 020 8313 4338 ✆ peter.turner@bromley.gov.uk

Pensions: Ms Janice Castle, Pensions Manager, Civic Centre, Stockwell Close, Bromley BR1 3UH ☎ 020 8461 7503 ✆ janice.castle@bromley.gov.uk

Fleet Management: Mr Paul Chilton, Transport Operations Manager, Central Depot, Baths Road, Bromley BR2 9RB ☎ 020 8313 4849 ✆ paul.chilton@bromley.gov.uk

Grounds Maintenance: Mr Dan Jones, Assistant Director - Streetscene & Greenspace, Civic Centre, Stockwell Close, Bromley BR1 3UH ☎ 020 8313 4211 ✆ dan.jones@bromley.gov.uk

BROMLEY

Highways: Mr Paul Symonds, Assistant Director - Transport & Highways, Civic Centre, Stockwell Close, Bromley BR1 3UH ☎ 020 8313 4540 ⌨ paul.symonds@bromley.gov.uk

Housing: Ms Sara Bowrey, Assistant Director - Housing Needs, Civic Centre, Stockwell Close, Bromley BR1 3UH ☎ 020 8313 4013 ⌨ sara.bowrey@bromley.gov.uk

Leisure and Cultural Services: Mr Colin Brand, Assistant Director - Leisure & Culture, Civic Centre, Stockwell Close, Bromley BR1 3UH ☎ 020 8313 4107 ⌨ colin.brand@bromley.gov.uk

Licensing: Mr Paul Lehane, Head of Food Safety & Licensing, Civic Centre, Stockwell Close, Bromley BR1 3UH ☎ 020 8313 4216 ⌨ paul.lehane@bromley.gov.uk

Lighting: Mr Garry Warner, Head of Highways, Civic Centre, Stockwell Close, Bromley BR1 3UH ☎ 020 8313 4929 ⌨ garry.warner@bromley.gov.uk

Member Services: Mr Graham Walton, Democratic Services Manager, Civic Centre, Stockwell Close, Bromley BR1 3UH ☎ 020 8461 7743 ⌨ graham.walton@bromley.gov.uk

Parking: Mr Benjamin Stephens, Head of Parking Shared Services, Civic Centre, Stockwell Close, Bromley BR1 3UH ☎ 020 8313 4514 ⌨ benjamin.stephens@bexley.gov.uk

Planning: Mr Jim Kehoe, Chief Planner, Civic Centre, Stockwell Close, Bromley BR1 3UH ☎ 020 8313 4441 ⌨ jim.kehoe@bromley.gov.uk

Public Libraries: Mr Tim Woolgar, Library Operations & Commissioning Manager, Bromley Central Library, High Street, Bromley BR1 1EX ☎ 020 8461 7232 ⌨ tim.woolgar@bromley.gov.uk

Recycling & Waste Minimisation: Mr John Woodruff, Head of Waste Services, Civic Centre, Stockwell Close, Bromley BR1 3UH ☎ 020 8313 4910 ⌨ john.woodruff@bromley.gov.uk

Road Safety: Mr Angus Culverwell, Head of Traffic & Road Safety, Civic Centre, Stockwell Close, Bromley BR1 3UH ☎ 020 8313 4959 ⌨ angus.culverwell@bromley.gov.uk

Social Services (Adult): Mr Stephen John, Statutory Lead - Adult Services, Civic Centre, Stockwell Close, Bromley BR1 3UH ☎ 020 8313 4197 ⌨ stephen.john@bromley.gov.uk

Social Services (Children): Ms Kay Weiss, Statutory Lead - Children's Services, Civic Centre, Stockwell Close, Bromley BR1 3UH ☎ 020 8313 4062 ⌨ kay.weiss@bromley.gov.uk

Public Health: Dr Nada Lemic, Director - Public Health, Bexley Civic Offices, 2 Watling Street, Bexleyheath DA6 7AT ☎ 020 8303 7777 ⌨ nada.lemic@bromley.gov.uk

Staff Training: Ms Antoinette Thorne, Head of Workforce Development, Civic Centre, Stockwell Close, Bromley BR1 3UH ☎ 020 8313 4380 ⌨ antoinette.thorne@bromley.gov.uk

Street Scene: Mr Peter McCready, Head of Area Management, Civic Centre, Stockwell Close, Bromley BR1 3UH ☎ 020 8313 4942 ⌨ peter.mccready@bromley.gov.uk

Town Centre: Mr Martin Pinnell, Head of Town Centre Management & Business Support, Civic Centre, Stockwell Close, Bromley BR1 3UH ☎ 020 8313 4457; 020 8461 7890 ⌨ martin.pinnell@bromley.gov.uk

Transport: Mr Paul Chilton, Transport Operations Manager, Central Depot, Baths Road, Bromley BR2 9RB ☎ 020 8313 4849 ⌨ paul.chilton@bromley.gov.uk

COUNCILLORS

Mayor: Payne, Ian (CON - Chislehurst)
ian.payne@bromley.gov.uk

Deputy Mayor: Gray, Hannah (CON - West Wickham)
hannah.gray@bromley.gov.uk

Leader of the Council: Carr, Stephen (CON - Bromley Common & Keston)
stephen.carr@bromley.gov.uk

Deputy Leader of the Council: Smith, Colin (CON - Bickley)
colin.smith@bromley.gov.uk

Group LeaderLivett, David (UKIP - Cray Valley West)
david.livett@bromely.gov.uk

Group LeaderWilkins, Angela (LAB - Crystal Palace)
angela.wilkins@bromley.gov.uk

Allen, Vanessa (LAB - Clock House)
vanessa.allen2@bromley.gov.uk

Arthur, Graham (CON - Hayes & Coney Hall)
graham.arthur@bromley.gov.uk

Auld, Douglas (CON - Petts Wood & Knoll)
douglas.auld@bromley.gov.uk

Bance, Kathy (LAB - Penge & Cator)
katherine.bance@bromley.gov.uk

Benington, Julian (CON - Biggin Hill)
julian.benington@bromley.gov.uk

Bennett, Nicholas (CON - West Wickham)
md@kentrefurbishment.co.uk

Bennett, Ruth (CON - Bromley Common & Keston)
ruth.bennett@bromley.gov.uk

Bosshard, Eric (CON - Chislehurst)
eric.bosshard@bromley.gov.uk

Botting, Kim (CON - Orpington)
kim.botting@bromley.gov.uk

Boughey, Katy (CON - Chislehurst)
katy.boughey@bromley.gov.uk

Brooks, Kevin (LAB - Penge & Cator)
kevin.brooks@bromley.gov.uk

Buttinger, Lydia (CON - Chelsfield & Pratts Bottom)
lydia.buttinger@bromley.gov.uk

Cartwright, David (CON - Mottingham & Chislehurst North)
david.cartwright@bromley.gov.uk

Collins, Alan (CON - Kelsey & Eden Park)
alan.collins@bromley.gov.uk

Cooke, Mary (CON - Shortlands)
mary.cooke@bromley.gov.uk

Dean, Peter (CON - Kelsey & Eden Park)
peter.dean@bromley.gov.uk

Dunn, Ian (LAB - Clock House)
ian.dunn@bromley.gov.uk

Dykes, Nicky (CON - Bromley Town)
nicky.dykes@bromley.gov.uk

Ellis, Judi (CON - Cray Valley West)
judith.ellis@bromley.gov.uk

Evans, Robert (CON - Farnborough & Crofton)
robert.evans@bromley.gov.uk

Fawthrop, Simon (CON - Petts Wood & Knoll)
simon.fawthrop@bromley.gov.uk

Fookes, Peter (LAB - Penge & Cator)
peter.fookes@bromley.gov.uk

Fortune, Peter (CON - Hayes & Coney Hall)
peter.fortune@bromley.gov.uk

Harmer, Ellie (CON - Plaistow & Sundridge)
ellie.harmer@bromley.gov.uk

Harmer, Will (CON - Bromley Town)
will.harmer@bromley.gov.uk

Huntington-Thresher, William (CON - Orpington)
william.huntington-thresher@bromley.gov.uk

Huntington-Thresher, Samaris (CON - Chelsfield & Pratts Bottom)
samaris.huntington-thresher@bromley.gov.uk

Jeffreys, David (CON - Shortlands)
david.jeffreys@bromley.gov.uk

Joel, Charles (CON - Farnborough & Crofton)
charles.joel@bromley.gov.uk

Lymer, Kate (CON - Bickley)
kate.lymer@bromley.gov.uk

Mellor, Russell (CON - Copers Cope)
russell.mellor@bromley.gov.uk

Michael, Alexa (CON - Bromley Common & Keston)
alexa.michael@bromley.gov.uk

Morgan, Peter (CON - Plaistow & Sundridge)
peter.morgan@bromley.gov.uk

Nathan, Terence (UKIP - Cray Valley West)
terence.nathan@bromley.gov.uk

Onslow, Keith (CON - Chelsfield & Pratts Bottom)
keith.onslow@bromley.gov.uk

Owen, Tony (CON - Petts Wood & Knoll)
tony.owen@bromley.gov.uk

Page, Angela (CON - Cray Valley East)
angela.page@bromley.gov.uk

Phillips, Sarah (CON - Clock House)
sarah.phillips@bromley.gov.uk

Philpott, Tom (CON - West Wickham)
trphilpott@hotmail.com

Pierce, Chris (CON - Cray Valley East)
chris.pierce@bromley.gov.uk

Reddin, Neil (CON - Hayes & Coney Hall)
neil.reddin@bromley.gov.uk

Rideout, Catherine (CON - Bickley)
catherine.rideout@bromley.gov.uk

Rideout, Charles (CON - Mottingham & Chislehurst North)
charles.rideout@bromley.gov.uk

Rutherford, Michael (CON - Bromley Town)
michael.rutherford@bromley.gov.uk

Scoates, Richard (CON - Darwin)
richard.scoates@bromley.gov.uk

Smith, Diane (CON - Kelsey & Eden Park)
diane.smith@bromley.gov.uk

Stevens, Melanie (CON - Biggin Hill)
melanie.stevens@bromley.gov.uk

Stevens, Tim (CON - Farnborough & Crofton)
tim.stevens@bromley.gov.uk

Te, Teresa (CON - Cray Valley East)
teresa.te@bromley.gov.uk

Tickner, Michael (CON - Copers Cope)
michael.tickner@bromley.gov.uk

Tunnicliffe, Pauline (CON - Orpington)
pauline.tunnicliffe@bromley.gov.uk

Turner, Michael (CON - Plaistow & Sundridge)
michael.turner@bromley.gov.uk

Wells, Stephen (CON - Copers Cope)
stephen.wells@bromley.gov.uk

Williams, Richard (LAB - Crystal Palace)
richard.williams@bromley.gov.uk

POLITICAL COMPOSITION
CON: 51, LAB: 7, UKIP: 2

COMMITTEE CHAIRS
Care Services: Ms Judi Ellis

Development Control: Mr Peter Dean

Education: Mr Nicholas Bennett

Environment: Mr William Huntington-Thresher

Health & Wellbeing: Mr David Jeffreys

Licensing: Mr Tim Stevens

Bromsgrove   D

Bromsgrove District Council, Parkside, Market Street,
Bromsgrove B61 8DA
☎ 01527 881288 ⌨ bromsgrovecsc@bromsgrove.gov.uk
🖳 www.bromsgrove.gov.uk

FACTS AND FIGURES
Parliamentary Constituencies: Bromsgrove
EU Constituencies: West Midlands
Election Frequency: Elections are of whole council

PRINCIPAL OFFICERS
Chief Executive: Mr Kevin Dicks, Chief Executive, Parkside,
Market Street, Bromsgrove B61 8AD ☎ 01527 881484
⌨ k.dicks@bromsgroveandredditch.gov.uk

BROMSGROVE

Deputy Chief Executive: Mrs Susan Hanley, Deputy Chief Executive, Parkside, Market Street, Bromsgrove B61 8DA
☎ 01527 534118 ⏚ s.hanley@bromsgroveandredditch.gov.uk

Senior Management: Ms Jayne Pickering, Executive Director & S151 Officer, Parkside, Market Street, Bromsgrove B61 8DA
☎ 01527 881400 ⏚ j.pickering@bromsgroveandredditch.gov.uk

Best Value: Ms Jayne Pickering, Executive Director & S151 Officer, Town Hall, Walter Stranz Square, Redditch B98 8AH
☎ 01527 881400 ⏚ j.pickering@bromsgroveandredditch.gov.uk

Building Control: Mr Adrian Wyre, Principal Building Control Surveyor, Parkside, Market Street, Bromsgrove B61 8DA
☎ 01527 881350 ⏚ a.wyre@bromsgroveandredditch.gov.uk

PR / Communications: Mrs Anne-Marie Harley, Communications & Publicity Manager, Parkside, Market Street, Bromsgrove B61 8DA
☎ 01527 881296 ⏚ a.harley@bromsgroveandredditch.gov.uk

Community Safety: Ms Judy Willis, Head of Community Services, Parkside, Market Street, Bromsgrove B61 8DA ☎ 01527 64252
⏚ j.willis@bromsgroveandredditch.gov.uk

Computer Management: Mrs Deb Poole, Head of Business Transformation & Organisational, Parkside, Market Street, Bromsgrove B61 8DA ☎ 01527 881256
⏚ d.poole@bromsgroveandredditch.gov.uk

Contracts: Ms Carmen Young, Procurement Officer, Parkside, Market Street, Bromsgrove B61 8DA ☎ 01527 548239
⏚ procurement@bromsgroveandredditch.gov.uk

Customer Service: Mrs Amanda Singleton, Head of Customer Access & Financial Support, Parkside, Market Street, Bromsgrove B61 8DA ☎ 01527 881241
⏚ a.singleton@bromsgroveandredditch.gov.uk

Economic Development: Mr Dean Piper, Head of Economic Development & Regeneration - North Worcestershire, Wyre Forest House, Finepoint Way, Kidderminster DY11 7WF ☎ 01562 932192
⏚ dean.piper@nwedr.org.uk

Economic Development: Mr Steve Singleton, Economic Development Manager - North Worcestershire, Wyre Forest House, Finepoint Way, Kidderminster DY11 7WF ☎ 01562 732168
⏚ steve.singleton@nwedr.org.uk

E-Government: Mrs Deb Poole, Head of Business Transformation & Organisational, Parkside, Market Street, Bromsgrove B61 8DA
☎ 01527 881256 ⏚ d.poole@bromsgroveandredditch.gov.uk

Electoral Registration: Mrs Claire Felton, Head of Legal, Equalities & Democratic Services, Parkside, Market Street, Bromsgrove B61 8DA ☎ 01527 881429
⏚ c.felton@bromsgroveandredditch.gov.uk

Emergency Planning: Mrs Susan Hanley, Deputy Chief Executive, Parkside, Market Street, Bromsgrove B61 8DA
☎ 01527 534118 ⏚ s.hanley@bromsgroveandredditch.gov.uk

Emergency Planning: Ms Rebecca Pritchett, North Worcestershire Civil Contingencies & Resilience Manager, Wyre Forest House, Finepoint Way, Kidderminster DY11 7WF
☎ 01562 732711 ⏚ rebecca.pritchett@wyreforestdc.gov.uk

Energy Management: Ms Carmen Young, Procurement Officer, Parkside, Market Street, Bromsgrove B61 8DA ☎ 01527 548239
⏚ procurement@bromsgroveandredditch.gov.uk

Environmental / Technical Services: Mr Guy Revans, Head of Environmental Services, Central Depot, Aston Road, Aston Fields, Bromsgrove B60 3EX ☎ 01527 64252 Ext 3292
⏚ g.revans@bromsgroveandredditch.gov.uk

Environmental Health: Mr Simon Wilkes, Head of Regulatory Services, Wyre Forest House, Finepoint Way, Kidderminster DY11 7WF ⏚ simon.wilkes@worcsregservices.gov.uk

Estates, Property & Valuation: Mrs Amanda Singleton, Head of Customer Access & Financial Support, Parkside, Market Street, Bromsgrove B61 8DA ☎ 01527 881241
⏚ a.singleton@bromsgroveandredditch.gov.uk

Events Manager: Mr Jonathan Cochrane, Arts & Events Manager, Parkside, Market Street, Bromsgrove B61 8DA ☎ 01527 881381
⏚ jonathan.cochrane@bromsgroveandredditch.gov.uk

Facilities: Ms Julie Heyes, Business Development Manager, Parkside, Market Street, Bromsgrove B61 8DA ☎ 01527 881377
⏚ j.heyes@bromsgroveandredditch.gov.uk

Finance: Ms Jayne Pickering, Executive Director & S151 Officer, Parkside, Market Street, Bromsgrove B61 8DA ☎ 01527 881400
⏚ j.pickering@bromsgroveandredditch.gov.uk

Treasury: Ms Sam Morgan, Financial Services Manager, Parkside, Market Street, Bromsgrove B61 8DA ☎ 01527 587088
⏚ sam.morgan@bromsgroveandredditch.gov.uk

Fleet Management: Mr Kevin Hirons, Environmental Business Development Manager, Parkside, Market Street, Bromsgrove B61 8DA ☎ 01527 881705 ⏚ k.hirons@bromsgroveandredditch.gov.uk

Health and Safety: Ms Dawn Ibbotson, Senior Advisor - Health, Safety & Wellbeing, Parkside, Market Street, Bromsgrove B61 8DA
☎ 01527 64252 Ext 1398
⏚ d.ibbotson@bromsgroveandredditch.gov.uk

Home Energy Conservation: Ms Kath Manning, Climate Change & Energy Support Manager, Parkside, Market Street, Bromsgrove B61 8DA ☎ 01527 587094
⏚ kath.manning@bromsgroveandredditch.gov.uk

Housing: Mr Derek Allen, Strategic Housing Manager, Parkside, Market Street, Bromsgrove B61 8DA ☎ 01527 881278
⏚ d.allen@bromsgroveandredditch.gov.uk

Legal: Mrs Claire Felton, Head of Legal, Equalities & Democratic Services, Parkside, Market Street, Bromsgrove B61 8DA
☎ 01527 881429 ⏚ c.felton@bromsgroveandredditch.gov.uk

Leisure and Cultural Services: Mr John Godwin, Head of Leisure, Parkside, Market Street, Bromsgrove B61 8DA ☎ 01527 881742 ~🖰 j.godwin@bromsgroveandredditch.gov.uk

Licensing: Mr Simon Wilkes, Head of Regulatory Services, Wyre Forest House, Finepoint Way, Kidderminster DY11 7WF ~🖰 simon.wilkes@worcsregservices.gov.uk

Lottery Funding, Charity and Voluntary: Ms Judy Willis, Head of Community Services, Parkside, Market Street, Bromsgrove B61 8DA ☎ 01527 64252 ~🖰 j.willis@bromsgroveandredditch.gov.uk

Member Services: Mrs Sheena Jones, Democratic Services Manager, Parkside, Market Street, Bromsgrove B61 8DA ☎ 01527 548240 ~🖰 s.jones@bromsgroveandredditch.gov.uk

Parking: Mr Guy Revans, Head of Environmental Services, Central Depot, Aston Road, Aston Fields, Bromsgrove B60 3EX ☎ 01527 64252 Ext 3292 ~🖰 g.revans@bromsgroveandredditch.gov.uk

Partnerships: Mrs Della McCarthy, Partnerships Manager, Parkside, Market Street, Bromsgrove B61 8DA ☎ 01527 881618 ~🖰 d.mccarthy@bromsgroveandreddictch.gov.uk

Personnel / HR: Mrs Deb Poole, Head of Business Transformation & Organisational, Parkside, Market Street, Bromsgrove B61 8DA ☎ 01527 881256 ~🖰 d.poole@bromsgroveandredditch.gov.uk

Planning: Mr Dale Birch, Development Control Manager, Parkside, Market Street, Bromsgrove B61 8DA ☎ 01527 881341 ~🖰 d.birch@bromsgroveandredditch.gov.uk

Procurement: Ms Carmen Young, Procurement Officer, Parkside, Market Street, Bromsgrove B61 8DA ☎ 01527 548239 ~🖰 procurement@bromsgroveandredditch.gov.uk

Recycling & Waste Minimisation: Mr Guy Revans, Head of Environmental Services, Central Depot, Aston Road, Aston Fields, Bromsgrove B60 3EX ☎ 01527 64252 Ext 3292 ~🖰 g.revans@bromsgroveandredditch.gov.uk

Regeneration: Mr Kevin Dicks, Chief Executive, Parkside, Market Street, Bromsgrove B61 8DA ☎ 01527 881484 ~🖰 k.dicks@bromsgroveandredditch.gov.uk

Road Safety: Ms Ruth Bamford, Head of Planning & Regeneration Services, Parkside, Market Street, Bromsgrove B61 8DA ☎ 01527 64252 Ext 3201 ~🖰 r.bamford@bromsgroveandredditch.gov.uk

Staff Training: Ms Becky Talbot, Human Resources & Organisational Development Manager, Parkside, Market Street, Bromsgrove B61 8DA ~🖰 b.talbot@bromsgroveandredditch.gov.uk

Street Scene: Mr Guy Revans, Head of Environmental Services, Central Depot, Aston Road, Aston Fields, Bromsgrove B60 3EX ☎ 01527 64252 Ext 3292 ~🖰 g.revans@bromsgroveandredditch.gov.uk

Tourism: Mr John Godwin, Head of Leisure, Parkside, Market Street, Bromsgrove B61 8DA ☎ 01527 881742 ~🖰 j.godwin@bromsgroveandredditch.gov.uk

Waste Collection and Disposal: Mr Guy Revans, Head of Environmental Services, Parkside, Market Street, Bromsgrove B61 8DA ☎ 01527 64252 Ext 3292 ~🖰 g.revans@bromsgroveandredditch.gov.uk

Waste Management: Mr Guy Revans, Head of Environmental Services, Parkside, Market Street, Bromsgrove B61 8DA ☎ 01527 64252 Ext 3292 ~🖰 g.revans@bromsgroveandredditch.gov.uk

COUNCILLORS

Chair: Spencer, C J (CON - Slideslow)
c.spencer@bromsgrove.gov.uk

Vice-Chair: Glass, (CON - Avoncroft)
m.glass@bromsgrove.gov.uk

Leader of the Council: Sherrey, Margaret (CON - Belbroughton & Romsley)
m.sherry@bromsgrove.gov.uk

Deputy Leader of the Council: Taylor, C (CON - Lickey Hills)
k.taylor@bromsgrove.gov.uk

Allen-Jones, C (CON - Belbroughton & Romsley)
c.allen-jones@bromsgrove.gov.uk

Baxter, Sue (R - Drakes Cross & Walkers Heath)
s.baxter@bromsgrove.gov.uk

Bloore, C (LAB - Sidemoor)
c.bloore@bromsgrove.gov.uk

Buxton, M T (LAB - Sanders Park)
m.buxton@bromsgrove.gov.uk

Colella, (IND - Hagley West)
s.colella@bromsgrove.gov.uk

Cooper, B T (CON - Marlbrock)
b.cooper@bromsgrove.gov.uk

Deeming, R J (CON - Cofton)
r.deeming@bromsgrove.gov.uk

Denaro, G N (CON - Wythall West)
g.denaro@bromsgrove.gov.uk

Dent, R L (CON - Bromsgrove Central)
r.dent@bromsgrove.gov.uk

Griffiths, J (CON - Alvechurch South)
j.griffiths@bromsgrove.gov.uk

Hotham, C A (IND - Barnt Green & Hopwood)
c.hotham@bromsgrove.gov.uk

Jenkins, (IND - Hagley East)
r.jenkins@bromsgrove.gov.uk

Jones, H (CON - Catshill North)
h.jones@bromsgrove.gov.uk

Laight, R J (CON - Lowes Hill)
r.laight@bromsgrove.gov.uk

Lammas, P (CON - Norton)
p.lammas@bromsgrove.gov.uk

Mallett, L (LAB - Hill Top)
l.mallett@bromsgrove.gov.uk

May, K J (CON - Perryfields)
k.may@bromsgrove.gov.uk

McDonald, P M (LAB - Rubery North)
p.mcdonald@bromsgrove.gov.uk

BROMSGROVE

McDonald, C M (LAB - Rubery South)
c.mcdonald@bromsgrove.gov.uk

Peters, (R - Hollywood)
s.peters@bromsgrove.gov.uk

Shannon, Sean (LAB - Charford)
s.shannon@bromsgrove.gov.uk

Smith, (CON - Alvechurch Village)
r.smith@bromsgrove.gov.uk

Thomas, (CON - Aston Fields)
p.thomas@bromsgrove.gov.uk

Thompson, M (LAB - Rock Hill)
m.thompson@bromsgrove.gov.uk

Turner, L J (R - Wythall East)
l.turner@bromsgrove.gov.uk

Webb, (CON - Catshill South)
s.webb@bromsgrove.gov.uk

Whittaker, Peter (CON - Tardebigge)
p.whittaker@bromsgrove.gov.uk

POLITICAL COMPOSITION
CON: 18, LAB: 7, R: 3, IND: 3

Broxbourne   D

Broxbourne Borough Council, Borough Offices, Bishops'
College, Churchgate, Cheshunt EN8 9XQ
☎ 01992 785555 🖶 01992 785578 ⌂ enquiry@broxbourne.gov.uk
🖳 www.broxbourne.gov.uk

FACTS AND FIGURES
Parliamentary Constituencies: Broxbourne
EU Constituencies: Eastern
Election Frequency: Elections are by thirds

PRINCIPAL OFFICERS

Chief Executive: Mr Jeff Stack, Chief Executive, Borough Offices,
Bishops' College, Churchgate, Cheshunt EN8 9XQ ☎ 01992
785553 ⌂ ceo@broxbourne.gov.uk

Senior Management: Mrs Sandra Beck, Director - Finance,
Borough Offices, Bishops' College, Churchgate, Cheshunt EN8
9XQ ☎ 01992 785555 ⌂ sandra.beck@broxbourne.gov.uk

Senior Management: Mr Peter Linkson, Director - Environmental
Services, Borough Offices, Bishops' College, Churchgate, Cheshunt
EN8 9XQ ☎ 01992 785555 ⌂ peter.linkson@broxbourne.gov.uk

Senior Management: Mr Gavin Miles, Head of Legal Services,
Borough Offices, Bishops' College, Churchgate, Cheshunt EN8 9NF
☎ 01992 785555 ⌂ gavin.miles@broxbourne.gov.uk

Building Control: Mr Keith Loxley, Building Control Manager,
Borough Offices, Bishop's College, Churchgate, Cheshunt EN8 9NF
☎ 01922 785555 ⌂ keith.loxley@broxbourne.gov.uk

PR / Communications: Mrs Nichola Needs, Communications
Manager, Borough Offices, Bishops' College, Churchgate, Cheshunt
EN8 9XQ ☎ 01992 785592 ⌂ nichola.needs@broxbourne.gov.uk

Community Safety: Mrs Nichola Pearce, Community Safety
Manager, Borough Offices, Bishops' College, Churchgate, Cheshunt
EN8 9XQ ☎ 01992 785555 ⌂ nicola.pearce@broxbourne.gov.uk

Computer Management: Mr Richard Pennell, Head of Personnel
& Payroll, Borough Offices, Bishops' College, Churchgate, Cheshunt
EN8 9XG ☎ 01992 758809 ⌂ richard.pennell@broxbourne.gov.uk

Customer Service: Mr Clive Head, Head of Business
Management, Borough Offices, Bishops' College, Churchgate,
Cheshunt EN8 9XQ ⌂ clive.head@broxbourne.gov.uk

Economic Development: Mrs Clare Watson, Head of Economic
Development, Borough Offices, Bishops' College, Churchgate,
Cheshunt EN8 9XQ ☎ 01992 785555
⌂ clare.watson@broxbourne.gov.uk

Electoral Registration: Mr Stephen Billington, Head of Support
Services, Borough Offices, Bishops' College, Churchgate, Cheshunt
EN8 9XQ ☎ 01992 785534 ⌂ stephen.billington@broxbourne.gov.uk

Emergency Planning: Mr Jeff Stack, Chief Executive, Borough
Offices, Bishops' College, Churchgate, Cheshunt EN8 9XQ
☎ 01992 785553 ⌂ ceo@broxbourne.gov.uk

Environmental Health: Ms Barbara Goult, Environmental Health
Manager, Borough Offices, Bishops' College, Churchgate, Cheshunt
EN8 9XQ ☎ 01992 785555 ⌂ barbara.goult@broxbourne.gov.uk

Facilities: Mr Mick Mager, Facilities Manager, Borough Offices,
Bishops' College, Churchgate, Cheshunt EN8 9XQ
☎ 01992 785555 ⌂ mick.mager@broxbourne.gov.uk

Finance: Mrs Sandra Beck, Director - Finance, Borough Offices,
Bishops' College, Churchgate, Cheshunt EN8 9XQ
☎ 01992 785555 ⌂ sandra.beck@broxbourne.gov.uk

Grounds Maintenance: Mr Dave Renouf, Green Spaces
Manager, Borough Offices, Bishops' College, Churchgate, Cheshunt
EN8 9XQ ☎ 01992 785555 ⌂ dave.renouf@broxbourne.gov.uk

Health and Safety: Mr Steve Jones, Health & Safety Co-
ordinator, Borough Offices, Bishops' College, Churchgate, Cheshunt
EN8 9XQ ☎ 01992 785555 ⌂ dave.renouf@broxbourne.gov.uk

Housing: Mr Stephen Tingley, Head of Housing & Benefits,
Borough Offices, Bishops' College, Churchgate, Cheshunt EN8
9XQ ☎ 01992 785555 ⌂ stephen.tingley@broxbourne.gov.uk

Legal: Mr Gavin Miles, Head of Legal Services, Borough Offices,
Bishops' College, Churchgate, Cheshunt EN8 9NF
☎ 01992 785555 ⌂ gavin.miles@broxbourne.gov.uk

Leisure and Cultural Services: Mr Steve Dupoy, Head of
Leisure & Culture, Borough Offices, Bishops' College, Churchgate,
Cheshunt EN8 9XQ ☎ 01992 785555
⌂ steven.dupoy@broxbourne.gov.uk

Licensing: Mr Stephen Billington, Head of Support Services,
Borough Offices, Bishops' College, Churchgate, Cheshunt EN8
9XQ ☎ 01992 785534 ⌂ stephen.billington@broxbourne.gov.uk

Member Services: Mr Stephen Billington, Head of Support Services, Borough Offices, Bishops' College, Churchgate, Cheshunt EN8 9XQ ☎ 01992 785534 ✆ stephen.billington@broxbourne.gov.uk

Parking: Ms Clare Fensome, Parking Services Manager, Borough Offices, Bishops' College, Churchgate, Cheshunt EN8 9XQ ☎ 01992 785555 ✆ clare.fensome@broxbourne.gov.uk

Personnel / HR: Mr Richard Pennell, Head of Personnel & Payroll, Borough Offices, Bishops' College, Churchgate, Cheshunt EN8 9XG ☎ 01992 758809 ✆ richard.pennell@broxbourne.gov.uk

Planning: Mr Douglas Cooper, Head of Planning & Development, Borough Offices, Bishops' College, Churchgate, Cheshunt EN8 9XQ ☎ 01992 785555 ✆ douglas.cooper@broxbourne.gov.uk

Procurement: Mr Clive Head, Head of Business Management, Borough Offices, Bishops' College, Churchgate, Cheshunt EN8 9XQ ✆ clive.head@broxbourne.gov.uk

Recycling & Waste Minimisation: Mr Peter Linkson, Director - Environmental Services, Borough Offices, Bishops' College, Churchgate, Cheshunt EN8 9XQ ☎ 01992 785555 ✆ peter.linkson@broxbourne.gov.uk

Staff Training: Mr Richard Pennell, Head of Personnel & Payroll, Borough Offices, Bishops' College, Churchgate, Cheshunt EN8 9XG ☎ 01992 758809 ✆ richard.pennell@broxbourne.gov.uk

Street Scene: Mrs Lisa Carroll, Street Scene Manager, Borough Offices, Bishops' College, Churchgate, Cheshunt EN8 9XQ ☎ 01992 785555 ✆ lisa.carroll@broxbourne.gov.uk

Town Centre: Mr Tony Cox, Town Centres & Regeneration Manager, Borough Offices, Bishops' College, Churchgate, Cheshunt EN8 9XQ ☎ 01992 785555 ✆ tony.cox@broxbourne.gov.uk

Waste Collection and Disposal: Mr Peter Linkson, Director - Environmental Services, Borough Offices, Bishops' College, Churchgate, Cheshunt EN8 9XQ ☎ 01992 785555 ✆ peter.linkson@broxbourne.gov.uk

Waste Management: Mr Peter Linkson, Director - Environmental Services, Borough Offices, Bishops' College, Churchgate, Cheshunt EN8 9XQ ☎ 01992 785555 ✆ peter.linkson@broxbourne.gov.uk

COUNCILLORS

Mayor: Greensmyth, Martin (CON - Rosedale & Bury Green) m.greensmyth@ntlworld.com

Deputy Mayor: Crump, Carol (CON - Cheshunt South & Theobalds) carolann.crump@sky.com

Leader of the Council: Mills-Bishop, Mark (CON - Goffs Oak) cllr.m.mills-bishop@broxbourne.gov.uk

Group LeaderAitken, Malcolm (LAB - Waltham Cross) malcolm.aitken549@btinternet.com

Ayling, Ken (CON - Hoddesdon Town & Rye Park) ken.ayling@ntlworld.com

Ball-Greenwood, Suzanne (CON - Flamstead End)

Bowman, Carol (LAB - Waltham Cross) carol.bowman@sky.com

Brown, Keith (CON - Hoddesdon North) keithbrown3@hotmail.com

Cocking, Lewis (CON - Wormley & Turnford) lewis4wormleyturnford@gmail.com

Gordon, Susie (CON - Broxbourne & Hoddesdon South) susiemac4broxbourne@gmail.com

Hart, Dee (CON - Flamstead End) dee.hart@hertfordshire.gov.uk

Harvey, Neil (LAB - Waltham Cross) neilandgillharvey@gmail.com

Holliday, David (CON - Broxbourne & Hoddesdon South) david4broxbourne@gmail.com

Hutchings, Tim (CON - Broxbourne & Hoddesdon South) trhutchings59@gmail.com

Iszatt, Mike (CON - Cheshunt North) iszatt@live.com

McCormick, Cody (CON - Cheshunt South & Theobalds) cheshuntcody@gmail.com

Mobbs, Yvonne (CON - Rosedale & Bury Green) yvonnemobbs@btinternet.com

Moule, Peter (CON - Goffs Oak) peter@billmoule.co.uk

Nicholson, Gordon (CON - Wormley & Turnford)

Pearce, Jeremy (CON - Goffs Oak) jeremy.n.pearce@gmail.com

Perryman, Bren (CON - Hoddesdon Town & Rye Park) cllr.b.perryman@broxbourne.gov.uk

Pitcher, Darren (CON - Rosedale & Bury Green)

Platt, David (UKIP - Hoddesdon Town & Rye Park) cllr.david.platt@gmail.com

Russell, Linda (CON - Cheshunt North) linda.russell@ntlworld.com

Seeby, Paul (CON - Flamstead End) cllr.p.seeby@broxbourne.gov.uk

Siracusa, Tony (CON - Cheshunt South & Theobalds) cllr.t.siracusa@broxbourne.gov.uk

Soteris, Penny (CON - Cheshunt North) p.soteris@hotmail.com

Taylor, David (CON - Wormley & Turnford) davidwjtaylor@gmail.com

White, Lyn (CON - Hoddesdon North) lyn.white@ntlworld.com

Wortley, Steve (CON - Hoddesdon North) s.wortley@icloud.com

POLITICAL COMPOSITION
CON: 26, LAB: 3, UKIP: 1

COMMITTEE CHAIRS

Planning: Mr Tony Siracusa

BROXTOWE

Broxtowe   D

Broxtowe Borough Council, Council Offices, Foster Avenue, Beeston NG9 1AB
☎ 0115 917 7777 📠 0115 917 3030
✆ customerservices@broxtowe.gov.uk 🖥 www.broxtowe.gov.uk

FACTS AND FIGURES
Parliamentary Constituencies: Ashfield, Broxtowe
EU Constituencies: East Midlands
Election Frequency: Elections are of whole council

PRINCIPAL OFFICERS

Chief Executive: Ms Ruth Hyde, Chief Executive, Town Hall, Foster Avenue, Beeston NG9 1AB ☎ 0115 917 3255
✆ ceo@broxtowe.gov.uk

Deputy Chief Executive: Mr Shane Flynn, Deputy Chief Executive & S151 Officer, Council Offices, Foster Avenue, Beeston NG9 1AB ☎ 0115 917 3232 ✆ shane.flynn@broxtowe.gov.uk

Senior Management: Mr Ted Czerniak, Director - Housing, Leisure & Property Services, Council Offices, Foster Avenue, Beeston NG9 1AB ☎ 0115 917 3419 ✆ ted.czerniak@broxtowe.gov.uk

Senior Management: Mr Phillip Horsfield, Director - Legal & Planning Services, Council Offices, Foster Avenue, Beeston NG9 1AB ☎ 0115 917 3230 ✆ phillip.horsfield@broxtowe.gov.uk

PR / Communications: Miss Sarah Yates, Corporate Communications Officer, Town Hall, Foster Avenue, Beeston NG9 1AB ☎ 0115 917 3825 ✆ sarah.yates@broxtowe.gov.uk

Community Planning: Mrs Marice Hawley, Principal Community Development Officer, Council Offices, Foster Avenue, Beeston NG9 1AB ☎ 0115 917 3492 ✆ marice.hawley@broxtowe.gov.uk

Community Safety: Mr David Gell, Head of Public Protection, Council Offices, Foster Avenue, Beeston NG9 1AB ☎ 0115 917 3504 ✆ david.gell@broxtowe.gov.uk

Computer Management: Mr Kevin Powell, CIO Officer, Town Hall, Foster Avenue, Beeston NG9 1AB ☎ 0115 917 3214 ✆ kevin.powell@broxtowe.gov.uk

Contracts: Mr Ted Czerniak, Director - Housing, Leisure & Property Services, Council Offices, Foster Avenue, Beeston NG9 1AB ☎ 0115 917 3419 ✆ ted.czerniak@broxtowe.gov.uk

Customer Service: Mr Robert Williams, Customer Services Manager, Council Offices, Foster Avenue, Beeston NG9 1AB ☎ 0115 917 3940 ✆ robert.williams@broxtowe.gov.uk

Direct Labour: Mr John Delaney, Head of Built Environment, Council Offices, Foster Avenue, Beeston NG9 1AB ☎ 0115 917 3655 ✆ john.delaney@broxtowe.gov.uk

Economic Development: Mr Steffan Saunders, Head of Neighbourhoods & Prosperity, Council Offices, Foster Avenue, Beeston NG9 1AB ☎ 0115 917 3482 ✆ steffan.saunders@broxtowe.gov.uk

E-Government: Mr Kevin Powell, CIO Officer, Town Hall, Foster Avenue, Beeston NG9 1AB ☎ 0115 917 3214 ✆ kevin.powell@broxtowe.gov.uk

Electoral Registration: Ms Ruth Hyde, Chief Executive, Town Hall, Foster Avenue, Beeston NG9 1AB ☎ 0115 917 3255 ✆ ceo@broxtowe.gov.uk

Emergency Planning: Mr Steve Newton, Health & Safety Officer, Council Offices, Foster Avenue, Beeston NG9 1AB ☎ 0115 917 3330 ✆ steve.newton@broxtowe.gov.uk

Environmental / Technical Services: Mr David Gell, Head of Public Protection, Council Offices, Foster Avenue, Beeston NG9 1AB ☎ 0115 917 3504 ✆ david.gell@broxtowe.gov.uk

Environmental Health: Mrs Suzanne Hickey, Principal Environmental Health Officer, Council Offices, Foster Avenue, Beeston NG9 1AB ☎ 0115 917 3612 ✆ sue.hickley@broxtowe.gov.uk

Estates, Property & Valuation: Mr Steffan Saunders, Head of Neighbourhoods & Prosperity, Council Offices, Foster Avenue, Beeston NG9 1AB ☎ 0115 917 3482 ✆ steffan.saunders@broxtowe.gov.uk

Finance: Mr Shane Flynn, Deputy Chief Executive & S151 Officer, Council Offices, Foster Avenue, Beeston NG9 1AB ☎ 0115 917 3232 ✆ shane.flynn@broxtowe.gov.uk

Treasury: Mr Shane Flynn, Deputy Chief Executive & S151 Officer, Council Offices, Foster Avenue, Beeston NG9 1AB ☎ 0115 917 3232 ✆ shane.flynn@broxtowe.gov.uk

Grounds Maintenance: Mr Tim Crawford, Parks & Environment Manager, Council Offices, Foster Avenue, Beeston NG9 1AB ☎ 0115 917 3643 ✆ tim.crawford@broxtowe.gov.uk

Health and Safety: Mr Steve Newton, Health & Safety Officer, Council Offices, Foster Avenue, Beeston NG9 1AB ☎ 0115 917 3330 ✆ steve.newton@broxtowe.gov.uk

Highways: Mr John Delaney, Head of Built Environment, Council Offices, Foster Avenue, Beeston NG9 1AB ☎ 0115 917 3655 ✆ john.delaney@broxtowe.gov.uk

Housing: Mr Ted Czerniak, Director - Housing, Leisure & Property Services, Council Offices, Foster Avenue, Beeston NG9 1AB ☎ 0115 917 3419 ✆ ted.czerniak@broxtowe.gov.uk

Housing Maintenance: Mr Gary Duckmanton, Building Maintenance Manager, Kimberley Depot, Eastwood Road, Kimberley, Nottingham NG16 2HX ☎ 0115 917 7777

Legal: Mr Phillip Horsfield, Director - Legal & Planning Services, Council Offices, Foster Avenue, Beeston NG9 1AB ☎ 0115 917 3230 ✆ phillip.horsfield@broxtowe.gov.uk

Leisure and Cultural Services: Mr Ashley Marriott, Head of Leisure & Culture, Council Offices, Foster Avenue, Beeston NG9 1AB ☎ 0115 917 3626 ✆ ashley.marriott@broxtowe.gov.uk

Licensing: Mr David Gell, Head of Public Protection, Council Offices, Foster Avenue, Beeston NG9 1AB ☎ 0115 917 3504
✆ david.gell@broxtowe.gov.uk

Lighting: Mr John Delaney, Head of Built Environment, Council Offices, Foster Avenue, Beeston NG9 1AB ☎ 0115 917 3655
✆ john.delaney@broxtowe.gov.uk

Lottery Funding, Charity and Voluntary: Mr Ashley Marriott, Head of Leisure & Culture, Council Offices, Foster Avenue, Beeston NG9 1AB ☎ 0115 917 3626
✆ ashley.marriott@broxtowe.gov.uk

Member Services: Mrs Sue Rodden, Head of Administrative Services, Council Offices, Foster Avenue, Beeston NG9 1AB
☎ 0115 917 3295 ✆ sue.rodden@broxtowe.gov.uk

Parking: Mr John Delaney, Head of Built Environment, Council Offices, Foster Avenue, Beeston NG9 1AB ☎ 0115 917 3655
✆ john.delaney@broxtowe.gov.uk

Partnerships: Ms Ruth Hyde, Chief Executive, Town Hall, Foster Avenue, Beeston NG9 1AB ☎ 0115 917 3255
✆ ceo@broxtowe.gov.uk

Personnel / HR: Mr Aaron Gidney, Head of Human Resources, Town Hall, Foster Avenue, Beeston NG9 1AB ☎ 0115 917 3552
✆ aaron.gidney@broxtowe.gov.uk

Planning: Mr Phillip Horsfield, Director - Legal & Planning Services, Council Offices, Foster Avenue, Beeston NG9 1AB
☎ 0115 917 3230 ✆ phillip.horsfield@broxtowe.gov.uk

Procurement: Mr Steve Cotterill, Procurement Officer, Council Offices, Foster Avenue, Beeston NG9 1AB ☎ 0115 917 3296
✆ steve.cotterill@broxtowe.gov.uk

Recycling & Waste Minimisation: Mr Paul Wolverson, Waste & Recycling Officer, Kimberley Depot, Eastwood Road, Kimberley, Nottingham NG16 2HX ☎ 0115 917 3106
✆ paul.wolverson@broxtowe.gov.uk

Regeneration: Mr Steffan Saunders, Head of Neighbourhoods & Prosperity, Council Offices, Foster Avenue, Beeston NG9 1AB
☎ 0115 917 3482 ✆ steffan.saunders@broxtowe.gov.uk

Staff Training: Mrs Sally Holowka, Training Officer, Town Hall, Foster Avenue, Beeston NG9 1AB ☎ 0115 917 3387
✆ sally.holowka@broxtowe.gov.uk

Sustainable Communities: Mrs Marice Hawley, Principal Community Development Officer, Council Offices, Foster Avenue, Beeston NG9 1AB ☎ 0115 917 3492
✆ marice.hawley@broxtowe.gov.uk

Sustainable Development: Mrs Marice Hawley, Principal Community Development Officer, Council Offices, Foster Avenue, Beeston NG9 1AB ☎ 0115 917 3492
✆ marice.hawley@broxtowe.gov.uk

Waste Collection and Disposal: Mr Paul Syson, Refuse & Cleansing Manager, Kimberley Depot, Eastwood Road, Kimberley, Nottingham NG16 2HX ☎ 0115 917 3062
✆ paul.syson@broxtowe.gov.uk

Waste Management: Mr Paul Wolverson, Waste & Recycling Officer, Kimberley Depot, Eastwood Road, Kimberley, Nottingham NG16 2HX ☎ 0115 917 3106 ✆ paul.wolverson@broxtowe.gov.uk

COUNCILLORS

Leader of the Council: Jackson, Richard (CON - Attenborough & Chilwell East)
richard.jackson@broxtowe.gov.uk

Deputy Leader of the Council: Owen, Jill (CON - Watnall & Nuthall West)
jill.owen@broxtowe.gov.uk

Atherton, Eileen (CON - Chilwell West)
eileen.atherton@broxtowe.gov.uk

Bagshaw, Susan (LAB - Eastwood Hilltop)
susan.bagshaw@broxtowe.gov.uk

Bagshaw, David (LAB - Eastwood St Mary's)
david.bagshaw@broxtowe.gov.uk

Ball, Lydia (CON - Awsworth, Cossall & Trowell)
lydia.ball@broxtowe.gov.uk

Briggs, Joan (CON - Attenborough & Chilwell East)
joan.briggs@broxtowe.gov.uk

Brindley, Tim (CON - Chilwell West)
tim.brindley@broxtowe.gov.uk

Brown, Mick (CON - Greasley)
mick.brown@broxtowe.gov.uk

Burnett, Derek (CON - Watnall & Nuthall West)
derek.burnett@broxtowe.gov.uk

Carr, Barbara (LD - Beeston North)
barbara.carr@broxtowe.gov.uk

Carr, Stephen (LD - Beeston North)
steve.carr@broxtowe.gov.uk

Crow, Mel (CON - Kimberley)
mel.crow@broxtowe.gov.uk

Cullen, Teresa (LAB - Beeston Rylands)
teresa.cullen@broxtowe.gov.uk

Darby, Ray (LAB - Stapleford South West)
ray.darby@broxtowe.gov.uk

Doddy, John Anthony (CON - Bramcote)
john.doddy@broxtowe.gov.uk

Easom, Shane (CON - Kimberley)
shane.easom@broxtowe.gov.uk

Elliott, Dawn (LAB - Beeston Rylands)
dawn.elliott@broxtowe.gov.uk

Goold, Jan (CON - Bramcote)
jan.goold@broxtowe.gov.uk

Handley, Margaret (CON - Greasley)
margaret.handley@broxtowe.gov.uk

Handley, John William (CON - Brinsley)
john.handley@broxtowe.gov.uk

Harper, Tony (CON - Eastwood Hall)
anthony.harper@broxtowe.gov.uk

BROXTOWE

Harvey, Graham (CON - Chilwell West)
graham.harvey@broxtowe.gov.uk

Harvey, Natalie (CON - Toton & Chilwell Meadows)
natalie.harvey@broxtowe.gov.uk

Kee, Mia (CON - Toton & Chilwell Meadows)

Kerry, Eric (CON - Attenborough & Chilwell East)
eric.kerry@broxtowe.gov.uk

Khaled, Halimah (CON - Toton & Chilwell Meadows)
halimah.khaled@broxtowe.gov.uk

Lally, Lynda (LAB - Beeston Central)
lynda.lally@broxtowe.gov.uk

Lally, Patrick (LAB - Beeston Central)
pat.lally@broxtowe.gov.uk

Longdon, John (CON - Stapleford North)
john.longdon@broxtowe.gov.uk

Marshall, Greg (LAB - Beeston West)

Marsters, Josie (LD - Eastwood St Mary's)
josie.marsters@broxtowe.gov.uk

McGrath, John (LAB - Stapleford South West)
john.mcgrath@broxtowe.gov.uk

McRae, Richard (IND - Stapleford North)
richard.mcrae@broxtowe.gov.uk

Owen, Philip (CON - Nuthall East & Strelley)
philip.owen@broxtowe.gov.uk

Patrick, Janet (LAB - Beeston West)
janet.patrick@broxtowe.gov.uk

Plackett, Martin (CON - Bramcote)
martin.plackett@broxtowe.gov.uk

Radulovic, Milan (LAB - Eastwood Hilltop)
milan.radulovic@broxtowe.gov.uk

Rice, Christopher (CON - Stapleford South East)
christopher.rice@broxtowe.gov.uk

Rigby, Kenneth (LD - Awsworth, Cossall & Trowell)
ken.rigby@broxtowe.gov.uk

Robinson, Richard (LAB - Kimberley)
richard.robinson@broxtowe.gov.uk

Rowland, Stuart (CON - Greasley)
stuart.rowland@broxtowe.gov.uk

Simpson, Paul (CON - Nuthall East & Strelley)
paul.simpson@broxtowe.gov.uk

Stockwell, Adam (CON - Stapleford South East)

POLITICAL COMPOSITION
CON: 27, LAB: 12, LD: 4, IND: 1

Buckinghamshire   C

Buckinghamshire County Council, County Hall, Walton Street, Aylesbury HP20 1YU
☎ 01296 395000 ⫧ customerservices@buckscc.gov.uk
🖳 www.buckscc.gov.uk

FACTS AND FIGURES
EU Constituencies: South East
Election Frequency: Elections are of whole council

PRINCIPAL OFFICERS

Chief Executive: Ms Rachael Shimmin, Chief Executive, County Hall, Walton Street, Aylesbury HP20 1YU
⫧ rshimmin@buckscc.gov.uk

Senior Management: Mr Trevor Boyd, Strategic Director - Adults & Family Wellbeing, County Hall, Walton Street, Aylesbury HP20 1YU ☎ 01296 382074 ⫧ tboyd@buckscc.gov.uk

Senior Management: Mr Neil Gibson, Strategic Director - Communities & Built Environment, County Hall, Walton Street, Aylesbury HP20 1YU ☎ 01296 383106 ⫧ negibson@buckscc.gov.uk

Senior Management: Mr David Johnston, MD of Children's Social Care & Learning, County Hall, Walton Street, Aylesbury HP20 1YU ☎ 01296 383104 ⫧ djohnston@buckscc.gov.uk

Senior Management: Dr J O'Grady, Director - Public Health, County Hall, Walton Street, Aylesbury HP20 1YU ☎ 01296 387623 ⫧ jaogrady@buckscc.gov.uk

Senior Management: Mr Hugh Peart, Director - Legal & Governance Services, County Hall, Walton Street, Aylesbury HP20 1YU ☎ 020 8424 1272 ⫧ hugh.peart@harrow.gov.uk

Senior Management: Mrs Gillian Quinton, MD - Business Enterprise & Services, County Hall, Walton Street, Aylesbury HP20 1YU ☎ 01296 383127 ⫧ gquinton@buckscc.gov.uk

Access Officer / Social Services (Disability): Ms Sarah Holding, School Relationship Manager, County Hall, Walton Street, Aylesbury HP20 1YU ☎ 01296 383038 ⫧ sholding@buckscc.gov.uk

Best Value: Ms Sarah Ashmead, Director - Strategy & Policy, County Hall, Walton Street, Aylesbury HP20 1YU ☎ 01296 383986 ⫧ sashmead@buckscc.gov.uk

Best Value: Mrs Gillian Quinton, MD - Business Enterprise & Services, County Hall, Walton Street, Aylesbury HP20 1YU ☎ 01296 383127 ⫧ gquinton@buckscc.gov.uk

Children / Youth Services: Mr Chris Munday, Service Director, County Hall, Walton Street, Aylesbury HP20 1YU ☎ 01296 387849 ⫧ ccmunday@buckscc.gov.uk

Children / Youth Services: Ms Laura Nankin, Head of Fair Access & Youth Provision, County Hall, Walton Street, Aylesbury HP20 1YU ☎ 01296 382078 ⫧ lnankin@buckscc.gov.uk

PR / Communications: Ms Celia Logan, Service Director - Customer Services & Communication, County Hall, Walton Street, Aylesbury HP20 1YU ☎ 01296 387416 ⫧ clogan@buckscc.gov.uk

Computer Management: Mrs S Payne, Head of Communications, County Hall, Walton Street, Aylesbury HP20 1YU ☎ 01296 382463 ⫧ spayne@buckscc.gov.uk

Consumer Protection and Trading Standards: Mr Phil Dart, Service Director - Localities & Safer Communities, 5-7 Walton Street, Aylesbury HP20 1UY ☎ 01296 382398 ⫧ pdart@buckscc.gov.uk

Contracts: Ms Tricia Hook, Senior Procurement Manager, County Hall, Walton Street, Aylesbury HP20 1YU ☎ 01296 383615 ⌂ phook@buckscc.gov.uk

Education: Mr Trevor Boyd, Strategic Director - Adults & Family Wellbeing, County Hall, Walton Street, Aylesbury HP20 1YU ☎ 01296 382074 ⌂ tboyd@buckscc.gov.uk

Education: Ms Sarah Holding, School Relationship Manager, County Hall, Walton Street, Aylesbury HP20 1YU ☎ 01296 383038 ⌂ sholding@buckscc.gov.uk

E-Government: Mrs S Payne, Head of Communications, County Hall, Walton Street, Aylesbury HP20 1YU ☎ 01296 382463 ⌂ spayne@buckscc.gov.uk

Electoral Registration: Mr Clive Parker, Head of Civic & Ceremonial Services, Legal and Democratic Services, County Hall, Walton Street, Aylesbury HP20 1UA ☎ 01296 383685 ⌂ cparker@buckscc.gov.uk

Emergency Planning: Mr Andrew Fyfe, Resilience Manager, County Hall, Walton Street, Aylesbury HP20 1YU ☎ 01296 382937 ⌂ afyfe@buckscc.gov.uk

Environmental / Technical Services: Mr Neil Gibson, Strategic Director - Communities & Built Environment, County Hall, Walton Street, Aylesbury HP20 1YU ☎ 01296 383106 ⌂ negibson@buckscc.gov.uk

Facilities: Mr Ian Boll, Director - Infrastructure & Regeneration, County Hall, Walton Street, Aylesbury HP20 1YU ☎ 01296 382113 ⌂ iboll@buckscc.gov.uk

Finance: Mr Richard Ambrose, Service Director - Finance & Commercial Services, County Hall, Walton Street, Aylesbury HP20 1YU ☎ 01296 383120 ⌂ rambrose@buckscc.gov.uk

Treasury: Mr Richard Ambrose, Service Director - Finance, Treasury & Commercial Services, County Hall, Walton Street, Aylesbury HP20 1YU ☎ 01296 383120 ⌂ rambrose@buckscc.gov.uk

Pensions: Ms Julie Edwards, Pensions Manager, County Hall, Walton Street, Aylesbury HP20 1YU ☎ 01296 395000 ⌂ jedwards@buckscc.gov.uk

Health and Safety: Ms Pat Beveridge, Health & Safety Advisor, County Hall, Walton Street, Aylesbury HP20 1YU ☎ 01296 382954 ⌂ pbeveridge@buckss.gov.uk

Highways: Mr Neil Gibson, Strategic Director - Communities & Built Environment, County Hall, Walton Street, Aylesbury HP20 1YU ☎ 01296 383106 ⌂ negibson@buckscc.gov.uk

Local Area Agreement: Ms Sarah Ashmead, Director - Strategy & Policy, County Hall, Walton Street, Aylesbury HP20 1YU ☎ 01296 383986 ⌂ sashmead@buckscc.gov.uk

Legal: Mr Hugh Peart, Director - Legal & Governance Services, Room 102 Labour Group Office, Civic Centre, Station Road, Harrow HA1 2UH ☎ 020 8424 1272 ⌂ hugh.peart@harrow.gov.uk

Leisure and Cultural Services: Mr Phil Dart, Service Director - Localities & Safer Communities, 5-7 Walton Street, Aylesbury HP20 1UY ☎ 01296 382398 ⌂ pdart@buckscc.gov.uk

Lifelong Learning: Mr Phil Dart, Service Director - Localities & Safer Communities, 5-7 Walton Street, Aylesbury HP20 1UY ☎ 01296 382398 ⌂ pdart@buckscc.gov.uk

Member Services: Mr Clive Parker, Head of Civic & Ceremonial Services, Legal and Democratic Services, County Hall, Walton Street, Aylesbury HP20 1UA ☎ 01296 383685 ⌂ cparker@buckscc.gov.uk

Personnel / HR: Mrs C Daltry, Service Director - Human Resources, County Hall, Walton Street, Aylesbury HP20 1YU ☎ 01296 382528 ⌂ cdaltry@buckscc.gov.uk

Planning: Mr David Sutherland, Resource Strategy Manager, County Hall, Walton Street, Aylesbury HP20 1UY ☎ 01296 383003 ⌂ dsutherland@buckscc.gov.uk

Public Libraries: Ms Celia Logan, Service Director - Customer Services & Communication, County Hall, Walton Street, Aylesbury HP20 1YU ☎ 01296 387416 ⌂ clogan@buckscc.gov.uk

Recycling & Waste Minimisation: Mr David Sutherland, Resource Strategy Manager, County Hall, Walton Street, Aylesbury HP20 1UY ☎ 01296 383003 ⌂ dsutherland@buckscc.gov.uk

Social Services (Adult): Mr Trevor Boyd, Strategic Director - Adults & Family Wellbeing, County Hall, Walton Street, Aylesbury HP20 1YU ☎ 01296 382074 ⌂ tboyd@buckscc.gov.uk

Social Services (Children): Mr David Johnston, MD of Children's Social Care & Learning, County Hall, Walton Street, Aylesbury HP20 1YU ☎ 01296 383104 ⌂ djohnston@buckscc.gov.uk

Families: Mr Trevor Boyd, Strategic Director - Adults & Family Wellbeing, County Hall, Walton Street, Aylesbury HP20 1YU ☎ 01296 382074 ⌂ tboyd@buckscc.gov.uk

Public Health: Dr J O'Grady, Director - Public Health, County Hall, Walton Street, Aylesbury HP20 1YU ☎ 01296 387623 ⌂ jaogrady@buckscc.gov.uk

Staff Training: Mrs Frances Mills, Head of People & Organisational Development, County Hall, Walton Street, Aylesbury HP20 1YU ☎ 01296 382945 ⌂ fmills@buckscc.gov.uk

Sustainable Communities: Ms Sarah Ashmead, Director - Strategy & Policy, County Hall, Walton Street, Aylesbury HP20 1YU ☎ 01296 383986 ⌂ sashmead@buckscc.gov.uk

Sustainable Communities: Mr Neil Gibson, Strategic Director - Communities & Built Environment, County Hall, Walton Street, Aylesbury HP20 1YU ☎ 01296 383106 ⌂ negibson@buckscc.gov.uk

Sustainable Development: Mrs Zoe Dixon, Senior Manager - Place Service, County Hall, Walton Street, Aylesbury HP20 1UZ ☎ 01296 382132 ⌂ zdixon@buckscc.gov.uk

BUCKINGHAMSHIRE

Traffic Management: Mr Neil Gibson, Strategic Director - Communities & Built Environment, County Hall, Walton Street, Aylesbury HP20 1YU ☎ 01296 383106 ✆ negibson@buckscc.gov.uk

Waste Management: Mr Gurbaksh Badhan, Waste Business Manager, County Hall, Walton Street, Aylesbury HP20 1YU ☎ 01296 387678 ✆ gbadhan@buckscc.gov.uk

COUNCILLORS

ChairLetheren, Valerie (CON - Terriers & Amersham Hill)
vletheren@buckscc.gov.uk

Vice-ChairBirchley, Patricia (CON - Chiltern Ridges)
pbirchley@buckscc.gov.uk

Leader of the Council: Tett, Martin (CON - Little Chalfont & Amersham Common)
mtett@buckscc.gov.uk

Deputy Leader of the Council: Appleyard, Mike (CON - The Wooburns, Bourne End & Hedsor)
mappleyard@buckscc.gov.uk

Group LeaderDavies, Avril (LD - Ivinghoe)
acdavies@buckscc.gov.uk

Group LeaderHuxley, Andy (UKIP - Aylesbury North West)
ahuxley@buckscc.gov.uk

Adams, Brian (UKIP - Aylesbury South West)
bradams@buckscc.gov.uk

Adams, Chris (UKIP - Wendover, Halton & Stoke Mandeville)
chadams@buckscc.gov.uk

Aston, Margaret (CON - Bernwood)
maston@buckscc.gov.uk

Bendyshe-Brown, Bill (CON - The Risboroughs)
bbendyshe-brown@buckscc.gov.uk

Blake, Janet (CON - Great Brickhill)
janetblake@buckscc.gov.uk

Brown, Noel (CON - Chess Valley)
nbrown@buckscc.gov.uk

Busby, Adrian (CON - Beaconsfield)
ajbusby@buckscc.gov.uk

Butcher, Timothy (CON - Chalfont St Giles)
trbutcher@buckscc.gov.uk

Carroll, David (CON - Ridgeway East)
dcarroll@buckscc.gov.uk

Chapple, William (CON - Aston Clinton & Bierton)
bchapple@buckscc.gov.uk

Chilver, John (CON - Winslow)
jchilver@buckscc.gov.uk

Clarke, Lesley (CON - Abbey)
lmclarke@buckscc.gov.uk

Dhillon, Dev (CON - Cliveden)
ddhillon@buckscc.gov.uk

Ditta, Chaudhary (LD - Totteridge & Bowerdean)
cditta@buckscc.gov.uk

Egleton, Trevor (CON - Stoke Poges & Westham)
tegleton@buckscc.gov.uk

Etholen, Carl (CON - Ridgeway West)
cetholen@buckscc.gov.uk

Glover, Netta (CON - Wing)
nglover@buckscc.gov.uk

Gomm, Phil (IND - Aylesbury East)
pgomm@buckscc.gov.uk

Hardy, Peter (CON - Gerrards Cross)
phardy@buckscc.gov.uk

Hayday, Darren (IND - West Wycombe)
dhayday@buckscc.gov.uk

Hazell, Lin (CON - Farnham Common & Burnham Beeches)
lhazell@buckscc.gov.uk

Irwin, Paul (UKIP - Stone & Waddesdon)
pirwin@buckscc.gov.uk

Khan, Raj (LD - Aylesbury North)
rkhan@buckscc.gov.uk

Lambert, Steven (LD - Aylesbury West)
slambert@buckscc.gov.uk

Macpherson, Angela (CON - Grendon Underwood)
angmacpherson@buckscc.gov.uk

Mallen, Wendy (CON - Downley)
wmallen@buckscc.gov.uk

Martin, David (CON - Chalfont St Peter)
dmartin@buckscc.gov.uk

Mohammed, Zahir (CON - Booker Cressex & Castlefield)
zamohammed@buckscc.gov.uk

Phillips, Martin (CON - Amersham & Chesham Bois)
mphillips@buckscc.gov.uk

Reed, Roger (CON - Denham)
roreed@buckscc.gov.uk

Roberts, Brian (CON - Aylesbury South East)
broberts@buckscc.gov.uk

Schofield, David (CON - Penn Wood & Old Amersham)
dschofield@buckscc.gov.uk

Scott, Richard (CON - Marlow)
rjscott@buckscc.gov.uk

Shakespeare, David (CON - Tylers Green & Loudwater)
dshakespeare@buckscc.gov.uk

Shaw, Mark (CON - Chesham)
markshaw@buckscc.gov.uk

Stevens, Alan (UKIP - Great Missenden)
alstevens@buckscc.gov.uk

Stuchbury, Robin (LAB - Buckingham West)
rstuchbury@buckscc.gov.uk

Teesdale, Jean (CON - Chiltern Villages)
jteesdale@buckscc.gov.uk

Vigor-Hedderly, Ruth (CON - Iver)
rvhedderly@buckscc.gov.uk

Wassell, Julia (IND - Ryemead & Micklefield)
jwassell@buckscc.gov.uk

Watson, David (CON - Flackwell Heath, Little Marlow & Marlow South East)
dwatson@buckscc.gov.uk

Whyte, Warren (CON - Buckingham East)
wwhyte@buckscc.gov.uk

Wood, Katrina (CON - Hazelmere)
kwood@buckscc.gov.uk

POLITICAL COMPOSITION
CON: 36, UKIP: 5, LD: 4, IND: 3, LAB: 1

COMMITTEE CHAIRS

Finance, Performance & Resources: Mr William Chapple

Health & Wellbeing: Mr Martin Tett

Burnley   D

Burnley Borough Council, Town Hall, Manchester Road, Burnley BB11 9SA
☎ 01282 425011 🖶 01282 450594 ⌨ contactburnley@burnley.gov.uk
💻 www.burnley.gov.uk

FACTS AND FIGURES
Parliamentary Constituencies: Burnley
EU Constituencies: North West
Election Frequency: Elections are by thirds

PRINCIPAL OFFICERS

Chief Executive: Ms Pam Smith, Chief Executive, Town Hall, Manchester Road, Burnley BB11 9SA ☎ 01282 477101 ⌨ psmith@burnley.gov.uk

Senior Management: Mr Mick Cartledge, Director - Community Services, Town Hall, Manchester Road, Burnley BB11 9SA ☎ 01282 477280 ⌨ mcartledge@burnley.gov.uk

Senior Management: Ms Helen Seechurn, Director - Resources, Town Hall, Manchester Road, Burnley BB11 9SA ☎ 01282 425011 ⌨ hseechurn@burnley.gov.uk

Architect, Building / Property Services: Mr Phil Moore, Head of Finance & Property Management, Town Hall, Manchester Road, Burnley BB11 9SA ☎ 01282 425011 ⌨ pmoore@burnley.gov.uk

Best Value: Mr Chris Gay, Performance & Committee Manager, Town Hall, Manchester Road, Burnley BB11 9SA ☎ 01282 425011 ⌨ cgay@burnley.gov.uk

PR / Communications: Mr Mike Waite, Head of Corporate Engagement & Cohesion, Town Hall, Manchester Road, Burnley BB11 9SA ☎ 01282 425011 ⌨ mwaite@burnley.gov.uk

Community Planning: Mr Mike Waite, Head of Corporate Engagement & Cohesion, Town Hall, Manchester Road, Burnley BB11 9SA ☎ 01282 425011 ⌨ mwaite@burnley.gov.uk

Community Safety: Mr Sam McConnell, Community Safety Manager, 18/20 Nicholas Street, Burnley BB11 2AP ☎ 01282 425011 ⌨ smcconnell@burnley.gov.uk

Computer Management: Mrs Sharon Hargraves, ICT Service Delivery Manager, Town Hall, Manchester Road, Burnley BB11 9SA ☎ 07976 969835 ⌨ shargraves@burnley.gov.uk

Contracts: Mr Chris Gay, Performance & Committee Manager, Town Hall, Manchester Road, Burnley BB11 9SA ☎ 01282 425011 ⌨ cgay@burnley.gov.uk

Corporate Services: Mr Rob Dobson, Corporate Policy Officer, Town Hall, Manchester Road, Burnley BB11 9SA ☎ 01282 425011 ⌨ rdobson@burnley.gov.uk

Customer Service: Mrs Sharon Hargraves, ICT Service Delivery Manager, Town Hall, Manchester Road, Burnley BB11 9SA ☎ 07976 969835 ⌨ shargraves@burnley.gov.uk

Economic Development: Ms Kate Ingram, Head of Regeneration & Planning Policy, 1st Floor, Parker Lane Offices, Parker Lane, Burnley BB11 2DT ☎ 01282 477310 ⌨ kingram@burnley.gov.uk

E-Government: Mrs Sharon Hargraves, ICT Service Delivery Manager, Town Hall, Manchester Road, Burnley BB11 9SA ☎ 07976 969835 ⌨ shargraves@burnley.gov.uk

Electoral Registration: Mrs Alison Morville, Elections Officer, Town Hall, Manchester Road, Burnley BB11 9SA ☎ 01282 425011 ⌨ amorville@burnley.gov.uk

Emergency Planning: Mr Mick Cartledge, Director - Community Services, Town Hall, Manchester Road, Burnley BB11 9SA ☎ 01282 477280 ⌨ mcartledge@burnley.gov.uk

Energy Management: Mr Phil Moore, Head of Finance & Property Management, Town Hall, Manchester Road, Burnley BB11 9SA ☎ 01282 425011 ⌨ pmoore@burnley.gov.uk

Environmental Health: Ms Karen Davies, Environmental Health & Licensing Manager, Parker Lane Offices, Parker Lane, Burnley BB11 2DT ☎ 01282 425011 ⌨ kdavies@burnley.gov.uk

Estates, Property & Valuation: Mr Phil Moore, Head of Finance & Property Management, Town Hall, Manchester Road, Burnley BB11 9SA ☎ 01282 425011 ⌨ pmoore@burnley.gov.uk

European Liaison: Ms Kate Ingram, Head of Regeneration & Planning Policy, 1st Floor, Parker Lane Offices, Parker Lane, Burnley BB11 2DT ☎ 01282 477310 ⌨ kingram@burnley.gov.uk

Events Manager: Mr Mike Waite, Head of Corporate Engagement & Cohesion, Town Hall, Manchester Road, Burnley BB11 9SA ☎ 01282 425011 ⌨ mwaite@burnley.gov.uk

Facilities: Mr Phil Moore, Head of Finance & Property Management, Town Hall, Manchester Road, Burnley BB11 9SA ☎ 01282 425011 ⌨ pmoore@burnley.gov.uk

Finance: Ms Helen Seechurn, Director - Resources, Town Hall, Manchester Road, Burnley BB11 9SA ☎ 01282 425011 ⌨ hseechurn@burnley.gov.uk

Fleet Management: Mr Mark Rogers, Operations Manager, 93 Rossendale Road, Burnley BB11 5DD ☎ 01282 425011 ⌨ mrogers@burnley.gov.uk

Grounds Maintenance: Mr Simon Goff, Head of Greenspaces & Amenities, 93 Rossendale Road, Burnley BB11 5DD ☎ 01282 425011 ⌨ sgoff@burnley.gov.uk

Health and Safety: Mr David Lawrence, Strategic Health & Safety Consultant, Town Hall, Manchester Road, Burnley BB11 9SA
☎ 01282 425011 ⌨ dlawrence@burnley.gov.uk

Home Energy Conservation: Mr Stephen Nutter, Project Officer, Parker Lane Offices, Parker Lane, Burnley BB11 2DT
☎ 01282 425011 ⌨ snutter@burnley.gov.uk

Housing: Mr Paul Gatrell, Head of Housing & Development Control, Parker Lane Offices, Parker Lane, Burnley BB11 2DT
☎ 01282 425011 ⌨ pgatrell@burnley.gov.uk

Legal: Mr Lukman Patel, Head of Governance, Law & Regulation, Town Hall, Manchester Road, Burnley BB11 9SA ☎ 01282 425011
⌨ lpatel@burnley.gov.uk

Licensing: Ms Karen Davies, Environmental Health & Licensing Manager, Parker Lane Offices, Parker Lane, Burnley BB11 2DT
☎ 01282 425011 ⌨ kdavies@burnley.gov.uk

Member Services: Mr Chris Gay, Performance & Committee Manager, Town Hall, Manchester Road, Burnley BB11 9SA ☎ 01282 425011 ⌨ cgay@burnley.gov.uk

Parking: Mrs Joanne Swift, Head of Street Scene, 18/20 Nicholas Street, Burnley BB11 2AP ☎ 01282 425011 ⌨ jswift@burnley.gov.uk

Partnerships: Mr Rob Dobson, Corporate Policy Officer, Town Hall, Manchester Road, Burnley BB11 9SA ☎ 01282 425011
⌨ rdobson@burnley.gov.uk

Personnel / HR: Ms Heather Brennan, Head of People & Development, Town Hall, Manchester Road, Burnley BB11 9SA
☎ 01282 425011 ⌨ hbrennan@burnley.gov.uk

Planning: Mr Paul Gatrell, Head of Housing & Development Control, Parker Lane Offices, Parker Lane, Burnley BB11 2DT
☎ 01282 425011 ⌨ pgatrell@burnley.gov.uk

Procurement: Mr Chris Gay, Performance & Committee Manager, Town Hall, Manchester Road, Burnley BB11 9SA ☎ 01282 425011 ⌨ cgay@burnley.gov.uk

Recycling & Waste Minimisation: Mrs Joanne Swift, Head of Street Scene, 18/20 Nicholas Street, Burnley BB11 2AP
☎ 01282 425011 ⌨ jswift@burnley.gov.uk

Regeneration: Ms Kate Ingram, Head of Regeneration & Planning Policy, 1st Floor, Parker Lane Offices, Parker Lane, Burnley BB11 2DT ☎ 01282 477310 ⌨ kingram@burnley.gov.uk

Staff Training: Ms Heather Brennan, Head of People & Development, Town Hall, Manchester Road, Burnley BB11 9SA
☎ 01282 425011 ⌨ hbrennan@burnley.gov.uk

Street Scene: Mrs Joanne Swift, Head of Street Scene, 18/20 Nicholas Street, Burnley BB11 2AP ☎ 01282 425011
⌨ jswift@burnley.gov.uk

Sustainable Communities: Ms Kate Ingram, Head of Regeneration & Planning Policy, 1st Floor, Parker Lane Offices, Parker Lane, Burnley BB11 2DT ☎ 01282 477310
⌨ kingram@burnley.gov.uk

Sustainable Development: Ms Kate Ingram, Head of Regeneration & Planning Policy, 1st Floor, Parker Lane Offices, Parker Lane, Burnley BB11 2DT ☎ 01282 477310
⌨ kingram@burnley.gov.uk

Tourism: Ms Kate Ingram, Head of Regeneration & Planning Policy, 1st Floor, Parker Lane Offices, Parker Lane, Burnley BB11 2DT ☎ 01282 477310 ⌨ kingram@burnley.gov.uk

Town Centre: Mr Phil Moore, Head of Finance & Property Management, Town Hall, Manchester Road, Burnley BB11 9SA
☎ 01282 425011 ⌨ pmoore@burnley.gov.uk

Waste Collection and Disposal: Mrs Joanne Swift, Head of Street Scene, 18/20 Nicholas Street, Burnley BB11 2AP
☎ 01282 425011 ⌨ jswift@burnley.gov.uk

Waste Management: Mrs Joanne Swift, Head of Street Scene, 18/20 Nicholas Street, Burnley BB11 2AP ☎ 01282 425011
⌨ jswift@burnley.gov.uk

COUNCILLORS

Mayor: Sumner, Jeff (LD - Rosehill with Burnley Wood)
jsumner@burnley.gov.uk

Deputy Mayor: Baker, Howard (LAB - Trinity)
hbaker@burnley.gov.uk

Leader of the Council: Townsend, Mark (LAB - Brunshaw)
mtownsend@burnley.gov.uk

Deputy Leader of the Council: Harbour, John (LAB - Gawthorpe)
jharbour@burnley.gov.uk

Birtwistle, Gordon (LD - Coal Clough with Deerplay)
gordon.bitwistle.mp@parliament.uk

Briggs, Charlie (LD - Gannow)
cbriggs@burnley.gov.uk

Brindle, Margaret (LD - Coal Clough with Deerplay)
mbrindle@burnley.gov.uk

Brindle, Bill (LD - Coal Clough with Deerplay)
bbrindle@burnley.gov.uk

Cant, Frank (LAB - Gawthorpe)
fcant@burnley.gov.uk

Carmichael, Ida (CON - Whittlefield with Ightenhill)
icarmichael@burnley.gov.uk

Chaudhary, Saeed (LAB - Daneshouse with Stoneyholme)
schauldhary@burnley.gov.uk

Cunningham, Jean (LAB - Hapton with Park)
jcunningham@burnley.gov.uk

Ellis, Trish (LAB - Lanehead)
tellis@burnley.gov.uk

Flemming, Danny (LAB - Rosehill with Burnley Wood)

Foster, Bea (LAB - Rosegrove with Lowerhouse)
bfoster@burnley.gov.uk

Frayling, Gary (LAB - Bank Hall)
gfrayling@burnley.gov.uk

Frost, Roger (LD - Briercliffe)
rfrost@burnley.gov.uk

Graham, Sue (LAB - Queensgate)
sgraham@burnley.gov.uk

Greenwood, Joanne (LAB - Hapton with Park)
joannegreenwood@burnley.gov.uk

Harrison, Tony (LAB - Brunshaw)
tharrison@burnley.gov.uk

Heginbotham, David (CON - Cliviger with Worsthorne)
dheginbotham@burnley.gov.uk

Hosker, Alan (UKIP - Hapton with Park)

Hussain, Shah (LAB - Daneshouse with Stoneyholme)
shussain@burnley.gov.uk

Ishtiaq, Mohammed (LAB - Queensgate)
mishtiaq@burnley.gov.uk

Johnstone, Marcus (LAB - Rosegrove with Lowerhouse)
mjohnstone@burnley.gov.uk

Kelly, Anne (LD - Briercliffe)
annekelly@burnley.gov.uk

Khan, Lubna (LAB - Bank Hall)

Khan, Wajid (LAB - Daneshouse with Stoneyholme)
wajidkhan@burnley.gov.uk

Khan, Arif (LAB - Queensgate)
arifkhan@burnley.gov.uk

Lishman, Margaret (LD - Briercliffe)
mlishman@burnley.gov.uk

Malik, Sobia (LAB - Bank Hall)
smalik@burnley.gov.uk

Martin, Tony (LAB - Trinity)
tmartin@burnley.gov.uk

Monk, Elizabeth (LAB - Trinity)
emonk@burnley.gov.uk

Mottershead, Neil (LD - Gannow)
nmottershead@burnley.gov.uk

Newhouse, Andrew (CON - Cliviger with Worsthorne)
anewhouse@burnley.gov.uk

Pate, Lian (LAB - Brunshaw)
lpate@burnley.gov.uk

Payne, Mark (LD - Gannow)
mpayne@burnley.gov.uk

Porter, Tom (LD - Whittlefield with Ightenhill)
tporter@burnley.gov.uk

Raja, Asif (LAB - Lanehead)
araja@burnley.gov.uk

Reynolds, Paul (LAB - Rosegrove with Lowerhouse)
preynolds@burnley.gov.uk

Roper, David (LD - Whittlefield with Ightenhill)
droper@burnley.gov.uk

Royle, Ann (LAB - Lanehead)
aroyle@burnley.gov.uk

Tatchell, Andrew (LAB - Gawthorpe)
atatchell@burnley.gov.uk

Towneley, Cosima (CON - Cliviger with Worsthorne)
mail@cositowneley.co.uk

White, Christine (LD - Rosehill with Burnley Wood)
cwhite@burnley.gov.uk

POLITICAL COMPOSITION
LAB: 27, LD: 13, CON: 4, UKIP: 1

COMMITTEE CHAIRS

Development Control: Mr Arif Khan

Licensing: Ms Ann Royle

Bury   M

Bury Metropolitan Borough Council, Town Hall, Knowsley Street, Bury BL9 0SW
☎ 0161 253 5000 🖷 0161 253 5119 ⁍ info@bury.gov.uk
🖳 www.bury.gov.uk

FACTS AND FIGURES
Parliamentary Constituencies: Bury North, Bury South
EU Constituencies: North West
Election Frequency: Elections are by thirds

PRINCIPAL OFFICERS

Chief Executive: Mr Michael Owen, Chief Executive, Town Hall, Knowsley Street, Bury BL9 0SW ☎ 0161 253 5000
⁍ m.a.owen@bury.gov.uk

Senior Management: Mr Mark Carriline, Executive Director - Children, Young People & Culture, 3 Knowsley Place, Duke Street, Bury BL9 0EJ ☎ 0161 253 5603 ⁍ m.carriline@bury.gov.uk

Senior Management: Mrs Pat Jones-Greenhalgh, Executive Director - Communities & Wellbeing, Town Hall, Knowsley Street, Bury BL9 0SW ☎ 0161 253 5405 ⁍ p.jones-greenhalgh@bury.gov.uk

Architect, Building / Property Services: Mr Alex Holland, Head - Property & Asset Management, Town Hall, Knowsley Street, Bury BL9 0SW ☎ 0161 253 5992 ⁍ a.holland@bury.gov.uk

Architect, Building / Property Services: Mr Michael Owen, Chief Executive, Town Hall, Knowsley Street, Bury BL9 0SW ☎ 0161 253 5000 ⁍ m.a.owen@bury.gov.uk

Best Value: Mr David Hipkiss, Head - Risk Management, Town Hall, Knowsley Street, Bury BL9 0SW ☎ 0161 253 5084 ⁍ d.hipkiss@bury.gov.uk

Building Control: Mr Rob Thorpe, Principal Building Control Officer, 3 Knowsley Place, Duke Street, Bury BL9 0EJ ☎ 0161 253 5289 ⁍ r.c.thorpe@bury.gov.uk

Catering Services: Mr Charles Walton, Head - Civics & Leisure Catering, Unit 3, Bradley Fold Trading Estate, Bradley Fold Road, Bolton BL2 6RF ☎ 0161 253 5709 ⁍ c.k.walton@bury.gov.uk

Children / Youth Services: Ms Kate Allam, IYSS Operational Manager, 3 Knowsley Place, Duke Street, Bury BL9 0EJ ☎ 0161 253 7921 ⁍ k.allam@bury.gov.uk

Children / Youth Services: Mr Mark Carriline, Executive Director - Children's Services, 3 Knowsley Place, Duke Street, Bury BL0 0EJ ☎ 0161 253 5603 ᐁ m.carriline@bury.gov.uk

Civil Registration: Mr Haydn Keenan, Head - Registration, Town Hall, Knowsley Street, Bury BL9 0SW ☎ 0161 253 6027 ᐁ w.keenan@bury.gov.uk

Community Planning: Mr David Fowler, Assistant Director - Localities, Town Hall, Knowsley Street, Bury BL9 0SW ☎ 0161 253 5518 ᐁ d.w.fowler@bury.gov.uk

Computer Management: Mr Stephen Denton, ICT Development & Programme Manager, Town Hall, Knowsley Street, Bury BL9 0SW ☎ 0161 253 6043 ᐁ s.denton@bury.gov.uk

Consumer Protection and Trading Standards: Ms Angela Lomax, Head of Trading Standards & Licensing, 3 Knowsley Place, Duke Street, Bury BL0 0EJ ☎ 0161 253 5049 ᐁ a.s.lomax@bury.gov.uk

Corporate Services: Mr Michael Owen, Chief Executive, Town Hall, Knowsley Street, Bury BL9 0SW ☎ 0161 253 5000 ᐁ m.a.owen@bury.gov.uk

Economic Development: Mr Crispian Logue, Head of Strategic Planning & Economic Development, 3 Knowsley Place, Duke Street, Bury BL0 0EJ ☎ 0161 253 5306 ᐁ c.logue@bury.gov.uk

Education: Mr Klare Rufo, Assistant Director - Learning & Culture, 3 Knowsley Place, Duke Street, Bury BL0 0EJ ☎ 0161 253 5477 ᐁ k.rufo@bury.go.uk

E-Government: Mr Michael Owen, Chief Executive, Town Hall, Knowsley Street, Bury BL9 0SW ☎ 0161 253 5000 ᐁ m.a.owen@bury.gov.uk

Electoral Registration: Mr Warren Rafferty, Elections & Land Charges Officer, Town Hall, Knowsley Street, Bury BL9 0SW ☎ 0161 253 6018 ᐁ w.j.rafferty@bury.gov.uk

Environmental / Technical Services: Mr Neil Long, Assistant Director - Operations, 3 Knowsley Place, Duke Street, Bury BL9 0EJ ☎ 0161 253 5735 ᐁ n.s.long@bury.gov.uk

Environmental Health: Mr David Fowler, Assistant Director - Localities, 3 Knowsley Place, Duke Street, Bury BL9 0EJ ☎ 0161 253 5518 ᐁ d.w.fowler@bury.gov.uk

Estates, Property & Valuation: Mr Alex Holland, Head - Property & Asset Management, Town Hall, Knowsley Street, Bury BL9 0SW ☎ 0161 253 5992 ᐁ a.holland@bury.gov.uk

European Liaison: Ms Tracey Flynn, Unit Manager - Economic Strategy, 3 Knowsley Place, Duke Street, Bury BL9 0EJ ☎ 0161 253 6040 ᐁ t.flynn@bury.gov.uk

Events Manager: Mr Neil Long, Assistant Director - Operations, 3 Knowsley Place, Duke Street, Bury BL9 0EJ ☎ 0161 253 5735 ᐁ n.s.long@bury.gov.uk

Facilities: Mr Neil Long, Assistant Director - Operations, 3 Knowsley Place, Duke Street, Bury BL9 0EJ ☎ 0161 253 5735 ᐁ n.s.long@bury.gov.uk

Fleet Management: Mr Stephen Fleming, Head - Transport Services & Workshop, Unit 34, Bradley Fold Trading Estate, Bradley Fold Road, Bolton BL2 6RF ☎ 0161 253 6624 ᐁ s.j.fleming@bury.gov.uk

Grounds Maintenance: Mr Neil Long, Assistant Director - Operations, 3 Knowsley Place, Duke Street, Bury BL9 0EJ ☎ 0161 253 5735 ᐁ n.s.long@bury.gov.uk

Health and Safety: Mr Alan Manchester, Principal Occupational Health, Safety & Emergency Planning, Town Hall, Knowsley Street, Bury BL9 0SW ☎ 0161 253 5143 ᐁ a.manchester@bury.gov.uk

Highways: Mr Neil Long, Assistant Director - Operations, 3 Knowsley Place, Duke Street, Bury BL9 0EJ ☎ 0161 253 5735 ᐁ n.s.long@bury.gov.uk

Housing: Mrs Sharon McCambridge, Chief Executive - Six Town Housing, 6 Knowsley Place, Angouleme Way, Bury BL9 0EL ☎ 0161 686 8000 ᐁ s.mccambridge@sixtownhousing.org

Housing Maintenance: Mr Wayne Campbell, Head - Repairs & Maintenance, 6 Knowsley Place, Angouleme Way, Bury BL9 0EL ☎ 0161 253 5000 ᐁ w.campbell@bury.gov.uk

Legal: Mrs Jayne Hammond, Assistant Director - Legal & Democratic Services, Town Hall, Knowsley Street, Bury BL9 0SW ☎ 0161 253 5237 ᐁ j.m.hammond@bury.gov.uk

Leisure and Cultural Services: Mr Neil Long, Assistant Director - Operations, 3 Knowsley Place, Duke Street, Bury BL9 0EJ ☎ 0161 253 5735 ᐁ n.s.long@bury.gov.uk

Licensing: Mr David Fowler, Assistant Director - Localities, 3 Knowsley Place, Duke Street, Bury BL9 0EJ ☎ 0161 253 5518 ᐁ d.w.fowler@bury.gov.uk

Licensing: Ms Angela Lomax, Head of Trading Standards & Licensing, 3 Knowsley Place, Duke Street, Bury BL0 0EJ ☎ 0161 253 5049 ᐁ a.s.lomax@bury.gov.uk

Lighting: Mr Phil Hewitt, Principal Engineer - Street Lighting, Bradley Fold Depot, Bradley Fold Road, Bolton BL2 6RS ☎ 0161 253 5000 ᐁ p.m.hewitt@bury.gov.uk

Member Services: Mr Leigh Webb, Democratic Services Manager, Town Hall, Knowsley Street, Bury BL9 0SW ☎ 0161 253 5399 ᐁ l.m.webb@bury.gov.uk

Parking: Mr John Foudy, Car Parking Manager, 3 Knowsley Place, Duke Street, Bury BL9 0EJ ☎ 0161 253 5445 ᐁ j.foudy@bury.gov.uk

Partnerships: Mr David Fowler, Assistant Director - Localities, 3 Knowsley Place, Duke Street, Bury BL9 0EJ ☎ 0161 253 5518 ᐁ d.w.fowler@bury.gov.uk

Personnel / HR: Ms Tracey Murphy, Acting Assistant Director - Personnel, Town Hall, Knowsley Street, Bury BL9 0SW ☎ 0161 253 5151 ✆ t.e.murphy@bury.gov.uk

Planning: Mr David Fowler, Assistant Director - Localities, 3 Knowsley Place, Duke Street, Bury BL9 0EJ ☎ 0161 253 5518 ✆ d.w.fowler@bury.gov.uk

Procurement: Mrs Sarah Janusz, Corporate Procurement Manager, Town Hall, Knowsley Street, Bury BL9 0SW ☎ 0161 253 6147 ✆ s.e.janusz@bury.gov.uk

Public Libraries: Rev Elizabeth Binns, Head of Libraries, Topping Fold Community Centre & Library, 36 Topping Fold Road, Bury BL9 7NG ☎ 0161 253 5973 ✆ e.binns@bury.gov.uk

Recycling & Waste Minimisation: Mr Glenn Stuart, Head - Waste Management, Unit 3, Bradley Fold Trading Estate, Bradley Fold Road, Bolton BL2 6RF ☎ 0161 253 6621 ✆ g.stuart@bury.gov.uk

Road Safety: Ms Jan Brabin, Principal Road Safety Officer, 3 Knowsley Place, Duke Street, Bury BL9 0EJ ☎ 0161 253 5787 ✆ j.brabin@bury.gov.uk

Social Services (Adult): Mrs Pat Jones-Greenhalgh, Executive Director - Communities & Wellbeing, Town Hall, Knowsley Street, Bury BL9 0SW ☎ 0161 253 5405 ✆ p.jones-greenhalgh@bury.gov.uk

Social Services (Children): Mr Mark Carriline, Executive Director - Children, Young People & Culture, 3 Knowsley Place, Duke Street, Bury BL9 0EJ ☎ 0161 253 5603 ✆ m.carriline@bury.gov.uk

Safeguarding: Ms Jackie Gower, Assistant Director - Social Care & Safeguarding, 3 Knowsley Place, Duke Street, Bury BL9 0EJ ☎ 0161 253 5603 ✆ j.gower@bury.gov.uk

Childrens Social Care: Ms Jackie Gower, Assistant Director - Social Care & Safeguarding, 3 Knowsley Place, Duke Street, Bury BL9 0EJ ☎ 0161 253 5603 ✆ j.gower@bury.gov.uk

Public Health: Ms Lesley Jones, Director - Public Health, 3 Knowsley Place, Duke Street, Bury BL9 0EJ ✆ l.jones@bury.gov.uk

Staff Training: Ms Tracey Murphy, Acting Assistant Director - Personnel, Town Hall, Knowsley Street, Bury BL9 0SW ☎ 0161 253 5151 ✆ t.e.murphy@bury.gov.uk

Sustainable Communities: Mr David Fowler, Assistant Director - Localities, 3 Knowsley Place, Duke Street, Bury BL9 0EJ ☎ 0161 253 5518 ✆ d.w.fowler@bury.gov.uk

Tourism: Mr David Fowler, Assistant Director - Localities, 3 Knowsley Place, Duke Street, Bury BL9 0EJ ☎ 0161 253 5518 ✆ d.w.fowler@bury.gov.uk

Tourism: Ms Jill Youlton, Tourism Development Officer, 3 Knowsley Place, Duke Street, Bury BL9 0EJ ☎ 0161 253 6075 ✆ j.youlton@bury.gov.uk

Traffic Management: Mr Dave Gilbin, Head of Engineering, 3 Knowsley Place, Duke Street, Bury BL9 0EJ ☎ 0161 253 5798 ✆ r.gilbin@bury.gov.uk

Transport: Mr Stephen Fleming, Head - Transport Services & Workshop, Unit 34, Bradley Fold Trading Estate, Bradley Fold Road, Bolton BL2 6RF ☎ 0161 253 6624 ✆ s.j.fleming@bury.gov.uk

Waste Collection and Disposal: Mr Glenn Stuart, Head - Waste Management, Unit 3, Bradley Fold Trading Estate, Bradley Fold Road, Bolton BL2 6RF ☎ 0161 253 6621 ✆ g.stuart@bury.gov.uk

Waste Management: Mr Glenn Stuart, Head - Waste Management, Unit 3, Bradley Fold Trading Estate, Bradley Fold Road, Bolton BL2 6RF ☎ 0161 253 6621 ✆ g.stuart@bury.gov.uk

COUNCILLORS

Mayor: Connolly, Mike (LAB - East)
m.connolly@bury.gov.uk

Deputy Mayor: Smith, Stella (LAB - East)
stella.smith@bury.gov.uk

Leader of the Council: Shori, Rishi (LAB - Radcliffe West)
r.shori@bury.gov.uk

Deputy Leader of the Council: Lewis, Jane (LAB - Radcliffe North)
j.lewis@bury.gov.uk

Group Leader: Gartside, Iain (CON - Tottington)
i.b.gartside@bury.gov.uk

Adams, Paul (LAB - Unsworth)
p.adams@bury.gov.uk

Bayley, Noel (LAB - St Marys)
n.bayley@bury.gov.uk

Bevan, Ian (CON - Ramsbottom)
i.bevan@bury.gov.uk

Black, Jane (LAB - St Marys)
j.black@bury.gov.uk

Briggs, Sharon (LAB - Radcliffe North)
s.briggs@bury.gov.uk

Caserta, Robert (CON - Pilkington Park)
r.caserta@bury.gov.uk

Cathcart, Rhyse (LAB - Radcliffe East)

Cummings, Tony (LAB - Radcliffe West)

D'Albert, Mary (LD - Holyrood)
m.dalbert@bury.gov.uk

Daly, James (CON - North Manor)
jdaly@cromptonhaliwell.co.uk

Fitzgerald, Elizabeth (LAB - Besses)
e.fitzgerald@bury.gov.uk

Grimshaw, Joan (LAB - Unsworth)
j.grimshaw@bury.gov.uk

Gunther, Dorothy (CON - North Manor)
d.l.gunther@bury.gov.uk

Hankey, Michael (CON - Elton)
m.hankey@bury.gov.uk

Haroon, Shaheena (LAB - Redvales)
s.haroon@bury.gov.uk

Harris, Jackie (CON - Church)

Hodkinson, Robert (CON - Ramsbottom)

BURY

Holt, Trevor (LAB - East)
t.holt@bury.gov.uk

Hussain, Khalid (CON - North Manor)
k.hussain@bury.gov.uk

James, Michael (LAB - Sedgley)
m.a.james@bury.gov.uk

Jones, David (LAB - Unsworth)
david.jones@bury.gov.uk

Keeley, Greg (CON - Tottington)
g.keeley@bury.gov.uk

Kelly, Judith (LAB - Redvales)

Kerrison, Sarah (LAB - Elton)
s.kerrison@bury.gov.uk

Kersh, Oliver (CON - Pilkington Park)

Mallon, John (LAB - Pilkington Park)
j.mallon@bury.gov.uk

Matthews, Alan (LAB - Besses)
a.k.matthews@bury.gov.uk

McKay, Annette (LAB - Moorside)

Nuttall, Susan (CON - Church)
sue.nuttall@bury.gov.uk

O'Brien, Eamonn (LAB - St Marys)
e.o'brien@bury.gov.uk

Parnell, Nick (LAB - Radcliffe East)
n.parnell@bury.gov.uk

Pickstone, Tim (LD - Holyrood)
t.d.pickstone@bury.gov.uk

Preston, Catherine (LAB - Radcliffe East)

Quinn, Alan (LD - Sedgley)
alan.quinn@bury.gov.uk

Schofield, Ian (CON - Ramsbottom)

Silbiger, David (CON - Sedgley)

Skillen, Rachel (LAB - Radcliffe West)

Southworth, Susan (LAB - Elton)
s.southworth@bury.gov.uk

Southworth, Sarah (LAB - Moorside)

Tariq, Tamoor (LAB - Redvales)
t.tariq@bury.gov.uk

Walker, Roy (CON - Church)
roy@edwardwalker.freeserve.co.uk

Walker, Jamie (LAB - Radcliffe North)

Walmsley, Sandra (LAB - Moorside)
sandra.walmsley@gov.uk

Whitby, Mary (LAB - Besses)
m.whitby@bury.gov.uk

Wright, Steve (LD - Holyrood)

Wright, Yvonne (CON - Tottington)
y.s.wright@bury.gov.uk

POLITICAL COMPOSITION
LAB: 31, CON: 16, LD: 4

COMMITTEE CHAIRS

Audit: Mr John Mallon

Licensing: Mr David Jones

Planning: Ms Jane Black

Caerphilly   W

Caerphilly County Borough Council, Penallta House,
Tredomen Park, Ystrad Mynach, Hengoed CF82 7PG
☎ 01443 815588 🖷 01443 864443 ✆ info@caerphilly.gov.uk
🖳 www.caerphilly.gov.uk

FACTS AND FIGURES
Parliamentary Constituencies: Caerphilly, Islwyn
EU Constituencies: Wales
Election Frequency: Elections are by thirds

PRINCIPAL OFFICERS

Chief Executive: Mr Chris Burns, Interim Chief Executive, Penallta
House, Tredomen Park, Ystrad Mynach, Hengoed CF82 7PG
☎ 01443 864410 ✆ chrisburns@caerphilly.gov.uk

Access Officer / Social Services (Disability): Mr Simon Dixon,
Disabled Access Officer, Tredomen House, Tredomen Park, Ystrad
Mynach, Hengoed CF82 7WF ☎ 01443 864085
✆ dixons@caerphilly.gov.uk

Architect, Building / Property Services: Mr Colin Jones, Head
of Performance & Property, Penallta House, Tredomen Park, Ystrad
Mynach, Hengoed CF82 7PG ☎ 01443 864382
✆ jonesrc@caerphilly.gov.uk

Best Value: Mr Stephen Harris, Acting Head of Corporate
Finance, Penallta House, Tredomen Park, Ystrad Mynach, Hengoed
CF82 7PG ☎ 01443 863022 ✆ harrisr@caerphilly.gov.uk

Building Control: Mr Jason Lear, Team Leader - Building Control,
Tredomen House, Tredomen Park, Ystrad Mynach, Hengoed CF82
7WF ☎ 01495 235091 ✆ learj@caerphilly.gov.uk

Catering Services: Ms Marcia Lewis, Principal Catering Officer,
Penallta House, Tredomen Park, Ystrad Mynach, Hengoed CF82
7PG ☎ 01443 864055 ✆ lewism3@caerphilly.gov.uk

Children / Youth Services: Mr Bleddyn Hopkins, Assistant
Director - Planning Strategy, Penallta House, Tredomen Park,
Ystrad Mynach, Hengoed CF82 7PG ☎ 01443 864355
✆ hopkib@caerphilly.gov.uk

Civil Registration: Ms Della Mahony, Superintendent Registrar,
Penallta House, Tredomen Park, Ystrad Mynach, Hengoed CF82
7PG ☎ 01443 863074

PR / Communications: Mr Paul Lewis, Acting Head of
Information, Technology & Citizen Engagement, Penallta House,
Tredomen Park, Ystrad Mynach, Hengoed CF82 7PG
☎ 01443 863267 ✆ lewisp@caerphilly.gov.uk

Community Planning: Mr Tim Stephens, Head of Planning &
Regeneration, Tredomen House, Tredomen Park, Ystrad Mynach,
Hengoed CF82 7WF ☎ 01495 235359 ✆ stepht@caerphilly.gov.uk

Community Safety: Mr Rob Hartshorn, Head of Public Protection, Penallta House, Tredomen Park, Ystrad Mynach, Hengoed CF82 7PG ☎ 01495 235315 ⏣ hartsr@caerphilly.gov.uk

Computer Management: Mr Paul Lewis, Acting Head of Information, Technology & Citizen Engagement, Penallta House, Tredomen Park, Ystrad Mynach, Hengoed CF82 7PG ☎ 01443 863267 ⏣ lewisp@caerphilly.gov.uk

Consumer Protection and Trading Standards: Mr Rob Hartshorn, Head of Public Protection, Council Offices, Pontllanfraith, Blackwood NP12 2YW ☎ 01495 235315 ⏣ hartsr@caerphilly.gov.uk

Contracts: Mr Stephen Harris, Acting Head of Corporate Finance, Penallta House, Tredomen Park, Ystrad Mynach, Hengoed CF82 7PG ☎ 01443 863022 ⏣ harrisr@caerphilly.gov.uk

Corporate Services: Ms Nicole Scammel, Acting Director - Corporate Services, Penallta House, Tredomen Park, Ystrad Mynach, Hengoed CF82 7PG ☎ 01443 864419 ⏣ scammn@caerphilly.gov.uk

Customer Service: Mr David Titley, Customer Services Manager, Penallta House, Tredomen Park, Ystrad Mynach, Hengoed CF82 7PG ☎ 01443 864548 ⏣ titled@caerphilly.gov.uk

Direct Labour: Mr Shaun Couzens, Chief Housing Officer, Tir-y-berth Depot, New Road, Tir-y-berth, Hengoed CF82 8NR ☎ 01443 863282 ⏣ couzes@caerphilly.gov.uk

Economic Development: Mr Dave Whetter, Head of Planning & Regeneration, Ty Dyffryn, Dyffryn Business Park, Ystrad Mynach, Hengoed CF82 7TW ☎ 01443 826209 ⏣ whettdj@caerphilly.gov.uk

Education: Ms Christina Harrhy, Corporate Director - Education & Community Services, Penallta House, Tredomen Park, Ystrad Mynach, Hengoed CF82 7PG ☎ 01443 864948 ⏣ harrhc@caerphilly.gov.uk

E-Government: Mr Paul Lewis, Acting Head of Information, Technology & Citizen Engagement, Penallta House, Tredomen Park, Ystrad Mynach, Hengoed CF82 7PG ☎ 01443 863267 ⏣ lewisp@caerphilly.gov.uk

Electoral Registration: Mr Dave Beecham, Electoral Services Manager, Ty Dyffryn, Dyffryn Business Park, Ystrad Mynach, Hengoed CF82 7TW ☎ 01443 864405 ⏣ beechd@caerphilly.gov.uk

Emergency Planning: Ms Sheryl Andrews, Emergency Planning Manager, Penallta House, Tredomen Park, Ystrad Mynach, Hengoed CF82 7PG ☎ 01495 235048 ⏣ andres@caerphilly.gov.uk

Energy Management: Mr Colin Jones, Head of Performance & Property, Penallta House, Tredomen Park, Ystrad Mynach, Hengoed CF82 7PG ☎ 01443 864382 ⏣ jonesrc@caerphilly.gov.uk

Environmental / Technical Services: Mr Chris Burns, Interim Chief Executive, Penallta House, Tredomen Park, Ystrad Mynach, Hengoed CF82 7PG ☎ 01443 864410 ⏣ chrisburns@caerphilly.gov.uk

Environmental Health: Mr Rob Hartshorn, Head of Public Protection, Council Offices, Pontllanfraith, Blackwood NP12 2YW ☎ 01495 235315 ⏣ hartsr@caerphilly.gov.uk

Estates, Property & Valuation: Mr Colin Jones, Head of Performance & Property, Penallta House, Tredomen Park, Ystrad Mynach, Hengoed CF82 7PG ☎ 01443 864382 ⏣ jonesrc@caerphilly.gov.uk

Events Manager: Mr Paul Hudson, Senior Events & Marketing Officer, Tredomen Business & Technology Centre, Tredomen Business Park, Ystrad Mynach, Hengoed CF82 7FN ☎ 01443 866228 ⏣ hudsop@caerphilly.gov.uk

Facilities: Mr Mark Faulkner, Senior Facilities Manager, Penallta House, Tredomen Park, Ystrad Mynach, Hengoed CF82 7PG ☎ 01443 864128 ⏣ faulkm@caerphilly.gov.uk

Finance: Mr Stephen Harris, Acting Head of Corporate Finance, Penallta House, Tredomen Park, Ystrad Mynach, Hengoed CF82 7PG ☎ 01443 863022 ⏣ harrisr@caerphilly.gov.uk

Fleet Management: Ms Mary Powell, Fleet Manager, Tir-y-berth Depot, New Road, Tir-y-berth, Hengoed CF82 8NR ☎ 01443 873720 ⏣ powelem@caerphilly.gov.uk

Grounds Maintenance: Mr Derek Price, Principal Parks & Open Spaces Officer, Unit B5, New Road, Tir y Berth, Hengoed CG82 8NR ☎ 01495 235470 ⏣ priced@caerphilly.gov.uk

Health and Safety: Ms Emma Townsend, Corporate Health & Safety Manager, Penallta House, Tredomen Park, Ystrad Mynach, Hengoed CF82 7PG ☎ 01443 864280 ⏣ townsej@caerphilly.gov.uk

Highways: Mr Terry Shaw, Head of Engineering Services, Ty Dyffryn, Dyffryn Business Park, Ystrad Mynach, Hengoed CF82 7TW ☎ 01495 235319 ⏣ shawt@caerphilly.gov.uk

Home Energy Conservation: Mr Steve Martin, Energy Officer, Cherry Tree House, Carlton Drive, Penyfan Industrial Estate, Crumlin, Newport NP11 4EA ☎ 01443 863215 ⏣ martins@caerphilly.gov.uk

Housing: Mr Shaun Couzens, Chief Housing Officer, Tir y Berth Depot, New Road, Hengoed CF82 8NR ☎ 01443 863282 ⏣ couzes@caerphilly.gov.uk

Housing Maintenance: Mr Shaun Couzens, Chief Housing Officer, Tir y Berth Depot, New Road, Hengoed CF82 8NR ☎ 01443 863282 ⏣ couzes@caerphilly.gov.uk

Legal: Ms Gail Williams, Interim Head of Legal Services & Monitoring Officer, Penallta House, Tredomen Park, Ystrad Mynach, Hengoed CF82 7PG ☎ 01443 863393 ⏣ willige@caerphilly.gov.uk

Leisure and Cultural Services: Mr Mark Williams, Head of Community & Leisure Services, Pontllanfraith House, Pontllanfraith, Blackwood NP12 2YW ☎ 01495 235070 ⏣ willims@caerphilly.gov.uk

Licensing: Ms Myra McSherry, Licensing Manager, Penallta House, Tredomen Park, Ystrad Mynach, Hengoed CF82 7PG ☎ 01443 866750 ⏣ mcshe@caerphilly.gov.uk

CAERPHILLY

Lifelong Learning: Mr Bleddyn Hopkins, Assistant Director - Planning Strategy, Penallta House, Tredomen Park, Ystrad Mynach, Hengoed CF82 7PG ☎ 01443 864355 ⌨ hopkib@caerphilly.gov.uk

Lighting: Mr Terry Shaw, Head of Engineering Services, Council Offices, Pontllanfraith, Blackwood NP12 2YW ☎ 01495 235319 ⌨ shawt@caerphilly.gov.uk

Lottery Funding, Charity and Voluntary: Mr Colin Jones, Head of Performance & Property, Penalta House, Tredomen Park, Ystrad Mynach, Hengoed CF82 7PG ☎ 01443 864382 ⌨ jonesrc@caerphilly.gov.uk

Member Services: Ms Karen Green, Cabinet Support Assistant, Penallta House, Tredomen Park, Ystrad Mynach, Hengoed CF82 7PG ☎ 01443 864369 ⌨ greenk@caerphilly.gov.uk

Parking: Mr Terry Shaw, Head of Engineering Services, Ty Dyffryn, Dyffryn Business Park, Ystrad Mynach, Hengoed CF82 7TW ☎ 01495 235319 ⌨ shawt@caerphilly.gov.uk

Partnerships: Mr Colin Jones, Head of Performance & Property, Penallta House, Tredomen Park, Ystrad Mynach, Hengoed CF82 7PG ☎ 01443 864382 ⌨ jonesrc@caerphilly.gov.uk

Personnel / HR: Ms Lynne Donovan, Head of People Management & Development, Penallta House, Tredomen Park, Ystrad Mynach, Hengoed CF82 7PG ☎ 01443 864570 ⌨ donovl@caerphilly.gov.uk

Planning: Mr Tim Stephens, Head of Planning & Regeneration, Tredomen House, Tredomen Park, Ystrad Mynach, Hengoed CF82 7WF ☎ 01495 235359 ⌨ stepht@caerphilly.gov.uk

Procurement: Mrs Elizabeth Lucas, Head of Procurement, Penallta House, Tredomen Park, Ystrad Mynach, Hengoed CF82 7PG ☎ 01443 863160 ⌨ lucasej@caerphilly.gov.uk

Public Libraries: Mr Gareth Evans, Senior Manager - Libraries, Penallta House, Tredomen Park, Ystrad Mynach, Hengoed CF82 7PG ☎ 01443 864033 ⌨ evansg1@caerphilly.gov.uk

Recycling & Waste Minimisation: Mr Mark Williams, Head of Community & Leisure Services, Unit B5, New Road, Tir y Berth, Hengoed CF82 8NR ☎ 01495 235070 ⌨ willims@caerphilly.gov.uk

Regeneration: Mr Dave Whetter, Head of Planning & Regeneration, Ty Dyffryn, Dyffryn Business Park, Ystrad Mynach, Hengoed CF82 7TW ☎ 01443 826209 ⌨ whettdj@caerphilly.gov.uk

Road Safety: Mr Terry Shaw, Head of Engineering Services, Ty Dyffryn, Dyffryn Business Park, Ystrad Mynach, Hengoed CF82 7TW ☎ 01495 235319 ⌨ shawt@caerphilly.gov.uk

Social Services: Mr Dave Street, Director - Social Services, Penallta House, Tredomen Park, Ystrad Mynach, Hengoed CF82 7PG ☎ 01443 864560 ⌨ streed@caerphilly.gov.uk

Social Services (Adult): Ms Jo Williams, Assistant Director - Adult Services, Penallta House, Tredomen Park, Ystrad Mynach, Hengoed CF82 7PG ☎ 01443 864611 ⌨ willij6@caerphilly.gov.uk

Social Services (Children): Mr Gareth Jenkins, Assistant Director - Children's Services, Penallta House, Tredomen Park, Ystrad Mynach, Hengoed CF82 7PG ☎ 01443 864520 ⌨ jenkig2@caerphilly.gov.uk

Staff Training: Ms Jane Haile, Interim Team Manager, 3 Foxes Lane, Oakdale Business Park, Oakdale, Caerphilly NP12 4AB ☎ 01443 863410 ⌨ hailej@caerphilly.gov.uk

Sustainable Communities: Mr Dave Whetter, Head of Planning & Regeneration, Ty Dyffryn, Dyffryn Business Park, Ystrad Mynach, Hengoed CF82 7TW ☎ 01443 826209 ⌨ whettdj@caerphilly.gov.uk

Sustainable Development: Mr Dave Whetter, Head of Planning & Regeneration, Ty Dyffryn, Dyffryn Business Park, Ystrad Mynach, Hengoed CF82 7TW ☎ 01443 826209 ⌨ whettdj@caerphilly.gov.uk

Tourism: Mr Paul Hudson, Senior Events & Marketing Officer, Tredomen Business & Technology Centre, Tredomen Business Park, Ystrad Mynach, Hengoed CF82 7FN ☎ 01443 866228 ⌨ hudsop@caerphilly.gov.uk

Town Centre: Mr Andrew Highway, Town Centre Development Manager, Tredomen Business and Technology Centre, Ystrad Mynach, Hengoed CF82 7FN ☎ 01443 866213 ⌨ highwa@caerphilly.gov.uk

Traffic Management: Mr Terry Shaw, Head of Engineering Services, Ty Dyffryn, Dyffryn Business Park, Ystrad Mynach, Hengoed CF82 7TW ☎ 01495 235319 ⌨ shawt@caerphilly.gov.uk

Transport: Mr Clive Campbell, Transportation Engineering Manager, Ty Dyffryn, Ty Dyffryn Business Park, Ystrad Mynach, Hengoed CF82 7TW ☎ 01495 235339 ⌨ campbc@caerphilly.gov.uk

Transport Planner: Mr Clive Campbell, Transportation Engineering Manager, Ty Dyffryn, Ty Dyffryn Business Park, Ystrad Mynach, Hengoed CF82 7TW ☎ 01495 235339 ⌨ campbc@caerphilly.gov.uk

Waste Collection and Disposal: Mr Mark Williams, Head of Community & Leisure Services, Unit B5, New Road, Tir y Berth, Hengoed CF82 8NR ☎ 01495 235070 ⌨ willims@caerphilly.gov.uk

Waste Management: Mr Mark Williams, Head of Community & Leisure Services, Unit B5, New Road, Tir y Berth, Hengoed CF82 8NR ☎ 01495 235070 ⌨ willims@caerphilly.gov.uk

Children's Play Areas: Mr Derek Price, Principal Parks & Open Spaces Officer, Unit B5, New Road, Tir y Berth, Hengoed CF82 8NR ☎ 01495 235470 ⌨ priced@caerphilly.gov.uk

COUNCILLORS

Mayor: Price, Dianne (LAB - Bargoed) dianneprice@caerphilly.gov.uk

Deputy Mayor: Bevan, John (LAB - Moriah) johnbevan@caerphilly.gov.uk

Leader of the Council: Reynolds, Keith (LAB - Aberbargoed) keithreynolds@caerphilly.gov.uk

Deputy Leader of the Council: Jones, Barbara (LAB - St James)
barbarajones@caerphilly.gov.uk

Deputy Leader of the Council: Poole, David (LAB - Pengam)
davidpoole@caerphilly.gov.uk

Group LeaderMann, Colin (PC - Llanbradach)
colinmann@caerphilly.gov.uk

Ackerman, Lyn (PC - Newbridge)
lynackerman@caerphilly.gov.uk

Adams, Michael (LAB - Pontllanfraith)
michaeladams@caerphilly.gov.uk

Aldworth, Elizabeth (LAB - Bedwas, Trethomas & Machen)
lizaldworth@caerphilly.gov.uk

Angel, Alan (PC - Ystrad Mynach)
alanangel@caerphilly.gov.uk

Baker, Kath (PC - Newbridge)
kathbaker@caerphilly.gov.uk

Bevan, Phil (PC - Morgan Jones)
philbevan@caerphilly.gov.uk

Binding, Lyndon (PC - Aber Valley)
lyndonbinding@caerphilly.gov.uk

Blackman, Anne (IND - Nelson)
anneblackman@caerphilly.gov.uk

Bolter, Dennis (PC - Hengoed)
dennisbolter@caerphilly.gov.uk

Carter, David (LAB - Bargoed)
davidcarter@caerphilly.gov.uk

Cook, Patrica (LAB - Blackwood)
patriciacook@caerphilly.gov.uk

Cuss, Carl (LAB - Twyn Carno)
carlcuss@caerphilly.gov.uk

David, Hefin (LAB - St Cattwg)
hefindavid@caerphilly.gov.uk

David, Wynne (LAB - St Cattwg)
wynnedavid@caerphilly.gov.uk

Davies, Tudor (LAB - Bargoed)
tudordavies@caerphilly.gov.uk

Davies, Huw (LAB - Penyrheol)
huwdavies@caerphilly.gov.uk

Dawson, Kevin (LAB - Pengam)
kevindawson@caerphilly.gov.uk

Dix, Nigel (LAB - Blackwood)
nigeldix@caerphilly.gov.uk

Elsbury, Colin (PC - St Martins)
colinelsbury@caerphilly.gov.uk

Evans, Mark (LAB - New Tredegar)
evansm6@caerphilly.gov.uk

Forehead, Elaine (LAB - St James)
elaineforehead@caerphilly.gov.uk

Forehead, Christine (LAB - St James)
christineforehead@caerphilly.gov.uk

Fussell, James (PC - St Martins)
jamesfussell@caerphilly.gov.uk

Gale, June (LAB - Bedwas, Trethomas & Machen)
junegalecaerphilly.gov.uk

Gardiner, Leon (LAB - Argoed)
leongardiner@caerphilly.gov.uk

George, Nigel (LAB - Risca East)
nigelgeorge@caerphilly.gov.uk

Gordon, Colin (LAB - Pontllanfraith)
colingordon@caerphilly.gov.uk

Gough, Rob (PC - Llanbradach)
robgough@caerphilly.gov.uk

Griffiths, Phyl (IND - Risca West)
phyllisgriffiths@caerphilly.gov.uk

Hardacre, David (LAB - Darren Valley)
davidhardacre@caerphilly.gov.uk

Harse, David (LAB - Moriah)

Havard, Derek (LAB - Bedwas, Trethomas & Machen)
derekhavard@caerphilly.gov.uk

Hawker, Chris (LAB - Cefn Fforest)
chrishawker@caerphilly.gov.uk

Higgs, Alan (LAB - Aberbargoed)
alanhiggs@caerphilly.gov.uk

Hughes, Graham (LAB - St Cattwg)
grahamhughes@caerphilly.gov.uk

James, Ken (LAB - Abercarn)
kenjames@caerphilly.gov.uk

James, Martyn (PC - Ystrad Mynach)
martynjames@caerphilly.gov.uk

Johnston, Gary (LAB - Newbridge)
garyjohnston@caerphilly.gov.uk

Jones, Lisa (LAB - Bedwas, Trethomas & Machen)
jonesl1@caerphilly.gov.uk

Jones, Janet (LAB - Ynysddu)
janetjones@caerphilly.gov.uk

Kent, Stephen (PC - St Martins)
stephenkent@caerphilly.gov.uk

Kirby, Gez (LAB - Pontllanfraith)
gezkirby@caerphilly.gov.uk

Leonard, Philippa (LAB - Risca East)
leonap@caerphilly.gov.uk

Lewis, Andrew (LAB - Crumlin)
andrewlewis@caerphilly.gov.uk

Lloyd, Keith (PC - Crumlin)
keithlloyd@caerphilly.gov.uk

Marsden, Philippa (LAB - Ynysddu)
marsdp@caerphilly.gov.uk

Morgan, Sean (LAB - Nelson)
seanmorgan@caerphilly.gov.uk

Oliver, Gaynor (LAB - Pontlottyn)
gaynoroliver@caerphilly.gov.uk

Preece, Denver (LAB - Abercarn)
denverpreece@caerphilly.gov.uk

Prew, Michael (PC - Morgan Jones)
michaelprew@caerphilly.gov.uk

Pritchard, James (LAB - Morgan Jones)
jamespritchard@caerphilly.gov.uk

Pritchard, Judith (PC - Hengoed)
judithpritchard@caerphilly.gov.uk

CAERPHILLY

Rees, Dave (IND - Risca West)
daverees@caerphilly.gov.uk

Rees, Allan (LAB - Blackwood)
reesa2@caerphilly.gov.uk

Roberts, John (PC - Aber Valley)
johnroberts@caerphilly.gov.uk

Saralis, Roy (LAB - Penmaen)
roysaralis@caerphilly.gov.uk

Sargent, Margaret (PC - Penyrheol)
margaretsargent@caerphilly.gov.uk

Simmonds, Julian (LAB - Crosskeys)
simmoj@caerphilly.gov.uk

Skivens, Steve (PC - Penyrheol)
stevenskivens@caerphilly.gov.uk

Stenner, Eluned (LAB - New Tredegar)
elunedstenner@caerphilly.gov.uk

Summers, Jean (LAB - Penmaen)
jeansummers@caerphilly.gov.uk

Taylor, John (PC - Aber Valley)
johntaylor@caerphilly.gov.uk

Whittle, Lindsay (PC - Penyrheol)
lindsaywhittle@caerphilly.gov.uk

Williams, Tom (LAB - Cefn Fforest)
tomwilliams@caerphilly.gov.uk

Woodyatt, Robin (LAB - Maesycwmmer)
robinwoodyatt@caerphilly.gov.uk

POLITICAL COMPOSITION
LAB: 48, PC: 20, IND: 3, Vacant: 1

COMMITTEE CHAIRS

Audit: Mr Dave Rees

Health, Social Care & Wellbeing: Miss Lyn Ackerman

Licensing: Mr Denver Preece

Planning: Mr David Carter

Calderdale   M

Calderdale Metropolitan Borough Council, Town Hall,
Crossley Street, Halifax HX1 1UJ
☎ 0845 245 6000 ☒ 01422 393102 ⌨ www.calderdale.gov.uk

FACTS AND FIGURES
Parliamentary Constituencies: Calder Valley, Halifax
EU Constituencies: Yorkshire and the Humber
Election Frequency: Elections are by thirds

PRINCIPAL OFFICERS

Chief Executive: Ms Merran McRae, Chief Executive, Town Hall,
Halifax HX1 1UJ ☎ 01422 393005
⌁ merran.mcrae@calderdale.gov.uk

Senior Management: Mr Paul Butcher, Director - Public Health,
Northgate House, Halifax HX1 1UN
⌁ paul.butcher@calderdale.gov.uk

Senior Management: Ms Bev Maybury, Director - Adults, Health
& Social Care, 1 Park Road, Halifax HX1 2TU ☎ 01422 393800
⌁ bev.maybury@calderdale.gov.uk

Senior Management: Mr Stuart Smith, Director - Children &
Young People, Northgate House, Halifax HX1 1UN ☎ 01422 392552
⌁ stuart.smith@calderdale.gov.uk

Senior Management: Mr Mark Thompson, Acting Director
- Economy & Environment (Head of Housing, Environment &
Renewal), Northgate House, Northgate, Halifax HX1 1UN ☎ 01422
392435 ⌁ mark.thompson@calderdale.gov.uk

Senior Management: Mr Robin Tuddenham, Director -
Communities & Service Support, Westgate House, Halifax HX1 1PS
☎ 01422 393018 ⌁ robin.tuddenham@calderdale.gov.uk

Access Officer / Social Services (Disability): Mr Iain Baines,
Head of Safeguarding & Quality, Northgate House, Halifax HX1
1UN ☎ 01422 393809 ⌁ iain.baines@calderdale.gov.uk

Access Officer / Social Services (Disability): Ms Pippa
Corner, Head of Partnerships & Personalisation, 1 Park Road,
Halifax HX1 2TU ☎ 01422 393864 ⌁ pippa.corner@calderdale.
gov.uk

Architect, Building / Property Services: Mr Stephen Hoyle,
Lead for Asset Management, Northgate House, Halifax HX1 1UN
☎ 01422 392058 ⌁ stephen.hoyle@calderdale.gov.uk

Architect, Building / Property Services: Ms Geraldine Rushton,
Disabilities Liaison Officer, Northgate House, Halifax HX1 1UN
☎ 01422 393099 ⌁ geraldine.rushton@calderdale.gov.uk

Building Control: Mr Mike Terry, Building Control Manager,
Westgate House, Halifax HX1 1PS ☎ 01422 392221
⌁ mike.terry@calderdale.gov.uk

Catering Services: Mr Graham Dixon, FM Operational Services
Manager, Northgate House, Halifax HX1 1UN ☎ 01422 392363
⌁ graham.dixon@calderdale.gov.uk

Children / Youth Services: Mr David Whalley, Head of Learning,
Northgate House, Halifax HX1 1UN ☎ 01422 392716
⌁ david.whalley@calderdale.gov.uk

Civil Registration: Mrs Andrea Breen, Acting Registration &
Licensing Services, Northgate House, Halifax HX1 1UN
☎ 01422 284470 ⌁ andrea.breen@calderdale.gov.uk

PR / Communications: Mrs Lucy Bradwell, PR & Public
Information Officer, Westgate House, Westgate, Halifax HX1 1PS
☎ 01422 393003 ⌁ lucy.bradwell@calderdale.gov.uk

Community Safety: Mr Derek Benn, Community Safety
Partnership Manager, Hoover Building, 21 West Parade, Halifax HX1
2TE ☎ 01422 393130 ⌁ derek.benn@calderdale.gov.uk

Contracts: Ms Deborah Gaunt, Corporate Procurement Officer,
Princess Buildings, Halifax HX1 1TP
☎ 01422 393176 ⌁ deborah.gaunt@calderdale.gov.uk

Contracts: Mrs Judith Wyllie, Commissioning & Partnership Services, Northgate House, Halifax HX1 1UN ☎ 01422 392527 🖂 judith.wyllie@calderdale.gov.uk

Customer Service: Ms Zohrah Zancudi, Head of Customer Service, 2nd Floor, Westgate House, Halifax HX1 1PS ☎ 01422 393201 🖂 zohrah.zancudi@calderdale.gov.uk

Economic Development: Mr Robert Campbell, Business & Economy Manager, Northgate House, Halifax HX1 1UN ☎ 01422 392235 🖂 robert.campbell@calderdale.gov.uk

Education: Ms Jackie Nellis, Head of Learning, Town Hall, Crossley Street, Halifax HX1 1UJ 🖂 jackie.nellis@calderdale.gov.uk

Electoral Registration: Ms Linda Clarkson, Principal Electoral Services Officer, Westgate House, Westgate, Halifax HX1 1PS ☎ 01422 393049 🖂 linda.clarkson@calderdale.gov.uk

Emergency Planning: Ms Amanda Webster, Senior Emergency Planning Advisor, Westgate House, Halifax HX1 1PS ☎ 01422 392870 🖂 amanda.webster@calderdale.gov.uk

Energy Management: Ms Helen Rhodes, Head of Housing, Environment & Renewal, Northgate House, Halifax HX1 1UN ☎ 01422 392485 🖂 helen.rhodes@calderdale.gov.uk

Environmental / Technical Services: Mr Peter Broadbent, Environmental Health Manager, Northgate House, Halifax HX1 1UN ☎ 01422 392345 🖂 peter.broadbent@calderdale.gov.uk

Environmental Health: Mr Peter Broadbent, Environmental Health Manager, Northgate House, Halifax HX1 1UN ☎ 01422 392345 🖂 peter.broadbent@calderdale.gov.uk

Estates, Property & Valuation: Mr Stephen Hoyle, Lead for Asset Management, Northgate House, Halifax HX1 1UN ☎ 01422 392058 🖂 stephen.hoyle@calderdale.gov.uk

Events Manager: Mr Peter Vardy, Recreation Officer - Licensing & Events, Ainley's Depot (Highway's Offices), c/o Highways & Engineering, Huddersfield Road, Elland HX5 9JR ☎ 01422 384796 🖂 peter.vardy@calderdale.gov.uk

Facilities: Ms Elaine Wynne, Lead for Facilities Management, Northgate House, Halifax HX1 1UN ☎ 01422 392066 🖂 elaine.wynne@calderdale.gov.uk

Finance: Mr Nigel Broadbent, Head of Finance, Princess Buildings, Halifax HX1 1TP ☎ 01422 393872 🖂 nigel.broadbent@calderdale.gov.uk

Fleet Management: Mr Paul Topham, Transport Manager, Economy & Environment, Battinson Road Depot, Queen's Road, Halifax HX1 4PL ☎ 01422 264350 🖂 paul.topham@calderdale.gov.uk

Grounds Maintenance: Ms Amanda Firth, Safer, Cleaner, Greener Manager, Spring Hall Mansion, Spring Hall, Halifax HX3 0AQ ☎ 01422 284441 🖂 amanda.firth@calderdale.gov.uk

Health and Safety: Mr Martin Allingham, Principal Health & Safety Adviser, Westgate House, Halifax HX1 1PS ☎ 01422 393080 🖂 martin.allingham@calderdale.gov.uk

Highways: Ms Carolyn Walton, Highways & Engineering Manager, Westgate House, Halifax HX1 1PS ☎ 01422 392167 🖂 carolyn.walton@calderdale.gov.uk

Home Energy Conservation: Mr Richard Armitage, Housing Projects Officer, Northgate House, Halifax HX1 1UN ☎ 01422 392474 🖂 richard.armitage@calderdale.gov.uk

Housing: Ms Heidi Wilson, Housing Access & Waste Management Manager, Northgate House, Halifax HX1 1UN ☎ 01422 392406 🖂 heidi.wilson@calderdale.gov.uk

Housing Maintenance: Ms Helen Rhodes, Head of Housing, Environment & Renewal, Northgate House, Halifax HX1 1UN ☎ 01422 392485 🖂 helen.rhodes@calderdale.gov.uk

Local Area Agreement: Mr Alan Duncan, LSP & Partnerships Manager, Town Hall, Halifax HX1 1UN ☎ 01422 392207 🖂 alan.duncan@calderdale.gov.uk

Legal: Mr Ian Hughes, Policy & Partnership Manager, Westgate House, Westgate, Halifax HX1 1PS ☎ 01422 393063 🖂 ian.hughes@calderdale.gov.uk

Licensing: Mrs Andrea Breen, Acting Registration & Licensing Services, Spring Hall Mansion, Huddersfield Road, Halifax HX3 0AQ ☎ 01422 284470 🖂 andrea.breen@calderdale.gov.uk

Lifelong Learning: Mrs Anne Craven, Service Manager - Commissioning Schools & Lifelong Learning, Northgate House, Halifax HX1 1UN ☎ 01422 392806 🖂 anne.craven@calderdale.gov.uk

Lighting: Ms Carolyn Walton, Highways & Engineering Manager, Westgate House, Halifax HX1 1PS ☎ 01422 392167 🖂 carolyn.walton@calderdale.gov.uk

Lottery Funding, Charity and Voluntary: Ms Sarah Barker, Commissioning & Monitoring Officer, 2nd Floor, Westgate House, Westgate, Halifax HX1 1PS ☎ 01422 393218 🖂 sarahj.barker@calderdale.gov.uk

Member Services: Mr Peter Burton, Democratic Services Manager, Town Hall, Halifax HX1 1UJ ☎ 01422 393011 🖂 peter.burton@calderdale.gov.uk

Parking: Ms Debbie Harrison, Parking Operations Manager, Multure House, Halifax HX1 1SP ☎ 01422 392185 🖂 debbie.harrison@calderdale.gov.uk

Partnerships: Mr Andrew Pitts, Head of Neighbourhoods, Westgate House, Westgate, Halifax HX1 1PS ☎ 01422 392600 🖂 andrew.pitts@calderdale.gov.uk

Personnel / HR: Ms Jackie Addison, Corporate Lead for HR, 3rd Floor, Westgate, Westgate, Halifax HX1 1PS ☎ 01422 288417 🖂 jackie.addison@calderdale.gov.uk

CALDERDALE

Planning: Mr Richard Seaman, Development Manager, Westgate House, Halifax HX1 1PS ☎ 01422 392241 ✆ richard.seaman@calderdale.gov.uk

Procurement: Ms Deborah Gaunt, Corporate Procurement Officer, Westgate House, Halifax HX1 1PS ☎ 01422 393176 ✆ deborah.gaunt@calderdale.gov.uk

Public Libraries: Ms Carole Knowles, Library Services Manager, Central Library, Northgate, Halifax HX1 1UN ☎ 01422 392623 ✆ carole.knowles@calderdale.gov.uk

Recycling & Waste Minimisation: Ms Heidi Wilson, Housing Access & Waste Management Manager, Northgate House, Halifax HX1 1UN ☎ 01422 392406 ✆ heidi.wilson@calderdale.gov.uk

Regeneration: Mr Robert Campbell, Business & Economy Manager, Northgate House, Halifax HX1 1UN ☎ 01422 392235 ✆ robert.campbell@calderdale.gov.uk

Road Safety: Ms Debbie Calcott, Network Manager, Mulcture House, Halifax HX1 1PS ☎ 01422 392185 ✆ debbie.calcott@calderdale.gov.uk

Social Services: Mr Iain Baines, Head of Safeguarding & Quality, Northgate House, Halifax HX1 1UN ☎ 01422 393809 ✆ iain.baines@calderdale.gov.uk

Social Services: Ms Beate Wagner, Head of Early Intervention Safeguarding, Northgate House, Halifax HX1 1UN ☎ 01422 392722 ✆ beate.wagner@calderdale.gov.uk

Social Services (Adult): Ms Pippa Corner, Head of Partnerships & Personalisation, 1 Park Road, Halifax HX1 2TU ☎ 01422 393864 ✆ pippa.corner@calderdale.gov.uk

Social Services (Children): Ms Julie Jenkins, Head of Early Intervention & Safeguarding, Northgate House, Halifax HX1 1UN ☎ 01422 392722 ✆ julie.jenkins@calderdale.gov.uk

Social Services (Children): Mr Stuart Smith, Director - Children & Young People, Northgate House, Halifax HX1 1UN ☎ 01422 392552 ✆ stuart.smith@calderdale.gov.uk

Fostering & Adoption: Mr Gary Pickles, Service Manager - Children Looked After, Northgate House, Halifax HX1 1UN ☎ 01422 392717 ✆ dean.howson@calderdale.gov.uk

Safeguarding: Ms Julie Jenkins, Head of Early Intervention & Safeguarding, Northgate House, Halifax HX1 1UN ☎ 01422 392722 ✆ julie.jenkins@calderdale.gov.uk

Families: Ms Julie Killey, Acting Strategic Commissioning - Children, Young People & Family, Northgate House, Halifax HX1 1UN ☎ 01422 392816 ✆ julie.killey@calderdale.gov.uk

Childrens Social Care: Mr Sean Walsh, Service Manager - Locality Teams, Northgate House, Halifax HX1 1UN ☎ 01422 392805 ✆ lisa.handley@calderdale.gov.uk

Public Health: Mr Paul Butcher, Director - Public Health, Northgate House, Halifax HX1 1UN ✆ paul.butcher@calderdale.gov.uk

Public Health: Mrs Caron Walker, Consultant in Public Health, Northgate House, Halifax HX1 1UN ☎ 01422 266156 ✆ caron.walker@calderdale.gov.uk

Public Health: Mr Dean Wallace, Consultant in Public Health, Northgate House, Halifax HX1 1UN ☎ 01422 266134 ✆ dean.wallace@calderdale.gov.uk

Staff Training: Ms Julie Comb, Corporate Lead - Workforce Development, 3rd Floor, Westgate House, Westgate, Halifax HX1 1PS ☎ 01422 288340 ✆ julie.comb@calderdale.gov.uk

Street Scene: Ms Amanda Firth, Safer, Cleaner, Greener Manager, Spring Hall Mansion, Spring Hall, Hali HX3 0AQ ☎ 01422 284441 ✆ amanda.firth@calderdale.gov.uk

Sustainable Communities: Mr Phil Ratcliffe, Development Strategy Manager, Northgate House, Hali HX1 1UN ☎ 01422 392255 ✆ phil.ratcliffe@calderdale.gov.uk

Tourism: Ms Katie Kinsella, Tourism Manager, Westgate House, Halifax HX1 1PS ☎ 01422 392293 ✆ katie.kinsella@calderdale.gov.uk

Traffic Management: Ms Carolyn Walton, Highways & Engineering Manager, Westgate House, Halifax HX1 1PS ☎ 01422 392167 ✆ carolyn.walton@calderdale.gov.uk

Transport: Mr Paul Topham, Transport Manager, Economy & Environment, Battinson Road Depot, Queen's Road, Halifax HX1 4PL ☎ 01422 264350 ✆ paul.topham@calderdale.gov.uk

Transport Planner: Mr Paul Topham, Transport Manager, Economy & Environment, Battinson Road Depot, Queen's Road, Halifax HX1 4PL ☎ 01422 264350 ✆ paul.topham@calderdale.gov.uk

Waste Collection and Disposal: Ms Heidi Wilson, Housing Access & Waste Management Manager, Northgate House, Halifax HX1 1UN ☎ 01422 392406 ✆ heidi.wilson@calderdale.gov.uk

Waste Management: Ms Heidi Wilson, Housing Access & Waste Management Manager, Northgate House, Halifax HX1 1UN ☎ 01422 392406 ✆ heidi.wilson@calderdale.gov.uk

Children's Play Areas: Ms Amanda Firth, Safer, Cleaner, Greener Manager, Spring Hall Mansion, Spring Hall, Halifax HX3 0AQ ☎ 01422 284441 ✆ amanda.firth@calderdale.gov.uk

COUNCILLORS

Mayor: Blagbrough, Howard (CON - Brighouse) councillor.hblagbrough@calderdale.gov.uk

Deputy Mayor: Carter, Geraldine (CON - Ryburn) councillor.gcarter@calderdale.gov.uk

Leader of the Council: Swift, Tim (LAB - Town) councillor.tswift@calderdale.gov.uk

Deputy Leader of the Council: Collins, Barry (LAB - Illingworth & Mixenden)
councillor.bcollins@calderdale.gov.uk

Group LeaderBaker, James (LD - Warley)
councillor.jbaker@calderdale.gov.uk

Group LeaderBenton, Scott (CON - Brighouse)
councillor.sbenton@calderdale.gov.uk

Ali, Ferman (LAB - Park)
councillor.fali@calderdale.gov.uk

Allen, Patricia (LD - Elland)
councillor.pallen@calderdale.gov.uk

Baines, Stephen (CON - Northowram & Shelf)
councillor.sbaines@calderdale.gov.uk

Beal, Christine (CON - Rastrick)
councillor.cbeal@calderdale.gov.uk

Bellenger, Paul (LD - Greetland & Stainland)
councillor.pbellenger@calderdale.gov.uk

Booth, Jayne (LAB - Todmorden)
councillor.jbooth@calderdale.gov.uk

Caffrey, Peter (CON - Northowram & Shelf)
councillor.pcaffrey@calderdale.gov.uk

Collins, Anne (LAB - Ovenden)
councillor.acollins@calderdale.gov.uk

Evans, Ashley (LD - Warley)
councillor.aevans@calderdale.gov.uk

Fenton-Glynn, Josh (LAB - Calder)
councillor.jfentonglynn@calderdale.gov.uk

Ford, John (CON - Elland)
councillor.jford@calderdale.gov.uk

Foster, Michelle (LAB - Warley)
councillor.mfoster@calderdale.gov.uk

Foster, Dot (LAB - Sowerby Bridge)
councillor.dfoster@calderdale.gov.uk

Gallagher, Angie (LAB - Elland)
councillor.agallagher@calderdale.gov.uk

Greenwood, Marilyn (LD - Greetland & Stainland)
councillor.mgreenwood@calderdale.gov.uk

Hall, Graham (CON - Hipperholme & Lightcliffe)
councillor.ghall@calderdale.gov.uk

Hardy, John (CON - Skircoat)
councillor.jhardy@calderdale.gov.uk

Holden, Robert (CON - Ryburn)
councillor.rholden@calderdale.gov.uk

Jayne May, Nicola (CON - Luddendenfoot)
councillor.nmay@calcerdale.gov.uk

Kirton, David (CON - Hipperholme & Lightcliffe)
councillor.dkirton@calderdale.gov.uk

Lambert, Lisa (LAB - Illingworth & Mixenden)
councillor.llambert@calderdale.gov.uk

Lynn, Jenny (LAB - Park)
councillor.jlynn@calderdale.gov.uk

Metcalfe, Bob (LAB - Town)
councillor.bmetcalfe@calderdale.gov.uk

Miles, Ali (LAB - Calder)
councillor.amiles@calderdale.gov.uk

Mitchell, Lynne (CON - Rastrick)
councillor.lmitchell@calderdale.gov.uk

Payne, Michael (CON - Sowerby Bridge)
councillor.mpayne@calderdale.gov.uk

Pearson, Chris (CON - Greetland & Stainland)
cpearson@calderdale.gov.uk

Peel, Colin (CON - Brighouse)
councillor.cpeel@calderdale.gov.uk

Pillai, Chris (CON - Rastrick)
councillor.cpillai@calderdale.gov.uk

Press, Susan (LAB - Todmorden)
councillor.spress@calderdale.gov.uk

Raistrick, Colin (IND - Hipperholme & Lightcliffe)
councillor.craistrick@calderdale.gov.uk

Rivron, Helen (LAB - Ovenden)
councillor.hrivron@calderdale.gov.uk

Scullion, Jane (LAB - Luddendenfoot)
councillor.jscullion@calderdale.gov.uk

Shoukat, Faisal (LAB - Park)
councillor.fshoukat@calderdale.gov.uk

Smith, Bryan (LAB - Ovenden)
councillor.bsmith@calderdale.gov.uk

Smith-Moorhouse, Jill (CON - Luddendenfoot)
councillor.jsmith-moorhouse@calderdale.gov.uk

Sutherland, Daniel (LAB - Illingworth & Mixenden)
councillor.dsutherland@calderdale.gov.uk

Sweeney, Steve (LAB - Todmorden)
councillor.ssweeney@calderdale.gov.uk

Swift, Megan (LAB - Town)
councillor.mswift@calderdale.gov.uk

Tagg, Andrew (CON - Skircoat)
councillor.atagg@calderdale.gov.uk

Taylor, Roger (CON - Northowram & Shelf)
councillor.rtaylor@calderdale.gov.uk

Thompson, Marcus (CON - Skircoat)
councillor.mthompson@calderdale.gov.uk

Thornber, Robert (CON - Ryburn)
councillor.rthornber@calderdale.gov.uk

Wilkinson, Adam (LAB - Sowerby Bridge)
councillor.awilkinson@calderdale.gov.uk

Young, Dave (LAB - Calder)
councillor.dyoung@calderdale.gov.uk

POLITICAL COMPOSITION
LAB: 23, CON: 22, LD: 5, IND: 1

COMMITTEE CHAIRS

Adults, Health & Social Care: Mrs Marilyn Greenwood

Audit: Mr Stephen Baines

Children & Young People: Mrs Geraldine Carter

Economy & Environment: Mr James Baker

Health & Wellbeing: Mr Tim Swift

Licensing: Mrs Patricia Allen

CALDERDALE

Licensing: Mr Robert Thornber

Planning: Mr David Kirton

Cambridge City   D

Cambridge City Council, Mandela House, 4 Regent Street,
Cambridge CB2 1BY
☎ 01223 457000 🖷 01223 457009 ◌ enquiries@cambridge.gov.uk
🖳 www.cambridge.gov.uk

FACTS AND FIGURES
Parliamentary Constituencies: Cambridge, Cambridgeshire South
EU Constituencies: Eastern
Election Frequency: Elections are by thirds

PRINCIPAL OFFICERS

Chief Executive: Ms Antoinette Jackson, Chief Executive, The
Guildhall, Cambridge CB2 3QJ ☎ 01223 457003
◌ antoinette.jackson@cambridge.gov.uk

Senior Management: Ms Liz Bisset, Strategic Adviser - Housing
& Welfare Reform, Mandela House, 4 Regent Street, Cambridge
CB2 1BY ☎ 01223 457801 ◌ liz.bisset@cambridge.gov.uk

Senior Management: Ms Suzanne McBride, Strategic Director,
The Guildhall, Cambridge CB2 3QJ ☎ 01223 457478
◌ suzanne.mcbride@cambridge.gov.uk

Senior Management: Mr Ray Ward, Strategic Director, The
Guildhall, Cambridge CB2 3QJ ☎ 01223 457007
◌ ray.ward@cambridge.gov.uk

Access Officer / Social Services (Disability): Mr Mark Taylor,
Disability Access Officer, The Guildhall, Cambridge CB2 3QJ
☎ 01223 457075 ◌ mark.taylor@cambridge.gov.uk

Architect, Building / Property Services: Mr Will Barfield, Asset
Manager, Mill Road Depot, Mill Road, Cambridge CB1 2AZ
☎ 01223 457843 ◌ will.barfield@cambridge.gov.uk

Building Control: Mr John Thompson, Building Control Manager,
The Guildhall, Cambridge CB2 3QJ ☎ 01223 457111
◌ john.thompson@3csharedservices.org

PR / Communications: Mr Ashley Perry, Corporate Marketing
Manager, The Guildhall, Cambridge CB2 3QJ ☎ 01223 457064
◌ ashley.perry@cambridge.gov.uk

Community Safety: Ms Lynda Kilkelly, Community Safety
Manager, Hobson House, 44 St. Andrew's Street, Cambridge
CB2 3AS ☎ 01223 457045 ◌ lynda.kilkelly@cambridge.gov.uk

Corporate Services: Mr Steve Crabtree, Head of Internal Audit,
The Guildhall, Cambridge CB2 3QJ ☎ 01223 458181
◌ steve.crabtree@cambridge.gov.uk

Corporate Services: Mr Andrew Limb, Head of Corporate
Strategy, The Guildhall, Cambridge CB2 3QJ ☎ 01223 457004
◌ andrew.limb@cambridge.gov.uk

Customer Service: Mr Jonathan James, Head of Customer
Services, Mandela House, 4 Regent Street, Cambridge CB2 1BY
☎ 01223 458601 ◌ jonathan.james@cambridge.gov.uk

Electoral Registration: Ms Vicky Breading, Electoral Services
Manager, The Guildhall, Cambridge CB2 3QJ ☎ 01223 457057
◌ vicky.breading@cambridge.gov.uk

Emergency Planning: Mr Paul Parry, Corporate H&S and
Emergency Planning Manager, The Guildhall, Cambridge CB2 3QJ
☎ 01223 458033 ◌ paul.parry@cambridge.gov.uk

Environmental Health: Mr Joel Carre, Head of Environmental
Services, Mill Road Depot, Mill Road, Cambridge CB1 2AZ
☎ 01223 458201 ◌ joel.carre@cambridge.gov.uk

Estates, Property & Valuation: Mr Dave Prinsep, Head of
Property Services, The Guildhall, Cambridge CB2 3QJ
☎ 01223 457318 ◌ dave.prinsep@cambridge.gov.uk

Finance: Ms Alison Cole, Head of Revenues & Benefits, Mandela
House, 4 Regent Street, Cambridge CB2 1BY ☎ 01223 457701
◌ alison.cole@cambridge.gov.uk

Finance: Ms Caroline Ryba, Head of Finance, The Guildhall,
Cambridge CB2 3QJ ☎ 01223 458134
◌ caroline.ryba@cambridge.gov.uk

Fleet Management: Mr David Cox, Fleet Manager, Mill Road
Depot, Mill Road, Cambridge CB1 2AZ ☎ 01223 458265
◌ david.cox@cambridge.gov.uk

Grounds Maintenance: Mr Joel Carre, Head of Environmental
Services, Mill Road Depot, Mill Road, Cambridge CB1 2AZ
☎ 01223 458201 ◌ joel.carre@cambridge.gov.uk

Health and Safety: Mr Paul Parry, Corporate H&S and
Emergency Planning Manager, The Guildhall, Cambridge CB2 3QJ
☎ 01223 458033 ◌ paul.parry@cambridge.gov.uk

Home Energy Conservation: Mr Justin Smith, Home Energy
Officer, Mandela House, 4 Regent Street, Cambridge CB2 1BY
☎ 01223 457954 ◌ justin.smith@cambridge.gov.uk

Housing: Mr Tom Bremner, Interim Head of Housing Services, City
Homes North, 171 Arbury Road, Cambridge CB4 2YG
☎ 01223 458401 ◌ tom.bremner@cambridge.gov.uk

Housing: Mr Alan Carter, Managing Director - Housing
Development Agency, Hobson House, 44 St. Andrew's Street,
Cambridge CB4 2YG ☎ 01223 457948
◌ alan.carter@cambridge.gov.uk

Housing Maintenance: Mr Dave Prinsep, Head of Property
Services, The Guildhall, Cambridge CB2 3QJ ☎ 01223 457318
◌ dave.prinsep@cambridge.gov.uk

Legal: Mr Tom Lewis, Head of Legal Practice, The Guildhall,
Cambridge CB2 3QJ ☎ 01223 457401 ◌ tom.lewis@cambridge.gov.uk

Leisure and Cultural Services: Ms Debbie Kaye, Head of Community Services, Hobson House, 44 St Andrew's Street, Cambridge CB2 3AS ☎ 01223 458633
⌂ debbie.kaye@cambridge.gov.uk

Licensing: Mr Joel Carre, Head of Environmental Services, Mill Road Depot, Mill Road, Cambridge CB1 2AZ ☎ 01223 458201
⌂ joel.carre@cambridge.gov.uk

Member Services: Ms Kathy Brown, EA to Leader & Members, The Guildhall, Cambridge CB2 3QJ ☎ 01223 457022
⌂ kathy.brown@cambridge.gov.uk

Member Services: Mr Gary Clift, Head of Democratic Services, The Guildhall, Cambridge CB2 3QJ ☎ 01223 457011
⌂ gary.clift@cambridge.gov.uk

Parking: Mr James Elms, Head of Commercial Services, Mill Road Depot, Mill Road, Cambridge CB1 2AZ ☎ 01223 458510
⌂ james.elms@cambridge.gov.uk

Personnel / HR: Ms Deborah Simpson, Head of Human Resources, The Guildhall, Cambridge CB2 3QJ ☎ 01223 458101
⌂ deborah.simpson@cambridge.gov.uk

Planning: Mr Stephen Kelly, Director - Planning & Economic Development, The Guildhall, Cambridge CB2 3QJ ☎ 01223 457103
⌂ stephen.kelly@cambridge.gov.uk

Procurement: Mr John Bridgwater, Strategic Procurement Adviser, The Guildhall, Cambridge CB2 3QJ ☎ 01223 458178
⌂ john.bridgwater@cambridge.gov.uk

Recycling & Waste Minimisation: Ms Kylie Laws, Waste Policy, Change & Innovations Manager, Dickerson Industrial Estate, Ely Road, Waterbeach, Cambridge CB25 9PG ☎ 01954 713192
⌂ kylie.laws@scambs.gov.uk

Staff Training: Ms Deborah Simpson, Head of Human Resources, The Guildhall, Cambridge CB2 3QJ ☎ 01223 458101
⌂ deborah.simpson@cambridge.gov.uk

Street Scene: Mr Joel Carre, Head of Environmental Services, Mill Road Depot, Mill Road, Cambridge CB1 2AZ ☎ 01223 458201
⌂ joel.carre@cambridge.gov.uk

Tourism: Mrs Emma Thornton, CEO - Visit Cambridge & Beyond, The Guildhall, Cambridge CB2 3QJ ☎ 01223 791517
⌂ emma.thornton@visitcambridge.org

Town Centre: Mrs Emma Thornton, CEO - Visit Cambridge & Beyond, The Guildhall, Cambridge CB2 3QJ ☎ 01223 791517
⌂ emma.thornton@visitcambridge.org

Waste Collection and Disposal: Mr Paul Vanston, Head of Waste Resources, Dickerson Industrial Estate, Ely Road, Waterbeach, Cambridge CB25 9PG ☎ 01954 713154
⌂ paul.vanston@cambridge.gov.uk

Waste Management: Mr Paul Vanston, Head of Waste Resources, Dickerson Industrial Estate, Ely Road, Waterbeach, Cambridge CB25 9PG ☎ 01954 713154
⌂ paul.vanston@cambridge.gov.uk

COUNCILLORS

Mayor: Benstead, Jeremy (LAB - Coleridge)
j_benstead@live.co.uk

Deputy Mayor: Holland, Marie-Louise (IND - Castle)
marie-louise.holland@cambridge.gov.uk

Leader of the Council: Herbert, Lewis (LAB - Coleridge)
lewis.herbert@cambridge.gov.uk

Deputy Leader of the Council: O'Reilly, Carina (LAB - Arbury)
carinaoreilly@gmail.com

Deputy Leader of the Council: Price, Kevin (LAB - King's Hedges)
kevin.price@cambridge.gov.uk

Group LeaderHipkin, John (IND - Castle)
castleindependent@gmail.com

Abbott, Margery (LAB - East Chesterton)
margery.abbott.labour@hotmail.co.uk

Ashton, Mark (LAB - Cherry Hinton)
mark.ashton@cambridge.gov.uk

Austin, Ysanne (LD - West Chesterton)
ysanne.austin@cambridge.gov.uk

Avery, Nicholas (LD - Trumpington)
nick.avery@cambridge.gov.uk

Avery, Nicholas (LD - Trumpington)
nick.avery@cambridge.gov.uk

Baigent, Dave (LAB - Romsey)
dave.baigent@cambridge.gov.uk

Barnett, Sophie (LAB - Romsey)
sophie.barnett@cambridge.gov.uk

Bick, Tim (LD - Market)
tim.bick@btinternet.com

Bird, Gerri (LAB - East Chesterton)
gerribird@sky.com

Blencowe, Kevin (LAB - Petersfield)
kevin.blencowe@gmail.com

Cantrill, Rod (LD - Newnham)
rcantrill@millingtonadvisory.com

Dryden, Robert (LAB - Cherry Hinton)
robert.dryden@cambridge.gov.uk

Gawthrope, Nigel (LAB - King's Hedges)
nigel.gawthrope@cambridge.gov.uk

Gehring, Markus (LD - Newnham)
markus.gehring@cambridge.gov.uk

Gillespie, Oscar (GRN - Market)
oscar.gillespie@cambridge.gov.uk

Hart, Caroline (LAB - Abbey)
caroline.hart@cambridge.gov.uk

Holt, Valerie (LD - Castle)
valerie.holt@cambridge.gov.uk

Johnson, Richard (LAB - Abbey)
richard.johnston@cambridge.gov.uk

CAMBRIDGE CITY

McPherson, Russell (LAB - Cherry Hinton)
russ.mcpherson@cambridge.gov.uk

Moore, Rosy (LAB - Coleridge)
rosy.moore@cambridge.gov.uk

Moore, Tim (LD - Queen Edith's)
tim.moore@cambridge.gov.uk

Nethsingha, Lucy (LD - Newnham)
nethsingha@btinternet.com

O'Connell, Zoe (LD - Trumpington)
zoe.coconnell@cambridge.gov.uk

Page-Croft, Jennifer (LD - Queen Edith's)
jennifer.croft@cambridge.gov.uk

Perry, Charlotte (LAB - Arbury)
charlotte.perry@cambridge.gov.uk

Pippas, George (LD - Queen Edith's)
george.pippas@cambridge.gov.uk

Ratcliffe, Dan (LAB - Market)
dan.ratcliffe@cambridge.gov.uk

Roberts, Peter (LAB - Abbey)
peter.roberts@cambridge.gov.uk

Robertson, Richard (LAB - Petersfield)
richard.robertson@cambridge.gov.uk

Sargeant, Mike (LAB - West Chesterton)
mikesargeant@ntlworld.com

Sarris, Peter (LAB - East Chesterton)
peter.sarris@cambridge.gov.uk

Sinnott, Ann (LAB - Petersfield)
ann.sinnott@cambridge.gov.uk

Smart, Martin (LAB - King's Hedges)
martin.smart@cambridge.gov.uk

Smith, Anna (LAB - Romsey)
anna.smith@cambridge.gov.uk

Todd-Jones, Mike (LAB - Arbury)
mike.todd-jones@cambridge.gov.uk

Tunnacliffe, Damien (LD - West Chesterton)
damientunnacliffe@yahoo.gov.uk

POLITICAL COMPOSITION
LAB: 26, LD: 13, IND: 2, GRN: 1

COMMITTEE CHAIRS

Environment: Ms Charlotte Perry

Housing: Mr Mike Todd-Jones

Licensing: Ms Gerri Bird

Planning: Mr John Hipkin

Cambridgeshire   C

Cambridgeshire County Council, Box ET 1021, Shire Hall,
Castle Hill, Cambridge CB3 0AP
☎ 0345 045 5200 🖷 01223 717201 🕾 info@cambridgeshire.gov.uk
🖳 www.cambridgeshire.gov.uk

FACTS AND FIGURES
Parliamentary Constituencies: Huntingdon

EU Constituencies: Eastern
Election Frequency: Elections are of whole council

PRINCIPAL OFFICERS

Chief Executive: Mrs Gillian Beasley, Chief Executive, Town Hall,
Bridge Street, Peterborough PE1 1HL ☎ 01733 452390
🕾 gillian.beasley@peterborough.gov.uk

Senior Management: Ms Sue Grace, Corporate Director -
Customer Service & Transformation, Box SH1103, Shire Hall, Castle
Hill, Cambridge CB3 0AP ☎ 01223 699248
🕾 sue.grace@cambridgeshire.gov.uk

Senior Management: Mr Graham Hughes, Executive Director -
Environment, Transport & Economy, Box CC1307, Shire Hall, Castle
Hill, Cambridge CB3 0AP ☎ 01223 699246
🕾 graham.hughes@cambridgeshire.gov.uk

Senior Management: Mr Adrian Loades, Executive Director -
Children, Families & Adults, CC 1001, Shire Hall, Cambridge CB3
0AP ☎ 01223 727993 🕾 adrian.loades@cambridgeshire.gov.uk

Senior Management: Mr Chris Maylon, Chief Finance Officer,
Box RES 1211, Shire Hall, Castle Hill, Cambridge CB3 0AP ☎ 01223
699796 🕾 chris.maylon@cambridgeshire.gov.uk

Senior Management: Dr Liz Robin, Director - Public Health, Box
ET 1021, Shire Hall, Castle Hill, Cambridge CB3 0AP ☎ 0345 045
5200 🕾 liz.robin@cambridgeshire.gov.uk

Best Value: Mr James Gemmell, Data & Performance Manager,
BH1107, Shire Hall, Castle Hill, Cambridge CB3 0AP ☎ 01223
699067 🕾 james.gemmell@cambridgeshire.gov.uk

Catering Services: Mr Rudy Imhoof, Interim Head of Catering &
Cleaning Services, CC 1105, Shire Hall, Castle Hill, Cambridge
CB3 0AP ☎ 01233 703509 🕾 rudy.imhoof@cambridgeshire.gov.uk

Children / Youth Services: Ms Sarah Ferguson, Service Director
- Children's Enhanced & Preventative Services, CC1001, Shire Hall,
Cambridge CB3 0AP ☎ 01223 727990
🕾 sarah.ferguson@cambridgeshire.gov.uk

Children / Youth Services: Mr Keith Grimwade, Director -
Learning, CC 1001, Shire Hall, Cambridge CB3 0AP
☎ 01223 727988 🕾 keith.grimwade@cambridgeshire.gov.uk

Children / Youth Services: Ms Theresa Leavy, Interim Director
- Social Care, Children & Young People's Services, CC 1001, Shire
Hall, Cambridge CB3 0AP ☎ 01223 727989
🕾 theresa.leavy@cambridgeshire.gov.uk

Children / Youth Services: Mr Adrian Loades, Executive
Director - Children, Families & Adults, CC 1001, Shire Hall,
Cambridge CB3 0AP
☎ 01223 727993 🕾 adrian.loades@cambridgeshire.gov.uk

Civil Registration: Ms Louise Clover, Support Manager -
Registrations & Coroners, Lawrence Court, Princes Street,
Huntingdon PE29 3PA ☎ 01223 715365
🕾 louise.clover@cambridgeshire.gov.uk

PR / Communications: Mr Simon Cobby, Strategic Marketing & Communications Manager, Box Res 1101, Shire Hall, Castle Hill, Cambridge CB3 0AP ☎ 01223 699281 ✎ simon.cobby@cambridgeshire.gov.uk

Community Planning: Mr Paul Nelson, Acting Head of Passenger Transport, CC 1212, Shire Hall, Castle Hill, Cambridge CB3 0AP ☎ 01223 715585 ✎ paul.nelson@cambridgeshire.gov.ui

Community Safety: Dr Liz Robin, Director - Public Health, CC 1108, Shire Hall, Castle Hill, Cambridge CB3 0AP ☎ 01223 725401 ✎ liz.robin@cambridgeshire.gov.uk

Computer Management: Mr John Platten, Channel Strategy Manager, SH 1001, Shire Hall, Castle Hill, Cambridge CB3 0AP ☎ 01223 699712 ✎ john.platten@cambridgeshire.gov.uk

Consumer Protection and Trading Standards: Ms Aileen Andrews, Operations Manager - Supporting Business & Communities, Box ET 4000, Sackville House, Sackville Way, Great Cambourne, Cambridge CB3 0AP ☎ 01954 284659 ✎ aileen.andrews@cambridgeshire.gov.uk

Corporate Services: Ms Sue Grace, Corporate Director - Customer Service & Transformation, Box SH1103, Shire Hall, Castle Hill, Cambridge CB3 0AP ☎ 01223 699248 ✎ sue.grace@cambridgeshire.gov.uk

Customer Service: Ms Sue Grace, Corporate Director - Customer Service & Transformation, Box SH1103, Shire Hall, Castle Hill, Cambridge CB3 0AP ☎ 01223 699248 ✎ sue.grace@cambridgeshire.gov.uk

Customer Service: Ms Jo Tompkins, Customer Services Manager, DA3 Contact Centre, St. Ives PE27 5JL ☎ 01480 373406 ✎ jo.tompkins@cambridgeshire.gov.uk

Economic Development: Mr Guy Mills, Enterprise & Economy Development Manager, SH1315, Shire Hall, Castle Hill, Cambridge CB3 0AP ☎ 01223 699929 ✎ guy.mills@cambridgeshire.gov.uk

Education: Mr Keith Grimwade, Director - Learning, CC 1001, Shire Hall, Cambridge CB3 0AP ☎ 01223 727988 ✎ keith.grimwade@cambridgeshire.gov.uk

Emergency Planning: Mr Stewart Thomas, Head of Emergency Planning, RES 1403, Shire Hall, Castle Hill, Cambridge CB3 0AP ☎ 01223 727944 ✎ stewart.thomas@cambridgeshire.gov.uk

Estates, Property & Valuation: Ms Lesley Currie, Capital Projects Manager, Box ET 1021, Shire Hall, Castle Hill, Cambridge CB3 0AP ☎ 01223 699711 ✎ lecurrie@northamptonshire.gov.uk

Facilities: Mr Jim Mowatt, Service Facilities Manager, RES1010, Shire Hall, Castle Hill, Cambridge CB3 0AP ☎ 01223 699098 ✎ jim.mowatt@cambridgeshire.gov.uk

Finance: Ms Sarah Heywood, Head of Finance & Performance (CFA), SH1395, Shire Hall, Castle Hill, Cambridge CB3 0AP ☎ 01223 699714 ✎ sarah.heywood@cambridgeshire.gov.uk

Finance: Mr Chris Maylon, Chief Finance Officer, Box RES 1211, Shire Hall, Castle Hill, Cambridge CB3 0AP ☎ 01223 699796 ✎ chris.maylon@cambridgeshire.gov.uk

Finance: Mr Ian Smith, Strategy Finance Manager, RES1303, Shire Hall, Castle Hill, Cambridge CB3 0AP ☎ 01223 699807 ✎ ian.smith@cambridgeshire.gov.uk

Treasury: Mr Mike Batty, Principal Accountant, RES1211, Shire Hall, Castle Hill, Cambridge CB3 0AP ☎ 01223 699942 ✎ mike.batty@cambridgeshire.gov.uk

Pensions: Mr Steve Dainty, Head of Pensions, Shire Hall, Shire Hall, Cambridge CB3 0AP ☎ 0345 045 5200 ✎ steve.dainty@cambridgeshire.gov.uk

Health and Safety: Mr Stuart Wood, Health & Safety Manager, RES 1413, Shire Hall, Castle Hill, Cambridge CB3 0AP ☎ 01223 699122 ✎ stuart.wood@cambridgeshire.gov.uk

Highways: Mr Richard Lumley, Head of Local Infrastructure & Street Management, SH1204, Shire Hall, Castle Hill, Cambridge CB3 0AP ☎ 01223 703839 ✎ richard.lumley@cambridgeshire.gov.uk

Legal: Mr Quentin Baker, Director - Legal Services, Shire Hall, Shire Hall, Cambridge CB3 0AP ☎ 01223 727961 ✎ quentin.baker@cambridgeshire.gov.uk

Lighting: Mr Richard Ling, Signals & Systems Manager, Welbrook Court, Girton, Cambridge CB3 0NA ☎ 01223 715916 ✎ richard.ling@cambridgeshire.gov.uk

Lottery Funding, Charity and Voluntary: Mr Robert Sanderson, Senior Democratic Services Officer, Box ET 1021, Shire Hall, Castle Hill, Cambridge CB3 0AP ☎ 01223 699181 ✎ robert.sanderson@cambridgeshire.gov.uk

Member Services: Ms Karin Aston, Member Services Officer, SH1102, Shire Hall, Castle Hill, Cambridge CB3 0AP ☎ 01223 699170 ✎ karin.astin@cambridgeshire.gov.uk

Parking: Mr Philip Hammer, Parking Operations Manager, RES1416, Shire Hall, Castle Hill, Cambridge CB3 0AP ☎ 01223 727901 ✎ philip.hammer@cambridgeshire.gov.uk

Planning: Mr Bob Menzies, Service Director - Strategy & Development, CC1307, Shire Hall, Castle Hill, Cambridge CB3 0AP ☎ 01223 715664 ✎ bob.menzies@cambridgeshire.gov.uk

Public Libraries: Ms Jill Terrell, Acting Head of Libraries, Archives & Information, Box CC 1218, Shire Hall, Castle Hill, Cambridge CB3 0AP ☎ 01223 703521 ✎ jill.terrell@cambridgeshire.gov.uk

Recycling & Waste Minimisation: Mr Donald Haymes, Waste Services Manager, Box CC 1215, Shire Hall, Castle Hill, Cambridge CB3 0AP ☎ 01223 728560 ✎ donald.haymes@cambridgeshire.gov.uk

Road Safety: Ms Amanda Mays, Road Safety Manager, CC1309, Cambridgeshire Highways, Welbrooke Court, Girton, Cambridge CB3 0NA ☎ 01223 715923 ✎ amanda.mays@cambridgeshire.gov.uk

CAMBRIDGESHIRE

Social Services: Ms Jean Fletcher, Head of Procurement (Social Care), Box CC 1006, Shire Hall, Castle Hill, Cambridge CB3 0AP ☎ 01223 729130 ⌁ jean.fletcher@cambridgeshire.gov.uk

Social Services: Ms Sarah-Jane Smedmore, Head of Safeguarding & Standards, CC1005, Shire Hall, Castle Hill, Cambridge CB3 0AP ☎ 01223 699920 ⌁ sarah-jane.smedmore@cambridgeshire.gov.uk

Social Services (Adult): Ms Charlotte Black, Director - Older People's Services & Mental Health, CC1323, Shire Hall, Castle Hill, Cambridge CB3 0AP ☎ 01223 727993 ⌁ charlotte.black@cambridgeshire.gov.uk

Social Services (Adult): Ms Claire Bruin, Service Director - Adult Social Care, Box CC1315, Castle Court, Shire Hall, Castle Hill, Cambridge CB3 0AP ☎ 01223 715665 ⌁ claire.bruin@cambridgeshire.gov.uk

Social Services (Adult): Mr Adrian Loades, Executive Director - Children, Families & Adults, CC 1001, Shire Hall, Cambridge CB3 0AP ☎ 01223 727993 ⌁ adrian.loades@cambridgeshire.gov.uk

Social Services (Children): Ms Theresa Leavy, Interim Director - Social Care, Children & Young People's Services, CC 1001, Shire Hall, Cambridge CB3 0AP ☎ 01223 727989 ⌁ theresa.leavy@cambridgeshire.gov.uk

Social Services (Children): Mr Adrian Loades, Executive Director - Children, Families & Adults, Box CC 1001, Shire Hall, Castle Hill, Cambridge CB3 0AP ☎ 01223 727993 ⌁ adrian.loades@cambridgeshire.gov.uk

Public Health: Dr Liz Robin, Director - Public Health, Box ET 1021, Shire Hall, Castle Hill, Cambridge CB3 0AP ☎ 0345 045 5200 ⌁ liz.robin@cambridgeshire.gov.uk

Staff Training: Mr Rob Parker, Organisational & Workforce Development Advisor, RES 1227, Shire Hall, Castle Hill, Cambridge CB3 0AP ☎ 01223 706337 ⌁ rob.parker@cambridgeshire.gov.uk

Traffic Management: Ms Sonia Hansen, Traffic Manager, SH 1204, Shire Hall, Castle Hill, Cambridge CB3 0AP ☎ 01223 713817 ⌁ sonia.hansen@cambridgeshire.gov.uk

Transport: Mr Paul Nelson, Acting Head of Passenger Transport, CC 1212, Shire Hall, Castle Hill, Cambridge CB3 0AP ☎ 01223 715585 ⌁ paul.nelson@cambridgeshire.gov.ui

COUNCILLORS

Leader of the Council: Count, Steve (CON - March North) steve.count@cambridgeshire.gov.uk

Ashcroft, Peter (UKIP - Huntingdon) peter.ashcroft@cambridgeshire.gov.uk

Ashwood, Barbara (LD - Trumpington) barbara.ashwood@cambridgeshire.gov.uk

Bailey, Anna (CON - Ely South & West) anna.bailey@cambridgeshire.gov.uk

Bates, Ian (CON - The Hemingfords & Fenstanton) ian.bates@cambridgeshire.gov.uk

Boden, Chris (CON - Wisbech North) chris.boden@cambridgeshire.gov.uk

Brown, Peter (CON - Huntingdon) sirpeter.brown@cambridgeshire.gov.uk

Brown, David (CON - Burwell) david.brown@cambridgeshire.gov.uk

Bullen, Paul (UKIP - St Ives) paul.bullen@cambridgeshire.gov.uk

Butcher, Ralph (CON - Whittlesey South) butcher919@btinternet.com

Bywater, Simon (UKIP - Sawtry & Ellington) simon.bywater@cambridgeshire.gov.uk

Cearns, Edward (LD - Market) edward.cearns@cambridgeshire.gov.uk

Chapman, Barry (CON - Little Paxton & St Neots North) barry.champan@cambridgeshire.gov.uk

Clapp, Paul (UKIP - Wisbech North) paul.clapp@cambridgeshire.gov.uk

Clark, John (CON - March West) johnclark786@btinternet.com

Connor, David (CON - Forty Foot) david.connor@cambridgeshire.gov.uk

Crawford, Sandra (LAB - Cherry Hinton) sandra.crawford@cambridgeshire.gov.uk

Criswell, Steve (CON - Somersham & Earith) steve.criswell@cambridgeshire.gov.uk

Dent, Adrian (CON - Bassingbourn) adrian.dent@cambridgeshire.gov.uk

Divine, Daniel (UKIP - Littleport) daniel.divine@cambridgeshire.gov.uk

Downes, Peter (LD - Brampton & Kimbolton) peter.downes@cambridgeshire.gov.uk

Dupre, Lorna (LD - Sutton) lorna@lornadupre.org.uk

Frost, Stephen (CON - Hardwick) stephen.frost@cambridgeshire.gov.uk

Giles, Derek (IND - St Neots Eaton Socon & Eynesbury) derek.giles@cambridgeshire.gov.uk

Gillick, Gordon (UKIP - Waldersey) gordon.gillick@cambridgeshire.gov.uk

Harford, Lynda (CON - Bar Hill) lyndaharford@icloud.com

Harty, David (CON - Little Paxton & St Neots North) david.harty@cambridgeshire.gov.uk

Henson, Roger (UKIP - Norman Cross) roger.henson@cambridgeshire.gov.uk

Hickford, Roger (CON - Linton) roger.hickford@cambridgeshire.gov.uk

Hipkin, John (IND - Castle) john.hipkin@cambridgeshire.gov.uk

Hoy, Samantha (CON - Whittlesey South) samphoy@googlemail.com

Hudson, Peter (CON - Willingham) peter.hudson@cambridgeshire.gov.uk

Hunt, William (CON - Haddenham)
william.hunt@cambridgeshire.gov.uk

Jenkins, David (LD - Cottenham, Histon & Impington)
ccc@davidjenkins.org.uk

Kavanagh, Noel (LAB - Coleridge)
noel.kavanagh@cambridgeshire.gov.uk

Kenney, Gail (CON - Sawston)
gail.kenney@cambridgeshire.gov.uk

Kindersley, Sebastian (LD - Gamlingay)
skindersley@hotmail.com

Lay, Alan (UKIP - King's Hedges)
alan_lay@sky.com

Leeke, Maurice (LD - Waterbeach)
maurice.leeke@cambridgeshire.gov.uk

Loynes, Mervyn (CON - Bourn)
mervyn.loynes@cambridgeshire.gov.uk

Mandley, Richard (UKIP - Chatteris)
shipmatedick@aol.com

Manning, Ian (LD - East Chesterton)
manning.ian@gmail.com

Mason, Mike (IND - Cottenham, Histon & Impington)
mike.mason@cambridgeshire.gov.uk

McGuire, Mac (CON - Norman Cross)
mac.mcguire@cambridgeshire.gov.uk

Moghadas, Zoe (LAB - Romsey)
zoe.moghadas@cambridgeshire.gov.uk

Nethsingha, Lucy (LD - Newnham)
nethsingha@btinternet.com

Onasanya, Fiona (LAB - King's Hedges)
fiona.onasanya@cambridgeshire.gov.uk

Orgee, Tony (CON - Sawston)
tony.orgee@cambridgeshire.gov.uk

Palmer, James (CON - Soham & Fordham Villages)
jpp@oakhouse@gmail.com

Reeve, Peter (UKIP - Ramsey)
reeve@ukip.org

Reynolds, Kevin (CON - St Ives)
kevin.reynolds@cambridgeshire.gov.uk

Rouse, Michael (CON - Ely North & East)
michael.rouse@cambridgeshire.gov.uk

Sales, Paul (LAB - Arbury)
cccpaul.sales@gmail.com

Schumann, Joshua (CON - Soham & Fordham Villages)
joshua.schumann@cambridgeshire.gov.uk

Scutt, Jocelynne (LAB - West Chesterton)
jocelynne.scutt@cambridgeshire.gov.uk

Shellens, Michael (LD - Godmanchester & Huntingdon East)
shellens@waitrose.com

Shuter, Mathew (CON - Woodditton)
mshuter@btinternet.com

Smith, Mandy (CON - Papworth & Swavesey)
mandysmith310@btinternet.com

Taylor, Simone (IND - St Neots Eaton Socon & Eynesbury)
simone45taylor@yahoo.com

Taylor, Amanda (LD - Queen Edith's)
amanda.taylor@cambridgeshire.gov.uk

Tew, Michael (UKIP - Warboys & Upwood)
michael.tew@cambridgeshire.gov.uk

Topping, Peter (CON - Duxford)
peter.topping@cambridgeshire.gov.uk

van de Ven, Susan (LD - Melbourn)
susanvendeven@yahoo.co.uk

Walsh, Ashley (LAB - Waldersey)
ashley.walsh@cambridgeshire.gov.uk

Whitehead, Joan (LAB - Abbey)
joan.whitehead@cambridgeshire.gov.uk

Williams, John (LD - Fulbourn)
john.williams@cambridgeshire.gov.uk

Wilson, Graham (LD - Godmanchester & Huntingdon East)
graham.wilson@cambridgeshire.gov.uk

Wisson, Julie (CON - Buckden, Gransden & The Offords)
julie.wisson@cambridgeshire.gov.uk

Yeulett, Frederick (CON - March East)
fred.yeulett@cambridgeshire.gov.uk

POLITICAL COMPOSITION
CON: 32, LD: 14, UKIP: 11, LAB: 8, IND: 4

COMMITTEE CHAIRS

Adults: Mr Michael Tew

Audit & Accounts: Mr Michael Shellens

Children & Young People: Ms Joan Whitehead

Economy & Environment: Mr Ian Bates

Health & Wellbeing: Mr Tony Orgee

Camden   L

Camden London Borough Council, Town Hall, Judd Street,
London WC1H 9JE
☎ 020 7974 4444 🖳 www.camden.gov.uk

FACTS AND FIGURES
Parliamentary Constituencies: Hampstead and Kilburn, Holborn
and St. Pancras
EU Constituencies: London
Election Frequency: Elections are of whole council

PRINCIPAL OFFICERS

Chief Executive: Mr Mike Cooke, Chief Executive, Town Hall,
Judd Street, London WC1H 9JE ☎ 020 7974 5686
⌁ mike.cooke@camden.gov.uk

Deputy Chief Executive: Ms Rachel Stopard, Deputy Chief
Executive - Transformation & Policy, 5 Pancras Square, London
N1C 4AG ☎ 020 7974 5621; 020 7974 5556
⌁ rachel.stopard@camden.gov.uk

Senior Management: Ms Julie Billett, Director - Public Health, 5
Pancras Square, London N1C 4AG ☎ 020 7527 1221
⌁ julie.billett@camden.gov.uk

CAMDEN

Senior Management: Mr Andrew Maughan, Borough Solicitor, 5 Pancras Square, London N1C 4AG ☎ 020 7974 5656 ⌂ andrew.maughan@camden.gov.uk

Senior Management: Mr Mike O'Donnell, Executive Director - Corporate Services, 5 Pancras Square, London N1C 4AG ☎ 020 7974 5933 ⌂ mike.odonnell@camden.gov.uk

Senior Management: Mr Martin Pratt, Executive Director - Supporting People, 5 Pancras Square, London N1C 4AG ☎ 020 7974 1505 ⌂ martin.pratt@camden.gov.uk

Senior Management: Ms Jenny Rowlands, Executive Director - Supporting Communities, 5 Pancras Square, London N1C 4AG ⌂ jenny.rowlands@camden.gov.uk

Access Officer / Social Services (Disability): Ms Anne Turner, Director - Children's Safeguarding & Social Work, 5 Pancras Square, London N1C 4AG ☎ 020 7974 6641 ⌂ anne.turner@camden.gov.uk

Architect, Building / Property Services: Ms Kate Casey, Director - Property Management, 5 Pancras Square, London N1C 4AG ⌂ kate.casey@camden.gov.uk

Building Control: Mr Nasser Rad, Head of Service - Building Control, 5 Pancras Square, London N1C 4AG ☎ 020 7974 2387 ⌂ nasser.rad@camden.gov.uk

Catering Services: Ms Jean Darko, Assistant Facilities Management Contract & Performance Manager, 5 Pancras Square, London N1C 4AG ☎ 020 7974 5072 ⌂ jean.darko@camden.gov.uk

Children / Youth Services: Ms Eve Stickler, Director - Early Intervention & Prevention, 5 Pancras Square, London N1C 4AG ☎ 020 7974 1177 ⌂ eve.stickler@camden.gov.uk

Civil Registration: Ms Jenni Grant, Registration Services Team Leader / Superintendent Registrar, Town Hall, Judd Street, London WC1H 9JE ☎ 020 7974 1057 ⌂ jenni.grant@camden.gov.uk

PR / Communications: Mr Robert Beasley, Interim Head of Communications, 5 Pancras Square, London N1C 4AG ☎ 020 7974 4444 ⌂ robert.beasley@camden.gov.uk

Community Safety: Mr Tom Preest, Assistant Director - Communities, 5 Pancras Square, London N1C 4AG ☎ 020 7974 3461 ⌂ tom.preest@camden.gov.uk

Computer Management: Mr Omid Shiraji, Interim Assistant Director - ICT, 5 Pancras Square, London N1C 4AG ☎ 020 7974 1023 ⌂ omid.shiraji@camden.gov.uk

Consumer Protection and Trading Standards: Mr Jim Foudy, Head of Regulatory Services, 5 Pancras Square, London N1C 4AG ☎ 020 7974 6962 ⌂ jim.foudy@camden.gov.uk

Corporate Services: Mr Mike O'Donnell, Executive Director - Corporate Services, 5 Pancras Square, London N1C 4AG ☎ 020 7974 5933 ⌂ mike.odonnell@camden.gov.uk

Customer Service: Ms Kate Robertson, Director - Customer Services, 5 Pancras Square, London N1C 4AG ☎ 020 7974 8109 ⌂ kate.robertson@camden.gov.uk

Economic Development: Ms Karen Galey, Head of Economic Development, 5 Pancras Square, London N1C 4AG ☎ 020 7974 4059 ⌂ karen.galey@camden.gov.uk

Education: Mr Peter Dudley, Director - Education (Achievement & Aspiration), 5 Pancras Square, London N1C 4AG ☎ 020 7974 3813 ⌂ peter.dudley@camden.gov.uk

Electoral Registration: Ms Clare Oakley, Elections Manager, Town Hall, Judd Street, London WC1H 9JE ☎ 020 7974 6372 ⌂ clare.oakley@camden.gov.uk

Emergency Planning: Mr Darren Wilsher, Head of Emergency Management, Borough Emergency Control Centre, Dennis Geffen Annexe, Camley Street, London NW1 0PS ☎ 020 7974 2797 ⌂ darren.wilsher@camden.gov.uk

Energy Management: Mr Harold Garner, Energy & Sustainability Manager, 5 Pancras Square, London N1C 4AG ☎ 020 7974 2701 ⌂ harold.garner@camden.gov.uk

Environmental / Technical Services: Mr Paul Dunphy, Acting Director - Place Management, 5 Pancras Square, London N1C 4AG ☎ 020 7974 2246 ⌂ paul.dunphy@camden.gov.uk

Environmental Health: Mr Winston Labarr, Business Compliance Manager, 5 Pancras Square, London N1C 4AG ☎ 020 7974 6369 ⌂ winston.labarr@camden.gov.uk

Events Manager: Ms Nicky Ezer, Manager - Events Service & Camden Centre, 5 Pancras Square, London N1C 4AG ☎ 020 7974 1932 ⌂ nicky.ezer@camden.gov.uk

Facilities: Mr Terry Gallagher, Senior Practitioner - Corporate Building Management, 5 Pancras Square, London N1C 4AG ☎ 020 7974 1626 ⌂ terry.gallager@camden.gov.uk

Finance: Mr Mike O'Donnell, Executive Director - Corporate Services, 5 Pancras Square, London N1C 4AG ☎ 020 7974 5933 ⌂ mike.odonnell@camden.gov.uk

Finance: Mr Jon Rowney, Deputy Director - Finance & Procurement, 5 Pancras Square, London N1C 4AG ☎ 020 7974 6960 ⌂ jon.rowney@camden.gov.uk

Treasury: Mr Nigel Mascarenhas, Head of Treasury & Financial Transactions, 5 Pancras Square, London N1C 4AG ☎ 020 7974 1904 ⌂ nigel.mascarenhas@camden.gov.uk

Pensions: Mr Nigel Mascarenhas, Head of Treasury & Financial Transactions, 5 Pancras Square, London N1C 4AG ☎ 020 7974 1904 ⌂ nigel.mascarenhas@camden.gov.uk

Fleet Management: Ms Josephine Allman, Head of Camden Accessible Travel Solutions, York Way Depot, 7 York Way, London N1C 4BE ☎ 020 7974 5560 ⌂ josephine.allman@camden.gov.uk

Grounds Maintenance: Mr Oliver Myers, Head of Sustainability & Green Space, 5 Pancras Square, London N1C 4AG
☎ 020 7974 6370 ✆ oliver.myers@camden.gov.uk

Health and Safety: Mr Darren Williams, Health & Safety Manager, 5 Pancras Square, London N1C 4AG ☎ 020 7974 2117
✆ darren.williams@camden.gov.uk

Highways: Mr George Loureda, Head of Engineering Service, 5 Pancras Square, London N1C 4AG ☎ 020 7974 6949
✆ george.loureda@camden.gov.uk

Housing: Mr Shaun Flook, Head of Housing Needs Group, 5 Pancras Square, London N1C 4AG ☎ 020 7974 1966
✆ shaun.flook@camden.gov.uk

Housing: Mr Rhys Makinson, Director - Housing Support Services, 5 Pancras Square, London N1C 4AG ☎ 020 7974 3518
✆ rhys.makinson@camden.gov.uk

Housing: Ms Mary McGowan, Director - Housing Management, 5 Pancras Square, London N1C 4AG ☎ 020 7974 5804
✆ mary.mcgowan@camden.gov.uk

Housing Maintenance: Mr Ross Barber, Team Mananger - Major Repairs, Ground Floor, Holmes Road Depot, 79 Holmes Road, London NW5 3AP ☎ 020 7974 6763 ✆ ross.barber@camden.gov.uk

Housing Maintenance: Mr Kim Wells, Head of Repairs, Holmes Road Depot, 79 Holmes Road, London NW5 3AP ☎ 020 7974 1746
✆ kim.wells@camden.gov.uk

Legal: Mr Andrew Maughan, Borough Solicitor, 5 Pancras Square, London N1C 4AG ☎ 020 7974 5656
✆ andrew.maughan@camden.gov.uk

Leisure and Cultural Services: Mr Sam Eastop, Head of Arts, Tourism & Libraries, 5 Pancras Square, London N1C 4AG
☎ 020 7974 6248 ✆ sam.eastop@camden.gov.uk

Leisure and Cultural Services: Ms Jessica Gibbons, Director - Community Services, 5 Pancras Square, London N1C 4AG
☎ 020 7974 4226 ✆ jessica.gibbons@camden.gov.uk

Leisure and Cultural Services: Mr Nigel Robinson, Head of Sport & Physical Activities, 5 Pancras Square, London N1C 4AG
☎ 020 7974 1614 ✆ nigel.robinson@camden.gov.uk

Licensing: Ms Vicky Wallas, Noise & Licensing Enforcement Manager, 5 Pancras Square, London N1C 4AG ☎ 020 7974 2190
✆ vicky.wallas@camden.gov.uk

Lighting: Mr George Loureda, Head of Engineering Services, 5 Pancras Square, London N1C 4AG ☎ 020 7974 6949
✆ george.loureda@camden.gov.uk

Member Services: Ms Olivia Mensah, Member Support Manager, Town Hall, Judd Street, London WC1H 9JE ☎ 020 7974 6409
✆ olivia.mensah@camden.gov.uk

Parking: Ms Nicolina Cooper, Head of Parking Services, 5 Pancras Square, London N1C 4AG ☎ 020 7974 4678
✆ nicolina.cooper@camden.gov.uk

Personnel / HR: Ms Joanna Brown, Assistant Director - HR, 5 Pancras Square, London N1C 4AG ☎ 020 7974 6302
✆ joanna.brown@camden.gov.uk

Planning: Mr David Joyce, Director - Regeneration & Planning, 5 Pancras Square, London N1C 4AG ☎ 020 7974 4098
✆ david.joyce@camden.gov.uk

Procurement: Ms Lorraine Colledge, Head of Strategic Procurement, 5 Pancras Square, London N1C 4AG
☎ 020 7974 2827 ✆ lorraine.colledge@camden.gov.uk

Public Libraries: Mr Sam Eastop, Head of Libraries & Registration Services, 5 Pancras Square, London N1C 4AG
☎ 020 7974 6248 ✆ sam.eastop@camden.gov.uk

Recycling & Waste Minimisation: Mr Richard Bradbury, Head of Environment Services, 5 Pancras Square, London N1C 4AG
☎ 020 7974 3725 ✆ richard.bradbury@camden.gov.uk

Regeneration: Mr David Joyce, Director - Regeneration & Planning, 5 Pancras Square, London N1C 4AG ☎ 020 7974 4098
✆ david.joyce@camden.gov.uk

Road Safety: Ms Louise McBride, Head of Transport Planning & Parking Strategy, 5 Pancras Square, London N1C 4AG
☎ 020 7974 5543 ✆ louise.mcbride@camden.gov.uk

Social Services: Ms Anne Turner, Director - Children's Safeguarding & Social Work, 5 Pancras Square, London N1C 4AG
☎ 020 7974 6641 ✆ anne.turner@camden.gov.uk

Social Services (Adult): Ms Vivienne Broadhurst, Director - Adult Social Care, 5 Pancras Square, London N1C 4AG ☎ 020 7974 6092
✆ vivienne.broadhurst@camden.gov.uk

Social Services (Children): Ms Anne Turner, Director - Children's Safeguarding & Social Work, 5 Pancras Square, London N1C 4AG ☎ 020 7974 6641 ✆ anne.turner@camden.gov.uk

Childrens Social Care: Ms Anne Turner, Director - Children's Safeguarding & Social Work, 5 Pancras Square, London N1C 4AG
☎ 020 7974 6641 ✆ anne.turner@camden.gov.uk

Public Health: Dr Julie Billett, Director - Public Health, 5 Pancras Square, London N1C 4AG ☎ 020 7527 1221
✆ julie.billett@camden.gov.uk

Staff Training: Ms Joanna Brown, Assistant Director - HR, 5 Pancras Square, London N1C 4AG ☎ 020 7974 6302
✆ joanna.brown@camden.gov.uk

Sustainable Development: Mr Oliver Myers, Head of Sustainability & Green Space, 5 Pancras Square, London N1C 4AG
☎ 020 7974 6370 ✆ oliver.myers@camden.gov.uk

CAMDEN

Tourism: Mr Sam Eastop, Head of Libraries & Registration Services, 5 Pancras Square, London N1C 4AG ☎ 020 7974 6248 🖱 sam.eastop@camden.gov.uk

Transport: Ms Louise McBride, Head of Transport Planning & Parking Strategy, 5 Pancras Square, London N1C 4AG ☎ 020 7974 5543 🖱 louise.mcbride@camden.gov.uk

Waste Management: Mr David Beadle, Managing Director of North London Waste Authority, c/o Unit 169, Lee Valley Technopark, Ashley Road, London N17 9LN ☎ 020 8489 5665 🖱 david.beadle@camden.gov.uk

Children's Play Areas: Ms Jane Hutcheson, Senior Locality Manager - Integrated Early Years Service, 5 Pancras Square, London N1C 4AG ☎ 020 7974 7076 🖱 jane.hutcheson@camden.gov.uk

COUNCILLORS

Mayor: Shah, Nadia (LAB - Regent's Park)
nadia.shah@camden.gov.uk

Deputy Mayor: Cotton, Richard (LAB - Camden Town with Primrose Hill)
richard.cotton@camden.gov.uk

Leader of the Council: Hayward, Sarah (LAB - King's Cross)
sarah.hayward@camden.gov.uk

Deputy Leader of the Council: Callaghan, Patricia (LAB - Camden Town with Primrose Hill)
patricia.callaghan@camden.gov.uk

Tomlinson, Paul (LAB - St Pancras & Somers Town)
paul.tomlinson@camden.gov.uk

Ali, Nasim (LAB - Regent's Park)
nasim.ali@camden.gov.uk

Apak, Meric (LAB - Kentish Town)
meric.apak@camden.gov.uk

Baillie, Siobhan (CON - Frognal & Fitzjohns)
siobhan.baillie@camden.gov.uk

Beales, Danny (LAB - Cantelowes)
danny.beales@camden.gov.uk

Beattie, Douglas (LAB - Kilburn)
douglas.beattie@camden.gov.uk

Berry, Sian (GRN - Highgate)
sian.berry@camden.gov.uk

Blackwell, Theo (LAB - Gospel Oak)
theo.blackwell@camden.gov.uk

Bucknell, Jonny (CON - Belsize)
jonny.bucknell@camden.gov.uk

Cooper, Oliver (CON - Hampstead Town)
oliver.cooper@camden.gov.uk

Currie, Tom (CON - Hampstead Town)
tom.currie@camden.gov.uk

Eslamdoust, Maryam (LAB - Kilburn)
maryam.eslamdoust@camden.gov.uk

Francis, Sabrina (LAB - Bloomsbury)
sabrina.francis@camden.gov.uk

Freeman, Roger (CON - Swiss Cottage)
roger.freeman@camden.gov.uk

Fulbrook, Julian (LAB - Holborn & Covent Garden)
julian.fulbrook@camden.gov.uk

Gardiner, Thomas (LAB - Kilburn)
thomas.gardiner@camden.gov.uk

Gimson, Sally (LAB - Highgate)
sally.gimson@camden.gov.uk

Gould, Georgia (LAB - Kentish Town)
georgia.gould@camden.gov.uk

Hai, Abdul (LAB - King's Cross)
abdul.hai@camden.gov.uk

Harrison, Adam (LAB - Bloomsbury)
adam.harrison@camden.gov.uk

Headlam-Wells, Jenny (LAB - Kentish Town)
jenny.headlam-wells@camden.gov.uk

Johnson, Heather (LAB - Regent's Park)
heather.johnson@camden.gov.uk

Jones, Phil (LAB - Cantelowes)
phil.jones@camden.gov.uk

Kelly, Alison (LAB - Haverstock)
alison.kelly@camden.gov.uk

Khatoon, Samata (LAB - St Pancras & Somers Town)
samata.khatoon@camden.gov.uk

Lewis, Oliver (LAB - Highgate)
oliver.lewis@camden.gov.uk

Leyland, Claire-Louise (CON - Belsize)
claire-louise.leyland@camden.gov.uk

Madlani, Rishi (LAB - Bloomsbury)
rishi.madlani@camden.gov.uk

Marshall, Andrew (CON - Swiss Cottage)
andrew.marshall@camden.gov.uk

Mason, Angela (LAB - Cantelowes)
angela.mason@camden.gov.uk

McCormack, Maeve (LAB - Gospel Oak)
maeve.mccormack@camden.gov.uk

Mennear, Andrew (CON - Frognal & Fitzjohns)
andrew.mennear@camden.gov.uk

Olad, Awale (LAB - Holborn & Covent Garden)
awale.olad@camden.gov.uk

Olszewski, Richard (LAB - Fortune Green)
richard.olszewski@camden.gov.uk

Pietragnoli, Lazzaro (LAB - Camden Town with Primrose Hill)
lazzaro.pietragnoli@camden.gov.uk

Pober, Angela (LAB - West Hampstead)
angela.pober@camden.gov.uk

Quadir, Abdul (LAB - Haverstock)
abdul.quadir@camden.gov.uk

Rea, Flick (LD - Fortune Green)
flick.rea@camden.gov.uk

Revah, Larraine (LAB - Gospel Oak)
larraine.revah@camden.gov.uk

Robinson, Roger (LAB - St Pancras & Somers Town)
roger.robinson@camden.gov.uk

Rosenberg, Phil (LAB - West Hampstead)
phil.rosenberg@camden.gov.uk

Roy, Leila (CON - Belsize)
leila.roy@camden.gov.uk

Russell, Lorna (LAB - Fortune Green)
lorna.russell@camden.gov.uk

Simpson, Jonathan (LAB - King's Cross)
jonathan.simpson@camden.gov.uk

Spinella, Gio (CON - Frognal & Fitzjohns)
gio.spinella@camden.gov.uk

Stark, Stephen (CON - Hampstead Town)
stephen.stark@camden.gov.uk

Vincent, Sue (LAB - Holborn & Covent Garden)
sue.vincent@camden.gov.uk

Williams, Don (CON - Swiss Cottage)
don.williams@camden.gov.uk

Wood, Abi (LAB - Haverstock)
abi.wood@camden.gov.uk

Yarde, James (LAB - West Hampstead)
james.yarde@camden.gov.uk

POLITICAL COMPOSITION
LAB: 40, CON: 12, LD: 1, GRN: 1

COMMITTEE CHAIRS

Audit: Ms Maeve McCormack

Children, Schools & Families: Ms Jenny Headlam-Wells

Development Control: Ms Heather Johnson

Health & Adult Social Care: Ms Alison Kelly

Health & Wellbeing: Ms Sarah Hayward

Housing: Mr Danny Beales

Licensing: Ms Maryam Eslamdoust

Pensions: Mr Rishi Madlani

Cannock Chase   D

Cannock Chase District Council, Civic Centre, PO Box 28, Cannock WS11 1BG
☎ 01543 462621 ☎ 01543 462317
customerservices@cannockchasedc.gov.uk
www.cannockchasedc.gov.uk

FACTS AND FIGURES
Parliamentary Constituencies: Cannock Chase
EU Constituencies: West Midlands
Election Frequency: Elections are by thirds

PRINCIPAL OFFICERS

Chief Executive: Mr Tony McGovern, Managing Director, Civic Centre, Beecroft Road, Cannock WS11 1BG ☎ 01543 464438
tonymcgovern@cannockchasedc.gov.uk

Deputy Chief Executive: Mr Bob Kean, Deputy Managing Director & Head of Finance, Civic Centre, PO Box 28, Beecroft Road, Cannock WS11 1BG ☎ 01543 464334
bobkeane@cannockchasedc.gov.uk

Senior Management: Mrs Judith Aupers, Head of Governance, Civic Centre, PO Box 28, Beecroft Road, Cannock WS11 1BG ☎ 01543 464411 judithaupers@cannockchasedc.gov.uk

Senior Management: Mr Mike Edmonds, Head of Commissioning, Civic Centre, PO Box 28, Beecroft Road, Cannock WS11 1BG ☎ 01543 464416 mikeedmonds@cannockchasedc.gov.uk

Senior Management: Mr Peter Kendrick, Head of Technology, Stafford Borough Council, Civic Centre, Riverside, Stafford ST16 3AQ ☎ 01785 619274 pkendrick@stafford.gov.uk

Senior Management: Mr Neville Raby, Head of Human Resources & Property Services, Civic Centre, Riverside, Stafford ST16 3AQ ☎ 01785 619205 nraby@staffordbc.gov.uk

Senior Management: Ms Nirmal Samrai, Head of Housing & Waste Management, Civic Centre, PO Box 28, Cannock WS11 1BG ☎ 01543 464210 nirmalsamrai@cannockchasedc.gov.uk

Senior Management: Mr Steve Shilvock, Head of Environmental Health, Civic Centre, Beecroft Road, Cannock WS11 1BG ☎ 01543 464597 steveshilvock@cannockchasedc.gov.uk

Senior Management: Mr Michael Tichford, Head of Economic Development, Civic Centre, PO Box 28, Cannock WS11 1BG ☎ 01543 464223 michaeltichford@cannockchasedc.gov.uk

Senior Management: Mr Alistair Welch, Head of Law & Administration, Civic Centre, PO Box 28, Cannock WS11 1BG

Architect, Building / Property Services: Mr Michael Tichford, Head of Economic Development, Civic Centre, PO Box 28, Cannock WS11 1BG ☎ 01543 464223 michaeltichford@cannockchasedc.gov.uk

Best Value: Mrs Judith Aupers, Head of Governance, Civic Centre, PO Box 28, Beecroft Road, Cannock WS11 1BG ☎ 01543 464411 judithaupers@cannockchasedc.gov.uk

Building Control: Mr Paul Beckley, Building Control Manager, Stafford Borough Council, Civic Centre, Riverside, Stafford ST16 3AQ ☎ 01785 619311 paulbeckley@cannockchasedc.gov.uk

PR / Communications: Miss Kerry Wright, Partnerships & Communications Manager, Civic Centre, PO Box 28, Cannock WS11 1BG ☎ 01543 464368 kerrywright@cannockchasedc.gov.uk

Community Safety: Miss Kerry Wright, Partnerships & Communications Manager, Civic Centre, PO Box 28, Cannock WS11 1BG ☎ 01543 464368 kerrywright@cannockchasedc.gov.uk

Computer Management: Mr Peter Kendrick, Head of Technology, Stafford Borough Council, Civic Centre, Riverside, Stafford ST16 3AQ ☎ 01785 619274 pkendrick@stafford.gov.uk

Contracts: Mrs Judith Aupers, Head of Governance, Civic Centre, PO Box 28, Beecroft Road, Cannock WS11 1BG ☎ 01543 464411 judithaupers@cannockchasedc.gov.uk

CANNOCK CHASE

Customer Service: Ms Amanda Wilkinson, Customer Services & Central Control Manager, Civic Centre, PO Box 28, Cannock WS11 1BG ☎ 01543 464365 ✆ amandawilkinson@cannockchase.gov.uk

Economic Development: Mr Michael Tichford, Head of Economic Development, Civic Centre, PO Box 28, Cannock WS11 1BG ☎ 01543 464223 ✆ michaeltichford@cannockchasedc.gov.uk

Electoral Registration: Mr Steve Partridge, Democratic Services Manager, Civic Centre, PO Box 28, Beecroft Road, Cannock WS11 1BG ☎ 01543 464588 ✆ stevepartridge@cannockchasedc.gov.uk

Emergency Planning: Mrs Judith Aupers, Head of Governance, Civic Centre, PO Box 28, Beecroft Road, Cannock WS11 1BG ☎ 01543 464411 ✆ judithaupers@cannockchasedc.gov.uk

Environmental Health: Mr Steve Shilvock, Head of Environmental Health, Civic Centre, Beecroft Road, Cannock WS11 1BG ☎ 01543 464597 ✆ steveshilvock@cannockchasedc.gov.uk

Estates, Property & Valuation: Mr Michael Tichford, Head of Economic Development, Civic Centre, PO Box 28, Cannock WS11 1BG ☎ 01543 464223 ✆ michaeltichford@cannockchasedc.gov.uk

European Liaison: Mr Glenn Watson, Economic Development Manager, Civic Centre, PO Box 28, Beecroft Road, Cannock WS11 1BG ☎ 01543 464529 ✆ glennwatson@cannockchasedc.gov.uk

Facilities: Mr Michael Tichford, Head of Economic Development, Civic Centre, PO Box 28, Cannock WS11 1BG ☎ 01543 464223 ✆ michaeltichford@cannockchasedc.gov.uk

Finance: Mr Bob Kean, Deputy Managing Director & Head of Finance, Civic Centre, PO Box 28, Beecroft Road, Cannock WS11 1BG ☎ 01543 464334 ✆ bobkeane@cannockchasedc.gov.uk

Treasury: Mr Bob Kean, Deputy Managing Director & Head of Finance, Civic Centre, PO Box 28, Beecroft Road, Cannock WS11 1BG ☎ 01543 464334 ✆ bobkeane@cannockchasedc.gov.uk

Grounds Maintenance: Mr Tom Walsh, Parks & Open Spaces Manager, Civic Centre, Beecroft Road, Cannock WS11 1BG ☎ 01543 434482 ✆ tomwalsh@cannockchasedc.gov.uk

Health and Safety: Mr Carl Morgan, Health & Safety Officer, Civic Centre, PO Box 28, Beecroft Road, Cannock WS11 1BG ☎ 01543 464227 ✆ carlmorgan@cannockchasedc.gov.uk

Housing: Ms Nirmal Samrai, Head of Housing & Waste Management, Civic Centre, PO Box 28, Cannock WS11 1BG ☎ 01543 464210 ✆ nirmalsamrai@cannockchasedc.gov.uk

Housing Maintenance: Ms Catherine Owen, Housing Maintenance Manager, Civic Centre, PO Box 28, Cannock WS11 1BG ☎ 01543 456831 ✆ catherineowen@cannockchasedc.gov.uk

Legal: Mr Alistair Welch, Head of Law & Administration, Civic Centre, Riverside, Stafford ST16 3AQ ☎ 01785 619204 ✆ awelch@staffordbc.gov.uk

Leisure and Cultural Services: Mr Mike Edmonds, Head of Commissioning, Civic Centre, PO Box 28, Beecroft Road, Cannock WS11 1BG ☎ 01543 464416 ✆ mikeedmonds@cannockchasedc.gov.uk

Licensing: Mr Steve Shilvock, Head of Environmental Health, Civic Centre, Beecroft Road, Cannock WS11 1BG ☎ 01543 464597 ✆ steveshilvock@cannockchasedc.gov.uk

Member Services: Mr Steve Partridge, Democratic Services Manager, Civic Centre, PO Box 28, Beecroft Road, Cannock WS11 1BG ☎ 01543 464588 ✆ stevepartridge@cannockchasedc.gov.uk

Partnerships: Miss Kerry Wright, Partnerships & Communications Manager, Civic Centre, PO Box 28, Cannock WS11 1BG ☎ 01543 464368 ✆ kerrywright@cannockchasedc.gov.uk

Personnel / HR: Mrs Anne Bird, Human Resources Manager, Civic Centre, PO Box 28, Cannock WS11 1BG ☎ 01543 464426 ✆ annebird@cannockchasedc.gov.uk

Personnel / HR: Mr Neville Raby, Head of Human Resources & Property Services, Civic Centre, Riverside, Stafford ST16 3AQ ☎ 01785 619205 ✆ nraby@staffordbc.gov.uk

Planning: Mr Michael Tichford, Head of Economic Development, Civic Centre, PO Box 28, Cannock WS11 1BG ☎ 01543 464223 ✆ michaeltichford@cannockchasedc.gov.uk

Procurement: Mrs Judith Aupers, Head of Governance, Civic Centre, PO Box 28, Beecroft Road, Cannock WS11 1BG ☎ 01543 464411 ✆ judithaupers@cannockchasedc.gov.uk

Recycling & Waste Minimisation: Mr Anthony Morris, Recycling & Climate Change Officer, Civic Centre, PO Box 28, Cannock WS11 1BG ☎ 01543 456812 ✆ anthonymorris@cannockchasedc.gov.uk

Regeneration: Mr Michael Tichford, Head of Economic Development, Civic Centre, PO Box 28, Cannock WS11 1BG ☎ 01543 464223 ✆ michaeltichford@cannockchasedc.gov.uk

Staff Training: Mrs Anne Bird, Human Resources Manager, Civic Centre, PO Box 28, Cannock WS11 1BG ☎ 01543 464426 ✆ annebird@cannockchasedc.gov.uk

Street Scene: Mr Tom Walsh, Parks & Open Spaces Manager, Civic Centre, Beecroft Road, Cannock WS11 1BG ☎ 01543 434482 ✆ tomwalsh@cannockchasedc.gov.uk

Tourism: Mrs Debbie Harris, Economic Services Manager, Civic Centre, PO Box 28, Cannock WS11 1BG ☎ 01543 464490 ✆ debbie.harris@cannockchase.gov.uk

Town Centre: Mr Glenn Watson, Economic Development Manager, Civic Centre, PO Box 28, Beecroft Road, Cannock WS11 1BG ☎ 01543 464529 ✆ glennwatson@cannockchasedc.gov.uk

Waste Collection and Disposal: Mr Joss Pressland, Waste & Engineering Services Manager, Civic Centre, PO Box 28, Cannock WS11 1BG ☎ 01543 456807 ✆ josspresland@cannockchasedc.gov.uk

Waste Management: Mr Joss Pressland, Waste & Engineering Services Manager, Civic Centre, PO Box 28, Cannock WS11 1BG
☎ 01543 456807 ◌ josspresland@cannockchasedc.gov.uk

Children's Play Areas: Mr Tom Walsh, Parks & Open Spaces Manager, Civic Centre, Beecroft Road, Cannock WS11 1BG
☎ 01543 434482 ◌ tomwalsh@cannockchasedc.gov.uk

COUNCILLORS

ChairStretton, Zaphne (LAB - Norton Canes)
zaphnestretton@cannockchasedc.gov.uk

Leader of the Council: Adamson, George (LAB - Hednesford Green Heath)
georgeadamson@cannockchasedc.gov.uk

Deputy Leader of the Council: Alcott, Gordon (LAB - Cannock North)
gordonalcott@cannockchasedc.gov.uk

Group LeaderHardman, Bill (UKIP - Rawnsley)
billhardman@cannockchasedc.gov.uk

Group LeaderSnape, Paul (CON - Cannock West)
paulsnape@cannockchasedc.gov.uk

Allen, Frank (LAB - Cannock North)
frankallen@cannockchasedc.gov.uk

Allt, Anne (CON - Western Springs)
anneallt@cannockchasedc.gov.uk

Bennett, Carl (LAB - Western Springs)
carlbennett@cannockchasedc.gov.uk

Bowater, Jim (CON - Etching Hill & the Heath)
jamesbowater@cannockchasedc.gov.uk

Burnett, Graham (CON - Hednesford Green Heath)
grahamburnett@cannockchasedc.gov.uk

Buttery, Martyn (UKIP - Hawks Green)
martynbuttery@cannockchasedc.gov.uk

Cartwright, Sheila (LAB - Hednesford North)
sheilacartwright@cannockchasedc.gov.uk

Christian, Joanne (CON - Hednesford South)
joannechristian@cannockchasedc.gov.uk

Cooper, Jessica (LAB - Cannock North)
jessicacooper@cannockchsedc.gov.uk

Davis, Muriel (LAB - Cannock East)
murieldavis@cannockchasedc.gov.uk

Dean, Alan (UKIP - Heath Hayes East & Wimblebury)
alandean@cannockchasedc.gov.uk

Dudson, Michellle (LAB - Hagley)
michellsdudson@cannockchasedc.gov.uk

Dudson, Alan (LAB - Brereton & Ravenhill)
alandudson@cannockchasedc.gov.uk

Foley, Darren (LAB - Brereton & Ravenhill)
darrenfoley@cannockchasedc.gov.uk

Freeman, Maureen (LAB - Cannock South)
maureenfreeman@cannockchasedc.gov.uk

Grice, Doris (LAB - Hednesford North)
d.grice316@btinternet.com

Grocott, Michael (IND - Western Springs)
michaelgrocott@cannockchasedc.gov.uk

Hoare, Mike (CON - Norton Canes)
michaelhoare@cannockchasedc.gov.uk

Johnson, Tony (LAB - Cannock East)
tonyjohnson@cannockchasedc.gov.uk

Johnson, Justin (CON - Etching Hill & the Heath)
justinjohnson@cannockchasedc.gov.uk

Kraujalis, John (LAB - Cannock South)
johnkraujalis@cannockchasedc.gov.uk

Lea, Colin (CON - Heath Hayes East & Wimblebury)
colinlea@cannockchasedc.gov.uk

Martin, Christine (LAB - Hagley)
christinemartin@cannockchasedc.gov.uk

Mitchell, Christine (LAB - Cannock East)
christinemitchell@cannockchasedc.gov.uk

Molineux, Gerald (LD - Brereton & Ravenhill)
geraldmolineux@cannockchasedc.gov.uk

Peake, Claire (CON - Rawnsley)
clairepeak@cannockchasedc.gov.uk

Pearson, Alan (LAB - Hednesford North)
alanpearson@cannockchasedc.gov.uk

Preece, John (LAB - Norton Canes)
jophnpreece@cannockchasedc.gov.uk

Smith, Doug (CON - Cannock West)

Snape, Daniel (CON - Hawks Green)

Sutherland, Mike (CON - Hawks Green)
michaelsutherland@cannockchasedc.gov.uk

Sutton, Hyra (CON - Cannock West)
hyrasutton@cannockchasedc.gov.uk

Todd, Diane (LAB - Heath Hayes East & Wimblebury)
dianetodd@cannockchasedc.gov.uk

Whitehouse, Stephanie (UKIP - Etching Hill & the Heath)
stephenaniewhitehouse@canonchasedc.gov.uk

Witton, Paul (LAB - Cannock South)
paulwitton@cannonchasedc.gov.uk

Woodhead, Paul (GRN - Hednesford South)
paulwoodhead@cannockchasedc.gov.uk

POLITICAL COMPOSITION
LAB: 21, CON: 13, UKIP: 4, IND: 1, LD: 1, GRN: 1

COMMITTEE CHAIRS

Audit: Mr Paul Witton

Environment: Ms Christine Martin

Licensing: Mrs Doris Grice

Planning: Ms Sheila Cartwright

Canterbury City   D

Canterbury City Council, Council Offices, Military Road, Canterbury CT1 1YW
☎ 01227 862000 🖷 01227 862020 🖳 www.canterbury.gov.uk

FACTS AND FIGURES
Parliamentary Constituencies: Canterbury
EU Constituencies: South East

CANTERBURY CITY

Election Frequency: Elections are of whole council

PRINCIPAL OFFICERS

Chief Executive: Mr Colin Carmichael, Chief Executive, Council Offices, Military Road, Canterbury CT1 1YW ☎ 01227 862082 🖰 colin.carmichael@canterbury.gov.uk

Deputy Chief Executive: Ms Velia Coffey, Deputy Chief Executive, Council Offices, Military Road, Canterbury CT1 1YW ☎ 01227 862149 🖰 velia.coffey@canterbury.gov.uk

Senior Management: Mr Ian Brown, Assistant Director - Planning & Regeneration, Council Offices, Military Road, Canterbury CT1 1YW ☎ 01227 862193 🖰 ian.brown@canterbury.gov.uk

Senior Management: Ms Lisa Fillery, Assistant Director - Finance & Procurement, Council Offices, Military Road, Canterbury CT1 1YW ☎ 01227 862000 🖰 lisa.fillery@canterbury.gov.uk

Senior Management: Ms Tricia Marshall, Director - Resources, Council Offices, Military Road, Canterbury CT1 1YW ☎ 01227 862393 🖰 tricia.marshall@canterbury.gov.uk

Senior Management: Mrs Janice McGuinness, Assistant Director - Commissioned Services, Council Offices, Military Road, Canterbury CT1 1YW ☎ 01227 862492 🖰 janice.mcguinness@canterbury.gov.uk

Senior Management: Ms Larissa Reed, Assistant Director - Direct Services, Council Offices, Military Road, Canterbury CT1 1YW ☎ 01227 862213 🖰 larissa.reed@canterbury.gov.uk

Senior Management: Ms Suzi Wakeham, Assistant Director - Strategy & Democracy, Council Offices, Military Road, Canterbury CT1 1YW ☎ 01227 862057 🖰 suzi.wakeham@canterbury.gov.uk

Architect, Building / Property Services: Mr Martin Bovingdon, Head of Property, Council Offices, Military Road, Canterbury CT1 1YW ☎ 01227 862088 🖰 martin.bovingdon@canterbury.gov.uk

Best Value: Mrs Lorna Ford, Head of Strategy, Council Offices, Military Road, Canterbury CT1 1YW ☎ 01227 862068 🖰 lorna.ford@canterbury.gov.uk

Building Control: Mr Mark Webb, Building Control Manager, Council Offices, Military Road, Canterbury CT1 1YW ☎ 01227 862502 🖰 mark.webb@canterbury.gov.uk

PR / Communications: Mrs Celia Glynn-Williams, Head of Communications, Council Offices, Military Road, Canterbury CT1 1YW ☎ 01227 862065 🖰 celia.glynn-williams@canterbury.gov.uk

Community Planning: Mr Ian Brown, Assistant Director - Planning & Regeneration, Council Offices, Military Road, Canterbury CT1 1YW ☎ 01227 862193 🖰 ian.brown@canterbury.gov.uk

Community Safety: Mr Doug Rattray, Head of Safer Neighbourhoods, Council Offices, Military Road, Canterbury CT1 1YW ☎ 01227 862363 🖰 doug.rattray@canterbury.gov.uk

Computer Management: Mr Sean Hale, Head of ICT, Council Offices, Military Road, Canterbury CT1 1YW ☎ 01227 862082 🖰 saen.hale@ekservices.org

Contracts: Mrs Janice McGuinness, Assistant Director - Commissioned Services, Council Offices, Military Road, Canterbury CT1 1YW ☎ 01227 862492 🖰 janice.mcguinness@canterbury.gov.uk

Corporate Services: Ms Tricia Marshall, Director - Resources, Council Offices, Military Road, Canterbury CT1 1YW ☎ 01227 862393 🖰 tricia.marshall@canterbury.gov.uk

Customer Service: Mr Andrew Stevens, Assistant Director - Customer Delivery, Council Offices, Military Road, Canterbury CT1 1YW ☎ 01227 862101 🖰 andrew.stevens@ekservices.org

Economic Development: Ms Caroline Hicks, Head of Business & Regeneration, Council Offices, Military Road, Canterbury CT1 1YW ☎ 01227 862054 🖰 caroline.hicks@canterbury.gov.uk

E-Government: Mrs Roz Edridge, Business Systems Manager, East Kent Services, Council Offices, Cecil Street, Margate CT9 1XZ ☎ 01843 577033 🖰 roz.edridge@ekservices.org

Electoral Registration: Ms Lyn McDaid, Elections Manager, Council Offices, Military Road, Canterbury CT1 1YW ☎ 01227 862006 🖰 lyn.mcdaid@canterbury.gov.uk

Emergency Planning: Mr Andy Jeffery, Emergency Planning & Events Officer, Council Offices, Military Road, Canterbury CT1 1YW ☎ 01227 862012 🖰 andy.jeffery@canterbury.gov.uk

Energy Management: Mr Philip Kiss, Building Services Engineer (Mechanical) & Energy Officer, Council Offices, Military Road, Canterbury CT1 1YW ☎ 01227 862481 🖰 philip.kiss@canterbury.gov.uk

Environmental / Technical Services: Ms Larissa Reed, Assistant Director - Direct Services, Council Offices, Military Road, Canterbury CT1 1YW ☎ 01227 862213 🖰 larissa.reed@canterbury.gov.uk

Environmental Health: Ms Larissa Reed, Assistant Director - Direct Services, Council Offices, Military Road, Canterbury CT1 1YW ☎ 01227 862213 🖰 larissa.reed@canterbury.gov.uk

Estates, Property & Valuation: Mr Martin Bovingdon, Head of Property, Council Offices, Military Road, Canterbury CT1 1YW ☎ 01227 862088 🖰 martin.bovingdon@canterbury.gov.uk

Events Manager: Mr Andy Jeffery, Emergency Planning & Events Officer, Council Offices, Military Road, Canterbury CT1 1YW ☎ 01227 862012 🖰 andy.jeffery@canterbury.gov.uk

Facilities: Mrs Alexis Jobson, Corporate Business Support Manager, Council Offices, Military Road, Canterbury CT1 1YW ☎ 01227 862255 🖰 alexis.jobson@canterbury.gov.uk

Finance: Ms Lisa Fillery, Assistant Director - Finance & Procurement, Council Offices, Military Road, Canterbury CT1 1YW ☎ 01227 862000 🖰 lisa.fillery@canterbury.gov.uk

Grounds Maintenance: Mrs Janice McGuinness, Assistant Director - Commissioned Services, Council Offices, Military Road, Canterbury CT1 1YW ☎ 01227 862492 🖰 janice.mcguinness@canterbury.gov.uk

Health and Safety: Mr Stephen Turner, Health & Safety Advisor, Council Offices, Military Road, Canterbury CT1 1YW
⌂ stephen.turner@canterbury.gov.uk

Housing: Ms Larissa Reed, Assistant Director - Direct Services, Council Offices, Military Road, Canterbury CT1 1YW
☎ 01227 862213 ⌂ larissa.reed@canterbury.gov.uk

Housing Maintenance: Mr David Ashby, Head of Asset Management, East Kent Housing Ltd, 3 - 5 Shorncliffe Road, Folkestone CT20 2SQ ☎ 01303 853749
⌂ david.ashby@eastkenthousing.org.uk

Legal: Ms Sarah Bowman, Head of Legal, Council Offices, Military Road, Canterbury CT1 1YW ☎ 01227 862017
⌂ sarah.bowman@canterbury.gov.uk

Leisure and Cultural Services: Mrs Janice McGuinness, Assistant Director - Commissioned Services, Council Offices, Military Road, Canterbury CT1 1YW ☎ 01227 862492
⌂ janice.mcguinness@canterbury.gov.uk

Licensing: Mr Doug Rattray, Head of Safer Neighbourhoods, Council Offices, Military Road, Canterbury CT1 1YW
☎ 01227 862363 ⌂ doug.rattray@canterbury.gov.uk

Lottery Funding, Charity and Voluntary: Ms Marie Royle, Head of Community Services, Council Offices, Military Road, Canterbury CT1 1YW ☎ 01227 862517 ⌂ marie.royle@canterbury.gov.uk

Member Services: Mr Matthew Archer, Head of Democratic Services, Council Offices, Military Road, Canterbury CT1 1YW
☎ 01227 862175 ⌂ matthew.archer@canterbury.gov.uk

Parking: Mr Doug Rattray, Head of Safer Neighbourhoods, Council Offices, Military Road, Canterbury CT1 1YW ☎ 01227 862363
⌂ doug.rattray@canterbury.gov.uk

Personnel / HR: Ms Juli Oliver-Smith, Head of EK Human Resources, East Kent HR Partnership, Dover District Council, White Cliffs Business Park, Whitfield, Dover CT16 3PJ ☎ 07917 473616
⌂ hrpartnership@dover.gov.uk

Planning: Mr Ian Brown, Assistant Director - Planning & Regeneration, Council Offices, Military Road, Canterbury CT1 1YW
☎ 01227 862193 ⌂ ian.brown@canterbury.gov.uk

Recycling & Waste Minimisation: Mrs Janice McGuinness, Assistant Director - Commissioned Services, Council Offices, Military Road, Canterbury CT1 1YW ☎ 01227 862492
⌂ janice.mcguinness@canterbury.gov.uk

Regeneration: Mr Ian Brown, Assistant Director - Planning & Regeneration, Council Offices, Military Road, Canterbury CT1 1YW
☎ 01227 862193 ⌂ ian.brown@canterbury.gov.uk

Staff Training: Ms Paula Radcliffe, Learning & Development Manager, Council Offices, Military Road, Canterbury CT1 1YW
☎ 01304 872799 ⌂ paula.radcliffe@canterbury.gov.uk

Sustainable Communities: Ms Suzi Wakeham, Assistant Director - Strategy & Democracy, Council Offices, Military Road, Canterbury CT1 1YW ☎ 01227 862057
⌂ suzi.wakeham@canterbury.gov.uk

Sustainable Development: Mr Ian Brown, Assistant Director - Planning & Regeneration, Council Offices, Military Road, Canterbury CT1 1YW ☎ 01227 862193 ⌂ ian.brown@canterbury.gov.uk

Tourism: Ms Caroline Hicks, Head of Business & Regeneration, Council Offices, Military Road, Canterbury CT1 1YW
☎ 01227 862054 ⌂ caroline.hicks@canterbury.gov.uk

Town Centre: Ms Caroline Hicks, Head of Business & Regeneration, Council Offices, Military Road, Canterbury CT1 1YW
☎ 01227 862054 ⌂ caroline.hicks@canterbury.gov.uk

Transport Planner: Mr Richard Moore, Transport & Environment Manager, Council Offices, Military Road, Canterbury CT1 1YW
☎ 01227 862419 ⌂ richard.moore@canterbury.gov.uk

Waste Collection and Disposal: Mrs Janice McGuinness, Assistant Director - Commissioned Services, Council Offices, Military Road, Canterbury CT1 1YW ☎ 01227 862492
⌂ janice.mcguinness@canterbury.gov.uk

COUNCILLORS

The Lord Mayor: Metcalfe, George (CON - Blean Forest)
george.metcalfe@canterbury.gov.uk

Sheriff: Doyle, Rosemary (CON - Chartham & Stone Street)
rosemary.doyle@canterbury.gov.uk

Leader of the Council: Cook, Simon (CON - Nailbourne)
simon.cook@canterbury.gov.uk

Deputy Leader of the Council: Todd, Patt (CON - Chestfield)
pat.todd@canterbury.gov.uk

Group Leader: Baldock, Alan (LAB - Northgate)
alan.baldock@canterbury.gov.uk

Group Leader: Dixey, Michael (LD - Westgate)
michael.dixey@canterbury.gov.uk

Group Leader: Hirst, David (UKIP - Greenhill)
david.hirst@canterbury.gov.uk

Baker, Neil (CON - Tankerton)
neil.baker@canterbury.gov.uk

Baker, Amy (CON - Blean Forest)
amy.baker@canterbury.gov.uk

Baker, Brian (CON - Gorrell)
brian.baker@canterbury.gov.uk

Bartley, Stephen (CON - Seasalter)
stephen.bartley@canterbury.gov.uk

Brazier, John (CON - Westgate)
john.brazier@canterbury.gov.uk

Butcher, Jean (LAB - Northgate)
jean.butcher@canterbury.gov.uk

Clark, Ashley (CON - Gorrell)
ashley.clark@canterbury.gov.uk

Cook, Andrew (CON - Heron)
andrew.cook@canterbury.gov.uk

CANTERBURY CITY

Eden-Green, Nick (LD - Wincheap)
nick.edengreen@canterbury.gov.uk

Fawcett, Oliver (CON - Barton)
oliver.fawcett@canterbury.gov.uk

Fisher, Bernadette (LAB - Gorrell)
bernadette.fisher@canterbury.gov.uk

Fitter-Harding, Ben (CON - Blean Forest)
ben.fitter@canterbury.gov.uk

Glover, Georgina (CON - Sturry)
georgina.glover@canterbury.gov.uk

Howes, Joe (CON - Heron)
joe.howes@canterbury.gov.uk

Jones, Robert (CON - Herne & Broomfield)
robert.jones@canterbury.gov.uk

Jones, Louise (CON - Barton)
louise.jones@canterbury.gov.uk

MacCaul, Charlotte (LD - Wincheap)
charlotte.maccaul@canterbury.gov.uk

Samper, Jennifer (CON - Chestfield)
jenny.samper@canterbury.gov.uk

Sonnex, Sharron (CON - Herne & Broomfield)
sharron.sonnex@canterbury.gov.uk

Spooner, Colin (CON - Seasalter)
colin.spooner@canterbury.gov.uk

Stockley, Ian (CON - Beltinge)
ian.stockley@canterbury.gov.uk

Stockley, Jeanette (CON - Beltinge)
jeanette.stockley@canterbury.gov.uk

Taylor, Heather (CON - Sturry)
heather.taylor@canterbury.gov.uk

Taylor, Ann (CON - Reculver)
ann.taylor@councillor.canterbury.gov.uk

Thomas, Ian (CON - Swalecliffle)
ian.thomas@canterbury.gov.uk

Thomas, Robert (CON - Chartham & Stone Street)
robert.thomas@canterbury.gov.uk

Thomas, David (CON - Heron)
david.thomas@canterbury.gov.uk

Walker, Stuart (CON - Little Stour & Adisham)
stuart.walker@canterbury.gov.uk

Waters, Sally (CON - St Stephen's)
sally.waters@canterbury.gov.uk

Westgate, Terry (CON - St Stephen's)
terry.westgate@canterbury.gov.uk

Williams, Steven (CON - Barton)
steven.williams@canterbury.gov.uk

Wimble, Geoff (UKIP - West Bay)

POLITICAL COMPOSITION
CON: 31, LAB: 3, LD: 3, UKIP: 2

COMMITTEE CHAIRS
Audit: Ms Georgina Glover

Planning: Ms Jennifer Samper

Cardiff   W

Cardiff Council, County Hall, Atlantic Wharf, Cardiff
CF10 4UW
☎ 029 2087 2087 ▤ 029 2087 2086 ✆ c2c@cardiff.gov.uk
▣ www.cardiff.gov.uk

FACTS AND FIGURES
Parliamentary Constituencies: Cardiff Central, Cardiff North,
Cardiff South and Penarth, Cardiff West, Pontypridd
EU Constituencies: Wales
Election Frequency: Elections are of whole council

PRINCIPAL OFFICERS

Chief Executive: Mr Paul Orders, Chief Executive, County Hall,
Atlantic Wharf, Cardiff CF10 4UW ☎ 029 2087 2401
✆ paul.orders@cardiff.gov.uk

Senior Management: Mr Nick Batchelar, Director - Education &
Lifelong Learning, County Hall, Atlantic Wharf, Cardiff CF10 4UW

Senior Management: Ms Davina Fiore, Director - Governance &
Legal Services, County Hall, Atlantic Wharf, Cardiff CF10 4UW
✆ d.fiore@cardiff.gov.uk

Senior Management: Mr Andrew Gregory, Director - City
Operations, County Hall, Atlantic Wharf, Cardiff CF10 4UW
✆ a.gregory@cardiff.gov.uk

Senior Management: Mr Neil Hanratty, Director - Economic
Development, County Hall, Atlantic Wharf, Cardiff CF10 4UW
☎ 029 2087 2052 ✆ nhanratty@cardiff.gov.uk

Senior Management: Ms Sarah McGill, Director - Communities,
Housing & Customer Services, Wilcox House, Dunleavy Drive, Celtic
Gateway, Cardiff CF11 0BA ☎ 029 2087 2900
✆ s.mcgill@cardiff.gov.uk

Senior Management: Ms Christine Salter, Corporate Director -
Resources & Monitoring Officer, County Hall, Atlantic Wharf, Cardiff
CF10 4UW ☎ 029 2087 2300 ✆ c.salter@cardiff.gov.uk

Senior Management: Mr Tony Young, Director - Social Services,
County Hall, Atlantic Wharf, Cardiff CF10 4UW

Architect, Building / Property Services: Mr Philip Dee, Project
Design Development Manager, County Hall, Atlantic Wharf, Cardiff
CF10 4UW ☎ 029 2233 0078 ✆ p.dee@cardiff.gov.uk

Catering Services: Mr Roberto Rossi, Catering Manager, County
Hall, Atlantic Wharf, Cardiff CF10 4UW ☎ 029 2087 2025
✆ r.rossi@cardiff.gov.uk

Children / Youth Services: Mr Nick Batchelar, Director -
Education & Lifelong Learning, County Hall, Atlantic Wharf, Cardiff
CF10 4UW

Children / Youth Services: Mr Tony Young, Director - Social
Services, County Hall, Atlantic Wharf, Cardiff CF10 4UW

PR / Communications: Mr Tim Gordon, Head of Corporate Communications & External Relations, County Hall, Atlantic Wharf, Cardiff CF10 4UW ☖ tgordon@cardiff.gov.uk

Consumer Protection and Trading Standards: Mr Dave Holland, Head of Service - Regulatory & Support Service, County Hall, Atlantic Wharf, Cardiff CF10 2TS ☎ 029 2087 2089 ☖ d.holland@cardiff.gov.uk

Corporate Services: Mr Jonathan Day, Business Development Manager, County Hall, Atlantic Wharf, Cardiff CF10 4UW ☎ 029 2078 8573 ☖ j.day@cardiff.gov.uk

Corporate Services: Mr Alan Richards, Superintendent Registrar, Park Place, Cardiff CF10 4UW ☎ 029 2087 1680 ☖ a.richards@cardiff.gov.uk

Economic Development: Mr Neil Hanratty, Director - Economic Development, County Hall, Atlantic Wharf, Cardiff CF10 4UW ☎ 029 2087 2052 ☖ nhanratty@cardiff.gov.uk

Education: Mr Chris Jones, Chief Education Officer, County Hall, Atlantic Wharf, Cardiff CF10 4UW ☎ 029 2087 2700 ☖ chjones@cardiff.gov.uk

Emergency Planning: Mr Gavin Macho, Principal Emergency Management Officer, Strategic Planning & Environment, Emergency Planning Unit, City Hall, Cardiff CF10 3ND ☎ 029 2087 1831 ☖ gmacho@cardiff.gov.uk

European Liaison: Mr Jonathan Day, Business Development Manager, County Hall, Atlantic Wharf, Cardiff CF10 4UW ☎ 029 2078 8573 ☖ j.day@cardiff.gov.uk

Finance: Ms Christine Salter, Corporate Director - Resources & Monitoring Officer, County Hall, Atlantic Wharf, Cardiff CF10 4UW ☎ 029 2087 2300 ☖ c.salter@cardiff.gov.uk

Pensions: Mr Gareth Henson, Manager of Pensions, County Hall, Atlantic Wharf, Cardiff CF10 4UW ☎ 029 2087 2975 ☖ g.henson@cardiff.gov.uk

Fleet Management: Mr Richard Jones, Tactical Manager - Fleet & Procurement, County Hall, Atlantic Wharf, Cardiff CF10 4UW ☎ 029 2087 2087 ☖ RiJones@cardiff.gov.uk

Grounds Maintenance: Mr Jon Maidment, Operational Manager for Parks & Sport, County Hall, Atlantic Wharf, Cardiff CF10 4UW ☎ 029 2087 2087 ☖ j.maidment@cardiff.gov.uk

Health and Safety: Miss Christina Lloyd, Operational Manager - Health & Safety, County Hall, Atlantic Wharf, Cardiff CF10 4UW ☎ 029 2087 2635 ☖ c.c.lloyd@cardiff.gov.uk

Highways: Mr Andrew Gregory, Director - City Operations, County Hall, Atlantic Wharf, Cardiff CF10 4UW ☖ a.gregory@cardiff.gov.uk

Housing: Ms Sarah McGill, Director - Communities, Housing & Customer Services, Wilcox House, Dunleavy Drive, Celtic Gateway, Cardiff CF11 0BA ☎ 029 2087 2900 ☖ s.mcgill@cardiff.gov.uk

Housing Maintenance: Ms Sarah McGill, Director - Communities, Housing & Customer Services, Wilcox House, Dunleavy Drive, Celtic Gateway, Cardiff CF11 0BA ☎ 029 2087 2900 ☖ s.mcgill@cardiff.gov.uk

Legal: Ms Davina Fiore, Director - Governance & Legal Services, County Hall, Atlantic Wharf, Cardiff CF10 4UW ☖ d.fiore@cardiff.gov.uk

Licensing: Mr Andrew Gregory, Director - City Operations, County Hall, Atlantic Wharf, Cardiff CF10 4UW ☖ a.gregory@cardiff.gov.uk

Lighting: Mr Gary Brown, Operational Manager - Highways Maintenance, County Hall, Atlantic Wharf, Cardiff CF10 4UW ☎ 029 2078 5280 ☖ gbrown@cardiff.gov.uk

Member Services: Ms Davina Fiore, Director - Governance & Legal Services, County Hall, Atlantic Wharf, Cardiff CF10 4UW ☖ d.fiore@cardiff.gov.uk

Parking: Mr Paul Carter, Head of Transportation & Network Management, County Hall, Atlantic Wharf, Cardiff CF10 4UW ☎ 029 2087 3243 ☖ p.carter@cardiff.gov.uk

Personnel / HR: Mr Laithe Bonni, Specialist Support Manager, County Hall, Atlantic Wharf, Cardiff CF10 4UW ☎ 029 2087 2655 ☖ l.bonni@cardiff.gov.uk

Personnel / HR: Mr Philip Lenz, Chief HR Officer, Room 470, County Hall, Atlantic Wharf, Cardiff CF10 4UW ☎ 029 2087 2000 ☖ plenz@cardiff.gov.uk

Planning: Mr James Clements, Head of Planning, County Hall, Atlantic Wharf, Cardiff CF10 4UW ☎ 029 2233 0827 ☖ j.clements@cardiff.gov.uk

Planning: Mr Andrew Gregory, Director - City Operations, County Hall, Atlantic Wharf, Cardiff CF10 4UW ☖ a.gregory@cardiff.gov.uk

Procurement: Ms Christine Salter, Corporate Director - Resources & Monitoring Officer, County Hall, Atlantic Wharf, Cardiff CF10 4UW ☎ 029 2087 2300 ☖ c.salter@cardiff.gov.uk

Public Libraries: Ms Nicola Richards, Central Library Manager, County Hall, Atlantic Wharf, Cardiff CF10 4UW ☎ 029 2053 7027 ☖ n.richards@cardiff.gov.uk

Recycling & Waste Minimisation: Ms Tara King, Chief Officer Waste Management & City Services, Lamby Way, Cardiff CF3 2EQ ☎ 029 2087 2087 ☖ t.king@cardiff.gov.uk

Regeneration: Mr Gareth Harcombe, Operational Manager - Regeneration, City Hall, Cathays Park, Cardiff CF10 3ND ☎ 029 2087 3489 ☖ gharcombe@cardiff.gov.uk

Road Safety: Ms Lisa Lewis, Lead Officer - Road Safety & Training, County Hall, Atlantic Wharf, Cardiff CF10 4UW ☎ 029 2078 8521 ☖ l.lewis@cardiff.gov.uk

CARDIFF

Tourism: Ms Sally Edwards Hart, Operational Manager - Venues & Tourism, County Hall, Atlantic Wharf, Cardiff CF10 4UW
☎ 029 2087 3360 ✆ sallyhart@cardiff.gov.uk

Tourism: Ms Kathryn Richards, Head of Marketing, Motorpoint Arena, Executive Suite 1, Mary Ann Street, Cardiff CF10 2EQ
☎ 029 2087 2452 ✆ k.richards@cardiff.gov.uk

Town Centre: Mr Paul Williams, City Centre Manager, County Hall, Atlantic Wharf, Cardiff CF10 4UW ☎ 029 2066 2986
✆ p.williams@cardiff.gov.uk

Transport: Mr Paul Carter, Head of Transportation & Network Management, County Hall, Atlantic Wharf, Cardiff CF10 4UW
☎ 029 2087 3243 ✆ p.carter@cardiff.gov.uk

Transport Planner: Mr Paul Carter, Head of Transportation & Network Management, County Hall, Atlantic Wharf, Cardiff CF10 4UW ☎ 029 2087 3243 ✆ p.carter@cardiff.gov.uk

Waste Collection and Disposal: Ms Tara King, Chief Officer Waste Management & City Services, Lamby Way, Cardiff CF3 2EQ
☎ 029 2087 2087 ✆ t.king@cardiff.gov.uk

COUNCILLORS

The Lord Mayor: Walsh, Monica (LAB - Trowbridge)
mowalsh@cardiff.gov.uk

Deputy Lord Mayor: Phillips, Georgina (LAB - Pontprennau & Old St. Mellons)
georgina.phillips@cardiff.gov.uk

Leader of the Council: Bale, Phil (LAB - Llanishen)
phil.bale@cardiff.gov.uk

Deputy Leader of the Council: Lent, Sue (LAB - Plasnewydd)
sue.lent@cardiff.gov.uk

Group LeaderMcEvoy, Neil (PC - Fairwater)
nmcevoy@cardiff.gov.uk

Group LeaderWalker, David (CON - Lisvane)
dwalker@cardiff.gov.uk

Group LeaderWoodman, Judith (LD - Pentwyn)
jwoodman@cardiff.gov.uk

Ahmed, Manzoor (LAB - Adamsdown)
manzoor.ahmed@cardiff.gov.uk

Ahmed, Ali (LAB - Butetown)
ali.ahmed@cardiff.gov.uk

Ali, Dilwar (LAB - Llandaff North)
dilwar.ali@cardiff.gov.uk

Aubrey, Gareth (LD - Llandaff)
gaubrey@cardiff.gov.uk

Bowden, Fenella (IND - Heath)
fbowden@cardiff.gov.uk

Boyle, Joe (LD - Penylan)
joe.boyle@cardiff.gov.uk

Bradbury, Peter (LAB - Caerau)
peter.bradbury@cardiff.gov.uk

Bridges, Ed (LD - Gabalfa)
ebridges@cardiff.gov.uk

Burfoot, Tricia (LD - Penylan)
pburfoot@cardiff.gov.uk

Carter, Joseph (LD - Pentwyn)
jcarter@cardiff.gov.uk

Chaundy, Paul (LD - Pentwyn)
pchaundy@cardiff.gov.uk

Clark, Elizabeth (LD - Cathays)
eclark@cardiff.gov.uk

Cook, Richard (LAB - Canton)
ricook@cardiff.gov.uk

Cook, Ralph (IND - Trowbridge)
ralphcook@cardiff.gov.uk

Cowan, Jayne (CON - Rhiwbina)
j.cowan@cardiff.gov.uk

Davies-Warner, Kirsty (LD - Llandaff)
kirsty.davies-warner@cardiff.gov.uk

Davis, Chris (LAB - Whitchurch & Tongwynlais)
chris.davies@cardiff.gov.uk

De'Ath, Daniel (LAB - Plasnewydd)
daniel.de'ath@cardiff.gov.uk

Derbyshire, Bob (LAB - Rumney)
bob.derbyshire@cardiff.gov.uk

Elsmore, Susan (LAB - Canton)
susan.elsmore@cardiff.gov.uk

Evans, Jonathan (LAB - Whitchurch & Tongwynlais)
jonathan.evans@cardiff.gov.uk

Ford, Lisa (PC - Fairwater)
lisaford@cardiff.gov.uk

Goddard, Susan (LAB - Ely)
sgoddard@cardiff.gov.uk

Goodway, Russell (LAB - Ely)
r.v.goodway@cardiff.gov.uk

Gordon, Iona (LAB - Riverside)
iona.gordon@cardiff.gov.uk

Govier, Ashley (LAB - Grangetown)
ashley.govier@cardiff.gov.uk

Graham, Andrew (CON - Llanishen)
andrew.graham@cardiff.gov.uk

Groves, David (LAB - Whitchurch & Tongwynlais)
david.groves@cardiff.gov.uk

Hill-John, Gavin (CON - Pentyrch)
gavin.hill-john@cardiff.gov.uk

Hinchey, Graham (LAB - Heath)
graham.hinchey@cardiff.gov.uk

Holden, Gareth (PC - Gabalfa)
gareth.holden@cardiff.gov.uk

Howells, Nigel (LD - Adamsdown)
nhowells@cardiff.gov.uk

Hudson, Lyn (CON - Heath)
lhudson@cardiff.gov.uk

Hunt, Garry (LAB - Llanishen)
garry.hunt@cardiff.gov.uk

Hyde, Keith (LD - Pentwyn)
khyde@cardiff.gov.uk

Javed, Mohammad (LAB - Plasnewydd)
mohammad.javed@cardiff.gov.uk

Jones, Margaret (LD - Cyncoed)
mjones@cardiff.gov.uk

Jones, Keith (LAB - Llanrumney)
keith.jones@cardiff.gov.uk

Joyce, Heather (LAB - Llanrumney)
hjoyce@cardiff.gov.uk

Kelloway, Bill (LD - Penylan)
bkelloway@cardiff.gov.uk

Knight, Sam (LAB - Cathays)
sam.knight@cardiff.gov.uk

Lloyd, Kate (LD - Cyncoed)
klloyd@cardiff.gov.uk

Lomax, Chris (LAB - Grangetown)
chris.lomax@cardiff.gov.uk

Magill, Julia (LAB - Llanishen)
julia.magill@cardiff.gov.uk

Marshall, Gretta (IND - Splott)
gretta.marshall@cardiff.gov.uk

McGarry, Mary (LAB - Plasnewydd)
mary.mcgarry@cardiff.gov.uk

McKerlish, Roderick (CON - Radyr and Morganstown)
rmckerlich@cardiff.gov.uk

Merry, Sarah (LAB - Cathays)
sarah.merry@cardiff.gov.uk

Michael, Michael (LAB - Trowbridge)
michael.michael@cardiff.gov.uk

Mitchell, Paul (LAB - Fairwater)
paul.mitchell@cardiff.gov.uk

Morgan, Derek (IND - Llanrumney)
derrickmorgan@cardiff.gov.uk

Murphy, Jim (LAB - Ely)
jim.murphy@cardiff.gov.uk

Parry, Jacqueline (LAB - Rumney)
JackieParry@cardiff.gov.uk

Patel, Ramesh (LAB - Canton)
rapatel@cardiff.gov.uk

Rees, Diane (CON - Pontprennau & Old St. Mellons)
direes@cardiff.gov.ukw

Rees, David (LD - Cyncoed)
davrees@cardiff.gov.uk

Robson, Adrian (CON - Rhiwbina)
arobson@cardiff.gov.uk

Sanders, Eleanor (IND - Rhiwbina)
eleanor.sanders@cardiff.gov.uk

Simmons, Elaine (LAB - Caerau)
elaine.simmons@cardiff.gov.uk

Stubbs, Ed (LAB - Splott)
ed.stubbs@cardiff.gov.uk

Thomas, Huw (LAB - Splott)
huw.thomas@cardiff.gov.uk

Thomas, Graham (CON - Creigiau & St Fagans)
graham.thomas@cardiff.gov.uk

Thomas, Ben (LAB - Whitchurch & Tongwynlais)
ben.thomas@cardiff.gov.uk

Thorne, Lynda (LAB - Grangetown)
lynda.thorne@cardiff.gov.uk

Weaver, Chris (LAB - Cathays)
christopher.weaver@cardiff.gov.uk

White, Susan (LAB - Llandaff North)
susan.white@cardiff.gov.uk

Wild, Caro (LAB - Riverside)
caro.wild@cardiff.gov.uk

Williams, Darren (LAB - Riverside)
darren.williams@cardiff.gov.uk

POLITICAL COMPOSITION
LAB: 43, LD: 15, CON: 9, IND: 5, PC: 3

COMMITTEE CHAIRS

Children & Young People: Mr Richard Cook

Community & Adult Services: Ms Mary McGarry

Economy & Culture: Mr Roderick McKerlish

Licensing: Ms Jacqueline Parry

Planning: Mr Michael Michael

Carlisle City   D

Carlisle City Council, Civic Centre, Carlisle CA3 8QG
☎ 01228 817000 🖨 01228 817048 ✆ customerservices@carlisle.gov.uk
🖥 www.carlisle.gov.uk

FACTS AND FIGURES
Parliamentary Constituencies: Carlisle, Penrith and The Border
EU Constituencies: North West
Election Frequency: Elections are by thirds

PRINCIPAL OFFICERS

Chief Executive: Dr Jason Gooding, Chief Executive, Civic Centre, Carlisle CA3 8QG ☎ 01228 817009 ✆ jason.gooding@carlisle.gov.uk

Deputy Chief Executive: Mr Darren Crossley, Deputy Chief Executive, Civic Centre, Carlisle CA3 8QG ☎ 01228 817004 ✆ darren.crossley@carlisle.gov.uk

Senior Management: Mr Mark Lambert, Director - Governance, Civic Centre, Carlisle CA3 8QG ☎ 01228 817019 ✆ mark.lambert@carlisle.gov.uk

Senior Management: Ms Jane Meek, Director - Economic Development, Civic Centre, Carlisle CA3 8QG ☎ 01228 817190 ✆ jane.meek@carlisle.gov.uk

Access Officer / Social Services (Disability): Ms Karen Scrivener, Access Officer, Civic Centre, Carlisle CA3 8QG ☎ 01228 817183 ✆ karen.scrivener@carlisle.gov.uk

Architect, Building / Property Services: Ms Barbara Vernon, Senior Estates Surveyor, Civic Centre, Carlisle CA3 8QG ☎ 01228 817422 ✆ barbara.vernon@carlisle.gov.uk

CARLISLE CITY

Best Value: Mr Steven O'Keeffe, Policy & Communications Manager, Civic Centre, Carlisle CA3 8QG ☎ 01228 817258 ⌁ steven.o'keefe@carlisle.gov.uk

Building Control: Mr Mark Bowman, Building Control Manager, Civic Centre, Carlisle CA3 8QG ☎ 01228 817189 ⌁ mark.bowman@carlisle.gov.uk

PR / Communications: Mr Steven O'Keeffe, Policy & Communications Manager, Civic Centre, Carlisle CA3 8QG ☎ 01228 817258 ⌁ steven.o'keefe@carlisle.gov.uk

Community Planning: Ms Emma Dixon, Partnership Manager, Civic Centre, Carlisle CA3 8QG ☎ 01228 817370 ⌁ emma.dixon@carlisle.gov.uk

Community Safety: Ms Ruth Crane, Communities & Family Development Officer, Civic Centre, Carlisle CA3 8QG ☎ 01228 817362 ⌁ ruth.crane@carlisle.gov.uk

Computer Management: Mr Michael Scott, DIS Manager, Civic Centre, Carlisle CA3 8QG ☎ 01228 817251 ⌁ michael.scott@carlisle.gov.uk

Contracts: Mr Gavin Capstick, Contracts & Community Services Manager, Civic Centre, Carlisle CA3 8QG ☎ 01228 817123 ⌁ gavin.capstick@carlisle.gov.uk

Corporate Services: Dr Jason Gooding, Chief Executive, Civic Centre, Carlisle CA3 8QG ☎ 01228 817009 ⌁ jason.gooding@carlisle.gov.uk

Customer Service: Mrs Jillian Gillespie, Customer Services Manager, Civic Centre, Carlisle CA3 8QG ☎ 01228 817461 ⌁ jillian.gillespie@carlisle.gov.uk

Economic Development: Ms Jane Meek, Director - Economic Development, Civic Centre, Carlisle CA3 8QG ☎ 01228 817190 ⌁ jane.meek@carlisle.gov.uk

Electoral Registration: Mr Ian Dixon, Electoral Services Officer, Civic Centre, Carlisle CA3 8QG ☎ 01228 817555 ⌁ ian.dixon@carlisle.gov.uk

Emergency Planning: Mr Steven O'Keeffe, Emergency Planning Manager, Civic Centre, Carlisle CA3 8QG ☎ 01228 817258 ⌁ steven.o'keefe@carlisle.gov.uk

Environmental / Technical Services: Mr Colin Bowley, Neighbourhood Services Manager, Civic Centre, Carlisle CA3 8QG ☎ 01228 817124 ⌁ colin.bowley@carlisle.gov.uk

Environmental Health: Mr Scott Burns, Environmental Health Manager, Civic Centre, Carlisle CA3 8QG ☎ 01228 817328 ⌁ scott.burns@carlisle.gov.uk

Estates, Property & Valuation: Ms Barbara Vernon, Senior Estates Surveyor, Civic Centre, Carlisle CA3 8QG ☎ 01228 817422 ⌁ barbara.vernon@carlisle.gov.uk

Events Manager: Ms Gill Forster-Spratt, Events Officer, Civic Centre, Carlisle CA3 8QG ☎ 01228 817156 ⌁ gill.forsterspratt@carlisle.gov.uk

Facilities: Mr Gavin Bannister, Building Maintenance Team Leader, Civic Centre, Carlisle CA3 8QG ☎ 01228 817250 ⌁ gavin.bannister@carlisle.gov.uk

Grounds Maintenance: Mr Colin Bowley, Neighbourhood Services Manager, Civic Centre, Carlisle CA3 8QG ☎ 01228 817124 ⌁ colin.bowley@carlisle.gov.uk

Health and Safety: Mr Arup Majhi, Safety & Health Environmental Manager, Civic Centre, Carlisle CA3 8QG ☎ 01228 817507 ⌁ arup.majhi@carlisle.gov.uk

Housing: Ms Emma Moraitis, HIA Team Leader, Civic Centre, Carlisle CA3 8QG ☎ 01228 817443 ⌁ emma.moraitis@carlisle.gov.uk

Legal: Mr Mark Lambert, Director - Governance, Civic Centre, Carlisle CA3 8QG ☎ 01228 817019 ⌁ mark.lambert@carlisle.gov.uk

Leisure and Cultural Services: Mr Gavin Capstick, Contracts & Community Services Manager, Civic Centre, Carlisle CA3 8QG ☎ 01228 817123 ⌁ gavin.capstick@carlisle.gov.uk

Licensing: Ms Susan Stashkiw, Licensing Manager, Civic Centre, Carlisle CA3 8QG ☎ 01228 817029 ⌁ susan.stashkiw@carlisle.gov.uk

Member Services: Mr Mark Lambert, Director - Governance, Civic Centre, Carlisle CA3 8QG ☎ 01228 817019 ⌁ mark.lambert@carlisle.gov.uk

Parking: Ms Sharon Jenkinson, City Centre Manager, Civic Centre, Carlisle CA3 8QG ☎ 01228 817549 ⌁ sharon.jenkinson@carlisle.gov.uk

Partnerships: Ms Emma Dixon, Partnership Manager, Civic Centre, Carlisle CA3 8QG ☎ 01228 817370 ⌁ emma.dixon@carlisle.gov.uk

Personnel / HR: Ms Julie Kemp, HR Advisory Services Team Leader, Civic Centre, Carlisle CA3 8QG ☎ 01228 817081 ⌁ julie.kemp@carlisle.gov.uk

Planning: Mr Christopher Hardman, Planning Manager, Civic Centre, Carlisle CA3 8QG ☎ 01228 817502 ⌁ chris.hardman@carlisle.gov.uk

Procurement: Ms Dawn Reid, Assistant Procurement Officer, Civic Centre, Carlisle CA3 8QG ☎ 01228 817595 ⌁ dawn.reid@carlisle.gov.uk

Recycling & Waste Minimisation: Mr Colin Bowley, Neighbourhood Services Manager, Civic Centre, Carlisle CA3 8QG ☎ 01228 817124 ⌁ colin.bowley@carlisle.gov.uk

Staff Training: Ms Linda Mattinson, Learning & Development Co-ordinator, Civic Centre, Carlisle CA3 8QG ☎ 01228 817076 ⌁ linda.mattinson@carlisle.gov.uk

Tourism: Ms Laura Thompson, Tourist Information Officer, Civic Centre, Carlisle CA3 8QG ☎ 01228 598596 ✆ laura.thompson@carlisle.gov.uk

Town Centre: Ms Sharon Jenkinson, City Centre Manager, Civic Centre, Carlisle CA3 8QG ☎ 01228 817549 ✆ sharon.jenkinson@carlisle.gov.uk

Waste Collection and Disposal: Mr Colin Bowley, Neighbourhood Services Manager, Civic Centre, Carlisle CA3 8QG ☎ 01228 817124 ✆ colin.bowley@carlisle.gov.uk

Waste Management: Mr Colin Bowley, Neighbourhood Services Manager, Civic Centre, Carlisle CA3 8QG ☎ 01228 817124 ✆ colin.bowley@carlisle.gov.uk

Children's Play Areas: Mr Phil Gray, Greenspaces & Bereavement Services Manager, Civic Centre, Carlisle CA3 8QG ☎ 01228 817485 ✆ phil.gray@carlisle.gov.uk

COUNCILLORS

Mayor: Stothard, Colin (LAB - Morton)
colin.stothard@carlisle.gov.uk

Deputy Mayor: Vasey, Patricia (CON - Belah)
trish.vasey@carlisle.gov.uk

Leader of the Council: Glover, Colin (LAB - Currock)
colin.glover@carlisle.gov.uk

Alcroft, Ruth (LAB - Denton Holme)

Allison, Trevor (LD - Dalston)
trevor.allison@carlisle.gov.uk

Bainbridge, James (CON - Stanwix Rural)
james.bainbridge@carlisle.gov.uk

Bell, John (LAB - Morton)
john.bell@carlisle.gov.uk

Betton, Robert (IND - Botcherby)
robert.betton@carlisle.gov.uk

Bloxham, Raynor (CON - Longtown & Rockcliffe)
ray.bloxham@carlisle.gov.uk

Bomford, Jeffrey (IND - Botcherby)

Bowditch, Steven (LAB - Yewdale)
steven.bowditch@carlisle.gov.uk

Bowman, Cyril (CON - Irthing)
cyril.bowman@carlisle.gov.uk

Bowman, Marilyn (CON - Stanwix Rural)
marilyn.bowman@carlisle.gov.uk

Bradley, Heather (LAB - Currock)
heather.bradley@carlisle.gov.uk

Burns, Robert (LAB - Harraby)
rob.burns@carlisle.gov.uk

Christian, Nigel (CON - Dalston)
Nigel.christian@carlisle.gov.uk

Coleman, Joanna (LAB - Castle)

Collier, John (CON - Burgh)
john.collier@carlisle.gov.uk

Dodd, Thomas (LAB - Yewdale)
tom.dodd@carlisle.gov.uk

Earp, Barry (CON - Wetheral)
barry.earp@carlisle.gov.uk

Ellis, Gareth (CON - Belah)
gareth.ellis@carlisle.gov.uk

Franklin, Jacqueline (LAB - Belle Vue)
jacqueline.franklin@carlisle.gov.uk

Harid, Abdul (LAB - Currock)
abdul.harid@carlisle.gov.uk

Higgs, Stephen (CON - Wetheral)
stephen.higgs@carlisle.gov.uk

Layden, Stephen (CON - Brampton)
stephen.layden@carlisle.gov.uk

Mallinson, Elizabeth (CON - Stanwix Urban)
liz.mallinson@carlisle.gov.uk

Mallinson, John (CON - Longtown & Rockcliffe)
john.mallinson@carlisle.gov.uk

McDevitt, Hugh (LAB - Denton Holme)
hugh.mcdevitt@carlisle.gov.uk

McDonald, Maureen (LAB - Yewdale)

McKerrell, Ann (CON - Dalston)
ann.mckerrell@carlisle.gov.uk

McNulty, Niall (LAB - Upperby)

Mitchelson, Mike (CON - Brampton)
mike.mitchelson@carlisle.gov.uk

Morton, David (CON - Belah)
david.morton@carlisle.gov.uk

Nedved, Paul (CON - Stanwix Urban)
paul.nedved@carlisle.gov.uk

Osgood, Barrie (LAB - Castle)
barrie.osgood@carlisle.gov.uk

Parsons, Doreen (CON - Great Corby & Geltsdale)
doreen.parsons@carlisle.gov.uk

Paton, John (IND - Botcherby)
jack.paton@carlisle.gov.uk

Patrick, Lucy (LAB - St Aidans)
lucy.patrick@carlisle.gov.uk

Quilter, Anne (LAB - St Aidans)
anne.quilter@carlisle.gov.uk

Riddle, Jessica (LAB - Belle Vue)
jessica.riddle@carlisle.gov.uk

Robson, Fiona (CON - Stanwix Urban)
fiona.robson@carlisle.gov.uk

Shepherd, David (CON - Lyne)
david.shepherd@carlisle.gov.uk

Sherriff, Lee (LAB - Harraby)
lee.sherriff@carlisle.gov.uk

Sidgwick, Therese (LAB - Morton)

Southward, Christopher (LAB - Denton Holme)
chris.southward@carlisle.gov.uk

Tickner, Les (LAB - Belle Vue)
les.tickner@carlisle.gov.uk

Tinnion, Raymond (IND - Hayton)

Warwick, Ann (LAB - Upperby)
ann.warwick@carlisle.gov.uk

CARLISLE CITY

Watson, Reginald (LAB - St Aidans)
reg.watson@Carlisle.gov.uk

Williams, Jo (LAB - Harraby)
jo.williams@carlisle.gov.uk

Wilson, David (LAB - Upperby)
david.wilson@carlisle.gov.uk

POLITICAL COMPOSITION
LAB: 26, CON: 20, IND: 4, LD: 1

COMMITTEE CHAIRS

Audit: Ms Lucy Patrick

Development Control: Mrs Ann Warwick

Environment & Economy: Mr Paul Nedved

Carmarthenshire   W

Carmarthenshire County Council, County Hall, Carmarthen SA31 1JP
☎ 01267 234567 🖨 01267 224911
🖰 information@carmarthenshire.gov.uk
🖳 www.carmarthenshire.gov.uk

FACTS AND FIGURES
Parliamentary Constituencies: Carmarthen East and Dinefwr, Carmarthen West and South Pembrokeshire, Llanelli
EU Constituencies: Wales
Election Frequency: Elections are of whole council

PRINCIPAL OFFICERS

Chief Executive: Mr Mark James, Chief Executive, County Hall, Carmarthen SA31 1JP ☎ 01267 224110
🖰 mjames@carmarthenshire.gov.uk

Assistant Chief Executive: Mr Paul Thomas, Assistant Chief Executive - People Management & Performance, Parc Dewi Sant, Carmarthen SA31 3HB ☎ 01267 246123
🖰 prthomas@carmarthenshire.gov.uk

Assistant Chief Executive: Ms Wendy Walters, Assistant Chief Executive - Regeneration & Policy, County Hall, Carmarthen SA31 1JP ☎ 01267 244112 🖰 wswalters@carmarthenshire.gov.uk

Senior Management: Mr Christopher Moore, Director - Corporate Services & S151 Officer, County Hall, Carmarthen SA31 1JP ☎ 01267 224160 🖰 cmoore@carmarthenshire.gov.uk

Senior Management: Mr Jake Morgan, Director - Community Services, County Hall, Carmarthen SA31 1JP ☎ 01267 244698
🖰 jakemorgan@carmarthenshire.gov.uk

Senior Management: Ms Ruth Mullen, Director - Environment, County Hall, Carmarthen SA31 1JP
🖰 rmullen@carmarthenshire.gov.uk

Senior Management: Mr Robert Sully, Director - Education & Children's Services, County Hall, Carmarthen SA31 1JP
☎ 01267 224888 🖰 rsully@carmarthenshire.gov.uk

Access Officer / Social Services (Disability): Mr Richard Elms, Civil Contingency Officer, Parc Myrddin, Wellfield Road, Carmarthen SA13 1DS ☎ 01267 228147 🖰 relms@carmarthenshire.gov.uk

Building Control: Ms Ruth Mullen, Director - Environment, County Hall, Carmarthen SA31 1JP 🖰 rmullen@carmarthenshire.gov.uk

Catering Services: Mrs Sandra Weigel, Catering Services Manager, Parc Dewi Sant, Carmarthen SA31 3HB ☎ 01267 246484 🖰 sjweigel@carmarthenshire.gov.uk

Children / Youth Services: Mr Stefan Smith, Head - Children's Services, Block 2, S David's Park, Jobswewl Road, Carmarthen SA31 3HB ☎ 01267 246530 🖰 sjsmith@carmarthenshire.gov.uk

Civil Registration: Mrs Andrea Rowlands, Civil Registration, Parc Myrddin, Richmond Terrace, Carmarthen SA31 1HQ ☎ 01267 228375 🖰 akrowlands@carmarthenshire.gov.uk

PR / Communications: Mrs Deina Hockenhull, Marketing & Media Manager, County Hall, Carmarthen SA31 1JP ☎ 01267 224654 🖰 dmhockenhull@carmarthenshire.gov.uk

Community Safety: Mrs Kate Thomas, Community Safety Manager, County Hall, Carmarthen SA31 1JP ☎ 01267 224202 🖰 khthomas@carmarthenshire.gov.uk

Computer Management: Mr Noelwyn Daniel, Performance & Information Manager, Parc Dewi Sant, Carmarthen SA31 3HB ☎ 01267 246217 🖰 ndaniel@carmarthenshire.gov.uk

Consumer Protection and Trading Standards: Mr Roger Edmunds, Trading Standards Manager, Ty Elwyn, Llanelli SA15 3AP ☎ 01554 742280 🖰 redmunds@carmarthenshire.gov.uk

Customer Service: Mrs Penelope Graepel, Customer Services Manager, County Hall, Carmarthen SA31 1JP ☎ 01558 825384 🖰 pgraepal@carmartenshire.gov.uk

Direct Labour: Ms Ruth Mullen, Director - Environment, County Hall, Carmarthen SA31 1JP 🖰 rmullen@carmarthenshire.gov.uk

Economic Development: Mr Stuart Walters, Regeneration Manager, Parc Ananwy, Business Resource Centre, Ammanford SA18 3EP ☎ 01269 590241 🖰 swalters@carmarthenshire.gov.uk

Education: Mr Robert Sully, Director - Education & Children's Services, County Hall, Carmarthen SA31 1JP ☎ 01267 224888 🖰 rsully@carmarthenshire.gov.uk

E-Government: Mr Phil Sexton, Head - Audit, Procurement & ICT, Parc Dewi Sant, Carmarthen SA31 3HB ☎ 01267 246217 🖰 psexton@carmarthenshire.gov.uk

Electoral Registration: Ms Amanda Bebb, Electoral Services Manager, Parc Myrddin, Richmond Terrace, Carmarthen SA31 1HQ ☎ 01267 228609 🖰 Abebb@carmarthenshire.gov.uk

Emergency Planning: Mr Richard Elms, Civil Contingency Manager, Parc Myrddin, Richmond Terrace, Carmarthen SA31 1HQ ☎ 01267 228195 🖰 relms@carmarthenshire.gov.uk

Environmental Health: Mr Robin Staines, Head - Public Protection & Housing, 3 Spilman Street, Carmarthen SA31 1LE ☎ 01267 228960 ⚲ rstaines@carmarthenshire.gov.uk

Estates, Property & Valuation: Mr Jonathan Fearn, Head - Corporate Property, Parc Dewi, Carmarthen SA31 3HB ☎ 01267 246244 ⚲ jfearn@carmarthenshire.gov.uk

European Liaison: Ms Helen Morgan, Development Manager, County Hall, Carmarthen SA31 1JP ☎ 01267 224859 ⚲ hlmorgan@carmarthenshire.gov.uk

Finance: Mr Christopher Moore, Director - Corporate Services & S151 Officer, County Hall, Carmarthen SA31 1JP ☎ 01267 224160 ⚲ cmoore@carmarthenshire.gov.uk

Pensions: Mr Kevin Gerard, Pensions Manager, County Hall, Carmarthen SA31 1JP ☎ 01267 224157 ⚲ kgerard@carmarthenshire.gov.uk

Pensions: Mr Anthony Parnell, Treasurer, Pensions & Investment Manager, County Hall, Carmarthen SA31 1JP ☎ 01267 224180 ⚲ aparnell@carmarthenshire.gov.uk

Fleet Management: Mr Steven Pilliner, Head - Transport & Engineering, Parc Myrddin, Carmarthen SA31 2HQ ☎ 01267 228150 ⚲ spilliner@carmarthenshire.gov.uk

Grounds Maintenance: Ms Ruth Mullen, Director - Environment, County Hall, Carmarthen SA31 1JP ⚲ rmullen@carmarthenshire.gov.uk

Health and Safety: Mr Mark Millward, Health & Safety Advisor, Parc Dewi Sant, Carmarthen SA31 3HB ☎ 01267 246131 ⚲ mmilward@carmarthenshire.gov.uk

Highways: Mr Steven Pilliner, Head - Transport & Engineering, Parc Myrddin, Carmarthen SA31 2HQ ☎ 01267 228150 ⚲ spilliner@carmarthenshire.gov.uk

Home Energy Conservation: Mr Robin Staines, Head - Public Protection & Housing, 3 Spilman Street, Carmarthen SA31 1LE ☎ 01267 228960 ⚲ rstaines@carmarthenshire.gov.uk

Housing: Mr Robin Staines, Head - Public Protection & Housing, 3 Spilmand Street, Carmarthen SA31 1LE ☎ 01267 228960 ⚲ rstaines@carmarthenshire.gov.uk

Housing Maintenance: Mr Robin Staines, Head - Public Protection & Housing, 3 Spilman Street, Carmarthen SA31 1LE ☎ 01267 228960 ⚲ rstaines@carmarthenshire.gov.uk

Legal: Mrs Linda Rees-Jones, Head - Administration & Law, County Hall, Carmarthen SA31 1JP ☎ 01267 224012 ⚲ LRJones@carmarthenshire.gov.uk

Leisure and Cultural Services: Mr Ian Jones, Head - Leisure, Parc Myrddin, Carmarthen SA13 1DS ☎ 01267 228309 ⚲ ijones@carmarthenshire.gov.uk

Licensing: Mrs Sue Watts, Public Health Services Manager, 3 Spilman Street, Carmarthen SA31 1LE ☎ 01267 228929 ⚲ sewatts@carmarthenshire.gov.uk

Lifelong Learning: Mr Matt Morden, Lifelong Skills Network Manager, County Hall, Carmarthen SA31 1JP ☎ 01267 246648 ⚲ msmorden@carmarthenshire.gov.uk

Lighting: Ms Ruth Mullen, Director - Environment, County Hall, Carmarthen SA31 1JP ⚲ rmullen@carmarthenshire.gov.uk

Member Services: Ms Gaynor Morgan, Democratic Services Manager, County Hall, Carmarthen SA31 1JP ☎ 01267 224026 ⚲ gmorgan@carmarthenshire.gov.uk

Parking: Mr John Mcevoy, Road Safety & Traffic Manager, Parc Myrddin, Carmarthen SA31 2HQ ☎ 01267 228190 ⚲ jmcevoy@carmarthenshire.gov.uk

Partnerships: Mrs Gwyneth Ayers, Corporate Policy & Partnerships Manager, County Hall, Carmarthen SA31 1JP ☎ 01267 224112 ⚲ gayers@carmarthenshire.gov.uk

Personnel / HR: Mr Paul Thomas, Assistant Chief Executive - People Management & Performance, Parc Dewi Sant, Carmarthen SA31 3HB ☎ 01267 246123 ⚲ prthomas@carmarthenshire.gov.uk

Planning: Mr Llinos Quelch, Head - Planning, County Hall, Carmarthen SA31 1JP ⚲ lquelch@carmarthenshire.gov.uk

Procurement: Mr Phil Sexton, Head - Audit, Procurement & ICT, Parc Dewi Sant, Carmarthen SA31 3HB ☎ 01267 246217 ⚲ psexton@carmarthenshire.gov.uk

Public Libraries: Mrs Jane Davies, Senior Cultural Services Manager, County Hall, Carmarthen SA31 1JP ☎ 01554 742180 ⚲ jdavies@carmarthenshire.gov.uk

Recycling & Waste Minimisation: Mr Ainsley Williams, Head - Waste Management, County Hall, Carmarthen SA31 1JP ⚲ aiwilliams@carmarthenshire.gov.uk

Regeneration: Mr Stuart Walters, Regeneration Manager, Parc Ananwy, Business Resource Centre, Ammanford SA18 3EP ☎ 01269 590241 ⚲ swalters@carmarthenshire.gov.uk

Road Safety: Mr John Mcevoy, Road Safety & Traffic Manager, Parc Myrddin, Carmarthen SA31 2HQ ☎ 01267 228190 ⚲ jmcevoy@carmarthenshire.gov.uk

Social Services: Mr Jake Morgan, Director - Community Services, County Hall, Carmarthen SA31 1JP ☎ 01267 244698 ⚲ jakemorgan@carmarthenshire.gov.uk

Social Services (Adult): Ms Avril Bracey, Head - Mental Health & Learning Disabilities, County Hall, Carmarthen SA31 1JP ☎ 01267 242492 ⚲ abracey@carmarthenshire.gov.uk

Social Services (Children): Mr Stefan Smith, Head - Children's Services, Block 2, S David's Park, Jobswewl Road, Carmarthen SA31 3HB ☎ 01267 246530 ⚲ sjsmith@carmarthenshire.gov.uk

CARMARTHENSHIRE

Street Scene: Ms Ruth Mullen, Director - Environment, County Hall, Carmarthen SA31 1JP ⏚ rmullen@carmarthenshire.gov.uk

Sustainable Development: Mr Kendal Davies, Sustainable Development Manager, County Hall, Carmarthen SA31 1JP ☎ 01267 228351 ⏚ jkdavies@carmarthenshire.gov.uk

Tourism: Mr Huw Parsons, Assistant Marketing & Media Manager, County Hall, Carmarthen SA31 1JP ⏚ hlparsons@carmarthenshire.gov.uk

Traffic Management: Mr John Mcevoy, Road Safety & Traffic Manager, Parc Myrddin, Carmarthen SA31 2HQ ☎ 01267 228190 ⏚ jmcevoy@carmarthenshire.gov.uk

Transport: Mr Steven Pilliner, Head - Transport & Engineering, Parc Myrddin, Carmarthen SA31 2HQ ☎ 01267 228150 ⏚ spilliner@carmarthenshire.gov.uk

Transport Planner: Mr Steven Pilliner, Head - Transport & Engineering, Parc Myrddin, Carmarthen SA31 2HQ ☎ 01267 228150 ⏚ spilliner@carmarthenshire.gov.uk

Waste Collection and Disposal: Mr Ainsley Williams, Head - Waste Management, County Hall, Carmarthen SA31 1JP ⏚ aiwilliams@carmarthenshire.gov.uk

Waste Management: Mr Ainsley Williams, Head - Waste Management, County Hall, Carmarthen SA31 1JP ⏚ aiwilliams@carmarthenshire.gov.uk

COUNCILLORS

Leader of the Council: Dole, Emlyn (PC - Llannon) edole@carmarthenshire.gov.uk

Deputy Leader of the Council: Jenkins, David (PC - Glanamman) dmjenkins@carmarthenshire.gov.uk

Deputy Leader of the Council: Palmer, Pamela (IND - Abergwili) papalmer@carmarthenshire.gov.uk

Allen, Susan (IND - Whitland) smallen@carmarthenshire.gov.uk

Bartlett, Ryan (LAB - Betws) rbartlett@carmarthenshire.gov.uk

Bowen, Theressa (IND - Llwynhendy) thbowen@carmarthenshire.gov.uk

Caiach, Sian (O - Hengoed) smcaiach@carmarthenshire.gov.uk

Campbell, Cefin (PC - Llanfihangel Aberbythych) cacampbell@carmarthenshire.gov.uk

Charles, John (PC - Llanegwad) mcharles@carmarthenshire.gov.uk

Cooper, Peter (LAB - Saron) apcooper@carmarthenshire.gov.uk

Cundy, Deryk (LAB - Bynea) dcundy@carmarthenshire.gov.uk

Davies, Terry (LAB - Gorslas) tedavies@carmarthenshire.gov.uk

Davies, Joseph (IND - Manordeib & Salem) josdavies@carmarthenshire.gov.uk

Davies, Alun (PC - Saron) alundavies@carmarthenshire.gov.uk

Davies, Daff (IND - Llansteffan) dbdavies@carmarthenshire.gov.uk

Davies, Ieuan (IND - Llanybydder) iwdavies@carmarthenshire.gov.uk

Davies, Sharen (LAB - Llwynhendy) sdavies@carmarthenshire.gov.uk

Davies, Glynog (PC - Quarter Bach) gidavies@carmarthenshire.gov.uk

Davies, Anthony (IND - Llandybie) antdavies@carmarthenshire.gov.uk

Davies Evans, Linda (PC - Llanfihangel-Ar-Arth) ldaviesevans@carmarthenshire.gov.uk

Defis, Tom (PC - Carmarthen Town West) tdefis@carmarthenshire.gov.uk

Devichand, Tegwen (LAB - Dafen) tdevichand@carmarthenshire.gov.uk

Edmunds, Jeffrey (LAB - Bigyn) jedmunds@carmarthenshire.gov.uk

Edwards, Penny (LAB - Hengoed) PennyEdwards@carmarthenshire.gov.uk

Evans, Colin (LAB - Pontamman) dcevans@carmarthenshire.gov.uk

Evans, Hazel (PC - Cenarth) hazelevans@carmarthenshire.gov.uk

Evans, Tyssul (PC - Llangyndeyrn) wtevans@carmarthenshire.gov.uk

Evans, Wyn (IND - Llanddarog) wjwevans@carmarthenshire.gov.uk

Gravell, Meryl (IND - Trimsaran) mgravell@carmarthenshire.gov.uk

Griffiths, Peter (PC - Carmarthen Town North) phughes-griffiths@carmarthenshire.gov.uk

Harries, Deian (PC - Ammanford) deharries@carmarthenshire.gov.uk

Higgins, Calum (LAB - Tycroes) chiggins@carmarthenshire.gov.uk

Hopkins, Gwyn (PC - Llangennech) wghopkins@carmarthenshire.gov.uk

Howell, Ken (PC - Llangeler) kenhowell@carmarthenshire.gov.uk

Hughes, Philip (IND - St Clears) pmhughes@carmarthenshire.gov.uk

Jackson, Ivor (IND - Llandovery) ijjackson@carmarthenshire.gov.uk

James, Andrew (IND - Llangadog) andjames@carmarthenshire.gov.uk

James, John (LAB - Burry Port) johnjames@carmarthenshire.gov.uk

Jenkins, John (INDNA - Elli) jpjenkins@carmarthenshire.gov.uk

Jones, Gareth (PC - Carmarthen Town North) gojones@carmarthenshire.gov.uk

Jones, Anthony (LAB - Llandybie)
awjones@carmarthenshire.gov.uk

Jones, Patricia (LAB - Burry Port)
pemjones@carmarthenshire.gov.uk

Jones, Irfon (IND - Cynwyl Elfed)
hijones@carmarthenshire.gov.uk

Jones, Jim (IND - Glyn)
tjjones@carmarthenshire.gov.uk

Lemon, Winston (PC - Glanymor)
wjlemon@carmarthenshire.gov.uk

Lenny, Alun (PC - Carmarthen Town South)
alunlenny@carmarthenshire.gov.uk

Lewis, Jean (PC - Trelech)
JeanLewis@carmarthenshire.gov.uk

Llewellyn, Roy (PC - Llanboidy)
djrllewellyn@carmarthenshire.gov.uk

Madge, Kevin (LAB - Garnant)
kmadge@carmarthenshire.gov.uk

Matthews, Shirley (LAB - Pembrey)
smatthews@carmarthenshire.gov.uk

Morgan, Giles (IND - Swiss Valley)
agmorgan@carmarthenshire.gov.uk

Morgan, Eryl (LAB - Bigyn)
emorgan@carmarthenshire.gov.uk

Owen, Jeff (PC - Tyisha)
jeffowen@carmarthenshire.gov.uk

Price, Darren (PC - Gorslas)
daprice@carmarthenshire.gov.uk

Richards, Hugh (IND - Felinfoel)
dwhrichards@carmarthenshire.gov.uk

Roberts, Beatrice (LAB - Glanymor)
loroberts@carmarthenshire.gov.uk

Shepardson, Hugh (IND - Pembrey)
hbshepardson@carmarthenshire.gov.uk

Speake, Alan (PC - Carmarthen Town West)
adtspeake@carmarthenshire.gov.uk

Stephens, Mair (IND - St Ishmael)
lmstephens@carmarthenshire.gov.uk

Theophilus, Thomas (IND - Cilycwm)
ttheophilus@carmarthenshire.gov.uk

Thomas, Edward (IND - Llandeilo)
egthomas@carmarthenshire.gov.uk

Thomas, Gwyneth (PC - Llangennech)
gwythomas@carmarthenshire.gov.uk

Thomas, Ryan (LAB - Kidwelly)
ryanthomas@carmarthenshire.gov.uk

Thomas, Siân (PC - Pen-y-Groes)
sethomas@sirgar.gov.uk

Thomas, Keri (LAB - Tyisha)
kpthomas@carmarthenshire.gov.uk

Thomas, Kim (LAB - Llannon)
mkthomas@carmarthenshire.gov.uk

Thomas, Jeffrey (PC - Carmarthen Town South)
jeffthomas@carmarthenshire.gov.uk

Thomas, Gareth (PC - Hendy)
gbthomas@sirgar.gov.uk

Thomas, Bill (LAB - Lliedi)
bthomas@carmarthenshire.gov.uk

Tremlett, Jane (IND - Laugharne Township)
jtremlett@carmarthenshire.gov.uk

Williams, Eirwyn (PC - Cynwyl Gaeo)
jewilliams@carmarthenshire.gov.uk

Williams, Janice (LAB - Lliedi)
janwilliams@carmarthenshire.gov.uk

Williams, Joy (PC - Pontyberem)
jswilliams@sirgar.gov.uk

Williams, Elwyn (PC - Llangunnor)
dewilliams@carmarthenshire.gov.uk

POLITICAL COMPOSITION
PC: 29, LAB: 22, IND: 21, INDNA: 1, O: 1

COMMITTEE CHAIRS

Education & Children: Mr Eirwyn Williams

Social Care & Health: Mrs Gwyneth Thomas

Castle Point   D

Castle Point Borough Council, Council Offices, Kiln Road,
Thundersley, Benfleet SS7 1TF
☎ 01268 882200 🖨 01268 882455 ✆ info@castlepoint.gov.uk
💻 www.castlepoint.gov.uk

FACTS AND FIGURES
Parliamentary Constituencies: Castle Point
EU Constituencies: Eastern
Election Frequency: Elections are by thirds

PRINCIPAL OFFICERS

Chief Executive: Mr David Marchant, Chief Executive, Council
Offices, Kiln Road, Thundersley, Benfleet SS7 1TF ☎ 01268 882200
✆ dmarchant@castlepoint.gov.uk

Deputy Chief Executive: Mrs Devinia Board, Strategic Director
- Transformation & Resources, Council Offices, Kiln Road,
Thundersley, Benfleet SS7 1TF ☎ 01268 882363
✆ dboard@castlepoint.gov.uk

Deputy Chief Executive: Mr Andrew Smith, Strategic Director -
Corporate Services & Monitoring Officer, Council Offices, Kiln Road,
Thundersley, Benfleet SS7 1TF ☎ 01268 882433
✆ asmith@castlepoint.gov.uk

Architect, Building / Property Services: Mr Jarl Jansen,
Facilities & Asset Manager, Council Offices, Kiln Road, Thundersley,
Benfleet SS7 1TF ☎ 01268 882408 ✆ jjansen@castlepoint.gov.uk

Best Value: Mr Craig Watts, Head - Performance & Support
Service, Council Offices, Kiln Road, Thundersley, Benfleet SS7 1TF
☎ 01268 882213 ✆ cwatts@castlepoint.gov.uk

CASTLE POINT

Building Control: Mr Gary Martindill, Principal Building Surveyor, Council Offices, Kiln Road, Thundersley, Benfleet SS7 1TF ☎ 01268 882288 ✆ gmartindill@castlepoint.gov.uk

PR / Communications: Miss Ann Horgan, Head - Governance, Council Offices, Kiln Road, Thundersley, Benfleet SS7 1TF ☎ 01268 882413 ✆ ahorgan@castlepoint.gov.uk

Community Planning: Mr Stephen Rogers, Head - Regeneration & Neighbourhoods, Council Offices, Kiln Road, Thundersley, Benfleet SS7 1TF ☎ 01268 882200 ✆ srogers@castlepoint.gov.uk

Community Safety: Mrs Mel Harris, Head - Partnerships & Safer Places, Council Offices, Kiln Road, Thundersley, Benfleet SS7 1TF ☎ 01268 882369 ✆ mharris@castlepoint.gov.uk

Computer Management: Mr Barry Delf, ICT Service Manager, Council Offices, Kiln Road, Thundersley, Benfleet SS7 1TF ☎ 01268 882412 ✆ bdelf@castlepoint.gov.uk

Contracts: Ms Fiona Wilson, Head - Law & Deputy Monitoring Officer, Council Offices, Kiln Road, Thundersley, Benfleet SS7 1TF ☎ 01268 882436 ✆ fwilson@castlepoint.gov.uk

Corporate Services: Mr Andrew Smith, Strategic Director - Corporate Services & Monitoring Officer, Council Offices, Kiln Road, Thundersley, Benfleet SS7 1TF ☎ 01268 882433 ✆ asmith@castlepoint.gov.uk

Customer Service: Ms Wendy Buck, Head of Housing & Communities, Council Offices, Kiln Road, Thundersley, Benfleet SS7 1TF ☎ 01268 882245 ✆ wbuck@castlepoint.gov.uk

Economic Development: Mr Stephen Rogers, Head - Regeneration & Neighbourhoods, Council Offices, Kiln Road, Thundersley, Benfleet SS7 1TF ☎ 01268 882200 ✆ srogers@castlepoint.gov.uk

Electoral Registration: Mr John Riley, Cabinet & Electoral Services Manager, Council Offices, Kiln Road, Thundersley, Benfleet SS7 1TF ☎ 01268 882417 ✆ jriley@castlepoint.gov.uk

Emergency Planning: Mr Jarl Jansen, Facilities & Asset Manager, Council Offices, Kiln Road, Thundersley, Benfleet SS7 1TF ☎ 01268 882408 ✆ jjansen@castlepoint.gov.uk

Energy Management: Mr Rob Lawrence, Property Technical Officer, Council Offices, Kiln Road, Thundersley, Benfleet SS7 1TF ☎ 01268 882200

Environmental / Technical Services: Mrs Trudie Bragg, Head - Environment, Council Offices, Kiln Road, Thundersley, Benfleet SS7 1TF ☎ 01268 882476 ✆ tbragg@castlepoint.gov.uk

Environmental Health: Mrs Trudie Bragg, Head - Environment, Council Offices, Kiln Road, Thundersley, Benfleet SS7 1TF ☎ 01268 882476 ✆ tbragg@castlepoint.gov.uk

Events Manager: Mrs Mel Harris, Head - Partnerships & Safer Places, Council Offices, Kiln Road, Thundersley, Benfleet SS7 1TF ☎ 01268 882369 ✆ mharris@castlepoint.gov.uk

Facilities: Mr Jarl Jansen, Facilities & Asset Manager, Council Offices, Kiln Road, Thundersley, Benfleet SS7 1TF ☎ 01268 882408 ✆ jjansen@castlepoint.gov.uk

Finance: Ms Chris Mills, Head - Resources & S151 Officer, Council Offices, Kiln Road, Thundersley, Benfleet SS7 1TF ☎ 01268 882215 ✆ cmills@castlepoint.gov.uk

Treasury: Ms Chris Mills, Head - Resources & S151 Officer, Council Offices, Kiln Road, Thundersley, Benfleet SS7 1TF ☎ 01268 882215 ✆ cmills@castlepoint.gov.uk

Grounds Maintenance: Mr Ryan Lynch, Operations Services Manager, Council Offices, Kiln Road, Thundersley, Benfleet SS7 1TF ☎ 01268 882377 ✆ rlynch@castlepoint.gov.uk

Health and Safety: Ms Chris Mills, Head - Resources & S151 Officer, Council Offices, Kiln Road, Thundersley, Benfleet SS7 1TF ☎ 01268 882215 ✆ cmills@castlepoint.gov.uk

Home Energy Conservation: Mr Simon Llewellyn, Environmental Health Operational Manager, Council Offices, Kiln Road, Thundersley, Benfleet SS7 1TF ☎ 01268 882303 ✆ sllewellyn@castlepoint.gov.uk

Housing: Ms Wendy Buck, Head of Housing & Communities, Council Offices, Kiln Road, Thundersley, Benfleet SS7 1TF ☎ 01268 882245 ✆ wbuck@castlepoint.gov.uk

Legal: Ms Fiona Wilson, Head - Law & Deputy Monitoring Officer, Council Offices, Kiln Road, Thundersley, Benfleet SS7 1TF ☎ 01268 882436 ✆ fwilson@castlepoint.gov.uk

Leisure and Cultural Services: Ms Diane Logue, Community Services & Corporate Support Manager, Council Offices, Kiln Road, Thundersley, Benfleet SS7 1TF ☎ 01268 882669 ✆ dlogue@castlepoint.gov.uk

Member Services: Miss Ann Horgan, Head - Governance, Council Offices, Kiln Road, Thundersley, Benfleet SS7 1TF ☎ 01268 882413 ✆ ahorgan@castlepoint.gov.uk

Parking: Mr Ryan Lynch, Operational Services Manager, Council Offices, Kiln Road, Thundersley, Benfleet SS7 1TF ☎ 01268 882377 ✆ rlynch@castlepoint.gov.uk

Partnerships: Mrs Mel Harris, Head - Partnerships & Safer Places, Council Offices, Kiln Road, Thundersley, Benfleet SS7 1TF ☎ 01268 882369 ✆ mharris@castlepoint.gov.uk

Personnel / HR: Ms B Cree, HR Manager, Council Offices, Kiln Road, Thundersley, Benfleet SS7 1TF ☎ 01268 882445 ✆ bcree@castlepoint.gov.uk

Personnel / HR: Ms Chris Mills, Head - Resources & S151 Officer, Council Offices, Kiln Road, Thundersley, Benfleet SS7 1TF ☎ 01268 882215 ✆ cmills@castlepoint.gov.uk

Planning: Mr Stephen Rogers, Head - Regeneration & Neighbourhoods, Council Offices, Kiln Road, Thundersley, Benfleet SS7 1TF ☎ 01268 882200 ✆ srogers@castlepoint.gov.uk

Procurement: Mr Jarl Jansen, Facilities & Asset Manager, Council Offices, Kiln Road, Thundersley, Benfleet SS7 1TF ☎ 01268 882408 ⌕ jjansen@castlepoint.gov.uk

Recycling & Waste Minimisation: Mrs Trudie Bragg, Head - Environment, Council Offices, Kiln Road, Thundersley, Benfleet SS7 1TF ☎ 01268 882476 ⌕ tbragg@castlepoint.gov.uk

Regeneration: Mr Stephen Rogers, Head - Regeneration & Neighbourhoods, Council Offices, Kiln Road, Thundersley, Benfleet SS7 1TF ☎ 01268 882200 ⌕ srogers@castlepoint.gov.uk

Staff Training: Ms Chris Mills, Head - Resources & S151 Officer, Council Offices, Kiln Road, Thundersley, Benfleet SS7 1TF ☎ 01268 882215 ⌕ cmills@castlepoint.gov.uk

Street Scene: Mr Ryan Lynch, Operational Services Manager, Council Offices, Kiln Road, Thundersley, Benfleet SS7 1TF ☎ 01268 882377 ⌕ rlynch@castlepoint.gov.uk

Sustainable Communities: Mr Stephen Rogers, Head - Regeneration & Neighbourhoods, Council Offices, Kiln Road, Thundersley, Benfleet SS7 1TF ☎ 01268 882200 ⌕ srogers@castlepoint.gov.uk

Sustainable Development: Mr Rob Lawrence, Property Technical Officer, Council Offices, Kiln Road, Thundersley, Benfleet SS7 1TF ☎ 01268 882200

Traffic Management: Mr Ryan Lynch, Operational Services Manager, Council Offices, Kiln Road, Thundersley, Benfleet SS7 1TF ☎ 01268 882377 ⌕ rlynch@castlepoint.gov.uk

Waste Collection and Disposal: Mrs Trudie Bragg, Head - Environment, Council Offices, Kiln Road, Thundersley, Benfleet SS7 1TF ☎ 01268 882476 ⌕ tbragg@castlepoint.gov.uk

Waste Management: Mrs Trudie Bragg, Head - Environment, Council Offices, Kiln Road, Thundersley, Benfleet SS7 1TF ☎ 01268 882476 ⌕ tbragg@castlepoint.gov.uk

Children's Play Areas: Mr Ryan Lynch, Operational Services Manager, Council Offices, Kiln Road, Thundersley, Benfleet SS7 1TF ☎ 01268 882377 ⌕ rlynch@castlepoint.gov.uk

COUNCILLORS

Mayor: Cole, Steven (CON - St. George's)
cllr.scole@castlepoint.gov.uk

Deputy Mayor: Wood, Brian (CON - St. George's)
cllr.bwood@castlepoint.gov.uk

Leader of the Council: Riley, Colin (CON - Victoria)
cllr.criley@castlepoint.gov.uk

Deputy Leader of the Council: Stanley, Jeffrey (CON - Boyce)
cllr.jstanley@castlepoint.gov.uk

Acott, Alan (IND - Canvey Island East)
cllr.aacott@castlepoint.gov.uk

Anderson, John (IND - Canvey Island Central)
cllr.janderson@castlepoint.gov.uk

Bayley, Alan (UKIP - Appleton)
cllr.abayley@castlepoint.gov.uk

Blackwell, Dave (IND - Canvey Island Central)
cllr.dblackwell@castlepoint.gov.uk

Campagna, Barry (IND - Canvey Island South)
cllr.bcampagna@castlepoint.gov.uk

Cross, David (CON - St. Mary's)
cllr.dcross@castlepoint.gov.uk

Dick, Bill (CON - St. Peter's)
cllr.wdick@castlepoint.gov.uk

Egan, Eoin (CON - Appleton)
cllr.eegan@castlepoint.gov.uk

Egan, Beverley (CON - St. Peter's)
cllr.began@castlepoint.gov.uk

Goodwin, Wendy (CON - Boyce)
cllr.wgoodwin@castlepoint.gov.uk

Greig, Peter (IND - Canvey Island Winter Garden)
cllr.pgreig@castlepoint.gov.uk

Hart, Simon (CON - Victoria)
cllr.shart@castlepoint.gov.uk

Harvey, Nick (IND - Canvey Island North)
cllr.nharvey@castlepoint.gov.uk

Howard, Ray (CON - Canvey Island West)
cllr.rhoward@castlepoint.gov.uk

Hudson, John (UKIP - Cedar Hall)
cllr.jhudson@castlepoint.gov.uk

Hurrell, Ron (UKIP - St. Peter's)
cllr.rhurrell@castlepoint.gov.uk

Isaacs, Godfrey (CON - St. James')
cllr.gisaacs@castlepoint.gov.uk

King, Jane (IND - Canvey Island West)
cllr.jking@castlepoint.gov.uk

Ladzrie, Norman (CON - St. James')
cllr.nladzrie@castlepoint.gov.uk

Maclean, Colin (CON - Cedar Hall)
cllr.cmaclean@castlepoint.gov.uk

May, Peter (IND - Canvey Island Central)
cllr.pmay@castlepoint.gov.uk

Mumford, Charles (CON - Canvey Island East)
cllr.cmumford@castlepoint.gov.uk

Palmer, Barry (IND - Canvey Island South)
cllr.bpalmer@castlepoint.gov.uk

Partridge, Alf (CON - St. Mary's)
cllr.apartridge@castlepoint.gov.uk

Payne, Janice (IND - Canvey Island South)
cllr.jpayne@castlepoint.gov.uk

Payne, John (IND - Canvey Island North)
cllr.japayne@castlepoint.gov.uk

Sach, Carole (IND - Canvey Island East)
cllr.csach@castlepoint.gov.uk

Sharp, Bill (CON - St. James')
cllr.wsharp@castlepoint.gov.uk

Sheldon, Andrew (CON - St. Mary's)
cllr.asheldon@castlepoint.gov.uk

CASTLE POINT

Skipp, Tom (CON - Appleton)
cllr.tskipp@castlepoint.gov.uk

Smith, Norman (CON - Boyce)
cllr.nsmith@castlepoint.gov.uk

Taylor, Allan (IND - Canvey Island Winter Garden)
cllr.ataylor@castlepoint.gov.uk

Varker, Paul (UKIP - Victoria)
cllr.pvarker@castlepoint.gov.uk

Walter, Clive (CON - St. George's)
cllr.cwalter@castlepoint.gov.uk

Wass, Liz (CON - Cedar Hall)
cllr.lwass@castlepoint.gov.uk

Watson, Neville (IND - Canvey Island Winter Garden)
cllr.nwatson@castlepoint.gov.uk

Watson, Grace (IND - Canvey Island North)
cllr.gwatson@castlepoint.gov.uk

POLITICAL COMPOSITION
CON: 22, IND: 15, UKIP: 4

COMMITTEE CHAIRS

Audit: Mr Norman Ladzrie

Development Control: Mr Simon Hart

Environment: Mr Clive Walter

Licensing: Mrs Beverley Egan

Places & Communities: Mr David Cross

Causeway Coast & Glens District Council   N

Causeway Coast & Glens District Council, Causeway Coast & Glens Borough Council, 66 Portstewart Road, Coleraine BT52 1EY
☎ 028 7034 7034 ⏚ info@causewaycoastandglens.gov.uk
🖥 www.causewaycoastandglens.gov.uk

PRINCIPAL OFFICERS

Chief Executive: Mr David Jackson, Chief Executive, Causeway Coast & Glens Borough Council, 66 Portstewart Road, Coleraine BT52 1EY ☎ 028 7034 7034
⏚ david.jackson@causewaycoastandglens.gov.uk

Deputy Chief Executive: Ms Moira Quinn, Director - Performance, Causeway Coast & Glens Borough Council, 66 Portstewart Road, Coleraine BT52 1EY ☎ 028 7034 7034
⏚ moira.quinn@causewaycoastandglens.gov.uk

Senior Management: Mr Richard Baker, Director - Leisure & Development, Causeway Coast & Glens Borough Council, 66 Portstewart Road, Coleraine BT52 1EY ☎ 028 7034 7034
⏚ richard.baker@causewaycoastandglens.gov.uk

Senior Management: Mr Stephen McMaw, Head of Convergence, Causeway Coast & Glens Borough Council, 66 Portstewart Road, Coleraine BT52 1EY ☎ 028 7034 7034
⏚ stephen.mcmaw@causewaycoastandglens.gov.uk

Senior Management: Mr Aiden McPeake, Director - Environmental Services, Causeway Coast & Glens Borough Council, 66 Portstewart Road, Coleraine BT52 1EY ☎ 028 7034 7034
⏚ aidan.mcpeake@causewaycoastandglens.gov.uk

Senior Management: Ms Moira Quinn, Director - Performance, Causeway Coast & Glens Borough Council, 66 Portstewart Road, Coleraine BT52 1EY ☎ 028 7034 7034
⏚ moira.quinn@causewaycoastandglens.gov.uk

Senior Management: Mr David Wright, Chief Finance Officer, Causeway Coast & Glens Borough Council, 66 Portstewart Road, Coleraine BT52 1EY ☎ 028 7034 7034
⏚ david.wright@causewaycoastandglens.gov.uk

Building Control: Mr Bryan Edgar, Head of Health & Built Environment, Causeway Coast & Glens Borough Council, 66 Portstewart Road, Coleraine BT52 1EY ☎ 028 7034 7034
⏚ bryan.edgar@causewaycoastandglens.gov.uk

Civil Registration: Mrs Janet McCaughey, Registrar of Births, Deaths, Marriages & Civil Partnerships, Causeway Coast & Glens Borough Council, 66 Portstewart Road, Coleraine BT52 1EY
☎ 028 7034 7034
⏚ janet.mccaughey@causewaycoastandglens.gov.uk

PR / Communications: Mrs Elizabeth Johnston, Head of Democratic & Customer Services, Causeway Coast & Glens Borough Council, 66 Portstewart Road, Coleraine BT52 1EY
☎ 028 7034 7034
⏚ elizabeth.johnston@causewaycoastandglens.gov.uk

Community Planning: Mrs Elizabeth Beattie, Head of Policy & Community Planning, Causeway Coast & Glens Borough Council, 66 Portstewart Road, Coleraine BT52 1EY ☎ 028 7772 2226
⏚ elizabeth.beattie@causewaycoastandglens.gov.uk

Community Safety: Mrs Bridget McCaughan, Policing & Community Safety Manager, Causeway Coast & Glens Borough Council, 66 Portstewart Road, Coleraine BT52 1EY ☎ 028 7776 0304 ⏚ bridget.mccaughan@causewaycoastandglens.gov.uk

Computer Management: Mr Patrick McColgan, Head of ICT, Causeway Coast & Glens Borough Council, 66 Portstewart Road, Coleraine BT52 1EY ☎ 028 7034 7034
⏚ patrick.mccolgan@causewaycoastandglens.gov.uk

Consumer Protection and Trading Standards: Mr Bryan Edgar, Head of Health & Built Environment, Causeway Coast & Glens Borough Council, 66 Portstewart Road, Coleraine BT52 1EY
☎ 028 7034 7034 ⏚ bryan.edgar@causewaycoastandglens.gov.uk

Customer Service: Mrs Elizabeth Johnston, Head of Democratic & Customer Services, Causeway Coast & Glens Borough Council, 66 Portstewart Road, Coleraine BT52 1EY ☎ 028 7034 7034
⏚ elizabeth.johnston@causewaycoastandglens.gov.uk

Economic Development: Mrs Elizabeth Beattie, Head of Policy & Community Planning, Causeway Coast & Glens Borough Council, 66 Portstewart Road, Coleraine BT52 1EY ☎ 028 7772 2226
⏚ elizabeth.beattie@causewaycoastandglens.gov.uk

CAUSEWAY COAST & GLENS DISTRICT COUNCIL

Emergency Planning: Mr Bryan Edgar, Head of Health & Built Environment, Causeway Coast & Glens Borough Council, 66 Portstewart Road, Coleraine BT52 1EY ☎ 028 7034 7034
✆ bryan.edgar@causewaycoastandglens.gov.uk

Energy Management: Mr John Richardson, Head of Capital Works, Energy & Infrastructure, Causeway Coast & Glens Borough Council, 66 Portstewart Road, Coleraine BT52 1EY
☎ 028 7034 7034 ✆ john.richardson@causewaycoastandglens.gov.uk

Environmental / Technical Services: Mr Aiden McPeake, Director - Environmental Services, Causeway Coast & Glens Borough Council, 66 Portstewart Road, Coleraine BT52 1EY
☎ 028 7034 7034 ✆ aidan.mcpeake@causewaycoastandglens.gov.uk

Environmental Health: Mr Bryan Edgar, Head of Health & Built Environment, Causeway Coast & Glens Borough Council, 66 Portstewart Road, Coleraine BT52 1EY ☎ 028 7034 7034
✆ bryan.edgar@causewaycoastandglens.gov.uk

Events Manager: Mrs Christine McKee, Events Manager, Causeway Coast & Glens Borough Council, 66 Portstewart Road, Coleraine BT52 1EY ☎ 028 7034 7034
✆ christine.mckee@causewaycoastandglens.gov.uk

Facilities: Mr Gareth Doyle, Head of Estates & Facilities Management, Causeway Coast & Glens Borough Council, 66 Portstewart Road, Coleraine BT52 1EY ☎ 028 7034 7034
✆ gareth.doyle@causewaycoastandglens.gov.uk

Finance: Mr David Wright, Chief Finance Officer, Causeway Coast & Glens Borough Council, 66 Portstewart Road, Coleraine BT52 1EY ☎ 028 7034 7034
✆ david.wright@causewaycoastandglens.gov.uk

Grounds Maintenance: Mr Gareth Doyle, Head of Estates & Facilities Management, Causeway Coast & Glens Borough Council, 66 Portstewart Road, Coleraine BT52 1EY ☎ 028 7034 7034
✆ gareth.doyle@causewaycoastandglens.gov.uk

Health and Safety: Ms Moira Quinn, Director - Performance, Causeway Coast & Glens Borough Council, 66 Portstewart Road, Coleraine BT52 1EY ☎ 028 7034 7034
✆ moira.quinn@causewaycoastandglens.gov.uk

Legal: Ms Moira Quinn, Director - Performance, Causeway Coast & Glens Borough Council, 66 Portstewart Road, Coleraine BT52 1EY
☎ 028 7034 7034 ✆ moira.quinn@causewaycoastandglens.gov.uk

Leisure and Cultural Services: Mrs Wendy McCullough, Head of Sport & Wellbeing, Causeway Coast & Glens Borough Council, 66 Portstewart Road, Coleraine BT52 1EY ☎ 028 7034 7034
✆ wendy.mccullough@causewaycoastandglens.gov.uk

Leisure and Cultural Services: Mrs Julie Welsh, Head of Community & Culture, Causeway Coast & Glens Borough Council, 66 Portstewart Road, Coleraine BT52 1EY ☎ 028 7034 7034
✆ julie.welsh@causewaycoastandglens.gov.uk

Licensing: Mr Bryan Edgar, Head of Health & Built Environment, Causeway Coast & Glens Borough Council, 66 Portstewart Road, Coleraine BT52 1EY ☎ 028 7034 7034
✆ bryan.edgar@causewaycoastandglens.gov.uk

Member Services: Mrs Pauline Donaghy, Democratic Services Manager, Causeway Coast & Glens Borough Council, 66 Portstewart Road, Coleraine BT52 1EY ☎ 028 7034 7034
✆ pauline.donaghy@causewaycoastandglens.gov.uk

Parking: Mr John Richardson, Head of Capital Works, Energy & Infrastructure, Causeway Coast & Glens Borough Council, 66 Portstewart Road, Coleraine BT52 1EY ☎ 028 7034 7034
✆ john.richardson@causewaycoastandglens.gov.uk

Personnel / HR: Mrs Brid Lofthouse, Head of HR & Organisation Development, Causeway Coast & Glens Borough Council, 66 Portstewart Road, Coleraine BT52 1EY ☎ 028 7034 7034
✆ brid.lofthouse@causewaycoastandglens.gov.uk

Planning: Mrs Denise Dickson, Head of Planning, Causeway Coast & Glens Borough Council, 66 Portstewart Road, Coleraine BT52 1EY ☎ 028 7034 7034
✆ denise.dickson@causewaycoastandglens.gov.uk

Procurement: Mr David Wright, Chief Finance Officer, Causeway Coast & Glens Borough Council, 66 Portstewart Road, Coleraine BT52 1EY ☎ 028 7034 7034
✆ david.wright@causewaycoastandglens.gov.uk

Recycling & Waste Minimisation: Mr Aidan Mullan, Head of Operations, Causeway Coast & Glens Borough Council, 66 Portstewart Road, Coleraine BT52 1EY ☎ 028 7034 7034
✆ aidan.mullan@causewaycoastandglens.gov.uk

Regeneration: Mrs Elizabeth Beattie, Head of Policy & Community Planning, Causeway Coast & Glens Borough Council, 66 Portstewart Road, Coleraine BT52 1EY ☎ 028 7772 2226
✆ elizabeth.beattie@causewaycoastandglens.gov.uk

Public Health: Mr Bryan Edgar, Head of Health & Built Environment, Causeway Coast & Glens Borough Council, 66 Portstewart Road, Coleraine BT52 1EY ☎ 028 7034 7034
✆ bryan.edgar@causewaycoastandglens.gov.uk

Staff Training: Mrs Brid Lofthouse, Head of HR & Organisation Development, Causeway Coast & Glens Borough Council, 66 Portstewart Road, Coleraine BT52 1EY ☎ 028 7034 7034
✆ brid.lofthouse@causewaycoastandglens.gov.uk

Tourism: Mr Peter Thompson, Head of Tourism & Recreation, Causeway Coast & Glens Borough Council, 66 Portstewart Road, Coleraine BT52 1EY ☎ 028 7034 7034
✆ peter.thompson@causewaycoastandglens.gov.uk

Town Centre: Mrs Elizabeth Beattie, Head of Policy & Community Planning, Causeway Coast & Glens Borough Council, 66 Portstewart Road, Coleraine BT52 1EY ☎ 028 7772 2226
✆ elizabeth.beattie@causewaycoastandglens.gov.uk

Waste Collection and Disposal: Mr Aidan Mullan, Head of Operations, Causeway Coast & Glens Borough Council, 66 Portstewart Road, Coleraine BT52 1EY ☎ 028 7034 7034
✆ aidan.mullan@causewaycoastandglens.gov.uk

CAUSEWAY COAST & GLENS DISTRICT COUNCIL

Waste Management: Mr Aidan Mullan, Head of Operations, Causeway Coast & Glens Borough Council, 66 Portstewart Road, Coleraine BT52 1EY ☎ 028 7034 7034
🖑 aidan.mullan@causewaycoastandglens.gov.uk

COUNCILLORS

Mayor: Hickey, Maura (SDLP - Causeway)
maura.hickey@colerainebc.gov.uk

Alderman: Campbell, Frank (DUP - Causeway)
frank.campbell@causewaycoastandglens.gov.uk

Alderman: Cole, Sam (DUP - Bann)
samuelcole@hotmail.co.uk

Alderman: Findlay, John (DUP - Ballymoney)
john.finlay@ballymoney.gov.uk

Alderman: Hillis, Norman (UUP - Causeway)
norman.hills@colerainebc.gov.uk

Alderman: King, William (UUP - Bann)
william.king@colerainebc.gov.uk

Alderman: McKeown, Tom (UUP - Ballymoney)
thomas.mckeown@ballymoney.gov.uk

Alderman: McKillop, Sharon (O - Causeway)
cllr.smckillop@moyle-council.org

Alderman: Robinson, Alan (DUP - Limavady)
george.robinson14@btopenworld.com

Baird, Joan (UUP - The Glens)
cllr.jbaird@moyle-council.org

Beattie, Orla (SDLP - Benbradagh)
orlabeattie@hotmail.com

Blair, William (O - Ballymoney)
william.blair@ballymoney.gov.uk

Callan, Aaron (UUP - Limavady)
aaron.callan@causewaycoastandglens.gov.uk

Chivers, Brenda (SF - Limavady)
bchivers5@aol.com

Clarke, Trevor (DUP - Coleraine)
trevor.clarke@colerainebc.gov.uk

Deighan, John (SDLP - Limavady)
john.deighan@causewaycoastandglens.gov.uk

Douglas, Boyd (O - Benbradagh)
boyd.douglas@btinternet.com

Duddy, George (DUP - Coleraine)
william.duddy@colerainebc.gov.uk

Fielding, Mark (DUP - Causeway)
mark.fielding@colerainebc.gov.uk

Fitzpatrick, Barney (ALL - Causeway)
bernard.fitzpatrick@colerainebc.gov.uk

Harding, David (UUP - Coleraine)
david.harding@colerainebc.gov.uk

Holmes, Richard (UUP - Bann)
richard.holmes@colerainebc.gov.uk

Hunter, Sandra (UUP - Causeway)
cllr.shunter@moyle-council.org

Knight-McQuillan, Michelle (DUP - Bann)
michelle.knight-mcquillan@colerainebc.gov.uk

Loftus, Roisin (SDLP - Bann)
roisin.loftus@colerainebc.gov.uk

McCandless, William (UUP - Coleraine)
william.mccandless@colerainebc.gov.uk

McCaul, Tony (SF - Benbradagh)
tonymccaul1952@hotmail.com

McCorkell, James (DUP - Limavady)
jamesmccorkell@btinternet.com

McGlinchey, Sean (SF - Benbradagh)
carolinewhite65@hotmail.com

McGuigan, Philip (SF - Ballymoney)
philipmcguigan@hotmail.com

McKillop, Margaret (SDLP - The Glens)
margaretanne.mckillop@causewaycoastandglens.gov.uk

McLean, Alan (DUP - Ballymoney)
alan.mclean@causewaycoastandglens.gov.uk

McShane, Cara (SF - The Glens)
caramcshane@hotmail.com

McShane, Padraig (IND - The Glens)
mcshaneshar@aol.com

Mulholland, Kieran (SF - The Glens)
kieranjmulholland@icloud.com

Nicholl, Dermot (SF - Benbradagh)
dermot.nicholl@hotmail.com

Quigley, Stephanie (SDLP - Coleraine)
stephanie.quigley@colerainebc.gov.uk

Stevenson, Ian (DUP - Ballymoney)
ian.stevenson@ballymoney.gov.uk

Watton, Russell (PUP - Coleraine)
russellwatton@hotmail.co.uk

Wilson, Darryl (UUP - Ballymoney)
darrylwilson1979@gmail.com

POLITICAL COMPOSITION
DUP: 11, UUP: 10, SF: 7, SDLP: 6, O: 3, PUP: 1, IND: 1, ALL: 1

COMMITTEE CHAIRS

Audit: Ms Cara McShane

Environmental Services: Mr William King

Leisure & Development: Mr Boyd Douglas

Planning: Ms Roisin Loftus

Central Bedfordshire   U

Central Bedfordshire, Priory House, Monks Walk, Chicksands, Shefford SG17 5TQ
☎ 0300 300 8000 🖑 customers@centralbedfordshire.gov.uk
🖳 www.centralbedfordshire.gov.uk

FACTS AND FIGURES
Parliamentary Constituencies: Bedfordshire Mid, Bedfordshire North East, Bedfordshire South West, Luton South, South West Bedfordshire

PRINCIPAL OFFICERS

Chief Executive: Mr Richard Carr, Chief Executive, Priory House, Monks Walk, Chicksands, Shefford SG17 5TQ ☎ 0300 300 4004 ♋ richard.carr@centralbedfordshire.gov.uk

Senior Management: Mr Marcel Coiffait, Director - Community Services, Priory House, Monks Walk, Chicksands, Shefford SG17 5TQ ☎ 0300 300 5637 ♋ marcel.coiffait@cenetralbedforshire.gov.uk

Senior Management: Ms Sue Harrison, Director - Children's Services, Priory House, Monks Walk, Chicksands, Shefford SG17 5TQ ☎ 0300 300 4229 ♋ sue.harrison@centralbedfordshire.gov.uk

Senior Management: Mr Jason Longhurst, Director - Regeneration & Business, Priory House, Monks Walk, Chicksands, Shefford SG17 5TQ ☎ 0300 300 4005 ♋ jason.longhurst@centralbedfordshire.gov.uk

Senior Management: Ms Julie Ogley, Director - Social Care, Health & Housing, Priory House, Monks Walk, Chicksands, Shefford SG17 5TQ ☎ 0300 300 4221 ♋ julie.ogley@centralbedfordshire.gov.uk

Senior Management: Ms Muriel Scott, Director - Public Health, Priory House, Monks Walk, Chicksands, Shefford SG17 5TQ ☎ 0300 300 5616 ♋ muriel.scott@centralbedfordshire.gov.uk

Senior Management: Mr Charles Warboys, Chief Finance Officer, Priory House, Monks Walk, Chicksands, Shefford SG17 5TQ ☎ 0300 300 6147 ♋ charles.warboys@centralbedfordshire.gov.uk

Architect, Building / Property Services: Mr Steven Girling, Assistant Director - Assets, Priory House, Monks Walk, Chicksands, Shefford SG17 5TQ ☎ 0300 300 5246 ♋ steven.girling@centralbedfordshire.gov.uk

Building Control: Mr Peter Keates, Head of Development & Regulation, Priory House, Monks Walk, Chicksands SG17 5TQ ☎ 0300 300 4380 ♋ peter.keates@centralbedfordshire.gov.uk

Children / Youth Services: Mr Gerard Jones, Assistant Director - Operations, Priory House, Monks Walk, Chicksands, Shefford SG17 5TQ ☎ 0300 300 4616 ♋ gerard.jones@wolverhampton.gov.uk

Children / Youth Services: Ms Karen Oellermann, Assistant Director - Commissioning & Partnerships, Watling House, High Street North, Dunstable LU6 1LF ☎ 0300 300 5265 ♋ karen.oellermann@centralbedfordshire.gov.uk

Children / Youth Services: Ms Helen Redding, Assistant Director - Learning, Commissioning & Partnerships, Priory House, Monks Walk, Chicksands, Shefford SG17 5TQ ☎ 0300 300 6067 ♋ helen.redding@centralbedfordshire.gov.uk

PR / Communications: Ms Karen Aspinall, Head of Communications, Priory House, Monks Walk, Chicksands, Shefford SG17 5TQ ☎ 0300 300 6286 ♋ karen.aspinall@centralbedfordshire.gov.uk

Community Safety: Ms Jeanette Keyte, Head of Community Safety & Parking, Priory House, Monks Walk, Chicksands, Shefford SG17 5TQ ☎ 0300 300 5252 ♋ jeanette.keyte@centralbedfordshire.gov.uk

Computer Management: Mr Stephan Conaway, Chief Information Officer, Priory House, Monks Walk, Chicksands, Shefford SG17 5TQ ☎ 0300 300 5386 ♋ stephan.conaway@centralbedfordshire.gov.uk

Consumer Protection and Trading Standards: Ms Susan Childerhouse, Head of Public Protection & Transport, Priory House, Monks Walk, Chicksands, Shefford SG17 5TQ ☎ 0300 300 4394 ♋ susan.childerhouse@centralbedfordshire.gov.uk

Customer Service: Ms Bernie McGill, Head of Customer Relations & Services, Priory House, Monks Walk, Chicksands, Shefford SG17 5TQ ☎ 0300 300 5614 ♋ bernie.mcgill@centralbedfordshire.gov.uk

Economic Development: Ms Kate McFarlane, Business Investment Group Manager, Priory House, Monks Walk, Chicksands, Shefford SG17 5TQ ☎ 0300 300 5858 ♋ kate.mcfarlane@centralbedfordshire.gov.uk

Education: Ms Sue Harrison, Director - Children's Services, Priory House, Monks Walk, Chicksands, Shefford SG17 5TQ ☎ 0300 300 4229 ♋ sue.harrison@centralbedfordshire.gov.uk

Education: Ms Helen Redding, Assistant Director - Learning, Commissioning & Partnerships, Priory House, Monks Walk, Chicksands, Shefford SG17 5TQ ☎ 0300 300 6067 ♋ helen.redding@centralbedfordshire.gov.uk

Electoral Registration: Mr Brian Dunleavey, Democratic Services Manager, Priory House, Monks Walk, Chicksands, Shefford SG17 5TQ ☎ 0300 300 4049 ♋ brian.dunleavey@centralbedfordshire.gov.uk

Emergency Planning: Ms Susan Childerhouse, Head of Public Protection & Transport, Priory House, Monks Walk, Chicksands, Shefford SG17 5TQ ☎ 0300 300 4394 ♋ susan.childerhouse@centralbedfordshire.gov.uk

Environmental Health: Ms Susan Childerhouse, Head of Public Protection & Transport, Priory House, Monks Walk, Chicksands, Shefford SG17 5TQ ☎ 0300 300 4394 ♋ susan.childerhouse@centralbedfordshire.gov.uk

Facilities: Mr Bernard Carter, Head of Facilities Management, Priory House, Monks Walk, Chicksands, Shefford SG17 5TQ ☎ 0300 300 8306 ♋ bernard.carter@centralbedfordshire.gov.uk

Finance: Mr Charles Warboys, Chief Finance Officer, Priory House, Monks Walk, Chicksands, Shefford SG17 5TQ ☎ 0300 300 6147 ♋ charles.warboys@centralbedfordshire.gov.uk

Health and Safety: Mr Lee Butler, Health, Safety & Wellbeing Manager, Priory House, Monks Walk, Chicksands, Shefford SG17 5TQ ☎ 0300 300 6793 ♋ lee.butler@centralbedfordshire.gov.uk

Highways: Mr Paul Mason, Assistant Director - Highways, Priory House, Monks Walk, Chicksands, Shefford SG17 5TQ ☎ 0300 300 4708 ♋ paul.mason@centralbedfordshire.gov.uk

Housing: Mr Tony Keaveney, Assistant Director - Housing, High Street North, Dunstable LU6 1LF ☎ 0300 300 5210 ♋ tony.keaveney@centralbedfordshire.gov.uk

CENTRAL BEDFORDSHIRE

Legal: Mr Quentin Baker, Monitoring Officer, Priory House, Monks Walk, Chicksands, Shefford SG17 5TQ ☎ 0300 300 4204 ✆ quentin.baker@centralbedfordshire.gov.uk

Leisure and Cultural Services: Ms Jill Dickinson, Head of Leisure, Libraries & Countryside, Priory House, Monks Walk, Chicksands, Shefford SG17 5TQ ☎ 0300 300 4258 ✆ jill.dickinson@centralbedfordshire.gov.uk

Licensing: Ms Susan Childerhouse, Head of Public Protection & Transport, Priory House, Monks Walk, Chicksands, Shefford SG17 5TQ ☎ 0300 300 4394 ✆ susan.childerhouse@centralbedfordshire.gov.uk

Member Services: Mr Brian Dunleavey, Democratic Services Manager, Priory House, Monks Walk, Chicksands, Shefford SG17 5TQ ☎ 0300 300 4049 ✆ brian.dunleavey@centralbedfordshire.gov.uk

Partnerships: Mr Peter Fraser, Head of Partnerships & Community Engagement, Priory House, Monks Walk, Chicksands, Shefford SG17 5TQ ☎ 0300 300 6740 ✆ peter.fraser@centralbedfordshire.gov.uk

Personnel / HR: Ms Catherine Jones, Chief People Officer, Priory House, Monks Walk, Chicksands, Shefford SG17 5TQ ☎ 0300 300 6048 ✆ catherine.jones@centralbedfordshire.gov.uk

Planning: Mr Andrew Davie, Development Infrastructure Group Manager, Priory House, Monks Walk, Chicksands, Shefford SG17 5TQ ☎ 0300 300 4426 ✆ andrew.davie@centralbedfordshire.gov.uk

Procurement: Mr Paul Meigh, Head of Procurement, Priory House, Monks Walk, Chicksands, Shefford SG17 5TQ ☎ 0300 300 6626 ✆ paul.meigh@centralbedfordshire.gov.uk

Public Libraries: Ms Jill Dickinson, Head of Leisure, Libraries & Countryside, Priory House, Monks Walk, Chicksands, Shefford SG17 5TQ ☎ 0300 300 4258 ✆ jill.dickinson@centralbedfordshire.gov.uk

Recycling & Waste Minimisation: Ms Tracey Harris, Assistant Director - Environmental Services, Priory House, Monks Walk, Chicksands, Shefford SG17 5TQ ☎ 0300 300 4646 ✆ tracey.harris@centralbedfordshire.gov.uk

Regeneration: Mr Jason Longhurst, Director - Regeneration & Business, Priory House, Monks Walk, Chicksands, Shefford SG17 5TQ ☎ 0300 300 4005 ✆ jason.longhurst@centralbedfordshire.gov.uk

Road Safety: Mr Paul Mason, Assistant Director - Highways, Priory House, Monks Walk, Chicksands, Shefford SG17 5TQ ☎ 0300 300 4708 ✆ paul.mason@centralbedfordshire.gov.uk

Social Services: Mr Stuart Mitchelmore, Assistant Director - Adult Social Care, Houghton Lodge, Ampthill, Bedford MK45 2TB ☎ 0300 300 4796 ✆ stuart.mitchelmore@centralbedfordshire.gov.uk

Social Services (Adult): Mr Stuart Mitchelmore, Assistant Director - Adult Social Care, Houghton Lodge, Ampthill, Bedford MK45 2TB ☎ 0300 300 4796 ✆ stuart.mitchelmore@centralbedfordshire.gov.uk

Social Services (Children): Mr Gerard Jones, Assistant Director - Operations, Priory House, Monks Walk, Chicksands, Shefford SG17 5TQ ☎ 0300 300 4616 ✆ gerard.jones@wolverhampton.gov.uk

Public Health: Ms Muriel Scott, Director - Public Health, 7 Hadleigh Close, Putnoe, Bedford MK41 8JW ☎ 0300 300 5616 ✆ muriel.scott@centralbedfordshire.gov.uk

Staff Training: Mr Craig Picknell, Senior HR Development & Learning Manager, Priory House, Monks Walk, Chicksands, Shefford SG17 5TQ ☎ 0300 300 4416 ✆ craig.picknell@centralbedfordshire.gov.uk

Traffic Management: Mr Paul Mason, Assistant Director - Highways, Priory House, Monks Walk, Chicksands, Shefford SG17 5TQ ☎ 0300 300 4708 ✆ paul.mason@centralbedfordshire.gov.uk

Waste Collection and Disposal: Ms Tracey Harris, Assistant Director - Environmental Services, Technology House, 239 Ampthill Road, Bedford MK42 9BD ☎ 0300 300 4646 ✆ tracey.harris@centralbedfordshire.gov.uk

Waste Management: Ms Tracey Harris, Assistant Director - Environmental Services, Technology House, 239 Ampthill Road, Bedford MK42 9BD ☎ 0300 300 4646 ✆ tracey.harris@centralbedfordshire.gov.uk

COUNCILLORS

ChairBowater, David (CON - Leighton Buzzard South) david.bowater@centralbedfordshire.gov.uk

Vice-ChairChapman, Fiona (CON - Flitwick) fiona.chapman@centralbedfordshire.gov.uk

Leader of the Council: Jamieson, James (CON - Westoning, Flitton & Greenfield) james.jamieson@centralbedfordshire.gov.uk

Deputy Leader of the Council: Jones, Maurice (CON - Biggleswade North) maurice.jones@centralbedfordshire.gov.uk

Barker, Angela (CON - Houghton Conquest & Haynes) angela.barker@centralbedfordshire.gov.uk

Berry, Raymond (CON - Leighton Buzzard South) raymond.berry@centralbedfordshire.gov.uk

Birt, Lewis (CON - Shefford) lewis.birt@centralbedfordshire.gov.uk

Blair, Michael (CON - Ampthill) michael.blair@centralbedfordshire.gov.uk

Brown, Anthony (CON - Shefford) anthony.brown@centralbedfordshire.gov.uk

Chatterley, John (CON - Dunstable Icknield) john.chatterley@centralbedfordshire.gov.uk

Clark, Sue (CON - Cranfield & Marston Moretaine) sue.clark@centralbedfordshire.gov.uk

Collins, Kevin (CON - Caddington) kevin.collins@centralbedfordshire.gov.uk

Costin, Norman (CON - Toddington) norman.costin@centralbedfordshire.gov.uk

Dalgarno, Ian (CON - Arlesey) ian.dalgarno@centralbedfordshire.gov.uk

Dixon, Steven (CON - Stotfold & Langford)
steven.dixon@centralbedfordshire.gov.uk

Dodwell, Amanda (CON - Leighton Buzzard South)
amanda.dodwell@centralbedfordshire.gov.uk

Downing, Paul (CON - Ampthill)
paul.downing@centralbedfordshire.gov.uk

Duckett, Paul (CON - Ampthill)
paul.duckett@centralbedfordshire.gov.uk

Ferguson, Ken (CON - Leighton Buzzard North)
ken.ferguson@centralbedfordshire.gov.uk

Firth, Frank (CON - Northill)
frank.firth@centralbedfordshire.gov.uk

Freeman, Jeannette (CON - Dunstable Northfields)
jeannette.freeman@centralbedfordshire.gov.uk

Ghent, Eugene (CON - Dunstable Manshead)
eugene.ghent@centralbedfordshire.gov.uk

Gomm, Charles (CON - Flitwick)
charles.gomm@centralbedfordshire.gov.uk

Goodchild, Susan (LD - Houghton Hall)
susan.goodchild@centralbedfordshire.gov.uk

Graham, Alison (IND - Silsoe & Shillington)
alison.graham@centralbedfordshire.gov.uk

Gurney, Doreen (CON - Potton)
doreen.gurney@centralbedfordshire.gov.uk

Hegley, Carole (CON - Dunstable Central)
carole.hegley@centralbedfordshire.gov.uk

Hollick, Peter (CON - Dunstable Watling)
peter.hollick@centralbedfordshire.gov.uk

Janes, Ken (CON - Eaton Bray)
ken.janes@centralbedfordshire.gov.uk

Johnstone, Roy (CON - Leighton Buzzard North)
roy.johnstone@centralbedfordshire.gov.uk

Kane, John (CON - Houghton Hall)
john.kane@centralbedfordshire.gov.uk

Lawrence, David (CON - Biggleswade South)
david.lawrence@centralbedfordshire.gov.uk

Lawrence, Jane (CON - Biggleswade North)
jane.lawrence@centralbedfordshire.gov.uk

Matthews, Ken (CON - Cranfield & Marston Moretaine)
ken.matthews@centralbedfordshire.gov.uk

Maudlin, Caroline (CON - Sandy)
caroline.maudlin@centralbedfordshire.gov.uk

McVicar, David (CON - Dunstable Icknield)
david.mcvicar@centralbedfordshire.gov.uk

Morris, Robert (CON - Cranfield & Marston Moretaine)
robert.morris@centralbedfordshire.gov.uk

Nicols, Tom (CON - Toddington)
tom.nicols@centralbedfordshire.gov.uk

Perham, Gordon (CON - Linslade)
gordon.perham@centralbedfordshire.gov.uk

Ryan, Antonia (CON - Parkside)
antonia.ryan@centralbedfordshire.gov.uk

Saunders, John (CON - Stotfold & Langford)

Saunders, Brian (CON - Stotfold & Langford)
brian.saunders@centralbedfordshire.gov.uk

Shelvey, David (CON - Arlesey)
david.shelvey@centralbedfordshire.gov.uk

Shingler, Ian (IND - Barton-le-Clay)
ian.shingler@centralbedfordshire.gov.uk

Smith, Peter (CON - Sandy)
peter.smith3@centralbedfordshire.gov.uk

Spurr, Brian (CON - Leighton Buzzard North)
brian.spurr@centralbedfordshire.gov.uk

Stay, Richard (CON - Caddington)
richard.stay@centralbedfordshire.gov.uk

Stock, Tracey (CON - Sandy)
tracey.stock@centralbedfordshire.gov.uk

Swain, Tony (LAB - Tithe Farm)
tony.swain@centralbedfordshire.gov.uk

Tubb, Gary (CON - Linslade)
gary.tubb@centralbedfordshire.gov.uk

Turner, Andrew (CON - Flitwick)
andrewturner@flitwickfirst.com

Versallion, Mark (CON - Heath & Reach)
mark.versallion@centralbedfordshire.gov.uk

Walker, Ben (CON - Linslade)
ben.walker@centralbedfordshire.gov.uk

Warren, Nigel (CON - Dunstable Northfields)
nigel.warren@centralbedfordshire.gov.uk

Wells, Budge (CON - Aspley & Woburn)
budge.wells@centralbedfordshire.gov.uk

Wenham, Richard (CON - Arlesey)
richard.wenham@centralbedfordshire.gov.uk

Woodward, Tim (CON - Biggleswade South)
cllrtim.woodward@centralbedfordshire.gov.uk

Young, Nigel (CON - Dunstable Watling)
nigel.young@centralbedfordshire.gov.uk

Zerny, Adam (IND - Potton)
adam.zerny@centralbedforshire.gov.uk

POLITICAL COMPOSITION
CON: 54, IND: 3, LAB: 1, LD: 1

COMMITTEE CHAIRS

Audit: Mr Michael Blair

Children's Services: Mr Mark Versallion

Development Management: Mr Ken Matthews

Health & Wellbeing: Mr Maurice Jones

Licensing: Mr Tom Nicols

Social Care, Health & Housing: Mr Peter Hollick

Ceredigion   W

Ceredigion County Council, Neuadd Cyngor Ceredigion,
Penmorfa, Aberaeron SA46 0PA
☎ 01545 570881 📠 01545 572009 🖱 reception@ceredigion.gov.uk 🖳
www.ceredigion.gov.uk

FACTS AND FIGURES
Parliamentary Constituencies: Ceredigion

CEREDIGION

EU Constituencies: Wales
Election Frequency: Elections are of whole council

PRINCIPAL OFFICERS

Chief Executive: Miss Bronwen Morgan, Chief Executive, Neuadd Cyngor Ceredigion, Penmorfa, Aberaeron SA46 0PA
☎ 01545 572004 chiefexecutive@ceredigion.ov.uk

Deputy Chief Executive: Mr Eifon Evans, Deputy Chief Executive, Neuadd Cyngor Ceredigion, Penmorfa, Aberaeron SA46 0PA
☎ 01545 572021 eifion.evans@ceredigion.gov.uk

Senior Management: Ms Sue Darnbrook, Strategic Director - Care, Protection & Lifestyle, Neuadd Cyngor Ceredigion, Penmorfa, Aberaeron SA46 0PA ☎ 01545 572620
sue.darnbrook@ceredigion.gov.uk

Senior Management: Mr Huw Morgan, Strategic Director - Sustainable Communities, Neuadd Cyngor Ceredigion, Penmorfa, Aberaeron SA46 0PA ☎ 01545 572562
huwt.morgan@ceredigion.gov.uk

Senior Management: Mr Barry Rees, Strategic Director - Learning & Partnerships, Neuadd Cyngor Ceredigion, Penmorfa, Aberaeron SA46 0PA ☎ 01545 572562
barry.rees@ceredigion.gov.uk

Access Officer / Social Services (Disability): Ms Donna Pritchard, Team Manager - Disabilities, Min Areon, Rhiw Goch, Aberaeron SA46 0DY ☎ 01545 570881
donnap@ceredigion.gov.uk

Architect, Building / Property Services: Mr Huw Morgan, Strategic Director - Sustainable Communities, County Hall, Market Street, Aberaeron SA46 0AS ☎ 01545 572562
huwt.morgan@ceredigion.gov.uk

Best Value: Mr Russell Hughes-Pickering, Head of Performance & Economy, Neuadd Cyngor Ceredigion, Penmorfa, Aberaeron SA46 0PA ☎ 01545 572121
russell.hughes-pickering@ceredigion.gov.uk

Building Control: Mr Huw Williams, Head of Lifestyle Services, Neuadd Cyngor Ceredigion, Penmorfa, Aberaeron SA46 0PA
☎ 01545 572151 huww@ceredigion.gov.uk

Catering Services: Ms Nia James, Catering Services Manager, Canolfan Rheidol, Rhodfa Padarn, Llanbadarn Fawr, Aberystwyth SY23 3UE ☎ 01970 633364 nia.james@ceredigion.gov.uk

Children / Youth Services: Ms Ann Sweeting, Principal Youth Officer, Canolfan Rheidol, Rhodfa Padarn, Llanbadarn Fawr, Aberystwyth SY23 3UE ☎ 01970 633712
anns@ceredigion.gov.uk

Civil Registration: Ms Elin Prysor, Monitoring Officer, Neuadd Cyngor Ceredigion, Penmorfa, Aberaeron SA46 0PA
☎ 01545 572120 elin.prysor@ceredigion.gov.uk

PR / Communications: Ms Siwan Davies, Corporate Communications Officer, Neuadd Cyngor Ceredigion, Penmorfa, Aberaeron SA46 0PA ☎ 01545 572003
siwan.davies2@ceredigion.gov.uk

Community Planning: Mr Alun Williams, Head of Policy Support, Neuadd Cyngor Ceredigion, Penmorfa, Aberaeron SA46 0PA
☎ 01545 574115 alun.williams2@ceredigion.gov.uk

Community Safety: Mr Alan Garrod, Manager - Community Safety, Neuadd Cyngor Ceredigion, Penmorfa, Aberaeron SA46 0PA ☎ 01545 572012 alang@ceredigion.gov.uk

Computer Management: Mr Arwyn Morris, Head of Information, Communications Technology & Customer Services, Canolfan Rheidol, Rhodfa Padarn, Llanbadarn Fawr, Aberystwyth SY23 3UE
☎ 01970 633200 arwyn.morris@ceredigion.gov.uk

Consumer Protection and Trading Standards: Mr Huw Williams, Head of Lifestyle Services, Neuadd Cyngor Ceredigion, Penmorfa, Aberaeron SA46 0PA ☎ 01545 572151
huww@ceredigion.gov.uk

Contracts: Mr Huw Morgan, Strategic Director - Sustainable Communities, County Hall, Market Street, Aberaeron SA46 0AS
☎ 01545 572562 huwt.morgan@ceredigion.gov.uk

Customer Service: Mr Arwyn Morris, Head of Information, Communications Technology & Customer Services, Canolfan Rheidol, Rhodfa Padarn, Llanbadarn Fawr, Aberystwyth SY23 3UE
☎ 01970 633200 arwyn.morris@ceredigion.gov.uk

Direct Labour: Mr Huw Morgan, Strategic Director - Sustainable Communities, County Hall, Market Street, Aberaeron SA46 0AS
☎ 01545 572562 huwt.morgan@ceredigion.gov.uk

Economic Development: Mr Russell Hughes-Pickering, Head of Performance & Economy, Neuadd Cyngor Ceredigion, Penmorfa, Aberaeron SA46 0PA ☎ 01545 572121
russell.hughes-pickering@ceredigion.gov.uk

Education: Mr Matthew Brown, Head of Learning Services, Canolfan Rheidol, Rhodfa Padarn, Llanbadarn Fawr, Aberystwyth SY22 3UE ☎ 01970 633631 matthew.brown@ceredigion.gov.uk

Education: Mr Barry Rees, Strategic Director - Learning & Partnerships, Neuadd Cyngor Ceredigion, Penmorfa, Aberaeron SA46 0PA ☎ 01545 572562 barry.rees@ceredigion.gov.uk

E-Government: Mr Arwyn Morris, Head of Information, Communications Technology & Customer Services, Canolfan Rheidol, Rhodfa Padarn, Llanbadarn Fawr, Aberystwyth SY23 3UE
☎ 01970 633200 arwyn.morris@ceredigion.gov.uk

Electoral Registration: Miss Bronwen Morgan, Chief Executive, Neuadd Cyngor Ceredigion, Penmorfa, Aberaeron SA46 0PA
☎ 01545 572004 chiefexecutive@ceredigion.ov.uk

Emergency Planning: Mr Alan Garrod, Manager - Community Safety, Neuadd Cyngor Ceredigion, Penmorfa, Aberaeron SA46 0PA ☎ 01545 572012 alang@ceredigion.gov.uk

Energy Management: Mr Huw Morgan, Strategic Director - Sustainable Communities, County Hall, Market Street, Aberaeron SA46 0AS ☎ 01545 572562 huwt.morgan@ceredigion.gov.uk

Environmental / Technical Services: Mr Paul Arnold, Head of Technical Services, Neuadd Cyngor Ceredigion, Penmorfa, Aberaeron SA46 0PA ☎ 01970 633902 ⌂ paul.arnold@ceredigion.gov.uk

Environmental / Technical Services: Mr Huw Williams, Head of Lifestyle Services, Neuadd Cyngor Ceredigion, Penmorfa, Aberaeron SA46 0PA ☎ 01545 572151 ⌂ huww@ceredigion.gov.uk

Environmental Health: Mr Huw Williams, Head of Lifestyle Services, Neuadd Cyngor Ceredigion, Penmorfa, Aberaeron SA46 0PA ☎ 01545 572151 ⌂ huww@ceredigion.gov.uk

Estates, Property & Valuation: Mr Jason Jones, Group Manager - Development & Estates, Neuadd Cyngor Ceredigion, Penmorfa, Aberaeron SA46 0PA ☎ 01545 572070 ⌂ jason.jones@ceredigion.gov.uk

European Liaison: Mr Mike Shaw, Group Manager - Community Regeneration & Europe, Neuadd Cyngor Ceredigion, Penmorfa, Aberaeron SA46 0PA ☎ 01545 572064 ⌂ mikes@ceredigion.gov.uk

Facilities: Mr Paul Arnold, Head of Technical Services, Neuadd Cyngor Ceredigion, Penmorfa, Aberaeron SA46 0PA ☎ 01970 633902 ⌂ paul.arnold@ceredigion.gov.uk

Finance: Mr Stephen Johnson, Head of Finance, Neuadd Cyngor Ceredigion, Penmorfa, Aberaeron SA46 0PA ☎ 01970 633101 ⌂ stephen.johnson@ceredigion.gov.uk

Fleet Management: Mr Huw Morgan, Strategic Director - Sustainable Communities, Neuadd Cyngor Ceredigion, Penmorfa, Aberaeron SA46 0PA ☎ 01545 572562 ⌂ huwt.morgan@ceredigion.gov.uk

Grounds Maintenance: Mr Huw Morgan, Strategic Director - Sustainable Communities, Neuadd Cyngor Ceredigion, Penmorfa, Aberaeron SA46 0PA ☎ 01545 572562 ⌂ huwt.morgan@ceredigion.gov.uk

Health and Safety: Mr Keith Holmes, Corporate Head - Health & Safety, Canolfan Rheidol, Rhodfa Padarn, Llanbadarn Fawr, Aberystwyth SY23 3UE ☎ 01970 627543 ⌂ keithh@ceredigion.gov.uk

Highways: Mr Huw Morgan, Strategic Director - Sustainable Communities, Neuadd Cyngor Ceredigion, Penmorfa, Aberaeron SA46 0PA ☎ 01545 572562 ⌂ huwt.morgan@ceredigion.gov.uk

Home Energy Conservation: Mr Huw Williams, Head of Lifestyle Services, Neuadd Cyngor Ceredigion, Penmorfa, Aberaeron SA46 0PA ☎ 01545 572151 ⌂ huww@ceredigion.gov.uk

Housing: Mr Huw Williams, Head of Lifestyle Services, Neuadd Cyngor Ceredigion, Penmorfa, Aberaeron SA46 0PA ☎ 01545 572151 ⌂ huww@ceredigion.gov.uk

Housing Maintenance: Mr Huw Morgan, Strategic Director - Sustainable Communities, Neuadd Cyngor Ceredigion, Penmorfa, Aberaeron SA46 0PA ☎ 01545 572562 ⌂ huwt.morgan@ceredigion.gov.uk

Legal: Mr Rhys Stephens, Group Manager - Legal Services, Neuadd Cyngor Ceredigion, Penmorfa, Aberaeron SA46 0PA ☎ 01545 572055 ⌂ rhys.stephens@ceredigion.gov.uk

Leisure and Cultural Services: Mr Darryl Evans, Recreation Manager, Canolfan Rheidol, Rhodfa Padarn, Llanbadarn Fawr, Aberystwyth SY23 3UE ☎ 01970 633587 ⌂ darryle@ceredigion.gov.uk

Licensing: Mr Dafydd Roberts, Consumer Services Manager, Neuadd Cyngor Ceredigion, Penmorfa, Aberaeron SA46 0PA ☎ 01545 572170 ⌂ dafydd.roberts@ceredigion.gov.uk

Lifelong Learning: Mr Barry Rees, Strategic Director - Learning & Partnerships, Neuadd Cyngor Ceredigion, Penmorfa, Aberaeron SA46 0PA ☎ 01545 572562 ⌂ barry.rees@ceredigion.gov.uk

Lighting: Mr Huw Morgan, Strategic Director - Sustainable Communities, Neuadd Cyngor Ceredigion, Penmorfa, Aberaeron SA46 0PA ☎ 01545 572562 ⌂ huwt.morgan@ceredigion.gov.uk

Lottery Funding, Charity and Voluntary: Mr Gareth Rowlands, Manager - Community Regeneration, Neuadd Cyngor Ceredigion, Penmorfa, Aberaeron SA46 0PA ☎ 01545 572066

Member Services: Miss Lowri Edwards, Group Manager - Democratic Services, Neuadd Cyngor Ceredigion, Penmorfa, Aberaeron SA46 0PA ☎ 01545 572005 ⌂ lowri.edwards@ceredigion.gov.uk

Parking: Mr Huw Morgan, Strategic Director - Sustainable Communities, Neuadd Cyngor Ceredigion, Penmorfa, Aberaeron SA46 0PA ☎ 01545 572562 ⌂ huwt.morgan@ceredigion.gov.uk

Partnerships: Mr Alun Williams, Head of Policy Support, Neuadd Cyngor Ceredigion, Penmorfa, Aberaeron SA46 0PA ☎ 01545 574115 ⌂ alun.williams2@ceredigion.gov.uk

Personnel / HR: Mrs Caroline Lewis, Head - Corporate Human Resources, Canolfan Rheidol, Rhodfa Padarn, Llanbadarn Fawr, Aberystwyth SY23 3UE ☎ 01970 633680 ⌂ caroline.lewis@ceredigion.gov.uk

Planning: Mr Huw Williams, Head of Lifestyle Services, Neuadd Cyngor Ceredigion, Penmorfa, Aberaeron SA46 0PA ☎ 01545 572151 ⌂ huww@ceredigion.gov.uk

Procurement: Mr Stephen Johnson, Head of Finance, Neuadd Cyngor Ceredigion, Penmorfa, Aberaeron SA46 0PA ☎ 01970 633101 ⌂ stephen.johnson@ceredigion.gov.uk

Public Libraries: Mr Arwyn Morris, Head of Information, Communications Technology & Customer Services, Canolfan Rheidol, Rhodfa Padarn, Llanbadarn Fawr, Aberystwyth SY23 3UE ☎ 01970 633200 ⌂ arwyn.morris@ceredigion.gov.uk

Recycling & Waste Minimisation: Mr Huw Morgan, Strategic Director - Sustainable Communities, Neuadd Cyngor Ceredigion, Penmorfa, Aberaeron SA46 0PA ☎ 01545 572562 ⌂ huwt.morgan@ceredigion.gov.uk

CEREDIGION

Regeneration: Mr Russell Hughes-Pickering, Head of Performance & Economy, Neuadd Cyngor Ceredigion, Penmorfa, Aberaeron SA46 0PA ☎ 01545 572121 ⁂ russell.hughes-pickering@ceredigion.gov.uk

Road Safety: Mr Huw Morgan, Strategic Director - Sustainable Communities, Neuadd Cyngor Ceredigion, Penmorfa, Aberaeron SA46 0PA ☎ 01545 572562 ⁂ huwt.morgan@ceredigion.gov.uk

Social Services: Ms Sue Darnbrook, Strategic Director - Care, Protection & Lifestyle, Neuadd Cyngor Ceredigion, Penmorfa, Aberaeron SA46 0PA ☎ 01545 572620 ⁂ sue.darnbrook@ceredigion.gov.uk

Social Services (Adult): Ms Carys James, Head of Adult & Commissioned Services, Min Aeron, South Road, Aberaeron SA46 0DY ☎ 01545 572620 ⁂ carys.james@ceredigion.gov.uk

Social Services (Children): Mr Elfed Hopkins, Head of Families & Children's Services, Min Aeron, Rhiw Goch, Aberaeron SA46 0DY ☎ 01545 572694 ⁂ elfed.hopkins@ceredigion.gov.uk

Staff Training: Ms Patricia Smith, Training Manager, Canolfan Rheidol, Rhodfa Padarn, Llanbadarn Fawr, Aberystwyth SY23 3UE ☎ 01545 575009 ⁂ patricia.smith@ceredigion.gov.uk

Street Scene: Mr Rhodri Llwyd, Group Manager - Highways Services, County Hall, Market Street, Aberaeron SA46 0AS ☎ 01545 572434 ⁂ rhodri.llwyd@ceredigion.gov.uk

Tourism: Mr A.E Jones, Manager - Marketing & Tourism Service, Lisburn House, Terrace Road, Aberystwyth SY23 2AG ☎ 01970 633061

Town Centre: Mr Jason Jones, Group Manager - Development & Estates, Neuadd Cyngor Ceredigion, Penmorfa, Aberaeron SA46 0PA ☎ 01545 572070 ⁂ jason.jones@ceredigion.gov.uk

Traffic Management: Mr Huw Morgan, Strategic Director - Sustainable Communities, Neuadd Cyngor Ceredigion, Penmorfa, Aberaeron SA46 0PA ☎ 01545 572562 ⁂ huwt.morgan@ceredigion.gov.uk

Transport: Mr Rhodri Llwyd, Group Manager - Highways Services, County Hall, Market Street, Aberaeron SA46 0AS ☎ 01545 572434 ⁂ rhodri.llwyd@ceredigion.gov.uk

Transport: Mr Huw Morgan, Strategic Director - Sustainable Communities, Neuadd Cyngor Ceredigion, Penmorfa, Aberaeron SA46 0PA ☎ 01545 572562 ⁂ huwt.morgan@ceredigion.gov.uk

Waste Collection and Disposal: Mr Huw Morgan, Strategic Director - Sustainable Communities, Neuadd Cyngor Ceredigion, Penmorfa, Aberaeron SA46 0PA ☎ 01545 572562 ⁂ huwt.morgan@ceredigion.gov.uk

Waste Management: Mr Huw Morgan, Strategic Director - Sustainable Communities, Neuadd Cyngor Ceredigion, Penmorfa, Aberaeron SA46 0PA ☎ 01545 572562 ⁂ huwt.morgan@ceredigion.gov.uk

COUNCILLORS

Chair: Mason, David (IND - Trefeurig)
dai.mason@ceredigion.gov.uk

Vice-Chair: Thomas, William Lynford (PC - Llanfihangel Ystrad)
lynford.thomas@ceredigion.gov.uk

Leader of the Council: Ap Gwynn, Ellen (PC - Ceulanamaesmawr)
ellen.apgwynn@ceredigion.gov.uk

Deputy Leader of the Council: Quant, Ray (IND - Borth)
ray.quant@ceredigion.gov.uk

Adams-Lewis, John (PC - Cardigan - Mwldan)
john.adams-lewis@ceredigion.gov.uk

Cole, John Mark (LD - Cardigan - Rhydyfuwch)
mark.cole@ceredigion.gov.uk

Davies, Euros (IND - Llanwenog)
euros.davies@ceredigion.gov.uk

Davies, Bryan (PC - Llanarth)
bryan.davies@ceredigion.gov.uk

Davies, John Aled (IND - Aberystwyth Rheidol)
aled.davis@ceredigion.gov.uk

Davies, Gareth (PC - Llanbadarn Fawr - Padarn)
gareth.davies@ceredigion.gov.uk

Davies, Thomas Peter (IND - Capel Dewi)
peter.davies@ceredigion.gov.uk

Davies, John Odwyn (PC - Llangybi)
odwyn.davies@ceredigion.gov.uk

Davies, Ceredig (LD - Aberystwyth Central)
ceredig.davies@ceredigion.gov.uk

Davies, Steve (PC - Aberystwyth Penparcau)
steve.davies2@ceredigion.gov.uk

Davies, Ifan (IND - Lledrod)
ifan.davies@ceredigion.gov.uk

Davies, Rhodri (PC - Melindwr)
rhodri.davies@ceredigion.gov.uk

Edwards, Dafydd (IND - Llansantffraid)
dafydd.edwards@live.co.uk

Evans, Elizabeth (LD - Aberaeron)
elizabeth.evans@ceredigion.gov.uk

Evans, Peter (PC - Llandysul Town)
peter.evans3@ceredigion.gov.uk

Evans, David Rhodri (IND - Llangeitho)
rhodri.evans2@ceredigion.gov.uk

Evans, Benjamin Towyn (PC - Llandyfriog)
towyn.evans@ceredigion.gov.uk

Harris, George (LAB - Lampeter)
hag.harries@ceredigion.gov.uk

Hinge, Paul (LD - Tirymynach)
paul.hinge@ceredigion.gov.uk

Hopley, Sarah Gillian (IND - New Quay)
gill.hopley@ceredigion.gov.uk

Hughes, Catherine (PC - Tregaron)
catherine.hughes@ceredigion.gov.uk

James, Gethin (INDNA - Aberporth)
gethin.james@ceredigion.gov.uk

James, Gwyn (IND - Penbryn)
gwyn.james@ceredigion.gov.uk

James, Paul (PC - Llanbadarn Fawr - Sulien)
paul.james@ceredigion.gov.uk

Jones, Rowland (LD - Ystwyth)
rowland.jones@ceredigion.gov.uk

Jones-Southgate, Lorrae (PC - Aberystwyth Penparcau)
lorrae.jones-southgate@ceredigion.gov.uk

Lewis, Thomas Maldwyn (IND - Troedyraur)
maldwyn.lewis@ceredigion.gov.uk

Lewis, Thomas (IND - Penparc)
thomaslewis34@mypostoffice.co.uk

Lloyd, Gareth (IND - Llandysiliogogo)
gareth.lloyd@ceredigion.gov.uk

Lloyd, Lyndon (PC - Beulah)

Lloyd Jones, Alun (PC - Llanfarian)
alun.lloydjones@ceredigion.gov.uk

Lumley, John (PC - Ciliau Aeron)
john.lumley@ceredigion.gov.uk

Miles, Catrin (PC - Cardigan - Teifi)
catrin.miles@ceredigion.gov.uk

Rees-Evans, David Rowland (LD - Llanrhystud)
rowland.rees-evans@ceredigion.gov.uk

Roberts, John (LD - Faenor)
john.roberts@ceredigion.gov.uk

Strong, Mark (PC - Aberystwyth North)
mark.strong@ceredigion.gov.uk

Williams, Alun (PC - Aberystwyth Bronglais)
alun.williams@ceredigion.gov.uk

Williams, Ivor (IND - Lampeter)
ivor.williams@ceredigion.gov.uk

POLITICAL COMPOSITION
PC: 19, IND: 14, LD: 7, INDNA: 1, LAB: 1

COMMITTEE CHAIRS

Audit: Mr David Rowland Rees-Evans

Development Control: Mr Rhodri Davies

Licensing: Mr Alun Lloyd Jones

Charnwood   D

Charnwood Borough Council, Southfields, Loughborough
LE11 2TX
☎ 01509 263151 ▤ 01509 263791 ✆ info@charnwood.gov.uk
▯ www.charnwood.gov.uk

FACTS AND FIGURES
Parliamentary Constituencies: Charnwood, Loughborough
EU Constituencies: East Midlands
Election Frequency: Elections are of whole council

PRINCIPAL OFFICERS

Chief Executive: Mr Geoff Parker, Chief Executive & Head of
Paid Services, Southfields, Loughborough LE11 2TR ☎ 01509
634600 ✆ geoff.parker@charnwood.gov.uk

Senior Management: Mr Simon Jackson, Strategic Director -
Corporate Services, Southfields, Loughborough LE11 2TX
☎ 01509 634583 ✆ simon.jackson@charnwood.gov.uk

Senior Management: Ms Eileen Mallon, Strategic Director -
Housing, Planning, Regulation & Regulatory Services, Southfields,
Loughborough LE11 2TX ☎ 01509 634662
✆ eileen.mallon@charnwood.gov.uk

Senior Management: Ms Christine Traill, Strategic Director
- Neighbourhoods & Community Wellbeing, Southfields,
Loughborough LE11 2TX ☎ 01509 634774
✆ chris.traill@charnwood.gov.uk

Architect, Building / Property Services: Mr Richard Bennett,
Head of Planning & Regeneration, Southfields, Loughborough LE11
2TX ☎ 01509 634763 ✆ richard.bennett@charnwood.gov.uk

Architect, Building / Property Services: Ms Clare Hodgson,
Head of Finance & Property Services, Southfields, Loughborough
LE11 2TX ☎ 01509 634583 ✆ clare.hodgson@charnwood.gov.uk

Architect, Building / Property Services: Mr Dave Wall,
Premises Manager, Southfields, Loughborough LE11 2TR
☎ 01509 634686 ✆ dave.wall@charnwood.gov.uk

Best Value: Mr Simon Jackson, Strategic Director - Corporate
Services, Southfields, Loughborough LE11 2TX ☎ 01509 634583
✆ simon.jackson@charnwood.gov.uk

Best Value: Mr Adrian Ward, Head of Strategic Support,
Southfields, Loughborough LE11 2TX ☎ 01509 634573
✆ adrian.ward@charnwood.gov.uk

Building Control: Mr Richard Bennett, Head of Planning &
Regeneration, Southfields, Loughborough LE11 2TX
☎ 01509 634763 ✆ richard.bennett@charnwood.gov.uk

Building Control: Ms Eileen Mallon, Strategic Director -
Housing, Planning, Regulation & Regulatory Services, Southfields,
Loughborough LE11 2TX ☎ 01509 634662
✆ eileen.mallon@charnwood.gov.uk

Catering Services: Mr Dave Wall, Premises Manager, Southfields,
Loughborough LE11 2TR ☎ 01509 634686
✆ dave.wall@charnwood.gov.uk

Children / Youth Services: Ms Julie Robinson, Head of
Neighbourhoods & Communities, Southfields, Loughborough LE11
2TX ☎ 01509 634590 ✆ julie.robinson@charnwood.gov.uk

Children / Youth Services: Ms Christine Traill, Strategic
Director - Neighbourhoods & Community Wellbeing, Southfields,
Loughborough LE11 2TX ☎ 01509 634774
✆ chris.traill@charnwood.gov.uk

PR / Communications: Mr Michael Roberts, Communications
Officer, Southfields, Loughborough LE11 2TX ☎ 01509 634517
✆ mike.roberts@charnwood.gov.uk

CHARNWOOD

PR / Communications: Mr Adrian Ward, Head of Strategic Support, Southfields, Loughborough LE11 2TX ☎ 01509 634573
📧 adrian.ward@charnwood.gov.uk

Community Planning: Ms Julie Robinson, Head of Neighbourhoods & Communities, Southfields, Loughborough LE11 2TX ☎ 01509 634590 📧 julie.robinson@charnwood.gov.uk

Community Safety: Ms Julie Robinson, Head of Neighbourhoods & Communities, Southfields, Loughborough LE11 2TX ☎ 01509 634590 📧 julie.robinson@charnwood.gov.uk

Computer Management: Mr Paul Bargewell, Technical Service & Strategy Manager, Southfields, Loughborough LE11 2TX ☎ 01509 634777 📧 paul.bargewell@charnwood.gov.uk

Computer Management: Mr David Platts, Head of Revenue, Benefits & Customer Service, Southfields, Loughborough LE11 2TX ☎ 01509 634850 📧 david.platts@charnwood.gov.uk

Corporate Services: Mr Simon Jackson, Strategic Director - Corporate Services, Southfields, Loughborough LE11 2TX ☎ 01509 634583 📧 simon.jackson@charnwood.gov.uk

Customer Service: Mr David Platts, Head of Revenue, Benefits & Customer Service, Southfields, Loughborough LE11 2TX ☎ 01509 634850 📧 david.platts@charnwood.gov.uk

Economic Development: Mr Richard Bennett, Head of Planning & Regeneration, Southfields, Loughborough LE11 2TX ☎ 01509 634763 📧 richard.bennett@charnwood.gov.uk

E-Government: Mr Paul Bargewell, Technical Service & Strategy Manager, Southfields, Loughborough LE11 2TX ☎ 01509 634777 📧 paul.bargewell@charnwood.gov.uk

E-Government: Mr David Platts, Head of Revenue, Benefits & Customer Service, Southfields, Loughborough LE11 2TX ☎ 01509 634850 📧 david.platts@charnwood.gov.uk

Electoral Registration: Mr Adrian Ward, Head of Strategic Support, Southfields, Loughborough LE11 2TX ☎ 01509 634573 📧 adrian.ward@charnwood.gov.uk

Emergency Planning: Mr Adrian Ward, Head of Strategic Support, Southfields, Loughborough LE11 2TX ☎ 01509 634573 📧 adrian.ward@charnwood.gov.uk

Energy Management: Mr Dave Wall, Premises Manager, Southfields, Loughborough LE11 2TR ☎ 01509 634686 📧 dave.wall@charnwood.gov.uk

Environmental / Technical Services: Mr Matthew Bradford, Head of Cleansing & Open Spaces, Southfields, Loughborough LE11 2TX ☎ 01509 634675 📧 matthew.bradford@charnwood.gov.uk

Environmental Health: Ms Eileen Mallon, Strategic Director - Housing, Planning, Regulation & Regulatory Services, Southfields, Loughborough LE11 2TX ☎ 01509 634662 📧 eileen.mallon@charnwood.gov.uk

Environmental Health: Mr Alan Twells, Head of Regulatory Services, Southfields, Loughborough LE11 2TX ☎ 01509 634650 📧 alan.twells@charnwood.gov.uk

Estates, Property & Valuation: Ms Clare Hodgson, Head of Finance & Property Services, Southfields, Loughborough LE11 2TX ☎ 01509 634583 📧 clare.hodgson@charnwood.gov.uk

Events Manager: Ms Sylvia Wright, Head of Leisure & Culture, Southfields, Loughborough LE11 2TX ☎ 01509 634658 📧 sylvia.wright@charnwood.gov.uk

Facilities: Mr Dave Wall, Premises Manager, Southfields, Loughborough LE11 2TR ☎ 01509 634686 📧 dave.wall@charnwood.gov.uk

Finance: Ms Clare Hodgson, Head of Finance & Property Services, Southfields, Loughborough LE11 2TX ☎ 01509 634583 📧 clare.hodgson@charnwood.gov.uk

Finance: Mr Simon Jackson, Strategic Director - Corporate Services, Southfields, Loughborough LE11 2TX ☎ 01509 634583 📧 simon.jackson@charnwood.gov.uk

Fleet Management: Mr Dave Woolsey, Fleet Manager, Southfields, Loughborough LE11 2TX ☎ 01509 634682 📧 dave.woolsey@charnwood.gov.uk

Grounds Maintenance: Mr Matthew Bradford, Head of Cleansing & Open Spaces, Southfields, Loughborough LE11 2TX ☎ 01509 634675 📧 matthew.bradford@charnwood.gov.uk

Health and Safety: Mr David Hicks, Health & Safety Officer, Southfields, Loughborough LE11 3DH ☎ 01509 634637 📧 david.hicks@charnwood.gov.uk

Health and Safety: Mr Adrian Ward, Head of Strategic Support, Southfields, Loughborough LE11 2TX ☎ 01509 634573 📧 adrian.ward@charnwood.gov.uk

Housing: Ms Christine Ansell, Head of Landlord Services, Southfields, Loughborough LE11 2TX ☎ 01509 634592 📧 christine.ansell@charnwood.gov.uk

Housing: Mrs Alison Simmons, Head of Strategic & Private Sector Housing, Southfields, Loughborough LE11 2TX ☎ 01509 634780 📧 alison.simmons@charnwood.gov.uk

Housing Maintenance: Ms Christine Ansell, Head of Landlord Services, Southfields, Loughborough LE11 2TX ☎ 01509 634592 📧 christine.ansell@charnwood.gov.uk

Legal: Mrs Sanjit Sull, Legal Services Manager, Southfields, Loughborough LE11 2TX ☎ 01509 634611 📧 sanjit.sull@charnwood.gov.uk

Legal: Mr Adrian Ward, Head of Strategic Support, Southfield Road, Loughborough LE11 2TR ☎ 01509 634612 📧 adrian.ward@charnwood.gov.uk

Leisure and Cultural Services: Ms Christine Traill, Strategic Director - Neighbourhoods & Community Wellbeing, Southfields, Loughborough LE11 2TX ☎ 01509 634774 ⌂ chris.traill@charnwood.gov.uk

Leisure and Cultural Services: Ms Sylvia Wright, Head of Leisure & Culture, Southfields, Loughborough LE11 2TX ☎ 01509 634658 ⌂ sylvia.wright@charnwood.gov.uk

Licensing: Mr Alan Twells, Head of Regulatory Services, Southfields, Loughborough LE11 2TX ☎ 01509 634650 ⌂ alan.twells@charnwood.gov.uk

Lottery Funding, Charity and Voluntary: Ms Julie Robinson, Head of Neighbourhoods & Communities, Southfields, Loughborough LE11 2TX ☎ 01509 634590 ⌂ julie.robinson@charnwood.gov.uk

Member Services: Mr Adrian Ward, Head of Strategic Support, Southfields, Loughborough LE11 2TX ☎ 01509 634573 ⌂ adrian.ward@charnwood.gov.uk

Parking: Mr Alan Twells, Head of Regulatory Services, Southfields, Loughborough LE11 2TX ☎ 01509 634650 ⌂ alan.twells@charnwood.gov.uk

Partnerships: Ms Julie Robinson, Head of Neighbourhoods & Communities, Southfields, Loughborough LE11 2TX ☎ 01509 634590 ⌂ julie.robinson@charnwood.gov.uk

Personnel / HR: Mr Adrian Ward, Head of Strategic Support, Southfields, Loughborough LE11 2TX ☎ 01509 634573 ⌂ adrian.ward@charnwood.gov.uk

Planning: Mr Richard Bennett, Head of Planning & Regeneration, Southfields, Loughborough LE11 2TX ☎ 01509 634763 ⌂ richard.bennett@charnwood.gov.uk

Planning: Ms Eileen Mallon, Strategic Director - Housing, Planning, Regulation & Regulatory Services, Southfields, Loughborough LE11 2TX ☎ 01509 634662 ⌂ eileen.mallon@charnwood.gov.uk

Procurement: Mr David Howkins, Purchasing Manager, Southfields, Loughborough LE11 2TX ☎ 01509 634672 ⌂ david.howkins@charnwood.gov.uk

Staff Training: Mr Kevin Brewin, Learning Co-ordinator, Southfields, Loughborough LE11 2TR ☎ 01509 634904 ⌂ kevin.brewin@charnwood.gov.uk

Staff Training: Mr Adrian Ward, Head of Strategic Support, Southfields, Loughborough LE11 2TX ☎ 01509 634573 ⌂ adrian.ward@charnwood.gov.uk

Street Scene: Mr Alan Twells, Head of Regulatory Services, Southfields, Loughborough LE11 2TX ☎ 01509 634650 ⌂ alan.twells@charnwood.gov.uk

Sustainable Communities: Ms Julie Robinson, Head of Neighbourhoods & Communities, Southfields, Loughborough LE11 2TX ☎ 01509 634590 ⌂ julie.robinson@charnwood.gov.uk

Tourism: Ms Christine Traill, Strategic Director - Neighbourhoods & Community Wellbeing, Southfields, Loughborough LE11 2TX ☎ 01509 634774 ⌂ chris.traill@charnwood.gov.uk

Town Centre: Mr Michael Bird, Markets & Fairs Manager, Southfields, Loughborough LE11 2TX ☎ 01509 634624 ⌂ market.fairs@charnwood.gov.uk

Town Centre: Ms Sylvia Wright, Head of Leisure & Culture, Southfields, Loughborough LE11 2TX ☎ 01509 634658 ⌂ sylvia.wright@charnwood.gov.uk

Transport Planner: Mr Richard Bennett, Head of Planning & Regeneration, Southfields, Loughborough LE11 2TX ☎ 01509 634763 ⌂ richard.bennett@charnwood.gov.uk

Waste Collection and Disposal: Mr Matthew Bradford, Head of Cleansing & Open Spaces, Southfields, Loughborough LE11 2TX ☎ 01509 634675 ⌂ matthew.bradford@charnwood.gov.uk

Waste Management: Mr Matthew Bradford, Head of Cleansing & Open Spaces, Southfields, Loughborough LE11 2TX ☎ 01509 634675 ⌂ matthew.bradford@charnwood.gov.uk

COUNCILLORS

Mayor: Gaskell, David (CON - Birstall Watermead) cllr.david.gaskell@charnwood.gov.uk

Leader of the Council: Slater, David (CON - Quorn & Mountsorrel Castle) cllr.david.slater@charnwood.gov.uk

Deputy Leader of the Council: Morgan, Jonathan (CON - Loughborough Outwoods) cllr.jonathan.morgan@charnwood.gov.uk

Group LeaderMiah, Jewel (LAB - Loughborough Lemyngton) cllr.jewel.miah@charnwood.gov.uk

Barkley, Thomas (CON - Syston West) cllr.thomas.barkley@charnwood.gov.uk

Bebbington, Bill (CON - Shepshed East) cllr.bill.bebbington@charnwood.gov.uk

Bentley, Iain (CON - Birstall Watermead) cllr.iain.bentley@charnwood.gov.uk

Bokor, Jenny (CON - The Wolds) cllr.jenny.bokor@charnwood.gov.uk

Bradshaw, Julie (LAB - Loughborough Ashby) cllr.julie.bradshaw@charnwood.gov.uk

Brookes, Matthew (CON - Thurmaston) cllr.matthew.brookes@charnwood.gov.uk

Campsall, Roy (IND - Loughborough Garendon) cllr.roy.campsall@charnwood.gov.uk

Capleton, John (CON - Mountsorrel) cllr.john.capleton@charnwood.gov.uk

Cooper, Beatrice (CON - Loughborough Dishley & Hathern) cllr.beatrice.cooper@charnwood.gov.uk

Forrest, Sandie (LAB - Loughborough Storer) cllr.sandra.forrest@charnwood.gov.uk

Fryer, Hilary (CON - Barrow & Sileby West) cllr.hilary.fryer@charnwood.gov.uk

CHARNWOOD

Gerrard, Sue (CON - East Gosgate)
cllr.sur.garrard@charnwood.gov.uk

Grimley, Daniel (CON - Queniborough)
cllr.daniel.grimley@charnwood.gov.uk

Hachem, Harley (CON - Loughborough Ashby)
cllr.harley.hachem@charnwood.gov.uk

Hadji-Nikolaou, Leon (CON - Rothley & Thurcaston)
cllr.leon.hadji-nikolaou@charnwood.gov.uk

Hampson, Stephen (CON - Syston East)
cllr.stephen.hampson@charnwood.gov.uk

Harper-Davies, Leigh (CON - Mountsorrel)
cllr.leigh.harper-davies@charnwood.gov.uk

Harris, Christine (LAB - Loughborough Lemyngton)
cllr.christine.harris@charnwood.gov.uk

Harris, Keith (LAB - Loughborough Dishley & Hathern)
cllr.kieth.harris@charnwood.gov.uk

Hayes, David (CON - Loughborough Shelhorpe)
cllr.david.hayes@charnwood.gov.uk

Jones, Renata (CON - Birstall Wanlip)
cllr.renata.jones@charnwood.gov.uk

Jukes, Ron (CON - Loughborough Outwoods)
cllr.ron.jukes@charnwood.gov.uk

Lowe, Mark (CON - Thurmaston)
cllr.mark.lowe@charnwood.gov.uk

Maynard Smith, Sarah (LAB - Loughborough Hastings)
cllr.sarah.maynard-smith@charnwood.gov.uk

Mercer, Paul (CON - Loughborough Southfields)
cllr.paul.mercer@charnwood.gov.uk

Murphy, Paul (CON - Sileby)
cllr.paul.murphy: charnwood.gov.uk

Pacey, Ken (CON - Syston East)
cllr.ken.pacey@charnwood.gov.uk

Page, Brian (CON - Rothley & Thurcaston)
cllr.brian.page@charnwood.gov.uk

Paling, Andy (CON - Sileby)
cllr.andrew.paling@charnwood.gov.uk

Parsons, Geoff (CON - Loughborough Nanpantan)
cllr.geoff.parsons@charnwood.gov.uk

Parton, Ted (CON - Loughborough Southfields)
cllr.ted.parton@charnwood.gov.uk

Poland, James (CON - Wreake Villages)
cllr.james.poland@charnwood.gov.uk

Radford, Christine (CON - Shepshed West)
cllr.christine.radford@charnwood.gov.uk

Ranson, Pauline (CON - Barrow & Sileby West)
cllr.pauline.ranson@charnwood.gov.uk

Savage, John (CON - Shepshed East)
cllr.john.savage@charnwood.gov.uk

Seaton, Brenda (CON - Thurmaston)
cllr.brenda.seaton@charnwood.gov.uk

Sharp, Robert (LAB - Loughborough Shelthorpe)
cllr.robert.sharp@charnwood.gov.uk

Shepherd, Richard (CON - Quorn & Mountsorrel Castle)
cllr.richard.shepherd@charnwood.gov.uk

Shergill, Serinda (CON - Birstall Wanlip)
cllr.serinda.shergill@charnwood.gov.uk

Smidowicz, Margaret (CON - Loughborough Nanpantan)
cllr.margaret.smidowicz@charnwood.gov.uk

Smith, Luke (CON - Loughborough Garendon)
cllr.luke.smith@charnwood.gov.uk

Snartt, David (CON - Forest Bradgate)
cllr.david.snartt@charnwood.gov.uk

Sutherington, John (LD - Anstey)
cllr.john.sutherington@charnwood.gov.uk

Tassell, Joan (CON - Shepshed West)
cllr.joan.tassell@charnwood.gov.uk

Taylor, Deborah (CON - Anstey)
cllr.deoborah.taylor@charnwood.gov.uk

Tillotson, Jenni (LAB - Loughborough Storer)
cllr.jenni.tillotson@charnwood.gov.uk

Vardy, Eric (CON - Syston West)
cllr.eric.vardy@charnwood.gov.uk

Williams, Anne (LAB - Loughborough Hastings)
cllr.anne.williams@charnwood.gov.uk

POLITICAL COMPOSITION
CON: 41, LAB: 9, LD: 1, IND: 1

Chelmsford D

Chelmsford City Council, Civic Centre, Duke Street,
Chelmsford CM1 1JE
☎ 01245 606606 🖶 01245 606310 ⌖ mailbox@chelmsford.gov.uk
🖥 www.chelmsford.gov.uk

FACTS AND FIGURES
Parliamentary Constituencies: Chelmsford
EU Constituencies: Eastern
Election Frequency: Elections are of whole council

PRINCIPAL OFFICERS

Chief Executive: Mr Steve Packham, Chief Executive, Civic
Centre, Duke Street, Chelmsford CM1 1JE ☎ 01245 606901
⌖ steve.packham@chelmsford.gov.uk

Senior Management: Mr Nick Eveleigh, Director - Finance &
Housing, PO Box 457, Civic Centre, Duke Street, Chelmsford CM1
1JE ☎ 01245 606419 ⌖ nick.eveleigh@chelmsford.gov.uk

Senior Management: Ms Louise Goodwin, Director - Corporate
Services, Civic Centre, Duke Street, Chelmsford CM1 1JE
☎ 01245 606802 ⌖ louise.goodwin@chelmsford.gov.uk

Senior Management: Mr David Green, Director - Sustainable
Communities, Civic Centre, Duke Street, Chelmsford CM1 1JE
☎ 01245 606503 ⌖ david.green@chelmsford.gov.uk

Senior Management: Mr Keith Nicholson, Director - Public
Places, Civic Centre, Duke Street, Chelmsford CM1 1JE
☎ 01245 606606 ⌖ keith.nicholson@chelmsford.gov.uk

Senior Management: Ms Averil Price, Director - Community Services, Civic Centre, Duke Street, Chelmsford CM1 1JE ☎ 01245 606473 ⊕ averil.price@chelmsford.gov.uk

Access Officer / Social Services (Disability): Mr Paul Houghton, Access Officer, Civic Centre, Duke Street, Chelmsford CM1 1JE ☎ 01245 606328 ⊕ paul.houghton@chelmsford.gov.uk

Building Control: Mr Andrew Savage, Building Control Manager, Civic Centre, Duke Street, Chelmsford CM1 1JE ☎ 01245 606541 ⊕ andrew.savage@chelmsford.gov.uk

PR / Communications: Ms Laura Ketley, Senior Communications Officer, Civic Centre, Duke Street, Chelmsford CM1 1JE ☎ 01245 606795 ⊕ laura.ketley@chelmsford.gov.uk

Community Planning: Mr David Green, Director - Sustainable Communities, Civic Centre, Duke Street, Chelmsford CM1 1JE ☎ 01245 606503 ⊕ david.green@chelmsford.gov.uk

Community Safety: Mr Spencer Clarke, Public Protection Manager, Civic Centre, Duke Street, Chelmsford CM1 1JE ☎ 01245 606477 ⊕ spencer.clarke@chelmsford.gov.uk

Computer Management: Mr Tony Preston, Corporate ICT Manager, Civic Centre, Duke Street, Chelmsford CM1 1JE ☎ 01245 606606 ⊕ tony.preston@chelmsford.gov.uk

Corporate Services: Ms Louise Goodwin, Director - Corporate Services, Civic Centre, Duke Street, Chelmsford CM1 1JE ☎ 01245 606802 ⊕ louise.goodwin@chelmsford.gov.uk

Customer Service: Mrs Elaine Peck, Customer Services Manager, Civic Centre, Duke Street, Chelmsford CM1 1JE ☎ 01245 606406 ⊕ elaine.peck@chelmsford.gov.uk

Economic Development: Mr Stuart Graham, Inward Investment, Economy & Growth Manager, Civic Centre, Duke Street, Chelmsford CM1 1JE ☎ 01245 606364 ⊕ stuart.graham@chelmsford.gov.uk

Electoral Registration: Mr Edward McCreadie, Electoral Services Team Manager, Civic Centre, Duke Street, Chelmsford CM1 1JE ☎ 01245 606607 ⊕ edward.mccreadie@chelmsford.gov.uk

Emergency Planning: Ms Karen Buttress, Community Safety Officer, Civic Centre, Duke Street, Chelmsford CM1 1JE ☎ 01245 606233 ⊕ karen.buttress@chelmsford.gov.uk

Energy Management: Ms Michelle Keene, Energy & Contracts Manager, Civic Centre, Duke Street, Chelmsford CM1 1JE ☎ 01245 606747 ⊕ michelle.keene@chelmsford.gov.uk

Environmental / Technical Services: Mr Paul Brookes, Public Health & Protection Services Manager, Civic Centre, Duke Street, Chelmsford CM1 1JE ☎ 01245 606436 ⊕ paul.brookes@chelmsford.gov.uk

Environmental Health: Mr Paul Brookes, Public Health & Protection Services Manager, Civic Centre, Duke Street, Chelmsford CM1 1JE ☎ 01245 606436 ⊕ paul.brookes@chelmsford.gov.uk

Estates, Property & Valuation: Mr Andrew Larges, Corporate Property Manager, Civic Centre, Duke Street, Chelmsford CM1 1JE ☎ 01245 606311 ⊕ andrew.large@chelmsford.gov.uk

Events Manager: Mr Ali Naqvi, Marketing & Engagement Team Manager, Civic Centre, Duke Street, Chelmsford CM1 1JE ☎ 01245 606282 ⊕ ali.naqvi@chelmsford.gov.uk

Facilities: Mr Richard Bishop, Building Services Manager, Civic Centre, Duke Street, Chelmsford CM1 1JE ☎ 01245 606882 ⊕ richard.bishop@chelmsford.gov.uk

Finance: Mr Nick Eveleigh, Director - Finance & Housing, PO Box 457, Civic Centre, Duke Street, Chelmsford CM1 1JE ☎ 01245 606419 ⊕ nick.eveleigh@chelmsford.gov.uk

Grounds Maintenance: Mr Richard Whiting, Grounds Maintenance & Operations Manager, Civic Centre, Duke Street, Chelmsford CM1 1JE ☎ 01245 605560 ⊕ richard.whiting@chelmsford.gov.uk

Housing: Mr Nick Eveleigh, Director - Finance & Housing, PO Box 457, Civic Centre, Duke Street, Chelmsford CM1 1JE ☎ 01245 606419 ⊕ nick.eveleigh@chelmsford.gov.uk

Legal: Ms Ann Coronel, Legal & Democratic Services Manager, Civic Centre, Duke Street, Chelmsford CM1 1JE ☎ 01245 606560 ⊕ ann.coronel@chelmsford.gov.uk

Leisure and Cultural Services: Ms Averil Price, Director - Community Services, Civic Centre, Duke Street, Chelmsford CM1 1JE ☎ 01245 606473 ⊕ averil.price@chelmsford.gov.uk

Licensing: Mr Matthew Evans, Licensing Lead Officer, Civic Centre, Duke Street, Chelmsford CM1 1JE ☎ 01245 606512 ⊕ matthew.evans@chelmsford.gov.uk

Member Services: Ms Ann Coronel, Legal & Democratic Services Manager, Civic Centre, Duke Street, Chelmsford CM1 1JE ☎ 01245 606560 ⊕ ann.coronel@chelmsford.gov.uk

Parking: Ms Rosa Tanfield, Parking & Highways Liaison Manager, Civic Centre, Duke Street, Chelmsford CM1 1JE ☎ 01245 606284 ⊕ rosa.tanfield@chelmsford.gov.uk

Personnel / HR: Ms Debbie Knibb, Service Manager - Human Resources, Civic Centre, Duke Street, Chelmsford CM1 1JE ☎ 01245 606711 ⊕ debbie.knibb@chelmsford.gov.uk

Planning: Mr David Green, Director - Sustainable Communities, Civic Centre, Duke Street, Chelmsford CM1 1JE ☎ 01245 606503 ⊕ david.green@chelmsford.gov.uk

Procurement: Mr Chris Lay, Procurement Manager, Civic Centre, Duke Street, Chelmsford CM1 1JE ☎ 01245 606485 ⊕ chris.lay@chelmsford.gov.uk

Recycling & Waste Minimisation: Mr Keith Nicholson, Director - Public Places, Civic Centre, Duke Street, Chelmsford CM1 1JE ☎ 01245 606606 ⊕ keith.nicholson@chelmsford.gov.uk

CHELMSFORD

Regeneration: Mr Stuart Graham, Inward Investment, Economy & Growth Manager, Civic Centre, Duke Street, Chelmsford CM1 1JE
☎ 01245 606364 ⌨ stuart.graham@chelmsford.gov.uk

Staff Training: Ms Kerry Knowles, HR Strategy & Development Manager, Civic Centre, Duke Street, Chelmsford CM1 1JE
☎ 01245 606592 ⌨ kerry.knowles@chelmsford.gov.uk

Sustainable Communities: Mr David Green, Director - Sustainable Communities, Civic Centre, Duke Street, Chelmsford CM1 1JE ☎ 01245 606503 ⌨ david.green@chelmsford.gov.uk

Sustainable Development: Mr David Green, Director - Sustainable Communities, Civic Centre, Duke Street, Chelmsford CM1 1JE ☎ 01245 606503 ⌨ david.green@chelmsford.gov.uk

Town Centre: Mr Mike Wrays, City Centre Manager, Civic Centre, Duke Street, Chelmsford CM1 1JE ☎ 01245 606253

Waste Collection and Disposal: Mr Keith Nicholson, Director - Public Places, Civic Centre, Duke Street, Chelmsford CM1 1JE
☎ 01245 606606 ⌨ keith.nicholson@chelmsford.gov.uk

Children's Play Areas: Mr Paul Van Damme, Parks & Greens Spaces Manager, Civic Centre, Duke Street, Chelmsford CM1 1JE
☎ 01245 606477 ⌨ spencer.clarke@chelmsford.gov.uk

COUNCILLORS

Mayor: Hughes, Patricia (CON - South Woodham - Elmwood & Woodville)
p.hughes@chelmsford.gov.uk

Deputy Mayor: Denston, Linda (CON - South Woodham - Elmwood & Woodville)
linda.denston@chelmsford.gov.uk

Leader of the Council: Whitehead, Roy (CON - South Hanningfield - Stock & Margaretting)
r.whitehead@chelmsford.gov.uk

Deputy Leader of the Council: Galley, John (CON - Boreham & the Leighs)
j.galley@chelmsford.gov.uk

Group LeaderRobinson, Stephen (LD - Patching Hall)
stephen.robinson@chelmsford.gov.uk

Ahmed, Liz (CON - Great Baddow East)
liz.ahmed@chelmsford.gov.uk

Alcock, Ron (CON - Chelmer Village & Beaulieu Park)
r.alcock@chelmsford.gov.uk

Ambor, Richard (CON - Little Baddow, Danbury & Sandon)
richard.ambor@chelmsford.gov.uk

Ashley, Lee (LD - St Andrews)
lee.ashley@chelmsford.gov.uk

Camp, Victoria (CON - Moulsham & Central)
victoria.camp@chelmsford.gov.uk

Chambers, Nicolette (CON - Chelmsford Rural West)
n.chambers@chelmsford.gov.uk

Chambers, Alan (CON - Waterhouse Farm)
alan.chambers@chelmsford.gov.uk

Chandler, Jenny (CON - Great Baddow West)
jenny.chandler@chelmsford.gov.uk

Cook, Simon (CON - Moulsham Lodge)
simon.cook@chelmsford.gov.uk

Cousins, Peter (CON - St Andrews)
peter.cousins@chelmsford.gov.uk

de Vries, Jon (CON - Patching Hall)
jon.devries@chelmsford.gov.uk

Deakin, Jude (LD - Marconi)
jude.deakin@chelmsford.gov.uk

Denston, Bob (CON - South Woodham - Elmwood & Woodville)
r.denston@chelmsford.gov.uk

Flack, Matt (CON - Bicknacre & East & West Hanningfield)
matt.flack@chelmsford.gov.uk

Fowell, Stephen (CON - St Andrews)
stephen.fowell@chelmsford.gov.uk

Garrett, Christine (CON - The Lawns)
christine.garrett@chelmsford.gov.uk

Grundy, Ian (CON - South Hanningfield, Stock & Margaretting)
i.grundy@chelmsford.gov.uk

Gulliver, Neil (CON - Chelmer Village & Beaulieu Park)
n.gulliver@chelmsford.gov.uk

Hindi, Sameh (CON - Moulsham & Central)
s.k.hindi@chelmsford.gov.uk

Holoway, Michael (CON - Patching Hall)
michael.holoway@chelmsford.gov.uk

Hutchinson, Paul (CON - Springfield North)
paul.hutchinson@chelmsford.gov.uk

Jeapes, Julia (CON - The Lawns)
julia.jeapes@chelmsford.gov.uk

John, Ashley (CON - South Woodham - Chetwood & Collingwood)
ashley.john@chelmsford.gov.uk

Knight, Barry (CON - Broomfield & The Walthams)
gbr.knight@chelmsford.gov.uk

Lumley, Duncan (CON - Chelmer Village & Beaulieu Park)
d.lumley@chelmsford.gov.uk

Madden, Dick (CON - Moulsham & Central)
dick.madden@chelmsford.gov.uk

Massey, Bob (CON - South Woodham - Chetwood & Collingwood)
bob.massey@chelmsford.gov.uk

McQuiggan, Anthony (CON - Goat Hall)
anthony.mcquiggan@chelmsford.gov.uk

Millane, Lance (CON - Rettendon & Runwell)
lance.millane@chelmsford.gov.uk

Mountain, Freda (LD - Goat Hall)
f.mountain@chelmsford.gov.uk

Murray, Jean (CON - Trinity)
jean.murray@chelmsford.gov.uk

Pontin, Sandra (CON - Broomfield & The Walthams)
sandra.pontin@chelmsford.gov.uk

Potter, Janette (CON - Galleywood)
japotter@chelmsford.gov.uk

Poulter, Richard (CON - Bicknacre & East & West Hanningfield)
r.poulter@chelmsford.gov.uk

Raven, James (CON - Broomfield & The Walthams)
james.raven@chelmsford.gov.uk

Ride, Raymond (CON - Rettendon & Runwell)
r.ride@chelmsford.gov.uk

Roper, Tim (CON - Writtle)
t.roper@chelmsford.gov.uk

Sach, Tony (CON - Writtle)
tony.sach@chelmsford.gov.uk

Scott, Stephanie (CON - Great Baddow East)
stephanie.scott@chelmsford.gov.uk

Seeley, Graham (CON - Trinity)
graham.seeley@chelmsford.gov.uk

Shepherd, Bob (CON - Little Baddow, Danbury & Sandon)
b.shepherd@chelmsford.gov.uk

Sismey, Malcolm (CON - South Woodham - Chetwood & Collingwood)
malcolm.sismey@chelmsford.gov.uk

Smith, Gillian (CON - Great Baddow East)
gillian.smith@chelmsford.gov.uk

Spence, Yvonne (CON - Marconi)
yvonne.spence@chelmsford.gov.uk

Springett, Mark (LD - Moulsham Lodge)
mark.springett@chelmsford.gov.uk

Stevenson, David (CON - Galleywood)
d.stevenson@chelmsford.gov.uk

Sullivan, Susan (CON - Springfield North)
susan.sullivan@chelmsford.gov.uk

Villa, Bob (CON - Great Baddow West)
bob.villa@chelmsford.gov.uk

Ward, Louis (CON - Springfield North)
louis.ward@chelmsford.gov.uk

Watson, Malcolm (CON - Waterhouse Farm)
malcolm.watson@chelmsford.gov.uk

Wilson, Philip (CON - Boreham & the Leighs)
philip.wilson@chelmsford.gov.uk

Wright, Ian (CON - Little Baddow, Danbury & Sandon)
i.wright@chelmsford.gov.uk

POLITICAL COMPOSITION
CON: 52, LD: 5

Cheltenham D

Cheltenham Borough Council, Municipal Offices, The Promenade, Cheltenham GL50 9SA
☎ 01242 262626 🖷 01242 227131 ◌ enquiries@cheltenham.gov.uk
🖳 www.cheltenham.gov.uk

FACTS AND FIGURES
Parliamentary Constituencies: Cheltenham
EU Constituencies: South West
Election Frequency: Elections are biennial

PRINCIPAL OFFICERS
Chief Executive: Mrs Pat Pratley, Head of Paid Service, Municipal Offices, Promenade, Cheltenham GL50 9SA ☎ 01242 264100
◌ pat.pratley@cheltenham.gov.uk

Senior Management: Mr Tim Atkins, Managing Director - Place & Economic Development, Municipal Offices, The Promenade, Cheltenham GL50 9SA ☎ 01242 775045
◌ tim.atkins@cheltenham.gov.uk

Senior Management: Mr David Neudegg, Managing Director, Council Offices, Trinity Road, Cirencester GL7 1PX
☎ 01285 623101 ◌ david.neudegg@2020partnership.uk

Senior Management: Mr Mark Sheldon, Director - Resources & Projects, Municipal Offices, The Promenade, Cheltenham GL50 9SA
☎ 01242 264123 ◌ mark.sheldon@cheltenham.gov.uk

Senior Management: Mr Ralph Young, Programme Director, Council Offices, Trinity Road, Cirencester GL7 1PX
☎ 01285 623600 ◌ ralph.young@cotswold.gov.uk

Architect, Building / Property Services: Mr David Roberts, Head of Property & Asset Management, Municipal Offices, The Promenade, Cheltenham GL50 9SA ☎ 01242 264151
◌ david.roberts@cheltenham.gov.uk

Building Control: Mr Iain Houston, Building Control Manager, Municipal Offices, The Promenade, Cheltenham GL50 9SA
☎ 01242 264293 ◌ iain.houston@cheltenham.gov.uk

Catering Services: Mr Chris Foster, Operations Manager, Town Hall, Imperial Square, Cheltenham GL50 1QA ☎ 01242 775878
◌ chris.foster@cheltenhamtrust.org.uk

PR / Communications: Mr Richard Gibson, Strategy & Engagement Manager, Municipal Offices, The Promenade, Cheltenham GL50 9SA ☎ 01242 235354
◌ richard.gibson@cheltenham.gov.uk

Community Planning: Mr Mike Redman, Director - Environment, Municipal Offices, The Promenade, Cheltenham GL50 9SA
☎ 01242 264160 ◌ mike.redman@cheltenham.gov.uk

Community Safety: Mrs Barbara Exley, Head of Public Protection, Municipal Offices, Promenade, Cheltenham GL50 9SA
☎ 01242 264220 ◌ barbara.exley@cheltenham.gov.uk

Community Safety: Mrs Yvonne Hope, Head of Public Protection, Municipal Offices, The Promenade, Cheltenham GL50 9SA
☎ 01242 775002 ◌ yvonne.hope@cheltenham.gov.uk

Computer Management: Mr Phil Martin, Head of Joint Business, Council Offices, Coleford GL16 8HG ☎ 01285 623114
◌ phil.martin@2020partnership.uk

Contracts: Mrs Shirin Wotherspoon, Principal Solicitor (Commercial), Tewkesbury Borough Council, Council Offices, Gloucester Road, Tewkesbury GL20 5TT ☎ 01684 272017
◌ shirin.wotherspoon@tewkesbury.gov.uk

Corporate Services: Mr Mark Sheldon, Director - Resources & Projects, Municipal Offices, The Promenade, Cheltenham GL50 9SA
☎ 01242 264123 ◌ mark.sheldon@cheltenham.gov.uk

Customer Service: Mr Mark Sheldon, Director - Resources & Projects, Municipal Offices, The Promenade, Cheltenham GL50 9SA
☎ 01242 264123 ◌ mark.sheldon@cheltenham.gov.uk

CHELTENHAM

Economic Development: Mr Mike Redman, Director - Environment, Municipal Offices, The Promenade, Cheltenham GL50 9SA ☎ 01242 264160 ⌂ mike.redman@cheltenham.gov.uk

Electoral Registration: Mrs Kim Smith, Elections & Electoral Registration Manager, Municipal Offices, The Promenade, Cheltenham GL50 9SA ☎ 01242 264948 ⌂ kim.smith@cheltenham.gov.uk

Emergency Planning: Mr Bryan Parsons, Corporate Governance, Risk & Compliance Officer, Municipal Offices, The Promenade, Cheltenham GL50 9SA ☎ 01242 264189 ⌂ bryan.parsons@cheltenham.gov.uk

Energy Management: Mr Garrie Dowling, Senior Property Surveyor, Municipal Offices, The Promenade, Cheltenham GL50 9SA ☎ 01242 264394 ⌂ garrie.dowling@cheltenham.gov.uk

Environmental Health: Mrs Barbara Exley, Head of Public Protection, Municipal Offices, Promenade, Cheltenham GL50 9SA ☎ 01242 264220 ⌂ barbara.exley@cheltenham.gov.uk

Estates, Property & Valuation: Mr David Roberts, Head of Property & Asset Management, Municipal Offices, The Promenade, Cheltenham GL50 9SA ☎ 01242 264151 ⌂ david.roberts@cheltenham.gov.uk

Events Manager: Mr Gary Newman, Events Manager, Town Hall, Imperial Square, Cheltenham GL50 1QA ☎ 01242 775876 ⌂ gary.newman@cheltenhamtrust.org.uk

Finance: Mr Mark Sheldon, Director - Resources & Projects, Municipal Offices, The Promenade, Cheltenham GL50 9SA ☎ 01242 264123 ⌂ mark.sheldon@cheltenham.gov.uk

Treasury: Mr Mark Sheldon, Director - Resources & Projects, Municipal Offices, The Promenade, Cheltenham GL50 9SA ☎ 01242 264123 ⌂ mark.sheldon@cheltenham.gov.uk

Fleet Management: Mr Mark Hulbert, Fleet Services Manager, Central Depot, Swindon Road, Cheltenham GL51 9JZ ☎ 01242 264361 ⌂ mark.hulbert@ubico.co.uk

Grounds Maintenance: Mr Adam Reynolds, Green Space Development Manager, Central Depot, Swindon Road, Cheltenham GL51 9JZ ☎ 01242 774669 ⌂ adam.reynolds@cheltenham.gov.uk

Health and Safety: Mrs Barbara Exley, Head of Public Protection, Municipal Offices, Promenade, Cheltenham GL50 9SA ☎ 01242 264220 ⌂ barbara.exley@cheltenham.gov.uk

Home Energy Conservation: Mr Mark Nelson, Enforcement Manager, Municipal Offices, The Promenade, Cheltenham GL50 9SA ☎ 01242 264165 ⌂ mark.nelson@cheltenham.gov.uk

Housing: Mr Martin Stacy, Lead Commissioner - Housing Services, Municipal Offices, The Promenade, Cheltenham GL50 9SA ☎ 01242 775214 ⌂ martin.stacy@cheltenham.gov.uk

Housing Maintenance: Mr Paul Stephenson, Chief Executive of Cheltenham Borough Homes, Cheltenham House, Clarence Street, Cheltenham GL50 3RD ☎ 01242 775319 ⌂ paul.stephenson@cheltborohomes.org

Legal: Ms Sara Freckleton, Borough Solicitor & Monitoring Officer, Council Offices, Gloucester Road, Tewkesbury GL20 5TT ☎ 01684 272010 ⌂ sara.freckleton@tewkesbury.gov.uk

Legal: Mr Peter Lewis, Head of Legal Services, Council Offices, Gloucester Road, Tewkesbury GL20 5TT ☎ 01684 272012 ⌂ peter.lewis@tewkesbury.gov.uk

Leisure and Cultural Services: Mrs Pat Pratley, Head of Paid Service, Municipal Offices, Promenade, Cheltenham GL50 9SA ☎ 01242 264100 ⌂ pat.pratley@cheltenham.gov.uk

Licensing: Mrs Barbara Exley, Head of Public Protection, Municipal Offices, Promenade, Cheltenham GL50 9SA ☎ 01242 264220 ⌂ barbara.exley@cheltenham.gov.uk

Lifelong Learning: Ms Julie Finch, CEO - Cheltenham Trust, Art Gallery & Museum, Clarence Street, Cheltenham GL50 3JT ☎ 01242 775093 ⌂ julie.finch@cheltenhamtrust.org.uk

Lottery Funding, Charity and Voluntary: Mr Richard Gibson, Strategy & Engagement Manager, Municipal Offices, The Promenade, Cheltenham GL50 9SA ☎ 01242 235354 ⌂ richard.gibson@cheltenham.gov.uk

Member Services: Mrs Rosalind Reeves, Democratic Services Manager, Municipal Offices, The Promenade, Cheltenham GL50 9SA ☎ 01242 774937 ⌂ rosalind.reeves@cheltenham.gov.uk

Parking: Mr Mike Redman, Director - Environment, Municipal Offices, The Promenade, Cheltenham GL50 9SA ☎ 01242 264160 ⌂ mike.redman@cheltenham.gov.uk

Partnerships: Mr Richard Gibson, Strategy & Engagement Manager, Municipal Offices, The Promenade, Cheltenham GL50 9SA ☎ 01242 235354 ⌂ richard.gibson@cheltenham.gov.uk

Personnel / HR: Ms Deborah Bainbridge, GO Shared Services Head of HR, Municipal Offices, The Promenade, Cheltenham GL50 9SA ☎ 01242 264186 ⌂ deborah.bainbridge@cheltenham.gov.uk

Planning: Ms Tracey Crews, Director - Planning, Municipal Offices, The Promenade, Cheltenham GL50 9SA ☎ 01242 774405 ⌂ tracey.crews@cheltenham.gov.uk

Procurement: Mr David Baker, Business Partner - Procurement, Municipal Offices, The Promenade, Cheltenham GL50 9SA ☎ 01242 775055 ⌂ david.baker@cheltenham.gov.uk

Recycling & Waste Minimisation: Ms Beth Boughton, Waste & Recycling Manager, Central Depot, Swindon Road, Cheltenham GL51 9JZ ☎ 01242 774644 ⌂ beth.boughton@ubico.co.uk

Regeneration: Mr Mike Redman, Director - Environment, Municipal Offices, The Promenade, Cheltenham GL50 9SA ☎ 01242 264160 ⌂ mike.redman@cheltenham.gov.uk

Staff Training: Mrs Jan Bridges, Learning & Organisational Development Manager, Municipal Offices, Promenade, Cheltenham GL50 9SA ☎ 01242 775189 ⌂ jan.bridges@cheltenham.gov.uk

Street Scene: Mr Wilf Tomaney, Townscape Manager, Municipal Offices, The Promenade, Cheltenham GL50 9SA ☎ 01242 264145 🖑 wilf.tomaney@cheltenham.gov.uk

Sustainable Communities: Mrs Pat Pratley, Head of Paid Service, Municipal Offices, Promenade, Cheltenham GL50 9SA ☎ 01242 264100 🖑 pat.pratley@cheltenham.gov.uk

Sustainable Development: Ms Gill Morris, Climate Change & Sustainability Officer, Municipal Offices, The Promenade, Cheltenham GL50 9SA ☎ 01242 264229 🖑 gill.morris@cheltenham.gov.uk

Tourism: Ms Julie Finch, CEO - Cheltenham Trust, Art Gallery & Museum, Clarence Street, Cheltenham GL50 3JT ☎ 01242 775093 🖑 julie.finch@cheltenhamtrust.org.uk

Town Centre: Mr Kevan Blackadder, Chelenham Business Partnership Manager, Cheltenham Business Partnership, 2 Trafalgar Square, Cheltenham GL50 1UH ☎ 01242 252626 🖑 manager@cheltenhambp.org.uk

Waste Collection and Disposal: Mr Rob Bell, Managing Director of UBICO, Central Depot, Swindon Road, Cheltenham GL51 9JZ ☎ 01242 264181 🖑 rob.bell@ubico.co.uk

Waste Management: Mr Scott Williams, Strategic Client Officer, Cotswold District Council, Trinity Road, Cirencester GL7 1PX ☎ 01285 623123 🖑 scott.williams@cotswold.gov.uk

COUNCILLORS

Directly Elected Mayor: Ryder, Chris (CON - Warden Hill)
Christine.Ryer@cheltenham.gov.uk

Deputy Mayor: Sudbury, Klara (LD - College)
cllr.klara.sudbury@cheltenham.gov.uk

Leader of the Council: Jordan, Stephen (LD - All Saints)
cllr.steve.jordan@cheltenham.gov.uk

Deputy Leader of the Council: Coleman, Chris (LD - St. Mark's)
cllr.chris.coleman@cheltenham.gov.uk

Group LeaderHarman, Tim (CON - Park)
cllr.tim.harman@cheltenham.gov.uk

Group LeaderStennett, Malcolm (O - Prestbury)
cllr.malcolm.stennett@cheltenham.gov.uk

Babbage, Matt (CON - Battledown)
cllr.matt.babbage@cheltenham.gov.uk

Baker, Paul (LD - Charlton Park)
cllr.paul.baker&cheltenham.gov.uk

Barnes, Garth (LD - College)
cllr.garth.barnes@cheltenham.gov.uk

Bickerton, Ian (IND - Leckhampton)
cllr.ian.bickerton@cheltenham.gov.uk

Britter, Nigel (LD - Benhall & the Reddings)
cllr.nigel.britter@cheltenham.gov.uk

Clucas, Flo (LD - Swindon Village)
cllr.flo.clucas@cheltenham.gov.uk

Collins, Mike (LD - Benhall & the Reddings)
cllr.mike.collins@cheltenham.gov.uk

Fisher, Bernard (LD - Swindon Village)
cllr.bernard.fisher@cheltenham.gov.uk

Flynn, Wendy (LD - Hesters Way)
cllr.wendy.flynn@cheltenham.gov.uk

Harvey, Steve (LD - Charlton Park)
cllr.steve.harvey@cheltenham.gov.uk

Hay, Rowena (LD - Oakley)
cllr.rowena.hay@cheltenham.gov.uk

Hay, Colin (LD - Oakley)
cllr.colin.hay@cheltenham.gov.uk

Hobley, Karl (LD - St. Pauls)

Holliday, Sandra (LD - St. Mark's)
cllr.sandra.holliday@cheltenham.gov.uk

Jeffries, Peter (LD - Springbank)
cllr.peter.jeffries@cheltenham.gov.uk

Lillywhite, Adam (O - Pittville)
cllr.adamlillywhite@cheltenham.gov.uk

Mason, Chris (CON - Lansdown)
cllr.chris.mason@cheltenham.gov.uk

McCloskey, Helena (LD - Charlton Kings)
cllr.helena.mccloskey@cheltenham.gov.uk

McCloskey, Paul (LD - Charlton Kings)
cllr.paul.mccloskey@cheltenham.gov.uk

McKinlay, Andrew (LD - Up Hatherley)
cllr.andrew.mckinlay@cheltenham.gov.uk

Murch, Dan (LD - All Saints)
cllr.dan.murch@cheltenham.gov.uk

Nelson, Chris (CON - Leckhampton)
cllr.chris.nelson@cheltenham.gov.uk

Oliver, Tony (LD - Warden Hill)

Parsons, Dennis (LD - Pittville)
cllr.dennis.parsons@cheltenham.gov.uk

Payne, John (O - Prestbury)
cllr.john.payne@cheltenham.gov.uk

Savage, Louis (CON - Battledown)
cllr.louis.sagage@cheltenham.gov.uk

Seacome, Diggory (CON - Lansdown)
cllr.diggory.seacome@cheltenham.gov.uk

Thornton, Pat (LD - St. Peter's)
cllr.pat.thornton@cheltenham.gov.uk

Walklett, Jon (LD - St. Pauls)
cllr.jon.walklett@cheltenham.gov.uk

Wheeler, Simon (LD - Hesters Way)
cllr.simon.wheeler@cheltenham.gov.uk

Whyborn, Roger (LD - Up Hatherley)
cllr.roger.whyborn@cheltenham.gov.uk

Wilkinson, Max (LD - Park)
cllr.max.wilkinson@cheltenham.gov.uk

Williams, Suzanne (LD - Springbank)
cllr.suzanne.williams@cheltenham.gov.uk

Willingham, David (LD - St. Peter's)
cllr.david.willingham@cheltenham.gov.uk

POLITICAL COMPOSITION
LD: 29, CON: 7, O: 3, IND: 1

CHELTENHAM

COMMITTEE CHAIRS

Audit: Mr Colin Hay

Licensing: Mrs Wendy Flynn

Planning: Mr Garth Barnes

Cherwell   D

Cherwell District Council, Bodicote House, Bodicote, Banbury OX15 4AA
☎ 01295 227001 ⏚ info@cherwell-dc.gov.uk
🖳 www.cherwell-dc.gov.uk

FACTS AND FIGURES
Parliamentary Constituencies: Banbury
EU Constituencies: South East
Election Frequency: Elections are by thirds

PRINCIPAL OFFICERS

Chief Executive: Mrs Sue Smith, Chief Executive, Bodicote House, Bodicote, Banbury OX15 4AA ☎ 01295 221573
⏚ sue.smith@cherwellandsouthnorthants.gov.uk

Senior Management: Mr Calvin Bell, Director - Development, Council Offices, Springfields, Towcester NN12 6AE ☎ 0300 003 0103 ⏚ calvin.bell@cherwellandsouthnorthants.gov.uk

Senior Management: Mr Ian Davies, Director - Operational Delivery, Bodicote House, Bodicote, Banbury OX15 4AA
☎ 01327 322302; 0300 003 0101
⏚ ian.davies@cherwellandsouthnorthants.gov.uk

Senior Management: Mr Martin Henry, Director - Resources & S151 Officer, Bodicote House, Bodicote, Banbury OX15 4AA
☎ 0300 003 0102 ⏚ martin.henry@cherwellandsouthnorthants.gov.uk

Access Officer / Social Services (Disability): Ms Caroline French, Corporate Policy Officer, Bodicote House, Bodicote, Banbury OX15 4AA ☎ 01295 227928
⏚ caroline.french@cherwell-dc.gov.uk

Access Officer / Social Services (Disability): Mr Andy Kidd, Joint Building Control Officer, The Forum, Moat Lane, Towcester NN12 6AD ⏚ andy.kidd@southnorthants.gov.uk

Architect, Building / Property Services: Mr Chris Stratford, Head of Regeneration & Housing, Bodicote House, Bodicote, Banbury OX15 4AA ☎ 01295 251871; 0300 003 0111
⏚ chris.stratford@cherwellandsouthnorthants.gov.uk

Building Control: Mr Andy Preston, Head of Development Management, The Forum, Moat Lane, Towcester NN12 6AD
☎ 0300 003 0109 ⏚ andy.preston@cherwellandsouthnorthants.gov.uk

PR / Communications: Mrs Janet Ferris, Corporate Communications & Marketing Manager, Bodicote House, Bodicote, Banbury OX15 4AA ☎ 0300 003 0114
⏚ janet.ferris@cherwellandsouthnorthants.gov.uk

Community Planning: Ms Claire Taylor, Performance Manager, Bodicote House, Bodicote, Banbury OX15 4AA ☎ 0300 003 0113
⏚ claire.taylor@cherwellandsouthnorthants.gov.uk

Community Safety: Mr Mike Grant, Safer Communities Manager, Bodicote House, Bodicote, Banbury OX15 4AA ☎ 01295 227989
⏚ mike.grant@cherwell-dc.gov.uk

Computer Management: Ms Balvinder Heran, Head of Customer Access, Bodicote House, Bodicote, Banbury OX15 4AA ☎ 01295 227903 ⏚ balvinder.heran@cherwellandsouthnorthants.gov.uk

Computer Management: Ms Jo Pitman, Head of Transformation, The Forum, Moat Lane, Towcester NN12 6AD ☎ 0300 003 0108
⏚ jo.pitman@cherwellandsouthnorthants.gov.uk

Corporate Services: Mr Chris Rothwell, Head of Community Services, Bodicote House, Bodicote, Banbury OX15 4AA
☎ 01295 251774; 0300 003 0104
⏚ chris.rothwell@cherwellandsouthnorthants.gov.uk

Customer Service: Ms Natasha Barnes, Customer Service Manager, Bodicote House, Bodicote, Banbury OX15 4AA
☎ 01295 227965 ⏚ natasha.barnes@southnorthants.gov.uk

Economic Development: Mr Adrian Colwell, Head of Strategic Planning & the Economy, Bodicote House, Bodicote, Banbury OX15 4AA ☎ 0300 003 0110
⏚ adrian.colwell@cherwellandsouthnorthants.gov.uk

Economic Development: Mr Steven Newman, Economic Development Officer, Bodicote House, Bodicote, Banbury OX15 4AA ☎ 01295 221860 ⏚ steven.newman@cherwell-dc.gov.uk

Electoral Registration: Mr James Doble, Democratic & Elections Manager, Bodicote House, Bodicote, Banbury OX15 4AA
☎ 01295 221587 ⏚ james.doble@cherwellandsouthnorthants.gov.uk

Emergency Planning: Mr Jan Southgate, Emergency Co-ordinator, Bodicote House, Bodicote, Banbury OX15 4AA
☎ 01295 227906 ⏚ jan.southgate@cherwell-dc.gov.uk

Energy Management: Ms Eloise Attwood, Team Leader - Service Development & Commercial, Bodicote House, Bodicote, Banbury OX15 4AA ☎ 01327 332095
⏚ eloise.attwood@cherwellandsouthnorthants.gov.uk

Environmental / Technical Services: Mr Ian Davies, Director - Operational Delivery, Bodicote House, Bodicote, Banbury OX15 4AA
☎ 01327 322302; 0300 003 0101
⏚ ian.davies@cherwellandsouthnorthants.gov.uk

Environmental / Technical Services: Mr Ed Potter, Head of Environmental Services, Thorpe Lane Depot, Banbury OX16 4UT
☎ 01295 227023; 0300 003 0105
⏚ ed.potter@cherwellandsouthnorthants.gov.uk

Estates, Property & Valuation: Mr Duncan Wigley, Estates Surveyor, Council Offices, Springfields, Towcester NN12 6AE
☎ 01327 322345 ⏚ duncan.wigley@southnorthants.gov.uk

Facilities: Ms Linda Barlow, Corporate Facilities Manager, Bodicote House, Bodicote, Banbury OX15 4AA ☎ 01295 221800
⏚ linda.barlow@cherwell-dc.gov.uk

Finance: Mr Paul Sutton, Head of Finance & Procurement, Bodicote House, Bodicote, Banbury OX15 4AA ☎ 0300 003 0116 📧 paul.sutton@cherwellandsouthnorthants.gov.uk

Health and Safety: Mr David Bennett, Corporate Health & Safety Adviser, Bodicote House, Bodicote, Banbury OX15 4AA ☎ 01295 221738 📧 dave.bennett@cherwellandsouthnorthants.gov.uk

Health and Safety: Ms Jackie Fitzsimons, Public Protection & Environmental Health Manager, The Forum, Moat Lane, Towcester NN12 6AD ☎ 01327 322283 📧 jackie.fitzsimmons@southnorthants.gov.uk

Home Energy Conservation: Mr Tim Mills, Private Sector Housing Manager, Bodicote House, Bodicote, Banbury OX15 4AA ☎ 01295 221655 📧 tim.mills@cherwell-dc.gov.uk

Housing: Mr Chris Stratford, Head of Regeneration & Housing, Bodicote House, Bodicote, Banbury OX15 4AA ☎ 01295 251871; 0300 003 0111 📧 chris.stratford@cherwellandsouthnorthants.gov.uk

Legal: Mr Nigel Bell, Solicitor, Bodicote House, Bodicote, Banbury OX15 4AA ☎ 01295 221687 📧 nigel.bell@cherwell-dc.gov.uk

Legal: Mr Kevin Lane, Head of Law & Governance, Council Offices, Springfields, Towcester NN12 6AE ☎ 0300 003 0107 📧 kevin.lane@cherwellandsouthnorthants.gov.uk

Leisure and Cultural Services: Mr Ian Davies, Director - Operational Delivery, Bodicote House, Bodicote, Banbury OX15 4AA ☎ 01327 322302; 0300 003 0101 📧 ian.davies@cherwellandsouthnorthants.gov.uk

Leisure and Cultural Services: Mr Chris Rothwell, Head of Community Services, Bodicote House, Bodicote, Banbury OX15 4AA ☎ 01295 251774; 0300 003 0104 📧 chris.rothwell@cherwellandsouthnorthants.gov.uk

Licensing: Ms Claire Bold, Licensing Team Leader, Bodicote House, Bodicote, Banbury OX15 4AA ☎ 01295 223741 📧 claire.bold@cherwell-dc.gov.uk

Member Services: Ms Natasha Clark, Democratic & Elections Team Leader, Bodicote House, Bodicote, Banbury OX15 4AA ☎ 01295 221589 📧 natasha.clark@cherwellandsouthnorthants.gov.uk

Parking: Ms Jo Powell, Vehicle, Parks & Town Team Leader, Bodicote House, Bodicote, Banbury OX15 4AA ☎ 01295 221766 📧 jo.powell@cherwell-dc.gov.uk

Personnel / HR: Ms Paula Goodwin, Shared HR & OD Manager, Bodicote House, Bodicote, Banbury OX15 4AA ☎ 01295 221735 📧 paula.goodwin@cherwellandsouthnorthants.gov.uk

Planning: Mr Adrian Colwell, Head of Strategic Planning & the Economy, Bodicote House, Bodicote, Banbury OX15 4AA ☎ 0300 003 0110 📧 adrian.colwell@cherwellandsouthnorthants.gov.uk

Planning: Mr John Westerman, Development Services Manager, 58 Appleby Close, Banbury OX16 0UX ☎ 01295 221821 📧 john.westerman@cherwell-dc.gov.uk

Procurement: Ms Viv Hitchens, Corporate Procurement Manager, Bodicote House, Bodicote, Banbury OX15 4AA 📧 viv.hitchens@cherwell-dc.gov.uk

Recycling & Waste Minimisation: Ms Eloise Attwood, Team Leader - Service Development & Commercial, Bodicote House, Bodicote, Banbury OX15 4AA ☎ 01327 332095 📧 eloise.attwood@cherwellandsouthnorthants.gov.uk

Street Scene: Mr Paul Almond, Street & Landscape Services Manager, Bodicote House, Bodicote, Banbury OX15 4AA ☎ 01295 221705 📧 paul.almond@cherwellandsouthnorthants.gov.uk

Sustainable Communities: Mr Chris Rothwell, Head of Community Services, Bodicote House, Bodicote, Banbury OX15 4AA ☎ 01295 251774; 0300 003 0104 📧 chris.rothwell@cherwellandsouthnorthants.gov.uk

Tourism: Ms Nicola Riley, Arts & Tourism Manager, Bodicote House, Bodicote, Banbury OX15 4AA ☎ 01295 221724 📧 nicola.riley@cherwell-dc.gov.uk

Waste Collection and Disposal: Mr Ed Potter, Head of Environmental Services, Thorpe Lane Depot, Banbury OX16 4UT ☎ 01295 227023; 0300 003 0105 📧 ed.potter@cherwellandsouthnorthants.gov.uk

COUNCILLORS

ChairHeath, Chris (CON - Adderbury, Bloxham & Bodicote) cllr.chris.heath@cherwell-dc.gov.uk

Vice-ChairBillington, Maurice (CON - Kidlington East) cllr.maurice.billington@cherwell-dc.gov.uk

Leader of the Council: Wood, Barry (CON - Fringford & Heyfords) cllr.barry.wood@cherwell-dc.gov.uk

Deputy Leader of the Council: Reynolds, George (CON - Cropredy, Sibfords & Wroxton) cllr.george.reynolds@cherwell-dc.gov.uk

Group LeaderWoodcock, Sean (LAB - Banbury Ruscote) sean.woodcock@cherwell-dc.gov.uk

Anderson, David (CON - Bicester South & Ambrosden) david.anderson@cherwell-dc.gov.uk

Atack, Ken (CON - Cropredy, Sibfords & Wroxton) cllr.ken.atack@cherwell-dc.gov.uk

Banfield, Hannah (LAB - Banbury Cross & Neithrop) hannah.banfield@cherwell-dc.gov.uk

Beere, Andrew (LAB - Banbury, Grimsbury & Hightown) cllr.andrew.beere@cherwell-dc.gov.uk

Bell, Claire (LAB - Banbury, Grimsbury & Hightown) claire.bell@cherwell-dc.gov.uk

Bishop, Mike (CON - Adderbury, Bloxham & Bodicote) mike.bishop@cherwell-dc.gov.uk

Brown, Hugo (CON - Deddington) hugo.brown@cherwell-dc.gov.uk

Cherry, Mark (LAB - Banbury Ruscote) councillormark.cherry@cherwell-dc.gov.uk

Corkin, Ian (CON - Fringford & Heyfords) ian.corkin@cherwell-dc.gov.uk

CHERWELL

Cotter, Nick (IND - Bicester South & Ambrosden)
nick.cotter@cherwell-dc.gov.uk

Dhesi, Surinder (LAB - Banbury Cross & Neithrop)
surinder.dhesi@cherwell-dc.gov.uk

Donaldson, John (CON - Banbury Hardwick)
cllr.john.donaldson@cherwell-dc.gov.uk

Gaul, Sean (CON - Bicester East)
sean.gaul@cherwell-dc.gov.uk

Griffiths, Carmen (CON - Kidlington East)
carmen.griffiths@cherwell-dc.gov.uk

Hallchurch, Timothy (CON - Launton & Otmoor)
cllr.timothy.hallchurch@cherwell-dc.gov.uk

Holland, Simon (CON - Launton & Otmoor)
cllr.simon.holland@cherwell-dc.gov.uk

Hughes, David (CON - Launton & Otmoor)
cllr.david.hughes@cherwell-dc.gov.uk

Hussain, Shaida (LAB - Banbury, Grimsbury & Hightown)
shaida.hussain@cherwell-dc.gov.uk

Ilott, Tony (CON - Banbury Hardwick)
cllr.tony.ilott@cherwell-dc.gov.uk

Kerford-Byrnes, Mike (CON - Deddington)
cllr.mike.kerfordbyrnes@cherwell-dc.gov.uk

Lis, Jolanta (CON - Bicester West)
jolantamaria.lis@cherwell-dc.gov.uk

MacKenzie-Wintle, Alan (CON - Kidlington West)
alan.mackenzie-wintle@cherwell-dc.gov.uk

Macnamara, James (CON - Fringford & Heyfords)
cllr.james.macnamara@cherwell-dc.gov.uk

Mawer, Nicholas (CON - Bicester North & Caversfield)
cllr.nicholas.mawer@cherwell-dc.gov.uk

Milne Home, Alastair (CON - Banbury Cross & Neithrop)
cllr.alastair.milnehome@cherwell-dc.gov.uk

Mould, Richard (CON - Bicester East)
richard.mould@cherwell-dc.gov.uk

Pickford, Debbie (CON - Bicester West)
cllr.debbie.pickford@cherwell-dc.gov.uk

Pratt, Lynn (CON - Bicester North & Caversfield)
cllr.lynn.pratt@cherwell-dc.gov.uk

Prestidge, Neil (CON - Kidlington East)
cllr.neil.prestidge@cherwell-dc.gov.uk

Randall, Nigel (CON - Adderbury, Bloxham & Bodicote)
nigel.randall@cherwell-dc.gov.uk

Rhodes, Sandra (CON - Kidlington West)
sandra.rhodes@cherwell-dc.gov.uk

Richards, Barry (LAB - Banbury Ruscote)
barry.richards@cherwell-dc.gov.uk

Sames, Dan (CON - Bicester South & Ambrosden)
cllr.daniel.sames@cherwell-dc.gov.uk

Sibley, Les (IND - Bicester West)
cllr.les.sibley@cherwell-dc.gov.uk

Simpson, Nigel (CON - Kidlington West)
nigel.simpson@cherwell-dc.gov.uk

Slaymaker, Jason (CON - Bicester North & Caversfield)
jason.slaymaker@cherwell-dc.gov.uk

Turner, Nicholas (CON - Banbury Hardwick)
cllr.nicholas.turner@cherwell-dc.gov.uk

Wallis, Tom (CON - Bicester East)
tom.wallis@cherwell-dc.gov.uk

Webb, Douglas (CON - Cropredy, Sibfords & Wroxton)
cllr.douglas.webb@cherwell-dc.gov.uk

Williams, Bryn (CON - Deddington)
bryn.williams@cherwell-dc.gov.uk

POLITICAL COMPOSITION
CON: 35, LAB: 8, IND: 2

COMMITTEE CHAIRS

Accounts, Audit & Risk: Mr Mike Kerford-Byrnes

Licensing: Mr Douglas Webb

Planning: Mr David Hughes

Cheshire East U

Cheshire East Council, Westfields, Middlewich Road,
Sandbach CW11 1HZ
☎ 0300 123 5500 ⏁ info@cheshireeast.gov.uk
🖳 www.cheshireeast.gov.uk

FACTS AND FIGURES
Parliamentary Constituencies: Congleton, Crewe and Nantwich,
Eddisbury, Macclesfield, Tatton
EU Constituencies: North West
Election Frequency: Elections are of whole council

PRINCIPAL OFFICERS

Chief Executive: Mr Mike Suarez, Chief Executive, Westfields,
Middlewich Road, Sandbach CW11 1HZ ☎ 01270 686018
⏁ mike.suarez@cheshireeast.gov.uk

Deputy Chief Executive: Ms Kath O'Dwyer, Deputy Chief
Executive & Executive Director - People, Westfields, Middlewich
Road, Sandbach CW11 1HZ ☎ 01270 686018 ⏁ kath.odwyer@
cheshireeast.gov.uk

Senior Management: Mr Peter Bates, Chief Operating Officer,
Westfields, Middlewich Road, Sandbach CW11 1HZ ☎ 01270 686013
⏁ peter.bates@cheshireeast.gov.uk

Senior Management: Ms Heather Grimbaldeston, Director -
Public Health, Westfields, Middlewich Road, Sandbach CW11 1HZ
☎ 01270 686242 ⏁ heather.grimbaldeston@cheshireeast.gov.uk

Senior Management: Mr Bill Norman, Director - Legal Services,
Westfields, Middlewich Road, Sandbach CW11 1HZ
⏁ bill.norman@cheshireeast.gov.uk

Senior Management: Ms Kath O'Dwyer, Deputy Chief Executive &
Executive Director - People, Westfields, Middlewich Road, Sandbach
CW11 1HZ ☎ 01270 686018 ⏁ kath.odwyer@cheshireeast.gov.uk

Senior Management: Mr Brian Reed, Head of Governance &
Democratic Services, Westfields, Middlewich Road, Sandbach
CW11 1HZ ☎ 01270 686670 ⏁ brian.reed@cheshireeast.gov.uk

Senior Management: Mr Andrew Round, Interim Executive Director - Place, Westfields, Middlewich Road, Sandbach CW11 1HZ ⏚ andrew.round@cheshireeast.gov.uk

Architect, Building / Property Services: Ms Denise Griffiths, Facilities Manager, 2nd Floor, Delamere House, Delamere Street, Crewe CW1 2JZ ☎ 01270 686125 ⏚ denise.griffiths@cheshireeast.gov.uk

Catering Services: Ms Joanne Cooper, Interim Catering Services Manager, Floor 1, Municipal Buildings, Earle Street, Crewe CW1 2BJ ☎ 01606 271565 ⏚ joanne.cooper@cheshireeast.gov.uk

Children / Youth Services: Mr Nigel Moorhouse, Director - Children's Social Care, Dalton House, Dalton Way, Middlewich CW10 0HU ☎ 01606 271775 ⏚ nigel.moorhouse@cheshireeast.gov.uk

Civil Registration: Ms Lindsey Parton, Registration Service & Business Manager, Westfields, Middlewich Road, Sandbach CW11 1HZ ☎ 01270 686477 ⏚ lindsey.parton@cheshireeast.gov.uk

Community Safety: Ms Stephanie Cordon, Head of Communities, Westfields, Middlewich Road, Sandbach CW11 1HZ ☎ 01270 686401 ⏚ steph.cordon@cheshireeast.gov.uk

Community Safety: Ms Kirstie Hercules, Principal Manager - Partnerships & Communities, Westfields, Middlewich Road, Sandbach CW11 1HZ ☎ 01270 686632 ⏚ kirstie.hercules@cheshireeast.gov.uk

Computer Management: Mr Gareth Pawlett, Corporate Manager ICT, 1st Floor, Delamere House, Delamere Street, Crewe CW1 2JZ ☎ 01270 686166

Consumer Protection and Trading Standards: Ms Tracey Bettaney, Principal Manager - Regulatory Services & Health, Municipal Buildings, Earle Street, Crewe CW1 2BJ ☎ 01270 686596 ⏚ tracey.bettaney@cheshireeast.gov.uk

Customer Service: Mr Paul Bayley, Principal Manager - Local Community Services, Macclesfield Town Hall, Market Place, Macclesfield SK10 1EA ☎ 01606 271567 ⏚ paul.bayley@cheshireeast.gov.uk

Economic Development: Mr Julian Cobley, Head of Investment, Westfields, Middlewich Road, Sandbach CW11 1HZ ☎ 01270 685906 ⏚ julian.cobley@cheshireeast.gov.uk

Education: Mr Fintan Bradley, Corporate Manager - Education Strategy, 2nd Floor, Westfields, Middlewich Road, Sandbach CW11 1HZ ☎ 01270 271504 ⏚ fintan.bradley@cheshireeast.gov.uk

Electoral Registration: Ms Diane Todd, Electoral Services Manager, Macclesfield Town Hall, Market Place, Macclesfield SK10 1EA ☎ 01270 686478 ⏚ diane.todd@cheshireeast.gov.uk

Emergency Planning: Mr Norman Powell, Lead Emergency Planning Officer, Ground Floor, Nicholas Street, Chester CM1 2NP ☎ 01244 973868

Energy Management: Mr Colin Farrelly, Corporate Energy Manager, 2nd Floor, Delamere House, Delamere Street, Crewe CW1 2JZ ☎ 01270 686161 ⏚ colin.farrelly@cheshireeast.gov.uk

Environmental Health: Ms Tracey Bettaney, Principal Manager - Regulatory Services & Health, Municipal Buildings, Earle Street, Crewe CW1 2BJ ☎ 01270 686596 ⏚ tracey.bettaney@cheshireeast.gov.uk

Estates, Property & Valuation: Ms Heather McManus, Interim Head of Assets, Delamere House, Delamere Street, Crewe CW1 2JZ ☎ 01270 686130 ⏚ heather.mcmanus@cheshireeast.gov.uk

Events Manager: Mr Andrew Latham, Events Manager, Oakley Building, Victoria Community Centre, West Street, Crewe CW1 2PZ ☎ 01270 686785 ⏚ andrew.latham@cheshireeast.gov.uk

Facilities: Ms Denise Griffiths, Facilities Manager, 2nd Floor, Delamere House, Delamere Street, Crewe CW1 2JZ ☎ 01270 686125 ⏚ denise.griffiths@cheshireeast.gov.uk

Finance: Mr Peter Bates, Chief Operating Officer, Westfields, Middlewich Road, Sandbach CW11 1HZ ☎ 01270 686013 ⏚ peter.bates@cheshireeast.gov.uk

Finance: Ms Judith Tench, Head of Corporate Resources & Stewardship, Westfields, Middlewich Road, Sandbach CW11 1HZ ☎ 01270 685859 ⏚ judith.tench@cheshireeast.gov.uk

Health and Safety: Ms Bronwen MacArthur-Williams, Corporate Health & Safety Manager, 5th Floor, Delamere House, Delamere Street, Crewe CW1 2JZ ☎ 01270 686331 ⏚ bronwen.macarthur-williams@cheshireeast.gov.uk

Highways: Mr Paul Traynor, Strategic Commissioning Manager - Highways, Floor 6, Delamere House, Delamere Street, Crewe CW1 2JZ ☎ 01260 371055 ⏚ paul.traynor@cheshireeast.gov.uk

Housing: Ms Karen Carsberg, Strategic Housing Manager, Westfields, Middlewich Road, Sandbach CW11 1HZ ☎ 01270 686654 ⏚ karen.carsberg@cheshireeast.gov.uk

Legal: Mr Bill Norman, Director - Legal Services, Westfields, Middlewich Road, Sandbach CW11 1HZ ⏚ bill.norman@cheshireeast.gov.uk

Leisure and Cultural Services: Mr Mark Wheelton, Corporate Commissioning Manager - Leisure, Westfields, Middlewich Road, Sandbach CW11 1HZ ☎ 01270 686679 ⏚ mark.wheelton@cheshireeast.gov.uk

Licensing: Ms Tracey Bettaney, Principal Manager - Regulatory Services & Health, Municipal Buildings, Earle Street, Crewe CW1 2BJ ☎ 01270 686596 ⏚ tracey.bettaney@cheshireeast.gov.uk

Lifelong Learning: Mr Peter Cavanagh, 14+ Skills Manager, Floor 7, Delamere House, Delamere Street, Crewe CW1 2JZ ☎ 01270 685992 ⏚ peter.cavanagh@cheshireeast.gov.uk

Parking: Ms Carolyn Noonan, Enforcement Notice Processing Supervisor, Macclesfield Town Hall, Market Place, Macclesfield SK10 1EA ☎ 01625 383760 ⏚ carolyn.noonan@cheshireeast.gov.uk

CHESHIRE EAST

Personnel / HR: Mr Phil Badley, Interim Head of Human Resources & Organisational Development, Westfields, Middlewich Road, Sandbach CW11 1HZ ☎ 01270 686027 ✆ phil.badley@cheshireeast.gov.uk

Planning: Mr Adrian Fisher, Head of Planning Strategy, Westfields, Middlewich Road, Sandbach CW11 1HZ ☎ 01270 686641 ✆ adrian.fisher@cheshireeast.gov.uk

Procurement: Ms Lianne Halliday, Procurement Manager, Westfields, Middlewich Road, Sandbach CW11 1HZ ☎ 01270 685766 ✆ lianne.halliday@cheshireeast.gov.uk

Public Libraries: Mr Paul Bayley, Principal Manager - Local Community Services, Macclesfield Town Hall, Market Place, Macclesfield SK10 1EA ☎ 01606 271567 ✆ paul.bayley@cheshireeast.gov.uk

Recycling & Waste Minimisation: Mr Ralph Kemp, Manager - Commissioning Waste & Environment, Pyms Lane Depot, Pyms Lane, Crewe CW1 3PJ ☎ 01270 686683 ✆ ralph.kemp@cheshireeast.gov.uk

Regeneration: Mr Jez Goodman, Regeneration Programme Manager, Westfields, Middlewich Road, Sandbach CW11 1HZ ☎ 01270 685906 ✆ jez.goodman@cheshireeast.gov.uk

Social Services: Mr Nigel Moorhouse, Director - Children's Social Care, Dalton House, Dalton Way, Middlewich CW10 0HU ☎ 01606 271775 ✆ nigel.moorhouse@cheshireeast.gov.uk

Social Services (Adult): Ms Sue Redmond, Interim Director - Adult Social Care, Westfields, Middlewich Road, Sandbach CW11 1HZ ✆ sue.redmond@cheshireeast.gov.uk

Public Health: Ms Heather Grimbaldeston, Director - Public Health, Westfields, Middlewich Road, Sandbach CW11 1HZ ☎ 01270 686242 ✆ heather.grimbaldeston@cheshireeast.gov.uk

Staff Training: Ms Lisa Burrows, Senior Manager - Strategic Workforce Development, Westfields, Middlewich Road, Sandbach CW11 1HZ ☎ 01270 686093 ✆ lisa.burrow@cheshireeast.gov.uk

Tourism: Mr Brendan Flanagan, Visitor Economy, Culture & Tatton Park Manager, Tatton Park, Tatton, Knutsford WA16 6QN ☎ 01625 374415 ✆ brendan.flanagan@cheshireeast.gov.uk

COUNCILLORS

Mayor: Hunter, Olivia (CON - High Legh)
olivia.hunter@cheshireeast.gov.uk

Deputy Mayor: Moran, Arthur (IND - Nantwich North & West)
arthur.moran@cheshireeast.gov.uk

Leader of the Council: Bailey, Rachel (CON - Audlem)
rachel.bailey@cheshireeast.gov.uk

Deputy Leader of the Council: Brown, David (CON - Congleton East)
david.brown@cheshireeast.gov.uk

Group LeaderBurkhill, Barry (R - Handforth)
barry.burkhill@cheshireeast.gov.uk

Group LeaderFletcher, Rod (LD - Alsager)
rod.fletcher@cheshireeast.gov.uk

Group LeaderNewton, David (LAB - Crewe East)
david.newton@cheshireeast.gov.uk

Andrew, Chris (CON - Macclesfield South)
chris.andrew@cheshireeast.gov.uk

Arnold, Ainsley (CON - Macclesfield Tytherington)
ainsley.arnold@cheshireeast.gov.uk

Baggott, Geoff (CON - Congleton East)
geoff.baggott@cheshireeast.gov.uk

Bailey, Damian (LAB - Crewe St Barnabas)
damian.bailey@cheshireeast.gov.uk

Bailey, Rhoda (CON - Odd Rode)
rhoda.bailey@cheshireeast.gov.uk

Barton, Gary (CON - Wilmslow West & Chorley)
gary.barton@cheshireeast.gov.uk

Bates, Paul (CON - Congleton West)
paul.bates@cheshireeast.gov.uk

Baxendale, Gordon (CON - Congleton West)
gordon.baxendale@cheshireeast.gov.uk

Beanland, Michael (CON - Poynton West & Adlington)
michael.beanland@cheshireeast.gov.uk

Bebbington, Derek (CON - Leighton)
derek.bebbington@cheshireeast.gov.uk

Brookfield, Suzanne (LAB - Crewe East)
suzanne.brookfield@cheshireeast.gov.uk

Brooks, Ellie (CON - Wilmslow West & Chorley)
ellie.brooks@cheshireeast.gov.uk

Browne, Craig (O - Alderley Edge)
craig.browne@cheshireeast.gov.uk

Butterill, Penny (IND - Nantwich North & West)
penny.butterill@cheshireeast.gov.uk

Carter, Steve (LAB - Macclesfield Hurdsfield)
stephen.carter@cheshireeast.gov.uk

Chapman, Clair (LAB - Crewe East)
clair.chapman@cheshireeast.gov.uk

Clowes, Janet (CON - Wybunbury)
janet.clowes@cheshireeast.gov.uk

Corcoran, Sam (LAB - Sandbach Heath & East)
sam.corcoran@cheshireeast.gov.uk

Davenport, Harold (CON - Disley)
harold.davenport@cheshireeast.gov.uk

Davies, Stan (CON - Wrenbury)
stanley.davies@cheshireeast.gov.uk

Deakin, Martin (CON - Alsager)
martin.deakin@cheshireeast.gov.uk

Dean, Tony (CON - Knutsford)
tony.dean@cheshireeast.gov.uk

Dooley, Beverley (CON - Macclesfield Central)
beverley.dooley@cheshireeast.gov.uk

Durham, Liz (CON - Broken Cross & Upton)
liz.durham@cheshireeast.gov.uk

Edgar, Steven (CON - Shavington)
steven.edgar@cheshireeast.gov.uk

Faseyi, Irene (LAB - Crewe Central)
irene.faseyi@cheshireeast.gov.uk

Findlow, Paul (CON - Prestbury)
paul.findlow@cheshireeast.gov.uk

Flude, Dorothy (LAB - Crewe South)
dorothy.flude@cheshireeast.gov.uk

Fox, Toni (R - Wilmslow Dean Row)
toni.fox@cheshireeast.gov.uk

Gaddum, Hilda (CON - Sutton)
hilda.gaddum@cheshireeast.gov.uk

Gardiner, Stewart (CON - Knutsford)
stewart.gardiner@cheshireeast.gov.uk

Gardner, Sam (CON - Macclesfield Tytherington)
sam.gardner@cheshireeast.gov.uk

Gilbert, Les (CON - Dane Valley)
les.gilbert@cheshireeast.gov.uk

Grant, Mo (LAB - Crewe North)
mo.grant@cheshireeast.gov.uk

Groves, Peter (CON - Nantwich South & Stapeley)
peter.groves@cheshireeast.gov.uk

Hammond, John (CON - Haslington)
john.hammond@cheshireeast.gov.uk

Hardy, Martin (CON - Broken Cross & Upton)
martin.hardy@cheshireeast.gov.uk

Harewood, Alift (LAB - Macclesfield West & Ivy)
alift.harewood@cheshireeast.gov.uk

Hayes, George (CON - Congleton West)
george.hayes@cheshireeast.gov.uk

Hogben, Stephen (LAB - Crewe South)
steven.hogben@cheshireeast.gov.uk

Hough, Derek (LD - Alsager)
derek.hough@cheshireeast.gov.uk

Jackson, Janet (LAB - Macclesfield Central)
janet.jackson@cheshireeast.gov.uk

Jeuda, Laura (LAB - Macclesfield South)
laura.jeuda@cheshireeast.gov.uk

Jones, Michael (CON - Bunbury)
michael.e.jones@cheshireeast.gov.uk

Kolker, Andrew (CON - Dane Valley)
andrew.kolker@cheshireeast.gov.uk

Macrae, Jamie (CON - Mobberley)
jamie.macrae@cheshireeast.gov.uk

Mahon, Dennis (R - Handforth)
dennis.mahon@cheshireeast.gov.uk

Mannion, Nick (LAB - Macclesfield West & Ivy)
nick.mannion@cheshireeast.gov.uk

Marren, David (CON - Haslington)
david.marren@cheshireeast.gov.uk

Martin, Andrew (CON - Nantwich South & Stapeley)
andrew.martin@cheshireeast.gov.uk

McGrory, Simon (IND - Middlewich)
simon.mcgrory@cheshireeast.gov.uk

Menlove, Rod (CON - Wilmslow East)
rod.menlove@cheshireeast.gov.uk

Merry, Gill (CON - Sandbach Elworth)
gillian.merry@cheshireeast.gov.uk

Moran, Barry (CON - Sandbach Town)
barry.moran@cheshireeast.gov.uk

Murray, Howard (CON - Poynton East & Pott Shrigley)

Parsons, Michael (IND - Middlewich)
michael.parsons@cheshireeast.gov.uk

Pochin, Sarah (CON - Willaston & Rope)
sarah.pochin@cheshireeast.gov.uk

Rhodes, Jill (LAB - Crewe West)
jill.rhodes@cheshireeast.gov.uk

Roberts, Brian (LAB - Crewe West)
brian.roberts@cheshireeast.gov.uk

Saunders, Jos (CON - Poynton East & Pott Shrigley)
jos.saunders@cheshireeast.gov.uk

Simon, Margaret (CON - Wistaston)
margaret.simon@cheshireeast.gov.uk

Smetham, Lesley (CON - Gawsworth)
lesley.smetham@cheshireeast.gov.uk

Stewart, Mike (CON - Poynton West & Adlington)
mike.stewart@cheshireeast.gov.uk

Stockton, Don (CON - Wilmslow Lacey Green)
don.stockton@cheshireeast.gov.uk

Stott, Amanda (O - Bollington)
amanda.stott@cheshireeast.gov.uk

Wait, Gail (CON - Sandbach Ettiley Heath & Wheelock)
gail.wait@cheshireeast.gov.uk

Walmsley, Bernice (IND - Middlewich)
bernice.walmsley@cheshireeast.gov.uk

Walton, George (CON - Chelford)
george.walton@cheshireeast.gov.uk

Wardlaw, Liz (CON - Odd Rode)
liz.wardlaw@cheshireeast.gov.uk

Warren, Mick (IND - Macclesfield East)
mick.warren@cheshireeast.gov.uk

Weatherill, Jaqueline (CON - Wistaston)
jacquie.weatherill@cheshireeast.gov.uk

Wells-Bradshaw, Hayley (CON - Knutsford)
hayley.wells-bradshaw@cheshireeast.gov.uk

Weston, Jonathan (CON - Bollington)
jonathan.weston@cheshireeast.gov.uk

Williams, Glen (CON - Congleton East)
glen.williams@cheshireeast.gov.uk

Wray, John (CON - Brereton Rural) john.wray@cheshireeast.gov.uk

POLITICAL COMPOSITION
CON: 53, LAB: 16, IND: 6, R: 3, LD: 2, O: 2

COMMITTEE CHAIRS

Audit & Governance: Ms Lesley Smetham

Children & Families: Ms Rhoda Bailey

Environment: Mr John Wray

Health & Adult Social Care: Ms Jos Saunders

Licensing: Mr Stan Davies

Planning: Mr Harold Davenport

CHESHIRE WEST & CHESTER

Cheshire West & Chester U

Cheshire West & Chester, HQ, 58 Nicholas Street, Chester CH1 2NP
☎ 0300 123 8123 ⎙ enquiries@cheshirewestandchester.gov.uk
▣ www.cheshirewestandchester.gov.uk

FACTS AND FIGURES
Parliamentary Constituencies: Chester, City of, Eddisbury, Ellesmere Port and Neston, Tatton, Weaver Vale

PRINCIPAL OFFICERS

Chief Executive: Mr Gerald Meehan, Chief Executive, HQ, 58 Nicholas Street, Chester CH1 2NP ☎ 01244 977454
⎙ gerald.meehan@cheshirewestandchester.gov.uk

Senior Management: Mr Charlie Seward, Deputy Chief Executive - Places, HQ, 58 Nicholas Street, Chester CH1 2NP
☎ 01244 972857 ⎙ charlie.seward@cheshirewestandchester.gov.uk

Access Officer / Social Services (Disability): Mr Graham Garnett, Senior Access Officer, HQ, 58 Nicholas Street, Chester CH1 2NP ☎ 01244 972609
⎙ graham.garnett@cheshirewestandchester.gov.uk

Architect, Building / Property Services: Mr Richard Green, Principal Property & Information Manager, HQ, 58 Nicholas Street, Chester CH1 2NP ☎ 01244 977465
⎙ richard.green@cheshirewestandchester.gov.uk

Best Value: Mr Lawrence Ainsworth, Director - Public Services Reform, HQ, 58 Nicholas Street, Chester CH1 2NP ☎ 01244 977147
⎙ lawrence.ainsworth@cheshirewestandchester.gov.uk

Building Control: Mr John Adcock, Building Control Consultancy Area Manager, HQ, 58 Nicholas Street, Chester CH1 2NP ☎ 01244 977797 ⎙ john.adcock@cheshirewestandchester.gov.uk

Children / Youth Services: Ms Helen Brackenbury, Interim Director - Integrated Early Support, HQ, 58 Nicholas Street, Chester CH1 2NP ⎙ helen.brackenbury@cheshirewestandchester.gov.uk

Children / Youth Services: Mr Mark Parkinson, Director - Education, HQ, 58 Nicholas Street, Chester CH1 2NP ☎ 01244 975923 ⎙ mark.parkinson@cheshirewestandchester.gov.uk

Children / Youth Services: Ms Emma Taylor, Director - Children's Social Care, HQ, 58 Nicholas Street, Chester CH1 2NP ☎ 01244 973512 ⎙ emma.taylor@cheshirewestandchester.gov.uk

PR / Communications: Mr Carl Holloway, Senior Communication & Marketing Manager, HQ, 58 Nicholas Street, Chester CH1 2NP ☎ 01244 972216 ⎙ carl.holloway@cheshirewestandchester.gov.uk

Community Planning: Ms Maria Byrne, Director - Place Operations, HQ, 58 Nicholas Street, Chester CH1 2NP
⎙ maria.byrne@cheshirewestandchester.gov.uk

Community Planning: Ms Alison Knight, Director - Places Strategy, HQ, 58 Nicholas Street, Chester CH1 2NP ☎ 01244 976785 ⎙ alison.knight@cheshirewestandchester.gov.uk

Community Safety: Ms Jane Makin, Senior Manager - Chester Locality & Community Safety Management, HQ, 58 Nicholas Street, Chester CH1 2NP ☎ 01244 973464

Computer Management: Ms Simone Thomas, Senior Manager - Business Technology Solutions, HQ, 58 Nicholas Street, Chester CH1 2NP ☎ 01244 972347
⎙ simone.thomas@cheshirewestandchester.gov.uk

Consumer Protection and Trading Standards: Ms Vanessa Griffiths, Regulatory Services Manager, HQ, 58 Nicholas Street, Chester CH1 2NP ☎ 01244 073987
⎙ vanessa.griffiths@cheshirewestandchester.gov.uk

Contracts: Mr Dave Thomas, Contract Development Manager, HQ, 58 Nicholas Street, Chester CH1 2NP ☎ 01244 977410
⎙ david.b.thomas@cheshire.gov.uk

Economic Development: Ms Alison Knight, Director - Places Strategy, HQ, 58 Nicholas Street, Chester CH1 2NP ☎ 01244 976785 ⎙ alison.knight@cheshirewestandchester.gov.uk

Education: Mr Mark Parkinson, Director - Education, HQ, 58 Nicholas Street, Chester CH1 2NP ☎ 01244 975923
⎙ mark.parkinson@cheshirewestandchester.gov.uk

Electoral Registration: Ms Penny Housley, Senior Manager - Civic Member & Scrutiny, HQ, 58 Nicholas Street, Chester CH1 2NP ☎ 01244 975972 ⎙ penny.housley@cheshirewestandchester.gov.uk

Emergency Planning: Mr Chris Samuel, Emergency Planning Team Manager, HQ, 58 Nicholas Street, Chester CH1 2NP ☎ 01244 976720 ⎙ chris.samuel@cheshirewestandchester.gov.uk

Energy Management: Ms Georgina Patel, Project Manager - Climate Change, HQ, 58 Nicholas Street, Chester CH1 2NP
☎ 01244 972427 ⎙ georgina.patel@cheshirewestandchester.gov.uk

Environmental / Technical Services: Ms Vanessa Griffiths, Regulatory Services Manager, HQ, 58 Nicholas Street, Chester CH1 2NP ☎ 01244 073987
⎙ vanessa.griffiths@cheshirewestandchester.gov.uk

Environmental / Technical Services: Mr John Outram, Technical Director, HQ, 58 Nicholas Street, Chester CH1 2NP
☎ 01244 977539 ⎙ john.outram@cheshirewestandchester.gov.uk

Estates, Property & Valuation: Mr Richard Green, Principal Property & Information Manager, HQ, 58 Nicholas Street, Chester CH1 2NP ☎ 01244 977465
⎙ richard.green@cheshirewestandchester.gov.uk

Facilities: Ms Sam Brousas, Director - Professional Services, HQ, 58 Nicholas Street, Chester CH1 2NP ☎ 01244 972739
⎙ samantha.brousas@cheshirewestandchester.gov.uk

Finance: Mr Mark Wynn, Director - Finance, HQ, 58 Nicholas Street, Chester CH1 2NP ☎ 01244 972537
⎙ mark.wynn@cheshirewestandchester.gov.uk

Treasury: Mr Mark Wynn, Director - Finance, HQ, 58 Nicholas Street, Chester CH1 2NP ☎ 01244 972537
⎙ mark.wynn@cheshirewestandchester.gov.uk

Pensions: Mr Nick Jones, Senior Financial Advisor (Pensions), HQ, 58 Nicholas Street, Chester CH1 2NP ☎ 01244 972652
🖰 nick.jones@cheshirewestandchester.gov.uk

Fleet Management: Ms Mary Jefferson, Section Leader - Transport Commissioning Service, HQ, 58 Nicholas Street, Chester CH1 2NP ☎ 01244 973052
🖰 mary.jefferson@cheshirewestandchester.gov.uk

Health and Safety: Mr Eric Burt, Health & Safety Manager, HQ, 58 Nicholas Street, Chester CH1 2NP ☎ 01244 972229
🖰 eric.burt@cheshirewestandchester.gov.uk

Highways: Mr Rob Brooks, Senior Manager - Place Network & Environment Manager, HQ, 58 Nicholas Street, Chester CH1 2NP ☎ 01244 973621 🖰 rob.brooks@cheshirewestandchester.gov.uk

Legal: Ms Vanessa Whiting, Director - Governance & Monitoring Officer, HQ, 58 Nicholas Street, Chester CH1 2NP ☎ 01244 977802
🖰 vanessa.whiting@cheshirewestandchester.gov.uk

Licensing: Ms Vanessa Whiting, Director - Governance & Monitoring Officer, HQ, 58 Nicholas Street, Chester CH1 2NP ☎ 01244 977802 🖰 vanessa.whiting@cheshirewestandchester.gov.uk

Lifelong Learning: Ms Gemma Davies, Senior Manager - Economic Growth, HQ, 58 Nicholas Street, Chester CH1 2NP ☎ 01244 976729 🖰 gemma.davies@cheshirewest.gov.uk

Lottery Funding, Charity and Voluntary: Ms Pam Bradley, Senior Manager - Rural Localities, HQ, 58 Nicholas Street, Chester CH1 2NP ☎ 01244 976996
🖰 pam.bradley@cheshirewestandchester.gov.uk

Member Services: Ms Andrea Thwaite, Team Leader - Civic & Member Support, HQ, 58 Nicholas Street, Chester CH1 2NP ☎ 01244 972283 🖰 andrea.thwaite@cheshirewestandchester.gov.uk

Parking: Ms Sarah Armstrong, Manager - Lifetime Services & Car Parking, First Floor, The Forum, Chester CH1 2HS ☎ 01244 973774 🖰 sarah.armstrong@cheshirewestandchester.gov.uk

Partnerships: Mr Alistair Jeffs, Director - Commissioning People, HQ, 58 Nicholas Street, Chester CM1 2NP ☎ 01244 972228
🖰 alistair.jeffs@cheshirewestandchester.gov.uk

Personnel / HR: Ms Sam Brousas, Director - Professional Services, HQ, 58 Nicholas Street, Chester CH1 2NP ☎ 01244 972739 🖰 samantha.brousas@cheshirewestandchester.gov.uk

Planning: Ms Fiona Hore, Planning Manager, The Forum Offices, Chester CH1 2HS ☎ 01244 972859
🖰 fiona.hore@cheshirewestandchester.gov.uk

Procurement: Mr Julian Ablett, Procurement Process & Planning Manager, HQ, 58 Nicholas Street, Chester CH1 2NP ☎ 01244 972952 🖰 julian.ablett@cheshirewestandchester.gov.uk

Public Libraries: Ms Rachel Foster, Library Services Manager, HQ, 58 Nicholas Street, Chester CH1 2NP ☎ 01244 972612
🖰 rachel.foster@cheshirewestandchester.gov.uk

Recycling & Waste Minimisation: Mr Steve Bakewell, Senior Manager - Waste Collection & Disposal, Phoenix House, Clough Road, Winsford CW7 4BD ☎ 01244 977847
🖰 steve.bakewell@cheshirewestandchester.gov.uk

Regeneration: Ms Alison Knight, Director - Places Strategy, HQ, 58 Nicholas Street, Chester CH1 2NP ☎ 01244 976785
🖰 alison.knight@cheshirewestandchester.gov.uk

Road Safety: Ms Sarah Collins, Senior Road Safety Officer, Rivacre Business Centre, Mill Lane, Ellesmere Port CH66 3TL ☎ 01244 976713 🖰 sarah.collins@cheshire.gov.uk

Social Services: Ms Emma Taylor, Director - Children's Social Care, HQ, 58 Nicholas Street, Chester CH1 2NP ☎ 01244 973512 🖰 emma.taylor@cheshirewestandchester.gov.uk

Social Services (Adult): Ms Jill Broomhall, Director - Prevention & Wellbeing, HQ, 58 Nicholas Street, Chester CH1 2NP ☎ 01244 972247 🖰 jill.broomhall@cheshirewestandchester.gov.uk

Social Services (Adult): Mr Alistair Jeffs, Director - Commissioning People, HQ, 58 Nicholas Street, Chester CM1 2NP ☎ 01244 972228 🖰 alistair.jeffs@cheshirewestandchester.gov.uk

Social Services (Children): Ms Emma Taylor, Director - Children's Social Care, HQ, 58 Nicholas Street, Chester CH1 2NP ☎ 01244 973512 🖰 emma.taylor@cheshirewestandchester.gov.uk

Families: Ms Helen Brackenbury, Interim Director - Integrated Early Support, HQ, 58 Nicholas Street, Chester CH1 2NP
🖰 helen.brackenbury@cheshirewestandchester.gov.uk

Public Health: Ms Fiona Reynolds, Interim Director of Public Health, HQ, 58 Nicholas Street, Chester CH1 2NP ☎ 01244 977030 🖰 fiona.reynolds@cheshirewestandchester.gov.uk

Staff Training: Ms Kelly Castle, Senior Organisational Development & Workforce Advisor, HQ, 58 Nicholas Street, Chester CH1 2NP ☎ 01244 976043 🖰 kelly.castle@cheshirewestandchester.gov.uk

Street Scene: Mr Simon Lammond, Senior Manager - Place Delivery, HQ, 58 Nicholas Street, Chester CH1 2NP
🖰 simon.lammond@cheshirewestandchester.gov.uk

Sustainable Communities: Mr George Ablett, Principal Sustainable Development Officer, HQ, 58 Nicholas Street, Chester CH1 2NP ☎ 01244 972419
🖰 george.ablett@cheshirewestandchester.gov.uk

Total Place: Ms Aleta Steele, Senior Manager - Locality Working, HQ, 58 Nicholas Street, Chester CH1 2NP ☎ 01244 972143 🖰 aleta.steele@cheshirewestandchester.gov.uk

Waste Collection and Disposal: Mr Steve Bakewell, Senior Manager - Waste Collection & Disposal, Phoenix House, Clough Road, Winsford CW7 4BD ☎ 01244 977847
🖰 steve.bakewell@cheshirewestandchester.gov.uk

CHESHIRE WEST & CHESTER

Waste Management: Mr Jody Sherratt, Contracts Manager (Waste), HQ, 58 Nicholas Street, Chester CH1 2NP ☎ 01244 973529 ⏚ jody.sherratt@cheshirewestandchester.gov.uk

COUNCILLORS

The Lord Mayor: Rooney, Peter (LAB - Ledsham & Manor)
peter.rooney@cheshirewestandchester.gov.uk

Deputy Lord Mayor: Daniels, Razia (CON - Handbridge Park)
razia.daniels@cheshirewestandchester.gov.uk

Chair: Rudd, Bob (LAB - Garden Quarter)
bob.rudd@cheshirewestandchester.gov.uk

Leader of the Council: Dixon, Samantha (LAB - Chester City)
samantha.dixon@cheshirewestandchester.gov.uk

Deputy Leader of the Council: Gittins, Louise (LAB - Little Neston & Burton)
louise.gittins@cheshirewestandchester.gov.uk

Group Leader: Riley, Lynn (CON - Frodsham)
lynn.riley@cheshirewestandchester.gov.uk

Anderson, Gareth (CON - Ledsham & Manor)
gareth.anderson@cheshirewestandchester.gov.uk

Armstrong, David (LAB - Winsford Swanlow & Dene)
david.armstrong@cheshirewestandchester.gov.uk

Armstrong, Val (LAB - Witton & Rudheath)
val.armstrong@cheshirewestandchester.gov.uk

Barker, Martin (IND - Parkgate)
martin.barker@cheshirewestandchester.gov.uk

Baynham, Michael (CON - Winsford Over & Verdin)
michael.baynham@cheshirewestandchester.gov.uk

Beacham, Richard (LAB - Newton)
richard.beacham@cheshirewestandchester.gov.uk

Beckett, Don (LAB - Winsford Over & Verdin)
don.beckett@cheshirewestandchester.gov.uk

Bisset, Robert (LAB - St. Paul's)
robert.bisset@cheshirewestandchester.gov.uk

Black, Alex (LAB - Hoole)
alex.black@cheshirewestandchester.gov.uk

Blackmore, Tom (LAB - Winsford Over & Verdin)
tom.blackmore@cheshirewestandchester.gov.uk

Board, Keith (CON - Great Boughton)
keith.board@cheshirewestandchester.gov.uk

Booher, Pamela (LAB - Winsford Wharton)
pam.booher@cheshirewestandchester.gov.uk

Bryan, Matt (LAB - Upton)
matt.bryan@cheshirewestandchester.gov.uk

Burns, Stephen (LAB - Winsford Swanlow & Dene)
stephen.burns@cheshirewestandchester.gov.uk

Chidley, Angie (LAB - Hoole)
angie.chidley@cheshirewestandchester.gov.uk

Clare, Lynn (LAB - Ellesmere Port Town)
lynn.clare@cheshirewestandchester.gov.uk

Clarke, Brian (LAB - Winsford Wharton)
brian.clarke@cheshirewestandchester.gov.uk

Claydon, Angela (LAB - St. Paul's)
angela.claydon@cheshirewestandchester.gov.uk

Crook, Jess (LAB - Ellesmere Port Town)
jessica.crook@cheshirewestandchester.gov.uk

Crowe, Brian (CON - Saughall & Mollington)
brian.crowe@cheshirewestandchester.gov.uk

Dawson, Andrew (CON - Frodsham)
andrew.dawson@cheshirewestandchester.gov.uk

Delaney, Martyn (LAB - Boughton)
martyn.delaney@cheshirewestandchester.gov.uk

Deynem, Hugo (CON - Tarvin & Kelsall)
hugo.deynem@cheshirewestandchester.gov.uk

Dolan, Paul (LAB - Winnington & Castle)
paul.dolan@cheshirewestandchester.gov.uk

Donovan, Paul (LAB - Sutton)
paul.donovan@cheshirewestandchester.gov.uk

Fifield, Charles (CON - Weaver & Cuddington)
charles.fifield@cheshirewestandchester.gov.uk

Gahan, Carol (LAB - Blacon)
carol.gahan@cheshirewestandchester.gov.uk

Gibbon, Lynn (CON - Marbury)
lynn.gibbon@cheshirewestandchester.gov.uk

Greenwood, Howard (CON - Farndon)
howard.greenwood@cheshirewestandchester.gov.uk

Hall, Pamela (CON - Great Boughton)
pamela.hall@cheshirewestandchester.gov.uk

Hammond, Don (CON - Marbury)
don.hammond@cheshirewestandchester.gov.uk

Henesy, Mark (LAB - Strawberry)
mark.henesy@cheshirewestandchester.gov.uk

Hogg, Myles (CON - Willaston & Thornton)
myles.hogg@cheshirewestandchester.gov.uk

Houlbrook, Jill (CON - Upton)
jill.houlbrook@cheshirewestandchester.gov.uk

Johnson, Eleanor (CON - Gowy)
eleanor.johnson@cheshirewestandchester.gov.uk

Jones, Mike (CON - Tattenhall)
mike.jones@cheshirewestandchester.gov.uk

Jones, Brian (LAB - Whitby)
brian.jones@cheshirewestandchester.gov.uk

Jones, Reggie (LAB - Blacon)
reggie.jones@cheshirewestandchester.gov.uk

Jones, Nige (CON - Little Neston & Burton)
nigel.jones@cheshirewestandchester.gov.uk

Kaur, Susan (CON - Hartford & Greenbank)
susan.kaur@cheshirewestandchester.gov.uk

Lawrenson, Tony (LAB - Witton & Rudheath)
tony.lawrenson@cheshirewestandchester.gov.uk

Leather, John (CON - Tarvin & Kelsall)
john.leather@cheshirewestandchester.gov.uk

McKie, Alan (CON - Helsby)
alan.mckie@cheshirewestandchester.gov.uk

Meardon, Nicole (LAB - Sutton)
nicole.meardon@cheshirewestandchester.gov.uk

Mercer, Jane (LAB - Lache)
jane.mercer@cheshirewestandchester.gov.uk

Merrick, Pat (LAB - Rossmore)
pat.merrick@cheshirewestandchester.gov.uk

Moore, Eveleigh (CON - Tarporley)
eveleigh.mooredutton@cheshirewestandchester.gov.uk

Naylor, Sam (LAB - Winnington & Castle)
sam.naylor@cheshirewestandchester.gov.uk

Nelson, Marie (LAB - Blacon)
marie.nelson@cheshirewestandchester.gov.uk

Oultram, Ralph (CON - Kingsley)
ralph.oultram@cheshirewestandchester.gov.uk

Parker, Margaret (CON - Chester Villages)
margaret.parker@cheshirewestandchester.gov.uk

Parker, Stuart (CON - Chester Villages)
stuart.parker@cheshirewestandchester.gov.uk

Parkes, Patricia (CON - Hartford & Greenbank)
patricia.parkes@cheshirewestandchester.gov.uk

Pearson, James (CON - Davenham & Moulton)
james.pearson@cheshirewestandchester.gov.uk

Roberts, Diane (LAB - Netherpool)
diane.roberts2@cheshirewestandchester.gov.uk

Sherlock, Tony (LAB - Grange)
tony.sherlock@cheshirewestandchester.gov.uk

Shore, Karen (LAB - Whitby)
karen.shore@cheshirewestandchester.gov.uk

Sinar, Gaynor (CON - Davenham & Moulton)
gaynor.sinar@cheshirewestandchester.gov.uk

Smith, Stephen (LAB - Elton)
ste.smith@cheshirewestandchester.gov.uk

Stocks, Mark (CON - Shakerley)
mark.stocks@cheshirewestandchester.gov.uk

Sullivan, Neil (CON - Handbridge Park)
neil.sullivan@cheshirewestandchester.gov.uk

Tonge, Harry (CON - Weaver & Cuddington)
harry.tonge@cheshirewestandchester.gov.uk

Watson, Gill (LAB - Newton)
gill.watson@cheshirewestandchester.gov.uk

Weltman, Helen (CON - Davenham & Moulton)
helen.weltman@cheshirewestandchester.gov.uk

Whitehurst, Chris (CON - Malpas)
chris.whitehurst@cheshirewestandchester.gov.uk

Williams, Andy (LAB - Neston)
andy.williams2@cheshirewestandchester.gov.uk

Williams, Paul (CON - Weaver & Cuddington)
paul.williams2@cheshirewestandchester.gov.uk

Williams, Mark (CON - Dodleston & Huntingdon)
mark.williams@cheshirewestandchester.gov.uk

Wright, Norman (CON - Marbury)
norman.wright@cheshirewestandchester.gov.uk

POLITICAL COMPOSITION
LAB: 38, CON: 36, IND: 1

COMMITTEE CHAIRS

Adult Social Care: Mr Paul Dolan

Audit & Governance: Mr Stephen Burns

Children & Families: Ms Nicole Meardon

Economic Development & Infrastructure: Mr Brian Clarke

Environment & Community: Mr Mark Henesy

Health & Wellbeing: Ms Samantha Dixon

Housing: Ms Angela Claydon

Planning: Mr Alex Black

Chesterfield   D

Chesterfield Borough Council, Town Hall, Rose Hill,
Chesterfield S40 1LP
☎ 01246 345345 🖷 01246 345252 ✒ info@chesterfield.gov.uk
🖳 www.chesterfield.gov.uk

FACTS AND FIGURES
Parliamentary Constituencies: Chesterfield
EU Constituencies: East Midlands
Election Frequency: Elections are of whole council

PRINCIPAL OFFICERS

Chief Executive: Mr Huw Bowen, Chief Executive, Town Hall,
Rose Hill, Chesterfield S40 1LP ☎ 01246 345305
✒ huw.bowen@chesterfield.gov.uk

Senior Management: Mr James Drury, Executive Director, Town
Hall, Rose Hill, Chesterfield S40 1LP ☎ 01246 345292
✒ james.drury@chesterfield.gov.uk

Senior Management: Mr Kevin Hanlon, Director - Resources,
Town Hall, Rose Hill, Chesterfield S40 1LP
✒ kevin.hanlon@chesterfield.gov.uk

Senior Management: Mr Michael Rich, Executive Director, Town
Hall, Rose Hill, Chesterfield S40 1LP ☎ 01246 345461
✒ michael.rich@chesterfield.gov.uk

Architect, Building / Property Services: Mr Roger Farrand,
Principal Architect, Town Hall, Rose Hill, Chesterfield S40 1LP
☎ 01246 345401 ✒ roger.farrand@chesterfield.gov.uk

Best Value: Miss Karen Brown, Business Transformation
Manager, Town Hall, Rose Hill, Chesterfield S40 1LP
☎ 01246 345293 ✒ karen.brown@chesterfield.gov.uk

Building Control: Mr Malcolm Clinton, Business Manager, Town
Hall, Rose Hill, Chesterfield S40 1LP ☎ 01246 345817; 01246
354900 ✒ malcolm.clinton@ne-derbyshire.gov.uk; malcolm.clinton@
bcnconsultancy.co.uk

PR / Communications: Mr John Fern, Communications &
Marketing Manager, Town Hall, Rose Hill, Chesterfield S40 1LP
☎ 01246 345245 ✒ john.fern@chesterfield.gov.uk

Community Safety: Ms Dianne Illsley, Community Safety Officer,
Town Hall, Rose Hill, Chesterfield S40 1LP ☎ 01246 345225
✒ diane.illsley@chesterfield.gov.uk

CHESTERFIELD

Corporate Services: Mrs Jenny Williams, Interim Head of Internal Audit, Town Hall, Rose Hill, Chesterfield S40 1LP ☎ 01246 345468 ✆ jenny.williams@chesterfield.gov.uk

Economic Development: Ms Lynda Sharp, Joint Economic Development Manager, Town Hall, Rose Hill, Chesterfield S40 1LP ☎ 01246 345255 ✆ lynda.sharp@chesterfield.gov.uk

Economic Development: Ms Laurie Thomas, Joint Economic Development Manager, Town Hall, Rose Hill, Chesterfield S40 1LP ☎ 01246 345255 ✆ laurie.thomas@chesterfield.gov.uk

E-Government: Mr Jonathan Alsop, ICT Projects Manager, Town Hall, Rose Hill, Chesterfield S40 1LP ☎ 01246 345249 ✆ jonathan.alsop@chesterfield.gov.uk

Electoral Registration: Mrs Sandra Essex, Democratic Services Manager, Town Hall, Rose Hill, Chesterfield S40 1LP ☎ 01246 345227 ✆ sandra.essex@chesterfield.gov.uk

Emergency Planning: Ms Sam Sherlock, Emergency Planning Officer, Town Hall, Rose Hill, Chesterfield S40 1LP ☎ 01246 345407 ✆ sam.sherlock@chesterfield.gov.uk

Energy Management: Mr Jon Vaughan, Energy Manager, Town Hall, Rose Hill, Chesterfield S40 1LP ☎ 01246 345415 ✆ jon.vaughan@chesterfield.gov.uk

Environmental Health: Mr Martin Key, Health & Wellbeing Manager, Town Hall, Rose Hill, Chesterfield S40 1LP ☎ 01246 345337 ✆ martin.key@chesterfield.gov.uk

Estates, Property & Valuation: Mr Matthew Sorby, Head of Asset Management, Town Hall, Rose Hill, Chesterfield S40 1LP ☎ 01246 345308 ✆ matthew.sorby@chesterfield.gov.uk

European Liaison: Ms Laurie Thomas, Joint Economic Development Manager, Town Hall, Rose Hill, Chesterfield S40 1LP ☎ 01246 345255 ✆ laurie.thomas@chesterfield.gov.uk

Finance: Mr Kevin Hanlon, Director - Resources, Town Hall, Rose Hill, Chesterfield S40 1LP ✆ kevin.hanlon@chesterfield.gov.uk

Health and Safety: Miss Karen Brown, Business Transformation Manager, Town Hall, Rose Hill, Chesterfield S40 1LP ☎ 01246 345293 ✆ karen.brown@chesterfield.gov.uk

Home Energy Conservation: Mr Paul Staniforth, Development Management & Conservation Manager, Town Hall, Rose Hill, Chesterfield S40 1LP ☎ 01246 345781 ✆ paul.staniforth@chesterfield.gov.uk

Housing: Mrs Alison Craig, Housing Manager, Town Hall, Rose Hill, Chesterfield S40 1LP ☎ 01246 345156 ✆ alison.craig@chesterfield.gov.uk

Legal: Mr Gerard Rogers, Local Government & Regulatory Law Manager, Town Hall, Rose Hill, Chesterfield S40 1LP ☎ 01246 345310 ✆ gerard.rogers@chesterfield.gov.uk

Licensing: Mr Trevor Durham, Licensing Manager, Town Hall, Rose Hill, Chesterfield S40 1LP ☎ 01246 345230 ✆ trevor.durham@chesterfield.gov.uk

Member Services: Mrs Sandra Essex, Democratic Services Manager, Town Hall, Rose Hill, Chesterfield S40 1LP ☎ 01246 345227 ✆ sandra.essex@chesterfield.gov.uk

Member Services: Mr Gerard Rogers, Local Government & Regulatory Law Manager, Town Hall, Rose Hill, Chesterfield S40 1LP ☎ 01246 345310 ✆ gerard.rogers@chesterfield.gov.uk

Parking: Mr Andy Bond, Town Centre Operations Manager, Tourist Information Centre, Rykneld Square, Chesterfield S40 1SB ☎ 01246 345991 ✆ andy.bond@chesterfield.gov.uk

Personnel / HR: Ms Jane Dackiewicz, HR & Payroll Service Solution Lead, Town Hall, Rose Hill, Chesterfield S40 1LP ☎ 01246 345257 ✆ jane.dackiewicz@chesterfield.gov.uk

Planning: Mr Paul Staniforth, Development Management & Conservation Manager, Town Hall, Rose Hill, Chesterfield S40 1LP ☎ 01246 345781 ✆ paul.staniforth@chesterfield.gov.uk

Procurement: Ms Rachel O'Neil, 01246 345833, Town Hall, Rose Hill, Chesterfield S40 1LP ✆ rachel.oneil@chesterfield.gov.uk

Recycling & Waste Minimisation: Mr Mike Brymer, Commercial Services Manager, Town Hall, Rose Hill, Chesterfield S40 1LP ☎ 01246 345325 ✆ michael.brymer@chesterfield.gov.uk

Regeneration: Mr Neil Johnson, Development & Growth Manager, Town Hall, Rose Hill, Chesterfield S40 1LP ☎ 01246 345789 ✆ neil.johnson@chesterfield.gov.uk

Staff Training: Ms Jane Dackiewicz, HR & Payroll Service Solution Lead, Town Hall, Rose Hill, Chesterfield S40 1LP ☎ 01246 345257 ✆ jane.dackiewicz@chesterfield.gov.uk

Street Scene: Mr Mike Brymer, Commercial Services Manager, Town Hall, Rose Hill, Chesterfield S40 1LP ☎ 01246 345325 ✆ michael.brymer@chesterfield.gov.uk

Tourism: Mr Neil Johnson, Development & Growth Manager, Town Hall, Rose Hill, Chesterfield S40 1LP ☎ 01246 345789 ✆ neil.johnson@chesterfield.gov.uk

Town Centre: Mr Andy Bond, Town Centre Operations Manager, Tourist Information Centre, Rykneld Square, Chesterfield S40 1SB ☎ 01246 345991 ✆ andy.bond@chesterfield.gov.uk

Waste Collection and Disposal: Mr Mike Brymer, Commercial Services Manager, Town Hall, Rose Hill, Chesterfield S40 1LP ☎ 01246 345325 ✆ michael.brymer@chesterfield.gov.uk

Waste Management: Mr Mike Brymer, Commercial Services Manager, Town Hall, Rose Hill, Chesterfield S40 1LP ☎ 01246 345325 ✆ michael.brymer@chesterfield.gov.uk

COUNCILLORS

Leader of the Council: Burrows, John (LAB - Brimington North) john.burrows@chesterfield.gov.uk

Deputy Leader of the Council: Gilby, Terry (LAB - Brimington North)
terry.gilby@chesterfield.gov.uk

Bagley, Helen (LAB - St Helen's)
helen.bagley@chesterfield.gov.uk

Barr, Peter (LD - Linacre)
peter.barr@chesterfield.gov.uk

Barr, Jeannie (LD - Linacre)
jeannie.barr@chesterfield.gov.uk

Bellamy, Andy (LAB - Brimington South)
andy.bellamy@chesterfield.gov.uk

Bexton, Richard (UKIP - Barrow Hill & New Whittington)
richard.bexton@chesterfield.gov.uk

Bingham, Barry (LD - Barrow Hill & New Whittington)
barry.bingham@chesterfield.gov.uk

Blank, Sharon (LAB - St Leonard's)
sharon.blank@chesterfield.gov.uk

Borrell, Howard (LD - West)
howard.borrell@chesterfield.gov.uk

Brady, Mick (LAB - Hasland)
mick.brady@chesterfileld.gov.uk

Brittain, Stuart (LAB - Rother)
stuart.brittain@chesterfield.gov.uk

Brown, Keith (LAB - Moor)
keith.brown@chesterfield.gov.uk

Brunt, Steve (LAB - Brockwell)
steve.brunt@chesterfield.gov.uk

Callan, Ian (LAB - Brimington South)
ian.callan@chesterfield.gov.uk

Catt, Ray (LAB - West)
raymong.catt@chesterfield.gov.uk

Caulfield, Kate (LAB - Moor)
kate.caulfield@chesterfield.gov.uk

Collins, Dean (LAB - Lowgates & Woodthorpe)
dean.collings@chesterfield.gov.uk

Collins, Lisa (LAB - Lowgates & Woodthorpe)
lisa.collings@chesterfield.gov.uk

Davenport, Maureen (LD - Brockwell)
maureen.davenport@chesterfield.gov.uk

Derbyshire, Lisa-Marie (LAB - Barrow Hill & New Whittington)
lisa-marie.derbyshire@chesterfield.gov.uk

Dickinson, John (LAB - Brockwell)
john.dickinson@chesterfield.gov.uk

Diouf, Alexis (LD - Walton)
alexis.diouf@chesterfield.gov.uk

Diouf, Vicky-Anne (LD - Walton)
vickey.diouf@chesterfield.gov.uk

Dyke, Barry (LAB - Hollingwood & Inkersall)
barry.dyke@chesterfield.gov.uk

Elliott, Helen (LAB - Hollingwood & Inkersall)
helen.elliott@chesterfield.gov.uk

Flood, Jenny (LAB - Rother)
jenny.flood@chesterfield.gov.uk

Gilby, Tricia (LAB - Brimington South)
tricia.gilby@chesterfield.gov.uk

Hill, Anthony (LAB - Hollingwood & Inkersall)
anthony.hill@chesterfield.gov.uk

Hitchin, Stephen (LAB - Holmebrook)
stephen.hitchin@chesterfield.gov.uk

Hollingworth, Sarah (LAB - Dunston)
sarah.hollingworth@chesterfield.gov.uk

Huckle, Ken (LAB - St Leonard's)
ken.huckle@chesterfield.gov.uk

Innes, Jean (LAB - Old Whittington)
jean.innes@chesterfield.gov.uk

Innes, Peter (LAB - Old Whittington)
peter.innes@chesterfield.gov.uk

Ludlow, Chris (LAB - Middlecroft & Poolsbrook)
chris.ludlow@chesterfield.gov.uk

Miles, Keith (LAB - Rother)
keith.miles@chesterfield.gov.uk

Murphy, Tom (LAB - St Helen's)
tom.murphy@chesterfield.gov.uk

Murphy, Avis (LAB - Loundsley Green)
avis.murphy@chesterfield.gov.uk

Niblock, Shirley (LD - West)
shirley.niblock@chesterfield.gov.uk

Parsons, Donald (LAB - Middlecroft & Poolsbrook)
donald.parsons@chesterfield.gov.uk

Perkins, Suzie (LAB - Holmebrook)
suzie.perkins@chesterfield.gov.uk

Rayner, Mark (LAB - Dunston)
mark.rayner@chesterfield.gov.uk

Redihough, Nicholas (LD - Walton)
nick.redihough@chesterfield.gov.uk

Sarvent, Kate (LAB - St. Leonard's)
kate.sarvent@chesterfield.gov.uk

Serjeant, Amanda (LAB - Hasland)
amanda.serjeant@chesterfield.gov.uk

Simmons, Gordon (LAB - Dunston)
gordon.simmons@chesterfield.gov.uk

Slack, Andy (LAB - Hasland)
andy.slack@chesterfield.gov.uk

Wall, Mick (LAB - Loundsley Green)
mick.wall@chesterfield.gov.uk

POLITICAL COMPOSITION
LAB: 38, LD: 9, UKIP: 1

COMMITTEE CHAIRS

Audit: Mr Mark Rayner

Licensing: Mr Andy Bellamy

Planning: Mr Stuart Brittain

Chichester   D

Chichester District Council, Council Offices, East Pallant House, East Pallant, Chichester PO19 1TY
☎ 01243 785166 🖷 01243 776766 ✆ contact@chichester.gov.uk
🖳 www.chichester.gov.uk

CHICHESTER

Parliamentary Constituencies: Chichester
EU Constituencies: South East
Election Frequency: Elections are of whole council

PRINCIPAL OFFICERS

Chief Executive: Mrs Diane Shepherd, Chief Executive, Council Offices, East Pallant House, East Pallant, Chichester PO19 1TY ☎ 01243 534709 ✆ dshepherd@chichester.gov.uk

Senior Management: Mr Steve Carvell, Executive Director, Council Offices, East Pallant House, East Pallant, Chichester PO19 1TJ ☎ 01243 534569 ✆ scarvell@chichester.gov.uk

Senior Management: Mr Paul Over, Executive Director, Council Offices, East Pallant House, East Pallant, Chichester PO19 1TY ☎ 01243 534639 ✆ pover@chichester.gov.uk

Senior Management: Mr John Ward, Head of Finance & Governance Services, Council Offices, East Pallant House, East Pallant, Chichester PO19 1TY ☎ 01243 534805 ✆ jward@chichester.gov.uk

Access Officer / Social Services (Disability): Mr John Bacon, Building & Facility Services Manager, Council Offices, East Pallant House, East Pallant, Chichester PO19 1TY ☎ 01243 534648 ✆ jbacon@chichester.gov.uk

Architect, Building / Property Services: Mr John Bacon, Building & Facility Services Manager, Council Offices, East Pallant House, East Pallant, Chichester PO19 1TY ☎ 01243 534648 ✆ jbacon@chichester.gov.uk

Best Value: Mr Joe Mildred, Corporate Policy Advice Manager, East Pallant House, East Pallant, Chichester PO19 1TY ☎ 01243 534728 ✆ jmildred@chichester.gov.uk

Building Control: Mr Russell Pugh, Building Control Service Manager, East Pallant House, East Pallant, Chichester PO19 1TY ☎ 01243 534565 ✆ rpugh@chichester.gov.uk

Children / Youth Services: Mr Stephen Hansford, Head of Service - Community, Council Offices, East Pallant House, East Pallant, Chichester PO19 1TY ☎ 01243 534789 ✆ shansford@chichester.gov.uk

PR / Communications: Ms Sarah Parker, Public Relations Manager, Council Offices, East Pallant House, East Pallant, Chichester PO19 1TY ☎ 01243 534537 ✆ sparker@chichester.gov.uk

Community Planning: Mr Stephen Hansford, Head of Service - Community, Council Offices, East Pallant House, East Pallant, Chichester PO19 1TY ☎ 01243 534789 ✆ shansford@chichester.gov.uk

Community Safety: Mr Stephen Hansford, Head of Service - Community, Council Offices, East Pallant House, East Pallant, Chichester PO19 1TY ☎ 01243 534789 ✆ shansford@chichester.gov.uk

Computer Management: Mrs Jane Dodsworth, Head of Service - Business Improvement, Council Offices, East Pallant House, East Pallant, Chichester PO19 1TY ☎ 01243 534729 ✆ jdodsworth@chichester.gov.uk

Contracts: Mrs Helen Belenger, Accountancy Services Manager, Council Offices, East Pallant House, East Pallant, Chichester PO19 1TY ☎ 01243 785166 Ext 1045 ✆ hbelenger@chichester.gov.uk

Corporate Services: Mr Joe Mildred, Corporate Policy Advice Manager, Council Offices, East Pallant House, East Pallant, Chichester PO19 1TY ☎ 01243 534728 ✆ jmildred@chichester.gov.uk

Customer Service: Mrs Jane Dodsworth, Head of Service - Business Improvement, Council Offices, East Pallant House, East Pallant, Chichester PO19 1TY ☎ 01243 534729 ✆ jdodsworth@chichester.gov.uk

Direct Labour: Mr Rod Darton, Head of Service - Contract Services, Chichester Contract Services, Stane Street, Westhampnett, Chichester PO18 0NS ☎ 01243 521177 ✆ rdarton@chichester.gov.uk

Economic Development: Mr Stephen Oates, Economic Development Manager, Council Offices, East Pallant House, East Pallant, Chichester PO19 1TY ☎ 01243 534600 ✆ soates@chichester.gov.uk

E-Government: Mrs Jane Dodsworth, Head of Service - Business Improvement, Council Offices, East Pallant House, East Pallant, Chichester PO19 1TY ☎ 01243 534729 ✆ jdodsworth@chichester.gov.uk

Electoral Registration: Ms Jo Timm, Electoral Services Manager, Council Offices, East Pallant House, East Pallant, Chichester PO19 1TY ☎ 01243 534592 ✆ jtimm@chichester.gov.uk

Emergency Planning: Mrs Louise Rudziak, Head of Service - Housing & Environment, East Pallant House, East Pallant, Chichester PO19 1TY ☎ 01243 785166 ✆ lrudziak@chichester.gov.uk

Energy Management: Mr John Bacon, Building & Facility Services Manager, Council Offices, East Pallant House, East Pallant, Chichester PO19 1TY ☎ 01243 534648 ✆ jbacon@chichester.gov.uk

Environmental / Technical Services: Mr John Bacon, Building & Facility Services Manager, Council Offices, East Pallant House, East Pallant, Chichester PO19 1TY ☎ 01243 534648 ✆ jbacon@chichester.gov.uk

Environmental / Technical Services: Mrs Louise Rudziak, Head of Service - Housing & Environment, East Pallant House, East Pallant, Chichester PO19 1TY ☎ 01243 785166 ✆ lrudziak@chichester.gov.uk

Environmental Health: Mrs Louise Rudziak, Head of Service - Housing & Environment, East Pallant House, East Pallant, Chichester PO19 1TY ☎ 01243 785166 ✆ lrudziak@chichester.gov.uk

Estates, Property & Valuation: Mr Peter LeGood, Valuation & Estates Manager, East Pallant House, East Pallant, Chichester PO19 1TY ☎ 01243 534668 ✆ plegood@chichester.gov.uk

European Liaison: Mr Stephen Oates, Economic Development Manager, Council Offices, East Pallant House, East Pallant, Chichester PO19 1TY ☎ 01243 534600 ✆ soates@chichester.gov.uk

Events Manager: Mr Ian Baker, Sport & Leisure Officer, Council Offices, East Pallant House, East Pallant, Chichester PO19 1TY ☎ 01243 534798 ✆ ibaker@chichester.gov.uk

Facilities: Mr John Bacon, Building & Facility Services Manager, Council Offices, East Pallant House, East Pallant, Chichester PO19 1TY ☎ 01243 534648 ✆ jbacon@chichester.gov.uk

Finance: Mr John Ward, Head of Finance & Governance Services, Council Offices, East Pallant House, East Pallant, Chichester PO19 1TY ☎ 01243 534805 ✆ jward@chichester.gov.uk

Treasury: Mr John Ward, Head of Finance & Governance Services, Council Offices, East Pallant House, East Pallant, Chichester PO19 1TY ☎ 01243 534805 ✆ jward@chichester.gov.uk

Fleet Management: Mr John Hoole, Workshop Manager, Stane Street, Westhampnett, Chichester PO18 0NS ☎ 01243 521183 ✆ jhoole@chichester.gov.uk

Grounds Maintenance: Mr Rod Darton, Head of Service - Contract Services, Chichester Contract Services, Stane Street, Westhampnett, Chichester PO18 0NS ☎ 01243 521177 ✆ rdarton@chichester.gov.uk

Grounds Maintenance: Mr Andy Howard, Green Spaces & Street Scene Manager, East Pallant House, East Pallant, Chichester PO19 1TY ☎ 01243 782747 ✆ ahoward@chichester.gov.uk

Health and Safety: Mr Warren Townsend, Health & Safety Manager, East Pallant House, East Pallant, Chichester PO19 1TY ☎ 01243 534605 ✆ wtownsend@chichester.gov.uk

Home Energy Conservation: Mr Tom Day, Environmental Co-ordinator, Council Offices, East Pallant House, East Pallant, Chichester PO19 1TY ☎ 01243 534854 ✆ tday@chichester.gov.uk

Housing: Mrs Louise Rudziak, Head of Service - Housing & Environment, East Pallant House, East Pallant, Chichester PO19 1TY ☎ 01243 785166 ✆ lrudziak@chichester.gov.uk

Legal: Mr Nicholas Bennett, Legal & Democratic Services Manager, Council Offices, East Pallant House, East Pallant, Chichester PO19 1TY ☎ 01243 534657 ✆ nbennett@chichester.gov.uk

Leisure and Cultural Services: Mrs Jane Hotchkiss, Head of Service - Commercial, Council Offices, East Pallant House, East Pallant, Chichester PO19 1TY ☎ 01243 534790 ✆ jhotchkiss@chichester.gov.uk

Licensing: Mrs Louise Rudziak, Head of Service - Housing & Environment, East Pallant House, East Pallant, Chichester PO19 1TY ☎ 01243 785166 ✆ lrudziak@chichester.gov.uk

Lifelong Learning: Mr Stephen Oates, Economic Development Manager, Council Offices, East Pallant House, East Pallant, Chichester PO19 1TY ☎ 01243 534600 ✆ soates@chichester.gov.uk

Lottery Funding, Charity and Voluntary: Mr Stephen Hansford, Head of Service - Community, Council Offices, East Pallant House, East Pallant, Chichester PO19 1TY ☎ 01243 534789 ✆ shansford@chichester.gov.uk

Member Services: Mr Nicholas Bennett, Legal & Democratic Services Manager, Council Offices, East Pallant House, East Pallant, Chichester PO19 1TY ☎ 01243 534657 ✆ nbennett@chichester.gov.uk

Parking: Mrs Jane Hotchkiss, Head of Service - Commercial, Council Offices, East Pallant House, East Pallant, Chichester PO19 1TY ☎ 01243 534790 ✆ jhotchkiss@chichester.gov.uk

Partnerships: Mr Stephen Hansford, Head of Service - Community, Council Offices, East Pallant House, East Pallant, Chichester PO19 1TY ☎ 01243 534789 ✆ shansford@chichester.gov.uk

Personnel / HR: Mrs Jane Dodsworth, Head of Service - Business Improvement, Council Offices, East Pallant House, East Pallant, Chichester PO19 1TY ☎ 01243 534729 ✆ jdodsworth@chichester.gov.uk

Planning: Mr Andrew Frost, Head of Planning Services, East Pallant House, East Pallant, Chichester PO19 1TY ☎ 01243 534892 ✆ afrost@chichester.gov.uk

Procurement: Mr Phil Pickard, Procurement Officer, East Pallant House, East Pallant, Chichester PO19 1TY ☎ 01243 785166

Recycling & Waste Minimisation: Mr Bob Riley, Contracts Manager, Chichester Contract Services, Stane Street, Westhampnett, Chichester PO18 0NS ☎ 01243 534615 ✆ briley@chichester.gov.uk

Regeneration: Mr Stephen Oates, Economic Development Manager, Council Offices, East Pallant House, East Pallant, Chichester PO19 1TY ☎ 01243 534600 ✆ soates@chichester.gov.uk

Staff Training: Mr Tim Radcliffe, Senior Personnel Manager, Council Offices, East Pallant House, East Pallant, Chichester PO19 1TY ☎ 01243 534528 ✆ tradcliffe@chichester.gov.uk

Sustainable Communities: Mr Stephen Hansford, Head of Service - Community, Council Offices, East Pallant House, East Pallant, Chichester PO19 1TY ☎ 01243 534789 ✆ shansford@chichester.gov.uk

Sustainable Development: Mrs Louise Rudziak, Head of Service - Housing & Environment, East Pallant House, East Pallant, Chichester PO19 1TY ☎ 01243 785166 ✆ lrudziak@chichester.gov.uk

Tourism: Mrs Jane Hotchkiss, Head of Service - Commercial, Council Offices, East Pallant House, East Pallant, Chichester PO19 1TY ☎ 01243 534790 ✆ jhotchkiss@chichester.gov.uk

Transport: Mr John Hoole, Workshop Manager, Stane Street, Westhampnett, Chichester PO18 0NS ☎ 01243 521183 ✆ jhoole@chichester.gov.uk

CHICHESTER

Waste Collection and Disposal: Mr Bob Riley, Contracts Manager, Chichester Contract Services, Stane Street, Westhampnett, Chichester PO18 0NS ☎ 01243 534615 ✆ briley@chichester.gov.uk

Waste Management: Mr Bob Riley, Contracts Manager, Chichester Contract Services, Stane Street, Westhampnett, Chichester PO18 0NS ☎ 01243 534615 ✆ briley@chichester.gov.uk

Children's Play Areas: Mrs Sarah Peyman, Sport & Leisure Development Manager , East Pallant House, East Pallant, Chichester PO19 1TY ☎ 01243 534791 ✆ speyman@chichester.gov.uk

COUNCILLORS

Chair: Hamilton, Elizabeth (CON - West Wittering)
ehamilton@chichester.gov.uk

Vice-Chair: Graves, Norma (CON - Fernhurst)
ngraves@chichester.gov.uk

Leader of the Council: Dignum, Tony (CON - Chichester North)
pdignum@chichester.gov.uk

Deputy Leader of the Council: Lintill, Eileen (CON - Petworth)
elintill@chichester.gov.uk

Group Leader: Apel, Clare (LD - Chichester West)
capel@chichester.gov.uk

Group Leader: Shaxson, Andrew (IND - Harting)
ashaxson@chichester.gov.uk

Barrett, Graeme (CON - West Wittering)
gbarrett@chichester.gov.uk

Barrow, Roger (CON - Selsey South)
rbarrow@chichester.gov.uk

Budge, Peter (CON - Chichester North)
pbudge@chichester.gov.uk

Connor, John (CON - Selsey North)
jconnor@chichester.gov.uk

Cullen, Miles (CON - Bosham)
mcullen@chichester.gov.uk

Curbishley, Ian (CON - East Wittering)
icurbishley@chichester.gov.uk

Dempster, Thomas (CON - Chichester East)
tdempster@chichster.gov.uk

Dignum, Pam (CON - Chichester South)
pdignum@chichester.gov.uk

Duncton, Janet (CON - Petworth)
janet@duncton.plus.com

Dunn, Mark (CON - Westbourne)
mdunn@chichester.gov.uk

Elliot, John (CON - Selsey South)
jelliot@chichester.gov.uk

Elliott, John (CON - Bury)
john.elliott811929@btopenworld.com

Finch, Bruce (CON - Southbourne)
bfinch@chichester.gov.uk

Galloway, Nigel (CON - Chichester South)
ngalloway@chichester.gov.uk

Hall, Mike (CON - Lavant)
mhall@chichester.gov.uk

Hardwick, Phillippa (CON - Fernhurst)
phardwick@chichester.gov.uk

Hayes, Robert (CON - Southbourne)
rhayes@chichester.gov.uk

Hicks, Graham (CON - Southbourne)
ghicks@chichester.gov.uk

Hixson, Les (CON - Chichester East)
ihixson@chichester.gov.uk

Hobbs, Francis (CON - Easebourne)
fhobbs@chichester.gov.uk

Jarvis, Paul (CON - North Mundham)
pjarvis@chichester.gov.uk

Keegan, Gillian (CON - Rogate)
gkeegan@chichester.gov.uk

Kilby, Jane (CON - Chichester East)
jkilby@chichester.gov.uk

Knightley, Denise (CON - Plaistow)
dknightley@chichester.gov.uk

Lloyd-Williams, Simon (CON - Chichester North)
slloyd-williams@chichester.gov.uk

Macey, Len (CON - Chichester South)
lmacey@chichester.gov.uk

McAra, Gordon (IND - Midhurst)
gmcara@chichester.gov.uk

Morley, Steve (IND - Midhurst)
smorley@chichester.gov.uk

Neville, Caroline (CON - Stedman)
cneville@chichester.gov.uk

Oakley, Simon (CON - Tangmere)
soakley@chichester.gov.uk

Plant, Penny (CON - Bosham)
pplant@chichester.gov.uk

Ploughman, Richard (LD - Chichester West)
rploughman@chichester.gov.uk

Potter, Henry (CON - Boxgrove)
hpotter@chichester.gov.uk

Purnell, Carol (CON - Selsey North)
cpurnell@chichester.gov.uk

Ransley, Josef (CON - Wisborough Green)
jransley@chichester.gov.uk

Ridd, John (CON - Donnington)
jridd@chichester.gov.uk

Tassell, Julie (CON - Funtington)
julie.tassell@virgin.net

Taylor, Susan (CON - East Wittering)
sttaylor@chichester.gov.uk

Thomas, Nick (CON - Plaistow)
nthomas@chichester.gov.uk

Tull, Tricia (CON - Sidlesham)
ttull@chichester.gov.uk

Wakeman, Darren (CON - Selsey North)
dwakeman@chichester.gov.uk

Westacott, Sandra (LD - Fishbourne)
sweatacott@chichester.gov.uk

POLITICAL COMPOSITION
CON: 42, IND: 3, LD: 3

COMMITTEE CHAIRS

Audit & Governance: Mrs Tricia Tull

Licensing: Mr John Ridd

Planning: Mr Robert Hayes

Chiltern   D

Chiltern District Council, King George V House, King George V Road, Amersham HP6 5AW
☎ 01494 729000 🖷 01494 586506 🖳 www.chiltern.gov.uk

FACTS AND FIGURES
Parliamentary Constituencies: Aylesbury, Chesham and Amersham
EU Constituencies: South East
Election Frequency: Elections are of whole council

PRINCIPAL OFFICERS

Chief Executive: Mr Bob Smith, Acting Chief Executive, King George V House, King George V Road, Amersham HP6 5AW ☎ 01494 732178 ✆ bsmith@chiltern.gov.uk

Senior Management: Mr Jim Burness, Director - Resources, King George V House, King George V Road, Amersham HP6 5AW ☎ 01494 732095 ✆ jburness@chiltern.gov.uk

Senior Management: Ms Anita Cacchioli, Interim Director - Services, King George V House, King George V Road, Amersham HP6 5AW ☎ 01494 732235 ✆ acacchioli@chiltern.gov.uk

Senior Management: Mr Bob Smith, Acting Chief Executive, King George V House, King George V Road, Amersham HP6 5AW ☎ 01494 732178 ✆ bsmith@chiltern.gov.uk

Access Officer / Social Services (Disability): Mr Peter Beckford, Head of Sustainable Development, King George V House, King George V Road, Amersham HP6 5AW ☎ 01895 837208; 01494 732036 ✆ pbeckford@chiltern.gov.uk

Architect, Building / Property Services: Mr Chris Marchant, Head of Environment, King George V House, King George V Road, Amersham HP6 5AW ☎ 01895 837360; 01494 732250 ✆ cmarchant@chiltern.gov.uk

Building Control: Mr Peter Beckford, Head of Sustainable Development, King George V House, King George V Road, Amersham HP6 5AW ☎ 01895 837208; 01494 732036 ✆ pbeckford@chiltern.gov.uk

Children / Youth Services: Mr Paul Nanji, Principal Leisure & Community Officer, King George V House, King George V Road, Amersham HP6 5AW ☎ 01494 732110 ✆ pnanji@chiltern.gov.uk

PR / Communications: Mrs Rachel Prance, Community & Partnerships Manager, King George V House, King George V Road, Amersham HP6 5AW ☎ 01494 732903 ✆ rprance@chiltern.gov.uk

Community Planning: Mr David Gardner, Community Projects & Revitalisation Officer, King George V House, King George V Road, Amersham HP6 5AW ☎ 01494 732759 ✆ dgardner@chiltern.gov.uk

Community Safety: Mrs Katie Galvin, Community Safety Manager, King George V House, King George V Road, Amersham HP6 5AW ☎ 01494 732265 ✆ kgalvin@chiltern.gov.uk

Computer Management: Mrs Simonette Dixon, Head of Business Support, King George V House, King George V Road, Amersham HP6 5AW ☎ 01494 732087 ✆ sdixon@chiltern.gov.uk

Customer Service: Mrs Nicola Ellis, Head of Customer Services, King George V House, King George V Road, Amersham HP6 5AW ☎ 01494 732231 ✆ nellis@chiltern.gov.uk

Economic Development: Mr Bob Smith, Acting Chief Executive, King George V House, King George V Road, Amersham HP6 5AW ☎ 01494 732178 ✆ bsmith@chiltern.gov.uk

E-Government: Mrs Simonette Dixon, Head of Business Support, King George V House, King George V Road, Amersham HP6 5AW ☎ 01494 732087 ✆ sdixon@chiltern.gov.uk

Electoral Registration: Miss Lesley Blue, Interim Democratic & Electoral Services Manager, King George V House, King George V Road, Amersham HP6 5AW ☎ 01494 732010 ✆ lblue@chiltern.gov.uk

Emergency Planning: Mrs Glynis Chanell, Corporate Resilience Officer, King George V House, King George V Road, Amersham HP6 5AW ☎ 01494 732059 ✆ gchanell@chiltern.gov.uk

Energy Management: Mr Ben Coakley, Environmental Health Manager, King George V House, King George V Road, Amersham HP6 5AW ☎ 01494 732060 ✆ ben.coakley@southbucks.gov.uk

Environmental / Technical Services: Mr Chris Marchant, Head of Environment, King George V House, King George V Road, Amersham HP6 5AW ☎ 01895 837360; 01494 732250 ✆ cmarchant@chiltern.gov.uk

Environmental Health: Mr Martin Holt, Head of Healthy Communities, King George V House, King George V Road, Amersham HP6 5AW ☎ 01494 732055 ✆ mholt@chiltern.gov.uk

Estates, Property & Valuation: Mr Chris Marchant, Head of Environment, King George V House, King George V Road, Amersham HP6 5AW ☎ 01895 837360; 01494 732250 ✆ cmarchant@chiltern.gov.uk

European Liaison: Mr Bob Smith, Acting Chief Executive, King George V House, King George V Road, Amersham HP6 5AW ☎ 01494 732178 ✆ bsmith@chiltern.gov.uk

Facilities: Mr Kevin Kelly, Facilities Manager, King George V House, King George V Road, Amersham HP6 5AW ☎ 01494 586814 ✆ kkelly@chiltern.gov.uk

CHILTERN

Facilities: Ms Ann Pedder, Premises Supervisor, King George V House, King George V Road, Amersham HP6 5AW
☎ 01494 732262 ✆ apedder@chiltern.gov.uk

Finance: Mr Rodney Fincham, Head of Finance, King George V House, King George V Road, Amersham HP6 5AW
☎ 01243 776766 ✆ rfincham.chiltern.gov.uk

Treasury: Mr Jim Burness, Director - Resources, King George V House, King George V Road, Amersham HP6 5AW
☎ 01494 732095 ✆ jburness@chiltern.gov.uk

Grounds Maintenance: Mr Chris Marchant, Head of Environment, King George V House, King George V Road, Amersham HP6 5AW
☎ 01895 837360; 01494 732250 ✆ cmarchant@chiltern.gov.uk

Health and Safety: Mrs Glynis Chanell, Corporate Resilience Officer, King George V House, King George V Road, Amersham HP6 5AW ☎ 01494 732059 ✆ gchanell@chiltern.gov.uk

Home Energy Conservation: Mrs Louise Quinn, Senior Housing Standards Officer, King George V House, King George V Road, Amersham HP6 5AW ☎ 01494 732209 ✆ lquinn@chiltern.gov.uk

Housing: Mr Michael Veryard, Housing Manager, King George V House, King George V Road, Amersham HP6 5AW
☎ 01494 732200 ✆ mveryard@chiltern.gov.uk

Legal: Mrs Joanna Swift, Head of Legal & Democratic Services, King George V House, King George V Road, Amersham HP6 5AW
☎ 01895 837229; 01494 732761 ✆ jswift@chiltern.gov.uk

Leisure and Cultural Services: Mr Martin Holt, Head of Healthy Communities, King George V House, King George V Road, Amersham HP6 5AW ☎ 01494 732055 ✆ mholt@chiltern.gov.uk

Licensing: Mr Nathan March, Licensing Manager, King George V House, King George V Road, Amersham HP6 5AW
☎ 01494 732249 ✆ nmarch@chiltern.gov.uk

Lottery Funding, Charity and Voluntary: Mr Martin Holt, Head of Healthy Communities, King George V House, King George V Road, Amersham HP6 5AW ☎ 01494 732055
✆ mholt@chiltern.gov.uk

Member Services: Miss Lesley Blue, Interim Democratic & Electoral Services Manager, King George V House, King George V Road, Amersham HP6 5AW ☎ 01494 732010
✆ lblue@chiltern.gov.uk

Parking: Ms Julie Rushton, Parking Manager, King George V House, King George V Road, Amersham HP6 5AW
☎ 01494 586877 ✆ jrushton@chiltern.gov.uk

Personnel / HR: Mrs Judy Benson, Joint Principal Personnel Officer, King George V House, King George V Road, Amersham HP6 5AW ☎ 01494 732015 ✆ jbenson@chiltern.gov.uk

Planning: Mr Peter Beckford, Head of Sustainable Development, King George V House, King George V Road, Amersham HP6 5AW
☎ 01895 837208; 01494 732036 ✆ pbeckford@chiltern.gov.uk

Procurement: Mr Jim Burness, Director - Resources, King George V House, King George V Road, Amersham HP6 5AW
☎ 01494 732095 ✆ jburness@chiltern.gov.uk

Recycling & Waste Minimisation: Ms Sally Gordon, Acting Senior Officer - Waste, King George V House, King George V Road, Amersham HP6 5AW ☎ 01494 586868 ✆ sgordon@chiltern.gov.uk

Regeneration: Mr Bob Smith, Acting Chief Executive, King George V House, King George V Road, Amersham HP6 5AW
☎ 01494 732178 ✆ bsmith@chiltern.gov.uk

Staff Training: Mrs Judy Benson, Joint Principal Personnel Officer, King George V House, King George V Road, Amersham HP6 5AW ☎ 01494 732015 ✆ jbenson@chiltern.gov.uk

Sustainable Development: Mr Ben Coakley, Environmental Health Manager, King George V House, King George V Road, Amersham HP6 5AW ☎ 01494 732060
✆ ben.coakley@southbucks.gov.uk

Waste Collection and Disposal: Ms Sally Gordon, Acting Senior Officer - Waste, King George V House, King George V Road, Amersham HP6 5AW ☎ 01494 586868 ✆ sgordon@chiltern.gov.uk

Waste Management: Mr Chris Marchant, Head of Environment, King George V House, King George V Road, Amersham HP6 5AW
☎ 01895 837360; 01494 732250 ✆ cmarchant@chiltern.gov.uk

COUNCILLORS

Chair: Harker, Mimi (CON - Chesham Bois & Weedon Hill)
mharker@chiltern.gov.uk

Vice-Chair: Shepherd, Nigel (CON - Amersham on the Hill)
nshepherd@chiltern.gov.uk

Leader of the Council: Darby, Isobel (CON - Chalfont Common)
idarby@chiltern.gov.uk

Deputy Leader of the Council: Stannard, Mike (CON - St Mary's & Waterside)
mstannard@chiltern.gov.uk

Group Leader: Jones, Peter (LD - Ballinger, South Heath & Chartridge)
peter.m.jones@btinternet.com

Bacon, Alan (LD - Asheridge Vale & Lowndes)
abacon@chiltern.gov.uk

Berry, Seb (IND - Great Missenden)
sberry@chiltern.gov.uk

Bray, Des (CON - Chalfont St Giles)
dbray @chiltern.gov.uk

Burton, Julie (CON - Penn & Coleshill)
jburton@chiltern.gov.uk

Cook, Jules (CON - Amersham Town)
jcook@chiltern.gov.uk

Culverhouse, Emily (CON - Hilltop & Townsend)
eculverhouse@chiltern.gov.uk

Flys, Mark (CON - Amersham Town)
mflys@chiltern.gov.uk

Ford, Christopher (CON - Gold Hill)
cford@chiltern.gov.uk

Garth, Andrew (CON - Ashley Green, Latimer & Chenies)
agarth@chiltern.gov.uk

Gladwin, John (CON - Prestwood & Heath End)
jgladwin@chiltern.gov.uk

Hardie, Alan (CON - Penn & Coleshill)
ahardie@chiltern.gov.uk

Harris, Graham (CON - Chesham Bois and Weedon Hill)
gharris@chiltern.gov.uk

Harrold, Murrey (CON - Central)
mharrold@chiltern.gov.uk

Hudson, Peter (CON - St Mary's & Waterside)
phudson@chiltern.gov.uk

Jackson, Carl (CON - Chalfont St Giles)
cjackson@chiltern.gov.uk

Jones, Robert (CON - Prestwood & Heath End)
rjones@chiltern.gov.uk

Jones, Caroline (CON - Amersham Common)
cmjones@chiltern.gov.uk

Lacey, Derek (IND - Ridgeway)
dlacey@chiltern.gov.uk

MacBean, Jane (CON - Asheridge Vale & Lowndes)
jmacbean@chiltern.gov.uk

Martin, Peter (CON - Little Chalfont)
pmartin@chiltern.gov.uk

Patel, Siddharth (CON - Seer Green)
spatel@chiltern.gov.uk

Phillips, Don (CON - Little Chalfont)
dphillips@chiltern.gov.uk

Rose, Nick (CON - Cholesbury, The Lee & Bellingdon)
nrose@chiltern.gov.uk

Rouse, Caroline (CON - Chalfont St Giles)
crouse@chiltern.gov.uk

Rush, Jonathan (CON - Central)
jrush@chiltern.gov.uk

Shaw, Mark (CON - Newtown)
mshaw@chiltern.gov.uk

Smith, Michael (CON - Holmer Green)
msmith@chiltern.gov.uk

Smith, Linda (CON - Chalfont Common)
lsmith@chiltern.gov.uk

Titterington, Mark (CON - Holmer Green)
mtittering@chiltern.gov.uk

Varley, Diana (CON - Little Missenden)
dvarley@chiltern.gov.uk

Varley, Nick (CON - Vale)
nvarley@chiltern.gov.uk

Wallace, Heather (CON - Prestwood & Heath End)
hwallace@chiltern.gov.uk

Walsh, Liz (CON - Amersham on The Hill)
lwalsh@chiltern.gov.uk

Wertheim, John (CON - Austenwood)
jwertheim@chiltern.gov.uk

Wilson, Fred (CON - Hilltop & Townsend)
fwilson@chiltern.gov.uk

POLITICAL COMPOSITION
CON: 36, IND: 2, LD: 2

COMMITTEE CHAIRS

Audit: Mr John Gladwin

Licensing: Mr Jonathan Rush

Planning: Mr Don Phillips

Chorley   D

Chorley Borough Council, Civic Offices, Union Street, Chorley PR7 1AL

☎ 01257 515151 🖷 01257 515150 🖳 www.chorley.gov.uk

FACTS AND FIGURES
Parliamentary Constituencies: Chorley
EU Constituencies: North West
Election Frequency: Elections are by thirds

PRINCIPAL OFFICERS

Chief Executive: Mr Gary Hall, Chief Executive, Town Hall, Market Street, Chorley PR7 1DP ☎ 01257 515151 ⌂ gary.hall@chorley.gov.uk

Deputy Chief Executive: Mr Jamie Carson, Deputy Chief Executive & Director - Early Intervention & Support, Civic Offices, Union Street, Chorley PR7 1AL ☎ 01257 515151 ⌂ jamie.carson@chorley.gov.uk

Senior Management: Mr Jamie Carson, Deputy Chief Executive & Director - Early Intervention & Support, Civic Offices, Union Street, Chorley PR7 1AL ☎ 01257 515151 ⌂ jamie.carson@chorley.gov.uk

Senior Management: Mr Asim Khan, Director - Customer & Digital, Civic Offices, Union Street, Chorley PR7 1AL ☎ 01257 515151 ⌂ asim.khan@chorley.gov.uk

Senior Management: Mr Chris Sinnott, Director - Policy & Governance, Town Hall, Market Street, Chorley PR7 1DP ☎ 01257 515151 ⌂ chris.sinnott@chorley.gov.uk

Architect, Building / Property Services: Mr Keith Davy, Property Services Manager, Town Hall, Market Street, Chorley PR7 1DP ☎ 01257 515151 ⌂ keith.davy@chorley.gov.uk

Building Control: Mr John Bethwaite, Building Control Team Leader, Civic Offices, Union Street, Chorley PR7 1AL ☎ 01257 515151 ⌂ john.bethwaite@chorley.gov.uk

PR / Communications: Mr Andrew Daniels, Communications & Events Manager, Town Hall, Market Street, Chorley PR7 1DP ☎ 01257 515151 ⌂ andrew.daniels@chorley.gov.uk

Community Safety: Mrs Louise Elo, Head of Early Intervention & Support, Civic Offices, Union Street, Chorley PR7 1AL ☎ 01257 515151 ⌂ louise.elo@chorley.gov.uk

Computer Management: Ms Debbie Wilson, ICT Services Manager, Civic Offices, Union Street, Chorley PR7 1AL ☎ 01257 515151 ⌂ debbie.wilson@chorley.gov.uk

CHORLEY

Customer Service: Ms Rebecca Huddleston, Head of Customer Transformation, Town Hall, Market Street, Chorley PR7 1DP
☎ 01257 515151 ✆ rebecca.huddleston@chorley.gov.uk

Economic Development: Ms Cath Burns, Employment Skills & Business Support Manager, Civic Offices, Union Street, Chorley PR7 1AL ☎ 01257 515151 ✆ cath.burns@chorley.gov.uk

E-Government: Ms Debbie Wilson, ICT Services Manager, Civic Offices, Union Street, Chorley PR7 1AL ☎ 01257 515151
✆ debbie.wilson@chorley.gov.uk

Electoral Registration: Mr Phil Davies, Electoral Services Manager, Town Hall, Market Street, Chorley PR7 1DP
☎ 01257 515151 ✆ phil.davies@chorley.gov.uk

Emergency Planning: Mrs Louise Elo, Head of Early Intervention & Support, Civic Offices, Union Street, Chorley PR7 1AL
☎ 01257 515151 ✆ louise.elo@chorley.gov.uk

Environmental / Technical Services: Mr Jamie Carson, Deputy Chief Executive & Director - Early Intervention & Support, Civic Offices, Union Street, Chorley PR7 1AL ☎ 01257 515151
✆ jamie.carson@chorley.gov.uk

Environmental Health: Mrs Louise Elo, Head of Early Intervention & Support, Civic Offices, Union Street, Chorley PR7 1AL ☎ 01257 515151 ✆ louise.elo@chorley.gov.uk

Events Manager: Mrs Louise Finch, Campaigns & Engagement Manager (Events), Town Hall, Market Street, Chorley PR7 1DP
☎ 01257 515151 ✆ louise.finch@chorley.gov.uk

Finance: Ms Susan Guinness, Head of Shared Financial Services, Town Hall, Market Street, Chorley PR7 1DP ☎ 01257 515151
✆ susan.guinness@chorley.gov.uk

Grounds Maintenance: Ms Jo Oliver, Waste & Streetscene Manager, Bengal Street Depot, Chorley PR7 1SA ☎ 01257 515151
✆ jo.oliver@chorley.gov.uk

Health and Safety: Mrs Denise Fisher, Health & Safety Advisor, Town Hall, Market Street, Chorley PR7 1DP ☎ 01257 515151
✆ denise.fisher@chorley.gov.uk

Housing: Mrs Fiona Daniels, Housing Options & Support Manager, Civic Offices, Union Street, Chorley PR7 1AL ☎ 01257 515151
✆ fiona.daniels@chorley.gov.uk

Legal: Mr Chris Moister, Head of Legal, Democratic & HR Services, Town Hall, Market Street, Chorley PR7 1DP ☎ 01257 515151
✆ chris.moister@chorley.gov.uk

Leisure and Cultural Services: Mr Jamie Carson, Deputy Chief Executive & Director - Early Intervention & Support, Civic Offices, Union Street, Chorley PR7 1AL ☎ 01257 515151
✆ jamie.carson@chorley.gov.uk

Licensing: Mr Jamie Carson, Deputy Chief Executive & Director - Early Intervention & Support, Civic Offices, Union Street, Chorley PR7 1AL ☎ 01257 515151 ✆ jamie.carson@chorley.gov.uk

Lottery Funding, Charity and Voluntary: Mr Chris Moister, Head of Legal, Democratic & HR Services, Town Hall, Market Street, Chorley PR7 1DP ☎ 01257 515151 ✆ chris.moister@chorley.gov.uk

Member Services: Ms Carol Russell, Democratic Services Manager, Town Hall, Market Street, Chorley PR7 1DP ☎ 01257 515151 ✆ carol.russell@chorley.gov.uk

Parking: Ms Alison Wilding, Customer Services Manager, Civic Offices, Union Street, Chorley PR7 1AL ☎ 01257 515151
✆ alison.windling@chorley.gov.uk

Partnerships: Mrs Victoria Willett, Performance & Partnerships Manager, Town Hall, Market Street, Chorley PR7 1DP
☎ 01257 515151 ✆ victoria.willett@chorley.gov.uk

Personnel / HR: Ms Camilla Oakes-Scofield, HR Services Manager, Town Hall, Market Street, Chorley PR7 1DP
☎ 01257 515151 ✆ camilla.scofield@chorley.gov.uk

Planning: Mr Asim Khan, Director - Customer & Digital, Civic Offices, Union Street, Chorley PR7 1AL ☎ 01257 515151
✆ asim.khan@chorley.gov.uk

Procurement: Mrs Janet Hinds, Principal Procurement Officer, Town Hall, Market Street, Chorley PR7 1DP ☎ 01257 515151
✆ janet.hinds@chorley.gov.uk

Recycling & Waste Minimisation: Ms Jo Oliver, Waste & Streetscene Manager, Bengal Street Depot, Chorley PR7 1SA
☎ 01257 515151 ✆ jo.oliver@chorley.gov.uk

Regeneration: Ms Cath Burns, Employment Skills & Business Support Manager, Civic Offices, Union Street, Chorley PR7 1AL
☎ 01257 515151 ✆ cath.burns@chorley.gov.uk

Staff Training: Mr Graeme Walmsley, Senior HR & OD Consultant, Town Hall, Market Street, Chorley PR7 1DP
☎ 01257 515151 ✆ graeme.walmsley@chorley.gov.uk

Street Scene: Mr Asim Khan, Director - Customer & Digital, Civic Offices, Union Street, Chorley PR7 1AL ☎ 01257 515151
✆ asim.khan@chorley.gov.uk

Sustainable Communities: Ms Cath Burns, Employment Skills & Business Support Manager, Civic Offices, Union Street, Chorley PR7 1AL ☎ 01257 515151 ✆ cath.burns@chorley.gov.uk

Sustainable Development: Ms Cath Burns, Employment Skills & Business Support Manager, Civic Offices, Union Street, Chorley PR7 1AL ☎ 01257 515151 ✆ cath.burns@chorley.gov.uk

Tourism: Mr Andrew Daniels, Communications & Events Manager, Town Hall, Market Street, Chorley PR7 1DP ☎ 01257 515151
✆ andrew.daniels@chorley.gov.uk

Town Centre: Mr Gary Hall, Chief Executive, Town Hall, Market Street, Chorley PR7 1DP ☎ 01257 515151 ✆ gary.hall@chorley.gov.uk

Waste Collection and Disposal: Ms Jo Oliver, Waste & Streetscene Manager, Bengal Street Depot, Chorley PR7 1SA
☎ 01257 515151 ✆ jo.oliver@chorley.gov.uk

Waste Management: Ms Jo Oliver, Waste & Streetscene Manager, Bengal Street Depot, Chorley PR7 1SA ☎ 01257 515151 ✆ jo.oliver@chorley.gov.uk

COUNCILLORS

Mayor: Dickinson, Doreen (CON - Lostock)
doreen.dickinson@chorley.gov.uk

Deputy Mayor: Perks, Mark (CON - Astley & Buckshaw)
mark.perks@chorley.gov.uk

Leader of the Council: Bradley, Alistair (LAB - Chorley South East)
alistair.bradley@chorley.gov.uk

Deputy Leader of the Council: Wilson, Peter (LAB - Adlington & Anderton)
peter.wilson@chorley.gov.uk

Group LeaderLeadbetter, Paul (CON - Chisnell)
paul.leadbetter@chorley.gov.uk

Group LeaderSnape, Ralph (IND - Chorley North West)
ralph.snape@chorley.gov.uk

Beaver, Aaron (LAB - Chorley North West)
aaron.beaver@chorley.gov.uk

Bell, Eric (CON - Clayton-le-Woods & Whittle-le-Woods)
eric.bell@chorley.gov.uk

Boardman, Martin (CON - Eccleston & Mawdesley)
martin.boardman@chorley.gov.uk

Bromilow, Charlie (LAB - Clayton-le-Woods North)
charlie.bromilow@chorley.gov.uk

Brown, Terry (LAB - Chorley East)
terence.brown@chorley.gov.uk

Caunce, Henry (CON - Eccleston & Mawdesley)
henry.caunce@chorley.gov.uk

Clark, Paul (LAB - Coppull)
paul.clark@chorley.gov.uk

Cronshaw, Jean (LAB - Clayton-le-Woods North)
jean.cronshaw@chorley.gov.uk

Cullens, Alan (CON - Clayton-le-Woods West & Cuerden)
alan.cullens@chorley.gov.uk

Dalton, John (CON - Lostock)
john.dalton@chorley.gov.uk

Dunn, Graham (LAB - Adlington & Anderton)
graham.dunn@chorley.gov.uk

Fitzsimmons, Jane (LAB - Coppull)
jane.fitzsimmons@chorley.gov.uk

France, Gordon (LAB - Pennine)
gordon.france@chorley.gov.uk

France, Christopher (LAB - Wheelton & Withnell)
chris.france@chorley.gov.uk

France, Margaret (LAB - Wheelton & Withnell)
margaret.france@chorley.gov.uk

Gee, Anthony (LAB - Chorley South West)
anthony.gee@chorley.gov.uk

Gee, Danny (LAB - Euxton North)
danny.gee@chorley.gov.uk

Gray, Tom (LAB - Euxton North)
tom.gray@chorley.gov.uk

Iddon, Keith (CON - Eccleston & Mawdesley)
keith.iddon@chorley.gov.uk

Jarnell, Mark (LAB - Euxton South)
mark.jarnell@chorley.gov.uk

Khan, Zara (LAB - Chorley East)
zara.khan@chorley.gov.uk

Khan, Hasina (LAB - Chorley East)
hasina.khan@chorley.gov.uk

Lees, Roy (LAB - Chorley South West)
roy.lees@chorley.gov.uk

Lees, Margaret (LAB - Chorley South West)
margaret.lees@chorley.gov.uk

Long, Sheila (CON - Brindle & Hoghton)
sheila.long@chorley.gov.uk

Lowe, Marion (LAB - Chorley North East)
marion.lowe@chorley.gov.uk

Lowe, Adrian (LAB - Chorley North East)
adrian.lowe@chorley.gov.uk

Lynch, Matthew (LAB - Astley & Buckshaw)
matthew.lynch@chorley.gov.uk

Molyneaux, June (LAB - Adlington & Anderton)
june.molyneaux@chorley.gov.uk

Morgan, Greg (CON - Clayton-le-Woods & Whittle-le-Woods)
greg.morgan@chorley.gov.uk

Morwood, Alistair (LAB - Chorley North East)
alistair.morwood@chorley.gov.uk

Muncaster, Michael (CON - Clayton-le-Woods West & Cuerden)
mick.muncaster@chorley.gov.uk

Murfitt, Steve (LAB - Clayton-le-Woods North)
steve.murfitt@chorley.gov.uk

Murray, Beverley (LAB - Chorley South East)
beverley.murray@chorley.gov.uk

Platt, Debra (CON - Euxton South)
debra.platt@chorley.gov.uk

Snape, Kim (LAB - Heath Charnock & Rivington)
kim.snape@chorley.gov.uk

Snape, Joyce (IND - Chorley North West)
joyce.snape@chorley.gov.uk

Toon, Richard (LAB - Coppull)
richard.toon@chorley.gov.uk

Walker, John (CON - Clayton-le-Woods & Whittle-le-Woods)
john.walker@chorley.gov.uk

Walmsley, Paul (LAB - Chorley South East)
paul.walmsley@chorley.gov.uk

Whittaker, Alan (LAB - Chisnell)
alan.whittaker@chorleyl.gov.uk

POLITICAL COMPOSITION
LAB: 31, CON: 14, IND: 2

COMMITTEE CHAIRS

Development Control: Miss June Molyneaux

Licensing: Mrs Marion Lowe

CHRISTCHURCH

Christchurch   D

Christchurch Borough Council, Civic Offices, Bridge Street, Christchurch BH23 1AZ
☎ 01202 495000 🖶 01202 495234
🖑 postmaster@christchurchandeastdorset.gov.uk
🖳 www.dorsetforyou.com

FACTS AND FIGURES
Parliamentary Constituencies: Christchurch County
EU Constituencies: South West
Election Frequency: Elections are of whole council

PRINCIPAL OFFICERS

Chief Executive: Mr David McIntosh, Chief Executive, Civic Offices, Bridge Street, Christchurch BH23 1AZ ☎ 01202 795000 🖑 dmcintosh@christchurchandeastdorset.gov.uk

Senior Management: Mr David Barnes, Strategic Director, Civic Offices, Bridge Street, Christchurch BH23 1AZ ☎ 01202 495077 🖑 dbarnes@christchurchandeastdorset.gov.uk

Senior Management: Ms Louise Miller, Strategic Director, Civic Offices, Bridge Street, Christchurch BH23 1AZ ☎ 01202 795611 🖑 lmiller@christchurchandeastdorset.gov.uk

Senior Management: Mr Ian Milner, Strategic Director, Civic Offices, Bridge Street, Christchurch BH23 1AZ ☎ 01202 795176 🖑 imilner@christchurchandeastdorset.gov.uk

Architect, Building / Property Services: Mr Ashley Harman, Property & Engineering Services Manager, Civic Offices, Bridge Street, Christchurch BH23 1AZ ☎ 01202 795076 🖑 aharman@christchurchandeastdorset.gov.uk

Best Value: Mr David Barnes, Strategic Director, Civic Offices, Bridge Street, Christchurch BH23 1AZ ☎ 01202 495077 🖑 dbarnes@christchurchandeastdorset.gov.uk

Building Control: Mr Martin Thompson, Building Control Manager, Civic Offices, Bridge Street, Christchurch BH23 1AZ ☎ 01202 795033 🖑 mthompson@christchurchandeastdorset.gov.uk

Children / Youth Services: Ms Judith Plumley, Head - Community & Economy, Civic Offices, Bridge Street, Christchurch BH23 1AZ ☎ 01202 795043 🖑 jplumpley@christchurchandeastdorset.gov.uk

PR / Communications: Mr Allan Wood, Communications Officer, Civic Offices, Bridge Street, Christchurch BH23 1AZ ☎ 01202 795455 🖑 awood@christchurchandeastdorset.gov.uk

Community Planning: Ms Judith Plumley, Head - Community & Economy, Civic Offices, Bridge Street, Christchurch BH23 1AZ ☎ 01202 795043 🖑 jplumpley@christchurchandeastdorset.gov.uk

Community Planning: Mr Simon Trueick, Community & Planning Policy Manager, Civic Offices, Bridge Street, Christchurch BH23 1AZ ☎ 01202 495038 🖑 strueick@christchurchandeastdorset.gov.uk

Community Safety: Ms Judith Plumley, Head - Community & Economy, Civic Offices, Bridge Street, Christchurch BH23 1AZ ☎ 01202 795043 🖑 jplumpley@christchurchandeastdorset.gov.uk

Computer Management: Ms Fiona Hughes, Partnership ICT Manager, Civic Offices, Bridge Street, Christchurch BH23 1AZ ☎ 01202 795148 🖑 fhughes@christchurchandeastdorset.gov.uk

Computer Management: Mr Matti Raudsepp, Head of Organisational Development, Civic Offices, Bridge Street, Christchurch BH23 1AZ ☎ 01202 795125 🖑 mraudsepp@christchurchandeastdorset.gov.uk

Corporate Services: Mr Matti Raudsepp, Head of Organisational Development, Civic Offices, Bridge Street, Christchurch BH23 1AZ ☎ 01202 795125 🖑 mraudsepp@christchurchandeastdorset.gov.uk

Customer Service: Mrs Debbie Cliff, Customer Services Manager, Civic Offices, Bridge Street, Christchurch BH23 1AZ ☎ 01202 579150 🖑 dcliff@christchurch.gov.uk

Customer Service: Mr Matti Raudsepp, Head of Organisational Development, Civic Offices, Bridge Street, Christchurch BH23 1AZ ☎ 01202 795125 🖑 mraudsepp@christchurchandeastdorset.gov.uk

Economic Development: Mr Nick James, Head of Growth & Economy, Civic Offices, Bridge Street, Christchurch BH23 1AZ 🖑 njames@christchurchandeastdorset.gov.uk

E-Government: Mr David Barnes, Strategic Director, Civic Offices, Bridge Street, Christchurch BH23 1AZ ☎ 01202 495077 🖑 dbarnes@christchurchandeastdorset.gov.uk

E-Government: Ms Fiona Hughes, Partnership ICT Manager, Civic Offices, Bridge Street, Christchurch BH23 1AZ ☎ 01202 795148 🖑 fhughes@christchurchandeastdorset.gov.uk

Electoral Registration: Mr Richard Jones, Democratic Services & Elections Manager, Council Offices, Furzehill, Wimborne BH21 4HN ☎ 01202 795171 🖑 rjones@christchurchandeastdorset.gov.uk

Emergency Planning: Mr Gary Foyle, Senior Recreation Services Officer, Civic Offices, Bridge Street, Christchurch BH23 1AZ ☎ 01202 795070 🖑 gfoyle@christchurchandeastdorset.gov.uk

Energy Management: Ms Rachel Sharpe, Sustainability Management Officer, Civic Offices, Bridge Street, Christchurch BH23 1AZ ☎ 01202 795047 🖑 rsharpe@christchurchandeastdorset.gov.uk

Environmental / Technical Services: Mr Lindsay Cass, Head of Property & Engineering, Civic Offices, Bridge Street, Christchurch BH23 1AZ ☎ 01202 795003 🖑 lcass@christchurchandeastdorset.gov.uk

Estates, Property & Valuation: Mr Philip Marston, Estates Officer, Civic Offices, Bridge Street, Christchurch BH23 1AZ ☎ 01202 795187 🖑 pmarston@christchurchandeastdorset.gov.uk

Facilities: Mrs Debbie Cliff, Customer Services Manager, Civic Offices, Bridge Street, Christchurch BH23 1AZ ☎ 01202 579150 🖑 dcliff@christchurch.gov.uk

Fleet Management: Mr Lindsay Cass, Head of Property & Engineering, Civic Offices, Bridge Street, Christchurch BH23 1AZ ☎ 01202 795003 🖑 lcass@christchurchandeastdorset.gov.uk

Grounds Maintenance: Mr Clive Sinden, Countryside & Open Spaces Manager, Civic Offices, Bridge Street, Christchurch BH23 1AZ ☎ 01202 795072 ⌖ csinden@christchurchandeastdorset.gov.uk

Health and Safety: Mr Andrew Broomfield, Team Leader - Food & Safety, Civic Offices, Bridge Street, Christchurch BH23 1AZ ☎ 01202 795464 ⌖ abroomfield@christchurchandeastdorset.gov.uk

Health and Safety: Ms Pauline Miller-McIlravey, Health & Safety Officer, Civic Offices, Bridge Street, Christchurch BH23 1AZ ☎ 01202 795198 ⌖ pmiller-mcilraey@christchurchandeastdorset.gov.uk

Housing: Ms Kathryn Blatchford, Strategic Housing Services Manager, Civic Offices, Bridge Street, Christchurch BH23 1AZ ☎ 01202 795158 ⌖ kblatchford@christchurchandeastdorset.gov.uk

Legal: Ms Sophia Nartey, Legal Services Manager, Civic Offices, Bridge Street, Christchurch BH23 1AZ ☎ 01202 795400 ⌖ snartey@christchurchandeastdorset.gov.uk

Licensing: Mr Steve Ricketts, Community Protection Team Leader, Civic Offices, Bridge Street, Christchurch BH23 1AZ ☎ 01202 795407 ⌖ sricketts@christchurchandeastdorset.gov.uk

Member Services: Mr Richard Jones, Democratic Services & Elections Manager, Council Offices, Furzehill, Wimborne BH21 4HN ☎ 01202 795171 ⌖ rjones@christchurchandeastdorset.gov.uk

Parking: Mr Ashley Harman, Property & Engineering Services Manager, Civic Offices, Bridge Street, Christchurch BH23 1AZ ☎ 01202 795076 ⌖ aharman@christchurchandeastdorset.gov.uk

Partnerships: Ms Judith Plumley, Head - Community & Economy, Civic Offices, Bridge Street, Christchurch BH23 1AZ ☎ 01202 795043 ⌖ jplumpley@christchurchandeastdorset.gov.uk

Personnel / HR: Mr Matti Raudsepp, Head of Organisational Development, Civic Offices, Bridge Street, Christchurch BH23 1AZ ☎ 01202 795125 ⌖ mraudsepp@christchurchandeastdorset.gov.uk

Personnel / HR: Ms Lynda Thomson, Organisational Development, Civic Offices, Bridge Street, Christchurch BH23 1AZ ☎ 01202 795168 ⌖ mharford@christchurchandeastdorset.gov.uk

Planning: Mr David Barnes, Strategic Director, Civic Offices, Bridge Street, Christchurch BH23 1AZ ☎ 01202 495077 ⌖ dbarnes@christchurchandeastdorset.gov.uk

Recycling & Waste Minimisation: Mr Lindsay Cass, Head of Property & Engineering, Civic Offices, Bridge Street, Christchurch BH23 1AZ ☎ 01202 795003 ⌖ lcass@christchurchandeastdorset.gov.uk

Regeneration: Mr David Barnes, Strategic Director, Civic Offices, Bridge Street, Christchurch BH23 1AZ ☎ 01202 495077 ⌖ dbarnes@christchurchandeastdorset.gov.uk

Staff Training: Ms Lynda Thomson, Organisational Development, Civic Offices, Bridge Street, Christchurch BH23 1AZ ☎ 01202 795168 ⌖ mharford@christchurchandeastdorset.gov.uk

Sustainable Communities: Ms Rachel Sharpe, Sustainability Management Officer, Civic Offices, Bridge Street, Christchurch BH23 1AZ ☎ 01202 495047 ⌖ rsharpe@christchurchandeastdorset.gov.uk

Sustainable Development: Ms Judith Plumley, Head - Community & Economy, Civic Offices, Bridge Street, Christchurch BH23 1AZ ☎ 01202 795043 ⌖ jplumpley@christchurchandeastdorset.gov.uk

Waste Collection and Disposal: Mr Lindsay Cass, Head of Property & Engineering, Civic Offices, Bridge Street, Christchurch BH23 1AZ ☎ 01202 795003 ⌖ lcass@christchurchandeastdorset.gov.uk

Waste Management: Mr Lindsay Cass, Head of Property & Engineering, Civic Offices, Bridge Street, Christchurch BH23 1AZ ☎ 01202 795003 ⌖ lcass@christchurchandeastdorset.gov.uk

COUNCILLORS

Mayor: Jamieson, Patricia (CON - West Highcliffe) cllr.tjamieson@christchurch.gov.uk

Deputy Mayor: Geary, Nicholas (CON - North Highcliffe & Walkford) cllr.ngeary@christchurch.gov.uk

Leader of the Council: Nottage, Ray (CON - Purewell & Stanpit) cllr.rnottage@christchurch.gov.uk

Deputy Leader of the Council: Bath, Claire (CON - Mudeford & Friars Cliff) cllr.cbath@christchurch.gov.uk

Abbott, Janet (UKIP - Grange) cllr.jabbott@christchurch.gov.uk

Barfield, Andy (CON - Mudeford & Friars Cliff) cllr.abarfield@christchurch.gov.uk

Bungey, Colin (IND - Jumpers) cllr.cbungey@christchurch.gov.uk

Davis, Bernie (CON - Purewell & Stanpit) cllr.bdavis@christchurch.gov.uk

Dedman, Lesley (CON - West Highcliffe) cllr.ldedman@christchurch.gov.uk

Derham Wilkes, Sally (CON - North Highcliffe & Walkford) cllr.sjderhamwilkes@christchurch.gov.uk

Flagg, David (CON - Burton & Winkton) cllr.dflagg@christchurch.gov.uk

Fox, Tavis (CON - Portfield) cllr.tfox@christchurch.gov.uk

Grace, Wendy (CON - Town Centre) cllr.wgrace@christchurch.gov.uk

Hall, Peter (CON - Town Centre) cllr.phall@christchurch.gov.uk

Hallam, Vicki (CON - Highcliffe) cllr.vhallam@christchurch.gov.uk

Jamieson, Colin (CON - Burton & Winkton) cllr.cpjamieson@christchurch.gov.uk

Jones, Denise (CON - Grange) cllr.denisejones@christchurch.gov.uk

CHRISTCHURCH

Jones, David (CON - West Highcliffe)
cllr.djones@christchurch.gov.uk

Lofts, John (CON - Highcliffe)
cllr.jlofts@christchurchanddorset.gov.uk

Neale, Frederick (IND - Jumpers)
cllr.fneale@christchurch.gov.uk

Phipps, Margaret (CON - St Catherine's & Hurn)
cllr.mphipps@christchurch.gov.uk

Smith, Lisle (CON - Portfield)
cllr.lsmith@christchurch.gov.uk

Spittle, Susan (CON - St. Catherine's & Hurn)
cllr.sspittle@christchurch.gov.uk

Watts, Trevor (CON - Mudeford & Friars Cliff)
cllr.trwatts@christchurch.gov.uk

POLITICAL COMPOSITION
CON: 21, IND: 2, UKIP: 1

COMMITTEE CHAIRS

Planning Control: Mrs Lisle Smith

City of London   L

City of London, PO Box 270, Guildhall, London EC2P 2EJ
☎ 020 7332 1400; 020 7606 3030 🖨 020 7796 2621; 020 7332 1119
🖰 pro@cityoflondon.gov.uk 🖳 www.cityoflondon.gov.uk

FACTS AND FIGURES
Parliamentary Constituencies: Cities of London and Westminster
EU Constituencies: London
Election Frequency: Common Councilmen- 4 years, Aldermen- 6 years

PRINCIPAL OFFICERS

Chief Executive: Mr John Barradell, Town Clerk & Chief Executive, PO Box 270, Guildhall, London EC2P 2EJ ☎ 020 7332 1400; 020 7796 2621 🖰 townclerk@cityoflondon.gov.uk

Assistant Chief Executive: Mr Peter Lisley, Assistant Town Clerk, PO Box 270, Guildhall, London EC2P 2EJ ☎ 020 7332 1438; 020 7796 2621 🖰 peter.lisley@cityoflondon.gov.uk

Assistant Chief Executive: Mr Simon Murrells, Assistant Town Clerk, PO Box 270, Guildhall, London EC2P 2EJ ☎ 020 7332 1418; 020 7796 2621 🖰 simon.murrells@cityoflondon.gov.uk

Senior Management: Mr Peter Bennett, City Surveyor, PO Box 270, Guildhall, London EC2P 2EJ ☎ 020 7332 1502; 020 7332 3031 🖰 peter.bennett@cityoflondon.gov.uk

Senior Management: Mr William Chapman, Private Secretary & Chief of Staff to the Lord Mayor, PO Box 270, Guildhall, London EC2P 2EJ ☎ 020 7379 9302 🖰 william.chapman@cityoflondon.gov.uk

Senior Management: Mr Michael Cogher, Comptroller & City Solicitor, PO Box 270, Guildhall, London EC2P 2EJ ☎ 020 7332 3699 🖰 michael.cogher@cityoflondon.gov.uk

Senior Management: Mr Paul Double, City Remembrancer, PO Box 270, Guildhall, London EC2P 2EJ ☎ 020 7332 1207 🖰 paul.double@cityoflondon.gov.uk

Senior Management: Mr Barry Ife, Principale of the Guildhall School of Music & Drama, PO Box 270, Guildhall, London EC2P 2EJ ☎ 020 7628 2571 🖰 barry.ife@cityoflondon.gov.uk

Senior Management: Mrs Sue Ireland, Director - Open Spaces, City of London Open Space Department, 1 Guildhall Yard, London EC2V 5AE ☎ 020 7332 3033; 020 7332 3522 🖰 sue.ireland@cityoflondon.gov.uk

Senior Management: Mr Peter Kane, Chamberlain, PO Box 270, Guildhall, London EC2P 2EJ ☎ 020 7332 1300 🖰 chamberlain@cityoflondon.gov.uk

Senior Management: Sir Nicholas Kenyon, Managing Director of the Barbican Centre, Barbican Centre, Silk Street, London EC2Y 8DS ☎ 020 7382 7001; 020 7382 7245 🖰 nkenyon@barbican.org.uk

Senior Management: Ms Chrissie Morgan, Director - Human Resources, PO Box 270, Guildhall, London EC2P 2EJ ☎ 020 7332 1424 🖰 chrissie.morgan@cityoflondon.gov.uk

Senior Management: Mr Damian Nussbaum, Director - Economic Development, PO Box 270, Guildhall, London EC2P 2EJ ☎ 020 7332 3600 🖰 damian.nussbaum@cityoflondon.gov.uk

Senior Management: Mr David Pearson, Director - Culture, Heritage & Libraries, PO Box 270, Guildhall, London EC2P 2EJ 🖰 david.pearson@cityoflondon.gov.uk

Senior Management: Mr David Smith, Director - Markets & Consumer Protection, PO Box 270, Guildhall, London EC2P 2EJ ☎ 020 7332 3967 🖰 david.smith@cityoflondon.gov.uk

PR / Communications: Mr Bob Roberts, Communications Director, PO Box 270, Guildhall, London EC2P 2EJ 🖰 bob.roberts@cityoflondon.gov.uk

Computer Management: Mr Bill Limond, Information Systems Director, 65 Basinghall Street, London EC2V 5DZ ☎ 020 7332 1307; 020 7332 3110 🖰 bill.limond@cityoflondon.gov.uk

Contracts: Mr Richard Jeffrey, Assistant City Solicitor, PO Box 270, Guildhall, London EC2P 2EJ ☎ 020 7332 1683 🖰 richard.jeffrey@cityoflondon.gov.uk

Customer Service: Ms Jill Bailey, Access to Services Programme Manager, PO Box 270, Guildhall, London EC2P 2EJ ☎ 020 7332 3422 🖰 jill.bailey@cityoflondon.gov.uk

Economic Development: Mr Damian Nussbaum, Director - Economic Development, PO Box 270, Guildhall, London EC2P 2EJ ☎ 020 7332 3600 🖰 damian.nussbaum@cityoflondon.gov.uk

European Liaison: Ms Audrey Nelson, Senior European Officer, PO Box 270, Guildhall, London EC2P 2EJ ☎ 020 7332 1054; 020 7332 3616 🖰 audrey.nelson@cityoflondon.gov.uk

Events Manager: Ms Fiona Hoban, Assistant Remembrancer (Ceremonial), PO Box 270, Guildhall, London EC2P 2EJ
☎ 020 7332 1261 ᐧᕊ fiona.hoban@cityoflondon.gov.uk

Finance: Mrs Carla-Maria Heath, Head of Revenues, PO Box 270, Guildhall, London EC2P 2EJ ☎ 020 7332 1387
ᐧᕊ carla-maria.heath@cityoflondon.gov.uk

Finance: Mr Peter Kane, Chamberlain, PO Box 270, Guildhall, London EC2P 2EJ ☎ 020 7332 1300 ᐧᕊ chamberlain@cityoflondon.gov.uk

Treasury: Mr Peter Kane, Chamberlain, PO Box 270, Guildhall, London EC2P 2EJ ☎ 020 7332 1300
ᐧᕊ chamberlain@cityoflondon.gov.uk

Treasury: Ms Kate Limna, Corporate Treasurer, PO Box 270, Guildhall, London EC2P 2EJ ☎ 020 7332 1309
ᐧᕊ kate.limna@cityoflondon.gov.uk

Pensions: Mr Charlie Partridge, Pensions Manager, PO Box 270, Guildhall, London EC2P 2EJ ☎ 020 7332 1133
ᐧᕊ charlie.partridge@cityoflondon.gov.uk

Fleet Management: Mr Douglas Wilkinson, Cleansing Services Assistant Director, Walbrook Wharf, Upper Thames Street, London EC4R 3TD ☎ 020 7332 4998; 020 7236 6560
ᐧᕊ douglas.wilkinson@cityoflondon.gov.uk

Grounds Maintenance: Mr Martin Rodman, Superintendant of West Ham Park & City Gardens, PO Box 270, Guildhall, London EC2P 2EJ ☎ 020 7374 4152; 020 7374 4116
ᐧᕊ martin.rodman@cityoflondon.gov.uk

Highways: Mr Paul Monaghan, Assistant Director - Engineering, PO Box 270, Guildhall, London EC2P 2EJ
ᐧᕊ paul.monaghan@cityoflondon.gov.uk

Highways: Mr Steve Presland, Transportation & Public Realm Director, PO Box 270, Guildhall, London EC2P 2EJ
☎ 020 7332 4999 ᐧᕊ steve.presland@cityoflondon.gov.uk

Housing Maintenance: Mr Edwin Stevens, Housing & Technical Services Director, 3 Lauderdale Place, Barbican, London EC2Y 8EN
☎ 020 7332 3015 ᐧᕊ edwin.stevens@cityoflondon.gov.uk

Legal: Mr Michael Cogher, Comptroller & City Solicitor, PO Box 270, Guildhall, London EC2P 2EJ ☎ 020 7332 3699
ᐧᕊ michael.cogher@cityoflondon.gov.uk

Leisure and Cultural Services: Mrs Sue Ireland, Director - Open Spaces, City of London Open Space Department, 1 Guildhall Yard, London EC2V 5AE ☎ 020 7332 3033; 020 7332 3522
ᐧᕊ sue.ireland@cityoflondon.gov.uk

Leisure and Cultural Services: Sir Nicholas Kenyon, Managing Director of the Barbican Centre, Barbican Centre, Silk Street, London EC2Y 8DS ☎ 020 7382 7001 ᐧᕊ nkenyon@barbican.org.uk

Leisure and Cultural Services: Mr David Pearson, Director - Culture, Heritage & Libraries, PO Box 270, Guildhall, London EC2P 2EJ ᐧᕊ david.pearson@cityoflondon.gov.uk

Licensing: Mr Bryn Aldridge, Trading Standards Consultant, Walbrook Wharf, Upper Thames Street, London EC4R 3TD
ᐧᕊ bryn.aldridge@cityoflondon.gov.uk

Lighting: Mr John Burke, Mechanical & Electrical Services Manager, PO Box 270, Guildhall, London EC2P 2EJ
☎ 020 7332 1102 ᐧᕊ john.burke@cityoflondon.gov.uk

Lottery Funding, Charity and Voluntary: Mr David Farnsworth, Director & Chief Grants Officer - City Bridge Trust, PO Box 270, Guildhall, London EC2P 2EJ ☎ 020 7332 3713
ᐧᕊ david.farnsworth@cityoflondon.gov.uk

Parking: Mr Ian Hughes, Assistant Highways Director, PO Box 270, Guildhall, London EC2P 2EJ ☎ 020 7332 1977
ᐧᕊ ian.hughes@cityoflondon.gov.uk

Personnel / HR: Ms Chrissie Morgan, Director - Human Resources, PO Box 270, Guildhall, London EC2P 2EJ
☎ 020 7332 1424 ᐧᕊ chrissie.morgan@cityoflondon.gov.uk

Planning: Ms Annie Hampson, Chief Planning Officer, PO Box 270, Guildhall, London EC2P 2EJ ☎ 020 7332 1700
ᐧᕊ annie.hampson@cityoflondon.gov.uk

Procurement: Mr Gary Dowding, Head of Business Enablement, PO Box 270, Guildhall, London EC2P 2EJ ☎ 020 7332 1828; 020 7332 1535 ᐧᕊ gary.dowding@cityoflondon.gov.uk

Public Libraries: Mr David Pearson, Director - Culture, Heritage & Libraries, PO Box 270, Guildhall, London EC2P 2EJ
ᐧᕊ david.pearson@cityoflondon.gov.uk

Road Safety: Mr Matthew Collins, Road Safety Team Leader, PO Box 270, Guildhall, London EC2P 2EJ ☎ 020 7332 1546; 020 7332 1806 ᐧᕊ matthew.collins@cityoflondon.gov.uk

Social Services (Adult): Mr Dave Mason, Interim Head of Adult Social Care, North Wing 2nd Floor, PO Box 270, Guildhall, London EC2P 2EJ ☎ 020 7332 1636 ᐧᕊ dave.mason@cityoflondon.gov.uk

Public Health: Dr Penny Bevan, Director - Public Health, Town Hall, Mare Street, London E8 1EA ᐧᕊ penny.bevan@hackney.gov.uk

Street Scene: Mr Steve Presland, Transportation & Public Realm Director, PO Box 270, Guildhall, London EC2P 2EJ
☎ 020 7332 4999 ᐧᕊ steve.presland@cityoflondon.gov.uk

Sustainable Communities: Mr Neal Hounsell, Assistant Director - Commissioning & Partnership, Department of Community and Children's Services, PO Box 270, Guildhall, London EC2P 2EJ
☎ 020 7332 1638 ᐧᕊ neal.hounsell@cityoflondon.gov.uk

Traffic Management: Mr Iain Simmons, Assistant Director - City Transportation, PO Box 270, Guildhall, London EC2P 2EJ
☎ 020 7332 1151; 020 7332 1806 ᐧᕊ iain.simmons@cityoflondon.gov.uk

Waste Collection and Disposal: Mr Jim Graham, Assistant Director - Operations / Cleansing, Walbrook Wharf, Upper Thames Street, London EC4R 3TD ☎ 020 7332 4972; 020 7236 6560
ᐧᕊ jim.graham@cityoflondon.gov.uk

CITY OF LONDON

Waste Collection and Disposal: Mr Steve Presland, Transportation & Public Realm Director, PO Box 270, Guildhall, London EC2P 2EJ ☎ 020 7332 4999 ✆ steve.presland@cityoflondon.gov.uk

Waste Management: Mr Lee Turner, Senior Waste Disposal Officer, Walbrook Wharf, Upper Thames Street, London EC4R 3TD ☎ 020 7332 4976; 020 7236 6560 ✆ lee.turner@cityoflondon.gov.uk

COUNCILLORS

The Lord Mayor: Evans, Jeffrey (NP - Cheap)
jeffrey.evans@cityoflondon.gov.uk

Alderman: Anstee, Nick (IND - Aldersgate)
nick.anstee@sjberwin.com

Alderman: Bear, Michael (NP - Portsoken)
michael.bear@cityoflondon.gov.uk

Alderman: Bowman, Charles (NP - Lime Street)
charles.bowman@uk.pwc.com

Alderman: Eskenzi, Anthony (NP - Farringdon Within)
anthony.eskenzi@cityoflondon.gov.uk

Alderman: Estlin, Peter (NP - Coleman Street)
peter.estlin@barclays.com

Alderman: Garbutt, John (NP - Walbrook)
john.garbutt@halbis.com

Alderman: Gowman, Alison (NP - Dowgate)
alison.gowman@dlapiper.com

Alderman: Graves, David (NP - Cripplegate)
david.graves@cityoflondon.gov.uk

Alderman: Hailes, Timothy (NP - Bassishaw)
tim.hailes@cityoflondon.gov.uk

Alderman: Haines, Gordon (NP - Queenhithe)
gordon.haines@cityoflondon.gov.uk

Alderman: Hewitt, Peter (NP - Aldgate)
peter.hewitt@aldgateward.com

Alderman: Howard, David (NP - Cornhill)
david.howard@charles-stanley.co.uk

Alderman: Judge, Paul (NP - Tower)
paul@paulrjudge.com

Alderman: Keaveny, Vincent (NP - Farringdon Within)
vincent.keaveny@cityoflondon.gov.uk

Alderman: Luder, Ian (NP - Castle Baynard)
ian.luder@cityoflondon.gov.uk

Alderman: Mainelli, Michael (NP - Broad Street)

Alderman: Malins, Julian (NP - Farringdon Without)
malins@btinternet.com

Alderman: Parmley, Andrew (NP - Vintry)
andrew.parmley@cityoflondon.gov.uk

Alderman: Richardson, Matthew (NP - Billingsgate)

Alderman: Richardson, Adam (NP - Farringdon Without)
adam@adamrichardson.co.uk

Alderman: Russell, William (NP - Bread Street)
thriplowbury@aol.com

Alderman: Scotland of Asthal, Patricia (IND - Bishopsgate)

Alderman: Wootton, David (NP - Langbourn)
david.wootton@cityoflondon.gov.uk

Common Councilman: Abrahams, George (NP - Farringdon Without)
georgea@georgeabrahams.co.uk

Common Councilman: Absalom, John (NP - Farringdon Without)
john.absalom@cityoflondon.gov.uk

Common Councilman: Anderson, Randall (IND - Aldersgate)
randall.anderson@cityoflondon.gov.uk

Common Councilman: Bain-Stewart, Alex (NP - Farringdon Within)
alex.bain-stewart@cityoflondon.gov.uk

Common Councilman: Barker, John (NP - Cripplegate)
john.barker@cityoflondon.gov.uk

Common Councilman: Barrow, Douglas (NP - Aldgate)

Common Councilman: Bennett, John (NP - Broad Street)
john.bennett@cityoflondon.gov.uk

Common Councilman: Bensted-Smith, Nicholas (NP - Cheap)

Common Councilman: Boden, Christopher (NP - Castle Baynard)
christopher.boden@cityoflondon.gov.uk

Common Councilman: Boleat, Mark (NP - Cordwainer)
mark.boleat@cityoflondon.gov.uk

Common Councilman: Bottomley, Keith (IND - Bridge & Bridge Without)
keith.bottomley@cityoflondon.gov.uk

Common Councilman: Bradshaw, David (NP - Cripplegate)
david.bradshaw@cityoflondon.gov.uk

Common Councilman: Campbell-Taylor, William Goodacre (LAB - Portsoken)
william.taylor@cityoflondon.gov.uk

Common Councilman: Cassidy, Michael (NP - Coleman Street)
michael.cassidy@dlapiper.com

Common Councilman: Chadwick, Roger (NP - Tower)
roger.chadwick@cityoflondon.gov.uk

Common Councilman: Challis, Nigel (NP - Castle Baynard)
nigel.challis@cityoflondon.gov.uk

Common Councilman: Chapman, John (NP - Langbourn)
johnc@jdconsultants.com

Common Councilman: Christian, Dominic (IND - Lime Street)
dominic.christian@aonbenfield.com

Common Councilman: Clark, Jamie (NP - Billingsgate)

Common Councilman: Colthurst, Henry (NP - Lime Street)

Common Councilman: Cotgrove, Dennis (NP - Lime Street)
dennis.cotgrove@cityoflondon.gov.uk

Common Councilman: De Sausmarez, James (IND - Candlewick)

Common Councilman: Deane, Alexander (NP - Farringdon Without)
alexanderdeane@ymail.com

Common Councilman: D'Olier Duckworth, Simon (NP - Bishopsgate)

Common Councilman: Dostalova, Karina (NP - Farringdon Within)

Common Councilman: Dove, William (NP - Bishopsgate)

Common Councilman: Dudley, Martin (IND - Aldersgate)
martin.dudley@cityoflondon.gov.uk

Common Councilman: Dunphy, Peter (NP - Cornhill)
petergdunphy@hotmail.com

Common Councilman: Edhem, Emma (NP - Castle Baynard)
emma_edhem@yahoo.co.uk

Common Councilman: Everett, Kevin (NP - Candlewick)
kevin.everett@cityoflondon.gov.uk

Common Councilman: Fairweather, Anne (IND - Tower)
anne.fairweather@cityoflondon.gov.uk

Common Councilman: Fernandes, Sophie (NP - Coleman Street)
sophieannefernandes@gmail.com

Common Councilman: Fraser, Stuart (NP - Coleman Street)
stuart.fraser@cityoflondon.gov.uk

Common Councilman: Fraser, Bill (NP - Vintry)
william.fraser@cityoflondon.gov.uk

Common Councilman: Fredericks, Marianne (NP - Tower)
marianne_fredericks@hotmail.com

Common Councilman: Frew, Lucy (NP - Walbrook)
lucy.frew@cityoflondon.gov.uk

Common Councilman: Gillon, George (NP - Cordwainer)
george.gillon@cityoflondon.gov.uk

Common Councilman: Ginsburg, Stanley (NP - Bishopsgate)
stanley.ginsburg@cityoflondon.gov.uk

Common Councilman: Haines, Stephen (NP - Cornhill)
stephen.haines@cityoflondon.gov.uk

Common Councilman: Harris, Brian (NP - Bridge & Bridge Without)
brian.harris@cityoflondon.gov.uk

Common Councilman: Harrower, George (IND - Bassishaw)

Common Councilman: Hayward, Christopher (NP - Broad Street)
chris@haywardinvestments.com

Common Councilman: Hoffman, Tom (NP - Vintry)
tom.hoffman@cityoflondon.gov.uk

Common Councilman: Holmes, Ann (NP - Farringdon Within)
ann.holmes@cityoflondon.gov.uk

Common Councilman: Hudson, Michael (NP - Castle Baynard)
city@mhlaw.co.uk

Common Councilman: Hyde, Wendy (NP - Bishopsgate)
wendy.hyde@cityoflondon.gov.uk

Common Councilman: James, Clare (NP - Farringdon Within)
clare.james@puntersouthall.com

Common Councilman: Jones, Henry (NP - Portsoken)
henry.jones@cityoflondon.gov.uk

Common Councilman: Jones, Gregory (NP - Farringdon Without)

Common Councilman: King, Alastair (NP - Queenhithe)
alastair.king@cityoflondon.gov.uk

Common Councilman: Lawrence, Greg (NP - Farringdon Without)
gregory.lawrence@cityoflondon.gov.uk

Common Councilman: Littlechild, Vivienne (NP - Cripplegate)
vivienne.littlechild@cityoflondon.gov.uk

Common Councilman: Lodge, Oliver (NP - Bread Street)
oliver.lodge@cityoflondon.gov.uk

Common Councilman: Lord, Charles Edward (NP - Farringdon Without)
edward.lord@cityoflondon.gov.uk

Common Councilman: Lumley, John (IND - Aldersgate)

Common Councilman: Martinelli, Peter (NP - Farringdon Without)
peter.martinelli@cityoflondon.gov.uk

Common Councilman: Mayhew, Jeremy (IND - Aldersgate)
jeremymayhew@btinternet.com

Common Councilman: McGuinness, Catherine (NP - Castle Baynard)
catherine.mcguinness@cityoflondon.gov.uk

Common Councilman: McMurtrie, Andrew (NP - Coleman Street)
andrew.mcmurtrie@cityoflondon.gov.uk

Common Councilman: Mead, Wendy (NP - Farringdon Without)
wendy.mead@cityoflondon.gov.uk

Common Councilman: Merrett, Robert (NP - Bassishaw)
robert.merrett@jpmorgan.com

Common Councilman: Mooney, Brian (NP - Queenhithe)
brian.mooney@btinternet.com

Common Councilman: Moore, Gareth (NP - Cripplegate)
gareth.moore@cityoflondon.gov.uk

Common Councilman: Morris, Hugh (NP - Aldgate)

Common Councilman: Moss, Alastair (NP - Cheap)
alastair.moss@hotmail.com

Common Councilman: Moys, Sylvia (NP - Aldgate)
sylvia.moys@cityoflondon.gov.uk

Common Councilman: Nash, Joyce (IND - Aldersgate)
joyce.nash@cityoflondon.gov.uk

Common Councilman: Newman, Barbara (IND - Aldersgate)
barbara.newman@cityoflondon.gov.uk

Common Councilman: Packham, Graham (NP - Castle Baynard)

Common Councilman: Patel, Dhruv (NP - Aldgate)
dhruv.patel@cityoflondon.gov.uk

Common Councilman: Pembroke, Anne (NP - Cheap)
ann.pembroke@cityoflondon.gov.uk

Common Councilman: Pleasance, Judith (NP - Langbourn)

Common Councilman: Pollard, Henry (NP - Dowgate)
henry_pollard@invescoperpetual.co.uk

Common Councilman: Price, Emma (NP - Farringdon Without)

Common Councilman: Priest, Henrika (NP - Castle Baynard)
henrika.priest@cityoflondon.gov.uk

Common Councilman: Punter, Christopher (NP - Cripplegate)
chris.punter@cityoflondon.gov.uk

Common Councilman: Quilter, Stephen (NP - Cripplegate)
vision@totalise.co.uk

Common Councilman: Regan, Richard (NP - Farringdon Within)
richard.regan@cityoflondon.gov.u

Common Councilman: Regis, Delis (NP - Portsoken)
delis.regis@cityoflondon.gov.uk

Common Councilman: Rogula, Elizabeth (NP - Lime Street)
er@btinternet.com

Common Councilman: Rounding, Virginia (NP - Farringdon Within)
virginia.rounding@cityoflondon.gov.uk

CITY OF LONDON

Common Councilman: Scott, John (NP - Broad Street)
john.scott@cityoflondon.gov.uk

Common Councilman: Shilson, Giles (NP - Bread Street)
giles.shilson@cityoflondon.gov.uk

Common Councilman: Simons, Jeremy (NP - Castle Baynard)
jeremy.simons@cityoflondon.gov.uk

Common Councilman: Sleigh, Tom (NP - Bishopsgate)
tom.sleigh@cityoflondon.gov.uk

Common Councilman: Smith, Graeme (NP - Farringdon Within)
graeme.smith@cityoflondon.gov.uk

Common Councilman: Snyder, Michael (NP - Cordwainer)
michael.snyder@cityoflondon.gov.uk

Common Councilman: Starling, Angela (NP - Cripplegate)
angela.starling@cityoflondon.gov.uk

Common Councilman: Streeter, Patrick (NP - Bishopsgate)

Common Councilman: Thompson, David (NP - Aldgate)

Common Councilman: Thomson, James (NP - Walbrook)
james.m.d.thomson@virgin.net

Common Councilman: Tomlinson, John (NP - Cripplegate)
john@johnandpaula.com

Common Councilman: Tumbridge, James (NP - Tower)
james.tumbridge@cityoflondon.gov.uk

Common Councilman: Welbank, Michael (NP - Billingsgate)
michael.welbank@cityoflondon.gov.uk

Common Councilman: Wheatley, Mark (NP - Dowgate)
markindowgate@gmail.com

Common Councilman: Woodhouse, Philip (NP - Langbourn)

Fletcher, John William (NP - Portsoken)

Gifford, Roger (NP - Cordwainer)
roger.gifford@seb.co.uk

Seaton, Ian (NP - Cornhill)

Woolf, Fiona (NP - Candlewick)
fiona.woolf@cms-cmck.com

Yarrow, Alan (NP - Bridge & Bridge Without)
alan.yarrow@dkib.com

POLITICAL COMPOSITION
NP: *, IND: 13, LAB: 1

Clackmannanshire   S

Clackmannanshire Council, Kilncraigs, Alloa FK10 1EB
☎ 01259 450000 🖶 01259 452010 ✆ cutomerservice@clacks.gov.uk
💻 www.clacksweb.org.uk

FACTS AND FIGURES
Parliamentary Constituencies: Ochil and Perthshire South
EU Constituencies: Scotland
Election Frequency: Elections are of whole council

PRINCIPAL OFFICERS

Chief Executive: Ms Elaine McPherson, Chief Executive,
Kilncraigs, Alloa FK10 1EB ☎ 01259 450000
✆ emcpherson@clacks.gov.uk

Deputy Chief Executive: Mrs Nikki Bridle, Depute Chief
Executive, Kilncraigs, Alloa FK10 1EB ☎ 01259 452373
✆ nbridle@clacks.gov.uk

Senior Management: Mr Stephen Coulter, Head of Resources &
Governance, Kilncraigs, Alloa FK10 1EB ☎ 01259 452373

Senior Management: Mr Stuart Crickmar, Head of Strategy &
Customer Services, Kilncraigs, Alloa FK10 1EB ☎ 01259 452127
✆ scrickmar@clacks.gov.uk

Senior Management: Mr Garry Dallas, Executive Director,
Kilncraigs, Alloa FK10 1EB ☎ 01259 450002
✆ gdallas@clacks.gov.uk

Senior Management: Ms Val de Souza, Head of Social Services
/ Chief Social Worker, Kilncraigs, Alloa FK10 1EB ☎ 01259 225017
✆ vdesouza@clacks.gov.uk

Senior Management: Mr Ahsan Khan, Head of Housing &
Community Safety, Kilncraigs, Alloa FK10 1EB ☎ 01259 452473
✆ akhan@clacks.gov.uk

Senior Management: Mr David Leng, Head of Education, Teith
House, Kerse Road, Stirling FK7 7QA ☎ 01786 442669
✆ dleng@clacks.gov.uk

Senior Management: Mr Gordon McNeil, Head of Development
& Environment, Kilncraigs, Alloa FK10 1EB ☎ 01259 452533
✆ gmcneil@clacks.gov.uk

Architect, Building / Property Services: Ms Eileen Turnbull,
Asset Manager, Kilncraigs, Greenside Street, Alloa FK10 1EB
☎ 01259 452460 ✆ eturnbull2@clacks.gov.uk

Best Value: Mr Derek Barr, Procurement Manager, Kilncraigs,
Alloa FK10 1EB ☎ 01259 452017 ✆ dbarr@clacks.gov.uk

Building Control: Mr Alistair Mackenzie, Team Leader - Building,
Standards & Licensing, Kilncraigs, Alloa FK10 1EB ☎ 01259 452554
✆ amackenzie@clacks.gov.uk

Catering Services: Ms Diane MacKenzie, Catering Manager,
Class Cuisine, 21 Main Street, Sauchie, Alloa FK10 3JR ☎ 01259
452190 ✆ dmackenzie@clacks.gov.uk

Children / Youth Services: Ms Mary Fox, Team Leader - Youth
Services, Kilncraigs, Alloa FK10 1EB ☎ 01259 450000
✆ mfox@clacks.gov.uk

Civil Registration: Mr Brian Forbes, Customer Services Manager,
Kilncraigs, Alloa FK10 1EB ☎ 01259 452187
✆ bforbes@clacks.gov.uk

PR / Communications: Ms Karen Payton, Communications &
Community Team Leader, Kilncraigs, Alloa FK10 1EB
☎ 01259 452027 ✆ kpayton@clacks.gov.uk

Community Planning: Ms Cherie Jarvie, Strategy & Performance
Manager, Kilncraigs, Alloa FK10 1EB ☎ 01259 452365
✆ cjarvie@clacks.gov.uk

Community Safety: Mr Ahsan Khan, Head of Housing & Community Safety, Kilncraigs, Alloa FK10 1EB ☎ 01259 452473 ⏚ akhan@clacks.gov.uk

Computer Management: Mr John Munro, ICT Service Manager, Kilncraigs, Alloa FK10 1EB ☎ 01259 452510 ⏚ jmunro@clacks.gov.uk

Consumer Protection and Trading Standards: Mr Ian Doctor, Service Manager - Environmental Health & Consumer Protection, Kilncraigs, Greenside Place, Alloa FK10 1EB ☎ 01259 452572 ⏚ idoctor@clacks.gov.uk

Contracts: Mr Derek Barr, Procurement Manager, Kilncraigs, Alloa FK10 1EB ☎ 01259 452017 ⏚ dbarr@clacks.gov.uk

Customer Service: Mr Brian Forbes, Customer Services Manager, Kilncraigs, Alloa FK10 1EB ☎ 01259 452187 ⏚ bforbes@clacks.gov.uk

Economic Development: Ms Julie Hamilton, Development Services Manager, Kilncraigs, Greenside Place, Alloa FK10 1EB ☎ 01259 450000 ⏚ jhamilton@clacks.gov.uk

Education: Mr Kevin Kelman, Senior Manager - Head of School Improvement, Viewforth, Stirling FK8 2ET ☎ 01786 233224 ⏚ kelmank@stirling.gov.uk

Education: Mr Alan Milliken, Head of Learning, Communities, Performance & Resources, Viewforth, Stirling FK8 2ET ☎ 01786 233225 ⏚ millikina@stirling.gov.uk

Electoral Registration: Mr Andrew Hunter, Senior Governance Officer, Kilncraigs, Alloa FK10 1EB ☎ 01259 452103 ⏚ ahunter2@clackmannanshire.gov.uk

Emergency Planning: Mr David Johnstone, Emergency Planning Officer, Kilncraigs, Alloa FK10 1EB ☎ 01259 452537 ⏚ djohnstone@clacks.gov.uk

Energy Management: Mr Richard Scobbie, Energy Officer, Kilncraigs, Alloa FK10 1EB ☎ 01259 450000 ⏚ rscobbie@clacks.gov.uk

Environmental / Technical Services: Mr Gordon McNeil, Head of Development & Environment, Kilncraigs, Alloa FK10 1EB ☎ 01259 452533 ⏚ gmcneil@clacks.gov.uk

Environmental Health: Mr Andrew Crawford, Environmental Health Team Leader, Kilncraigs, Greenside Street, Alloa FK10 1EB ☎ 01259 452581 ⏚ acrawford@clacks.gov.uk

Estates, Property & Valuation: Mr George Adamson, Team Leader - Estates, Kilncraigs, Alloa FK10 1EB ☎ 01259 452647

Facilities: Ms Eileen Turnbull, Asset Manager, Kilncraigs, Alloa FK10 1EB ☎ 01259 452460 ⏚ eturnbull2@clacks.gov.uk

Finance: Mrs Lindsay Sim, Chief Accountant, Kilncraigs, Alloa FK10 1EB ☎ 01259 452078 ⏚ lsim@clacks.gov.uk

Grounds Maintenance: Mr Kenny Inglis, Land Services Team Leader, Kilncraigs, Alloa FK10 1EB ☎ 01259 226933 ⏚ kinglis@clacks.gov.uk

Health and Safety: Mrs Sarah Robertson, Health & Safety Adviser, Kilncraigs, Alloa FK10 1EB ☎ 01259 452174 ⏚ hands@clacks.gov.uk

Housing: Mr Ahsan Khan, Head of Housing & Community Safety, Kilncraigs, Alloa FK10 1EB ☎ 01259 452473 ⏚ akhan@clacks.gov.uk

Housing Maintenance: Ms Jennifer Queripel, Service Manager - Housing Operations, Kilncraigs, Alloa FK10 1EB ☎ 01259 452475 ⏚ jqueripel@clacks.gov.uk

Legal: Mr Andrew Wyse, Team Leader - Legal Services, Kilncraigs, Greenside Street, Alloa FK10 1EB ☎ 01259 452088 ⏚ awyse@clacks.gov.uk

Licensing: Ms June Andison, Administrator / Licensing, Kilncraigs, Alloa FK10 1EB ☎ 01259 452093 ⏚ jandison@clacks.gov.uk

Lighting: Mr Scott Walker, Manager - Roads & Transportation, Kilncraigs, Alloa FK10 1EB ☎ 01259 450000 ⏚ swalker@clacks.gov.uk

Member Services: Mrs Alison Bryce, Business Support Manager, Kilncraigs, Alloa FK10 1EB ☎ 01259 452003 ⏚ abryce@clacks.gov.uk

Planning: Mr Grant Baxter, Principal Planner, Kilncraigs, Alloa FK10 1EB ☎ 01259 450000 ⏚ gbaxter@clacks.gov.uk

Procurement: Mr Derek Barr, Procurement Manager, Kilncraigs, Alloa FK10 1EB ☎ 01259 452017 ⏚ dbarr@clacks.gov.uk

Public Libraries: Mr Brian Forbes, Customer Services Manager, Kilncraigs, Alloa FK10 1EB ☎ 01259 452187 ⏚ bforbes@clacks.gov.uk

Recycling & Waste Minimisation: Mr Graeme Cunningham, Manager - Environment, Kilncraigs, Alloa FK10 1EB ☎ 01259 452548 ⏚ gcunningham@clacks.gov.uk

Road Safety: Mr Alan Murray, Team Leader - Roads & Transportation, Kilncraigs, Alloa FK10 1EB ☎ 01259 450000 ⏚ amurry@clacks.gov.uk

Social Services: Ms Val de Souza, Head of Social Services / Chief Social Worker, Kilncraigs, Alloa FK10 1EB ☎ 01259 225017 ⏚ vdesouza@clacks.gov.uk

Traffic Management: Mr Alan Murray, Team Leader - Roads & Transportation, Kilncraigs, Alloa FK10 1EB ☎ 01259 450000 ⏚ amurry@clacks.gov.uk

Transport Planner: Mr Alan Murray, Team Leader - Roads & Transportation, Kilncraigs, Alloa FK10 1EB ☎ 01259 450000 ⏚ amurry@clacks.gov.uk

Waste Collection and Disposal: Mr Graeme Cunningham, Environment Manager, Kilncraigs House, Greenside Street, Alloa FK10 1EB ☎ 01259 452548 ⏚ gcunningham@clacks.gov.uk

CLACKMANNANSHIRE

Waste Management: Mr Graeme Cunningham, Environment Manager, Kilncraigs House, Greenside Street, Alloa FK10 1EB
☎ 01259 452548 ⏱ gcunningham@clacks.gov.uk

COUNCILLORS

Provost: Stewart, Derek (LAB - Clackmannanshire Central)
dstewart2@clacks.gov.uk

Deputy Provost: Stalker, Jim (LAB - Clackmannanshire West)
jstalker@clacks.gov.uk

Leader of the Council: McGill, Robert (LAB - Clackmannanshire North)
rmcgill@clacks.gov.uk

Deputy Leader of the Council: Watt, Graham (LAB - Clackmannanshire Central)
gwatt3@clacks.gov.uk

Balsillie, Donald (SNP - Clackmannanshire North)
dbalsillie@clacks.gov.uk

Cadenhead, Janet (LAB - Clackmannanshire South)
jcadenhead@clacks.gov.uk

Campbell, Alastair (CON - Clackmannanshire East)
acampbell@clacks.gov.uk

Drummond, Archie (IND - Clackmannanshire North)
adrummond@clacks.gov.uk

Earle, Kenneth (LAB - Clackmannanshire South)
kearle@clacks.gov.uk

Forson, Ellen (SNP - Clackmannanshire South)
eforson@clacks.gov.uk

Hamilton, Irene (SNP - Clackmannanshire East)
ihamilton@clacks.gov.uk

Holden, Craig (SNP - Clackmannanshire South)
cholden@clacks.gov.uk

Martin, Kathleen (LAB - Clackmannanshire East)
kmartin@clacks.gov.uk

Matchett, George (LAB - Clackmannanshire West)
gmatchett@clacks.gov.uk

McAdam, Walter (SNP - Clackmannanshire North)
wmcadam@clacks.gov.uk

Murphy, Tina (SNP - Clackmannanshire West)
tmurphy@clacks.gov.uk

Sharp, Les (SNP - Clackmannanshire West)
lsharp@clacks.gov.uk

Womersley, Gary (SNP - Clackmannanshire Central)
gwomersley@clacks.gov.uk

POLITICAL COMPOSITION
LAB: 8, SNP: 8, CON: 1, IND: 1

COMMITTEE CHAIRS

Audit & Finance: Mrs Janet Cadenhead

Planning: Mr Alastair Campbell

Colchester   D

Colchester Borough Council, Rowan House, 33 Sheepen Road, Colchester CO3 3WG

☎ 01206 282222 🖨 01206 282288
⏱ customerservicecentre@colchester.gov.uk
🖥 www.colchester.gov.uk

FACTS AND FIGURES
Parliamentary Constituencies: Colchester, Harwich and Essex North
EU Constituencies: Eastern
Election Frequency: Elections are by thirds

PRINCIPAL OFFICERS

Chief Executive: Mr Adrian Pritchard, Chief Executive, Rowan House, 33 Sheepen Road, Colchester CO3 3WG ☎ 01206 282211
⏱ adrian.pritchard@colchester.gov.uk

Assistant Chief Executive: Mr Matthew Sterling, Assistant Chief Executive, Rowan House, 33 Sheepen Road, Colchester CO3 3WG
☎ 01206 282577 ⏱ matthew.sterling@colchester.gov.uk

Senior Management: Mrs Pam Donnelly, Executive Director - Customer Operations & Partnerships, Rowan House, 33 Sheepen Road, Colchester CO3 3WG ☎ 01206 282884
⏱ pamela.donnelly@colchester.gov.uk

Senior Management: Mrs Ann Hedges, Chief Operating Officer - Delivery & Performance, Rowan House, 33 Sheepen Road, Colchester CO3 3WG ☎ 01206 282212
⏱ ann.hedges@colchester.gov.uk

Senior Management: Mr Ian Vipond, Strategic Director - Commerical & Place, Rowan House, 33 Sheepen Road, Colchester CO3 3WG ☎ 01206 282717 ⏱ ian.vipond@colchester.gov.uk

Building Control: Mr Tony Tarran, Building Control Manager, Rowan House, 33 Sheepen Road, Colchester CO3 3WG
☎ 01206 508646 ⏱ tony.tarran@colchester.gov.uk

Children / Youth Services: Mrs Lucie Breadman, Head - Community Services, Rowan House, 33 Sheepen Road, Colchester CO3 3WG ☎ 01206 282726 ⏱ lucie.breadman@colchester.gov.uk

PR / Communications: Ms Joanne Partlett, Communications Manager, Rowan House, 33 Sheepen Road, Colchester CO3 3WG
☎ 01206 282310 ⏱ joanne.partlett@colchester.gov.uk

Community Planning: Mr Gareth Mitchell, Head - Commercial Services, Rowan House, 33 Sheepen Road, Colchester CO3 3WG
☎ 01206 506972 ⏱ gareth.mitchell@colchester.gov.uk

Computer Management: Mr Kieran Johnston, Strategic ICT & Communications Manager, Rowan House, 33 Sheepen Road, Colchester CO3 3WG ☎ 01206 507880
⏱ kieran.johnston@colchester.gov.uk

Contracts: Mr Julian Wilkins, Principal Lawyer, Rowan House, 33 Sheepen Road, Colchester CO3 3WG ☎ 01206 282257
⏱ julian.wilkins@colchester.gov.uk

Corporate Services: Mr Matthew Sterling, Assistant Chief Executive, Rowan House, 33 Sheepen Road, Colchester CO3 3WG
☎ 01206 282577 ⏱ matthew.sterling@colchester.gov.uk

Customer Service: Ms Leonie Rathbone, Head of Customer Services, Rowan House, 33 Sheepen Road, Colchester CO3 3WG ☎ 01206 507887 ⌨ leonie.rathbone@colchester.gov.uk

Economic Development: Mr Nigel Myers, Economic Development Manager, Rowan House, 33 Sheepen Road, Colchester CO3 3WG ☎ 01206 282878 ⌨ nigel.myers@colchester.gov.uk

E-Government: Mr Kieran Johnston, Strategic ICT & Communications Manager, Rowan House, 33 Sheepen Road, Colchester CO3 3WG ☎ 01206 507880 ⌨ kieran.johnston@colchester.gov.uk

Electoral Registration: Mrs Sarah Cheek, Electoral Services Manager, Rowan House, 33 Sheepen Road, Colchester CO3 3WG ☎ 01206 282271 ⌨ sarah.cheek@colchester.gov.uk

Emergency Planning: Ms Hayley McGrath, Corporate Governance Manager, Rowan House, 33 Sheepen Road, Colchester CO3 3WG ☎ 01206 508902 ⌨ hayley.mcgrath@colchester.gov.uk

Environmental Health: Mr Rory Doyle, Public Health & Enforcement Service Manager, Rowan House, 33 Sheepen Road, Colchester CO3 3WG ☎ 01206 507855 ⌨ rory.doyle@colchester.gov.uk

Environmental Health: Mrs Beverley Jones, Head of Professional Services, Rowan House, 33 Sheepen Road, Colchester CO3 3WG ☎ 01206 282593 ⌨ beverley.jones@colchester.gov.uk

Estates, Property & Valuation: Ms Fiona Duhamel, Economic Growth Manager, Rowan House, 33 Sheepen Road, Colchester CO3 3WG ☎ 01206 282252 ⌨ fiona.duhamel@colchester.gov.uk

Events Manager: Mr Will Jenkins, Events Manager, PO Box 5215, Town Hall, Colchester CO1 1GG ☎ 01206 282962 ⌨ will.jenkins@colchester.gov.uk

Facilities: Mr Lee Spalding, Corporate Asset Manager, Rowan House, 33 Sheepen Road, Colchester CO3 3WG ☎ 01206 506905 ⌨ lee.spalding@colchester.gov.uk

Finance: Mr Sean Plummer, Finance Manager (Section 151 Officer), Rowan House, 33 Sheepen Road, Colchester CO3 3WG ☎ 01206 282347 ⌨ sean.plummer@colchester.gov.uk

Fleet Management: Mr Chris Dowsing, Group Manager - Recycling, Waste & Fleet, Rowan House, 33 Sheepen Road, Colchester CO3 3WG ☎ 01206 282752 ⌨ chris.dowsing@colchester.gov.uk

Grounds Maintenance: Mr Bob Penny, Parks & Recreation Manager, Rowan House, 33 Sheepen Road, Colchester CO3 3WG ☎ 01206 282903 ⌨ bob.penny@colchester.gov.uk

Health and Safety: Mrs Pam Donnelly, Executive Director - Customer Operations & Partnerships, Rowan House, 33 Sheepen Road, Colchester CO3 3WG ☎ 01206 282884 ⌨ pamela.donnelly@colchester.gov.uk

Health and Safety: Mr Rory Doyle, Public Health & Enforcement Service Manager, Rowan House, 33 Sheepen Road, Colchester CO3 3WG ☎ 01206 507855 ⌨ rory.doyle@colchester.gov.uk

Home Energy Conservation: Ms Melanie Rundle, Community Welfare Co-ordinator, Rowan House, 33 Sheepen Road, Colchester CO3 3WG ☎ 01206 282541 ⌨ melaine.rundle@colchester.gov.uk

Housing: Mr Nicorum Flaherty, Housing Options Co-ordinator, Rowan House, 33 Sheepen Road, Colchester CO3 3WG ☎ 01206 282981 ⌨ nicorum.flaherty@colchester.gov.uk

Legal: Mr Andrew Weavers, Legal Services Manager & Monitoring Officer, Rowan House, 33 Sheepen Road, Colchester CO3 3WG ☎ 01206 282213 ⌨ andrew.weavers@colchester.gov.uk

Leisure and Cultural Services: Mr Tim Swallow, Sport & Leisure Operations Manager, Rowan House, 33 Sheepen Road, Colchester CO3 3WG ☎ 01206 282106 ⌨ tim.swallow@colchester.gov.uk

Licensing: Ms Sally Harrington, Planning & Licensing Service Manager, Rowan House, 33 Sheepen Road, Colchester CO3 3WG ☎ 01206 506464 ⌨ sally.harrington@colchester.gov.uk

Member Services: Ms Amanda Chidgey, Democratic Services Manager, Rowan House, 33 Sheepen Road, Colchester CO3 3WG ☎ 01206 282227 ⌨ amanda.chidgey@colchester.gov.uk

Parking: Mr Richard Walker, Parking Partnership Group Manager, Rowan House, 33 Sheepen Road, Colchester CO3 3WG ☎ 01206 282708 ⌨ richard.walker@colchester.gov.uk

Personnel / HR: Ms Jessica Douglas, Strategic People & Performance Manager, Rowan House, 33 Sheepen Road, Colchester CO3 3WG ☎ 01206 282239 ⌨ jessica.douglas@colchester.gov.uk

Planning: Mrs Beverley Jones, Head of Professional Services, Rowan House, 33 Sheepen Road, Colchester CO3 3WG ☎ 01206 282593 ⌨ beverley.jones@colchester.gov.uk

Recycling & Waste Minimisation: Mr Chris Dowsing, Group Manager - Recycling, Waste & Fleet, Rowan House, 33 Sheepen Road, Colchester CO3 3WG ☎ 01206 282752 ⌨ chris.dowsing@colchester.gov.uk

Regeneration: Ms Fiona Duhamel, Economic Growth Manager, Rowan House, 33 Sheepen Road, Colchester CO3 3WG ☎ 01206 282252 ⌨ fiona.duhamel@colchester.gov.uk

Street Scene: Mr Matthew Young, Head - Operational Services, Rowan House, 33 Sheepen Road, Colchester CO3 3WG ☎ 01206 282902 ⌨ matthew.young@colchester.gov.uk

Sustainable Communities: Mrs Lucie Breadman, Head - Community Services, Rowan House, 33 Sheepen Road, Colchester CO3 3WG ☎ 01206 282726 ⌨ lucie.breadman@colchester.gov.uk

Sustainable Development: Mr Gareth Mitchell, Head - Commercial Services, Rowan House, 33 Sheepen Road, Colchester CO3 3WG ☎ 01206 506972 ⌨ gareth.mitchell@colchester.gov.uk

COLCHESTER

Tourism: Mr Gareth Mitchell, Head - Commercial Services, Rowan House, 33 Sheepen Road, Colchester CO3 3WG ☎ 01206 506972 ✎ gareth.mitchell@colchester.gov.uk

Tourism: Ms Karen Turnbull, Enterprise & Tourism Development Manager, Rowan House, 33 Sheepen Road, Colchester CO3 3WG ☎ 01206 282915 ✎ karen.turnbull@colchester.gov.uk

Town Centre: Mr Howard Davies, Town Centre Project Manager, Rowan House, 33 Sheepen Road, Colchester CO3 3WG ☎ 01206 507885 ✎ howard.davies@colchester.gov.uk

Transport Planner: Mr Gareth Mitchell, Head - Commercial Services, Rowan House, 33 Sheepen Road, Colchester CO3 3WG ☎ 01206 506972 ✎ gareth.mitchell@colchester.gov.uk

Total Place: Mr Ian Vipond, Strategic Director - Commerical & Place, Rowan House, 33 Sheepen Road, Colchester CO3 3WG ☎ 01206 282717 ✎ ian.vipond@colchester.gov.uk

Waste Collection and Disposal: Mr Chris Dowsing, Group Manager - Recycling, Waste & Fleet, Rowan House, 33 Sheepen Road, Colchester CO3 3WG ☎ 01206 282752 ✎ chris.dowsing@colchester.gov.uk

Waste Management: Mr Chris Dowsing, Group Manager - Recycling, Waste & Fleet, Rowan House, 33 Sheepen Road, Colchester CO3 3WG ☎ 01206 282752 ✎ chris.dowsing@colchester.gov.uk

Children's Play Areas: Mr Bob Penny, Parks & Recreation Manager, Rowan House, 33 Sheepen Road, Colchester CO3 3WG ☎ 01206 282903 ✎ bob.penny@colchester.gov.uk

COUNCILLORS

Leader of the Council: Smith, Paul (LD - St Anne's & St John's) cllr.paul.smith@colchester.gov.uk

Deputy Leader of the Council: Young, Tim (LAB - Greenstead) cllr.tim.young@colchester.gov.uk

Arnold, Christopher (CON - Rural North) cllr.christopher.arnold@colchester.gov.uk

Barber, Lewis (CON - Lexden & Braiswick) cllr.lewis.barber@colchester.gov.uk

Barlow, Nick (LD - Castle) cllr.nick.barlow@colchester.gov.uk

Barton, Lyn (LD - Shrub End) cllr.linda.barton@colchester.gov.uk

Bentley, Kevin (CON - Marks Tey & Layer) cllr.kevin.bentley@colchester.gov.uk

Bourne, Tina (LAB - Greenstead) cllr.tina.bourne@colchester.gov.uk

Buston, Roger (CON - Prettygate) cllr.roger.buston@colchester.gov.uk

Chaplin, Karen (LD - Shrub End) cllr.karen.chaplin@colchester.gov.uk

Chapman, Nigel (CON - Rural North) cllr.nigel.chapman@colchester.gov.uk

Chillingworth, Peter (CON - Rural North) cllr.peter.chillingworth@colchester.gov.uk

Chuah, Helen (LD - St Anne's & St John's) cllr.helen.chuah@colchester.gov.uk

Coleman, Phil (LD - Mile End) cllr.phil.coleman@colchester.gov.uk

Cope, Nick (LD - New Town & Christ Church) cllr.nick.cope@colchester.gov.uk

Cory, Mark (LD - Wivenhoe) cllr.mark.cory@colchester.gov.uk

Davidson, Robert (CON - Mersea & Pyefleet) cllr.robert.davidson@colchester.gov.uk

Davies, Beverly (CON - Prettygate) cllr.beverly.davies@colchester.gov.uk

Elliott, John (CON - Tiptree) cllr.john.elliott@colchester.gov.uk

Ellis, Andrew (CON - Marks Tey & Layer) cllr.andrew.ellis@colchester.gov.uk

Ellis, Daniel (CON - Castle) cllr.daniel.ellis@colchester.gov.uk

Feltham, Annie (LD - New Town & Christ Church) cllr.annie.feltham@colchester.gov.uk

Fox, Adam (LAB - Old Heath & The Hythe) cllr.adam.fox@colchester.gov.uk

Goss, Martin (LD - Mile End) cllr.martin.goss@colchester.gov.uk

Graham, Dominic (LD - Mile End) cllr.dominic.graham@colchester.gov.uk

Harris, David (LAB - Berechurch) cllr.david.harris@colchester.gov.uk

Hazell, Pauline (CON - Shrub End) cllr.pauline.hazell@colchester.gov.uk

Higgins, Theresa (LD - New Town & Christ Church) cllr.theresa.higgins@colchester.gov.uk

Hogg, Mike (LD - St Anne's & St John's) cllr.mike.hogg@colchester.gov.uk

Jarvis, Brian (CON - Lexden & Braiswick) cllr.brian.jarvis@colchester.gov.uk

Jowers, John (CON - Mersea & Pyefleet) cllr.john.jowers@colchester.gov.uk

Laws, Darius (CON - Castle) cllr.darius.laws@colchester.gov.uk

Liddy, Cyril (LAB - Wivenhoe) cllr.cyril.liddy@colchester.gov.uk

Lilley, Michael (LAB - Old Heath & The Hythe) cllr.mike.lilley@colchester.gov.uk

Lissimore, Sue (CON - Prettygate) cllr.sue.lissimore@colchester.gov.uk

Loveland, Derek (CON - Tiptree) cllr.derek.loveland@colchester.gov.uk

Maclean, Fiona (CON - Stanway) cllr.fiona.maclean@colchester.gov.uk

Maclean, Jackie (CON - Marks Tey & Layer) cllr.jackie.maclean@colchester.gov.uk

Moore, Patricia (CON - Mersea & Pyefleet)
cllr.patricia.moore@colchester.gov.uk

Oxford, Gerard (IND - Highwoods)
cllr.gerald.oxford@colchester.gov.uk

Oxford, Philip (IND - Highwoods)
cllr.philip.oxford@colchester.gov.uk

Oxford, Beverley (IND - Highwoods)
cllr.beverley.oxford@colchester.gov.uk

Pearson, Chris (LAB - Berechurch)
cllr.chris.pearson@colchester.gov.uk

Scordis, Lee (LAB - Old Heath & The Hythe)
cllr.lee.scordis@colchester.gov.uk

Scott, Rosalind (LAB - Wivenhoe)
cllr.rosalind.scott@colchester.gov.uk

Scott-Boutell, Jessica (LD - Stanway)
cllr.jessica.scott-boutell@colchester.gov.uk

Scott-Boutell, Lesley (LD - Stanway)

Warnes, Martyn (LAB - Berechurch)
cllr.martyn.warnes@colchester.gov.uk

Willetts, Dennis (CON - Lexden & Braiswick)
cllr.dennis.willetts@colchester.gov.uk

Wood, Barbara (CON - Tiptree)
cllr.barbara.wood@colchester.gov.uk

Young, Julie (LAB - Greenstead)
cllr.julie.young@colchester.gov.uk

POLITICAL COMPOSITION
CON: 22, LD: 15, LAB: 11, IND: 3

COMMITTEE CHAIRS

Audit & Governance: Mr Chris Pearson

Licensing: Mr Nick Cope

Planning: Ms Theresa Higgins

Conwy   W

Conwy County Borough Council, Bodlondeb, Bangor Road, Conwy LL32 8DU
☎ 01492 574000 📠 01492 592114 ◌ information@conwy.gov.uk
💻 www.conwy.gov.uk

FACTS AND FIGURES
Parliamentary Constituencies: Aberconwy, Clwyd West
EU Constituencies: Wales
Election Frequency: Elections are of whole council

PRINCIPAL OFFICERS

Chief Executive: Mr Iwan Davies, Chief Executive, Bodlondeb, Bangor Road, Conwy LL32 8DU ☎ 01492 576015; 01492 576135 ◌ iwan.davies@conwy.gov.uk

Senior Management: Mr Andrew Kirkham, Strategic Director - Finance & Efficiencies, Bodlondeb, Bangor Road, Conwy LL32 8DU ☎ 01492 576170 ◌ andrew.kirkham@conwy.gov.uk

Senior Management: Ms Jane Richardson, Strategic Director - Economy & Place, Bodlondeb, Bangor Road, Conwy LL32 8DU
☎ 01492 576001 ◌ jane.richardson@conwy.gov.uk

Senior Management: Ms Jenny Williams, Strategic Director - Social Care & Education, Government Buildings, Dinerth Road, Rhos-on-Sea, Conwy LL28 4UL ☎ 01492 575687; 01492 575687 ◌ jenny.williams@conwy.gov.uk

Access Officer / Social Services (Disability): Ms Claire Lister, Head of Integrated Adult & Community Services, Government Buildings, Dinerth Road, Rhos-on-Sea, Conwy LL28 4UL
☎ 01492 575378 ◌ claire.lister@conwy.gov.uk

Architect, Building / Property Services: Mr Bleddyn Evans, County Valuer & Asset Manager, Bodlondeb, Bangor Road, Conwy LL32 8DU ☎ 01492 574283; 01492 574040
◌ bleddyn.evans@conwy.gov.uk

Building Control: Ms Paula Jones, Development & Building Control Manager, Civic Offices, Colwyn Bay LL29 8AR
☎ 01492 575271 ◌ paula.jones@conwy.gov.uk

Catering Services: Mr Dafydd Williams, Catering Manager, Government Buildings, Dinerth Road, Rhos-on-Sea, LL28 4UL
☎ 01492 575580 ◌ dafydd.aled.williams@conwy.gov.uk

Children / Youth Services: Ms Jane Williams, Section Head - Conwy Youth Services, Bodlondeb, Bangor Road, Conwy LL32 8DU
☎ 01492 575051 ◌ jane.williams@conwy.gov.uk

Children / Youth Services: Ms Jenny Williams, Strategic Director - Social Care & Education, Government Buildings, Dinerth Road, Rhos on Sea, Colwyn Bay LL28 4UL ☎ 01492 575687; 01492 575687 ◌ jenny.williams@conwy.gov.uk

Civil Registration: Mrs Delyth Jones, Head of Law & Governance, Bodlondeb, Bangor Road, Conwy LL32 8DU
☎ 01492 576075 ◌ delyth.e.jones@conwy.gov.uk

PR / Communications: Mrs Rachael Gill, Marketing & Communications Manager, Bodlondeb, Bangor Road, Conwy LL32 8DU ☎ 01492 575941 ◌ rachael.gill@conwy.gov.uk

Community Planning: Ms Marianne Jackson, Head of Community Development Services, Library Building, Mostyn Street, Llandudno LL30 2NG ☎ 01492 576314
◌ marianne.jackson@conwy.gov.uk

Community Safety: Ms Sian Taylor, Community Safety Manager, Civic Offices, Colwyn Bay LL29 8AR ☎ 01492 575190
◌ sian.taylor@conwy.gov.uk

Computer Management: Mr Huw McKee, Head of IT & Digital Transformation, Bodlondeb, Bangor Road, Conwy LL32 8DU
☎ 01492 576020 ◌ huw.mckee@conwy.gov.uk

Consumer Protection and Trading Standards: Mr John Donnelly, Principal Licensing & Registration Officer, Civic Offices, Colwyn Bay LL29 8AR ☎ 01492 575197
◌ john.donnelly@conwy.gov.uk

Contracts: Ms Diane Sandham, Corporate Procurement & Contracts Manager, Bodlondeb, Bangor Road, Conwy LL32 8DU ☎ 01492 574117 ✆ diane.sandham@conwy.gov.uk

Economic Development: Mr Rob Dix, Section Head - Business & Enterprise, 28 Wynnstay Road, Colwyn Bay LL29 8NB ☎ 01492 574506 ✆ rob.dix@conwy.gov.uk

Economic Development: Ms Marianne Jackson, Head of Community Development Services, Library Building, Mostyn Street, Llandudno LL30 2NG ☎ 01492 576314 ✆ marianne.jackson@conwy.gov.uk

Education: Dr Lowri Gravell, Interim Head of Education Services, Government Buildings, Dinerth Road, Rhos on Sea, Colwyn Bay LL28 4UL ☎ 01492 575599 ✆ dr.lowri.gravell@conwy.gov.uk

E-Government: Mrs Sarah Davies, E-Government Manager, Bodlondeb, Bangor Road, Conwy LL32 8DU ☎ 01492 576290 ✆ sarah.davies@conwy.gov.uk

Electoral Registration: Mrs Sian Williams, Democratic Services Manager, Bodlondeb, Bangor Road, Conwy LL32 8DU ☎ 01492 576062 ✆ sian.williams@conwy.gov.uk

Emergency Planning: Mr Jonathan Williams, Civil Contingencies Manager, Bodlondeb, Conwy LL32 8DU ☎ 01492 576099 ✆ jonathan.williams@nwc-reps.org.uk

Energy Management: Ms Amanda Jones, Business Improvement Manager, Mochdre Offices, Conwy Road, Mochdre, Colwyn Bay LL28 5AB ☎ 01492 575398 ✆ amanda.j.jones@conwy.gov.uk

Energy Management: Mr Steven Teale, Facilities Manager, Mochdre Offices, Conwy Road, Mochdre, Colwyn Bay LL28 5AB ☎ 01492 574104 ✆ steven.teale@conwy.gov.uk

Environmental / Technical Services: Mr Geraint Edwards, Head of Environment, Roads & Facilities, Mochdre Offices, Conway Road, Mochdre, LL28 5AB ☎ 01492 575207; 01492 575199 ✆ geraint.edwards@conwy.gov.uk

Environmental Health: Mr Matthew Frankcom, Public Protection Manager, Civic Offices, Colwyn Bay LL29 8AR ☎ 01492 575225 ✆ matthew.frankcom@conwy.gov.uk

Estates, Property & Valuation: Mr Bleddyn Evans, County Valuer & Asset Manager, Town Hall, Lloyd Street, Llandudno LL30 2UP ☎ 01492 574283; 01492 574040 ✆ bleddyn.evans@conwy.gov.uk

European Liaison: Mrs Barbara Burchell, Principal European Project Development Officer, Library Building, Mostyn Street, Llandudno LL30 2RP ☎ 01492 576011 ✆ barbara.burchell@conwy.gov.uk

European Liaison: Mr Rob Dix, Section Head - Business & Enterprise, 28 Wynnstay Road, Colwyn Bay LL29 8NB ☎ 01492 574506 ✆ rob.dix@conwy.gov.uk

Events Manager: Mrs Rachael Gill, Marketing & Communications Manager, Bodlondeb, Bangor Road, Conwy LL32 8DU ☎ 01492 575941 ✆ rachael.gill@conwy.gov.uk

Facilities: Mr Steven Teale, Facilities Manager, Mochdre Offices, Conwy Road, Mochdre, Colwyn Bay LL28 5AB ☎ 01492 574104 ✆ steven.teale@conwy.gov.uk

Finance: Mr Andrew Kirkham, Strategic Director - Finance & Efficiencies, Bodlondeb, Conwy LL32 8DU ☎ 01492 576170 ✆ andrew.kirkham@conwy.gov.uk

Fleet Management: Mr Andrew Dawson, Transport Manager, Mochdre Offices, Conway Road, Mochdre, Colwyn Bay LL28 5AB ☎ 01492 575966 ✆ andrew.dawson2@conwy.gov.uk

Grounds Maintenance: Mr Lyn Davies, Open Spaces Manager, Mochdre Offices, Conway Road, Mochdre, Colwyn Bay LL28 5AB ☎ 01492 575299 ✆ lyn.davies@conwy.gov.uk

Health and Safety: Mr Richard Evans, Corporate Occupational Health & Safety Manager, Bron y Nant, Dinerth Road, Rhos on Sea, Colwyn Bay LL28 4YL ☎ 01492 576090 ✆ richard.h.evans@conwy.gov.uk

Highways: Mr Andrew Wilkinson, Head of Neighbourhood Services, Mochdre Offices, Conway Road, Mochdre, Colwyn Bay LL28 5AB ☎ 01492 577619 ✆ andrew.j.wilkinson@conwy.gov.uk

Home Energy Conservation: Mrs Sam Parry, Housing Services Manager, Civic Offices, Colwyn Bay LL29 8AR ☎ 01492 574224 ✆ sam.parry@conwy.gov.uk

Housing: Mrs Sam Parry, Housing Services Manager, Civic Offices, Colwyn Bay LL29 8AR ☎ 01492 574224 ✆ sam.parry@conwy.gov.uk

Legal: Mrs Delyth Jones, Head of Law & Governance, Bodlondeb, Bangor Road, Conwy LL32 8DU ☎ 01492 576075 ✆ delyth.e.jones@conwy.gov.uk

Leisure and Cultural Services: Ms Marianne Jackson, Head of Community Development Services, Library Building, Mostyn Street, Llandudno LL30 2NG ☎ 01492 576314 ✆ marianne.jackson@conwy.gov.uk

Licensing: Mr John Donnelly, Principal Licensing & Registration Officer, Civic Offices, Colwyn Bay LL29 8AR ☎ 01492 575197 ✆ john.donnelly@conwy.gov.uk

Lifelong Learning: Dr Lowri Gravell, Interim Head of Education Services, Government Buildings, Dinerth Road, Rhos on Sea, Colwyn Bay LL28 4UL ☎ 01492 575599 ✆ dr.lowri.gravell@conwy.gov.uk

Lighting: Mr Victor Turner, Traffic & Network Manager, The Heath, Penmaenmawr Road, Llanfairfechan, LL33 0PF ☎ 01492 575402 ✆ victor.turner@conwy.gov.uk

Member Services: Mrs Sian Williams, Democratic Services Manager, Bodlondeb, Bangor Road, Conwy LL32 8DU ☎ 01492 576062 ✆ sian.williams@conwy.gov.uk

Parking: Mr Victor Turner, Traffic & Network Manager, The Heath, Penmaenmawr Road, Llanfairfechan, LL33 0PF ☎ 01492 575402 ✆ victor.turner@conwy.gov.uk

Personnel / HR: Mr Phillip Davies, Head of Corporate Personnel Services, Bodlondeb, Bangor Road, Conwy LL32 8DU ☎ 01492 576124; 01492 576135 🖰 phillip.davies@conwy.gov.uk

Planning: Ms Paula Jones, Development & Building Control Manager, Civic Offices, Colwyn Bay LL29 8AR ☎ 01492 575271 🖰 paula.jones@conwy.gov.uk

Procurement: Mr Mike Halstead, Head of Audit & Procurement, Bodlondeb, Bangor Road, Conwy LL32 8DU ☎ 01492 574000; 01492 592114 🖰 mike.halstead@conwy.gov.uk

Public Libraries: Ms Ann Lloyd Williams, Section Head: Rural Community Development, Culture & Information, Library Building, Mostyn Street, Llandudno LL30 2NG ☎ 01492 575571 🖰 ann.lloyd.williams@conwy.gov.uk

Recycling & Waste Minimisation: Mr Jon Eastwood, Waste Manager, Mochdre Offices, Conway Road, Mochdre, Colwyn Bay LL28 5AB ☎ 01492 575127 🖰 jon.eastwood@conwy.gov.uk

Recycling & Waste Minimisation: Mr Andrew Wilkinson, Head of Neighbourhood Services, Mochdre Offices, Conway Road, Mochdre, Colwyn Bay LL28 5AB ☎ 01492 577619 🖰 andrew.j.wilkinson@conwy.gov.uk

Regeneration: Mr Rob Dix, Section Head - Business & Enterprise, 28 Wynnstay Road, Colwyn Bay LL29 8NB ☎ 01492 574506 🖰 rob.dix@conwy.gov.uk

Regeneration: Ms Marianne Jackson, Head of Community Development Services, Library Building, Mostyn Street, Llandudno LL30 2NG ☎ 01492 576314 🖰 marianne.jackson@conwy.gov.uk

Road Safety: Mr Victor Turner, Traffic & Network Manager, The Heath, Penmaenmawr Road, Llanfairfechan, LL33 0PF ☎ 01492 575402 🖰 victor.turner@conwy.gov.uk

Social Services: Ms Jenny Williams, Strategic Director - Social Care & Education, Government Buildings, Dinerth Road, Rhos on Sea, Colwyn Bay LL28 4UL ☎ 01492 575687; 01492 575687 🖰 jenny.williams@conwy.gov.uk

Social Services (Adult): Ms Claire Lister, Head of Integrated Adult & Community Services, Government Buildings, Dinerth Road, Rhos-on-Sea, Conwy LL28 4UL ☎ 01492 575378 🖰 claire.lister@conwy.gov.uk

Social Services (Children): Ms Kate Devonport, Head of Service - Children, Families & Safeguarding, Civic Offices, Annexe, Colwyn Bay LL29 8AR ☎ 01492 575166 🖰 kate.devonport@conwy.gov.uk

Staff Training: Mr Phillip Davies, Head of Corporate Personnel Services, Bodlondeb, Bangor Road, Conwy LL32 8DU ☎ 01492 576124; 01492 576135 🖰 phillip.davies@conwy.gov.uk

Street Scene: Mr Lyn Davies, Open Spaces Manager, Mochdre Offices, Conway Road, Mochdre, Colwyn Bay LL28 5AB ☎ 01492 575299 🖰 lyn.davies@conwy.gov.uk

Sustainable Communities: Ms Marianne Jackson, Head of Community Development Services, Library Building, Mostyn Street, Llandudno LL30 2NG ☎ 01492 576314 🖰 marianne.jackson@conwy.gov.uk

Sustainable Development: Ms Marianne Jackson, Head of Community Development Services, Library Building, Mostyn Street, Llandudno LL30 2NG ☎ 01492 576314 🖰 marianne.jackson@conwy.gov.uk

Tourism: Ms Marianne Jackson, Head of Community Development Services, Library Building, Mostyn Street, Llandudno LL30 2NG ☎ 01492 576314 🖰 marianne.jackson@conwy.gov.uk

Town Centre: Ms Marianne Jackson, Head of Community Development Services, Library Building, Mostyn Street, Llandudno LL30 2NG ☎ 01492 576314 🖰 marianne.jackson@conwy.gov.uk

Traffic Management: Mr Victor Turner, Traffic & Network Manager, The Heath, Penmaenmawr Road, Llanfairfechan, LL33 0PF ☎ 01492 575402 🖰 victor.turner@conwy.gov.uk

Transport: Mr Andrew Dawson, Transport Manager, Mochdre Offices, Conway Road, Mochdre, Colwyn Bay LL28 5AB ☎ 01492 575966 🖰 andrew.dawson2@conwy.gov.uk

Transport Planner: Mr Gethin George, Integrated Transport (Policy) Officer, Library Building, Mostyn Street, Llandudno LL30 2NG ☎ 01492 575562 🖰 gethin.george@conwy.gov.uk

Waste Collection and Disposal: Mr Jon Eastwood, Waste Manager, Mochdre Offices, Conway Road, Mochdre, Colwyn Bay LL28 5AB ☎ 01492 575127 🖰 jon.eastwood@conwy.gov.uk

Waste Collection and Disposal: Mr Andrew Wilkinson, Head of Neighbourhood Services, Mochdre Offices, Conway Road, Mochdre, Colwyn Bay LL28 5AB ☎ 01492 577619 🖰 andrew.j.wilkinson@conwy.gov.uk

Waste Management: Mr Jon Eastwood, Waste Manager, Mochdre Offices, Conway Road, Mochdre, Colwyn Bay LL28 5AB ☎ 01492 575127 🖰 jon.eastwood@conwy.gov.uk

Waste Management: Mr Andrew Wilkinson, Head of Neighbourhood Services, Mochdre Offices, Conway Road, Mochdre, Colwyn Bay LL28 5AB ☎ 01492 577619 🖰 andrew.j.wilkinson@conwy.gov.uk

Children's Play Areas: Mr Lyn Davies, Open Spaces Manager, Mochdre Offices, Conway Road, Mochdre, Colwyn Bay LL28 5AB ☎ 01492 575299 🖰 lyn.davies@conwy.gov.uk

COUNCILLORS

ChairCossey, Brian (LD - Colwyn)
cllr.brian.cossey@conwy.gov.uk

Vice-ChairLewis, Peter (IND - Uwchaled)
cllr.peter.lewis@conwy.gov.uk

Leader of the Council: Roberts, Dilwyn (PC - Llangernyw)
cllr.dilwyn.roberts@conwy.gov.uk

CONWY

Deputy Leader of the Council: Hughes, Ronnie (LAB - Tudno)
cllr.ronnie.hughes@conwy.gov.uk

Allardice, Sarah Louise (LAB - Conwy)
cllr.sara.allardice@conwy.gov.uk

Anderson, Stuart (IND - Bae Cinmel / Kinmel Bay)
cllr.dr.stuart.anderson@conwy.gov.uk

Bradfield, Frank (CON - Craig Y Don)
cllr.frank.bradfield@conwy.gov.uk

Carlisle, Cheryl (CON - Colwyn)
cllr.cheryl.carlisle@conwy.gov.uk

Cater, Christopher (IND - Penrhyn)
cllr.christopher.cater@conwy.gov.uk

Cotton, Samantha (CON - Deganwy)
cllr.samantha.cotton@conwy.gov.uk

Cowans, Dave (IND - Eirias)
cllr.dave.cowans@conwy.gov.uk

Darwin, William (IND - Bae Cinmel / Kinmel Bay)
cllr.bill.darwin@conwy.gov.uk

Doyle, Mary (CON - Rhiw)
cllr.mary.doyle@conwy.gov.uk

Edwards, Goronwy (IND - Caerhun)
cllr.goronwy.edwards@conwy.gov.uk

Edwards, Philip (PC - Llandrillo-yn-Rhos)
cllr.phil.edwards@conwy.gov.uk

Eeles, Keith (IND - Llanddulas)
cllr.keith.eeles@conwy.gov.uk

Evans, Philip (IND - Tudno)
cllr.philip.evans@conwy.gov.uk

Fallon, Julie (CON - Deganwy)
cllr.julie.fallon@conwy.gov.uk

Groom, Linda (IND - Penrhyn)
cllr.linda.groom@conwy.gov.uk

Hinchliff, Andrew (LAB - Bryn)
cllr.andrew.hinchliff@conwy.gov.uk

Hughes, Meirion (PC - Pensarn)
cllr.meirion.hughes@conwy.gov.uk

Hughes, Chris (LAB - Glyn)
cllr.chris.hughes@conwy.gov.uk

Jenkins, Ian (PC - Gower)
cllr.ian.jenkins@conwy.gov.uk

Jones, Ray (LAB - Pandy)
cllr.ray.jones@conwy.gov.uk

Jones, Gareth (PC - Craig Y Don)
cllr.gareth.jones@conwy.gov.uk

Jones, Wyn Ellis (PC - Uwch Conwy)
cyng.wyn.ellis.jones@conwy.gov.uk

Khan, Abdul (PC - Glyn)
cllr.abdul.khan@conwy.gov.uk

Knightly, Laura (CON - Tywyn)
cllr.laura.knightly@conwy.gov.uk

Lloyd, Ifor (IND - Betws-Yn-Rhos)
cllr.ifor.glyn.lloyd@conwy.gov.uk

Lloyd-Williams, Susan (PC - Llansannan)
cllr.sue.lloyd-williams@conwy.gov.uk

Lyon, Margaret (IND - Gogarth)
cllr.margaret.lyon@conwy.gov.uk

MacLennan, John (CON - Pentre Mawr)
cllr.john.maclennan@conwy.gov.uk

MacRae, Delyth (PC - Gele)
cllr.delyth.macrae@conwy.gov.uk

McCaffrey, Anne (IND - Capelulo)
cllr.anne.mccaffrey@conwy.gov.uk

Miles, Dewi (IND - Mostyn)
cllr.dewi.miles@conwy.gov.uk

Milne, Donald (CON - Llandrillo-yn-Rhos)
cllr.donald.milne@conwy.gov.uk

Parry, Roger (CON - Llandrillo-yn-Rhos)
cllr.roger.parry@conwy.gov.uk

Parry, Edgar (IND - Crwst)
cllr.edgar.parry@conwy.gov.uk

Priestley, Michael (LD - Marl)
cllr.michael.priestley@conwy.gov.uk

Rees, Graham (IND - Llansanffraid)
cllr.graham.rees@conwy.gov.uk

Roberts, Elizabeth (PC - Betws Y Coed)
cllr.liz.roberts@conwy.gov.uk

Roberts, John (LD - Rhiw)
cllr.john.roberts@conwy.gov.uk

Roberts, Austin (PC - Eglwysbach)
cllr.austin.roberts@conwy.gov.uk

Roberts, Dave (CON - Llandrillo-yn-Rhos)
cllr.david.m.roberts@conwy.gov.uk

Rogers-Jones, Hilary (PC - Trefriw)
cllr.hilary.rogers-jones@conwy.gov.uk

Rowlands, Samuel (CON - Pentre Mawr)
cllr.sam.rowlands@conwy.gov.uk

Rowlands, Tim (CON - Gele)
cllr.tim.rowlands@conwy.gov.uk

Saville, Harry (CON - Gogarth)
cllr.harry.saville@conwy.gov.uk

Shotter, Susan (LD - Marl)
cllr.susan.shotter@conwy.gov.uk

Smith, Nigel (IND - Bae Cinmel / Kinmel Bay)
cllr.nigel.smith@conwy.gov.uk

Smith, Deion (LAB - Llysfaen)
cllr.deion.smith@conwy.gov.uk

Squire, Bob (IND - Eirias)
cllr.bob.squire@conwy.gov.uk

Stevens, Ken (LAB - Pant Yr Afon / Penmaenan)
cllr.ken.stevens@conwy.gov.uk

Stott, Trevor (LD - Rhiw)
cllr.trevor.stott@conwy.gov.uk

Stubbs, Rick (LAB - Abergele Pensarn)
cllr.rick.stubbs@conwy.gov.uk

Tansley, Adrian (LAB - Mochdre)
cllr.adrian.tansley@conwy.gov.uk

Vaughan, Joan (IND - Conwy)
cllr.joan.vaughan@conwy.gov.uk

Wood, Andrew (IND - Gele)
cllr.andrew.wood@conwy.gov.uk

POLITICAL COMPOSITION
IND: 19, CON: 13, PC: 12, LAB: 9, LD: 5, Vacant: 1

COMMITTEE CHAIRS
Audit: Mr Samuel Rowlands

Licensing: Mr Ken Stevens

Planning: Mr Nigel Smith

Copeland   D

Copeland Borough Council, The Copeland Centre, Catherine
Street, Whitehaven CA28 7SJ
☎ 01946 598300 ⏚ info@copeland.gov.uk 🖳 www.copeland.gov.uk

FACTS AND FIGURES
Parliamentary Constituencies: Copeland
EU Constituencies: North West
Election Frequency: Elections are of whole council

PRINCIPAL OFFICERS

Senior Management: Mrs Julie Betteridge, Director - Customer
& Community Services, The Copeland Centre, Catherine Street,
Whitehaven CA28 7SJ ☎ 01946 598415
⏚ julie.betteridge@copeland.gov.uk

Senior Management: Mrs Pat Graham, Managing Director, The
Copeland Centre, Catherine Street, Whitehaven CA28 7SJ
☎ 01946 598440 ⏚ pat.graham@copeland.gov.uk

Building Control: Mr Mark Key, Building Control Manager, The
Copeland Centre, Catherine Street, Whitehaven CA28 7SJ
☎ 01946 598407 ⏚ mark.key@copeland.gov.uk

Computer Management: Mr Martin Stroud, ICT Manager, The
Copeland Centre, Catherine Street, Whitehaven CA28 7SJ
☎ 01946 598481 ⏚ martin.stroud@copeland.gov.uk

Consumer Protection and Trading Standards: Ms Jackie
O'Reilly, Environmental Health Manager, The Copeland Centre,
Catherine Street, Whitehaven CA28 7SJ ☎ 01946 598304
⏚ jackie.oreilly@copeland.gov.uk

Contracts: Mr Martyn Morton, Property Programmes Manager, The
Copeland Centre, Catherine Street, Whitehaven CA28 7SJ
☎ 01946 598495

Corporate Services: Mrs Fiona Rooney, Interim Director -
Commercial & Corporate Resources, The Copeland Centre,
Catherine Street, Whitehaven CA28 7SJ ☎ 01946 598457
⏚ fiona.rooney@copeland.gov.uk

Customer Service: Mrs Julie Betteridge, Director - Customer
& Community Services, The Copeland Centre, Catherine Street,
Whitehaven CA28 7SJ ☎ 01946 598415
⏚ julie.betteridge@copeland.gov.uk

Economic Development: Mrs Sarah Mitchell, Economic
& Community Regeneration Manager, The Copeland Centre,
Catherine Street, Whitehaven CA28 7SJ ☎ 01946 598438
⏚ sarah.mitchell@copeland.gov.uk

Electoral Registration: Miss Stephanie Shaw, Elections
Manager, The Copeland Centre, Catherine Street, Whitehaven
CA28 7SJ ☎ 01946 598533 ⏚ stephanie.shaw@copeland.gov.uk

Emergency Planning: Ms Jackie O'Reilly, Environmental Health
Manager, The Copeland Centre, Catherine Street, Whitehaven
CA28 7SJ ☎ 01946 598304 ⏚ jackie.oreilly@copeland.gov.uk

Environmental Health: Ms Jackie O'Reilly, Environmental Health
Manager, The Copeland Centre, Catherine Street, Whitehaven
CA28 7SJ ☎ 01946 598335 ⏚ joreilly@copelandbc.gov.uk

Finance: Mrs Fiona Rooney, Interim Director - Commercial &
Corporate Resources, The Copeland Centre, Catherine Street,
Whitehaven CA28 7SJ ☎ 01946 598457
⏚ fiona.rooney@copeland.gov.uk

Fleet Management: Mrs Janice Carrol, Waste Services Manager,
Whitehaven Commerical Park, Moresby Parks, Whitehaven CA28
8YD ☎ 01946 593024 ⏚ janice.carrol@copeland.gov.uk

Grounds Maintenance: Mr John Davis, Parks Manager,
Whitehaven Commercial Park, Moresby Parks, Whitehaven CA28
8YD ☎ 02946 593022 ⏚ john.davis@copeland.gov.uk

Housing: Mrs Debbie Cochrane, Housing Policy Manager, The
Copeland Centre, Catherine Street, Whitehaven CA28 7SJ
☎ 01946 598427 ⏚ debbie.cochrane@copeland.gov.uk

Local Area Agreement: Mrs Julie Betteridge, Director -
Customer & Community Services, The Copeland Centre, Catherine
Street, Whitehaven CA28 7SJ ☎ 01946 598415
⏚ julie.betteridge@copeland.gov.uk

Legal: Mr Clinton Boyce, Legal Services Manager, The Copeland
Centre, Catherine Street, Whitehaven CA28 7SJ ☎ 01946 598516
⏚ clinton.boyce@copeland.gov.uk

Member Services: Mrs Lindsay Tomlinson, Democratic Services
Manager, The Copeland Centre, Catherine Street, Whitehaven
CA28 7SJ ☎ 01946 598526 ⏚ lindsay.tomlinson@copeland.gov.uk

Parking: Mrs Janice Carrol, Waste Services Manager, Whitehaven
Commerical Park, Moresby Parks, Whitehaven CA28 8YD
☎ 01946 593024 ⏚ janice.carrol@copeland.gov.uk

Partnerships: Mrs Julie Betteridge, Director - Customer &
Community Services, The Copeland Centre, Catherine Street,
Whitehaven CA28 7SJ ☎ 01946 598415
⏚ julie.betteridge@copeland.gov.uk

Planning: Mr Nick Hayhurst, Senior Development Control Officer,
The Copeland Centre, Catherine Street, Whitehaven CA28 7SJ
☎ 01946 598331 ⏚ nick.hayhurst@copeland.gov.uk

COPELAND

Planning: Mr Chris Hoban, Senior Planning Policy Officer, The Copeland Centre, Catherine Street, Whitehaven CA28 7SJ
☎ 01946 598439 ⏚ chris.hoban@copeland.gov.uk

Recycling & Waste Minimisation: Ms Janice Carrol, Waste Services Manager, Whitehaven Commercial Park, Moresby Parks, Whitehaven CA28 8YD ☎ 01946 852915
⏚ jcarrol@copelandbc.gov.uk

Regeneration: Mrs Sarah Mitchell, Economic & Community Regeneration Manager, The Copeland Centre, Catherine Street, Whitehaven CA28 7SJ ☎ 01946 598438

Sustainable Communities: Mrs Julie Betteridge, Director - Customer & Community Services, The Copeland Centre, Catherine Street, Whitehaven CA28 7SJ ☎ 01946 598415
⏚ julie.betteridge@copeland.gov.uk

Sustainable Development: Mrs Pat Graham, Director - Economic Growth, The Copeland Centre, Catherine Street, Whitehaven CA28 7SJ ☎ 01946 598440
⏚ pat.graham@copeland.gov.uk

Waste Collection and Disposal: Ms Janice Carrol, Waste Services Manager, Whitehaven Commercial Park, Moresby Parks, Whitehaven CA28 8YD ☎ 01946 852915
⏚ jcarrol@copelandbc.gov.uk

Waste Management: Mrs Janice Carrol, Waste Services Manager, Whitehaven Commerical Park, Moresby Parks, Whitehaven CA28 8YD ☎ 01946 593024
⏚ janice.carrol@copeland.gov.uk

COUNCILLORS

ChairTyson, Peter (LAB - Sandwith)
peter.tyson@copeland.gov.uk

Vice-ChairNorwood, Alistair (CON - Hillcrest)
alistair.norwood@copeland.gov.uk

Mayor: Starkie, Mike (IND - No Ward)
elected.mayor@copeland.gov.uk

Deputy Leader of the Council: Hogg, Lena (LAB - Egremont South)
lena.hogg@copeland.gov.uk

Arrighi, Carla (IND - Harbour)
carla.arrighi@copeland.gov.uk

Banks, David (LAB - Cleator Moor South)
david.banks@copeland.gov.uk

Barbour, Martin (CON - Moresby)

Bowman, Jackie (LAB - Distington)
jackie.bowman@copeland.gov.uk

Bowman, John (LAB - Distington)
john.bowman@copeland.gov.uk

Bradshaw, Anne (LAB - Bransty)
ann.bradshaw@copland.gov.uk

Branney, Hugh (LAB - Cleator Moor North)
hugh.branney@copeland.gov.uk

Burness, Denise (LAB - Holborn Hill)

Burns, John (LAB - Egremont North)
john.burns@copeland.gov.uk

Clarkson, Yvonne (CON - Beckermet)
yvonne.clarkson@copeland.gov.uk

Cole, Raymond (CON - Newtown)
raymond.cole@copeland.gov.uk

Connolly, Peter (LAB - Frizington)
peter.connnolly@copeland.gov.uk

Dirom, John (CON - Ennerdale)
john.dirom@copeland.gov.uk

Everett, Gwynneth (LAB - Frizington)
gwynneth.everett@copeland.gov.uk

Ferguson, Neil (LAB - Egremont South)
neil.ferguson@copeland.gov.uk

Forster, Jeanette (LAB - Hensingham)
jeanette.forster@copeland.gov.uk

Forster, Allan (LAB - Hensingham)
norman.williams@copeland.gov.uk

Gill, Ray (LAB - Hensingham)
ray.gill@copeland.gov.uk

Gleaves, Frederick (CON - Holborn Hill)
fred.gleaves@copeland.gov.uk

Guest, Michael (IND - Kells)
michael.guest@copeland.gov.uk

Hill, Ian (CON - St Bees)
ian.hill@copeland.gov.uk

Hitchen, Keith (CON - Bootle)
keith.hitchen@copeland.gov.uk

Holliday, Allan (LAB - Kells)
allan.holliday@copeland.gov.uk

Holliday, Allan (LAB - Mirehouse)
allan.holliday@copeland.gov.uk

Hully, Joan (LAB - Cleator Moor North)
membersservices@copeland.gov.uk

Jacob, Alan (CON - Gosforth)
alan.jacob@copeland.gov.uk

Jones-Bulman, Linda (LAB - Cleator Moor North)
linda.jones-bulman@copland.gov.uk

Kane, John (LAB - Hillcrest)
john.kane@copeland.gov.uk

Kelly, Bob (LAB - Newtown)
bob.kelly@copeland.gov.uk

Kirkbride, William (LAB - Harbour)

Lewthwaite, Jean (CON - Egremont North)
jean.lewthwaite@copeland.gov.uk

Maulding, Charles (IND - Harbour)
charles.maulding@copeland.gov.uk

McVeigh, Michael (LAB - Egremont South)
micheal.mcveigh@copeland.gov.uk

Meteer, Sam (IND - Beckermet)
simon.meteer@copeland.gov.uk

Moore, David (CON - Seascale)
david.moore@copeland.gov.uk

O'Kane, Brian (CON - Bransty)
brian.okane@copland.gov.uk

Pollen, Sam (LAB - Egremont North)
sam.pollen@copeland.gov.uk

Pratt, Andy (CON - Seascale)
andy.pratt@copeland.gov.uk

Reay, Christopher (LAB - Mirehouse)
christopher.reay@copeland.gov.uk

Riley, David (LAB - Cleator Moor South)
david.riley@copeland.gov.uk

Roberts, Graham (CON - Bransty)
graham.roberts@copeland.gov.uk

Scurrah, Gilbert (CON - Millom Without)
membersservices@copeland.gov.uk

Stephenson, Peter (LAB - Sandwith)
peter.stephenson@copeland.gov.uk

Sunderland, Graham (IND - Arlecdon)
graham.sunderland@copeland.gov.uk

Troughton, Gillian (LAB - Distington)
gillian.troughton@copeland.gov.uk

Whalley, Paul (LAB - Mirehouse)
paul.whalley@copeland.gov.uk

Wilson, Douglas (CON - Haverigg)
douglas.wilson@copeland.gov.uk

Wilson, Fee (CON - Newtown)
felicity.wilson@copeland.gov.uk

POLITICAL COMPOSITION
LAB: 29, CON: 17, IND: 6

COMMITTEE CHAIRS

Licensing: Mr Graham Roberts

Planning: Mr Michael McVeigh

Corby   D

Corby Borough Council, The Corby Cube, George Street, Corby NN17 1QG
☎ 01536 464000 📠 01536 400200 🖥 www.corby.gov.uk

FACTS AND FIGURES
Parliamentary Constituencies: Corby
EU Constituencies: East Midlands
Election Frequency: Every 4 years

PRINCIPAL OFFICERS

Chief Executive: Mr Norman Stronach, Chief Executive, The Cube, Parkland Gateway, George Street, Corby NN17 1QG ☎ 01536 464156 ✆ norman.stronach@corby.gov.uk

Senior Management: Mr Adrian Sibley, Director - Corporate Services, Deene House, New Post Office Square, Corby NN17 1GD ☎ 01536 464125 ✆ adrian.sibley@corby.gov.uk

Senior Management: Mr Iain Smith, Head of Service - Planning & Environmental Services, Deene House, New Post Office Square, Corby NN17 1GD ☎ 01536 464061 ✆ iain.smith@corby.gov.uk

Senior Management: Mr Chris Stephenson, Head of Service - Culture & Leisure, Deene House, New Post Office Square, Corby NN17 1GD ☎ 01536 464041 ✆ chris.stephenson@corby.gov.uk

Senior Management: Mr Jonathan Waterworth, Interim Head of Service - CB Property, Deene House, New Post Office Square, Corby NN17 1GD ☎ 01536 464686 ✆ jonathan.waterworth@corby.gov.uk

Access Officer / Social Services (Disability): Mr Colin Cox, Principal Building Control Officer, Deene House, New Post Office Square, Corby NN17 1GD ☎ 01536 464172 ✆ colin.cox@corby.gov.uk

Building Control: Mr Colin Cox, Principal Building Control Officer, Deene House, New Post Office Square, Corby NN17 1GD ☎ 01536 464172 ✆ colin.cox@corby.gov.uk

PR / Communications: Ms Kimberley Buzzard, Communications Officer, The Cube, Parklands Gateway, George Street, Corby NN17 1QG ☎ 01536 464020 ✆ kimberley.buzzard@corby.gov.uk

Community Safety: Ms Antonia Malpas, Principal Community Safety Officer, Deene House, New Post Office Square, Corby NN17 1GD ☎ 01536 464647 ✆ antonia.malpas@corby.gov.uk

Community Safety: Mr Craig Spence, Senior Neighbourhood Manager, Deene House, New Post Office Square, Corby NN17 1GD ☎ 01536 464625 ✆ craig.spence@corby.gov.uk

Computer Management: Mr Will McAlindon, ICT Manager, Deene House, New Post Office Square, Corby NN17 1GD ☎ 01536 464089 ✆ will.mcalindon@corby.gov.uk

Contracts: Mr Chris Everett, Procurement Officer, Deene House, New Post Office Square, Corby NN17 1GD ☎ 01536 464685 ✆ chris.everett@corby.gov.uk

Corporate Services: Mr Adrian Sibley, Director - Corporate Services, Deene House, New Post Office Square, Corby NN17 1GD ☎ 01536 464125 ✆ adrian.sibley@corby.gov.uk

Corporate Services: Mr Norman Stronach, Chief Executive, The Cube, Parklands Gateway, George Street, Corby NN17 1QG ☎ 01536 464156 ✆ norman.stronach@corby.gov.uk

Customer Service: Ms Samantha Dickinson, Recovery & Customer First Manager, The Cube, Parkland Gateway, George Street, Corby NN17 1QG ☎ 01536 464136 ✆ samantha.dickinson@corby.gov.uk

Direct Labour: Mr Iain Smith, Head of Service - Planning & Environmental Services, Deene House, New Post Office Square, Corby NN17 1GD ☎ 01536 464061 ✆ iain.smith@corby.gov.uk

Electoral Registration: Mr Aaron O'Sullivan, Electoral Services Officer, The Cube, Parkland Gateway, George Street, Corby NN17 1QG ☎ 01536 464012 ✆ aaron.o'sullivan@corby.gov.uk

Environmental / Technical Services: Mr Iain Smith, Head of Service - Planning & Environmental Services, Deene House, New Post Office Square, Corby NN17 1GD ☎ 01536 464061 ✆ iain.smith@corby.gov.uk

Environmental Health: Mr Iain Smith, Head of Service - Planning & Environmental Services, Deene House, New Post Office Square, Corby NN17 1GD ☎ 01536 464061 ✆ iain.smith@corby.gov.uk

CORBY

Estates, Property & Valuation: Mr Jonathan Waterworth, Interim Head of Service - CB Property, The Cube, Parklands Gateway, George Street, Corby NN17 1QG ☎ 01536 464686 ✉ jonathan.waterworth@corby.gov.uk

Facilities: Mr Jonathan Waterworth, Interim Head of Service - CB Property, The Cube, Parklands Gateway, George Street, Corby NN17 1QG ☎ 01536 464686 ✉ jonathan.waterworth@corby.gov.uk

Finance: Ms Claire Edwards, Financial Services Manager, Deene House, New Post Office Square, Corby NN17 1GD ☎ 01536 464101 ✉ claire.edwards@corby.gov.uk

Health and Safety: Mr Iain Smith, Head of Service - Planning & Environmental Services, Deene House, New Post Office Square, Corby NN17 1GD ☎ 01536 464061 ✉ iain.smith@corby.gov.uk

Housing: Ms Cath Maglone, Landlord Services Manager, Deene House, New Post Office Square, Corby NN17 1GD ☎ 01536 463074 ✉ cath.maglone@corby.gov.uk

Housing Maintenance: Mr Iain Smith, Head of Service - Planning & Environmental Services, Deene House, New Post Office Square, Corby NN17 1GD ☎ 01536 464061 ✉ iain.smith@corby.gov.uk

Legal: Mr Nigel Channer, Legal Services Manager, Deene House, New Post Office Square, Corby NN17 1GD ☎ 01536 464679 ✉ nigel.channer@corby.gov.uk

Leisure and Cultural Services: Mr Chris Stephenson, Head of Service - Culture & Leisure, Deene House, New Post Office Square, Corby NN17 1GD ☎ 01536 464041 ✉ chris.stephenson@corby.gov.uk

Licensing: Mr Iain Smith, Head of Service - Planning & Environmental Services, Deene House, New Post Office Square, Corby NN17 1GD ☎ 01536 464061 ✉ iain.smith@corby.gov.uk

Lottery Funding, Charity and Voluntary: Mr Chris Stephenson, Head of Service - Culture & Leisure, Deene House, New Post Office Square, Corby NN17 1GD ☎ 01536 464041 ✉ chris.stephenson@corby.gov.uk

Member Services: Mr Paul Goult, Democratic Services Manager & Monitoring Officer, The Cube, Parkland Gateway, George Street, Corby NN17 1QG ☎ 01536 464013 ✉ paul.goult@corby.gov.uk

Personnel / HR: Mrs Stella Jinks, Human Resources Manager, Deene House, New Post Office Square, Corby NN17 1GD ☎ 01536 464032 ✉ stella.jinks@corby.gov.uk

Planning: Mr Rob Temperley, Principal Planning Officer, Deene House, New Post Office Square, Corby NN17 1GD ☎ 01536 464161 ✉ rob.temperley@corby.gov.uk

Procurement: Mr Chris Everett, Procurement Officer, Deene House, New Post Office Square, Corby NN17 1GD ☎ 01536 464685 ✉ chris.everett@corby.gov.uk

Regeneration: Mr Norman Stronach, Chief Executive, The Cube, Parklands Gateway, Corby NN17 1QB ☎ 01536 464156 ✉ norman.stronach@corby.gov.uk

Staff Training: Mrs Stella Jinks, Human Resources Manager, Deene House, New Post Office Square, Corby NN17 1GD ☎ 01536 464032 ✉ stella.jinks@corby.gov.uk

Street Scene: Mr Iain Smith, Head of Service - Planning & Environmental Services, Deene House, New Post Office Square, Corby NN17 1GD ☎ 01536 464061 ✉ iain.smith@corby.gov.uk

Sustainable Communities: Mr Norman Stronach, Chief Executive, The Cube, Parklands Gateway, Corby NN17 1GD ☎ 01536 464156 ✉ norman.stronach@corby.gov.uk

Sustainable Development: Ms Sara Earl, Sustainability Officer, Deene House, New Post Office Square, Corby NN17 1GD ☎ 01536 464685 ✉ sara.earl@corby.gov.uk

Waste Collection and Disposal: Mr Iain Smith, Head of Service - Planning & Environmental Services, Deene House, New Post Office Square, Corby NN17 1GD ☎ 01536 464061 ✉ iain.smith@corby.gov.uk

Waste Management: Mr Iain Smith, Head of Service - Planning & Environmental Services, Deene House, New Post Office Square, Corby NN17 1GD ☎ 01536 464061 ✉ iain.smith@corby.gov.uk

Children's Play Areas: Mr Lloyd Baines-Davies, Community Recreation & Events Officer, Deene House, New Post Office Square, Corby NN17 1GD ☎ 01536 464674 ✉ lloyd.bainesdavies@corby.gov.uk

COUNCILLORS

Mayor: McEwan, Peter (LAB - Oakley North)
peter.mcewan@corby.gov.uk

Leader of the Council: Beattie, Tom (LAB - Lodge Park)
tom.beattie@corby.gov.uk

Deputy Leader of the Council: Addison, Jean (LAB - Rowlett)
jean.addison@corby.gov.uk

Group Leader: McKellar, Robert (CON - Weldon & Gretton)
robert.mckellar@corby.gov.uk

Beattie, Paul (LAB - Beanfield)
paul.beattie@corby.gov.uk

Beeby, Raymond (LAB - Oakley North)
ray.beeby@corby.gov.uk

Brown, Ann (LAB - Beanfield)
ann.brown@corby.gov.uk

Butcher, Mary (LAB - Beanfield)
mary.butcher@corby.gov.uk

Caine, Judy (LAB - Oakley South)
judy.caine@corby.gov.uk

Carratt, Kenneth (LAB - Kingswood & Hazel Leys)
kenneth.carratt@corby.gov.uk

Cassidy, Colleen (LAB - Danesholme)
colleen.cassidy@corby.gov.uk

Colquhoun, William (LAB - Stanion & Corby Village)
william.colquhoun@corby.gov.uk

Dady, Anthony (LAB - Central)
anthony.dady@corby.gov.uk

Elliston, Elise (LAB - Kingswood & Hazel Leys)
elise.elliston@corby.gov.uk

Eyles, Bob (LAB - Lodge Park)
bob.eyles@corby.gov.uk

Ferguson, Lawrence (LAB - Central)
lawrence.ferguson@corby.gov.uk

Goult, Lucy (LAB - Lloyds)
Lucy.goult@corby.gov.uk

Keane, Matt (LAB - Lodge Park)
matt.keane@corby.gov.uk

Latta, Willie (LAB - Rowlett)
william.latta@corby.gov.uk

McGhee, John (LAB - Kingswood & Hazel Leys)
jmcghee@northamptonshire.gov.uk

Pengelly, Mark (LAB - Lloyds)
mark.pengelly@corby.gov.uk

Petch, Peter (LAB - Danesholme)
peter.petch@corby.gov.uk

Rahman, Mohammed (LAB - Oakley South)
Mohammed.rahman@corby.gov.uk

Reay, Matt (LAB - Lloyds)
matt.reay@corby.gov.uk

Riley, Julie (LAB - Stanion & Corby Village)
julie.riley@corby.gov.uk

Rutt, Robert (CON - Rural West)
robert.rutt@corby.gov.uk

Sims, David (CON - Oakley South)
dsimonsonline.gmail.com

Watt, Kevin (CON - Weldon & Gretton)
kevin.watt@corby.gov.uk

Watts, Bridget (CON - Weldon & Gretton)
bridget.watts@corby.gov.uk

POLITICAL COMPOSITION
LAB: 24, CON: 5

COMMITTEE CHAIRS

Audit: Mr Bob Eyles

Cornwall   U

Cornwall, County Hall, Treyew Road, Truro TR1 3AY
☎ 0300 123 4100 ⌁ customerservices@cornwall.gov.uk
🖳 www.cornwall.gov.uk

FACTS AND FIGURES
Parliamentary Constituencies: Camborne and Redruth, St. Austell and Newquay, St. Ives, Truro and Falmouth
EU Constituencies:
Election Frequency:

PRINCIPAL OFFICERS

Chief Executive: Ms Kate Kennally, Chief Executive, County Hall, Treyew Road, Truro TR1 3AY ☎ 0300 123 4100
⌁ kkennally@cornwall.gov.uk

Senior Management: Mr John Betty, Interim Strategic Director - Economic Growth & Development, County Hall, Treyew Road, Truro TR1 3AY ⌁ jbetty@cornwall.gov.uk

Senior Management: Mr Trevor Doughty, Strategic Director - Children, Families & Adults, County Hall, Treyew Road, Truro TR1 3AY ☎ 01872 322403 ⌁ tdoughty@cornwall.gov.uk

Senior Management: Mr Paul Masters, Strategic Director - Neighbourhoods, County Hall, Treyew Road, Truro TR1 3AY ☎ 01872 322121 ⌁ pmasters@cornwall.gov.uk

Senior Management: Ms Cath Robinson, Chief Operating Officer - Customer & Support Services (S151 Officer), County Hall, Treyew Road, Truro TR1 3AY ☎ 01872 324449 ⌁ crobinson@cornwall.gov.uk

Architect, Building / Property Services: Mr Adam Birchall, Property Forward Planning Manager, Pydar House, 4th Floor, Pydar Street, Truro TR1 1EA ☎ 01872 323083 ⌁ abirchall@cornwall.gov.uk

Building Control: Mr Phil Mason, Service Director - Planning & Sustainable Development, Room 209, Restormel Offices, 39 Penwinnick Road, St. Austell PL25 5DR ☎ 01726 223452 ⌁ phil.mason@cornwall.gov.uk

Children / Youth Services: Mr Trevor Doughty, Strategic Director - Children, Families & Adults, County Hall, Treyew Road, Truro TR1 3AY ☎ 01872 322403 ⌁ tdoughty@cornwall.gov.uk

Civil Registration: Ms Anne McSeveney, Assistant Head of Customers & Communities (Face to Face), Dalvenie House, Country Hall, Treyew Road, Truro TR1 3AY ☎ 01872 224300 ⌁ amcseveney@cornwall.gov.uk

PR / Communications: Ms Patricia Hewitt, Corporate Communications Manager, Room 3S, New County Hall, Treyew Road, Truro TR1 3AY ☎ 01872 322186 ⌁ phewitt@cornwall.gov.uk

Community Safety: Mr Paul Walker, Chief Fire Officer & Service Director - Community Resilience, 4th Floor, New County Hall, Treyew Road, Truro TR1 3AY ☎ 01872 323739 ⌁ pwalker@fire.cornwall.gov.uk

Computer Management: Mr David Picknett, Head of Information Technology, County Hall, Truro TR1 3AY ☎ 0300 1234 100 ⌁ dpicknett@cornwall.gov.uk

Consumer Protection and Trading Standards: Mr Allan Hampshire, Service Director - Neighbourhood & Public Realm, County Hall, Treyew Road, Truro TR1 3AY ☎ 01872 224409 ⌁ allan.hampshire@cornwall.gov.uk

Corporate Services: Mr Paul Masters, Strategic Director - Neighbourhoods, County Hall, Treyew Road, Truro TR1 3AY ☎ 01872 322121 ⌁ pmasters@cornwall.gov.uk

Customer Service: Mr Mark Read, Service Director - Customer Access & Digital Services, Room 204, Central 2 Office, 39 Penwinnick Road, St. Austell PL25 5DR ☎ 01726 223316 ⌁ mark.read@cornwall.gov.uk

CORNWALL

Education: Ms Jane Black, Service Director - Education & Early Years, County Hall, Treyew Road, Truro TR1 3AY
✆ jblack@cornwall.gov.uk

Education: Mr Trevor Doughty, Strategic Director - Children, Families & Adults, County Hall, Treyew Road, Truro TR1 3AY
☎ 01872 322403 ✆ tdoughty@cornwall.gov.uk

Electoral Registration: Mr Richard Williams, Service Director - Assurance, Room 470, New County Hall, Treyew Road, Truro TR1 3AY ☎ 01872 322120 ✆ rawilliams@cornwall.gov.uk

Emergency Planning: Mr Richard Fedorowicz, Head of Emergency Management, County Hall, Treyew Road, Truro TR1 3AY ☎ 01872 323121 ✆ rfedorowicz@cornwall.gov.uk

Energy Management: Mr Adam Birchall, Property Forward Planning Manager, Pydar House, 4th Floor, Pydar Street, Truro TR1 1EA ☎ 01872 323083 ✆ abirchall@cornwall.gov.uk

Environmental / Technical Services: Mr Nigel Blackler, Service Director - Transport & Infrastructure, County Hall, Treyew Road, Truro TR1 3AY ☎ 01872 324124 ✆ nblackler@cornwall.gov.uk

Environmental Health: Mr Allan Hampshire, Service Director - Neighbourhood & Public Realm, County Hall, Treyew Road, Truro TR1 3AY ☎ 01872 224409 ✆ allan.hampshire@cornwall.gov.uk

Estates, Property & Valuation: Mr Adam Birchall, Property Forward Planning Manager, Pydar House, 4th Floor, Pydar Street, Truro TR1 1EA ☎ 01872 323083 ✆ abirchall@cornwall.gov.uk

European Liaison: Ms Sandra Rothwell, CEO - Cornwall & Isles of Scilly Local Environment Partnership, 3rd Floor, New County Hall, Treyew Road, Truro TR1 3AY ☎ 01872 224385
✆ srothwell@cornwall.gov.uk

Finance: Mr Andy Brown, Interim Service Director - Resources, County Hall, Treyew Road, Truro TR1 3AY
✆ abrown@cornwall.gov.uk

Finance: Ms Cath Robinson, Chief Operating Officer - Customer & Support Services (S151 Officer), County Hall, Treyew Road, Truro TR1 3AY ☎ 01872 324449 ✆ crobinson@cornwall.gov.uk

Treasury: Mr Clive Sturthridge, Treasury Officer, County Hall, Treyew Road, Truro TR1 3AY ☎ 01872 322228
✆ csturthridge@cornwall.gov.uk

Pensions: Mr Matthew Trebilcock, Pensions Investment Manager, New County Hall, Treyew Road, Truro TR1 3AY ☎ 01872 322322 ✆ mtrebilcock@cornwall.gov.uk

Fleet Management: Mr Arthur Hooper, Managing Director of CORMAC Solutions Ltd, North Building, Central GP Centre, Castle Canyke Road, Bodmin PL31 1DZ ☎ 01872 324559
✆ ahooper@cornwall.gov.uk

Health and Safety: Mr Sean Oates, Health, Safety & Wellbeing Manager, Fowey Building, New County Hall, Treyew Road, Truro TR1 3AY ☎ 01872 322182 ✆ soates1@cornwall.gov.uk

Highways: Mr Arthur Hooper, Managing Director of CORMAC Solutions Ltd, County Hall, Treyew Road, Truro TR1 3AY
☎ 01872 324559 ✆ ahooper@cornwall.gov.uk

Housing: Ms Jane Barlow, Managing Director of Cornwall Housing, Council Offices, 2nd Floor, Dolcoath Avenue, Camborne TR14 8SX ☎ 01209 614322 ✆ jane.barlow@cornwall.gov.uk

Housing Maintenance: Ms Jane Barlow, Managing Director of Cornwall Housing, Council Offices, 2nd Floor, Dolcoath Avenue, Camborne TR14 8SX ☎ 01209 614322 ✆ jane.barlow@cornwall.gov.uk

Legal: Mr Richard Williams, Service Director - Assurance, Room 470, New County Hall, Treyew Road, Truro TR1 3AY
☎ 01872 322120 ✆ rawilliams@cornwall.gov.uk

Leisure and Cultural Services: Mr Simon Blamey, Managing Director of Tempus Leisure Ltd, Windwhistle House, Cooksland Road, Bodmin PL31 2RH ☎ 01208 262805
✆ sblamey@tempusleisure.org.uk

Licensing: Mr Allan Hampshire, Service Director - Neighbourhood & Public Realm, Room C3.11, Carrick House, Pydar Street, Truro TR1 1EB ☎ 01872 224409 ✆ allan.hampshire@cornwall.gov.uk

Member Services: Mr Richard Williams, Service Director - Assurance, Room 470, New County Hall, Treyew Road, Truro TR1 3AY ☎ 01872 322120 ✆ rawilliams@cornwall.gov.uk

Parking: Mr Jon Haskins, Parking Manager, Room E2: 20, Carrick House, Truro TR1 1EB ☎ 01872 224264 ✆ jhaskins@cornwall.gov.uk

Partnerships: Ms Rachael Bice, Partnerships & Rural Policy Lead, Pydar House, 4th Floor, Pydar Street, Truro TR1 1EA
☎ 01872 224314 ✆ rbice@cornwall.gov.uk

Personnel / HR: Ms Julie Wood, Assistant Head of People Management, Development & Wellbeing, County Hall, Treyew Road, Truro TR1 3AY ☎ 01872 322153 ✆ jwood@cornwall.gov.uk

Planning: Mr Phil Mason, Service Director - Planning & Sustainable Development, County Hall, Treyew Road, Truro TR1 3AY ☎ 01726 223452 ✆ phil.mason@cornwall.gov.uk

Procurement: Mr Ray Hughes, Assistant Head of Business Planning & Development (Commercial Services), Room 2W, New County Hall, Truro TR1 3AY ☎ 01872 326510
✆ rhughes@cornwall.gov.uk

Public Libraries: Mr Mark Read, Service Director - Customer Access & Digital Services, Room 204, Central 2 Office, 39 Penwinnick Road, St. Austell PL25 5DR ☎ 01726 223316
✆ mark.read@cornwall.gov.uk

Recycling & Waste Minimisation: Mr Peter Marsh, Interim Service Director - Environment, The Exchange, New County Hall, Treyew Road, Truro TR1 3AY ☎ 01872 326932
✆ pmarsh@cornwall.gov.uk

Regeneration: Mr Phil Mason, Service Director - Planning & Sustainable Development, County Hall, Treyew Road, Truro TR1 3AY ☎ 01726 223452 ✆ phil.mason@cornwall.gov.uk

Road Safety: Mr Paul Walker, Chief Fire Officer & Service Director - Community Resilience, 4th Floor, New County Hall, Treyew Road, Truro TR1 3AY ☎ 01872 323739 ✆ pwalker@fire.cornwall.gov.uk

Social Services: Mr Trevor Doughty, Strategic Director - Children, Families & Adults, County Hall, Treyew Road, Truro TR1 3AY ☎ 01872 322403 ✆ tdoughty@cornwall.gov.uk

Social Services (Adult): Mr Trevor Doughty, Strategic Director - Children, Families & Adults, County Hall, Treyew Road, Truro TR1 3AY ☎ 01872 322403 ✆ tdoughty@cornwall.gov.uk

Social Services (Adult): Ms Claire Leandro, Service Director - Adult Care Services, County Hall, Treyew Road, Truro TR1 3AY ✆ cleandro@cornwall.gov.uk

Social Services (Children): Mr Jack Cordery, Service Director - Children & Family Services, Room 424, New County Hall, Treyew Road, Truro TR1 3AY ☎ 01872 323637 ✆ jcordery@cornwall.gov.uk

Childrens Social Care: Ms Marion Russell, Principal Child & Family Social Worker, County Hall, Treyew Road, Truro TR1 3AY ☎ 0300 1234 100 ✆ marion.russell@cornwall.gov.uk

Public Health: Ms Caroline Court, Interim Service Director - Wellbeing & Public Health, County Hall, Treyew Road, Truro TR1 3AY ✆ ccourt@cornwall.gov.uk

Staff Training: Ms Julie Wood, Assistant Head of People Management, Development & Wellbeing, County Hall, Treyew Road, Truro TR1 3AY ☎ 01872 322153 ✆ jwood@cornwall.gov.uk

Tourism: Mr Malcom Bell, Head of Tourism, Pydar House, Pydar Street, Truro TR1 1EA ☎ 01872 322820 ✆ malcolm.bell@cornwallenterprise.co.uk

Town Centre: Mr Rob Andrew, Assistant Head of Service for Communities & Devolution, County Hall, Treyew Road, Truro TR1 3AY ☎ 01872 224239 ✆ randrew@cornwall.gov.uk

Traffic Management: Mr Arthur Hooper, Managing Director of CORMAC Solutions Ltd, North Building, Central GP Centre, Castle Canyke Road, Bodmin PL31 1DZ ☎ 01872 324559 ✆ ahooper@cornwall.gov.uk

Transport: Mr Nigel Blackler, Service Director - Transport & Infrastructure, County Hall, Treyew Road, Truro TR1 3AY ☎ 01872 324124 ✆ nblackler@cornwall.gov.uk

Transport Planner: Mr Nigel Blackler, Service Director - Transport & Infrastructure, County Hall, Treyew Road, Truro TR1 3AY ☎ 01872 324124 ✆ nblackler@cornwall.gov.uk

Waste Collection and Disposal: Mr Peter Marsh, Interim Service Director - Environment, The Exchange, New County Hall, Treyew Road, Truro TR1 3AY ☎ 01872 326932 ✆ pmarsh@cornwall.gov.uk

Waste Management: Mr Peter Marsh, Interim Service Director - Environment, The Exchange, New County Hall, Treyew Road, Truro TR1 3AY ☎ 01872 326932 ✆ pmarsh@cornwall.gov.uk

Children's Play Areas: Mr Jon James, Natural Environment Manager, Room 102, Scorrier Depot, Radnor Road, Scorrier, Redruth TR16 5EH ☎ 01209 614387 ✆ jjames@cornwall.gov.uk

COUNCILLORS

ChairKerridge, Ann (LD - Bodmin St Mary's) akerridge@cornwall.gov.uk

Vice-ChairMay, Mary (IND - Penryn West) mamay@cornwall.gov.uk

Leader of the Council: Pollard, John (IND - Hayle North) jpollard1@cornwall.gov.uk

Deputy Leader of the Council: Paynter, Adam (LD - Launceston North & North Petherwin) apaynter@cornwall.gov.uk

Group Leader:Cole, Dick (O - St Enoder) ricole@cornwall.gov.uk

Group Leader:Dwelly, Tim (LAB - Penzance East) tdwelly@cornwall.gov.uk

Group Leader:Ferguson, Fiona (CON - Truro Trehaverne) fiferguson@cornwall.gov.uk

Group Leader:Keeling, John (CON - Breage, Germoe & Sithney) jkeeling@cornwall.gov.uk

Group Leader:McWilliam, Stephanie (UKIP - Lynher) smcwilliam@cornwall.gov.uk

Group Leader:Mitchell, Andrew (IND - St Ives West) amitchell1@cornwall.gov.uk

Andrewes, Tim (INDNA - St Ives East) tandrewes@cornwall.gov.uk

Atherton, Candy (LAB - Falmouth Smithick) catherton@cornwall.gov.uk

Austin, Bob (LD - Saltash West) baustin@cornwall.gov.uk

Bastin, John (CON - Constantine, Mawnan & Budock) jbastin@cornwall.gov.uk

Batters, Chris (LD - Lanivet & Blisland) cbatters@cornwall.gov.uk

Bay, Benedicte (CON - Lostwithiel) bbay@cornwall.gov.uk

Biscoe, Bert (IND - Truro Boscawen) bertbiscoe@btinternet.com

Brown, Glenton (LD - Tintagel) gbrown@cornwall.gov.uk

Brown, Malcolm (LD - St Austell Bethel) mbrown3@cornwall.gov.uk

Brown, Geoff (LD - Newquay Central) geoff.brown@cornwall.gov.uk

Bull, Jackie (LD - St Austell Poltair) jbull@cornwall.gov.uk

Burden, Neil (IND - Stokeclimsland) nburden@cornwall.gov.uk

Buscombe, Richard (LD - Padstow) rbuscombe@cornwall.gov.uk

Callan, Michael (IND - Perranporth) mcallan@cornwall.gov.uk

CORNWALL

Candy, Jim (LD - Trelawny)
jcandy@cornwall.gov.uk

Chamberlain, Steve (CON - Feock & Playing Place)
schamberlain1@cornwall.gov.uk

Chopak, Nicky (LD - Poundstock)
nchopal@cornwall.gov.uk

Coombe, John (IND - Hayle South)
jcoombe@cornwall.gov.uk

Curnow, Des (IND - St Stephen-In-Brannel)
descurrow@cornwall.gov.uk

Deeble, Tim (IND - Threemilestone & Gloweth)
tdeeble@cornwall.gov.uk

Dolley, Lisa (IND - Redruth North)
ldolley@cornwall.gov.uk

Dolphin, Paula (LD - Grenville & Stratton)
pdolphin@cornwall.gov.uk

Duffin, Joyce (LD - Mount Hawke & Portreath)
jmduffin@cornwall.gov.uk

Dyer, John (CON - Chacewater, Kenwyn & Baldhu)
fjdyer@cornwall.gov.uk

Eathorne-Gibbons, Mike (IND - Ladock, St Clement & St Erme)
meathornegibbons@cornwall.gov.uk

Eddowes, Mike (CON - Redruth Central)
meddowes@cornwall.gov.uk

Egerton, Bob (INDNA - Probus, Tregony & Grampound)
begerton@cornwall.gov.uk

Ekinsmyth, David (LD - Illogan)
dekinsmyth@cornwall.gov.uk

Elliott, Derek (UKIP - Four Lanes)
delliott@cornwall.gov.uk

Ellison, Joe (IND - Saltash North)
jellison1@cornwall.gov.uk

Evans, Geoffrey (CON - Falmouth Arwenack)
gfevans@cornwall.gov.uk

Farrington, Jade (LD - Launceston South)
jfarrington@cornwall.gov.uk

Fitter, John (CON - St Mawgan & Colan)
jfitter@cornwall.gov.uk

Flashman, Jim (CON - St Dominick, Harrowbarrow & Kelly Bray)
jflashman@cornwall.gov.uk

Fonk, Mario (LD - Gulval & Heamoor)
mfonk@cornwall.gov.uk

Frank, Hilary (LD - Saltash South)
hfrank@cornwall.gov.uk

French, Tom (CON - St Austell Bay)
tfrench@cornwall.gov.uk

George, Michael (LD - Liskeard West & Dobwalls)
mgeorge1@cornwall.gov.uk

German, Julian (IND - Roseland)
jgerman@cornwall.gov.uk

Greenslade, Fred (IND - St Dennis & Nanpean)
fred.greenslade@cornwall.gov.uk

Hall, Vivian (CON - Altarnun)
vhall@cornwall.gov.uk

Hannaford, Edwina (LD - Looe West, Lansallos & Lanteglos)
ehannaford@cornwall.gov.uk

Harding, Roger (CON - Newlyn & Mousehole)
rharding@cornwall.gov.uk

Harris, Malcolm (IND - St Mewan)
mharris2@cornwall.gov.uk

Harvey, Pat (IND - St Columb Major)
pharvey@cornwall.gov.uk

Hawken, Sally (IND - Liskeard East)
shawken@cornwall.gov.uk

Haycock, Judith (IND - Helston South)
jhaycock@cornwall.gov.uk

Herd, John (CON - Camborne Pendarves)
jherd@cornwall.gov.uk

Heyward, Sandra (IND - St Austell Gover)
sheyward@cornwall.gov.uk

Hobbs, Brian (LD - Torpoint East)
bhobbs@cornwall.gov.uk

Holley, Derek (IND - Saltash East)
dholley@cornwall.gov.uk

Holmes, Roger (IND - Liskeard North)
rholmes@cornwall.gov.uk

Hughes, David (LD - Fowey & Tywardreath)
dhughes@cornwall.gov.uk

James, Sue (LD - St Just In Penwith)
sjames@cornwall.gov.uk

Jenkin, Loveday (O - Crowan & Wendron)
letjenkin@cornwall.gov.uk

Jewell, Alan (CON - Falmouth Boslowick)
ajewell@cornwall.gov.uk

Kaczmarek, Mark (IND - Carharrack, Gwennap & St Day)
mkaczmarek@cornwall.gov.uk

Kenny, Joanna (LD - Newquay Pentire)
jkenny@cornwall.gov.uk

King, Gary (IND - Mount Charles)
gking@cornwall.gov.uk

Kirk, Dorothy (LAB - Gunnislake & Calstock)
dkirk@cornwall.gov.uk

Knightley, Steve (LD - Wadebridge East)
sknightley@cornwall.gov.uk

Lambshead, Patrick (CON - Newquay Tretherras)
plambshead@cornwall.gov.uk

Long, Andrew (O - Callington)
ajlong@cornwall.gov.uk

Luke, Matthew (O - Penwithick & Boscoppa)
mluke1@cornwall.gov.uk

Maddern, Bill (CON - St Buryan)
william.maddern@cornwall.gov.uk

Mann, Roy (CON - Ludgvan)
rmann@cornwall.gov.uk

Martin, Tony (CON - Penryn East & Mylor)
tomartin@cornwall.gov.uk

Martin, Phil (IND - Helston North)
pmartin@cornwall.gov.uk

Massey, Gemma (LD - Launceston Central)

McHugh, Karen (LD - Wadebridge West)

McKenna, Jim (IND - Penzance Promenade)
jmckenna@cornwall.gov.uk

Mitchell, Pete (LD - St Agnes)
pmitchell1@cornwall.gov.uk

Moyle, Malcolm (LAB - Pool & Tehidy)
mmoyle@cornwall.gov.uk

Mustoe, James (CON - Mevagissey)
jmustoe@cornwall.gov.uk

Nicholas, Sue (CON - Marazion & Perranuthoe)
sunicholas@cornwall.gov.uk

Nolan, Rob (LD - Truro Redanick)
rnolan@cornwall.gov.uk

Olivier, Cornelius (LAB - Penzance Central)
colivier@cornwall.gov.uk

Parsons, David (LD - Bude)
dparsons@cornwall.gov.uk

Pascoe, Lionel (CON - Gwinear-Gwithian & St Erth)
lpascoe1@cornwall.gov.uk

Pearce, Nigel (LD - Bude)
nigelpearce33@hotmail.com

Pearn, Mike (CON - Torpoint West)
mpearn@cornwall.gov.uk

Penhaligon, Liz (CON - Lelant & Carbis Bay)
epenhaligon@cornwall.gov.uk

Penny, Andy (IND - St Minver & St Endellion)
apenny@cornwall.gov.uk

Pugh, Daniel (CON - St Germans & Landulph)
dpugh@cornwall.gov.uk

Rich, Loic (IND - Truro Tregolls)
lrich@cornwall.gov.uk

Rix, Simon (LD - Bugle)
srix@cornwall.gov.uk

Robinson, Jude (LAB - Camborne Treswithian)

Rogerson, Pat (LD - Bodmin St Leonard)
progerson@cornwall.gov.uk

Rogerson, Steve (LD - Bodmin St Petroc)
srogerson@cornwall.gov.uk

Rotchell, Rob (LD - Camelford)
rrotchell@cornwall.gov.uk

Rowe, Jeremy (LD - St Issey & St Tudy)
jerowe@cornwall.gov.uk

Rule, Carolyn (IND - Mullion & Grade-Ruan)
carorule@cornwall.gov.uk

Sanger, Walter (CON - St Keverne & Meneage)
wsanger@cornwall.gov.uk

Saunby, David (IND - Falmouth Trescobeas)

Scrafton, Douglas (LD - Par & St Blazey Gate)
dscrafton@cornwall.gov.uk

Seeva, Phil (CON - Menheniot)

Sleeman, Dave (LD - Newquay Treloggan)
dsleeman@cornwall.gov.uk

Stoneman, Jon (CON - Camborne Trelowarren)
jstoneman@cornwall.gov.uk

Taylor, Roy (LD - St Blazey)
roytaylor@cornwall.gov.uk

Thomas, John (IND - Lanner & Stithians)
john.thomas@cornwall.gov.uk

Thomas, Ian (IND - Redruth South)
ithomas@cornwall.gov.uk

Toms, Armand (IND - Looe East)
atoms@cornwall.gov.uk

Toms, Hanna (LAB - Falmouth Penwerris)
htoms@cornwall.gov.uk

Trubody, George (IND - Rame Peninsular)
gtrubody@conrwall.gov.uk

Wallis, Andrew (IND - Porthleven & Helston West)
awallis@cornwall.gov.uk

Watson, Derris (LD - St Cleer)
dwatson@cornwall.gov.uk

Webber, Robert (LAB - Camborne Treslothan)
rwebber@cornwall.gov.uk

White, Paul (CON - Camborne Roskear)
pwhite@cornwall.gov.uk

Williams, Peter (CON - Mabe, Perranarworthal & St Gluvias)
prgwilliams@cornwall.gov.uk

Wood, John (IND - Roche)
johnwood@cornwall.gov.uk

POLITICAL COMPOSITION
LD: 39, IND: 35, CON: 30, LAB: 8, O: 4, Vacant: 3, UKIP: 2, INDNA: 2

COMMITTEE CHAIRS

Economy & Culture: Mr Tim Dwelly

Housing & Environment: Mr Armand Toms

Licensing: Mr Malcolm Brown

Pensions: Mr Derek Holley

Planning: Mr Rob Nolan

Cotswold   D

Cotswold District Council, Council Offices, Trinity Road, Cirencester GL7 1PX
☎ 01285 623000 📠 01285 623900 ✍ cdc@cotswold.gov.uk
🖥 www.cotswold.gov.uk

FACTS AND FIGURES
Parliamentary Constituencies: Cotswold
EU Constituencies: South West
Election Frequency: Elections are of whole council

PRINCIPAL OFFICERS

Chief Executive: Mr Frank Wilson, Head of Paid Service, Council Offices, Trinity Road, Cirencester GL7 1PX ☎ 01285 623101
✍ frank.wilson@cotswold.gov.uk

COTSWOLD

Senior Management: Ms Christine Gore, Strategic Director - Communities & Planning, Council Offices, Trinity Road, Cirencester GL7 1PX ☎ 01285 623500 ⌗ christine.gore@cotswold.gov.uk

Senior Management: Mr David Neudegg, Managing Director, Council Offices, Trinity Road, Cirencester GL7 1PX ☎ 01285 623101 ⌗ david.neudegg@2020partnership.uk

Senior Management: Mr Ralph Young, Programme Director, Council Offices, Trinity Road, Cirencester GL7 1PX ☎ 01285 623600 ⌗ ralph.young@cotswold.gov.uk

Architect, Building / Property Services: Mrs Bhavna Patel, Head of Legal & Property Services, Council Offices, Trinity Road, Cirencester GL7 1PX ☎ 01285 623219 ⌗ bhavna.patel@cotswold.gov.uk

Best Value: Ms Kath Hoare, Business Improvement Manager, Council Offices, Trinity Road, Cirencester GL7 1PX ☎ 01285 623573 ⌗ kath.hoare@2020partnership.uk

Building Control: Mr Andrew Jones, Building Control Manager, Council Offices, Trinity Road, Cirencester GL7 1PX ☎ 01285 623633 ⌗ andrew.jones@cotswold.gov.uk

PR / Communications: Mr Bob McNally, Press & Media Liaison Officer, Council Offices, Trinity Road, Cirencester GL7 1PX ☎ 01285 623120 ⌗ bob.mcnally@cotswold.gov.uk

Community Planning: Mr Mike Clark, Corporate Planning Manager, Council Offices, Woodgreen, Witney OX28 1NB ☎ 01285 623565 ⌗ mike.clark@cotswold.gov.uk

Community Safety: Mr Tony Dix, Community Safety Officer, Council Offices, Woodgreen, Witney OX28 1NB ⌗ tony.dix@westoxon.gov.uk

Computer Management: Mr John Chorlton, ICT Operations Manager, Council Offices, Trinity Road, Cirencester GL7 1PX ☎ 01285 623000 ⌗ john.chorlton@cotswold.gov.uk

Contracts: Mr Phil Martin, Head of Business Information & Change, Council Offices, Woodgreen, Witney OX28 1NB ☎ 01993 861201 ⌗ phil.martin@westoxon.gov.uk

Customer Service: Mrs Sarah Cantwell, Customer Services Manager, Council Offices, Trinity Road, Cirencester GL7 1PX ☎ 01285 623068 ⌗ sarah.cantwell@cotswold.gov.uk

Economic Development: Ms Diane Shelton, Head of Leisure & Communities, Council Offices, Woodgreen, Witney OX28 1NB ☎ 01285 623560 ⌗ diana.shelton@westoxfordshire.gov.uk

E-Government: Mr Dave Pennington, Web Developer, Council Offices, Trinity Road, Cirencester GL7 1PX ☎ 01285 623000 ⌗ dave.pennington@cotswold.gov.uk

Electoral Registration: Mr Nigel Adams, Head of Democratic Services, Council Offices, Trinity Road, Cirencester GL7 1PX ☎ 01285 623202 ⌗ nigel.adams@cotswold.gov.uk

Emergency Planning: Mrs Claire Locke, Head of Environmental Services, Council Offices, Trinity Road, Cirencester GL7 1PX ☎ 01285 623427 ⌗ claire.locke@cotswold.gov.uk

Energy Management: Mr Gary Packer, Sustainable Energy Officer, Council Offices, Trinity Road, Cirencester GL7 1PX ☎ 01285 623428 ⌗ gary.packer@cotswold.gov.uk

Environmental / Technical Services: Mrs Claire Locke, Head of Environmental Services, Council Offices, Trinity Road, Cirencester GL7 1PX ☎ 01285 623427 ⌗ claire.locke@cotswold.gov.uk

Environmental Health: Mr Bill Oddy, Head of Community Safety, Council Offices, Trinity Road, Cirencester GL7 1PX ☎ 01993 861631 ⌗ bill.oddy@2020partnership.uk

Estates, Property & Valuation: Mrs Bhavna Patel, Head of Legal & Property Services, Council Offices, Trinity Road, Cirencester GL7 1PX ☎ 01285 623219 ⌗ bhavna.patel@cotswold.gov.uk

Finance: Ms Jenny Poole, Head of Finance & Audit, Council Offices, Trinity Road, Cirencester GL7 1PX ☎ 01285 623313 ⌗ jenny.poole@cotswold.gov.uk

Health and Safety: Mr Mark Lane, Health & Safety Manager, Council Offices, Trinity Road, Cirencester GL7 1PX ☎ 01285 623111 ⌗ mark.lane@cotswold.gov.uk

Home Energy Conservation: Mr Gary Packer, Sustainable Energy Officer, Council Offices, Trinity Road, Cirencester GL7 1PX ☎ 01285 623428 ⌗ gary.packer@cotswold.gov.uk

Housing: Ms Philippa Lowe, Head of Planning & Strategic Housing, Council Offices, Trinity Road, Cirencester GL7 1PX ☎ 01285 623000 ⌗ philippa.lowe@cotswold.gov.uk

Legal: Mrs Bhavna Patel, Head of Legal & Property Services, Council Offices, Trinity Road, Cirencester GL7 1PX ☎ 01285 623219 ⌗ bhavna.patel@cotswold.gov.uk

Leisure and Cultural Services: Ms Diane Shelton, Head of Leisure & Communities, Council Offices, Woodgreen, Witney OX28 1NB ☎ 01285 623560 ⌗ diana.shelton@westoxfordshire.gov.uk

Licensing: Mr Matthew Kirby, Interim Head of Public Protection, Council Offices, Trinity Road, Cirencester GL7 1PX ☎ 01285 623442 ⌗ amanda.morgan@cotswold.gov.uk

Member Services: Mr Nigel Adams, Head of Democratic Services, Council Offices, Trinity Road, Cirencester GL7 1PX ☎ 01285 623202 ⌗ nigel.adams@cotswold.gov.uk

Parking: Ms Maria Wheatley, Parking Services Manager, Council Offices, Trinity Road, Cirencester GL7 1PX ☎ 01285 623228 ⌗ maria.wheatley@cotswold.gov.uk

Personnel / HR: Ms Deborah Bainbridge, Head of Human Resources, Council Offices, Woodgreen, Witney OX28 1NB ☎ 01285 623148 ⌗ deborah.bainbridge@cotswold.gov.uk

Planning: Ms Philippa Lowe, Head of Planning & Strategic Housing, Council Offices, Trinity Road, Cirencester GL7 1PX
☎ 01285 623000 ⌨ philippa.lowe@cotswold.gov.uk

Procurement: Ms Kath Hoare, Business Improvement Manager, Council Offices, Trinity Road, Cirencester GL7 1PX
☎ 01285 623573 ⌨ kath.hoare@2020partnership.uk

Procurement: Ms Sarah Turner, Business Solutions Manager, Municipal Offices, The Promenade, Cheltenham GL50 9SA
⌨ sarah.turner@cotswold.gov.uk

Staff Training: Mrs Jan Bridges, Learning & Organisational Development Manager, Municipal Offices, Promenade, Cheltenham GL50 9SA ☎ 01242 775189 ⌨ jan.bridges@cheltenham.gov.uk

Staff Training: Ms Jenny Poole, Head of Finance & Audit, Council Offices, Trinity Road, Cirencester GL7 1PX ☎ 01285 623313 ⌨ jenny.poole@cotswold.gov.uk

Tourism: Ms Sally Graff, Tourism Manager, Council Offices, Trinity Road, Cirencester GL7 1PX ☎ 01608 650881 ⌨ sally.graff@cotswold.gov.uk

Waste Collection and Disposal: Mrs Claire Locke, Head of Environmental Services, Council Offices, Trinity Road, Cirencester GL7 1PX ☎ 01285 623427 ⌨ claire.locke@cotswold.gov.uk

Waste Management: Mrs Claire Locke, Head of Environmental Services, Council Offices, Trinity Road, Cirencester GL7 1PX
☎ 01285 623427 ⌨ claire.locke@cotswold.gov.uk

COUNCILLORS

ChairAnnett, Mark (CON - Campden & Vale)
mark.annett@cotswold.gov.uk

Leader of the Council: Stowe, Lynden (CON - Campden & Vale)
lynden.stowe@cotswold.gov.uk

Deputy Leader of the Council: Parsons, Nicholas (CON - Ermin)
nicholas.parsons@cotswold.gov.uk

Group LeaderHarris, Joseph (LD - St Michael's)
joe.harris@cotswold.gov.uk

Andrews, Stephen (CON - Lechdale, Kempsford & Fairford South)
stephen.andrews@cotswold.gov.uk

Beale, Julian (CON - Fosseridge)
julian.beale@cotswold.gov.uk

Beccle, Abagail (CON - Fairford North)
abagail.beccle@cotswold.gov.uk

Berry, Tony (CON - Kemble)
tony.berry@cotswold.gov.uk

Brassington, Ray (LD - Four Acres)
ray.brassington@cotswold.gov.uk

Cheung, Tatyan (LD - New Mills)
tatyan.cheung@cotswold.gov.uk

Coakley, Sue (CON - Lechdale, Kempsford & Fairford South)
sue.coakley@cotswold.gov.uk

Coggins, Alison (CON - Moreton West)
alison.coggins@cotswold.gov.uk

Coleman, Patrick (LD - Stratton)
patrick.coleman@cotswold.gov.uk

Dare, Barry (CON - Stow)
barry.dare@cotswold.gov.uk

Dutton, Robert (CON - Moreton East)
robert.dutton@cotswold.gov.uk

Forde, Jenny (LD - Chedworth & Churn Valley)
jenny.forde@cotswold.gov.uk

Fowles, David (CON - The Ampneys & Hampton)
david.fowles@cotswold.gov.uk

Hancock, Christopher (CON - Northleach)
christopher.hancock@cotswold.gov.uk

Harris, Mark (LD - Abbey)
mark.harris@cotswold.gov.uk

Heaven, Maggie (CON - Tetbury & East Rural)
maggie.heaven@cotswold.gov.uk

Hicks, Jenny (LD - Watermoor)
jenny.hicks@cotswold.gov.uk

Hirst, Stephen (CON - Tetbury Town)
stephen.hirst@cotswold.gov.uk

Hughes, Roly (LD - Chesterton)
roly.hughes@cotswold.gov.uk

Hughes, Robin (CON - Sandywell)
robin.hughes@cotswold.gov.uk

Jepson, Sue (CON - Blockley)
sue.jepson@cotswold.gov.uk

Keeling, Richard (CON - Bourton Vale)
richard.keeling@cotswold.gov.uk

Layton, Juliet (LD - South Cerney Village)
juliet.layton@cotswold.gov.uk

MacKenzie-Charrington, Mark (CON - The Rissingtons)
mark.mackenzie-charrington@cotswold.gov.uk

Parsons, Shaun (CON - Siddington & Cerney Rural)
shaun.parsons@cotswold.gov.uk

Parsons, Jim (CON - Grumbolds Ash with Avening)
jim.parsons@cotswold.gov.uk

Robbins, Nigel (LD - The Beeches)
nigel.robbins@cotswold.gov.uk

Stevenson, Tina (CON - Tetbury with Upton)
tina.stevenson@cotswold.gov.uk

Theodoulou, Raymond (CON - Coln Valley)
raymond.theodoulou@cotswold.gov.uk

Wilkins, Len (CON - Bourton Village)
len.wilkins@cotswold.gov.uk

POLITICAL COMPOSITION
CON: 24, LD: 10

COMMITTEE CHAIRS

Audit: Mr Len Wilkins

Planning & Licensing: Mr Stephen Hirst

COVENTRY CITY

Coventry City Council, The Council House, Earl Street, Coventry CV1 5RR
☎ 024 7683 4333 ⏀ customer.services@coventry.gov.uk
▭ www.coventry.gov.uk

FACTS AND FIGURES
Parliamentary Constituencies: Coventry North East, Coventry North West, Coventry South
EU Constituencies: West Midlands
Election Frequency: Elections are by thirds

PRINCIPAL OFFICERS

Chief Executive: Mr Martin Reeves, Chief Executive, The Council House, Earl Street, Coventry CV1 5RR ☎ 024 7683 1100 ⏀ martin.reeves@coventry.gov.uk

Senior Management: Dr Jane Moore, Director - Public Health, The Council House, Earl Street, Coventry CV1 5RR ☎ 024 7683 2884 ⏀ jane.moore@coventry.gov.uk

Senior Management: Ms Gail Quinton, Executive Director - People, Civic Centre, 1 Little Park Street, Coventry CV1 5RS ☎ 024 7683 3405 ⏀ gail.quinton@coventry.gov.uk

Senior Management: Mr Chris West, Executive Director - Resources, The Council House, Earl Street, Coventry CV1 5RR ☎ 024 7683 3700 ⏀ chris.west@coventry.gov.uk

Senior Management: Mr Martin Yardley, Executive Director - Place, Floor 13, Civic Centre 4, Much Park Street, Coventry CV1 2PY ☎ 024 7683 1200 ⏀ martin.yardley@coventry.gov.uk

Architect, Building / Property Services: Mr Nigel Clews, Assistant Director - Property Asset Management, Civic Centre 4, Much Park Street, Coventry CV1 2PY ☎ 024 7683 4001 ⏀ nigel.clews@coventry.gov.uk

Building Control: Mr Stuart Claridge, Team Manager - Building Control, Civic Centre 4, Much Park Street, Coventry CV1 2PY ☎ 024 7683 2057 ⏀ stuart.claridge@coventry.gov.uk

Catering Services: Mr Marcus Lynch, Manager of St. Mary's Guildhall, St. Mary's Guildhall, Bayley Lane, Coventry CV1 5RN ☎ 024 7683 3327 ⏀ marcus.lynch@coventry.gov.uk

Children / Youth Services: Ms Yolanda Corden, Interim Assistant Director - Children's Social Care & Early Intervention Services, 2nd Floor, Civic Centre 1, Little Park Street, Coventry CV1 5RS ☎ 024 7689 1901 ⏀ yolanda.corden@coventry.gov.uk

Children / Youth Services: Mr John Gregg, Director - Children's Services, Civic Centre 1, Coventry CV1 5RS ☎ 024 7683 3621 ⏀ john.gregg@coventry.gov.uk

Children / Youth Services: Mrs Isabel Merrifield, Assistant Director - Strategy Commissioning and Policy, The Council House, Earl Street, Coventry CV1 5RR ☎ 024 7683 3403 ⏀ isabel.merrifield@coventry.gov.uk

Children / Youth Services: Ms Kirston Nelson, Director - Adult Education & Libraries, Civic Centre 1, Coventry CV1 5RS ☎ 024 7683 3621 ⏀ kirtson.nelson@coventry.gov.uk

Civil Registration: Ms Bernadette Pennington, Superintendent Registrar, The Register Office, Chelesmore Manor House, Manor House Drive, Coventry CV1 2ND ☎ 024 7683 3138 ⏀ bernadette.pennington@coventry.gov.uk

PR / Communications: Ms Fran Collingham, Assistant Director - Communications, Council House, Earl Street, Coventry CV1 5RS ☎ 024 7683 1088 ⏀ fran.collingham@coventry.gov.uk

Community Planning: Mr Simon Brake, Director - Primary Care, Sustainability & Integration, Civic Centre 1, Little Park Street, Coventry CV1 5RS ☎ 024 7683 1652 ⏀ simon.brake@coventry.gov.uk

Community Planning: Mr Peter Fahy, Director - Adult Services, The Council House, Earl Street, Coventry CV1 5RR ☎ 024 7683 3555 ⏀ peter.fahy@coventry.gov.uk

Community Planning: Ms Gail Quinton, Executive Director - People, Civic Centre, 1 Little Park Street, Coventry CV1 5RS ☎ 024 7683 3405 ⏀ gail.quinton@coventry.gov.uk

Community Safety: Mr Liam Nagle, Offender Management Strategic Officer, Ground Floor, Christchurch House, Coventry CV1 2QL ☎ 024 7683 2063 ⏀ liam.nagle@coventry.gov.uk

Computer Management: Mr Mark Chester, Infrastructure Operations Manager, The Council House, Earl Street, Coventry CV1 5RR ☎ 024 7678 7970 ⏀ mark.chester@coventry.gov.uk

Computer Management: Ms Lisa Commane, Assistant Director - ICT, Transformation & Customer Services, The Council House, Earl Street, Coventry CV1 5RR ☎ 024 7683 3990 ⏀ lisa.commane@coventry.gov.uk

Consumer Protection and Trading Standards: Mr Hamish Simmonds, Head of Regulatory Services, 5th Floor, Broadgate House, Broadgate, Coventry CV1 5RS ☎ 024 7683 1871 ⏀ hamish.simmonds@coventry.gov.uk

Contracts: Mr Mick Burn, Head of Procurement & Commissioning, Spire House, Floor 5, Coventry CV1 2PW ☎ 024 7683 3767 ⏀ mick.burn@coventry.gov.uk

Economic Development: Mr Richard Moon, Senior Development Executive, Civic Centre 4, Much Park Street, Coventry CV1 2PY ☎ 024 7683 2350 ⏀ richard.moon@coventry.gov.uk

Economic Development: Mr Martin Yardley, Executive Director - Place, Floor 13, Civic Centre 4, Much Park Street, Coventry CV1 2PY ☎ 024 7683 1200 ⏀ martin.yardley@coventry.gov.uk

Education: Ms Kirston Nelson, Director - Adult Education & Libraries, Civic Centre 1, Coventry CV1 5RS ☎ 024 7683 3621 ⏀ kirtson.nelson@coventry.gov.uk

Electoral Registration: Ms Liz Read, Electoral Services Manager, The Council House, Earl Street, Coventry CV1 5RR ☎ 024 7683 3177 ⏀ liz.read2@coventry.gov.uk

Emergency Planning: Mr Michael Enderby, Head of CSW Resillience, The Council House, Earl Street, Coventry CV1 5RR ☎ 0121 704 8179 ⏚ michael.enderby@coventry.gov.uk

Energy Management: Mr Kevin Palmer, Energy Manager, City Development, Tower Block, Much Park Street, Coventry CV1 2QE ☎ 024 7683 2713 ⏚ kevin.palmer@coventry.gov.uk

Environmental / Technical Services: Mr Craig Hickin, Head of Environmental Services, 315 Broadgate House, Broadgate, Coventry CV1 1NH ☎ 024 7683 2585 ⏚ craig.hackin@coventry.gov.uk

Environmental Health: Mr Craig Hickin, Head of Environmental Services, 315 Broadgate House, Broadgate, Coventry CV1 1NH ☎ 024 7683 2585 ⏚ craig.hackin@coventry.gov.uk

Estates, Property & Valuation: Mr Nigel Clews, Assistant Director - Property Asset Management, Civic Centre 4, Much Park Street, Coventry CV1 2PY ☎ 024 7683 4001 ⏚ nigel.clews@coventry.gov.uk

Events Manager: Ms Lee House, Senior Event Officer, Floor 2, West Orchard House, Corporation Street, Coventry CV1 1GF ☎ 024 7683 2351 ⏚ lee.house@coventry.gov.uk

Facilities: Mr Ian Johnson, Corporate Property Services Manager, Civic Centre 4, Much Park Street, Coventry CV1 2PY ☎ 024 7683 3054 ⏚ ian.johnson@coventry.gov.uk

Finance: Mr Barry Hastie, Assistant Director - Finance, The Council House, Earl Street, Coventry CV1 5RR ☎ 024 7683 3710 ⏚ barry.hastie@coventry.gov.uk

Finance: Mr Chris West, Executive Director - Resources, The Council House, Earl Street, Coventry CV1 5RR ☎ 024 7683 3700 ⏚ chris.west@coventry.gov.uk

Fleet Management: Ms Sarah Elliott, Head of Fleet & Waste Services, Whitley Depot, London Road, Coventry CV3 4AR ☎ 024 7683 3024 ⏚ sarah.elliott@coventry.gov.uk

Grounds Maintenance: Mr Andrew Walster, Assistant Director - Streetscene & Greenspace, Civic Centre 4, Much Park Street, Coventry CV1 2PY ☎ 024 7683 2621 ⏚ andrew.walster@coventry.gov.uk

Health and Safety: Ms Angela White, Occupational Health & Safety Manager, Christchurch Annexe, Greyfriars Lane, Coventry CV1 2PY ☎ 024 7683 3285 ⏚ angela.white@coventry.gov.uk

Highways: Mr Colin Knight, Assistant Director - Planning, Transport & Highways, Tower Block, Much Park Street, Coventry CV1 2PY ☎ 024 7683 2322 ⏚ colin.knight@coventry.gov.uk

Highways: Ms Karen Seager, Group Manager Highways, The Council House, Earl Street, Coventry CV1 5RR ☎ 024 7683 4014 ⏚ karen.seager@coventry.gov.uk

Home Energy Conservation: Mr Michael Checkley, Sustainability & Low Carbon Manager, Civic Centre 4, Much Park Street, Coventry CV1 2PY ☎ 024 7683 2155 ⏚ michael.checkley@coventry.gov.uk

Housing: Mr Ayaz Maqsood, Head of Housing, Spire House, New Union Street, Coventry CV1 2PW ☎ 024 7683 1958 ⏚ ayaz.magsood@coventry.gov.uk

Legal: Ms Helen Lynch, Legal Services Manager, Christchurch House, Greyfriars Lane, Coventry CV1 2QL ☎ 028 7683 3011 ⏚ helen.lynch@coventry.gov.uk

Legal: Ms Julie Newman, People Manager - Legal Services, Christchurch House, Greyfriars Lane, Coventry CV1 2QL ☎ 024 7683 3544 ⏚ julie.newman@coventry.gov.uk

Licensing: Ms Davina Blackburn, Licensing Manager, Broadgate House, Coventry CV1 1NH ☎ 024 7683 1874 ⏚ davina.blackburn@coventry.gov.uk

Lottery Funding, Charity and Voluntary: Mr Andy Williams, Resources & New Projects Manager, Civic Centre 4, Much Park Street, Coventry CV1 2PY ☎ 024 7683 3731 ⏚ andy.willliams@coventry.gov.uk

Member Services: Mr Adrian West, Members & Elections Team Leader, The Council House, Earl Street, Coventry CV1 5RR ☎ 024 7683 2286 ⏚ adrian.west@coventry.gov.uk

Parking: Mr Paul Bowman, Team Manager - Parking Services, Civic Centre 4, Much Park Street, Coventry CV1 2PY ☎ 024 7683 4243 ⏚ paul.bowman@coventry.gov.uk

Partnerships: Ms Dawn Ford, Coventry Partnership & Communities Manager, Civic Centre 4, Much Park Street, Coventry CV1 2PY ☎ 024 7683 4356 ⏚ dawn.ford@coventry.gov.uk

Planning: Ms Tracy Miller, Head of Planning, Civic Centre 4, Much Park Street, Coventry CV1 2PY ☎ 024 7683 1240 ⏚ tracy.miller@coventry.gov.uk

Procurement: Mr Mick Burn, Head of Procurement & Commissioning, Spire House, Floor 5, Coventry CV1 2PW ☎ 024 7683 3767 ⏚ mick.burn@coventry.gov.uk

Public Libraries: Mr Peter Barnett, Head of Libraries, Advice, Health & Information Services, Civic Centre 1, Little Park Street, Coventry CV1 1RS ☎ 024 7683 1579 ⏚ peter.barnett@coventry.gov.uk

Recycling & Waste Minimisation: Mr Anthony Campbell, Waste & Recyling Manager, Whitley Depot, London Road, Coventry CV3 4AR ☎ 024 7683 4309 ⏚ anthony.campbell@coventry.gov.uk

Regeneration: Ms Lucy Hobbs, Community Regeneration Manager, Civic Centre 4, Much Park Street, Coventry CV1 2PY ☎ 024 7683 2642 ⏚ lucy.hobbs@coventry.gov.uk

Road Safety: Ms Caron Archer, Senior Engineer - Traffic Management, Civic Centre 4, Much Park Street, Coventry CV1 2PY ☎ 024 7683 2062 ⏚ caron.archer@coventry.gov.uk

Social Services (Adult): Mr Peter Fahy, Director - Adult Services, The Council House, Earl Street, Coventry CV1 5RR ☎ 024 7683 3555 ⏚ peter.fahy@coventry.gov.uk

COVENTRY CITY

Social Services (Children): Ms Yolanda Corden, Interim Assistant Director - Children's Social Care & Early Intervention Services, 2nd Floor, Civic Centre 1, Little Park Street, Coventry CV1 5RS ☎ 024 7689 1901 ✆ yolanda.corden@coventry.gov.uk

Safeguarding: Ms Jivan Sembi, Head of Children's Regulatory Services, Civic Centre 1, Coventry CV1 5RS ☎ 024 7683 3443 ✆ jivan.sembi@coventry.gov.uk

Public Health: Dr Jane Moore, Director - Public Health, The Council House, Earl Street, Coventry CV1 5RR ☎ 024 7683 2884 ✆ jane.moore@coventry.gov.uk

Street Scene: Mr Andrew Walster, Assistant Director - Streetscene & Greenspace, Whitley Depot, London Road, Coventry CV3 4AR ☎ 024 7683 2621 ✆ andrew.walster@coventry.gov.uk

Sustainable Communities: Mr Andrew Walster, Assistant Director - Streetscene & Greenspace, Whitley Depot, London Road, Coventry CV3 4AR ☎ 024 7683 2621 ✆ andrew.walster@coventry.gov.uk

Sustainable Development: Mr Michael Checkley, Sustainability & Low Carbon Manager, Civic Centre 4, Much Park Street, Coventry CV1 2PY ☎ 024 7683 2155 ✆ michael.checkley@coventry.gov.uk

Tourism: Mr David Cockcroft, Assistant Director - City Centre & Development Services, Tower Block, Much Park Street, Coventry CV1 2PY ☎ 024 7660 3964 ✆ david.cockcroft@discover.co.uk

Town Centre: Mr David Cockcroft, Assistant Director - City Centre & Development Services, Tower Block, Much Park Street, Coventry CV1 2PY ☎ 024 7660 3964 ✆ david.cockcroft@discover.co.uk

Traffic Management: Mr Colin Knight, Assistant Director - Planning, Transport & Highways, Tower Block, Much Park Street, Coventry CV1 2PY ☎ 024 7683 2322 ✆ colin.knight@coventry.gov.uk

Transport: Mr Colin Knight, Assistant Director - Planning, Transport & Highways, Tower Block, Much Park Street, Coventry CV1 2PY ☎ 024 7683 2322 ✆ colin.knight@coventry.gov.uk

COUNCILLORS

The Lord Mayor: Harvard, Lindsley (LAB - Longford)
lindsley@harvard.freeserve.co.uk

Deputy Mayor: Skipper, Tony (LAB - Radford)
tony.skipper@coventry.gov.uk

Leader of the Council: Duggins, George (LAB - Longford)
george.duggins@coventry.gov.uk

Deputy Leader of the Council: Khan, Abdul (LAB - Foleshill)
abdul.khan@coventry.gov.uk

Abbott, Faye (LAB - Wyken)
faye.abbott@coventry.gov.uk

Akhtar, Perez (LAB - Whoberley)
perez.aktar@coventry.gov.uk

Akhtar, Naeem (LAB - St Michaels)
naeem.akhtar@coventry.gov.uk

Ali, Rois (LAB - Cheylesmore)
rois.ali@coventry.gov.uk

Andrews, Allan (CON - Earlsdon)
allan.andrews@coventry.gov.uk

Auluck, Randhir (LAB - Upper Stoke)

Bailey, Roger (CON - Cheylesmore)
roger.bailey@coventry.gov.uk

Bains, Sucha (LAB - Upper Stoke)
sucha.bains@coventry.gov.uk

Bigham, Linda (LAB - Longford)
linda.bigham@coventry.gov.uk

Birdi, Jaswant (CON - Bablake)
jaswant.birdi@coventry.gov.uk

Blundell, John (CON - Wainbody)
john.blundell@coventry.gov.uk

Brown, Richard (LAB - Cheylesmore)
richard.brown@coventry.gov.uk

Caan, Kamram (LAB - Upper Stoke)
kamran.caan@coventry.gov.uk

Clifford, Joe (LAB - Holbrook)
joseph.clifford@coventry.gov.uk

Crookes, Gary (CON - Wainbody)
gary.crookes@coventry.gov.uk

Gannon, Damian (LAB - Sherbourne)
damian.gannon@coventry.gov.uk

Hammon, Michael (CON - Earlsdon)
michael.hammon@coventry.gov.uk

Innes, Jayne (LAB - Whoberley)
jayne.innes@coventry.gov.uk

Kaur, Balvinder (LAB - Foleshill)
balvinder.dhanjal@coventry.gov.uk

Kelly, Lynette (LAB - Sherbourne)
lynette.kelly@coventry.gov.uk

Kershaw, David (LAB - Bablake)
david.kershaw@coventry.gov.uk

Khan, Tariq (LAB - Foleshill)
tariq.khan@coventry.gov.uk

Lakha, Ram (LAB - Binley & Willenhall)
ram.lakha@coventry.gov.uk

Lancaster, Rachel (LAB - Holbrook)
rachel.lancaster@coventry.gov.uk

Lapsa, Marcus (CON - Westwood)
marcus.lapsa@coventry.gov.uk

Lepoidevin, Julia (CON - Woodlands)
julia.lepoidevin@coventry.gov.uk

Lucas, Ann (LAB - Holbrook)
ann.lucas@coventry.gov.uk

Male, Peter (CON - Woodlands)
peter.male@coventry.gov.uk

Maton, Kevin (LAB - Henley)
kevin.maton@coventry.gov.uk

Mayer, Tim (CON - Westwood)
tim.mayer@coventry.gov.uk

McNicholas, John (LAB - Lower Stoke)
john.mcnicholas@coventry.gov.uk

Miks, Catherine (LAB - Lower Stoke)
catherine.miks@coventry.gov.uk

Mullhall, Keiran (LAB - Radford)
keiran.mulhall@coventry.gov.uk

Mutton, John (LAB - Binley & Willenhall)
john.mutton@coventry.gov.uk

Mutton, Mal (LAB - Radford)
mal.mutton@coventry.gov.uk

O'Boyle, Jim (LAB - St Michaels)
jim.o'boyle@coventry.gov.uk

Ridley, Gary (CON - Woodlands)
gary.ridley@coventry.gov.uk

Ruane, Ed (LAB - Henley)
ed.ruane@coventry.gov.uk

Sawdon, Tim (CON - Wainbody)
tim.sawdon@coventry.gov.uk

Seaman, Patricia (LAB - Henley)
patricia.seaman@coventry.gov.uk

Singh, Rupinder (LAB - Lower Stoke)
rupinder.singh@coventry.gov.uk

Singh, Bally (LAB - Whoberley)
bally.singh@coventry.gov.uk

Skinner, David (CON - Westwood)
david.skinner@coventry.gov.uk

Sweet, Hazel (LAB - Wyken)
hazel.sweet@coventry.gov.uk

Taylor, Ken (CON - Earlsdon)
ken.taylor@coventry.gov.uk

Thay, Robert (LAB - Wyken)
robert.thay@coventry.gov.uk

Thomas, Christine (LAB - Binley & Willenhall)
christine.thomas@coventry.gov.uk

Walsh, Seamus (LAB - Sherbourne)
seamus.walsh@coventry.gov.uk

Welsh, David (LAB - St. Michaels)
david.welsh@coventry.gov.uk

Williams, Glen (CON - Bablake)
glenn.williams@coventry.gov.uk

POLITICAL COMPOSITION
LAB: 39, CON: 15

Craven   D

Craven District Council, 1 Belle Vue Square, Broughton Road, Skipton BD23 1FJ
☎ 01756 700600 📠 01756 700658 📧 contactus@cravendc.gov.uk
🖥 www.cravendc.gov.uk

FACTS AND FIGURES
Parliamentary Constituencies: Skipton and Ripon
EU Constituencies: Yorkshire and the Humber
Election Frequency: Elections are by thirds

PRINCIPAL OFFICERS

Chief Executive: Mr Paul Shevlin, Chief Executive, 1 Belle Vue Square, Broughton Road, Skipton BD23 1FJ ☎ 01756 706201 📧 pshevlin@cravendc.gov.uk

Senior Management: Ms Nicola Chick, Strategic Manager - Financial Services (S151 Officer), 1 Belle Vue Square, Broughton Road, Skipton BD23 1FJ ☎ 01756 706418 📧 nchick@cravendc.gov.uk

Senior Management: Mr Paul Ellis, Director - Services, 1 Belle Vue Square, Broughton Road, Skipton BD23 1FJ ☎ 01756 706413 📧 pellis@cravendc.gov.uk

Senior Management: Ms Samia Hussain, Corporate Head of Business Support, 1 Belle Vue Square, Broughton Road, Skipton BD23 1FJ ☎ 01756 706207 📧 shussain@cravendc.gov.uk

Senior Management: Mr David Smurthwaite, Strategic Manager - Planning & Regeneration, 1 Belle Vue Square, Broughton Road, Skipton BD23 1FJ ☎ 01756 706409 📧 dsmurthwaite@cravendc.gov.uk

Architect, Building / Property Services: Mr Ian Halton, Assets & Commercial Services Manager, 1 Belle Vue Square, Broughton Road, Skipton BD23 1FJ ☎ 01756 706329 📧 ihalton@cravendc.gov.uk

Best Value: Mrs Claire Hudson, Value for Money & Improvement Manager, 1 Belle Vue Square, Broughton Road, Skipton BD23 1FJ ☎ 01756 706493 📧 chudson@cravendc.gov.uk

Building Control: Mr Andrew Allott, Senior Building Control Surveyor, 1 Belle Vue Square, Broughton Road, Skipton BD23 1FJ ☎ 01756 706441 📧 aallott@cravendc.gov.uk

PR / Communications: Mrs Sharon Hudson, Communications & Partnerships Manager, 1 Belle Vue Square, Broughton Road, Skipton BD23 1FJ ☎ 01756 706246 📧 shudson@cravendc.gov.uk

Community Safety: Ms Stacey Reffin, Craven Community Safety Partnership Co-ordinator, 1 Belle Vue Square, Broughton Road, Skipton BD23 1FJ ☎ 01756 700600 📧 sreffin@cravendc.gov.uk

Computer Management: Mr Darren Maycock, ICT & Transformation Manager, 1 Belle Vue Square, Broughton Road, Skipton BD23 1FJ ☎ 01756 706270 📧 dmaycock@cravendc.gov.uk

Customer Service: Mr David Carre, Interim Revenues, Benefits & Customer Services Manager, 1 Belle Vue Square, Broughton Road, Skipton BD23 1FJ ☎ 01756 706482 📧 dcarre@cravendc.gov.uk

Economic Development: Ms Sharon Sunter, Economic Development Manager, 1 Belle Vue Square, Broughton Road, Skipton BD23 1FJ ☎ 01756 706213 📧 ssunter@cravendc.gov.uk

Electoral Registration: Mr Andrew Mather, Member Services Manager, 1 Belle Vue Square, Broughton Road, Skipton BD23 1FJ ☎ 01756 706226 📧 amather@cravendc.gov.uk

Emergency Planning: Mr Paul Shevlin, Chief Executive, 1 Belle Vue Square, Broughton Road, Skipton BD23 1FJ ☎ 01756 706201 📧 pshevlin@cravendc.gov.uk

CRAVEN

Environmental Health: Mr Wyn Ashton, Environmental Services & Housing Manager, 1 Belle Vue Square, Broughton Road, Skipton BD23 1FJ ☎ 01756 706338 ⁷ washton@cravendc.gov.uk

Estates, Property & Valuation: Mr Ian Halton, Assets & Commercial Services Manager, 1 Belle Vue Square, Broughton Road, Skipton BD23 1FJ ☎ 01756 706329 ⁷ ihalton@cravendc.gov.uk

Grounds Maintenance: Mr Paul Connelly, Facilities Manager, 1 Belle Vue Square, Broughton Road, Skipton BD23 1FJ ☎ 01756 706293 ⁷ pconnelly@cravendc.gov.uk

Health and Safety: Ms Samia Hussain, Corporate Head of Business Support, 1 Belle Vue Square, Broughton Road, Skipton BD23 1FJ ☎ 01756 706207 ⁷ shussain@cravendc.gov.uk

Housing: Mr Wyn Ashton, Environmental Services & Housing Manager, 1 Belle Vue Square, Broughton Road, Skipton BD23 1FJ ☎ 01756 706338 ⁷ washton@cravendc.gov.uk

Legal: Ms Annette Moppett, Solicitor to the Council & Monitoring Officer, 1 Belle Vue Square, Broughton Road, Skipton BD23 1FJ ☎ 01756 706325 ⁷ amoppett@cravendc.gov.uk

Leisure and Cultural Services: Ms Hazel Smith, Business Manager - Leisure Services, 1 Belle Vue Square, Broughton Road, Skipton BD23 1FJ ☎ 01756 706310 ⁷ hsmith@cravendc.gov.uk

Leisure and Cultural Services: Mr David Smurthwaite, Strategic Manager - Planning & Regeneration, 1 Belle Vue Square, Broughton Road, Skipton BD23 1FJ ☎ 01756 706409 ⁷ dsmurthwaite@cravendc.gov.uk

Licensing: Ms Samia Hussain, Corporate Head of Business Support, 1 Belle Vue Square, Broughton Road, Skipton BD23 1FJ ☎ 01756 706207 ⁷ shussain@cravendc.gov.uk

Member Services: Mr Andrew Mather, Member Services Manager, 1 Belle Vue Square, Broughton Road, Skipton BD23 1FJ ☎ 01756 706226 ⁷ amather@cravendc.gov.uk

Parking: Ms Hazel Smith, Business Manager - Leisure Services, 1 Belle Vue Square, Broughton Road, Skipton BD23 1FJ ☎ 01756 706310 ⁷ hsmith@cravendc.gov.uk

Partnerships: Mrs Sharon Hudson, Communications & Partnerships Manager, 1 Belle Vue Square, Broughton Road, Skipton BD23 1FJ ☎ 01756 706246 ⁷ shudson@cravendc.gov.uk

Personnel / HR: Ms Samia Hussain, Corporate Head of Business Support, 1 Belle Vue Square, Broughton Road, Skipton BD23 1FJ ☎ 01756 706207 ⁷ shussain@cravendc.gov.uk

Planning: Mr Ian Swain, Development Control Manager, 1 Belle Vue Square, Broughton Road, Skipton BD23 1FJ ☎ 01756 706465 ⁷ wgudger@cravendc.gov.uk

Procurement: Ms Carol Lee, Procurement, Payments & Risk Manager, 1 Belle Vue Square, Broughton Road, Skipton BD23 1FJ ☎ 01756 706271 ⁷ clee@cravendc.gov.uk

Regeneration: Mr David Smurthwaite, Strategic Manager - Planning & Regeneration, 1 Belle Vue Square, Broughton Road, Skipton BD23 1FJ ☎ 01756 706409 ⁷ dsmurthwaite@cravendc.gov.uk

Tourism: Ms Sharon Sunter, Economic Development Manager, 1 Belle Vue Square, Broughton Road, Skipton BD23 1FJ ☎ 01756 706213 ⁷ ssunter@cravendc.gov.uk

COUNCILLORS

ChairMason, Robert (IND - West Craven)
cllr.rmason@cravendc.gov.uk

Leader of the Council: Foster, Richard (CON - Grassington)
cllr.rfoster@cravendc.gov.uk

Deputy Leader of the Council: Mulligan, Patrick (CON - Aire Valley-with-Lothersdale)
cllr.pmulligan@cravendc.gov.uk

Group LeaderBarrett, Philip (IND - Glusburn)
cllr.pbarrett@cravendc.gov.uk

Baxandall, Roger (UKIP - Glusburn)
cllr.rbaxandall@cravendc.gov.uk

Brockbank, Linda (CON - Bentham)
cllr.lbrockbank@cravendc.gov.uk

Dawson, John (CON - Skipton North)
cllr.jdawson@cravendc.gov.uk

Fairbank, Patricia (CON - Aire Valley with Lothersdale)

Graham, Tanya (CON - Upper Wharfedale)

Harbron, Christopher (CON - Skipton East)
cllr.charbron@cravendc.gov.uk

Heseltine, Robert (IND - Skipton South)
cllr.rheseltine@cravendc.gov.uk

Hull, Wendy (CON - Settle & Ribble Banks)
cllr.whull@cravendc.gov.uk

Ireton, David (IND - Ingleton & Clapham)
cllr.direton@cravendc.gov.uk

Jaquin, Eric (LD - Skipton East)
cllr.ejaquin@cravendc.gov.uk

Lis, Carl (CON - Ingleton & Clapham)
cllr.clis@cravendc.gov.uk

Madeley, Peter (LAB - Skipton West)
cllr.pmadeley@cravendc.gov.uk

Mercer, William (LAB - Cowling)

Moorby, Robert (IND - Hellifield & Long Preston)
cllr.cmoorby@cravendc.gov.uk

Morrell, Stephen (IND - Sutton-in-Craven)
cllr.smorrell@cravendc.gov.uk

Myers, Simon (CON - Gargrave & Malhamdale)
cllr.smyers@cravendc.gov.uk

Pighills, David (IND - Barden Fell)

Place, Stephen (IND - Sutton-in-Craven)
cllr.splace@cravendc.gov.uk

Rose, Chris (LAB - Skipton West)

Shuttleworth, Brian (IND - Embsay with Eastby)
cllr.bshuttleworth@cravendc.gov.uk

Solloway, Andrew (IND - Skipton South)
cllr.asolloway@cravendc.gov.uk

Staveley, David (CON - Settle & Ribblebanks)
cllr.dstaveley@cravendc.gov.uk

Sutcliffe, Alan (CON - Gargrave & Malhamdale)
cllr.asutcliffe@cravendc.gov.uk

Thompson, Ian (CON - Bentham)
cllr.ithompson@cravendc.gov.uk

Welch, Richard (CON - Penyghent)
cllr.rwelch@cravendc.gov.uk

Whitaker, Paul (CON - Skipton North)

POLITICAL COMPOSITION
CON: 15, IND: 10, LAB: 3, LD: 1, UKIP: 1

COMMITTEE CHAIRS

Audit & Governance: Mr Christopher Harbron

Licensing: Mr Simon Myers

Crawley   D

Crawley Borough Council, Town Hall, The Boulevard, Crawley
RH10 1UZ
☎ 01293 438000 🖷 01293 511803 ⌐ crawleybc@crawley.gov.uk
🖳 www.crawley.gov.uk

FACTS AND FIGURES
Parliamentary Constituencies: Crawley
EU Constituencies: South East
Election Frequency: Elections are by thirds

PRINCIPAL OFFICERS

Chief Executive: Mr Lee Harris, Chief Executive, Town Hall, The
Boulevard, Crawley RH10 1UZ ☎ 01293 438626
⌐ lee.harris@crawley.gov.uk

Deputy Chief Executive: Mr Peter Browning, Deputy Chief
Executive, Town Hall, The Boulevard, Crawley RH10 1UZ
☎ 01293 438754 ⌐ peter.browning@crawley.gov.uk

Senior Management: Ms Ann-Maria Brown, Head of Legal &
Democratic Services, Town Hall, The Boulevard, Crawley RH10 1UZ
☎ 01293 438292 ⌐ ann-maria.brown@crawley.gov.uk

Senior Management: Mrs Karen Hayes, Head of Finance,
Revenues & Benefits, Town Hall, The Boulevard, Crawley RH10 1UZ
☎ 01293 438263 ⌐ karen.hayes@crawley.gov.uk

Senior Management: Ms Diana Maughan, Head of Strategic
Planning & Housing, Town Hall, The Boulevard, Crawley RH10 1UZ
☎ 01293 438234 ⌐ diana.maughan@crawley.gov.uk

Senior Management: Mr Clem Smith, Head of Economic &
Environmental Services, Town Hall, The Boulevard, Crawley RH10
1UZ ☎ 01293 438567 ⌐ clem.smith@crawley.gov.uk

Access Officer / Social Services (Disability): Mr Damian
Brewer, Access Officer of Horsham District Council, Town Hall, The
Boulevard, Crawley RH10 1UZ ☎ 01403 215648
⌐ damian.brewer@crawley.gov.uk

Building Control: Ms Vanessa Good, Building Development &
Marketing Manager, Town Hall, The Boulevard, Crawley RH10 1UZ
☎ 01403 215157 ⌐ vanessa.good@horsham.gov.uk

PR / Communications: Mr Allan Hambly, Communications
Manager, Town Hall, The Boulevard, Crawley RH10 1UZ
☎ 01293 438781 ⌐ allan.hambly@crawley.gov.uk

Community Planning: Ms Carrie Burton, Transformation
Manager, Town Hall, The Boulevard, Crawley RH10 1UZ
☎ 01293 438473 ⌐ carrie.burton@crawley.gov.uk

Community Safety: Mrs Trish Emmans, Community Safety
Officer, Town Hall, The Boulevard, Crawley RH10 1UZ
☎ 01293 438482 ⌐ trish.emmans@crawley.gov.uk

Computer Management: Mrs Lucasta Grayson, Head of People
& Technology, Town Hall, The Boulevard, Crawley RH10 1UZ
☎ 01293 438213 ⌐ lucasta.grayson@crawley.gov.uk

Contracts: Ms Jo Newton-Smith, Procurement Manager, Town
Hall, The Boulevard, Crawley RH10 1UZ ☎ 01403 215299
⌐ jo.newton-smith@crawley.gov.uk

Customer Service: Mrs Lucasta Grayson, Head of People &
Technology, Town Hall, The Boulevard, Crawley RH10 1UZ
☎ 01293 438213 ⌐ lucasta.grayson@crawley.gov.uk

Direct Labour: Mr Peter Browning, Deputy Chief Executive, Town
Hall, The Boulevard, Crawley RH10 1UZ ☎ 01293 438754
⌐ peter.browning@crawley.gov.uk

Economic Development: Mr Clem Smith, Head of Economic &
Environmental Services, Town Hall, The Boulevard, Crawley RH10
1UZ ☎ 01293 438567 ⌐ clem.smith@crawley.gov.uk

Economic Development: Ms Lise Sorensen, Economic
Development Officer, Town Hall, The Boulevard, Crawley RH10 1UZ
☎ 01293 438519 ⌐ lise.sorensen@crawley.gov.uk

E-Government: Mrs Lucasta Grayson, Head of People &
Technology, Town Hall, The Boulevard, Crawley RH10 1UZ
☎ 01293 438213 ⌐ lucasta.grayson@crawley.gov.uk

Electoral Registration: Ms Ann-Maria Brown, Head of Legal &
Democratic Services, Town Hall, The Boulevard, Crawley RH10 1UZ
☎ 01293 438292 ⌐ ann-maria.brown@crawley.gov.uk

Electoral Registration: Mr Andrew Oakley, Electoral Services
Manager, Town Hall, The Boulevard, Crawley RH10 1UZ
☎ 01293 438346 ⌐ andrew.oakley@crawley.gov.uk

Emergency Planning: Mr Andrew Gaffney, Emergency Planning
Officer, Town Hall, The Boulevard, Crawley RH10 1UZ
☎ 01293 468454 ⌐ andy.gaffney@crawley.gov.uk

CRAWLEY

Energy Management: Mr Brett Hagen, Environment Manager, Town Hall, The Boulevard, Crawley RH10 1UZ ☎ 01293 438543 ✆ brett.hagen@crawley.gov.uk

Environmental / Technical Services: Mr Peter Browning, Deputy Chief Executive, Town Hall, The Boulevard, Crawley RH10 1UZ ☎ 01293 438754 ✆ peter.browning@crawley.gov.uk

Environmental / Technical Services: Mr Clem Smith, Head of Economic & Environmental Services, Town Hall, The Boulevard, Crawley RH10 1UZ ☎ 01293 438567 ✆ clem.smith@crawley.gov.uk

Environmental Health: Mr Clem Smith, Head of Economic & Environmental Services, Town Hall, The Boulevard, Crawley RH10 1UZ ☎ 01293 438567 ✆ clem.smith@crawley.gov.uk

European Liaison: Mr Lee Harris, Chief Executive, Town Hall, The Boulevard, Crawley RH10 1UZ ☎ 01293 438626 ✆ lee.harris@crawley.gov.uk

Facilities: Mr Mike Pidgeon, Facilities Manager, Town Hall, The Boulevard, Crawley RH10 1UZ ☎ 01293 438291 ✆ mike.pidgeon@crawley.gov.uk

Finance: Mrs Karen Hayes, Head of Finance, Revenues & Benefits, Town Hall, The Boulevard, Crawley RH10 1UZ ☎ 01293 438263 ✆ karen.hayes@crawley.gov.uk

Grounds Maintenance: Mrs Karen Rham, Parks & Green Spaces Officer, Town Hall, The Boulevard, Crawley RH10 1UZ ☎ 01293 535624 ✆ karen.rham@crawley.gov.uk

Health and Safety: Mr Andrew Gaffney, Emergency Planning Officer, Town Hall, The Boulevard, Crawley RH10 1UZ ☎ 01293 468454 ✆ andy.gaffney@crawley.gov.uk

Home Energy Conservation: Mr Brett Hagen, Environment Manager, Town Hall, The Boulevard, Crawley RH10 1UZ ☎ 01293 438543 ✆ brett.hagen@crawley.gov.uk

Housing: Mrs Karen Dodds, Head of Crawley Homes, Town Hall, The Boulevard, Crawley RH10 1UZ ☎ 01293 438256 ✆ karen.dodds@crawley.gov.uk

Housing: Ms Diana Maughan, Head of Strategic Planning & Housing, Town Hall, The Boulevard, Crawley RH10 1UZ ☎ 01293 438234 ✆ diana.maughan@crawley.gov.uk

Housing Maintenance: Mr Tim Honess, Maintenance Operations Manager, Town Hall, The Boulevard, Crawley RH10 1UZ ☎ 01293 438253 ✆ tim.honess@crawley.gov.uk

Legal: Ms Ann-Maria Brown, Head of Legal & Democratic Services, Town Hall, The Boulevard, Crawley RH10 1UZ ☎ 01293 438292 ✆ ann-maria.brown@crawley.gov.uk

Leisure and Cultural Services: Mr Christian Harris, Head of Community Services, Town Hall, The Boulevard, Crawley RH10 1UZ ☎ 01293 438420 ✆ christian.harris@crawley.gov.uk

Licensing: Mr Tony Baldock, Environmental Health Manager, Town Hall, The Boulevard, Crawley RH10 1UZ ☎ 01293 438220 ✆ tony.baldock@crawley.gov.uk

Lottery Funding, Charity and Voluntary: Mr Nigel Sheehan, Head of Partnership Services, Town Hall, The Boulevard, Crawley RH10 1UZ ☎ 01293 438728 ✆ nigel.sheehan@crawley.gov.uk

Member Services: Ms Ann-Maria Brown, Head of Legal & Democratic Services, Town Hall, The Boulevard, Crawley RH10 1UZ ☎ 01293 438292 ✆ ann-maria.brown@crawley.gov.uk

Parking: Mr Steve Kirby, Enforcement & Technical Services Manager, Town Hall, The Boulevard, Crawley RH10 1UZ ☎ 01293 438961 ✆ steve.kirby@crawley.gov.uk

Personnel / HR: Mrs Lucasta Grayson, Head of People & Technology, Town Hall, The Boulevard, Crawley RH10 1UZ ☎ 01293 438213 ✆ lucasta.grayson@crawley.gov.uk

Planning: Mrs Jean McPherson, Development Control Manager, Town Hall, The Boulevard, Crawley RH10 1UZ ☎ 01293 438577 ✆ jean.mcpherson@crawley.gov.uk

Procurement: Ms Jo Newton-Smith, Procurement Manager, Town Hall, The Boulevard, Crawley RH10 1UZ ☎ 01293 438363 ✆ jo.newton-smith@crawley.gov.uk

Recycling & Waste Minimisation: Mr Nigel Sheehan, Head of Partnership Services, Town Hall, The Boulevard, Crawley RH10 1UZ ☎ 01293 438728 ✆ nigel.sheehan@crawley.gov.uk

Staff Training: Mrs Carron Burton, HR & Development Manager, Town Hall, The Boulevard, Crawley RH10 1UZ ☎ 01293 438095 ✆ carron.burton@crawley.gov.uk

Street Scene: Mr Graham Rowe, Street Scene Services & Cleansing Manager, Town Hall, The Boulevard, Crawley RH10 1UZ ☎ 01293 438460 ✆ graham.rowe@crawley.gov.uk

Sustainable Communities: Mr Peter Browning, Deputy Chief Executive, Town Hall, The Boulevard, Crawley RH10 1UZ ☎ 01293 438754 ✆ peter.browning@crawley.gov.uk

Sustainable Development: Mr Brett Hagen, Environment Manager, Town Hall, The Boulevard, Crawley RH10 1UZ ☎ 01293 438543 ✆ brett.hagen@crawley.gov.uk

Town Centre: Mr Alfredo Mendes, Town Centre Co-ordinator, Town Hall, The Boulevard, Crawley RH10 1UZ ☎ 01293 438237 ✆ alfredo.mendes@crawley.gov.uk

Transport: Mr Graham Rowe, Street Scene Services & Cleansing Manager, Town Hall, The Boulevard, Crawley RH10 1UZ ☎ 01293 438460 ✆ graham.rowe@crawley.gov.uk

Waste Collection and Disposal: Mr Nigel Sheehan, Head of Partnership Services, Town Hall, The Boulevard, Crawley RH10 1UZ ☎ 01293 438728 ✆ nigel.sheehan@crawley.gov.uk

COUNCILLORS

Leader of the Council: Lamb, Peter (LAB - Northgate)
peter.lamb@crawley.gov.uk

Deputy Leader of the Council: Joyce, Stephen (LAB - Langley Green)
stephen.joyce@crawley.gov.uk

Ayling, Marion (LAB - Bewbush)
marion.ayling@crawley.gov.uk

Belben, Tina (CON - Pound Hill North)
tina.belben@crawley.gov.uk

Bloom, Howard (CON - Pound Hill South & Worth)
howard.bloom@crawley.gov.uk

Burgess, Bob (CON - Three Bridges)
bob.burgess@crawley.gov.uk

Burgess, Brenda (CON - Three Bridges)
brenda.burgess@crawley.gov.uk

Burrett, Richard (CON - Pound Hill North)
richard.burrett@crawley.gov.uk

Cheshire, Chris (LAB - Bewbush)
chris.cheshire@crawley.gov.uk

Crow, Duncan (CON - Furnace Green)
duncan.crow@crawley.gov.uk

Eade, Carol (CON - Furnace Green)
carol.eade@crawley.gov.uk

Fiveash, Rory (LAB - West Green)
rory.fiveash@crawley.gov.uk

Guidera, Francis (CON - Tilgate)
frances.guidera@crawley.gov.uk

Irvine, Ian (LAB - Broadfield North)
ian.irvine@crawley.gov.uk

Jaggard, Kim (CON - Maidenbower)

Jones, Michael (LAB - Bewbush)
michael.jones@crawley.gov.uk

Lanzer, Bob (CON - Pound Hill South & Worth)
bob.lanzer@crawley.gov.uk

Lunnon, Timothy (LAB - Broadfield South)
hayley.thorne@crawley.gov.uk

McCarthy, Kevan (CON - Pound Hill)
kevan.mccarthy@crawley.gov.uk

Mecrow, Beryl (CON - Pound Hill South & Worth)

Mullins, Chris (LAB - Gossops Green)
chris.mullins@crawley.gov.uk

Peck, Duncan (CON - Maidenbower)
duncan.peck@crawley.gov.uk

Pickett, Mike (LAB - Southgate)
mike.pickett@crawley.gov.uk

Portal Castro, Carlos (LAB - Tilgate)
carlos.castro@crawley.gov.uk

Quinn, Brian (LAB - Broadfield North)
brian.quinn@crawley.gov.uk

Rana, Tahira (LAB - Broadfield South)
tahira.rana@crawley.gov.uk

Sharma, Raj (LAB - Southgate)

Skudder, Andrew (LAB - Langley Green)

Smith, Peter (LAB - Ifield)
peter.smith@crawley.gov.uk

Smith, Brenda (LAB - Langley Green)
brenda.smith@crawley.gov.uk

Stanley, John (LAB - Ifield)
hayley.thorne@crawley.gov.uk

Stone, Martin (CON - Ifield)
martin.stone@crawley.gov.uk

Sudan, Karen (LAB - West Green)
karen.sudan@crawley.gov.uk

Tarrant, Jan (CON - Southgate)

Thomas, Geraint (LAB - Northgate)
geraint.thomas@crawley.gov.uk

Trussell, Ken (CON - Maidenbower)
ken.trussell@crawley.gov.uk

Vitler, Lisa (CON - Gossops Green)

POLITICAL COMPOSITION
LAB: 20, CON: 17

COMMITTEE CHAIRS

Audit: Ms Karen Sudan

Licensing: Mr Mike Pickett

Planning: Mr Ian Irvine

Croydon   L

Croydon London Borough Council, The Town Hall, Katherine Street, Croydon CR0 1NX
☎ 020 8726 6000 🖷 020 8760 5657 🖳 www.croydon.gov.uk

FACTS AND FIGURES
Parliamentary Constituencies: Croydon Central, Croydon North, Croydon South
EU Constituencies: London
Election Frequency: Elections are of whole council

PRINCIPAL OFFICERS

Chief Executive: Ms Jo Negrini, Chief Executive, 9th Floor, Zone B, Bernard Weatherill House, 8 Mint Walk, Croydon CR0 1EA
☎ 020 8726 6000 ✍ jo.negrini@croydon.gov.uk

Senior Management: Mr Graham Cadle, Director - Customer & Transformation, The Town Hall, Katherine Street, Croydon CR0 1NX
☎ 020 8726 6000 Extn 63295 ✍ graham.cadle@croydon.gov.uk

Senior Management: Ms Heather Cheesbrough, Director - Planning & Strategic Transport, The Town Hall, Katherine Street, Croydon CR0 1NX ☎ 020 8726 6000
✍ heather.cheesbrough@croydon.gov.uk

Senior Management: Ms Heather Daley, Director - Human Resources, The Town Hall, Katherine Street, Croydon CR0 1NX
☎ 020 8760 6561 ✍ heather.daley@croydon.gov.uk

Senior Management: Ms Jane Doyle, Director - Universal People Services, The Town Hall, Katherine Street, Croydon CR0 1NX ☎ 020 8726 6000 ◌ jane.doyle@croydon.gov.uk

Senior Management: Ms Rachel Flowers, Director - Public Health, The Town Hall, Katherine Street, Croydon CR0 1NX ◌ rachel.flowers@croydon.gov.uk

Senior Management: Mr Mark Fowler, Director - Gateway & Welfare Services, The Town Hall, Katherine Street, Croydon CR0 1NX ☎ 020 8726 6000 ◌ mark.fowler@croydon.gov.uk

Senior Management: Mr Steve Iles, Director - Streets, The Town Hall, Katherine Street, Croydon CR0 1NX ☎ 020 8726 6000 Ext 52821 ◌ steve.iles@croydon.gov.uk

Senior Management: Ms Sarah Ireland, Director - Strategy, Communities & Commissioning, The Town Hall, Katherine Street, Croydon CR0 1NX ☎ 020 8726 6000 Extn 62070 ◌ sarah.ireland@croydon.gov.uk

Senior Management: Mr Colm Lacey, Director - Development, The Town Hall, Katherine Street, Croydon CR0 1NX ☎ 020 8726 6000 ◌ colm.lacey@croydon.gov.uk

Senior Management: Mr Ian Lewis, Director - Children, Family Intervention & Children's Social Care, The Town Hall, Katherine Street, Croydon CR0 1NX ☎ 020 8726 6000 ◌ ian.lewis@croydon.gov.uk

Senior Management: Mr Mark Meehan, Director - Housing Need, The Town Hall, Katherine Street, Croydon CR0 1NX ☎ 020 8726 6000 ◌ mark.meehan@croydon.gov.uk

Senior Management: Mr Andy Opie, Director - Safety, The Town Hall, Katherine Street, Croydon CR0 1NX ☎ 020 8726 6000 Extn 65686 ◌ andy.opie@croydon.gov.uk

Senior Management: Ms Barbara Peacock, Executive Director - People, The Town Hall, Katherine Street, Croydon CR0 1NX ☎ 020 8726 6000 Ext 65787 ◌ barbara.peacock@croydon.gov.uk

Senior Management: Mr Richard Simpson, Executive Director - Resources & S151 Officer, The Town Hall, Katherine Street, Croydon CR0 1NX

Senior Management: Ms Pratima Solanki, Director - Adult Social Care & All-Age Disability, The Town Hall, Katherine Street, Croydon CR0 1NX ☎ 020 8760 5727 ◌ pratima.solanki@croydon.gov.uk

Senior Management: Mr Stephen Tate, Director - District Centres & Regeneration, The Town Hall, Katherine Street, Croydon CR0 1NX ☎ 020 8726 6000 ◌ stephen.tate@croydon.gov.uk

Architect, Building / Property Services: Mr Stephen Wingrave, Head of Asset Management & Estates, The Town Hall, Katherine Street, Croydon CR0 1NX ☎ 020 8726 6000 Extn 61512 ◌ stephen.wingrave@croydon.gov.uk

Building Control: Mr Mike Kiely, Director - Planning, The Town Hall, Katherine Street, Croydon CR0 1NX ☎ 020 8760 5599 ◌ mike.kiely@croydon.gov.uk

Catering Services: Ms Allyson Lloyd, Corporate Catering Manager, The Town Hall, Katherine Street, Croydon CR0 1NX ☎ 020 8760 5467 ◌ allyson.lloyd@croydon.gov.uk

Children / Youth Services: Ms Barbara Peacock, Executive Director - People, The Town Hall, Katherine Street, Croydon CR0 1NX ☎ 020 8726 6000 Ext 65787 ◌ barbara.peacock@croydon.gov.uk

PR / Communications: Ms Hayley Lewis, Head of Communications & Engagement, The Town Hall, Katherine Street, Croydon CR0 1NX

Community Safety: Mr Andy Opie, Director - Safety, The Town Hall, Katherine Street, Croydon CR0 1NX ☎ 020 8726 6000 Extn 65686 ◌ andy.opie@croydon.gov.uk

Computer Management: Mr Nathan Elvery, Chief Executive, 9th Floor, Zone B, Bernard Weatherill House, 8 Mint Walk, Croydon CR0 1EA ☎ 020 8726 6000 Extn 62416 ◌ nathan.elvery@croydon.gov.uk

Consumer Protection and Trading Standards: Mr Paul Foster, Head of Regulatory Services, The Town Hall, Katherine Street, Croydon CR0 1NX ☎ 020 8726 6000 Extn 65475 ◌ paul.foster@croydon.gov.uk

Contracts: Ms Sarah Ireland, Director - Strategy, Communities & Commissioning, The Town Hall, Katherine Street, Croydon CR0 1NX ☎ 020 8726 6000 Extn 62070 ◌ sarah.ireland@croydon.gov.uk

Customer Service: Mr Graham Cadle, Director - Customer & Transformation, The Town Hall, Katherine Street, Croydon CR0 1NX ☎ 020 8726 6000 Extn 63295 ◌ graham.cadle@croydon.gov.uk

Economic Development: Ms Lisa McCance, Head of Economic Development, The Town Hall, Katherine Street, Croydon CR0 1NX ☎ 020 8760 5655 ◌ lisa.mccance@croydon.gov.uk

E-Government: Mr Nathan Elvery, Chief Executive, 9th Floor, Zone B, Bernard Weatherill House, 8 Mint Walk, Croydon CR0 1EA ☎ 020 8726 6000 Extn 62416 ◌ nathan.elvery@croydon.gov.uk

Electoral Registration: Mr Lea Goddard, Head of Registration Services & Electoral, Town Hall, Katherine Street, Croydon CR9 1DE ☎ 020 8726 6000 Extn 65730 ◌ lea.goddard@croydon.gov.uk

Emergency Planning: Mr Maurice Egan, Corporate Security Manager, The Town Hall, Katherine Street, Croydon CR0 1NX ☎ 020 8760 5678 ◌ mo.egan@croydon.gov.uk

Estates, Property & Valuation: Mr Stephen Wingrave, Head of Asset Management & Estates, The Town Hall, Katherine Street, Croydon CR0 1NX ☎ 020 8726 6000 Extn 61512 ◌ stephen.wingrave@croydon.gov.uk

Finance: Mr Nigel Cook, Head of Pensions & Treasury, The Town Hall, Katherine Street, Croydon CR0 1NX ☎ 020 8726 6000 ◌ nigel.cook@croydon.gov.uk

Finance: Mr Nathan Elvery, Chief Executive, The Town Hall, Katherine Street, Croydon CR0 1NX ☎ 020 8726 6000 Extn 62416 ◌ nathan.elvery@croydon.gov.uk

Treasury: Mr Nigel Cook, Head - Treasury & Pensions, The Town Hall, Katherine Street, Croydon CR0 1NX ☎ 020 8726 6000 ✆ nigel.cook@croydon.gov.uk

Treasury: Mr Derek Fernandes, Treasury Manager, The Town Hall, Katherine Street, Croydon CR0 1NX ☎ 020 8726 6000 Extn 62526 ✆ derek.fernandes@croydon.gov.uk

Pensions: Mr Nigel Cook, Head of Pensions & Treasury, The Town Hall, Katherine Street, Croydon CR0 1NX ☎ 020 8726 6000 ✆ nigel.cook@croydon.gov.uk

Health and Safety: Ms Liz Johnston, Health & Safety Senior Consultant, The Town Hall, Katherine Street, Croydon CR0 1NX ☎ 020 8726 6000 Extn 62001 ✆ elizabeth.johnston@croydon.gov.uk

Highways: Mr Steve Iles, Director - Streets, The Town Hall, Katherine Street, Croydon CR0 1NX ☎ 020 8726 6000 Ext 52821 ✆ steve.iles@croydon.gov.uk

Housing: Mr Mark Meehan, Director - Housing Need, The Town Hall, Katherine Street, Croydon CR0 1NX ☎ 020 8726 6000 ✆ mark.meehan@croydon.gov.uk

Housing: Mr Stephen Tate, Director - District Centres & Regeneration, The Town Hall, Katherine Street, Croydon CR0 1NX ☎ 020 8726 6000 ✆ stephen.tate@croydon.gov.uk

Housing Maintenance: Mr Dave Sutherland, Divisional Director - Housing Management Services, The Town Hall, Katherine Street, Croydon CR0 1NX ☎ 020 8726 6000 Extn 4957 ✆ dave.sutherland@croydon.gov.uk

Housing Maintenance: Mr Stephen Tate, Director - District Centres & Regeneration, The Town Hall, Katherine Street, Croydon CR0 1NX ☎ 020 8726 6000 ✆ stephen.tate@croydon.gov.uk

Legal: Mrs Julie Belvir, Director - Democratic & Legal Services, The Town Hall, Katherine Street, Croydon CR0 1NX ☎ 020 8726 6000 Extn 64985 ✆ julie.belvir@croydon.gov.uk

Leisure and Cultural Services: Mr Malcolm Kendall, Head of Environmental & Leisure Services, The Town Hall, Katherine Street, Croydon CR0 1NX ☎ 020 8726 6000 ✆ malcolm.kendall@croydon.gov.uk

Licensing: Mr Michael Goddard, Licensing Team Leader, The Town Hall, Katherine Street, Croydon CR0 1NX ☎ 020 8726 6000 ✆ michael.goddard@croydon.gov.uk

Lottery Funding, Charity and Voluntary: Mr David Freeman, Policy Manager, The Town Hall, Katherine Street, Croydon CR0 1NX ☎ 020 8726 6000 ✆ david.freeman@croydon.gov.uk

Member Services: Mr Solomon Agutu, Head of Democratic Services & Scrutiny, The Town Hall, Katherine Street, Croydon CR0 1NX ☎ 020 8726 6000 extn 62920 ✆ soloman.agutu@croydon.gov.uk

Personnel / HR: Ms Heather Daley, Director - Human Resources, The Town Hall, Katherine Street, Croydon CR0 1NX ☎ 020 8760 6561 ✆ heather.daley@croydon.gov.uk

Planning: Mr Mike Kiely, Director - Planning, The Town Hall, Katherine Street, Croydon CR0 1NX ☎ 020 8760 5599 ✆ mike.kiely@croydon.gov.uk

Planning: Mr Rory Macleod, Head of Planning Control, The Town Hall, Katherine Street, Croydon CR0 1NX ☎ 020 8726 6000 Ext 65578 ✆ rory.macleod@croydon.gov.uk

Procurement: Ms Sarah Ireland, Director - Strategy, Communities & Commissioning, The Town Hall, Katherine Street, Croydon CR0 1NX ☎ 020 8726 6000 Extn 62070 ✆ sarah.ireland@croydon.gov.uk

Public Libraries: Ms Aileen Cahill, Head of Libraries, Central Library, Katharine Street, Croydon CR9 1ET ☎ 020 8726 6000 Extn 1123 ✆ aileen.cahill@croydon.gov.uk

Recycling & Waste Minimisation: Mr Malcolm Kendall, Head of Environmental & Leisure Services, Stubbs Mead Depot, Factory Lane, Croydon CR0 3RL ☎ 020 8726 6000 ✆ malcolm.kendall@croydon.gov.uk

Regeneration: Mr Stephen Tate, Director - District Centres & Regeneration, The Town Hall, Katherine Street, Croydon CR0 1NX ☎ 020 8726 6000 ✆ stephen.tate@croydon.gov.uk

Road Safety: Mr Mike Barton, Strategic Technical Manager, The Town Hall, Katherine Street, Croydon CR0 1NX ☎ 020 8760 6197 ✆ mike.barton@croydon.gov.uk

Social Services: Mr Mark Fowler, Director - Gateway & Welfare Services, The Town Hall, Katherine Street, Croydon CR0 1NX ☎ 020 8726 6000 ✆ mark.fowler@croydon.gov.uk

Social Services: Mrs Hannah Miller, Executive Director of Housing & Social Services, The Town Hall, Katherine Street, Croydon CR0 1NX ☎ 020 8760 5490 ✆ hannah.miller@croydon.gov.uk

Social Services (Adult): Mr Mark Fowler, Director - Gateway & Welfare Services, The Town Hall, Katherine Street, Croydon CR0 1NX ☎ 020 8726 6000 ✆ mark.fowler@croydon.gov.uk

Social Services (Adult): Ms Pratima Solanki, Director - Adult Social Care & All-Age Disability, The Town Hall, Katherine Street, Croydon CR0 1NX ☎ 020 8760 5727 ✆ pratima.solanki@croydon.gov.uk

Social Services (Children): Mr Ian Lewis, Director - Children, Family Intervention & Children's Social Care, The Town Hall, Katherine Street, Croydon CR0 1NX ☎ 020 8726 6000 ✆ ian.lewis@croydon.gov.uk

Public Health: Ms Rachel Flowers, Director - Public Health, The Town Hall, Katherine Street, Croydon CR0 1NX ✆ rachel.flowers@croydon.gov.uk

Staff Training: Ms Sarah Garner, Head of Learning, Organisational Change & Cultural Development, The Town Hall, Katherine Street, Croydon CR0 1NX ☎ 020 86047207 ✆ sarah.garner@croydon.gov.uk

CROYDON

Street Scene: Mr Andy Opie, Director – Safety, The Town Hall, Katherine Street, Croydon CR0 1NX ☎ 020 8726 6000 Extn 65686
✆ andy.opie@croydon.gov.uk

Traffic Management: Mr Dave Tomlinson, Traffic Manager, The Town Hall, Katherine Street, Croydon CR0 1NX ☎ 020 8760 5425
✆ dave.tomlinson@croydon.gov.uk

Transport: Mr Ian Plowright, Head of Strategic Transport, The Town Hall, Katherine Street, Croydon CR0 1NX ☎ 020 8726 6000 Extn 62927 ✆ ian.plowright@croydon.gov.uk

Waste Collection and Disposal: Mr Malcolm Kendall, Head of Environmental & Leisure Services, Stubbs Mead Depot, Factory Lane, Croydon CR0 3RL ☎ 020 8726 6000
✆ malcolm.kendall@croydon.gov.uk

Waste Management: Mr Malcolm Kendall, Head of Environmental & Leisure Services, Stubbs Mead Depot, Factory Lane, Croydon CR0 3RL ☎ 020 8726 6000
✆ malcolm.kendall@croydon.gov.uk

COUNCILLORS

ChairHay-Justice, Patricia (LAB – Addiscombe)
patricia.hay-justice@croydon.gov.uk

Mayor: Trakas-Lawlor, Wayne (LAB – South Norwood)
wayne.lawlor@croydon.gov.uk

Deputy Mayor: Letts, Toni (LAB – Selhurst)
toni.letts@croydon.gov.uk

Leader of the Council: Newman, Tony (LAB – Woodside)
tony.newman@croydon.gov.uk

Deputy Leader of the Council: Butler, Alison (LAB – Bensham Manor)
alison.butler@croydon.gov.uk

Deputy Leader of the Council: Collins, Stuart (LAB – Broad Green)
stuart.collins@croydon.gov.uk

Group LeaderPollard, Tim (CON – Sanderstead)
councillor@timpollard.co.uk

Ali, Hamida (LAB – Woodside)
hamida.ali@croydon.gov.uk

Audsley, Jamie (LAB – Bensham Manor)
jamie.audsley@croydon.gov.uk

Avis, Jane (LAB – South Norwood)
jane.avis@croydon.gov.uk

Bains, Jeet (CON – Coulsdon West)
jeet.bains@croydon.gov.uk

Bashford, Sara (CON – Selsdon & Ballards)
sara.bashford@croydon.gov.uk

Bee, Kathy (LAB – South Norwood)
kathy.bee@croydon.gov.uk

Bennett, Sue (CON – Shirley)
sue.bennett@croydon.gov.uk

Bird, Margaret (CON – Coulsdon East)
margaret.bird@croydon.gov.uk

Bonner, Carole (LAB – Fieldway)
carole.bonner@croydon.gov.uk

Brew, Simon (CON – Purley)
simon.brew@croydon.gov.uk

Buttinger, Jan (CON – Kenley)
jan.buttinger@croydon.gov.uk

Canning, Robert (LAB – Waddon)
robert.canning@croydon.gov.uk

Chatterjee, Richard (CON – Shirley)
richard.chatterjee@croydon.gov.uk

Chowdhury, Sherwan (LAB – Norbury)
sherwan.chowdhury@croydon.gov.uk

Clancy, Luke (CON – Coulsdon West)
luke.clancy@croydon.gov.uk

Clouder, Pat (LAB – Thornton Heath)
pat.clouder@croydon.gov.uk

Creatura, Mario (CON – Coulsdon West)
mario.creatura@croydon.gov.uk

Cummings, Jason (CON – Heathfield)
jason.cummings@croydon.gov.uk

Fisher, Mike (CON – Shirley)
mike.fisher@croydon.gov.uk

Fitzsimons, Sean (LAB – Addiscombe)
sean.fitzsimons@croydon.gov.uk

Flemming, Alisa (LAB – Upper Norwood)
alisa.flemming@croydon.gov.uk

Gatland, Maria (CON – Croham)
maria.gatland@croydon.gov.uk

Godfrey, Timothy (LAB – Selhurst)
timothy.godfrey@croydon.gov.uk

Hale, Lynne (CON – Sanderstead)
lynne.hale@croydon.gov.uk

Hall, Simon (LAB – Fieldway)
simon.hall@croydon.gov.uk

Henson, Maddie (LAB – Ashburton)
maddie.henson@croydon.gov.uk

Hollands, Steve (CON – Kenley)
steven.hollands@croydon.gov.uk

Hopley, Yvette (CON – Sanderstead)
yvette.hopley@croydon.gov.uk

Jewitt, Karen (LAB – Thornton Heath)
karen.jewitt@croydon.gov.uk

Kabir, Humayun (LAB – Bensham Manor)
humayun.kabir@croydon.gov.uk

Khan, Shafi (LAB – Norbury)
shafi.khan@croydon.gov.uk

Khan, Bernadette (LAB – West Thornton)
bernadette.khan@croydon.gov.uk

King, Stuart (LAB – West Thornton)
stuart.king@croydon.gov.uk

Kyeremeh, Matthew (IND – Thornton Heath)
matthew.kyeremeh@croydon.gov.uk

Lewis, Oliver (LAB – New Addington)
oliver.lewis@croydon.gov.uk

Mann, Stephen (LAB – Ashburton)
stephen.mann@croydon.gov.uk

Mansell, Maggie (LAB - Norbury)
maggie.mansell@croydon.gov.uk

Mead, Margaret (CON - Heathfield)
margaret.mead@croydon.gov.uk

Mead, Dudley (CON - Selsdon & Ballards)
dudley.mead@croydon.gov.uk

Mohan, Vidhi (CON - Fairfield)
vidhi.mohan@croydon.gov.uk

Neal, Michael (CON - Croham)
michael.neal@croydon.gov.uk

O'Connell, Steve (CON - Kenley)
steve.o'connell@croydon.gov.uk

Pelling, Andrew (LAB - Waddon)
andrew.pelling@croydon.gov.uk

Perry, Jason (CON - Croham)
jason.perry@croydon.gov.uk

Pollard, Helen (CON - Fairfield)
helen.pollard@croydon.gov.uk

Prince, Joy (LAB - Waddon)
joy.prince@croydon.gov.uk

Quadir, Badsha (CON - Purley)
badsha.quadia@croydon.gov.uk

Rendle, Andrew (LAB - Ashburton)
andrew.rendle@croydon.gov.uk

Ryan, Pat (LAB - Upper Norwood)
pat.ryan@croydon.gov.uk

Scott, Paul (LAB - Woodside)
paul.scott@croydon.gov.uk

Selva, Mike (LAB - Broad Green)
mike.selva@croydon.gov.uk

Shahul-Hameed, Manju (LAB - Broad Green)
the.mayor@croydon.gov.uk

Speakman, Donald (CON - Purley)
donaldspeakman@croydon.gov.uk

Stranack, Andy (CON - Heathfield)
andy.stranack@croydon.gov.uk

Thomas, Phil (CON - Selsdon & Ballards)
phil.thomas@croydon.gov.uk

Thompson, James (CON - Coulsdon East)
james.thompson@croydon.gov.uk

Watson, Mark (LAB - Addiscombe)
mark.watson@croydon.gov.uk

Wentworth, John (LAB - Upper Norwood)
john.wentworth@croydon.gov.uk

Winborn, Sue (CON - Fairfield)
susan.winborn@croydon.gov.uk

Wood, David (LAB - Selhurst)
david.wood@croydon.gov.uk

Woodley, Louisa (LAB - New Addington)
louisa.woodley@croydon.gov.uk

Wright, Chris (CON - Coulsdon East)
chris.wright@croydon.gov.uk

Young, Callton (LAB - West Thornton)
callton.young@croydon.gov.uk

POLITICAL COMPOSITION
LAB: 39, CON: 30, IND: 1

COMMITTEE CHAIRS

Audit: Mr Pat Ryan

Licensing: Ms Jane Avis

Pensions: Mr John Wentworth

Planning: Mr Paul Scott

Cumbria   C

Cumbria County Council, The Courts, English Street, Carlisle CA3 8NA

☎ 01228 606060 🖨 01228 606327 ✆ information@cumbriacc.gov.uk
🖥 www.cumbria.gov.uk

FACTS AND FIGURES
EU Constituencies: North West
Election Frequency: Elections are of whole council

PRINCIPAL OFFICERS

Chief Executive: Mrs Diane Wood, Chief Executive, The Courts, English Street, Carlisle CA3 8NA ☎ 01228 226301
✆ diane.wood@cumbria.gov.uk

Senior Management: Mr Colin Cox, Director - Public Health, The Courts, English Street, Carlisle CA3 8NA
✆ colin.cox@cumbria.gov.uk

Senior Management: Mr Dominic Donnini, Corporate Director - Economy & Highways, The Courts, English Street, Carlisle CA3 8NA ☎ 01228 226260 ✆ dominic.donnini@cumbria.gov.uk

Senior Management: Mr Paul Hancock, Chief Fire Officer, The Courts, English Street, Carlisle CA3 8NA
✆ paul.hancock@cumbria.gov.uk

Senior Management: Mr John Macilwraith, Corporate Director - Children & Familes Services, The Courts, English Street, Carlisle CA3 8NA ☎ 01228 226868 ✆ john.macilwraith@cumbria.gov.uk

Senior Management: Ms Dawn Roberts, Corporate Director - Resources & Transformation, The Courts, English Street, Carlisle CA3 8NA ✆ dawn.roberts@cumbria.gov.uk

Senior Management: Ms Brenda Smith, Corporate Director - Health, Care & Community Services, The Courts, English Street, Carlisle CA3 8NA ✆ brenda.smith@cumbria.gov.uk

Architect, Building / Property Services: Mr Mike Smith, Assistant Director - Capital Programmes & Property, Parkhouse Building, Baron Way, Carlisle CA6 4SJ ☎ 07717 003727
✆ mike.smith@cumbria.gov.uk

Best Value: Mr Duncan McQueen, Senior Manager - Performance & Intelligence, The Courts, Carlisle CA3 8NA ☎ 01228 226293
✆ duncan.mcqueen@cumbria.gov.uk

CUMBRIA

Building Control: Mr Mike Smith, Assistant Director - Capital Programmes & Property, Parkhouse Building, Baron Way, Carlisle CA6 4SJ ☎ 07717 003727 ✆ mike.smith@cumbria.gov.uk

Children / Youth Services: Ms Lyn Burns, Assistant Director - Children & Families, The Courts, English Street, Carlisle CA3 8NA ☎ 01228 226859 ✆ lyn.burns@cumbria.gov.uk

Children / Youth Services: Mr John Macilwraith, Corporate Director - Children & Familes Services, The Courts, English Street, Carlisle CA3 8NA ☎ 01228 226868 ✆ john.macilwraith@cumbria.gov.uk

PR / Communications: Ms Sara Turnbull, Communications Manager, The Courts, English Street, Carlisle CA3 8NA ☎ 01228 226614 ✆ sara.turnbull@cumbria.gov.uk

Community Safety: Mr Jim Onions, Chief Fire Officer, The Courts, English Street, Carlisle CA3 8NA ☎ 01768 812565 ✆ jim.onions@cumbria.gov.uk

Computer Management: Mr Ian Williamson, Senior Manager - ICT Delivery, English Gate Plaza, Botchergate, Carlisle CA1 1RP ☎ 01228 223410 ✆ ian.williamson@cumbria.gov.uk

Consumer Protection and Trading Standards: Ms Angela Jones, Assistant Director - Environment & Community Services, South Lakeland House, Lowther Street, Kendal LA9 4DQ ☎ 07920 814141 ✆ angela.jones@cumbria.gov.uk

Contracts: Mr Conway Stewart, Senior Manager - Corporate Procurement & CM, The Courts, English Street, Carlisle CA3 8NA ☎ 01228 221744 ✆ conway.stewart@cumbria.gov.uk

Corporate Services: Mr Alan Ratcliffe, Assistant Director - Business Services, The Courts, English Street, Carlisle CA3 8NA ☎ 01228 221013 ✆ alan.ratcliffe@cumbria.gov.uk

Customer Service: Mr Jim Grisenthwaite, Assistant Director - Community Services, The Courts, English Street, Carlisle CA3 8NA ☎ 01228 221540 ✆ jim.grisenthwaite@cumbria.gov.uk

Education: Mr John Macilwraith, Corporate Director - Children & Familes Services, The Courts, English Street, Carlisle CA3 8NA ☎ 01228 226868 ✆ john.macilwraith@cumbria.gov.uk

Emergency Planning: Ms Angela Jones, Assistant Director - Environment & Community Services, South Lakeland House, Lowther Street, Kendal LA9 4DQ ☎ 07920 814141 ✆ angela.jones@cumbria.gov.uk

Energy Management: Ms Angela Jones, Assistant Director - Environment & Community Services, South Lakeland House, Lowther Street, Kendal LA9 4DQ ☎ 07920 814141 ✆ angela.jones@cumbria.gov.uk

Estates, Property & Valuation: Mr Mike Smith, Assistant Director - Capital Programmes & Property, Parkhouse Building, Baron Way, Carlisle CA6 4SJ ☎ 07717 003727 ✆ mike.smith@cumbria.gov.uk

Facilities: Mr Mike Smith, Assistant Director - Capital Programmes & Property, Parkhouse Building, Baron Way, Carlisle CA6 4SJ ☎ 07717 003727 ✆ mike.smith@cumbria.gov.uk

Finance: Mr Dominic Donnini, Corporate Director - Economy & Highways, The Courts, English Street, Carlisle CA3 8NA ☎ 01228 226260 ✆ dominic.donnini@cumbria.gov.uk

Treasury: Ms Julie Crellin, Assistant Director - Finance & S151 Officer, The Courts, English Street, Carlisle CA3 8NA ☎ 01228 227291 ✆ julie.crellin@cumbria.gov.uk

Pensions: Mrs Fiona Miller, Senior Manager - Pensions & Finance, The Courts, English Street, Carlisle CA3 8NA ☎ 01228 226280 ✆ fiona.miller@cumbria.gov.uk

Fleet Management: Mr David Jenkinson, Interim Fleet & ITT Manager, Mintsfeet Depot, Mintsfeet Road North, Kendal LA9 6LZ ☎ 01539 713103 ✆ david.jenkins@cumbria.gov.uk

Grounds Maintenance: Mr Mike Smith, Assistant Director - Capital Programmes & Property, Parkhouse Building, Baron Way, Carlisle CA6 4SJ ☎ 07717 003727 ✆ mike.smith@cumbria.gov.uk

Health and Safety: Mr Julian Stainton, Senior Manager - Health, Safety & Wellbeing, Carlisle Fire Station East, Eastern Way, Carlisle CA1 3RA ☎ 07500227793 ✆ julian.stainton@cumbria.gov.uk

Highways: Mr Andrew Moss, Assistant Director - Highways & Transport, Parkhouse Building, Baron Way, Carlisle CA6 4SJ ☎ 01228 221388 ✆ andrew.moss@cumbria.gov.uk

Local Area Agreement: Ms Clare Killeen, Strategic Policy Advisor, The Courts, English Street, Carlisle CA3 8NA ☎ 01228 226514 ✆ clare.killeen@cumbria.gov.uk

Legal: Ms Caroline Elwood, Interim Monitoring Officer, The Courts, English Street, Carlisle CA3 8NA ☎ 01228 227350 ✆ caroline.elwood@cumbria.gov.uk

Leisure and Cultural Services: Mr Jim Grisenthwaite, Assistant Director - Community Services, The Courts, English Street, Carlisle CA3 8NA ☎ 01228 221540 ✆ jim.grisenthwaite@cumbria.gov.uk

Lighting: Mr Andrew Moss, Assistant Director - Highways & Transport, Parkhouse Building, Baron Way, Carlisle CA6 4SJ ☎ 01228 221388 ✆ andrew.moss@cumbria.gov.uk

Parking: Mr Andrew Moss, Assistant Director - Highways & Transport, The Courts, English Street, Carlisle CA3 8NA ☎ 01228 221388 ✆ andrew.moss@cumbria.gov.uk

Partnerships: Mrs Helen Blake, Senior Manager - Policy, Planning & Communities, The Courts, English Street, Carlisle CA3 8NA ☎ 01228 226687 ✆ helen.blake@cumbria.gov.uk

Procurement: Mr Conway Stewart, Senior Manager - Corporate Procurement & CM, The Courts, English Street, Carlisle CA3 8NA ☎ 01228 221744 ✆ conway.stewart@cumbria.gov.uk

Public Libraries: Mr Jim Grisenthwaite, Assistant Director - Community Services, The Courts, English Street, Carlisle CA3 8NA ☎ 01228 221540 ⊕ jim.grisenthwaite@cumbria.gov.uk

Recycling & Waste Minimisation: Mr Ian Stephenson, Waste Services Manager, Parkhouse Building, Baron Way, Carlisle CA6 4SJ ☎ 07825 723046 ⊕ ian.stephenson@cumbria.gov.uk

Road Safety: Mr Chris Broadbent, Road Safety Co-ordinator, Parkhouse Building, Baron Way, Carlisle CA6 4SJ ☎ 07826 874354 ⊕ chris.broadbent@cumbria.gov.uk

Social Services: Ms Sally Burton, Interim Corporate Director - Health & Care Services, The Courts, English Street, Carlisle CA3 8NA ☎ 01228 227110 ⊕ sally.burton@cumbria.gov.uk

Social Services (Adult): Ms Lyn Burns, Assistant Director - Children & Families, The Courts, English Street, Carlisle CA3 8NA ☎ 01228 226859 ⊕ lyn.burns@cumbria.gov.uk

Social Services (Adult): Ms Amanda Evans, Assistant Director - Adult Social Care, The Courts, English Street, Carlisle CA3 8NA ☎ 01228 227116 ⊕ amanda.evans@cumbria.gov.uk

Social Services (Children): Mr John Macilwraith, Corporate Director - Children & Familes Services, The Courts, English Street, Carlisle CA3 8NA ☎ 01228 226868 ⊕ john.macilwraith@cumbria.gov.uk

Childrens Social Care: Mr John Macilwraith, Corporate Director - Children & Familes Services, The Courts, English Street, Carlisle CA3 8NA ☎ 01228 226868 ⊕ john.macilwraith@cumbria.gov.uk

Public Health: Mr Colin Cox, Director - Public Health, The Courts, English Street, Carlisle CA3 8NA ⊕ colin.cox@cumbria.gov.uk

Sustainable Communities: Mrs Helen Blake, Senior Manager - Policy, Planning & Communities, The Courts, English Street, Carlisle CA3 8NA ☎ 01228 226687 ⊕ helen.blake@cumbria.gov.uk

Sustainable Communities: Mr Jim Grisenthwaite, Assistant Director - Community Services, The Courts, English Street, Carlisle CA3 8NA ☎ 01228 221540 ⊕ jim.grisenthwaite@cumbria.gov.uk

Sustainable Communities: Mr Jim Onions, Chief Fire Officer, The Courts, English Street, Carlisle CA3 8NA ☎ 01768 812565 ⊕ jim.onions@cumbria.gov.uk

Traffic Management: Mr Andrew Moss, Assistant Director - Highways & Transport, Parkhouse Building, Baron Way, Carlisle CA6 4SJ ☎ 01228 221388 ⊕ andrew.moss@cumbria.gov.uk

Transport: Mr Andrew Moss, Assistant Director - Highways & Transport, Parkhouse Building, Baron Way, Carlisle CA6 4SJ ☎ 01228 221388 ⊕ andrew.moss@cumbria.gov.uk

Transport Planner: Mr Andrew Moss, Assistant Director - Highways & Transport, Parkhouse Building, Baron Way, Carlisle CA6 4SJ ☎ 01228 221388 ⊕ andrew.moss@cumbria.gov.uk

Waste Collection and Disposal: Mr Ian Stephenson, Waste Services Manager, Parkhouse Building, Baron Way, Carlisle CA6 4SJ ☎ 07825 723046 ⊕ ian.stephenson@cumbria.gov.uk

Waste Management: Mr Ian Stephenson, Waste Services Manager, Parkhouse Building, Baron Way, Carlisle CA6 4SJ ☎ 07825 723046 ⊕ ian.stephenson@cumbria.gov.uk

COUNCILLORS

ChairCook, Geoffrey (LD - Kendal Highgate) geoffrey.cook@cumbriacc.gov.uk

Vice-ChairSkillicorn, Wendy (LAB - Kells & Sandwith) wendy.skillicorn@cumbria.gov.uk

Leader of the Council: Young, Stewart (LAB - Upperby) stewart.young@cumbria.gov.uk

Deputy Leader of the Council: Bell, Patricia (LD - Penrith East) patricia.bell@cumbriacc.gov.uk

Group LeaderAirey, James (CON - Ulverston West) james.airey@cumbria.gov.uk

Group LeaderHolliday, Joseph (IND - St John's & Great Clifton) joe.holliday@cumbria.gov.uk

Group LeaderRobinson, Mary (IND - Alston & East Fellside) mary.robinson@cumbria.gov.uk

Allison, Trevor (INDNA - Dalston & Burgh) trevor.allison@cumbria.gov.uk

Barry, Alan (LAB - St Michael's) alan.barry@cumbria.gov.uk

Bateman, Olivia (CON - Kirkby Stephen) libby.bateman@cumbria.gov.uk

Bell, John (LAB - Morton) john.bell@cumbria.gov.uk

Betton, Robert (INDNA - Botcherby) robert.betton@cumbria.gov.uk

Bingham, Roger (CON - Lower Kentdale) roger.bingham@cumbria.gov.uk

Bland, James (CON - Lyth Valley) james.bland@cumbria.gov.uk

Bowditch, Christine (LAB - Belle Vue)

Bowness, Joseph (CON - Bothel & Wharrels) alan.bowness@cumbria.gov.uk

Burns, Anne (LAB - Hindpool) anne.burns@cumbriacc.gov.uk

Carrick, Hilary (CON - Penrith North) hilary.carrick@cumbria.gov.uk

Cassidy, Frank (LAB - Walney South)

Clark, Alan (LAB - Dearham & Broughton) alan.clarck@cumbria.gov.uk

Clarkson, Norman (CON - Gosforth) norman.clarkson@cumbriacc.gov.uk

Collins, Stan (LD - Upper Kent) stan.collins@cumbriacc.gov.uk

Cotton, Nicholas (LD - Sedbergh & Kirkby Lonsdale) nicholas.cotton@cumbria.gov.uk

CUMBRIA

Crawford, Brian (CON - Millom)
brian.crawford@cumbria.gov.uk

Doughty, Barry (LAB - Dalton North)
barry.doughty@cumbria.gov.uk

Earl, Deborah (LAB - Harraby South)
deborah.earl@cumbria.gov.uk

Evans, Shirley (LD - Kendal Nether)
shirley.evans@cumbria.gov.uk

Fairbairn, Duncan (CON - Thursby)
duncan.fairbairn@cumbria.gov.uk

Fearon, Helen (CON - Penrith West)
helen.fearon@cumbria.gov.uk

Feeney-Johnson, Clare (LD - Kendal Castle)
clare.feeney-johnson@cumbria.gov.uk

Fisher, Lawrence (CON - Brampton)
lawrence.fisher@cumbriacc.gov.uk

Fletcher, David (LD - High Furness)
david.fletcher@cumbria.gov.uk

Furneaux, Beth (LAB - Yewdale)
beth.furneaux@cumbria.gov.uk

Graham, William (INDNA - Corby & Hayton)
william.graham@cumbria.gov.uk

Gray, Brenda (LD - Kendal South)
brenda.gray@cumbria.gov.uk

Halliday, Heidi (LD - Lakes)
heidi.halliday@cumbria.gov.uk

Hamilton, Kevin (LAB - Risedale)
kevin.hamilton@cumbria.gov.uk

Hawkins, Michael (LAB - Mirehouse)
mike.hawkins@cumbria.gov.uk

Hitchen, Keith (CON - Millom Without)
keith.hitchen@cumbria.gov.uk

Hughes, Neil (LD - Eden Lakes)
neil.hughes@cumbria.gov.uk

Humes, Gerald (LAB - Moss Bay & Moorclose)
gerald.humes@cumbria.gov.uk

Jones, Colin (LD - Windermere)
colin.jones@cumbria.gov.uk

Kennon, Alan (CON - Cockermouth South)
alan.kennon@cumbria.gov.uk

Knowles, Timothy (LAB - Cleator Moor East & Frizington)
timothy.knowles@cumbriacc.gov.uk

Liddle, Roger (LAB - Wigton)
roger.liddle@cumbria.gov.uk

Lister, Jim (CON - Aspatria)
jim.lister@cumbria.gov.uk

Little, Keith (LAB - Maryport South)
keith.little@cumbria.gov.uk

Lysser, Andrew (IND - Keswick)
andrew.lysser@cumbria.gov.uk

Mallinson, Elizabeth (CON - Stanwix Urban)
elizabeth.mallinson@cumbria.gov.uk

Mallinson, John (CON - Houghton & Irthington)
john.mallinson@cumbria.gov.uk

Markley, Anthony (CON - Solway Coast)
anthony.markley@cumbria.gov.uk

Marriner, Nicholas (CON - Wetheral)
nick.marriner@cumbria.gov.uk

McCarron-Holmes, Carni (LAB - Maryport North)
carni.mccarron-holmes@cumbria.gov.uk

McDevitt, Hugh (LAB - Denton Holme)
hugh.mcdevitt@cumbria.gov.uk

McEwan, William (LAB - Ormsgill)
william.mcewan@cumbria.gov.uk

McGuckin, Alan (LAB - Castle)
alan.mcguckin@cumbria.gov.uk

Morgan, Frank (LAB - Cleator Moor West)
frank.morgan@cumbriacc.gov.uk

Murphy, Jane (LAB - Newbarns & Parkside)
jane.murphy@cumbria.gov.uk

Murphy, John (LAB - Old Barrow)
john.murphy1@cumbria.gov.uk

Nicholson, Eric (CON - Cockermouth North)
eric.nicholson@cumbriacc.gov.uk

Rae, Marjorie (IND - Harrington)
marjorie.rae@cumbria.gov.uk

Roberts, David (CON - Hawcoat)
david.roberts@cumbria.gov.uk

Sanderson, Sue (LD - Cartmel)

Southward, David (LAB - Egremont)
david.southward@cumbria.gov.uk

Stephenson, Martin (CON - Appleby)
martin.stephenson@cumbria.gov.uk

Stewart, Ian (LD - Kent Estuary)
ian.stewart@cumbria.gov.uk

Strong, Gary (CON - Penrith Rural)
gary.b.strong@cumbria.gov.uk

Tarbitt, Val (CON - Longtown)
val.tarbitt@cumbria.gov.uk

Thornton, Peter (LD - Kendal Strickland & Fell)
peter.thornton@cumbria.gov.uk

Tibble, Celia (LAB - Seaton)

Toole, Alan (IND - Belah)
alan.toole@cumbria.gov.uk

Troughton, Gillian (LAB - Howgate)
gillian.troughton@cumbria.gov.uk

Wall, Helen (LAB - Roosecote)
helen.wall@cumbria.gov.uk

Watson, Reg (LAB - Currock)
reg.watson@cumbria.gov.uk

Wearing, Bill (CON - Grange)
bill.wearing@cumbria.gov.uk

Weber, Cyril (LAB - Harraby North)
cyril.weber@cumbria.gov.uk

Weir, Eileen (LAB - Bransty)
eileen.weir@cumbria.gov.uk

Wentworth Waites, Tom (CON - Greystoke & Hesket)
tom.wentworth-waites@cumbria.gov.uk

Wharrier, Christine (LAB - Hillcrest & Hensingham)
christine.wharrier@cumbria.gov.uk

Willis, Janet (LD - Low Furness)
janet.willis@cumbria.gov.uk

Wilson, Ernie (LAB - Dalton South)
ernie.wilson~cumbria.gov.uk

Wilson, Mark (LAB - Ulverston East)
mark.wilson2@cumbria.gov.uk

Wormstrup, Henry (LAB - Egremont North & St Bees)
henry.wormstrup@cumbria.gov.uk

Worth, Melvyn (LAB - Walney North)
melvyn.worth@cumbria.gov.uk

POLITICAL COMPOSITION
LAB: 36, CON: 25, LD: 15, IND: 5, INDNA: 3

COMMITTEE CHAIRS

Adults: Mr Mark Wilson

Audit: Mr Timothy Knowles

Children & Young People: Mr Duncan Fairbairn

Communities & Place: Mr Michael Hawkins

Development Control & Regulation: Mr Alan Clark

Health & Wellbeing: Mr Stewart Young

Pensions: Mr Melvyn Worth

Dacorum   D

Dacorum Borough Council, Civic Centre, Marlowes, Hemel Hempstead HP1 1HH
☎ 01442 228000 ᐧᵔ customer.services@dacorum.gov.uk
🖳 www.dacorum.gov.uk

FACTS AND FIGURES
Parliamentary Constituencies: Hemel Hempstead
EU Constituencies: Eastern
Election Frequency: Elections are of whole council

PRINCIPAL OFFICERS

Chief Executive: Mrs Sally Marshall, Chief Executive, Civic Centre, Marlowes, Hemel Hempstead HP1 1HH ☎ 01442 228213 ᐧᵔ sally.marshall@dacorum.gov.uk

Senior Management: Mr James Deane, Corporate Director - Finance & Operations (Section 151 Officer), Civic Centre, Marlowes, Hemel Hempstead HP1 1HH ᐧᵔ james.deane@dacorum.gov.uk

Senior Management: Mr Mark Gaynor, Corporate Director - Housing & Regeneration, Civic Centre, Marlowes, Hemel Hempstead HP1 1HH ☎ 01442 228500 ᐧᵔ mark.gaynor@dacorum.gov.uk

Building Control: Ms Sara Whelan, Group Manager - Development & Planning, Civic Centre, Marlowes, Hemel Hempstead HP1 1HH ☎ 01442 228671 ᐧᵔ sara.whelan@dacorum.gov.uk

Children / Youth Services: Ms Julie Still, Group Manager - Resident Services, Civic Centre, Marlowes, Hemel Hempstead HP1 1HH ☎ 01442 228453 ᐧᵔ julie.still@dacorum.gov.uk

Community Safety: Ms Julie Still, Group Manager - Resident Services, Civic Centre, Marlowes, Hemel Hempstead HP1 1HH ☎ 01442 228453 ᐧᵔ julie.still@dacorum.gov.uk

Computer Management: Mr Ben Trueman, Group Manager - Information, Communication & Technology, Civic Centre, Marlowes, Hemel Hempstead HP1 1HH ☎ 01442 228171 ᐧᵔ ben.trueman@dacorum.gov.uk

Corporate Services: Ms Lesley Crisp, Strategic Planning & Regeneration Officer, Civic Centre, Marlowes, Hemel Hempstead HP1 1HH ☎ 01756 700600 ᐧᵔ lesley.crisp@dacorum.gov.uk

Corporate Services: Mr Jim Doyle, Group Manager - Democratic Services, Civic Centre, Marlowes, Hemel Hempstead HP1 1HH ☎ 01442 228222 ᐧᵔ jim.doyle@dacorum.gov.uk

Economic Development: Ms Lesley Crisp, Strategic Planning & Regeneration Officer, Civic Centre, Marlowes, Hemel Hempstead HP1 1HH ☎ 01756 700600 ᐧᵔ lesley.crisp@dacorum.gov.uk

Economic Development: Mrs Chris Taylor, Group Manager - Strategic Planning & Regeneration, Civic Centre, Marlowes, Hemel Hempstead HP1 1HH ☎ 01442 867805 ᐧᵔ chris.taylor@dacorum.gov.uk

E-Government: Mr Ben Trueman, Group Manager - Information, Communication & Technology, Civic Centre, Marlowes, Hemel Hempstead HP1 1HH ☎ 01442 228171 ᐧᵔ ben.trueman@dacorum.gov.uk

Electoral Registration: Mr Jim Doyle, Group Manager - Democratic Services, Civic Centre, Marlowes, Hemel Hempstead HP1 1HH ☎ 01442 228222 ᐧᵔ jim.doyle@dacorum.gov.uk

Emergency Planning: Mr Chris Troy, Group Manager - Regulatory Services, Civic Centre, Marlowes, Hemel Hempstead HP1 1HH ☎ 01442 228473 ᐧᵔ chris.troy@dacorum.gov.uk

Environmental Health: Mr Chris Troy, Group Manager - Regulatory Services, Civic Centre, Marlowes, Hemel Hempstead HP1 1HH ☎ 01442 228473 ᐧᵔ chris.troy@dacorum.gov.uk

Estates, Property & Valuation: Ms Adriana Livingstone, Team Leader - Estates & Valuation, Civic Centre, Marlowes, Hemel Hempstead HP1 1HH ☎ 01442 228776 ᐧᵔ adriana.livingstone@dacroum.gov.uk

Finance: Mr James Deane, Corporate Director - Finance & Operations (Section 151 Officer), Civic Centre, Marlowes, Hemel Hempstead HP1 1HH ᐧᵔ james.deane@dacorum.gov.uk

Grounds Maintenance: Mr Simon Coultas, Assistant Operations Manager, Civic Centre, Marlowes, Hemel Hempstead HP1 1HH ☎ 01442 228032 ᐧᵔ simon.coultas@dacorum.gov.uk

Health and Safety: Mr Chris Troy, Group Manager - Regulatory Services, Civic Centre, Marlowes, Hemel Hempstead HP1 1HH ☎ 01442 228473 ᐧᵔ chris.troy@dacorum.gov.uk

DACORUM

Housing: Mr Elliott Brooks, Assistant Director - Housing, Civic Centre, Marlowes, Hemel Hempstead HP1 1HH
elliott.brooks@dacorum.gov.uk

Housing Maintenance: Mr Neil Brown, Programme & Procurement Team Leader, Civic Centre, Marlowes, Hemel Hempstead HP1 1HH ☎ 01442 228639

Legal: Mr Mark Brookes, Solicitor to the Council & Monitoring Officer, Civic Centre, Marlowes, Hemel Hempstead HP1 1HH
☎ 01442 228236 mark.brookes@dacorum.gov.uk

Licensing: Mr Ross Hill, Team Leader - Licensing, Civic Centre, Marlowes, Hemel Hempstead HP1 1HH ross.hill@dacorum.gov.uk

Member Services: Mr Jim Doyle, Group Manager - Democratic Services, Civic Centre, Marlowes, Hemel Hempstead HP1 1HH
☎ 01442 228222 jim.doyle@dacorum.gov.uk

Parking: Mr Steve Barnes, Parking Services Team Leader, Civic Centre, Marlowes, Hemel Hempstead HP1 1HH ☎ 01442 249484
steve.barnes@dacorum.gov.uk

Personnel / HR: Mr Matthew Rawdon, Group Manager - People, Civic Centre, Marlowes, Hemel Hempstead HP1 1HH
☎ 01442 228513 matthew.rawdon@dacorum.gov.uk

Planning: Mr James Doe, Assistant Director - Planning, Development & Regeneration, Civic Centre, Marlowes, Hemel Hempstead HP1 1HH ☎ 01442 228000
james.doe@dacorum.gov.uk

Procurement: Mr Ben Hosier, Group Manager - Commissioning, Procurement & Compliance, Civic Centre, Marlowes, Hemel Hempstead HP1 1HH ☎ 01442 228215
ben.hosier@dacorum.gov.uk

Recycling & Waste Minimisation: Mr Craig Thorpe, Group Manager - Environmental Services, Civic Centre, Marlowes, Hemel Hempstead HP1 1HH ☎ 01442 228030
craig.thorpe@dacorum.gov.uk

Regeneration: Mr Mark Gaynor, Corporate Director - Housing & Regeneration, Civic Centre, Marlowes, Hemel Hempstead HP1 1HH
☎ 01442 228500 mark.gaynor@dacorum.gov.uk

Street Scene: Mr David Austin, Assistant Director - Neighbourhood Delivery, Civic Centre, Marlowes, Hemel Hempstead HP1 1HH ☎ 01442 228355 david.austin@dacorum.gov.uk

Town Centre: Mr James Doe, Assistant Director - Planning, Development & Regeneration, Civic Centre, Marlowes, Hemel Hempstead HP1 1HH ☎ 01442 228000
james.doe@dacorum.gov.uk

Transport Planner: Mr James Doe, Assistant Director - Planning, Development & Regeneration, Civic Centre, Marlowes, Hemel Hempstead HP1 1HH ☎ 01442 228000
james.doe@dacorum.gov.uk

Waste Collection and Disposal: Mr Craig Thorpe, Group Manager - Environmental Services, Civic Centre, Marlowes, Hemel Hempstead HP1 1HH ☎ 01442 228030
craig.thorpe@dacorum.gov.uk

Waste Management: Mr Craig Thorpe, Group Manager - Environmental Services, Civic Centre, Marlowes, Hemel Hempstead HP1 1HH ☎ 01442 228030 craig.thorpe@dacorum.gov.uk

COUNCILLORS

Mayor: McLean, Bob (CON - Kings Langley)
bob.mclean@dacorum.gov.uk

Deputy Mayor: Collins, David (CON - Berkhamsted Castle)
david.collins@dacorum.gov.uk

Leader of the Council: Williams, Andrew (CON - Boxmoor)
andrew.williams@dacorum.gov.uk

Deputy Leader of the Council: Griffiths, Margaret (CON - Leverstock Green)
margaret.griffiths@dacorum.gov.uk

Adeleke, Gbola (CON - Bovingdon, Flaunden & Chipperfield)
gbola.adeleke@dacorum.gov.uk

Adshead, Sharon (CON - Adeyfield West)
sharon.adshead@dacorum.gov.uk

Anderson, Alan (CON - Kings Langley)
alan.anderson@dacorum.gov.uk

Ashburn, Julian (CON - Berkhamsted West)
julian.ashburn@dacorum.gov.uk

Ashead, Graham (CON - Adeyfield East)
graham.ashead@dacorum.gov.uk

Banks, Julie (CON - Grovehill)
julie.banks@dacorum.gov.uk

Barnes, Adam (CON - Bovingdon, Flaunden & Chipperfield)
adam.barnes@dacorum.gov.uk

Bassadone, Hazel (CON - Leverstock Green)
hazel.bassadone@dacorum.gov.uk

Bhinder, Alexander (CON - Grovehill)
alexander.bhinder@dacorum.gov.uk

Birnie, John (CON - Bennetts End)
joh.birnie@dacorum.gov.uk

Brown, Christine (CON - Hemel Hempstead Town)
christine.brown@dacorum.gov.uk

Chapman, Herbert (CON - Watling)
herbert.chapman@dacorum.gov.uk

Clark, Michael (CON - Apsley & Corner Hall)
michael.clark@dacorum.gov.uk

Collins, Elaine (CON - Berkhamsted East)
elaine.collins@dacorum.gov.uk

Conway, Olive (CON - Tring West & Rural)
olive.conway@dacorum.gov.uk

Douris, Terry (CON - Ashridge)
terry.douris@dacorum.gov.uk

Elliot, Graeme (CON - Chaulden & Warners End)
graeme.elliott@dacorum.gov.uk

Fantham, Alan (CON - Northchurch)
alan.fantham@dacorum.gov.uk

Fethney, Tony (LAB - Highfield)
tony.fethney@dacorum.gov.uk

Fisher, Anne (LAB - Hemel Hempstead Town)
anne.fisher@dacorum.gov.uk

Guest, Fiona (CON - Chaulden & Warners End)
fiona@dandfguest.eclipse.co.uk

Harden, Neil (CON - Boxmoor)
neil.harden@dacorum.gov.uk

Hearn, Penelope (CON - Tring East)
penny.hearn@dacorum.gov.uk

Hearn, Stephen (CON - Tring Central)
stephen.hearn@dacorum.gov.uk

Hicks, Mike (CON - Tring West & Rural)
mike.hicks@dacorum.gov.uk

Howard, Tina (CON - Apsley & Corner Hall)
tina.howard@dacorum.gov.uk

Imarni, Isy (CON - Gadebridge)
isy.imarni@dacorum.gov.uk

Link, Brenda (LD - Highfield)
brenda.link@dacorum.gov.uk

Maddern, Jan (CON - Nash Mills)
jan.maddern@dacorum.gov.uk

Mahmood, Suqlain (CON - Bennetts End)
suqlain.mahmood@dacorum.gov.uk

Marshall, Janice (CON - Boxmoor)
janice.marshall@dacorum.gov.uk

Matthews, Peter (CON - Berkhamsted West)
peter.matthews@dacorum.gov.uk

Mills, Stan (CON - Aldbury & Wigginton)
stan.mills@dacorum.gov.uk

Peter, Colin (CON - Apsley & Corner Hall)
colin.peter@dacorum.gov.uk

Ransley, Roxanne (LD - Tring Central)
roxanne.ransley@dacorum.gov.uk

Riddick, Stewart (CON - Bovingdon, Flaunden & Chipperfield)
stewart.riddick@dacorum.gov.uk

Ritchie, Tom (CON - Berkhamsted Castle)
tom.ritchie@dacorum.gov.uk

Silwal, Goverdhan (CON - Grovehill)
goverdhan.silwal@dacorum.gov.uk

Sutton, Rosie (CON - Woodhall Farm)
rosie.sutton@dacorum.gov.uk

Sutton, Graham (CON - Leverstock Green)
graham.sutton@dacorum.gov.uk

Taylor, Roger (CON - Gadebridge)
roger.taylor@dacorum.gov.uk

Timmis, Jane (CON - Watling)
jane.timmis@dacorum.gov.uk

Tindall, Ron (LD - Adeyfield West)
ron.tindall@dacorum.go.uk

Whitman, John (CON - Chaulden & Warners End)
john.whitman@dacorum.gov.uk

Wyatt-Lowe, William (CON - Adeyfield East)
william.wyatt-lowe@dacorum.gov.uk

Wyatt-Lowe, Colette (CON - Woodhall Farm)
colette.wyatt-lowe@dacorum.gov.uk

POLITICAL COMPOSITION
CON: 45, LD: 3, LAB: 2

COMMITTEE CHAIRS

Audit: Mr Roger Taylor

Development Control: Mr David Collins

Finance & Resources: Mr Herbert Chapman

Housing & Community: Mr Suqlain Mahmood

Licensing: Ms Penelope Hearn

Planning & Environment: Mr Alan Anderson

Darlington   U

Darlington Borough Council, Town Hall, Feethams, Darlington DL1 5QT
☎ 01325 380651 🖷 01325 382032
⌁ customerservices@darlington.gov.uk 🖳 www.darlington.gov.uk

FACTS AND FIGURES
Parliamentary Constituencies: Darlington
EU Constituencies: North East
Election Frequency: Elections are of whole council

PRINCIPAL OFFICERS

Chief Executive: Ms Ada Burns, Chief Executive, Town Hall, Feethams, Darlington DL1 5QT ☎ 01325 405813
⌁ ada.burns@darlington.gov.uk

Senior Management: Ms Miriam Davidson, Director - Public Health, Town Hall, Feethams, Darlington DL1 5QT ☎ 01325 406203
⌁ miriam.davidson@darlington.gov.uk

Senior Management: Ms Suzanne Joyner, Director - Children & Adults' Services, Town Hall, Feethams, Darlington DL1 5QT
☎ 01325 405814 ⌁ suzanne.joyner@darlington.gov.uk

Senior Management: Mr Paul Wildsmith, Director - Neighbourhood Services & Resources, Town Hall, Feethams, Darlington DL1 5QT
☎ 01325 405829 ⌁ paul.wildsmith@darlington.gov.uk

Senior Management: Mr Ian Williams, Director - Economic Growth, Town Hall, Feethams, Darlington DL1 5QT ☎ 01325 406379
⌁ ian.williams@darlington.gov.uk

Architect, Building / Property Services: Mr Brian Robson, Head of Capital Projects, Yarm Road Business Park, 17 Allington Way, Darlington DL1 4QB ☎ 01325 406608
⌁ brian.robson@darlington.gov.uk

Catering Services: Mr Graham Carey, Catering Manager, Dolphin Centre, Horsemarket, Darlington DL1 5RP ☎ 01325 406970
⌁ graham.carey@darlington.gov.uk

DARLINGTON

Children / Youth Services: Mr David Mason, Head of Looked After Children, Edge of Care & Youth, Town Hall, Feethams, Darlington DL1 5QT ☎ 01325 405884 ⏚ david.mason@darlington.gov.uk

Civil Registration: Mr Anthony Hall, Superintendent Registrar, The Registrar Office, Backhouse Hall, Bull Wynd, Darlington DL1 5RG ☎ 01325 406400 ⏚ anthony.hall@darlington.gov.uk

PR / Communications: Mr Neil Bowerbank, Head of Communications, Town Hall, Feethams, Darlington DL1 5QT ☎ 01325 406052 ⏚ neil.bowerbank@darlington.gov.uk

Computer Management: Mr Ian Miles, Assistant Director - Central Services, Town Hall, Feethams, Darlington DL1 5QT ☎ 01642 527012 ⏚ ian.miles@xentrall.org.uk

Customer Service: Mrs Linda Todd, Head of Democratic & Customer Services, Town Hall, Feethams, Darlington DL1 5QT ☎ 01325 405807 ⏚ linda.todd@darlington.gov.uk

Education: Ms Rachel Kershaw, Head of School & Pupil Support Services, Town Hall, Feethams, Darlington DL1 5QT ☎ 01325 405885 ⏚ rachel.kershaw@darlington.gov.uk

E-Government: Mr Ian Miles, Assistant Director - Central Services, Town Hall, Feethams, Darlington DL1 5QT ☎ 01642 527012 ⏚ ian.miles@xentrall.org.uk

Electoral Registration: Ms Lynne Wood, Elections Manager, Town Hall, Feethams, Darlington DL1 5QT ☎ 01325 388287 ⏚ lynne.wood@darlington.gov.uk

Emergency Planning: Mr Bill Westland, Assistant Director - Regulatory Services, Town Hall, Feethams, Darlington DL1 5QT ☎ 01325 406303 ⏚ bill.westland@darlington.gov.uk

Energy Management: Mr Guy Metcalfe, Head of Property Asset Management, Town Hall, Feethams, Darlington DL1 5QT ☎ 01325 406725 ⏚ guy.metcalfe@darlington.gov.uk

Environmental / Technical Services: Mr Brian Graham, Head of Environmental Services, Yarm Road Business Park, 17 Allington Way, Darlington DL1 4QB ☎ 01325 406607 ⏚ brian.graham@darlington.gov.uk

Estates, Property & Valuation: Mr Guy Metcalfe, Head of Property Asset Management, Town Hall, Feethams, Darlington DL1 5QT ☎ 01325 406725 ⏚ guy.metcalfe@darlington.gov.uk

Events Manager: Mrs Marion Ogle, Library & Events Manager, Dolphin Centre, Horsemarket, Darlington DL1 5RP ☎ 01325 406990 ⏚ marion.ogle@darlington.gov.uk

Finance: Mr Paul Wildsmith, Director - Neighbourhood Services & Resources, Town Hall, Feethams, Darlington DL1 5QT ☎ 01325 405829 ⏚ paul.wildsmith@darlington.gov.uk

Grounds Maintenance: Mr Brian Graham, Head of Environmental Services, Yarm Road Business Park, 17 Allington Way, Darlington DL1 4QB ☎ 01325 406607 ⏚ brian.graham@darlington.gov.uk

Health and Safety: Ms Joanne Skelton, Health & Safety Manager, Town Hall, Feethams, Darlington DL1 5QT ☎ 01325 406256 ⏚ joanne.skelton@darlington.gov.uk

Highways: Mr Steve Brannan, Head of Highway Asset Management, Yarm Road Business Park, 17 Allington Way, Darlington DL1 4QB ☎ 01325 406663 ⏚ steve.brannan@darlington.gov.uk

Highways: Mr Dave Winstanley, Assistant Director - Transport & Capital Projects, Yarm Road Business Park, 17 Allington Way, Darlington DL1 4QB ☎ 01325 406618 ⏚ david.winstanley@darlington.gov.uk

Housing: Mrs Pauline Mitchell, Assistant Director - Housing & Building Services, Town Hall, Feethams, Darlington DL1 5QT ☎ 01325 405831 ⏚ pauline.mitchell@darlington.gov.uk

Housing Maintenance: Ms Hazel Neasham, Head of Housing, Town Hall, Feethams, Darlington DL1 5QT ☎ 01325 405933 ⏚ hazel.neasham@darlington.gov.uk

Legal: Mr Luke Swinhoe, Assistant Director - Law & Governance, Town Hall, Feethams, Darlington DL1 5QT ☎ 01325 405490 ⏚ luke.swinhoe@darlington.gov.uk

Leisure and Cultural Services: Mr Mike Crawshaw, Head of Culture, Dolphin Centre, Horsemarket, Darlington DL1 5RP ☎ 01325 406980 ⏚ mike.crawshaw@darlington.gov.uk

Lifelong Learning: Mr Mike Crawshaw, Head of Culture, Dolphin Centre, Horsemarket, Darlington DL1 5RP ☎ 01325 406980 ⏚ mike.crawshaw@darlington.gov.uk

Member Services: Mrs Linda Todd, Head of Democratic & Customer Services, Town Hall, Feethams, Darlington DL1 5QT ☎ 01325 405807 ⏚ linda.todd@darlington.gov.uk

Partnerships: Mr Seth Pearson, Executive Director - Darlington Partnership, Town Hall, Feethams, Darlington DL1 5QT ☎ 01325 406090 ⏚ seth.pearson@darlington.gov.uk

Personnel / HR: Mrs Elizabeth Davison, Assistant Director - Finance & Human Resources, Town Hall, Feethams, Darlington DL1 5QT ☎ 01325 405830 ⏚ elizabeth.davison@darlington.gov.uk

Planning: Mr John Anderson, Assistant Director - Economic Initiative, Town Hall, Feethams, Darlington DL1 5QT ☎ 01325 406322 ⏚ john.anderson@darlington.gov.uk

Procurement: Ms Sarah Hutchinson, Principal Lawyer (Commercial), Town Hall, Feethams, Darlington DL1 5QT ☎ 01325 405489 ⏚ sarah.hutchinson@darlington.gov.uk

Public Libraries: Mr Mike Crawshaw, Head of Culture, Dolphin Centre, Horsemarket, Darlington DL1 5RP ☎ 01325 406980 ⏚ mike.crawshaw@darlington.gov.uk

Recycling & Waste Minimisation: Ms Phillippa Scrafton, Waste & Recycling Service Development Officer, Yarm Road Business Park, 17 Allington Way, Darlington DL1 4QB ☎ 01325 406648 ⏚ phillippa.scrafton@darlington.gov.uk

Regeneration: Mr John Anderson, Assistant Director - Economic Initiative, Town Hall, Feethams, Darlington DL1 5QT
☎ 01325 406322 ᐧᵇ john.anderson@darlington.gov.uk

Road Safety: Mr Andrew Casey, Head of Highway Network Management, Yarm Road Business Park, 17 Allington Way, Darlington DL1 4QB ☎ 01325 406701
ᐧᵇ andrew.casey@darlington.gov.uk

Social Services (Adult): Mr Kevin Kelly, Acting Assistant Director - Adult Social Care, Town Hall, Feethams, Darlington DL1 5QT
☎ 01325 406126 ᐧᵇ kevin.kelly@darlington.gov.uk

Families: Ms Yvonne Coates, Head of First Contact & Locality Services, Town Hall, Feethams, Darlington DL1 5QT
☎ 01325 405864 ᐧᵇ yvonne.coates@darlington.gov.uk

Childrens Social Care: Mr David Mason, Head of Looked After Children, Edge of Care & Youth, Town Hall, Feethams, Darlington DL1 5QT ☎ 01325 405884 ᐧᵇ david.mason@darlington.gov.uk

Public Health: Ms Miriam Davidson, Director - Public Health, Town Hall, Feethams, Darlington DL1 5QT ☎ 01325 406203
ᐧᵇ miriam.davidson@darlington.gov.uk

Street Scene: Mr Brian Graham, Head of Environmental Services, Yarm Road Business Park, 17 Allington Way, Darlington DL1 4QB
☎ 01325 406607 ᐧᵇ brian.graham@darlington.gov.uk

Traffic Management: Mr Andrew Casey, Head of Highway Network Management, Yarm Road Business Park, 17 Allington Way, Darlington DL1 4QB ☎ 01325 406701 ᐧᵇ andrew.casey@darlington.gov.uk

Transport: Ms Melanie Stainthorpe, Schools Admissions & Transport Manager, Town Hall, Feethams, Darlington DL1 5QT
☎ 01325 405908 ᐧᵇ melanie.stainthorpe@darlington.gov.uk

Waste Collection and Disposal: Mr Brian Graham, Head of Environmental Services, Yarm Road Business Park, 17 Allington Way, Darlington DL1 4QB ☎ 01325 406607
ᐧᵇ brian.graham@darlington.gov.uk

Waste Management: Mr Brian Graham, Head of Environmental Services, Yarm Road Business Park, 17 Allington Way, Darlington DL1 4QB ☎ 01325 406607 ᐧᵇ brian.graham@darlington.gov.uk

Children's Play Areas: Mr Brian Graham, Head of Environmental Services, Yarm Road Business Park, 17 Allington Way, Darlington DL1 4QB ☎ 01325 406607 ᐧᵇ brian.graham@darlington.gov.uk

COUNCILLORS

Leader of the Council: Dixon, Bill (LAB - Eastbourne)
bill.dixon@darlington.gov.uk

Deputy Leader of the Council: Harker, Stephen (LAB - Pierremont)
stephen.harker@darlington.gov.uk

Baldwin, Paul (LAB - Cockerton East)
paul.baldwin@darlington.gov.uk

Carson, Bob (LAB - Pierremont)
bob.carson@darlington.gov.uk

Cartwright, Gill (CON - Harrowgate Hill)
gill.cartwright@darlington.gov.uk

Copeland, Veronica (LAB - Banktop)
veronica.copeland@darlington.gov.uk

Cossins, Jan (LAB - Cockerton West)
jan.cossins@darlington.gov.uk

Coultas, Alan (CON - Hummersknott)
alan.coultas@darlington.gov.uk

Crichlow, Roderick (LAB - Eastbourne)
roderick.crichlow@darlington.gov.uk

Crudass, Paul (CON - Heighington & Coniscliffe)
paul.crudass@darlington.gov.uk

Crumbie, Helen (LAB - Lascelles)
helen.crumbie@darlington.gov.uk

Culley, Pauline (CON - Mowden)
pauline.culley@darlington.gov.uk

Curry, Anne-Marie (LD - North Road)
annemarie.curry@darlington.gov.uk

Donoghue, Bob (CON - Park West)
bob.donoghue@darlington.gov.uk

Galletley, Ian (CON - College)
ian.galletley@darlington.gov.uk

Grundy, Richard (CON - Faverdale)
richard.grundy@darlington.gov.uk

Haszeldine, Ian (LAB - Lingfield)
ian.haszeldine@darlington.gov.uk

Haszeldine, Lynne (LAB - Lingfield)
lynne.haszeldine@darlington.gov.uk

Hughes, Cyndi (LAB - Park East)
cyndi.hughes@darlington.gov.uk

Hughes, Linda (LAB - Pierremont)
linda.hughes@darlington.gov.uk

Johnson, Charles (CON - Hummersknott)
charles.johnson@darlington.gov.uk

Jones, Doris (CON - Middleton St George)
doris.jones@darlington.gov.uk

Jones, Brian (CON - Sadberge & Whessoe)
brian.jones@darlington.gov.uk

Kane, Sonia (LAB - Northgate)
sonia.kane@darlington.gov.uk

Kelley, Joe (LD - Hurworth)
joe.kelley@darlington.gov.uk

Kelly, Katie (LAB - Stephenson)
katie.kelly@darlington.gov.uk

Knowles, Marjory (LAB - Harrowgate Hill)
marjory.knowles@darlington.gov.uk

Lawton, Fred (LD - North Road)
fred.lawton@darlington.gov.uk

Lee, Gerald (CON - Heighington & Coniscliffe)
gerald.lee@darlington.gov.uk

Lister, Eleanor (LAB - Northgate)
eleanor.lister@darlington.gov.uk

Lyonette, David (LAB - Haughton West)
david.lyonette@darlington.gov.uk

DARLINGTON

McEwan, Chris (LAB - Haughton East)
chris.mcewan@darlington.gov.uk

Mills, Rachel (CON - Brinkburn & Faverdale)
rachel.mills@darlington.gov.uk

Newall, Wendy (LAB - Lascelles)
wendy.newall@darlington.gov.uk

Nicholson, Kevin (IND - Eastbourne)
kevin.nicholson@darlington.gov.uk

Nicholson, Michael (LAB - Park East)
michael.nicholson@darlington.gov.uk

Nutt, Thomas (LAB - Haughton North)
thomas.nutt@darlington.gov.uk

Regan, David (LAB - Cockerton West)
david.regan@darlington.gov.uk

Richmond, Tony (CON - College)

Richmond, Sue (LAB - Cockerton East)
sue.richmond@darlington.gov.uk

Scott, Andrew (LAB - Haughton West)
andrew.scott@darlington.gov.uk

Scott, Heather (CON - Park West)
heather.scott@darlington.gov.uk

Stenson, Bill (CON - Mowden)
bill.stenson@darlington.gov.uk

Storr, Dawn (LAB - North Road)
dawn.storr@darlington.gov.uk

Taylor, Jan (LAB - Central)
jan.taylor@darlington.gov.uk

Taylor, Chris (LAB - Banktop)
chris.taylor@darlington.gov.uk

Tostevin, Lorraine (CON - Hurworth)
lorraine.tostevin@darlington.gov.uk

Wallis, Nick (LAB - Haughton West)
nick.wallis@darlington.gov.uk

Wright, Malcolm (LAB - Central)
malcolm.wright@darlington.gov.uk

York, Steve (CON - Middleton St George)
steve.york@darlington.gov.uk

POLITICAL COMPOSITION
LAB: 29, CON: 17, LD: 3, IND: 1

COMMITTEE CHAIRS

Adults & Housing: Ms Sue Richmond

Audit: Mr Paul Baldwin

Children & Housing: Ms Eleanor Lister

Children & Young People: Mr Chris Taylor

Health & Wellbeing: Mr Andrew Scott

Licensing: Mr Thomas Nutt

Planning: Mr Paul Baldwin

Dartford Borough Council, Civic Centre, Home Gardens, Dartford DA1 1DR

☎ 01322 343434 📠 01322 343422 🖥 www.dartford.gov.uk

FACTS AND FIGURES
Parliamentary Constituencies: Dartford
EU Constituencies: South East
Election Frequency: Elections are of whole council

PRINCIPAL OFFICERS

Chief Executive: Mr Graham Harris, Managing Director, Civic Centre, Home Gardens, Dartford DA1 1DR ☎ 01322 343434 ⌁ graham.harris@dartford.gov.uk

Senior Management: Mrs Sheri Green, Strategic Director & Monitoring Officer, Civic Centre, Home Gardens, Dartford DA1 1DR ☎ 01322 343434 ⌁ sheri.green@dartford.gov.uk

Senior Management: Ms Sarah Martin, Strategic Director - Internal Services & S151 Officer, Civic Centre, Home Gardens, Dartford DA1 1DR ☎ 01322 343434 ⌁ sarah.martin@dartford.gov.uk

Building Control: Mr Andrew Nichols, Building & Control Manager, Civic Centre, Home Gardens, Dartford DA1 1DR ☎ 01322 343434 ⌁ andrew.nichols@dartford.gov.uk

PR / Communications: Ms Helen Clark, Press & Design Officer, Civic Centre, Home Gardens, Dartford DA1 1DR ☎ 01322 343069 ⌁ helen.clark@dartford.gov.uk

Community Planning: Ms Teresa Ryszkowska, Head of Regeneration, Civic Centre, Home Gardens, Dartford DA1 1DR ☎ 01322 343631 ⌁ teresa.ryszkowska@dartford.gov.uk

Community Safety: Mrs Sheri Green, Strategic Director & Monitoring Officer, Civic Centre, Home Gardens, Dartford DA1 1DR ☎ 01322 343434 ⌁ sheri.green@dartford.gov.uk

Computer Management: Mrs Sheri Green, Strategic Director & Monitoring Officer, Civic Centre, Home Gardens, Dartford DA1 1DR ☎ 01322 343434 ⌁ sheri.green@dartford.gov.uk

Corporate Services: Mr Andrew Hall, Corporate Building Surveyor, Civic Centre, Home Gardens, Dartford DA1 1DR ☎ 01322 343489 ⌁ andrew.hall@dartford.gov.uk

Customer Service: Mrs Carol Russell, Customer Services Manager, Civic Centre, Home Gardens, Dartford DA1 1DR ☎ 01322 343030 ⌁ carol.russell@dartford.gov.uk

E-Government: Mrs Sheri Green, Strategic Director & Monitoring Officer, Civic Centre, Home Gardens, Dartford DA1 1DR ☎ 01322 343434 ⌁ sheri.green@dartford.gov.uk

Electoral Registration: Mr Graham Harris, Managing Director, Civic Centre, Home Gardens, Dartford DA1 1DR ☎ 01322 343434 ⌁ graham.harris@dartford.gov.uk

Emergency Planning: Mr Mark Salisbury, Enforcement & Regulatory Services Manager, Civic Centre, Home Gardens, Dartford DA1 1DR ☎ 01322 343434 ⁊ mark.salisbury@dartford.gov.uk

Environmental Health: Mrs Annie Sargent, Environmental Health Manager, Dartford Borough Council, Civic Centre, Home Gardens, Dartford DA1 1DR ☎ 01322 343434 ⁊ annie.sargent@dartford.gov.uk

Estates, Property & Valuation: Mr Andrew Hall, Corporate Building Surveyor, Civic Centre, Home Gardens, Dartford DA1 1DR ☎ 01322 343489 ⁊ andrew.hall@dartford.gov.uk

Finance: Mr Tim Sams, Financial Services Manager, Civic Centre, Home Gardens, Dartford DA1 1DR ☎ 01322 343434 ⁊ tim.sams@dartford.gov.uk

Fleet Management: Ms Lynn Stewart, Senior Finance Assistant, Civic Centre, Home Gardens, Dartford DA1 1DR ☎ 01322 343434 ⁊ lynn.stewart@dartford.gov.uk

Grounds Maintenance: Mr Dave Thomas, Waste & Recycling Manager, Civic Centre, Home Gardens, Dartford DA1 1DR ☎ 01322 343434 ⁊ dave.thomas@dartford.gov.uk

Health and Safety: Mrs Annie Sargent, Environmental Health Manager, Dartford Borough Council, Civic Centre, Home Gardens, Dartford DA1 1DR ☎ 01322 343434 ⁊ annie.sargent@dartford.gov.uk

Home Energy Conservation: Ms Sandra Woodfall, Environmental Promotions Officer, Civic Centre, Home Gardens, Dartford DA1 1DR ☎ 01322 343434 ⁊ sandra.woodfall@dartford.gov.uk

Housing: Mr Peter Dosad, Head of Housing, Civic Centre, Home Gardens, Dartford DA1 1DR ☎ 01322 343434 ⁊ peter.dosad@dartford.gov.uk

Legal: Ms Marie Kelly-Stone, Head of Legal Services, Civic Centre, Home Gardens, Dartford DA1 1DR ☎ 01322 343434 ⁊ marie.kelly-stone@dartford.gov.uk

Leisure and Cultural Services: Mr Adrian Gowan, Policy & Corporate Support Manager, Civic Centre, Home Gardens, Dartford DA1 1DR ☎ 01322 343434 ⁊ adrian.gowan@dartford.gov.uk

Licensing: Mr Mark Salisbury, Enforcement & Regulatory Services Manager, Civic Centre, Home Gardens, Dartford DA1 1DR ☎ 01322 343434 ⁊ mark.salisbury@dartford.gov.uk

Member Services: Mr Alan Twyman, Member Services Manager, Civic Centre, Home Gardens, Dartford DA1 1DR ☎ 01322 343434 ⁊ alan.twyman@dartford.gov.uk

Parking: Mr Lewis Boudville, Parking Services Manager, Civic Centre, Home Gardens, Dartford DA1 1DR ☎ 01322 434434 ⁊ lewis.boudville@dartford.gov.uk

Planning: Ms Teresa Ryszkowska, Head of Regeneration, Civic Centre, Home Gardens, Dartford DA1 1DR ☎ 01322 343631 ⁊ teresa.ryszkowska@dartford.gov.uk

Procurement: Mr Bami Cole, Audit, Risk & Anti-Fraud Manager, Dartford Borough Council, Civic Centre, Home Gardens, Dartford DA1 1DR ☎ 01322 343023 ⁊ bami.cole@dartford.gov.uk

Recycling & Waste Minimisation: Mr Dave Thomas, Waste & Parks Manager, Civic Centre, Home Gardens, Dartford DA1 1DR ☎ 01322 343334 ⁊ dave.thomas@dartford.gov.uk

Regeneration: Ms Teresa Ryszkowska, Head of Regeneration, Civic Centre, Home Gardens, Dartford DA1 1DR ☎ 01322 343631 ⁊ teresa.ryszkowska@dartford.gov.uk

Sustainable Development: Ms Sandra Woodfall, Environmental Promotions Officer, Civic Centre, Home Gardens, Dartford DA1 1DR ☎ 01322 343434 ⁊ sandra.woodfall@dartford.gov.uk

Town Centre: Mr Lewis Kirnon, Town Centre Liaison Officer, Civic Centre, Home Gardens, Dartford DA1 1DR ☎ 01322 343434 ⁊ lewis.kirnon@dartford.gov.uk

Waste Collection and Disposal: Mr Dave Thomas, Waste & Recycling Manager, Civic Centre, Home Gardens, Dartford DA1 1DR ☎ 01322 343434 ⁊ dave.thomas@dartford.gov.uk

Waste Management: Mr Dave Thomas, Waste & Recycling Manager, Civic Centre, Home Gardens, Dartford DA1 1DR ☎ 01322 343434 ⁊ dave.thomas@dartford.gov.uk

COUNCILLORS

Mayor: Burrell, John (CON - Stone) john.burrell@dartford.gov.uk

Deputy Mayor: Currans, Rosanna (CON - Brent) rossanna.currens@darford.gov.uk

Leader of the Council: Kite, Jeremy (CON - Longfield, New Barn & Southfleet) jeremy.kite@dartford.gov.uk

Deputy Leader of the Council: Shippam, Chris (CON - Town) chris.shippam@dartford.gov.uk

Allen, Ann (CON - Joydens Wood) ann.allen@dartford.gov.uk

Armitt, Ian (CON - Bean & Darenth) ian.armitt@dartford.gov.uk

Bardoe, Arron (CON - West Hill) arron.bardoe@dartford.gov.uk

Brown, Steve (CON - Longfield, New Barn & Southfleet) steve.brown@dartford.gov.uk

Canham, Lucy (CON - Stone) Lucy.Canham@dartford.gov.uk

Coleman, Pat (CON - Sutton-at-Hone & Hawley)

Cutler, Paul (CON - Castle) paul.cutler@dartford.gov.uk

Davis, Matthew (CON - Town) matthew.davis@dartford.gov.uk

Garden, Brian (CON - Joydens Wood) brian.garden@dartford.gov.uk

Hammock, David (CON - Bean & Darenth) david.hammock@dartford.gov.uk

DARTFORD

Hawkes, Jonathon (LAB - Stone)
jonathon.hawkes@dartford.gov.uk

Hayes, John (R - Swanscombe)
john.hayes@dartford.gov.uk

Hunnisett, Derek (CON - Wilmington)

Jarnell, Steven (CON - Newtown)
steven.jarnell@dartford.gov.uk

Jones, Joshua (LAB - Princes)
Joshua.Jones@dartford.gov.uk

Kaini, Bachchu (LAB - Joyce Green)
bachchu.kaini@dartford.gov.uk

Kelly, Keith (CON - Greenhithe)
keith.kelly@dartford.gov.uk

Kelly, Patrick (LAB - Princes)
patrick.kelly@dartford.gov.uk

Kelly, Maria (CON - Greenhithe)
maria.kelly@dartfordl.gov.uk

Lampkin, Eddy (CON - Wilmington)
eddy.lampkin@dartford.gov.uk

Lees, Richard (R - Swanscombe)
Richard.Lees@dartford.gov.uk

Lloyd, Andy (CON - Heath)
andy.lloyd@dartford.gov.uk

Maddison, Mark (LAB - Joyce Green)
mark.maddison@dartford.gov.uk

Madison, Tom (LAB - Littlebrook)
tom.maddison@dartford.gov.uk

McLean, Calvin (CON - Newtown)
Calvin.McLean@dartford.gov.uk

Mote, David (CON - Greenhithe)
david.mote@dartford.gov.uk

Ozog, Julie (CON - Newtown)
Julie.Ozog@dartford.gov.uk

Ozog, Jan (CON - West Hill)
jan.ozog@dartford.gov.uk

Paige, Daisy (LAB - Littlebrook)
dais.paige@dartford.gov.uk

Perfitt, Roger (CON - Longfield, New Barn & Southfleet)

Peters, Marilyn (CON - Joydens Wood)
marilyn.peters@kcl.ac.uk

Read, Bryan (R - Swanscombe)
bryan.read@dartford.gov.uk

Reynolds, Denzil (CON - West Hill)
Denzil.Reynolds@dartford.gov.uk

Reynolds, Lucas (CON - Sutton-at-Hone & Hawley)
Lucas.Reynolds@dartford.gov.uk

Sandhu, Avtar (CON - Brent)
avtar.sandhu@dartford.gov.uk

Shanks, Rebecca (CON - Bean & Darenth)
rebecca.shanks@dartford.gov.uk

Storey, Rebecca (CON - Princes)

Swinerd, Drew (CON - Brent)
drew.swinerd@dartford.gov.uk

Thurlow, Patsy (CON - Heath)

Wells, Richard (CON - Heath)
richard.wells@dartford.gov.uk

POLITICAL COMPOSITION
CON: 34, LAB: 7, R: 3

COMMITTEE CHAIRS

Audit: Mr David Hammock

Development Control: Mr Derek Hunnisett

Licensing: Mr Arron Bardoe

Daventry   D

Daventry District Council, Lodge Road, Daventry NN11 4FP
☎ 01327 871100 🖷 01327 300011 ✍ comments@daventrydc.gov.uk
🖳 www.daventrydc.gov.uk

FACTS AND FIGURES
Parliamentary Constituencies: Daventry, Kettering
EU Constituencies: East Midlands
Election Frequency: Elections are by thirds

PRINCIPAL OFFICERS

Chief Executive: Mr Ian Vincent, Chief Executive & Returning Officer, Council Offices, Lodge Road, Daventry NN11 4FP
☎ 01327 871100 ✍ ivincent@daventrydc.gov.uk

Deputy Chief Executive: Mr Simon Bovey, Deputy Chief Executive & Monitoring Officer, Council Offices, Lodge Road, Daventry NN11 4FP ☎ 01327 871100 ✍ sbovey@daventrydc.gov.uk

Senior Management: Mr Simon Bowers, Business Manager, Council Offices, Lodge Road, Daventry NN11 4FP ☎ 01327 302435 ✍ sbowers@daventrydc.gov.uk

Senior Management: Mr Tony Gillet, Resources Manager, Council Offices, Lodge Road, Daventry NN11 4FP ☎ 01327 302276 ✍ tgillet@daventrydc.gov.uk

Senior Management: Mrs Audra Statham, Chief Financial Officer, Lodge Road, Daventry NN11 4FP ☎ 01327 302354 ✍ astatham@daventry.gov.uk

Senior Management: Mrs Maria Taylor, Community Manager, Council Offices, Lodge Road, Daventry NN11 4FP ☎ 01327 302229 ✍ mtaylor@daventrydc.gov.uk

Architect, Building / Property Services: Mr Simon Bowers, Business Manager, Council Offices, Lodge Road, Daventry NN11 4FP ☎ 01327 302435 ✍ sbowers@daventrydc.gov.uk

PR / Communications: Mrs Becky Hutson, Communications & Marketing Manager, Lodge Road, Daventry NN11 4FP
☎ 01327 302404 ✍ bhutson@daventrydc.gov.uk

Community Safety: Mr Kevin Fagan, Community Partnership Team Manager, Lodge Road, Daventry NN11 4FP ☎ 01327 302424 ✍ kfagan@daventrydc.gov.uk

Computer Management: Mr Neil Smith, Senior IT Officer, Lodge Road, Daventry NN11 4FP ☎ 01327 302331 ⌁ nsmith@daventrydc.gov.uk

Customer Service: Ms Katie Jones, Customer Service Manager, Lodge Road, Daventry NN11 4FP ☎ 01327 302417 ⌁ kjones@daventrydc.gov.uk

Economic Development: Mr Simon Bowers, Business Manager, Council Offices, Lodge Road, Daventry NN11 4FP ☎ 01327 302435 ⌁ sbowers@daventrydc.gov.uk

Electoral Registration: Mrs Jane Lyons, Principal Elections Officer, Lodge Road, Daventry NN11 4FP ☎ 01327 302321 ⌁ jlyons@daventrydc.gov.uk

Emergency Planning: Mr Simon Bowers, Business Manager, Council Offices, Lodge Road, Daventry NN11 4FP ☎ 01327 302435 ⌁ sbowers@daventrydc.gov.uk

Environmental Health: Mrs Maria Taylor, Community Manager, Council Offices, Lodge Road, Daventry NN11 4FP ☎ 01327 302229 ⌁ mtaylor@daventrydc.gov.uk

Estates, Property & Valuation: Mr Simon Bowers, Business Manager, Council Offices, Lodge Road, Daventry NN11 4FP ☎ 01327 302435 ⌁ sbowers@daventrydc.gov.uk

Facilities: Mr Simon Bowers, Business Manager, Council Offices, Lodge Road, Daventry NN11 4FP ☎ 01327 302435 ⌁ sbowers@daventrydc.gov.uk

Finance: Mrs Audra Statham, Chief Financial Officer, Lodge Road, Daventry NN11 4FP ☎ 01327 302354 ⌁ astatham@daventry.gov.uk

Treasury: Mrs Audra Statham, Chief Financial Officer, Lodge Road, Daventry NN11 4FP ☎ 01327 302354 ⌁ astatham@daventry.gov.uk

Health and Safety: Mrs Maria Taylor, Community Manager, Council Offices, Lodge Road, Daventry NN11 4FP ☎ 01327 302229 ⌁ mtaylor@daventrydc.gov.uk

Home Energy Conservation: Mrs Maria Taylor, Community Manager, Council Offices, Lodge Road, Daventry NN11 4FP ☎ 01327 302229 ⌁ mtaylor@daventrydc.gov.uk

Home Energy Conservation: Mrs Maria Taylor, Corporate Manager - Community, Council Offices, Lodge Road, Daventry NN11 4FP ☎ 01327 302229 ⌁ mtaylor@daventrydc.gov.uk

Housing: Mrs Maria Taylor, Corporate Manager - Community, Council Offices, Lodge Road, Daventry NN11 4FP ☎ 01327 302229 ⌁ mtaylor@daventrydc.gov.uk

Legal: Mr Tony Gillet, Resources Manager, Council Offices, Lodge Road, Daventry NN11 4FP ☎ 01327 302276 ⌁ tgillet@daventrydc.gov.uk

Licensing: Mrs Maria Taylor, Community Manager, Council Offices, Lodge Road, Daventry NN11 4FP ☎ 01327 302229 ⌁ mtaylor@daventrydc.gov.uk

Member Services: Miss Fiona Rye, PA to Deputy Chief Executive, Lodge Road, Daventry NN11 4FP ☎ 01327 302400 ⌁ frye@daventrydc.gov.uk

Personnel / HR: Mr Tony Gillet, Resources Manager, Council Offices, Lodge Road, Daventry NN11 4FP ☎ 01327 302276 ⌁ tgillet@daventrydc.gov.uk

Planning: Mrs Maria Taylor, Community Manager, Council Offices, Lodge Road, Daventry NN11 4FP ☎ 01327 302229 ⌁ mtaylor@daventrydc.gov.uk

Procurement: Mr Simon Bowers, Business Manager, Council Offices, Lodge Road, Daventry NN11 4FP ☎ 01327 302435 ⌁ sbowers@daventrydc.gov.uk

Recycling & Waste Minimisation: Mr Simon Bowers, Business Manager, Council Offices, Lodge Road, Daventry NN11 4FP ☎ 01327 302435 ⌁ sbowers@daventrydc.gov.uk

Regeneration: Mr Simon Bowers, Business Manager, Council Offices, Lodge Road, Daventry NN11 4FP ☎ 01327 302435 ⌁ sbowers@daventrydc.gov.uk

Staff Training: Ms Rosemary Daniels, Governance Manager, Lodge Road, Daventry NN11 4FP ☎ 01327 302412 ⌁ rdaniel@daventrydc.gov.uk

Sustainable Communities: Mrs Maria Taylor, Community Manager, Council Offices, Lodge Road, Daventry NN11 4FP ☎ 01327 302229 ⌁ mtaylor@daventrydc.gov.uk

Town Centre: Mr Simon Bowers, Business Manager, Council Offices, Lodge Road, Daventry NN11 4FP ☎ 01327 302435 ⌁ sbowers@daventrydc.gov.uk

COUNCILLORS

Leader of the Council: Millar, Chris (CON - Long Buckby) cmillar@daventrydc.gov.uk

Deputy Leader of the Council: Griffin, Elizabeth (CON - Woodford) egriffin@daventrydc.gov.uk

Amos, Johnnie (CON - Weedon) jamos@daventrydc.gov.uk

Auger, Richard (CON - Welford) rauger@daventrydc.gov.uk

Brown, Adam (CON - Weedon) abrown@daventrydc.gov.uk

Bunting, Nick (CON - Brixworth) nbunting@daventrydc.gov.uk

Carr, Nigel (UKIP - Abbey North) ncarr@daventrydc.gov.uk

Carter, Ann (CON - Walgrave) acarter@daventrydc.gov.uk

Chantler, Alan (CON - Yelvertoft) aechantler@daventrydc.gov.uk

Connors, Sean (UKIP - Drayton) sconnors@daventrydc.gov.uk

DAVENTRY

Cribbin, Daniel (CON - Moulton)
dcribbin@daventrydc.gov.uk

Eddon, Deanna (CON - Abbey South)
deddon@daventrydc.gov.uk

Fraser-Allen, Fabienne (CON - Brixworth)
ffraser-allen@daventrydc.gov.uk

Frenchman, Barry (CON - Spratton)
bfrenchman@daventrydc.gov.uk

Gilford, Jo (CON - Woodford)
jmgilford@daventrydc.gov.uk

Hills, Alan (CON - Hill)
ahills@daventrydc.gov.uk

Howard, Wayne (CON - Hill)
whoward@daventrydc.gov.uk

Howard, Amy (CON - Drayton)
ahoward@daventrydc.gov.uk

Irving-Swift, Cecile (CON - Welford)
cirving-swift@daventrydc.gov.uk

James, David (CON - Abbey North)
djames@daventrydc.gov.uk

Lomax, Catherine (LD - Barby & Kilsby)
clomax@daventrydc.gov.uk

Micklewright, Richard (CON - Ravensthorpe)
rmicklewright@daventrydc.gov.uk

Morgan, Colin (CON - Abbey South)
cmorgan@daventrydc.gov.uk

Osborne, Diana (CON - Long Buckby)
dosborne@daventrydc.gov.uk

Osborne, Steve (CON - Long Buckby)
sosborne@daventrydc.gov.uk

Parker, Kevin (CON - Brixworth)
kparker@daventrydc.gov.uk

Patchett, Bob (CON - Woodford)
bpatchett@daventrydc.gov.uk

Poole, Colin (CON - Hill)
cpoole@daventrydc.gov.uk

Pritchard, Jason (LAB - Braunston & Welton)
jpritchard@daventrydc.gov.uk

Randall, Wendy (LAB - Drayton)
wrandall@daventrydc.gov.uk

Ritchie, Ken (LAB - Abbey North)
kritchie@daventrydc.gov.uk

Robertson, Ian (CON - Barby & Kilsby)
irobertson@daventrydc.gov.uk

Shephard, John (CON - Spratton)
jshephard@daventrydc.gov.uk

Smith, David (CON - Weedon)
dsmith1@daventrydc.gov.uk

Warren, Mike (CON - Moulton)
mwarren@daventrydc.gov.uk

Wesley, Mark (CON - Abbey South)
mwesley@daventrydc.gov.uk

POLITICAL COMPOSITION
CON: 30, LAB: 3, UKIP: 2, LD: 1

COMMITTEE CHAIRS

Licensing: Mrs Ann Carter

Planning: Mr Steve Osborne

Denbighshire   W

Denbighshire County Council, County Hall, Wynnstay Road, Ruthin LL15 1YN
☎ 01824 706101 ▣ 01824 707446 ✆ customerservicecentre@ denbighshire.gov.uk or canolfangwasanaethcwsmer@sirddinbych.gov.uk
▣ www.denbighshire.gov.uk or www.sirddinbych.gov.uk

FACTS AND FIGURES
Parliamentary Constituencies: Clwyd South, Clwyd West, Vale of Clwyd
EU Constituencies: Wales
Election Frequency: Elections are of whole council

PRINCIPAL OFFICERS

Chief Executive: Dr Mohammed Mehmet, Chief Executive, County Hall, Wynnstay Road, Ruthin LL15 1YN ☎ 01824 706128
✆ mohammed.mehmet@denbighshire.gov.uk

Senior Management: Ms Rebecca Maxwell, Corporate Director - Economy & Public Realm, County Hall, Wynnstay Road, Ruthin LL15 1YN

Senior Management: Ms Nicola Stubbins, Corporate Director - Social Services, County Hall, Wynnstay Road, Ruthin LL15 1YN ☎ 01824 706149 ✆ nicola.stubbins@denbighshire.gov.uk

Senior Management: Mr Richard Weigh, Section 151 Officer, County Hall, Wynnstay Road, Ruthin LL15 1YN
✆ richard.weigh@denbighshire.gov.uk

Senior Management: Mr Gary Williams, Head of Legal, HR & Democratic Services, County Hall, Wynnstay Road, Ruthin LL15 1YN ☎ 01824 712562 ✆ gary.williams@denbighshire.gov.uk

Architect, Building / Property Services: Mr David Matthews, Valuation & Estates Team Manager, County Hall, Wynnstay Road, Ruthin LL15 1YN ☎ 01824 706798
✆ david.matthews@denbighshire.gov.uk

Building Control: Mr Robin Johnston, Building Control Officer, Caledfryn, Smithfield Road, Denbigh LL16 3RJ ☎ 01824 706714
✆ robin.johnston@denbighshire.gov.uk

Catering Services: Ms Hayley Jones, Catering Manager, Kinmel Park Depot, Bodelwyddan, LL18 5UX ☎ 01824 712131
✆ hayley.jones@denbighshire.gov.uk

Catering Services: Mr Ian Kemp, Catering Services Manager, Kinmel Park Depot, Bodelwyddan, LL18 5UX ☎ 01824 712125
✆ ian.kemp@denbighshire.gov.uk

Children / Youth Services: Mr Jamie Groves, Interim Head of Finance & Assets, County Hall, Wynnstay Road, Ruthin LL15 1YN
☎ 01824 712723 ✆ jamie.groves@denbighshire.gov.uk

Civil Registration: Mr Gary Williams, Head of Legal, HR & Democratic Services, County Hall, Wynnstay Road, Ruthin LL15 1YN
☎ 01824 712562 ⊸ gary.williams@denbighshire.gov.uk

PR / Communications: Mr Gareth Watson, Team Leader - Communication & Campaign Management, County Hall, Wynnstay Road, Ruthin LL15 1YN ☎ 01824 706222
⊸ gareth.watson@denbighshire.gov.uk

Computer Management: Mr Barry Eaton, Business Transformation & ICT Manager, County Hall, Wynnstay Road, Ruthin LL15 1YN ☎ 01824 706211
⊸ barry.eaton@denbighshire.gov.uk

Consumer Protection and Trading Standards: Mr Graham Boase, Head of Planning & Public Protection, County Hall, Wynnstay Road, Ruthin LL15 1YN ☎ 01824 706925
⊸ graham.boase@denbighshire.gov.uk

Customer Service: Ms Jackie Walley, Head of Customers & Education Support, County Hall, Wynnstay Road, Ruthin LL15 1YN
⊸ jackie.walley@denbighshire.gov.uk

Economic Development: Mr Mike Horrocks, Economic & Business Development Manager, County Hall, Wynnstay Road, Ruthin LL15 1YN ☎ 07824 509279
⊸ mike.horrocks@denbighshire.gov.uk

Education: Ms Karen Evans, Head of Education & Children's Services, County Hall, Wynnstay Road, Ruthin LL15 1YN
☎ 01824 708009 ⊸ karen.evans@denbighshire.gov.uk

E-Government: Mr Barry Eaton, Business Transformation & ICT Manager, County Hall, Wynnstay Road, Ruthin LL15 1YN
☎ 01824 706211 ⊸ barry.eaton@denbighshire.gov.uk

Electoral Registration: Mr Gareth Evans, County Electoral Services Administrator, County Hall, Wynnstay Road, Ruthin LL15 1YN ☎ 01824 706114 ⊸ g.evans@denbighshire.gov.uk

Emergency Planning: Mr Philip Harrison, Emergency Planning Co-ordinator, County Hall, Mold CH7 6NJ ☎ 01352 752121
⊸ phillip.harrison@flintshire.gov.uk

Environmental / Technical Services: Mr Tony Ward, Head of Highways & Environmental Services, County Hall, Wynnstay Road, Ruthin LL15 1YN ☎ 01824 706397 ⊸ tony.ward@denbighshire.gov.uk

Environmental Health: Mr Graham Boase, Head of Planning & Public Protection, Caledfryn, Smithfield Road, Denbigh LL16 3RJ ☎ 01824 706925 ⊸ graham.boase@denbighshire.gov.uk

Estates, Property & Valuation: Mr David Mathews, Valuation & Estates Team Manager, Caledfryn, Smithfield Road, Denbigh LL16 3RJ ☎ 01824 706798 ⊸ david.mathews@denbighshire.gov.uk

Events Manager: Ms Sian Davies, Events Manager, Rhyl Pavillion Theatre, The Promenade, Rhyl LL18 3AQ ☎ 01745 332414

Fleet Management: Mr Chris Brown, Transport Manager, Fleet Depot, Expressway Business Park, Bodelwyddan, Rhyl LL18 5SQ
⊸ chris.brown@denbighshire.gov.uk

Health and Safety: Mr Gerry Lapington, Senior Corporate Health & Safety Advisor, County Hall, Wynnstay Road, Ruthin LL15 1YN
⊸ gerry.lapington@denbighshire.gov.uk

Highways: Mr Tony Ward, Head of Highways & Environmental Services, County Hall, Wynnstay Road, Ruthin LL15 1YN
☎ 01824 706397 ⊸ tony.ward@denbighshire.gov.uk

Home Energy Conservation: Mr Gareth Roberts, Housing & Renewal Officer, Ty Nant, 6/8 Nant Hall Road, Prestatyn LL19 9LL
☎ 01824 706679 ⊸ gareth.roberts@denbighshire.gov.uk

Housing Maintenance: Mr Alan Jones, Principal Officer - Maintenance, Housing & Community Development, Kinmel Park Depot, Abergele Road, Bodelwyddan, Rhyl LL18 5UX
⊸ alan.jones@denbighshire.gov.uk

Legal: Mr Gary Williams, Head of Legal, HR & Democratic Services, County Hall, Wynnstay Road, Ruthin LL15 1YN
☎ 01824 712562 ⊸ gary.williams@denbighshire.gov.uk

Leisure and Cultural Services: Mr Jamie Groves, Interim Head of Finance & Assets, County Hall, Wynnstay Road, Ruthin LL15 1YN
☎ 01824 712723 ⊸ jamie.groves@denbighshire.gov.uk

Leisure and Cultural Services: Mr Huw Rees, Acting Head of Countryside Services, Yr Hen Garchar, Ruthin LL15 1QA
☎ 01824 708228 ⊸ huw.rees@denbighshire.gov.uk

Lighting: Mr Andy Clark, Work Unit Manager, Kinmel Park Depot, Abergele Road, Bodelwyddan, LL18 5UX ☎ 01824 712140
⊸ andy.clark@denbighshire.gov.uk

Member Services: Mr Eleri Woodford, Member Support & Development Manager, County Hall, Wynnstay Road, Ruthin LL15 1YN ☎ 01824 706196 ⊸ eleri.woodford@denbighshire.gov.uk

Partnerships: Mr Alan Smith, Head of Business Planning & Performance, County Hall, Wynnstay Road, Ruthin LL15 1AT
☎ 01824 706246 ⊸ alan.smith@denbighshire.gov.uk

Personnel / HR: Mr Gary Williams, Head of Legal, HR & Democratic Services, County Hall, Wynnstay Road, Ruthin LL15 1YN
☎ 01824 712562 ⊸ gary.williams@denbighshire.gov.uk

Planning: Mr Graham Boase, Head of Planning & Public Protection, Caledfryn, Smithfield Road, Denbigh LL16 3RJ
☎ 01824 706925 ⊸ graham.boase@denbighshire.gov.uk

Procurement: Mr Arwel Staples, Strategic Procurement Manager, County Hall, Wynnstay Road, Ruthin LL15 1YN ☎ 01824 706042
⊸ arwel.staples@denbighshire.gov.uk

Public Libraries: Mr Robert Arwyn Jones, Principal Librarian, County Hall, Wynnstay Road, Ruthin LL15 1YN ☎ 01824 708203
⊸ arwyn.jones@denbighshire.gov.uk

Recycling & Waste Minimisation: Mr Alan Roberts, Senior Waste Management Officer, Kinmel Park Depot, Engine Hill, LL18 5UX ☎ 01824 712408 ⊸ alan.l.roberts@denbighshire.gov.uk

DENBIGHSHIRE

Regeneration: Mr Mike Horrocks, Economic & Business Development Manager, County Hall, Wynnstay Road, Ruthin LL15 1YN ☎ 07824 509279 ⏱ mike.horrocks@denbighshire.gov.uk

Road Safety: Mr Alan Hinchcliffe, Road Safety Officer, Caledfryn, Smithfield Road, Denbigh LL16 3RJ ⏱ alan.hinchcliffe@denbighshire.gov.uk

Social Services: Mr Phil Gilroy, Head of Adult Services (Community & Intermediate Care), County Hall, Wynnstay Road, Ruthin LL15 1YN ☎ 01824 706654 ⏱ phil.gilroy@denbighshire.gov.uk

Social Services: Ms Nicola Stubbins, Corporate Director - Social Services, County Hall, Wynnstay Road, Ruthin LL15 1YN ☎ 01824 706149 ⏱ nicola.stubbins@denbighshire.gov.uk

Social Services (Children): Mr Leighton Rees, Head of Children & Family Services, Ty Nant, Nant Hall Road, Prestatyn LL19 9LL ⏱ leighton.rees@denbighshire.gov.uk

Staff Training: Mr John Rees, Principal Personnel Officer, Employee & Member Development, County Hall, Wynnstay Road, Ruthin LL15 1YN ⏱ john.rees@denbighshire.gov.uk

Tourism: Ms Sian Owen, Lead Officer - Destination, Marketing & Communications, County Hall, Wynnstay Road, Ruthin LL15 1YN ☎ 01824 706125 ⏱ sian.owen@denbighshire.gov.uk

Waste Collection and Disposal: Mr Alan Roberts, Senior Waste Management Officer, Kinmel Park Depot, Engine Hill, LL18 5UX ☎ 01824 712408 ⏱ alan.l.roberts@denbighshire.gov.uk

Waste Management: Mr Alan Roberts, Senior Waste Management Officer, Kinmel Park Depot, Engine Hill, LL18 5UX ☎ 01824 712408 ⏱ alan.l.roberts@denbighshire.gov.uk

COUNCILLORS

ChairDavies, Ann (CON - Rhuddlan)
j.ann.davies@denbighshire.gov.uk

Vice-ChairMullen-James, Win (LAB - Rhyl South East)
win.mullen-james@denbighshire.gov.uk

Leader of the Council: Evans, Hugh (IND - Llanfair Dyffryn Clwyd / Gwyddelwern)
hugh.evans@denbighshire.gov.uk

Deputy Leader of the Council: Williams, Eryl (PC - Efenechtyd)
eryl.williams@denbighshire.gov.uk

Group LeaderButterfield, Joan (LAB - Rhyl West)
joan.butterfield@denbighshire.gov.uk

Group LeaderHolland, Martyn (CON - Llanarmon-yn-lâl/ Llandegla)
martyn.holland@denbighshire.gov.uk

Group LeaderRoberts, Arwel (PC - Rhuddlan)
arwel.roberts@denbighshire.gov.uk

Group LeaderWelch, Joe (IND - Llanrhaeadr-yng-Nghinmeirch)
joseph.welch@denbighshire.gov.uk

Armstrong, Ian (LAB - Rhyl West)
ian.armstrong@denbighshire.gov.uk

Bartley, Raymond (IND - Denbigh Lower)
ray.bartley@denbighshire.gov.uk

Blakeley, Brian (LAB - Rhyl South East)
brian.blakeley@denbighshire.gov.uk

Chamberlain-Jones, Jeanette (LAB - Rhyl South)
jeanette.c.jones@denbighshire.gov.uk

Cowie, Bill (IND - St Asaph West)
bill.cowie@denbighshire.gov.uk

Davies, Stuart (IND - Llangollen)
stuart.a.davies@denbighshire.gov.uk

Davies, Meirick Lloyd (PC - Trefnant)
meirick.davies@denbighshire.gov.uk

Duffy, Peter (LAB - Prestatyn Central)
peter.duffy@denbighshire.gov.uk

Evans, Peter (IND - Prestatyn Meliden)
peter.evans@denbighshire.gov.uk

Feeley, Bobby (IND - Ruthin)
bobby.feeley@denbighshire.gov.uk

Guy-Davies, Carys (LAB - Prestatyn North)
carys.guy-davies@denbighshire.gov.uk

Hilditch-Roberts, Huw (IND - Ruthin)
huw.hilditch-roberts@denbighshire.gov.uk

Hughes, Colin (LAB - Denbigh Upper & Henllan)
colin.hughes@denbighshire.gov.uk

Hughes, Rhys (PC - Llangollen)
rhys.hughes@denbighshire.gov.uk

Irving, Hugh (CON - Prestatyn Central)
hugh.irving@denbighshire.gov.uk

Jones, Alice (PC - Bodelwyddan)
alice.jones@denbighshire.gov.uk

Jones, Huw (PC - Corwen)
huw.jones@denbighshire.gov.uk

Jones, Pat (LAB - Rhyl South West)
pat.jones@denbighshire.gov.uk

Kensler, Gwyneth (PC - Denbigh Central)
gwyneth.kensler@denbighshire.gov.uk

Lloyd-Williams, Geraint (LAB - Denbigh Upper & Henllan)
geraint.lloyd-williams@denbighshire.gov.uk

McLellan, Jason (LAB - Prestatyn North)
jason.mcclellan@denbighshire.gov.uk

Mellor, Barry (LAB - Rhyl East)
barry.mellor@denbighshire.gov.uk

Murray, Bob (LAB - Prestatyn South West)
bob.murray@denbighshire.gov.uk

Owens, Dewi (CON - St Asaph East)
dewi.owens@denbighshire.gov.uk

Parry, Merfyn (IND - Llandyrnog)
merfyn.parry@denbighshire.gov.uk

Penlington, Paul (LAB - Prestatyn North)
paul.penlington@denbighshire.gov.uk

Prendergast, Pete (LAB - Rhyl South West)
pete.prendergast@denbighshire.gov.uk

Sampson, Anton (CON - Prestatyn East)
anton.sampson@denbighshire.gov.uk

Sandilands, Gareth (LAB - Prestatyn South West)
gareth.sandilands@denbighshire.gov.uk

Simmons, David (LAB - Rhyl East)
david.simmons@denbighshire.gov.uk

Smith, Barbara (IND - Tremeirchion)
barbara.smith@denbighshire.gov.uk

Smith, David (IND - Ruthin)
david.smith@denbighshire.gov.uk

Tasker, Bill (LAB - Rhyl South East)
bill.tasker@denbighshire.gov.uk

Thompson-Hill, Julian (CON - Prestatyn East)
julian.thompson-hill@denbighshire.gov.uk

Williams, David (IND - Dyserth)
david.g.williams@denbighshire.gov.uk

Williams, Cefyn (PC - Llandrillo)
cefyn.williams@denbighshire.gov.uk

Williams, Cheryl (LAB - Rhyl South)
cheryl.williams@denbighshire.gov.uk

Williams, Huw (CON - Llanbedr Dyffryn Clwyd/ Llangynhafal)
huw.o.williams@denbighshire.gov.uk

Young, Mark (IND - Denbigh Lower)
mark.young@denbighshire.gov.uk

POLITICAL COMPOSITION
LAB: 19, IND: 13, PC: 8, CON: 7

COMMITTEE CHAIRS

Licensing: Mr Cefyn Williams

Planning: Mr Raymond Bartley

Derby City   U

Derby City Council, 1st Floor, The Council House, Corporation Street, Derby DE1 2FS
☎ 01332 293111 🖨 01332 255500 ✆ customerservices@derby.gov.uk
🖥 www.derby.gov.uk

FACTS AND FIGURES
Parliamentary Constituencies: Derby North, Derby South, Derbyshire Mid
EU Constituencies: East Midlands
Election Frequency: Elections are by thirds

PRINCIPAL OFFICERS

Chief Executive: Mr Paul Robinson, Chief Executive, 1st Floor, The Council House, Corporation Street, Derby DE1 2FS
☎ 01332 643555 ✆ paul.robinson@derby.gov.uk

Senior Management: Dr Robyn Dewis, Consultant in Public Health Medicine, 1st Floor, The Council House, Corporation Street, Derby DE1 2FS ☎ 01332 643073 ✆ robyn.dewis@derby.gov.uk

Senior Management: Ms Christine Durrant, Strategic Director - Communities & Place, 1st Floor, Council House, Corporation Street, Derby DE1 2FS ☎ 01332 642434 ✆ christine.durrant@derby.gov.uk

Senior Management: Mr Andy Smith, Strategic Director - Children & Young People, 1st Floor, Council House, Corporation Street, Derby DE1 2FS ☎ 01332 643557 ✆ andy.smith@derby.gov.uk

Best Value: Mr Gordon Stirling, Director - Strategic Services & Organisational Development, 1st Floor, Council House, Corporation Street, Derby DE1 2FS ☎ 01332 643430
✆ gordon.stirling@derby.gov.uk

Building Control: Mr Paul Clarke, Head of Planning, 1st Floor, Council House, Corporation Street, Derby DE1 2FS ☎ 01332 641642
✆ paul.clarke@derby.gov.uk

Building Control: Mr Mick Henman, Head of Building Consultancy & Emergency Planning, 1st Floor, Council House, Corporation Street, Derby DE1 2FS ☎ 01332 642096
✆ mick.henman@derby.gov.uk

Catering Services: Mrs Sandra Cole, Head of Service Facilities, 1st Floor, Council House, Corporation Street, Derby DE1 2FS
☎ 01332 642142 ✆ sandra.cole@derby.gov.uk

Children / Youth Services: Mr Andrew Kaiser, Head of Service, 1st Floor, The Council House, Corporation Street, Derby DE1 2FS
☎ 01332 641340 ✆ kaiser.andrew@derby.gov.uk

Children / Youth Services: Ms Sally Penrose, Specialist Services - Fostering & Adoption, Fostering & Adoption Centre, Perth Street, Derby DE21 6XX ☎ 01332 643817 ✆ sally.penrose@derby.gov.uk

Civil Registration: Mr James Clark, Registration Services Manager, Royal Oak House, Market Place, Derby DE1 3AR
☎ 01332 642534 ✆ james.clark@derby.gov.uk

PR / Communications: Ms Yvonne Wilkinson, Head of Communications, 1st Floor, Council House, Corporation Street, Derby DE1 2FS ☎ 01332 643501 ✆ yvonne.wilkinson@derby.gov.uk

Computer Management: Mr Nick O'Reilly, Director - Digital, 1st Floor, The Council House, Corporation Street, Derby DE1 2FS
☎ 01332 643254 ✆ nick.oreilly@derby.gov.uk

Consumer Protection and Trading Standards: Mr John Tomlinson, Service Director - Communities, Environment & Regulatory Services, Ground Floor, Council House, Corporation Street, Derby DE1 2FS ☎ 01332 642435
✆ john.tomlinson@derby.gov.uk

Corporate Services: Mr Richard Boneham, Head of Governance & Assurance, 1st Floor, The Council House, Corporation Street, Derby DE1 2FS ☎ 01332 643280 ✆ richard.boneham@derby.gov.uk

Corporate Services: Ms Lynda Innocent, Head of ISS, 1st Floor, The Council House, Corporation Street, Derby DE1 2FS
☎ 01332 643235 ✆ lynda.innocent@derby.gov.uk

Customer Service: Mr Bernard Fenton, Head of Customer Services, Ground Floor, The Council House, Corporation Street, Derby DE1 2FS ☎ 01332 643758 ✆ bernard.fenton@derby.gov.uk

DERBY CITY

Education: Mr Gurmail Nizzer, Acting Director - Commissioning & Head of School Organisation, 1st Floor, Council House, Corporation Street, Derby DE1 2FS ☎ 01332 642720 ✆ gurmail.nizzer@derby.gov.uk

Education: Mr Andy Smith, Strategic Director - Children & Young People, 1st Floor, Council House, Corporation Street, Derby DE1 2FS ☎ 01332 643557 ✆ andy.smith@derby.gov.uk

Electoral Registration: Mr Mick Styne, Electoral Services & Land Charges Manager, 1st Floor, Council House, Corporation Street, Derby DE1 2FS ☎ 01332 641663 ✆ mick.styne@derby.gov.uk

Energy Management: Mr Richard Murrell, Principal Home Energy Advisor, 1st Floor, Council House, Corporation Street, Derby DE1 2FS ☎ 01332 642016 ✆ richard.murrell@derby.gov.uk

Environmental Health: Mr Michael Kay, Head of Environmental Health & Licensing, Ground Floor, Council House, Corporation Street, Derby DE1 2FS ☎ 01332 641940 ✆ michael.kay@derby.gov.uk

Estates, Property & Valuation: Ms Jayne Sower-Warrington, Head of Strategic Asset Management & Estates, 2nd Floor, Council House, Corporation Street, Derby DE1 2FS ☎ 01332 643327 ✆ jayne.sower-warrington@derby.gov.uk

Facilities: Ms Sandra Cole, Head of Facilities Management, 2nd Floor, Council House, Corporation Street, Derby DE1 2FS ☎ 01332 642142 ✆ sandra.cole@derby.gov.uk

Facilities: Mr Ian Shepherd, Corporate Facilities Manager, 2nd Floor, Council House, Corporation Street, Derby DE1 2FS ☎ 01332 643338 ✆ ian.shepherd@derby.gov.uk

Finance: Mr Martyn Marples, Director - Finance, 1st Floor, Council House, Corporation Street, Derby DE1 2FS ☎ 01332 643377 ✆ martyn.marples@derby.gov.uk

Fleet Management: Mr Richard Kniveton, Fleet & Depot Manager, 15 Stores Road, Derby DE21 4BD ☎ 01332 641514 ✆ richard.kniveton@derby.gov.uk

Grounds Maintenance: Mr Dave Bartram, Head of Highways & Engineering, 15 Stores Road, Derby DE21 4BD ☎ 01332 641516 ✆ dave.bartram@derby.gov.uk

Highways: Mr Dave Bartram, Head of Highways & Engineering, 15 Stores Road, Derby DE21 4BD ☎ 01332 641516 ✆ dave.bartram@derby.gov.uk

Home Energy Conservation: Mr Richard Murrell, Principal Home Energy Advisor, 1st Floor, Council House, Corporation Street, Derby DE1 2FS ☎ 01332 642016 ✆ richard.murrell@derby.gov.uk

Housing: Ms Maria Murphy, Director - Derby Homes, 839 London Road, Derby DE24 8UZ ☎ 01332 888522 ✆ maria.murphy@derbyhomes.org

Legal: Ms Janie Berry, Director - Governance & Monitoring, 1st Floor, The Council House, Corporation Street, Derby DE1 2FS ☎ 01332 643616 ✆ janie.berry@derby.gov.uk

Leisure and Cultural Services: Dr Peter Meakin, Culture Development Manager, Assembly Rooms, Market Place, Derby DE1 3AH ☎ 01332 255806 ✆ peter.meakin@derby.gov.uk

Leisure and Cultural Services: Mr David Potton, Head of Libraries, Ground Floor, Council House, Corporation Street, Derby DE1 2FS ☎ 01332 641719 ✆ david.potton@derby.gov.uk

Licensing: Mr John Tomlinson, Service Director - Communities, Environment & Regulatory Services, Ground Floor, Council House, Corporation Street, Derby DE1 2FS ☎ 01332 642435 ✆ john.tomlinson@derby.gov.uk

Lifelong Learning: Ms Cath Harcula, Head of Service, Allen Park Centre, Derby DE24 9DE ☎ 01332 642304 ✆ cath.harcula@derby.gov.uk

Member Services: Mr David Walsh, Head of Democracy, 1st Floor, Council House, Corporation Street, Derby DE1 2FS ☎ 01332 643655 ✆ david.walsh@derby.gov.uk

Planning: Mr Paul Clarke, Head of Planning, 1st Floor, Council House, Corporation Street, Derby DE1 2FS ☎ 01332 641642 ✆ paul.clarke@derby.gov.uk

Procurement: Mr Martyn Marples, Director - Finance, 1st Floor, Council House, Corporation Street, Derby DE1 2FS ☎ 01332 643377 ✆ martyn.marples@derby.gov.uk

Procurement: Ms Linda Spiby, Acting Head - Procurement, 1st Floor, Council House, Corporation Street, Derby DE1 2FS ☎ 01332 643274 ✆ linda.spiby@derby.gov.uk

Public Libraries: Mr David Potton, Head of Libraries, Ground Floor, Council House, Corporation Street, Derby DE1 2FS ☎ 01332 641719 ✆ david.potton@derby.gov.uk

Public Libraries: Ms Jennie Preedy, Network Co-ordination Manager, Ground Floor, Council House, Corporation Street, Derby DE1 2FS ☎ 01332 641723 ✆ jennie.preedy@derby.gov.uk

Recycling & Waste Minimisation: Mr Mick McLachlan, Head of Waste Management, 15 Stores Road, Derby DE21 4BE ☎ 01332 641503 ✆ mick.mclachlan@derby.gov.uk

Regeneration: Mr Greg Jennings, Head of Regeneration Projects, 2nd Floor, Council House, Corporation Street, Derby DE1 2FS ☎ 01332 641617 ✆ greg.jennings@derby.gov.uk

Social Services (Children): Ms Hazel Lymbery, Director - Delivering Differently, 2nd Floor, Council House, Corporation Street, Derby DE1 2FS ☎ 01332 642644 ✆ hazel.lymbery@derby.gov.uk

Safeguarding: Ms Maureen Darbon, Director - Early Intervention & Integrated Safeguarding, 1st Floor, The Council House, Corporation Street, Derby DE1 2FS ☎ 01332 256790 ✆ maureen.darbon@derby.gov.uk

Public Health: Dr Robyn Dewis, Consultant in Public Health Medicine, 1st Floor, The Council House, Corporation Street, Derby DE1 2FS ☎ 01332 643073 ✆ robyn.dewis@derby.gov.uk

Tourism: Ms Claire Davenport, Director - Leisure, Culture & Tourism, 2nd Floor, Council House, Corporation Street, Derby DE1 2FS ☎ 01332 642433 ✆ claire.davenport@derby.gov.uk

Tourism: Mr Alan Smith, Head of Economic Regeneration, 2nd Floor, Council House, Corporation Street, Derby DE1 2FS ☎ 01332 641624 ✆ alan.smith@derby.gov.uk

Traffic Management: Mr David Gartside, Head of Traffic & Transportation, Ground Floor, Council House, Corporation Street, Derby DE1 2FS ☎ 01332 641821 ✆ david.gartside@derby.gov.uk

Transport: Mr Tony Gascoigne, Central & West Area Group Manager, Ground Floor, Council House, Corporation Street, Derby DE1 2FS ☎ 01332 641779 ✆ tony.gascoigne@derby.gov.uk

Waste Management: Mr Mick McLachlan, Head of Waste Management, 15 Stores Road, Derby DE21 4BE ☎ 01332 641503 ✆ mick.mclachlan@derby.gov.uk

COUNCILLORS

Leader of the Council: Banwait, Ranjit (LAB - Boulton)
ranjit.banwait@derby.gov.uk

Deputy Leader of the Council: Rawson, Martin (LAB - Derwent)
martin.rawson@derby.gov.uk

Afzal, Asaf (LAB - Abbey)
asaf.afzal@derby.gov.uk

Anderson, Dom (LAB - Boulton)
dom.anderson@derby.gov.uk

Ashburner, Eric (LD - Littleover)
eric.ashburner@derby.gov.uk

Barker, Mick (CON - Oakwood)
mick.barker@derby.gov.uk

Bayliss, Paul (LAB - Alvaston)
paul.bayliss@derby.gov.uk

Bolton, Sara (LAB - Chaddesden)
sara.bolton@derby.gov.uk

Care, Lucy (LD - Littleover)
lucy.care@derby.gov.uk

Carr, Michael (LD - Littleover)
michael.carr@derby.gov.uk

Dhindsa, Hardyal (LAB - Normanton)
hardyal.dhindsa@derby.gov.uk

Eldret, Lisa (LAB - Darley)
lisa.eldret@derby.gov.uk

Evans, John (UKIP - Alvaston)
john.evans@derby.gov.uk

Froggatt, Diane (LAB - Mackworth)
diane.froggatt@derby.gov.uk

Graves, Alan (UKIP - Alvaston)

Grimadell, Alan (CON - Chellaston)
alan.grimadell@derby.gov.uk

Harwood, Frank (CON - Oakwood)
frank.harwood@derby.gov.uk

Hassall, Steve (CON - Allestree)
steve.hassall@derby.gov.uk

Hezelgrave, Paul (LAB - Abbey)

Holmes, Alison (CON - Mickleover)
alison.holmes2@derby.gov.uk

Holmes, Matthew (CON - Mickleover)
matthew.holmes@derby.gov.uk

Hudson, Richard (CON - Derwent)
richard.hudson@derby.gov.uk

Hussain, Fareed (LAB - Arboretum)
fareed.hussain@derby.gov.uk

Ingall, Philip John (CON - Chellaston)
philip.ingall@derby.gov.uk

Jackson, Barbara (LAB - Boulton)
barbara.jackson@derby.gov.uk

Keith, John (CON - Mickleover)
john.keith@derby.gov.uk

Khan, Jangir (LAB - Normanton)
jangir.khan@derby.gov.uk

Khan, Shiraz (LD - Arboretum)
shiraz.khan@derby.gov.uk

Marshall, Sean (LAB - Chellaston)
sean.marshall@derby.gov.uk

Naitta, Joe (LD - Blagreaves)
joe.naitta@derby.gov.uk

Nawaz, Gulfraz (LAB - Arboretum)
gulfraz.nawaz@derby.gov.uk

Pegg, Paul (LAB - Mackworth)
paul.pegg@derby.gov.uk

Poulter, Christopher Paul (CON - Spondon)
christopher.poulter@derby.gov.uk

Raju, Amo (LAB - Blagreaves)
amo.raju@derby.gov.uk

Repton, Martin (LAB - Darley)
martin.repton@derby.gov.uk

Roulstone, Nicola (CON - Spondon)
nicola.roulstone@derby.gov.uk

Russell, Sarah (LAB - Abbey)
sarah.russell@derby.gov.uk

Sandhu, Balbir (LAB - Normanton)
balbir.sandhu@derby.gov.uk

Shanker, Baggy (LAB - Sinfin)
baggy.shankar@derby.gov.uk

Skelton, Ruth (LD - Blagreaves)
ruth.skelton@derby.gov.uk

Smale, Jonathan (CON - Chaddesden)
jonathan.smale@derby.gov.uk

Stanton, Jack (LAB - Darley)
jack.stanton@derby.gov.uk

Turner, Robin (LAB - Sinfin)
robin.turner@derby.gov.uk

Webb, Roy (CON - Allestree)
roy.webb@derby.gov.uk

West, Joanna (LAB - Sinfin)
joanna.west@derby.gov.uk

Whitby, John (LAB - Mackworth)
john.whitby@derby.gov.uk

DERBY CITY

Williams, Evonne (CON - Spondon)
evonne.williams@derby.gov.uk

Winter, Linda (LAB - Chaddesden)
linda.winter@derby.gov.uk

Wood, Robin (CON - Oakwood)
robin.wood@derby.gov.uk

Wright, Bill (UKIP - Derwent)

POLITICAL COMPOSITION
LAB: 26, CON: 15, LD: 6, UKIP: 3

COMMITTEE CHAIRS

Audit & Accounts: Mr Paul Hezelgrave

Licensing: Mr Balbir Sandhu

Planning: Mr Shiraz Khan

Derbyshire   C

Derbyshire County Council, County Hall, Matlock DE4 3AG
☎ 01629 533190 ⌨ contact.centre@derbyshire.gov.uk
🖳 www.derbyshire.gov.uk

FACTS AND FIGURES
EU Constituencies: East Midlands
Election Frequency: Elections are of whole council

PRINCIPAL OFFICERS

Chief Executive: Mr Ian Stephenson, Chief Executive, County Hall, Matlock DE4 3AG ☎ 01629 538100 ⌨ ian.stephenson@derbyshire.gov.uk

Assistant Chief Executive: Ms Mags Young, Assistant Chief Executive, County Hall, Matlock DE4 3AG ☎ 01629 538501 ⌨ mags.young@derbyshire.gov.uk

Senior Management: Mr Mike Ashworth, Strategic Director - Economy, Transport & Communities, County Hall, Matlock DE4 3AG ☎ 01629 538544 ⌨ mike.ashworth@derbyshire.gov.uk

Senior Management: Ms Judith Greenhalgh, Strategic Director - Corporate Resources, County Hall, Matlock DE4 3AG ☎ 01629 538300 ⌨ judith.greenhalgh@derbyshire.gov.uk

Senior Management: Ms Joy Hollister, Strategic Director - Adult Care, County Hall, Matlock DE4 3AG ⌨ joy.hollister@derbyshire.gov.uk

Senior Management: Ms Jane Parfrement, Strategic Director - Children's Services, County Hall, Matlock DE4 3AG ☎ 01629 532005 ⌨ jane.parfrement@derbyshire.gov.uk

Architect, Building / Property Services: Mr David Beard, Group Manager - Property Services, Chatsworth Hall, Chesterfield Road, Matlock DE4 3FW ☎ 01629 536337 ⌨ david.beard@derbyshire.gov.uk

Architect, Building / Property Services: Mrs Sarah Morris, Assistant Director - Corporate Property, Corporate Resources Department, Chatsworth Hall, Chesterfield Road, Matlock DE4 3FW ☎ 01629 536260 ⌨ sarah.morris@derbyshire.gov.uk

Best Value: Mrs Ester Croll, Policy Manager, County Hall, Matlock DE4 3AG ☎ 01629 538267 ⌨ ester.croll@derbyshire.gov.uk

Building Control: Mr Kevin Firth, Head of Development, County Hall, Matlock DE4 3AG ☎ 01629 536567 ⌨ kevin.firth@derbyshire.gov.uk

Catering Services: Ms Sheila Murdoch, Catering & Domestic Services Manager, County Hall, Matlock DE4 3AG ☎ 01629 532183 ⌨ sheila.murdoch@derbyshire.gov.uk

Children / Youth Services: Ms Kathryn Boulton, Service Director - Schools & Learning, County Hall, Matlock DE4 3AG ☎ 01629 532750 ⌨ kathryn.boulton@derbyshire.gov.uk

Children / Youth Services: Mrs Isobel Fleming, Service Director - Performance Quality & Commissioning, County Hall, Matlock DE4 3AG ☎ 01629 532211 ⌨ isobel.fleming@derbyshire.gov.uk

Children / Youth Services: Ms Alison Noble, Service Director - Early Help & Safeguarding, County Hall, Matlock DE4 3AG ☎ 01629 532005 ⌨ alison.noble@derbyshire.gov.uk

Children / Youth Services: Ms Jane Parfrement, Strategic Director - Children's Services, County Hall, Matlock DE4 3AG ☎ 01629 532005 ⌨ jane.parfrement@derbyshire.gov.uk

Civil Registration: Ms Gemma Duckworth, Business Services Manager, County Hall, Matlock DE4 3AG ☎ 01629 538324 ⌨ gemma.duckworth@derbyshire.gov.uk

PR / Communications: Ms Mags Young, Assistant Chief Executive, County Hall, Matlock DE4 3AG ☎ 01629 538501 ⌨ mags.young@derbyshire.gov.uk

Community Planning: Mr Wes Downes, Policy Manager, County Hall, Matlock DE4 3AG ☎ 01629 538439 ⌨ wes.downes@derbyshire.gov.uk

Computer Management: Mr Bob Busby, Core Systems Programme Manager, County Hall, Matlock DE4 3AG ☎ 01629 536806 ⌨ bob.busby@derbyshire.gov.uk

Consumer Protection and Trading Standards: Mr Rob Taylour, Head of Trading Standards, County Hall, Matlock DE4 3AG ☎ 01629 539830 ⌨ rob.taylour@derbyshire.gov.uk

Corporate Services: Ms Judith Greenhalgh, Strategic Director - Corporate Resources, County Hall, Matlock DE4 3AG ☎ 01629 538300 ⌨ judith.greenhalgh@derbyshire.gov.uk

Economic Development: Mr Frank Horsley, Head of Economic Regeneration, County Hall, Matlock DE4 3AG ☎ 01629 538348 ⌨ frank.horsley@derbyshire.gov.uk

E-Government: Mr David Hickman, Director - Transformation, County Hall, Matlock DE4 3AG ☎ 01629 535801 ✆ david.hickman@derbyshire.gov.uk

Emergency Planning: Ms Elizabeth Partington, Emergency Planning Manager, County Hall, Matlock DE4 3AG ✆ liz.partington@derbyshire.gov.uk

Energy Management: Ms Kathryn Sowerby-Warrington, Carbon & Energy Manager, County Hall, Matlock DE4 3AG ☎ 01629 538440 ✆ kathryn.warrington@derbyshire.gov.uk

Environmental / Technical Services: Mrs Allison Thomas, Service Director - Transport & Environment, County Hall, Matlock DE4 3AG ☎ 01629 533300 ✆ allison.thomas@derbyshire.gov.uk

Estates, Property & Valuation: Mr Steve Dolby, Group Manager - Estates, Chatsworth Hall, Chesterfield Road, Matlock DE4 3FW ☎ 01629 536333 ✆ steve.dolby@derbyshire.gov.uk

European Liaison: Mr Frank Horsley, Head of Economic Regeneration, County Hall, Matlock DE4 3AG ☎ 01629 538348 ✆ frank.horsley@derbyshire.gov.uk

Events Manager: Miss Stephanie Walsh, Economic Development Officer, County Hall, Matlock DE4 3AG ☎ 01629 538464 ✆ stephanie.walsh@derbyshire.gov.uk

Facilities: Mr Geoff Pickford, Service Director - Highways, County Hall, Matlock DE4 3AG ☎ 01629 538194 ✆ geoff.pickford@derbyshire.gov.uk

Finance: Mr Peter Handford, Director - Finance, County Hall, Matlock DE4 3AG ☎ 01629 538700 ✆ peter.handford@derbyshire.gov.uk

Treasury: Mr Peter Handford, Director - Finance, County Hall, Matlock DE4 3AG ☎ 01629 538700 ✆ peter.handford@derbyshire.gov.uk

Pensions: Mr Nigel Dowey, Pensions Manager, County Hall, Matlock DE4 3AG ☎ 01629 538827 ✆ nigel.dowey@derbyshire.gov.uk

Pensions: Ms Dawn Kinley, Pension Investment Officer, County Hall, Matlock DE4 3AG ☎ 01629 538893 ✆ dawn.kinley@derbyshire.gov.uk

Fleet Management: Mr Brian Hattersley, Principal Engineer - Fleet Services, County Transport, Fleet Management, Ripley Road, Ambergate, Derby DE4 2ER ☎ 01629 532110 ✆ brian.hattersley@derbyshire.gov.uk

Grounds Maintenance: Mr Andy Goodall, Group Manager - Property Services, County Hall, Matlock DE4 3AG ☎ 01629 536686 ✆ andy.goodall@derbyshire.gov.uk

Health and Safety: Mr John Davis, Corporate Health & Safety Consultant, County Hall, Matlock DE4 3AG ☎ 01629 536950 ✆ john.davis@derbyshire.gov.uk

Highways: Mr Geoff Pickford, Service Director - Highways, County Hall, Matlock DE4 3AG ☎ 01629 538194 ✆ geoff.pickford@derbyshire.gov.uk

Legal: Mr John McElvaney, Director - Legal Services, County Hall, Matlock DE4 3AG ☎ 01629 580000 ✆ john.mcelvaney@derbyshire.gov.uk

Licensing: Mr Rob Taylour, Head of Trading Standards, County Hall, Matlock DE4 3AG ☎ 01629 539830 ✆ rob.taylour@derbyshire.gov.uk

Lighting: Mr Geoff Pickford, Service Director - Highways, County Hall, Matlock DE4 3AG ☎ 01629 538194 ✆ geoff.pickford@derbyshire.gov.uk

Lottery Funding, Charity and Voluntary: Ms Sarah Eaton, Head of Policy & Research, County Hall, Matlock DE4 3AG ☎ 01629 538268 ✆ sarah.eaton@derbyshire.gov.uk

Member Services: Ms Michelle Archer, Business Manager - Member & Management Support, County Hall, Matlock DE4 3AG ✆ michelle.archer@derbyshire.gov.uk

Personnel / HR: Mr Toni Compai, Director - HR, County Hall, Matlock DE4 3AG ☎ 01629 536927 ✆ toni.compai@derbyshire.gov.uk

Planning: Mrs Allison Thomas, Service Director - Transport & Environment, County Hall, Matlock DE4 3AG ☎ 01629 533300 ✆ allison.thomas@derbyshire.gov.uk

Procurement: Mrs Michelle Smith, Corporate Procurement Manager, County Hall, Matlock DE4 3AG ☎ 01629 536870 ✆ michelle.smith@derbyshire.gov.uk

Public Libraries: Mr Don Gibbs, Service Director - Libraries & Heritage, County Hall, Matlock DE4 3AG ☎ 01629 536572 ✆ don.gibbs@derbyshire.gov.uk

Recycling & Waste Minimisation: Ms Claire Brailsford, Head of Waste Management, County Hall, Matlock DE4 3AG ☎ 01629 539775 ✆ claire.brailsford@derbyshire.gov.uk

Regeneration: Mr Frank Horsley, Head of Economic Regeneration, County Hall, Matlock DE4 3AG ☎ 01629 538348 ✆ frank.horsley@derbyshire.gov.uk

Road Safety: Mr Geoff Pickford, Service Director - Highways, County Hall, Matlock DE4 3AG ☎ 01629 538194 ✆ geoff.pickford@derbyshire.gov.uk

Social Services (Adult): Ms Joy Hollister, Strategic Director - Adult Care, County Hall, Matlock DE4 3AG ✆ joy.hollister@derbyshire.gov.uk

Social Services (Adult): Mr Roger Miller, Assistant Director - Prevention & Personalisation, County Hall, Matlock DE4 3AG ☎ 01629 532002 ✆ roger.miller@derbyshire.gov.uk

DERBYSHIRE

Social Services (Adult): Mr Simon Stevens, Assistant Director - Direct Care, County Hall, Matlock DE4 3AG ☎ 01629 532001 ✆ simon.stevens@derbyshire.gov.uk

Social Services (Adult): Ms Julie Voller, Assistant Director - Strategy & Commissioning, County Hall, Matlock DE4 3AG ☎ 01629 532004 ✆ julie.voller@derbyshire.gov.uk

Public Health: Mr Dean Wallace, Director - Public Health, County Hall, Matlock DE4 3AG ☎ 01629 538437 ✆ dean.wallace@derbyshire.gov.uk

Staff Training: Mr Toni Compai, Director - HR, County Hall, Matlock DE4 3AG ☎ 01629 536927 ✆ toni.compai@derbyshire.gov.uk

Tourism: Miss Stephanie Walsh, Economic Development Officer, County Hall, Matlock DE4 3AG ☎ 01629 538464 ✆ stephanie.walsh@derbyshire.gov.uk

Traffic Management: Mr Geoff Pickford, Service Director - Highways, County Hall, Matlock DE4 3AG ☎ 01629 538194 ✆ geoff.pickford@derbyshire.gov.uk

Transport: Mr Brian Hattersley, Principal Engineer - Fleet Services, County Transport, Fleet Management, Ripley Road, Ambergate, Derby DE4 2ER ☎ 01629 532110 ✆ brian.hattersley@derbyshire.gov.uk

Waste Collection and Disposal: Ms Claire Brailsford, Head of Waste Management, County Hall, Matlock DE4 3AG ☎ 01629 539775 ✆ claire.brailsford@derbyshire.gov.uk

Waste Management: Ms Claire Brailsford, Head of Waste Management, County Hall, Matlock DE4 3AG ☎ 01629 539775 ✆ claire.brailsford@derbyshire.gov.uk

COUNCILLORS

Leader of the Council: Western, Anne (LAB - Barlborough & Clowne)
anne.western@derbyshire.gov.uk

Deputy Leader of the Council: Smith, Paul (LAB - Alfreton & Somercotes)
paul.smith@derbyshire.gov.uk

Allen, David (LAB - Birdholme)
dave.allen@derbyshire.gov.uk

Atkins, Elizabeth (LD - New Mills)
beth.atkins@derbyshire.gov.uk

Bambrick, Sean (LAB - Swadlincote North)
sean.bambrick@derbyshire.gov.uk

Birkin, Glennice (LAB - Ilkeston East)
glennice.birkin@derbyshire.gov.uk

Bisknell, Caitlin (LAB - Buxton North & East)
caitlin.bisknell@derbyshire.gov.uk

Blank, Sharon (LAB - Spire)
sharon.blank@derbyshire.gov.uk

Booth, Michelle (LAB - Ilkeston West)
michelle.booth@derbyshire.gov.uk

Botham, Andy (LAB - Matlock)
andy.botham@derbyshire.gov.uk

Bradford, Stuart (CON - Duffield & Belper South)
stuart.bradford@derbyshire.gov.uk

Brittain, Stuart (LAB - Loundsley Green & Newbold)
stuart.brittain@derbyshire.gov.uk

Bull, Steve (CON - Ashbourne)
steve.bull@derbyshire.gov.uk

Buttery, Kevin (CON - Horsley)
kevin.buttery@derbyshire.gov.uk

Charles, Diane (LAB - Eckington & Killamarsh)
diane.charles@derbyshire.gov.uk

Chilton, Linda (CON - Melbourne)
linda.chilton@derbyshire.gov.uk

Collins, Dean (LAB - Staveley North & Whittington)
dean.collins@derbyshire.gov.uk

Cox, Celia (LAB - Heanor Central)
celia.cox@derbyshire.gov.uk

Coyle, Jim (LAB - Pinxton & South Normanton West)
jim.coyle@derbyshire.gov.uk

Davison, Robert (LAB - Aston)
rob.davison@derbyshire.gov.uk

Dixon, Joan (LAB - Bolsover South West & Scarcliffe)
joan.dixon@derbyshire.gov.uk

Dunn, Paul (LAB - Swadlincote Central)
paul.dunn@derbyshire.gov.uk

Ellis, Stuart (CON - Dronfield West & Walton)
stuart.ellis@derbyshire.gov.uk

Ford, Martyn (CON - Etwall & Repton)
martyn.ford@derbyshire.gov.uk

Freeborn, Steve (LAB - Ripley East & Codnor)
steve.freeborn@derbyshire.gov.uk

Frudd, John (LAB - Ilkeston South)
john.frudd@derbyshire.gov.uk

Gilby, Tricia (LAB - Brimington)

Gillott, Kevin (LAB - Clay Cross South)
kevin.gillott@derbyshire.gov.uk

Greenhalgh, Damien (LAB - Glossop & Charlesworth)
damien.greenhalgh@derbyshire.gov.uk

Hart, Carol (CON - Breadsall & West Hallam)
carol.hart@derbyshire.gov.uk

Hill, Janet (LAB - Dronfield East)
janet.hill2@derbyshire.gov.uk

Hill, Julie (LAB - Sutton)
julie.hill@derbsyshire.gov.uk

Hosker, Roland (LAB - Long Eaton)
roland.hosker@derbyshire.gov.uk

Innes, Jean (LAB - St Mary's)
jean.innes@derbyshire.gov.uk

Jones, Paul (LAB - Greater Heanor)
paul.jones@derbyshire.gov.uk

Kemp, Tony (CON - Buxton West)
tony.kemp@derbyshire.gov.uk

Lauro, Kath (LAB - Linton)
kath.lauro@derbyshire.gov.uk

Lewis, Barry (CON - Wingerworth & Shirland)
barry.lewis@derbyshire.gov.uk

Lomax, David (LD - Whaley Bridge)
david.lomax@derbyshire.gov.uk

Major, Wayne (CON - Sandiacre)
wayne.major@derbyshire.gov.uk

Marshall-Clarke, Steve (LAB - Alfreton & Somercotes)
steve.marshall-clarke@derbyshire.gov.uk

McGregor, Duncan (LAB - Bolsover North)
duncan.mcgregor@derbyshire.gov.uk

Mihaly, Ron (LAB - Boythorpe & Brampton South)
ron.mihaly@derbyshire.gov.uk

Moesby, Clive (LAB - Tibshelf)
clive.moesby@derbyshire.gov.uk

Morgan, Keith (LD - Walton & West)
keith.morgan@derbyshire.gov.uk

Neill, Clare (LAB - Petersham)
clare.neill@derbyshire.gov.uk

Owen, John (LAB - Belper)
john.owen@derbyshire.gov.uk

Parkinson, Robert (CON - Breaston)
robert.parkinson@derbyshire.gov.uk

Patten, Julie (CON - Hilton)
julie.patten@derbyshire.gov.uk

Ratcliffe, Irene (LAB - Wirksworth)
irene.ratcliffe@derbyshire.gov.uk

Ridgway, Brian (LAB - Eckington & Killamarsh)
brian.ridgway@derbyshire.gov.uk

Southerd, Trevor (LAB - Swadlincote South)
trevor.southerd@derbyshire.gov.uk

Spencer, Simon (CON - Dovedale)
simon.spencer@derbyshire.gov.uk

Stockdale, Marion (LAB - Shirebrook & Pleasley)
marian.stockdale@derbyshire.gov.uk

Street, Jocelyn (CON - Chapel & Hope Valley)
jocelyn.street@derbyshire.gov.uk

Taylor, David (CON - Alport & Derwent)
david.taylor@derbyshire.gov.uk

Twigg, Judith (CON - Bakewell)
judith.twigg@derbyshire.gov.uk

Walton, Daniel (CON - Sawley)
daniel.walton@derbyshire.gov.uk

Wilcox, Ellie (LAB - Glossop & Charlesworth)
ellie.wilcox@derbyshire.gov.uk

Wilcox, Dave (LAB - Etherow)
dave.wilcox@derbyshire.gov.uk

Wild, Joanne (CON - Derwent Valley)
jo.wild@derbyshire.gov.uk

Williams, John (LAB - Staveley)
john.williams@derbyshire.gov.uk

Williams, Dave (LAB - Ripley West & Heage)
david.williams@derbyshire.gov.uk

Wright, Brian (LAB - Clay Cross North)
brian.wright@derbyshire.gov.uk

POLITICAL COMPOSITION
LAB: 43, CON: 18, LD: 3

Derbyshire Dales   D

Derbyshire Dales District Council, Town Hall, Matlock
DE4 3NN
☎ 01629 761100 🖷 01629 761148 🖳 www.derbyshiredales.gov.uk

FACTS AND FIGURES
Parliamentary Constituencies: Derbyshire Dales, High Peak
EU Constituencies: East Midlands
Election Frequency: Elections are of whole council

PRINCIPAL OFFICERS
Chief Executive: Mrs Dorcas Bunton, Chief Executive, Town Hall,
Matlock DE4 3NN ☎ 01629 761126
🖑 dorcas.bunton@derbyshiredales.gov.uk

Deputy Chief Executive: Mr Paul Wilson, Corporate Director &
Deputy Chief Executive, Town Hall, Matlock DE4 3NN
☎ 01629 761324 🖑 paul.wilson@derbyshiredales.gov.uk

Architect, Building / Property Services: Mrs Karen Henriksen,
Head of Resources, Town Hall, Matlock DE4 3NN ☎ 01629 761203
🖑 karen.henriksen@derbyshiredales.gov.uk

Best Value: Dr Steve Capes, Head of Regeneration & Policy,
Town Hall, Matlock DE4 3NN ☎ 01629 761371
🖑 steve.capes@derbyshiredales.gov.uk

Building Control: Mr David Harris, Building Control Manager,
Town Hall, Matlock DE4 3NN ☎ 01629 761320
🖑 david.harris@derbyshiredales.gov.uk

PR / Communications: Mr Jim Fearn, Communications &
Marketing Manager, Town Hall, Matlock DE4 3NN ☎ 01629 761195
🖑 jim.fearn@derbyshiredales.gov.uk

Community Planning: Mr Giles Dann, Policy & Economic
Development Manager, Town Hall, Matlock DE4 3NN ☎ 01629
761211 🖑 giles.dann@derbyshiredales.gov.uk

Community Safety: Mr Ashley Watts, Head of Community
Development, Town Hall, Matlock DE4 3NN ☎ 01629 761367 🖑
ashley.watts@derbyshiredales.gov.uk

Computer Management: Mr Nick Blaney, Joint IT Services
Manager, Town Hall, Matlock DE4 3NN ☎ 01246 217103; 01246
217103; 01246 717097 🖑 nick.blaney@ne-derbyshire.gov.uk

Corporate Services: Ms Sandra Lamb, Head of Corporate
Services, Town Hall, Matlock DE4 3NN ☎ 01629 761281
🖑 sandra.lamb@derbyshiredales.gov.uk

Customer Service: Ms Sandra Lamb, Head of Corporate
Services, Town Hall, Matlock DE4 3NN ☎ 01629 761281
🖑 sandra.lamb@derbyshiredales.gov.uk

DERBYSHIRE DALES

Economic Development: Mr Giles Dann, Policy & Economic Development Manager, Town Hall, Matlock DE4 3NN ☎ 01629 761211 ✆ giles.dann@derbyshiredales.gov.uk

E-Government: Mr Nick Blaney, Joint IT Services Manager, Town Hall, Matlock DE4 3NN ☎ 01246 717097 ✆ nick.blaney@ne-derbyshire.gov.uk

Electoral Registration: Mrs Dorcas Bunton, Chief Executive, Town Hall, Matlock DE4 3NN ☎ 01629 761126 ✆ dorcas.bunton@derbyshiredales.gov.uk

Emergency Planning: Mrs Dorcas Bunton, Chief Executive, Town Hall, Matlock DE4 3NN ☎ 01629 761126 ✆ dorcas.bunton@derbyshiredales.gov.uk

Energy Management: Mr Mike Galsworthy, Estates & Facilities Manager, Town Hall, Matlock DE4 3NN ☎ 01629 761362 ✆ mike.galsworthy@derbyshiredales.gov.uk

Environmental / Technical Services: Mrs Heidi McDougall, Head of Environmental Services, Town Hall, Matlock DE4 3NN ☎ 01629 761372 ✆ heidi.mcdougall@derbyshiredales.gov.uk

Environmental Health: Mr Tim Braund, Head of Regulatory Services, Town Hall, Matlock DE4 3NN ☎ 01629 761118 ✆ tim.braund@derbyshiredales.gov.uk

Estates, Property & Valuation: Mr Mike Galsworthy, Estates & Facilities Manager, Town Hall, Matlock DE4 3NN ☎ 01629 761362 ✆ mike.galsworthy@derbyshiredales.gov.uk

Events Manager: Mrs Nicola Goodwin, Events Manager, Town Hall, Matlock DE4 3NN ☎ 01629 761390 ✆ nicola.wildgoose@derbyshiredales.gov.uk

Facilities: Mr Mike Galsworthy, Estates & Facilities Manager, Town Hall, Matlock DE4 3NN ☎ 01629 761362 ✆ mike.galsworthy@derbyshiredales.gov.uk

Finance: Mrs Karen Henriksen, Head of Resources, Town Hall, Matlock DE4 3NN ☎ 01629 761203 ✆ karen.henriksen@derbyshiredales.gov.uk

Fleet Management: Mr Peter McEvoy, Operations Manager, Town Hall, Matlock DE4 3NN ☎ 01629 761357 ✆ peter.mcevoy@derbyshiredales.gov.uk

Grounds Maintenance: Mrs Heidi McDougall, Head of Environmental Services, Town Hall, Matlock DE4 3NN ☎ 01629 761372 ✆ heidi.mcdougall@derbyshiredales.gov.uk

Health and Safety: Mr Tim Braund, Head of Regulatory Services, Town Hall, Matlock DE4 3NN ☎ 01629 761118 ✆ tim.braund@derbyshiredales.gov.uk

Home Energy Conservation: Mr Tim Braund, Head of Regulatory Services, Town Hall, Matlock DE4 3NN ☎ 01629 761118 ✆ tim.braund@derbyshiredales.gov.uk

Housing: Mr Rob Cogings, Head of Housing, Town Hall, Matlock DE4 3NN ☎ 01629 761354 ✆ robert.cogings@derbyshiredales.gov.uk

Legal: Miss Katie Hamill, Solicitor, Town Hall, Matlock DE4 3NN ☎ 01629 761319 ✆ katie.hamill@derbyshiredales.gov.uk

Leisure and Cultural Services: Mr Ashley Watts, Head of Community Development, Town Hall, Matlock DE4 3NN ☎ 01629 761367 ✆ ashley.watts@derbyshiredales.gov.uk

Licensing: Mr Tim Braund, Head of Regulatory Services, Town Hall, Matlock DE4 3NN ☎ 01629 761118 ✆ tim.braund@derbyshiredales.gov.uk

Lottery Funding, Charity and Voluntary: Ms Sandra Lamb, Head of Corporate Services, Town Hall, Matlock DE4 3NN ☎ 01629 761281 ✆ sandra.lamb@derbyshiredales.gov.uk

Member Services: Ms Sandra Lamb, Head of Corporate Services, Town Hall, Matlock DE4 3NN ☎ 01629 761281 ✆ sandra.lamb@derbyshiredales.gov.uk

Parking: Mrs Heidi McDougall, Head of Environmental Services, Town Hall, Matlock DE4 3NN ☎ 01629 761372 ✆ heidi.mcdougall@derbyshiredales.gov.uk

Partnerships: Dr Steve Capes, Head of Regeneration & Policy, Town Hall, Matlock DE4 3NN ☎ 01629 761371 ✆ steve.capes@derbyshiredales.gov.uk

Personnel / HR: Mr Tim Furniss, HR Officer, Town Hall, Matlock DE4 3NN ☎ 01629 761155 ✆ tim.furniss@derbyshiredales.gov.uk

Personnel / HR: Mrs Deborah Unwin, HR Manager, Town Hall, Matlock DE4 3NN ☎ 01629 761364 ✆ deborah.unwin@derbyshiredales.gov.uk

Planning: Mr Tim Braund, Head of Regulatory Services, Town Hall, Matlock DE4 3NN ☎ 01629 761118 ✆ tim.braund@derbyshiredales.gov.uk

Procurement: Ms Sandra Lamb, Head of Corporate Services, Town Hall, Matlock DE4 3NN ☎ 01629 761281 ✆ sandra.lamb@derbyshiredales.gov.uk

Recycling & Waste Minimisation: Mrs Heidi McDougall, Head of Environmental Services, Town Hall, Matlock DE4 3NN ☎ 01629 761372 ✆ heidi.mcdougall@derbyshiredales.gov.uk

Recycling & Waste Minimisation: Mrs Sally Rose, Waste & Recycling Manager, Town Hall, Matlock DE4 3NN ☎ 01629 761112 ✆ sally.rose@derbyshiredales.gov.uk

Regeneration: Dr Steve Capes, Head of Regeneration & Policy, Town Hall, Matlock DE4 3NN ☎ 01629 761371 ✆ steve.capes@derbyshiredales.gov.uk

Staff Training: Mrs Deborah Unwin, HR Manager, Town Hall, Matlock DE4 3NN ☎ 01629 761364 ✆ deborah.unwin@derbyshiredales.gov.uk

Street Scene: Mrs Heidi McDougall, Head of Environmental Services, Town Hall, Matlock DE4 3NN ☎ 01629 761372
✆ heidi.mcdougall@derbyshiredales.gov.uk

Sustainable Development: Mrs Dorcas Bunton, Chief Executive, Town Hall, Matlock DE4 3NN ☎ 01629 761126
✆ dorcas.bunton@derbyshiredales.gov.uk

Tourism: Ms Gill Chapman, Tourism Officer, Town Hall, Matlock DE4 3NN ☎ 01629 761145 ✆ gill.chapman@derbyshiredales.gov.uk

Transport: Mr Peter McEvoy, Operations Manager, Town Hall, Matlock DE4 3NN ☎ 01629 761357
✆ peter.mcevoy@derbyshiredales.gov.uk

Children's Play Areas: Mrs Heidi McDougall, Head of Environmental Services, Town Hall, Matlock DE4 3NN
☎ 01629 761372 ✆ heidi.mcdougall@derbyshiredales.gov.uk

COUNCILLORS

Leader of the Council: Rose, Lewis (CON - Carsington Water)
lewis.rose@derbyshiredales.gov.uk

Deputy Leader of the Council: Catt, Albert (CON - Doveridge & Sudbury)
albert.catt@derbyshiredales.gov.uk

Atkin, Jason (CON - Darley Dale)
jason.atkin@derbyshiredales.gov.uk

Botham, Deborah (LAB - Matlock St. Giles)
deborah.botham@derbyshiredales.gov.uk

Bower, Jennifer (CON - Tideswell)
jennifer.bower@derbyshiredales.gov.uk

Bright, Richard (CON - Hulland)
richard.bright@derbyshiredales.gov.uk

Bull, Stephen (CON - Ashbourne North)
stephen.bull@derbyshiredales.gov.uk

Burfoot, Susan (LD - Matlock All Saints)
sue.burfoot@derbyshiredales.gov.uk

Burfoot, Martin (LD - Matlock All Saints)
martin.burfoot@derbyshiredales.gov.uk

Chapman, David (CON - Hartington & Taddington)
david.chapman@derbyshiredales.gov.uk

Chell, Phil (CON - Ashbourne South)
philip.chell@derbyshiredales.gov.uk

Donnelly, Thomas (CON - Ashbourne South)
thomas.donnelly@derbyshiredales.gov.uk

Elliott, Graham (O - Lathkill & Bradford)
graham.elliott@derbyshiredales.gov.uk

Elliott, Ann (CON - Matlock All Saints)
ann.elliott@derbyshiredales.gov.uk

Fitzherbert, Richard (CON - Dovedale & Parwich)
richard.fitzherbert@derbyshiredales.gov.uk

Flitter, Steve (LD - Matlock St. Giles)
steve.flitter@derbyshiredales.gov.uk

Froggatt, Helen (CON - Bakewell)
helen.froggatt@derbyshiredales.gov.uk

Furness, Chris (CON - Bradwell)
chris.furness@derbyshiredales.gov.uk

Hill, Alyson (CON - Bakewell)
alyson.hill@derbyshiredales.gov.uk

Hobson, Susan (CON - Chatsworth)
susan.hobson@derbyshiredales.gov.uk

Horton, Neil (CON - Litton & Longstone)
neil.horton@derbyshiredales.gov.uk

Jenkins, Angus (CON - Brailsford)
angus.jenkins@derbyshiredales.gov.uk

Massey, Vicky (CON - Hathersage & Eyam)
vicky.massey@derbyshiredales.gov.uk

Millward, Anthony (CON - Ashbourne North)
tony.millward@derbyshiredales.gov.uk

Monks, Jean (CON - Hathersage & Eyam)
jean.monks@derbyshiredales.gov.uk

Morley, Tony (CON - Norbury)
tony.morley@derbyshiredales.gov.uk

Pawley, Joyce (LAB - Masson)
joyce.pawley@derbyshiredales.gov.uk

Purdy, Garry (CON - Masson)
garry.purdy@derbyshiredales.gov.uk

Ratcliffe, Mike (LAB - Wirksworth)
mike.ratclife@derbyshiredales.gov.uk

Ratcliffe, Irene (LAB - Wirksworth)
irene.ratcliffe@derbyshiredales.gov.uk

Salt, Mark (CON - Darley Dale)
mark.salt@derbyshiredales.gov.uk

Shirley, Andrew (CON - Clifton & Bradley)
andrew.shirley@derbyshiredales.gov.uk

Slack, Peter (LAB - Wirksworth)
peter.slack@derbyshiredales.gov.uk

Statham, Andrew (CON - Darley Dale)
andrew.statham@derbyshiredales.gov.uk

Stevens, Jacquie (CON - Matlock St. Giles)
jacquie.stevens@derbyshiredales.gov.uk

Swindell, Colin (IND - Winster & South Darley)
colin.swindell@derbyshiredales.gov.uk

Tibenham, John (CON - Calver)
john.tibenham@derbyshiredales.gov.uk

Tilbrook, Philippa (CON - Bakewell)
philippa.tilbrook@derbyshiredales.gov.uk

Wild, Joanne (CON - Stanton)
joanna.wild@derbyshiredales.gov.uk

POLITICAL COMPOSITION
CON: 29, LAB: 5, LD: 3, O: 1, IND: 1

COMMITTEE CHAIRS
Community & Environment: Ms Joanne Wild

Licensing: Ms Jean Monks

Planning: Mr Garry Purdy

DERRY CITY & STRABANE DISTRICT COUNCIL

Derry City & Strabane District Council, Derry City Council, 98 Strand Road, Derry BT48 7NN
☎ 028 7125 3253 ✆ info@derrystrabane.com
🖥 www.derrystrabane.com

PRINCIPAL OFFICERS

Chief Executive: Mr John Kelpie, Chief Executive, Derry City Council, 98 Strand Road, Derry BT48 7NN
✆ john.kelpie@derrycityandstrabanedistrict.com

Building Control: Mr Frank Morrison, Head of Capital Development & Building Control, Derry City Council, 98 Strand Road, Derry BT48 7NN ☎ 028 7125 3253
✆ frank.morrison@derrycityandstrabanedistrict.com

Community Planning: Ms Teresa Bradley, Principal Community Development Officer, Derry City Council, 98 Strand Road, Derry BT48 7NN ☎ 028 7125 3253
✆ teresa.bradley@derrycityandstrabanedistrict.com

Corporate Services: Mr Stephen Gillespie, Director - Business & Culture, Derry City Council, 98 Strand Road, Derry BT48 7NN ☎ 028 7125 3253
✆ stephen.gillespie@derrycityandstrabanedistrict.com

Corporate Services: Mr Kevin O'Connor, Head of Business, Derry City Council, 98 Strand Road, Derry BT48 7NN ☎ 028 7125 3253
✆ kevin.o'connor@derrycityandstrabanedistrict.com

Economic Development: Ms Linda Williams, Head of Economic Development & Marketing, Derry City Council, 98 Strand Road, Derry BT48 7NN ☎ 028 7125 3253
✆ linda.williams@derrycityandstrabanedistrict.com

Environmental / Technical Services: Mr Conor Canning, Head of Environment, Derry City Council, 98 Strand Road, Derry BT48 7NN ☎ 028 7125 3253
✆ conor.canning@derrycityandstrabanedistrict.com

Environmental / Technical Services: Ms Karen Phillips, Director - Environment & Regeneration, Derry City Council, 98 Strand Road, Derry BT48 7NN ☎ 028 7125 3253
✆ karen.phillips@derrycityandstrabanedistrict.com

Environmental Health: Mr Barry Doherty, Senior Environmental Health Officer, Derry City Council, 98 Strand Road, Derry BT48 7NN ☎ 028 7137 6513 ✆ barry.doherty@derrystrabane.com

Events Manager: Ms Karen Leonard, Festival & Events Manager, Derry City Council, 98 Strand Road, Derry BT48 7NN
☎ 028 7125 3253 ✆ karen.leonard@derrycityandstrabanedistrict.com

Finance: Mr Alfie Dallas, Head of Strategic Finance & Funding, Derry City Council, 98 Strand Road, Derry BT48 7NN ✆ alfie.dallas@derrystrabane.com

Fleet Management: Mr Ciaran McCartie, Property & Fleet Manager, Derry City Council, 98 Strand Road, Derry BT48 7NN
☎ 028 7125 3253
✆ ciaran.mccartie@derrycityandstrabanedistrict.com

Grounds Maintenance: Mr Danny McCartney, Grounds Maintenance Manager, Derry City Council, 98 Strand Road, Derry BT48 7NN ☎ 028 7135 5997
✆ danny.mccartney@derrycityandstrabanedistrict.com

Legal: Mr Philip Kingston, Senior Solicitor, Derry City Council, 98 Strand Road, Derry BT48 7NN ☎ 028 7125 3253
✆ philip.kingston@derrycityandstrabanedistrict.com

Leisure and Cultural Services: Mr Stephen Gillespie, Director - Business & Culture, Derry City Council, 98 Strand Road, Derry BT48 7NN ☎ 028 7125 3253
✆ stephen.gillespie@derrycityandstrabanedistrict.com

Leisure and Cultural Services: Ms Aeidin McCarter, Head of Culture, Derry City Council, 98 Strand Road, Derry BT48 7NN
☎ 028 7125 3253 ✆ aeidin.mccarter@derrycityandstrabanedistrict.com

Personnel / HR: Ms Debbie Rogers, Head of HR, Derry City Council, 98 Strand Road, Derry BT48 7NN ☎ 028 7125 3253
✆ debbie.rogers@derrycityandstrabanedistrict.com

Planning: Ms Maura Fox, Head of Planning, Derry City Council, 98 Strand Road, Derry BT48 7NN ☎ 028 7137 6580
✆ maura.fox@derrycityandstrabanedistrict.com

Planning: Ms Suzanne McCracken, Development Management Principal Planning Officer, Derry City Council, 98 Strand Road, Derry BT48 7NN ☎ 028 7137 6522
✆ suzanne.mccracken@derrycityandstrabanedistrict.com

Waste Management: Ms Nicola Doherty, Waste Services Manager, Derry City Council, 98 Strand Road, Derry BT48 7NN
☎ 028 7125 3253
✆ nicola.doherty@derrycityandstrabanedistrict.com

COUNCILLORS

Mayor: McCallion, Elisha (SF - Ballyarnett)
elisha.mccallion@derrycityandstrabanedistrict.com

Alderman: Bresland, Allan (DUP - Sperrin)
allan.bresland@derrycityandstrabanedistrict.com

Alderman: Devenney, Maurice (IND - Faughan)
maurice.devenney@derrycityandstrabanedistrict.com

Alderman: Hamilton, Mary (UUP - Waterside)
mary.hamilton@derrycityandstrabanedistrict.com

Alderman: Hamilton, Rhonda (DUP - Sperrin)
rhonda.hamilton@derrycityandstrabanedistrict.com

Alderman: Hussey, Derek (UUP - Derg)
derek.hussey@derrycityandstrabanedistrict.com

Alderman: Kerrigan, Thomas (DUP - Derg)
thomas.kerrigan@derrycityandstrabanedistrict.com

Alderman: McClintock, Hilary (DUP - Waterside)
hilary.mcclintock@derrystrabane.com

Alderman: Ramsey, David (DUP - Waterside)
david.ramsey@derrystrabane.com

Alderman: Thompson, Drew (DUP - Waterside)
drew.thompson@derrystrabane.com

Alderman: Warke, Graham (DUP - Faughan)
graham.warke@derrycityandstrabanedistrict.com

Boyle, John (SDLP - Foyleside)
john.boyle@derrycityandstrabanedistrict.com

Campbell, Kevin (SF - The Moor)
kevin.campbell@derrycityandstrabanedistrict.com

Carlin, Karina (SF - Sperrin)
karina.carlin@derrycityandstrabanedistrict.com

Carr, Sean (IND - The Moor)
sean.carr@derrycityandstrabanedistrict.com

Cooper, Michael (SF - Foyleside)
michael.cooper@derrycityandstrabanedistrict.com

Cusack, Shauna (SDLP - Foyleside)
shauna.cusack@derrycityandstrabanedistrict.com

Dobbins, Angela (SDLP - Ballyarnett)
angela.dobbins@derrycityandstrabanedistrict.com

Donnelly, Gary (IND - The Moor)
gary.donnelly@derrycityandstrabanedistrict.com

Duffy, Sandra (SF - Ballyarnett)
sandra.duffy@derrycityandstrabanedistrict.com

Fleming, Paul (SF - Faughan)
paul.fleming@derrycityandstrabanedistrict.com

Gallagher, Paul (IND - Sperrin)
paul.gallagher@derrycityandstrabanedistrict.com

Gardiner, Tina (SDLP - Waterside)
tina.gardiner@derrystrabane.com

Hassan, Tony (SF - Ballyarnett)
tony.hassan@derrycityandstrabanedistrict.com

Hastings, Hugh (Gus) (SDLP - Faughan)
gus.hastings@derrycityandstrabanedistrict.com

Jackson, Christopher (SF - Waterside)
christopher.jackson@derrystrabane.com

Kelly, Dan (SF - Sperrin)
dan.kelly@derrycityandstrabanedistrict.com

Kelly, Patsy (SDLP - Sperrin)
patsy.kelly@derrycityandstrabanedistrict.com

Kelly, Colly (SF - The Moor)
colly.kelly@derrycityandstrabanedistrict.com

Logue, Patricia (SF - The Moor)
patricia.logue@derrycityandstrabanedistrict.com

McGinley, Eric (SF - Foyleside)
eric.mcginley@derrycityandstrabanedistrict.com

McGuire, Kieran (SF - Derg)
kieran.mcguire@derrycityandstrabanedistrict.com

McHugh, Maolíosa (SF - Derg)
maoliosa.mchugh@derrycityandstrabanedistrict.com

McHugh, Ruairi (SF - Derg)
ruairi.mchugh@derrycityandstrabanedistrict.com

McKeever, Jim (SDLP - Faughan)
jim.mckeever@derrycityandstrabanedistrict.com

McMahon, Brian (SF - Sperrin)
brian.mcmahon@derrycityandstrabanedistrict.com

O'Reilly, Darren (IND - Foyleside)
darren.oreilly@derrycityandstrabanedistrict.com

Reilly, Martin (SDLP - Waterside)
martin.reilly@derrystrabane.com

Robinson, Warren (IND - Ballyarnett)
warren.robinson@derrystrabane.com

Tierney, Brian (SDLP - Ballyarnett)
brian.tierney@derrycityandstrabanedistrict.com

POLITICAL COMPOSITION
SF: 16, SDLP: 9, DUP: 7, IND: 6, UUP: 2

COMMITTEE CHAIRS

Assurance, Audit & Risk: Mr Eric McGinley

Environment & Regeneration: Mr Brian Tierney

Health & Community: Mr Ruairi McHugh

Planning: Ms Karina Carlin

Devon   C

Devon County Council, County Hall, Topsham Road, Exeter
EX2 4QD
☎ 0345 155 1015 ⌂ customer@devon.gov.uk 🖳 www.devon.gov.uk

FACTS AND FIGURES
Parliamentary Constituencies: Devon Central, Devon East, Devon
North, Devon South West, Devon West and Torridge, Exeter, Newton
Abbot, Plymouth Moor View, Plymouth Sutton and Devonport, Tiverton
and Honiton, Totnes
EU Constituencies: South West
Election Frequency: Elections are of whole council

PRINCIPAL OFFICERS

Chief Executive: Dr Phil Norrey, Chief Executive, County Hall,
Topsham Road, Exeter EX2 4QD ☎ 01392 383201
⌂ phil.norrey@devon.gov.uk

Senior Management: Mr Mary Davis, County Treasurer, County
Hall, Topsham Road, Exeter EX2 4QD ☎ 01392 383310
⌂ mary.davis@devon.gov.uk

Senior Management: Ms Jo Olsson, Interim Chief Officer -
Children's Services, County Hall, Topsham Road, Exeter EX2 4QD
⌂ jo.olsson@devon.gov.uk

Senior Management: Dr Virginia Pearson, Chief Officer -
Communities, Public Health, Environment & Prosperity, County Hall,
Topsham Road, Exeter EX2 4QD ☎ 01392 386398
⌂ virginia.pearson@devon.gov.uk

Senior Management: Mr Jan Shadbolt, County Solicitor, County
Hall, Topsham Road, Exeter EX2 4QD ☎ 01392 382285
⌂ jan.shadbolt@devon.gov.uk

Senior Management: Mrs Jennie Stephens, Chief Officer - Adult
Care & Health, County Hall, Topsham Road, Exeter EX2 4QR
☎ 01392 383299 ⌂ jennie.stephens@devon.gov.uk

DEVON

Access Officer / Social Services (Disability): Ms Carolyn Elliott, Assistant Director - Community Service & Social Care, Bay House, Nicholson Road, Torquay TQ2 7TD ☎ 01803 210534 ✆ carolyn.elliott3@nhs.net

Architect, Building / Property Services: Mr Matthew Jones, Corporate Asset Manager - Estates, County Hall, Topsham Road, Exeter EX2 4QD ☎ 01392 383000 ✆ matthew.jones@devon.gov.uk

Building Control: Mr Mike Deaton, Planning Development Manager, Lucombe House, County Hall, Topsham Road, Exeter EX2 4QW ☎ 01392 382130 ✆ mike.deaton@devon.gov.uk

Catering Services: Ms Fran Perry, Function & Food Procurement Manager, Capital Court, Sowton, Exeter EX2 7FW ☎ 01392 351157 ✆ fran.perry@ncsgrp.co.uk

Civil Registration: Ms Trish Harrogate, Registration Services Manager, Larkbeare House, Topsham Road, Exeter EX2 4NG ☎ 01392 385618 ✆ trish.harrogate@devon.gov.uk

PR / Communications: Mr Peter Doyle, Head of External Affairs, County Hall, Topsham Road, Exeter EX2 4QW ☎ 01392 383264 ✆ peter.doyle@devon.gov.uk

Community Safety: Mr John Smith, Head of Organisational Development, County Hall, Topsham Road, Exeter EX2 4QD ☎ 01392 383021 ✆ john.smith@devon.gov.uk

Computer Management: Mr Rob Parkhouse, Head of Digital Transformation & Business Support, County Hall, Topsham Road, Exeter EX2 4QJ ☎ 01392 382458 ✆ rob.parkhouse@devon.gov.uk

Consumer Protection and Trading Standards: Mr Paul Thomas, Head of Trading Standards & Adult Community Learning, County Hall, Topsham Road, Exeter EX2 4QD ☎ 01392 382728 ✆ paul.thomas@devon.gov.uk

Contracts: Mr Justin Bennetts, Strategic Procurement Manager, County Hall, Topsham Road, Exeter EX2 4QD ☎ 01392 383000 ✆ justin.bennetts@devon.gov.uk

Customer Service: Mr Roger Jenkins, Customer Service Centre Manager, Customer Service Centre, 7 Millennium Place, Lowman Way, Tiverton EX16 6SB ☎ 01392 383000 ✆ roger.jenkins@devon.gov.uk

Economic Development: Ms Keri Denton, Head of Economy, Enterprise & Skills, County Hall, Topsham Road, Exeter EX2 4QD ☎ 01392 383684 ✆ keri.denton@devon.gov.uk

Education: Ms Dawn Stabb, Head of Education & Learning, County Hall, Topsham Road, Exeter EX2 4QD ✆ dawn.stabb@devon.gov.uk

Emergency Planning: Mr Simon Kitchen, Head of Policy, Strategy & Organisation Change, County Hall, Topsham Road, Exeter EX2 4QD ☎ 01392 382699 ✆ simon.kitchen@devon.gov.uk

Environmental / Technical Services: Mr Dave Black, Head of Planning, Transportation & Environment, County Hall, Topsham Road, Exeter EX2 4QD ☎ 01392 383247 ✆ dave.black@devon.gov.uk

Estates, Property & Valuation: Mr Matthew Jones, Corporate Asset Manager - Estates, County Hall, Topsham Road, Exeter EX2 4QD ☎ 01392 383000 ✆ matthew.jones@devon.gov.uk

European Liaison: Ms Keri Denton, Head of Economy, Enterprise & Skills, County Hall, Topsham Road, Exeter EX2 4QD ☎ 01392 383684 ✆ keri.denton@devon.gov.uk

Events Manager: Ms Jenny Caldwell, Marketing & Communications Manager, County Hall, Topsham Road, Exeter EX2 4QD ☎ 01392 382739 ✆ jenny.caldwell@devon.gov.uk

Facilities: Ms Linda Stevenson, County Hall Facilities Manager, County Hall, Topsham Road, Exeter EX2 4QD ☎ 01392 383000 ✆ linda.stevenson@devon.gov.uk

Treasury: Ms Mary Davis, County Treasurer, County Hall, Topsham Road, Exeter EX2 4QD ☎ 01392 383310 ✆ mary.davis@devon.gov.uk

Pensions: Ms Charlotte Thompson, Head of Pension Services, County Hall, Topsham Road, Exeter EX2 4QD ☎ 01392 381933 ✆ charlotte.thompson@devon.gov.uk

Grounds Maintenance: Ms Linda Stevenson, County Hall Facilities Manager, County Hall, Topsham Road, Exeter EX2 4QD ☎ 01392 383000 ✆ linda.stevenson@devon.gov.uk

Health and Safety: Ms Margaret Bullock, County Health & Safety Wellbeing Manager, Great Moor House, Sowton, Exeter EX2 7NL ☎ 01392 382788 ✆ margaret.bullock@devon.gov.uk

Highways: Mr David Whitton, Chief Officer - Highways, Infrastructure Development & Waste, County Hall, Topsham Road, Exeter EX2 4QD ☎ 01392 382701 ✆ david.whitton@devon.gov.uk

Legal: Mr Jan Shadbolt, County Solicitor, County Hall, Topsham Road, Exeter EX2 4QD ☎ 01392 382285 ✆ jan.shadbolt@devon.gov.uk

Lighting: Mr Maurizio Dalesio, Team Leader - Street Lighting, County Hall, Topsham Road, Exeter EX2 4QD ☎ 01392 382114 ✆ maurizio.dalesio@devon.gov.uk

Member Services: Mr Rob Hooper, Democratic Services & Scrutiny Manager, County Hall, Topsham Road, Exeter EX2 4QD ☎ 01392 382300 ✆ rob.hooper@devon.gov.uk

Member Services: Mrs Alison Howell, Member Services Officer, County Hall, Topsham Road, Exeter EX2 4QD ☎ 01392 382888 ✆ alison.howell@devon.gov.uk

Member Services: Ms Karen Strahan, Deputy Democratic Services & Scrutiny Manager, County Hall, Topsham Road, Exeter EX2 4QD ☎ 01392 382264 ✆ karen.strahan@devon.gov.uk

Personnel / HR: Mr John Smith, Head of Organisational Development, County Hall, Topsham Road, Exeter EX2 4QD ☎ 01392 383021 ✆ john.smith@devon.gov.uk

Planning: Mr Dave Black, Head of Planning, Transportation & Environment, County Hall, Topsham Road, Exeter EX2 4QD
☎ 01392 383247 ⌂ dave.black@devon.gov.uk

Procurement: Mr Justin Bennetts, Strategic Procurement Manager, County Hall, Topsham Road, Exeter EX2 4QD
☎ 01392 383000 ⌂ justin.bennetts@devon.gov.uk

Public Libraries: Ms Ciara Eastell, Head of Libraries, Great Moor House, Bittern Road, Sowton, Exeter EX2 7NL ☎ 01392 384315
⌂ ciara.eastell@devon.gov.uk

Recycling & Waste Minimisation: Ms Wendy Barratt, County Waste Manager, County Hall, Topsham Road, Exeter EX2 4QD
☎ 01392 382901 ⌂ wendy.barratt@devon.gov

Road Safety: Mr Jeremy Phillips, Sustainable & Safer Travel Team Manager, County Hall, Topsham Road, Exeter EX2 4QD
☎ 01392 383289 ⌂ jeremy.phillips@devon.gov.uk

Social Services: Mr Tim Golby, Head of Social Care Commissioning, County Hall, Topsham Road, Exeter EX2 4QD
☎ 01392 383527 ⌂ tim.golby@devon.gov.uk

Social Services (Adult): Mr Tim Golby, Head of Adult Commissioning & Health, County Hall, Topsham Road, Exeter EX2 4QD ⌂ tim.golby@devon.gov.uk

Social Services (Adult): Mrs Jennie Stephens, Chief Officer - Adult Care & Health, County Hall, Topsham Road, Exeter EX2 4QR
☎ 01392 383299 ⌂ jennie.stephens@devon.gov.uk

Social Services (Adult): Ms Keri Storey, Head of Adult Care Operations & Health, County Hall, Topsham Road, Exeter EX2 4QD
⌂ keri.storey@devon.gov.uk

Social Services (Children): Ms Vivien Lines, Interim Head of Children's Social Care, County Hall, Topsham Road, Exeter EX2 4QD ⌂ vivien.lines@devon.gov.uk

Social Services (Children): Ms Jo Olsson, Interim Chief Officer - Children's Services, County Hall, Topsham Road, Exeter EX2 4QD
⌂ jo.olsson@devon.gov.uk

Fostering & Adoption: Ms Karen Cleave, Professional & Governance Lead, County Hall, Topsham Road, Exeter EX2 4QD
☎ 01392 38 5635 ⌂ karen.cleave@devon.gov.uk

Safeguarding: Ms Fiona Fitzpatrick, Consultant, County Hall, Topsham Road, Exeter EX2 4QD ☎ 01392 383000
⌂ fiona.fitzpatrick@devon.gov.uk

Safeguarding: Ms Nicky Scutt, Senior Manager - Safeguarding & Specialist Services, County Hall, Topsham Road, Exeter EX2 4QD
☎ 01392 382741 ⌂ nicky.scutt@devon.gov.uk

Families: Ms Karen Cleave, Professional & Governance Lead, County Hall, Topsham Road, Exeter EX2 4QD ☎ 01392 38 5635
⌂ karen.cleave@devon.gov.uk

Childrens Social Care: Ms Vivien Lines, Interim Head of Children's Social Care, County Hall, Topsham Road, Exeter EX2 4QD ⌂ vivien.lines@devon.gov.uk

Public Health: Dr Virginia Pearson, Chief Officer - Communities, Public Health, Environment & Prosperity, County Hall, Topsham Road, Exeter EX2 4QD ☎ 01392 386398
⌂ virginia.pearson@devon.gov.uk

Staff Training: Mr Bill Heasman, HR Business Partner - Performance, Room 220, County Hall, Topsham Road, Exeter EX2 4QD ☎ 01392 382344 ⌂ bill.heasman@devon.gov.uk

Sustainable Communities: Mr John Smith, Head of Organisational Development, County Hall, Topsham Road, Exeter EX2 4QD ☎ 01392 383021 ⌂ john.smith@devon.gov.uk

Tourism: Ms Keri Denton, Head of Economy, Enterprise & Skills, Lucombe House, County Hall, Topsham Road, Exeter EX2 4QD
☎ 01392 383684 ⌂ keri.denton@devon.gov.uk

Transport: Mr Dave Black, Head of Planning, Transportation & Environment, County Hall, Topsham Road, Exeter EX2 4QD
☎ 01392 383247 ⌂ dave.black@devon.gov.uk

Transport Planner: Mr Dave Black, Head of Planning, Transportation & Environment, County Hall, Topsham Road, Exeter EX2 4QD ☎ 01392 383247 ⌂ dave.black@devon.gov.uk

Waste Collection and Disposal: Ms Wendy Barratt, County Waste Manager, County Hall, Topsham Road, Exeter EX2 4QD
☎ 01392 382901 ⌂ wendy.barratt@devon.gov

Waste Management: Mr David Whitton, Chief Officer - Highways, Infrastructure Development & Waste, County Hall, Topsham Road, Exeter EX2 4QD ☎ 01392 382701 ⌂ david.whitton@devon.gov.uk

COUNCILLORS

ChairMoulding, Andrew (CON - Axminster)
andrew.moulding@devon.gov.uk

Vice-ChairRowe, Rosemary (CON - South Brent & Dartington)
rose.rowe@devon.gov.uk

Leader of the Council: Hart, John (CON - Bickleigh & Wembury)
john.hart@devon.gov.uk

Deputy Leader of the Council: Clatworthy, John (CON - Dawlish)
john.clatworthy@devon.gov.uk

Ball, Kevin (CON - Okehampton Rural)
kevin.ball@devon.gov.uk

Barisic, Eve (CON - Newton Abbot North)
eve.barisic@devon.gov.uk

Barker, Stuart (CON - Ashburton & Buckfastleigh)
stuart.barker@devon.gov.uk

Berry, John (CON - Cullompton Rural)
john.berry@devon.gov.uk

Biederman, Frank (IND - Fremington Rural)
frank.biederman@devon.gov.uk

Bowden, Peter (CON - Broadclyst & Whimple)
peter.bowden@devon.gov.uk

DEVON

Boyd, Andy (CON - Torrington Rural)
andy.boyd@devon.gov.uk

Brazil, Julian (LD - Kingsbridge & Stokenham)
julian.brazil@devon.gov.uk

Brook, Jerry (CON - Chudleigh Rural)
jerry.brook@devon.gov.uk

Channon, Christine (CON - Budleigh)
christine.channon@devon.gov.uk

Chugg, Caroline (CON - Braunton Rural)
caroline.chugg@devon.gov.uk

Clarence, Chris (CON - Teign Estuary)
chris.clarence@devon.gov.uk

Colthorpe, Polly (CON - Tiverton West)
polly.colthorpe@devon.gov.uk

Connett, Alan (LD - Exminster & Kenton)
alan.connett@devon.gov.uk

Croad, Roger (CON - Ivybridge)
roger.croad@devon.gov.uk

Davis, Andrea (CON - Combe Martin Rural)
andrea.davis@devon.gov.uk

Dempster, Tony (UKIP - Kingsteignton)
tony.dempster@devon.gov.uk

Dewhirst, Alistair (LD - Teignbridge South)
alistair.dewhirst@devon.gov.uk

Dezart, Gaston (UKIP - Bideford East)
gaston.dezart@devon.gov.uk

Diviani, Paul (CON - Honiton St Paul's)
paul.diviani@devon.gov.uk

Eastman, Andrew (CON - Northam)
andrew.eastman@devon.gov.uk

Edgell, Richard (CON - Chulmleigh & Swimbridge)
richard.edgell@devon.gov.uk

Edmunds, Mike (IND - Ilfracombe)
mike.edmunds@devon.gov.uk

Foggin, Olwen (LAB - Heavitree & Whipton Barton)
olwen.foggin@devon.gov.uk

Gilbert, Rufus (CON - Thurlestone, Salcombe & Allington)
rufus.gilbert@devon.gov.uk

Greenslade, Brian (LD - Barnstaple North)
brian.greenslade@devon.gov.uk

Gribble, George (CON - Bovey Tracey Rural)
george.gribble@devon.gov.uk

Hannaford, Rob (LAB - Exwick & St Thomas)
rob.hannaford@devon.gov.uk

Hannan, Andy (LAB - Priory & St Leonard's)
andy.hannan@devon.gov.uk

Hannon, Des (LD - Tiverton East)
des.hannon@devon.gov.uk

Hawkins, Jonathan (CON - Dartmouth & Kingswear)
jonathan.hawkins@devon.gov.uk

Hill, Roy (LAB - Alphington & Cowick)
roy.hill@devon.gov.uk

Hone, John (UKIP - Exmouth, Brixington & Withycombe)
john.hone@devon.gov.uk

Hook, Gordon (LD - Newton Abbot South)
gordon.hook@devon.gov.uk

Hosking, Richard (CON - Yealmpton)
richard.hosking@devon.gov.uk

Hughes, Stuart (CON - Sidmouth Sidford)
stuart.hughes@devon.gov.uk

Hughes, Bernard (CON - Exmouth Halsdon & Woodbury)
bernard.hughes@devon.gov.uk

Julian, Robin (UKIP - Bideford South & Hartland)
robin.julian@devon.gov.uk

Knight, Jim (CON - Seaton Coastal)
jim.knight@devon.gov.uk

Leadbetter, Andrew (CON - St Loyes & Topsham)
andrew.leadbetter@devon.gov.uk

Matthews, John (CON - Barnstaple South)
john.matthews@devon.gov.uk

McInnes, James (CON - Hatherleigh & Chagford)
james.mcinnes@devon.gov.uk

Morse, Emma (LAB - Pinhoe & Mincinglake)
emma.morse@devon.gov.uk

Owen, Jill (LAB - St David's & St James)
jill.owen@devon.gov.uk

Parsons, Barry (CON - Holsworthy Rural)
barry.parsons@devon.gov.uk

Prowse, Percy (CON - Duryard & Pennsylvania)
percy.prowse@devon.gov.uk

Radford, Ray (CON - Willand & Uffculme)
ray.radford@devon.gov.uk

Randall-Johnson, Sara (CON - Honiton St Michael's)
sara.randalljohnson@devon.gov.uk

Sanders, Philip (CON - Yelverton Rural)
philip.sanders@devon.gov.uk

Sellis, Debo (CON - Tavistock)
debo.sellis@devon.gov.uk

Squires, Margaret (CON - Newton St Cyres & Sandford)
margaret.squires@devon.gov.uk

Vint, Robert (IND - Totnes Rural)
robert.vint@devon.gov.uk

Way, Nick (LD - Crediton Rural)
nick.way@devon.gov.uk

Westlake, Richard (LAB - Newtown & Polsloe)
richard.westlake@devon.gov.uk

Wragg, Eileen (LD - Exmouth Littleham & Town)
eileen.wragg@devon.gov.uk

Wright, Claire (IND - Ottery St Mary)
claire.wright@devon.gov.uk

Yabsley, Jeremy (CON - South Molton Rural)
jeremy.yabsley@devon.gov.uk

Younger-Ross, Richard (LD - Teignmouth)
richard.younger-ross@devon.gov.uk

POLITICAL COMPOSITION
CON: 38, LD: 9, LAB: 7, UKIP: 4, IND: 4

COMMITTEE CHAIRS

Audit: Mr Richard Edgell

Development Management: Mr Jerry Brook

Health & Wellbeing: Miss Andrea Davis

Pensions: Mr Rufus Gilbert

Doncaster   M

Doncaster Metropolitan Borough Council, Civic Office, Waterdale, Doncaster DN1 3BU
☎ 01302 736000 ✆ customer.services@doncaster.gov.uk
🖳 www.doncaster.gov.uk

FACTS AND FIGURES
Parliamentary Constituencies: Don Valley, Doncaster Central, Doncaster North
EU Constituencies: Yorkshire and the Humber
Election Frequency: Elections are by thirds

PRINCIPAL OFFICERS

Chief Executive: Mrs Jo Miller, Chief Executive, Civic Office, Waterdale, Doncaster DN1 3BU ☎ 01302 862230 ✆ jo.miller@doncaster.gov.uk

Senior Management: Mr Damian Allen, Director - Learning, Opportunities & Skills, Civic Office, Waterdale, Doncaster DN1 3BU
☎ 01302 737102 ✆ damian.allen@doncaster.gov.uk

Senior Management: Ms Kim Curry, Interim Director - Adults, Health & Wellbeing, Civic Office, Waterdale, Doncaster DN1 3BU
✆ kim.curry@doncaster.gov.uk

Senior Management: Mr Peter Dale, Director - Regeneration & Environment, Civic Office, Waterdale, Doncaster DN1 3BU
☎ 01302 862505 ✆ peter.dale@doncaster.gov.uk

Senior Management: Dr Rupert Suckling, Director - Public Health, Civic Office, Waterdale, Doncaster DN1 3BU
☎ 01302 734010 ✆ rupert.suckling@doncaster.gov.uk

Senior Management: Mr Simon Wiles, Director - Finance & Corporate Services, Civic Office, Waterdale, Doncaster DN1 3BU
☎ 01302 736907 ✆ simon.wiles@doncater.gov.uk

Access Officer / Social Services (Disability): Mr Pat Higgs, Director - Adults, Health & Wellbeing, Civic Office, Waterdale, Doncaster DN1 3BU ☎ 01302 737620 ✆ pat.higgs@doncaster.gov.uk

Architect, Building / Property Services: Mr Adam Midgley, Head of Property & Construction Services, Civic Office, Waterdale, Doncaster DN1 3BU ☎ 01302 737316 ✆ adam.midgley@doncaster.gov.uk

Building Control: Mr Richard Purcell, Head of Planning, Civic Office, Waterdale, Doncaster DN1 3BU ☎ 01302 734862 ✆ richard.purcell@doncaster.gov.uk

Catering Services: Ms Andrea Swaby, Catering Manager, Civic Office, Waterdale, Doncaster DN1 3BU ☎ 01302 862544 ✆ andrea.swaby@doncaster.gov.uk

Children / Youth Services: Mr Damian Allen, Director - Learning, Opportunities & Skills, Civic Office, Waterdale, Doncaster DN1 3BU
☎ 01302 737102 ✆ damian.allen@doncaster.gov.uk

Civil Registration: Ms Vivien Green, Superintendent Registrar, Register Office, Elmfield Park, South Parade, Doncaster DN1 2EB
☎ 01302 736432 ✆ vivien.green@doncaster.gov.uk

PR / Communications: Ms Steph Cunningham, Head of Communications, Civic Office, Waterdale, Doncaster DN1 3BU
☎ 01302 737988 ✆ steph.cunningham@doncaster.gov.uk

Community Planning: Mr Scott Cardwell, Assistant Director - Development, Civic Office, Waterdale, Doncaster DN1 3BU
☎ 01302 737655 ✆ scott.cardwell@doncaster.gov.uk

Community Safety: Ms Karen Johnson, Assistant Director - Communities, Civic Office, Waterdale, Doncaster DN1 3BU
☎ 01302 862507 ✆ karen.johnson@doncaster.gov.uk

Computer Management: Ms Julie Grant, Assistant Director - Customers, Digital & ICT, Civic Office, Waterdale, Doncaster DN1 3BU ☎ 01302 862496 ✆ julie.grant@doncaster.gov.uk

Consumer Protection and Trading Standards: Mr Dave McMurdo, Trading Standards Manager, Civic Office, Waterdale, Doncaster DN1 3BU ☎ 01302 737522
✆ dave.mcmurdo@doncaster.gov.uk

Contracts: Ms Denise Bann, Head of Procurement, Civic Office, Waterdale, Doncaster DN1 3BU ☎ 01302 862222
✆ denise.bann@doncaster.gov.uk

Corporate Services: Mr Simon Wiles, Director - Finance & Corporate Services, Civic Office, Waterdale, Doncaster DN1 3BU
☎ 01302 736907 ✆ simon.wiles@doncater.gov.uk

Customer Service: Ms Julie Grant, Assistant Director - Customers, Digital & ICT, Civic Office, Waterdale, Doncaster DN1 3BU ☎ 01302 862496 ✆ julie.grant@doncaster.gov.uk

Economic Development: Mr Scott Cardwell, Assistant Director - Development, Civic Office, Waterdale, Doncaster DN1 3BU
☎ 01302 737655 ✆ scott.cardwell@doncaster.gov.uk

Education: Mr Damian Allen, Director - Learning, Opportunities & Skills, Civic Office, Waterdale, Doncaster DN1 3BU ☎ 01302 737102
✆ damian.allen@doncaster.gov.uk

Electoral Registration: Mr Scott Fawcus, Assistant Director - Legal & Democratic Services, Civic Office, Waterdale, Doncaster DN1 3BU ☎ 01302 734640 ✆ scott.fawcus@doncaster.gov.uk

Emergency Planning: Ms Gill Gillies, Assistant Director - Environment, Civic Office, Waterdale, Doncaster DN1 3BU
☎ 01302 736018 ✆ gill.gillies@doncaster.gov.uk

DONCASTER

Energy Management: Mr Dave Wilkinson, Assistant Director - Trading Services & Assets, Civic Office, Waterdale, Doncaster DN1 3BU ☎ 01302 737501 ⌁ dave.wilkinson@doncaster.gov.uk

Environmental / Technical Services: Mr Dave Wilkinson, Assistant Director - Trading Services & Assets, Civic Office, Waterdale, Doncaster DN1 3BU ☎ 01302 737501 ⌁ dave.wilkinson@doncaster.gov.uk

Environmental Health: Ms Gill Gillies, Assistant Director - Environment, Civic Office, Waterdale, Doncaster DN1 3BU ☎ 01302 736018 ⌁ gill.gillies@doncaster.gov.uk

Estates, Property & Valuation: Mr Dave Wilkinson, Assistant Director - Trading Services & Assets, Civic Office, Waterdale, Doncaster DN1 3BU ☎ 01302 737501 ⌁ dave.wilkinson@doncaster.gov.uk

European Liaison: Mr Christian Foster, Head of Strategy & Performance, Civic Office, Waterdale, Doncaster DN1 3BU ☎ 01302 736614 ⌁ christian.foster@doncaster.gov.uk

Facilities: Mr Drew Oxley, Head of Facilities Management, Civic Office, Waterdale, Doncaster DN1 3BU ☎ 01302 736857 ⌁ drew.oxley@doncaster.gov.uk

Finance: Mr Simon Wiles, Director - Finance & Corporate Services, Civic Office, Waterdale, Doncaster DN1 3BU ☎ 01302 736907 ⌁ simon.wiles@doncaster.gov.uk

Fleet Management: Mr Mick Hepple, Fleet Manager, North Bridge Depot, North Bridge Road, Doncaster DN5 9AN ☎ 01302 736810 ⌁ mick.hepple@doncaster.gov.uk

Grounds Maintenance: Ms Gill Gillies, Assistant Director - Environment, Civic Office, Waterdale, Doncaster DN1 3BU ☎ 01302 736018 ⌁ gill.gillies@doncaster.gov.uk

Health and Safety: Mr Peter Harrison, Corporate Health & Safety Manager, Civic Office, Waterdale, Doncaster DN1 3BU ☎ 01302 736095 ⌁ peter.harrison@doncaster.gov.uk

Highways: Mr Lee Garrett, Head of Service - Waste & Highways, Civic Office, Waterdale, Doncaster DN1 3BU ☎ 01302 734499 ⌁ lee.garrett@doncaster.gov.uk

Home Energy Conservation: Mr Richard James Smith, Energy Manager, Civic Office, Waterdale, Doncaster DN1 3BU ☎ 01302 862514 ⌁ richardjames.smith@doncaster.gov.uk

Housing: Mr Scott Cardwell, Assistant Director - Development, Civic Office, Waterdale, Doncaster DN1 3BU ☎ 01302 737655 ⌁ scott.cardwell@doncaster.gov.uk

Housing Maintenance: Ms Susan Jordan, Chief Executive - St Leger Homes of Doncaster, St Leger Court, White Road Way, Doncaster DN4 5ND ☎ 01302 862700 ⌁ susan.jordan@stlegerhomes.co.uk

Local Area Agreement: Mr Lee Tillman, Assistant Director - Strategy & Performance, Civic Office, Waterdale, Doncaster DN1 3BU ☎ 01302 734552 ⌁ lee.tillman@doncaster.gov.uk

Legal: Mr Scott Fawcus, Assistant Director - Legal & Democratic Services, Civic Office, Waterdale, Doncaster DN1 3BU ☎ 01302 734640 ⌁ scott.fawcus@doncaster.gov.uk

Leisure and Cultural Services: Mr Nick Stopforth, Head of Libraries & Culture, Civic Office, Waterdale, Doncaster DN1 3BU ☎ 01302 734298 ⌁ nick.stopforth@doncaster.gov.uk

Licensing: Mr Paul Williams, Business Safety & Licensing Manager, Civic Office, Waterdale, Doncaster DN1 3BU ☎ 01302 737837 ⌁ pj.williams@doncaster.gov.uk

Lifelong Learning: Ms Jennefer Holmes, Head of Service - Skills & Enterprise, Civic Office, Waterdale, Doncaster DN1 3BU ☎ 01302 735810 ⌁ jennefer.holmes@doncaster.gov.uk

Lighting: Mr Andy Rutherford, Head of Service - Streetscene & Highways Operations, Civic Office, Waterdale, Doncaster DN1 3BU ☎ 01302 734494 ⌁ andy.rutherford@doncaster.gov.uk

Lottery Funding, Charity and Voluntary: Mr Christian Foster, Head of Strategy & Performance, Civic Office, Waterdale, Doncaster DN1 3BU ☎ 01302 736614 ⌁ christian.foster@doncaster.gov.uk

Member Services: Mr Andrew Sercombe, Member Support & Scrutiny Manager, Civic Office, Waterdale, Doncaster DN1 3BU ☎ 01302 734354 ⌁ andrew.sercombe@doncaster.gov.uk

Parking: Mr Mark Benton, Team Manager - Vehicles & Contracts, North Bridge Depot, North Bridge Road, Doncaster DN5 9AN ☎ 01302 734001 ⌁ mark.benton@doncaster.gov.uk

Partnerships: Mr Christian Foster, Head of Strategy & Performance, Civic Office, Waterdale, Doncaster DN1 3BU ☎ 01302 736614 ⌁ christian.foster@doncaster.gov.uk

Personnel / HR: Ms Jill Parker, Assistant Director - HR & Communications, Civic Office, Waterdale, Doncaster DN1 3BU ☎ 01302 734444 ⌁ jill.parker@doncaster.gov.uk

Planning: Mr Richard Purcell, Head of Planning, Civic Office, Waterdale, Doncaster DN1 3BU ☎ 01302 734862 ⌁ richard.purcell@doncaster.gov.uk

Procurement: Ms Denise Bann, Head of Procurement, Civic Office, Waterdale, Doncaster DN1 3BU ☎ 01302 862222 ⌁ denise.bann@doncaster.gov.uk

Public Libraries: Mr Nick Stopforth, Head of Libraries & Culture, Civic Office, Waterdale, Doncaster DN1 3BU ☎ 01302 734298 ⌁ nick.stopforth@doncaster.gov.uk

Recycling & Waste Minimisation: Ms Gill Gillies, Assistant Director - Environment, Civic Office, Waterdale, Doncaster DN1 3BU ☎ 01302 736018 ⌁ gill.gillies@doncaster.gov.uk

Regeneration: Mr Scott Cardwell, Assistant Director - Development, Civic Office, Waterdale, Doncaster DN1 3BU ☎ 01302 737655 ⌁ scott.cardwell@doncaster.gov.uk

Road Safety: Mr Lee Garrett, Head of Service - Waste & Highways, Civic Office, Waterdale, Doncaster DN1 3BU
☎ 01302 734499 ✐ lee.garrett@doncaster.gov.uk

Social Services (Adult): Ms Kim Curry, Interim Director - Adults, Health & Wellbeing, Civic Office, Waterdale, Doncaster DN1 3BU
✐ kim.curry@doncaster.gov.uk

Social Services (Children): Mr Paul Moffat, Chief Executive - Doncaster Children's Trust, The Blue Building, 38 - 40 High Street, Doncaster DN1 1DE ☎ 01302 735809 ✐ paul.moffat@dcstrust.co.uk

Fostering & Adoption: Ms Heather Hollingworth, Team Manager, The Blue Building, 38 - 40 High Street, Doncaster DN1 1DE
☎ 01302 736908 ✐ heather.hollingworth@dcstrust.co.uk

Safeguarding: Mr Richard Fawcett, Head of Service - Safeguarding & Standards, The Blue Building, 38 - 40 High Street, Doncaster DN1 1DE ☎ 01302 734523
✐ richard.fawcett@dcstrust.co.uk

Families: Mr Mark Douglas, Chief Operating Officer, The Blue Building, 38 - 40 High Street, Doncaster DN1 1DE
☎ 01302 734323 ✐ mark.douglas@dcstrust.co.uk

Childrens Social Care: Mr Paul Moffat, Chief Executive - Doncaster Children's Trust, The Blue Building, 38 - 40 High Street, Doncaster DN1 1DE ☎ 01302 735809 ✐ paul.moffat@dcstrust.co.uk

Public Health: Dr Rupert Suckling, Director - Public Health, Civic Office, Waterdale, Doncaster DN1 3BU ☎ 01302 734010
✐ rupert.suckling@doncaster.gov.uk

Staff Training: Ms Jill Parker, Assistant Director - Human Resources & Communications, Civic Office, Waterdale, Doncaster DN1 3BU ☎ 01302 737004 ✐ jill.parker@doncaster.gov.uk

Street Scene: Mr Andy Rutherford, Head of Service - Streetscene & Highways Operations, Civic Office, Waterdale, Doncaster DN1 3BU ☎ 01302 734494 ✐ andy.rutherford@doncaster.gov.uk

Sustainable Communities: Ms Gill Gillies, Assistant Director - Environment, Civic Office, Waterdale, Doncaster DN1 3BU
☎ 01302 736018 ✐ gill.gillies@doncaster.gov.uk

Tourism: Ms Lorna Reeve, Destination Manager, Civic Office, Waterdale, Doncaster DN1 3BU ☎ 01302 734066
✐ lorna.reeve@doncaster.gov.uk

Town Centre: Mr Adrian Pickersgill, Head of Commercial Services, Civic Office, Waterdale, Doncaster DN1 3BU ☎ 01302 862777
✐ adrian.pickersgill@doncaster.gov.uk

Traffic Management: Mr Lee Garrett, Head of Service - Waste & Highways, Civic Office, Waterdale, Doncaster DN1 3BU
☎ 01302 734499 ✐ lee.garrett@doncaster.gov.uk

Transport: Mr Lee Garrett, Head of Service - Waste & Highways, Civic Office, Waterdale, Doncaster DN1 3BU ☎ 01302 734499
✐ lee.garrett@doncaster.gov.uk

Transport Planner: Mr Steve Shannon, Strategic Infrastructure Manager, Civic Office, Waterdale, Doncaster DN1 3BU
☎ 01302 862310 ✐ steve.shannon@doncaster.gov.uk

Waste Collection and Disposal: Mr Lee Garrett, Head of Service - Waste & Highways, Civic Office, Waterdale, Doncaster DN1 3BU ☎ 01302 734499 ✐ lee.garrett@doncaster.gov.uk

Waste Management: Mr Lee Garrett, Head of Service - Waste & Highways, Civic Office, Waterdale, Doncaster DN1 3BU
☎ 01302 734499 ✐ lee.garrett@doncaster.gov.uk

Children's Play Areas: Ms Gill Gillies, Assistant Director - Environment, Civic Office, Waterdale, Doncaster DN1 3BU
☎ 01302 736018 ✐ gill.gillies@doncaster.gov.uk

COUNCILLORS

Mayor: Jones, Ros (LAB - No Ward)
ros.jones@doncaster.gov.uk

Deputy Mayor: Jones, Glyn (LAB - Hexthorpe & Balby North)
glyn.jones@doncaster.gov.uk

Group LeaderHart, James (CON - Tickhill & Wadworth)
james.hart@doncaster.gov.uk

Allen, Nick (CON - Bessacarr)
nick.allen@doncaster.gov.uk

Ball, Nigel (LAB - Conisbrough)
nigel.ball@doncaster.gov.uk

Beech, Iris (LAB - Norton & Askern)
iris.beech@doncaster.gov.uk

Blackham, Joe (LAB - Thorne & Moorends)
joe.blackham@doncaster.gov.uk

Blake, Rachael (LAB - Rossington & Bawtry)
rachael.blake@doncaster.gov.uk

Butler, Elsie (LAB - Edlington & Warmsworth)
elsie.butler@doncaster.gov.uk

Chapman, Bev (O - Mexborough)
bev.chapman@doncaster.gov.uk

Cole, Phil (LAB - Edlington & Warmsworth)
phil.cole@doncaster.gov.uk

Cooke, John (IND - Rossington & Bawtry)
john.cooke@doncaster.gov.uk

Corden, Tony (LAB - Armthorpe)
tony.corden@doncaster.gov.uk

Cox, Jane (CON - Finningley)
jane.cox@doncaster.gov.uk

Cox, Steve (CON - Finningley)
steve.cox@doncaster.gov.uk

Credland, Jessie (UKIP - Hatfield)
jessie.credland@doncaster.gov.uk

Curran, Linda (LAB - Hatfield)
linda.curran@doncaster.gov.uk

Derx, George (LAB - Stainforth & Barnby Dun)
george.derx@doncaster.gov.uk

Durant, Susan (LAB - Thorne & Moorends)
susan.durant@doncaster.gov.uk

DONCASTER

Fennelly, Nuala (LAB - Balby South)
nuala.fennelly@doncaster.gov.uk

Gethin, Neil (LAB - Bessacarr)
neil.gethin@doncaster.gov.uk

Gibbons, Sean (O - Mexborough)
sean.gibbons@doncaster.gov.uk

Haith, Pat (LAB - Roman Ridge)
pat.haith@doncaster.gov.uk

Healy, John (LAB - Balby South)
john.healy@doncaster.gov.uk

Hodson, Rachel (LAB - Adwick & Carcroft)
rachel.hodson@doncaster.gov.uk

Hogarth, Charlie (LAB - Bentley)
charlie.hogarth@doncaster.gov.uk

Holland, Sandra (LAB - Conisbrough)
sandra.holland@doncaster.gov.uk

Houlbrook, Mark (LAB - Thorne & Moorends)
mark.houlbrook@doncaster.gov.uk

Hughes, Eva (LAB - Wheatley Hills & Intake)
eva.hughes@doncaster.gov.uk

Jones, Richard Allen (CON - Finningley)
richard.jones@doncaster.gov.uk

Jones, Alan (LAB - Norton & Askern)
a.jones@doncaster.gov.uk

Keegan, Ken (LAB - Stainforth & Barnby Dun)
kenneth.keegan@doncaster.gov.uk

Khan, Majid (LAB - Bessacarr)
majid.khan@doncaster.gov.uk

Kidd, Jane (LAB - Wheatley Hills & Intake)
jane.kidd@doncaster.gov.uk

Kitchen, Ted (LAB - Adwick & Carcroft)
edwin.kitchen@doncaster.gov.uk

Knight, Pat (LAB - Hatfield)
pat.knight@doncaster.gov.uk

Knowles, Sue (LAB - Town)
s.knowles@doncaster.gov.uk

McGuinness, Chris (LAB - Armthorpe)
chris.mcguinness@doncaster.gov.uk

McGuinness, Sue (LAB - Armthorpe)
sue.mcguinness@doncaster.gov.uk

McHale, John (LAB - Town)
john.mchale@doncaster.gov.uk

Mordue, Bill (LAB - Bentley)
bill.mordue@doncaster.gov.uk

Mounsey, John (LAB - Adwick & Carcroft)
john.mounsey@doncaster.gov.uk

Nevett, David (LAB - Edenthorpe & Kirk Sandall)
david.nevett@doncaster.gov.uk

Nightingale, Jane (LAB - Bentley)
jane.nightingale@doncaster.gov.uk

Pickering, Andy (O - Mexborough)
andy.pickering@doncaster.gov.uk

Ransome, Cynthia (CON - Sprotbrough)
cynthia.ransome@doncaster.gov.uk

Robinson, Andrea (LAB - Edenthorpe & Kirk Sandall)
andrea.robinson@doncaster.gov.uk

Rodgers, Kevin (LAB - Roman Ridge)
kevin.rodgers@doncaster.gov.uk

Sahman, Craig (LAB - Conisbrough)
craig.sahman@doncaster.gov.uk

Shaw, Dave (LAB - Town)
dave.shaw@doncaster.gov.uk

Smith, Alan (CON - Tickhill & Wadworth)
alan.smith2@doncaster.gov.uk

Stone, Clive (UKIP - Rossington & Bawtry)
clive.stone@doncaster.gov.uk

White, Austen (LAB - Norton & Askern)
austen.white@doncaster.gov.uk

Wilkinson, Sue (LAB - Hexthorpe & Balby North)
sue.wilkinson@doncaster.gov.uk

Wood, Jonathan (CON - Sprotbrough)
jonathan.wood@doncaster.gov.uk

Wray, Paul (LAB - Wheatley Hills & Intake)
paul.wray@doncaster.gov.uk

POLITICAL COMPOSITION
LAB: 42, CON: 8, O: 3, UKIP: 2, IND: 1

COMMITTEE CHAIRS

Audit: Mr Austen White

Communities & Environment: Ms Jane Kidd

Health & Adult Social Care: Ms Rachael Blake

Health & Wellbeing: Ms Pat Knight

Licensing: Mr Ken Keegan

Planning: Ms Iris Beech

Regeneration & Housing: Mr Paul Wray

Dorset   C

Dorset County Council, County Hall, Colliton Park, Dorchester DT1 1XJ
☎ 01305 221000 🖷 01305 224839 🖳 dorsetdirect@dorsetcc.gov.uk
🖳 www.dorsetforyou.com; www.dorsetforyou.com

FACTS AND FIGURES
EU Constituencies: South West
Election Frequency: Elections are of whole council

PRINCIPAL OFFICERS

Chief Executive: Ms Debbie Ward, Chief Executive, County Hall, Colliton Park, Dorchester DT1 1XJ ☎ 01305 224195 🖳 d.ward@dorsetcc.gov.uk

Assistant Chief Executive: Mr Patrick Ellis, Assistant Chief Executive, County Hall, Colliton Park, Dorchester DT1 1XJ ☎ 01305 224116 🖳 p.ellis@dorsetcc.gov.uk

Senior Management: Ms Helen Coombes, Interim Director - Adult & Community Services, County Hall, Colliton Park, Dorchester DT1 1XJ ☎ 01305 224317 ⌁ helen.coombes@dorsetcc.gov.uk

Senior Management: Mr Mike Harries, Director - Environment & the Economy, County Hall, Colliton Park, Dorchester DT1 1XJ ☎ 01305 224216 ⌁ m.j.harries@dorsetcc.gov.uk

Senior Management: Mr Patrick Myers, Head of Corporate Development, County Hall, Colliton Park, Dorchester DT1 1XJ ☎ 01305 228302 ⌁ p.myers@dorsetcc.gov.uk

Senior Management: Dr David Phillips, Director - Public Health, Princes House, Princes Street, Dorchester DT1 1TP ☎ 01305 225868 ⌁ d.phillips@poole.gov.uk

Senior Management: Mrs Sarah Tough, Director - Children's Services, County Hall, Colliton Park, Dorchester DT1 1XJ ☎ 01305 224165 ⌁ s.tough@dorsetcc.gov.uk

Access Officer / Social Services (Disability): Mr Harry Capron, Head of Adult Care, County Hall, Colliton Park, Dorchester DT1 1XJ ☎ 01305 224363 ⌁ H.Capron@dorsetcc.gov.uk

Architect, Building / Property Services: Mr Mike Harries, Director - Environment & the Economy, County Hall, Colliton Park, Dorchester DT1 1XJ ☎ 01305 224216 ⌁ m.j.harries@dorsetcc.gov.uk

Building Control: Mr Mike Harries, Director - Environment & the Economy, County Hall, Colliton Park, Dorchester DT1 1XJ ☎ 01305 224216 ⌁ m.j.harries@dorsetcc.gov.uk

Catering Services: Mrs Sue Hawkins, Care Catering Services Manager, County Hall, Colliton Park, Dorchester DT1 1XJ ☎ 01305 225930 ⌁ s.hawkins@dorsetcc.gov.uk

Civil Registration: Ms Jo Wenborne-Allen, Registration Service Manager, Dorset History Centre, Bridport Road, Dorchester DT1 1RP ☎ 01305 228909 ⌁ j.wenborne@dorsetcc.gov.uk

Community Safety: Mr Andy Frost, Strategic Manager - Drug Addiction & Community Safety, County Hall, Colliton Park, Dorchester DT1 1XJ ☎ 01305 224331 ⌁ a.frost@dorsetcc.gov.uk

Community Safety: Mrs Kay Wilson-White, Community Safety Business Manager, County Hall, Colliton Park, Dorchester DT1 1XJ ☎ 01305 224768 ⌁ k.wilson-white@dorsetcc.gov.uk

Computer Management: Mr Richard Pascoe, Head of ICT & Customer Services, County Hall, Colliton Park, Dorchester DT1 1XJ ☎ 01305 224712 ⌁ r.j.pascoe@dorsetcc.gov.uk

Consumer Protection and Trading Standards: Mr Ivan Hancock, Trading Standards Service Manager, Colliton Annexe, Colliton Park, Dorchester DT1 1XJ ☎ 01305 224956 ⌁ l.n.hancock@dorsetcc.gov.uk

Contracts: Ms Karen Andrews, Group Manager - Corporate Development, County Hall, Colliton Park, Dorchester DT1 1XJ ☎ 01305 221260 ⌁ k.andrews@dorsetcc.gov.uk

Customer Service: Mr Simon Bailey, Customer Services Manager, County Hall, Colliton Park, Dorchester DT1 1XJ ☎ 01305 221762 ⌁ simon.bailey@dorset.gov.uk

Economic Development: Mr Dave Walsh, Team Leader - Economy & Enterprise, County Hall, Colliton Park, Dorchester DT1 1XJ ☎ 01305 224254 ⌁ d.walsh@dorsetcc.gov.uk

Education: Mr Phillip Minns, Head of Learning & Inclusion Services, County Hall, Colliton Park, Dorchester DT1 1XJ ☎ 01305 224770 ⌁ p.minns@dorsetcc.gov.uk

Education: Mrs Sarah Tough, Director - Children's Services, County Hall, Colliton Park, Dorchester DT1 1XJ ☎ 01305 224165 ⌁ s.tough@dorsetcc.gov.uk

E-Government: Mr Richard Pascoe, Head of ICT & Customer Services, County Hall, Colliton Park, Dorchester DT1 1XJ ☎ 01305 224712 ⌁ r.j.pascoe@dorsetcc.gov.uk

Electoral Registration: Mr Lee Gallagher, Democratic Services Manager, County Hall, Colliton Park, Dorchester DT1 1XJ ☎ 01305 224191 ⌁ l.d.gallagher@dorsetcc.gov.uk

Emergency Planning: Mr Simon Parker, County Emergency Planning Officer, County Hall, Colliton Park, Dorchester DT1 1XJ ☎ 01305 224510 ⌁ s.parker@dorsetcc.gov.uk

Energy Management: Mr Mike Petitdemange, Sustainable Community Team Leader, Princes House, Princes Street, Dorchester DT1 1TP ☎ 01305 225279 ⌁ m.j.petitdemange@dorsetcc.gov.uk

Environmental / Technical Services: Mr Peter Moore, Head of Environment, County Hall, Colliton Park, Dorchester DT1 1XJ ☎ 01305 224285 ⌁ p.k.moore@dorsetcc.gov.uk

Environmental / Technical Services: Mr Matthew Piles, Head of Economy, County Hall, Colliton Park, Dorchester DT1 1XJ ☎ 01305 221336 ⌁ m.d.piles@dorsetcc.gov.uk

Estates, Property & Valuation: Mr Peter Scarlett, Estates & Assets Service Manager, County Hall, Colliton Park, Dorchester DT1 1XJ ☎ 01305 221940 ⌁ p.scarlett@dorsetcc.gov.uk

European Liaison: Mr Jon Bird, European Policy & Funding Officer, County Hall, Colliton Park, Dorchester DT1 1XJ ☎ 01305 221895 ⌁ j.bird@dorsetcc.gov.uk

Facilities: Mr Andrew Turner, Team Leader - Operational Estate Management, County Hall, Colliton Park, Dorchester DT1 1XJ ☎ 01305 221943 ⌁ a.p.turner@dorsetcc.gov.uk

Finance: Mr Richard Bates, Head of Financial Services, County Hall, Colliton Park, Dorchester DT1 1XJ ☎ 01305 224303 ⌁ r.m.bates@dorsetcc.gov.uk

Finance: Mr Jim McManus, Chief Accountant, County Hall, Colliton Park, Dorchester DT1 1XJ ☎ 01305 221235 ⌁ j.mcmanus@dorsetcc.gov.uk

DORSET

Finance: Mr Andy Smith, Group Finance Manager, County Hall, Colliton Park, Dorchester DT1 1XJ ☎ 01305 224031 ⌨ a.g.smith@dorsetcc.gov.uk

Treasury: Mr Nick Buckland, Chief Treasury & Pension Manager, County Hall, Colliton Park, Dorchester DT1 1XJ ☎ 01305 224763 ⌨ n.j.buckland@dorsetcc.gov.uk

Pensions: Mr Nick Buckland, Chief Treasury & Pension Manager, County Hall, Colliton Park, Dorchester DT1 1XJ ☎ 01305 224763 ⌨ n.j.buckland@dorsetcc.gov.uk

Fleet Management: Mr Sean Adams, Fleet Services Manager, County Hall, Colliton Park, Dorchester DT1 1XJ ☎ 01305 221263 ⌨ s.w.adams@dorsetcc.gov.uk

Fleet Management: Mr Andrew Martin, Head of Dorset Highways, County Hall, Colliton Park, Dorchester DT1 1XJ ☎ 01305 228182 ⌨ a.j.martin@dorsetcc.gov.uk

Health and Safety: Mr Ian Burke, Health & Safety Manager, Charminster Depot, Wanchard Lane, Charminster, Dorchester DT2 9RP ☎ 01963 365923 ⌨ i.s.burke@dorsetcc.gov.uk

Highways: Mr Andrew Martin, Head of Dorset Highways, County Hall, Colliton Park, Dorchester DT1 1XJ ☎ 01305 228182 ⌨ a.j.martin@dorsetcc.gov.uk

Legal: Mr Jonathan Mair, Head of Legal & Democratic Services, County Hall, Colliton Park, Dorchester DT1 1XJ ☎ 01305 224181 ⌨ j.e.mair@dorsetcc.gov.uk

Leisure and Cultural Services: Mr Paul Leivers, Head of Early Help & Community Services, Library Headquarters, Colliton Park, Dorchester DT1 1XJ ☎ 01305 224453 ⌨ p.leivers@dorsetcc.gov.uk

Licensing: Mr Ivan Hancock, Trading Standards Service Manager, Colliton Annexe, Colliton Park, Dorchester DT1 1XJ ☎ 01305 224956 ⌨ l.n.hancock@dorsetcc.gov.uk

Lifelong Learning: Mr Paul Leivers, Head of Early Help & Community Services, Library Headquarters, Colliton Park, Dorchester DT1 1XJ ☎ 01305 224453 ⌨ p.leivers@dorsetcc.gov.uk

Lighting: Mr Rod Mainstone, Streetlighting Team Leader, County Hall, Colliton Park, Dorchester DT1 1XJ ☎ 01305 225355 ⌨ r.l.mainstone@dorsetcc.gov.uk

Lottery Funding, Charity and Voluntary: Mr Chris Scally, Corporate Policy & Performance Officer, County Hall, Colliton Park, Dorchester DT1 1XJ ☎ 01305 228624 ⌨ c.scally@dorsetcc.gov.uk

Member Services: Mr Lee Gallagher, Democratic Services Manager, County Hall, Colliton Park, Dorchester DT1 1XJ ☎ 01305 224191 ⌨ l.d.gallagher@dorsetcc.gov.uk

Parking: Mr Simon Gledhill, Network Management Services Manager, County Hall, Colliton Park, Dorchester DT1 1XJ ☎ 01305 228141 ⌨ s.t.gledhill@dorsetcc.gov.uk

Partnerships: Ms Jay Mercer, Head of Strategy, Partnerships & Performance, County Hall, Colliton Park, Dorchester DT1 1XJ ☎ 01305 228244 ⌨ jay.mercer@dorsetcc.gov.uk

Personnel / HR: Miss Sheralyn Huntingford, Head of Human Resources & Organisational Development, County Hall, Colliton Park, Dorchester DT1 1XJ ☎ 01305 224617 ⌨ s.huntingford@dorsetcc.gov.uk

Procurement: Ms Karen Andrews, Group Manager - Corporate Development, County Hall, Colliton Park, Dorchester DT1 1XJ ☎ 01305 221260 ⌨ k.andrews@dorsetcc.gov.uk

Public Libraries: Mr Paul Leivers, Head of Early Help & Community Services, Library Headquarters, Colliton Park, Dorchester DT1 1XJ ☎ 01305 224453 ⌨ p.leivers@dorsetcc.gov.uk

Recycling & Waste Minimisation: Ms Gemma Clinton, Head of Strategy, Princes House, Princes Street, Dorchester DT1 1TP ☎ 01305 224716 ⌨ g.clinton@dorsetcc.gov.uk

Regeneration: Mr Dave Walsh, Team Leader - Economy & Enterprise, County Hall, Colliton Park, Dorchester DT1 1XJ ☎ 01305 224254 ⌨ d.walsh@dorsetcc.gov.uk

Road Safety: Mr Andrew Shaw, Dorset Travel Team Service Manager, County Hall, Colliton Park, Dorchester DT1 1XJ ☎ 01305 224237 ⌨ a.d.shaw@dorsetcc.gov.uk

Social Services (Adult): Mr Harry Capron, Head of Adult Care, County Hall, Colliton Park, Dorchester DT1 1XJ ☎ 01305 224363 ⌨ H.Capron@dorsetcc.gov.uk

Social Services (Adult): Ms Helen Coombes, Interim Director - Adult & Community Services, County Hall, Colliton Park, Dorchester DT1 1XJ ☎ 01305 224317 ⌨ helen.coombes@dorsetcc.gov.uk

Social Services (Adult): Ms Jay Mercer, Head of Strategy, Partnerships & Performance, County Hall, Colliton Park, Dorchester DT1 1XJ ☎ 01305 228244 ⌨ jay.mercer@dorsetcc.gov.uk

Social Services (Children): Mrs Anne Salter, Head of Strategy, Partnerships & Performance, County Hall, Colliton Park, Dorchester DT1 1XJ ☎ 01305 224163 ⌨ a.salter@dorsetcc.gov.uk

Social Services (Children): Mrs Sarah Tough, Director - Children's Services, County Hall, Colliton Park, Dorchester DT1 1XJ ☎ 01305 224165 ⌨ s.tough@dorsetcc.gov.uk

Fostering & Adoption: Mrs Vanessa Glenn, Head of Family Support, County Hall, Colliton Park, Dorchester DT1 1XJ ☎ 01305 224328 ⌨ v.glenn@dorsetcc.gov.uk

Safeguarding: Mr Michael Hall, Designated Safeguarding Manager, County Hall, Colliton Park, Dorchester DT1 1XJ ☎ 01305 228375 ⌨ michael.hall@dorsetcc.gov.uk

Families: Mrs Vanessa Glenn, Head of Family Support, County Hall, Colliton Park, Dorchester DT1 1XJ ☎ 01305 224328 ⌨ v.glenn@dorsetcc.gov.uk

Looked after Children: Mrs Vanessa Glenn, Head of Family Support, County Hall, Colliton Park, Dorchester DT1 1XJ ☎ 01305 224328 ✆ v.glenn@dorsetcc.gov.uk

Childrens Social Care: Mrs Penny Lodwick, Senior Manager - Family Support, Ferndown Local Officer, Penny's Walk, Ferndown BH22 9JY ☎ 01202 868222 ✆ p.lodwick@dorsetcc.gov.uk

Childrens Social Care: Mr Stuart Riddle, Senior Manager - Family Support, Children's Services Directorate, County Hall, Colliton Street, Dorchester DT1 1XJ ☎ 01305 225089 ✆ S.Riddle@dorsetcc.gcsx.gov.uk

Childrens Social Care: Mr Kevin Stenlake, Senior Manager - Family Support, Sturminster Newton Local Office, Bath Road, Dorchester DT10 1DR ☎ 01258 475681 ✆ k.j.stenlake@dorsetcc.gov.uk

Public Health: Dr David Phillips, Director - Public Health, Princes House, Princes Street, Dorchester DT1 1TP ☎ 01305 225868 ✆ d.phillips@poole.gov.uk

Staff Training: Mrs Helen Sotheran, Learning & Development Manager, County Hall, Colliton Park, Dorchester DT1 1XJ ☎ 01305 224088 ✆ h.l.sotheran@dorsetcc.gov.uk

Street Scene: Ms Karen Punchard, Director - Dorset Waste Partnership, Princes House, Princes Street, Dorchester DT1 1TP ☎ 01305 225459 ✆ k.punchard@dorsetwastepartnership.gov.uk

Sustainable Development: Ms Kate Hall, Community Energy Team Leader, County Hall, Colliton Park, Dorchester DT1 1XJ ☎ 01305 224774 ✆ k.m.hall@dorsetcc.gov.uk

Tourism: Mr Dave Walsh, Team Leader - Economy & Enterprise, County Hall, Colliton Park, Dorchester DT1 1XJ ☎ 01305 224254 ✆ d.walsh@dorsetcc.gov.uk

Transport: Mr Chris Hook, Travel Operations Manager, County Hall, Colliton Park, Dorchester DT1 1XJ ☎ 01305 225141 ✆ c.p.hook@dorsetcc.gov.uk

Transport Planner: Mr Matthew Piles, Head of Economy, County Hall, Colliton Park, Dorchester DT1 1XJ ☎ 01305 221336 ✆ m.d.piles@dorsetcc.gov.uk

Waste Collection and Disposal: Ms Karen Punchard, Director - Dorset Waste Partnership, Princes House, Princes Street, Dorchester DT1 1TP ☎ 01305 225459 ✆ k.punchard@dorsetwastepartnership.gov.uk

Waste Management: Ms Karen Punchard, Director - Dorset Waste Partnership, Princes House, Princes Street, Dorchester DT1 1TP ☎ 01305 225459 ✆ k.punchard@dorsetwastepartnership.gov.uk

COUNCILLORS

ChairCattaway, Andrew (CON - Stour Vale)
a.r.cattaway@dorsetcc.gov.uk

Vice-ChairCox, Hilary (CON - Winterborne)
h.a.cox@dorsetcc.gov.uk

Leader of the Council: Gould, Robert (CON - Sherborne)
r.gould@dorsetcc.gov.uk

Deputy Leader of the Council: Finney, Peter (CON - West Moors & Holt)
p.finney@dorsetcc.gov.uk

Group LeaderDover, Janet (LD - Colehill & Stapehill)
j.dover@dorsetcc.gov.uk

Group LeaderKimber, Paul (LAB - Portland Tophill)
p.kimber@dorsetcc.gov.uk

Batstone, Pauline (CON - Blackmore Vale)
p.h.batstone@dorsetcc.gov.uk

Biggs, Richard (LD - Dorchester)
r.m.biggs@dorsetcc.gov.uk

Butler, Steve (CON - Cranborne Chase)
steve.butler@dorsetcc.gov.uk

Byatt, Mike (LAB - Weymouth Town)
m.byatt@dorsetcc.gov.uk

Canning, Andy (LD - Linden Lea)
a.canning@dorsetcc.gov.uk

Coatsworth, Ronald (CON - Bride Valley)
r.w.coatsworth@dorsetcc.gov.uk

Cook, Robin (CON - Minister)
r.cook@dorsetcc.gov.uk

Coombs, Toni (CON - Verwood & Three Legged Cross)
t.b.coombs@dorsetcc.gov.uk

Cooper, Barrie (LD - Blandford)
b.g.cooper@dorsetcc.gov.uk

Croney, Deborah (CON - Hambledon)
d.croney@dorsetcc.gov.uk

Dedman, Lesley (CON - Mudeford & Highcliffe)
l.m.dedman@dorsetcc.gov.uk

Drane, Fred (LD - Lytchett)
f.h.drane@dorsetcc.gov.uk

Ezzard, Beryl (LD - Wareham)
b.r.ezzard@dorsetcc.gov.uk

Flower, Spencer (CON - Verwood & Three Legged Cross)
s.g.flower@dorsetcc.gov.uk

Gardner, Ian (CON - Chickerell & Chesil Bank)
i.gardner@dorsetcc.gov.uk

Hall, Peter (CON - Christchurch Central)
p.r.hall@dorsetcc.gov.uk

Hall, Matthew (LD - Sherborne Rural)
mnwh1976@sky.com

Harris, David (LD - Westham)
david.harris@dorsetcc.gov.uk

Haynes, Jill (CON - Three Valleys)
jill.haynes@dorsetcc.gov.uk

Jamieson, Colin (CON - Highcliffe & Walkford)
c.jamieson@dorsetcc.gov.uk

Jefferies, Susan (LD - Corfe Mullen)
s.jefferies@dorsetcc.gov.uk

Jeffery, Mervyn (LD - Shaftesbury)
m.jeffrey@dorsetcc.gov.uk

Jones, David (CON - Burton Grange)
david.jones@dorsetcc.gov.uk

DORSET

Jones, Trevor (LD - Dorchester)
d.t.jones@dorsetcc.gov.uk

Kayes, Ros (LD - Bridport)
r.kayes@dorsetcc.gov.uk

Knox, Rebecca (CON - Beaminster)
r.knox@dorsetcc.gov.uk

Lovell, Mike (CON - Purbeck Hills)
m.w.lovell@dorsetcc.gov.uk

Mannings, David (LD - Lodmoor)
d.g.mannings@dorsetcc.gov.uk

Phipps, Margaret (CON - Commons)
m.phipps@dorsetcc.gov.uk

Richardson, Peter (CON - St Leonards & St Ives)
p.richardson@dorsetcc.gov.uk

Smith, Ian (UKIP - Ferndown)
i.m.smith@dorsetcc.gov.uk

Sutton, Clare (GRN - Rodwell)
clare.sutton@dorsetcc.gov.uk

Tewkesbury, Mark (LAB - Broadwey)
m.tewkesbury@dorsetcc.gov.uk

Trite, William (CON - Swanage)
w.trite@dorsetcc.gov.uk

Turner, Daryl (CON - Marshwood Vale)
d.w.turner@dorsetcc.gov.uk

Walsh, David (CON - Gillingham)
david.walsh@dorsetcc.gov.uk

Wharf, Peter (CON - Egdon Heath)
p.k.wharf@dorsetcc.gov.uk

Wheller, Kate (LAB - Portland Harbour)
k.wheller@dorsetcc.gov.uk

Wilson, John (CON - Ferndown)
j.l.wilson@dorsetcc.gov.uk

POLITICAL COMPOSITION
CON: 26, LD: 13, LAB: 4, GRN: 1, UKIP: 1

COMMITTEE CHAIRS

Audit & Governance: Mr Trevor Jones

Health & Wellbeing: Mrs Rebecca Knox

People & Communities: Mr David Walsh

Dover   D

Dover District Council, Council Offices, White Cliffs Business
Park, Dover CT16 3PJ
☎ 01304 821199 🖷 01304 872300 ᷐ customerservices@dover.gov.uk
🖳 www.dover.gov.uk

FACTS AND FIGURES
Parliamentary Constituencies: Dover
EU Constituencies: South East
Election Frequency: Elections are of whole council

PRINCIPAL OFFICERS

Chief Executive: Mr Nadeem Aziz, Chief Executive, Council
Offices, White Cliffs Business Park, Dover CT16 3PJ
☎ 01304 872400 ᷐ nadeemaziz@dover.gov.uk

Senior Management: Mr Mike Davis, Director - Finance, Housing
& Community, Council Offices, White Cliffs Business Park, Dover
CT16 3PJ ☎ 01304 872107 ᷐ mikedavis@dover.gov.uk

Senior Management: Mr David Randall, Director - Governance,
Council Offices, White Cliffs Business Park, Dover CT16 3PJ
☎ 01304 872141 ᷐ davidrandall@dover.gov.uk

Senior Management: Mr Roger Walton, Director - Environment
& Corporate Assets, Council Offices, White Cliffs Business Park,
Dover CT16 3PJ ☎ 01304 872240 ᷐ rogerwalton@dover.gov.uk

Architect, Building / Property Services: Mr Roger Walton,
Director - Environment & Corporate Assets, Council Offices, White
Cliffs Business Park, Dover CT16 3PJ ☎ 01304 872240
᷐ rogerwalton@dover.gov.uk

Building Control: Mr Roger Walton, Director - Environment &
Corporate Assets, Council Offices, White Cliffs Business Park,
Dover CT16 3PJ ☎ 01304 872240 ᷐ rogerwalton@dover.gov.uk

PR / Communications: Mr Mike Davis, Director - Finance,
Housing & Community, Council Offices, White Cliffs Business Park,
Dover CT16 3PJ ☎ 01304 872107 ᷐ mikedavis@dover.gov.uk

Community Safety: Mr Roger Walton, Director - Environment
& Corporate Assets, Council Offices, White Cliffs Business Park,
Dover CT16 3PJ ☎ 01304 872240 ᷐ rogerwalton@dover.gov.uk

Computer Management: Mr Sean Hale, Head of ICT, EK
Services, Military Road, Canterbury CT1 1YW ☎ 01227 862341
᷐ sean.hale@ekservices.org

Contracts: Mr Mike Davis, Director - Finance, Housing &
Community, Council Offices, White Cliffs Business Park, Dover
CT16 3PJ ☎ 01304 872107 ᷐ mikedavis@dover.gov.uk

Corporate Services: Mr David Randall, Director - Governance,
Council Offices, White Cliffs Business Park, Dover CT16 3PJ
☎ 01304 872141 ᷐ davidrandall@dover.gov.uk

Economic Development: Mr Nadeem Aziz, Chief Executive,
Council Offices, White Cliffs Business Park, Dover CT16 3PJ
☎ 01304 872400 ᷐ nadeemaziz@dover.gov.uk

E-Government: Mrs Roz Edridge, Business Systems Manager,
East Kent Services, Council Offices, Cecil Street, Margate CT9 1XZ
☎ 01843 577033 ᷐ roz.edridge@ekservices.org

Electoral Registration: Mr Nadeem Aziz, Chief Executive,
Council Offices, White Cliffs Business Park, Dover CT16 3PJ
☎ 01304 872400 ᷐ nadeemaziz@dover.gov.uk

Emergency Planning: Mr David Randall, Director - Governance,
Council Offices, White Cliffs Business Park, Dover CT16 3PJ
☎ 01304 872141 ᷐ davidrandall@dover.gov.uk

Energy Management: Mr Roger Walton, Director - Environment & Corporate Assets, Council Offices, White Cliffs Business Park, Dover CT16 3PJ ☎ 01304 872240 ⌁ rogerwalton@dover.gov.uk

Environmental / Technical Services: Mr Roger Walton, Director - Environment & Corporate Assets, Council Offices, White Cliffs Business Park, Dover CT16 3PJ ☎ 01304 872240 ⌁ rogerwalton@dover.gov.uk

Environmental Health: Mr David Randall, Director - Governance, Council Offices, White Cliffs Business Park, Dover CT16 3PJ ☎ 01304 872141 ⌁ davidrandall@dover.gov.uk

Estates, Property & Valuation: Mr Roger Walton, Director - Environment & Corporate Assets, Council Offices, White Cliffs Business Park, Dover CT16 3PJ ☎ 01304 872240 ⌁ rogerwalton@dover.gov.uk

Events Manager: Mr Mike Davis, Director - Finance, Housing & Community, Council Offices, White Cliffs Business Park, Dover CT16 3PJ ☎ 01304 872107 ⌁ mikedavis@dover.gov.uk

Facilities: Mr Roger Walton, Director - Environment & Corporate Assets, Council Offices, White Cliffs Business Park, Dover CT16 3PJ ☎ 01304 872240 ⌁ rogerwalton@dover.gov.uk

Finance: Mr Mike Davis, Director - Finance, Housing & Community, Council Offices, White Cliffs Business Park, Dover CT16 3PJ ☎ 01304 872107 ⌁ mikedavis@dover.gov.uk

Treasury: Mr Mike Davis, Director - Finance, Housing & Community, Council Offices, White Cliffs Business Park, Dover CT16 3PJ ☎ 01304 872107 ⌁ mikedavis@dover.gov.uk

Fleet Management: Mr Mike Davis, Director - Finance, Housing & Community, Council Offices, White Cliffs Business Park, Dover CT16 3PJ ☎ 01304 872107 ⌁ mikedavis@dover.gov.uk

Grounds Maintenance: Mr Roger Walton, Director - Environment & Corporate Assets, Council Offices, White Cliffs Business Park, Dover CT16 3PJ ☎ 01304 872240 ⌁ rogerwalton@dover.gov.uk

Health and Safety: Mr David Randall, Director - Governance, Council Offices, White Cliffs Business Park, Dover CT16 3PJ ☎ 01304 872141 ⌁ davidrandall@dover.gov.uk

Home Energy Conservation: Mr Roger Walton, Director - Environment & Corporate Assets, Council Offices, White Cliffs Business Park, Dover CT16 3PJ ☎ 01304 872240 ⌁ rogerwalton@dover.gov.uk

Housing: Mr Mike Davis, Director - Finance, Housing & Community, Council Offices, White Cliffs Business Park, Dover CT16 3PJ ☎ 01304 872107 ⌁ mikedavis@dover.gov.uk

Housing Maintenance: Mr David Ashby, Head of Asset Management, East Kent Housing Ltd, 3 - 5 Shorncliffe Road, Folkestone CT20 2SQ ☎ 01303 853749 ⌁ david.ashby@eastkenthousing.org.uk

Legal: Mr Harvey Rudd, Solicitor to the Council, Council Offices, White Cliffs Business Park, Dover CT16 3PJ ☎ 01304 872321 ⌁ harveyrudd@dover.gov.uk

Leisure and Cultural Services: Mr Roger Walton, Director - Environment & Corporate Assets, Council Offices, White Cliffs Business Park, Dover CT16 3PJ ☎ 01304 872240 ⌁ rogerwalton@dover.gov.uk

Licensing: Mr David Randall, Director - Governance, Council Offices, White Cliffs Business Park, Dover CT16 3PJ ☎ 01304 872141 ⌁ davidrandall@dover.gov.uk

Lighting: Mr Roger Walton, Director - Environment & Corporate Assets, Council Offices, White Cliffs Business Park, Dover CT16 3PJ ☎ 01304 872240 ⌁ rogerwalton@dover.gov.uk

Lottery Funding, Charity and Voluntary: Mr Mike Davis, Director - Finance, Housing & Community, Council Offices, White Cliffs Business Park, Dover CT16 3PJ ☎ 01304 872107 ⌁ mikedavis@dover.gov.uk

Member Services: Mr David Randall, Director - Governance, Council Offices, White Cliffs Business Park, Dover CT16 3PJ ☎ 01304 872141 ⌁ davidrandall@dover.gov.uk

Parking: Mr Roger Walton, Director - Environment & Corporate Assets, Council Offices, White Cliffs Business Park, Dover CT16 3PJ ☎ 01304 872240 ⌁ rogerwalton@dover.gov.uk

Partnerships: Mr Mike Davis, Director - Finance, Housing & Community, Council Offices, White Cliffs Business Park, Dover CT16 3PJ ☎ 01304 872107 ⌁ mikedavis@dover.gov.uk

Personnel / HR: Ms Juli Oliver-Smith, Head of EK Human Resources, East Kent HR Partnership, Dover District Council, White Cliffs Business Park, Whitfield, Dover CT16 3PJ ☎ 07917 473616 ⌁ hrpartnership@dover.gov.uk

Planning: Mr Nadeem Aziz, Chief Executive, Council Offices, White Cliffs Business Park, Dover CT16 3PJ ☎ 01304 872400 ⌁ nadeemaziz@dover.gov.uk

Procurement: Mr Mike Davis, Director - Finance, Housing & Community, Council Offices, White Cliffs Business Park, Dover CT16 3PJ ☎ 01304 872107 ⌁ mikedavis@dover.gov.uk

Recycling & Waste Minimisation: Mr Roger Walton, Director - Environment & Corporate Assets, Council Offices, White Cliffs Business Park, Dover CT16 3PJ ☎ 01304 872240 ⌁ rogerwalton@dover.gov.uk

Regeneration: Mr Tim Ingleton, Head of Inward Investment, Council Offices, White Cliffs Business Park, Dover CT16 3PJ ☎ 01304 872423 ⌁ timingleton@dover.gov.uk

Staff Training: Mr David Randall, Director - Governance, Council Offices, White Cliffs Business Park, Dover CT16 3PJ ☎ 01304 872141 ⌁ davidrandall@dover.gov.uk

DOVER

Street Scene: Mr Roger Walton, Director - Environment & Corporate Assets, Council Offices, White Cliffs Business Park, Dover CT16 3PJ ☎ 01304 872240 ⌨ rogerwalton@dover.gov.uk

Sustainable Communities: Mr Mike Davis, Director - Finance, Housing & Community, Council Offices, White Cliffs Business Park, Dover CT16 3PJ ☎ 01304 872107 ⌨ mikedavis@dover.gov.uk

Tourism: Mr Roger Walton, Director - Environment & Corporate Assets, Council Offices, White Cliffs Business Park, Dover CT16 3PJ ☎ 01304 872240 ⌨ rogerwalton@dover.gov.uk

Traffic Management: Mr Roger Walton, Director - Environment & Corporate Assets, Council Offices, White Cliffs Business Park, Dover CT16 3PJ ☎ 01304 872240 ⌨ rogerwalton@dover.gov.uk

Waste Collection and Disposal: Mr Roger Walton, Director - Environment & Corporate Assets, Council Offices, White Cliffs Business Park, Dover CT16 3PJ ☎ 01304 872240 ⌨ rogerwalton@dover.gov.uk

Waste Management: Mr Roger Walton, Director - Environment & Corporate Assets, Council Offices, White Cliffs Business Park, Dover CT16 3PJ ☎ 01304 872240 ⌨ rogerwalton@dover.gov.uk

COUNCILLORS

ChairChandler, Susan (CON - Little Stour & Ashstone)
cllrsusanchandler@dover.gov.uk

Vice-ChairHannent, David (CON - Whitfield)
cllrdavid.hannent@dover.gov.uk

Leader of the Council: Watkins, Paul (CON - St Margaret's-at-Cliffe)
cllrpaulwatkins@dover.gov.uk

Deputy Leader of the Council: Connolly, Michael (CON - Little Stour & Ashstone)
cllrmichaelconolly@dover.gov.uk

Group LeaderEddy, Mike (LAB - Mill Hill)
cllrmichaeleddy@dover.gov.uk

Group LeaderRichardson, Andrew (UKIP - Maxton, Elms Vale & Priory)
cllrandrew.richardon@dover.gov.uk

Back, Jim (CON - Whitfield)
cllrjames.back@dover.gov.uk

Bannister, Simon (LAB - Buckland)
cllrsimon.bannister@dover.gov.uk

Bartlett, Trevor (CON - Little Stour & Ashstone)
cllrtrevorbartlett@dover.gov.uk

Beresford, Pauline (CON - River)
cllrpauline.beresford@dover.gov.uk

Bond, Trevor (CON - Middle Deal & Sholden)
cllrtrevorbond@dover.gov.uk

Brivio, Pamela (LAB - Tower Hamlets)
cllrpamela.brivio@dover.gov.uk

Butcher, Bernard (CON - Sandwich)
cllrbernardbutcher@dover.gov.uk

Carter, Paul (CON - Sandwich)
cllrpaul.carter@dover.gov.uk

Collor, Nigel (CON - Castle)
cllrnigelcollor@dover.gov.uk

Cosin, Margaret (LAB - Mill Hill)
cllrmargaret.cosin@dover.gov.uk

Cronk, David (LAB - Middle Deal & Sholden)
cllrdavid.cronk@dover.gov.uk

Dixon, Nicholas (CON - River)
cllrnicholas.dixon@dover.gov.uk

Friend, Adrian (CON - North Deal)
cllradrian.friend@dover.gov.uk

Frost, Bob (CON - North Deal)
cllrbobfrost@dover.gov.uk

Gardner, Bill (LAB - North Deal)
billkimi@hotmail.co.uk

Glayzer, Ben (UKIP - Tower Hamlets)
cllrben.glayzer@dover.gov.uk

Hawkins, Pam (LAB - Middle Deal & Sholden)
cllrpamela.hawkins@dover.gov.uk

Heath, Patrick (CON - Walmer)
cllrpatrickheath@dover.gov.uk

Heron, John (LAB - Maxton, Elms Vale & Priory)
cllrjohn.heron@dover.gov.uk

Hill, Susan (LAB - Buckland)
cllr.susan.hill@dover.gov.uk

Holloway, Michael (CON - Sandwich)
cllrmichael.holloway@dover.gov.uk

Johnstone, Thomas (LAB - Aylesham)
cllr.thomas.johnstone@dover.gov.uk

Jones, Sue (LAB - St Radigunds)
cllrsue.jones@dover.gov.uk

Keen, Linda (LAB - Aylesham)
linda.keen@clara.co.uk

Kenton, Nicholas (CON - Eastry)
cllrnicholaskenton@dover.gov.uk

Le Chevalier, Sue (CON - Ringwould)
cllrsuzannelechevalier@dover.gov.uk

Le Chevalier, Paul (CON - Walmer)
cllrpaullechevalier@dover.gov.uk

Manion, Stephen (CON - Eastry)
cllrstephenmanion@dover.gov.uk

Mills, Kevin (LAB - St Radigunds)
cllrkevinmills@dover.gov.uk

Morris, Keith (CON - St Margaret's-at-Cliffe)
cllrkeith.morris@dover.gov.uk

Murphy, Derek (CON - Walmer)
cllrderek.murphy@dover.gov.uk

Ovenden, Marjorie (Mog) (CON - Eythorne & Shepherdswell)
cllrmogovenden@dover.gov.uk

Pollitt, Sid (LAB - Mill Hill)
cllrsid.pollitt@dover.gov.uk

Rapley, Georgette (UKIP - Town & Pier)
cllrgeorgette.rapley@dover.gov.uk

Rose, Mark (CON - Lydden and Temple Ewell)
cllrmark.rose@dover .gov.uk

Sargent, Daniel (LAB - Buckland)
cllrdaniel.sargent@dover.gov.uk

Scales, Frederick (CON - Capel-le-Ferne)
cllrfrederickscales@dover.gov.uk

Walker, Peter (LAB - Eythorne & Shepherdswell)
cllrpeterwalker@dover.gov.uk

Wallace, Peter (LAB - Maxton, Elms Vale & Priory)
cllrpeterwallace@dover.gov.uk

POLITICAL COMPOSITION
CON: 25, LAB: 17, UKIP: 3

COMMITTEE CHAIRS

Planning: Mr Frederick Scales

Dudley M

Dudley Metropolitan Borough Council, The Council House, Priory Road, Dudley DY1 1HF
☎ 0300 555 2345 🖷 01384 815275 ⌁ dudleycouncilplus@dudley.gov.uk
🖳 www.dudley.gov.uk

FACTS AND FIGURES
Parliamentary Constituencies: Dudley North, Dudley South, Halesowen and Rowley Regis, Stourbridge
EU Constituencies: West Midlands
Election Frequency: Elections are by thirds

PRINCIPAL OFFICERS

Chief Executive: Ms Sarah Norman, Chief Executive, The Council House, Priory Road, Dudley DY1 1HF ☎ 01384 815201
⌁ sarah.norman@dudley.gov.uk

Senior Management: Dr Deborah Harkins, Chief Officer - Health & Wellbeing, Falcon House, 8th Floor, The Minories, Dudley DY2 8PG ☎ 01384 816239 ⌁ deborah.harkins@dudley.gov.uk

Senior Management: Mr Alan Lunt, Strategic Director - Place, The Council House, Priory Road, Dudley DY1 1HF ☎ 01384 814150 ⌁ alan.lunt@dudley.gov.uk

Senior Management: Mr Tony Oakman, Strategic Director - People, The Council House, Priory Road, Dudley DY1 1HF ☎ 01384 815800 ⌁ tony.oakman@dudley.gov.uk

Access Officer / Social Services (Disability): Mr Matt Bowsher, Chief Officer - Adult Social Care, 3 - 5 St James's Road, Dudley DY1 1HZ ☎ 01384 815886 ⌁ matt.bowsher@dudley.gov.uk

Catering Services: Ms Penny Rushen, General Manager, Saltwells Education Centre, Bowling Green Road, Netherton DY2 9LY ☎ 01384 814320 ⌁ penny.rushen@dudley.gov.uk

Children / Youth Services: Ms Amanda Grove, Head of Youth Service, 7 St. James's Road, Dudley DY1 1HP
⌁ amanda.grove@dudley.gov.uk

Civil Registration: Ms Jayne Catley, Head of Customer Services, Dudley Council Plus, 259 Castle Street, Dudley DY1 1LQ
☎ 01384 818349 ⌁ jayne.catley@dudley.gov.uk

PR / Communications: Mr Phil Parker, Head of Communication & Public Affairs, The Council House, Priory Road, Dudley DY1 1HF
☎ 01384 818047 ⌁ phil.parker@dudley.gov.uk

Community Safety: Ms Sue Haywood, Head of Community Safety, Brierley Hill Police Station, Bank Street, Brierley Hill DY5 3DH ☎ 01384 815215 ⌁ sue.haywood@dudley.gov.uk

Computer Management: Mrs Sandra Taylor, Head of ICT Services, 3 - 3 St. James's Road, Dudley DY1 1HZ ☎ 01384 815600 ⌁ sandra.taylor@dudley.gov.uk

Consumer Protection and Trading Standards: Dr Deborah Harkins, Chief Officer - Health & Wellbeing, Falcon House, 8th Floor, The Minories, Dudley DY2 8PG ☎ 01384 816239 ⌁ deborah.harkins@dudley.gov.uk

Contracts: Mr Iain Newman, Chief Officer - Finance & Legal Services, The Council House, Priory Road, Dudley DY1 1HF
☎ 01384 814802 ⌁ iain.newman@dudley.gov.uk

Corporate Services: Mr Steve Cooper, Head of Corporate Landlord Services, 4 Ednam Road, Dudley DY1 1HL ☎ 01384 815319 ⌁ steve.cooper@dudley.gov.uk

Customer Service: Ms Jayne Catley, Head of Customer Services, Dudley Council Plus, 259 Castle Street, Dudley DY1 1LQ
☎ 01384 818349 ⌁ jayne.catley@dudley.gov.uk

Education: Ms Suzanne Edwards, Lead for Education Outcomes, Westox House, Trinity Road, Dudley DY1 1JB ☎ 01384 818029 ⌁ suzanne.edwards@dudley.gov.uk

Electoral Registration: Ms Alison Malkin, Head of Electoral Services, Electoral Services, Old Crown Court, Priory Street, Dudley DY1 1EY ☎ 01384 815274 ⌁ alison.malkin@dudley.gov.uk

Emergency Planning: Ms Sarah Hill, Acting Head of Resilience, The Laundry Block, Himley Hall & Park, Dudley DY3 4DF
☎ 01384 817080 ⌁ sarah.hill@dudley.gov.uk

Environmental / Technical Services: Mr Matt Williams, Chief Officer - Environmental Services, Lister Road Depot, Lister Road, Netherton, Dudley DY2 8JW ☎ 01384 814510 ⌁ matt.williams@dudley.gov.uk

Environmental Health: Dr Deborah Harkins, Chief Officer - Health & Wellbeing, Falcon House, 8th Floor, The Minories, Dudley DY2 8PG ☎ 01384 816239 ⌁ deborah.harkins@dudley.gov.uk

Estates, Property & Valuation: Ms Mary Cox, Team Manager - Valuation & Transactual Services, 4 Ednam Road, Dudley DY1 1HL
☎ 01384 815345 ⌁ mary.cox@dudley.gov.uk

Events Manager: Ms Sally Newell, Himley Estate Manager, Himley Hall & Park, Himley Park, Dudley DY3 4DF ☎ 01384 817823 ⌁ sally.newell@dudley.gov.uk

Facilities: Mr Steve Cooper, Head of Corporate Landlord Services, 4 Ednam Road, Dudley DY1 1HL ☎ 01384 815319 ⌁ steve.cooper@dudley.gov.uk

DUDLEY

Finance: Mr Iain Newman, Chief Officer - Finance & Legal Services, The Council House, Priory Road, Dudley DY1 1HF
☎ 01384 814802 ◦ iain.newman@dudley.gov.uk

Fleet Management: Mr Matt Williams, Chief Officer - Environmental Services, Lister Road Depot, Lister Road, Netherton, Dudley DY2 8JT ☎ 01384 814510 ◦ matt.williams@dudley.gov.uk

Grounds Maintenance: Mr Matt Williams, Chief Officer - Environmental Services, Lister Road Depot, Lister Road, Netherton, Dudley DY2 8JT ☎ 01384 814510 ◦ matt.williams@dudley.gov.uk

Health and Safety: Mr Simon Reece, Corporate Health & Safety Manager, The Council House, Priory Road, Dudley DY1 1HF
☎ 01384 814722 ◦ simon.reece@dudley.gov.uk

Highways: Mr Matt Williams, Chief Officer - Environmental Services, Lister Road Depot, Lister Road, Netherton, Dudley DY2 8JT ☎ 01384 814510 ◦ matt.williams@dudley.gov.uk

Home Energy Conservation: Mr Andrew Leigh, Head of Service - Housing Strategy, Harbour Buildings, Ground Floor, Waterfront West, Brierley Hill DY5 1LN ☎ 01384 815007
◦ andrew.leigh@dudley.gov.uk

Housing: Mr Mark Rodgers, Chief Officer - Housing, Harbour Buildings, 1st Floor, Waterfront West, Brierley Hill DY5 1LN
☎ 01384 815076 ◦ mark.rodgers@dudley.gov.uk

Housing Maintenance: Mr Ian Gardner, Head of Housing Maintenance, The Council House, Priory Road, Dudley DY1 1HF
☎ 01384 812113 ◦ ian.gardner@dudley.gov.uk

Legal: Mr Mohammed Farooq, Head of Law & Governance, The Council House, Priory Road, Dudley DY1 1HF ☎ 01384 815301
◦ mohammed.farooq@dudley.gov.uk

Leisure and Cultural Services: Mr Stuart Connelly, Head of Service - Vistor, Economy & Cultural Services, 4 Ednam Road, Dudley DY1 1HL ☎ 01384 813972 ◦ stuart.connelly@dudley.gov.uk

Leisure and Cultural Services: Mr Andy Webb, Interim Head of Sport & Leisure, 4 Ednam Road, Dudley DY1 1HL ☎ 01384 815579
◦ andy.webb@dudley.gov.uk

Licensing: Mr Mohammed Farooq, Head of Law & Governance, The Council House, Priory Road, Dudley DY1 1HF ☎ 01384 815301
◦ mohammed.farooq@dudley.gov.uk

Lifelong Learning: Ms Viv Webb, Deputy Head of Adult Community Learning, Archives & Local History Centre, Tipton Road, Dudley DY1 4SQ ☎ 01384 813975 ◦ viv.webb@dudley.gov.uk

Lighting: Mr Matt Williams, Chief Officer - Environmental Services, Lister Road Depot, Lister Road, Netherton, Dudley DY2 8JT
☎ 01384 814510 ◦ matt.williams@dudley.gov.uk

Member Services: Mr Steve Griffiths, Democratic Services Manager, The Council House, Priory Road, Dudley DY1 1HF
☎ 01384 815235 ◦ steve.griffiths@dudley.gov.uk

Parking: Mr Garry Dean, Head of Street & Green Care, Lister Road Depot, Lister Road, Netherton, Dudley DY2 8JW
☎ 01384 814506 ◦ garry.dean@dudley.gov.uk

Personnel / HR: Mrs Sharon Harthill, Head of HR Services, 87 - 88 Regent House, King Street, Dudley DY2 8PR ☎ 01384 512125
◦ sharon.harthill@dudley.gov.uk

Personnel / HR: Mr Adrian McCormick, Chief Officer - Transformation & Performance, 87 - 88 Regent House, King Street, Dudley DY2 8PR ☎ 01384 313449
◦ adrian.mccormick@dudley.gov.uk

Planning: Mrs Helen Martin, Head of Planning & Development, 4 Ednam Road, Dudley DY1 1HL ☎ 01384 814186
◦ helen.martin@dudley.gov.uk

Procurement: Mr Christopher Morgan, Procurement Manager, The Council House, Priory Road, Dudley DY1 1HF ☎ 01384 814862
◦ christopher.morgan@dudley.gov.uk

Public Libraries: Ms Jen Beardsmore, Head of Libraries & Archives, Dudley Library, St. James's Road, Dudley DY1 1HP
☎ 01384 815551 ◦ jen.beardsmore@dudley.gov.uk

Recycling & Waste Minimisation: Mr Matt Williams, Chief Officer - Environmental Services, Lister Road Depot, Lister Road, Netherton, Dudley DY2 8JT ☎ 01384 814510
◦ matt.williams@dudley.gov.uk

Social Services (Adult): Mr Matt Bowsher, Chief Officer - Adult Social Care, 3 - 5 St. James's Road, Dudley DY1 1HP
☎ 01384 815805 ◦ matt.bowsher@dudley.gov.uk

Social Services (Children): Mr Merlin Joseph, Interim Chief Officer - Children's Services, Westox House, Trinity Road, Dudley DY1 1JB ☎ 01384 814200 ◦ merlin.joseph@dudley.gov.uk

Safeguarding: Ms Anne Harris, Head of Adult Safeguarding, Brierley Hill Health & Social Care Centre, Venture Way, Brierley Hill DY5 1RU ☎ 01384 815870 ◦ anne.harris@dudley.gov.uk

Safeguarding: Mr Howard Woolfenden, Interim Head of Safeguarding, 3 - 5 St. James's Road, Dudley DY1 1HZ
☎ 01384 817409 ◦ howard.woolfenden@dudley.gov.uk

Public Health: Dr Deborah Harkins, Chief Officer - Health & Wellbeing, Falcon House, 8th Floor, The Minories, Dudley DY2 8PG
☎ 01384 816239 ◦ deborah.harkins@dudley.gov.uk

Staff Training: Mrs Sarah Treneer, Head of Learning & Organisational Development, 87 - 88 Regent House, King Street, Dudley DY2 8PR ☎ 01384 814727 ◦ sarah.treneer@dudley.gov.uk

Street Scene: Mr Matt Williams, Chief Officer - Environmental Services, Lister Road Depot, Lister Road, Netherton, Dudley DY2 8JT ☎ 01384 814510 ◦ matt.williams@dudley.gov.uk

Sustainable Communities: Ms Karen Jackson, Public Health Consultant, Falcon House, 8th Floor, The Minories, Dudley DY2 8PG ☎ 01384 816698 ◦ karen.jackson@dudley.gov.uk

Tourism: Ms Nicola Beckley, Tourism Development Officer, 4 Ednam Road, Dudley DY1 1HL ☎ 01384 817611 ⏚ nicola.beckley@dudley.gov.uk

Transport: Mr Matt Williams, Chief Officer - Environmental Services, Lister Road Depot, Lister Road, Netherton, Dudley DY2 8JT ☎ 01384 814510 ⏚ matt.williams@dudley.gov.uk

Transport Planner: Mr Matt Williams, Chief Officer - Environmental Services, Lister Road Depot, Lister Road, Netherton, Dudley DY2 8JT ☎ 01384 814510 ⏚ matt.williams@dudley.gov.uk

Waste Collection and Disposal: Mr Matt Williams, Chief Officer - Environmental Services, Lister Road Depot, Lister Road, Netherton, Dudley DY2 8JT ☎ 01384 814510 ⏚ matt.williams@dudley.gov.uk

Waste Management: Mr Matt Williams, Chief Officer - Environmental Services, Lister Road Depot, Lister Road, Netherton, Dudley DY2 8JT ☎ 01384 814510 ⏚ matt.williams@dudley.gov.uk

Children's Play Areas: Ms Liz Stuffins, Greenspace Team Leader, Lister Road Depot, Lister Road, Netherton DY2 8JT ☎ 01384 816991 ⏚ liz.stuffins@dudley.gov.uk

COUNCILLORS

Mayor: Hanif, Mohammed (LAB - Lye & Stourbridge North) cllr.mohammed.hanif@dudley.gov.uk

Deputy Mayor: Tyler, Dave (LAB - Kingswinford North & Wall Heath) cllr.dave.tyler@dudley.gov.uk

Leader of the Council: Lowe, Peter (LAB - Lye & Stourbridge North) cllr.peter.lowe@dudley.gov.uk

Deputy Leader of the Council: Foster, Judy (LAB - Brockmoor & Pensnett) cllr.judy.foster@dudley.gov.uk

Ahmed, Khurshid (LAB - St James's) cllr.khurshid.ahmed@dudley.gov.uk

Ahmed, Asif (LAB - St James's) cllr.asif.ahmed@dudley.gov.uk

Ali, Shaukat (LAB - St Thomas's) cllr.shaukat.ali@dudley.gov.uk

Anderton, Star (UKIP - Coseley East) cllr.star.etheridge@dudleymbc.org.uk

Aston, Adam (LAB - Upper Gornal & Woodsetton) cllr.adam.aston@dudley.gov.uk

Aston, Margaret (LAB - Castle & Priory) cllr.margaret.aston@dudley.gov.uk

Attwood, Mike (CON - Norton) cllr.mike.attwood@dudley.gov.uk

Baines, Julie (LAB - Amblecote) cllr.julie.baines@dudleymbc.org.uk

Barlow, Nicolas (CON - Wollaston & Stourbridge Town) cllr.nicolas.barlow@dudley.gov.uk

Bayton, Cathryn (LAB - St James's) cathrynbayton66@gmail.com

Bills, Hilary (LAB - Halesowen North) cllr.hilary.bills@dudley.gov.uk

Body, Richard (LAB - Cradley & Wollescote) cllr.richard.body@dudley.gov.uk

Bradley, Paul (UKIP - Amblecote) pwbradley69@googlemail.com

Brothwood, Paul (UKIP - Wordsley) cllr.paul.brothwood@dudley.gov.uk

Buttery, Ruth (CON - Hayley Green & Cradley South)

Casey, Keiran (LAB - Upper Gornal & Woodsetton) cllr.keiran.casey@dudley.gov.uk

Clark, Steve (CON - Wollaston & Stourbridge Town) cllr.steve.clark@dudley.gov.uk

Cooper, Ian (LAB - Belle Vale) cllr.ian.cooper@dudley.gov.uk

Cotterill, Bryan (LAB - Quarry Bank & Dudley Wood) cllr.bryan.cotterill@dudley.gov.uk

Cowell, Jackie (LAB - Quarry Bank & Dudley Wood) cllr.jackie.cowell@dudley.gov.uk

Craigie, Serena (LAB - Brierley Hill) cllr.serena.craigie@dudleymbc.org.uk

Crumpton, Timothy (LAB - Cradley & Wollescote) cllr.timothy.crumpton@dudley.gov.uk

Elcock, Colin (CON - Norton) cllr.colin.elcock@dudleymbc.org.uk

Etheridge, Bill (UKIP - Sedgley) cllr.bill.etheridge@dudley.gov.uk

Evans, Michael (CON - Sedgley) cllr.michael.evans@dudley.gov.uk

Finch, Ken (LAB - Castle & Priory) cllr.ken.finch@dudley.gov.uk

Finch, Alan (LAB - Castle & Priory) cllr.alan.finch@dudley.gov.uk

Goddard, Andrea (CON - Hayley Green & Cradley South) cllr.andrea.goddard@dudley.gov.uk

Gregory, Nick (CON - Halesowen South) cllr.nick.gregory@dudley.gov.uk

Harley, Patrick (CON - Kingswinford South) cllr.patrick.harley@dudley.gov.uk

Harris, Rachel (LAB - Brierley Hill) cllr.rachel.harris@dudley.gov.uk

Henley, Stuart (UKIP - Halesowen North) cllr.stuart.henley@dudley.gov.uk

Hill, Jeff (CON - Hayley Green & Cradley South) cllr.jeff.hill@Dudley.gov.uk

Hopwood, Alan (CON - Wollaston & Stourbridge Town) cllr.alan.hopwood@dudleymbc.org.uk

Islam, Zafar (LAB - Brierley Hill) cllr.zafar.islam@dudley.gov.uk

Johnson, Luke (CON - Kingswinford South) cllr.luke.johnson@dudleymbc.org.uk

Jones, Les (CON - Pedmore & Stourbridge East) cllr.les.jones@dudley.gov.uk

Jordan, Karen (LAB - Brockmoor & Pensnett) cllr.karen.jordan@dudley.gov.uk

Kettle, Ian (CON - Pedmore & Stourbridge East) cllr.ian.kettle@dudley.gov.uk

DUDLEY

Lawrence, Ed (CON - Kingswinford North & Wall Heath)
mail@edlawrence.co.uk

Lees, Angus (CON - Pedmore & Stourbridge East)
cllr.angus.lees@dudleymbc.org.uk

Lewis, Kerry (UKIP - Wordsley)
cllr.kerry.lewis@dudleymbc.org.uk

Martin, John (LAB - Brockmoor & Pensnett)
cllr.john.martin@dudley.gov.uk

Miller, Peter (CON - Kingswinford South)
cllr.peter.miller@dudley.gov.uk

Millward, Anne (CON - Gornal)
cllr.anne.millward@dudley.gov.uk

Mottram, Melvyn (LAB - Coseley East)
cllr.melvyn.mottram@dudley.gov.uk

Partridge, Gaye (LAB - Cradley & Wollescote)
cllr.gaye.partridge@dudley.gov.uk

Perks, Dean (UKIP - Upper Gornal & Woodsetton)
cllr.dean.perks@dudley.gov.uk

Perks, Christine (LAB - Netherton, Woodside & St Andrews)
cllr.christine.perks@dudleymbc.org.uk

Phipps, Simon (CON - Belle Vale)
cllr.simon.phipps@dudley.gov.uk

Richards, Nicola (CON - Kingswinford North & Wall Heath)
cllr.nicola.richards@dudley.gov.uk

Ridney, Susan (LAB - Coseley East)
cllr.sue.ridney@dudleymbc.org.uk

Rogers, Heather (CON - Norton)
cllr.heather.rogers@dudley.gov.uk

Rogers, Matt (CON - Wordsley)
cllr.matt.rogers@dudleymbc.org.uk

Scott-Dow, Roger (UKIP - Gornal)
cllr.roger.scott-dow@dudley.gov.uk

Shakespeare, Karen (CON - Halesowen North)
cllr.karen.shakespeare@dudley.gov.uk

Simms, Glenis (LAB - St Thomas's)
cllr.glenis.simms@dudleymbc.org.uk

Sparks, David (LAB - Quarry Bank & Dudley Wood)
cllr.david.sparks@dudley.gov.uk

Stanley, David (CON - Gornal)
cllr.david.stanley@dudleymbc.org.uk

Taylor, Elaine (LAB - Netherton, Woodside & St Andrews)
cllr.elaine.taylor@dudley.gov.uk

Taylor, Laura (CON - Belle Vale)
cllr.laura.taylor@dudleymbc.org.uk

Taylor, Alan (CON - Halesowen South)
cllr.alan.taylor@dudley.gov.uk

Tyler, Simon (CON - Amblecote)
cllr.simon.tyler@dudley.gov.uk

Vickers, David (CON - Halesowen South)
cllr.david.vickers@dudley.gov.uk

Wale, Vanessa (LAB - Lye & Stourbridge North)

Waltho, Steve (LAB - St Thomas's)
cllr.steve.waltho@dudley.gov.uk

Westwood, Tina (CON - Sedgley)
cllr.tine.westwood@dudley.gov.uk

Zada, Qadar (LAB - Netherton, Woodside & St Andrews)
cllr.qadar.zada@dudley.gov.uk

POLITICAL COMPOSITION
LAB: 35, CON: 29, UKIP: 8

COMMITTEE CHAIRS

Children's Services: Ms Anne Millward

Health & Wellbeing: Ms Rachel Harris

Licensing: Mr Ken Finch

Dumfries & Galloway   S

Dumfries & Galloway Council, Council Offices, English Street, Dumfries DG1 2DD

☎ 0303 333 3000 ◦∯ contact@dumgal.gov.uk 🖳 www.dumgal.gov.uk

FACTS AND FIGURES
Parliamentary Constituencies: Dumfries and Galloway, Dumfriesshire, Clydesdale and Tweedale
EU Constituencies: Scotland
Election Frequency: Elections are of whole council

PRINCIPAL OFFICERS

Chief Executive: Mr Gavin Stevenson, Chief Executive, Council Offices, English Street, Dumfries DG1 2DD ☎ 01387 260001 ◦∯ chief.executive@dumgal.gov.uk

Senior Management: Mr Derek Crichton, Director - Communities, Council Offices, English Street, Dumfries DG1 2DD

Senior Management: Mr Colin Grant, Director - Children, Young People & Lifelong Learning, Council Offices, English Street, Dumfries DG1 2DD ◦∯ cgrant@dumgal.gov.uk

Senior Management: Ms Lorna Meahan, Director - Corporate Services, Council Offices, English Street, Dumfries DG1 2DD ☎ 01387 260003 ◦∯ lorna.meahan@dumgal.gov.uk

Senior Management: Mr Alistair Speedie, Director - Economy, Environment & Infrastructure, Militia House, English Street, Dumfries DG1 2HR ☎ 01387 260376 ◦∯ alistair.speedie@dumgal.gov.uk

Civil Registration: Mrs Alison Quigley, Chief Registrar, 15 Ednam Street, Annan DG12 5EF ☎ 01461 204914 ◦∯ alisonq@dumgal.gov.uk

PR / Communications: Ms Claire Aitken, Communications Manager, Council Offices, English Street, Dumfries DG1 2DD ☎ 01387 260058 ◦∯ claire.aitken@dumgal.gov.uk

Community Safety: Mr Martin Ogilvie, Emergency Planning & Community Safety Manager, Council Offices, English Street, Dumfries DG1 2DD ☎ 01387 260046 ◦∯ martin.ogilvie@dumgal.gov.uk

Consumer Protection and Trading Standards: Ms Sandra Harkness, Service Manager - Trading Standards, Municipal Chambers, Buccleuch Street, Dumfries DG1 2AD ☎ 03033 333000

Contracts: Mr Alistair Speedie, Director - Economy, Environment & Infrastructure, Militia House, English Street, Dumfries DG1 2HR ☎ 01387 260376 ⌕ alistair.speedie@dumgal.gov.uk

Economic Development: Mr Ewan Green, Operations Manager - Economic Development, Council Offices, English Street, Dumfries DG1 2DD

Education: Mr Colin Grant, Director - Children, Young People & Lifelong Learning, Council Offices, English Street, Dumfries DG1 2DD ⌕ cgrant@dumgal.gov.uk

Electoral Registration: Mr Keith Mossop, Assessor & Electoral Registration Officer, Council Offices, English Street, Dumfries DG1 2DD ☎ 01387 260627 ⌕ ero@dumgal.gov.uk

Emergency Planning: Mr Martin Ogilvie, Emergency Planning & Community Safety Manager, Council Offices, English Street, Dumfries DG1 2DD ☎ 01387 260046 ⌕ martin.ogilvie@dumgal.gov.uk

Energy Management: Mr John Currie, Service Leader - Energy, County House, 2 Great King Street, Dumfries DG1 1AE ☎ 01387 260718 ⌕ johncu@dumgal.gov.uk

Finance: Mr Paul Garrett, Operations Manager, Council Offices, English Street, Dumfries DG1 2DD

Pensions: Ms Islay Herrick, Pensions Assistant, Monreith House, Bankend Road, Dumfries DG1 4ZE ☎ 01387 273853 ⌕ islay.herrick@dumgal.gov.uk

Highways: Mr Alistair Speedie, Director - Economy, Environment & Infrastructure, Militia House, English Street, Dumfries DG1 2HR ☎ 01387 260376 ⌕ alistair.speedie@dumgal.gov.uk

Housing: Mr John Lynch, Operations Manager - Strategic Housing & Commissioning, Carmont House, Bankend Road, Dumfries DG1 4ZJ ☎ 01387 245123 ⌕ johnl@dumgal.gov.uk

Legal: Mr Willie Taylor, Service Manager - Courts & Licensing, Council Offices, English Street, Dumfries DG1 2DD ☎ 01387 245913 ⌕ willie.taylor@dumgal.gov.uk

Leisure and Cultural Services: Mr Richard Grieveson, Head - Resource Planning & Community Services, Marchmount House, Dumfries DG1 1PY ☎ 01387 273875 ⌕ richard.grieveson@dumgal.gov.uk

Licensing: Mr Willie Taylor, Service Manager - Courts & Licensing, Council Offices, English Street, Dumfries DG1 2DD ☎ 01387 245913 ⌕ willie.taylor@dumgal.gov.uk

Lighting: Mr Alistair Speedie, Director - Economy, Environment & Infrastructure, Militia House, English Street, Dumfries DG1 2HR ☎ 01387 260376 ⌕ alistair.speedie@dumgal.gov.uk

Lottery Funding, Charity and Voluntary: Ms Emma Berger, Voluntary Sector Manager, Municipal Offices, Buccleuch Street, Dumfries DG1 2AD ☎ 01387 260000 ⌕ emma.berger@dumgal.gov.uk

Parking: Mr Alistair Speedie, Director - Economy, Environment & Infrastructure, Militia House, English Street, Dumfries DG1 2HR ☎ 01387 260376 ⌕ alistair.speedie@dumgal.gov.uk

Personnel / HR: Mr Paul Clarkin, Operations Manager - Human Resources, Council Offices, English Street, Dumfries DG1 2DD ☎ 01387 273842 ⌕ paul.clarkin@dumgal.gov.uk

Planning: Mr Alistair Speedie, Director - Economy, Environment & Infrastructure, Militia House, English Street, Dumfries DG1 2HR ☎ 01387 260376 ⌕ alistair.speedie@dumgal.gov.uk

Procurement: Mrs Rhona Lewis, Head of Legal & Democratic Services, Council Offices, English Street, Dumfries DG1 2DD ⌕ rlewis@dumgal.gov.uk

Recycling & Waste Minimisation: Mr Alistair Speedie, Director - Economy, Environment & Infrastructure, Militia House, English Street, Dumfries DG1 2HR ☎ 01387 260376 ⌕ alistair.speedie@dumgal.gov.uk

Social Services: Mr Peter David, Senior Social Work Manager, Council Offices, English Street, Dumfries DG1 2DD

Social Services: Mr Geoff Dean, Senior Social Work Manager, Longacres Road, Kirkcudbright DG6 4AT ☎ 01557 339260

Fostering & Adoption: Ms Sandra Ritchie, Fostering & Adoption Manager, 122-124 Irish Street, Dumfries DG1 2AW ☎ 01387 273700 ⌕ sandra.ritchie@dumgal.gov.uk

Staff Training: Mr Paul Clarkin, Operations Manager - Human Resources, Marchmount House, Dumfries DG1 1PY ☎ 01387 273842 ⌕ paul.clarkin@dumgal.gov.uk

Traffic Management: Mr Alistair Speedie, Director - Economy, Environment & Infrastructure, Militia House, English Street, Dumfries DG1 2HR ☎ 01387 260376 ⌕ alistair.speedie@dumgal.gov.uk

Waste Management: Mr Alistair Speedie, Director - Economy, Environment & Infrastructure, Militia House, English Street, Dumfries DG1 2HR ☎ 01387 260376 ⌕ alistair.speedie@dumgal.gov.uk

COUNCILLORS

Leader of the Council: Nicholson, Ronnie (LAB - North West Dumfries)
ronnie.nicholson@dumgal.gov.uk

Deputy Leader of the Council: Thompson, Ted (LAB - Iochar)
ted.thompson@dumgal.gov.uk

Group LeaderCarruthers, Ian (IND - Annandale South)
ian.carruthers@dumgal.gov.uk

Group LeaderFerguson, Andy (SNP - North West Dumfries)
andy.ferguson@dumgal.gov.uk

DUMFRIES & GALLOWAY

Group LeaderMaitland, Jane (IND - Dee)
jane.maitland@dumgal.gov.uk

Group LeaderNicol, Graham (CON - Mid Galloway)
graham.nicol@dumgal.gov.uk

Bell, Graham (CON - North West Dumfries)
john.bell2@dumgal.gov.uk

Blake, Ian (CON - Abbey)
ian.blake@dumgal.gov.uk

Brodie, Richard (IND - Annandale South)
richard.brodie@dumgal.gov.uk

Carruthers, Karen (IND - Annandale East & Eskdale)
karen.carruthers3@dumgal.gov.uk

Carson, Finlay (CON - Castle Douglas & Glenkens)
finlay.carson@dumgal@gov.uk

Collins, Brian (SNP - Castle Douglas & Glenkens)
brian.collins@dumgal.gov.uk

Davidson, Rob (SNP - Abbey)
rob.davidson@dumgal.gov.uk

Dempster, James (LAB - Mid & Upper Nithsdale)
jim.dempster@dumgal.gov.uk

Dick, Iain (SNP - Stranraer & North Rhins)
iain.dick@dumgal.gov.uk

Diggle, Peter (CON - Annandale North)
peter.diggle@dumgal.gov.uk

Dryburgh, Archie (LAB - Annandale East & Eskdale)
archie.dryburgh@dumgal.gov.uk

Dykes, Gillian (CON - Mid & Upper Nithsdale)
gill.dykes@dumgal.gov.uk

Forster, Grahame (INDNA - Wigtown West)
grahame.forster@dumgal.gov.uk

Geddes, Alistair (SNP - Mid Galloway)

Gilroy, Patsy (CON - Dee)
patsy.gilroy@dumgal.gov.uk

Groom, Jack (CON - Nith)
jack.groom@dumgal.gov.uk

Hongmei Jin, Yen (SNP - Lochar)
yen.hongmeijin@dumgal.gov.uk

Hyslop, Ivor (CON - Lochar)
ivor.hyslop@dumgal.gov.uk

Leaver, Jeff (LAB - Lochar)
jeff.leaver@dumgal.gov.uk

MacGregor, Gail (CON - Annandale North)
gail.macgregor@dumgal.gov.uk

Male, Denis (CON - Annandale East & Eskdale)
denis.male@dumgal.gov.uk

Marshall, Sean (LAB - Annandale South)
sean.marshall@dumgal.gov.uk

Martin, John (LAB - Nith)
john.martin@dumgal.gov.uk

McAughtrie, Tom (LAB - Abbey)
tom.mcaughtrie@dumgal.gov.uk

McClung, Jim (SNP - Wigtown West)
jim.mcclung@dumgal.gov.uk

McColm, Jim (IND - Mid Galloway)
jim.mccolm@dumgal.gov.uk

McCutcheon, Marion (LAB - Stranraer & North Rhins)
marion.mccutcheon@dumgal.gov.uk

McKie, David (LAB - North West Dumfries)
david.mckie@dumgal.gov.uk

Oglivie, Ronald (LAB - Annandale South)
ronal.ogilvie@dumgal.gov.uk

Peacock, Craig (IND - Annandale East & Eskdale)
craig.peacock@dumgal.gov.uk

Prentice, George (IND - Castle Douglas & Glenkens)
george.prentice@dumgal.gov.uk

Scobie, William (NP - Stranraer & North Rhins)
william.scobie@dumgal.gov.uk

Smyth, Colin (LAB - Nith)
colin.smyth@dumgal.gov.uk

Stitt, David (LAB - Abbey)
davie.stitt@dumgal.gov.uk

Syme, John (LAB - Mid & Upper Nithsdale)
john.syme@dumgal.gov.uk

Tait, Graeme (CON - Annandale North)
graeme.tait2@dumgal.gov.uk

Thompson, Stephen (SNP - Annandale North)
stephen.thompson@dumgal.gov.uk

Tuckfield, Roberta (CON - Wigtown West)
roberta.tuckfield@dumgal.gov.uk

Witts, Alistair (SNP - Nith)
alistair.witts@dumgal.gov.uk

Wood, Andrew (SNP - Mid & Upper Nithsdale)
andrew.wood@dumgal.gov.uk

Wyper, Colin (INDNA - Dee)
colin.wyper@dumgal.gov.uk

POLITICAL COMPOSITION
LAB: 14, CON: 13, SNP: 10, IND: 7, INDNA: 2, NP: 1

COMMITTEE CHAIRS

Audit: Mrs Gillian Dykes

Children, Young People & Lifelong Learning: Mr Jeff Leaver

Communities: Mr Tom McAughtrie

Economy, Environment & Infrastructure: Mr Colin Smyth

Planning: Mr John Martin

Dundee City   S

Dundee City Council, 21 City Square, Dundee DD1 3BY
☎ 01382 434000 🖷 01382 434666
✆ customerservices@dundeecity.gov.uk 🖳 www.dundeecity.gov.uk

FACTS AND FIGURES
Parliamentary Constituencies: Dundee East, Dundee West
EU Constituencies: Scotland
Election Frequency: Elections are of whole council

PRINCIPAL OFFICERS

Chief Executive: Mr David Martin, Chief Executive, 21 City Square, Dundee DD1 3BY ☎ 01382 434201 ✐ david.martin@dundeecity.gov.uk

Senior Management: Mr Stewart Murdoch, Director - Leisure & Communities, Central Library, Dundee DD1 2DB ☎ 01382 437460 ✐ stewart.murdoch@dundeecity.gov.uk

Access Officer / Social Services (Disability): Ms Dorothy Wilson, Access Officer, Dundee House, 50 North Lindsay Street, Dundee DD1 1LS ☎ 01382 433865 ✐ dorothy.wilson@dundeecity.gov.uk

Architect, Building / Property Services: Mr Rob Pedersen, City Architectural Services Officer, Dundee House, 50 North Lindsay Street, Dundee DD1 1LS ☎ 01382 433640 ✐ rob.pedersen@dundeecity.gov.uk

Best Value: Mr Paul Carroll, Performance & Improvement Manager, 21 City Square, Dundee DD1 3BY ☎ 01382 434452 ✐ paul.carroll@dundeecity.gov.uk

Building Control: Mr Kenneth Findlay, Team Leader - Building Control, Dundee House, 50 North Lindsay Street, Dundee DD1 1LS ☎ 01382 433001 ✐ ken.findlay@dundeecity.gov.uk

Children / Youth Services: Ms Jane Martin, Manager - Children's Services & Criminal Justice, Friarfield House, Barrack Street, Dundee DD1 1PQ ☎ 01382 435017 ✐ jane.martin@dundeecity.gov.uk

Civil Registration: Ms Jayne Allan, Registrar, 21 City Square, Dundee DD1 3BY ☎ 01382 435225 ✐ jayne.allan@dundeecity.gov.uk

PR / Communications: Ms Merrill Smith, Head of Corporate Communications, 21 City Square, Dundee DD1 3BY ☎ 01382 434500 ✐ merrill.smith@dundeecity.gov.uk

Community Planning: Mr Peter Allan, Community Planning Manager, 21 City Square, Dundee DD1 3BY ☎ 01382 434465 ✐ peter.allan@dundeecity.gov.uk

Community Safety: Mr Tom Stirling, Head of Community Safety & Protection, 21 City Square, Dundee DD1 3BY ☎ 01382 433203 ✐ tom.stirling@dundeecity.gov.uk

Computer Management: Ms Janet Robertson, Head of HR & Business Support, Dundee House, 50 North Lindsay Street, Dundee DD1 1LS ☎ 01382 433335 ✐ janet.robertson@dundeecity.gov.uk

Consumer Protection and Trading Standards: Mr Ken Daly, Trading Standards Manager, Claverhouse West Industrial Park, Jack Martin Way, Dundee DD1 ☎ 01382 436263 ✐ ken.daly@dundeecity.gov.uk

Contracts: Mrs Elaine Zwirlein, Director - Neighbourhood Services, 50 North Lindsay Street, Dundee DD1 1LS ☎ 01382 434538 ✐ elaine.zwirlein@dundeecity.gov.uk

Corporate Services: Ms Marjory Stewart, Director - Corporate Services, Dundee House, 50 North Lindsay Street, Dundee DD1 1LS ☎ 01382 433555 ✐ marjory.stewart@dundeecity.gov.uk

Direct Labour: Mrs Elaine Zwirlein, Director - Neighbourhood Services, 50 North Lindsay Street, Dundee DD1 1LS ☎ 01382 434538 ✐ elaine.zwirlein@dundeecity.gov.uk

Economic Development: Mr Mike Galloway, Director - City Development, Dundee House, 50 North Lindsay Street, Dundee DD1 1LS ☎ 01382 433610 ✐ mike.galloway@dundeecity.gov.uk

Education: Mr Michael Wood, Director - Children & Families, Dundee House, 50 North Lindsay Street, Dundee DD1 1LS ☎ 01382 433088 ✐ michael.wood@dundeecity.gov.uk

E-Government: Mr Paul Carroll, Performance & Improvement Manager, 21 City Square, Dundee DD1 3BY ☎ 01382 434452 ✐ paul.carroll@dundeecity.gov.uk

Electoral Registration: Mr Roger Mennie, Head of Legal & Democratic Services, 21 City Square, Dundee DD1 3BY ☎ 01382 434577 ✐ roger.mennie@dundeecity.gov.uk

Emergency Planning: Mr Graeme Mackenzie, Risk & Business Continuity Manager, Dundee House, 50 North Lindsay Street, Dundee DD1 1NZ ☎ 01382 433301 ✐ graeme.mackenzie@dundeecity.gov.uk

Energy Management: Mr Alex Gibson, Team Leader - Property Services, 3 City Square, Dundee DD1 3BA ☎ 01382 434814 ✐ alex.gibson@dundeecity.gov.uk

Environmental Health: Mr Kenny Kerr, Head of Environmental Protection, 34 Harefield Road, Dundee DD2 3JW ☎ 01382 436201 ✐ kenny.kerr@dundeecity.gov.uk

Estates, Property & Valuation: Mr Mike Galloway, Director - City Development, Dundee House, 50 North Lindsay Street, Dundee DD1 1LS ☎ 01382 433610 ✐ mike.galloway@dundeecity.gov.uk

European Liaison: Mr Gregor Hamilton, Head of Planning & Economic Development, Dundee House, 50 Nirth Lindsay Street, Dundee DD1 1LS ☎ 01382 433520 ✐ gregor.hamilton@dundeecity.gov.uk

Finance: Ms Marjory Stewart, Director - Corporate Services, Dundee House, 50 North Lindsay Street, Dundee DD1 1NZ ☎ 01382 433555 ✐ marjory.stewart@dundeecity.gov.uk

Treasury: Ms Marjory Stewart, Director - Corporate Services, Dundee House, 50 North Lindsay Street, Dundee DD1 1LS ☎ 01382 433555 ✐ marjory.stewart@dundeecity.gov.uk

Pensions: Ms Catherine Carruthers, Depute Pensions Manager, Dundee House, 50 North Lindsay Street, Dundee DD1 1LS ☎ 01382 437925 ✐ catherine.carruthers@dundeecity.gov.uk

Grounds Maintenance: Mr Rod Houston, Land Services Manager, 353 Clepington Road, Dundee DD3 8PL ☎ 01382 434747 ✐ rod.houston@dundeecity.gov.uk

Health and Safety: Mr Neil Doherty, Council Health & Safety Co-ordinator, 8 City Square, Dundee DD1 3BG ☎ 01382 434878 ✐ neil.doherty@dundeecity.gov.uk

DUNDEE CITY

Highways: Mr Fergus Wison, City Engineer, Dundee House, 50 North Lindsay Street, Dundee DD1 1LS ☎ 01382 433711 ⏚ fergus.wilson@dundeecity.gov.uk

Home Energy Conservation: Ms Heather McQuillan, HECA Officer, Housing Investment Unit, Dundee House, 50 North Lindsay Street, Dundee DD1 1NB ☎ 01382 434872 ⏚ heather.mcquillan@dundeecity.gov.uk

Housing: Mrs Elaine Zwirlein, Director - Neighbourhood Services, 50 North Lindsay Street, Dundee DD1 1LS ☎ 01382 434538 ⏚ elaine.zwirlein@dundeecity.gov.uk

Housing Maintenance: Mrs Elaine Zwirlein, Director - Neighbourhood Services, 50 North Lindsay Street, Dundee DD1 1LS ☎ 01382 434538 ⏚ elaine.zwirlein@dundeecity.gov.uk

Legal: Mr Roger Mennie, Head of Legal & Democratic Services, 21 City Square, Dundee DD1 3BY ☎ 01382 434577 ⏚ roger.mennie@dundeecity.gov.uk

Leisure and Cultural Services: Mr Stewart Murdoch, Director - Leisure & Communities, Central Library, Dundee DD1 2DB ☎ 01382 437460 ⏚ stewart.murdoch@dundeecity.gov.uk

Licensing: Mr Roger Mennie, Head of Legal & Democratic Services, 21 City Square, Dundee DD1 3BY ☎ 01382 434577 ⏚ roger.mennie@dundeecity.gov.uk

Lifelong Learning: Mr Stewart Murdoch, Director - Leisure & Communities, Central Library, Dundee DD1 2DB ☎ 01382 437460 ⏚ stewart.murdoch@dundeecity.gov.uk

Lighting: Mr Lindsay McGregor, Team Leader - Street Lighting, Dundee House, 50 North Lindsay Street, Dundee DD1 1LS ☎ 01382 834132 ⏚ lindsay.mcgregor@dundeecity.gov.uk

Lottery Funding, Charity and Voluntary: Ms Diane Milne, Senior Policy Officer, Dundee House, 50 North Lindsay Street, Dundee DD1 1LS ☎ 01382 434653 ⏚ diane.milne@dundeecity.gov.uk

Member Services: Mr Paul Carroll, Performance & Improvement Manager, 21 City Square, Dundee DD1 3BY ☎ 01382 434452 ⏚ paul.carroll@dundeecity.gov.uk

Parking: Mr Mike Galloway, Director - City Development, Dundee House, 50 North Lindsay Street, Dundee DD1 1LS ☎ 01382 433610 ⏚ mike.galloway@dundeecity.gov.uk

Personnel / HR: Ms Janet Robertson, Head of HR & Business Support, Dundee House, 50 North Lindsay Street, Dundee DD1 1LS ☎ 01382 433335 ⏚ janet.robertson@dundeecity.gov.uk

Planning: Mr Mike Galloway, Director - City Development, Dundee House, 50 North Lindsay Street, Dundee DD1 1LS ☎ 01382 433610 ⏚ mike.galloway@dundeecity.gov.uk

Public Libraries: Mr Stewart Murdoch, Director - Leisure & Communities, Central Library, Dundee DD1 2DB ☎ 01382 437460 ⏚ stewart.murdoch@dundeecity.gov.uk

Recycling & Waste Minimisation: Mr Kenny Kerr, Head of Environmental Protection, 34 Harefield Road, Dundee DD2 3JW ☎ 01382 436201 ⏚ kenny.kerr@dundeecity.gov.uk

Road Safety: Mr Neil Gellatly, Head of Transportation, Dundee House, 50 North Lindsay Street, Dundee DD1 1LS ☎ 01382 433116 ⏚ neil.gellatly@dundeecity.gov.uk

Social Services: Ms Diane McCulloch, Community Care Manager, Claverhouse East Industrial Park, Jack Martin Way, Dundee DD4 9FF ☎ 01382 438302 ⏚ diane.mcculloch@dundeecity.gov.uk

Social Services (Adult): Ms Diane McCulloch, Community Care Manager, Claverhouse East Industrial Park, Jack Martin Way, Dundee DD4 9FF ☎ 01382 438302 ⏚ diane.mcculloch@dundeecity.gov.uk

Social Services (Children): Ms Jane Martin, Manager - Children's Services & Criminal Justice, Friarfield House, Barrack Street, Dundee DD1 1PQ ☎ 01382 435017 ⏚ jane.martin@dundeecity.gov.uk

Staff Training: Ms Janet Robertson, Head of HR & Business Support, Dundee House, 50 North Lindsay Street, Dundee DD1 1LS ☎ 01382 433335 ⏚ janet.robertson@dundeecity.gov.uk

Town Centre: Mrs Sarah Craig, City Centre Manager, 3 City Square, Dundee DD1 3BA ☎ 01382 434548 ⏚ sarah.craig@dundeecity.gov.uk

Traffic Management: Mr Neil Gellatly, Head of Transportation, Dundee House, 50 North Lindsay Street, Dundee DD1 1LS ☎ 01382 433116 ⏚ neil.gellatly@dundeecity.gov.uk

Transport: Mr Mike Galloway, Director - City Development, Dundee House, 50 North Lindsay Street, Dundee DD1 1LS ☎ 01382 433610 ⏚ mike.galloway@dundeecity.gov.uk

Transport Planner: Mr Mike Galloway, Director - City Development, Dundee House, 50 North Lindsay Street, Dundee DD1 1LS ☎ 01382 433610 ⏚ mike.galloway@dundeecity.gov.uk

Waste Collection and Disposal: Mr Kenny Kerr, Head of Environmental Protection, 34 Harefield Road, Dundee DD2 3JW ☎ 01382 436201 ⏚ kenny.kerr@dundeecity.gov.uk

Waste Management: Mr Kenny Kerr, Head of Environmental Protection, 34 Harefield Road, Dundee DD2 3JW ☎ 01382 436201 ⏚ kenny.kerr@dundeecity.gov.uk

Children's Play Areas: Mr Gary Robertson, Head of Environmental Management, 3 City Square, Dundee DD1 3BA ☎ 01382 436894 ⏚ gary.robertson@dundeecity.gov.uk

COUNCILLORS

Provost: Duncan, Bob (SNP - Lochee) bob.duncan@dundeecity.gov.uk

Alexander, John (SNP - Strathmartine) john.alexander@dundeecity.gov.uk

Asif, Mohammed (LAB - Coldside)
mohammed.asif@dundeecity.gov.uk

Bidwell, Laurie (LAB - The Ferry)
laurie.bidwell@dundeecity.gov.uk

Black, Jimmy (SNP - Coldside)
jimmy.black@dundeecity.gov.uk

Borthwick, Ian (IND - Strathmartine)
ian.borthwick@dundeecity.gov.uk

Bowes, David (SNP - Coldside)
david.bowes@dundeecity.gov.uk

Brennan, Lesley (LAB - East End)
lesley.brennan@dundeecity.gov.uk

Campbell, Bill (SNP - West End)
bill.campbell@dundeecity.gov.uk

Cordell, Kevin (SNP - The Ferry)
kevin.cordell@dundeecity.gov.uk

Cruikshank, Georgia (LAB - Maryfield)
georgia.cruikshank@dundeecity.gov.uk

Dawson, Will (SNP - East End)
will.dawson@dundeecity.gov.uk

Ferguson, Tom (LAB - Lochee)
tom.ferguson@dundeecity.gov.uk

Gordon, Brian (LAB - North East)
brian.gordon@dundeecity.gov.uk

Guild, Kenneth (SNP - The Ferry)
ken.guild@dundeecity.gov.uk

Hunter, Stewart (SNP - Strathmartine)
stewart.hunter@dundeecity.gov.uk

Keenan, Kevin (LAB - Strathmartine)
kevin.keenan@dundeecity.gov.uk

Lynn, Ken (SNP - Maryfield)
ken.lynn@dundeecity.gov.uk

MacPherson, Fraser (LD - West End)
fraser.macpherson@dundeecity.gov.uk

McCready, Richard (LAB - West End)
richard.mccready@dundeecity.gov.uk

McDonald, Vari (SNP - West End)
vari.mcdonald@dundeecity.gov.uk

McGovern, Norma (LAB - Lochee)
Norma.mcgovern@dundeecity.gov.uk

Melville, Craig (SNP - Maryfield)
craig.melville@dundeecity.gov.uk

Murray, Gregor (SNP - North East)
gregor.murray@dundeecity.gov.uk

Roberts, Christina (SNP - East End)
christina.roberts@dundeecity.gov.uk

Ross, Alan (SNP - Lochee)
alan.ross@dundeecity.gov.uk

Sawers, Willie (SNP - North East)
willie.sawers@dundeecity.gov.uk

Scott, Derek (CON - The Ferry)
derek.scott@dundeecity.gov.uk

Wright, Helen (LAB - Coldside)
helen.wright@dundeecity.gov.uk

POLITICAL COMPOSITION
SNP: 16, LAB: 10, LD: 1, CON: 1, IND: 1

Durham U

Durham, Durham County Council, County Hall, Durham DH1 5QF
☎ 03000 260000 🖥 www.durham.gov.uk

FACTS AND FIGURES
Parliamentary Constituencies: Bishop Auckland, Durham North, Durham North West, Durham, City of, Easington, Sedgefield

PRINCIPAL OFFICERS

Chief Executive: Mr Terry Collins, Chief Executive, Durham County Council, County Hall, Durham DH1 5UQ ☎ 03000 267331 ⏚ terry.collins@durham.gov.uk

Senior Management: Mr John Hewitt, Corporate Director - Resources, Durham County Council, County Hall, Durham DH1 5QF ⏚ john.hewitt@durham.gov.uk

Senior Management: Ms Lorraine O'Donnell, Director - Transformation & Partnership, Durham County Council, County Hall, Durham DH1 5QF ☎ 03000 268060 ⏚ lorraine.odonnell@durham.gov.uk

Senior Management: Ms Gill O'Neill, Director - Public Health, Durham County Council, County Hall, Durham DH1 5QF ⏚ gill.o'neill@durham.gov.uk

Senior Management: Ms Jane Robinson, Corporate Director - Adult & Health Services, Durham County Council, County Hall, Durham DH1 5QF ⏚ jane.robinson@durham.gov.uk

Senior Management: Mr Ian Thompson, Corporate Director - Regeneration & Economic Development, Durham County Council, County Hall, Durham DH1 5QF ☎ 03000 267330 ⏚ ian_thompson@durham.gov.uk

Senior Management: Ms Margaret Whellans, Interim Corporate Director - Children & Young People's Services, Durham County Council, County Hall, Durham DH1 5QF ⏚ margaret.whellans@durham.gov.uk

Access Officer / Social Services (Disability): Ms Jeanette Stephenson, Community Safety & Involvement Manager, Durham County Council, County Hall, Durham DH1 5QF ☎ 03000 267390 ⏚ jeanette.stephenson@durham.gov.uk

Architect, Building / Property Services: Mr David Taylor, Property, Planning & Projects Manager, Durham County Council, County Hall, Durham DH1 5QF ☎ 03000 269727 ⏚ david.taylor3@durham.gov.uk

Best Value: Mr Roger Goodes, Head - Policy & Communications, Durham County Council, County Hall, Durham DH1 5UL ☎ 03000 268050 ⏚ roger.goodes@durham.gov.uk

Building Control: Mr Paul Burr, Building & Facilities Maintenance Manager, Durham County Council, County Hall, Durham DH1 5QF ☎ 03000 268263 ⏚ paul.burr@durham.gov.uk

DURHAM

Children / Youth Services: Ms Gill Eshelby, Strategic Manager - Co Durham Youth Offending Service, Durham County Council, County Hall, Durham DH1 5QF ☎ 03000 265989 ⌁ gill.eshelby@durham.gov.uk

Children / Youth Services: Ms Carol Payne, Head of Children's Services, Durham County Council, County Hall, Durham DH1 5QF ☎ 03000 268983 ⌁ carole.payne@durham.gov.uk

Children / Youth Services: Ms Margaret Whellans, Interim Corporate Director - Children & Young People's Services, Durham County Council, County Hall, Durham DH1 5QF ⌁ margaret.whellans@durham.gov.uk

PR / Communications: Mr Roger Goodes, Head - Policy & Communications, Durham County Council, County Hall, Durham DH1 5QF ☎ 03000 268050 ⌁ roger.goodes@durham.gov.uk

Community Planning: Ms Jenny Haworth, Head - Planning & Performance, Durham County Council, County Hall, Durham DH1 5QF ☎ 03000 268071 ⌁ jenny.haworth@durham.gov.uk

Computer Management: Mr Keith Forster, Strategic Manager - Performance & Systems, Durham County Council, County Hall, Durham DH1 5QF ☎ 03000 267396 ⌁ keith.forster@durham.gov.uk

Computer Management: Mr Phil Jackman, Head - ICT Services, Durham County Council, County Hall, Durham DH1 5QF ☎ 03000 268372 ⌁ phil.jackman@durham.gov.uk

Consumer Protection and Trading Standards: Mr Owen Cleugh, Consumer Protection Manager, Durham County Council, County Hall, Durham DH1 5QF ☎ 03000 260925 ⌁ owen.cleugh@durham.gov.uk

Consumer Protection and Trading Standards: Ms Joanne Waller, Head - Environment, Health & Consumer Protection, Durham County Council, County Hall, Durham DH1 5UQ ☎ 03000 260924 ⌁ joanne.waller@durham.gov.uk

Contracts: Ms Denise Elliot, Strategic Commissioning Manager, Durham County Council, County Hall, Durham DH1 5QF ☎ 03000 267389 ⌁ denise.elliot@durham.gov.uk

Contracts: Mr Dave Shipman, Strategic Commissioning Manager, Durham County Council, County Hall, Durham DH1 5QF ☎ 03000 267391 ⌁ dave.shipman@durham.gov.uk

Corporate Services: Mr Kevin Edworthy, Corporate Policy & Planning Team Leader, Durham County Council, County Hall, Durham DH1 5QF ☎ 03000 268045 ⌁ kevin.edworthy@durham.gov.uk

Corporate Services: Ms Vanessa Glover, Corporate News Manager, Durham County Council, County Hall, Durham DH1 5QF ☎ 03000 268070 ⌁ vanessa.glover@durham.gov.uk

Corporate Services: Mr Tom Gorman, Corporate Scrutiny & Performance Manager, Durham County Council, County Hall, Durham DH1 5QF ☎ 03000 268027 ⌁ tom.gorman@durham.gov.uk

Corporate Services: Ms Su Jordan, CCU Programme Officer Manager, Durham County Council, County Hall, Durham DH1 5QF ☎ 03000 268055 ⌁ su.jordan@durham.gov.uk

Customer Service: Mr Lawrence Serewicz, Principal Information Manager, Durham County Council, County Hall, Durham DH1 5QF ☎ 03000 268038 ⌁ lawrence.serewicz@durham.gov.uk

Economic Development: Ms Sarah Robson, Head - Economic Development & Housing, Durham County Council, County Hall, Durham DH1 5QF ☎ 03000 267332 ⌁ sarah_robson@durham.gov.uk

Economic Development: Mr Graham Wood, Economic Development Manager, Durham County Council, County Hall, Durham DH1 5QF ☎ 03000 262002 ⌁ graham.wood@durham.gov.uk

Education: Ms Caroline O'Neill, Head of Education, Durham County Council, County Hall, Durham DH1 5QF ☎ 03000 268982 ⌁ caroline.oneill@durham.gov.uk

Education: Mr Paul Shadforth, Interim Strategic Manager - SEN, Durham County Council, County Hall, Durham DH1 5QF ☎ 03000 267756 ⌁ paul.shadforth@durham.gov.uk

Electoral Registration: Ms Colette Longbottom, Legal & Democratic Services, Durham County Council, County Hall, Durham DH1 5QF ☎ 03000 269732 ⌁ colette.longbottom@durham.gov.uk

Environmental / Technical Services: Mr John Reed, Head - Technical Services, Durham County Council, County Hall, Durham DH1 5QF ☎ 03000 267454 ⌁ john.reed@durham.gov.uk

Environmental Health: Mr Gary Hutchinson, Environment Protection Manager, Durham County Council, County Hall, Durham DH1 5QF ☎ 03000 261007 ⌁ gary.hutchinson@durham.gov.uk

Environmental Health: Ms Joanne Waller, Head - Environment, Health & Consumer Protection, Durham County Council, County Hall, Durham DH1 5UQ ☎ 03000 260924 ⌁ joanne.waller@durham.gov.uk

Environmental Health: Mr Michael Yeadon, Health Protection Manager, Durham County Council, County Hall, Durham DH1 5QF ☎ 03000 264655 ⌁ michael.yeadon@durham.gov.uk

Estates, Property & Valuation: Mr Gerard Darby, Asset Services Manager, Durham County Council, County Hall, Durham DH1 5QF ☎ 03000 267024 ⌁ gerard.darby@durham.gov.uk

Events Manager: Ms Michelle Gorman, Managing Director - Visit County Durham, Durham County Council, County Hall, Durham DH1 5QF ☎ 03000 261219 ⌁ michelle.gorman@durham.gov.uk

Finance: Mr Phillip Curran, Finance Manager - Neighbourhoods, Durham County Council, County Hall, Durham DH1 5QF ☎ 03000 261967 ⌁ philip.curran@durham.gov.uk

Finance: Mr Paul Darby, Head - Financial & HR Services, Durham County Council, County Hall, Durham DH1 5QF ☎ 03000 261930 ⌁ paul.darby@durham.gov.uk

Finance: Mr Jeff Garfoot, Head - Corporate Finance & HR, Durham County Council, County Hall, Durham DH1 5QF ☎ 03000 261946 ⌨ jeff.garfoot@durham.gov.uk

Finance: Mr Andrew Gilmore, Finance Manager, Durham County Council, County Hall, Durham DH1 5QF ☎ 03000 263497 ⌨ andrew.gilmore@durham.gov.uk

Finance: Ms Beverly White, Finance Manager - Pensions & Technical, Durham County Council, County Hall, Durham DH1 5QF ⌨ beverly.white@durham.gov.uk

Pensions: Mr Nick Orton, Pensions Manager, Durham County Council, County Hall, Durham DH1 5QF ☎ 03000 269798 ⌨ nick.orton@durham.gov.uk

Fleet Management: Mr Norman Ramsey, County Fleet Manager, Durham County Council, County Hall, Durham DH1 5QF ☎ 03000 269262 ⌨ norman.ramsey@durham.gov.uk

Health and Safety: Mr Kevin Lough, Occupational Health & Safety Manager, Durham County Council, County Hall, Durham DH1 5QF ☎ 03000 267308 ⌨ kevin.lough@durham.gov.uk

Highways: Mr Mark Readman, Highways Services Manager, Durham County Council, County Hall, Durham DH1 5QF ☎ 03000 269261 ⌨ mark.readman@durham.gov.uk

Housing: Ms Sarah Robson, Head - Economic Development & Housing, Durham County Council, County Hall, Durham DH1 5QF ☎ 03000 267332 ⌨ sarah_robson@durham.gov.uk

Housing Maintenance: Ms Kath Heathcote, Housing Regeneration Manager, Durham County Council, County Hall, Durham DH1 5QF ☎ 03000 265264 ⌨ kath.heathcote@durham.gov.uk

Legal: Ms Colette Longbottom, Legal & Democratic Services, Durham County Council, County Hall, Durham DH1 5QF ☎ 03000 269732 ⌨ colette.longbottom@durham.gov.uk

Legal: Mr Bryan Smith, Litigation Manager, Durham County Council, County Hall, Durham DH1 5QF ☎ 03000 269732 ⌨ bryan.smith@durham.gov.uk

Leisure and Cultural Services: Mr Nigel Dodds, Strategic Manager - Culture & Sport, Durham County Council, County Hall, Durham DH1 5QF ⌨ nigel.dodds@durham.gov.uk

Leisure and Cultural Services: Mr Stephen Howell, Head - Culture & Sport, Durham County Council, County Hall, Durham DH1 5UQ ☎ 03000 264550 ⌨ stephen.howell@durham.gov.uk

Member Services: Mrs Ros Layfield, Committee, Member & Civic Service Manager, Durham County Council, County Hall, Durham DH1 5QF ⌨ ros.layfield@durham.gov.uk

Partnerships: Mr Gordon Elliott, Head - Partnership & Community Engagement, Durham County Council, County Hall, Durham DH1 5UF ☎ 03000 263605 ⌨ gordon.elliott@durham.gov.uk

Personnel / HR: Ms Lorraine Anderson, HR Manager - Operations & Data, Durham County Council, County Hall, Durham DH1 5QF ☎ 03000 265857 ⌨ lorraine.anderson@durham.gov.uk

Personnel / HR: Ms Joanne Kemp, Human Resources & Organisational Development Manager, Durham County Council, County Hall, Durham DH1 5QF ☎ 03000 265856 ⌨ joanne.kemp@durham.gov.uk

Planning: Ms Jenny Haworth, Head - Planning & Performance, Durham County Council, County Hall, Durham DH1 5QF ☎ 03000 268071 ⌨ jenny.haworth@durham.gov.uk

Planning: Ms Andrea Petty, Policy & Planning Manager, Durham County Council, County Hall, Durham DH1 5QF ☎ 03000 267312 ⌨ andrea.petty@durham.gov.uk

Planning: Mr Stuart Timmiss, Head - Planning & Assets, Durham County Council, County Hall, Durham DH1 5QF ☎ 03000 267334 ⌨ stuart.timmiss@durham.gov.uk

Procurement: Ms Jane Bowie, Interim Head of Commissioning, Durham County Council, County Hall, Durham DH1 5QF ☎ 03000 268041 ⌨ jane.bowie@durham.gov.uk

Procurement: Mr Darren Knowd, Corporate Procurement Manager, Durham County Council, County Hall, Durham DH1 5QF ☎ 03000 265416 ⌨ darren.knowd@durham.gov.uk

Regeneration: Mr Peter Coe, Regeneration & Development Manager, Durham County Council, County Hall, Durham DH1 5QF ☎ 03000 262042 ⌨ peter.coe@durham.gov.uk

Social Services (Adult): Mr Lee Alexander, Strategic Manager - Safeguarding, Practice Development & Access, Durham County Council, County Hall, Durham DH1 5QF ☎ 03000 268180 ⌨ lee.alexander@durham.gov.uk

Social Services (Adult): Mr Philip Emberson, Strategic Manager - Physical Disability & Sensory Impairment, Durham County Council, County Hall, Durham DH1 5QF ☎ 03000 268245 ⌨ philip.emberson@durham.gov.uk

Social Services (Adult): Mrs Lesley Jeavons, Head - Adult Care, Durham County Council, County Hall, Durham DH1 5UG ☎ 03000 267354 ⌨ lesley.jeavons@durham.gov.uk

Social Services (Adult): Ms Tracy Joisce, Strategic Manager - Learning Disabilities, Mental Health, Substance Misuse & Transitions, Durham County Council, County Hall, Durham DH1 5QF ☎ 03000 268243 ⌨ tracy.joisce@durham.gov.uk

Social Services (Children): Mr Mark Gurney, Strategic Manager - Child Protection & Disability, Durham County Council, County Hall, Durham DH1 5QF ☎ 03000 265758 ⌨ mark.gurney@durham.gov.uk

Social Services (Children): Ms Carol Payne, Head of Children's Services, Durham County Council, County Hall, Durham DH1 5QF ☎ 03000 268983 ⌨ carole.payne@durham.gov.uk

DURHAM

Social Services (Children): Ms Karen Robb, Strategic Manager - Looked After & Permanence, Durham County Council, County Hall, Durham DH1 5QF ☎ 03000 265759 ◌ karen.robb@durham.gov.uk

Public Health: Ms Gill O'Neill, Director - Public Health, Durham County Council, County Hall, Durham DH1 5QF ◌ gill.o'neill@durham.gov.uk

Staff Training: Ms Joanne Kemp, Human Resources & Organisational Development Manager, Durham County Council, County Hall, Durham DH1 5QF ☎ 03000 265856 ◌ joanne.kemp@durham.gov.uk

Street Scene: Mr Jimmy Bennett, Clean & Green Manager, Durham County Council, County Hall, Durham DH1 5QF ☎ 03000 266047 ◌ james.bennett@durham.gov.uk

Street Scene: Mr Ian Hoult, Neighbourhood Protection Manager, Durham County Council, County Hall, Durham DH1 5QF ☎ 03000 265571 ◌ ian.hoult@durham.gov.uk

Street Scene: Mr Keith Parkinson, Refuse & Recycling Manager, Durham County Council, County Hall, Durham DH1 5QF ☎ 03000 268371 ◌ keith.parkinson@durham.gov.uk

Sustainable Communities: Mr Peter Appleton, Head - Planning & Service Strategy, Durham County Council, County Hall, Durham DH1 5QF ☎ 03000 267388 ◌ peter.appleton@durham.gov.uk

Transport: Mr Adrian White, Head - Transport & Contract Services, Durham County Council, County Hall, Durham DH1 5UQ ☎ 03000 267455 ◌ adrian.white@durham.gov.uk

Transport Planner: Mr Andrew Leadbetter, Sustainable Transport Manager, Durham County Council, County Hall, Durham DH1 5QF ☎ 03000 268512 ◌ andrew.leadbetter@durham.gov.uk

Total Place: Ms Jenny Haworth, Head - Planning & Performance, Durham County Council, County Hall, Durham DH1 5QF ☎ 03000 268071 ◌ jenny.haworth@durham.gov.uk

Waste Management: Mr John Shannon, Strategic Waste Manager, Durham County Council, County Hall, Durham DH1 5QF ☎ 03000 266098 ◌ john.shannon@durham.gov.uk

COUNCILLORS

ChairBell, Edward (LAB - Deneside)
edward.bell@durham.gov.uk

Vice-ChairDixon, Mike (LAB - Aycliffe North & Middridge)
mike.dixon@durham.gov.uk

Leader of the Council: Henig, Simon (LAB - Chester-le-Street West Central)
simon.henig@durham.gov.uk

Deputy Leader of the Council: Napier, Alan (LAB - Murton)
alan.napier@durham.gov.uk

Adam, Eddy (LAB - Aycliffe West)
eddy.adam@durham.gov.uk

Allen, Joy (LAB - Bishop Auckland Town)
joy.allen@durham.gov.uk

Alvey, Jimmy (LAB - Peterlee West)
jimmy.alvey@durham.gov.uk

Armstrong, Lawson (LAB - Chester-le-Street East)
lawson.armstrong@durham.gov.uk

Armstrong, Joseph (LAB - Esh & Witton Gilbert)
joseph.armstrong@durham.gov.uk

Armstrong, Barbara (LAB - Esh & Witton Gilbert)
barbara.armstrong@durham.gov.uk

Avery, Brian (IND - Ferryhill)
brian.avery@durham.gov.uk

Batey, Alison (LAB - Pelton)
alison.batey@durham.gov.uk

Bell, Alan (IND - Lumley)
alan.bell@durham.gov.uk

Bell, David (LAB - Deerness)
dbell@durham.gov.uk

Bell, Richard (CON - Barnard Castle West)
richard.bell@durham.gov.uk

Bell, Jennifer (LAB - Deneside)
jennifer.bell@durham.gov.uk

Bennett, Harry (LAB - Peterlee East)
harry.bennett@durham.gov.uk

Blakey, Jan (LAB - Coxhoe)
jan.blakey@durham.gov.uk

Bleasdale, Gerry (LAB - Seaham)
gerry.bleasdale@durham.gov.uk

Bonner, Anne (LAB - Deerness)
anne.bonner@durham.gov.uk

Boyes, David (LAB - Easington)
david.boyes@durham.gov.uk

Brookes, Peter (LAB - Trimdon & Thornley)
peter.brookes@durham.gov.uk

Brown, Jane (LAB - Delves Lane)
jane.brown@durham.gov.uk

Carr, Joanne (LAB - Burnopfield & Dipton)
joanne.carr@durham.gov.uk

Carr, Colin (LAB - Pelton)
colin.carr@durham.gov.uk

Chaplow, Jean (LAB - Deerness)
jean.chaplow@durham.gov.uk

Charlton, Joyce (IND - Tanfield)
joyce.charlton@durham.gov.uk

Clare, John (LAB - Aycliffe North & Middridge)
john.clare@durham.gov.uk

Clark, June (LAB - Horden)
j.clark@durham.gov.uk

Conway, Patrick (LAB - Belmont)
patrick.conway@durham.gov.uk

Cordon, James (LAB - Pelton)
james.cordon@durham.gov.uk

Corrigan, Kate (LAB - Belmont)
katie.corrigan@durham.gov.uk

Crathorne, Pauline (LAB - Ferryhill)
pauline.crathorne@durham.gov.uk

Crute, Robert (LAB - Blackhalls)
rob.crute@durham.gov.uk

Davidson, Keith (LAB - Chester-le-Street South)
keith.davidson@durham.gov.uk

Davinson, Mark (LAB - Craghead & South Moor)
mark.davinson@durham.gov.uk

Dearden, Katherine (LAB - Stanley)
katherine.dearden@durham.gov.uk

Forster, Sonia (LAB - Dawdon)
sonia.forster@durham.gov.uk

Foster, Neil (LAB - Tudhoe)
neil.foster@durham.gov.uk

Freeman, David (LD - Elvet & Gilesgate)
david.freeman@durham.gov.uk

Geldard, Ian (LAB - Spennymoor)
ian.geldard@durham.gov.uk

Glass, Bob (LAB - Delves Lane)
bob.glass@durham.gov.uk

Graham, Barbara (LAB - Tudhoe)
barbara.graham@durham.gov.uk

Gray, Joan (LAB - Aycliffe North & Middridge)
joan.gray@durham.gov.uk

Gunn, Olwyn (LAB - Willington & Hunwick)
olwyn.gunn@durham.gov.uk

Hall, David (LAB - Sherburn)
dhall@durham.gov.uk

Hampson, Carole (LAB - Craghead & South Moor)
carole.hampson@durham.gov.uk

Hart, John (LAB - Tow Law)
john.hart@durham.gov.uk

Henderson, Ted (CON - Barnard Castle West)
ted.henderson@durham.gov.uk

Henig, Katherine (LAB - Chester-le-Street South)
katherine.henig@durham.gov.uk

Hicks, Derek (IND - Consett South)
derek.hicks@durham.gov.uk

Hillary, Jed (LAB - Aycliffe East)
jed.hillary@durham.gov.uk

Hodgson, Michele (LAB - Annfield Plain)
michele.hodgson@durham.gov.uk

Holland, Grenville (LD - Nevilles Cross)
grenville.holland@durham.gov.uk

Hopgood, Amanda (LD - Framwellgate & Newton Hall)
amanda.hopgood@durham.gov.uk

Hopper, Kate (LAB - Aycliffe West)
kate.hopper@durham.gov.uk

Hovvells, Lucy (LAB - Trimdon & Thornley)
lucy.hovvells@durham.gov.uk

Huntington, Eunice (LAB - Shotton & South Hetton)
eunice.huntington@durham.gov.uk

Iveson, Sarah (LAB - Aycliffe East)
sarah.iveson@durham.gov.uk

Jewell, Ivan (LAB - Burnopfield & Dipton)
ivan.jewell@durham.gov.uk

Johnson, Ossie (LAB - Lanchester)
ossie.johnson@durham.gov.uk

Kay, Charlie (LAB - Coundon)
charlie.kay@durham.gov.uk

Kellett, Bill (LAB - Sherburn)
bill.kellett@durham.gov.uk

Laing, Audrey (LAB - Peterlee East)
audrey.laing@durham.gov.uk

Lawton, Pat (LAB - Spennymoor)
pat.lawton@durham.gov.uk

Lee, June (LAB - Woodhouse Close)
june.lee@durham.gov.uk

Lethbridge, John (LAB - Woodhouse Close)
john.lethbridge@durham.gov.uk

Liddle, Heather (LAB - Sacriston)
heather.liddle@durham.gov.uk

Lindsay, John (LAB - Ferryhill)
john.lindsay@durham.gov.uk

Liversidge, Alan (LAB - Shotton & South Hetton)
alan.liversidge@durham.gov.uk

Lumsdon, Rachel (LAB - Sedgefield)
rachel.lumsdon@durham.gov.uk

Maitland, Joyce (LAB - Murton)
joyce.maitland@durham.gov.uk

Marshall, Linda (LAB - Chester-le-Street West Central)
linda.marshall@durham.gov.uk

Marshall, Carl (LAB - Stanley)
carl.marshall@durham.gov.uk

Martin, Nigel (LD - Nevilles Cross)
nigel.martin@durham.gov.uk

Maslin, Joan (IND - Passfield)
joan.maslin@durham.gov.uk

May, Peter (IND - North Lodge)
peter.may@durham.gov.uk

Measor, Jan (LAB - Peterlee West)
jan.measor@durham.gov.uk

Milburn, Olga (LAB - Tanfield)
olga.milburn@durham.gov.uk

Moir, Bill (LAB - Belmont)
bill.moir@durham.gov.uk

Morrison, Sue (LAB - Seaham)
sue.morrison@durham.gov.uk

Nearney, Thomas (LAB - Annfield Plain)
thomas.nearney@durham.gov.uk

Nicholls, Morris (LAB - Trimdon & Thornley)
morris.nicholls@durham.gov.uk

Nicholson, Henry (LAB - Shildon & Dene Valley)
henry.nicholson@durham.gov.uk

Oliver, Peter (IND - Benfieldside)
peter.oliver@durham.gov.uk

Ormerod, Richard (LD - Elvet & Gilesgate)
richard.ormerod@durham.gov.uk

Patterson, Andrea (LAB - Crook)
andrea.patterson@durham.gov.uk

DURHAM

Pemberton, Trish (LAB - Shildon & Dene Valley)
trish.pemberton@durham.gov.uk

Plews, Maria (LAB - Coxhoe)
maria.plews@durham.gov.uk

Potts, Christine (LAB - Chilton)
christine.potts@durham.gov.uk

Pounder, Lynn (LAB - Blackhalls)
lynn.pounder@durham.gov.uk

Richardson, George (CON - Barnard Castle East)
george.richardson@durham.gov.uk

Robinson, John (LAB - Sedgefield)
john.robinson@durham.gov.uk

Robinson, Stephen (IND - Benfieldside)
s.robinson@durham.gov.uk

Rowlandson, James (CON - Barnard Castle East)
james.rowlandson@durham.gov.uk

Savory, Anita (IND - Weardale)
anita.savory@durham.gov.uk

Shaw, Kevin (LAB - Dawdon)
kevin.shaw@durham.gov.uk

Shield, Alan (IND - Leadgate & Medomsley)
alan.shield@durham.gov.uk

Shuttleworth, John (IND - Weardale)
jshuttleworth@durham.gov.uk

Simmons, Mamie (LD - Framwellgate & Newton Hall)
mamie.simmons@durham.gov.uk

Simpson, Mick (LAB - Bishop Middleham & Cornforth)
m.simpson@durham

Smith, Tracie (LAB - Chester-le-Street North)
tracie.smith@durham.gov.uk

Smith, Heather (LAB - Evenwood)
heather.smith@durham.gov.uk

Stanton, Maureen (LAB - Crook)
maureen.stanton@durham.gov.uk

Stelling, Watts (IND - Leadgate & Medomsley)
watts.stelling@durham.gov.uk

Stephens, Brian (LAB - Shildon & Dene Valley)
brian.stephens@durham.gov.uk

Stoker, David (LD - Durham South)
david.stoker@durham.gov.uk

Stradling, Paul (LAB - Horden)
paul.stradling@durham.gov.uk

Surtees, Angela (LAB - Easington)
a.surtees@durham.gov.uk

Taylor, Paul (LAB - Brandon)
paul.taylor@durham.gov.uk

Taylor, Leo (LAB - Wingate)
leo.taylor@durham.gov.uk

Temple, Owen (LD - Consett North)
owen.temple@durham.gov.uk

Thompson, Kevin (IND - Spennymoor)
kevin.thompson@durham.gov.uk

Tinsley, Fraser (LAB - Willington & Hunwick)
fraser.tinsley@durham.gov.uk

Tomlinson, Eddie (LAB - Crook)
eddie.tomlinson@durham.gov.uk

Turnbull, John (LAB - Brandon)
john.turnbull@durham.gov.uk

Turner, Andy (LAB - Evenwood)
andy.turner@durham.gov.uk

Watson, Alex (IND - Consett North)
alex.watson@durham.gov.uk

Wilkes, Mark (LD - Framwellgate & Newton Hall)
mark.wilkes@durham.gov.uk

Williams, Mac (LAB - Coxhoe)
mac.williams@durham.gov.uk

Willis, Audrey (IND - Lumley)
audrey.willis@durham.gov.uk

Wilson, Simon (LAB - Sacriston)
swilson@durham.gov.uk

Wilson, Christine (LAB - West Auckland)
c.wilson@durham.gov.uk

Yorke, Robert (LAB - West Auckland)
robert.yorke@durham.gov.uk

Young, Richard (IND - Lanchester)
richie.young@durham.gov.uk

Zair, Samuel (IND - Bishop Auckland Town)
sam.zair@durham.gov.uk

POLITICAL COMPOSITION
LAB: 96, IND: 17, LD: 9, CON: 4

COMMITTEE CHAIRS

Adults, Health & Wellbeing: Mr John Robinson

Audit: Mr Edward Bell

Children & Young People: Ms Christine Potts

Economy & Enterprise: Mr Robert Crute

Environment & Sustainable Communities: Ms Barbara Graham

Health & Wellbeing: Ms Lucy Hovvells

Licensing: Mr Colin Carr

Pensions: Mr Andy Turner

Planning: Mr Keith Davidson

Safer & Stronger Communities: Mr David Boyes

Ealing   L

Ealing London Borough Council, Perceval House, 14-16 Uxbridge Road, Ealing, London W5 2HL
☎ 020 8825 5000 🖳 www.ealing.gov.uk

FACTS AND FIGURES
Parliamentary Constituencies: Ealing Central and Acton, Ealing North, Ealing, Southall
EU Constituencies: London
Election Frequency: Elections are of whole council

PRINCIPAL OFFICERS

Chief Executive: Mr Paul Najsarek, Chief Executive, Perceval House, 14-16 Uxbridge Road, Ealing, London W5 2HL ✆ najsarekp@ealing.gov.uk

Senior Management: Dr Jackie Chin, Director - Public Health, Perceval House, 14-16 Uxbridge Road, Ealing, London W5 2HL ☎ 020 8825 6448 ✆ chinj@ealing.gov.uk

Senior Management: Ms Judith Finlay, Executive Director - Children, Adults & Public Health, Perceval House, 14-16 Uxbridge Road, Ealing, London W5 2HL ☎ 020 8825 7106 ✆ finlayj@ealing.gov.uk

Senior Management: Mr Pat Hayes, Executive Director - Regeneration & Housing, Perceval House, 14-16 Uxbridge Road, London W5 2HL ☎ 020 8825 7889 ✆ pat.hayes@ealing.gov.uk

Senior Management: Mr Ian O'Donnell, Executive Director - Corporate Resources, Perceval House, 14-16 Uxbridge Road, London W5 2HL ☎ 020 8825 5269 ✆ odonnelli@ealing.gov.uk

Senior Management: Mr Keith Townsend, Executive Director - Environment & Customer Services, Perceval House, 14-16 Uxbridge Road, Ealing, London W5 2NL ☎ 020 8825 6306 ✆ keith.townsend@ealing.gov.uk

Architect, Building / Property Services: Mr Mike Ibbitson, Director - Business Services Group, Perceval House, 14-16 Uxbridge Road, Ealing, London W5 2HL ✆ ibbitsonm@ealing.gov.uk

Best Value: Mr Matthew Booth, Director - Policy & Performance, Perceval House, 14-16 Uxbridge Road, Ealing, London W5 2HL ☎ 020 8825 8556 ✆ boothm@ealing.gov.uk

Building Control: Ms Aileen Jones, Head of Planning Services, Perceval House, 14-16 Uxbridge Road, Ealing, London W5 2HL ☎ 020 8825 8371 ✆ jonesa@ealing.gov.uk

Building Control: Mr Noel Rutherford, Director - Built Environment, Perceval House, 14-16 Uxbridge Road, Ealing, London W5 2HL ☎ 020 8825 6639 ✆ rutherfn@ealing.gov.uk

Children / Youth Services: Ms Elaine Cunningham, Head of Youth & Connexions Service, Perceval House, 14-16 Uxbridge Road, Ealing, London W5 2HL ☎ 020 8825 7578 ✆ ecunningham@ealing.gov.uk

Children / Youth Services: Ms Judith Finlay, Executive Director - Children, Adults & Public Health, Perceval House, 14-16 Uxbridge Road, Ealing, London W5 2HL ☎ 020 8825 7106 ✆ finlayj@ealing.gov.uk

Civil Registration: Ms Franschene Allen, Registration Services Manager, Ealing Town Hall, New Broadway, London W5 2BY ☎ 020 8825 9277 ✆ fran.allen@ealing.gov.uk

Computer Management: Mr Mike Ibbitson, Director - Business Services Group, Perceval House, 14-16 Uxbridge Road, Ealing, London W5 2HL ✆ ibbitsonm@ealing.gov.uk

Consumer Protection and Trading Standards: Mr Mark Wiltshire, Head of Regulatory Services, Perceval House, 14-16 Uxbridge Road, Ealing, London W5 2HL ☎ 020 8825 8197 ✆ wiltshirema@ealing.gov.uk

Contracts: Mrs Kate Graefe, Head of Strategic Procurement, Perceval House, 14-16 Uxbridge Road, Ealing, London W5 2HL ☎ 020 8825 9843 ✆ graefek@ealing.gov.uk

Customer Service: Ms Alison Reynolds, Director - Customer Services, Perceval House, 14-16 Uxbridge Road, Ealing, London W5 2HL ☎ 020 8825 5329 ✆ reynolda@ealing.gov.uk

Economic Development: Ms Lucy Taylor, Assistant Director - Regeneration & Planning Policy, Perceval House, 14-16 Uxbridge Road, Ealing, London W5 2HL ☎ 020 8825 9036 ✆ taylorl@ealing.gov.uk

Education: Ms Eileen Lustig, Head of Admissions, Perceval House, 14-16 Uxbridge Road, Ealing, London W5 2HL ☎ 020 8825 5059 ✆ elustig@ealing.gov.uk

Electoral Registration: Mr Ross Jackson, Head of Elections & Members' Services, Perceval House, 14-16 Uxbridge Road, Ealing, London W5 2HL ☎ 020 8825 6854 ✆ jacksonr@ealing.gov.uk

Emergency Planning: Ms Donna Wootton, Interim Head of Civil Protection, Perceval House, 14-16 Uxbridge Road, Ealing, London W5 2HL ☎ 020 8825 9494 ✆ woottond@ealing.gov.uk

Environmental / Technical Services: Mr Darren Henaghan, Interim Director - Environment, Perceval House, 14-16 Uxbridge Road, Ealing, London W5 2HL ☎ 020 8825 8576 ✆ henaghand@ealing.gov.uk

Environmental Health: Mr Mark Wiltshire, Head of Regulatory Services, Perceval House, 14-16 Uxbridge Road, Ealing, London W5 2HL ☎ 020 8825 8197 ✆ wiltshirema@ealing.gov.uk

European Liaison: Mr Calum Murdoch, External Funding Officer, Perceval House, 14-16 Uxbridge Road, Ealing, London W5 2HL ☎ 020 8825 7443 ✆ murdochc@ealing.gov.uk

Events Manager: Ms Jane Coughlan, Head of Hospitality & Events, Perceval House, 14-16 Uxbridge Road, Ealing, London W5 2HL ☎ 020 8825 6700 ✆ coughlanj@ealing.gov.uk

Facilities: Miss Fiona Elliot, Head of Hospitality & Events, Perceval House, 14-16 Uxbridge Road, Ealing, London W5 2HL ☎ 020 8825 6061 ✆ elliotf@ealing.gov.uk

Finance: Ms Maria Christofi, Corporate Director - Resources, Perceval House, 14-16 Uxbridge Road, Ealing, London W5 2HL ☎ 020 8825 6193 ✆ mchristofi@ealing.gov.uk

Treasury: Mr Ian O'Donnell, Executive Director - Corporate Resources, Perceval House, 14-16 Uxbridge Road, London W5 2HL ☎ 020 8825 5269 ✆ odonnelli@ealing.gov.uk

Pensions: Ms Bridget Uku, Group Manager - Treasury & Investments, Perceval House, 14-16 Uxbridge Road, Ealing, London W5 2HL ☎ 020 8825 5981 ✆ ukub@ealing.gov.uk

EALING

Fleet Management: Mrs Kate Graefe, Head of Strategic Procurement, Perceval House, 14-16 Uxbridge Road, Ealing, London W5 2HL ☎ 020 8825 9843 ◌ graefek@ealing.gov.uk

Grounds Maintenance: Mr Darren Henaghan, Interim Director - Environment, Perceval House, 14-16 Uxbridge Road, Ealing, London W5 2HL ☎ 020 8825 8576 ◌ henaghand@ealing.gov.uk

Health and Safety: Ms Sue Emery, Interim Head of Health & Safety, Perceval House, 14-16 Uxbridge Road, Ealing, London W5 2HL ☎ 020 8825 6942 ◌ emerysu@ealing.gov.uk

Highways: Mr Shahid Iqbal, Assistant Director - Highways, Perceval House, 14-16 Uxbridge Road, Ealing, London W5 2HL ☎ 020 8825 7802 ◌ iqbalsp@ealing.gov.uk

Housing: Mr Mark Meehan, Assistant Director - Housing Demand, Perceval House, 14-16 Uxbridge Road, Ealing, London W5 2HL ☎ 020 8825 9046 ◌ meehanm@ealing.gov.uk

Local Area Agreement: Mr Jarvis Garrett, Head of Improvement & Efficiency, Perceval House, 14-16 Uxbridge Road, Ealing, London W5 2HL ☎ 020 8825 7893 ◌ garrettj@ealing.gov.uk

Legal: Ms Helen Harris, Director - Legal & Democratic Services, Perceval House, 14-16 Uxbridge Road, Ealing, London W5 2HL ☎ 020 8825 8615 ◌ harrish@ealing.gov.uk

Leisure and Cultural Services: Mr Chris Bunting, Assistant Director - Leisure, Perceval House, 14-16 Uxbridge Road, Ealing, London W5 2HL ☎ 020 8825 6429 ◌ buntingc@ealing.gov.uk

Leisure and Cultural Services: Ms Carole Stewart, Assistant Director - Arts, Heritage & Libraries, Perceval House, 14-16 Uxbridge Road, Ealing, London W5 2HL ☎ 020 8825 7216 ◌ stewartc@ealing.gov.uk

Licensing: Ms Loraine Abbott, Regulatory Services Officer, Perceval House, 14-16 Uxbridge Road, Ealing, London W5 2HL ☎ 020 8825 6298 ◌ abbottl@ealing.gov.uk

Lifelong Learning: Ms Sharon Thomas, Adult Learning Manager, Perceval House, 14-16 Uxbridge Road, Ealing, London W5 2HL ☎ 020 8825 5279 ◌ thomassh@ealing.gov.uk

Lottery Funding, Charity and Voluntary: Mr Nigel Fogg, Grants Unit Manager, Perceval House, 14-16 Uxbridge Road, Ealing, London W5 2HL ☎ 020 8825 7589 ◌ foggn@ealing.gov.uk

Member Services: Ms Helen Harris, Director - Legal & Democratic Services, Perceval House, 14-16 Uxbridge Road, Ealing, London W5 2HL ☎ 020 8825 8615 ◌ harrish@ealing.gov.uk

Member Services: Mr Ross Jackson, Head of Elections & Members' Services, Perceval House, 14-16 Uxbridge Road, Ealing, London W5 2HL ☎ 020 8825 6854 ◌ jacksonr@ealing.gov.uk

Parking: Mr Barry Francis, Assistant Director - Parking, Perceval House, 14-16 Uxbridge Road, Ealing, London W5 2HL ☎ 020 8825 6252 ◌ francisb@ealing.gov.uk

Partnerships: Mr Matthew Booth, Director - Policy & Performance, Perceval House, 14-16 Uxbridge Road, Ealing, London W5 2HL ☎ 020 8825 8556 ◌ boothm@ealing.gov.uk

Personnel / HR: Mr David Veale, Assistant Director - HR & Organisational Development, Perceval House, 14-16 Uxbridge Road, Ealing, London W5 2HL ☎ 020 8825 7359 ◌ vealed@ealing.gov.uk

Planning: Ms Aileen Jones, Head of Planning Services, Perceval House, 14-16 Uxbridge Road, Ealing, London W5 2HL ☎ 020 8825 8371 ◌ jonesa@ealing.gov.uk

Procurement: Mrs Kate Graefe, Head of Strategic Procurement, Perceval House, 14-16 Uxbridge Road, Ealing, London W5 2HL ☎ 020 8825 9843 ◌ graefek@ealing.gov.uk

Public Libraries: Ms Carole Stewart, Assistant Director - Arts, Heritage & Libraries, Perceval House, 14-16 Uxbridge Road, Ealing, London W5 2HL ☎ 020 8825 7216 ◌ stewartc@ealing.gov.uk

Recycling & Waste Minimisation: Mr Earl McKenzie, Assistant Director - Street Services, Perceval House, 14-16 Uxbridge Road, Ealing, London W5 2LX ☎ 020 8825 5194 ◌ mckenzie@ealing.gov.uk

Regeneration: Ms Lucy Taylor, Assistant Director - Regeneration & Planning Policy, Perceval House, 14-16 Uxbridge Road, Ealing, London W5 2HL ☎ 020 8825 9036 ◌ taylorl@ealing.gov.uk

Road Safety: Mr Shahid Iqbal, Assistant Director - Highways, Perceval House, 14-16 Uxbridge Road, Ealing, London W5 2HL ☎ 020 8825 7802 ◌ iqbalsp@ealing.gov.uk

Social Services (Adult): Mr Stephen Day, Director - Adult Services, Perceval House, 14-16 Uxbridge Road, Ealing, London W5 2HL ☎ 020 8825 6286 ◌ days@ealing.gov.uk

Social Services (Children): Ms Judith Finlay, Executive Director - Children, Adults & Public Health, Perceval House, 14-16 Uxbridge Road, Ealing, London W5 2HL ☎ 020 8825 7106 ◌ finlayj@ealing.gov.uk

Safeguarding: Ms Finola Culbert, Assistant Director - Safeguarding & Support, Perceval House, 14-16 Uxbridge Road, Ealing, London W5 2HL ☎ 020 8825 5177 ◌ culbertl@ealing.gov.uk

Looked after Children: Ms Bridie McDonagh, Looked after Children, Perceval House, 14-16 Uxbridge Road, Ealing, London W5 2HL ☎ 020 8825 6648 ◌ bmcdonagh@ealing.gov.uk

Public Health: Dr Jackie Chin, Director - Public Health, Perceval House, 14-16 Uxbridge Road, Ealing, London W5 2HL ☎ 020 8825 6448 ◌ chinj@ealing.gov.uk

Staff Training: Ms Liz Chiles, HR Business Partner, Perceval House, 14-16 Uxbridge Road, Ealing, London W5 2HL ☎ 020 8825 9345 ◌ chilesl@ealing.gov.uk

Sustainable Communities: Ms Joanne Mortensen, Programme Manager, Perceval House, 14-16 Uxbridge Road, Ealing, London W5 2HL ☎ 020 8825 9183 ◌ mortensenj@ealing.gov.uk

Sustainable Development: Ms Joanne Mortensen, Programme Manager, Perceval House, 14-16 Uxbridge Road, Ealing, London W5 2HL ☎ 020 8825 9183 ◌ mortensenj@ealing.gov.uk

Town Centre: Ms Lucy Taylor, Assistant Director - Regeneration & Planning Policy, Perceval House, 14-16 Uxbridge Road, Ealing, London W5 2HL ☎ 020 8825 9036 ◌ taylorl@ealing.gov.uk

Traffic Management: Mr Shahid Iqbal, Assistant Director - Highways, Perceval House, 14-16 Uxbridge Road, Ealing, London W5 2HL ☎ 020 8825 7802 ◌ iqbalsp@ealing.gov.uk

Transport: Mr Francis Torto, Transport Development Manager, Perceval House, 14-16 Uxbridge Road, Ealing, London W5 2HL ☎ 020 8825 7382 ◌ tortof@ealing.gov.uk

Transport Planner: Mr Nick O'Donnell, Assistant Director - Strategic Transport, Perceval House, 14-16 Uxbridge Road, Ealing, London W5 2HL ☎ 020 8825 8078 ◌ odonnelln@ealing.gov.uk

Waste Management: Mr Earl McKenzie, Assistant Director - Street Services, Perceval House, 14-16 Uxbridge Road, Ealing, London W5 2LX ☎ 020 8825 5194 ◌ mckenzie@ealing.gov.uk

Children's Play Areas: Mr Jeff Parkinson, Children's Services Manager, Perceval House, 14-16 Uxbridge Road, Ealing, London W5 2HL ☎ 020 8825 8267 ◌ jeff.parkinson@ealing.gov.uk

COUNCILLORS

Leader of the Council: Bell, Julian (LAB - Greenford Broadway)
julian.bell@ealing.gov.uk

Deputy Leader of the Council: Dheer, Ranjit (LAB - Dormers Wells)
ranjit.dheer@ealing.gov.uk

Ahmed, Munir (LAB - Perivale)
munir.ahmed@ealing.gov.uk

Ahmed-Shaikh, Natasha (LAB - Northolt Mandeville)
natasha.ahmeddhaikh@ealing.gov.uk

Anand, Jasbir (LAB - Southall Green)
jasbir.anand@ealing.gov.uk

Aslam, Mohammad (LAB - Norwood Green)
mohammad.aslam@ealing.gov.uk

Bagha, Tej (LAB - Dormers Wells)
tej.bagha@ealing.gov.uk

Ball, Jon (LD - Ealing Common)
jon.ball@ealing.gov.uk

Blacker, Josh (LAB - South Acton)
josh.blacker@ealing.gov.uk

Busuttil, Gary (LD - Southfield)
gary.busuttil@ealing.gov.uk

Byrne, Theresa (LAB - North Greenford)
theresa.byrne@ealing.gov.uk

Camadoo, Joanna (LAB - Elthorne)
joanna.camadoo@ealing.gov.uk

Cogan, Patrick (LAB - North Greenford)
patrick.cogan@ealing.gov.uk

Conlan, Paul (LAB - Walpole)
paul.conlan@ealing.gov.uk

Conti, Fabio (CON - Northfield)

Crawford, Daniel (LAB - Acton Central)
daniel.crawford@ealing.gov.uk

Crawford, Kate (LAB - East Acton)
katherine.crawford@ealing.gov.uk

Dabrowska, Joanna (CON - Ealing Common)
joanna.dabrowska@ealing.gov.uk

Dhami, Tejinder (LAB - Dormers Wells)
tejinder.dhami@ealing.gov.uk

Dhindsa, Kamaljit (LAB - Southall Green)
kamaljit.dhindsa@ealing.gov.uk

Gavan, Kieron (LAB - East Acton)
kieron.gavan@ealing.gov.uk

Gordon, Yoel (LAB - Elthorne)
yoel.gordon@ealing.gov.uk

Gulaid, Abdullah (LAB - Acton Central)
abdullah.gulaid@ealing.gov.uk

Hynes, Steve (LAB - Northolt Mandeville)
steve.hynes@ealing.gov.uk

Johnson, Yvonne (LAB - South Acton)
yvonne.johnson@ealing.gov.uk

Jones, Penny (LAB - Hobbayne)
penny.jones@ealing.gov.uk

Kang, Swarn (LAB - Southall Green)
swarn.kang@ealing.gov.uk

Kaur Dheer, Harbhajan (LAB - Greenford Broadway)
harbhajan.kaur@ealing.gov.uk

Kelly, Anthony (LAB - Greenford Green)
anthony.kelly@ealing.gov.uk

Khan, Sarfraz (LAB - Southall Broadway)
sarfraz.khan@ealing.gov.uk

Kohli, Sanjai (LAB - Southall Broadway)
sanjai.kohli@ealing.gov.uk

Kumar, Seema (CON - Ealing Broadway)
seema.kumar@ealing.gov.uk

Mahfouz, Bassam (LAB - Northolt West End)
bassam.mahfouz@ealing.gov.uk

Mahmood, Tariq (LAB - Perivale)
tariq.mahmood@ealing.gov.uk

Malcolm, Gary (LD - Southfield)
gary.malcolm@ealing.gov.uk

Mann, Rajinder (LAB - Norwood Green)
rajinder.mann@ealing.gov.uk

Mann, Gurmit (LAB - Norwood Green)
gurmit.mann@ealing.gov.uk

Manro, Shital (LAB - North Greenford)
shital.manro@ealing.gov.uk

Martin, Dee (LAB - Northolt West End)
dee.martin@ealing.gov.uk

Mason, Peter (LAB - Elthorne)
peter.mason@ealing.gov.uk

McCartan, Ciaran (LAB - Hobbayne)
ciaran.mccartan@ealing.gov.uk

EALING

Midha, Mohinder (LAB - Lady Margaret)
mohinder.midha@ealing.gov.uk

Millican, David (CON - Northfield)
david.millican@ealing.gov.uk

Mohan, Karam (LAB - Lady Margaret)
karam.mohan@ealing.gov.uk

Morrissey, Joy (CON - Hanger Hill)
morrisseyj@ealing.gov.uk

Mullins, Theresa (CON - Northfield)
theresa.mullins@ealing.gov.uk

Murray, Lynne (LAB - Cleveland)
lynne.murray@ealing.gov.uk

Murtagh, Timothy (LAB - Greenford Broadway)
tim.murtagh@ealing.gov.uk

Nagpal, Kamaljit (LAB - Southall Broadway)
kamaljit.nagpal@ealing.gov.uk

Padda, Swaran (LAB - Lady Margaret)
swaran.padda@ealing.gov.uk

Proud, Ian (CON - Cleveland)
ian.proud@ealing.gov.uk

Rai, Binda (LAB - Walpole)
binda.rai@ealing.gov.uk

Raza, Aysha (LAB - Greenford Green)
aysha.raza@ealing.gov.uk

Reece, Roz (CON - Ealing Common)
roz.reece@ealing.gov.uk

Rodgers, David (LAB - Cleveland)
david.rodgers@ealing.gov.uk

Sabiers, Mik (LAB - South Acton)
mik.sabiers@ealing.gov.uk

Sharma, Charan (LAB - Perivale)
charan.sharma@ealing.gov.uk

Shaw, Gareth (LAB - Walpole)
gareth.shaw@ealing.gov.uk

Stafford, Gregory (CON - Hanger Hill)
gregory.stafford@ealing.gov.uk

Stafford, Alexander (CON - Ealing Broadway)
alex.stafford@ealing.gov.uk

Steed, Andrew (LD - Southfield)
andrew.steed@ealing.gov.uk

Summers, Chris (LAB - Northolt Mandeville)
chris.summers@ealing.gov.uk

Sumner, Nigel (CON - Hanger Hill)
nigel.sumner@ealing.gov.uk

Tailor, Hitesh (LAB - East Acton)
hitesh.tailor@ealing.gov.uk

Walker, Patricia (LAB - Acton Central)
patricia.walker@ealing.gov.uk

Wall, Lauren (LAB - Northolt West End)
lauren.wall@ealing.gov.uk

Wall, Ray (LAB - Hobbayne)
ray.wall@ealing.gov.uk

Woodroofe, Simon (LAB - Greenford Green)
simon.woodroofe@ealing.gov.uk

Young, Anthony (CON - Ealing Broadway)
anthony.young@ealing.gov.uk

POLITICAL COMPOSITION
LAB: 53, CON: 12, LD: 4

COMMITTEE CHAIRS

Audit: Mr Timothy Murtagh

Health & Adult Social Services: Mr Daniel Crawford

Health & Wellbeing: Mr Julian Bell

Licensing: Ms Kate Crawford

East Ayrshire   S

East Ayrshire Council, Council Headquarters, London Road, Kilmarnock KA3 7BU
☎ 01563 576000 🖶 01563 576500 ✆ the.council@east-ayrshire.gov.uk
🖥 www.east-ayrshire.gov.uk

FACTS AND FIGURES
Parliamentary Constituencies: Ayr, Carrick and Cumnock, Kilmarnock and Loudoun
EU Constituencies: Scotland
Election Frequency: Elections are of whole council

PRINCIPAL OFFICERS

Chief Executive: Ms Fiona Lees, Chief Executive, Council Headquarters, London Road, Kilmarnock KA3 7BU
☎ 01563 576019 ✆ fiona.lees@east-ayrshire.gov.uk

Deputy Chief Executive: Mr Chris McAleavey, Deputy Chief Executive - Safer Communities, Council Headquarters, London Road, Kilmarnock KA3 7BU ☎ 01563 576076
✆ chris.mcaleavey@east-ayrshire.gov.uk

Deputy Chief Executive: Mr Alex McPhee, Deputy Chief Executive - Economy & Skills / Chief Financial Officer, Council Headquarters, London Road, Kilmarnock KA3 7BU
☎ 01563 576279 ✆ alex.mcphee@east-ayrshire.gov.uk

Architect, Building / Property Services: Mr Andrew Kennedy, Head of Facilities & Property Management, Council Headquarters, London Road, Kilmarnock KA3 7BU ☎ 01563 576089
✆ andrew.kennedy@east-ayrshire.gov.uk

Best Value: Ms Gwen Barker, Policy, Planning & Performance Manager, Council Headquarters, London Road, Kilmarnock KA3 7BU ☎ 01563 554602 ✆ gwen.barker@east-ayrshire.gov.uk

Building Control: Mr David McDowall, Building Standards & Development Manager, The Johnnie Walker Bond, 15 Strand Street, Kilmarnock KA1 1HU ☎ 01563 576767
✆ david.mcdowall@east-ayrshire.gov.uk

Catering Services: Mr Andrew Kennedy, Head of Facilities & Property Management, Council Headquarters, London Road, Kilmarnock KA3 7BU ☎ 01563 576089
✆ andrew.kennedy@east-ayrshire.gov.uk

Civil Registration: Ms Catherine Dunlop, Senior Registrar, Burns Monument Centre, Kay Park, Kilmarnock KA3 7RU
☎ 01563 576692 ⁻🖰 catherine.dunlop@east-ayrshire.gov.uk

PR / Communications: Ms Lynne Buchanan, Communications Manager, Council Headquarters, London Road, Kilmarnock KA3 7BU ☎ 01563 576520 ⁻🖰 lynne.buchanan@east-ayrshire.gov.uk

Community Planning: Ms Gwen Barker, Policy, Planning & Performance Manager, Council Headquarters, London Road, Kilmarnock KA3 7BU ☎ 01563 554602
⁻🖰 gwen.barker@east-ayrshire.gov.uk

Community Safety: Ms Katie Kelly, Head of Housing & Communities, Council Headquarters, London Road, Kilmarnock KA3 7BU ☎ 01563 576598 ⁻🖰 katie.kelly@east-ayrshire.gov.uk

Computer Management: Mr Craig McArthur, Head of Finance Service, Council Headquarters, London Road, Kilmarnock KA3 7BU
☎ 01563 576513 ⁻🖰 craig.mcarthur@east-ayrshire.gov.uk

Consumer Protection and Trading Standards: Mr Paul Todd, Regulatory Services Manager, Civic Centre South, John Dickie Street, Kilmarnock KA1 1HW ☎ 01563 576913
⁻🖰 paul.todd@east-ayrshire.gov.uk

Contracts: Mr Stuart McCall, Legal Services Manager, Council Headquarters, London Road, Kilmarnock KA3 7BU
☎ 01563 576085 ⁻🖰 stuart.mccall@east-ayrshire.gov.uk

Direct Labour: Mr Derek Spence, Housing Asset Services Manager, Burnside Street, Kilmarnock, KA1 4EX ☎ 01563 555501 ⁻🖰 derek.spence@east-ayrshire.gov.uk

Economic Development: Mr Michael Keane, Head of Planning & Economic Development, The Johnnie Walker Bond, 15 Strand Street, Kilmarnock KA1 1HU ☎ 01563 576767 ⁻🖰 michael.keane@eastayrshire.gov.uk

Education: Mr Alan Ward, Head of Education, Council Headquarters, London Road, Kilmarnock KA3 7BU
☎ 01563 576126 ⁻🖰 alan.ward@east-ayrshire.gov.uk

E-Government: Mr Roy Hair, Systems & Performance Manager, Opera House, John Finnie Street, Kilmarnock KA1 1DD
☎ 01563 576817 ⁻🖰 roy.hair@east-ayrshire.gov.uk

E-Government: Mr Craig McArthur, Head of Finance Service, Council Headquarters, London Road, Kilmarnock KA3 7BU
☎ 01563 576513 ⁻🖰 craig.mcarthur@east-ayrshire.gov.uk

Electoral Registration: Ms Julie McGarry, Administration Manager, Council Headquarters, London Road, Kilmarnock KA3 7BU ☎ 01563 576147 ⁻🖰 julie.mcgarry@east-ayrshire.gov.uk

Emergency Planning: Ms Lesley Jeffrey, Civil Contingencies Officer, Building 372, Alpha Freight Area, Robertson Road, Glasgow Prestwick International Airport, Prestwick KA9 2PL
☎ 01292 692185 ⁻🖰 acct@south-ayrshire.gov.uk

Energy Management: Mrs Sarah Farrell, Energy Adviser, 2 The Cross, Kilmarnock KA1 1LR ☎ 01563 555224
⁻🖰 sarah.farrell@east-ayrshire.gov.uk

Environmental / Technical Services: Ms Katie Kelly, Head of Housing & Communities, Council Headquarters, London Road, Kilmarnock KA3 7BU ☎ 01563 576598
⁻🖰 katie.kelly@east-ayrshire.gov.uk

Environmental Health: Mr Paul Todd, Regulatory Services Manager, Civic Centre South, John Dickie Street, Kilmarnock KA1 1HW ☎ 01563 576913 ⁻🖰 paul.todd@east-ayrshire.gov.uk

Finance: Mr Alex McPhee, Deputy Chief Executive - Economy & Skills / Chief Financial Officer, Council Headquarters, London Road, Kilmarnock KA3 7BU ☎ 01563 576279
⁻🖰 alex.mcphee@east-ayrshire.gov.uk

Grounds Maintenance: Mr Robert McCulloch, Outdoor Amenities Manager, Outdoor Amenities, Western Road Depot, Kilmarnock KA3 1LL ☎ 01563 554066 ⁻🖰 robert.mcculloch@east-ayrshire.gov.uk

Health and Safety: Mr David Doran, Health & Safety Manager, Council Headquarters, London Road, Kilmarnock KA3 7BU
☎ 01563 576095 ⁻🖰 david.doran@east-ayrshire.gov.uk

Highways: Mr Stewart Turner, Head of Roads - Ayrshire Roads Alliance, The Johnnie Walker Bond, 15 Strand Street, Kilmarnock KA1 1HU ☎ 01563 503164 ⁻🖰 stewart.turner@ayrshireroadsalliance.org

Housing: Ms Katie Kelly, Head of Housing & Communities, Council Headquarters, London Road, Kilmarnock KA3 7BU
☎ 01563 576598 ⁻🖰 katie.kelly@east-ayrshire.gov.uk

Housing: Mr Chris McAleavey, Deputy Chief Executive - Safer Communities, Council Headquarters, London Road, Kilmarnock KA3 7BU ☎ 01563 576076 ⁻🖰 chris.mcaleavey@east-ayrshire.gov.uk

Housing Maintenance: Ms Katie Kelly, Head of Housing & Communities, Council Headquarters, London Road, Kilmarnock KA3 7BU ☎ 01563 576598 ⁻🖰 katie.kelly@east-ayrshire.gov.uk

Legal: Mr David Mitchell, Chief Governance Officer, Council Headquarters, London Road, Kilmarnock KA3 7BU
☎ 01563 576061 ⁻🖰 david.mitchell@east-ayrshire.gov.uk

Leisure and Cultural Services: Mr John Griffiths, Chief Executive - East Ayrshire Leisure, The Palace Theatre, 9 Green Street, Kilmarnock KA1 3BN ☎ 01563 554710
⁻🖰 john.griffiths@east-ayrshire.gov.uk

Licensing: Mr David Mitchell, Chief Governance Officer, Council Headquarters, London Road, Kilmarnock KA3 7BU
☎ 01563 576061 ⁻🖰 david.mitchell@east-ayrshire.gov.uk

Lighting: Mr Stewart Turner, Head of Roads - Ayrshire Roads Alliance, The Johnnie Walker Bond, 15 Strand Street, Kilmarnock KA1 1HU ☎ 01563 503164 ⁻🖰 stewart.turner@ayrshireroadsalliance.org

Member Services: Mr David Mitchell, Chief Governance Officer, Council Headquarters, London Road, Kilmarnock KA3 7BU
☎ 01563 576061 ⁻🖰 david.mitchell@east-ayrshire.gov.uk

Parking: Mr Stewart Turner, Head of Roads - Ayrshire Roads Alliance, The Johnnie Walker Bond, 15 Strand Street, Kilmarnock KA1 1HU ☎ 01563 503164 ⁻🖰 stewart.turner@ayrshireroadsalliance.org

EAST AYRSHIRE

Partnerships: Ms Gwen Barker, Policy, Planning & Performance Manager, Council Headquarters, London Road, Kilmarnock KA3 7BU ☎ 01563 554602 ⏴ gwen.barker@east-ayrshire.gov.uk

Personnel / HR: Mr Chris McAleavey, Deputy Chief Executive - Safer Communities, Council Headquarters, London Road, Kilmarnock KA3 7BU ☎ 01563 576076 ⏴ chris.mcaleavey@east-ayrshire.gov.uk

Personnel / HR: Mr Paul McGowan, Head of Human Resources, Council Headquarters, London Road, Kilmarnock KA3 7BU ☎ 01563 576092 ⏴ paul.mcgowan@east-ayrshire.gov.uk

Planning: Mr Michael Keane, Head of Planning & Economic Development, The Johnnie Walker Bond, 15 Strand Street, Kilmarnock KA1 1HU ☎ 01563 576767 ⏴ michael.keane@eastayrshire.gov.uk

Planning: Mr Alex McPhee, Deputy Chief Executive - Economy & Skills / Chief Financial Officer, Council Headquarters, London Road, Kilmarnock KA3 7BU ☎ 01563 576279 ⏴ alex.mcphee@east-ayrshire.gov.uk

Procurement: Ms Lesley McLean, Procurement Manager, Council Headquarters, London Road, Kilmarnock KA3 7BU ☎ 01563 576186 ⏴ lesley.mclean@east-ayrshire.gov.uk

Public Libraries: Mr John Griffiths, Chief Executive - East Ayrshire Leisure, The Palace Theatre, 9 Green Street, Kilmarnock KA1 3BN ☎ 01563 554710 ⏴ john.griffiths@east-ayrshire.gov.uk

Recycling & Waste Minimisation: Ms Katie Kelly, Head of Housing & Communities, Council Headquarters, London Road, Kilmarnock KA3 7BU ☎ 01563 576598 ⏴ katie.kelly@east-ayrshire.gov.uk

Regeneration: Mr Michael Keane, Head of Planning & Economic Development, The Johnnie Walker Bond, 15 Strand Street, Kilmarnock KA1 1HU ☎ 01563 576767 ⏴ michael.keane@eastayrshire.gov.uk

Road Safety: Mr Jim Melville, Road Safety Officer, The Johnnie Walker Bond, 15 Strand Street, Kilmarnock KA3 1HU ☎ 01563 503132 ⏴ jim.melville@east-ayrshire.gov.uk

Social Services: Mr Eddie Fraser, Director - Health & Social Care Partnership, Council Headquarters, London Road, Kilmarnock KA3 7BU ☎ 01563 576546 ⏴ eddie.fraser@east-ayrshire.gov.uk

Social Services: Ms Pamela Milliken, Head of Primary Care & Out of Hours Community Response Services, Council Headquarters, London Road, Kilmarnock KA3 7BU ☎ 01563 576020 ⏴ pamela.milliken@east-ayrshire.gov.uk

Social Services (Adult): Ms Annemargaret Black, Head of Community Health & Care Services, Council Headquarters, London Road, Kilmarnock KA3 7BU ☎ 01563 576090 ⏴ annemargaret.black@east-ayrshire.gov.uk

Social Services (Children): Ms Susan Taylor, Head of Children's Health, Care & Justice, Council Headquarters, London Road, Kilmarnock KA3 7BU ☎ 01563 576920 ⏴ susan.taylor@east-ayrshire.gov.uk

Staff Training: Ms Ailie Macpherson, Organisational Development Manager, Greenholm Street, Kilmarnock KA1 4DJ ☎ 01563 503441 ⏴ allie.macpherson@east-ayrshire.gov.uk

Street Scene: Mr Stewart Turner, Head of Roads - Ayrshire Roads Alliance, The Johnnie Walker Bond, 15 Strand Street, Kilmarnock KA1 1HU ☎ 01563 503164 ⏴ stewart.turner@ayrshireroadsalliance.org

Sustainable Development: Mr Michael Keane, Head of Planning & Economic Development, The Johnnie Walker Bond, 15 Strand Street, Kilmarnock KA1 1HU ☎ 01563 576767 ⏴ michael.keane@eastayrshire.gov.uk

Town Centre: Ms Fiona Nicolson, Town Centre Manager - Kilmarnock & Cumnock, CARS Office, 34 John Finnie Street, Kilmarnock KA1 1DD ☎ 01563 503014 ⏴ fiona.nicolson@east-ayrshire.gov.uk

Traffic Management: Mr Stewart Turner, Head of Roads - Ayrshire Roads Alliance, The Johnnie Walker Bond, 15 Strand Street, Kilmarnock KA1 1HU ☎ 01563 503164 ⏴ stewart.turner@ayrshireroadsalliance.org

Transport Planner: Mr Stewart Turner, Head of Roads - Ayrshire Roads Alliance, The Johnnie Walker Bond, 15 Strand Street, Kilmarnock KA1 1HU ☎ 01563 503164 ⏴ stewart.turner@ayrshireroadsalliance.org

Waste Collection and Disposal: Ms Katie Kelly, Head of Housing & Communities, Council Headquarters, London Road, Kilmarnock KA3 7BU ☎ 01563 576598 ⏴ katie.kelly@east-ayrshire.gov.uk

Waste Management: Ms Katie Kelly, Head of Housing & Communities, Council Headquarters, London Road, Kilmarnock KA3 7BU ☎ 01563 576598 ⏴ katie.kelly@east-ayrshire.gov.uk

Children's Play Areas: Ms Katie Kelly, Head of Housing & Communities, Council Headquarters, London Road, Kilmarnock KA3 7BU ☎ 01563 576598 ⏴ katie.kelly@east-ayrshire.gov.uk

COUNCILLORS

Leader of the Council: Reid, Douglas (SNP - Kilmarnock West & Crosshouse)
douglas.reid@east-ayrshire.gov.uk

Deputy Leader of the Council: Cook, Tom (CON - Kilmarnock West & Crosshouse)
tom.cook@east-ayrshire.gov.uk

Bell, John (SNP - Doon Valley)
john.bell@east-ayrshire.gov.uk

Buchanan, Jim (SNP - Kilmarnock East & Hurlford)
jim.buchanan@east-ayrshire.gov.uk

Campbell, John (SNP - Kilmarnock East & Hurlford)
john.campbell@east-ayrshire.gov.uk

Coffey, Helen (SNP - Kilmarnock North)
helen.coffey@east-ayrshire.gov.uk

Cowan, Elaine (SNP - Kilmarnock North)
elaine.cowan@east-ayrshire.gov.uk

Crawford, William (LAB - Cumnock & New Cumnock)
william.crawford@east-ayrshire.gov.uk

Cree, Gordon (LAB - Kilmarnock East & Hurlford)
gordon.cree@east-ayrshire.gov.uk

Dinwoodie, Elaine (LAB - Doon Valley)
elaine.dinwoodie@east-ayrshire.gov.uk

Freel, Ellen (IND - Annick)
ellen.freel2@east-ayrshire.gov.uk

Jones, Lillian (LAB - Kilmarnock West & Crosshouse)
lillian.jones@east-ayrshire.gov.uk

Knapp, John (LAB - Kilmarnock South)
john.knapp@east-ayrshire.gov.uk

Linton, Iain (SNP - Kilmarnock West & Crosshouse)
iain.linton@east-ayrshire.gov.uk

MacColl, Eoghann (SNP - Annick)
eoghann.maccoll@east-ayrshire.gov.uk

Mair, George (LAB - Irvine Valley)
george.mair@east-ayrshire.gov.uk

McDill, Bobby (SNP - Irvine Valley)
robert.mcdill@east-ayrshire.gov.uk

McFadzean, John (CON - Irvine Valley)
john.mcfadzean@east-ayrshire.gov.uk

McGhee, John (LAB - Annick)
john.mcghee@east-ayrshire.gov.uk

McGhee, Neil (LAB - Ballochmyle)
neil.mcghee@east-ayrshire.gov.uk

McIntyre, Drew (LAB - Kilmarnock East & Hurlford)
andrew.mcintyre@east-ayrshire.gov.uk

McKay, Maureen (LAB - Kilmarnock North)
maureen.mckay@east-ayrshire.gov.uk

Menzies, William (LAB - Cumnock & New Cumnock)
william.menzies@east-ayrshire.gov.uk

Morrice, Kathy (SNP - Cumnock & New Cumnock)
kathy.morrice@east-ayrshire.gov.uk

Pirie, Moira (LAB - Doon Valley)
moira.pirie@east-ayrshire.gov.uk

Primrose, Stephanie (SNP - Ballochmyle)
stephanie.primrose@east-ayrshire.gov.uk

Roberts, Jim (SNP - Ballochmyle)
jim.roberts@east-ayrshire.gov.uk

Ross, Hugh (SNP - Kilmarnock South)
hugh.ross@east-ayrshire.gov.uk

Ross, Eric (LAB - Cumnock & New Cumnock)
eric.ross@east-ayrshire.gov.uk

Shaw, David (LAB - Ballochmyle)
david.shaw@east-ayrshire.gov.uk

Todd, Jim (SNP - Kilmarnock South)
jim.todd@east-ayrshire.gov.uk

Whitham, Elena (SNP - Irvine Valley)
elena.whitham@east-ayrshire.gov.uk

POLITICAL COMPOSITION
SNP: 15, LAB: 14, CON: 2, IND: 1

East Cambridgeshire · D

East Cambridgeshire District Council, The Grange, Nutholt
Lane, Ely CB7 4EE
☎ 01353 665555 ▤ 01353 665240
⌂ customerservices@eastcambs.gov.uk ▢ www.eastcambs.gov.uk

FACTS AND FIGURES
Parliamentary Constituencies: Cambridgeshire South East
EU Constituencies: Eastern
Election Frequency: Elections are of whole council

PRINCIPAL OFFICERS

Chief Executive: Mr John Hill, Chief Executive, The Grange,
Nutholt Lane, Ely CB7 4EE ☎ 01353 616274
⌂ john.hill@eastcambs.gov.uk

Senior Management: Ms Jo Brooks, Director - Operations, The
Grange, Nutholt Lane, Ely CB7 4EE ☎ 01353 616498
⌂ jo.brooks@eastcambs.gov.uk

Senior Management: Ms Emma Grima, Director - Commercial,
The Grange, Nutholt Lane, Ely CB7 4EE ☎ 01353 616960
⌂ emma.grima@eastcambs.gov.uk

Senior Management: Mr Andy Radford, Director - Resources,
The Grange, Nutholt Lane, Ely CB7 4EE ☎ 01353 616303
⌂ andy.radford@eastcambs.gov.uk

Access Officer / Social Services (Disability): Mr Jason
Johnson, Building Control Manager, The Grange, Nutholt Lane, Ely
CB7 4EE ☎ 01353 616208 ⌂ jason.johnson@eastcambs.gov.uk

Building Control: Mr Jason Johnson, Building Control Manager,
The Grange, Nutholt Lane, Ely CB7 4EE ☎ 01353 616208
⌂ jason.johnson@eastcambs.gov.uk

PR / Communications: Ms Jo Brooks, Director - Operations, The
Grange, Nutholt Lane, Ely CB7 4EE ☎ 01353 616498
⌂ jo.brooks@eastcambs.gov.uk

Community Planning: Mr Lewis Bage, Communities &
Partnerships Manager, The Grange, Nutholt Lane, Ely CB7 4EE
☎ 01353 616374 ⌂ lewis.bage@eastcambs.gov.uk

Community Safety: Ms Angela Parmenter, Housing &
Community Safety Manager, The Grange, Nutholt Lane, Ely CB7
4EE ☎ 01353 616374 ⌂ angela.parmenter@eastcambs.gov.uk

Computer Management: Mr Mark Chadwick, Principal ICT
Officer (Support & Information Security), The Grange, Nutholt Lane,
Ely CB7 4EE ☎ 01353 616216 ⌂ mark.chadwick@eastcambs.gov.uk

Customer Service: Mrs Annette Wade, Customer Services
Manager, The Grange, Nutholt Lane, Ely CB7 4EE ☎ 01353 616310
⌂ annette.wade@eastcambs.gov.uk

Direct Labour: Mr Spencer Clark, Open Spaces & Facilities
Manager, The Grange, Nutholt Lane, Ely CB7 4EE ☎ 01353 616364
⌂ spencer.clark@eastcambs.gov.uk

EAST CAMBRIDGESHIRE

Economic Development: Mr Darren Hill, Business Development Manager, The Grange, Nutholt Lane, Ely CB7 4EE ☎ 01353 616450 ⏚ darren.hill@eastcambs.gov.uk

E-Government: Mr Mark Chadwick, Principal ICT Officer (Support & Information Security), The Grange, Nutholt Lane, Ely CB7 4EE ☎ 01353 616216 ⏚ mark.chadwick@eastcambs.gov.uk

Electoral Registration: Mrs Joan Cox, Electoral Services Officer, The Grange, Nutholt Lane, Ely CB7 4EE ☎ 01353 616460 ⏚ joan.cox@eastcambs.gov.uk

Emergency Planning: Mr John Hill, Chief Executive, The Grange, Nutholt Lane, Ely CB7 4EE ☎ 01353 616274 ⏚ john.hill@eastcambs.gov.uk

Energy Management: Mrs Liz Knox, Environmental Services Manager, The Grange, Nutholt Lane, Ely CB7 4EE ☎ 01353 616313 ⏚ liz.knox@eastcambs.gov.uk

Environmental Health: Mrs Liz Knox, Environmental Services Manager, The Grange, Nutholt Lane, Ely CB7 4EE ☎ 01353 616313 ⏚ liz.knox@eastcambs.gov.uk

European Liaison: Mr Darren Hill, Business Development Manager, The Grange, Nutholt Lane, Ely CB7 4EE ☎ 01353 616450 ⏚ darren.hill@eastcambs.gov.uk

Events Manager: Mrs Tracey Harding, Tourism & Town Centres Manager, The Grange, Nutholt Lane, Ely CB7 4EE ☎ 01363 665555 ⏚ tracey.harding@eastcambs.gov.uk

Facilities: Mrs Nicole Pema, HR Manager, The Grange, Nutholt Lane, Ely CB7 4EE ☎ 01353 665555 ⏚ nicole.pema@eastcambs.gov.uk

Grounds Maintenance: Mr Spencer Clark, Open Spaces & Facilities Manager, The Grange, Nutholt Lane, Ely CB7 4EE ☎ 01353 616364 ⏚ spencer.clark@eastcambs.gov.uk

Health and Safety: Mr David Vincent, Health & Safety Officer, The Grange, Nutholt Lane, Ely CB7 4EE ☎ 01353 616239 ⏚ david.vincent@eastcambs.gov.uk

Home Energy Conservation: Mrs Liz Knox, Environmental Services Manager, The Grange, Nutholt Lane, Ely CB7 4EE ☎ 01353 616313 ⏚ liz.knox@eastcambs.gov.uk

Housing: Ms Jo Brooks, Director - Operations, The Grange, Nutholt Lane, Ely CB7 4EE ☎ 01353 616498 ⏚ jo.brooks@eastcambs.gov.uk

Legal: Ms Maggie Camp, Legal Services Manager, The Grange, Nutholt Lane, Ely CB7 4EE ☎ 01353 616277 ⏚ maggie.camp@eastcambs.gov.uk

Leisure and Cultural Services: Mr Victor Le Grand, Senior Leisure Services Officer, The Grange, Nutholt Lane, Ely CB7 4EE ☎ 01353 616361 ⏚ victor.legrand@eastcambs.gov.uk

Licensing: Mrs Liz Knox, Environmental Services Manager, The Grange, Nutholt Lane, Ely CB7 4EE ☎ 01353 616313 ⏚ liz.knox@eastcambs.gov.uk

Member Services: Mrs Tracy Couper, Democratic Services Manager, The Grange, Nutholt Lane, Ely CB7 4EE ☎ 01353 616278 ⏚ tracy.couper@eastcambs.gov.uk

Parking: Mrs Tracey Harding, Tourism & Town Centres Manager, The Grange, Nutholt Lane, Ely CB7 4EE ☎ 01363 665555 ⏚ tracey.harding@eastcambs.gov.uk

Personnel / HR: Mrs Nicole Pema, HR Manager, The Grange, Nutholt Lane, Ely CB7 4EE ☎ 01353 665555 ⏚ nicole.pema@eastcambs.gov.uk

Planning: Ms Rebecca Saunt, Planning Manager, The Grange, Nutholt Lane, Ely CB7 4EE ☎ 01353 665555 ⏚ rebecca.saunt@eastcambs.gov.uk

Recycling & Waste Minimisation: Mr Dave White, Waste Strategy Team Leader, The Grange, Nutholt Lane, Ely CB7 4EE ☎ 01353 616232 ⏚ dave.white@eastcambs.gov.uk

Staff Training: Mrs Nicole Pema, HR Manager, The Grange, Nutholt Lane, Ely CB7 4EE ☎ 01353 665555 ⏚ nicole.pema@eastcambs.gov.uk

Tourism: Mrs Tracey Harding, Tourism & Town Centres Manager, The Grange, Nutholt Lane, Ely CB7 4EE ☎ 01363 665555 ⏚ tracey.harding@eastcambs.gov.uk

Town Centre: Mrs Tracey Harding, Tourism & Town Centres Manager, The Grange, Nutholt Lane, Ely CB7 4EE ☎ 01363 665555 ⏚ tracey.harding@eastcambs.gov.uk

Waste Collection and Disposal: Mr Dave White, Waste Strategy Team Leader, The Grange, Nutholt Lane, Ely CB7 4EE ☎ 01353 616232 ⏚ dave.white@eastcambs.gov.uk

Waste Management: Mr Dave White, Waste Strategy Team Leader, The Grange, Nutholt Lane, Ely CB7 4EE ☎ 01353 616232 ⏚ dave.white@eastcambs.gov.uk

Children's Play Areas: Mr Spencer Clark, Open Spaces & Facilities Manager, The Grange, Nutholt Lane, Ely CB7 4EE ☎ 01353 616364 ⏚ spencer.clark@eastcambs.gov.uk

COUNCILLORS

Chair: Allen, Michael (CON - Burwell)
michael.allen@eastcambs.gov.uk

Vice-Chair: Creesswell, Peter (CON - Cheveley)
peter.cresswell@eastcambs.gov.uk

Leader of the Council: Palmer, James (CON - Soham North)

Deputy Leader of the Council: Roberts, Charles (CON - Stretham)
charles.roberts@eastcambs.gov.uk

Group LeaderDupre, Lorna (LD - Sutton)

Alderson, Allen (CON - Swaffhams)

Ambrose-Smith, David (CON - Littleport East)
david.ambrose-smith@eastcambs.gov.uk

Ambrose-Smith, Christine (CON - Littleport West)
christine.ambrose-smith@eastcambs.gov.uk

Austen, Sue (LD - Ely West)
sue.austen@eastcambs.gov.uk

Bailey, Anna (CON - Downham Villages)
anna.bailey@eastcambs.gov.uk

Beckett, Derrick (IND - Isleham)
derrick.beckett@eastcambs.gov.uk

Bovingdon, Ian (CON - Soham South)
ian.bovingdon@eastcambs.gov.uk

Bradley, Mike (CON - Downham Villages)
mike.bradley@eastcambs.gov.uk

Brown, David (CON - Burwell)
david.brown@eastcambs.gov.uk

Chaplin, David (CON - Bottisham)
david.chaplin@eastcambs.gov.uk

Cheetham, Steve (CON - Haddenham)
steve.cheetham@eastcambs.gov.uk

Cox, Paul (CON - Littleport West)
paul.cox@eastcambs.gov.uk

Edwards, Lavinia (CON - Burwell)
lavinia.edwards@eastcambs.gov.uk

Every, Lis (CAP - Ely East)

Green, Coralie (CON - Ely South)
coralie.green@eastcambs.gov.uk

Griffin-Singh, Elaine (CON - Ely North)
elaine.griffin-singh@eastcambs.gov.uk

Hitchin, Neil (CON - Ely West)
neil.hitchin@eastcambs.gov.uk

Hobbs, Richard (CON - Ely East)
richard.hobbs@eastcambs.gov.uk

Huffer, Julia (CON - Fordham Villages)
julia.huffer@eastcambs.gov.uk

Hugo, Mark (CON - Haddenham)
mark.hugo@eastcambs.gov.uk

Hunt, Bill (CON - Stretham)
bill.hunt@eastcambs.gov.uk

Hunt, Tom (CON - Ely South)
tom.hunt@eastcambs.gov.uk

Morris, Chris (CON - Dullingham Villages)
chris.morris@eastcambs.gov.uk

Pearson, Andrew (CON - Ely North)
andrew.pearson@eastcambs.gov.uk

Ross, Hamish (CON - Soham South)

Rouse, Mike (CON - Ely North)
mike.rouse@eastcambs.gov.uk

Schuman, Dan (CON - Soham South)
dan.shcuman@eastcambs.gov.uk

Schumann, Joshua (CON - Fordham Villages)
joshua.schumann@eastcambs.gov.uk

Sennitt, Carol (CON - Soham North)
carol.sennitt@eastcambs.gov.uk

Sharp, Alan (CON - Bottisham)

Shuter, Mathew (CON - Cheveley)
Mathew.shuter@eastcambs.gov.uk

Smith, Stuart (CON - Haddenham)
stuart.smith@eastcambs.gov.uk

Stubbs, Lisa (CON - Sutton)

Webber, Jo (CON - Littleport East)
jo.webber@eastcambs.gov.uk

POLITICAL COMPOSITION
CON: 35, LD: 2, CAP: 1, IND: 1

COMMITTEE CHAIRS

Planning: Mr Joshua Schumann

East Devon   D

East Devon District Council, Council Offices, Knowle,
Sidmouth EX10 8HL
☎ 01395 516551 🖷 01395 517507 ⌨ csc@eastdevon.gov.uk
🖳 www.eastdevon.gov.uk

FACTS AND FIGURES
EU Constituencies: South West
Election Frequency: Elections are of whole council

PRINCIPAL OFFICERS

Chief Executive: Mr Mark Williams, Chief Executive, Council
Offices, Knowle, Sidmouth EX10 8HL ☎ 01395 571695
⌨ mwilliams@eastdevon.gov.uk

Deputy Chief Executive: Mr Richard Cohen, Deputy Chief
Executive of Development, Regeneration & Partnerships, Council
Offices, Knowle, Sidmouth EX10 8HL ☎ 01395 571552
⌨ rcohen@eastdevon.gov.uk

Senior Management: Mr Simon Davey, Strategic Lead - Finance,
Council Offices, Knowle, Sidmouth EX10 8HL ☎ 01395 517490
⌨ sdavey@eastdevon.gov.uk

Senior Management: Mr John Golding, Strategic Lead - Housing
& Environment, Council Offices, Knowle, Sidmouth EX10 8HL
☎ 01395 517567 ⌨ jgolding@eastdevon.gov.uk

Senior Management: Mr Henry Gordon Lennox, Strategic Lead -
Legal, Democratic Services, Licensing & Monitoring Officer, Council
Offices, Knowle, Sidmouth EX10 8HL ☎ 01395 517401
⌨ hgordonlennox@eastdevon.gov.uk

Senior Management: Ms Karen Jenkins, Strategic Lead -
Organisational Development & Transformation, Council Offices,
Knowle, Sidmouth EX10 8HL ☎ 01395 516551
⌨ kjenkin@eastdevon.gov.uk

Architect, Building / Property Services: Mr Paul Seager,
Building Control Manager, Council Offices, Knowle, Sidmouth EX10
8HL ☎ 01395 517482 ⌨ buildingcontrol@eastdevon.gov.uk

Building Control: Mr Paul Seager, Building Control Manager,
Council Offices, Knowle, Sidmouth EX10 8HL ☎ 01395 517482
⌨ buildingcontrol@eastdevon.gov.uk

EAST DEVON

PR / Communications: Mrs Richenda Oldham, Communications Officer, Council Offices, Knowle, Sidmouth EX10 8HL
☎ 01395 517559 ◌ roldham@eastdevon.gov.uk

Community Safety: Mr G Moore, Community Safety Officer, Exmouth Police Station, North Street, Sidmouth EX8 1JZ
☎ 01395 273802 ◌ gmoore@eastdevon.gov.uk

Computer Management: Mr Chris Powell, Chief Operations Manager, Council Offices, Knowle, Sidmouth EX10 8HL
☎ 01395 517433 ◌ cpowell@eastdevon.gov.uk

Computer Management: Mr Chris Powell, Chief Operations Officer, Civic Centre, Paris Street, Exeter EX1 1JN
☎ 01392 265600 ◌ cjpowell@eastdevon.gov.uk

Customer Service: Ms Cherise Foster, Customer Service Manager, Council Offices, Knowle, Sidmouth EX10 8HL
☎ 01395 517535 ◌ cfoster@eastdevon.gov.uk

Economic Development: Mrs Alison Hayward, Economy & Regeneration Manager, Council Offices, Knowle, Sidmouth EX10 8HL ☎ 01395 517406 ◌ ahayward@eastdevon.gov.uk

E-Government: Mr Chris Powell, Chief Operations Manager, Council Offices, Knowle, Sidmouth EX10 8HL ☎ 01395 517433 ◌ cpowell@eastdevon.gov.uk

Electoral Registration: Ms Jill Humphreys, Electoral Services Manager, Council Offices, Knowle, Sidmouth EX10 8HL
☎ 01395 517550 ◌ jumphreys@eastdevon.gov.uk

Emergency Planning: Ms Pam Harvey, Emergency Planning Officer, Council Offices, Knowle, Sidmouth EX10 8HL
☎ 01935 462462 ◌ pharvey@eastdevon.gov.uk

Environmental Health: Mr Andrew Ennis, Service Lead - Environmental Health & Car Parks, Council Offices, Knowle, Sidmouth EX10 8HL ☎ 01395 571583 ◌ aennis@eastdevon.gov.uk

Facilities: Mr Simon Allchurch, Senior Building Surveyor, Council Offices, Knowle, Sidmouth EX10 8HL ☎ 01395 516551
◌ sallchurch@eastdevon.gov.uk

Finance: Mr Simon Davey, Strategic Lead - Finance, Council Offices, Knowle, Sidmouth EX10 8HL ☎ 01395 517490
◌ sdavey@eastdevon.gov.uk

Pensions: Ms Charlotte Thompson, Pensions Manager, Pension Service, Estuary House, Peninsula Park, Rydon Lane, Exeter EX2 7XB ☎ 01392 688210 ◌ charlotte.thompson@devon.gov.uk

Health and Safety: Mr S Cross, Safety Advisor, Council Offices, Knowle, Sidmouth EX10 8HL ☎ 01395 516551
◌ scross@eastdevon.gov.uk

Housing: Mr John Golding, Strategic Lead - Housing & Environment, Council Offices, Knowle, Sidmouth EX10 8HL
☎ 01395 517567 ◌ jgolding@eastdevon.gov.uk

Legal: Mr Henry Gordon Lennox, Strategic Lead - Legal, Democratic Services, Licensing & Monitoring Officer, Council Offices, Knowle, Sidmouth EX10 8HL ☎ 01395 517401
◌ hgordonlennox@eastdevon.gov.uk

Licensing: Mr Stephen Saunders, Licensing Manager, Council Offices, Knowle, Sidmouth EX10 8HL ☎ 01395 516551
◌ ssaunders@eastdevon.gov.uk

Lottery Funding, Charity and Voluntary: Miss Jamie Buckley, Funding Officer, Council Offices, Knowle, Sidmouth EX10 8HL
☎ 01395 517569 ◌ jbuckley@eastdevon.gov.uk

Member Services: Mr Henry Gordon Lennox, Strategic Lead - Legal, Democratic Services, Licensing & Monitoring Officer, Council Offices, Knowle, Sidmouth EX10 8HL ☎ 01395 517401
◌ hgordonlennox@eastdevon.gov.uk

Personnel / HR: Ms Karen Jenkins, Strategic Lead - Organisational Development & Transformation, Council Offices, Knowle, Sidmouth EX10 8HL ☎ 01395 516551
◌ kjenkin@eastdevon.gov.uk

Planning: Mr Ed Freeman, Service Lead - Planning Strategy & Development Management, Council Offices, Knowle, Sidmouth EX10 8HL ◌ efreeman@eastdevon.gov.uk

Procurement: Mr Colin Slater, Procurement Officer, Council Offices, Knowle, Sidmouth EX10 8HL ☎ 01395 516551
◌ procurement@eastdevon.gov.uk

Street Scene: Mr Andrew Hancock, Service Lead - Street Scene, Council Offices, Knowle, Sidmouth EX10 8HL
◌ ahancock@eastdevon.gov.uk

COUNCILLORS

Chair: Hughes, Stuart (CON - Sidmouth Sidford)
shughes@eastdevon.gov.uk

Vice-Chair: Parr, Helen (CON - Coly Valley)
hparr@eastdevon.gov.uk

Leader of the Council: Diviani, Paul (CON - Yarty)
pdiviani@eastdevon.gov.uk

Deputy Leader of the Council: Moulding, Andrew (CON - Axminster Town)
amoulding@eastdevon.gov.uk

Allen, Mike (CON - Honiton St Michaels)
mallen@eastdevon.gov.uk

Armstrong, Megan (IND - Exmouth Halsdon)
marmstrong@eastdevon.gov.uk

Bailey, Brian (CON - Exmouth Withycombe Raleigh)
bbailey@eastdevon.gov.uk

Barratt, David (IND - Sidmouth Rural)
dbarratt@eastdevon.gov.uk

Barrow, Dean (CON - Honiton St Pauls)
dbarrow@eastdevon.gov.uk

Bond, Susie (IND - Feniton & Buckerell)
sbond@eastdevon.gov.uk

Booth, Matthew (IND - Sidmouth Town)
mbooth@@eastdevon.gov.uk

Bowden, Peter (CON - Whimple)
pbowden@eastdevon.gov.uk

Brown, Colin (CON - Dunkeswell)
cbrown@eastdevon.gov.uk

Burrows, Peter (LD - Seaton)
pburrows@eastdevon.gov.uk

Carter, Paul (CON - Ottery St Mary Rural)
pcarter@eastdevon.gov.uk

Chapman, David (CON - Exmouth Brixington)
dchapman@eastdevon.gov.uk

Chapman, Maddy (CON - Exmouth Brixington)
mchapman@eastdevonn.gov.uk

Chubb, Iain (CON - Newbridges)
ichubb@eastdevon.gov.uk

Coppell, Matt (IND - Ottery St Mary Rural)
mcoppell@eastdevon.gov.uk

Dent, Alan (CON - Budleigh)
adent@eastdevon.gov.uk

Dyson, John (IND - Sidmouth Town)
jdyson@eastdevon.gov.uk

Elson, Jill (CON - Exmouth Halsdon)
jelson@eastdevon.gov.uk

Faithfull, Peter (IND - Ottery St Mary Town)
pfaithfull@eastdevon.gov.uk

Gardner, Cathy (IND - Sidmouth Town)
cgardner@eastdevon.gov.uk

Gazzard, Steve (LD - Exmouth Town)
sgazzard@eastdevon.gov.uk

Giles, Roger (IND - Ottery St Mary Town)
rgiles@eastdevon.gov.uk

Godbeer, Graham (CON - Coly Valley)
ggodbeer@eastdevon.gov.uk

Graham, Pat (LD - Exmouth Town)
pgraham@eastdevon.gov.uk

Grundy, Simon (CON - Exe Valley)
sgrundy@eastdevon.gov.uk

Hale, Maria (CON - Broadclyst)
mhale@eastdevon.gov.uk

Hall, Steve (CON - Budleigh)
shall@eastdevon.gov.uk

Hall, Ian (CON - Axminster Rural)
ihall@eastdevon.gov.uk

Hartnell, Marcus (CON - Seaton)
mhartnell@eastdevon.gov.uk

Howe, Michael (CON - Clyst Valley)
mhowe@eastdevon.gov.uk

Hull, Douglas (LD - Axminster Town)
dhull@eastdevon.gov.uk

Humphreys, John (CON - Exmouth Littleham)
jhumphreys@eastdevon.gov.uk

Ingham, Ben (IND - Woodbury & Lympstone)
bingham@eastdevon.gov.uk

Jung, Geoff (IND - Raleigh)
gjung@eastdevon.gov.uk

Key, David (CON - Otterhead)
dkey@eastdevon.gov.uk

Knight, Jim (CON - Seaton)
jknight@eastdevon.gov.uk

Longhurst, Rob (IND - Woodbury & Lympstone)
rlonghurst@eastdevon.gov.uk

Manley, Dawn (IND - Sidmouth Sidford)
dmanley@eastdevon.gov.uk

Nash, Bill (CON - Exmouth Town)
bnash@eastdevon.gov.uk

Nicholas, Cherry (CON - Exmouth Brixington)
cnicholas@eastdevon.gov.uk

O'Leary, John (CON - Honiton St Pauls)
joleary@eastdevon.gov.uk

Pepper, Christopher (CON - Broadclyst)
cpepper@eastdevon.gov.uk

Pook, Geoff (IND - Beer & Branscome)
gpook@eastdevon.gov.uk

Ranger, Val (IND - Newton Poppleford & Harpford)
vranger@eastdevon.gov.uk

Rixson, Marianne (IND - Sidmouth Sidford)
mrixson@eastdevon.gov.uk

Skinner, Philip (CON - Tale Vale)
pskinner@eastdevon.gov.uk

Stott, Pauline (CON - Exmouth Halsdon)
pstott@eastdevon.gov.uk

Taylor, Brenda (LD - Exmouth Withycombe Raleigh)
btaylor@eastdevon.gov.uk

Thomas, Ian (CON - Trinity)
ithomas@eastdevon.gov.uk

Twiss, Phil (CON - Honiton St Michaels)
ptwiss@eastdevon.gov.uk

Williamson, Mark (CON - Exmouth Littleham)
mwilliamson@eastdevon.gov.uk

Wragg, Eileen (LD - Exmouth Town)
ewragg@eastdevon.gov.uk

Wright, Tom (CON - Budleigh)
twright@eastdevon.gov.uk

POLITICAL COMPOSITION
CON: 35, IND: 16, LD: 6

COMMITTEE CHAIRS

Audit: Mr Mark Williamson

Development Management: Mr David Key

Licensing: Mr Steve Hall

East Dorset　　　　　　　　　　　　　　　　**D**

East Dorset District Council, Council Offices, Furzehill,
Wimborne BH21 4HN
☎ 01202 886201 🖶 01202 841390 🖵 www.dorsetforyou.com

EAST DORSET

FACTS AND FIGURES
Parliamentary Constituencies: Christchurch County, Dorset Mid and Poole North
EU Constituencies: South West
Election Frequency: Elections are of whole council

PRINCIPAL OFFICERS

Chief Executive: Mr David McIntosh, Chief Executive, Council Offices, Furzehill, Wimborne BH21 4HN ☎ 01202 795000 ✆ dmcintosh@christchurchandeastdorset.gov.uk

Senior Management: Mr David Barnes, Strategic Director, Council Offices, Furzehill, Wimborne BH21 4HN ☎ 01202 495077 ✆ dbarnes@christchurchandeastdorset.gov.uk

Senior Management: Mr Ian Milner, Strategic Director, Civic Offices, Bridge Street, Christchurch BH23 1AZ ☎ 01202 795176 ✆ imilner@christchurchandeastdorset.gov.uk

Access Officer / Social Services (Disability): Mr David Gale, Building Control Partnership Manager, Council Offices, Furzehill, Wimborne BH21 4HN ☎ 01202 795058 ✆ dgale@christchurchandeastdorset.gov.uk

Architect, Building / Property Services: Mr Ashley Harman, Property & Estates Manager, Council Offices, Furzehill, Wimborne BH21 4HN ☎ 01202 795482 ✆ aharman@christchurchandeastdorset.gov.uk

Building Control: Mr David Gale, Building Control Partnership Manager, Council Offices, Furzehill, Wimborne BH21 4HN ☎ 01202 795058 ✆ dgale@christchurchandeastdorset.gov.uk

Children / Youth Services: Ms Judith Plumley, Head - Community & Economy, Council Offices, Furzehill, Wimborne BH21 4HN ☎ 01202 795043 ✆ jplumpley@christchurchandeastdorset.gov.uk

PR / Communications: Mr Allan Wood, Communications Officer, Council Offices, Furzehill, Wimborne BH21 4HN ☎ 01202 795455 ✆ awood@christchurchandeastdorset.gov.uk

Community Planning: Mr Ian Milner, Strategic Director, Civic Offices, Bridge Street, Christchurch BH23 1AZ ☎ 01202 795176 ✆ imilner@christchurchandeastdorset.gov.uk

Community Safety: Ms Julia Howlett, Community Safety Officer, Council Offices, Furzehill, Wimborne BH21 4HN ☎ 01202 795198 ✆ jhowlett@christchurchandeastdorset.gov.uk

Computer Management: Ms Fiona Hughes, Partnership ICT Manager, Civic Offices, Bridge Street, Christchurch BH23 1AZ ☎ 01202 795148 ✆ fhughes@christchurchandeastdorset.gov.uk

Customer Service: Ms Debbie Cliff, Customer Services Team Leader, Civic Offices, Bridge Street, Christchurch BH23 1AZ ✆ dcliff@christchurchandeastdorset.gov.uk

Economic Development: Mr Nick James, Manager - Economic Development, Council Offices, Furzehill, Wimborne BH21 4HN ☎ 01202 795328 ✆ njames@christchurchandeastdorset.gov.uk

Electoral Registration: Mr Richard Jones, Democratic Services & Elections Manager, Council Offices, Furzehill, Wimborne BH21 4HN ☎ 01202 795171 ✆ rjones@christchurchandeastdorset.gov.uk

Emergency Planning: Mr Jonathan Ross, Engineering & Parking Manager, Council Offices, Furzehill, Wimborne BH21 4HN ☎ 01202 795159 ✆ jross@christchurchandeastdorset.gov.uk

Environmental / Technical Services: Mr Lindsay Cass, Head of Property & Engineering, Council Offices, Furzehill, Wimborne BH21 4HN ☎ 01202 795003 ✆ lcass@christchurchandeastdorset.gov.uk

Environmental Health: Mr Sean Whitney, Public Health & Protection Manager, Council Offices, Furzehill, Wimborne BH21 4HN ☎ 01202 795387 ✆ swhitney@christchurchandeastdorset.gov.uk

European Liaison: Mr Nick James, Manager - Economic Development, Council Offices, Furzehill, Wimborne BH21 4HN ☎ 01202 795328 ✆ njames@christchurchandeastdorset.gov.uk

Facilities: Mr Ashley Harman, Property & Estates Manager, Council Offices, Furzehill, Wimborne BH21 4HN ☎ 01202 795482 ✆ aharman@christchurchandeastdorset.gov.uk

Finance: Mr Ian Milner, Strategic Director, Civic Offices, Bridge Street, Christchurch BH23 1AZ ☎ 01202 795176 ✆ imilner@christchurchandeastdorset.gov.uk

Health and Safety: Mr Sean Whitney, Public Health & Protection Manager, Council Offices, Furzehill, Wimborne BH21 4HN ☎ 01202 795387 ✆ swhitney@christchurchandeastdorset.gov.uk

Housing: Ms Kathryn Blatchford, Strategic Housing Services Manager, Civic Offices, Bridge Street, Christchurch BH23 1AZ ☎ 01202 795158 ✆ kblatchford@christchurchandeastdorset.gov.uk

Legal: Ms Sophia Nartey, Legal Services Manager, Council Offices, Furzehill, Wimborne BH21 4HN ☎ 01202 795400 ✆ snarty@christchurchandeastdorset.gov.uk

Leisure and Cultural Services: Mr Matti Raudsepp, Head of Organisational Development, Council Offices, Furzehill, Wimborne BH21 4HN ☎ 01202 795125 ✆ mraudsepp@christchurchandeastdorset.gov.uk

Licensing: Mr Steve Ricketts, Community Protection Team Leader, Council Offices, Furzehill, Wimborne BH21 4HN ☎ 01202 795407 ✆ sricketts@christchurchandeastdorset.gov.uk

Lottery Funding, Charity and Voluntary: Mr Matti Raudsepp, Head of Organisational Development, Council Offices, Furzehill, Wimborne BH21 4HN ☎ 01202 795125 ✆ mraudsepp@christchurchandeastdorset.gov.uk

Member Services: Mr Richard Jones, Democratic Services & Elections Manager, Council Offices, Furzehill, Wimborne BH21 4HN ☎ 01202 795171 ✆ rjones@christchurchandeastdorset.gov.uk

Parking: Mr Jonathan Ross, Engineering & Parking Manager, Council Offices, Furzehill, Wimborne BH21 4HN ☎ 01202 795159 ✆ jross@christchurchandeastdorset.gov.uk

Personnel / HR: Ms Clare Selby, HR Team Leader, Council Offices, Furzehill, Wimborne BH21 4HN
cselby@christchurchandeastdorset.gov.uk

Planning: Mr Simon Trueick, Partnership Planning Policy Manager, Council Offices, Furzehill, Wimborne BH21 4HN ☎ 01202 795399
strueick@christchurchandeastdorset.gov.uk

Recycling & Waste Minimisation: Mr Lindsay Cass, Head of Property & Engineering, Council Offices, Furzehill, Wimborne BH21 4HN ☎ 01202 795003 lcass@christchurchandeastdorset.gov.uk

Waste Management: Mr Lindsay Cass, Head of Property & Engineering, Council Offices, Furzehill, Wimborne BH21 4HN
☎ 01202 795003 lcass@christchurchandeastdorset.gov.uk

COUNCILLORS

Leader of the Council: Flower, Spencer (IND - Verwood West)
cllr.sflower@eastdorsetdc.gov.uk

Deputy Leader of the Council: Gibson, Simon (CON - Verwood East)
cllr.sgibson@eastdorsetdc.gov.uk

Bartlett, Shane (LD - Wimborne Minster)
cllr.sbartlett@eastdorsetdc.gov.uk

Bryan, Ray (CON - St Leonards)
cllr.rbryan@eastdorsetdc.gov.uk

Burns, Sarah (CON - Corfe Mullen)
cllr.sburns@eastdorsetdc.gov.uk

Burt, Derek (CON - Corfe Mullen)
cllr.dburt@eastdorsetdc.gov.uk

Butler, Steve (CON - Crane)
cllr.sbutler@eastdorsetdc.gov.uk

Clarke, Alex (CON - West Moors & Holt)
cllr.aclarke@eastdorsetdc.gov.uk

Cook, Robin (CON - Stour)
cllr.rcook@eastdorsetdc.gov.uk

Coombes, Toni (CON - Verwood West)
cllr.tcoombes@eastdorsetdc.gov.uk

Dover, Janet (LD - Colehill East)
cllr.jdover@eastdorsetdc.gov.uk

Dyer, Mike (CON - St Leonards)
cllr.mdyer@eastdorsetdc.gov.uk

Goringe, Barry (CON - St Leonards)
cllr.bgoringe@eastdorsetdc.gov.uk

Harrison, Paul (CON - Corfe Mullen)
cllr.pharrison@eastdorsetdc.gov.uk

Johnson, KD (CON - Colehill East)
cllr.kdjohnson@eastdorsetdc.gov.uk

Logan, Gina (CON - Alderholt)
cllr.glogan@eastdorsetdc.gov.uk

Lugg, Cathy (CON - Ameysford)
cllr.clugg@eastdorsetdc.gov.uk

Lugg, Steven (CON - Ferndown Central)
cllr.slugg@eastdoresetdc.gov.uk

Manuel, Barbara (CON - Parley)
cllr.bmanuel@eastdorsetdc.gov.uk

Morgan, David (LD - Wimborne Minster)
cllr.dmorgan@eastdorsetdc.gov.uk

Mortimer, Boyd (CON - Verwood East)
cllr.bmortimer@eastdorsetdc.gov.uk

Ogglesby, Peter (CON - Ferndown Central)
cllr.pogglesby@eastdorsetdc.gov.uk

Packer, David (CON - Colehill West)
david.packer@btinternet.com

Robinson, Julie (CON - Ferndown Central)
cllr.jrobinson@eastdorsetdc.gov.uk

Russell, George (CON - Hampreston & Longham)
cllr.grussell@eastdorsetdc.gov.uk

Shortell, David (CON - West Moors & Holt)
cllr.dshortell@eastdorsetdc.gov.uk

Skeats, Andy (CON - West Moors & Holt)
cllr.askeats@eastdorsetdc.gov.uk

Tong, Simon (CON - Handley Vale)
cllr.stong@eastdorsetdc.gov.uk

POLITICAL COMPOSITION
CON: 24, LD: 3, IND: 1

COMMITTEE CHAIRS

Planning: Mr Mike Dyer

East Dunbartonshire   S

East Dunbartonshire Council, 12 Strathkelvin Place, Kirkintilloch, Glasgow G66 1TJ
☎ 0300 123 4510 customerservices@eastdunbarton.gov.uk
🖳 www.eastdunbarton.gov.uk

FACTS AND FIGURES
Parliamentary Constituencies: Cumbernauld, Kilsyth and Kirkintilloch East
EU Constituencies: Scotland
Election Frequency: Elections are of whole council

PRINCIPAL OFFICERS

Chief Executive: Mr Gerry Cornes, Chief Executive, 12 Strathkelvin Place, Kirkintilloch, Glasgow G66 1TJ ☎ 0141 578 8082; 0141 578 8082 gerry.cornes@eastdunbarton.gov.uk

Senior Management: Ms Ann Davie, Deputy Chief Executive - Education, People & Business, 12 Strathkelvin Place, Kirkintilloch, Glasgow G66 1TJ ☎ 0141 578 8025
ann.davie@eastdunbarton.gov.uk

Senior Management: Mr Keith Gardiner, Chief Social Worker, 12 Strathkelvin Place, Kirkintilloch, Glasgow G66 1TJ ☎ 0300 123 4510
keith.gardiner@eastdunbarton.gov.uk

Senior Management: Mr Thomas Glen, Deputy Chief Executive - Place, Neighbourhood & Corporate Assets, 12 Strathkelvin Place, Kirkintilloch, Glasgow G66 1TJ ☎ 0141 578 8420
thomas.glen@eastdunbarton.gov.uk

EAST DUNBARTONSHIRE

Senior Management: Mr Jamie Robertson, Strategic Lead - Finance, Audit & Performance, 12 Strathkelvin Place, Kirkintilloch, Glasgow G66 1TJ ☎ 0300 123 4510 ✆ jamie.robertson@eastdunbarton.gov.uk

PR / Communications: Ms Angela Fegan, Communications Manager, 12 Strathkelvin Place, Kirkintilloch, Glasgow G66 1TJ ☎ 0300 123 4510 ✆ angela.fegan@eastdunbarton.gov.uk

Computer Management: Mr Vince McNulty, ICT Manager, 12 Strathkelvin Place, Kirkintilloch, Glasgow G66 1TJ ☎ 0300 123 4510 ✆ vince.mcnulty@eastdunbarton.gov.uk

Consumer Protection and Trading Standards: Ms Evonne Bauer, Community Protection Manager, Southbank House, Environment Group, Kirkintilloch, Glasgow G66 1XH ☎ 0300 123 4510 ✆ evonne.bauer@eastdunbarton.gov.uk

Customer Service: Ms Ellen Beattie, Customer Services Manager, Broomhill Industrial Estate, Kilsyth Road, Kirkintilloch, Glasgow G66 1QF ☎ 0300 123 4510 ✆ ellen.beattie@eastdunbarton.gov.uk

Economic Development: Mr Thomas Glen, Deputy Chief Executive - Place, Neighbourhood & Corporate Assets, 12 Strathkelvin Place, Kirkintilloch, Glasgow G66 1TJ ☎ 0141 578 8420 ✆ thomas.glen@eastdunbarton.gov.uk

Education: Ms Jacqueline MacDonald, Chief Education Officer, 12 Strathkelvin Place, Kirkintilloch, Glasgow G66 1TJ ☎ 0300 123 4510 ✆ jacqueline.macdonald@eastdunbarton.gov.uk

Electoral Registration: Mr Martin Cunningham, Manager of Democratic Services, 12 Strathkelvin Place, Kirkintilloch, Glasgow G66 1TJ ☎ 0141 578 8000 ✆ martin.cunningham@eastdunbarton.gov.uk

Estates, Property & Valuation: Mr Alan Bauer, Major Assets & Facilities Manager, 12 Strathkelvin Place, Kirkintilloch, Glasgow G66 1TJ ☎ 0300 123 4510 ✆ alan.bauer@eastdunbarton.gov.uk

Finance: Mr Jamie Robertson, Strategic Lead - Finance, Audit & Performance, 12 Strathkelvin Place, Kirkintilloch, Glasgow G66 1TJ ☎ 0300 123 4510 ✆ jamie.robertson@eastdunbarton.gov.uk

Fleet Management: Mr Paul Curran, Fleet Manager, Broomhill Industrial Estate, Kisyth Road, Kirkintilloch, Glasgow G66 1TF ☎ 0300 123 4510 ✆ paul.curran@eastdunbarton.gov.uk

Health and Safety: Mr Jamie Robertson, Strategic Lead - Finance, Audit & Performance, 12 Strathkelvin Place, Kirkintilloch, Glasgow G66 1TJ ☎ 0300 123 4510 ✆ jamie.robertson@eastdunbarton.gov.uk

Housing: Mr Grant Macintosh, Housing Services Manager, Broomhill Industrial Estate, Kilsyth Road, Kirkintilloch, Glasgow G66 1TF ☎ 0300 123 4510 ✆ grant.mackintosh@eastdunbarton.gov.uk

Leisure and Cultural Services: Mr Mark Grant, East Dunbartonshire Leisure & Culture Trust General Manager, William Patrick Library, 2/3 West High Street, Kirkintilloch, Glasgow G66 1AD ☎ 0141 777 3143 ✆ mark.grant@eastdunbarton.gov.uk

Licensing: Mr Martin Cunningham, Manager of Democratic Services, 12 Strathkelvin Place, Kirkintilloch, Glasgow G66 1TJ ☎ 0141 578 8000 ✆ martin.cunningham@eastdunbarton.gov.uk

Member Services: Mr Martin Cunningham, Manager of Democratic Services, 12 Strathkelvin Place, Kirkintilloch, Glasgow G66 1TJ ☎ 0141 578 8000 ✆ martin.cunningham@eastdunbarton.gov.uk

Partnerships: Mr Thomas Glen, Deputy Chief Executive - Place, Neighbourhood & Corporate Assets, 12 Strathkelvin Place, Kirkintilloch, Glasgow G66 1TJ ☎ 0141 578 8420 ✆ thomas.glen@eastdunbarton.gov.uk

Personnel / HR: Ms Ann Davie, Deputy Chief Executive - Education, People & Business, 12 Strathkelvin Place, Kirkintilloch, Glasgow G66 1TJ ☎ 0141 578 8025 ✆ ann.davie@eastdunbarton.gov.uk

Planning: Mr Thomas Glen, Deputy Chief Executive - Place, Neighbourhood & Corporate Assets, 12 Strathkelvin Place, Kirkintilloch, Glasgow G66 1TJ ☎ 0141 578 8420 ✆ thomas.glen@eastdunbarton.gov.uk

Procurement: Ms Kirsty Chisholm, Procurement Manager, 12 Strathkelvin Place, Kirkintilloch, Glasgow G66 1TJ ☎ 0300 123 4510 ✆ kirsty.chisholm@eastdunbarton.gov.uk

Public Libraries: Mr Mark Grant, East Dunbartonshire Leisure & Culture Trust General Manager, William Patrick Library, 2/3 West High Street, Kirkintilloch, Glasgow G66 1AD ☎ 0141 777 3143 ✆ mark.grant@eastdunbarton.gov.uk

Social Services: Mr Keith Gardiner, Chief Social Worker, 12 Strathkelvin Place, Kirkintilloch, Glasgow G66 1TJ ☎ 0300 123 4510 ✆ keith.gardiner@eastdunbarton.gov.uk

Social Services (Adult): Mr Keith Gardiner, Chief Social Worker, 12 Strathkelvin Place, Kirkintilloch, Glasgow G66 1TJ ☎ 0300 123 4510 ✆ keith.gardiner@eastdunbarton.gov.uk

Social Services (Children): Mr Keith Gardiner, Chief Social Worker, 12 Strathkelvin Place, Kirkintilloch, Glasgow G66 1TJ ☎ 0300 123 4510 ✆ keith.gardiner@eastdunbarton.gov.uk

Staff Training: Ms Ceri Paterson, Organisational Development Manager, 12 Strathkelvin Place, Kirkintilloch, Glasgow G66 1TJ ☎ 0300 123 4510 ✆ ceri.patterson@eastdunbarton.gov.uk

COUNCILLORS

Provost: Walker, Una (LAB - Bishopbriggs North & Torrance) una.walker@eastdunbarton.gov.uk

Cumming, Duncan (IND - Bearsden North) duncan.cumming@eastdunbarton.gov.uk

Dempsey, John (LAB - Campsie & Kirkintilloch North) john.dempsey@eastdunbarton.gov.uk

Geekie, Rhondda (LAB - Lenzie & Kirkintilloch South) rhondda.geekie@eastdunbarton.gov.uk

Ghai, Ashay (LD - Bearsden North) ashay.ghai@eastdunbarton.gov.uk

Gibbons, Jim (SNP - Milngavie)
jim.gibbons@eastdunbarton.gov.uk

Gotts, Eric (LD - Milngavie)
eric.gotts@eastdunbarton.gov.uk

Hendry, Billy (CON - Bishopbriggs North & Torrance)
billy.hendry@eastdunbarton.gov.uk

Henry, Maureen (LAB - Milngavie)
maureen.henry@eastdunbarton.gov.uk

Jamieson, John (SNP - Kirkintilloch East & Twechar)
john.jamieson@eastdunbarton.gov.uk

Jarvis, Anne (CON - Lenzie & Kirkintilloch South)
anne.jarvis@eastdunbarton.gov.uk

Low, Gordon (SNP - Bishopbriggs South)
gordon.low@eastdunbarton.gov.uk

Macdonald, Stewart (LAB - Kirkintilloch East & Twechar)
stewart.macdonald@eastdunbarton.gov.uk

Mackay, Ian (SNP - Bearsden North)
ian.mackay@eastdunbarton.gov.uk

McNair, Anne (SNP - Bishopbriggs North & Torrance)
anne.mcnair@eastdunbarton.gov.uk

Moir, Alan (LAB - Bishopbriggs South)
alan.moir@eastdunbarton.gov.uk

Moody, Vaughan (LD - Bearsden South)
vaughan.moody@eastdunbarton.gov.uk

O'Donnell, Michael (LAB - Bishopbriggs South)
michael.o'donnell@eastdunbarton.gov.uk

Renwick, Gillian (SNP - Lenzie & Kirkintilloch South)
gillian.renwick@eastdunbarton.gov.uk

Ritchie, David (SNP - Campsie & Kirkintilloch North)
david.ritchie@eastdunbarton.gov.uk

Shergill, Manjinder (LAB - Bearsden South)
manjinder.shergill@eastdunbarton.gov.uk

Small, Keith (SNP - Bearsden South)
keith.small@eastdunbarton.gov.uk

Welsh, Gemma (LAB - Campsie & Kirkintilloch North)
gemma.welsh@eastdunbarton.gov.uk

Young, Jack (IND - Kirkintilloch East & Twechar)
jack.young@eastdunbarton.gov.uk

POLITICAL COMPOSITION
LAB: 9, SNP: 8, LD: 3, CON: 2, IND: 2

COMMITTEE CHAIRS

Development & Regeneration: Mr Alan Moir

Licensing: Mr John Dempsey

Planning: Mr Billy Hendry

Policy & Resources: Ms Rhondda Geekie

Social Work: Mr Michael O'Donnell

East Hampshire   D

East Hampshire District Council, Penns Place, Petersfield
GU31 4EX
☎ 01730 266551 🖳 www.easthants.gov.uk

FACTS AND FIGURES
Parliamentary Constituencies: Hampshire East
EU Constituencies: South East
Election Frequency: Elections are of whole council

PRINCIPAL OFFICERS

Chief Executive: Ms Sandy Hopkins, Joint Chief Executive, Penns Place, Petersfield GU31 4EX ☎ 023 9244 6150
⊶ sandy.hopkins@havant.gov.uk

Senior Management: Mrs Dawn Adey, Head of Research & Marketing, Penns Place, Petersfield GU31 4EX ☎ 023 9244 6392
⊶ dawn.adey@havant.gov.uk

Senior Management: Mr James Hassett, Interim Executive Director - Operations, Penns Place, Petersfield GU31 4EX
⊶ james.hassett@easthants.gov.uk

Senior Management: Mr Tom Horwood, Executive Director - Strategy & Governance, Penns Place, Petersfield GU31 4EX
☎ 01730 234025; 023 9244 6151 ⊶ tom.horwood@easthants.gov.uk

Senior Management: Mrs Claire Hughes, Head of Communications & Community Engagement, Penns Place, Petersfield GU31 4EX
☎ 02392 446633 ⊶ claire.hughes@havant.gov.uk

Senior Management: Ms Gill Kneller, Executive Director - Commercial, Penns Place, Petersfield GU31 4EX ☎ 01730 234004; 023 9244 6151 ⊶ gill.kneller@easthants.gov.uk

Senior Management: Mr Steve Pearce, Project Director - RegenCo., Penns Place, Petersfield GU31 4EX ☎ 01790 234005
⊶ steve.pearce@easthants.gov.uk

Senior Management: Mr Andrew Pritchard, Head of Environmental Services, Penns Place, Petersfield GU31 4EX
☎ 01730 234326 ⊶ andrew.pritchard@easthants.gov.uk

Architect, Building / Property Services: Mr Chris Fairhead, Land & Property Manager, Penns Place, Petersfield GU31 4EX
☎ 01730 234040 ⊶ chris.fairhead@easthants.gov.uk

Building Control: Mrs Julia Potter, Head of Development, Penns Place, Petersfield GU31 4EX ☎ 01730 234376; 023 9244 6520
⊶ julia.potter@easthants.gov.uk

Children / Youth Services: Mr Tim Slater, Executive Head of Organisational Development & Programmes, Penns Place, Petersfield GU31 4EX ☎ 01730 234613 ⊶ tim.slater@havant.gov.uk

PR / Communications: Mrs Dawn Adey, Head of Research & Marketing, Penns Place, Petersfield GU31 4EX ☎ 023 9244 6392
⊶ dawn.adey@havant.gov.uk

Community Planning: Mrs Claire Hughes, Head of Communications & Community Engagement, Penns Place, Petersfield GU31 4EX ☎ 02392 446633
⊶ claire.hughes@havant.gov.uk

Community Safety: Mr Ryan Gulliver, Community Safety Manager, Penns Place, Petersfield GU31 4EX ☎ 01730 234167
⊶ ryan.gulliver@easthants.gov.uk

EAST HAMPSHIRE

Computer Management: Mrs Susan Parker, Head of Programmes Redesign & Quality, Penns Place, Petersfield GU31 4EX ☎ 023 9244 6493 ✆ susan.parker@havant.gov.uk

Contracts: Ms Nicola Watts, Joint Environmental Services Manager, Penns Place, Petersfield GU31 4EX ☎ 01730 234383 ✆ nicola.watts@easthants.gov.uk

Corporate Services: Mr Tom Horwood, Executive Director - Strategy & Governance, Penns Place, Petersfield GU31 4EX ☎ 01730 234025; 023 9244 6151 ✆ tom.horwood@easthants.gov.uk

Corporate Services: Ms Gill Kneller, Executive Director - Commercial, Penns Place, Petersfield GU31 4EX ☎ 01730 234004; 023 9244 6151 ✆ gill.kneller@easthants.gov.uk

Customer Service: Mr Brian Wood, Head of Customer Services, Penns Place, Petersfield GU31 4EX ☎ 01730 234026 ✆ brian.wood@easthants.gov.uk

Economic Development: Mr Dan Grindey, Business, Economy & Town Services Manager, Penns Place, Petersfield GU31 4EX ☎ 023 9244 6177 ✆ dan.grindley@easthants.gov.uk

Electoral Registration: Mrs Lianne Richards, Elections Manager, Penns Place, Petersfield GU31 4EX ☎ 01730 234370 ✆ eservices@easthants.gov.uk

Emergency Planning: Mr Stuart Pinkney, Safety & Emergency Planning Officer, Penns Place, Petersfield GU31 4EX ☎ 023 9244 6675 ✆ stuart.pinkney@havant.gov.uk

Energy Management: Ms Gill Kneller, Executive Director - Commercial, Penns Place, Petersfield GU31 4EX ☎ 01730 234004; 023 9244 6151 ✆ gill.kneller@easthants.gov.uk

Energy Management: Mr Jon Sanders, Service Manager - Facilities, Penns Place, Petersfield GU31 4EX ☎ 023 9244 6566 ✆ jon.sanders@easthants.gov.uk

Environmental / Technical Services: Mr Andrew Pritchard, Head of Environmental Services, Penns Place, Petersfield GU31 4EX ☎ 01730 234326 ✆ andrew.pritchard@easthants.gov.uk

Environmental Health: Mrs Natalie Meagher, Head of Neighbourhood Support, Penns Place, Petersfield GU31 4EX ☎ 023 9244 6561 ✆ natalie.meagher@easthants.gov.uk

Environmental Health: Mr Andrew Pritchard, Head of Environmental Services, Penns Place, Petersfield GU31 4EX ☎ 01730 234326 ✆ andrew.pritchard@easthants.gov.uk

Estates, Property & Valuation: Mr Chris Fairhead, Land & Property Manager, Penns Place, Petersfield GU31 4EX ☎ 01730 234040 ✆ chris.fairhead@easthants.gov.uk

Facilities: Mr Jon Sanders, Service Manager - Facilities, Penns Place, Petersfield GU31 4EX ☎ 023 9244 6566 ✆ jon.sanders@easthants.gov.uk

Finance: Mr Simon Little, Service Manager - Finance, Penns Place, Petersfield GU31 4EX ☎ 02392 446624 ✆ simon.little@havant.gov.uk

Finance: Mr Stuart McGregor, Head of Finance & Assets, Penns Place, Petersfield GU31 4EX ☎ 01730 234171 ✆ stuart.mcgregor@easthants.gov.uk

Health and Safety: Ms Rebecca Mundy, Health & Safety Advisor, Penns Place, Petersfield GU31 4EX ✆ rebecca.mundy@easthants.gov.uk

Housing: Ms Tracey Howard, Head of Housing, Public Service Plaza, Civic Centre Road, Havant PO9 2AX ☎ 023 9244 6626 ✆ tracey.howard@easthants.gov.uk

Housing: Mr Tim Slater, Executive Head of Economy & Communities, Penns Place, Petersfield GU31 4EX ☎ 023 9244 6276 ✆ tim.slater@easthants.gov.uk

Legal: Mrs Jane Eaton, Director - Corporate Resources, Penns Place, Petersfield GU31 4EX ☎ 01730 234035; 023 9244 6151 ✆ jane.eaton@havant.gov.uk

Legal: Mr Abe Ezekiel, Head of Legal Services, Penns Place, Petersfield GU31 4EX ✆ abe.ezekiel@easthants.gov.uk

Leisure and Cultural Services: Mr Tim Slater, Executive Head of Organisational Development & Programmes, Penns Place, Petersfield GU31 4EX ☎ 01730 234613 ✆ tim.slater@havant.gov.uk

Licensing: Mrs Natalie Meagher, Head of Neighbourhood Support, Penns Place, Petersfield GU31 4EX ☎ 023 9244 6561 ✆ natalie.meagher@easthants.gov.uk

Member Services: Mrs Penny Milne, Democratic Services Officer, Penns Place, Petersfield GU31 4EX ☎ 023 9244 6234 ✆ penny.milne@havant.gov.uk

Parking: Mrs Natalie Meagher, Head of Neighbourhood Support, Penns Place, Petersfield GU31 4EX ☎ 023 9244 6561 ✆ natalie.meagher@easthants.gov.uk

Personnel / HR: Mr Jeremy Webb, Head of Organisational Development, Penns Place, Petersfield GU31 4EX ☎ 023 9244 6139 ✆ jeremy.webb@easthants.gov.uk

Planning: Mr Simon Jenkins, Head of Planning, Penns Place, Petersfield GU31 4EX ✆ simon.jenkins@easthants.gov.uk

Procurement: Mr Carl Mathias, Strategic Procurement Manager, Penns Place, Petersfield GU31 4EX ☎ 01730 234351 ✆ carl.mathias@easthants.gov.uk

Recycling & Waste Minimisation: Mr Andrew Pritchard, Head of Environmental Services, Penns Place, Petersfield GU31 4EX ☎ 01730 234326 ✆ andrew.pritchard@easthants.gov.uk

Regeneration: Mr Steve Pearce, Project Director - RegenCo., Penns Place, Petersfield GU31 4EX ☎ 01790 234005 ✆ steve.pearce@easthants.gov.uk

Staff Training: Mr Jeremy Webb, Head of Organisational Development, Penns Place, Petersfield GU31 4EX
☎ 023 9244 6139 ⏚ jeremy.webb@easthants.gov.uk

Town Centre: Mr Chris Fairhead, Land & Property Manager, Penns Place, Petersfield GU31 4EX ☎ 01730 234040 ⏚ chris.fairhead@easthants.gov.uk

Waste Collection and Disposal: Ms Nicola Watts, Joint Environmental Services Manager, Penns Place, Petersfield GU31 4EX ☎ 01730 234383 ⏚ nicola.watts@easthants.gov.uk

Waste Management: Mr Andrew Pritchard, Head of Environmental Services, Penns Place, Petersfield GU31 4EX
☎ 01730 234326 ⏚ andrew.pritchard@easthants.gov.uk

COUNCILLORS

Chair: Ashcroft, David (CON - Selborne)
david.ashcroft@easthants.gov.uk

Vice-Chair: Evans, Lynn (CON - Horndean (Murray))
lynn.evans@easthants.gov.uk

Leader of the Council: Cowper, Ferris (CON - Grayshott)
ferris.cowper@easthants.gov.uk

Deputy Leader of the Council: Millard, Richard (CON - Headley)
richard.millard@easthants.gov.uk

Group Leader: Waterhouse, Alan (LD - Whitehill (Pinewood))
alan.waterhouse@easthants.gov.uk

Abdey, James (CON - Petersfield (St Peters))
james.abdey@easthants.gov.uk

Ayer, Robert (IND - Petersfield (Rother))
bob.ayer@easthants.gov.uk

Bentley, Ben (CON - Petersfield (Causeway))
ben.bentley@easthants.gov.uk

Brandt, Edward (CON - Alton (Westbrooke))
edward.brandt@easthants.gov.uk

Butler, Julie (CON - Petersfield (Heath))
julie.butler@easthants.gov.uk

Carew, Adam (LD - Whitehill (Walldown))
adam.carew@easthants.gov.uk

Carter, Ken (CON - Binsted & Bentley)
ken.carter@easthants.gov.uk

Costigan, Tony (CON - Downland)
tonylcostigan@easthants.gov.uk

Drew, Nick (CON - Froxfield & Steep)
nick.drew@easthants.gov.uk

Evans, David (CON - Horndean (Kings))
david.evans@easthants.gov.uk

Glass, Angela (CON - Bramshott & Liphook)
angela.glass@easthants.gov.uk

Hill, Graham (CON - Alton (Whitedown))
graham.hill@easthants.gov.uk

Jackson, Deborah (CON - Four Marks & Medstead)
deborah.jackson@easthants.gov.uk

Johnson, Malcolm (CON - Rowlands Castle)
malcolm.johnson@easthants.gov.uk

Joy, Andrew (CON - Alton (Ashdell))
andrew.joy@easthants.gov.uk

Kendall, Mike (CON - Liss)
mike.kendall@easthants.gov.uk

Louisson, Charles (CON - Ropely & Tisted)
charles.louisson@easthants.gov.uk

Mocatta, Robert (CON - East Meon)
robert.mocatta@easthants.gov.uk

Moon, Ken (CON - Clanfield & Finchdean)
ken.moon@easthants.gov.uk

Mouland, Bill (CON - Bramshott & Liphook)
bill.mouland@easthants.gov.uk

Muldoon, Tony (LD - Whitehill (Deadwater))
tony.muldoon@easthants.gov.uk

Noble, Nicky (CON - Petersfield (St Mary))
nicky.noble@esathants.gov.uk

Orme, David (CON - Alton (Wooteys))
david.orme@easthants.gov.uk

Parker-Smith, Yvonne (CON - Lindford)
yvonne.parker-smith@easthants.gov.uk

Phillips, Dean (CON - Alton (Eastbrooke))
dean.phillips@easthants.gov.uk

Pienaar, Laetitia (CON - Liss)
laetitia.pienaar@easthants.gov.uk

Pond, Sally (LD - Whitehill (Chase))
sally.pond@esathants.gov.uk

Saunders, Robert (CON - Alton (Amery))
robert.saunders@easthants.gov.uk

Schillemore, Sara (CON - Horndean (Catherington & Lovedean))
sara.schillemore@easthants.gov.uk

Shepherd, Guy (CON - Horndean (Downs))
guy.shepherd@easthants.gov.uk

Smith, Mervyn (CON - Whitehill (Hogmoor))
mervyn.smith@easthants.gov.uk

Spencer, Thomas (CON - Petersfield (Bell Hill))
thomas.spencer@easthants.gov.uk

Standish, Rebecca (CON - Bramshott & Liphook)
rebecca.standish@easthants.gov.uk

Thomas, Ingrid (CON - Four Marks & Medstead)
ingrid.thomas@easthants.gov.uk

Tickell, Elaine (CON - Horndean (Hazelton & Blendworth))
elaine.tickell@easthants.gov.uk

Watts, Glynis (CON - Holybourne & Froyle)
glynis.watts@easthants.gov.uk

Williams, Anthony (CON - Headley)
anthony.williams@easthants.gov.uk

Wren, Nigel (CON - Clanfield & Finchdean)
nigel.wren@easthants.gov.uk

POLITICAL COMPOSITION
CON: 38, LD: 4, IND: 1

COMMITTEE CHAIRS

Audit: Mr Anthony Williams

Licensing: Mr Robert Ayer

EAST HERTFORDSHIRE

East Herts Council, The Causeway, Bishop's Stortford
CM23 2EN
☎ 01279 655261 ✆ info@eastherts.gov.uk 🖳 www.eastherts.gov.uk

FACTS AND FIGURES
Parliamentary Constituencies: Hertford and Stortford,
Hertfordshire North East
EU Constituencies: Eastern
Election Frequency: Elections are of whole council

PRINCIPAL OFFICERS

Chief Executive: Ms Liz Watts, Chief Executive, The Causeway,
Bishop's Stortford CM23 2EN ✆ liz.watts@eastherts.gov.uk

Senior Management: Ms Adele Taylor, Director - Finance &
Support Services, Wallfields, Pegs Lane, Hertford SG13 8EQ
☎ 01279 655261 ✆ adele.taylor@eastherts.gov.uk

Architect, Building / Property Services: Mr Steve Whinnett,
Principal Building Surveyor, Wallfields, Pegs Lane, Hertford SG13
8EQ ☎ 01279 655261 ✆ steve.whinnett@eastherts.gov.uk

Best Value: Ms Ceri Pettit, Corporate Planning & Performance
Manager, Council Offices, The Causeway, Bishop's Stortford CM23
2EN ☎ 01279 502240 ✆ ceri.pettit@eastherts.gov.uk

Building Control: Mr Kevin Steptoe, Head of Planning & Building
Control, East Herts Council, Wallfields, Pegs Lane, Hertford SG13
8EQ ☎ 01992 531407 ✆ kevin.steptoe@eastherts.gov.uk

PR / Communications: Ms Lorna Georgiou, Communications
Team Leader, Wallfields, Pegs Lane, Hertford SG13 8EQ
☎ 01279 655261 ✆ lorna.georgiou@eastherts.gov.uk

Computer Management: Mr David Frewin, Network & Systems
Support Manager, Wallfields, Pegs Lane, Hertford SG13 8EQ
☎ 01279 502158 ✆ david.frewin@eastherts.gov.uk

Computer Management: Mr Henry Lewis, Head of Service
- Share Business & Technology Services, Daneshill House,
Danestrete, Stevenage SG1 1HN ☎ 01438 242496
✆ henry.lewis@stevenage.gov.uk

Contracts: Mr Cliff Cardoza, Head of Environmental Services,
Wallfields, Pegs Lane, Hertford SG13 8EQ ☎ 01279 655261
✆ cliff.cardoza@eastherts.gov.uk

Customer Service: Mr Neil Sloper, Head of Customer Services &
Parking, Wallfields, Pegs Lane, Hertford SG13 8EQ ☎ 01992 531611
✆ neil.sloper@eastherts.gov.uk

Economic Development: Mr Ben Wood, Head of Service -
Communications, Strategy & Policy, Wallfields, Pegs Lane, Hertford
SG13 8EQ ☎ 01992 531699 ✆ benjamin.wood@eastherts.gov.uk

Electoral Registration: Mr Kevin Williams, Acting Head of
Service - Democratic & Legal Services, The Causeway, Bishop's
Stortford CM23 2EN ☎ 01279 655261
✆ kevin.williams@eastherts.gov.uk

Environmental / Technical Services: Mr Cliff Cardoza, Head of
Environmental Services, Wallfields, Pegs Lane, Hertford SG13 8EQ
☎ 01279 655261 ✆ cliff.cardoza@eastherts.gov.uk

Estates, Property & Valuation: Ms Anna Osbourne, Assets &
Estates Manager, Wallfields, Pegs Lane, Hertford SG13 8EQ
☎ 01992 531655 ✆ anna.osbourne@eastherts.gov.uk

European Liaison: Mr Paul Pullin, Economic Development
Manager, Wallfields, Pegs Lane, Hertford SG13 8EQ
☎ 01992 531606 ✆ paul.pullin@eastherts.gov.uk

Facilities: Mr Roy Crow, Facilities & Property Manager, Wallfields,
Pegs Lane, Hertford SG13 8EQ ☎ 01992 531695
✆ roy.crow@eastherts.gov.uk

Finance: Ms Adele Taylor, Director - Finance & Support Services,
Wallfields, Pegs Lane, Hertford SG13 8EQ ☎ 01279 655261
✆ adele.taylor@eastherts.gov.uk

Grounds Maintenance: Mr Ian Sharratt, Environmental Manager
- Open Spaces, Wallfields, Pegs Lane, Hertford SG13 8EQ
☎ 01992 531525 ✆ ian.sharratt@eastherts.gov.uk

Health and Safety: Mr Peter Dickinson, Health & Safety Officer,
Wallfields, Pegs Lane, Hertford SG13 8EQ ☎ 01992 531636
✆ peter.dickinson@eastherts.gov.uk

Home Energy Conservation: Mr David Thorogood,
Environmental Co-ordinator, Wallfields, Pegs Lane, Hertford SG13
8EQ ☎ 01279 655261 ✆ david.thorogood@eastherts.gov.uk

Housing: Ms Claire Bennett, Housing Strategy & Policy Manager,
Wallfields, Pegs Lane, Hertford SG13 8EQ ☎ 01992 531603
✆ claire.bennet@eastherts.gov.uk

Leisure and Cultural Services: Mr Mark Kingsland, Leisure
Services Manager, Wallfields, Pegs Lane, Hertford SG13 8EQ
☎ 01279 655880 ✆ mark.kingsland@eastherts.gov.uk

Licensing: Mr Oliver Rawlings, Senior Specialist Licensing Officer,
Wallfields, Pegs Lane, Hertford SG13 8EQ ☎ 01992 531629
✆ oliver.rawlings@eastherts.gov.uk

Lottery Funding, Charity and Voluntary: Ms Claire Pullen,
Engagement & Partnerships Officer of Grants, Wallfields, Pegs
Lane, Hertford SG13 8EQ ☎ 01992 531593
✆ claire.pullen@eastherts.gov.uk

Member Services: Mr Kevin Williams, Acting Head of Service -
Democratic & Legal Services, The Causeway, Bishop's Stortford
CM23 2EN ☎ 01279 655261 ✆ kevin.williams@eastherts.gov.uk

Parking: Mr Andrew Pulham, Parking Services Manager, Wallfields,
Pegs Lane, Hertford SG13 8EG ☎ 01279 502030
✆ andrew.pulham@eastherts.gov.uk

Partnerships: Ms Mekhola Ray, Engagement & Partnerships
Team Leader, Wallfields, Pegs Lane, Hertford SG13 8EQ
☎ 01992 531613 ✆ mekhola.ray@eastherts.gov.uk

Personnel / HR: Ms Emma Freeman, Head of Service - Human Resources & Organisation Development, Wallfields, Pegs Lane, Hertford SG13 8EQ ☎ 01992 531635
✆ emma.freeman@eastherts.gov.uk

Planning: Mr Kevin Steptoe, Head of Planning & Building Control, Wallfields, Pegs Lane, Hertford SG13 8EQ ☎ 01992 531407
✆ kevin.steptoe@eastherts.gov.uk

Recycling & Waste Minimisation: Mr David Allen, Waste Services Manager, Wallfields, Pegs Lane, Hertford SG13 8EQ ☎ 01992 531549 ✆ david.allen@eastherts.gov.uk

Sustainable Development: Mr David Thorogood, Environmental Co-ordinator, Wallfields, Pegs Lane, Hertford SG13 8EQ ☎ 01279 655261 ✆ david.thorogood@eastherts.gov.uk

Tourism: Ms Tilly Andrews, Economic & Tourism Development Officer, Wallfields, Pegs Lane, Hertford SG13 8EQ ☎ 01992 531506 ✆ tilly.andrews@eastherts.gov.uk

Town Centre: Mr Paul Pullin, Economic Development Manager, Wallfields, Pegs Lane, Hertford SG13 8EQ ☎ 01992 531606 ✆ paul.pullin@eastherts.gov.uk

Traffic Management: Mr Andrew Pulham, Parking Services Manager, Wallfields, Pegs Lane, Hertford SG13 8EQ ☎ 01279 502030 ✆ andrew.pulham@eastherts.gov.uk

Waste Collection and Disposal: Mr Cliff Cardoza, Head of Environmental Services, Wallfields, Pegs Lane, Hertford SG13 8EQ ☎ 01279 655261 ✆ cliff.cardoza@eastherts.gov.uk

Waste Management: Mr Cliff Cardoza, Head of Environmental Services, Wallfields, Pegs Lane, Hertford SG13 8EQ ☎ 01279 655261 ✆ cliff.cardoza@eastherts.gov.uk

Children's Play Areas: Mrs Jackie Bruce, Service Development Officer, Wallends, Pegs Lane, Hertford SG13 8EQ ☎ 01992 531654 ✆ jackie.bruce@eastherts.gov.uk

COUNCILLORS

Chair: Crofton, Ken (CON - Walkern)
henry.crofton@eastherts.gov.uk

Vice-Chair: Jones, Jeff (CON - Buntingford)
jeff.jones@eastherts.gov.uk

Leader of the Council: Haysey, Linda (CON - Hertford Rural South)
linda.haysey@eastherts.gov.uk

Deputy Leader of the Council: Jones, Gary (CON - Bishop's Stortford (Silverleys))
gary.jones@eastherts.gov.uk

Abbott, Daniel (CON - Bishop's Stortford (Meads))
daniel.abbott@eastherts.gov.uk

Alder, Angela (CON - Sawbridgeworth)
angela.alder@eastherts.gov.uk

Allen, Mike (CON - Stanstead Abbotts)
mike.allen@eastherts.gov.uk

Andrews, David (CON - Thundridge & Standon)
david.andrews@eastherts.gov.uk

Ballam, Phyllis (CON - Ware (Christchurch))
phyllis.ballam@eastherts.gov.uk

Brush, Kevin (CON - Hertford (Castle))
kevin.brush@eastherts.gov.uk

Buckmaster, Eric (IND - Sawbridgeworth)

Bull, Stan (CON - Buntingford)
stan.bull@eastherts.gov.uk

Cartwright, James (CON - Puckeridge)
james.cartwright@eastherts.gov.uk

Casey, Mike (CON - Bishop's Stortford (All Saints))
mike.casey@eastherts.gov.uk

Cheswright, Rose (CON - Great Amwell)
rosemary.cheswright@eastherts.gov.uk

Cousins, Steve (CON - Hertford (Sele))
steve.cousins@eastherts.gov.uk

Cutting, George (CON - Bishop's Stortford (Central))
george.cutting@eastherts.gov.uk

Deering, Bob (CON - Hertford (Castle))
bob.deering@eastherts.gov.uk

Devonshire, Ian (CON - Much Hadham)
ian.devonshire@eastherts.gov.uk

Drake, Holly (CON - Bishop's Stortford (Central))
holly.drake@eastherts.gov.uk

Freeman, Michael (CON - Watton-at-Stone)
michael.freeman@eastherts.gov.uk

Goodeve, Jan (CON - Hertford (Kingsmead))
jan.goodeve@eastherts.gov.uk

Harris-Quinney, Ben (CON - Braughing)
ben.harris.quinney@eastherts.gov.uk

Henson, Ryan (CON - Hertford (Sele))
ryan.henson@eastherts.gov.uk

Hollebon, Diane (CON - Bishop's Stortford (South))
diane.hollebon@eastherts.gov.uk

Hudson, Robert (CON - Hunsdon)
robert.brunton@eastherts.gov.uk

Jackson, Tony (CON - Datchworth & Aston)
anthony.jackson@eastherts.gov.uk

Kaye, Jonathan (CON - Ware (Christchurch))
jonathan.kaye@eastherts.gov.uk

Kenealy, Paul (CON - The Mundens & Cottered)
paul.kenealy@eastherts.gov.uk

McAndrew, Graham (CON - Bishop's Stortford (South))
graham.mcandrew@eastherts.gov.uk

McMullen, Michael (CON - Hertford Rural North)
michael.mcmullen@eastherts.gov.uk

Moore, Patricia (CON - Hertford (Bengeo))
patricia.moore@easthearts.gov.uk

Mortimer, William (CON - Sawbridgeworth)
william.mortimer@eastherts.gov.uk

Oldridge, David (CON - Ware (Trinity))
david.oldridge@eastherts.gov.uk

Page, Tim (CON - Bishop's Stortford (Silverleys))
tim.page@eastherts.gov.uk

Phillips, Paul (IND - Hertford (Bengeo))
paul.phillips@eastherts.gov.uk

EAST HERTFORDSHIRE

Pope, Mark (CON - Ware (Chadwell))
mark.pope@eastherts.gov.uk

Reed, Stephen (CON - Ware (Trinity))
stephen.reed@easthearts.gov.uk

Ruffles, Peter (CON - Hertford (Bengeo))
peter.ruffles@eastherts.gov.uk

Rutland-Barsby, Suzanne (CON - Hertford (Castle))
suzanne.rutland-barsby@eastherts.gov.uk

Snowden, Charlotte (CON - Hertford Heath)
charlotte.snowden@eastherts.gov.uk

Stainsby, Stan (CON - Bishop's Stortford (All Saints))
stan.stainsby@eastherts.gov.uk

Standley, Roz (CON - Ware (St Mary's))
roz.standley@eastherts.gov.uk

Stevenson, Mari (CON - Hertford (Kingsmead))
mari.stevenson@eastherts.gov.uk

Symonds, Norma (CON - Bishop's Stortford (Central))
norma.symonds@eastherts.gov.uk

Taylor, Jeanette (CON - Ware (St Mary's))
jeanette.taylor@eastherts.gov.uk

Warnell, Keith (CON - Bishop's Stortford (Meads))
keith.warnell@eastherts.gov.uk

Williamson, Geoffrey (CON - Little Hadham)
geoffrey.williamson@eastherts.gov.uk

Woodward, Colin (CON - Bishop's Stortford (All Saints))
colin.woodward@eastherts.gov.uk

Wyllie, John (CON - Bishop's Stortford (South))
john.wyllie@eastherts.gov.uk

POLITICAL COMPOSITION
CON: 48, IND: 2

COMMITTEE CHAIRS

Audit: Mr Mark Pope

Development Management: Mr Tim Page

Environment: Mr John Wyllie

Health & Wellbeing: Ms Angela Alder

Licensing: Mr Robert Hudson

East Lindsey   D

East Lindsey District Council, Tedder Hall, Manby Park, Louth
LN11 8UP
☎ 01507 601111 🖷 01507 600206 ✆ customerservices@e-lindsey.gov.uk
🖳 www.e-lindsey.gov.uk

FACTS AND FIGURES
Parliamentary Constituencies: Boston and Skegness, Louth and
Horncastle
EU Constituencies: East Midlands
Election Frequency: Elections are of whole council

PRINCIPAL OFFICERS

Chief Executive: Mr Stuart Davy, Chief Executive, Tedder Hall,
Manby Park, Louth LN11 8UP ☎ 01507 613411
✆ stuart.davy@e-lindsey.gov.uk

Deputy Chief Executive: Mr Robert Barlow, Deputy Chief
Executive & Strategic Director - Resources / S151 Officer, Tedder
Hall, Manby Park, Louth LN11 8UP ☎ 01507 613411
✆ robert.barlow@boston.gov.uk

Senior Management: Ms Victoria Burgess, Strategic
Development Manager, Tedder Hall, Manby Park, Louth LN11 8UP
☎ 01507 613214 ✆ victoria.burgess@e-lindsey.gov.uk

Senior Management: Ms Semantha Neal, Strategic Development
Manager, Tedder Hall, Manby Park, Louth LN11 8UP
☎ 01507 613440 ✆ semantha.neal@e-lindsey.gov.uk

Senior Management: Ms Alison Penn, Director, Tedder Hall,
Manby Park, Louth LN11 8UP ☎ 01507 329411
✆ alison.penn@e-lindsey.gov.uk

Senior Management: Ms Michelle Sacks, Monitoring Officer,
Tedder Hall, Manby Park, Louth LN11 8UP ☎ 01507 613203
✆ michelle.sacks@e-lindsey.gov.uk

Senior Management: Mr Gary Sargeant, Corporate Asset
Manager, Tedder Hall, Manby Park, Louth LN11 8UP
☎ 01507 613020 ✆ gary.sargeant@e-lindsey.gov.uk

Architect, Building / Property Services: Mr Gary Sargeant,
Corporate Asset Manager, Tedder Hall, Manby Park, Louth LN11
8UP ☎ 01507 613020 ✆ gary.sargeant@e-lindsey.gov.uk

Building Control: Mr Paul Smith, Building Control Team Leader,
Tedder Hall, Manby Park, Louth LN11 8UP ☎ 01507 613189
✆ paul.smith@e-lindsey.gov.uk

Children / Youth Services: Ms Semantha Neal, Strategic
Development Manager, Tedder Hall, Manby Park, Louth LN11 8UP
☎ 01507 613440 ✆ semantha.neal@e-lindsey.gov.uk

PR / Communications: Mr James Gilbert, Communications &
Consultation Tourism Manager, Tedder Hall, Manby Park, Louth
LN11 8UP ☎ 01507 613415 ✆ james.gilbert@e-lindsey.gov.uk

Community Safety: Mr Jonathan Challen, Private Sector Housing
Team Leader, Tedder Hall, Manby Park, Louth LN11 8UP
☎ 01507 613051 ✆ jonathan.challen@e-lindsey.gov.uk

Economic Development: Mr Jonathan Burgess, Economic
Development Team Leader, Tedder Hall, Manby Park, Louth LN11
8UP ☎ 01507 613117 ✆ jonathan.burgess@e-lindsey.gov.uk

Electoral Registration: Mrs Sue Brewitt, Elections Officer,
Tedder Hall, Manby Park, Louth LN11 8UP ☎ 01507 613430
✆ sue.brewitt@e-lindsey.gov.uk

Emergency Planning: Mr Mike Harrison, Environmental Health
Team Leader, Tedder Hall, Manby Park, Louth LN11 8UP
☎ 01507 613470 ✆ mike.harrison@e-lindsey.gov.uk

Energy Management: Mr Gary Sargeant, Corporate Asset
Manager, Tedder Hall, Manby Park, Louth LN11 8UP
☎ 01507 613020 ✆ gary.sargeant@e-lindsey.gov.uk

Environmental / Technical Services: Mr Mike Harrison, Environmental Health Team Leader, Tedder Hall, Manby Park, Louth LN11 8UP ☎ 01507 613470 ⌂ mike.harrison@e-lindsey.gov.uk

Environmental Health: Mr Mike Harrison, Environmental Health Team Leader, Tedder Hall, Manby Park, Louth LN11 8UP ☎ 01507 613470 ⌂ mike.harrison@e-lindsey.gov.uk

Estates, Property & Valuation: Mr Edward Cox, Principal Valuer, Tedder Hall, Manby Park, Louth LN11 8UP ☎ 01507 613021 ⌂ edward.cox@e-lindsey.gov.uk

Estates, Property & Valuation: Mr Gary Sargeant, Corporate Asset Manager, Tedder Hall, Manby Park, Louth LN11 8UP ☎ 01507 613020 ⌂ gary.sargeant@e-lindsey.gov.uk

Events Manager: Mr James Brindle, Director - Development & Partnerships, Office 10, Fairfield Enterprise Centre, Lincoln Way, Louth LN11 0LS ☎ 01507 613450 ⌂ james.brindle@mvtlc.org

Facilities: Mr Mark Humphreys, Managing Director - Magna Vitae Trust for Leisure & Culture, Office 10, Fairfield Enterprise Centre, Lincoln Way, Louth LN11 0LS ☎ 01507 613441 ⌂ mark.humphreys@e-lindsey.gov.uk

Finance: Mr Robert Barlow, Deputy Chief Executive & Strategic Director - Resources / S151 Officer, Tedder Hall, Manby Park, Louth LN11 8UP ☎ 01507 613411 ⌂ robert.barlow@boston.gov.uk

Treasury: Mr Robert Barlow, Deputy Chief Executive & Strategic Director - Resources / S151 Officer, Tedder Hall, Manby Park, Louth LN11 8UP ☎ 01507 613411 ⌂ robert.barlow@boston.gov.uk

Fleet Management: Mr Nick Davis, Team Leader - Refuse & Recycling, Tedder Hall, Manby Park, Louth LN11 8UP ☎ 01507 613540 ⌂ nick.davis@e-lindsey.gov.uk

Grounds Maintenance: Mr Danny Wilson, Neighbourhood Services Manager, Tedder Hall, Manby Park, Louth LN11 8UP ☎ 01507 613536 ⌂ danny.wilson@e-lindsey.gov.uk

Health and Safety: Mr Mike Gallagher, Health & Safety Advisor, Tedder Hall, Manby Park, Louth LN11 8UP ☎ 01507 613235 ⌂ michael.gallagher@cpbs.com

Home Energy Conservation: Mr Jonathan Challen, Private Sector Housing Team Leader, Tedder Hall, Manby Park, Louth LN11 8UP ☎ 01507 613051 ⌂ jonathan.challen@e-lindsey.gov.uk

Housing: Mr Jason Oxby, Housing Advice & Homelessness Team Leader, Tedder Hall, Manby Park, Louth LN11 8UP ☎ 01507 613120 ⌂ jason.oxby@e-lindsey.gov.uk

Leisure and Cultural Services: Mr Mark Humphreys, Managing Director - Magna Vitae Trust for Leisure & Culture, Office 10, Fairfield Industrial Estate, Lincoln Way, Louth LN11 0LS ☎ 01507 613441 ⌂ mark.humphreys@e-lindsey.gov.uk

Licensing: Mr Adrian Twiddy, Principal Licensing Officer, Tedder Hall, Manby Park, Louth LN11 8UP ☎ 01507 613011 ⌂ adrian.twiddy@e-lindsey.gov.uk

Lottery Funding, Charity and Voluntary: Mr James Ward, Community Development Officer, Tedder Hall, Manby Park, Louth LN11 8UP ☎ 01507 613073 ⌂ james.ward@e-lindsey .gov.uk

Member Services: Mrs Ann Good, Senior Democratic Services Officer & Civic Officer, Tedder Hall, Manby Park, Louth LN11 8UP ☎ 01507 613420 ⌂ ann.good@e-lindsey@gov.uk

Parking: Mr Duncan Hollingworth, Team Leader - Enforcement, Tedder Hall, Manby Park, Louth LN11 8UP ☎ 01507 613558 ⌂ duncan.hollingworth@e-lindsey.gov.uk

Partnerships: Mr John Medler, Team Leader - Performance, Commissioning & Governance, Tedder Hall, Manby Park, Louth LN11 8UP ☎ 01507 613072 ⌂ john.medler@e-lindsey.gov.uk

Planning: Mr Chris Panton, Planning Team Leader, Tedder Hall, Manby Park, Louth LN11 8UP ☎ 01507 613158 ⌂ chris.panton@e-lindsey.gov.uk

Planning: Ms Anne Shorland, Planning & Housing Policy Manager, Tedder Hall, Manby Park, Louth LN11 8UP ☎ 01507 613141 ⌂ anne.shorland@e-lindsey.gov.uk

Recycling & Waste Minimisation: Mr Nick Davis, Team Leader - Refuse & Recycling, Tedder Hall, Manby Park, Louth LN11 8UP ☎ 01507 613540 ⌂ nick.davis@e-lindsey.gov.uk

Regeneration: Mr Jonathan Burgess, Economic Development Team Leader, Tedder Hall, Manby Park, Louth LN11 8UP ☎ 01507 613117 ⌂ jonathan.burgess@e-lindsey.gov.uk

Staff Training: Mr James Makinson-Sanders, Member Development Officer, Tedder Hall, Manby Park, Louth LN11 8UP ☎ 01507 613234 ⌂ james.makinson-sanders@cpbs.com

Street Scene: Mr Danny Wilson, Neighbourhood Services Manager, Tedder Hall, Manby Park, Louth LN11 8UP ☎ 01507 613536 ⌂ danny.wilson@e-lindsey.gov.uk

Tourism: Mr James Gilbert, Communications & Consultation Tourism Manager, Tedder Hall, Manby Park, Louth LN11 8UP ☎ 01507 613415 ⌂ james.gilbert@e-lindsey.gov.uk

Town Centre: Mr Jonathan Burgess, Economic Development Team Leader, Tedder Hall, Manby Park, Louth LN11 8UP ☎ 01507 613117 ⌂ jonathan.burgess@e-lindsey.gov.uk

Waste Collection and Disposal: Mr Nick Davis, Team Leader - Refuse & Recycling, Tedder Hall, Manby Park, Louth LN11 8UP ☎ 01507 613540 ⌂ nick.davis@e-lindsey.gov.uk

Waste Management: Mr Nick Davis, Team Leader - Refuse & Recycling, Tedder Hall, Manby Park, Louth LN11 8UP ☎ 01507 613540 ⌂ nick.davis@e-lindsey.gov.uk

COUNCILLORS

Leader of the Council: Leyland, Craig (CON - Woodhall Spa) craig.leyland@e-lindsey.gov.uk

Deputy Leader of the Council: Marsh, Graham (CON - Alford) graham.marsh@e-lyndsey.gov.uk

EAST LINDSEY

Aldridge, Terry (IND - Holton le Clay & North Thoresby)
terry.aldridge@e-lindsey.gov.uk

Andrews, David (CON - Tetford & Donington)
david.andrews@e-lindsey.gov.uk

Ashton, Tom (CON - Sibsey & Stickney)
tom.ashton@e-lindsey.gov.uk

Avison, Richard (CON - Horncastle)
richard.avison@e-lindsey.gov.uk

Avison, Stanley (CON - Coningsby / Mareham)
stanley.avison@e-lindsey.gov.uk

Blackburn, Susan (UKIP - Skegness Winthorpe)
susan.blackburn@e-lindsey.gov.uk

Bowkett, Wendy (CON - Wainfleet)
wendy.bowkett@e-lindsey.gov.uk

Brookes, Danny (UKIP - Skegness Winthorpe)
danny.brookes@e-lindsey.gov.uk

Brown, Terence (UKIP - Mablethorpe)
terence.brown@e-lindsey.gov.uk

Buckley, David (CON - Fulstow)
david.buckley@e-lindsey.gov.uk

Byford, John (UKIP - Skegness, Scarborough & Seacroft)
john.byford@e-lindsey.gov.uk

Campbell-Wardman, Sandra (LD - Horncastle)
sandra.campbell-wardman@e-lindsey.gov.uk

Cooper, Neil (CON - Burgh le Marsh)
neil.cooper@e-lindsey.gov.uk

Cooper, Pauline (CON - Croft)
pauline.cooper@e-lindsey.gov.uk

Cullen, Graham (LAB - Mablethorpe)
graham.cullen@e-lindsey.gov.uk

Dannatt, Mark (UKIP - Skegness St Clements)
mark.dannatt@e-lindsey.gov.uk

Davie, Colin (CON - Ingoldmells)
colin.davie@e-lindsey.gov.uk

Dennis, Sid (CON - Skegness St Clements)
sidney.dennis@e-lindsey.gov.uk

Devereux, Sarah (IND - Alford)
sarah.devereux@e-lyndsey.gov.uk

Dickinson, Carleen (UKIP - Friskney)
carleen.dickinson@e-lindsey.gov.uk

Dodds, Sarah (LAB - Louth Priory & St James)
sarah.dodds@e-lindsey.gov.uk

Edginton, Dick (CON - Skegness, Scarborough & Seacroft)
david.edginton@e-lindsey.gov.uk

Flitcroft, Aimee (UKIP - Coningsby / Mareham)
aimee.flitcroft@e-lindsey.gov.uk

Foster, Martin (IND - Coningsby / Mareham)
martin.foster@e-lindsey.gov.uk

Fry, Richard (CON - Binbrook)
richard.fry@e-lindsey.gov.uk

Gorst, Susanna (CON - Woodhall Spa)
susanna.gorst@e-lindsey.gov.uk

Gray, William (CON - Roughton)
william.gray@e-lindsey.gov.uk

Green, Chris (CON - Louth St Margaret's)
chris.green@e-lindsey.gov.uk

Grist, Adam (CON - Legbourne)
adam.grist@e-lindsey.gov.uk

Grover, Will (CON - Hagworthingham)
will.gover@e-lindsey.gov.uk

Guyatt, Nick (CON - Wragby)
nick.guyatt@e-lindsey.gov.uk

Harrison, Sandra (CON - Withern & Theddlethorpe)
sandra.harrison@e-lindsey.gov.uk

Hibbert-Greaves, Paul (CON - Chapel St Leonards)
paul.hibbert-greaves@e.lindsey.gov.uk

Horton, George (IND - Louth St Michael's)
george.horton@e-lindsey.gov.uk

Howard, Tony (LAB - Mablethorpe)
tony.howard@e-lindsey.gov.uk

Jackson, Rosalind (LAB - Louth Trinity)
rosalind.jackson@e-lindsey.gov.uk

Jones, Neil (CON - Sibsey & Stickney)
langmick@talktalk.net

Kirk, Steve (CON - Skegness, Scarborough & Seacroft)
steve.kirk@e-lindsey.gov.uk

Knowles, Terry (IND - Grimoldby)
terence.knowles@e-lindsey.gov.uk

Makinson-Sanders, Jill (IND - Louth St Mary's)
jill.makinson-sanders@e-lindsey.gov.uk

Martin, Fiona (LD - Horncastle)
fiona.martin@e-lindsey.gov.uk

Matthews, Helen (CON - Sutton on Sea)
helen.matthews@e-lindsey.gov.uk

McNally, Daniel (UKIP - Marshchapel & Somercotes)
daniel.mcnally@e-lindsey.gov.uk

Palmer, Robert (CON - Marshchapel & Somercotes)
robert.palmer@e-lindsey.gov.uk

Palmer, Stephen (IND - Sutton on Sea)
stephen.palmer@e-lindsey.gov.uk

Swanson, Jim (IND - Halton Holegate)
jim.swanson@e-lindsey.gov.uk

Treanor, Fran (CON - Louth North Holme)
fran.treanor@e-lindsey.gov.uk

Turton-Leivers, Mel (CON - Chapel St Leonards)
mel.turton-l@e-lindsey.gov.uk

Vassar, Alan (CON - Willoughby / Sloothby)
alan.vassar@e-lindsey.gov.uk

Walker, Siobhan (CON - Holton le Clay & North Thoresby)
siobhan.walker@e-lindsey.gov.uk

Watson, Pauline (CON - Louth Priory & St James)
pauline.watson@e-lindsey.gov.uk

Watson, Stuart (CON - Tetney)
stuart.watson@e-lindsey.gov.uk

Williams, Rod (CON - Spilsby)
roderick.williams@e-lindsey.gov.uk

POLITICAL COMPOSITION
CON: 33, IND: 8, UKIP: 8, LAB: 4, LD: 2

COMMITTEE CHAIRS

Audit: Mr Rod Williams

Licensing: Mr Robert Palmer

Planning: Mr Neil Cooper

East Lothian   S

East Lothian Council, John Muir House, Brewery Park, Haddington EH41 3HA
☎ 01620 827827 ◌ customerservices@eastlothian.gov.uk
🖳 www.eastlothian.gov.uk

FACTS AND FIGURES
Parliamentary Constituencies: East Lothian
EU Constituencies: Scotland
Election Frequency: Elections are of whole council

PRINCIPAL OFFICERS

Chief Executive: Ms Angela Leitch, Chief Executive, John Muir House, Brewery Park, Haddington EH41 3HA ☎ 01620 827413 ◌ chiefexecutive@eastlothian.gov.uk

Deputy Chief Executive: Mr Alex McCrorie, Deputy Chief Executive - Resources & People Services, John Muir House, Haddington EH41 3HA ☎ 01620 827827 ◌ amccrorie@eastlothian.gov.uk

Deputy Chief Executive: Ms Monica Patterson, Deputy Chief Executive - Partnerships & Community Services, John Muir House, Brewery Park, Haddington EH41 3HA ☎ 01620 827827 ◌ mpatterson@eastlothian.gov.uk

Architect, Building / Property Services: Ms Liz McLean, Service Manager - Strategic Asset & Capital Plan Management, Penston House, Macmerry Industrial Estate, Macmerry, EH33 1EX ☎ 01620 827353 ◌ lmclean@eastlothian.gov.uk

Best Value: Mr Paolo Vestri, Service Manager - Corporate Policy & Improvement, John Muir House, Brewery Park, Haddington EH41 3HA ☎ 01620 827320 ◌ pvestri@eastlothian.gov.uk

Building Control: Mr Frank Fairgrieve, Principal Building Surveyor, John Muir House, Brewery Park, Haddington EH41 3HA ☎ 01620 827357 ◌ ffairfield@eastlothian.gov.uk

PR / Communications: Mr Paolo Vestri, Service Manager - Corporate Policy & Improvement, John Muir House, Brewery Park, Haddington EH41 3HA ☎ 01620 827320 ◌ pvestri@eastlothian.gov.uk

Community Planning: Mr Paolo Vestri, Service Manager - Corporate Policy & Improvement, John Muir House, Haddington EH41 3HA ☎ 01620 827320 ◌ pvestri@eastlothian.gov.uk

Community Safety: Mr Kenny Black, Safer Communities Team Leader, The George Johnstone Centre, 35 Winton Place, Tranent EH33 1AE ☎ 01620 829919 ◌ kblack@eastlothian.gov.uk

Computer Management: Mr Alan Cruickshank, Service Manager - IT Infrastructure, John Muir House, Brewery Park, Haddington EH41 3HA ☎ 01620 827220 ◌ acruickshank@eastlothian.gov.uk

Corporate Services: Mr Jim Lamond, Head of Council Resources, John Muir House, Brewery Park, Haddington EH41 3HA ☎ 01620 827278 ◌ jlamond@eastlothian.gov.uk

Customer Service: Ms Eileen Morrison, Service Manager - Customer Services, John Muir House, Haddington EH33 1EX ☎ 01620 827211 ◌ emorrison@eastlothian.gov.uk

Economic Development: Mr Douglas Proudfoot, Head of Development, John Muir House, Brewery Park, Haddington EH41 3HA ☎ 01620 827827 ◌ dproudfoot@eastlothian.gov.uk

Education: Mr Richard Parker, Service Manager - Education, John Muir House, Brewery Park, Haddington EH41 3HA ☎ 01620 827494 ◌ rparker@eastlothian.gov.uk

Education: Ms Fiona Robertson, Head of Education, John Muir House, Brewery Park, Haddington EH41 3HA ☎ 01620 827834 ◌ frobertson@eastlothian.gov.uk

Electoral Registration: Mr Jim Lamond, Head of Council Resources, John Muir House, Haddington EH41 3HA ☎ 01620 827278 ◌ jlamond@eastlothian.gov.uk

Emergency Planning: Mr Sandy Baptie, Emergency Planning Officer, John Muir House, Brewery Park, Haddington EH41 3HA ☎ 01620 827779 ◌ sbaptie@eastlothian.gov.uk

Emergency Planning: Mr Paolo Vestri, Service Manager - Corporate Policy & Improvement, John Muir House, Brewery Park, Haddington EH41 3HA ☎ 01620 827320 ◌ pvestri@eastlothian.gov.uk

Environmental Health: Mr Derek Oliver, Service Manager - Environmental Health, John Muir House, Brewery Park, Haddington EH41 3HA ☎ 01620 827286 ◌ doliver@eastlothian.gov.uk

Estates, Property & Valuation: Ms Liz McLean, Service Manager - Strategic Asset & Capital Plan Management, Penston House, Macmerry Industrial Estate, Macmerry, EH33 1EX ☎ 01620 827353 ◌ lmclean@eastlothian.gov.uk

European Liaison: Ms Susan Smith, Economic Development Manager, John Muir House, Brewery Park, Haddington EH41 3HA ☎ 01620 827174 ◌ ssmith@eastlothian.gov.uk

Facilities: Mr Ray Montgomery, Head of Infrastructure, John Muir House, Brewery Park, Haddington EH41 3HA ☎ 01620 827658 ◌ rmontgomery@eastlothian.gov.uk

Finance: Ms Sarah Fortune, Service Manager - Business Finance, John Muir House, Brewery Park, Haddington EH41 3HA ☎ 01620 827702 ◌ sfortune@eastlothian.gov.uk

Finance: Mr Jim Lamond, Head of Council Resources, John Muir House, Brewery Park, Haddington EH41 3HA ☎ 01620 827278 ◌ jlamond@eastlothian.gov.uk

Finance: Mr Alex McCrorie, Deputy Chief Executive - Resources & People Services, John Muir House, Haddington EH41 3HA ☎ 01620 827827 ◌ amccrorie@eastlothian.gov.uk

EAST LOTHIAN

Fleet Management: Mr Ray Montgomery, Head of Infrastructure, John Muir House, Haddington EH41 3HA ☎ 01620 827658 ✆ rmontgomery@eastlothian.gov.uk

Grounds Maintenance: Mr Stuart Pryde, Principal Amenities Officer - Landscape & Countryside, Block C, Brewery Park, Haddington EH41 3HA ☎ 01620 827430 ✆ spryde@eastlothian.gov.uk

Health and Safety: Mr Chris Lawson, Health & Safety Manager, Penston House, Macmerry Industrial Estate, Tranent EH33 1EX ☎ 01620 807337 ✆ clawson@eastlothian.gov.uk

Health and Safety: Mr Paolo Vestri, Service Manager - Corporate Policy & Improvement, John Muir House, Brewery Park, Haddington EH41 3HA ☎ 01620 827320 ✆ pvestri@eastlothian.gov.uk

Highways: Mr Ray Montgomery, Head of Infrastructure, John Muir House, Haddington EH41 3HA ☎ 01620 827658 ✆ rmontgomery@eastlothian.gov.uk

Housing: Ms Caitlin McCorry, Service Manager - Community Housing, Penston House, Macmerry Industrial Estate, Tranent EH33 1EX ☎ 01620 827190 ✆ cmccorry@eastlothian.gov.uk

Legal: Mr Jim Lamond, Head of Council Resources, John Muir House, Brewery Park, Haddington EH41 3HA ☎ 01620 827278 ✆ jlamond@eastlothian.gov.uk

Licensing: Ms Kirstie MacNeill, Service Manager - Licensing, Administration & Democratic Services, John Muir House, Brewery Park, Haddington EH41 3HA ☎ 01620 827164 ✆ kmacneill@eastlothian.gov.uk

Lighting: Mr Glen Kane, Senior Lighting Officer, John Muir House, Brewery Park, Haddington EH41 3HA ☎ 01620 827827 ✆ gkane@eastlothian.gov.uk

Lottery Funding, Charity and Voluntary: Ms Esther Wilson, Service Manager - Economic Development & Strategic Investment, John Muir House, Brewery Park, Haddington EH41 3HA ☎ 01620 827361 ✆ ewilson@eastlothian.gov.uk

Member Services: Ms Lel Gillingwater, Democratic Services Manager, John Muir House, Haddington EH41 3HA ☎ 01620 827225 ✆ lgillingwater@eastlothian.gov.uk

Member Services: Mr Jim Lamond, Head of Council Resources, John Muir House, Brewery Park, Haddington EH41 3HA ☎ 01620 827278 ✆ jlamond@eastlothian.gov.uk

Member Services: Ms Jill Totney, Democratic Services Manager, John Muir House, Brewery Park, Haddington EH41 3HA ☎ 01620 827225 ✆ jtotney@eastlothian.gov.uk

Partnerships: Mr Tom Shearer, Head of Communities & Partnerships, John Muir House, Brewery Park, Haddington EH41 3HA ☎ 01620 827413 ✆ tshearer@eastlothian.gov.uk

Personnel / HR: Ms Sue Cormack, Service Manager - Human Resources, John Muir House, Brewery Park, Haddington EH41 3HA ☎ 01620 827401 ✆ scormack@eastlothian.gov.uk

Personnel / HR: Mr Jim Lamond, Head of Council Resources, John Muir House, Brewery Park, Haddington EH41 3HA ☎ 01620 827278 ✆ jlamond@eastlothian.gov.uk

Planning: Mr Iain McFarlane, Service Manager - Planning, John Muir House, Brewery Park, Haddington EH41 3HA ☎ 01620 827292 ✆ imcfarlane@eastlothian.gov.uk

Procurement: Ms Morag Ferguson, Service Manager - Legal & Procurement, John Muir House, Brewery Park, Haddington EH41 3HA ☎ 01620 827770 ✆ mferguson@eastlothian.gov.uk

Public Libraries: Ms Eileen Morrison, Service Manager - Customer Services, John Muir House, Haddington EH33 1EX ☎ 01620 827211 ✆ emorrison@eastlothian.gov.uk

Public Libraries: Mr Tom Shearer, Head of Communities & Partnerships, John Muir House, Brewery Park, Haddington EH41 3HA ☎ 01620 827413 ✆ tshearer@eastlothian.gov.uk

Recycling & Waste Minimisation: Mr Tom Reid, Waste Services Manager, Kinwegar Waste Services Depot, Wallyford, Musselburgh EH21 8JU ☎ 01620 827830 ✆ treid@westlothian.gov.uk

Social Services: Mr David Small, Director - Health & Social Care Partnership, John Muir House, Brewery Park, Haddington EH41 3HA ☎ 01620 827778 ✆ david.a.small@nhslothian.scot.nhs.uk

Social Services (Adult): Ms Trish Leddy, Head of Adult Wellbeing, John Muir House, Brewery Park, Haddington EH41 3HA ☎ 01620 827827 ✆ tleddy@eastlothian.gov.uk

Social Services (Children): Ms Sharon Saunders, Head of Children's Wellbeing, John Muir House, Brewery Park, Haddington EH41 3HA ☎ 01620 827827 ✆ ssaunders@eastlothian.gov.uk

Staff Training: Mr Paolo Vestri, Service Manager - Corporate Policy & Improvement, John Muir House, Brewery Park, Haddington EH41 3HA ☎ 01620 827320 ✆ pvestri@eastlothian.gov.uk

Tourism: Ms Esther Wilson, Service Manager - Economic Development & Strategic Investment, John Muir House, Brewery Park, Haddington EH41 3HA ☎ 01620 827361 ✆ ewilson@eastlothian.gov.uk

Traffic Management: Mr Ray Montgomery, Head of Infrastructure, John Muir House, Haddington EH41 3HA ☎ 01620 827658 ✆ rmontgomery@eastlothian.gov.uk

Waste Collection and Disposal: Mr Tom Reid, Waste Services Manager, Kinwegar Waste Services Depot, Wallyford, Musselburgh EH21 8JU ☎ 01620 827830 ✆ treid@westlothian.gov.uk

Waste Management: Mr Ray Montgomery, Head of Infrastructure, John Muir House, Brewery Park, Haddington EH41 3HA ☎ 01620 827658 ✆ rmontgomery@eastlothian.gov.uk

Waste Management: Mr Tom Reid, Waste Services Manager, Kinwegar Waste Services Depot, Wallyford, Musselburgh EH21 8JU ☎ 01620 827830 ✆ treid@westlothian.gov.uk

COUNCILLORS

Provost: Broun-Lindsay, Ludovic (CON - Haddington & Lammermuir)
lbroun-linday@eastlothian.gov.uk

Leader of the Council: Innes, Willie (LAB - Preston/Seton/Gosford)
winnes@eastlothian.gov.uk

Deputy Leader of the Council: Veitch, Michael (CON - Dunbar & East Linton)
mveitch1@eastlothian.gov.uk

Akhtar, Shamin (LAB - Fa'side)
sakhtar@eastlothian.gov.uk

Berry, David (IND - North Berwick Coastal)
dberry@eastlothian.gov.uk

Brown, Steven (SNP - Preston / Seton / Gosford)
sbrown1@eastlothian.gov.uk

Caldwell, John (IND - Musselburgh East & Carberry)
jcaldwell1@eastlothian.gov.uk

Currie, Stuart (SNP - Musselburgh East & Carberry)
scurrie@eastlothian.gov.uk

Day, Tim (CON - North Berwick Coastal)
tday@eastlothian.gov.uk

Forrest, Andrew (LAB - Musselburgh East & Carberry)
aforrest2@eastlothian.gov.uk

Gillies, Jim (LAB - Fa'side)
jgillies@eastlothian.gov.uk

Goodfellow, Jim (LAB - North Berwick Coastal)
jgoodfellow@eastlothian.gov.uk

Grant, Donald (LAB - Fa'side)
dgrant@eastlothian.gov.uk

Hampshire, Norman (LAB - Dunbar & East Linton)
nhampshire@eastlothian.gov.uk

Libberton, Margaret (LAB - Preston / Seton / Gosford)
mlibberton1@eastlothian.gov.uk

MacKenzie, Peter (SNP - Preston / Seton / Gosford)
pmackenzie@eastlothian.gov.uk

McAllister, Fraser (SNP - Musselburgh West)
fmcallister@eastlothian.gov.uk

McLennan, Paul (SNP - Dunbar & East Linton)
pmclennan@eastlothian.gov.uk

McLeod, Kenny (SNP - Fa'side)
kmcleod1@eastlothian.gov.uk

McMillan, John (LAB - Haddington & Lammermuir)
jmcmillan@eastlothian.gov.uk

McNeil, John (LAB - Musselburgh West)
jmcneil@eastlothian.gov.uk

Trotter, Tom (SNP - Haddington & Lammermuir)
ttrotter@eastlothian.gov.uk

Williamson, John (SNP - Musselburgh West)
jwilliamson@eastlothian.gov.uk

POLITICAL COMPOSITION
LAB: 10, SNP: 8, CON: 3, IND: 2

COMMITTEE CHAIRS

Audit: Mr Kenny McLeod

Education: Cllr Shamin Akhtar

Planning: Mr Norman Hampshire

East Northamptonshire   D

East Northamptonshire District Council, East Northamptonshire House, Cedar Drive, Thrapston NN14 4LZ
☎ 01832 742000 🖷 01832 734839
⌕ customerservices@east-northamptonshire.gov.uk
💻 www.east-northamptonshire.gov.uk

FACTS AND FIGURES
Parliamentary Constituencies: Corby, Wellingborough
EU Constituencies: East Midlands
Election Frequency: Elections are of whole council

PRINCIPAL OFFICERS

Chief Executive: Mr David Oliver, Chief Executive, East Northamptonshire House, Cedar Drive, Thrapston NN14 4LZ
☎ 01832 742106 ⌕ doliver@east-northamptonshire.gov.uk

Senior Management: Mr Glenn Hammons, Chief Finance Officer & Section 151 Officer, East Northamptonshire House, Cedar Drive, Thrapston NN14 4LZ ☎ 01832 742267
⌕ ghammons@east-northamptonshire.gov.uk

Senior Management: Ms Sharn Matthews, Executive Director & Monitoring Officer, East Northamptonshire House, Cedar Drive, Thrapston NN14 4LZ ☎ 01832 742108
⌕ smatthews@east-northamptonshire.gov.uk

Building Control: Mr Bryan Rance, Building Control Manager, East Northamptonshire House, Cedar Drive, Thrapston NN14 4LZ
☎ 01832 742122 ⌕ brance@east-northamptonshire.gov.uk

Children / Youth Services: Mr Mike Greenway, Community Partnerships Manager, East Northamptonshire Council, Cedar Drive, Thrapston NN10 4LZ ☎ 01832 742244
⌕ mgreenway@east-northamptonshire.gov.uk

PR / Communications: Mrs Louise Spolton, Communications Manager, East Northamptonshire House, Cedar Drive, Thrapston NN14 4LZ ☎ 01832 742217 ⌕ lspolton@east-northamptonshire.gov.uk

Community Planning: Mr Mike Greenway, Community Partnerships Manager, East Northamptonshire Council, Cedar Drive, Thrapston NN10 4LZ ☎ 01832 742244
⌕ mgreenway@east-northamptonshire.gov.uk

Community Safety: Mr Mike Greenway, Community Development Manager, East Northamptonshire Council, Cedar Drive, Thrapston NN10 4LZ ☎ 01832 742244
⌕ mgreenway@east-northamptonshire.gov.uk

Corporate Services: Mrs Katy Everitt, Head of Resources & Organisational Development, East Northamptonshire House, Cedar House, Thrapston NN14 4LZ ☎ 01832 742113
⌕ personnel@east-northamptonshire.gov.uk

EAST NORTHAMPTONSHIRE

Customer Service: Ms Julia Smith, Interim Head of Customer & Community Services, East Northamptonshire House, Cedar Drive, Thrapston NN14 4LZ ☎ 01832 742066
✉ jsmith@east-northamptonshire.gov.uk

Economic Development: Ms Sharn Matthews, Executive Director & Monitoring Officer, East Northamptonshire House, Cedar Drive, Thrapston NN14 4LZ ☎ 01832 742108
✉ smatthews@east-northamptonshire.gov.uk

E-Government: Ms Angela Hook, Corporate Support Manager, East Northamptonshire House, Cedar Drive, Thrapston NN14 4LZ ☎ 01832 742203 ✉ ahook@east-northamptonshire.gov.uk

Environmental Health: Mr Mike Deacon, Head of Environmental Services, East Northamptonshire House, Cedar Drive, Thrapston NN14 4LZ ☎ 01832 742060
✉ environmentalservices@east-northamptonshire.gov.uk

Facilities: Mr Richard Hankins, Amenities Manager, East Northamptonshire House, Cedar Drive, Thrapston NN14 4LZ
☎ 01832 742031 ✉ rhankins@east-northamptonshire.gov.uk

Finance: Mr Glenn Hammons, Chief Finance Officer & Section 151 Officer, East Northamptonshire House, Cedar Drive, Thrapston NN14 4LZ ☎ 01832 742267
✉ ghammons@east-northamptonshire.gov.uk

Grounds Maintenance: Mr Richard Hankins, Amenities Manager, East Northamptonshire House, Cedar Drive, Thrapston NN14 4LZ
☎ 01832 742031 ✉ rhankins@east-northamptonshire.gov.uk

Housing: Ms Carol Conway, Housing Strategy & Delivery Manager, East Northamptonshire House, Cedar Drive, Thrapston NN14 4LZ
☎ 01832 742078 ✉ cconway@east-northamptonshire.gov.uk

Licensing: Mr Mike Deacon, Head of Environmental Services, East Northamptonshire House, Cedar Drive, Thrapston NN14 4LZ
☎ 01832 742060
✉ environmentalservices@east-northamptonshire.gov.uk

Partnerships: Mr Mike Greenway, Community Partnerships Manager, East Northamptonshire House, Cedar Drive, Thrapston NN14 4LZ ☎ 01832 742244
✉ mgreenway@east-northamptonshire.gov.uk

Personnel / HR: Mrs Katy Everitt, Head of Resources & Organisational Development, East Northamptonshire House, Cedar House, Thrapston NN14 4LZ ☎ 01832 742113
✉ personnel@east-northamptonshire.gov.uk

Planning: Mr Paul Bland, Head of Planning Services, East Northamptonshire House, Cedar Drive, Thrapston NN14 4LZ
☎ 01832 742218 ✉ pbland@east-northamptonshire.gov.uk

Recycling & Waste Minimisation: Ms Charlotte Tompkins, Waste Services Manager, East Northamptonshire House, Cedar Drive, Thrapston NN14 4LZ ☎ 01832 742208
✉ waste@east-northamptonshire.gov.uk

Regeneration: Mr Mike Greenway, Community Partnerships Manager, East Northamptonshire House, Cedar Drive, Thrapston NN14 4LZ ☎ 01832 742244 ✉ mgreenway@east-northamptonshire.gov.uk

Staff Training: Mrs Katy Everitt, Head of Resources & Organisational Development, East Northamptonshire House, Cedar House, Thrapston NN14 4LZ ☎ 01832 742113
✉ personnel@east-northamptonshire.gov.uk

Sustainable Communities: Mr Mike Greenway, Community Partnerships Manager, East Northamptonshire House, Cedar Drive, Thrapston NN14 4LZ ☎ 01832 742244
✉ mgreenway@east-northamptonshire.gov.uk

Sustainable Development: Mr Mike Greenway, Community Partnerships Manager, East Northamptonshire Council, Cedar Drive, Thrapston NN10 4LZ ☎ 01832 742244
✉ mgreenway@east-northamptonshire.gov.uk

Tourism: Miss Karen Williams, Tourism Development & Promotion Officer, East Northamptonshire House, Cedar Drive, Thrapston NN14 4LZ ☎ 01832 742064 ✉ kwilliams@east-northamptonshire.gov.uk

Waste Collection and Disposal: Ms Charlotte Tompkins, Waste Services Manager, East Northamptonshire House, Cedar Drive, Thrapston NN14 4LZ ☎ 01832 742208
✉ waste@east-northamptonshire.gov.uk

Waste Management: Ms Charlotte Tompkins, Waste Services Manager, East Northamptonshire House, Cedar Drive, Thrapston NN14 4LZ ☎ 01832 742208 ✉ waste@east-northamptonshire.gov.uk

COUNCILLORS

Chair: Reichhold, Rupert (CON - Oundle)

Vice-ChairWright, Colin (CON - Rushden Pemberton)
cwright@east-northamptonshire.gov.uk

Leader of the Council: North, Steven (CON - Rushden Sartoris)
snorth@east-northamptonshire.gov.uk

Deputy Leader of the Council: Harwood, Glenn (CON - Higham Ferrers Lancaster)
gharwood@east-northamptonshire.gov.uk

Group Leader: Gell, Richard (IND - Higham Ferrers Chichele)
rgell@east-northamptonshire.gov.uk

Beattie, Rosalie (CON - Thrapston Market)
rbeattie@east-northamptonshire.gov.uk

Boto, Tony (CON - Raunds Saxon)
tboto@east-northamptonshire.gov.uk

Brackenbury, Wendy (CON - Thrapston Lakes)
wbrackenbury@east-northamptonshire.gov.uk

Brackenbury, David (CON - Lower Nene)
dbrackenbury@east-northamptonshire.gov.uk

Carter, Val (IND - Thrapston Lakes)
vcarter@east-northamtonshire.gov.uk

Farrar, John (LAB - Irthlingborough John Pyel)
jfarrar@east-northamptonshire.gov.uk

Glithero, Roger (CON - Kings Forest)
rglithero@east-northamptonshire.gov.uk

Greenwood-Smith, Glenvil (CON - Raunds Windmill)
glenvil@east-northamptonshire.gov.uk

Harrison, Helen (CON - Fineshade)
hharrison@east-northamptonshire.gov.uk

Hillson, Marika (CON - Irthlingborough Waterloo)
mhillson@east-northamptonshire.gov.uk

Hobbs, Sylvia (CON - Irthlingborough Waterloo)
shobbs@east-northamptonshire.gov.uk

Hollomon, Marian (CON - Rushden Hayden)
mhollomon@east-northamptonshire.gov.uk

Howell, Helen (DUP - Stanwick)
hhowell@east-northamptonshire.gov.uk

Hughes, Dudley (CON - Woodford)
dhughes@east-northamptonshire.gov.uk

Hughes, Sylvia (CON - Lyveden)
shughes@east-northamptonshire.gov.uk

Jenney, Barbara (CON - Rushden Hayden)
bjenney@east-northamptonshire.gov.uk

Jenney, David (CON - Rushden Bates)
djenney@east-northamptonshire.gov.uk

Jones, Lance (CON - Raunds Saxon)
ljones@east-hamptonshire.gov.uk

Lewis, Richard (CON - Rushden Hayden)
rlewis@east-northamptonshire.gov.uk

Maxwell, Dorothy (CON - Rushden Spencer)
dmaxwell@east-northamptonshire.gov.uk

Mercer, Andy (CON - Rushden Spencer)
amercer@east-northamptonshire.gov.uk

Mercer, Gill (CON - Rushden Pemberton)
gmercer@east-northamptonshire.gov.uk

Peacock, Sarah (CON - Rushden Spencer)
speacock@east-northamptonshire.gov.uk

Pinnock, Ron (CON - Rushden Sartoris)
rpinnock@east-northamptonshire.gov.uk

Pinnock, Janet (CON - Rushden Pemberton)
jpinnock@east-northamptonshire.gov.uk

Powell, Roger (CON - Irthlingborough John Pyel)
rpowell@east-northamptonshire.gov.uk

Raven-Hill, Valerie (CON - Prebendal)
vraven@east-nothamptonshire.gov.uk

Saunston, Anna (CON - Higham Ferrers Chichele)
asaunton@east-northamptonshire.gov.uk

Shacklock, Geoff (CON - Barnwell)
gshacklock@east-northamptonshire.gov.uk

Smith, Alex (CON - Thrapston Market)
asmith@east-northamptonshire.gov.uk

Stearn, Phillip (CON - Oundle)
pstearn@east-northamptonshire.gov.uk

Underwood, Robin (CON - Rushden Bates)
runderwood@east-northamptonshire.gov.uk

Vowles, Jake (CON - Oundle)
jvowles@east-northamptonshire.gov.uk

Wathen, Peter (CON - Raunds Windmill)
pwathen@east-northamptonshire.gov.uk

Whiting, Pam (CON - Higham Ferrers Lancaster)
pwhiting@east-northamptonshire.gov.uk

POLITICAL COMPOSITION
CON: 36, IND: 2, LAB: 1, DUP: 1

COMMITTEE CHAIRS

Audit: Mr Colin Wright

Licensing: Mr Glenvil Greenwood-Smith

East Renfrewshire   S

East Renfrewshire Council, Council Headquarters, Eastwood Park, Rouken Glen Road, Giffnock G46 6UG
☎ 0141 577 3000 ᕀ customerservices@eastrenfrewshire.gov.uk
🖳 www.eastrenfrewshire.gov.uk

FACTS AND FIGURES
Parliamentary Constituencies: Renfrewshire East
EU Constituencies: Scotland
Election Frequency: Elections are of whole council

PRINCIPAL OFFICERS

Chief Executive: Mrs Lorraine McMillan, Chief Executive, Council Headquarters, Eastwood Park, Rouken Glen Road, Giffnock G46 6UG ☎ 0141 577 3009 ᕀ lorraine.mcmillan@eastrenfrewshire.gov.uk

Deputy Chief Executive: Mrs Caroline Innes, Deputy Chief Executive, Council Headquarters, Eastwood Park, Rouken Glen Road, Giffnock G46 6UG ☎ 0141 577 3161 ᕀ caroline.innes@eastrenfrewshire.gov.uk

Senior Management: Mr Andrew Cahill, Director - Environment, 2 Spiersbridge Way, Spiersbridge Business Park, Thornliebank G46 8NG ☎ 0141 577 3036 ᕀ andrew.cahill@eastrenfrewshire.gov.uk

Senior Management: Mrs Julie Murray, CHCP Director, Council Headquarters, Eastwood Park, Rouken Glen Road, Giffnock G46 6UG ☎ 0141 577 3840 ᕀ julie.murray@eastrenfrewshire.gov.uk

Senior Management: Ms Mhairi Shaw, Director - Education, Barrhead Council Offices, 211 Main Street, Barrhead G78 1SY ☎ 0141 577 3404 ᕀ mhairi.shaw@eastrenfrewshire.gov.uk

Children / Youth Services: Mrs Julie Murray, CHCP Director, Council Headquarters, Eastwood Park, Rouken Glen Road, Giffnock G46 6UG ☎ 0141 577 3840 ᕀ julie.murray@eastrenfrewshire.gov.uk

Children / Youth Services: Ms Kate Rocks, Head of Children's Services, 1 Burnfield Avenue, Giffnock G46 7TT ☎ 0141 577 3841 ᕀ kate.rocks@eastrenfrewshire.gov.uk

Civil Registration: Mr Jim Clarke, Registrar, Council Headquarters, Eastwood Park, Rouken Glen Road, Giffnock G46 6UG ☎ 0141 577 3452 ᕀ jim.clarke@eastrenfrewshire.gov.uk

PR / Communications: Mrs Emma Edwards, Communications Manager, Council Headquarters, Eastwood Park, Rouken Glen Road, Giffnock G46 6UG ☎ 0141 577 8536 ᕀ emma.edwards@eastrenfrewshire.gov.uk

Community Planning: Mr Jamie Reid, Community Resources Manager, Council Headquarters, Eastwood Park, Rouken Glen Road, Giffnock G46 6UG ☎ 0141 577 8557 ᕀ jamie.reid@eastrenfrewshire.gov.uk

EAST RENFREWSHIRE

Community Safety: Mr Jim Sneddon, Head of Democratic Services, Council Headquarters, Eastwood Park, Rouken Glen Road, Giffnock G46 6UG ☎ 0141 577 3744 ◌ jim.sneddon@eastrenfrewshire.gov.uk

Consumer Protection and Trading Standards: Mr Andrew Corry, Head of Environmental Services, Council Headquarters, Eastwood Park, Rouken Glen Road, Giffnock G46 6UG ☎ 0141 577 3756 ◌ andrew.corry@eastrenfrewshire.gov.uk

Contracts: Ms Diane Pirie, Chief Procurement Manager, Council Headquarters, Eastwood Park, Rouken Glen Road, Giffnock G46 6UG ☎ 0141 577 3676 ◌ diane.pirie@eastrenfrewshire.gov.uk

Customer Service: Ms Louise Smith, Head of Customer & Business Change Services, Council Headquarters, Eastwood Park, Rouken Glen Road, Giffnock G46 6UG ☎ 0141 577 3000 ◌ louise.smith@eastrenfrewshire.gov.uk

Economic Development: Mrs Gillian McNamara, Regeneration & Economic Development Manager, 2 Spiersbridge Way, Spiersbridge Business Park, Thornliebank G46 8NG ☎ 0141 577 3753 ◌ gillian.mcnamara@eastrenfrewshire.gov.uk

Education: Ms Fiona Morrison, Head of Education Services (Performance & Provision), Barrhead Council Offices, 211 Main Street, Barrhead G78 1SY ☎ 0141 577 3229 ◌ fiona.morrison@eastrenfrewshire.gov.uk

Education: Mr Mark Ratter, Head of Education Services, Barrhead Council Offices, 211 Main Street, Barrhead G78 1SY ☎ 0141 577 3481 ◌ mark.ratter@eastrenfrewshire.gov.uk

Education: Ms Mhairi Shaw, Director - Education, Barrhead Council Offices, 211 Main Street, Barrhead G78 1SY ☎ 0141 577 3404 ◌ mhairi.shaw@eastrenfrewshire.gov.uk

Environmental / Technical Services: Mr Andrew Cahill, Director - Environment, 2 Spiersbridge Way, Spiersbridge Business Park, Thornliebank G46 8NG ☎ 0141 577 3036 ◌ andrew.cahill@eastrenfrewshire.gov.uk

Environmental Health: Mr Andrew Corry, Head of Environmental Services, 2 Spiersbridge Way, Spiersbridge Business Park, Thornliebank G46 8NG ☎ 0141 577 3756 ◌ andrew.corry@eastrenfrewshire.gov.uk

Events Manager: Mr Malcolm Wright, Events Co-ordinator, Council Headquarters, Eastwood Park, Rouken Glen Road, Giffnock G46 6UG ☎ 0141 577 4854 ◌ malcolm.wright@eastrenfrewshire.gov.uk

Finance: Ms Margaret McCrossan, Head of Accountancy Services, Council Headquarters, Eastwood Park, Rouken Glen Road, Giffnock G46 6UG ☎ 0141 577 3035 ◌ margaret.mccrossan@eastrenfrewshire.gov.uk

Health and Safety: Mr Steve Murray, Principal Health & Safety Advisor, 2 Spiersbridge Way, Spiersbridge Business Park, Thornliebank G46 8NG ☎ 0141 577 3323 ◌ steve.murray@eastrenfrewshire.gov.uk

Housing: Mr Phil Dawes, Housing of Environment, 2 Spiersbridge Way, Spiersbridge Business Park, Thornliebank G46 8NG ☎ 0141 577 3186 ◌ phil.dawes@eastrenfrewshire.gov.uk

Legal: Mr Gerry Mahon, Chief Solicitor to the Council, Council Headquarters, Eastwood Park, Rouken Glen Road, Giffnock G46 6UG ☎ 0141 577 3024 ◌ gerry.mahon@eastrenfrewshire.gov.uk

Member Services: Ms Margaret Pettigrew, Member Services Officer, Council Headquarters, Eastwood Park, Rouken Glen Road, Giffnock G46 6UG ☎ 0141 577 3107 ◌ margaret.pettigrew@eastrenfrewshire.gov.uk

Partnerships: Mrs Julie Murray, CHCP Director, Council Headquarters, Eastwood Park, Rouken Glen Road, Giffnock G46 6UG ☎ 0141 577 3840 ◌ julie.murray@eastrenfrewshire.gov.uk

Personnel / HR: Ms Sharon Beattie, Human Resources Manager, Council Headquarters, Eastwood Park, Rouken Glen Road, Giffnock G46 6UG ☎ 0141 577 3161 ◌ sharon.beattie@eastrenfrewshire.gov.uk

Planning: Ms Gillian McCarney, Planning & Building Standards Manager, 2 Spiersbridge Way, Spiersbridge Business Park, Thornliebank RG46 8NG ☎ 0141 577 3116 ◌ gillian.mccarney@eastrenfrewshire.gov.uk

Procurement: Ms Diane Pirie, Chief Procurement Manager, Council Headquarters, Eastwood Park, Rouken Glen Road, Giffnock G46 6UG ☎ 0141 577 3676 ◌ diane.pirie@eastrenfrewshire.gov.uk

Recycling & Waste Minimisation: Mr Andrew Corry, Head of Environmental Services, Council Headquarters, Eastwood Park, Rouken Glen Road, Giffnock G46 6UG ☎ 0141 577 3756 ◌ andrew.corry@eastrenfrewshire.gov.uk

Regeneration: Mrs Gillian McNamara, Regeneration & Economic Development Manager, 2 Spiersbridge Way, Spiersbridge Business Park, Thornliebank G46 8NG ☎ 0141 577 3753 ◌ gillian.mcnamara@eastrenfrewshire.gov.uk

Social Services: Mrs Julie Murray, CHCP Director, Council Headquarters, Eastwood Park, Rouken Glen Road, Giffnock G46 6UG ☎ 0141 577 3840 ◌ julie.murray@eastrenfrewshire.gov.uk

Social Services (Adult): Mrs Julie Murray, CHCP Director, Council Headquarters, Eastwood Park, Rouken Glen Road, Giffnock G46 6UG ☎ 0141 577 3840 ◌ julie.murray@eastrenfrewshire.gov.uk

Social Services (Children): Mrs Julie Murray, CHCP Director, Council Headquarters, Eastwood Park, Rouken Glen Road, Giffnock G46 6UG ☎ 0141 577 3840 ◌ julie.murray@eastrenfrewshire.gov.uk

Sustainable Development: Mr Andrew Cahill, Director - Environment, 2 Spiersbridge Way, Spiersbridge Business Park, Thornliebank G46 8NG ☎ 0141 577 3036 ◌ andrew.cahill@eastrenfrewshire.gov.uk

Waste Management: Mr Andrew Corry, Head of Environmental Services, Council Headquarters, Eastwood Park, Rouken Glen Road, Giffnock G46 6UG ☎ 0141 577 3756 ◌ andrew.corry@eastrenfrewshire.gov.uk

COUNCILLORS

Provost: Carmichael, Alastair (SNP - Busby, Clarkston & Eaglesham)
alastair.carmichael@eastrenfrewshire.gov.uk

Deputy Provost: Cunningham, Betty (LAB - Barrhead)
betty.cunningham@eastrenfrewshire.gov.uk

Leader of the Council: Fletcher, Jim (LAB - Giffnock & Thornliebank)
jim.fletcher@eastrenfrewshire.gov.uk

Deputy Leader of the Council: Buchanan, Tony (SNP - Neilston, Uplawmoor & Newton Mearns North)
tony.buchanan@eastrenfrewshire.gov.uk

Group Leader: Wallace, Gordon (CON - Giffnock & Thornliebank)
gordon.wallace@eastrenfrewshire.gov.uk

Devlin, Danny (IND - Barrhead)
danny.devlin@eastrenfrewshire.gov.uk

Gilbert, Charlie (CON - Neilston, Uplawmoor & Newton Mearns North)
charlie.gilbert@eastrenfrewshire.gov.uk

Grant, Barbara (CON - Newton Mearns South)
barbara.grant@eastrenfrewshire.gov.uk

Green, Elaine (LAB - Neilston, Uplawmoor & Newton Mearns North)
elaine.green@eastrenfrewshire.gov.uk

Hay, Kenny (LAB - Barrhead)
kenny.hay@eastrenfrewshire.gov.uk

Lafferty, Alan (LAB - Busby, Clarkston & Eaglesham)
alan.lafferty@eastrenfrewshire.gov.uk

McAlpine, Ian (LAB - Newton Mearns South)
ian.mcalpine@eastrenfrewshire.gov.uk

McCaskill, Gordon (CON - Netherlee, Stamplerland & Williamwood)
gordon.mccaskil@eastrenfrewshire.gov.uk

Miller, Stewart (CON - Busy, Clarkston & Eaglesham)
stewart.miller@eastrenfrewshire.gov.uk

Montague, Mary (LAB - Netherlee, Stamplerland & Williamwood)
mary.montague@eastrenfrewshire.gov.uk

O'Kane, Paul (LAB - Neilston, Uplawmoor & Newton Mearns North)
paul.o'kane@eastrenfrewshire.gov.uk

Reilly, Tommy (SNP - Barrhead)
tommy.reilly@eastrenfrewshire.gov.uk

Robertson, Ralph (IND - Netherlee, Stamplerland & Williamwood)
ralph.robertson@eastrenfrewshire.gov.uk

Swift, Jim (CON - Newton Mearns South)
jim.swift@eastrenfrewshire.gov.uk

Waters, Vincent (SNP - Giffnock & Thornliebank)
vincent.waters@eastrenfrewshire.gov.uk

POLITICAL COMPOSITION
LAB: 8, CON: 6, SNP: 4, IND: 2

East Riding of Yorkshire   U

East Riding of Yorkshire Council, County Hall, Beverley HU17 9BA
☎ 01482 393939 ⏚ customer.services@eastriding.gov.uk
🖳 www.eastriding.gov.uk

FACTS AND FIGURES
Parliamentary Constituencies: Beverley & Holderness, Haltemprice and Howden, Yorkshire East

EU Constituencies: Yorkshire and the Humber
Election Frequency: Elections are of whole council

PRINCIPAL OFFICERS

Chief Executive: Mr Nigel Pearson, Chief Executive, County Hall, Beverley HU17 9BA ☎ 01482 391000
⏚ nigel.pearson@eastriding.gov.uk

Senior Management: Mr Tim Allison, Director - Public Health, County Hall, Beverley HU17 9BA ☎ 01482 391551; 01482 672068
⏚ tim.allison@eastriding.gov.uk; tim.allison@nhs.net

Senior Management: Mr Kevin Hall, Director - Children, Families & Schools, County Hall, Beverley HU17 9BA ☎ 01482 392000
⏚ kevin.hall@eastriding.gov.uk

Senior Management: Mrs Caroline Lacey, Director - Corporate Resources, County Hall, Beverley HU17 9BA ☎ 01482 394100
⏚ caroline.lacey@eastriding.gov.uk

Senior Management: Mr Nigel Leighton, Director - Environment & Neighbourhood Services, County Hall, Beverley HU17 9BA
☎ 01482 395000 ⏚ nigel.leighton@eastriding.gov.uk

Senior Management: Mr Alan Menzies, Director - Planning & Economic Regeneration, County Hall, Beverley HU17 9BA
☎ 01482 391600 ⏚ alan.menzies@eastriding.gov.uk

Senior Management: Mr John Skidmore, Director - Corporate Strategy & Commissioning, County Hall, Beverley HU17 9BA
☎ 01482 396000 ⏚ john.skidmore@eastriding.gov.uk

Access Officer / Social Services (Disability): Miss Lianne Therkelson, Area Manager, County Hall, Beverley HU17 9BA
☎ 01482 396416 ⏚ lianne.therkelson@eastriding.gov.uk

Architect, Building / Property Services: Mr Dave Waudby, Head of Infrastructure & Facilities, County Hall, Beverley HU17 9BA
☎ 01482 395800 ⏚ dave.waudby@eastriding.gov.uk

Best Value: Mr Simon Laurie, VFM & Consultancy Manager, County Hall, Beverley HU17 9BA ☎ 01482 391480
⏚ simon.laurie@eastriding.gov.uk

Building Control: Mr Chris Ducker, Building Control Manager, County Hall, Beverley HU17 9BA ☎ 01482 393810
⏚ chris.ducker@eastriding.gov.uk

Catering Services: Mr Alan Woods, Catering Service Manager, County Hall, Beverley HU17 9BA ☎ 01482 395121
⏚ alan.woods@eastriding.gov.uk

Children / Youth Services: Mr Kevin Hall, Director - Children, Families & Schools, County Hall, Beverley HU17 9BA
☎ 01482 392000 ⏚ kevin.hall@eastriding.gov.uk

Civil Registration: Ms Patricia Mann, Superintendent Registrar, Walkergate House, Beverley HU17 9BP ☎ 01482 393601
⏚ patricia.mann@eastriding.gov.uk

PR / Communications: Mr Nick Procter, Communications Manager, County Hall, Beverley HU17 9BA ☎ 01482 391440 ⌂ nick.procter@eastriding.gov.uk

Community Planning: Mr Simon Lowe, Policy, Partnerships & Intelligence Manager, County Hall, Beverley HU17 9BA ☎ 01482 391422 ⌂ simon.lowe@eastriding.gov.uk

Community Safety: Mr Max Hough, Crime & Disorder / Domestic Violence Services Manager, County Hall, Beverley HU17 9BA ☎ 01482 396421 ⌂ max.hough@eastriding.gov.uk

Computer Management: Mr Kevin Woodcock, ICT Business Solutions & Development Manager, County Hall, Beverley HU17 9BA ☎ 01482 394521 ⌂ kevin.woodcock@eastriding.gov.uk

Consumer Protection and Trading Standards: Mr Colin Briggs, Trading Standards Services Manager, Calibration Test Centre, Brudenell Way, Hull HU6 9DX ☎ 01482 396238 ⌂ colin.briggs@eastriding.gov.uk

Corporate Services: Mr Malcolm Sims, Director - Corporate Resources, County Hall, Beverley HU17 9BA ☎ 01482 393000 ⌂ malcolm.sims@eastriding.gov.uk

Customer Service: Mr Dave Morley, Head of Customer Services, County Hall, Beverley HU17 9BA ☎ 01482 395101 ⌂ dave.morley@eastriding.gov.uk

Customer Service: Ms Amanda Wilde, Customer Service Strategy & Digital Services Manager, County Hall, Beverley HU17 9BA ☎ 01482 393360 ⌂ amanda.wilde@eastriding.gov.uk

Economic Development: Mr Paul Bell, Head of Economic Development, County Hall, Beverley HU17 9BA ☎ 01482 391610 ⌂ paul.bell@eastriding.gov.uk

Education: Mr Mike Furbank, Head of Children & Young People, Education & Schools, County Hall, Beverley HU17 9BA ☎ 01482 392400 ⌂ mike.furbank@eastriding.gov.uk

E-Government: Mr Kevin Woodcock, ICT Business Solutions & Development Manager, County Hall, Beverley HU17 9BA ☎ 01482 394521 ⌂ kevin.woodcock@eastriding.gov.uk

Electoral Registration: Mrs Diane Hindhaugh, Assistant Democratic Services Manager, County Hall, Beverley HU17 9BA ☎ 01482 393150 ⌂ diane.hindhaugh@eastriding.gov.uk

Emergency Planning: Mr Alan Bravey, Emergency Planning Manager, County Hall, Beverley HU17 9BA ☎ 01482 393050 ⌂ alan.bravey@eastriding.gov.uk

Energy Management: Ms Karen Williamson, Strategic Investment & Development Manager, County Hall, Beverley HU17 9BA ☎ 01482 393907 ⌂ karen.williamson@eastriding.gov.uk

Environmental / Technical Services: Mr Mike Featherby, Head of Steetscene Services, County Hall, Beverley HU17 9BA ☎ 01482 395505 ⌂ mike.featherby@eastriding.gov.uk

Estates, Property & Valuation: Mr John Read, Valuation & Estates Manager, County Hall, Beverley HU17 9BA ☎ 01482 393930 ⌂ john.read@eastriding.gov.uk

European Liaison: Miss Claire Watts, External Funding & Policy Manager, County Hall, Beverley HU17 9BA ☎ 01482 391618 ⌂ claire.watts@eastriding.gov.uk

Events Manager: Mr Will Hall, Conference & Events Officer, County Hall, Beverley HU17 9BA ☎ 01482 391668 ⌂ william.hall@eastriding.gov.uk

Facilities: Mr Darren Stevens, Head of Culture & Information, County Hall, Beverley HU17 9BA ☎ 01482 392500 ⌂ darren.stevens@eastriding.gov.uk

Finance: Mrs Caroline Lacey, Director - Corporate Resources, County Hall, Beverley HU17 9BA ☎ 01482 394100 ⌂ caroline.lacey@eastriding.gov.uk

Treasury: Mrs Caroline Lacey, Director - Corporate Resources, County Hall, Beverley HU17 9BA ☎ 01482 394100 ⌂ caroline.lacey@eastriding.gov.uk

Pensions: Mr Graham Ferry, Pensions Manager, East Riding Pension Fund, PO Box 118, Council Offices, Church Street, Goole DN14 5BU ☎ 01482 394171 ⌂ graham.ferry@eastriding.gov.uk

Fleet Management: Mr Carl Gillyon, Fleet Services, Vehicle Maintenance Unit, Annie Reed Road, Beverley HU17 0LF ☎ 01482 395506 ⌂ carl.gillyon@eastriding.gov.uk

Grounds Maintenance: Mr Andy Harper, Operations Manager GMU Tech / Forestry, County Hall, Beverley HU17 9BA ☎ 01482 395863 ⌂ andy.harper@eastriding.gov.uk

Health and Safety: Mr Garry Smith, Safety Manager, County Hall, Beverley HU17 9BA ☎ 01482 391110 ⌂ garry.smith@eastriding.gov.uk

Highways: Mr Mike White, Group Manager - Technical Services, County Hall, Beverley HU17 9BA ☎ 01482 395684 ⌂ mike.white@eastriding.gov.uk

Home Energy Conservation: Mrs Jane Mears, Senior Environmental Health Officer, Town Hall, Quay Road, Bridlington YO16 4LT ☎ 01482 396278 ⌂ jane.mears@eastriding.gov.uk

Housing: Mr Richard Ikin, Housing & Safe Communities, County Hall, Beverley HU17 9BA ☎ 01482 396120 ⌂ dick.ikin@eastriding.gov.uk

Housing Maintenance: Mr Danny Hill, Housing Maintenance Unit Manager, 1st Floor, Beverley Depot, Annie Reed Road, Beverley HU17 0LE ☎ 01482 395817 ⌂ danny.hill@eastriding.gov.uk

Legal: Mr Mathew Buckley, Head of Legal & Democratic Services, County Hall, Beverley HU17 9BA ☎ 01482 393100 ⌂ mathew.buckley@eastriding.gov.uk

Legal: Ms Lisa-Jane Nicholson, Acting Litigation & Regulatory Services Manager, County Hall, Beverley HU17 9BA ☎ 01482 393143 ⌂ lisajane.nicholson@eastriding.gov.uk

Leisure and Cultural Services: Mr Darren Stevens, Head of Culture & Information, County Hall, Beverley HU17 9BA
☎ 01482 392500 ⤴ darren.stevens@eastriding.gov.uk

Licensing: Ms Tina Holtby, Licensing Manager, County Hall, Beverley HU17 9BA ☎ 01482 396291 ⤴ tina.holtby@eastriding.gov.uk

Lifelong Learning: Mr Mike Furbank, Head of Children & Young People, Education & Schools, County Hall, Beverley HU17 9BA
☎ 01482 392400 ⤴ mike.furbank@eastriding.gov.uk

Lighting: Mr Iain Ferguson, Lighting Engineer, County Hall, Beverley HU17 9BA ☎ 01482 395645 ⤴ iain.ferguson@eastriding.gov.uk

Lottery Funding, Charity and Voluntary: Mr Simon Lowe, Policy, Partnerships & Intelligence Manager, County Hall, Beverley HU17 9BA ☎ 01482 391422 ⤴ simon.lowe@eastriding.gov.uk

Member Services: Mrs Diane Hindhaugh, Assistant Democratic Services Manager, County Hall, Beverley HU17 9BA ☎ 01482 393150 ⤴ diane.hindhaugh@eastriding.gov.uk

Parking: Mrs Paula Danby, Service Manager, Mallard House, 6 Beck View Road, Beverley HU17 0JT ☎ 01482 395570 ⤴ paula.danby@eastriding.gov.uk

Partnerships: Ms Gillian Barley, Corporate Strategy & Performance Manager, County Hall, Beverley HU17 9BA
☎ 01482 391427 ⤴ gillian.barley@eastriding.gov.uk

Personnel / HR: Mr David Smith, Head of Human Resources & Support Services, County Hall, Beverley HU17 9BA
☎ 01482 391100 ⤴ david.smith@eastriding.gov.uk

Planning: Mr Stephen Hunt, Interim Head of Planning & Development Management, County Hall, Beverley HU17 9BA
☎ 01482 391740 ⤴ stephen.hunt@eastriding.gov.uk

Procurement: Mr Pete Arden, Procurement Manager, County Hall, Beverley HU17 9BA ☎ 01482 395551
⤴ pete.arden@eastriding.gov.uk

Public Libraries: Mr Kevin Hadfield, Libraries, Archives & Museums Service Manager, County Hall, Beverley HU17 9BA
☎ 01482 395221 ⤴ kevin.hadfield@eastriding.gov.uk

Recycling & Waste Minimisation: Mr Mike Featherby, Head of Steetscene Services, County Hall, Beverley HU17 9BA ☎ 01482 395505 ⤴ mike.featherby@eastriding.gov.uk

Regeneration: Ms Sue Lang, Regeneration & Funding Group Manager, County Hall, Beverley HU17 9BA ☎ 01482 391617
⤴ sue.lang@eastriding.gov.uk

Road Safety: Mr Kevin Hall, Director - Children, Families & Schools, County Hall, Beverley HU17 9BA ☎ 01482 392000
⤴ kevin.hall@eastriding.gov.uk

Social Services (Adult): Ms Rosy Pope, Head of Adult Services, County Hall, Beverley HU17 9BA ☎ 01482 396400
⤴ rosy.pope@eastriding.gov.uk

Social Services (Children): Ms Pam Allen, Head of Children & Young People's Support & Safeguarding Services, County Hall, Beverley HU17 9BA ☎ 01482 396404 ⤴ pam.allen@eastriding.gov.uk

Staff Training: Mrs Tina Tate, Learning & Development Manager, Council Offices, Main Road, Skirlaugh, Hull HU11 5HN
☎ 01482 391170 ⤴ tina.tate@eastriding.gov.uk

Street Scene: Mr Mike Featherby, Head of Steetscene Services, County Hall, Beverley HU17 9BA ☎ 01482 395505
⤴ mike.featherby@eastriding.gov.uk

Sustainable Communities: Mr Jeremy Pickles, Principal Sustainable Communities & Coast Officer, County Hall, Beverley HU17 9BA ☎ 01482 391720 ⤴ jeremy.pickles@eastriding.gov.uk

Sustainable Development: Mr Jeremy Pickles, Principal Sustainable Communities & Coast Officer, County Hall, Beverley HU17 9BA ☎ 01482 391720 ⤴ jeremy.pickles@eastriding.gov.uk

Tourism: Mr Andy Gray, Tourism Manager, County Hall, Beverley HU17 9BA ☎ 01482 391526 ⤴ andy.gray@eastriding.gov.uk

Town Centre: Ms Sue Lang, Regeneration & Funding Group Manager, County Hall, Beverley HU17 9BA ☎ 01482 391617
⤴ sue.lang@eastriding.gov.uk

Traffic Management: Mr Mike White, Group Manager - Technical Services, Beverley Depot, 2nd Floor, Beverley HU17 0JP
☎ 01482 395684 ⤴ mike.white@eastriding.gov.uk

Transport: Ms Paula Danby, Service Manager, Mallard House, 6 Beck View Road, Beverley HU17 0JT ☎ 01482 395570
⤴ paula.danby@eastriding.gov.uk

Transport: Ms Claire Hoskins, Interim Strategic Transport Planning Manager, County Hall, Beverley HU17 9BA ☎ 01482 391747
⤴ claire.hoskins@eastriding.gov.uk

Transport Planner: Ms Claire Hoskins, Interim Strategic Transport Planning Manager, County Hall, Beverley HU17 9BA
☎ 01482 391747 ⤴ claire.hoskins@eastriding.gov.uk

Waste Management: Ms Debbie Mansell, Waste Contracts & Recycling Manager, Willerby Depot, Viking Close, Willerby, Hull HU10 6DZ ☎ 01482 392560 ⤴ debbie.mansell@eastriding.gov.uk

Children's Play Areas: Ms Louise Adams, Sport, Play & Arts Service Manager, County Hall, Beverley HU17 9BA
☎ 01482 392520 ⤴ louise.adams@eastriding.gov.uk

COUNCILLORS

Leader of the Council: Parnaby, Stephen (CON - Beverley Rural)
councillor.parnaby@eastriding.gov.uk

Deputy Leader of the Council: Owen, Jonathan (CON - East Wolds & Coastal)
councillor.owen@eastriding.gov.uk

Abraham, Julie (CON - South Hunsley)
councillor.abraham@eastriding.gov.uk

EAST RIDING OF YORKSHIRE

Aird, Elaine (CON - St Marys)
councillor.aird@eastriding.gov.uk

Aitken, Victoria (CON - Howdenshire)
councillor.aitken@eastriding.gov.uk

Barrett, John (CON - Snaith Airmyn & Rawcliffe & Marshlands)
councillor.barrett@eastriding.gov.uk

Bayram, Linda (CON - Howdenshire)
councillor.bayram@eastriding.gov.uk

Bayram, Charlie (CON - Howden)
councillor.bayram@eastriding.gov.uk

Billinger, Iain (LAB - Hessle)
councillor.billinger@eastriding.gov.uk

Birmingham, Bradley (CON - Beverley Rural)
councillor.birmingham@eastriding.gov.uk

Boatman, Mally (LAB - Goole South)
councillor.boatman@eastriding.gov.uk

Bryan, Mike (CON - South West Holderness)
councillor.bryan@eastriding.gov.uk

Burton, Richard (CON - Bridlington Central & Old Town)
councillor.rburton@eastriding.gov.uk

Burton, Andy (CON - Wolds Weighton)
councillor.burton@eastriding.gov.uk

Chadwick, Margaret (CON - Bridlington South)
councillor.chadwick@eastriding.gov.uk

Charis, Irene (CON - St Marys)
councillor.charis@eastriding.gov.uk

Cracknell, Jackie (CON - South East Holderness)
councillor.cracknell@eastriding.gov.uk

Davison, Philip (LD - Hessle)
councillor.davison@eastriding.gov.uk

Dennis, John (CON - South West Holderness)
councillor.dennis@eastriding.gov.uk

Elvidge, David (CON - Minster & Woodmansey)
councillor.elvidge@eastriding.gov.uk

Evison, Jane (CON - East Wolds & Coastal)
councillor.evison@eastriding.gov.uk

Finlay, Shelagh (LAB - Bridlington South)
councillor.finlay@eastriding.gov.uk

Fox, Caroline (CON - Snaith Airmyn & Rawcliffe & Marshlands)
councillor.fox@eastriding.gov.uk

Fraser, Symon (CON - Driffield & Rural)
councillor.fraser@eastriding.gov.uk

Galbraith, Tony (CON - Dale)
councillor.gailbraith@eastriding.gov.uk

Green, Helen (CON - Cottingham South)
councillor.green@eastriding.gov.uk

Hall, Barbara (CON - Driffield & Rural)
councillor.hall@eastriding.gov.uk

Hardy, Mary-Rose (LD - Tranby)
councillor.hardy@eastriding.gov.uk

Harold, Kerri (CON - Minster & Woodmansey)
councillor.harold@eastriding.gov.uk

Harrap, Richard (CON - Bridlington North)
councillor.harrap@eastriding.gov.uk

Head, Josie (IND - Goole North)
councillor.head@eastriding.gov.uk

Healing, Lyn (CON - South East Holderness)
councillor.healing@eastriding.gov.uk

Hogan, Paul (LAB - Hessle)
councillor.hogan@eastriding.gov.uk

Holtby, John (CON - Mid Holderness)
councillor.holtby@eastriding.gov.uk

Horton, Shaun (CON - Willerby & Kirk Ella)
councillor.horton@eastriding.gov.uk

Jefferson, Barbara (IND - North Holderness)
councillor.jefferson@eastriding.gov.uk

Jump, Ros (IND - Cottingham North)
councillor.jump@eastriding.gov.uk

Kingston, Mary (CON - Tranby)
councillor.hardy@eastriding.gov.uk

Lisseter, Paul (CON - East Wolds & Coastal)
councillor.lisseter@eastriding.gov.uk

Mathieson, Geraldine (IND - Cottingham North)
cllr@mathieson1.karoo.co.uk

Matthews, Chris (CON - Bridlington North)
councillor.mathews@eastriding.gov.uk

McMaster, Gary (CON - Willerby & Kirk Ella)
councillor.mcmaster@eastriding.gov.uk

Medini, Mike (CON - Cottingham South)
councillor.medini@eastriding.gov.uk

Meredith, Richard (CON - Dale)
councillor.meredith@eastriding.gov.uk

Milns, Malcolm (UKIP - Bridlington Central & Old Town)
councillor.milns@eastriding.gov.uk

Milns, Thelma (UKIP - Bridlington North)
councillor.thelma@eastriding.gov.uk

Mole, Claude (CON - Pocklington Provincial)
councillor.mole@eastriding.gov.uk

Moore, Keith (LAB - Goole North)
councillor.moore@eastriding.gov.uk

O'Neil, Pat (LAB - Goole South)
councillor.o'neil@eastriding.gov.uk

Peacock, Dominic (CON - Minster & Woodmansey)
councillor.peacock@eastriding.gov.uk

Pearson, Bryan (CON - St Marys)
councillor.pearson@eastriding.gov.uk

Pollard, Phyllis (CON - Beverley Rural)
councillor.pollard@eastriding.gov.uk

Robinson, David (UKIP - Bridlington South)
councillor.robson@eastriding.gov.uk

Rudd, David (CON - Wolds Weighton)
councillor.rudd@eastriding .gov.uk

Sharpe, Dee (CON - Willerby & Kirk Ella)
coucillor.sharpe@eastriding.gov.uk

Skow, Brian (CON - Mid Holderness)
councillor.skow@eastriding.gov.uk

Smith, Pat (CON - Dale)
councillor.smith@eastriding.gov.uk

EAST STAFFORDSHIRE

Stathers, Mike (CON - Wolds Weighton)
councillor.stathers@eastriding.gov.uk

Steel, Sue (CON - South West Holderness)
councillor.steel@eastriding.gov.uk

Strangeway, Andy (IND - Pocklington Provincial)
info@island-man.co.uk

Temple, Felicity (CON - Driffield & Rural)
councillor.temple@eastriding.gov.uk

Turner, Peter (CON - Mid Holderness)
councillor.turner@eastriding.gov.uk

Walker, Vanessa (CON - South Hunsley)
councillor.walker@eastriding.gov.uk

West, Kay (CON - Pocklington Provincial)
councillor.west@eastriding.gov.uk

Whittle, John (IND - North Holderness)
councillor.whittle@eastriding.gov.uk

Wilkinson, Nigel (CON - Howdenshire)
councillor.nigel@eastriding.gov.uk

POLITICAL COMPOSITION
CON: 49, IND: 6, LAB: 6, UKIP: 3, LD: 2, Vacant: 1

East Staffordshire   D

East Staffordshire Borough Council, The Maltsters, Wetmore
Road, Burton-on-Trent DE14 1LS
☎ 01283 508000 🖶 01283 535412 ✆ reception@eaststaffsbc.gov.uk
🖳 www.eaststaffsbc.gov.uk

FACTS AND FIGURES
Parliamentary Constituencies: Burton
EU Constituencies: West Midlands
Election Frequency: Elections are of whole council

PRINCIPAL OFFICERS

Chief Executive: Mr Andy O'Brien, Chief Executive, The Maltsters,
Wetmore Road, Burton-on-Trent DE14 1LS ☎ 01283 508300
✆ andy.o'brien@eaststaffsbc.gov.uk

Senior Management: Mr Paul Costiff, Head of Service, The
Maltsters, Wetmore Road, Burton-on-Trent DE14 1LS
☎ 01283 505407 ✆ paul.costiff@eaststaffsbc.gov.uk

Senior Management: Mr Sal Khan, Head of Service, The
Maltsters, Wetmore Road, Burton-on-Trent DE14 1LS
☎ 01283 508674 ✆ sal.khan@eaststaffsbc.gov.uk

Senior Management: Mr Mark Rizk, Head of Service, The
Malsters, Wetmore Road, Burton-on-Trent DE14 1LS
☎ 01283 508867 ✆ mark.rizk@eaststaffsbc.gov.uk

Building Control: Mr Paul Costiff, Head of Service, The Maltsters,
Wetmore Road, Burton-on-Trent DE14 1LS ☎ 01283 505407
✆ paul.costiff@eaststaffsbc.gov.uk

PR / Communications: Mr Chris Ebberley, Corporate &
Commercial Manager, The Maltsters, Wetmore Road, Burton-on-Trent
DE14 1LS ☎ 01283 508772 ✆ chris.ebberley@eaststaffsbc.gov.uk

Community Safety: Mr Mark Rizk, Head of Service, The Malsters,
Wetmore Road, Burton-on-Trent DE14 1LS ☎ 01283 508867
✆ mark.rizk@eaststaffsbc.gov.uk

Computer Management: Mr Guy Thornhill, ICT Manager, The
Maltsters, Wetmore Road, Burton-on-Trent DE14 1LS
☎ 01283 504351 ✆ guy.thornhill@eaststaffbc.gov.uk

Contracts: Mr Chris Ebberley, Corporate & Commercial Manager,
The Maltsters, Wetmore Road, Burton-on-Trent DE14 1LS
☎ 01283 508772 ✆ chris.ebberley@eaststaffsbc.gov.uk

Corporate Services: Mr Sal Khan, Head of Service, The Maltsters,
Wetmore Road, Burton-on-Trent DE14 1LS ☎ 01283 508674
✆ sal.khan@eaststaffsbc.gov.uk

Customer Service: Mr Sal Khan, Head of Service, The Maltsters,
Wetmore Road, Burton-on-Trent DE14 1LS ☎ 01283 508674
✆ sal.khan@eaststaffsbc.gov.uk

Economic Development: Mr Paul Costiff, Head of Service, The
Maltsters, Wetmore Road, Burton-on-Trent DE14 1LS
☎ 01283 505407 ✆ paul.costiff@eaststaffsbc.gov.uk

E-Government: Mr Sal Khan, Head of Service, The Maltsters,
Wetmore Road, Burton-on-Trent DE14 1LS ☎ 01283 508674
✆ sal.khan@eaststaffsbc.gov.uk

Electoral Registration: Mr Chris Ebberley, Corporate &
Commercial Manager, The Maltsters, Wetmore Road, Burton-on-Trent
DE14 1LS ☎ 01283 508772 ✆ chris.ebberley@eaststaffsbc.gov.uk

Emergency Planning: Mr Chris Ebberley, Corporate & Commercial
Manager, The Maltsters, Wetmore Road, Burton-on-Trent DE14 1LS
☎ 01283 508772 ✆ chris.ebberley@eaststaffsbc.gov.uk

Environmental Health: Mr Paul Costiff, Head of Service, The
Maltsters, Wetmore Road, Burton-on-Trent DE14 1LS
☎ 01283 505407 ✆ paul.costiff@eaststaffsbc.gov.uk

Estates, Property & Valuation: Mr Paul Costiff, Head of Service,
The Maltsters, Wetmore Road, Burton-on-Trent DE14 1LS
☎ 01283 505407 ✆ paul.costiff@eaststaffsbc.gov.uk

Events Manager: Mr Mark Rizk, Head of Service, The Malsters,
Wetmore Road, Burton-on-Trent DE14 1LS ☎ 01283 508867
✆ mark.rizk@eaststaffsbc.gov.uk

Facilities: Mr Mark Rizk, Head of Service, The Malsters, Wetmore
Road, Burton-on-Trent DE14 1LS ☎ 01283 508867
✆ mark.rizk@eaststaffsbc.gov.uk

Finance: Mr Sal Khan, Head of Service, The Maltsters, Wetmore
Road, Burton-on-Trent DE14 1LS ☎ 01283 508674
✆ sal.khan@eaststaffsbc.gov.uk

Fleet Management: Mr Paul Farrer, Environment Manager, The
Maltsters, Wetmore Road, Burton-on-Trent DE14 1LS
☎ 01283 505899 ✆ paul.farrer@eaststaffsbc.gov.uk

EAST STAFFORDSHIRE

Grounds Maintenance: Mr Michael Hovers, Communities & Open Spaces Manager, The Maltsters, Wetmore Road, Burton-on-Trent DE14 1LS ☎ 01283 508776 ◌ paul.farrer@eaststaffsbc.gov.uk

Health and Safety: Mr Michael Hovers, Communities & Open Spaces Manager, The Maltsters, Wetmore Road, Burton-on-Trent DE14 1LS ☎ 01283 508776 ◌ paul.farrer@eaststaffsbc.gov.uk

Home Energy Conservation: Mr Paul Costiff, Head of Service, The Maltsters, Wetmore Road, Burton-on-Trent DE14 1LS ☎ 01283 505407 ◌ paul.costiff@eaststaffsbc.gov.uk

Housing: Mr Paul Costiff, Head of Service, The Maltsters, Wetmore Road, Burton-on-Trent DE14 1LS ☎ 01283 505407 ◌ paul.costiff@eaststaffsbc.gov.uk

Legal: Mrs Angela Wakefield, Monitoring Officer & Legal Services Manager, The Malsters, Wetmore Road, Burton-on-Trent DE14 1LS ☎ 01283 508267 ◌ angela.wakefield@eaststaffsbc.gov.uk

Leisure and Cultural Services: Mr Mark Rizk, Head of Service, The Malsters, Wetmore Road, Burton-on-Trent DE14 1LS ☎ 01283 508867 ◌ mark.rizk@eaststaffsbc.gov.uk

Licensing: Mr Paul Costiff, Head of Service, The Maltsters, Wetmore Road, Burton-on-Trent DE14 1LS ☎ 01283 505407 ◌ paul.costiff@eaststaffsbc.gov.uk

Member Services: Mr Chris Ebberley, Corporate & Commercial Manager, The Maltsters, Wetmore Road, Burton-on-Trent DE14 1LS ☎ 01283 508772 ◌ chris.ebberley@eaststaffsbc.gov.uk

Parking: Mr Paul Costiff, Head of Service, The Maltsters, Wetmore Road, Burton-on-Trent DE14 1LS ☎ 01283 505407 ◌ paul.costiff@eaststaffsbc.gov.uk

Partnerships: Mr Paul Costiff, Head of Service, The Maltsters, Wetmore Road, Burton-on-Trent DE14 1LS ☎ 01283 505407 ◌ paul.costiff@eaststaffsbc.gov.uk

Personnel / HR: Mr Andy O'Brien, Chief Executive, The Maltsters, Wetmore Road, Burton-on-Trent DE14 1LS ☎ 01283 508300 ◌ andy.o'brien@eaststaffsbc.gov.uk

Planning: Mr Sal Khan, Head of Service, The Maltsters, Wetmore Road, Burton-on-Trent DE14 1LS ☎ 01283 508674 ◌ sal.khan@eaststaffsbc.gov.uk

Procurement: Mr Chris Ebberley, Corporate & Commercial Manager, The Maltsters, Wetmore Road, Burton-on-Trent DE14 1LS ☎ 01283 508772 ◌ chris.ebberley@eaststaffsbc.gov.uk

Recycling & Waste Minimisation: Mr Paul Farrer, Environment Manager, Town Hall, Burton-on-Trent DE14 2EB ☎ 01283 505899 ◌ paul.farrer@eaststaffsbc.gov.uk

Regeneration: Mr Paul Costiff, Head of Service, The Maltsters, Wetmore Road, Burton-on-Trent DE14 1LS ☎ 01283 505407 ◌ paul.costiff@eaststaffsbc.gov.uk

Staff Training: Mr Sal Khan, Head of Service, The Maltsters, Wetmore Road, Burton-on-Trent DE14 1LS ☎ 01283 508674 ◌ sal.khan@eaststaffsbc.gov.uk

Street Scene: Mr Paul Farrer, Environment Manager, Town Hall, Burton-on-Trent DE14 2EB ☎ 01283 505899 ◌ paul.farrer@eaststaffsbc.gov.uk

Tourism: Mr Paul Costiff, Head of Service, The Maltsters, Wetmore Road, Burton-on-Trent DE14 1LS ☎ 01283 505407 ◌ paul.costiff@eaststaffsbc.gov.uk

Waste Collection and Disposal: Mr Paul Farrer, Environment Manager, Town Hall, Burton-on-Trent DE14 2EB ☎ 01283 505899 ◌ paul.farrer@eaststaffsbc.gov.uk

Waste Management: Mr Paul Farrer, Environment Manager, Town Hall, Burton-on-Trent DE14 2EB ☎ 01283 505899 ◌ paul.farrer@eaststaffsbc.gov.uk

COUNCILLORS

Mayor: Toon, Beryl (CON - Rolleston on Dove)
beryl.toon@eaststaffsbc.gov.uk

Leader of the Council: Grosvenor, Richard (CON - Branston)
richard.grosvenor@eaststaffsbc.gov.uk

Ackroyd, Patricia (CON - Branston)
patricia.ackroyd@eaststaffsbc.gov.uk

Allen, George (CON - Heath)
george.allen@eaststaffsbc.gov.uk

Andjelkovic, Sonia (LAB - Eton Park)
sonia.andjelkovic@eaststaffsbc.gov.uk

Barker, Edward (CON - Weaver)
edward.barker@eaststaffsbc.gov.uk

Bowering, Michael (CON - Branston)
michael.bowering@eaststaffsbc.gov.uk

Builth, Ken (LAB - Horninglow)
ken.builth@eaststaffsbc.gov.uk

Carlton, Rebecca (CON - Stretton)
rebecca.carlton@eaststaffsbc.gov.uk

Chaudhry, Ali (LAB - Anglesey)
ali.chaudhry@eaststaffsbc.gov.uk

Clarke, Ron (LAB - Eton Park)
ron.clarke@eaststaffsbc.gov.uk

Dyche, Steven (UKIP - Stapenhill)
steven.dyche@eaststaffsbc.gov.uk

Faulkner, Raymond (CON - Winshill)
raymond.faulkner@eaststaffsbc.gov.uk

Fitzpatrick, Michael (LAB - Stapenhill)
michael.fitzpatrick@eaststaffsbc.gov.uk

Fletcher, Dennis (LAB - Winshill)
dennis.fletcher@eaststaffsbc.gov.uk

Ganley, William (LAB - Shobnall)
william.ganley@eaststaffsbc.gov.uk

Gaskin, Simon (CON - Tutbury and Outwoods)
simon.gaskin@eaststaffsbc.gov.uk

Goodfellow, Duncan (CON - Tutbury and Outwoods)
duncan.goodfellow@eaststaffsbc.gov.uk

Haberfield, Karen (CON - Town)
karen.haberfield@eaststaffsbc.gov.uk

Hall, Greg (CON - Bagots)
greg.hall@eaststaffsbc.gov.uk

Hussain, Syed (LAB - Anglesey)
syed.hussain@eaststaffsbc.gov.uk

Jessel, Julia (CON - Needwood)
julia.jessel@eaststaffsbc.gov.uk

Johnson, Alan (CON - Yoxall)
alan.johnson@eaststaffsbc.gov.uk

Johnston, Bob (LAB - Horninglow)
robert.johnston@eaststaffsbc.gov.uk

Jones, Jacqui (CON - Needwood)
jacqui.jones@eaststaffsbc.gov.uk

Killoran, Julie (CON - Stretton)
julie.killoran@eaststaffsbc.gov.uk

Leese, David (CON - Winshill)
david.leese@eaststaffsbc.gov.uk

Legg, Alison (LAB - Stapenhill)
alison.legg@eaststaffsbc.gov.uk

McGarry, Susan (CON - Town)
susan.mcgarry@eaststaffsbc.gov.uk

McKiernan, Shelagh (LAB - Shobnall)
shelagh.mckiernan@eaststaffsbc.gov.uk

Milner, Len (CON - Stretton)
len.milner@eaststaffsbc.gov.uk

Mott, Julian (LAB - Horninglow)
julian.mott@eaststaffsbc.gov.uk

Peters, Bernard (CON - Brizlincote)
bernard.peters@eaststaffsbc.gov.uk

Rodgers, Michael (LD - Burton)
michael.rodgers@eaststaffsbc.gov.uk

Shelton, Lynne (CON - Heath)
lynne.shelton@eaststaffsbc.gov.uk

Smith, Stephen (CON - Crown)
stephen.smith@eaststaffsbc.gov.uk

Smith, Chris (CON - Churnett)
chris.smith@eaststaffsbc.gov.uk

Whittaker, Colin (CON - Abbey)
colin.whittaker@eaststaffsbc.gov.uk

Wileman, Colin (CON - Brizlincote)
colin.wileman@eaststaffsbc.gov.uk

POLITICAL COMPOSITION
CON: 25, LAB: 12, LD: 1, UKIP: 1

East Sussex   C

East Sussex County Council, County Hall, St Anne's Crescent,
Lewes BN7 1UE
☎ 0345 608 0190 ▪ www.eastsussex.gov.uk

FACTS AND FIGURES
Parliamentary Constituencies: Bexhill and Battle, Eastbourne,

Hastings and Rye, Lewes, Wealden
EU Constituencies: South East
Election Frequency: Elections are of whole council

PRINCIPAL OFFICERS

Chief Executive: Ms Becky Shaw, Chief Executive, County Hall, St
Anne's Crescent, Lewes BN7 1UE ☎ 01273 481950
✆ becky.shaw@eastsussex.gov.uk

Assistant Chief Executive: Mr Philip Baker, Assistant Chief
Executive, County Hall, St Anne's Crescent, Lewes BN7 1UE
☎ 01273 481564 ✆ philip.baker@eastsussex.gov.uk

Senior Management: Mr Rupert Clubb, Director - Communities,
Economy & Transport, County Hall, St Anne's Crescent, Lewes BN7
1UE ☎ 01273 482200 ✆ rupert.clubb@eastsussex.gov.uk

Senior Management: Mr Kevin Foster, Chief Operating Officer,
County Hall, St Anne's Crescent, Lewes BN7 1UE ☎ 01273 481412
✆ kevin.foster@eastsussex.gov.uk

Senior Management: Mr Stuart Gallimore, Director - Children's
Services, County Hall, St Anne's Crescent, Lewes BN7 1UE
☎ 01273 481316 ✆ stuart.gallimore@eastsussex.gov.uk

Senior Management: Mr Keith Hinkley, Director - Adult Social
Care & Health, County Hall, St Anne's Crescent, Lewes BN7 1UE
☎ 01273 481288 ✆ keith.hinkley@eastsussex.gov.uk

Senior Management: Ms Cynthia Lyons, Acting Director - Public
Health, County Hall, St Anne's Crescent, Lewes BN7 1UE
☎ 01273 336032 ✆ cynthia.lyons@eastsussex.gov.uk

Access Officer / Social Services (Disability): Mr Keith
Hinkley, Director - Adult Social Care & Health, County Hall, St
Anne's Crescent, Lewes BN7 1UE ☎ 01273 481288
✆ keith.hinkley@eastsussex.gov.uk

Architect, Building / Property Services: Mr John Stebbings,
Acting Chief Property Officer, County Hall, St Anne's Crescent, Lewes
BN7 1UE ☎ 020 8213 2554 ✆ john.stebbings@surreycc.gov.uk

Catering Services: Mr Andrew Little, Senior Contracts Officer -
Catering, County Hall, St Anne's Crescent, Lewes BN7 1UE
☎ 01273 482402 ✆ andrew.little@eastsussex.gov.uk

Children / Youth Services: Mr Stuart Gallimore, Director -
Children's Services, County Hall, St Anne's Crescent, Lewes BN7
1UE ☎ 01273 481316 ✆ stuart.gallimore@eastsussex.gov.uk

Civil Registration: Mr Steve Quayle, Proper Officer for
Registration, West D, County Hall, St Anne's Crescent, Lewes BN7
1UE ☎ 01273 337148 ✆ steve.quayle@eastsussex.gov.uk

Community Planning: Mrs Sarah Feather, Policy Manager -
Equalities, County Hall, St Anne's Crescent, Lewes BN7 1UE
☎ 01273 335712 ✆ sarah.feather@eastsussex.gov.uk

Computer Management: Mr Matt Scott, Orbis Chief Information
Officer, County Hall, St Anne's Crescent, Lewes BN7 1UE
☎ 01273 335677 ✆ matt.scott@eastsussex.gov.uk

EAST SUSSEX

Consumer Protection and Trading Standards: Ms Lucy Corrie, Head of Communities, St Mary's House, 52 St. Leonard's Road, Eastbourne BN21 3UU ☎ 01323 463421 ⌨ lucy.corrie@eastsussex.gov.uk

Contracts: Mr Mark Billington, Contracts Manager, County Hall, St Anne's Crescent, Lewes BN7 1UE ☎ 07884 262583 ⌨ mark.billington@eastsussex.gov.uk

Corporate Services: Mr Kevin Foster, Chief Operating Officer, County Hall, St Anne's Crescent, Lewes BN7 1UE ☎ 01273 481412 ⌨ kevin.foster@eastsussex.gov.uk

Customer Service: Ms Anita Cundall, Customer Services Manager, County Hall, St Anne's Crescent, Lewes BN7 1UE ☎ 01273 481870 ⌨ anita.cundall@eastsussex.gov.uk

Economic Development: Mr James Harris, Assistant Director - Economy, County Hall, St Anne's Crescent, Lewes BN7 1UE ☎ 01273 482158 ⌨ james.harris@eastsussex.gov.uk

Education: Mr Stuart Gallimore, Director - Children's Services, County Hall, St Anne's Crescent, Lewes BN7 1UE ☎ 01273 481316 ⌨ stuart.gallimore@eastsussex.gov.uk

Emergency Planning: Mr David Broadley, Emergency Planning Manager, St Mary's House, 52 St Leonard's Road, Eastbourne BN21 3UU ☎ 01323 747085 ⌨ david.broadley@eastsussex.gov.uk

Energy Management: Mr Andrew Burrows, Principal Client Officer, County Hall, St Anne's Crescent, Lewes BN7 1UE ⌨ andrew.burrows@eastsussex.gov.uk

Environmental / Technical Services: Mr Carl Valentine, Head of Transport & Operational Services, County Hall, St Anne's Crescent, Lewes BN7 1UE ☎ 01273 336199 ⌨ carl.valentine@eastsussexcc.gov.uk

Estates, Property & Valuation: Mr John Stebbings, Acting Chief Property Officer, County Hall, St Anne's Crescent, Lewes BN7 1UE ☎ 020 8213 2554 ⌨ john.stebbings@surreycc.gov.uk

European Liaison: Mr James Harris, Assistant Director - Economy, County Hall, St Anne's Crescent, Lewes BN7 1UE ☎ 01273 482158 ⌨ james.harris@eastsussex.gov.uk

Facilities: Mr Paul Barnard, Corporate Accommodation & Facilities Manager, County Hall, St. Anne's Crescent, Lewes BN7 1UE ☎ 01273 482120 ⌨ paul.barnard@eastsussex.gov.uk

Finance: Mr Kevin Foster, Chief Operating Officer, County Hall, St Anne's Crescent, Lewes BN7 1UE ☎ 01273 481412 ⌨ kevin.foster@eastsussex.gov.uk

Pensions: Mr Ola Owalabi, Head of Accounts & Pensions, County Hall, St Anne's Crescent, Lewes BN7 1UE ☎ 01273 482017 ⌨ ola.owolabi@eastsussex.gov.uk

Fleet Management: Mr Terry Myall, Fleet Management Officer, County Hall, St Anne's Crescent, Lewes BN7 1UE ☎ 01273 482935 ⌨ terry.myall@eastsussex.gov.uk

Health and Safety: Ms Judy Benoy, Senior Health & Safety Adviser, County Hall, St Anne's Crescent, Lewes BN7 1UE ☎ 01273 481227 ⌨ judy.benoy@eastsussex.gov.uk

Highways: Mr Rupert Clubb, Director - Communities, Economy & Transport, County Hall, St Anne's Crescent, Lewes BN7 1SW ☎ 01273 482200 ⌨ rupert.clubb@eastsussex.gov.uk

Local Area Agreement: Ms Becky Shaw, Chief Executive, County Hall, St Anne's Crescent, Lewes BN7 1SW ☎ 01273 481950 ⌨ becky.shaw@eastsussex.gov.uk

Legal: Mr Philip Baker, Assistant Chief Executive, County Hall, St Annes Crescent, Lewes BN7 1UN ☎ 01273 481564 ⌨ philip.baker@eastsussex.gov.uk

Leisure and Cultural Services: Ms Sally Staples, Cultural Strategy Manager, County Hall, St Anne's Crescent, Lewes BN7 1UE ☎ 01273 481871 ⌨ arts@eastsussex.gov.uk

Lighting: Mr Simon Hall, Street Lighting & Traffic Signals Team Manager, Ringmer Depot, The Broyle, Ringmer, Lewes BN8 5NP ☎ 01273 482781 ⌨ simon.hall@eastsussex.gov.uk

Member Services: Mr Paul Dean, Member Services Manager, Room C3F County Hall, St. Anne's Crescent, Lewes BN7 1SW ☎ 01273 481751 ⌨ paul.dean@eastsussex.gov.uk

Parking: Mr David Weeks, Team Manager - Parking, 6th Floor, St Mary's House, 52 St Leonard's Road, Eastbourne BN21 3UU ☎ 01323 466230 ⌨ david.weeks@eastsussex.gov.uk

Personnel / HR: Ms Sarah Mainwaring, Interim Assistant Director - Personnel & Training, County Hall, St Anne's Crescent, Lewes BN7 1UE ☎ 01273 482060 ⌨ sarah.mainwaring@eastsussex.gov.uk

Planning: Ms Sarah Iles, Team Manager - Planning & Development, County Hall, St Anne's Crescent, Lewes BN7 1UE ☎ 01273 481631 ⌨ sarah.iles@eastsussex.gov.uk

Procurement: Ms Laura Langstaff, Head of Procurement, County Hall, St Anne's Crescent, Lewes BN7 1UE ☎ 01273 335601 ⌨ laura.langstaff@surreycc.gov.uk

Public Libraries: Mr Nick Skelton, Assistant Director - Communities, County Hall, St Anne's Crescent, Lewes BN7 1UE ☎ 01273 482994 ⌨ nick.skelton@eastsussex.gov.uk

Recycling & Waste Minimisation: Mr Justin Foster, Waste Team Manager, County Hall, St Anne's Crescent, Lewes BN7 1UE ☎ 01273 395157 ⌨ justin.foster@eastsussex.gov.uk

Regeneration: Mr James Harris, Assistant Director - Economy, County Hall, St Anne's Crescent, Lewes BN7 1UE ☎ 01273 482158 ⌨ james.harris@eastsussex.gov.uk

Road Safety: Mr Brian Banks, Team Manager - Road Safety, County Hall, St Anne's Crescent, Lewes BN7 1UE ☎ 01424 724558 ⌨ brian.banks@eastsussex.gov.uk

Social Services: Mr Keith Hinkley, Director - Adult Social Care & Health, County Hall, St Anne's Crescent, Lewes BN7 1UE
☎ 01273 481288 ⌨ keith.hinkley@eastsussex.gov.uk

Social Services (Adult): Mr Mark Stainton, Assistant Director - Adult Social Care - Operations, County Hall, St Anne's Crescent, Lewes BN7 1UE ☎ 01273 481238
⌨ mark.stainton@eastsussex.gov.uk

Social Services (Children): Ms Liz Rugg, Assistant Director - Early Help & Social Care, County Hall, St Anne's Crescent, Lewes BN7 1UE ☎ 01273 481274 ⌨ liz.rugg@eastsussex.gov.uk

Social Services (Children): Mr Douglas Sinclair, Head of Children's Safeguards & Quality Assurance, County Hall, St Anne's Crescent, Lewes BN7 1UE ☎ 01273 481289
⌨ douglas.sinclair@eastsussex.gov.uk

Public Health: Ms Cynthia Lyons, Acting Director - Public Health, County Hall, St Anne's Crescent, Lewes BN7 1UE
☎ 01273 336032 ⌨ cynthia.lyons@eastsussex.gov.uk

Staff Training: Mr Ed Howarth, HR Manager, County Hall, St Anne's Crescent, Lewes BN7 1UE ☎ 01273 481527
⌨ ed.howarth@eastsussex.gov.uk

Sustainable Communities: Ms Becky Shaw, Chief Executive, County Hall, St Anne's Crescent, Lewes BN7 1SW ☎ 01273 481950
⌨ becky.shaw@eastsussex.gov.uk

Sustainable Development: Mr Rupert Clubb, Director - Transport & Environment, County Hall, St Anne's Crescent, Lewes BN7 1UE ☎ 01273 4822000 ⌨ rupert.clubb@eastsussex.gov.uk

Sustainable Development: Mr Carl Valentine, Head of Transport & Operational Services, County Hall, St Anne's Crescent, Lewes BN7 1UE ☎ 01273 336199 ⌨ carl.valentine@eastsussexcc.gov.uk

Traffic Management: Mr Rupert Clubb, Director - Communities, Economy & Transport, County Hall, St Anne's Crescent, Lewes BN7 1SW ☎ 01273 482200 ⌨ rupert.clubb@eastsussex.gov.uk

Transport: Mr Rupert Clubb, Director - Communities, Economy & Transport, County Hall, St Anne's Crescent, Lewes BN7 1SW
☎ 01273 482200 ⌨ rupert.clubb@eastsussex.gov.uk

Transport: Mr Roger Williams, Head of Service - Highways, Ringmer Depot, The Broyle, Ringmer, Lewes BN8 5NP
☎ 01273 481000 ⌨ roger.williams@eastsussex.gov.uk

Waste Collection and Disposal: Mr Rupert Clubb, Director - Communities, Economy & Transport, County Hall, St Anne's Crescent, Lewes BN7 1SW ☎ 01273 482200
⌨ rupert.clubb@eastsussex.gov.uk

Waste Management: Mr Rupert Clubb, Director - Communities, Economy & Transport, County Hall, St Anne's Crescent, Lewes BN7 1SW ☎ 01273 482200 ⌨ rupert.clubb@eastsussex.gov.uk

COUNCILLORS

Chair: Ensor, Michael (CON - Bexhill King Offa)
cllr.michael.ensor@eastsussex.gov.uk

Vice-Chair: Pragnell, Peter (CON - Hastings - Ashdown & Conquest)
cllr.peter.pragnell@eastsussex.gov.uk

Leader of the Council: Glazier, Keith (CON - Rye & Eastern Rother)
cllr.keith.glazier@eastsussex.gov.uk

Deputy Leader of the Council: Elkin, David (CON - Eastbourne - Sovereign)
cllr.david.elkin@eastsussex.gov.uk

Group LeaderHowson, Phil (UKIP - Peacehaven & Telscombe Towns)
cllr.phillip.howson@eastsussexcc.gov.uk

Group LeaderO'Keeffe, Ruth (IND - Lewes)
roklewes@gmail.com

Group LeaderShing, Stephen (IND - Polegate, Willingdon & East Dean)
cllr.stephen.shing@eastsussex.gov.uk

Group LeaderTutt, David (LD - Eastbourne - St Anthony's)
cllr.david.tutt@eastsussex.gov.uk

Group LeaderWebb, Trevor (LAB - Hastings - Central St Leonards & Gensing)
cllr.trevor.webb@eastsussex.gov.uk

Barnes, John (CON - Rother North West)
cll.john.barnes@eastsussex.gov.uk

Belsey, Colin (CON - Eastbourne - Ratton)
cllr.colin.belsey@eastsussex.gov.uk

Bennett, Nick (CON - Alfriston, East Hoathly & Hellingly)
cllr.nick.bennett@eastsussex.gov.uk

Bentley, Bill (CON - Hailsham & Herstmonceux)
cllr.bill.bentley@eastsussexcc.gov.uk

Blanch, Mike (LD - Eastbourne - Hampden Park)
Cllr.mike.blanch@eastsussex.gov.uk

Buchanan, Ian (UKIP - Peacehaven & Telscombe Towns)
cllr.ian.buchanan@eastsussex.gov.uk

Butler, Carla (LD - Newhaven & Ouse Valley West)
cllr.carla.butler@eastsussex.gov.uk

Carstairs, Frank (UKIP - Seaford Sutton)
cllr.frank.carstairs@eastsussex.gov.uk

Charlton, Peter (UKIP - Ouse Valley East)
cllr.peter.charlton@eastsussex.gov.uk

Charman, Tania (LAB - Hastings - Old Hastings & Tressell)
cllr.tania.charman@eastsussex.gov.uk

Clark, Charles (IND - Bexhill East)
cllr.charles.clark@eastsussex.gov.uk

Daniel, Godfrey (LAB - Hastings - Braybrooke & Castle)
cllr.godfrey.daniel@eastsussex.gov.uk

Davies, Angharad (CON - Northern Rother)
cllr.Angharad.Davies@eastsussex.gov.uk

Dowling, Chris (CON - Framfield & Horam)
cllr.chris.dowling@eastsussex.gov.uk

Dowling, Claire (CON - Uckfield)
cllr.claire.dowling@eastsussex.gov.uk

Earl, Stuart (IND - Bexhill West)
cllr.stuart.earl@eastsussex.gov.uk

Field, Kathryn (LD - Battle and Crowhurst)
kathryn.fied@btopenworld.com

EAST SUSSEX

Forward, Kim (LAB - Hastings - Maze Hill & West St Leonards)
cllr.kim.forward@eastsussex.gov.uk

Galley, Roy (CON - Buxted Maresfield)
cllr.roy.galley@eastsussex.gov.uk

Keeley, Laurence (UKIP - Hailsham & Hertsmonceux)
cllr.laurence.keeley@eastsussex.gov.uk

Lambert, Carolyn (LD - Seaford Blatchington)
cllr.carolyn.lambert@eastsussex.gov.uk

Maynard, Carl (CON - Brede Valley & Marsham)
cllr.carl.maynard@eastsussex.gov.uk

Phillips, Michael (UKIP - Bexhill King Offa)
cllr.michael.phillips@eastsussex.govl.uk

Pursglove, Mike (UKIP - Pevensey & Westham)
cllr.michael.pursglov@eastsussex.gov.uk

Rodohan, Pat (LD - Eastbourne - Upperton)
cllr.Pat.Rodohan@eastsussex.gov.uk

Rogers, Judy (LAB - Hastings - St Helen's & Silverhill)
cllr.judy.rogers@eastsussex.gov.uk

Scott, Philip (LAB - Hastings - Holllington & Wishing Tree)
cllr.phil.scott@eastsussex.gov.uk

Sheppard, Jim (CON - Chailey)
cllr.jim.sheppard@eastsussex.gov.uk

Shing, Daniel (IND - Polegate, Willingdon & East Dean)
cllr.daniel.shing@eastsussex.gov.uk

Shuttleworth, Alan (LD - Eastbourne - Langney)
cllr.alan.shuttleworth@eastsussex.gov.uk

Simmons, Rupert (CON - Heathfield)
cllr.rupert.simmons@eastsussex.gov.uk

St Pierre, Rosalyn (LD - Ringmer & Lewes Bridge)
cllr.rosalyn.stpierre@eastsussexcc.gov.uk

Standley, Bob (CON - Wadhurst)
cllr.bob.standley@eastsussex.gov.uk

Stogdon, Richard (CON - Crowborough)
cllr.richard.stogdon@eastsussex.gov.uk

Taylor, Barry (CON - Eastbourne - Meads)
cllr.barry.taylor@eastsussex.gov.uk

Tidy, Sylvia (CON - Crowborough)
cllr.sylvia.tidy@eastsussex.gov.uk

Ungar, John (LD - Eastbourne - Old Town)
cllr.john.ungar@eastsussex.gov.uk

Wallis, Steve (LD - Eastbourne - Devonshire)
cllr.steve.wallis@eastsussex.gov.uk

Whetstone, Francis (CON - Forest Row)
cllr.francis.whetstone@eastsussex.gov.uk

Wincott, Michael (LAB - Hastings - Baird & Ore)
cllr.michael.wincott@eastsussex.gov.uk

POLITICAL COMPOSITION
CON: 20, LD: 10, UKIP: 7, LAB: 7, IND: 5

COMMITTEE CHAIRS

Audit, Best Value & Community Services: Mr Mike Blanch

Children's Services: Mrs Kathryn Field

Economy, Transport & Environment: Mr Richard Stogdon

Education: Mr Nick Bennett

Health & Wellbeing: Mr Keith Glazier

Pensions: Mr Richard Stogdon

Planning: Mr Godfrey Daniel

Eastbourne   D

Eastbourne Borough Council, 1 Grove Road, Eastbourne
BN21 4TW
☎ 01323 415000 📠 01323 415130 📧 enquiries@eastbourne.gov.uk
🖥 www.eastbourne.gov.uk

FACTS AND FIGURES
Parliamentary Constituencies: Eastbourne
EU Constituencies: South East
Election Frequency: Elections are of whole council

PRINCIPAL OFFICERS

Chief Executive: Mr Robert Cottrill, Chief Executive, 1 Grove Road,
Eastbourne BN21 4TW ☎ 01323 415046
📧 robert.cottrill@eastbourne.gov.uk

Deputy Chief Executive: Mr Alan Osborne, Deputy Chief
Executive, 1 Grove Road, Eastbourne BN21 4TW ☎ 01323 415149
📧 alan.osborne@eastbourne.gov.uk

Senior Management: Mr Henry Branson, Senior Head of
Projects, Performance & Technology, 1 Grove Road, Eastbourne
BN21 4TW ☎ 01323 415155 📧 henry.branson@eastbourne.gov.uk

Senior Management: Mr Philip Evans, Senior Head of Tourism &
Enterprise, 1 Grove Road, Eastbourne BN21 4TW ☎ 01323 410000
📧 philip.evans@eastbourne.gov.uk

Senior Management: Mr Peter Finnis, Senior Head of Corporate
Development & Governance, Town Hall, Grove Road, Eastbourne
BN21 4UG ☎ 01323 415003 📧 peter.finnis@eastbourne.gov.uk

Senior Management: Mr Ian Fitzpatrick, Senior Head of
Community, 1 Grove Road, Eastbourne BN21 4TW ☎ 01323 415935
📧 ian.fitzpatrick@eastbourne.gov.uk

Senior Management: Ms Nazeya Hussain, Senior Head of
Regeneration, Planning & Assets, 1 Grove Road, Eastbourne BN21
4TW ☎ 01323 415240 📧 nazeya.hussain@eastbourne.gov.uk

Best Value: Mr William Tompsett, Senior Corporate Development
Officer, 1 Grove Road, Eastbourne BN21 4TW ☎ 01323 415418
📧 william.tompsett@eastbourne.gov.uk

Building Control: Mr Leigh Palmer, Senior Specialist Advisor, 1
Grove Road, Eastbourne BN21 4TW ☎ 01323 410000
📧 leigh.palmer@eastbourne.gov.uk

Catering Services: Mrs Annie Wills, Head of Tourism &
Enterprise, 1 Grove Road, Eastbourne BN21 4TW ☎ 01323 415410
📧 annie.wills@eastbourne.gov.uk

PR / Communications: Mrs Annie Wills, Head of Tourism &
Enterprise, 1 Grove Road, Eastbourne BN21 4TW ☎ 01323 415410
📧 annie.wills@eastbourne.gov.uk

Community Planning: Mr Ian Fitzpatrick, Senior Head of Community, 1 Grove Road, Eastbourne BN21 4TW ☎ 01323 415935 ᛒ ian.fitzpatrick@eastbourne.gov.uk

Community Safety: Mr Ian Fitzpatrick, Senior Head of Community, 1 Grove Road, Eastbourne BN21 4TW ☎ 01323 415935 ᛒ ian.fitzpatrick@eastbourne.gov.uk

Computer Management: Mr Henry Branson, Senior Head of Projects, Performance & Technology, 1 Grove Road, Eastbourne BN21 4TW ☎ 01323 415155 ᛒ henry.branson@eastbourne.gov.uk

Contracts: Ms Rachel Ayres, Corporate Procurement Specialist, 1 Grove Road, Eastbourne BN21 4TW ☎ 01273 415989 ᛒ rachel.ayres@eastbourne.gov.uk

Corporate Services: Mr Peter Finnis, Senior Head of Corporate Development & Governance, Town Hall, Grove Road, Eastbourne BN21 4UG ☎ 01323 415003 ᛒ peter.finnis@eastbourne.gov.uk

Customer Service: Mr Ian Fitzpatrick, Senior Head of Community, 1 Grove Road, Eastbourne BN21 4TW ☎ 01323 415935 ᛒ ian.fitzpatrick@eastbourne.gov.uk

Economic Development: Mrs Kerry Barrett, Specialist Advisor (Economic Development), 1 Grove Road, Eastbourne BN21 4TW ☎ 01323 415054 ᛒ kerry.barrett@eastbourne.gov.uk

Economic Development: Ms Sara Taylor, Specialist Advisor (Economic Development), 1 Grove Road, Eastbourne BN21 4TW ☎ 01323 415609 ᛒ sara.taylor@eastbourne.gov.uk

E-Government: Mr Henry Branson, Senior Head of Projects, Performance & Technology, 1 Grove Road, Eastbourne BN21 4TW ☎ 01323 415155 ᛒ henry.branson@eastbourne.gov.uk

Electoral Registration: Mr Peter Finnis, Senior Head of Corporate Development & Governance, Town Hall, Grove Road, Eastbourne BN21 4UG ☎ 01323 415003 ᛒ peter.finnis@eastbourne.gov.uk

Electoral Registration: Mrs Tracey Pannett, Electoral Services Manager, Town Hall, Grove Road, Eastbourne BN21 4UG ☎ 01323 415074 ᛒ tracey.pannett@eastbourne.gov.uk

Emergency Planning: Mr Peter Finnis, Senior Head of Corporate Development & Governance, Town Hall, Grove Road, Eastbourne BN21 4UG ☎ 01323 415003 ᛒ peter.finnis@eastbourne.gov.uk

Energy Management: Mr Nick Adlam, Specialist Advisor - Energy, 1 Grove Road, Eastbourne BN21 4TW ☎ 01323 415963 ᛒ nick.adlam@eastbourne.gov.uk

Environmental Health: Mrs Sue Oliver, Manager - Specialist Advisor Team, 1 Grove Road, Eastbourne BN21 4TW ☎ 01323 415360 ᛒ sue.oliver@eastbourne.gov.uk

Estates, Property & Valuation: Mr Paul Friend, Corporate Property Manager, 1 Grove Road, Eastbourne BN21 4TW ☎ 01323 415261 ᛒ paul.friend@eastbourne.gov.uk

Events Manager: Mr Mike Marchant, Events Development Manager, 1 Grove Road, Eastbourne BN21 4TW ☎ 01323 415407 ᛒ mike.marchant@eastbourne.gov.uk

Facilities: Mr Lee Beckham, Facilities Manager, Town Hall, Grove Road, Eastbourne BN21 4UG ☎ 01323 415038 ᛒ lee.beckham@eastbourne.gov.uk

Finance: Mr Alan Osborne, Deputy Chief Executive, 1 Grove Road, Eastbourne BN21 4TW ☎ 01323 415149 ᛒ alan.osborne@eastbourne.gov.uk

Grounds Maintenance: Mr Gareth Williams, Senior Specialist Advisor, 1 Grove Road, Eastbourne BN21 4TW ☎ 01323 415281 ᛒ gareth.williams@eastbourne.gov.uk

Health and Safety: Mrs Sue Oliver, Manager - Specialist Advisor Team, 1 Grove Road, Eastbourne BN21 4TW ☎ 01323 415360 ᛒ sue.oliver@eastbourne.gov.uk

Health and Safety: Ms Caroline Wallis, Environmental Health & Amenities Manager, 1 Grove Road, Eastbourne BN21 4TW ☎ 01323 415360 ᛒ sue.oliver@eastbourne.gov.uk

Home Energy Conservation: Mr Nick Adlam, Specialist Advisor - Energy, 1 Grove Road, Eastbourne BN21 4TW ☎ 01323 415963 ᛒ nick.adlam@eastbourne.gov.uk

Housing: Mr Ian Fitzpatrick, Senior Head of Community, 1 Grove Road, Eastbourne BN21 4TW ☎ 01323 415935 ᛒ ian.fitzpatrick@eastbourne.gov.uk

Legal: Ms Celia Cullen, Director - Shared Legal Services Unit, Lewes House, 32 High Street, Lewes BN7 2LX ☎ 01273 471600 ᛒ celia.cullen@lewes.gov.uk

Legal: Mr Peter Finnis, Senior Head of Corporate Development & Governance, Town Hall, Grove Road, Eastbourne BN21 4UG ☎ 01323 415003 ᛒ peter.finnis@eastbourne.gov.uk

Leisure and Cultural Services: Mr Philip Evans, Senior Head of Tourism & Enterprise, 1 Grove Road, Eastbourne BN21 4TW ☎ 01323 410000 ᛒ philip.evans@eastbourne.gov.uk

Licensing: Mr Jay Virgo, Senior Specialist Advisor, 1 Grove Road, Eastbourne BN21 4TW ☎ 01323 415933 ᛒ jay.virgo@eastbourne.gov.uk

Member Services: Ms Katie Cullum, Head of Local Democracy, 1 Grove Road, Eastbourne BN21 4TW ☎ 01323 415031 ᛒ katie.cullum@eastbourne.gov.uk

Partnerships: Mr Ian Fitzpatrick, Senior Head of Community, 1 Grove Road, Eastbourne BN21 4TW ☎ 01323 415935 ᛒ ian.fitzpatrick@eastbourne.gov.uk

Personnel / HR: Ms Becky Cooke, Strategic Organisational Development Manager, 1 Grove Road, Eastbourne BN21 4TW ☎ 01323 415106 ᛒ becky.cooke@eastbourne.gov.uk

EASTBOURNE

Planning: Ms Nazeya Hussain, Senior Head of Regeneration, Planning & Assets, 1 Grove Road, Eastbourne BN21 4TW
☎ 01323 415240 ◌ nazeya.hussain@eastbourne.gov.uk

Planning: Mr Leigh Palmer, Senior Specialist Advisor, 1 Grove Road, Eastbourne BN21 4TW ☎ 01323 410000
◌ leigh.palmer@eastbourne.gov.uk

Procurement: Ms Rachel Ayres, Corporate Procurement Specialist, 1 Grove Road, Eastbourne BN21 4TW ☎ 01273 415989
◌ rachel.ayres@eastbourne.gov.uk

Recycling & Waste Minimisation: Mrs Sue Oliver, Manager - Specialist Advisor Team, 1 Grove Road, Eastbourne BN21 4TW
☎ 01323 415360 ◌ sue.oliver@eastbourne.gov.uk

Regeneration: Ms Nazeya Hussain, Senior Head of Regeneration, Planning & Assets, 1 Grove Road, Eastbourne BN21 4TW
☎ 01323 415240 ◌ nazeya.hussain@eastbourne.gov.uk

Staff Training: Ms Elaine Wyatt, Resourcing & Development Manager, Town Hall, Grove Road, Eastbourne BN21 4UG
☎ 01323 415005 ◌ elaine.wyatt@eastbourne.gov.uk

Sustainable Communities: Mr Ian Fitzpatrick, Senior Head of Community, 1 Grove Road, Eastbourne BN21 4TW ☎ 01323 415935
◌ ian.fitzpatrick@eastbourne.gov.uk

Sustainable Development: Mrs Kerry Barrett, Specialist Advisor (Economic Development), 1 Grove Road, Eastbourne BN21 4TW
☎ 01323 415054 ◌ kerry.barrett@eastbourne.gov.uk

Tourism: Mrs Annie Wills, Head of Tourism & Enterprise, 1 Grove Road, Eastbourne BN21 4TW ☎ 01323 415410
◌ annie.wills@eastbourne.gov.uk

COUNCILLORS

Mayor: Hearn, Pat (LD - Hampden Park)
councillor.hearn@eastbourne.gov.uk

Deputy Mayor: Miah, Harun (LD - Langney)
councillor.miah@eastbourne.gov.uk

Leader of the Council: Tutt, David (LD - St Anthony's)
councillor.tutt@eastbourne.gov.uk

Deputy Leader of the Council: Mattock, Gill (LD - St Anthony's)
councillor.mattock@eastbourne.gov.uk

Group LeaderFreebody, Tony (CON - Ratton)
councillorfreebody@eastbourne.gov.uk

Bannister, Margaret (LD - Devonshire)
councillor.bannister@eastbourne.gov.uk

Belsey, Colin (CON - Ratton)
councillor.belsey@eastbourne.gov.uk

Blakebrouh, Raymond (CON - Sovereign)
councillor.blakebrough@eastbourne.gov.uk

Choudhury, Sammy (LD - Upperton)
councillor.choudhury@eastbourne.gov.uk

Coles, Janet (LD - Old Town)
councillor.coles@eastbourne.gov.uk

di Cara, Penny (CON - Sovereign)
councillor.dicara@eastbourne.gov.uk

Dow, Jonathan (LD - Old Town)
councillor.dow@eastbourne.gov.uk

Holt, Steve (LD - Devonshire)
councillor.holt@eastbourne.gov.uk

Jenkins, Gordon (CON - Sovereign)
councillor.jenkins@eastbourne.gov.uk

Murdoch, Colin (CON - Ratton)
councillor.murdoch@eastbourne.gov.uk

Murray, Jim (LD - Hampden Park)
councillor.murray@eastbourne.gov.uk

Robinson, Marget (LD - Upperton)
councillor.robinson@eastbourne.gov.uk

Rodohan, Pat (LD - Upperton)
councillor.rodohan@eastbourne.gov.uk

Sabri, Dean (LD - St Anthony's)
councillor.sabri@eastbourne.gov.uk

Shuttleworth, Alan (LD - Langney)
councillor.shuttleworth@eastbourne.gov.uk

Smart, Robert (CON - Meads)
councillor.smart@eastbourne.gov.uk

Smethers, Kathy (CON - Meads)
councillor.smethers@eastbourne.gov.uk

Swansborough, Colin (LD - Hampdon Park)
councillor.swansborough@eastbourne.gov.uk

Taylor, Barry (CON - Meads)
councillor.taylor@eastbourne.gov.uk

Tester, Troy (LD - Langney)
councillor.tester@eastbourne.gov.uk

Ungar, John (LD - Old Town)
councillor.ungar@eastbourne.gov.uk

Wallis, Steven (LD - Devonshire)
councillor.wallis@eastbourne.gov.uk

POLITICAL COMPOSITION
LD: 18, CON: 9

COMMITTEE CHAIRS

Audit: Mr Colin Swansborough

Licensing: Mr Jonathan Dow

Planning: Mr Jim Murray

Eastleigh   D

Eastleigh Borough Council, Civic Offices, Leigh Road, Eastleigh SO50 9YN
☎ 023 8068 8000 ▤ 023 8064 3952
◌ boroughcouncil@eastleigh.gov.uk ▯ www.eastleigh.gov.uk

FACTS AND FIGURES
Parliamentary Constituencies: Eastleigh
EU Constituencies: South East
Election Frequency: Elections are by thirds

PRINCIPAL OFFICERS

Chief Executive: Mr Nick Tustian, Chief Executive, Civic Offices, Leigh Road, Eastleigh SO50 9YN ☎ 023 8068 8101
⌂ nick.tustian@eastleigh.gov.uk

Senior Management: Mrs Sarah King, Corporate Director - Support Services & Chief Financial Officer, Civic Offices, Leigh Road, Eastleigh SO50 9YN ☎ 023 8068 8000
⌂ sarah.king@eastleigh.gov.uk

Senior Management: Ms Annie Righton, Interim Corporate Director, Civic Offices, Leigh Road, Eastleigh SO50 9YN

Senior Management: Mr Andrew Trayer, Corporate Director - Service Delivery, Contract Services, Botley Road, Hedge End, Eastleigh SO30 2RA ☎ 023 8068 8370
⌂ andrew.trayer@eastleigh.gov.uk

Senior Management: Mrs Natalie Wigman, Corporate Director - Strategy, Civic Offices, Leigh Road, Eastleigh SO50 9YN
☎ 023 8068 8405 ⌂ natalie.wigman@eastleigh.gov.uk

Architect, Building / Property Services: Mr Paul Ramshaw, Head - Regeneration & Planning Policy, Civic Offices, Leigh Road, Eastleigh SO50 9YN ☎ 023 8068 8132
⌂ paul.ramshaw@eastleigh.gov.uk

Building Control: Mr Neil Ferris, Head - Building Control, Civic Offices, Leigh Road, Eastleigh SO50 9YN ☎ 023 8068 8272
⌂ neil.ferris@eastleigh.gov.uk

PR / Communications: Mr Steve Collins, Communications Officer, Civic Offices, Leigh Road, Eastleigh SO50 9YN
☎ 023 8068 8135 ⌂ steve.collins@eastleigh.gov.uk

Community Planning: Ms Helen Coleman, Health & Community Team Manager, Civic Offices, Leigh Road, Eastleigh SO50 9YN
☎ 023 8068 8017 ⌂ helen.coleman@eastleigh.gov.uk

Community Safety: Mr Melvin Hartley, Head - Community Safety & Emergency Planning Officer, Civic Offices, Leigh Road, Eastleigh SO50 9YN ☎ 023 8068 8234 ⌂ melvin.hartley@eastleigh.gov.uk

Computer Management: Mr Jim Nicholson, Digital Solutions Manager, Civic Offices, Leigh Road, Eastleigh SO50 9YN
☎ 023 8068 8072 ⌂ jim.nicholson@eastleigh.gov.uk

Customer Service: Ms Jessica Mendez, Customer Services Manager, Civic Offices, Leigh Road, Eastleigh SO50 9YN
☎ 023 8068 8000 ⌂ jessica.mendez@eastleigh.gov.uk

Direct Labour: Mr Andrew Trayer, Corporate Director - Service Delivery, Contract Services, Botley Road, Hedge End, Eastleigh SO30 2RA ☎ 023 8068 8370 ⌂ andrew.trayer@eastleigh.gov.uk

Economic Development: Mrs Natalie Wigman, Corporate Director - Strategy, Civic Offices, Leigh Road, Eastleigh SO50 9YN
☎ 023 8068 8405 ⌂ natalie.wigman@eastleigh.gov.uk

Electoral Registration: Mrs Samantha Jones, Elections Officer, Civic Offices, Leigh Road, Eastleigh SO50 9YN ☎ 023 8068 8201
⌂ sam.jones@eastleigh.gov.uk

Emergency Planning: Mr Melvin Hartley, Head - Community Safety & Emergency Planning Officer, Civic Offices, Leigh Road, Eastleigh SO50 9YN ☎ 023 8068 8234
⌂ melvin.hartley@eastleigh.gov.uk

Estates, Property & Valuation: Mr Paul Phillips, Regeneration & Planning Policy Officer, Civic Offices, Leigh Road, Eastleigh SO50 9YN ☎ 023 8068 8000 ⌂ paul.phillips@eastleigh.gov.uk

Facilities: Mrs Diane Hunter, Facilities Manager, Civic Offices, Leigh Road, Eastleigh SO50 9YN ☎ 023 8068 8000
⌂ diana.hunter@eastleigh.gov.uk

Finance: Mrs Loraine Kemp, Head - Revenue & Benefits, Civic Offices, Leigh Road, Eastleigh SO50 9YN ☎ 023 8068 8000
⌂ loraine.kemp@eastleigh.gov.uk

Finance: Mrs Sarah King, Corporate Director - Support Services & Chief Financial Officer, Civic Offices, Leigh Road, Eastleigh SO50 9YN ☎ 023 8068 8000 ⌂ sarah.king@eastleigh.gov.uk

Fleet Management: Mr Andrew Trayer, Corporate Director - Service Delivery, Contract Services, Botley Road, Hedge End, Eastleigh SO30 2RA ☎ 023 8068 8370
⌂ andrew.trayer@eastleigh.gov.uk

Grounds Maintenance: Mr Paul Naylor, Streetscene Manager, Civic Offices, Leigh Road, Eastleigh SO50 9YN ☎ 023 8065 0970
⌂ paul.naylor@eastleigh.gov.uk

Health and Safety: Ms Phillippa Banner, Corporate Health & Safety Officer, Civic Offices, Leigh Road, Eastleigh SO50 9YN
☎ 023 8068 8358 ⌂ philippa.banner@eastleigh.gov.uk

Housing: Mr Nick James, Senior Housing Advisor, Civic Offices, Leigh Road, Eastleigh SO50 9YN ☎ 023 8068 8326
⌂ nick.james@oxford.gov.uk

Legal: Mr Richard Ward, Head - Legal & Democratic Services, Civic Offices, Leigh Road, Eastleigh SO50 9YN ☎ 023 8068 8103
⌂ richard.ward@eastleigh.gov.uk

Licensing: Mr Richard Ward, Head - Legal & Democratic Services, Civic Offices, Leigh Road, Eastleigh SO50 9YN ☎ 023 8068 8103
⌂ richard.ward@eastleigh.gov.uk

Lottery Funding, Charity and Voluntary: Mrs Cheryl Butler, Head - Culture, Civic Offices, Leigh Road, Eastleigh SO50 9YN
☎ 023 8068 8187 ⌂ cheryl.butler@eastleigh.gov.uk

Member Services: Mr Jon Brown, Head - Democratic Services, Civic Offices, Leigh Road, Eastleigh SO50 9YN ☎ 023 8068 8000
⌂ jon.brown@eastleigh.gov.uk

Parking: Mr Wayne Bailey, Parking Services Manager, Civic Offices, Leigh Road, Eastleigh SO50 9YN ☎ 023 8068 8000
⌂ wayne.bailey@eastleigh.gov.uk

Personnel / HR: Ms Theresa Ferris, HR Manager, Civic Offices, Leigh Road, Eastleigh SO50 9YN ☎ 023 8068 8000
⌂ theresa.ferris@eastleigh.gov.uk

EASTLEIGH

Planning: Mrs Louise O'Driscoll, Head - Development Management, Civic Offices, Leigh Road, Eastleigh SO50 9YN ☎ 023 8068 8248 ✆ louise.odriscoll@eastleigh.gov.uk

Regeneration: Mr Paul Ramshaw, Head - Regeneration & Planning Policy, Civic Offices, Leigh Road, Eastleigh SO50 9YN ☎ 023 8068 8132 ✆ paul.ramshaw@eastleigh.gov.uk

Staff Training: Ms Theresa Ferris, HR Manager, Civic Offices, Leigh Road, Eastleigh SO50 9YN ☎ 023 8068 8000 ✆ theresa.ferris@eastleigh.gov.uk

Street Scene: Mr Paul Naylor, Streetscene Manager, Civic Offices, Leigh Road, Eastleigh SO50 9YN ☎ 023 8065 0970 ✆ paul.naylor@eastleigh.gov.uk

Traffic Management: Mr Stuart Robinson-Woledge, Traffic & Construction Manager, Civic Offices, Leigh Road, Eastleigh SO50 9YN ☎ 023 8068 8229 ✆ stuart.robinson-woledge@eastleigh.gov.uk

Transport: Mr Ed Vokes, Head - Transportation & Engineering, Civic Offices, Leigh Road, Eastleigh SO50 9YN ☎ 023 8068 8234 ✆ ed.vokes@eastleigh.gov.uk

Waste Collection and Disposal: Mr Colin Ellis, Senior Inspector & Refuse Collection, Contract Services, Botley Road, Hedge End, Eastleigh SO30 2RA ☎ 023 8068 8000 ✆ colin.ellis@eastleigh.gov.uk

Waste Management: Mr Colin Ellis, Senior Inspector & Refuse Collection, Contract Services, Botley Road, Hedge End, Eastleigh SO30 2RA ☎ 023 8068 8000 ✆ colin.ellis@eastleigh.gov.uk

COUNCILLORS

Mayor: Scott, Desmond (LD - Fair Oak & Horton Heath) des.scott@eastleigh.gov.uk

Deputy Mayor: Sollitt, Maureen (LD - Eastleigh North) maureen.sollitt@eastleigh.gov.uk

Leader of the Council: House, Keith (LD - Hedge End Wildern) keith.house@eastleigh.gov.uk

Deputy Leader of the Council: Winstanley, Anne (LD - Bishopstoke West) anne.winstanley@eastleigh.gov.uk

Airey, David (LD - Netley Abbey) david.airey@eastleigh.gov.uk

Allingham, Margaret (LD - Hedge End St Johns)

Asman, Janice (LD - West End North) janiceasman@gmail.com

Atkinson, Margaret (CON - Hiltingbury East) margaret.atkinson@eastleigh.gov.uk

Bain, Sarah (LD - Eastleigh North) sarah.bain@eastleigh.gov.uk

Balaam, Mark (LD - Eastleigh Central) mark.balaam@eastleigh.gov.uk

Bicknell, Paul (LD - Eastleigh South) paul.bicknell@eastleigh.gov.uk

Bloom, Louise (LD - Hedge End Grange Park) louise.bloom@eastleigh.gov.uk

Boulton, Carol (LD - West End South) carol.boulton@eastleigh.gov.uk

Broadhurst, Alan (LD - Chandler's Ford West) alan.broadhurst@eastleigh.gov.uk

Broadhurst, Haulwen (LD - Chandler's Ford East) haulwen.broadhurst@eastleigh.gov.uk

Clarke, Daniel (LD - West End South) daniel.clarke@eastleigh.gov.uk

Craig, Tonia (LD - Burlesden & Old Netley) tonia.craig@eastleigh.gov.uk

Cross, Malcolm (LD - Hamble-le-Rice & Butlocks Heath) malcolm.cross@eastleigh.gov.uk

Garton, Cynthia (LD - Hedge End St Johns) cynthia.garton@eastleigh.gov.uk

Grajewski, Judith (CON - Hiltingbury West) judith.grajewski@eastleigh.gov.uk

Hall, Jerry (CON - Hedge End St Johns) jerry.hall@eastleigh.gov.uk

Hatfield, Daniel (CON - Hiltingbury East)

Holden-Brown, Pamela (LD - Chandler's Ford East) pamela.holden-brown@eastleigh.gov.uk

Holes, Steve (LD - Burlesdon & Old Netley) steve.holes@eastleigh.gov.uk

Hughes, Michael (CON - Hiltingbury West) michael.hughes@eastleigh.gov.uk

Irish, Wayne (LD - Eastleigh Central) wayne.irish@eastleigh.gov.uk

Kyrle, Rupert (LD - Botley) rupert.kyrle@eastleigh.gov.uk

Lear, Elizabeth (CON - Hamble-le-Rice & Butlocks Heath) elizabeth.lear@eastleigh.gov.uk

Mann, Darshan (LD - Eastleigh South) darshan.mann@eastleigh.gov.uk

Mignot, Trevor (LD - Bishopstoke East) trevor.mignot@eastleigh.gov.uk

Myerscough, Angel (LD - Botley)

Norman, Emma (LD - Hedge End Wildern) emma.norman@eastleigh.gov.uk

Parkinson-MacLachlan, Vickieye (NP - Bishopstoke West) vickieye.parkins-maclachlan@eastleigh.gov.uk

Pragnell, David (LD - Chandler's Ford West) david.pragnell@eastleigh.gov.uk

Pretty, Derek (LD - Hedge End Grange Park) derek.pretty@eastleigh.gov.uk

Rich, Jane (LD - Bursledon & Old Netley) jane.rich@eastleigh.gov.uk

Roling, Angela (LD - Bishopstoke East) angela.roling@eastleigh.gov.uk

Rushton, Rob (LD - Fair Oak & Horton Heath) rob.rushton@eastleigh.gov.uk

Smith, Roger (LD - Fair Oak & Horton Heath) roger.smith@eastleigh.gov.uk

Sollitt, Steve (LD - Eastleigh South) steve.sollitt@eastleigh.gov.uk

Tennent, Bruce (LD - West End North)
bruce.tennent@eastleigh.gov.uk

Thomas, Chris (LD - Eastleigh North)
chris.thomas@eastleigh.gov.uk

Trenchard, Keith (LD - Eastleigh Central)
keithsmobile@gmx.com

van Niekerk, Lizette (LD - Netley Abbey)
lizette.vanniekerk@eastleigh.gov.uk

POLITICAL COMPOSITION
LD: 37, CON: 6, NP: 1

COMMITTEE CHAIRS

Audit: Mr Steve Holes

Licensing: Mr David Airey

Eden   D

Eden District Council, Town Hall, Penrith CA11 7QF
☎ 01768 817817 🖷 01768 890470 ✆ customer.services@eden.gov.uk
🖳 www.eden.gov.uk

FACTS AND FIGURES
Parliamentary Constituencies: Penrith and The Border,
Westmorland and Lonsdale
EU Constituencies: North West
Election Frequency: Elections are of whole council

PRINCIPAL OFFICERS

Chief Executive: Mr Robin Hooper, Chief Executive, Town Hall,
Penrith CA11 7QF ☎ 01768 212200 ✆ chief.exec@eden.gov.uk

Senior Management: Mr Clive Howey, Interim Director - Finance,
Town Hall, Penrith CA11 7QF ☎ 01768 212213
✆ clive.howey@eden.gov.uk

Senior Management: Mr Matthew Neal, Director - Governance,
Town Hall, Penrith CA11 7QF ☎ 01768 212337 ✆ m.neal@eden.
gov.uk

Access Officer / Social Services (Disability): Ms Sally
Hemsley, Communities Officer, Mansion House, Penrith CA11 7YG
☎ 01768 212483 ✆ sallye.hemsley@eden.gov.uk

Architect, Building / Property Services: Ms Jane Langston,
Technical Services Manager, Mansion House, Penrith CA11 7YG
☎ 01768 212448 ✆ jane.langston@eden.gov.uk

Building Control: Mr Allan Park, Principal Building Control Officer
(North), Mansion House, Penrith CA11 7YG ☎ 01768 212373
✆ allan.park@eden.gov.uk

Building Control: Mr Alaistair Richmond, Principal Building
Control Officer (South), Mansion House, Penrith CA11 7YG
☎ 01768 212342 ✆ alaistair.richmond@eden.gov.uk

PR / Communications: Mr Barry Cooper, Communications
Officer, Town Hall, Penrith CA11 7QF ☎ 01768 212137
✆ barry.cooper@eden.gov.uk

PR / Communications: Ms Deborah Garnett, Information
Governance Manager, Town Hall, Penrith CA11 7QF
☎ 01768 212268 ✆ deborah.garnett@eden.gov.uk

Community Planning: Ms Sally Hemsley, Communities Officer,
Town Hall, Penrith CA11 7QF ☎ 01768 212483
✆ sallye.hemsley@eden.gov.uk

Community Safety: Mr Doug Huggon, Leisure Services Manager,
Mansion House, Penrith CA11 7YG ☎ 01768 212323
✆ doug.huggon@eden.gov.uk

Computer Management: Mr Ben Wright, Shared IT Services
Manager, Town Hall, Penrith CA11 7QF ☎ 01768 212206
✆ ben.wright@eden.gov.uk

Contracts: Mr Neil Buck, Contracts Manager, Mansion House,
Penrith CA11 7YG ☎ 01768 212337 ✆ neil.buck@eden.gov.uk

Contracts: Ms Jane Langston, Technical Services Manager,
Mansion House, Penrith CA11 7YG ☎ 01768 212448
✆ jane.langston@eden.gov.uk

Corporate Services: Mrs Linda Methven, Customer Services &
Transformation Manager, Town Hall, Penrith CA11 7QF
☎ 01768 212130 ✆ linda.methven@eden.gov.uk

Customer Service: Mrs Linda Methven, Customer Services &
Transformation Manager, Town Hall, Penrith CA11 7QF
☎ 01768 212130 ✆ linda.methven@eden.gov.uk

Economic Development: Mr Alan Houghton, Economic
Regeneration Officer, Mansion House, Penrith CA11 7YG
☎ 01768 212169 ✆ alan.houghton@eden.gov.uk

Economic Development: Mr Oliver Shimell, Commercial Services
Manager, Town Hall, Penrith CA11 7QF ☎ 01768 212143
✆ oliver.shimell@eden.gov.uk

E-Government: Mr Ben Wright, Shared IT Services Manager,
Town Hall, Penrith CA11 7QF ☎ 01768 212206
✆ ben.wright@eden.gov.uk

Electoral Registration: Ms Karen Thompson, Electoral Services
Manager, Town Hall, Penrith CA11 7QF ☎ 01768 212122
✆ karen.thompson@eden.gov.uk

Emergency Planning: Mr Clive Howey, Interim Director - Finance,
Town Hall, Penrith CA11 7QF ☎ 01768 212213
✆ clive.howey@eden.gov.uk

Environmental Health: Mr Robert Docherty, Head of
Environmental Services, Mansion House, Penrith CA11 7YG
☎ 01768 212328 ✆ robert.docherty@eden.gov.uk

Estates, Property & Valuation: Ms Jane Langston, Technical
Services Manager, Mansion House, Penrith CA11 7YG
☎ 01768 212448 ✆ jane.langston@eden.gov.uk

Events Manager: Mr Barry Cooper, Communications Officer,
Mansion House, Penrith CA11 7YG ☎ 01768 212137
✆ barry.cooper@eden.gov.uk

EDEN

Facilities: Mr Paul Brunsdon, Facilities Officer, Mansion House, Penrith CA11 7YG ☎ 01768 212371 ⌂ paul.brundson@eden.gov.uk

Facilities: Ms Jane Langston, Technical Services Manager, Mansion House, Penrith CA11 7YG ☎ 01768 212448 ⌂ jane.langston@eden.gov.uk

Finance: Mr Clive Howey, Interim Director - Finance, Town Hall, Penrith CA11 7QF ☎ 01768 212213 ⌂ clive.howey@eden.gov.uk

Grounds Maintenance: Mr Neil Buck, Contracts Manager, Mansion House, Penrith CA11 7YG ☎ 01768 212337 ⌂ neil.buck@eden.gov.uk

Grounds Maintenance: Ms Jane Langston, Technical Services Manager, Mansion House, Penrith CA11 7YG ☎ 01768 212448 ⌂ jane.langston@eden.gov.uk

Health and Safety: Mrs Tina Mason, Contracts Officer, Mansion House, Penrith CA11 7YG ☎ 01768 212368 ⌂ tina.mason@eden.gov.uk

Health and Safety: Mrs Bibian McRoy, Human Resources Manager, Town Hall, Penrith CA11 7QF ☎ 01768 212243 ⌂ bibian.mcroy@eden.gov.uk

Housing: Mr Robert Docherty, Head of Environmental Services, Mansion House, Penrith CA11 7YG ☎ 01768 212328 ⌂ robert.docherty@eden.gov.uk

Housing: Mr Graham Tomlinson, Principal EHO (Housing), Mansion House, Penrith CA11 7YG ☎ 01768 212364 ⌂ graham.tomlinson@eden.gov.uk

Legal: Mr Matthew Neal, Director - Governance, Town Hall, Penrith CA11 7QF ☎ 01768 212337 ⌂ m.neal@eden.gov.uk

Legal: Mrs Lisa Tremble, Legal Services Manager, Town Hall, Penrith CA11 7QF ☎ 01768 212249 ⌂ lisa.tremble@eden.gov.uk

Leisure and Cultural Services: Mr Doug Huggon, Leisure Services Manager, Mansion House, Penrith CA11 7YG ☎ 01768 212323 ⌂ doug.huggon@eden.gov.uk

Leisure and Cultural Services: Mr Ian Parker, Assistant Leisure Officer, Town Hall, Penrith CA11 7QF ☎ 01768 212473 ⌂ ian.parker@eden.gov.uk

Licensing: Mr Matthew Neal, Director - Governance, Town Hall, Penrith CA11 7QF ☎ 01768 212337 ⌂ m.neal@eden.gov.uk

Licensing: Mrs Lisa Tremble, Legal Services Manager, Town Hall, Penrith CA11 7QF ☎ 01768 212249 ⌂ lisa.tremble@eden.gov.uk

Member Services: Miss Lauren Rushen, Member Services Team Leader, Town Hall, Penrith CA11 7QF ☎ 01768 212142 ⌂ lauren.rushen@eden.gov.uk

Member Services: Mrs Lisa Tremble, Legal Services Manager, Town Hall, Penrith CA11 7QF ☎ 01768 212249 ⌂ lisa.tremble@eden.gov.uk

Parking: Ms Jane Langston, Technical Services Manager, Mansion House, Penrith CA11 7YG ☎ 01768 212448 ⌂ jane.langston@eden.gov.uk

Partnerships: Ms Sally Hemsley, Communities Officer, Town Hall, Penrith CA11 7QF ☎ 01768 212483 ⌂ sallye.hemsley@eden.gov.uk

Personnel / HR: Mrs Bibian McRoy, Human Resources Manager, Town Hall, Penrith CA11 7QF ☎ 01768 212243 ⌂ bibian.mcroy@eden.gov.uk

Procurement: Mr Clive Howey, Interim Director - Finance, Town Hall, Penrith CA11 7QF ☎ 01768 212213 ⌂ clive.howey@eden.gov.uk

Recycling & Waste Minimisation: Ms Jane Langston, Technical Services Manager, Mansion House, Penrith CA11 7YG ☎ 01768 212448 ⌂ jane.langston@eden.gov.uk

Regeneration: Mr Alan Houghton, Economic Regeneration Officer, Mansion House, Penrith CA11 7YG ☎ 01768 212169 ⌂ alan.houghton@eden.gov.uk

Staff Training: Mrs Bibian McRoy, Human Resources Manager, Town Hall, Penrith CA11 7QF ☎ 01768 212243 ⌂ bibian.mcroy@eden.gov.uk

Street Scene: Ms Sally Hemsley, Communities Officer, Town Hall, Penrith CA11 7QF ☎ 01768 212483 ⌂ sallye.hemsley@eden.gov.uk

Sustainable Communities: Ms Sally Hemsley, Communities Officer, Town Hall, Penrith CA11 7QF ☎ 01768 212483 ⌂ sallye.hemsley@eden.gov.uk

Sustainable Development: Mr Phil Megson, Principal Planning Policy Officer, Mansion House, Penrith CA11 7YG ☎ 01768 212157 ⌂ phil.megson@eden.gov.uk

Tourism: Miss Jessica Goodfellow, Tourism Manager (Job Share), Mansion House, Penrith CA11 7YG ☎ 01768 212165 ⌂ jessica.goodfellow@eden.gov.uk

Tourism: Ms Sally Hemsley, Communities Officer, Mansion House, Penrith CA11 7YG ☎ 01768 212483 ⌂ sallye.hemsley@eden.gov.uk

Town Centre: Mrs Yvonne Burrows, Town Centres Officer (Job Share), Mansion House, Penrith CA11 7YG ☎ 01768 212150 ⌂ yvonne.burrows@eden.gov.uk

Waste Collection and Disposal: Ms Jane Langston, Technical Services Manager, Mansion House, Penrith CA11 7YG ☎ 01768 212448 ⌂ jane.langston@eden.gov.uk

Waste Management: Ms Jane Langston, Technical Services Manager, Mansion House, Penrith CA11 7YG ☎ 01768 212448 ⌂ jane.langston@eden.gov.uk

Children's Play Areas: Mr Neil Buck, Contracts Manager, Mansion House, Penrith CA11 7YG ☎ 01768 212337 ⌂ neil.buck@eden.gov.uk

Children's Play Areas: Mr Doug Huggon, Leisure Services Manager, Mansion House, Penrith CA11 7YG ☎ 01768 212323
✉ doug.huggon@eden.gov.uk

COUNCILLORS

Chair: Tonkin, Michael (O - Morland)
mike.tonkin@eden.gov.uk

Vice-Chair: Raine, Joan (CON - Crosby Ravensworth)
joan.raine@eden.gov.uk

Leader of the Council: Beaty, Kevin (CON - Skelton)
kevin.beaty@eden.gov.uk

Deputy Leader of the Council: Grisedale, Lesley (CON - Hesket)
lesley.grisedale@eden.gov.uk

Group Leader: Howse, Robin (LD - Penrith North)
robin.howse@eden.gov.uk

Group Leader: Robinson, Mary (O - Kirkoswald)
mary.robinson@eden.gov.uk

Armstrong, Allan (CON - Long Marton)
allan.armstrong@eden.gov.uk

Banks, Douglas (IND - Langwathby)
douglas.banks@eden gov.uk

Breen, Paula (CON - Penrith Carleton)
paula.breen@eden.gov.uk

Chambers, Ian (CON - Eamont)
ian.chambers@eden.gov.uk

Clark, Margaret (IND - Penrith South)
margaret.clark@eden.gov.uk

Connell, Andrew (LD - Appleby (Bongate))
andrew.connell@eden.gov.uk

Derbyshire, Judith (LD - Dacre)
judith.derbyshire@eden.gov.uk

Eyles, Michael (LD - Penrith East)
michael.eyles@eden.gov.uk

Godwin, Pat (IND - Alston Moor)
patricia.godwin@eden.gov.uk

Hogg, Alistair (CON - Ullswater)

Holden, Deborah (LD - Penrith North)
deb.holden@eden.gov.uk

Jackson, Scott (CON - Penrith North)
scott.jackson@eden.gov.uk

Kendall, Valerie (CON - Kirkby Stephen)
valerie.kendall@eden.gov.uk

Ladhams, Trevor (IND - Kirkby Stephen)
trevor.ladhams@eden.gov.uk

Lynch, John (CON - Penrith East)
john.lynch@eden.gov.uk

Martin, Elaine (CON - Hesket)
elaine.martin@eden.gov.uk

Meadowcroft, Angela (CON - Revenstonedale)
angela.meadowcroft@eden.gov.uk

Nicolson, Gordon (CON - Lazonby)
gordon.nicolson@eden.gov.uk

Orchard, Sheila (CON - Hartside)

Owen, John (CON - Shap)
john.owen@eden.gov.uk

Patterson, William (IND - Warcop)
william.patterson@eden.gov.uk

Sawrey-Cookson, Henry (O - Kirkby Thore)
henry.sawrey-cookson@eden.gov.uk

Sealby, Richard (CON - Greystoke)
richard.sealby@eden.gov.uk

Slee, Michael (CON - Askham)
michael.slee@eden.gov.uk

Smith, Malcolm (IND - Brough)
malcolm.smith@eden.gov.uk

Taylor, Virginia (LD - Penrith West)
virginia.taylor@eden.gov.uk

Temple, Malcolm (CON - Penrith South)
malcolm.temple@eden.gov.uk

Thompson, John (CON - Penrith West)
john.thompson@eden.gov.uk

Todd, Adrian (CON - Orton with Tebay)
adrian.todd@eden.gov.uk

Tompkins, John (LD - Penrith Pategill)
john.tompkins@eden.gov.uk

POLITICAL COMPOSITION
CON: 20, LD: 7, IND: 6, O: 3

COMMITTEE CHAIRS

Accounts & Governance: Ms Paula Breen

Environment & Economy: Mr Ian Chambers

Housing & Community: Mrs Joan Raine

Licensing: Mr John Owen

Planning: Mr John Thompson

Edinburgh, City of   S

City of Edinburgh Council, Waverley Court, 4 East Market Street, Edinburgh EH8 8BG
☎ 0131 200 2000 ✉ council.info@edinburgh.gov.uk
🖥 www.edinburgh.gov.uk

FACTS AND FIGURES
Parliamentary Constituencies: Edinburgh East, Edinburgh North and Leith, Edinburgh South, Edinburgh South West, Edinburgh West
EU Constituencies: Scotland
Election Frequency: Elections are of whole council

PRINCIPAL OFFICERS

Chief Executive: Mr Andrew Kerr, Chief Executive, Waverley Court, 4 East Market Street, Edinburgh EH8 8BG ☎ 0131 469 3002 ✉ andrew.kerr@edinburgh.gov.uk

Senior Management: Mr Alistair Gaw, Acting Executive Director - Communities & Families, Waverley Court, Level 1.9, 4 East Market Street, Edinburgh EH8 8BG ☎ 0131 529 3494 ✉ alistair.gaw@edinburgh.gov.uk

EDINBURGH, CITY OF

Senior Management: Mr Paul Lawrence, Executive Director - Place, Waverley Court, 4 East Market Street, Edinburgh EH8 8BG
☎ 0131 529 7325 ◌ paul.lawrence@edinburgh.gov.uk

Senior Management: Ms Michelle Miller, Head of Service & Chief Social Work Officer, Waverley Court, Level 1.9, 4 East Market Street, Edinburgh EH8 8BG ☎ 0131 553 8520
◌ michelle.miller@edinburgh.gov.uk

Architect, Building / Property Services: Mr Peter Watton, Acting Head of Corporate Property, Waverley Court, Level 1.9, 4 East Market Street, Edinburgh EH8 8BG ☎ 0131 529 5962
◌ peter.long@edinburgh.gov.uk

Building Control: Mr David Leslie, Service Manager - City Wide Planning, Waverley Court, Level 1.9, 4 East Market Street, Edinburgh EH8 8BG ☎ 0131 529 3948 ◌ peter.long@edinburgh.gov.uk

Catering Services: Ms Helen Allan, Facilities Manager - South, Waverley Court, 4 East Market Street, Edinburgh EH8 8BG
☎ 0131 529 6208 ◌ helen.allan@edinburgh.gov.uk

Children / Youth Services: Mr Alistair Gaw, Acting Executive Director - Communities & Families, Waverley Court, Level 1.9, 4 East Market Street, Edinburgh EH8 8BG ☎ 0131 529 3494
◌ alistair.gaw@edinburgh.gov.uk

Civil Registration: Ms Karen Watson, Deputy Chief Registrar, Lothian Chambers, Room 2a, 59-63 George IV Bridge, Edinburgh EH1 1RN ☎ 0131 529 2617 ◌ karen.watson@edinburgh.gov.uk

PR / Communications: Mr Michael Pinkerton, Acting Head of Communications, Waverley Court, Level 2.1, 4 East Market Street BC2.1, Edinburgh EH8 8BG ☎ 0131 529 6151
◌ michael.pinkerton@edinburgh.gov.uk

Community Safety: Ms Susan Mooney, Head of Housing & Regulatory Services, Waverley Court, Level G.6, 4 East Market Street, Edinburgh EH8 8BG ☎ 0131 529 7587
◌ susan.mooney@edinburgh.gov.uk

Computer Management: Mrs Claudette Jones, Chief Information Officer, Waverley Court, Level C.4, East Market Street, Edinburgh EH8 8BG ☎ 0131 529 7847 ◌ claudette.jones@edinburgh.gov.uk

Consumer Protection and Trading Standards: Ms Susan Mooney, Head of Housing & Regulatory Services, Waverley Court, Level G.6, 4 East Market Street, Edinburgh EH8 8BG
☎ 0131 529 7587 ◌ susan.mooney@edinburgh.gov.uk

Customer Service: Mr Neil Jamieson, Deputy Head of Customer Services, Waverley Court, 4 East Market Street, Edinburgh EH8 8BG ☎ 0131 469 6150 ◌ neil.jamieson@edinburgh.gov.uk

Education: Mr Andy Gray, Head of Schools & Lifelong Learning, Waverley Court, 4 East Market Street, Edinburgh EH8 8BG
☎ 0131 529 2217 ◌ andy.gray@edinburgh.gov.uk

E-Government: Mrs Claudette Jones, Chief Information Officer, Waverley Court, Level C.4, East Market Street, Edinburgh EH8 8BG
☎ 0131 529 7847 ◌ claudette.jones@edinburgh.gov.uk

Emergency Planning: Ms Mary-Ellen Lang, Council Corporate Resilience Manager, Level 2/1, Waverley Court, 4 East Market Street, Edinburgh EH8 8BG ☎ 0131 529 4684
◌ mary-ellen.lang@edinburgh.gov.uk

Environmental Health: Ms Susan Mooney, Head of Housing & Regulatory Services, Waverley Court, Level G.6, 4 East Market Street, Edinburgh EH8 8BG ☎ 0131 529 7587
◌ susan.mooney@edinburgh.gov.uk

Estates, Property & Valuation: Mr Peter Watton, Acting Head of Corporate Property, Waverley Court, Level 1.9, 4 East Market Street, Edinburgh EH8 8BG ☎ 0131 529 5962
◌ peter.long@edinburgh.gov.uk

European Liaison: Ms Elaine Ballantyne, Head of External Relations & Investor Support, Waverley Court, Level G.1, 4 East Market Street, Edinburgh EH8 8BG ☎ 0131 469 3854
◌ elaine.ballantyne@edinburgh.gov.uk

Facilities: Ms Helen Allan, Facilities Manager - South, Waverley Court, 4 East Market Street, Edinburgh EH8 8BG ☎ 0131 529 6208
◌ helen.allan@edinburgh.gov.uk

Finance: Mr Hugh Dunn, Acting Executive Director - Resources, Waverley Court, Level G.6, 4 East Market Street, Edinburgh EH8 8BG ☎ 0131 469 3150 ◌ hugh.dunn@edinburgh.gov.uk

Treasury: Ms Innes Edwards, Principal Treasury & Banking Manager, Waverley Court, Level 2.5, 4 East Market Street, Edinburgh EH8 8BG ☎ 0131 469 6291
◌ innes.edwards@edinburgh.gov.uk

Pensions: Ms Clare Scott, Chief Executive - Lothian Pension, Atria One, 144 Morrison Street, Edinburgh EH8 8BG ☎ 0131 469 3865
◌ clare.scott@edinburgh.gov.uk

Fleet Management: Mr David Lyon, Head of Service, Waverley Court, Level 1.9, 4 East Market Street, Edinburgh EH8 8BG
☎ 0131 529 7047 ◌ david.lyon@edinburgh.gov.uk

Health and Safety: Ms Susan Tannahill, Council Health & Safety Manager, Waverley Court, 4 East Market Street, Edinburgh EH8 8BG ☎ 0131 553 8336 ◌ susan.tannaill@edinburgh.gov.uk

Highways: Mr David Lyon, Head of Service, Waverley Court, Level 1.9, 4 East Market Street, Edinburgh EH8 8BG ☎ 0131 529 7047
◌ david.lyon@edinburgh.gov.uk

Housing: Ms Susan Mooney, Head of Housing & Regulatory Services, Waverley Court, Level G.6, 4 East Market Street, Edinburgh EH8 8BG ☎ 0131 529 7587
◌ susan.mooney@edinburgh.gov.uk

Housing Maintenance: Mr Alex Burns, Edinburgh Building Services Manager, 33 Murrayburn Road, Edinburgh EH8 8BG
☎ 0131 529 5890 ◌ alexander.burns@edinburgh.gov.uk

Legal: Mr Nick Smith, Interim Head of Legal & Risk, Waverley Court, Level 3.3, 4 East Market Street, Edinburgh EH8 8BG
☎ 0131 529 4377 ◌ nick.smith@edinburgh.gov.uk

Leisure and Cultural Services: Ms Lynne Halfpenny, Director - Culture, Waverley Court, Level 1.9, 4 East Market Street, Edinburgh EH8 8BG ☎ 0131 529 3657 ◌ lynne.halfpenny@edinburgh.gov.uk

Licensing: Ms Susan Mooney, Head of Housing & Regulatory Services, Waverley Court, Level G.6, 4 East Market Street, Edinburgh EH8 8BG ☎ 0131 529 7587 ◌ susan.mooney@edinburgh.gov.uk

Lighting: Mr David Lyon, Head of Service, Waverley Court, Level 1.9, 4 East Market Street, Edinburgh EH8 8BG ☎ 0131 529 7047 ◌ david.lyon@edinburgh.gov.uk

Member Services: Mr Andy Nichol, Head of Members' Services, Waverley Court, Level 2, 4 East Market Street, Edinburgh EH8 8BG ☎ 0131 529 4461 ◌ andy.nichol@edinburgh.gov.uk

Parking: Mr David Lyon, Head of Service, Waverley Court, Level 1.9, 4 East Market Street, Edinburgh EH8 8BG ☎ 0131 529 7047 ◌ david.lyon@edinburgh.gov.uk

Personnel / HR: Ms Katy Miller, Head of Human Resources, Waverley Court, 4 East Market Street, Edinburgh EH8 8BG ☎ 0131 469 5522 ◌ katy.miller@edinburgh.gov.uk

Planning: Mr David Leslie, Service Manager - City Wide Planning, Waverley Court, Level 1.9, 4 East Market Street, Edinburgh EH8 8BG ☎ 0131 529 3948 ◌ peter.long@edinburgh.gov.uk

Procurement: Mr Nick Smith, Interim Head of Legal & Risk, Waverley Court, Level 3.3, 4 East Market Street, Edinburgh EH8 8BG ☎ 0131 529 4377 ◌ nick.smith@edinburgh.gov.uk

Public Libraries: Ms Susan Mooney, Head of Housing & Regulatory Services, Waverley Court, Level G.6, 4 East Market Street, Edinburgh EH8 8BG ☎ 0131 529 7587 ◌ susan.mooney@edinburgh.gov.uk

Regeneration: Ms Susan Mooney, Head of Housing & Regulatory Services, Waverley Court, Level G.6, 4 East Market Street, Edinburgh EH8 8BG ☎ 0131 529 7587 ◌ susan.mooney@edinburgh.gov.uk

Road Safety: Mr David Lyon, Head of Service, Waverley Court, Level 1.9, 4 East Market Street, Edinburgh EH8 8BG ☎ 0131 529 7047 ◌ david.lyon@edinburgh.gov.uk

Social Services: Ms Michelle Miller, Head of Service & Chief Social Work Officer, Waverley Court, Level 1.9, 4 East Market Street, Edinburgh EH8 8BG ☎ 0131 553 8520 ◌ michelle.miller@edinburgh.gov.uk

Social Services (Children): Mr Alistair Gaw, Acting Executive Director - Communities & Families, Waverley Court, Level 1.9, 4 East Market Street, Edinburgh EH8 8BG ☎ 0131 529 3494 ◌ alistair.gaw@edinburgh.gov.uk

Fostering & Adoption: Mr Alistair Gaw, Acting Executive Director - Communities & Families, Waverley Court, Level 1.9, 4 East Market Street, Edinburgh EH8 8BG ☎ 0131 529 3494 ◌ alistair.gaw@edinburgh.gov.uk

Families: Mr Alistair Gaw, Acting Executive Director - Communities & Families, Waverley Court, Level 1.9, 4 East Market Street, Edinburgh EH8 8BG ☎ 0131 529 3494 ◌ alistair.gaw@edinburgh.gov.uk

Staff Training: Ms Katy Miller, Head of Human Resources, Waverley Court, 4 East Market Street, Edinburgh EH8 8BG ☎ 0131 469 5522 ◌ katy.miller@edinburgh.gov.uk

Sustainable Development: Mr Nick Croft, Corporate Policy & Strategy Manager, Waverley Court, 4 East Market Street, Edinburgh EH8 8BG ☎ 0131 469 3726 ◌ nick.croft@edinburgh.gov.uk

Traffic Management: Mr David Lyon, Head of Service, Waverley Court, Level 1.9, 4 East Market Street, Edinburgh EH8 8BG ☎ 0131 529 7047 ◌ david.lyon@edinburgh.gov.uk

Transport: Mr David Lyon, Head of Service, Waverley Court, Level 1.9, 4 East Market Street, Edinburgh EH8 8BG ☎ 0131 529 7047 ◌ david.lyon@edinburgh.gov.uk

Waste Collection and Disposal: Mr Jim Hunter, Acting Head of Environment, Waverley Court, Level 1.9, 4 East Market Street, Edinburgh EH8 8BG ☎ 0131 469 5342 ◌ jim.hunter@edinburgh.gov.uk

Waste Management: Mr Jim Hunter, Acting Head of Environment, Waverley Court, Level 1.9, 4 East Market Street, Edinburgh EH8 8BG ☎ 0131 469 5342 ◌ jim.hunter@edinburgh.gov.uk

COUNCILLORS

Leader of the Council: Burns, Andrew (LAB - Fountainbridge & Craiglockhart)
andrew.burns@edinburgh.gov.uk

Aitken, Elaine (CON - Colinton & Fairmilehead)
elaine.aitken@edinburgh.gov.uk

Aldridge, Robert (LD - Drum Brae & Gyle)
robert.aldridge@edinburgh.gov.uk

Bagshaw, Nigel (SGP - Inverleith)
nigel.bagshaw@edinburgh.gov.uk

Balfour, Jeremy (CON - Corstorphine & Murrayfield)
jeremy.balfour@edinburgh.gov.uk

Barrie, Gavin (SNP - Inverleith)
gavin.barrie@edinburgh.gov.uk

Blacklock, Angela (LAB - Leith Walk)
angela.blacklock@edinburgh.gov.uk

Booth, Chas (SGP - Leith)
chas.booth@edinburgh.gov.uk

Bridgman, Michael (SNP - Portobello & Craigmillar)
michael.bridgman@edinburgh.gov.uk

Burgess, Steve (GRN - Southside & Newington)
steve.burgess@edinburgh.gov.uk

Cairns, Ronald (SNP - Drum Brae & Gyle)
ronald.cairns@edinburgh.gov.uk

Cardownie, Stephen (SNP - Forth)
steve.cardownie@edinburgh.gov.uk

Chapman, Maggie (GRN - Leith Walk)
maggie.chapman@edinburgh.gov.uk

EDINBURGH, CITY OF

Child, Maureen (LAB - Portobello & Craigmillar)
maureen.child@edinburgh.gov.uk

Cook, Bill (LAB - Liberton & Gilmerton)
bill.cook@edinburgh.gov.uk

Cook, Nick (CON - Liberton & Gilmerton)
nick.cook@edinburgh.gov.uk

Corbett, Gavin (SGP - Fountainbridge & Craiglockhart)
gavin.corbett@edinburgh.gov.uk

Day, Cammy (LAB - Forth)
cammy.day@edinburgh.gov.uk

Dixon, Denis (SNP - Sighthill & Gorgie)
denis.dixon@edinburgh.gov.uk

Doran, Karen (LAB - City Centre)
karen.doran@edinburgh.gov.uk

Edie, Paul (LD - Corstorphine & Murrayfield)
paul.edie@edinburgh.gov.uk

Fullerton, Catherine (SNP - Sighthill & Gorgie)
cathy.fullerton@edinburgh.gov.uk

Gardner, Nick (LAB - Leith Walk)
nick.gardner@edinburgh.gov.uk

Godzik, Paul (LAB - Meadows & Morningside)
paul.godzik@edinburgh.gov.uk

Griffiths, Joan (LAB - Craigentinny & Duddingston)
joan.griffiths@edinburgh.gov.uk

Hart, Norma (LAB - Liberton & Gilberton)
norma.austinhart@edinburgh.gov.uk

Henderson, Ricky (LAB - Pentland Hills)
ricky.henderson@edinburgh.gov.uk

Henderson, Bill (SNP - Pentland Hills)
bill.rhenderson@edinburgh.gov.uk

Heslop, Dominic (CON - Pentland Hills)
dominic.heslop@edinburgh.gov.uk

Hinds, Lesley (LAB - Inverleith)
lesley.hinds@edinburgh.gov.uk

Howat, Sandy (SNP - Meadows & Morningside)
sandy.howat@edinburgh.gov.uk

Jackson, Allan (CON - Forth)
allan.jackson@edinburgh.gov.uk

Keil, Karen (LAB - Drum Brae & Gyle)
karen.keil@edinburgh.gov.uk

Key, David (SNP - Fountainbridge & Craiglockhart)
david.key@edinburgh.gov.uk

Lewis, Richard (SNP - Colinton & Fairmilehead)
richard.lewis@edinburgh.gov.uk

Lunn, Alex (LAB - Craigentinny & Duddingston)
alex.lunn@edinburgh.gov.uk

Main, Melanie (SGP - Meadows & Morningside)
melanie.main@edinburgh.gov.uk

McInnes, Mark (CON - Meadows & Morningside)
mark.mcinnes@edinburgh.gov.uk

McVey, Adam (SNP - Leith)
adam.mcvey@edinburgh.gov.uk

Milligan, Eric (LAB - Sighthill & Gorgie)
eric.milligan@edinburgh.gov.uk

Mowat, Joanna (CON - City Centre)
joanna.mowat@edinburgh.gov.uk

Munro, Gordon (LAB - Leith)
gordon.munro@edinburgh.gov.uk

Orr, Jim (SNP - Southside & Newington)
jim.orr@edinburgh.gov.uk

Paterson, Lindsay (CON - Almond)
linday.paterson@edinburgh.gov.uk

Perry, Ian (LAB - Southside & Newington)
ian.perry@edinburgh.gov.uk

Rankin, Alasdair (SNP - City Centre)
alasdair.rankin@edinburgh.gov.uk

Redpath, Vicki (LAB - Forth)
vicki.redpath@edinburgh.gov.uk

Robson, Keith (LAB - Liberton & Gilmerton)
keith.robson@edinburgh.gov.uk

Rose, Cameron (CON - Southside & Newington)
cameron.rose@edinburgh.gov.uk

Ross, Frank (SNP - Corstorphine & Murrayfield)
frank.ross@edinburgh.gov.uk

Rust, Jason (CON - Colinton & Fairmilehead)
jason.rust@edinburgh.gov.uk

Shields, Alastair (LD - Almond)
alastair.shields@edinburgh.gov.uk

Tymkewwycz, Stefan (SNP - Craigentinny & Duddingston)
stefan.tymkewycz@edinburgh.gov.uk

Walker, David (LAB - Portobello & Craigmillar)
david.walker1@edinburgh.gov.uk

Whyte, Iain (CON - Inverleith)
iain.whyte@edinburgh.gov.uk

Wilson, Donald (LAB - Sighthill & Gorgie)
donald.wilson@edinburgh.gov.uk

Work, Norman (SNP - Almond)
norman.work@edinburgh.gov.uk

POLITICAL COMPOSITION
LAB: 21, SNP: 16, CON: 11, SGP: 4, LD: 3, GRN: 2

Elmbridge   D

Elmbridge Borough Council, Civic Centre, High Street, Esher
KT10 9SD
☎ 01372 474474 🖷 01372 474972 📧 civiccentre@elmbridge.gov.uk
🖥 www.elmbridge.gov.uk

FACTS AND FIGURES
Parliamentary Constituencies: Esher and Walton
EU Constituencies: South East
Election Frequency: Elections are by thirds

PRINCIPAL OFFICERS

Chief Executive: Mr Robert Moran, Chief Executive, Civic Centre,
High Street, Esher KT10 9SD ☎ 01372 474380
📧 chiefexec@elmbridge.gov.uk

Deputy Chief Executive: Mrs Sarah Selvanathan, Strategic Director & Deputy Chief Executive, Civic Centre, High Street, Esher KT10 9SD ☎ 01372 474100 ☝ sdr@elmbridge.gov.uk

Senior Management: Mr Ray Lee, Strategic Director, Civic Centre, High Street, Esher KT10 9SD ☎ 01372 474700 ☝ sds@elmbridge.gov.uk

Senior Management: Mrs Sarah Selvanathan, Strategic Director & Deputy Chief Executive, Civic Centre, High Street, Esher KT10 9SD ☎ 01372 474100 ☝ sdr@elmbridge.gov.uk

Architect, Building / Property Services: Mrs Alexandra Williams, Head of Asset Management & Property Services, Civic Centre, High Street, Esher KT10 9SD ☎ 01372 474218 ☝ awilliams@elmbridge.gov.uk

Best Value: Mrs Natalie Anderson, Head of Organisational Development, Civic Centre, High Street, Esher KT10 9SD ☎ 01372 474111 ☝ corporatepolicy@elmbridge.gov.uk

Building Control: Mr Mark Webb, Building Control Manager, Civic Centre, High Street, Esher KT10 9SD ☎ 01372 474801 ☝ bcon@elmbridge.gov.uk

PR / Communications: Mrs Natalie Anderson, Head of Organisational Development, Civic Centre, High Street, Esher KT10 9SD ☎ 01372 474111 ☝ corporatepolicy@elmbridge.gov.uk

Community Safety: Ms Annabel Crouch, Community Safety Co-ordinator, Civic Centre, High Street, Esher KT10 9SD ☎ 01372 474398 ☝ communitysafety@elmbridge.gov.uk

Computer Management: Mr Mark Lumley, Head of Information Systems, Civic Centre, High Street, Esher KT10 9SD ☝ isd@elmbridge.gov.uk

Contracts: Mr Alan Harrison, Head of Legal Services, Civic Centre, High Street, Esher KT10 9SD ☎ 01372 474192 ☝ legalservices@elmbridge.gov.uk

Corporate Services: Mrs Deanna Harris, Head of Internal Audit Partnership, Civic Centre, High Street, Esher KT10 9SD ☎ 01372 474108 ☝ internalaudit@elmbridge.gov.uk

Corporate Services: Mrs Sarah Selvanathan, Strategic Director & Deputy Chief Executive, Civic Centre, High Street, Esher KT10 9SD ☎ 01372 474100 ☝ sdr@elmbridge.gov.uk

Customer Service: Ms Dawn Crewe, Head of Customer Service, Civic Centre, High Street, Esher KT10 9SD ☎ 01372 474703 ☝ corporatepolicy@elmbridge.gov.uk

Economic Development: Mrs Natalie Anderson, Head of Organisational Development, Civic Centre, High Street, Esher KT10 9SD ☎ 01372 474111 ☝ corporatepolicy@elmbridge.gov.uk

Electoral Registration: Miss Alex Mammous, Electoral Services Manager, Civic Centre, High Street, Esher KT10 9SD ☎ 01372 474182 ☝ electoral@elmbridge.gov.uk

Emergency Planning: Mrs Gill Marchbank, Emergency Planning & Business Continuity Officer, Civic Centre, High Street, Esher KT10 9SD ☎ 01372 474208 ☝ gmarchbank@elmbridge.gov.uk

Environmental / Technical Services: Mr Anthony Jeziorski, Head of Environmental Care, Civic Centre, High Street, Esher KT10 9SD ☎ 01372 474762 ☝ envcare@elmbridge.gov.uk

Estates, Property & Valuation: Mrs Alexandra Williams, Head of Asset Management & Property Services, Civic Centre, High Street, Esher KT10 9SD ☎ 01372 474218 ☝ awilliams@elmbridge.gov.uk

Facilities: Mrs Alexandra Williams, Head of Asset Management & Property Services, Civic Centre, High Street, Esher KT10 9SD ☎ 01372 474218 ☝ awilliams@elmbridge.gov.uk

Finance: Mr Andrew Cooper, Head of Finance & Treasury, Civic Centre, High Street, Esher KT10 9SD ☎ 01372 474123 ☝ acooper@elmbridge.gov.uk

Finance: Mrs Sarah Selvanathan, Strategic Director & Deputy Chief Executive, Civic Centre, High Street, Esher KT10 9SD ☎ 01372 474100 ☝ sdr@elmbridge.gov.uk

Treasury: Mr Andrew Cooper, Head of Finance & Treasury, Civic Centre, High Street, Esher KT10 9SD ☎ 01372 474123 ☝ acooper@elmbridge.gov.uk

Grounds Maintenance: Mr Ian Burrows, Head of Leisure & Cultural Services, Civic Centre, High Street, Esher KT10 9SD ☎ 01372 474572 ☝ leisure@elmbridge.gov.uk

Health and Safety: Mr Richard Simms, Health & Safety Advisor, Civic Centre, High Street, Esher KT10 9SD ☎ 01372 474215 ☝ rsimms@elmbridge.gov.uk

Housing: Ms Julie Cook, Head of Housing Services, Civic Centre, High Street, Esher KT10 9SD ☎ 01372 474640 ☝ jcook@elmbridge.gov.uk

Legal: Mr Alan Harrison, Head of Legal Services, Civic Centre, High Street, Esher KT10 9SD ☎ 01372 474192 ☝ legalservices@elmbridge.gov.uk

Leisure and Cultural Services: Mr Ian Burrows, Head of Leisure & Cultural Services, Civic Centre, High Street, Esher KT10 9SD ☎ 01372 474572 ☝ leisure@elmbridge.gov.uk

Lottery Funding, Charity and Voluntary: Mrs Gail McKenzie, Preventative & Support Services Manager, Civic Centre, High Street, Esher KT10 9SD ☎ 01372 474549 ☝ commservices@elmbridge.gov.uk

Member Services: Ms Beverley Greenstein, Head of Executive & Member Services, Civic Centre, High Street, Esher KT10 9SD ☎ 01372 474173 ☝ committee@elmbridge.gov.uk

Parking: Mr Anthony Jeziorski, Head of Environmental Care, Civic Centre, High Street, Esher KT10 9SD ☎ 01372 474762 ☝ envcare@elmbridge.gov.uk

ELMBRIDGE

Partnerships: Mrs Natalie Anderson, Head of Organisational Development, Civic Centre, High Street, Esher KT10 9SD
☎ 01372 474111 ⌂ corporatepolicy@elmbridge.gov.uk

Personnel / HR: Mrs Natalie Anderson, Head of Organisational Development, Civic Centre, High Street, Esher KT10 9SD
☎ 01372 474111 ⌂ corporatepolicy@elmbridge.gov.uk

Procurement: Mr Alan Harrison, Head of Legal Services, Civic Centre, High Street, Esher KT10 9SD ☎ 01372 474192
⌂ legalservices@elmbridge.gov.uk

Recycling & Waste Minimisation: Mr Anthony Jeziorski, Head of Environmental Care, Civic Centre, High Street, Esher KT10 9SD
☎ 01372 474762 ⌂ envcare@elmbridge.gov.uk

Regeneration: Mr Ray Lee, Strategic Director, Civic Centre, High Street, Esher KT10 9SD ☎ 01372 474700 ⌂ sds@elmbridge.gov.uk

Staff Training: Ms Becky Atwood, Personnel Manager, Civic Centre, High Street, Esher KT10 9SD ☎ 01372 474214
⌂ personnel@elmbridge.gov.uk

Street Scene: Mr Anthony Jeziorski, Head of Environmental Care, Civic Centre, High Street, Esher KT10 9SD ☎ 01372 474762
⌂ envcare@elmbridge.gov.uk

Sustainable Development: Mr Mark Behrendt, Planning Policy Manager, Civic Centre, High Street, Esher KT10 9SD
☎ 01372 474829

Waste Collection and Disposal: Mr Anthony Jeziorski, Head of Environmental Care, Civic Centre, High Street, Esher KT10 9SD
☎ 01372 474762 ⌂ envcare@elmbridge.gov.uk

Waste Management: Mr Anthony Jeziorski, Head of Environmental Care, Civic Centre, High Street, Esher KT10 9SD
☎ 01372 474762 ⌂ envcare@elmbridge.gov.uk

COUNCILLORS

Mayor: Shipley, Tannia (R - Hinchley Wood & Weston Green)
tshiply@elmbridge.gov.uk

Deputy Mayor: Lake, Racheal (CON - Walton North)
rlake@elmbridge.gov.uk

Leader of the Council: Selleck, Stuart (R - Molesey East)
sselleck@elmbridge.gov.uk

Deputy Leader of the Council: Davis, Andrew (LD - Weybridge Riverside)
adavis@elmbridge.gov.uk

Ahmed, Ruby (R - Molesey West)
rahmed@elmbridge.gov.uk

Archer, David (CON - Esher)
darcher@elmbridge.gov.uk

Axton, Mike (R - Molesey West)
maxton@elmbridge.gov.uk

Bennison, Mike (CON - Cobham & Downside)
mbennison@elmbridge.gov.uk

Brown, Lewis (CON - Oatlands & Burwood Park)
lbrown@elmbridge.gov.uk

Browne, James (CON - Cobham & Downside)

Burley, Andrew (CON - Oxshott & Stoke D'Abernon)
aburley@elmbridge.gov.uk

Chappell, Oliver (CON - Oxshott & Stoke D'Abernon)
ochappell@elmbridge.gov.uk

Cheyne, Barry (CON - Oatlands & Burwood Park)
bcheyne@elmbridge.gov.uk

Coomes, Alex (LD - Claygate)
acoomes@elmbridge.gov.uk

Cross, Kim (LD - Claygate)
kcross@elmbridge.gov.uk

Cross, Christine (CON - Walton South)
ccross@elmbridge.gov.uk

Dearlove, Glenn (CON - Oatlands & Burwood Park)
gdearlove@elmbridge.gov.uk

Donaldson, Ian (CON - Weybridge St George's Hill)
idonaldson@elmbridge.gov.uk

Eldridge, Victor (R - Molesey West)
veldridge@elmbridge.gov.uk

Elmer, Christine (CON - Walton South)
celmer@elmbridge.gov.uk

Fairbank, Barry (LD - Long Ditton)
bfairbank@elmbridge.gov.uk

Foale, Simon (CON - Weybridge St George's Hill)
sfoale@elmbridge.gov.uk

Freeman, Michael (CON - Weybridge Riverside)
mfreeman@elmbridge.gov.uk

Green, Roy (O - Hersham Village)

Haig-Brown, Nigel (R - Hinchley Wood & Weston Green)
nhaig-brown@elmbridge.gov.uk

Harman, Peter (R - Weybridge St George's Hill)
pharman@elmbridge.gov.uk

Heaney, Peter (R - Esher)

Hill, Anne (O - Hersham Village)

Houston, Neil (LD - Long Ditton)
nhouston@elmbridge.gov.uk

Howard, Malcolm (CON - Walton South)
mhoward@elmbridge.gov.uk

Kapadia, Shweta (LD - Long Ditton)
skapadia@elmbridge.gov.uk

Kelly, Andrew (CON - Walton North)
akelly@elmbridge.gov.uk

Kopitko, Alan (CON - Walton North)
akopitko@elmbridge.gov.uk

Lyon, Ruth (R - Thames Ditton)
rlyon@elmbridge.gov.uk

Marshall, Mary (LD - Claygate)
mmarshall@elmbridge.gov.uk

Mitchell, Dorothy (CON - Cobham & Downside)
dmitchell@elmbridge.gov.uk

Muddyman, Andy (CON - Weybridge Riverside)
amuddyman@elmbridge.gov.uk

Oliver, Tim (CON - Esher)
toliver@elmbridge.gov.uk

Palmer, Alan (O - Walton Central)
apalmer@elmbridge.gov.uk

Popham, Tony (R - Molesey East)
tpopham@elmbridge.gov.uk

Randolph, Karen (R - Thames Ditton)
krandolph@elmbridge.gov.uk

Regan, Ivan (R - Molesey East)
iregan@elmbridge.gov.uk

Sadler, Chris (O - Walton Central)
csadler@elmbridge.gov.uk

Sheldon, Mary (CON - Hersham Village)
msheldon@elmbridge.gov.uk

Turner, Janet (R - Hinchley Wood & Weston Green)
jturner@elmbridge.gov.uk

Vickers, James (CON - Oxshott & Stoke D'Abernon)
jvickers@elmbridge.gov.uk

Welch Bland, Tricia (R - Thames Ditton)
twelshbland@elmbridge.gov.uk

Woolgar, Graham (O - Walton Central)
gwoolgar@elmbridge.gov.uk

POLITICAL COMPOSITION
CON: 22, R: 14, LD: 7, O: 5

COMMITTEE CHAIRS

Audit: Mr Alex Coomes

Licensing: Mr Ivan Regan

Planning: Mrs Shweta Kapadia

Enfield   L

Enfield London Borough Council, Civic Centre, Silver Street,
Enfield EN1 3XA
☎ 020 8379 1000 📠 020 8379 4453 🖥 www.enfield.gov.uk

FACTS AND FIGURES
Parliamentary Constituencies: Edmonton, Enfield North, Enfield,
Southgate
EU Constituencies: London
Election Frequency: Elections are of whole council

PRINCIPAL OFFICERS

Chief Executive: Mr Rob Leak, Chief Executive, PO Box 61, Civic
Centre, Silver Street, Enfield EN1 3XY ☎ 020 8379 3901
⁸ chief.executive@enfield.gov.uk

Senior Management: Dr Shahed Ahmad, Director - Public
Health, Civic Centre, Silver Street, Enfield EN1 3XA
☎ 020 8379 3211 ⁸ shahed.ahmad@enfield.gov.uk

Senior Management: Mr Gary Barnes, Assistant Director -
Business Development, Civic Centre, Silver Street, Enfield EN1 3XA
☎ 020 8379 3600; 020 8379 3475 ⁸ gary.barnes@enfield.gov.uk

Senior Management: Mr Ian Davis, Director - Regeneration &
Environment, PO Box 52, Civic Centre, Silver Street, Enfield EN1
3XD ☎ 020 8379 3500 ⁸ ian.davis@enfield.gov.uk

Senior Management: Mr Tony Gilling, Assistant Director -
Human Resources, PO Box 61, Civic Centre, Silver Street, Enfield
EN1 3XA ☎ 020 8379 4141 ⁸ tony.gilling@enfield.gov.uk

Senior Management: Mr Ray James, Director - Health, Housing
& Adult Social Care, PO Box 59, Civic Centre, Silver Street, Enfield
EN1 3XL ☎ 020 8379 4160 ⁸ ray.james@enfield.gov.uk

Senior Management: Mr James Rolfe, Director - Finance,
Resources & Customer Services, PO Box 54, Civic Centre, Silver
Street, Enfield EN1 3XF ☎ 020 8379 4600
⁸ james.rolfe@enfield.gov.uk

Senior Management: Mr Tony Theodoulou, Acting Director
- Schools & Children's Services, PO Box 56, Civic Centre, Silver
Street, Enfield EN1 3XL ☎ 020 8379 4610
⁸ tony.theodoulou@enfield.gov.uk

Architect, Building / Property Services: Mr Keith Crocombe,
Assistant Director - Property Services, PO Box 51, Civic Centre,
Silver Street, Enfield EN1 3XB ☎ 020 8379 4605
⁸ keith.crocombe@enfield.gov.uk

Best Value: Ms Alison Trew, Head of Performance Management,
Civic Centre, Silver Street, Enfield EN1 3XA ☎ 020 8379 3186
⁸ alison.trew@enfield.gov.uk

Building Control: Mr Bob Griffiths, Assistant Director - Planning,
Highways & Transformation, PO Box 52, Civic Centre, Silver Street,
Enfield EN1 3XD ☎ 020 8379 3676 ⁸ bob.griffiths@enfield.gov.uk

Catering Services: Ms Jenny Tosh, Chief Education Officer, PO
Box 56, Civic Centre, Silver Street, Enfield EN1 3XQ
☎ 020 8379 3350 ⁸ jenny.tosh@enfield.gov.uk

Children / Youth Services: Mr Tony Theodoulou, Acting Director
- Schools & Children's Services, PO Box 56, Civic Centre, Silver
Street, Enfield EN1 3XL ☎ 020 8379 4610
⁸ tony.theodoulou@enfield.gov.uk

Civil Registration: Mr James Kinsella, Head of Electoral,
Registration & Governance Services, Civic Centre, Silver Street,
Enfield EN1 3XA ☎ 020 8379 4041 ⁸ james.kinsella@enfield.gov.uk

PR / Communications: Mr David Greely, Head of
Communications, PO Box 61, Civic Centre, Silver Street, Enfield EN1
3XY ☎ 020 8379 5122 ⁸ david.greely@enfield.gov.uk

Community Planning: Mr Shaun Rogan, Head of Policy,
Partnerships, Engagement & Consultation, Civic Centre, Silver Street,
Enfield EN1 3XY ☎ 020 8379 3836 ⁸ shaun.rogan@enfield.gov.uk

Community Safety: Ms Andrea Clemons, Head of Community
Safety, PO Box 52, Civic Centre, Silver Street, Enfield EN1 3XD
☎ 020 8379 4085 ⁸ andrea.clemons@enfield.gov.uk

Computer Management: Mr James Rolfe, Director - Finance,
Resources & Customer Services, PO Box 54, Civic Centre, Silver
Street, Enfield EN1 3XF ☎ 020 8379 4600
⁸ james.rolfe@enfield.gov.uk

Consumer Protection and Trading Standards: Ms Sue McDaid, Head of Trading Standards & Licensing, Civic Centre, Silver Street, Enfield EN1 3XA ☎ 020 8379 3680 ✆ sue.mcdaid@enfield.gov.uk

Contracts: Mr Bob Griffiths, Assistant Director - Planning, Highways & Transformation, PO Box 52, Civic Centre, Silver Street, Enfield EN1 3XD ☎ 020 8379 3676 ✆ bob.griffiths@enfield.gov.uk

Corporate Services: Mr James Rolfe, Director - Finance, Resources & Customer Services, PO Box 54, Civic Centre, Silver Street, Enfield EN1 3XF ☎ 020 8379 4600 ✆ james.rolfe@enfield.gov.uk

Customer Service: Mr James Rolfe, Director - Finance, Resources & Customer Services, PO Box 54, Civic Centre, Silver Street, Enfield EN1 3XF ☎ 020 8379 4600 ✆ james.rolfe@enfield.gov.uk

Direct Labour: Mr Bob Griffiths, Assistant Director - Planning, Highways & Transformation, PO Box 52, Civic Centre, Silver Street, Enfield EN1 3XD ☎ 020 8379 3676 ✆ bob.griffiths@enfield.gov.uk

Economic Development: Mr Michael Toyer, Acting Assistant Director - Business & Economic Development, PO Box 52, Civic Centre, Silver Street, Enfield EN1 3XD ☎ 020 8379 5485 ✆ michael.toyer@enfield.gov.uk

Education: Ms Jenny Tosh, Chief Education Officer, PO Box 56, Civic Centre, Silver Street, Enfield EN1 3XQ ☎ 020 8379 3350 ✆ jenny.tosh@enfield.gov.uk

Electoral Registration: Mr James Kinsella, Head of Electoral, Registration & Governance Services, Civic Centre, Silver Street, Enfield EN1 3XA ☎ 020 8379 4041 ✆ james.kinsella@enfield.gov.uk

Emergency Planning: Ms Andrea Clemons, Head of Community Safety, PO Box 52, Civic Centre, Silver Street, Enfield EN1 3XD ☎ 020 8379 4085 ✆ andrea.clemons@enfield.gov.uk

Energy Management: Ms Nicky Fiedler, Assistant Director - Public Realm, PO Box 52, Civic Centre, Silver Street, Enfield EN1 3XD ☎ 020 8379 2016 ✆ nicky.fiedler@enfild.gov.uk

Environmental / Technical Services: Mr Ian Davis, Director - Regeneration & Environment, PO Box 52, Civic Centre, Silver Street, Enfield EN1 3XD ☎ 020 8379 3500 ✆ ian.davis@enfield.gov.uk

Environmental Health: Mr Ian Davis, Director - Regeneration & Environment, PO Box 52, Civic Centre, Silver Street, Enfield EN1 3XD ☎ 020 8379 3500 ✆ ian.davis@enfield.gov.uk

Estates, Property & Valuation: Mr Keith Crocombe, Assistant Director - Property Services, PO Box 51, Civic Centre, Silver Street, Enfield EN1 3XB ☎ 020 8379 4605 ✆ keith.crocombe@enfield.gov.uk

Facilities: Mr Stuart Simper, Acting Head of Facilities Management, PO Box 54, Civic Centre, Silver Street, Enfield EN1 3XF ☎ 020 8379 3032 ✆ stuart.simper@enfield.gov.uk

Finance: Ms Isabel Brittain, Assistant Director - Finance, PO Box 54, Civic Centre, Silver Street, Enfield EN1 3XF ☎ 020 8379 4744 ✆ isabel.brittain@enfield.gov.uk

Treasury: Ms Jayne Fitzgerald, Head of Corporate Finance, 4th Floor, Civic Centre, Silver Street, Enfield EN1 3XF ☎ 020 8379 5571 ✆ jayne.fitzgerald@enfield.gov.uk

Pensions: Mr Paul Reddaway, Head of Pensions, 4th Floor, Civic Centre, Silver Street, Enfield EN1 3XF ☎ 020 8379 4730 ✆ paul.reddaway@enfield.gov.uk

Fleet Management: Mr Bob Griffiths, Assistant Director - Planning, Highways & Transformation, PO Box 52, Civic Centre, Silver Street, Enfield EN1 3XD ☎ 020 8379 3676 ✆ bob.griffiths@enfield.gov.uk

Grounds Maintenance: Mr Bob Griffiths, Assistant Director - Planning, Highways & Transformation, PO Box 52, Civic Centre, Silver Street, Enfield EN1 3XD ☎ 020 8379 3676 ✆ bob.griffiths@enfield.gov.uk

Health and Safety: Mr John Griffiths, Corporate Safety Manager, PO Box 61, Civic Centre, Silver Street, Enfield EN1 3XY ☎ 020 8379 3696 ✆ john.griffiths@enfield.gov.uk

Highways: Mr Bob Griffiths, Assistant Director - Planning, Highways & Transformation, PO Box 52, Civic Centre, Silver Street, Enfield EN1 3XD ☎ 020 8379 3676 ✆ bob.griffiths@enfield.gov.uk

Home Energy Conservation: Ms Nicky Fiedler, Assistant Director - Public Realm, PO Box 52, Civic Centre, Silver Street, Enfield EN1 3XD ☎ 020 8379 2016 ✆ nicky.fiedler@enfield.gov.uk

Housing: Ms Sally McTernan, Assistant Director - Community Housing Services, Civic Centre, Silver Street, Enfield EN1 3XA ☎ 020 8379 4465 ✆ sally.mcternan@enfield.gov.uk

Housing Maintenance: Ms Sally McTernan, Assistant Director - Community Housing Services, Civic Centre, Silver Street, Enfield EN1 3XA ☎ 020 8379 4465 ✆ sally.mcternan@enfield.gov.uk

Local Area Agreement: Ms Alison Trew, Head of Performance Management, Civic Centre, Silver Street, Enfield EN1 3XA ☎ 020 8379 3186 ✆ alison.trew@enfield.gov.uk

Legal: Ms Asmat Hussain, Assistant Director - Legal & Governance Services, PO Box 54, Civic Centre, Silver Street, Enfield EN1 3XF ☎ 020 8379 6438 ✆ asmat.hussain@enfield.gov.uk

Leisure and Cultural Services: Mr Paul Everitt, Head of Leisure & Culture, PO Box 56, Civic Centre, Silver Street, Enfield EN1 3XQ ☎ 020 8379 4569 ✆ paul.everitt@enfield.gv.uk

Licensing: Ms Sue McDaid, Head of Trading Standards & Licensing, Civic Centre, Silver Street, Enfield EN1 3XA ☎ 020 8379 3680 ✆ sue.mcdaid@enfield.gov.uk

Lifelong Learning: Mr Tony Theodoulou, Acting Director - Schools & Children's Services, PO Box 56, Civic Centre, Silver Street, Enfield EN1 3XL ☎ 020 8379 4610 ✆ tony.theodoulou@enfield.gov.uk

Lighting: Mr Bob Griffiths, Assistant Director - Planning, Highways & Transformation, PO Box 52, Civic Centre, Silver Street, Enfield EN1 3XD ☎ 020 8379 3676 ⊕ bob.griffiths@enfield.gov.uk

Lottery Funding, Charity and Voluntary: Mr Shaun Rogan, Head of Policy, Partnerships, Engagement & Consultation, Civic Centre, Silver Street, Enfield EN1 3XY ☎ 020 8379 3836 ⊕ shaun.rogan@enfield.gov.uk

Member Services: Ms Asmat Hussain, Assistant Director - Legal & Governance Services, PO Box 54, Civic Centre, Silver Street, Enfield EN1 3XF ☎ 020 8379 6438 ⊕ asmat.hussain@enfield.gov.uk

Parking: Mr David Morris, Head of Parking, Civic Centre, Silver Street, Enfield EN1 3XA ☎ 020 8379 6556 ⊕ david.morris@enfield.gov.uk

Partnerships: Mr Shaun Rogan, Head of Policy, Partnerships, Engagement & Consultation, Civic Centre, Silver Street, Enfield EN1 3XY ☎ 020 8379 3836 ⊕ shaun.rogan@enfield.gov.uk

Personnel / HR: Mr Tony Gilling, Assistant Director - Human Resources, PO Box 61, Civic Centre, Silver Street, Enfield EN1 3XA ☎ 020 8379 4141 ⊕ tony.gilling@enfield.gov.uk

Planning: Mr Bob Griffiths, Assistant Director - Planning, Highways & Transformation, PO Box 52, Civic Centre, Silver Street, Enfield EN1 3XD ☎ 020 8379 3676 ⊕ bob.griffiths@enfield.gov.uk

Procurement: Ms Lynn Ferguson, Assistant Director - Procurement, PO Box 54, Civic Centre, Silver Street, Enfield EN1 3XF ☎ 020 8379 1513 ⊕ lynn.ferguson@enfield.gov.uk

Public Libraries: Ms Sally McTernan, Assistant Director - Community Housing Services, Civic Centre, Silver Street, Enfield EN1 3XA ☎ 020 8379 4465 ⊕ sally.mcternan@enfield.gov.uk

Recycling & Waste Minimisation: Ms Nicky Fiedler, Assistant Director - Public Realm, PO Box 52, Civic Centre, Silver Street, Enfield EN1 3XD ☎ 020 8379 2016 ⊕ nicky.fiedler@enfield.gov.uk

Regeneration: Mr Peter George, Assistant Director - Regeneration, Civic Centre, Silver Street, Enfield EN1 3XA ☎ 020 8379 3318 ⊕ peter.george@enfield.gov.uk

Road Safety: Mr David Taylor, Head of Traffic & Transportation, PO Box 52, Civic Centre, Silver Street, Enfield EN1 3XD ☎ 020 8379 3576 ⊕ david.b.taylor@enfield.gov.uk

Social Services: Mr Ray James, Director - Health, Housing & Adult Social Care, PO Box 59, Civic Centre, Silver Street, Enfield EN1 3XL ☎ 020 8379 4160 ⊕ ray.james@enfield.gov.uk

Social Services (Adult): Mr Ray James, Director - Health, Housing & Adult Social Care, PO Box 59, Civic Centre, Silver Street, Enfield EN1 3XL ☎ 020 8379 4160 ⊕ ray.james@enfield.gov.uk

Social Services (Children): Mr Tony Theodoulou, Acting Director - Schools & Children's Services, PO Box 56, Civic Centre, Silver Street, Enfield EN1 3XL ☎ 020 8379 4610 ⊕ tony.theodoulou@enfield.gov.uk

Public Health: Dr Shahed Ahmad, Director - Public Health, Civic Centre, Silver Street, Enfield EN1 3XA ☎ 020 8379 3211 ⊕ shahed.ahmad@enfield.gov.uk

Staff Training: Mr Tony Gilling, Assistant Director - Human Resources, PO Box 61, Civic Centre, Silver Street, Enfield EN1 3XA ☎ 020 8379 4141 ⊕ tony.gilling@enfield.gov.uk

Street Scene: Mr Ian Davis, Director - Regeneration & Environment, PO Box 52, Civic Centre, Silver Street, Enfield EN1 3XD ☎ 020 8379 3500 ⊕ ian.davis@enfield.gov.uk

Sustainable Communities: Mr Michael Toyer, Acting Assistant Director - Business & Economic Development, PO Box 52, Civic Centre, Silver Street, Enfield EN1 3XD ☎ 020 8379 5485 ⊕ michael.toyer@enfield.gov.uk

Sustainable Development: Mr Peter George, Assistant Director - Regeneration, Civic Centre, Silver Street, Enfield EN1 3XA ☎ 020 8379 3318 ⊕ peter.george@enfield.gov.uk

Tourism: Mr Paul Everitt, Head of Leisure & Culture, PO Box 56, Civic Centre, Silver Street, Enfield EN1 3XQ ☎ 020 8379 4569 ⊕ paul.everitt@enfield.gv.uk

Town Centre: Mr Bob Griffiths, Assistant Director - Planning, Highways & Transformation, PO Box 52, Civic Centre, Silver Street, Enfield EN1 3XD ☎ 020 8379 3676 ⊕ bob.griffiths@enfield.gov.uk

Traffic Management: Mr Bob Griffiths, Assistant Director - Planning, Highways & Transformation, PO Box 52, Civic Centre, Silver Street, Enfield EN1 3XD ☎ 020 8379 3676 ⊕ bob.griffiths@enfield.gov.uk

Transport: Mr Bob Griffiths, Assistant Director - Planning, Highways & Transformation, PO Box 52, Civic Centre, Silver Street, Enfield EN1 3XD ☎ 020 8379 3676 ⊕ bob.griffiths@enfield.gov.uk

Transport Planner: Mr Bob Griffiths, Assistant Director - Planning, Highways & Transformation, PO Box 52, Civic Centre, Silver Street, Enfield EN1 3XD ☎ 020 8379 3676 ⊕ bob.griffiths@enfield.gov.uk

Waste Collection and Disposal: Ms Nicky Fiedler, Assistant Director - Public Realm, PO Box 52, Civic Centre, Silver Street, Enfield EN1 3XD ☎ 020 8379 2016 ⊕ nicky.fiedler@enfield.gov.uk

Waste Management: Ms Nicky Fiedler, Assistant Director - Public Realm, PO Box 52, Civic Centre, Silver Street, Enfield EN1 3XD ☎ 020 8379 2016 ⊕ nicky.fiedler@enfield.gov.uk

COUNCILLORS

Mayor: Lappage, Bernie (LAB - Jubilee) cllr.bernie.lappage@enfield.gov.uk

Deputy Mayor: Hamilton, Christine (LAB - Enfield Highway) cllr.christine.hamilton@enfield.gov.uk

Leader of the Council: Taylor, Doug (LAB - Ponders End) cllr.doug.taylor@enfield.gov.uk

Deputy Leader of the Council: Georgiou, Achilleas (LAB - Bowes) cllr.achilleas.georgiou@enfield.gov.uk

ENFIELD

Group Leader: Neville, Terence (CON - Grange)
cllr.terence.neville@enfield.gov.uk

Abdullahi, Abdul (LAB - Edmonton Green)
cllr.abdul.abdullahi@enfield.gov.uk

Anderson, Daniel (LAB - Southgate Green)
cllr.daniel.anderson@enfield.gov.uk

Bakir, Ali (LAB - Upper Edmonton)
cllr.ali.bakir@enfield.gov.uk

Barry, Dinah (LAB - Winchmore Hill)
cllr.dinah.barry@enfield.gov.uk

Bond, Chris (LAB - Southbury)
cllr.chris.taylor@enfield.gov.uk

Brett, Yasemin (LAB - Bowes)
cllr.yasemin.brett@enfield.gov.uk

Cazimoglu, Alev (LAB - Jubilee)
cllr.alev.cazimoglu@enfield.gov.uk

Cazzimoglu, Nesil (LAB - Jubilee)

Celebi, Erin (CON - Bush Hill Park)
cllr.erin.celebi@enfield.gov.uk

Chamberlain, Lee (CON - Bush Hill Park)
cllr.lee.chamberlain@enfield.gov.uk

Charalambous, Jason (CON - Cockfosters)
cllr.jason.charalambous@enfield.gov.uk

Charalambous, Bambos (LAB - Palmers Green)
cllr.bambos.charalambous@enfield.gov.uk

Chibah, Katherine (LAB - Turkey Street)
cllr.katherine.chibah@enfield.gov.uk

David-Sanders, Lee (CON - Highlands)
cllr.lee.david-sanders@enfield.gov.uk

Delman, Dogan (CON - Highlands)
cllr.dogan.delman@enfield.gov.uk

Dines, Nick (CON - Chase)
cllr.nick.dines@enfield.gov.uk

Dogan, Guney (LAB - Lower Edmonton)
cllr.guney.dogan@enfield.gov.uk

Doyle, Sarah (LAB - Bush Hill Park)
cllr.sarah.doyle@enfield.gov.uk

During, Christina (LAB - Edmonton Green)
cllr.christina.during@enfield.gov.uk

Ekechi, Patricia (LAB - Upper Edmonton)
cllr.patricia.ekechi@enfield.gov.uk

Erbil, Nesimi (IND - Lower Edmonton)
cllr.nesimi.erbil@enfield.gov.uk

Esendagli, Turgut (LAB - Enfield Highway)
cllr.turgut.esendagli@enfield.gov.uk

Fallart, Peter (CON - Chase)
cllr.peter.fallart@enfield.gov.uk

Fonyonga, Krystle (LAB - Enfield Lock)
cllr.krystle.fonyonga@enfield.gov.uk

Georgiou, Alessandro (CON - Southgate Green)
cllr.alessandro.georgiou@enfield.gov.uk

Hasan, Ahmet (LAB - Enfield Highway)
cllr.ahmet.hasan@enfield.gov.uk

Hayward, Robert (CON - Southgate)
cllr.robert.hayward@enfield.gov.uk

Hayward, Elaine (CON - Winchmore Hill)
cllr.elaine.hayward@enfield.gov.uk

Hurer, Ertan (CON - Winchmore Hill)
cllr.ertan.hurer@enfield.gov.uk

Hurman, Suna (LAB - Haselbury)
cllr.suna.hurman@enfield.gov.uk

Jemal, Jansev (LAB - Southbury)
cllr.jansev.jemal@enfield.gov.uk

Jiagge, Doris (LAB - Upper Edmonton)
cllr.doris.jiagge@enfield.gov.uk

Jukes, Eric (CON - Grange)
cllr.eric.jukes@enfield.gov.uk

Keazor, Nneka (LAB - Enfield Lock)
cllr.nneka.keazor@enfield.gov.uk

Kepez, Adeline (LAB - Lower Edmonton)
cllr.adeline.kepez@enfield.gov.uk

Laban, Joanne (CON - Town)
cllr.joanne.laban@enfield.gov.uk

Lavender, Michael (CON - Cockfosters)
cllr.michael.lavender@enfield.gov.uk

Lemonides, Dino (LAB - Turkey Street)
cllr.dino.lemonides@enfield.gov.uk

Levy, Derek (LAB - Southbury)
cllr.derek.levy@enfield.gov.uk

Maguire, Mary (LAB - Palmers Green)
cllr.mary.maguire@enfield.gov.uk

McGowan, Donald (LAB - Ponders End)
cllr.donald.mcgowan@enfield.gov.uk

Milne, Andy (CON - Grange)
cllr.andy.milne@enfield.gov.uk

Orhan, Ayfer (LAB - Ponders End)
cllr.ayfer.orhan@enfield.gov.uk

Oykener, Ahmet (LAB - Palmers Green)
cllr.ahmet.oykener@enfield.gov.uk

Pearce, Anne-Marie (CON - Cockfosters)
cllr.anne.pearce@enfield.gov.uk

Pearce, Daniel (CON - Southgate)
cllr.daniel.pearce@enfield.gov.uk

Pite, Vicki (LAB - Chase)
cllr.vicki.pite@enfield.gov.uk

Rye, Michael (CON - Town)
cllr.michael.rye@enfield.gov.uk

Savva, George (LAB - Haselbury)
cllr.george.savva@enfield.gov.uk

Simon, Toby (LAB - Turkey Street)
cllr.toby.simon@enfield.gov.uk

Sitkin, Alan (LAB - Bowes)
cllr.alan.sitkin@enfield.gov.uk

Smith, Edward (CON - Southgate)
cllr.edward.smith@enfield.gov.uk

Stafford, Andrew (LAB - Edmonton Green)
cllr.andrew.stafford@enfield.gov.uk

Steven, Jim (CON - Town)
cllr.jim.steven@enfield.gov.uk

Stewart, Claire (LAB - Southgate Green)
cllr.claire.stewart@enfield.gov.uk

Ulus, Haydar (IND - Haselbury)
cllr.haydar.ulus@enfield.gov.uk

Uzoanya, Ozzie (LAB - Enfield Lock)
Cllr.Ozzie.Uzoanya@enfield.gov.uk

Vince, Glynis (CON - Highlands)
cllr.glynis.vince@enfield.gov.uk

POLITICAL COMPOSITION
LAB: 39, CON: 22, IND: 2

COMMITTEE CHAIRS

Audit: Ms Mary Maguire

Licensing: Mr Chris Bond

Pensions: Ms Dinah Barry

Planning: Mr Toby Simon

Epping Forest   D

Epping Forest District Council, Civic Offices, High Street,
Epping CM16 4BZ
☎ 01992 564000 🖨 01992 578018 ✆ contactus@eppingforestdc.gov.uk
💻 www.eppingforestdc.gov.uk

FACTS AND FIGURES
Parliamentary Constituencies: Epping Forest
EU Constituencies: Eastern
Election Frequency: Elections are by thirds

PRINCIPAL OFFICERS
Chief Executive: Mr Glen Chipp, Chief Executive, Civic Offices,
High Street, Epping CM16 4BZ ☎ 01992 564080
✆ gchipp@eppingforestdc.gov.uk

Deputy Chief Executive: Mr Derek McNab, Director -
Neighbourhoods & Deputy Chief Executive, Civic Offices, High
Street, Epping CM16 4BZ ☎ 01992 564051
✆ dmcnab@eppingforestdc.gov.uk

Senior Management: Mr Alan Hall, Director - Communities, Civic
Offices, High Street, Epping CM16 4BZ ☎ 01992 564004
✆ ahall@eppingforestdc.gov.uk

Senior Management: Ms Colleen O'Boyle, Director -
Governance; Solicitor to the Council, Civic Offices, High Street,
Epping CM16 4BZ ☎ 01992 564475
✆ coboyle@eppingforestdc.gov.uk

Senior Management: Mr Bob Palmer, Director - Resources &
S151 Chief Financial Officer, Civic Offices, High Street, Epping CM16
4BZ ☎ 01992 564279 ✆ bpalmer@eppingforestdc.gov.uk

PR / Communications: Mr Thomas Carne, Public Relations &
Marketing Officer, Civic Offices, High Street, Epping CM16 4BZ
☎ 01992 564039 ✆ tcarne@eppingforestdc.gov.uk

Community Planning: Ms Julie Chandler, Assistant Director -
Community Services & Safety, Civic Offices, High Street, Epping
CM16 4BZ ☎ 01992 564214 ✆ jchandler@eppingforestdc.gov.uk

Community Planning: Mr Derek McNab, Director -
Neighbourhoods & Deputy Chief Executive, Civic Offices, High
Street, Epping CM16 4BZ ☎ 01992 564051
✆ dmcnab@eppingforestdc.gov.uk

Community Planning: Mr James Nolan, Assistant Director -
Neighbourhood Services, Civic Offices, High Street, Epping CM16
4BZ ☎ 01992 564083 ✆ jnolan@eppingforestdc.gov.uk

Community Planning: Ms Kassandra Polyzoides, Assistant
Director - Forward Planning & Economic Development, Civic
Offices, High Street, Epping CM16 4BZ ☎ 01992 564119
✆ kpolyzoides@eppingforestdc.gov.uk

Community Planning: Ms Kassandra Polyzoides, Assistant
Director - Forward Planning & Economic Development, Civic
Offices, High Street, Epping CM16 4BZ ☎ 01992 564119
✆ kpolyzoides@eppingforestdc.gov.uk

Community Planning: Ms Gill Wallis, Community Development
Officer, Civic Offices, High Street, Epping CM16 4BZ
☎ 01992 564557 ✆ gwallis@eppingforestdc.gov.uk

Community Safety: Ms Caroline Wiggins, Communities Safety
Manager, Civic Offices, High Street, Epping CM16 4BZ
☎ 01992 564122 ✆ cwiggins@eppingforestdc.gov.uk

Computer Management: Mr David Newton, Assistant Director
- ICT & Facilities Management, Civic Offices, High Street, Epping
CM16 4BZ ☎ 01992 564580 ✆ dnewton@eppingforestdc.gov.uk

Corporate Services: Mr Simon Hill, Assistant Director -
Governance & Performance Management, Civic Offices, High
Street, Epping CM16 4BZ ☎ 01992 564249
✆ shill@eppingforestdc.gov.uk

Corporate Services: Mr Nigel Richardson, Assistant Director -
Development Management, Civic Offices, High Street, Epping CM16
4BZ ☎ 01992 564110 ✆ nrichardson@eppingforestdc.gov.uk

Customer Service: Ms Jenny Filby, Complaints Officer, Civic
Offices, High Street, Epping CM16 4BZ ☎ 01992 564512
✆ jfilby@eppingforestdc.gov.uk

Economic Development: Ms Kassandra Polyzoides, Assistant
Director - Forward Planning & Economic Development, Civic
Offices, High Street, Epping CM16 4BZ ☎ 01992 564119
✆ kpolyzoides@eppingforestdc.gov.uk

Electoral Registration: Mr Glen Chipp, Chief Executive, Civic
Offices, High Street, Epping CM16 4BZ ☎ 01992 564080
✆ gchipp@eppingforestdc.gov.uk

Environmental / Technical Services: Mr Qasim Durrani,
Assistant Director - Technical Services, Civic Offices, High Street,
Epping CM16 4BZ ☎ 01992 564055
✆ qdurrani@eppingforestdc.gov.uk

Facilities: Mr David Newton, Assistant Director - ICT & Facilities
Management, Civic Offices, High Street, Epping CM16 4BZ
☎ 01992 564580 ✆ dnewton@eppingforestdc.gov.uk

EPPING FOREST

Finance: Mr Peter Maddock, Assistant Director - Accountancy, Civic Offices, High Street, Epping CM16 4BZ ☎ 01992 564602 ☝ pmaddock@eppingforestdc.gov.uk

Finance: Mr Bob Palmer, Director - Resources & S151 Chief Financial Officer, Civic Offices, High Street, Epping CM16 4BZ ☎ 01992 564279 ☝ bpalmer@eppingforestdc.gov.uk

Treasury: Mr Peter Maddock, Assistant Director - Accountancy, Civic Offices, High Street, Epping CM16 4BZ ☎ 01992 564602 ☝ pmaddock@eppingforestdc.gov.uk

Housing: Mr James Nolan, Assistant Director - Neighbourhood Services, Civic Offices, High Street, Epping CM16 4BZ ☎ 01992 564083 ☝ jnolan@eppingforestdc.gov.uk

Housing: Mr Paul Pledger, Assistant Director - Housing Property, Civic Offices, High Street, Epping CM16 4BZ ☎ 01992 564248 ☝ ppledger@eppingforestdc.gov.uk

Housing: Ms Lyndsay Swan, Assistant Director - Private Sector Housing & Community Support, Civic Offices, High Street, Epping CM16 4BZ ☎ 01992 564146 ☝ lswann@eppingforestdc.gov.uk

Housing: Mr Roger Wilson, Assistant Director - Housing Operations, Civic Offices, High Street, Epping CM16 4BZ ☎ 01992 564419 ☝ rwilson@eppingforestdc.gov.uk

Housing Maintenance: Mr Roger Wilson, Assistant Director - Housing Operations, Civic Offices, High Street, Epping CM16 4BZ ☎ 01992 564419 ☝ rwilson@eppingforestdc.gov.uk

Legal: Mr Simon Hill, Assistant Director - Governance & Performance Management, Civic Offices, High Street, Epping CM16 4BZ ☎ 01992 564249 ☝ shill@eppingforestdc.gov.uk

Legal: Ms Alison Mitchell, Assistant Director - Legal Services, Civic Offices, High Street, Epping CM16 4BZ ☎ 01992 564017 ☝ amitchell@eppingforestdc.gov.uk

Legal: Ms Colleen O'Boyle, Director - Governance; Solicitor to the Council, Civic Offices, High Street, Epping CM16 4BZ ☎ 01992 564475 ☝ coboyle@eppingforestdc.gov.uk

Leisure and Cultural Services: Mr James Warwick, Assistant Community Health & Wellbeing Manager, Civic Offices, High Street, Epping CM16 4BZ ☎ 01992 564350 ☝ jwarwick@eppingforestdc.gov.uk

Member Services: Ms Wendy MacLeod, Senior Electoral Services Manager, Civic Offices, High Street, Epping CM16 4BZ ☎ 01992 564023 ☝ wmacleod@eppingforestdc.gov.uk

Member Services: Mr Stephen Tautz, Senior Democratic Services Manager, Civic Offices, High Street, Epping CM16 4BZ ☎ 01992 564180 ☝ stautz@eppingforestdc.gov.uk

Personnel / HR: Ms Paula Maginnis, Assistant Director - Human Resources, Civic Offices, High Street, Epping CM16 4BZ ☎ 01992 564536 ☝ pmaginnis@eppingforestdc.gov.uk

Public Libraries: Mr Tony O'Connor, Museum, Heritage & Culture Manager, Civic Offices, High Street, Epping CM16 4BZ ☎ 01992 716882 ☝ toconnor@eppingforestdc.gov.uk

Staff Training: Ms Paula Maginnis, Assistant Director - Human Resources, Civic Offices, High Street, Epping CM16 4BZ ☎ 01992 564536 ☝ pmaginnis@eppingforestdc.gov.uk

Tourism: Mr Tony O'Connor, Museum, Heritage & Culture Manager, Civic Offices, High Street, Epping CM16 4BZ ☎ 01992 716882 ☝ toconnor@eppingforestdc.gov.uk

COUNCILLORS

ChairLea, Jeanne (CON - Waltham Abbey North East)

Vice-ChairStallan, David (CON - North Weald Bassett) dave.stallan@tesco.net

Leader of the Council: Whitbread, Chris (CON - Epping Lindsey & Thornwood Common) cwhitbread@eppingforest.gov.uk

Deputy Leader of the Council: Stavrou, Syd (CON - Waltham Abbey High Beach) sydstavrou@yahoo.com

Avey, Nigel (CON - Epping Hemnall) nigel.avey@btinternet.com

Baldwin, Roger (R - Loughton Forest) baldwin.ri@gmail.com

Bassett, Richard (CON - Lower Nazeing) richard.d.bassett@ntlworld.com

Beales, Amy (R - Loughton Forest) amy.beales@googlemail.com

Bedford, Nigel (CON - Shelley) n.bedford@ntlworld.com

Boyce, Tony (CON - Moreton & Fyfield) tonyboyce@aol.com

Brady, Heather (CON - Passingford) heatherbrady@hotmail.co.uk

Breare-Hall, Will (CON - Epping Lindsey & Thornwood Common) wsbh@hotmail.co.uk

Brookes, Rose (R - Loughton Roding) vietrose01@aol.com

Butler, Rod (UKIP - Waltham Abbey Honey Lane) rod.butler@btconnect.com

Chambers, Gavin (CON - Buckhurst Hill West) gavin.chamberstraining@gmail.com

Chana, Kewel (CON - Grange Hill) kewalchana@yahoo.co.uk

Dorrell, David (UKIP - Waltham Abbey Paternoster) dave@cyprus.plus.com

Gadsby, Ricki (CON - Waltham Abbey South West)

Girling, Leon (R - Loughton Broadway) leongirling@gmail.com

Grigg, Anne (CON - North Weald Bassett)

Heap, Simon (GRN - Buckhurst Hill East) saheap.councillor@gmail.com

Hughes, Lynn (CON - Broadley Common, Epping Upland & Nazeing)
eppinglynn@live.com

Jennings, Judy (R - Loughton St Mary's)
cllrjjennings@hotmail.co.uk

Jennings, Bob (R - Loughton St John's)
cllrrobertjennings@hotmail.com

Jones, Sue (CON - Theydon Bois)
sue.jones193@ntlworld.com

Kane, Sam (CON - Waltham Abbey Honey Lane)
sam.kane@wacg.info

Kane, Helen (CON - Waltham Abbey South West)
helen@samkane.co.uk

Kauffman, Howard (R - Loughton St Mary's)

Keska, Paul (CON - Chipping Ongar, Greensted & Marden Ash)
cllr.ps.keska@hotmail.co.uk

Knapman, John (CON - Chigwell Village)
jknapman@msn.com

Knight, Yolanda (CON - Lower Nazeing)
yogard@hotmail.co.uk

Lion, Alan (CON - Grange Hill)
al.lion@btinternet.com

McEwen, Maggie (CON - High Ongar, Willingale & The Rodings)
heath.lands@btinternet.com

Mead, Louise (R - Loughton Fairmead)
cllrlouisemead@hotmail.com

Mitchell, Ann (CON - Waltham Abbey North East)
lillianmitchell@sky.com

Mohindra, Gagan (CON - Grange Hill)
gaganmohindra1@gmail.com

Morgan, Richard (IND - Hastingwood, Matching & Sheering Village)

Murray, Stephen (IND - Loughton Roding)

Neville, Steven (GRN - Buckhurst Hill East)
cllrstevenjsneville@gmail.com

Patel, Aniket (CON - Buckhurst Hill West)
patelaniket17@yahoo.co.uk

Philip, John (CON - Theydon Bois)
john.philip1@ntlworld.com

Pond, Chris (R - Loughton Broadway)
cllrccp@outlook.com

Pond, Caroline (R - Loughton St John's)
caroline_pond@hotmail.com

Roberts, Chris (R - Loughton Alderton)
chrisroberts_lra@yahoo.gov.uk

Roberts, Debra (GRN - Loughton Alderton)
cllrdebrarobertslra@gmail.com

Rolfe, Brian (CON - Lambourne)
cllrbrianrolfe@hotmail.co.uk

Sandler, Brian (CON - Chigwell Row)
bpsandler@aol.com

Sartin, Mary (CON - Roydon)
marysartin@yahoo.com

Shiell, Glynis (CON - Waltham Abbey Honey Lane)

Surtees, Brian (LD - Chipping Ongar, Greensted & Marden Ash)
bsurtees@seetrus.com

Wagland, Lesley (CON - Chigwell Village)
lwebber@live.co.uk

Waller, Gary (CON - Lower Sheering)
gary.waller@which.net

Watson, Sylvia (CON - Buckhurst Hill West)
sylvia_watson@btconnect.com

Webster, Elizabeth (CON - Waltham Abbey Paternoster)
cllr.elizabeth.webster@essexcc.gov.uk

Whitbread, Holly (CON - Epping Lindsey & Thornwood Common)
holly.whitbread@btinternet.com

Whitehouse, Janet (LD - Epping Hemnall)
janet.whitehouse@eflibdems.org.uk

Whitehouse, Jon (LD - Epping Hemnall)
jon@jonwhitehouse.org.uk

Wixley, David (R - Loughton Fairmead)
david.wixley@talktalk.net

POLITICAL COMPOSITION
CON: 36, R: 12, GRN: 3, LD: 3, UKIP: 2, IND: 2

COMMITTEE CHAIRS

Development Mangement: Mr Brian Sandler

Licensing: Mr Brian Surtees

Epsom & Ewell   D

Epsom & Ewell Borough Council, Town Hall, The Parade,
Epsom KT18 5BY
☎ 01372 732000 🖷 01372 732020 ✆ contactus@epsom-ewell.gov.uk
🖳 www.epsom-ewell.gov.uk

FACTS AND FIGURES
Parliamentary Constituencies: Epsom and Ewell
EU Constituencies: South East
Election Frequency: Elections are of whole council

PRINCIPAL OFFICERS

Chief Executive: Mrs Frances Rutter, Chief Executive, Town Hall,
The Parade, Epsom KT18 5BY ☎ 01372 732104
✆ frutter@epsom-ewell.gov.uk

Senior Management: Ms Kathryn Beldon, Director - Finance &
Resources, Town Hall, The Parade, Epsom KT18 5BY
☎ 01372 732102 ✆ mbeldon@epsom-ewell.gov.uk

Building Control: Mr Mark Berry, Head of Place Development,
Town Hall, The Parade, Epsom KT18 5BY ☎ 01372 732391
✆ mberry@epsom-ewell.gov.uk

PR / Communications: Mr Mark Rouson, Communications
Officer, Town Hall, The Parade, Epsom KT18 5BY ☎ 01372 732080
✆ mrouson@epson-ewell.gov.uk

Community Safety: Mr Kelvin Shooter, Community Safety Officer,
Town Hall, The Parade, Epsom KT18 5BY ☎ 01372 732133
✆ kshooter@epsom-ewell.gov.uk

EPSOM & EWELL

Computer Management: Mr Mark Lumley, Head of ICT, Town Hall, The Parade, Epsom KT18 5BY ☎ 01372 732174
✉ mlumley@epsom-ewell.gov.uk

Customer Service: Mrs Joy Stevens, Head of Customer Services & Business Support, Town Hall, The Parade, Epsom KT18 5BY
☎ 01372 732701 ✉ jstevens@epsom-ewell.gov.uk

Direct Labour: Mr Ian Dyer, Head of Operational Services, Longmead Depot, Blenheim Road, Epsom KT19 9AP
☎ 01372 732520 ✉ idyer@epsom-ewell.gov.uk

Electoral Registration: Ms Kerry Blundell, Electoral Registration Officer, Town Hall, The Parade, Epsom KT18 5BY ☎ 01372 732152
✉ kblundell@epsom-ewell.gov.uk

Environmental Health: Mr Rod Brown, Head - Housing & Environmental Services, Town Hall, The Parade, Epsom KT18 5BY
☎ 01372 732546 ✉ rbrown@epsom-ewell.gov.uk

Facilities: Mr Andrew Lunt, Head of Venues & Facilities, Town Hall, The Parade, Epsom KT18 5BY ☎ 01372 732302
✉ alunt@epsom-ewell.gov.uk

Finance: Ms Judith Doney, Head of Revenues & Benefits, Town Hall, The Parade, Epsom KT18 5BY ☎ 01372 732000
✉ jdoney@epsom-ewell.gov.uk

Finance: Mr Lee Duffy, Head of Financial Services, Town Hall, The Parade, Epsom KT18 5BY ☎ 01372 732210
✉ lduffy@epsom-ewell.gov.uk

Health and Safety: Ms Pauline Baxter, Corporate Health & Safety Officer, Town Hall, The Parade, Epsom KT18 5BY
☎ 01372 732410 ✉ pbaxter@epsom-ewell.gov.uk

Housing: Ms Annette Snell, Housing Manager, Town Hall, The Parade, Epsom KT18 5BY ☎ 01372 732436
✉ asnell@epsom-ewell.gov.uk

Legal: Mr Simon Young, Head of Legal & Democratic Services, Town Hall, The Parade, Epsom KT18 5BY ☎ 01372 732148
✉ syoung@epsom-ewell.gov.uk

Leisure and Cultural Services: Dr Sam Beak, Leisure Developments Manager, Town Hall, The Parade, Epsom KT18 5BY
☎ 01372 732460 ✉ sbeak@epsom-ewell.gov.uk

Licensing: Mrs Rachel Jackson, Licensing Officer, Town Hall, The Parade, Epsom KT18 5BY ☎ 01372 732449
✉ rjackson@epsom-ewell.gov.uk

Member Services: Miss Fiona Cotter, Democratic Services Manager, Town Hall, The Parade, Epsom KT18 5BY
☎ 01372 732124 ✉ fcotter@epsom-ewell.gov.uk

Parking: Mr Richard Chevalier, Parking Manager, Town Hall, The Parade, Epsom KT18 5BY ☎ 01372 732000
✉ rchevalier@epsom-ewell.gov.uk

Personnel / HR: Mrs Shona Mason, Head of HR & OD, Town Hall, The Parade, Epsom KT18 5BY ☎ 01372 732127
✉ smason@epsom-ewell.gov.uk

Planning: Mr Mark Berry, Head of Place Development, Town Hall, The Parade, Epsom KT18 5BY ☎ 01372 732391
✉ mberry@epsom-ewell.gov.uk

Recycling & Waste Minimisation: Mr Ian Dyer, Head of Operational Services, Longmead Depot, Blenheim Road, Epsom KT19 9AP ☎ 01372 732520 ✉ idyer@epsom-ewell.gov.uk

Waste Collection and Disposal: Mr Ian Dyer, Head of Operational Services, Longmead Depot, Blenheim Road, Epsom KT19 9AP ☎ 01372 732520 ✉ idyer@epsom-ewell.gov.uk

Waste Management: Mr Ian Dyer, Head of Operational Services, Longmead Depot, Blenheim Road, Epsom KT19 9AP
☎ 01372 732520 ✉ idyer@epsom-ewell.gov.uk

COUNCILLORS

Mayor: Crawford, George (R - Cuddington)
gcrawford@epsom-ewell.gov.uk

Arthur, Michael (R - Ewell)
marthur@epsom-ewell.gov.uk

Axelrod, Anthony (R - Town)
taxelrod@epsom-ewell.gov.uk

Baker, Richard (R - Stamford)
rbaker@epsom-ewell.gov.uk

Bansil, Rekha (R - Woodcote)
rbansil@epsom-ewell.gov.uk

Beckett, John (R - Auriol)
jbeckett@epsom-ewell.gov.uk

Bridger, Stephen (R - Stamford)
sbridger@epsom-ewell.gov.uk

Chinn, Katherine (LAB - Court)
kchin@epsom-ewell.gov.uk

Clarke, Alexander (CON - College)
aclarke@epsom-ewell.gov.uk

Dallen, Lucie (R - Cuddington)
ldallen@epsom-ewell.gov.uk

Dallen, Neil (R - Town)
ndallen@epsom-ewell.gov.uk

Dalton, Hannah (R - Stoneleigh)
hdalton@epsom-ewell.gov.uk

Dudley, Graham (R - Nonsuch)
gdudley@epsom-ewell.gov.uk

Foote, Robert (R - Cuddington)

Frost, Chris (R - Nonsuch)
cfrost@epsom-ewell.gov.uk

Frost, Liz (R - Woodcote)
lfrost@epsom-ewell.gov.uk

Geleit, Robert (LAB - Court)
rgeleit@epsom-ewell.gov.uk

Kington, Eber (R - Ewell Court)
ekington@merton.atl.org.uk

Kokou-Tchri, Omer (CON - College)
okokou-tchri@epsom-ewell.gov.uk

Mason, Janet (R - Ruxley)
jmason@epsom-ewell.gov.uk

Mountain, Christina (R - Woodcote)
tmountain@epsom-ewell.gov.uk

Nash, Barry (R - West Ewell)
bnash@epsom-ewell.gov.uk

O'Donavan, Peter (R - Ewell Court)
po'donovan@epsom-ewell.gov.uk

Olney, Martin (R - Stamford)
molney@epsom-ewell.gov.uk

Partirdge, Keith (R - Ruxley)
kpartridge@epsom-ewell.gov.uk

Race, Jane (CON - College)
jrace@epsom-ewell.gov.uk

Reeve, David (R - Stoneleigh)
dreeve@epsom-ewell.gov.uk

Reynolds, Humphrey (R - Ewell)
hreynolds@epsom-ewell.gov.uk

Robbins, Guy (R - Ewell Court)
grobbins@epsom-ewell.gov.uk

Romagnuolo, Vincent (LAB - Court)
wromagnuolo@epsom-ewell.gov.uk

Smitherham, Clive (R - West Ewell)
csmitherham@epsom-ewell.gov.uk

Steer, Jean (R - West Ewell)
jsteer@epsom-ewell.gov.uk

Sursham, Alan (R - Ruxley)
asursham@epsom-ewell.gov.uk

Teasdale, Michael (R - Stoneleigh)
mteasdale@epsom-ewell.gov.uk

Webb, Peter (R - Auriol)
pwebb@epsom-ewell.gov.uk

Wood, David (R - Nonsuch)
dwood@epsom-ewell.gov.uk

Woodbridge, Clive (R - Ewell)
cwoodbridge@epsom-ewell.gov.uk

Wormington, Estelle (R - Town)
twormington@epsom-ewell.gov.uk

POLITICAL COMPOSITION
R: 32, CON: 3, LAB: 3

COMMITTEE CHAIRS

Audit: Mr David Reeve

Community & Wellbeing: Mr Barry Nash

Environment: Mrr John Beckett

Licensing: Mr Robert Geleit

Licensing: Mr Neil Dallen

Licensing: Mr Clive Smitherham

Licensing: Mrs Jean Steer

Planning: Cllr Humphrey Reynolds

EREWASH

Erewash   **D**

Erewash Borough Council, Town Hall, Wharncliffe Road,
Ilkeston DE7 5RP
☎ 0845 907 2244 ⊕ enquiries@erewash.gov.uk
⌨ www.erewash.gov.uk

FACTS AND FIGURES
Parliamentary Constituencies: Erewash
EU Constituencies: Eastern
Election Frequency: Elections are of whole council

PRINCIPAL OFFICERS

Chief Executive: Mr Jeremy Jaroszek, Chief Executive, Town Hall,
Ilkeston DE7 5RP ☎ 0115 907 1199
⊕ jeremy.jaroszek@erewash.gov.uk

Deputy Chief Executive: Mr Ian Sankey, Director - Resources &
Deputy Chief Executive, Town Hall, Ilkeston DE7 5RP
☎ 0115 907 1157 ⊕ ian.sankey@erewash.gov.uk

Senior Management: Ms Lorraine Poyser, Director - Community
Services, Town Hall, Ilkeston DE7 5RP ☎ 0115 907 2244
⊕ lorraine.poyser@erewash.gov.uk

Senior Management: Mr Phillip Wright, Director - Operational
Services, Merlin House, Merlin Way, Ilkeston DE7 4RA
☎ 0115 907 2244 ⊕ phillip.wright@erewash.gov.uk

Architect, Building / Property Services: Mr Tom Haddock,
Property & Estates Manager, Town Hall, Long Eaton NG10 1HU
☎ 0115 907 2244 ⊕ tom.haddock@erewash.gov.uk

Best Value: Mrs Rachel Fernandez, Performance & Community
Manager, Town Hall, Ilkeston DE7 5RP ☎ 0115 907 2244
⊕ rachel.fernandez@erewash.gov.uk

Building Control: Mr Peter Baker, Building Control Manager,
Town Hall, Long Eaton NG10 1HU ☎ 0115 907 2221
⊕ peter.baker@erewash.gov.uk

PR / Communications: Mr Stewart Millar, Communications &
Culture Manager, Town Hall, Ilkeston DE7 5RP ☎ 0115 907 1159
⊕ stewart.millar@erewash.gov.uk

Community Safety: Ms Lorraine Poyser, Director - Community
Services, Town Hall, Ilkeston DE7 5RP ☎ 0115 907 2244
⊕ lorraine.poyser@erewash.gov.uk

Computer Management: Mr Neil Webster, ICT Manager, Town
Hall, Long Eaton NG10 1HU ☎ 0115 907 2244
⊕ neil.webster@erewash.gov.uk

Contracts: Mr Howard Lane, Lead Service Procurement Manager,
Bassetlaw District Council, Queens Building, Potter Street, Worksop
S80 2AH ☎ 01909 533449 ⊕ howard.lane@bassetlaw.gov.uk

Corporate Services: Mr Ian Sankey, Director - Resources &
Deputy Chief Executive, Town Hall, Ilkeston DE7 5RP ☎ 0115 907
1157 ⊕ ian.sankey@erewash.gov.uk

EREWASH

Customer Service: Mrs Rachel Fernandez, Performance & Community Manager, Town Hall, Ilkeston DE7 5RP ☎ 0115 907 2244 ⊕ rachel.fernandez@erewash.gov.uk

Economic Development: Mr Steve Birkinshaw, Head of Planning & Regeneration, Town Hall, Long Easton NG10 1HU ☎ 0115 907 2244 ⊕ steve.birkinshaw@erewash.gov.uk

Electoral Registration: Mrs Hayley Brailsford, Electoral Services Manager, Town Hall, Ilkeston DE7 5RP ☎ 0115 907 1112 ⊕ hayley.brailsford@erewash.gov.uk

Emergency Planning: Mr David Bramwell, Head of Green Space & Street Scene, Merlin House, Merlin Way, Ilkeston DE7 4RA ☎ 0115 907 2244 ⊕ dave.bramwell@erewash.gov.uk

Environmental / Technical Services: Mr Phillip Wright, Director - Operational Services, Merlin House, Merlin Way, Ilkeston DE7 4RA ☎ 0115 907 2244 ⊕ phillip.wright@erewash.gov.uk

Environmental Health: Mr Nick Thurstan, Head of Environment & Housing Services, Merlin House, Merlin Way, Ilkeston DE7 4RA ☎ 0115 931 6031 ⊕ nick.thurstan@erewash.gov.uk

Estates, Property & Valuation: Mr Brendan Morris, Head of Law & Corporate Governance, Town Hall, Ilkeston DE7 5RP ☎ 0115 907 1032 ⊕ brendan.morris@erewash.gov.uk

Events Manager: Mr Stewart Millar, Communications & Culture Manager, Town Hall, Ilkeston DE7 5RP ☎ 0115 907 1159 ⊕ stewart.millar@erewash.gov.uk

Facilities: Mr Tom Haddock, Property & Estates Manager, Town Hall, Long Eaton NG10 1HU ☎ 0115 907 2244 ⊕ tom.haddock@erewash.gov.uk

Finance: Mr David Watson, Head of Finance & Deputy Section 151 Officer, Town Hall, Ilkeston DE7 5RP ☎ 0115 907 2244 Ext 3438 ⊕ david.watson@erewash.gov.uk

Treasury: Mrs Judy Fay, Chief Accountant, Town Hall, Wharncliffe Road, Ilkeston DE7 5RP ☎ 0115 907 2244 ⊕ judy.fay@erewash.gov.uk

Fleet Management: Mr Joe Kirby, Area Supervisor (Waste / Fleet Manager), Merlin House, Merlin Way, Ilkeston DE7 4RA ☎ 0115 907 2244 ⊕ joe.kirby@erewash.gov.uk

Grounds Maintenance: Mr David Bramwell, Head of Green Space & Street Scene, Merlin House, Merlin Way, Ilkeston DE7 4RA ☎ 0115 907 2244 ⊕ dave.bramwell@erewash.gov.uk

Health and Safety: Ms Liz Street, Environmental Health Manager, Merlin House, Merlin Way, Ilkeston DE7 4RA ☎ 0115 907 2244 ⊕ elizabeth.street@erewash.gov.uk

Home Energy Conservation: Ms Liz Street, Environmental Health Manager, Merlin House, Merlin Way, Ilkeston DE7 4RA ☎ 0115 907 2244 ⊕ elizabeth.street@erewash.gov.uk

Housing: Mr Nick Thurstan, Head of Environment & Housing Services, Merlin House, Merlin Way, Ilkeston DE7 4RA ☎ 0115 931 6031 ⊕ nick.thurstan@erewash.gov.uk

Legal: Mr Brendan Morris, Head of Law & Corporate Governance, Town Hall, Ilkeston DE7 5RP ☎ 0115 907 1032 ⊕ brendan.morris@erewash.gov.uk

Leisure and Cultural Services: Mr Tim Spencer, Head of Leisure Services, Sandiacre Friesland Sports Centre, Nursery Avenue, Sandiacre NG10 5AE ☎ 0115 907 2244 ⊕ tim.spencer@erewash.gov.uk

Licensing: Mrs Carolyn Singleton, Licensing Manager, Town Hall, Spinney Drive, Long Eaton NG10 4HU ☎ 0115 907 2244 Ext 3121 ⊕ carolyn.singleton@erewash.gov.uk

Member Services: Mr Brendan Morris, Head of Law & Corporate Governance, Town Hall, Ilkeston DE7 5RP ☎ 0115 907 1032 ⊕ brendan.morris@erewash.gov.uk

Parking: Mr Scott Cartledge, Neighbourhood Warden Manager, Merlin House, Merlin Way, Ilkeston DE7 4RA ☎ 0115 907 2244 ⊕ scott.cartledge@erewash.gov.uk

Partnerships: Ms Lorraine Poyser, Director - Community Services, Town Hall, Ilkeston DE7 5RP ☎ 0115 907 2244 ⊕ lorraine.poyser@erewash.gov.uk

Personnel / HR: Mrs Jennifer Browne, Head of Personnel & ICT, Town Hall, Long Eaton NG10 1HU ☎ 0115 907 2244 ⊕ jennifer.browne@erewash.gov.uk

Planning: Mr Steve Birkinshaw, Head of Planning & Regeneration, Town Hall, Long Easton NG10 1HU ☎ 0115 907 2244 ⊕ steve.birkinshaw@erewash.gov.uk

Procurement: Mr Howard Lane, Lead Service Procurement Manager, Bassetlaw District Council, Queens Building, Potter Street, Worksop S80 2AH ☎ 01909 533449 ⊕ howard.lane@bassetlaw.gov.uk

Recycling & Waste Minimisation: Ms Julie Harvey, Waste & Fleet Manager, Town Hall, Wharncliffe Road, Ilkeston DE7 5RP ☎ 0115 907 2244 ⊕ julie.harvey@erewash.gov.uk

Regeneration: Mr Steve Birkinshaw, Head of Planning & Regeneration, Town Hall, Long Easton NG10 1HU ☎ 0115 907 2244 ⊕ steve.birkinshaw@erewash.gov.uk

Staff Training: Ms Joanna Till, Personnel Manager, Town Hall, Long Eaton NG10 1HU ☎ 0115 907 2244 ⊕ joanna.till@erewash.gov.uk

Street Scene: Mr David Bramwell, Head of Green Space & Street Scene, Merlin House, Merlin Way, Ilkeston DE7 4RA ☎ 0115 907 2244 ⊕ dave.bramwell@erewash.gov.uk

Sustainable Development: Mr Ian Sankey, Director - Resources & Deputy Chief Executive, Town Hall, Ilkeston DE7 5RP ☎ 0115 907 1157 ⊕ ian.sankey@erewash.gov.uk

Tourism: Mr Tim Spencer, Head of Leisure Services, Sandiacre Friesland Sports Centre, Nursery Avenue, Sandiacre NG10 5AE
☎ 0115 907 2244 ◌ tim.spencer@erewash.gov.uk

Waste Collection and Disposal: Mr Phillip Wright, Director - Operational Services, Merlin House, Merlin Way, Ilkeston DE7 4RA
☎ 0115 907 2244 ◌ phillip.wright@erewash.gov.uk

Waste Management: Mr Phillip Wright, Director - Operational Services, Merlin House, Merlin Way, Ilkeston DE7 4RA ☎ 0115 907 2244 ◌ phillip.wright@erewash.gov.uk

Children's Play Areas: Mr David Bramwell, Head of Green Space & Street Scene, Merlin House, Merlin Way, Ilkeston DE7 4RA
☎ 0115 907 2244 ◌ dave.bramwell@erewash.gov.uk

COUNCILLORS

Mayor: Stevenson, Abey (CON - Little Eaton & Stanley)
councillor.abey.stevenson@erewash.gov.uk

Deputy Mayor: Hopkinson, Mary (CON - Little Hallam)
councillor.mary.hopkinson@erewash.gov.uk

Leader of the Council: Corbett, Christopher (CON - Wilsthorpe)
councillor.chris.corbett@erewash.gov.uk

Deputy Leader of the Council: Hart, Carol (CON - West Hallam & Dale Abbey)
councillor.carol.hart@erewash.gov.uk

Group LeaderDawson, James (LAB - Awsworth Road)
councillor.james.dawson@erewash.gov.uk

Athwal, Kewal (CON - Wilsthorpe)
councillor.kewal.athwal@erewash.gov.uk

Beardsley, Susan (CON - Little Hallam)
councillor.sue.beardsley@erewash.gov.uk

Bilbie, Leonie (CON - Sandiacre)
councillor.leonie.bilbie@erewash.gov.uk

Bilbie, Steve (CON - Sandiacre)
councillor.steve.bilbie@erewash.gov.uk

Birkin, Glennice (LAB - Awsworth Road)
councillor.glennice.birkin@erewash.gov.uk

Bonam, Joanne (CON - Sawley)
councillor.jo.bonam@erewash.gov.uk

Broughton, Bruce (CON - West Hallam & Dale Abbey)
councillor.bruce.broughton@erewash.gov.uk

Brown, Caroline (LAB - Long Eaton Central)
councillor.caroline.brown@erewash.gov.uk

Clare, Valerie (CON - Draycott & Risley)
councillor.val.clare@erewash.gov.uk

Custance, Val (CON - Shipley View)
councillor.val.custance@erewash.gov.uk

Doyle, David (LAB - Nottingham Road)
councillor.david.doyle@erewash.gov.uk

Frudd, John (LAB - Kirk Hallam & Stanton by Dale)
councillor.john.frudd@erewash.gov.uk

Green, Stephen (LAB - Kirk Hallam & Stanton by Dale)

Griffiths, Howard (LAB - Derby Road East)

Griffiths, Margaret (LAB - Derby Road East)

Harris, Richard (CON - Derby Road West)
councillor.richard.harris@erewash.gov.uk

Harrison, Barbara (CON - West Hallam & Dale Abbey)
councillor.barbara.harrison@erewash.gov.uk

Hickton, Garry (CON - Derby Road West)

Hickton, Gerri (CON - Derby Road West)
councillor.gerri.hickton@erewash.gov.uk

Holbrook, Terence (CON - Ockbrook & Borrowash)
councillor.terry.holbrook@erewash.gov.uk

Hosker, Leah (LAB - Long Eaton Central)
councillor.leah.hosker@erewash.gov.uk

Major, Wayne (CON - Sandiacre)
councillor.wayne.major@erewash.gov.uk

McCandless, Andrew (CON - Draycott & Risley)
councillor.andrew.mccandless@erewash.gov.uk

McGraw, Linda (LAB - Kirk Hallam & Stanton by Dale)

Mellors, Denise (LAB - Nottingham Road)
councillor.denise.mellors@erewash.gov.uk

Miller, Kevin (CON - Breaston)
councillor.kevin.miller@erewash.gov.uk

Parkinson, Robert (CON - Breaston)
councillor.robert.parkinson@erewash.gov.uk

Pepios, Peter (CON - Long Eaton Central)
councillor.peter.pepios@erewash.gov.uk

Phillips, Frank (LAB - Larklands)
councillor.frank.phillips@erewash.gov.uk

Phillips, Pam (LAB - Larklands)
councillor.pam.phillips@erewash.gov.uk

Phillips, Alex (LAB - Hallam Fields)

Powell, Michael (CON - Wilsthorpe)
councillor.michael.powell@erewash.gov.uk

Sewell, John (CON - Sawley)
councillor.john.sewell@erewash.gov.uk

Shelton, Paul (CON - Shipley View)
councillor.paul.shelton@erewash.gov.uk

Summerfield, Alan (CON - Little Eaton & Stanley)
councillor.alan.summerfield@erewash.gov.uk

Tatham, Phillips (LAB - Larklands)

Treacy, Danny (LAB - Cotmanhay)
councillor.danny.treacy@erewash.gov.uk

Wallis, Michael (CON - Ockbrook & Borrowash)
councillor.michael.wallis@erewash.gov.uk

Walton, Daniel (CON - Sawley)
councillor.daniel.walton@erewash.gov.uk

White, Michael (CON - Ockbrook & Borrowash)
councillor.michael.white@erewash.gov.uk

Wilson, Jane (LAB - Cotmanhay)
councillor.jane.wilson@erewash.gov.uk

Wright, Jonathan (CON - Hallam Fields)
councillor.jon.wright@erewash.gov.uk

POLITICAL COMPOSITION
CON: 30, LAB: 17

EREWASH

COMMITTEE CHAIRS

Audit: Mr Alan Summerfield

Licensing: Mr Kewal Athwal

Planning: Mr Robert Parkinson

Essex C

Essex County Council, County Hall, Market Road, Chelmsford CM1 1LX

☎ 0345 743 0430 ✆ contact@essex.gov.uk 🖵 www.essex.gov.uk

FACTS AND FIGURES
Parliamentary Constituencies: Maldon
EU Constituencies: Eastern
Election Frequency: Elections are of whole council

PRINCIPAL OFFICERS

Chief Executive: Mr Gavin Jones, Chief Executive, County Hall, Market Road, Chelmsford CM1 1LX ✆ gavin.jones@essex.gov.uk

Senior Management: Mr James Bullion, Director - Adult Operations, County Hall, Market Road, Chelmsford CM1 1LX ✆ james.bullion@essex.gov.uk

Senior Management: Ms Sonia Davidson-Grant, Executive Director - Place Commissioning, County Hall, Market Road, Chelmsford CM1 1LX ✆ sonia.davidson-grant@essex.gov.uk

Senior Management: Dr Mike Gogarty, Director - Public Health, County Hall, Market Road, Chelmsford CM1 1LX ✆ mike.gogarty@essex.gov.uk

Senior Management: Mr Dave Hill, Executive Director - People Commissioning, County Hall, Market Road, Chelmsford CM1 1LX ☎ 01245 431891 ✆ dave.hill@essex.gov.uk

Senior Management: Ms Margaret Lee, Executive Director - Corporate Services & Customer Operations, County Hall, Market Road, Chelmsford CM1 1LX ☎ 08457 430430 ✆ margaret.lee@essex.gov.uk

Senior Management: Ms Helen Lincoln, Executive Director - People Operations, County Hall, Market Road, Chelmsford CM1 1LX ☎ 01245 437157 ✆ helen.lincoln@essex.gov.uk

Senior Management: Mr David Wilde, Executive Director - Place Operations & Chief Information Officer, County Hall, Market Road, Chelmsford CM1 1LX ☎ 01245 433172 ✆ david.wilde@essex.gov.uk

Access Officer / Social Services (Disability): Ms Liz Chidgey, MD - Essex Cares Ltd, County Hall, Market Road, Chelmsford CM1 1LX ☎ 01245 434123 ✆ liz.chidgey@essex.gov.uk

Building Control: Mr Roy Leavitt, Head - Development Control, County Hall, Market Road, Chelmsford CM1 1LX ☎ 01245 437522 ✆ roy.leavitt@essex.gov.uk

Children / Youth Services: Ms Stephanie Bishop, Head - Fostering & Adoption, County Hall, Market Road, Chelmsford CM1 1LX ☎ 08457 430430 ✆ stephanie.bishop@essex.gov.uk

Children / Youth Services: Mr Tim Coulson, Director - Education & Learning, County Hall, Market Road, Chelmsford CM1 1LX ☎ 01245 436031 ✆ tim.coulson@essex.gov.uk

Children / Youth Services: Ms Helen Lincoln, Executive Director - People Operations, County Hall, Market Road, Chelmsford CM1 1LX ☎ 08457 430430 ✆ helen.lincoln@essex.gov.uk

Civil Registration: Mr Philip Thomson, Director - Essex Legal Services, New Bridge House, 60-68 New London Road, Chelmsford CM2 0PD ☎ 01245 506760 ✆ philip.thomson@essex.gov.uk

Computer Management: Mr David Wilde, Executive Director - Place Operations & Chief Information Officer, County Hall, Market Road, Chelmsford CM1 1LX ☎ 01245 433172 ✆ david.wilde@essex.gov.uk

Contracts: Mr Mark Paget, Corporate Lead - Supply Chain Management & Contract Management, County Hall, Market Road, Chelmsford CM1 1LX ☎ 01245 431846 ✆ mark.paget@essex.gov.uk

Corporate Services: Ms Katie Hadgraft, Head - Employee Communications & Engagement, County Hall, Market Road, Chelmsford CM1 1LX ☎ 01245 434010 ✆ katie.hadgraft@essex.gov.uk

Corporate Services: Mr Mark Hobson, Director - Corporate Operations, County Hall, Market Road, Chelmsford CM1 1LX ☎ 01245 431026 ✆ mark.hobson@essex.gov.uk

Corporate Services: Ms Denise Murray, Head of Finance, County Hall, Market Road, Chelmsford CM1 1LX ☎ 01245 436721 ✆ denise.murray@essex.gov.uk

Education: Mr Tim Coulson, Director - Education & Learning, County Hall, Market Road, Chelmsford CM1 1LX ☎ 01245 436031 ✆ tim.coulson@essex.gov.uk

Education: Mr Graham Ranby, Lead Strategic Comissioner - Planning & Provision, County Hall, Market Road, Chelmsford CM1 1LX ☎ 01245 436704 ✆ graham.ranby@essex.gov.uk

Emergency Planning: Mr Adam Eckley, Acting Chief Fire Officer & Head of Emergency Planning, County Hall, Market Road, Chelmsford CM1 1LX ☎ 01245 430366 ✆ adam.eckley@essex.gov.uk

European Liaison: Ms Lorraine George, EU Funding Lead, County Hall, Market Road, Chelmsford CM1 1QH ☎ 01245 430472 ✆ lorraine.george@essex.gov.uk

Events Manager: Ms Sharon Collier, Events Management & Community Budgets, County Hall, Market Road, Chelmsford CM1 1QH ☎ 01245 436569 ✆ sharon.collier@essex.gov.uk

Finance: Ms Margaret Lee, Executive Director - Corporate Services & Customer Operations, County Hall, Market Road, Chelmsford CM1 1LX ☎ 08457 430430 ✆ margaret.lee@essex.gov.uk

Finance: Mr Peter Tanton, Head - Internal Audit, County Hall, Market Road, Chelmsford CM1 1LX ☎ 01245 43110 ✆ peter.tanton@essex.gov.uk

Treasury: Mr Robin Paddock, Treasurer & Deputy Chief Executive, 3 Hoffmanns Way, Chelmsford CM1 1GU ☎ 01245 291614 ⌀ robin.paddock@essex.gov.uk

Pensions: Ms Anne-Marie Allen, Investment Officer, County Hall, Market Road, Chelmsford CM1 1LX ☎ 01245 431733 ⌀ annemarie.allen@essex.gov.uk

Pensions: Ms Jody Evans, Pension Service Manager, County Hall, Market Road, Chelmsford CM1 1LX ☎ 01245 431700 ⌀ jody.evans@essex.gov.uk

Pensions: Mr Kevin McDonald, Director - Pensions & Investment, County Hall, Market Road, Chelmsford CM1 1LX ⌀ kevin.mcdonald@essex.gov.uk

Fleet Management: Mr John Pope, Head - Passenger Transport, County Hall, Market Road, Chelmsford CM1 1QH ☎ 01245 437506 ⌀ john.pope@essex.gov.uk

Grounds Maintenance: Mr Tim Dixon, Head - Country Parks, County Hall, Market Road, Chelmsford CM1 1LX ☎ 08457 430430 ⌀ tim.dixon@essex.gov.uk

Health and Safety: Ms Janet Ross, Health, Safety & Risk Manager, County Hall, Market Road, Chelmsford CM1 1QH ☎ 08457 430430 ⌀ janet.ross@essex.gov.uk

Highways: Mr Paul Bird, Director - Transport & Infrastructure, County Hall, Market Road, Chelmsford CM1 1QH ☎ 08457 430430 ⌀ paul.bird@essex.gov.uk

Legal: Mr Philip Thomson, Director - Essex Legal Services, New Bridge House, 60-68 New London Road, Chelmsford CM2 0PD ☎ 01245 506760 ⌀ philip.thomson@essex.gov.uk

Personnel / HR: Mr Keir Lynch, Executive Director - Strategy, Transformation & Commissioning Support, County Hall, Market Road, Chelmsford CM1 1LX ☎ 01245 431117 ⌀ keir.lynch@essex.gov.uk

Planning: Mr Paul Bird, Director - Transport & Infrastructure, County Hall, Market Road, Chelmsford CM1 1QH ☎ 08457 430430 ⌀ paul.bird@essex.gov.uk

Recycling & Waste Minimisation: Mr Jason Searles, Head - Commissioning Sustainable Essex Integration & Waste, County Hall, Market Road, Chelmsford CM1 1QH ☎ 08457 430430 ⌀ jason.searles@essex.gov.uk

Road Safety: Ms Katie Brimley, Road Safety ETP Team Leader, County Hall, Market Road, Chelmsford CM1 1LX ☎ 01245 437781 ⌀ katie.brimley@essex.gov.uk

Social Services (Children): Ms Helen Lincoln, Executive Director - People Operations, County Hall, Market Road, Chelmsford CM1 1LX ☎ 01245 437157 ⌀ helen.lincoln@essex.gov.uk

Public Health: Dr Mike Gogarty, Director - Public Health, County Hall, Market Road, Chelmsford CM1 1LX ⌀ mike.gogarty@essex.gov.uk

Staff Training: Mr Jeff Wren, Head - Leadership & Development, County Hall, Market Road, Chelmsford CM1 1LX ☎ 01245 437806 ⌀ jeff.wren@essex.gov.uk

Tourism: Ms Mary Tebje, Tourism Manager, County Hall, Market Road, Chelmsford CM1 1LX ☎ 03330 134185 ⌀ mary.tebje@essex.gov.uk

Traffic Management: Ms Nicola Foster, Group Manager - Road Safety, County Hall, Market Road, Chelmsford CM1 1LX ☎ 01245 437004 ⌀ nicola.foster@essex.gov.uk

Traffic Management: Mr John Pope, Head - Passenger Transport, County Hall, Market Road, Chelmsford CM1 1QH ☎ 01245 437506 ⌀ john.pope@essex.gov.uk

Transport: Mr John Pope, Head - Passenger Transport, County Hall, Market Road, Chelmsford CM1 1QH ☎ 01245 437506 ⌀ john.pope@essex.gov.uk

Transport Planner: Mr Christopher Stevenson, Head - Commissioning: Integrated Transport, County Hall, Market Road, Chelmsford CM1 1LX ☎ 08457 430430 ⌀ chris.stevenson@essex.gov.uk

Children's Play Areas: Mr Tim Dixon, Head - Country Parks, County Hall, Market Road, Chelmsford CM1 1LX ☎ 08457 430430 ⌀ tim.dixon@essex.gov.uk

COUNCILLORS

Chair: Aldridge, John (CON - Broomfield & Writtle)
cllr.john.aldridge@essexcc.gov.uk

Leader of the Council: Finch, David (CON - Hedingham)
cllr.david.finch@essexcc.gov.uk

Deputy Leader of the Council: Bentley, Kevin (CON - Stanway & Pyefleet)
cllr.kevin.bentley@essex.gov.uk

Group Leader: Abbott, James (GRN - Witham Northern)
cllr.james.abbott@essex.gov.uk

Group Leader: Henderson, Ivan (LAB - Harwich)
cllr.ivan.henderson@essex.gov.uk

Group Leader: Hoy, Michael (GRN - Rochford West)
cllr.michael.hoy@essex.gov.uk

Group Leader: Le Gresley, Nigel (UKIP - Wickford Crouch)
cllr.nigel.legresley@essex.gov.uk

Group Leader: Mackrory, Michael (LD - Springfield)
cllr.mike.mackrory@essexcc.gov.uk

Aspinell, Barry (LD - Brentwood North)
cllr.barry.aspinell@essex.gov.uk

Barker, Susan (CON - Dunmow)
cllr.susan.barker@essexcc.gov.uk

Bass, Rodney (CON - Heybridge & Tollesbury)
cllr.rodney.bass@essexcc.gov.uk

Bayley, Alan (UKIP - South Benfleet)
cllr.alan.bayley@essex.gov.uk

Blackwell, Dave (INDNA - Canvey Island East)
cllr.dave.blackwell@essex.gov.uk

Bobbin, Keith (LAB - Pitsea)
cllr.keith.bobbin@essex.gov.uk

ESSEX

Boyce, Bob (CON - Southminster)
cllr.bob.boyce@essexcc.gov.uk

Brown, Anne (CON - Constable)
cllr.anne.brown@essex.gov.uk

Buckley, Malcolm (CON - Wickford Crouch)
cllr.malcolm.buckley@essex.gov.uk

Butland, Graham (CON - Braintree Town)
cllr.graham.butland@essex.gov.uk

Canning, Stephen (CON - Bocking)
cllr.stephen.canning@essex.gov.uk

Chandler, Jenny (CON - Great Baddow)
cllr.jenny.chandler@essex.gov.uk

Channer, Penny (CON - Maldon)
cllr.penny.channer@essex.gov.uk

Clempner, Karen (LAB - Harlow West)
cllr.karen.clempner@essex.gov.uk

Cutmore, Terry (CON - Rochford North)
cllr.terry@cutmore@essex.gov.uk

Danvers, Michael (LAB - Harlow North)
cllr.michael.danvers@essex.gov.uk

Deakin, Judith (LD - Chelmsford West)
cllr.jude.deakin@essex.gov.uk

Donaldson, Magaret (LD - Abbey)
cllr.margaret.fisher@essex.gov.uk

Durcan, Anthony (LAB - Harlow West)
cllr.tony.durcan@essex.gov.uk

Ellis, Mark (UKIP - Laindon Park & Fryerns)
cllr.mark.ellis@essex.gov.uk

Erskine, Andrew (INDNA - Tendring Rural East)
cllr.andy.erskine@essex.gov.uk

Ferguson, Frank (UKIP - Laindon Park & Fryerns)

Gadsby, Ricki (CON - Waltham Abbey)
cllr.ricki.gadsby@essex.gov.uk

Gibbs, Keith (UKIP - Rayleigh South)
cllr.keith.gibbs@essex.gov.uk

Goggin, Alan (CON - Brightlingsea)
alan.goggin@essex.gov.uk

Gooding, Raymond (CON - Stanstead)
cllr.ray.gooding@essexcc.gov.uk

Grundy, Ian (CON - Stock)
cllr.ian.grundy@essex.gov.uk

Guglielmi, Carlo (CON - Tendring Rural West)
cllr.carlo.gugleilmi@essex.gov.uk

Harris, Dave (LAB - Maypole)
cllr.dave.harris@essex.gov.uk

Hedley, Anthony (CON - Billericay & Burstead)
cllr.anthony.hedley@essexcc.gov.uk

Higgins, Theresa (LD - Parsons Heath & East Gates)
cllr.theresa.higgins@essex.gov.uk

Hirst, Roger (CON - Brentwood Hutton)
cllr.roger.hirst@essex.gov.uk

Honeywood, Paul (CON - Clacton West)
cllr.paul.honeywood@essex.gov.uk

Howard, Raymond (CON - Canvey Island West)
cllr.ray.howard@essexcc.gov.uk

Hume, Norman (CON - South Woodham Ferrers)
cllr.norman.hume@essex.gov.uk

Huntman, Jamie (UKIP - Thundersley)
cllr.jamie.huntman@essex.gov.uk

Jackson, Anthony (CON - North Weald & Nazeing)
cllr.anthony.jackson@essex.gov.uk

Johnson, Edward (CON - Harlow South East)
cllr.edward.johnson@essexcc.gov.uk

Jowers, John (CON - Mersea & Tiptree)
cllr.john.jowers@essex.gov.uk

Kendall, David (LD - Brentwood South)
cllr.david.kendall@essex.gov.uk

Knapman, John (CON - Chigwell & Loughton Broadway)
cllr.john.knapman@essex.gov.uk

Lissimore, Sue (CAP - Drury)
cllr.sue.lissimore@essex.gov.uk

Lodge, John (INDNA - Saffron Walden)
cllr.john.lodge@essex.gov.uk

Louis, Derrick (CON - Witham Southern)
cllr.derrek.louis@essex.gov.uk

Madden, Dick (IND - Chelmsford Central)
cllr.dick.madden@essex.gov.uk

Maddocks, Malcolm (CON - Rayleigh North)
cllr.malcolm.maddocks@essex.gov.uk

McEwen, Maggie (CON - Ongar & Rural)
cllr.maggie.mcewen@essex.gov.uk

McGeorge, Melissa (LAB - Pitsea)
cllr.melissa.mcgeorge@essex.gov.uk

Metcalfe, Valerie (CON - Buckhurst Hill & Loughton South)
Cllr.valerie.metcalfe@essex.gov.uk

Naylor, Ann (CON - Brentwood Rural)
cllr.ann.naylor@essexcc.gov.uk

Newton, Patricia (CON - Braintree Eastern)
cllr.lady.newton@essex.gov.uk

Page, Michael (CON - Frinton & Walton)
cllr.mick.page@essexcc.gov.uk

Pike, Joe (CON - Halstead)
cllr.joe.pike@essex.gov.uk

Pond, Chris (R - Loughton Central)
cllr.chris.pond@essexcc.gov.uk

Reeves, Jillian (CON - Hadleigh)
cllr.jillian.reeves@essexcc.gov.uk

Robinson, Stephen (LD - Chelmsford North)
cllr.stephen.robinson@essex.gov.uk

Sargeant, Colin (INDNA - Clacton East)
cllr.colin.sargeant@essex.gov.uk

Seagers, Colin (CON - Rochford South)
cllr.colin.seagers@essex.gov.uk

Smith, Kerry (UKIP - Basildon Westley Heights)
cllr.kerry.smith@essex.gov.uk

Spence, John (CON - Chelmer)
cllr.john.spence@essex.gov.uk

Turrell, Anne (LD - Mile End & Highwoods)
cllr.anne.turrell@essexcc.gov.uk

Twitchen, Kay (CON - Billericay & Burstead)
cllr.kay.twitchen@essexcc.gov.uk

Walsh, Simon (CON - Thaxted)
cllr.simon.walsh@essex.gov.uk

Walters, Roger (CON - Three Fields with Great Notley)
cllr.roger.walters@essex.gov.uk

Whitehouse, Jon (LD - Epping & Theydon Bois)
cllr.jon.whitehouse@essex.gov.uk

Wood, Andy (CON - Clacton North)
cllr.andy.wood@essex.gov.uk

Young, Julie (LAB - Wivenhoe St Andrew)
cllr.julie.young@essex.gov.uk

POLITICAL COMPOSITION
CON: 41, LD: 9, LAB: 8, UKIP: 7, INDNA: 4, GRN: 2, R: 1, CAP: 1, IND: 1

COMMITTEE CHAIRS
Audit: Mr Terry Cutmore

Health & Wellbeing: Mr Graham Butland

Pensions: Mr Rodney Bass

People & Families: Mr Ian Grundy

Exeter City   D

Exeter City Council, Civic Centre, Paris Street, Exeter EX1 1JN
☎ 01392 277888 🖶 01392 265265 ✆ customer.services@exeter.gov.uk
💻 www.exeter.gov.uk

FACTS AND FIGURES
Parliamentary Constituencies: Exeter
EU Constituencies: South West
Election Frequency: Elections are by thirds

PRINCIPAL OFFICERS

Chief Executive: Mr Karime Hassan, Chief Executive & Growth Director, Civic Centre, Paris Street, Exeter EX1 1JN ☎ 01392 265188 ✆ karime.hassan@exeter.gov.uk

Deputy Chief Executive: Mr Mark Parkinson, Deputy Chief Executive, Civic Centre, Paris Street, Exeter EX1 1JN
☎ 01392 265105 ✆ mark.parkinson@exeter.gov.uk

Senior Management: Ms Bindu Arjoon, Assistant Director - Customer Access, Civic Centre, Paris Street, Exeter EX1 1JN
☎ 01392 265199 ✆ bindu.arjoon@exeter.gov.uk

Senior Management: Mr Richard Ball, Assistant Director - Economy, Civic Centre, Paris Street, Exeter EX1 1JN
☎ 01392 265140 ✆ richard.ball@exeter.gov.uk

Senior Management: Mr Roger Coombes, Assistant Director - Housing, Civic Centre, Paris Street, Exeter EX1 1JN
☎ 01392 265468 ✆ roger.coombes@exeter.gov.uk

Senior Management: Mr Bruce Luxton, Corporate Manager Policy - Communications & Community Engagement, Civic Centre, Paris Street, Exeter EX1 1JN ☎ 01392 265166
✆ bruce.luxton@exeter.gov.uk

Senior Management: Mr Robert Norley, Assistant Director - Environment, Civic Centre, Paris Street, Exeter EX1 1RQ
☎ 01392 265170 ✆ robert.norley@exeter.gov.uk

Senior Management: Mr Richard Short, Assistant Director - City Development, Civic Centre, Paris Street, Exeter EX1 1JN
☎ 01392 265219 ✆ richard.short@exeter.gov.uk

Senior Management: Mrs Sarah Ward, Assistant Director - Public Realm, Civic Centre, Paris Street, Exeter EX1 1JN
☎ 01392 265215 ✆ sarah.ward@exeter.gov.uk

PR / Communications: Mr Steve Upsher, Policy, Communications & Community Engagement Officer, Civic Centre, Paris Street, Exeter EX1 1JN ☎ 01392 265103
✆ steve.upsher@exeter.gov.uk

Computer Management: Mr Chris Powell, Chief Operations Officer, Civic Centre, Paris Street, Exeter EX1 1JN
☎ 01392 265600 ✆ cjpowell@eastdevon.gov.uk

Contracts: Mr Michael Carson, Corporate Manager - Property, Civic Centre, Paris Street, Exeter EX1 1JN ☎ 01392 265169
✆ michael.carson@exeter.gov.uk

Corporate Services: Mr John Street, Corporate Manager - Democratic & Civic Support, Civic Centre, Paris Street, Exeter EX1 1JN ☎ 01392 265106 ✆ john.street@exeter.gov.uk

Customer Service: Ms Bindu Arjoon, Assistant Director - Customer Access, Civic Centre, Paris Street, Exeter EX1 1JN
☎ 01392 265199 ✆ bindu.arjoon@exeter.gov.uk

Customer Service: Mr John Street, Corporate Manager - Democratic & Civic Support, Civic Centre, Paris Street, Exeter EX1 1JN ☎ 01392 265106 ✆ john.street@exeter.gov.uk

Economic Development: Mr Richard Ball, Assistant Director - Economy, Civic Centre, Paris Street, Exeter EX1 1JN
☎ 01392 265140 ✆ richard.ball@exeter.gov.uk

Electoral Registration: Mr Jeff Chalk, Electoral Services Manager, Civic Centre, Paris Street, Exeter EX1 1JN
☎ 01392 265640 ✆ jeff.chalk@exeter.gov.uk

Electoral Registration: Mr John Street, Corporate Manager - Democratic & Civic Support, Civic Centre, Paris Street, Exeter EX1 1JN ☎ 01392 265106 ✆ john.street@exeter.gov.uk

Emergency Planning: Mr Bruce Luxton, Corporate Manager Policy - Communications & Community Engagement, Civic Centre, Paris Street, Exeter EX1 1JN ☎ 01392 265166
✆ bruce.luxton@exeter.gov.uk

Environmental / Technical Services: Mr Robert Norley, Assistant Director - Environment, Civic Centre, Paris Street, Exeter EX1 1RQ ☎ 01392 265170 ✆ robert.norley@exeter.gov.uk

Environmental Health: Mr Robert Norley, Assistant Director - Environment, Civic Centre, Paris Street, Exeter EX1 1RQ
☎ 01392 265170 ✆ robert.norley@exeter.gov.uk

EXETER CITY

Estates, Property & Valuation: Mr Michael Carson, Corporate Manager - Property, Civic Centre, Paris Street, Exeter EX1 1JN ☎ 01392 265169 ✉ michael.carson@exeter.gov.uk

Events Manager: Ms Valerie Wilson, Festivals & Events Manager, Civic Centre, Paris Street, Exeter EX1 1JN ☎ 01392 265205 ✉ val.wilson@exeter.gov.uk

Facilities: Mr John Street, Corporate Manager - Democratic & Civic Support, Civic Centre, Paris Street, Exeter EX1 1JN ☎ 01392 265106 ✉ john.street@exeter.gov.uk

Finance: Mr David Hodgson, Assistant Director - Finance, Civic Centre, Paris Street, Exeter EX1 1JN ☎ 01392 265292 ✉ david.hodgson@exeter.gov.uk

Treasury: Mr David Hodgson, Assistant Director - Finance, Civic Centre, Paris Street, Exeter EX1 1JN ☎ 01392 265292 ✉ david.hodgson@exeter.gov.uk

Grounds Maintenance: Mr Paul Faulkner, Parks & Open Spaces Manager, Belle Isle Nursery, Belle Isle Drive, Exeter EX2 4RY ☎ 01392 262638 ✉ paul.faulkner@exeter.gov.uk

Health and Safety: Mr Robert Norley, Assistant Director - Environment, Civic Centre, Paris Street, Exeter EX1 1RQ ☎ 01392 265170 ✉ robert.norley@exeter.gov.uk

Home Energy Conservation: Mr Keith Williams, Environmental Health Manager of Private Sector Housing, Civic Centre, Paris Street, Exeter EX1 1RQ ☎ 01392 265777 ✉ keith.williams@exeter.gov.uk

Housing: Mr Roger Coombes, Assistant Director - Housing, Civic Centre, Paris Street, Exeter EX1 1JN ☎ 01392 265468 ✉ roger.coombes@exeter.gov.uk

Legal: Miss Baan Al-Khafaji, Corporate Manager Legal, Civic Centre, Paris Street, Exeter EX1 1JN ☎ 01392 265874 ✉ bkhafaji@exeter.gov.uk

Licensing: Mr Robert Norley, Assistant Director - Environment, Civic Centre, Paris Street, Exeter EX1 1RQ ☎ 01392 265170 ✉ robert.norley@exeter.gov.uk

Member Services: Ms Sarah Selway, Democratic Services Manager, Civic Centre, Paris Street, Exeter EX1 1JN ☎ 01392 265275 ✉ sarah.selway@exeter.gov.uk

Member Services: Mr John Street, Corporate Manager - Democratic & Civic Support, Civic Centre, Paris Street, Exeter EX1 1JN ☎ 01392 265106 ✉ john.street@exeter.gov.uk

Parking: Mrs Sarah Ward, Assistant Director - Public Realm, Civic Centre, Paris Street, Exeter EX1 1JN ☎ 01392 265215 ✉ sarah.ward@exeter.gov.uk

Personnel / HR: Mr Mark Parkinson, Deputy Chief Executive, Civic Centre, Paris Street, Exeter EX1 1JN ☎ 01392 265105 ✉ mark.parkinson@exeter.gov.uk

Planning: Mr Richard Short, Assistant Director - City Development, Civic Centre, Paris Street, Exeter EX1 1JN ☎ 01392 265219 ✉ richard.short@exeter.gov.uk

Recycling & Waste Minimisation: Mr Robert Norley, Assistant Director - Environment, Civic Centre, Paris Street, Exeter EX1 1RQ ☎ 01392 265170 ✉ robert.norley@exeter.gov.uk

Staff Training: Mrs June Callister, Learning & Development Partner, Civic Centre, Paris Street, Exeter EX1 1JN ☎ 01392 265666 ✉ june.callister@exeter.gov.uk

Street Scene: Mrs Sarah Ward, Assistant Director - Public Realm, Civic Centre, Paris Street, Exeter EX1 1JN ☎ 01392 265215 ✉ sarah.ward@exeter.gov.uk

Tourism: Mr Richard Ball, Assistant Director - Economy, Civic Centre, Paris Street, Exeter EX1 1JN ☎ 01392 265140 ✉ richard.ball@exeter.gov.uk

Tourism: Ms Victoria Hatfield, Tourism Development Manager, Civic Centre, Paris Street, Exeter EX1 1JJ ☎ 01392 265104 ✉ victoria.hatfield@exeter.gov.uk

Waste Management: Mr Robert Norley, Assistant Director - Environment, Civic Centre, Paris Street, Exeter EX1 1RQ ☎ 01392 265170 ✉ robert.norley@exeter.gov.uk

COUNCILLORS

The Lord Mayor: Thompson, Cynthia (CON - Pinhoe) cllr.cynthia.thompson@exeter.gov.uk

Deputy Lord Mayor: Holland, Peter (CON - Pennsylvania) cllr.peter.holland@exeter.gov.uk

Leader of the Council: Edwards, Peter (LAB - Mincinglake & Whipton) cllr.peter.edwards@exeter.gov.uk

Group Leader: Leadbetter, Andrew (CON - Topsham) cllr.andrew.leadbetter@exeter.gov.uk

Ashwood, Rose (LAB - St Loyes) cllr.rose.ashwood@exeter.gov.uk

Baldwin, Margaret (CON - Topsham) cllr.margaret.baldwin@exeter.gov.uk

Bialyk, Philip (LAB - Exwick) cllr.philip.bialyk@exeter.gov.uk

Branston, Richard (LAB - Newtown & St Leonard's) cllr.richard.branston@exeter.gov.uk

Brimble, Stephen (LAB - Mincinglake & Whipton) cllr.stephen.brimble@exeter.gov.uk

Bull, Paul (LAB - St Thomas) cllr.paul.bull@exeter.gov.uk

Denham, Rosie (LAB - Heavitree) cllr.rosie.denham@exeter.gov.uk

Foale, Bob (LAB - Alphington) cllr.bob.foale@exeter.gov.uk

Foggin, Owlen (LAB - Heavitree) cllr.olwen.foggin@exeter.gov.uk

Gottschalk, Daniel (LAB - Pennsylvania)
cllr.daniel.gottschalk@exeter.gov.uk

Hannaford, Rob (LAB - St Thomas)
cllr.rob.hannaford@exeter.gov.uk

Hannan, Kate (LAB - Priory)
cllr.kate.hannan@exeter.gov.uk

Harvey, David (LAB - Pinhoe)
cllr.david.harvey@exeter.gov.uk

Henson, David (CON - St Loyes)
cllr.david.henson@exeter.gov.uk

Henson, Yolanda (CON - St Loyes)
cllr.yolanda.henson@exeter.gov.uk

Keen, Lewis (LAB - St David's)
cllr.lewis.keen@exeter.gov.uk

Lamb, Robert (LAB - St David's)
cllr.robert.lamb@exeter.gov.uk

Lyons, Rachel (LAB - Pennsylvania)
cllr.rachel.lyons@exeter.gov.uk

Mitchell, Kevin (LD - Duryard & St James)
cllr.kevin.mitchell@exeter.gov.uk

Morse, Emma (LAB - Mincinglake & Whipton)
cllr.emma.morse@exeter.gov.uk

Musgrave, Chris (LAB - Alphington)
cllr.chris.musgrave@exeter.gov.uk

Newby, Rob (CON - Topsham)
cllr.rob.newby@exeter.gov.uk

Owen, Keith (LAB - Duryard & St James)
cllr.keith.owen@exeter.gov.uk

Packham, Hannah (LAB - St Thomas)
cllr.hannah.packham@exeter.gov.uk

Pearson, Ollie (LAB - Exwick)
cllr.ollie.pearson@exeter.gov.uk

Prowse, Percy (CON - Duryard & St James)
cllr.percy.prowse@exeter.gov.uk

Robson, Lesley (LAB - Priory)
cllr.lesley.robson@exeter.gov.uk

Sheldon, Greg (LAB - Heavitree)
cllr.greg.sheldon@exeter.gov.uk

Sills, Luke (LAB - St David's)
cllr.luke.sills@exeter.gov.uk

Spackman, Roger (LAB - Newtown & St Leonard's)
cllr.roger.spackman@exeter.gov.uk

Sutton, Rachel (LAB - Exwick)
cllr.rachel.sutton@exeter.gov.uk

Vizard, Natalie (LAB - Newtown & St Leonard's)
cllr.natalie.vizard@exeter.gov.uk

Wardle, Tony (LAB - Priory)
cllr.tony.wardle@exeter.gov.uk

Warwick, Steve (LAB - Alphington)
cllr.steve.warwick@exeter.gov.uk

Wood, Duncan (LAB - Pinhoe)
cllr.duncan.wood@exeter.gov.uk

POLITICAL COMPOSITION
LAB: 30, CON: 8, LD: 1

COMMITTEE CHAIRS

Audit: Ms Natalie Vizard

Licensing: Mr Roger Spackman

Planning: Ms Rachel Sutton

Falkirk   S

Falkirk Council, Municipal Buildings, Falkirk FK1 5RS
☎ 01324 506070 · contact.centre@falkirk.gov.uk
🖳 www.falkirk.gov.uk

FACTS AND FIGURES
Parliamentary Constituencies: Falkirk, Linlithgow and Falkirk East
EU Constituencies: Scotland
Election Frequency: Elections are of whole council

PRINCIPAL OFFICERS

Chief Executive: Mrs Mary Pitcaithly, Chief Executive, Municipal Buildings, Falkirk FK1 5RS ☎ 01324 506002
· mary.pitcaithly@falkirk.gov.uk

Senior Management: Ms Rhona Geisler, Director - Development Services, Abbotsford House, David's Loan, Falkirk FK2 7YZ
☎ 01324 504949 · rhona.geisler@falkirk.gov.uk

Senior Management: Ms Kathy McCarroll, Chief Social Worker & Head of Social Work, Sealock House, 2 Inchyra House, Grangemouth FK3 9XB ☎ 01324 508791
· kathy.mccarroll@falkirk.gov.uk

Senior Management: Mr Robert Naylor, Director - Children's Services, Sealock House, 2 Inchyra House, Grangemouth FK3 9XB
☎ 01324 506600 · robert.naylor@falkirk.gov.uk

Senior Management: Mr Stuart Ritchie, Director - Corporate & Housing Services, Municipal Buildings, Falkirk FK1 5RS
☎ 01324 506005 · stuart.ritchie@falkirk.gov.uk

Architect, Building / Property Services: Mr Robert McMaster, Head of Roads & Design Services, Abbotsford House, David's Loan, Falkirk FK2 7YZ ☎ 01324 504953
· robert.mcmaster@falkirk.gov.uk

Best Value: Mr Stuart Ritchie, Director - Corporate & Housing Services, Municipal Buildings, Falkirk FK1 5RS ☎ 01324 506005
· stuart.ritchie@falkirk.gov.uk

Building Control: Mr Ian Dryden, Development Manager, Falkirk Council Development Services, Abbotsford House, David's Loan, Falkirk FK2 7HZ ☎ 01324 504756 · ian.dryden@falkirk.gov.uk

Catering Services: Ms Judith Borg, Catering Co-ordinator, Municipal Buildings, Falkirk FK1 5RS ☎ 01324 590461
· judith.borg@falkirk.gov.uk

Civil Registration: Ms Gillian McIntyre, Customer & Development Manager, Municipal Buildings, Falkirk FK1 5RS ☎ 01324 506104
· gillian.mcintyre@falkirk.gov.uk

FALKIRK

PR / Communications: Ms Caroline Binnie, Communications Manager, Municipal Buildings, Falkirk FK1 5RS ☎ 01324 506051 ✆ caroline.binnie@falkirk.gov.uk

Community Planning: Ms Fiona Campbell, Head of Policy, Technology & Improvement, Municipal Buildings, Falkirk FK1 5RS ☎ 01324 506004 ✆ fiona.campbell@falkirk.gov.uk

Community Safety: Ms Fiona Campbell, Head of Policy, Technology & Improvement, Municipal Buildings, Falkirk FK1 5RS ☎ 01324 506004 ✆ fiona.campbell@falkirk.gov.uk

Computer Management: Ms Fiona Campbell, Head of Policy, Technology & Improvement, Municipal Buildings, Falkirk FK1 5RS ☎ 01324 506004 ✆ fiona.campbell@falkirk.gov.uk

Consumer Protection and Trading Standards: Mr Douglas Duff, Head of Economic Development & Environmental Services, Falkirk Council Development Services, Abbotsford House, David's Loan, Falkirk FK2 7YZ ☎ 01324 504952 ✆ douglas.duff@falkirk.gov.uk

Contracts: Mr David McGhee, Head of Procurement & Housing Property, Suite 4, The Forum, Callendar Business Park, Falkirk FK1 1XR ☎ 01324 590788 ✆ david.mcghee@falkirk.gov.uk

Corporate Services: Mr Stuart Ritchie, Director - Corporate & Housing Services, Municipal Buildings, Falkirk FK1 5RS ☎ 01324 506005 ✆ stuart.ritchie@falkirk.gov.uk

Customer Service: Ms Karen Algie, Head of Human Resources & Business Transformation, Municipal Buildings, Falkirk FK1 5RS ☎ 01324 506223 ✆ karen.algie@falkirk.gov.uk

Direct Labour: Mr David McGhee, Head of Procurement & Housing Property, Suite 4, The Forum, Callendar Business Park, Falkirk FK1 1XR ☎ 01324 590788 ✆ david.mcghee@falkirk.gov.uk

Economic Development: Mr Douglas Duff, Head of Economic Development & Environmental Services, Falkirk Council Development Services, Abbotsford House, David's Loan, Falkirk FK2 7YZ ☎ 01324 504952 ✆ douglas.duff@falkirk.gov.uk

Education: Mr Gary Greenhorn, Head of Service - Planning & Resources, Sealock House, 2 Inchyra Road, Grangemouth FK3 9XB ☎ 01324 506681 ✆ gary.greenhorn@swindon.gov.uk

Education: Mr David Mackay, Head of Education, Sealock House, 2 Inchyra Road, Grangemouth FK3 9XB ☎ 01324 506684 ✆ david.mackay@falkirk.gov.uk

Education: Mr Robert Naylor, Director - Children's Services, Sealock House, 2 Inchyra House, Grangemouth FK3 9XB ☎ 01324 506600 ✆ robert.naylor@falkirk.gov.uk

E-Government: Ms Fiona Campbell, Head of Policy, Technology & Improvement, Municipal Buildings, Falkirk FK1 5RS ☎ 01324 506004 ✆ fiona.campbell@falkirk.gov.uk

Emergency Planning: Mr Malcolm Wilson, Civil Contingencies Co-ordinator, Development Services, Abbotsford House, David's Loan, Falkirk FK2 7YZ ☎ 01324 501000 ✆ m.wilson@falkirk.gov.uk

Energy Management: Mr Robert McMaster, Head of Roads & Design Services, Abbotsford House, David's Loan, Falkirk FK2 7YZ ☎ 01324 504953 ✆ robert.mcmaster@falkirk.gov.uk

Environmental / Technical Services: Ms Rhona Geisler, Director - Development Services, Abbotsford House, David's Loan, Falkirk FK2 7YZ ☎ 01324 504949 ✆ rhona.geisler@falkirk.gov.uk

Environmental Health: Mr Graeme Webster, Interim Manager - Environmental Health, Trading Standards & Community Safety, Abbotsford House, David's Loan, Falkirk FK2 7YZ ☎ 01324 504762 ✆ graeme.webster@falkirk.gov.uk

Estates, Property & Valuation: Mr Douglas Duff, Head of Economic Development & Environmental Services, Falkirk Council Development Services, Abbotsford House, David's Loan, Falkirk FK2 7YZ ☎ 01324 504952 ✆ douglas.duff@falkirk.gov.uk

European Liaison: Ms Fiona Campbell, Head of Policy, Technology & Improvement, Municipal Buildings, Falkirk FK1 5RS ☎ 01324 506004 ✆ fiona.campbell@falkirk.gov.uk

Finance: Mr Danny Cairney, Acting Depute Chief Finance Officer, Municipal Buildings, Falkirk FK1 5RS ✆ danny.cairney@falkirk.gov.uk

Finance: Mr Bryan Smail, Chief Finance Officer, Municipal Buildings, Falkirk FK1 5RS ☎ 01324 506300 ✆ bryan.smail@falkirk.gov.uk

Finance: Mrs Amanda Templeman, Acting Depute Chief Finance Officer, Municipal Buildings, Falkirk FK1 5RS ☎ 01324 506371 ✆ amanda.templeman@falkirk.gov.uk

Pensions: Mr Alistair McGirr, Pensions Manager, Municipal Buildings, Falkirk FK1 5RS ☎ 01324 506304 ✆ alistair.mcgirr@falkirk.gov.uk

Fleet Management: Mr Carl Bullough, Acting Head of Operational Services, Dalgrain Depot, McCafferty Way, Grangemouth FK3 8EB ☎ 01324 590420 ✆ carl.bullough@falkirk.gov.uk

Grounds Maintenance: Mr Steve Bentley, Housing Strategy & Private Sector Housing Manager, Dalgrain Depot, McCafferty Way, Grangemouth FK3 8EB ☎ 01324 500833 ✆ steve.bentley@falkirk.gov.uk

Health and Safety: Ms Karen Algie, Head of Human Resources & Business Transformation, Municipal Buildings, Falkirk FK1 5RS ☎ 01324 506223 ✆ karen.algie@falkirk.gov.uk

Highways: Mr Robert McMaster, Head of Roads & Design Services, Abbotsford House, David's Loan, Falkirk FK2 7YZ ☎ 01324 504953 ✆ robert.mcmaster@falkirk.gov.uk

Home Energy Conservation: Mr Steve Bentley, Housing Strategy & Private Sector Housing Manager, Dalgrain Depot, McCafferty Way, Grangemouth FK3 8EB ☎ 01324 500833 ✆ steve.bentley@falkirk.gov.uk

Housing: Ms Jennifer Litts, Head of Housing Services, Suite 4, The Forum, Callendar Business Park, Falkirk FK1 1XR ☎ 01324 590789 ✆ jennifer.litts@falkirk.gov.uk

Housing Maintenance: Ms Jennifer Litts, Head of Housing Services, Suite 4, The Forum, Callendar Business Park, Falkirk FK1 1XR ☎ 01324 590789 ⌁ jennifer.litts@falkirk.gov.uk

Legal: Ms Rose Mary Glackin, Chief Governance Officer, Municipal Buildings, Falkirk FK1 5RS ☎ 01324 506076 ⌁ rosemary.glackin@falkirk.gov.uk

Licensing: Ms Alison Barr, Consumer Protection Manager, Municipal Buildings, Falkirk FK1 5RS ☎ 01324 501265 ⌁ alison.barr@falkirk.gov.uk

Lighting: Mr Graham Speirs, Area Lighting Engineer, Falkirk Council Development Services, Abbotsford House, David's Loan, Falkirk FK2 7YZ ☎ 01324 504823 ⌁ graham.speirs@falkirk.gov.uk

Lottery Funding, Charity and Voluntary: Ms Fiona Campbell, Head of Policy, Technology & Improvement, Municipal Buildings, Falkirk FK1 5RS ☎ 01324 506004 ⌁ fiona.campbell@falkirk.gov.uk

Member Services: Mr Harry Forster, Member Services Administrator, Municipal Buildings, Falkirk FK1 5RS ☎ 01324 506152 ⌁ harry.forster@falkirk.gov.uk

Parking: Mr Russell Steedman, Network Co-ordinator, Abbotsford House, David's Loan, Falkirk FK1 5RS ☎ 01324 504830 ⌁ russell.steedman@falkirk.gov.uk

Personnel / HR: Ms Karen Algie, Head of Human Resources & Business Transformation, Municipal Buildings, Falkirk FK1 5RS ☎ 01324 506223 ⌁ karen.algie@falkirk.gov.uk

Planning: Mr Ian Dryden, Development Manager, Falkirk Council Development Services, Abbotsford House, David's Loan, Falkirk FK2 7HZ ☎ 01324 504756 ⌁ ian.dryden@falkirk.gov.uk

Procurement: Mr David McGhee, Head of Procurement & Housing Property, Suite 4, The Forum, Callendar Business Park, Falkirk FK1 1XR ☎ 01324 590788 ⌁ david.mcghee@falkirk.gov.uk

Recycling & Waste Minimisation: Mr Robin Baird, Interim Waste Manager, Abbotsford House, David's Loan, Falkirk FK2 7YZ ☎ 01324 590437 ⌁ robin.baird@falkirk.gov.uk

Regeneration: Ms Fiona Campbell, Head of Policy, Technology & Improvement, Municipal Buildings, Falkirk FK1 5RS ☎ 01324 506004 ⌁ fiona.campbell@falkirk.gov.uk

Road Safety: Mr Greg Pender, Engineering Design Manager, Falkirk Council Development Services, Abbotsford House, David's Loan, Falkirk FK2 7YZ ☎ 01324 504827 ⌁ greg.pender@falkirk.gov.uk

Social Services (Adult): Mr Joe McElholm, Head of Adult Services, Denny Town House, Glasgow Road, Denny FK6 5DL ☎ 01324 504026 ⌁ joe.mcelholm@falkirk.gov.uk

Social Services (Children): Ms Kathy McCarroll, Chief Social Worker & Head of Social Work, Sealock House, 2 Inchyra Road, Grangemouth FK3 9XB ☎ 01324 508791 ⌁ kathy.mccarroll@falkirk.gov.uk

Staff Training: Ms Karen Algie, Head of Human Resources & Business Transformation, Municipal Buildings, Falkirk FK1 5RS ☎ 01324 506223 ⌁ karen.algie@falkirk.gov.uk

Street Scene: Mr Raymond Smith, Roads Manager, Development Services, Roads Unit, Earls Road, Grangemouth FK3 8XD ☎ 01324 504812 ⌁ raymond.smith@falkirk.gov.uk

Sustainable Communities: Mr Robert McMaster, Head of Roads & Design Services, Abbotsford House, David's Loan, Falkirk FK2 7YZ ☎ 01324 504953 ⌁ robert.mcmaster@falkirk.gov.uk

Sustainable Development: Mr Robert McMaster, Head of Roads & Design Services, Abbotsford House, David's Loan, Falkirk FK2 7YZ ☎ 01324 504953 ⌁ robert.mcmaster@falkirk.gov.uk

Tourism: Mr Pete Reid, Growth & Investment Manager, Falkirk Council Development Serivces, Abbotsford House, David's Loan, Falkirk FK2 7YZ ☎ 01324 590971 ⌁ pete.reid@falkirk.gov.uk

Town Centre: Mr Alex Fleming, Town Centre Manager, Old Burgh Buildings, 12 - 14 Newmarket Street, Falkirk FK1 1JE ☎ 01324 611293 ⌁ alex@falkirkdelivers.com

Traffic Management: Mr Russell Steedman, Network Co-ordinator, Abbotsford House, David's Loan, Falkirk FK1 5RS ☎ 01324 504830 ⌁ russell.steedman@falkirk.gov.uk

Transport: Mr Carl Bullough, Acting Head of Operational Services, Dalgrain Depot, McCafferty Way, Grangemouth FK3 8EB ☎ 01324 590420 ⌁ carl.bullough@falkirk.gov.uk

Transport Planner: Mrs Julie Cole, Acting Transport Planning Manager, Development Services, Abbotsford House, David's Loan, Falkirk FK2 7YZ ☎ 01324 404820 ⌁ julie.cole@falkirk.gov.uk

Waste Collection and Disposal: Mr Carl Bullough, Acting Head of Operational Services, Dalgrain Depot, McCafferty Way, Grangemouth FK3 8EB ☎ 01324 590420 ⌁ carl.bullough@falkirk.gov.uk

Waste Collection and Disposal: Mr Carl Bullough, Acting Head of Operational Services, Dalgrain Depot, McCafferty Way, Grangemouth FK3 8EB ☎ 01324 590420 ⌁ carl.bullough@falkirk.gov.uk

Waste Management: Mr Carl Bullough, Acting Head of Operational Services, Dalgrain Depot, McCafferty Way, Grangemouth FK3 8EB ☎ 01324 590420 ⌁ carl.bullough@falkirk.gov.uk

COUNCILLORS

Leader of the Council: Martin, Craig (LAB - Carse Kinnaird & Tryst) craig.martin@falkirk.gov.uk

Alexander, David (SNP - Falkirk North) david.alexander@falkirk.gov.uk

Balfour, David (SNP - Grangemouth) david.balfour@falkirk.gov.uk

Bird, Stephen (SNP - Carse Kinnaird & Tryst) stephen.bird@falkirk.gov.uk

Black, Allyson (LAB - Grangemouth) allyson.black@falkirk.gov.uk

FALKIRK

Blackwood, Jim (LAB - Denny & Banknock)
jim.blackwood@falkirk.gov.uk

Buchanan, Billy (INDNA - Bonnybridge & Larbert)
william.buchanan@falkirk.gov.uk

Carleschi, Steven (SNP - Carse Kinnaird & Tryst)
steven.carleschi@falkirk.gov.uk

Chalmers, Colin (SNP - Falkirk South)
colin.chalmers@falkirk.gov.uk

Coleman, Tom (SNP - Bonnybridge & Larbert)
thomas.coleman@falkirk.gov.uk

Goldie, Gerry (LAB - Falkirk South)
gerry.goldie@falkirk.gov.uk

Goldie, Dennis (LAB - Falkirk South)
dennis.goldie@falkirk.gov.uk

Gow, Linda (LAB - Bonnybridge & Larbert)
linda.gow@falkirk.gov.uk

Hughes, Gordon (SNP - Upper Braes)
gordon.hughes@falkirk.gov.uk

Jackson, Steven (SNP - Lower Braes)
steven.jackson@falkirk.gov.uk

MacDonald, Charles (LAB - Carse Kinnaird & Tryst)
charles.macdonald@falkirk.gov.uk

Mahoney, Adrian (LAB - Bo'ness & Blackness)
adrian.mahoney@falkirk.gov.uk

Martin, Craig (LAB - Falkirk North)
craigr.martin@falkirk.gov.uk

McCabe, Brian (INDNA - Denny & Banknock)
brian.mccabe@falkirk.gov.uk

McLuckie, John (LAB - Upper Braes)
john.mcluckie@falkirk.gov.uk

McNally, John (SNP - Denny & Banknock)
john.mcnally@falkirk.gov.uk

Meiklejohn, Cecil (SNP - Falkirk North)
cecil.meiklejohn@falkirk.gov.uk

Murray, Roise (LAB - Upper Braes)
rosie.murray@falkirk.gov.uk

Nicol, Malcolm (CON - Lower Braes)
malcolm.nicol@falkirk.gov.uk

Nimmo, Alan (LAB - Lower Braes)
alan.nimmo@falkirk.gov.uk

Oliver, Martin (SNP - Denny & Banknock)
martin.oliver@falkirk.gov.uk

Paterson, Joan (LAB - Grangemouth)
joan.paterson@falkirk.gov.uk

Patrick, John (CON - Falkirk South)
john.patrick@falkirk.gov.uk

Reid, Pat (LAB - Falkirk North)
pat.reid@falkirk.gov.uk

Ritchie, Ann (SNP - Bo'ness & Blackness)
ann.ritchie@falkirk.gov.uk

Spears, Robert (INDNA - Grangemouth)
robert.spears@falkirk.gov.uk

Turner, Sandy (SNP - Bo'ness & Blackness)
sandy.turner@falkirk.gov.uk

POLITICAL COMPOSITION
LAB: 14, SNP: 13, INDNA: 3, CON: 2

Fareham D

Fareham Borough Council, Civic Offices, Civic Way, Fareham PO16 7AZ

☎ 01329 236100 🖶 01329 822732 ✎ customerservices@fareham.gov.uk

🖥 www.fareham.gov.uk

FACTS AND FIGURES
Parliamentary Constituencies: Fareham
EU Constituencies: South East
Election Frequency: Elections are biennial

PRINCIPAL OFFICERS

Chief Executive: Mr Peter Grimwood, Chief Executive, Civic Offices, Civic Way, Fareham PO16 7AZ ☎ 01329 824300 ✎ cx@fareham.gov.uk

Senior Management: Mr Paul Doran, Director - Operations, Civic Offices, Civic Way, Fareham PO16 7AZ ☎ 01329 824572 ✎ pdoran@fareham.gov.uk

Senior Management: Mr Richard Jolley, Director - Planning & Regulation, Civic Offices, Civic Way, Fareham PO16 7AZ ☎ 01329 824388 ✎ rjolley@fareham.gov.uk

Senior Management: Mr Andy Wannell, Director - Finance & Resources, Civic Offices, Civic Way, Fareham PO16 7AZ ☎ 01329 824620 ✎ awannell@fareham.gov.uk

Access Officer / Social Services (Disability): Mr John Shaw, Head of Building Control, Civic Offices, Civic Way, Fareham PO16 7AZ ☎ 01329 824450 ✎ jshaw@fareham.gov.uk

Architect, Building / Property Services: Mr Shaun Barnett, Planned Maintenance Manager, Civic Offices, Civic Way, Fareham PO16 7AZ ☎ 01329 236100 ✎ sbarnett@fareham.gov.uk

Architect, Building / Property Services: Mr Graham Lloyd, Head of Estates, Civic Offices, Civic Way, Fareham PO16 7AZ ☎ 01329 824320 ✎ glloyd@fareham.gov.uk

Building Control: Mr John Shaw, Head of Building Control, Civic Offices, Civic Way, Fareham PO16 7AZ ☎ 01329 824450 ✎ jshaw@fareham.gov.uk

PR / Communications: Mrs Lindsey Ansell, Head of Corporate Services, Civic Offices, Civic Way, Fareham PO16 7AZ ☎ 01329 824567 ✎ lansell@fareham.gov.uk

Community Planning: Mr Richard Jolley, Director - Planning & Regulation, Civic Offices, Civic Way, Fareham PO16 7AZ ☎ 01329 824388 ✎ rjolley@fareham.gov.uk

Community Safety: Ms Narinder Bains, Community Safety Manager, Civic Offices, Civic Way, Fareham PO16 7AZ ☎ 01329 824496 ✎ nbains@fareham.gov.uk

Computer Management: Ms Sarah Robinson, Head of Personnel & ICT, Civic Offices, Civic Way, Fareham PO16 7AZ ☎ 01329 824564 ⌁ srobinson@fareham.gov.uk

Corporate Services: Mrs Lindsey Ansell, Head of Corporate Services, Civic Offices, Civic Way, Fareham PO16 7AZ ☎ 01329 824567 ⌁ lansell@fareham.gov.uk

Corporate Services: Ms Elaine Hammell, Head of Audit & Assurance, Civic Offices, Civic Way, Fareham PO16 7AZ ☎ 01329 236100 ⌁ ehammell@fareham.gov.uk

Customer Service: Mrs Lindsey Ansell, Head of Corporate Services, Civic Offices, Civic Way, Fareham PO16 7AZ ☎ 01329 824567 ⌁ lansell@fareham.gov.uk

E-Government: Mr Peter Grimwood, Chief Executive, Civic Offices, Civic Way, Fareham PO16 7AZ ☎ 01329 824300 ⌁ cx@fareham.gov.uk

Electoral Registration: Ms Leigh Usher, Head of Democratic Services, Civic Offices, Civic Way, Fareham PO16 7AZ ☎ 01329 824553 ⌁ lusher@fareham.gov.uk

Emergency Planning: Mr Paul Doran, Director - Operations, Civic Offices, Civic Way, Fareham PO16 7AZ ☎ 01329 824572 ⌁ pdoran@fareham.gov.uk

Energy Management: Mr Ian Cousins, Property Manager, Civic Offices, Civic Way, Fareham PO16 7AZ ☎ 01329 824835 ⌁ icousins@fareham.gov.uk

Environmental / Technical Services: Mr Paul Doran, Director - Operations, Civic Offices, Civic Way, Fareham PO16 7AZ ☎ 01329 824572 ⌁ pdoran@fareham.gov.uk

Environmental Health: Mr Ian Rickman, Head of Environmental Health, Civic Offices, Civic Way, Fareham PO16 7AZ ☎ 01329 824773 ⌁ irickman@fareham.gov.uk

Estates, Property & Valuation: Mr Graham Lloyd, Head of Estates, Civic Offices, Civic Way, Fareham PO16 7AZ ☎ 01329 824320 ⌁ glloyd@fareham.gov.uk

Facilities: Mr Tony Hopkins, Facilities Manager, Civic Offices, Civic Way, Fareham PO16 7AZ ☎ 01329 236100 ⌁ thopkins@fareham.gov.uk

Finance: Mr Andy Wannell, Director - Finance & Resources, Civic Offices, Civic Way, Fareham PO16 7AZ ☎ 01329 824620 ⌁ awannell@fareham.gov.uk

Fleet Management: Ms Kitty Rose, Refuse & Recycling Manager, Civic Offices, Civic Way, Fareham PO16 7AZ ☎ 01329 236100 ⌁ krose@fareham.gov.uk

Grounds Maintenance: Mr Paul Doran, Director - Operations, Civic Offices, Civic Way, Fareham PO16 7AZ ☎ 01329 824572 ⌁ pdoran@fareham.gov.uk

Health and Safety: Mr Keith Perkins, Health & Safety Officer, Civic Offices, Civic Way, Fareham PO16 7AZ ☎ 01329 236100 ⌁ kperkins@fareham.gov.uk

Housing: Mrs Caroline Newman, Head of Housing, Revenues & Benefits, Civic Offices, Civic Way, Fareham PO16 7AZ ☎ 01329 824645 ⌁ cnewman@fareham.gov.uk

Housing Maintenance: Mr Ian Cousins, Property Manager, Civic Offices, Civic Way, Fareham PO16 7AZ ☎ 01329 824835 ⌁ icousins@fareham.gov.uk

Legal: Mr Richard Ivory, Head of Legal & Democratic Services, Civic Offices, Civic Way, Fareham PO16 7AZ ☎ 02380 832794 ⌁ richard.ivory@southampton.gov.uk

Leisure and Cultural Services: Mr Mark Bowler, Head of Leisure & Community, Civic Offices, Civic Way, Fareham PO16 7AZ ☎ 01329 824420 ⌁ mbowler@fareham.gov.uk

Licensing: Ms Helen Spires, Licensing Manager, Civic Offices, Civic Way, Fareham PO16 7AZ ☎ 01329 824411 ⌁ hspires@fareham.gov.uk

Lottery Funding, Charity and Voluntary: Mr Mark Bowler, Head of Leisure & Community, Civic Offices, Civic Way, Fareham PO16 7AZ ☎ 01329 824420 ⌁ mbowler@fareham.gov.uk

Member Services: Ms Leigh Usher, Head of Democratic Services, Civic Offices, Civic Way, Fareham PO16 7AZ ☎ 01329 824553 ⌁ lusher@fareham.gov.uk

Parking: Mr K Wright, Head of Parking & Enforcement, Civic Offices, Civic Way, Fareham PO16 7AZ ☎ 01329 236100 ⌁ kwright@fareham.gov.uk

Personnel / HR: Ms Sarah Robinson, Head of Personnel & ICT, Civic Offices, Civic Way, Fareham PO16 7AZ ☎ 01329 824564 ⌁ srobinson@fareham.gov.uk

Planning: Mr Richard Jolley, Director - Planning & Regulation, Civic Offices, Civic Way, Fareham PO16 7AZ ☎ 01329 824388 ⌁ rjolley@fareham.gov.uk

Planning: Mr Lee Smith, Head of Development Control, Civic Offices, Civic Way, Fareham PO16 7AZ ☎ 01329 236100 ⌁ lsmith@fareham.gov.uk

Procurement: Mr Gary Jarvis, Procurement Officer, Civic Offices, Civic Way, Fareham PO16 7AZ ☎ 01329 824508 ⌁ gjarvis@fareham.gov.uk

Recycling & Waste Minimisation: Mr Paul Doran, Director - Operations, Civic Offices, Civic Way, Fareham PO16 7AZ ☎ 01329 824572 ⌁ pdoran@fareham.gov.uk

Regeneration: Ms Claire Burnett, Head of Planning Strategy & Regeneration, Civic Offices, Civic Way, Fareham PO16 7AZ ☎ 01329 236100 ⌁ cburnett@fareham.gov.uk

FAREHAM

Staff Training: Ms Sarah Robinson, Head of Personnel & ICT, Civic Offices, Civic Way, Fareham PO16 7AZ ☎ 01329 824564 📧 srobinson@fareham.gov.uk

Street Scene: Mr Paul Doran, Director - Operations, Civic Offices, Civic Way, Fareham PO16 7AZ ☎ 01329 824572 📧 pdoran@fareham.gov.uk

Sustainable Communities: Mr Richard Jolley, Director - Planning & Regulation, Civic Offices, Civic Way, Fareham PO16 7AZ ☎ 01329 824388 📧 rjolley@fareham.gov.uk

Sustainable Development: Mr Richard Jolley, Director - Planning & Regulation, Civic Offices, Civic Way, Fareham PO16 7AZ ☎ 01329 824388 📧 rjolley@fareham.gov.uk

Town Centre: Mr Mark Bowler, Head of Leisure & Community, Civic Offices, Civic Way, Fareham PO16 7AZ ☎ 01329 824420 📧 mbowler@fareham.gov.uk

Traffic Management: Mr Chris Oldham, Traffic & Design Manager, Civic Offices, Civic Way, Fareham PO16 7AZ ☎ 01329 236100 📧 coldham@fareham.gov.uk

Transport: Ms Kitty Rose, Refuse & Recycling Manager, Civic Offices, Civic Way, Fareham PO16 7AZ ☎ 01329 236100 📧 krose@fareham.gov.uk

Transport Planner: Mr Oli Seebohm, Principal Transport Planner, Civic Offices, Civic Way, Fareham PO16 7AZ ☎ 01329 236100 📧 oseebohm@fareham.gov.uk

Waste Collection and Disposal: Ms Kitty Rose, Refuse & Recycling Manager, Civic Offices, Civic Way, Fareham PO16 7AZ ☎ 01329 236100 📧 krose@fareham.gov.uk

Waste Management: Mr Paul Doran, Director - Operations, Civic Offices, Civic Way, Fareham PO16 7AZ ☎ 01329 824572 📧 pdoran@fareham.gov.uk

Children's Play Areas: Mrs Sue Woodbridge, Public & Open Spaces Manager, Civic Offices, Civic Way, Fareham PO16 7AZ ☎ 01329 236100 📧 swoodbridge@fareham.gov.uk

COUNCILLORS

Mayor: Hockley, Connie (CON - Titchfield)
chockley@fareham.gov.uk

Deputy Mayor: Fazackarley, Geoff (LD - Portchester East)
gfazackarley@fareham.gov.uk

Leader of the Council: Woodward, Sean (CON - Sarisbury)
swoodward@fareham.gov.uk

Deputy Leader of the Council: Cartwright, Trevor (CON - Warsash)
tcartwright@fareham.gov.uk

Group LeaderPrice, Roger (LD - Portchester East)
rprice@fareham.gov.uk

Barton, Keith (CON - Fareham South)
kbarton@fareham.gov.uk

Bayford, Brian (CON - Park Gate)
bbayford@fareham.gov.uk

Bayford, Susan (CON - Locks Heath)
sbayford@fareham.gov.uk

Bell, Susan (CON - Portchester West)
sbell@fareham.gov.uk

Birkett, Fred (CON - Fareham North West)
fbirkett@fareham.gov.uk

Brady, Maryam (LD - Fareham East)
mbrady@fareham.gov.uk

Bryant, Pamela (CON - Fareham North)
pbryant@fareham.gov.uk

Butts, Jonathan (CON - Sarisbury)
jbutts@fareham.gov.uk

Clubley, Louise (CON - Fareham North)
lclubley@fareham.gov.uk

Cunningham, Shaun (LD - Portchester East)
scunningham@fareham.gov.uk

Davies, Peter (CON - Fareham North West)
pdavies@fareham.gov.uk

Ellis, Tina (CON - Fareham West)
tellis@fareham.gov.uk

Englefield, Jack (IND - Titchfield Common)
jenglefield@fareham.gov.uk

Evans, Keith (CON - Locks Heath)
kevans@fareham.gov.uk

Ford, Michael (CON - Warsash)
mford@fareham.gov.uk

Harper, Tiffany (CON - Titchfield)
tharper@fareham.gov.uk

Heneghan, Carolyn (UKIP - Stubbington)
cheneghan@fareham.gov.uk

Keeble, Leslie (CON - Fareham West)
lkeeble@fareham.gov.uk

Mandry, Arthur (CON - Hill Head)
amandry@fareham.gov.uk

Mandry, Kay (CON - Hill Head)
kmandry@fareham.gov.uk

Martin, Simon (CON - Park Gate)
smartin@fareham.gov.uk

Pankhurst, Sarah (CON - Titchfield Common)
spankhurt@fareham.gov.uk

Steadman, Dennis (CON - Fareham South)
dsteadman@fareham.gov.uk

Trott, Katrina (LD - Fareham East)
ktrott@fareham.gov.uk

Walker, Nick (CON - Portchester West)
nwalker@fareham.gov.uk

Wood, Christopher (UKIP - Stubbington)
cwood@fareham.gov.uk

POLITICAL COMPOSITION
CON: 23, LD: 5, UKIP: 2, IND: 1

COMMITTEE CHAIRS

Audit: Ms Tiffany Harper

Health & Housing: Mr Brian Bayford

Leisure & Community: Mrs Sarah Pankhurst

Licensing: Mrs Pamela Bryant

Fenland   D

Fenland District Council, Fenland Hall, County Road, March
PE15 8NQ
☎ 01354 654321 📠 01354 622259 ✆ info@fenland.gov.uk
🖥 www.fenland.gov.uk

FACTS AND FIGURES
Parliamentary Constituencies: Cambridgeshire North East
EU Constituencies: Eastern
Election Frequency: Elections are of whole council

PRINCIPAL OFFICERS

Chief Executive: Mr Paul Medd, Chief Executive, Fenland Hall,
County Road, March PE15 8NQ ☎ 01354 622303
✆ paulmedd@fenland.gov.uk

Architect, Building / Property Services: Mr Gary Garford,
Corporate Director, Fenland Hall, County Road, March PE15 8NQ
☎ 01354 622373 ✆ garygarford@fenland.gov.uk

Building Control: Mr Rob Bridge, Corporate Director, Fenland
Hall, County Road, March PE15 8NQ ☎ 01354 622201
✆ robbridge@fenland.gov.uk

PR / Communications: Ms Carol Pilson, Corporate Director,
Fenland Hall, County Road, March PE15 8NQ ☎ 01354 622360
✆ cpilson@fenland.gov.uk

Community Planning: Mr Gary Garford, Corporate Director,
Fenland Hall, County Road, March PE15 8NQ ☎ 01354 622373
✆ garygarford@fenland.gov.uk

Community Safety: Mr Dan Horn, Head of Housing &
Community Support, Fenland Hall, County Road, March PE15 8NQ
☎ 01354 622470 ✆ dhorn@fenland.gov.uk

Computer Management: Mr Rob Bridge, Corporate Director,
Fenland Hall, County Road, March PE15 8NQ ☎ 01354 622201
✆ robbridge@fenland.gov.uk

Computer Management: Mr Geoff Kent, Head of Customer
Services, Fenland Hall, County Road, March PE15 8NQ
☎ 01354 654321 ✆ gkent@fenland.gov.uk

Contracts: Mr Shaun Beales, Purchasing & Procurement Manager,
Fenland Hall, County Road, March PE15 8NQ ☎ 01354 622429
✆ sbeales@fenland.gov.uk

Customer Service: Mr Geoff Kent, Head of Customer Services,
Fenland Hall, County Road, March PE15 8NQ ☎ 01354 654321
✆ gkent@fenland.gov.uk

Economic Development: Mr Justin Wingfield, Head of Business
& Economy, Fenland Hall, County Road, March PE15 8NQ
☎ 01354 622472 ✆ jwingfield@fenland.gov.uk

E-Government: Mr Rob Bridge, Corporate Director, Fenland Hall,
County Road, March PE15 8NQ ☎ 01354 622201
✆ robbridge@fenland.gov.uk

Electoral Registration: Mrs Anna Goodall, Head of Governance
& Legal, Fenland Hall, County Road, March PE15 8NQ
☎ 01354 622357 ✆ agoodall@fenland.gov.uk

Emergency Planning: Mr David Vincent, Health & Safety Advisor,
Fenland Hall, County Road, March PE15 8NQ ☎ 01354 622353
✆ dvincent@fenland.gov.uk

Energy Management: Mr Richard Cassidy, Corporate Director,
Fenland Hall, County Road, March PE15 8NQ ☎ 01354 622300
✆ richardcassidy@fenland.gov.uk

Environmental / Technical Services: Mr Richard Cassidy,
Corporate Director, Fenland Hall, County Road, March PE15 8NQ
☎ 01354 622300 ✆ richardcassidy@fenland.gov.uk

Environmental Health: Mrs Annabel Tighe, Environmental Health
Manager, Fenland Hall, County Road, March PE15 8NQ
☎ 01354 602497 ✆ atighe@fenland.gov.uk

Estates, Property & Valuation: Mr Justin Wingfield, Head of
Business & Economy, Fenland Hall, County Road, March PE15 8NQ
☎ 01354 622472 ✆ jwingfield@fenland.gov.uk

Events Manager: Ms Isabel Edgington, Senior Environmental
Projects Officer, Fenland Hall, County Road, March PE15 8NQ
☎ 01354 602167 ✆ iedgington@fenland.gov.uk

Facilities: Mr Gary Garford, Corporate Director, Fenland Hall,
County Road, March PE15 8NQ ☎ 01354 622373
✆ garygarford@fenland.gov.uk

Finance: Mr Rob Bridge, Corporate Director, Fenland Hall, County
Road, March PE15 8NQ ☎ 01354 622201
✆ robbridge@fenland.gov.uk

Fleet Management: Mr Mark Gregory, Fleet & Technical
Manager, Fenland Hall, County Road, March PE15 8NQ
☎ 01354 602119 ✆ mgregory@fenland.gov.uk

Grounds Maintenance: Mr Bob Ollier, Parks & Open Spaces
Manager, Fenland Hall, County Road, March PE15 8NQ
☎ 01354 602149 ✆ rollier@fenland.gov.uk

Health and Safety: Mr David Vincent, Health & Safety Advisor,
Fenland Hall, County Road, March PE15 8NQ ☎ 01354 622353
✆ dvincent@fenland.gov.uk

Home Energy Conservation: Mr Richard Cassidy, Corporate
Director, Fenland Hall, County Road, March PE15 8NQ
☎ 01354 622300 ✆ richardcassidy@fenland.gov.uk

Housing: Mr Dan Horn, Head of Housing & Community Support,
Fenland Hall, County Road, March PE15 8NQ ☎ 01354 622470
✆ dhorn@fenland.gov.uk

FENLAND

Local Area Agreement: Ms Carol Pilson, Corporate Director, Fenland Hall, County Road, March PE15 8NQ ☎ 01354 622360 cpilson@fenland.gov.uk

Legal: Mrs Anna Goodall, Head of Governance & Legal, Fenland Hall, County Road, March PE15 8NQ ☎ 01354 622357 agoodall@fenland.gov.uk

Leisure and Cultural Services: Mr Phil Hughes, Head of Parks & Leisure, Fenland Hall, County Road, March PE15 8NQ ☎ 01354 622520 phughes@fenland.gov.uk

Licensing: Mr Dan Horn, Head of Housing & Community Support, Fenland Hall, County Road, March PE15 8NQ ☎ 01354 622470 dhorn@fenland.gov.uk

Lottery Funding, Charity and Voluntary: Mr Dan Horn, Head of Housing & Community Support, Fenland Hall, County Road, March PE15 8NQ ☎ 01354 622470 dhorn@fenland.gov.uk

Member Services: Mrs Anna Goodall, Head of Governance & Legal, Fenland Hall, County Road, March PE15 8NQ ☎ 01354 622357 agoodall@fenland.gov.uk

Parking: Mr Trevor Watson, Head of Assets & Projects, Fenland Hall, County Road, March PE15 8NQ ☎ 01354 622518 tdwatson@fenland.gov.uk

Personnel / HR: Mrs Sam Anthony, Head of HR & OD, Fenland Hall, County Road, March PE15 8NQ ☎ 01354 622268 santhony@fenland.gov.uk

Planning: Mr Nick Harding, Head of Shared Planning, Fenland Hall, County Road, March PE15 8NQ ☎ 01354 622308 nharding@fenland.gov.uk

Procurement: Mr Rob Bridge, Corporate Director, Fenland Hall, County Road, March PE15 8NQ ☎ 01354 622201 robbridge@fenland.gov.uk

Recycling & Waste Minimisation: Mr Mark Mathews, Head of Environmental Services, Fenland Hall, County Road, March PE15 8NQ ☎ 01354 602164 mmathews@fenland.gov.uk

Regeneration: Mr Gary Garford, Corporate Director, Fenland Hall, County Road, March PE15 8NQ ☎ 01354 622373 garygarford@fenland.gov.uk

Staff Training: Mrs Sam Anthony, Head of HR & OD, Fenland Hall, County Road, March PE15 8NQ ☎ 01354 622268 santhony@fenland.gov.uk

Street Scene: Mrs Annabel Tighe, Environmental Health Manager, Fenland Hall, County Road, March PE15 8NQ ☎ 01354 602497 atighe@fenland.gov.uk

Sustainable Communities: Mr Dan Horn, Head of Housing & Community Support, Fenland Hall, County Road, March PE15 8NQ ☎ 01354 622470 dhorn@fenland.gov.uk

Tourism: Mr Phil Hughes, Head of Parks & Leisure, Fenland Hall, County Road, March PE15 8NQ ☎ 01354 622520 phughes@fenland.gov.uk

Town Centre: Mr Gary Garford, Corporate Director, Fenland Hall, County Road, March PE15 8NQ ☎ 01354 622373 garygarford@fenland.gov.uk

Transport Planner: Mr Gary Garford, Corporate Director, Fenland Hall, County Road, March PE15 8NQ ☎ 01354 622373 garygarford@fenland.gov.uk

Waste Collection and Disposal: Mr Mark Mathews, Head of Environmental Services, Fenland Hall, County Road, March PE15 8NQ ☎ 01354 602164 mmathews@fenland.gov.uk

Waste Management: Mr Mark Mathews, Head of Environmental Services, Fenland Hall, County Road, March PE15 8NQ ☎ 01354 602164 mmathews@fenland.gov.uk

COUNCILLORS

ChairCox, Carol (CON - Clarkson - Wisbech) ccox@fenland.gov.uk

Vice-ChairMayor: , Kay (CON - Bassenhally - Whittlesey) kaymayor@fenland.gov.uk

Leader of the Council: Clark, John (CON - March East) jclark@fenland.gov.uk

Bligh, Sarah (CON - Parson Drove & Wisbech St Mary) sbligh@fenland.gov.uk

Boden, Chris (CON - Bassenhally - Whittlesey) cboden@fenland.gov.uk

Booth, Gavin (O - Parson Drove & Wisbech St Mary) gbooth@fenland.gov.uk

Bucknor, Michael (IND - Waterlees - Village) mbucknor@fenland.gov.uk

Bucknor, Virginia (IND - Waterlees - Village) vbucknor@fenland.gov.uk

Buckton, Mark (CON - Manea) mbuckton@fenland.gov.uk

Butcher, Ralph (CON - Benwick, Coates & Eastrea) rbutcher@fenland.gov.uk

Clark, Sam (CON - Roman Bank - Wisbech) samclark@fenland.gov.uk

Connor, David (CON - Doddington & Wimblington) dconnor@fenland.gov.uk

Cornwell, Mike (CON - March North) mcornwell@fenland.gov.uk

Count, Steve (CON - March North) scount@fenland.gov.uk

Court, Stephen (CON - March North) scourt@fenland.gov.uk

Davis, Maureen (CON - Doddington & Wimblington) mdavis@fenland.gov.uk

French, Jan (CON - March West) jfrench@fenland.gov.uk

Garratt, Steve (CON - Lattersey - Whittlesey)
sgarratt@fenland.gov.uk

Green, David (CON - Birch - Chatteris)
davidgreen@fenland.gov.uk

Hay, Anne (CON - The Mills - Chatteris)
ahay@fenland.gov.uk

Hodgson, David (CON - Staithe - Wisbech)
dhodgson@fenland.gov.uk

Hoy, Samantha (CON - Hill - Wisbech)
shoy@fenland.gov.uk

Humphrey, Michael (CON - Roman Bank - Wisbech)
mhumphrey@fenland.gov.uk

King, Simon (CON - Hill - Wisbech)
sking@fenland.gov.uk

Laws, Dee (CON - Stonald)
dlaws@fenland.gov.uk

Mason, David (CON - St Andrews - Whittlesey)
dmason@fenland.gov.uk

Miscandlon, Alex (CON - Benwick, Coates & Eastrea)
amiscandlon@fenland.gov.uk

Murphy, Peter (CON - Wenneye - Chatteris)
pmurphy@fenland.gov.uk

Newell, Florence (CON - Slade Lode - Chatteris)
fnewell@fenland.gov.uk

Oliver, David (CON - Peckover - Wisbech)
doliver@fenland.gov.uk

Owen, Kit (CON - March West)
kowen@fenland.gov.uk

Pugh, Andrew (CON - March East)
apugh@fenland.gov.uk

Seaton, Christopher (CON - Roman Bank - Wisbech)
cseaton@fenland.gov.uk

Skoulding, Robert (IND - March West)
rskoulding@fenland.gov.uk

Sutton, Will (CON - Elm & Christchurch)
wsutton@fenland.gov.uk

Tanfield, Michelle (CON - Elm & Christchurch)
mtanfield@fenland.gov.uk

Tibbs, Garry (CON - Kirkgate - Wisbech)
gtibbs@fenland.gov.uk

Tierney, Steve (CON - Medworth - Wisbech)
stierney@fenland.gov.uk

Yeulett, Fred (CON - March East)
fyeulett@fenland.gov.uk

POLITICAL COMPOSITION
CON: 35, IND: 3, O: 1

COMMITTEE CHAIRS

Licensing: Mr Michael Humphrey

Planning: Mr Alex Miscandlon

Fermanagh & Omagh District Council   N

Fermanagh & Omagh District Council, Fermanagh District Council, Townhall, 2 Townhall Street, Enniskillen BT74 7BA
☎ 0300 303 1777 ✆ info@fermanaghomagh.com
🖳 www.fermanaghomagh.com

PRINCIPAL OFFICERS

Chief Executive: Mr Brendan Hegarty, Chief Executive, Fermanagh District Council, Townhall, 2 Townhall Street, Enniskillen BT74 7BA ✆ brendan.hegarty@fermanaghomagh.com

Senior Management: Ms Thelma Browne, Lead Officer - HR & OD, Fermanagh District Council, Townhall, 2 Townhall Street, Enniskillen BT74 7BA ☎ 0300 303 1777 ✆ thelma.browne@fermanaghomagh.com

Senior Management: Mr Robert Gibson, Director - Community, Health & Leisure, Fermanagh District Council, Townhall, 2 Townhall Street, Enniskillen BT74 7BA ☎ 0300 303 1777 ✆ robert.gibson@fermanaghomagh.com

Senior Management: Ms Catherine Leonard, Head of Finance, Fermanagh District Council, Townhall, 2 Townhall Street, Enniskillen BT74 7BA ☎ 0300 303 1777 ✆ catherine.leonard@fermanaghomagh.com

Senior Management: Ms Joan McCaffrey, Director - Corporate Services & Governance, Fermanagh District Council, Townhall, 2 Townhall Street, Enniskillen BT74 7BA ☎ 0300 303 1777 ✆ joan.mccaffrey@fermanaghomagh.com

Senior Management: Ms Alison McCullagh, Director - Regeneration & Planning, Fermanagh District Council, Townhall, 2 Townhall Street, Enniskillen BT74 7BA ☎ 0300 303 1777 ✆ alison.mccullagh@fermanaghomagh.com

Senior Management: Mr Kevin O'Gara, Director - Environment & Place, Fermanagh District Council, Townhall, 2 Townhall Street, Enniskillen BT74 7BA ☎ 0300 303 1777 ✆ kevin.ogara@fermanaghomagh.com

Building Control: Mr Gregory Young, Head of Building Control & Licensing, Fermanagh District Council, Townhall, 2 Townhall Street, Enniskillen BT74 7BA ☎ 0300 303 1777 ✆ gregory.young@fermanaghomagh.com

Civil Registration: Mrs Hazel Alderdice, Registrar, The Grange, Mountjoy Road, Omagh BT79 7BL ☎ 0300 303 1777 ✆ hazel.alderdice@fermanaghomagh.com

Community Planning: Mrs Kim McLaughlin, Head of Community Planning & Performance, The Grange, Mountjoy Road, Omagh BT79 7BL ☎ 0300 303 1777 ✆ kim.mclaughlin@fermanaghomagh.com

Computer Management: Mr Donal Cox, ICT Project Manager, Fermanagh District Council, Townhall, 2 Townhall Street, Enniskillen BT74 7BA ✆ donal.cox@fermanaghomagh.com

FERMANAGH & OMAGH DISTRICT COUNCIL

Contracts: Mr Ronan McSherry, Head of Contracts & Operations Management, Fermanagh District Council, Townhall, 2 Townhall Street, Enniskillen BT74 7BA ☎ 0300 303 1777 ⌂ ronan.sherry@fermanaghomagh.com

Corporate Services: Ms Joan McCaffrey, Director - Corporate Services & Governance, Fermanagh District Council, Townhall, 2 Townhall Street, Enniskillen BT74 7BA ☎ 0300 303 1777 ⌂ joan.mccaffrey@fermanaghomagh.com

Customer Service: Mrs Sonya McAnulla, Head of Democratic & Customer Services, The Grange, Mountjoy Road, Omagh BT79 7BL ☎ 0300 303 1777 ⌂ sonya.mcanulla@fermanaghomagh.com

Economic Development: Mr Kieran McCrory, Head of Tourism & Economic Development, The Grange, Mountjoy Road, Omagh BT79 7BL ☎ 0300 303 1777 ⌂ kieran.mccrory@fermanaghomagh.com

Emergency Planning: Ms Joan McCaffrey, Director - Corporate Services & Governance, Fermanagh District Council, Townhall, 2 Townhall Street, Enniskillen BT74 7BA ☎ 0300 303 1777 ⌂ joan.mccaffrey@fermanaghomagh.com

Environmental / Technical Services: Mr Kevin O'Gara, Director - Environment & Place, Fermanagh District Council, Townhall, 2 Townhall Street, Enniskillen BT74 7BA ☎ 0300 303 1777 ⌂ kevin.ogara@fermanaghomagh.com

Environmental Health: Ms Fiona Douglas, Head of Environmental Health, Fermanagh District Council, Townhall, 2 Townhall Street, Enniskillen BT74 7BA ☎ 0300 303 1777 ⌂ fiona.douglas@fermanaghomagh.com

Environmental Health: Mr Robert Gibson, Director - Community, Health & Leisure, Fermanagh District Council, Townhall, 2 Townhall Street, Enniskillen BT74 7BA ☎ 0300 303 1777 ⌂ robert.gibson@fermanaghomagh.com

Estates, Property & Valuation: Mr Sean Kelly, Head of Operations & Estates, The Grange, Mountjoy Road, Omagh BT79 7BL ☎ 0300 303 1777 ⌂ sean.kelly@fermanaghomagh.com

Finance: Ms Catherine Leonard, Head of Finance, Fermanagh District Council, Townhall, 2 Townhall Street, Enniskillen BT74 7BA ☎ 0300 303 1777 ⌂ catherine.leonard@fermanaghomagh.com

Fleet Management: Mr Ronan McSherry, Head of Contracts & Operations Management, Fermanagh District Council, Townhall, 2 Townhall Street, Enniskillen BT74 7BA ☎ 0300 303 1777 ⌂ ronan.sherry@fermanaghomagh.com

Health and Safety: Mr Mark Farrell, Health & Safety Manager, Fermanagh District Council, Townhall, 2 Townhall Street, Enniskillen BT74 7BA ☎ 0300 303 1777 ⌂ mark.farrell@fermanaghomagh.com

Leisure and Cultural Services: Mr Robert Gibson, Director - Community, Health & Leisure, Fermanagh District Council, Townhall, 2 Townhall Street, Enniskillen BT74 7BA ☎ 0300 303 1777 ⌂ robert.gibson@fermanaghomagh.com

Leisure and Cultural Services: Ms Liz Wilson, Head of Leisure, Recreation & Sport, Fermanagh District Council, Townhall, 2 Townhall Street, Enniskillen BT74 7BA ☎ 0300 303 1777 ⌂ liz.wilson@fermanaghomagh.com

Licensing: Mr Gregory Young, Head of Building Control & Licensing, Fermanagh District Council, Townhall, 2 Townhall Street, Enniskillen BT74 7BA ☎ 0300 303 1777 ⌂ gregory.young@fermanaghomagh.com

Member Services: Mrs Sonya McAnulla, Head of Democratic & Customer Services, The Grange, Mountjoy Road, Omagh BT79 7BL ☎ 0300 303 1777 ⌂ sonya.mcanulla@fermanaghomagh.com

Personnel / HR: Ms Thelma Browne, Lead Officer - HR & OD, Fermanagh District Council, Townhall, 2 Townhall Street, Enniskillen BT74 7BA ☎ 0300 303 1777 ⌂ thelma.browne@fermanaghomagh.com

Planning: Ms Alison McCullagh, Director - Regeneration & Planning, Fermanagh District Council, Townhall, 2 Townhall Street, Enniskillen BT74 7BA ☎ 0300 303 1777 ⌂ alison.mccullagh@fermanaghomagh.com

Planning: Ms Deirdre McSorley, Head of Planning, Fermanagh District Council, Townhall, 2 Townhall Street, Enniskillen BT74 7BA ☎ 0300 303 1777 ⌂ deirdre.mcsorley@fermanaghomagh.com

Procurement: Ms Nuala Conlan, Procurement Manager, Fermanagh District Council, Townhall, 2 Townhall Street, Enniskillen BT74 7BA ⌂ nuala.conlan@fermanaghomagh.com

Recycling & Waste Minimisation: Mr John McCullagh, Head of Waste & Recycling, Fermanagh District Council, Townhall, 2 Townhall Street, Enniskillen BT74 7BA ☎ 0300 303 1777 ⌂ john.mccullagh@fermanaghomagh.com

Regeneration: Ms Alison McCullagh, Director - Regeneration & Planning, Fermanagh District Council, Townhall, 2 Townhall Street, Enniskillen BT74 7BA ☎ 0300 303 1777 ⌂ alison.mccullagh@fermanaghomagh.com

Tourism: Mr Kieran McCrory, Head of Tourism & Economic Development, The Grange, Mountjoy Road, Omagh BT79 7BL ☎ 0300 303 1777 ⌂ kieran.mccrory@fermanaghomagh.com

Waste Management: Mr John McCullagh, Head of Waste & Recycling, Fermanagh District Council, Townhall, 2 Townhall Street, Enniskillen BT74 7BA ☎ 0300 303 1777 ⌂ john.mccullagh@fermanaghomagh.com

COUNCILLORS

Chair: Garrity, Mary (SDLP - West Tyrone)
mary.garrity@fermanaghomagh.com

Vice-Chair: Wilson, Bert (UUP - Mid Tyrone)
bert.wilson@fermanaghomagh.com

Baird, Alex (UUP - Erne West)
alex.baird@fermanaghomagh.com

Barton, Rosemary (UUP - Erne North)
rosemary.barton@fermanaghomagh.com

Buchanan, Mark (DUP - West Tyrone)
mark.buchanan@fermanaghomagh.com

Campbell, Glenn (SF - West Tyrone)
glenn.campbell@fermanaghomagh.com

Clarke, Sean (SF - Mid Tyrone)
sean.clarke@fermanaghomagh.com

Coyle, Debbie (SF - Enniskillen)
debbie.coyle@fermanaghomagh.com

Coyle, John (SDLP - Erne North)
john.coyle@fermanaghomagh.com

Deehan, Josephine (SDLP - Omagh)
josephine.deehan@fermanaghomagh.com

Doherty, Barry (SF - Erne West)
barry.doherty@fermanaghomagh.com

Donnelly, Joanne (SDLP - Omagh)
joanne.donnelly@fermanaghomagh.com

Donnelly, Frankie (SF - West Tyrone)
frankie.donnelly@fermanaghomagh.com

Donnelly, Sean (SF - Mid Tyrone)
sean.donnelly@fermanaghomagh.com

Elliott, Keith (DUP - Enniskillen)
keith.elliott@fermanaghomagh.com

Farrell, Raymond (UUP - Erne North)
raymond.farrell@fermanghomagh.com

Feely, Anthony (SF - Erne West)
anthony.feely@fermanaghomagh.com

Feely, John (SF - Erne North)
john.feely@fermanaghomagh.com

Fitzgerald, Anne Marie (SF - Mid Tyrone)
annemarie.fitzgerald@fermanaghomagh.com

Gallagher, Brendan (SDLP - Erne West)
brendan.gallagher@fermanaghomagh.com

Greene, Sheamus (SF - Erne East)
sheamus.greene@fermanaghomagh.com

Irvine, Robert (UUP - Enniskillen)
robert.irvine@fermanaghomagh.com

Maguire, Tommy (SF - Enniskillen)
tommy.maguire@fermanaghomagh.com

Mahon, David (DUP - Erne North)
david.mahon@fermanaghomagh.com

McAnespy, Sorcha (SF - Omagh)
sorcha.mcanespy@fermanaghomagh.com

McCaffrey, Brian (SF - Erne East)
brian.mccaffrey@fermanaghomagh.com

McCann, Stephen (SF - West Tyrone)
stephen.mccann@fermanaghomagh.com

McColgan, Marty (SF - Omagh)
marty.mccolgan@fermanaghomagh.com

McNally, Barry (SF - Mid Tyrone)
bary.mcnally@fermanaghomagh.com

McPhillips, Richie (SDLP - Erne East)
richie.mcphillips@fermanaghomagh.com

O'Reilly, Thomas (SF - Erne East)
thomas.oreilly@fermanaghomagh.com

Rainey, Allan (UUP - West Tyrone)
allan.rainey@fermanaghomagh.com

Robinson, Paul (DUP - Erne East)
paul.robinson@fermanaghomagh.com

Rogers, Patricia (SDLP - Enniskillen)
patricia.rogers@fermanaghomagh.com

Shields, Rosemarie (SDLP - Mid Tyrone)
rosemarie.shields@fermanaghomagh.com

Smyth, Chris (UUP - Omagh)
chris.smyth@fermanaghomagh.com

Swift, Bernice (IND - Erne West)
bernice.swift@fermanaghomagh.com

Thompson, Errol (DUP - Omagh)
errol.thompson@fermanaghomagh.com

Thornton, Howard (UUP - Enniskillen)
howard.thornton@fermanaghomagh.com

Warrington, Victor (UUP - Erne East)
victor.warrington@fermanaghomagh.com

POLITICAL COMPOSITION
SF: 17, UUP: 9, SDLP: 8, DUP: 5, IND: 1

Fife   S

Fife Council, Fife House, North Street, Glenrothes KY7 5LT
☎ 0345 155 0000 ⏱ fife.council@fife.gov.uk 🖳 www.fifedirect.org.uk

FACTS AND FIGURES
Parliamentary Constituencies: Dunfermline and West Fife, Fife
North East, Glenrothes, Kirkcaldy and Cowdenbeath
EU Constituencies: Scotland
Election Frequency: Elections are of whole council

PRINCIPAL OFFICERS

Chief Executive: Mr Steve Grimmond, Chief Executive, Fife
House, North Street, Glenrothes KY7 5LT ☎ 03451 555555 Ext
444143 ⏱ steve.grimmond@fife.gov.uk

Senior Management: Mr Michael Enston, Executive Director -
Communities, Fife House, North Street, Glenrothes KY7 5LT
☎ 03451 555555 Ext 441198 ⏱ michael.enston@fife.gov.uk

Senior Management: Mr Michael Kellett, Executive Director -
Health & Social Care, Fife House, North Street, Glenrothes
KY7 5LT ⏱ michael.kellett@fife.gov.uk

Senior Management: Ms Shelagh McLean, Executive Director
- Education & Children's Services, Fife House, North Street,
Glenrothes KY7 5LT ⏱ shelagh.mclean@fife.gov.uk

Senior Management: Ms Eileen Rowland, Executive Director -
Finance & Corporate Services, Fife House, North Street, Glenrothes
KY7 5LT ☎ 03451 555555 Ext 444120 ⏱ eileen.rowland@fife.gov.uk

Senior Management: Mr Keith Winter, Executive Director -
Enterprise & Environment, Fife House, North Street, Glenrothes
KY7 5LT ☎ 03451 555555 Ext 442284 ⏱ keith.winter@fife.gov.uk

Architect, Building / Property Services: Mr Alan Paul, Senior Manager - Property Services, Bankhead Central, Bankhead Park, Glenrothes KY7 6GH ☎ 03451 555555 Ext 440464 ⏱ alan.paul@fife.gov.uk

Best Value: Mr Michael Enston, Executive Director - Communities, Fife House, North Street, Glenrothes KY7 5LT ☎ 03451 555555 Ext 441198 ⏱ michael.enston@fife.gov.uk

Building Control: Mr Robin Presswood, Head of Economy, Planning & Employability Services, 3rd Floor, Kingdom House, Kingdom Avenue, Glenrothes KY7 5LY ☎ 03451 555555 Ext 442260 ⏱ robin.presswood@fife.gov.uk

Catering Services: Mr Ken Gourlay, Head of Assets, Transportation & Environment, Ground Floor, Bankhead Central, Bankhead Park, Glenrothes KY7 6GH ☎ 03451 555555 Ext 440473 ⏱ ken.gourlay@fife.gov.uk

Community Planning: Mr Michael Enston, Executive Director - Communities, Fife House, North Street, Glenrothes KY7 5LT ☎ 03451 555555 Ext 441198 ⏱ michael.enston@fife.gov.uk

Community Safety: Mr Michael Enston, Executive Director - Communities, Fife House, North Street, Glenrothes KY7 5LT ☎ 03451 555555 Ext 441198 ⏱ michael.enston@fife.gov.uk

Computer Management: Mr Charlie Anderson, Head of Business Technology Services, 6th Floor, Fife House, North Street, Glenrothes KY7 5LT ☎ 03451 555555 Ext 444241 ⏱ charlie.anderson@fife.gov.uk

Consumer Protection and Trading Standards: Mr Roy Stewart, Senior Manager - Protective Services, Kingdom House, Kingdom Avenue, Glenrothes KY7 5LY ☎ 03451 555555Ext 450466 ⏱ roy.steward@fife.gov.uk

Contracts: Mr John Cosgrove, Head of Procurement, Fife House, North Street, Glenrothes KY7 5LT ☎ 03451 555555 Ext 445926 ⏱ John.Cosgrove@fife.gov.uk

Corporate Services: Ms Eileen Rowland, Executive Director - Finance & Corporate Services, Fife House, North Street, Glenrothes KY7 5LT ☎ 03451 555555 Ext 444120 ⏱ eileen.rowland@fife.gov.uk

Customer Service: Ms Lynne Harvie, Head of Customer Service Improvement, Fife House, North Street, Glenrothes KY7 5LT ☎ 03451 555555 Ext 444263 ⏱ lynne.harvie@fife.gov.uk

Direct Labour: Mr Ken Gourlay, Head of Assets, Transportation & Environment, Ground Floor, Bankhead Central, Bankhead Park, Glenrothes KY7 6GH ☎ 03451 555555 Ext 440473 ⏱ ken.gourlay@fife.gov.uk

Economic Development: Mr Robin Presswood, Head of Economy, Planning & Employability Services, 3rd Floor, Kingdom House, Kingdom Avenue, Glenrothes KY7 5LY ☎ 03451 555555 Ext 442260 ⏱ robin.presswood@fife.gov.uk

Education: Ms Shelagh McLean, Executive Director - Education & Children's Services, Fife House, North Street, Glenrothes KY7 5LT ⏱ shelagh.mclean@fife.gov.uk

E-Government: Mr Charlie Anderson, Head of Business Technology Services, 6th Floor, Fife House, North Street, Glenrothes KY7 5LT ☎ 03451 555555 Ext 444241 ⏱ charlie.anderson@fife.gov.uk

Electoral Registration: Mr Lawrence Cooper, Depute Electoral Registration Officer & Service Manager, Fife House, North Street, Glenrothes KY7 5TL ⏱ lawrence.cooper@fife.gov.uk

Emergency Planning: Mrs Lori Hutcheson, Team Manager, 1st Floor, Fife House, North Street, Glenrothes KY7 5LT ☎ 03451 555555 Ext 442342 ⏱ lori.hutcheson@fife.gov.uk

Energy Management: Mr Ken Gourlay, Head of Assets, Transportation & Environment, Ground Floor, Bankhead Central, Bankhead Park, Glenrothes KY7 6GH ☎ 03451 555555 Ext 440473 ⏱ ken.gourlay@fife.gov.uk

Environmental / Technical Services: Mr Ken Gourlay, Head of Assets, Transportation & Environment, Ground Floor, Bankhead Central, Bankhead Park, Glenrothes KY7 6GH ☎ 03451 555555 Ext 440473 ⏱ ken.gourlay@fife.gov.uk

Environmental Health: Mr Roy Stewart, Senior Manager - Protective Services, Kingdom House, Kingdom Avenue, Glenrothes KY7 5LY ☎ 03451 555555Ext 450466 ⏱ roy.steward@fife.gov.uk

Estates, Property & Valuation: Mr Alan Paul, Senior Manager - Property Services, Bankhead Central, Bankhead Park, Glenrothes KY7 6GH ☎ 03451 555555 Ext 440464 ⏱ alan.paul@fife.gov.uk

European Liaison: Mr Michael Enston, Executive Director - Communities, Fife House, North Street, Glenrothes KY7 5LT ☎ 03451 555555 Ext 441198 ⏱ michael.enston@fife.gov.uk

Events Manager: Linda Temple, Cultural Partnership & Event Strategy Manager, Kingdom House, Kingdom Avenue, Glenrothes KY7 5LY ☎ 03451 555555 Ext 493296 ⏱ linda.temple@fife.gov.uk

Facilities: Mr Ken Gourlay, Head of Assets, Transportation & Environment, Ground Floor, Bankhead Central, Bankhead Park, Glenrothes KY7 6GH ☎ 03451 555555 Ext 440473 ⏱ ken.gourlay@fife.gov.uk

Finance: Mr Keith O'Donnell, Head of Finance, Fife House, North Street, Glenrothes KY7 5LT ☎ 03451 555555 Ext 440973 ⏱ keith.odonnell@fife.gov.uk

Treasury: Ms Eileen Rowland, Executive Director - Finance & Corporate Services, Fife House, North Street, Glenrothes KY7 5LT ☎ 03451 555555 Ext 444120 ⏱ eileen.rowland@fife.gov.uk

Pensions: Ms Eileen Rowland, Executive Director - Finance & Corporate Services, Fife House, North Street, Glenrothes KY7 5LT ☎ 03451 555555 Ext 444120 ⏱ eileen.rowland@fife.gov.uk

Fleet Management: Mr Ken Gourlay, Head of Assets, Transportation & Environment, Ground Floor, Bankhead Central, Bankhead Park, Glenrothes KY7 6GH ☎ 03451 555555 Ext 440473 ⏱ ken.gourlay@fife.gov.uk

Grounds Maintenance: Mr Ken Gourlay, Head of Assets, Transportation & Environment, Ground Floor, Bankhead Central, Bankhead Park, Glenrothes KY7 6GH ☎ 03451 555555 Ext 440473 ✆ ken.gourlay@fife.gov.uk

Health and Safety: Ms Sharon McKenzie, Head of Human Resources, Fife House, North Street, Glenrothes KY7 5LT ☎ 03451 555555 Ext 444265 ✆ sharon.mckenzie@fife.gov.uk

Highways: Mr Ken Gourlay, Head of Assets, Transportation & Environment, Ground Floor, Bankhead Central, Bankhead Park, Glenrothes KY7 6GH ☎ 03451 555555 Ext 440473 ✆ ken.gourlay@fife.gov.uk

Home Energy Conservation: Mr John Mills, Head of Housing Services, Rothesay House, North Street, Glenrothes KY5 5LT ☎ 03451 555555 Ext 480269 ✆ john.mills@fife.gov.uk

Housing: Mr John Mills, Head of Housing Services, Rothesay House, North Street, Glenrothes KY5 5LT ☎ 03451 555555 Ext 480269 ✆ john.mills@fife.gov.uk

Housing Maintenance: Mr John Mills, Head of Housing Services, Rothesay House, North Street, Glenrothes KY5 5LT ☎ 03451 555555 Ext 480269 ✆ john.mills@fife.gov.uk

Legal: Mr Iain Matheson, Head of Legal Services, Fife House, North Street, Glenrothes KY7 5LT ☎ 03451 555555 Ext 442180 ✆ iain.mattheson@fife.gov.uk

Licensing: Mr Iain Matheson, Head of Legal Services, Fife House, North Street, Glenrothes KY7 5LT ☎ 03451 555555 Ext 442180 ✆ iain.mattheson@fife.gov.uk

Lighting: Mr Ken Gourlay, Head of Assets, Transportation & Environment, Ground Floor, Bankhead Central, Bankhead Park, Glenrothes KY7 6GH ☎ 03451 555555 Ext 440473 ✆ ken.gourlay@fife.gov.uk

Lottery Funding, Charity and Voluntary: Mr Paul Vaughan, Head of Community & Corporate Development, Fife House, North Street, Glenrothes KY7 5LT ☎ 03451 555555 Ext 441241 ✆ paul.vaughan@fife.gov.uk

Member Services: Ms Eileen Rowland, Executive Director - Finance & Corporate Services, Fife House, North Street, Glenrothes KY7 5LT ☎ 03451 555555 Ext 444120 ✆ eileen.rowland@fife.gov.uk

Parking: Mr Ken Gourlay, Head of Assets, Transportation & Environment, Ground Floor, Bankhead Central, Bankhead Park, Glenrothes KY7 6GH ☎ 03451 555555 Ext 440473 ✆ ken.gourlay@fife.gov.uk

Partnerships: Mr Michael Enston, Executive Director - Communities, Fife House, North Street, Glenrothes KY7 5LT ☎ 03451 555555 Ext 441198 ✆ michael.enston@fife.gov.uk

Personnel / HR: Ms Sharon McKenzie, Head of Human Resources, Fife House, North Street, Glenrothes KY7 5LT ☎ 03451 555555 Ext 444265 ✆ sharon.mckenzie@fife.gov.uk

Planning: Mr Robin Presswood, Head of Economy, Planning & Employability Services, 3rd Floor, Kingdom House, Kingdom Avenue, Glenrothes KY7 5LY ☎ 03451 555555 Ext 442260 ✆ robin.presswood@fife.gov.uk

Procurement: Mr John Cosgrove, Head of Procurement, Fife House, North Street, Glenrothes KY7 5LT ☎ 03451 555555 Ext 445926 ✆ John.Cosgrove@fife.gov.uk

Public Libraries: Ms Heather Stuart, Chief Executive Officer - Fife Cultural Trust, Libraries & Museums HQ, 16 East Fergus Place, Kirkcaldy KY1 1XR ☎ 03451 555555 Ext 472796 ✆ heather.stuart@fife.gov.uk

Recycling & Waste Minimisation: Mr Ken Gourlay, Head of Assets, Transportation & Environment, Ground Floor, Bankhead Central, Bankhead Park, Glenrothes KY7 6GH ☎ 03451 555555 Ext 440473 ✆ ken.gourlay@fife.gov.uk

Regeneration: Mr Robin Presswood, Head of Economy, Planning & Employability Services, 3rd Floor, Kingdom House, Kingdom Avenue, Glenrothes KY7 5LY ☎ 03451 555555 Ext 442260 ✆ robin.presswood@fife.gov.uk

Road Safety: Mr Ken Gourlay, Head of Assets, Transportation & Environment, Ground Floor, Bankhead Central, Bankhead Park, Glenrothes KY7 6GH ☎ 03451 555555 Ext 440473 ✆ ken.gourlay@fife.gov.uk

Social Services: Mr Michael Kellett, Executive Director - Health & Social Care, Fife House, North Street, Glenrothes KY7 5LT ✆ michael.kellett@fife.gov.uk

Social Services (Adult): Mr Michael Kellett, Executive Director - Health & Social Care, Fife House, North Street, Glenrothes KY7 5LT ✆ michael.kellett@fife.gov.uk

Social Services (Children): Mr Michael Kellett, Executive Director - Health & Social Care, Fife House, North Street, Glenrothes KY7 5LT ✆ michael.kellett@fife.gov.uk

Staff Training: Ms Sharon McKenzie, Head of Human Resources, Fife House, North Street, Glenrothes KY7 5LT ☎ 03451 555555 Ext 444265 ✆ sharon.mckenzie@fife.gov.uk

Sustainable Communities: Mr Paul Vaughan, Head of Community & Corporate Development, Fife House, North Street, Glenrothes KY7 5LT ☎ 03451 555555 Ext 441241 ✆ paul.vaughan@fife.gov.uk

Sustainable Development: Mr Ken Gourlay, Head of Assets, Transportation & Environment, Ground Floor, Bankhead Central, Bankhead Park, Glenrothes KY7 6GH ☎ 03451 555555 Ext 440473 ✆ ken.gourlay@fife.gov.uk

Town Centre: Mr Robin Presswood, Head of Economy, Planning & Employability Services, 3rd Floor, Kingdom House, Kingdom Avenue, Glenrothes KY7 5LY ☎ 03451 555555 Ext 442260 ✆ robin.presswood@fife.gov.uk

FIFE

Traffic Management: Mr Ken Gourlay, Head of Assets, Transportation & Environment, Ground Floor, Bankhead Central, Bankhead Park, Glenrothes KY7 6GH ☎ 03451 555555 Ext 440473 ✆ ken.gourlay@fife.gov.uk

Transport: Mr Ken Gourlay, Head of Assets, Transportation & Environment, Ground Floor, Bankhead Central, Bankhead Park, Glenrothes KY7 6GH ☎ 03451 555555 Ext 440473 ✆ ken.gourlay@fife.gov.uk

Transport Planner: Mr Ken Gourlay, Head of Assets, Transportation & Environment, Ground Floor, Bankhead Central, Bankhead Park, Glenrothes KY7 6GH ☎ 03451 555555 Ext 440473 ✆ ken.gourlay@fife.gov.uk

Waste Collection and Disposal: Mr Derek Crowe, Senior Manager - Engineering & Waste Services, 1st Floor, Bankhead Central, Bankhead Park, Glenrothes KY7 6GH ☎ 03451 555555 Ext 450441 ✆ derek.crowe@fife.gov.uk

Waste Management: Mr Derek Crowe, Senior Manager - Engineering & Waste Services, 1st Floor, Bankhead Central, Bankhead Park, Glenrothes KY7 6GH ☎ 03451 555555 Ext 450441 ✆ derek.crowe@fife.gov.uk

COUNCILLORS

Provost: Leishman, Jim (LAB - Dunfermline Central)

Leader of the Council: Ross, David (LAB - Kirkcaldy North)

Adams, Tom (LAB - Leven, Kennoway and Largo)

Alexander, David (SNP - Leven, Kennoway and Largo)

Bain, Ann (SNP - The Lochs)

Bain, Alistair (SNP - Cowdenbeath)

Beare, John (SNP - Glenrothes North, Leslie and Markinch)

Brett, Tim (LD - Tay Bridgehead)

Brown, Bill (IND - Glenrothes West and Kinglassie)

Brown, Lawrence (LAB - Kirkcaldy East)

Callaghan, Pat (LAB - Rosyth)

Callaghan, Alice (LAB - West Fife and Coastal Villages)

Campbell, Alex (LAB - The Lochs)

Campbell, William (LAB - Dunfermline North)

Carrington, Kay (LAB - Kirkcaldy East)

Chapman, Douglas (SNP - Rosyth)

Chisholm, Ian (SNP - Lochgelly and Cardenden)

Clarke, William (IND - The Lochs)

Clelland, Bobby (LAB - West Fife and Coastal Villages)

Connor, Bill (SNP - Tay Bridgehead)

Craik, Altany (LAB - Glenrothes West and Kinglassie)

Crichton, Ian (LAB - Glenrothes Central and Thornton)

Crooks, Neil (LAB - Kirkcaldy North)

Dempsey, Dave (CON - Inverkeithing and Dalgety Bay)

Docherty, John (SNP - East Neuk and Landward)

Erskine, Linda (LAB - Lochgelly and Cardenden)

Ferguson, William (IND - West Fife and Coastal Villages)

George, Peter (LAB - Burntisland, Kinghorn & Western Kirkcaldy)

Goodall, Brian (SNP - Dunfermline South)

Graham, David (LAB - Buckhaven, Methil & Wemyss)

Grant, Fiona (SNP - Glenrothes North, Leslie and Markinch)

Guichan, Gary (LAB - Cowdenbeath)

Haffey, Charles (LAB - Leven, Kennoway and Largo)

Hamilton, Judy (LAB - Kirkcaldy Central)

Hanvey, Neale (SNP - Dunfermline Central)

Heer, Andy (CON - Howe of Fife and Tay Coast)

Hood, Mark (LAB - Lochgelly and Cardenden)

Hunter, Alistair (SNP - Leven, Kennoway and Largo)

Kay, George (SNP - Burntisland, Kinghorn & Western Kirkcaldy)

Kennedy, Margaret (LD - Cupar)

Laird, Lesley (LAB - Inverkeithing and Dalgety Bay)

Law, Helen (LAB - Dunfermline North)

Leslie, Susan (LD - Burntisland, Kinghorn & Western Kirkcaldy)

Lindsay, Carol (SNP - Kirkcaldy North)

Lockhart, Peter (LAB - Cowdenbeath)

Lothian, Donald (LD - Howe of Fife and Tay Coast)

MacDiarmid, David (SNP - Howe of Fife and Tay Coast)

MacGregor, Donald (LD - East Neuk and Landward)

MacPhail, Stuart (SNP - Kirkcaldy Central)

Marjoram, Karen (SNP - Cupar)

Martin, Tony (LD - Dunfermline South)

McCartney, Keith (SNP - St Andrews)

McGarry, Alice (SNP - Inverkeithing and Dalgety Bay)

Melville, Frances (LD - St Andrews)

Mogg, David (SNP - Dunfermline North)

Morrison, Dorothea (CON - St Andrews)

Morrison, Kay (LAB - Glenrothes North, Leslie and Markinch)

O'Brien, John (SNP - Buckhaven, Methil & Wemyss)

Penman, Marie (SNP - Kirkcaldy East)

Pollock, Billy (LAB - Dunfermline South)

Poole, Bryan (IND - Cupar)

Riches, Elizabeth (LD - East Neuk and Landward)

Rodger, Andrew (IND - Buckhaven, Methil & Wemyss)

Rosiejak, Joe (LD - Dunfermline Central)

Selbie, Kenny (LAB - Kirkcaldy Central)

Shirkie, Mike (LAB - Rosyth)

Sinclair, Fay (SNP - Dunfermline South)

Sloan, Ian (LAB - Glenrothes Central and Thornton)

Stewart, Kate (SNP - West Fife and Coastal Villages)

Taylor, Margaret (LD - Tay Bridgehead)

Thomson, Brian (LAB - St Andrews)

Vettraino, Ross (SNP - Glenrothes Central and Thornton)

Walker, Craig (SNP - Glenrothes West and Kinglassie)

Wincott, John (LAB - Glenrothes North, Leslie and Markinch)

Yates, Gavin (LAB - Inverkeithing and Dalgety Bay)

Young, Jim (LAB - Buckhaven, Methil & Wemyss)

Young, Bob (LAB - Dunfermline Central)

POLITICAL COMPOSITION
LAB: 33, SNP: 26, LD: 10, IND: 5, CON: 3

Flintshire   W

Flintshire County Council, County Hall, Mold CH7 6NF
☎ 01352 752121 🖷 01352 758240 ⌕ info@flintshire.gov.uk
🖳 www.flintshire.gov.uk

FACTS AND FIGURES
Parliamentary Constituencies: Alyn and Deeside, Delyn
EU Constituencies: Wales
Election Frequency: Elections are by thirds

PRINCIPAL OFFICERS

Chief Executive: Mr Colin Everett, Chief Executive, County Hall, Mold CH7 6NB ☎ 01352 702100 ⌕ chief.executive@flintshire.gov.uk

Senior Management: Mr Neil Ayling, Chief Officer - Social Services, County Hall, Mold CH7 6NF ☎ 01352 702500 ⌕ neil.j.ayling@flintshire.gov.uk

Senior Management: Mr Ian Bancroft, Chief Officer - Organisational Change, County Hall, Mold CH7 6NF ☎ 01352 704180 ⌕ ian.bancroft@flintshire.gov.uk

Senior Management: Mr Ian Budd, Chief Officer - Education & Youth, County Hall, Mold CH7 6NF ☎ 01352 704010 ⌕ ian.budd@flintshire.gov.uk

Senior Management: Ms Clare Budden, Chief Officer - Community & Enterprise, County Offices, Chapel Street, Flint CH6 5BD ☎ 01352 703800 ⌕ clare.budden@flintshire.gov.uk

Senior Management: Ms Sharon Carnie, Interim Chief Officer - People & Resources, County Hall, Mold CH7 6NF ☎ 01352 752121 ⌕ sharon.carnie@flintshire.gov.uk

Senior Management: Mr Neal Cockerton, Chief Officer - Organisational Change, County Hall, Mold CH7 6NF ☎ 01352 703169 ⌕ neal.cockerton@flintshire.gov.uk

Senior Management: Mr Andy Farrow, Chief Officer - Planning & Environment, County Hall, Mold CH7 6NB ☎ 01352 703201 ⌕ andy.farrow@flintshire.gov.uk

Senior Management: Mr Steve Jones, Chief Officer - Streetscene & Transportation, County Hall, Mold CH7 6NF ☎ 01352 704700 ⌕ stephen.o.jones@flintshire.gov.uk

Senior Management: Mr Gareth Owens, Chief Officer - Governance, County Hall, Mold CH7 6NF ☎ 01352 702344 ⌕ gareth.legal@flintshire.gov.uk

Access Officer / Social Services (Disability): Ms Jo Taylor, Disability, Progression & Recovery Service Manager, County Hall, Mold CH7 6NF ☎ 01352 701350 ⌕ jo.taylor@flintshire.gov.uk

Architect, Building / Property Services: Mr Andy Smith, Property & Design Consultancy Manager, County Offices, Chapel Street, Flint CH6 5BD ☎ 01352 752121 ⌕ andy.smith@flintshire.gov.uk

Best Value: Mrs Karen Armstrong, Corporate Business & Communication Executive Officer, County Hall, Mold CH7 6NT ☎ 01352 702740 ⌕ karen.armstrong@flintshire.gov.uk

Building Control: Mr Glyn Jones, Development Manager, County Hall, Mold CH7 6NF ☎ 01352 703248 ⌕ glyn.p.jones@flintshire.gov.uk

Children / Youth Services: Miss Kim Brookes, Business Manager, County Hall, Mold CH7 6NF ☎ 01352 704025 ⌕ kim.brookes@flintshire.gov.uk

Children / Youth Services: Mrs Ann Roberts, Families First Lead & Youth Services Manager, County Hall, Mold CH7 6NF ☎ 01352 704112 ⌕ ann.s.roberts@flintshire.gov.uk

Civil Registration: Mrs Denise Naylor, Customer Services Manager, County Hall, Mold CH7 6NT ☎ 01352 702421 ⌕ denise.naylor@flintshire.gov.uk

PR / Communications: Ms Barbara Milne, Corporate Communications Manager, County Hall, Mold CH7 6NB ☎ 01352 752121 ⌕ barbara.milne@flintshire.gov.uk

Community Planning: Mrs Karen Armstrong, Corporate Business & Communication Executive Officer, County Hall, Mold CH7 6NT ☎ 01352 702740 ⌕ karen.armstrong@flintshire.gov.uk

Community Safety: Mrs Sian Jones, Public Protection Manager - Community, County Hall, Mold CH7 6NT ☎ 01352 702132 ⌕ sian.l.jones@flintshire.gov.uk

Computer Management: Mr Aled Griffith, Network & IT Support Services Manager, County Hall, Mold CH7 6NF ☎ 01352 702801 ⌕ aled.griffith@flintshire.gov.uk

Computer Management: Ms Mandy Humphreys, IT Business Services Manager, County Hall, Mold CH7 6NF ☎ 01352 702821 ⌕ mandy.humphreys@flintshire.gov.uk

Consumer Protection and Trading Standards: Mrs Sylvia Portbury, Public Protection Service Manager - Business, County Hall, Mold CH7 6NF ☎ 01352 703378 ⌕ sylvia.portbury@flintshire.gov.uk

Corporate Services: Mr Gareth Owens, Chief Officer - Governance, County Hall, Mold CH7 6NF ☎ 01352 702344 ⌕ gareth.legal@flintshire.gov.uk

FLINTSHIRE

Customer Service: Mrs Denise Naylor, Customer Services Manager, County Hall, Mold CH7 6NT ☎ 01352 702421 🖰 denise.naylor@flintshire.gov.uk

E-Government: Mr Gareth Owens, Chief Officer - Governance, County Hall, Mold CH7 6NF ☎ 01352 702344 🖰 gareth.legal@flintshire.gov.uk

Electoral Registration: Mrs Lyn Phillips, Electoral Services Manager, County Hall, Mold CH7 6NF ☎ 01352 702329 🖰 lyn.phillips@flintshire.gov.uk

Emergency Planning: Mr Phil Harrison, Regional Emergency Planning Manager, County Hall, Mold CH7 6NF ☎ 01352 702120 🖰 philip.harrison@flintshire.gov.uk

Estates, Property & Valuation: Mr Tony Bamford, Corporate Valuer, County Offices, Chapel Street, Flint CH6 5BD ☎ 01352 703102 🖰 tony.bamford@flintshire.gov.uk

Events Manager: Mr Darell Jones, Streetlighting Manager, Alltami Depot, Alltami, Mold CH7 6LG ☎ 01352 701290 🖰 darell.jones@flintshire.gov.uk

Facilities: Mr Steve Jones, Facilities Services Manager, County Hall, Mold CH7 6NF ☎ 01352 704039 🖰 steve.w.jones@flintshire.gov.uk

Finance: Mr Gary Ferguson, Corporate Finance Manager, County Hall, Mold CH7 6NF ☎ 01352 702271 🖰 gary.ferguson@flintshire.gov.uk

Pensions: Mr Philip Latham, Clwyd Pension Fund Manager, County Hall, Mold CH7 6NF ☎ 01352 702264 🖰 philip.latham@flintshire.gov.uk

Fleet Management: Mr Barry Wilkinson, Fleet Services Operations Manager, Alltami Depot, Alltami, Mold CH7 6LG ☎ 01352 752121 🖰 barry.wilkinson@flintshire.gov.uk

Grounds Maintenance: Mr Paddy Wilkinson, Highway Network Manager, County Hall, Mold CH7 6NF ☎ 01352 752121 🖰 paddy.wilkinson@flintshire.gov.uk

Health and Safety: Ms Vanessa Johnson, Corporate Health & Safety Manager, County Hall, Mold CH7 6NB ☎ 01352 702962 🖰 vanessa.johnson@flintshire.gov.uk

Highways: Mr Anthony Stanford, Senior Engineer - Traffic, County Hall, Mold CH7 6NF ☎ 01352 704817 🖰 anthony.stanford@flintshire.gov.uk

Housing: Mr Gavin Griffith, Regeneration Manager, County Hall, Mold CH7 6NF ☎ 01352 703428 🖰 gavin.griffith@flintshire.gov.uk

Housing Maintenance: Ms Nikki Evans, Senior Manager - Council Housing, County Hall, Mold CH7 6NF ☎ 01352 701658 🖰 nikki.evans@flintshire.gov.uk

Legal: Mrs Sian Jones, Public Protection Manager - Community, County Hall, Mold CH7 6NT ☎ 01352 702132 🖰 sian.l.jones@flintshire.gov.uk

Leisure and Cultural Services: Mr Mike Welch, Principal Leisure Services Officer, County Hall, Mold CH7 6NF ☎ 01352 702452 🖰 mike.welch@flintshire.gov.uk

Licensing: Mr Scott Rowley, Interim Environmental Protection Manager, County Hall, Mold CH7 6NF ☎ 01352 752121 🖰 scott.rowley@flintshire.gov.uk

Lifelong Learning: Mr Ian Budd, Chief Officer - Education & Youth, County Hall, Mold CH7 6NF ☎ 01352 704010 🖰 ian.budd@flintshire.gov.uk

Lighting: Mr Darell Jones, Streetlighting Manager, Alltami Depot, Alltami, Mold CH7 6LG ☎ 01352 701290 🖰 darell.jones@flintshire.gov.uk

Member Services: Mrs Karen Jones, Chairman's & Members' Assistant, County Hall, Mold CH7 6NF ☎ 01352 702151 🖰 karen.jones@flintshire.gov.uk

Member Services: Mrs Lesley Wood, Chairman's & Members' Assistant, County Hall, Mold CH7 6NR ☎ 01352 702151 🖰 lesley.wood@flintshire.gov.uk

Parking: Mrs Joanna Jones, Parking Manager, County Hall, Mold CH7 6NF ☎ 01352 752121 🖰 joanna.l.jones@flintshire.gov.uk

Partnerships: Mrs Karen Armstrong, Corporate Business & Communication Executive Officer, County Hall, Mold CH7 6NT ☎ 01352 702740 🖰 karen.armstrong@flintshire.gov.uk

Personnel / HR: Mrs Karen Carney, Lead Business Partner, County Hall, Mold CH7 6NF ☎ 01352 702139 🖰 sharon.carney@flintshire.gov.uk

Planning: Mr Glyn Jones, Development Manager, County Hall, Mold CH7 6NF ☎ 01352 703248 🖰 glyn.p.jones@flintshire.gov.uk

Procurement: Ms Arwel Staples, Strategic Procurement Manager, County Hall, Mold CH7 6NF ☎ 01352 702267 🖰 arwel.staples@flintshire.gov.uk

Public Libraries: Ms Kate Lenard, Principal Librarian, County Hall, Mold CH7 6NF 🖰 kate.lenard@flintshire.gov.uk

Recycling & Waste Minimisation: Mr Harvey Mitchell, Waste & Ancillary Service Manager, Alltami Depot, Mold Road, Alltami, Mold CH7 6LG ☎ 01352 701710 🖰 harvey.mitchell@flintshire.gov.uk

Regeneration: Mr Niall Waller, Enterprise & Regeneration Manager, County Hall, Mold CH7 6NF ☎ 01352 702137 🖰 niall.waller@flintshire.gov.uk

Road Safety: Mr Paddy Wilkinson, Highway Network Manager, County Hall, Mold CH7 6NF ☎ 01352 752121 🖰 paddy.wilkinson@flintshire.gov.uk

Social Services: Mr Neil Ayling, Chief Officer - Social Services, County Hall, Mold CH7 6NF ☎ 01352 702500 🖰 neil.j.ayling@flintshire.gov.uk

Social Services (Adult): Mrs Christine Duffy, Senior Manager - Adult First Contact & Localities Service, County Hall, Mold CH7 6NF ☎ 01352 702561 ᛁ christine.duffy@flintshire.gov.uk

Social Services (Adult): Mrs Susie Lunt, Senior Manager - Integrated Services, Lead Adults, County Hall, Mold CH7 6NF ☎ 01352 701407 ᛁ susie.lunt@flintshire.gov.uk

Social Services (Children): Mr Ray Dickson, Service Manager - Children's Fieldwork Services, County Hall, Mold CH7 6NF ☎ 01352 701003 ᛁ ray.dickson@flintshire.gov.uk

Social Services (Children): Mr Peter Robson, Children's Resources Service Manager, County Hall, Mold CH7 6NF ☎ 01352 701028 ᛁ peter.robson@flintshire.gov.uk

Staff Training: Mrs Heather Johnson, Corporate Training Officer, Northop Campus, Deeside College, Northop, Mold CH7 6AA ☎ 01352 752121 ᛁ heather.johnson@flintshire.gov.uk

Street Scene: Mr Paddy Wilkinson, Highway Network Manager, County Hall, Mold CH7 6NF ☎ 01352 752121 ᛁ paddy.wilkinson@flintshire.gov.uk

Tourism: Mr David Evans, Tourism Manager, County Hall, Mold CH7 6NB ☎ 01352 702468 ᛁ david.p.evans@flintshire.gov.uk

Town Centre: Mr Niall Waller, Enterprise & Regeneration Manager, County Hall, Mold CH7 6NF ☎ 01352 702137 ᛁ niall.waller@flintshire.gov.uk

Transport: Mrs Kate Wilby, Transportation Manager, County Hall, Mold CH7 6NF ☎ 01352 704530 ᛁ katie.wilby@flintshire.gov.uk

Waste Collection and Disposal: Mr Kevin Edwards, Operations Manager - Waste, Alltami Depot, Mold Road, Alltami, Mold CH7 6LG ☎ 01352 701718 ᛁ kevin.edwards@flintshire.gov.uk

Waste Management: Mr Harvey Mitchell, Waste & Ancillary Service Manager, County Hall, Mold CH7 6NB ☎ 01352 701710 ᛁ harvey.mitchell@flintshire.gov.uk

Children's Play Areas: Mr Mike Welch, Principal Leisure Services Officer, County Hall, Mold CH7 6NF ☎ 01352 702452 ᛁ mike.welch@flintshire.gov.uk

COUNCILLORS

ChairCurtis, Peter (LAB - Holywell Central) peter.curtis@flintshire.gov.uk

Vice-ChairLloyd, Brian (IND - Mold West) brian.lloyd@flintshire.gov.uk

Leader of the Council: Shotton, Aaron (LAB - Connah's Quay Central) aaron.shotton@flintshire.gov.uk

Deputy Leader of the Council: Attridge, Bernie (LAB - Connah's Quay Central) bernie.attridge@flintshire.gov.uk

Group LeaderCarver, Clive (CON - Hawarden) clive.carver@flintshire.gov.uk

Group LeaderHughes, Raymond (IND - Leeswood) raymond.hughes@flintshire.gov.uk

Group LeaderMatthews, Nancy (LD - Gwernymyndd) nancy.matthews@flintshire.gov.uk

Group LeaderPeers, Mike (IND - Buckley Pentrobin) mike.peers@flintshire.gov.uk

Group LeaderSharps, Tony (IND - Northop Hall) tony.sharps@flintshire.gov.uk

Aldridge, Alex (LAB - Flint Coleshill) alex.aldridge@flintshire.gov.uk

Banks, Glyn (LAB - Ffynnongroyw) glyn.banks@flintshire.gov.uk

Bateman, Haydn (IND - Mold Broncoed) haydn.bateman@flintshire.gov.uk

Bateman, Marion (IND - Northop) marion.bateman@flintshire.gov.uk

Bithell, Chris (LAB - Mold East) christopher.bithell@flintshire.gov.uk

Brown, Helen (IND - Aston) helen.brown@flintshire.gov.uk

Butler, Derek (LAB - Broughton South) derek.butler@flintshire.gov.uk

Cox, David (LAB - Flint Coleshill) davidcox3b@gmail.com

Cunningham, Paul (LAB - Flint Trelawny) paul.cunningham@flintshire.gov.uk

Davies, Ron (LAB - Shotton Higher) rsdavi3s@aol.com

Davies-Cooke, Adele (CON - Gwernaffield) adele.daviescooke@flintshire.gov.uk

Diskin, Glenys (LAB - Mancot) glenys.diskin@flintshire.gov.uk

Diskin, Alan (LAB - Mancot) alan.diskin@flintshire.gov.uk

Dolphin, Chris (LD - Whitford) chris_dolphin@hotmail.co.uk

Dolphin, Rosetta (IND - Greenfield) rosetta_dolphin@hotmail.co.uk

Dunbar, Ian (LAB - Connah's Quay South) ian.dunbar@flintshire.gov.uk

Dunbobbin, Andy (LAB - Connah's Quay Golftyn) andrew.dunbobbin@flintshire.gov.uk

Dunn, Brian (IND - Connah's Quay Wepre) brian.dunn@flintshire.gov.uk

Ellis, Carol (IND - Buckley Mountain) carol.ellis@flintshire.gov.uk

Evans, David (LAB - Shotton East) david.evans@flintshire.gov.uk

Falshaw, Jim (CON - Caerwys) jim.falshaw@flintshire.gov.uk

Gay, Veronica (IND - Saltney Stonebridge) veronica.gay@flintshire.gov.uk

Guest, Robin (CON - Mold South) robin.guest@flintshire.gov.uk

FLINTSHIRE

Halford, Alison (CON - Ewloe)
alison.halford@flintshire.gov.uk

Hampson, Ron (LAB - Buckley Bistre West)
ronald.hampson@flintshire.gov.uk

Hardcastle, George (IND - Aston)
george.hardcastle@flintshire.gov.uk

Healey, David (LAB - Caergwrle)
david.healey@flintshire.gov.uk

Hinds, Cindy (LAB - Pen-y-Ffordd)
cindy.r.dennis@gmail.com

Hutchinson, Dennis (IND - Buckley Pentrobin)
dennis.hutchinson@flintshire.gov.uk

Isherwood, Hilary (CON - Llanfynydd)
hilary.isherwood@flintshire.gov.uk

Johnson, Joe (LAB - Holywell East)
joe.johnson@flintshire.gov.uk

Johnson, Rita (IND - Flint Oakenholt)
rita.johnson@flintshire.gov.uk

Jones, Christine (LAB - Sealand)
christine.m.jones@flintshire.gov.uk

Jones, Kevin (LAB - Bagillt East)
kevin.jones@flintshire.gov.uk

Jones, Richard (IND - Buckley Bistre East)
richard.b.jones@flintshire.gov.uk

Legg, Colin (IND - Halkyn)
colin.legg@flintshire.gov.uk

Lightfoot, Phil (IND - Higher Kinnerton)
phil.lightfoot@flintshire.gov.uk

Lloyd, Richard (LAB - Saltney Mold Junction)
richard.lloyd@flintshire.gov.uk

Lowe, Mike (LAB - Broughton South)
mike.lowe@flintshire.gov.uk

Mackie, Dave (IND - Ewloe)
david.mackie@flintshire.gov.uk

McGuill, Hilary (LD - Argoed)
hilary.mcguill@flintshire.gov.uk

Minshull, Ann (LAB - Shotton West)
ann.minshull@flintshire.gov.uk

Mullin, Billy (LAB - Broughton North East)
billy.mullin@flintshire.gov.uk

Newhouse, Tim (IND - Hope)
tim@mucc.info

Parker, Sara (LD - New Brighton)
sara.parker@flintshire.gov.uk

Perfect, Vicky (LAB - Flint Trelawny)
vicky.perfect@flintshire.gov.uk

Phillips, Neville (LD - Buckley Bistre West)
neville.phillips@flintshire.gov.uk

Reece, Mike (LAB - Bagillt West)
mikereece@talktalk.net

Roberts, Ian (LAB - Flint Castle)
ian.roberts@flintshire.gov.uk

Roberts, Gareth (PC - Holywell West)
h.gareth.roberts@flintshire.gov.uk

Roney, David (IND - Mostyn)
david.roney@flintshire.gov.uk

Shotton, Paul (LAB - Connah's Quay Golftyn)
paul.shotton@flintshire.gov.uk

Smith, Ian (LAB - Connah's Quay South)
ian.smith@flintshire.gov.uk

Steele-Mortimer, Nigel (CON - Trelawnyd & Gwaenysgor)
nigel.steele-mortimer@flintshire.gov.uk

Thomas, Owen (CON - Cilcain)
owen.thomas@flintshire.gov.uk

Thomas, Carolyn (IND - Treuddyn)
carolyn.thomas@flintshire.gov.uk

Williams, David (IND - Pen-y-Ffordd)
david.m.williams@flintshire.gov.uk

Williams, Sharon (LAB - Gronant)
sharon.williams@flintshire.gov.uk

Wisinger, David (LAB - Queensferry)
david.wisinger@flintshire.gov.uk

Woolley, Arnold (IND - Buckley Bistre East)
arnold.woolley@flintshire.gov.uk

Wright, Matt (CON - Brynford)
matt.wright@flintshire.gov.uk

POLITICAL COMPOSITION
LAB: 32, IND: 23, CON: 9, LD: 5, PC: 1

COMMITTEE CHAIRS

Community & Enterprise: Mr Ron Hampson

Planning & Development Control: Mr David Wisinger

Social & Health Care: Mrs Carol Ellis

Forest Heath   D

Forest Heath District Council, West Suffolk House, Western Way, Bury St. Edmunds IP33 3YU
☎ 01638 719000 ✆ customer.services@westsuffolk.gov.uk
🖳 www.westsuffolk.gov.uk

FACTS AND FIGURES
EU Constituencies: Eastern
Election Frequency: Elections are of whole council

PRINCIPAL OFFICERS

Chief Executive: Mr Ian Gallin, Joint Chief Executive, West Suffolk House, Western Way, Bury St. Edmunds IP33 3YU ☎ 01284 757001 ✆ ian.gallin@westsuffolk.gov.uk

Senior Management: Ms Davina Howes, Head of Families & Communities, West Suffolk House, Western Way, Bury St. Edmunds IP33 3YU ☎ 01284 757070 ✆ davina.howes@westsuffolk.gov.uk

Senior Management: Ms Jill Korwin, Director, West Suffolk House, Western Way, Bury St. Edmunds IP33 3YU
☎ 01284 757252 ✆ jill.korwin@westsuffolk.gov.uk

Senior Management: Ms Rachael Mann, Head of Resources & Performance, West Suffolk House, Western Way, Bury St. Edmunds IP33 3YU ☎ 01638 719245 ✆ rachael.mann@westsuffolk.gov.uk

Senior Management: Mr Simon Phelan, Head of Housing, West Suffolk House, Western Way, Bury St. Edmunds IP33 3YB
☎ 01638 719440 ⏱ simon.phelan@westsuffolk.gov.uk

Senior Management: Mrs Karen Points, Head of HR, Legal & Democratic Services, West Suffolk House, Western Way, Bury St. Edmunds IP33 3YU ☎ 01285 757015
⏱ karen.points@westsuffolk.gov.uk

Senior Management: Mr Mark Walsh, Head of Operations, West Suffolk House, Western Way, Bury St. Edmunds IP33 3YU
☎ 01284 757300 ⏱ mark.walsh@westsuffolk.gov.uk

Senior Management: Mr Alex Wilson, Director, West Suffolk House, Western Way, Bury St. Edmunds IP33 3YU
☎ 01284 757695 ⏱ alex.wilson@westsuffolk.gov.uk

Senior Management: Mr Steven Wood, Head of Planning & Growth, West Suffolk House, Western Way, Bury St. Edmunds IP33 3YU ☎ 01284 757306 ⏱ steven.wood@westsuffolk.gov.uk

Architect, Building / Property Services: Mr Michael Lindsell, Service Manager - Property Services, West Suffolk House, Western Way, Bury St. Edmunds IP33 3YB ☎ 01284 757385
⏱ michael.lindsell@westsuffolk.gov.uk

Building Control: Mr Rob Fysh, Principal Building Control Surveyor, West Suffolk House, Western Way, Bury St. Edmunds IP33 3YB ☎ 01284 757379 ⏱ rob.fysh@westsuffolk.gov.uk

PR / Communications: Ms Marianne Hulland, Service Manager - Corporate Communications, West Suffolk House, Western Way, Bury St. Edmunds IP33 3YU ☎ 01284 757034
⏱ marrianna.hulland@westsuffolk.gov.uk

Computer Management: Mr James Wager, ICT Infrastructure Support Manager, West Suffolk House, Western Way, Bury St. Edmunds IP33 3EY ☎ 01284 757205
⏱ james.wager@westsuffolk.gov.uk

Corporate Services: Ms Liz Barnard, Service Manager - Corporate Policy, Forest Heath District Council, College Heath Road, Mildenhall IP28 7EY ☎ 01638 719454
⏱ liz.barnard@westsuffolk.gov.uk

Corporate Services: Ms Tanya Sturman, Service Manager - Corporate Policy, Forest Heath District Council, College Heath Road, Mildenhall IP28 7EY ☎ 01638 719473
⏱ tanya.sturman@westsuffolk.gov.uk

Customer Service: Mr Chris Bolton, Service Manager - Customer Services & Transformation, Forest Heath District Council, College Heath Road, Mildenhall IP28 7EY ☎ 01638 719320
⏱ chris.bolton@westsuffolk.gov.uk

Economic Development: Mrs Andrea Mayley, Service Manager - Economic Development & Growth, District Offices, College Heath Road, Mildenhall IP28 7EY ☎ 01284 757343
⏱ andrea.mayley@westsuffolk.gov.uk

Electoral Registration: Mrs Fiona Osman, Service Manager - Democratic Services & Elections, District Offices, College Heath Road, Mildenhall IP28 7EY ☎ 01285 757105
⏱ fiona.osman@westsuffolk.gov.uk

Emergency Planning: Mr Alan Points, District Emergency Planning Officer, West Suffolk House, Western Way, Bury St. Edmunds IP33 1YU ☎ 01284 758461
⏱ alan.points@westsuffolk.gov.uk

Energy Management: Mr Andrew Oswald, Environment & Energy Team Leader, West Suffolk House, Western Way, Bury St. Edmunds IP33 3YB ☎ 01284 757622 ⏱ andrew.oswald@westsuffolk.gov.uk

Environmental / Technical Services: Mr Peter Gudde, Service Manager - Environmental Health, West Suffolk House, Western Way, Bury St. Edmunds IP33 3YB ☎ 01284 757042
⏱ peter.gudde@westsuffolk.gov.uk

Environmental Health: Mr Peter Gudde, Service Manager - Environmental Health, West Suffolk House, Western Way, Bury St. Edmunds IP33 3YB ☎ 01284 757042
⏱ peter.gudde@westsuffolk.gov.uk

Estates, Property & Valuation: Ms Charlotte Squirrell, Senior Estates Surveyor, West Suffolk House, Western Way, Bury St. Edmunds IP33 3YB ☎ 01284 757361
⏱ charlotte.squirrell@westsuffolk.gov.uk

Events Manager: Mr Nick Wells, Entertainment & Events Manager, West Suffolk House, Western Way, Bury St. Edmunds IP33 3YB ☎ 01284 758103 ⏱ nick.wells@westsuffolk.gov.uk

Facilities: Ms Teresa Claydon, Facilities & CCTV Manager, West Suffolk House, Western Way, Bury St. Edmunds IP33 3YB
☎ 01284 757398 ⏱ teresa.claydon@westsuffolk.gov.uk

Fleet Management: Mr Philip Clifford, Fleet & Technical Manager, West Suffolk House, Western Way, Bury St. Edmunds IP33 3YU ☎ 01284 757459 ⏱ philip.clifford@westsuffolk.gov.uk

Grounds Maintenance: Mr Chris Silverwood, Service Manager - Operations, Waste & Street Scene, West Suffolk House, Western Way, Bury St. Edmunds IP33 3YB ☎ 01284 757472
⏱ chris.silverwood@westsuffolk.gov.uk

Health and Safety: Mr Martin Hosker, Health & Safety Manager, West Suffolk House, Western Way, Bury St. Edmunds IP33 3YU
☎ 01284 757010 ⏱ martin.hosker@westsuffolk.gov.uk

Housing: Mr Tony Hobby, Service Manager - Housing Operations, Forest Heath District Council, College Heath Road, Mildenhall IP28 7EY ☎ 01638 719348 ⏱ tony.hobby@westsuffolk.gov.uk

Housing: Mr Simon Phelan, Head of Housing, West Suffolk House, Western Way, Bury St. Edmunds IP33 3YU ☎ 01638 719440
⏱ simon.phelan@westsuffolk.gov.uk

Housing Maintenance: Mr Andrew Newman, Service Manager - Housing Standards, Forest Heath District Council, College Heath Road, Mildenhall IP28 7EY ☎ 01638 719276
⏱ andrew.newman@westsuffolk.gov.uk

FOREST HEATH

Legal: Mr Steven Boyle, Interim Service Manager - Legal, West Suffolk House, Western Way, Bury St. Edmunds IP33 3YB·
☎ 01285 757165 ◌ steven.boyle@westsuffolk.gov.uk

Leisure and Cultural Services: Mr Damien Parker, Service Manager - Operations, Leisure & Culture, West Suffolk House, Western Way, Bury St. Edmunds IP33 3YB ☎ 01284 757090
◌ damien.parker@westsuffolk.gov.uk

Licensing: Mr Tom Wright, Business Regulation & Licensing Manager, West Suffolk House, Western Way, Bury St. Edmunds IP33 3YU ☎ 01638 719223 ◌ tom.wright@westsuffolk.gov.uk

Member Services: Mrs Karen Points, Head of HR, Legal & Democratic Services, West Suffolk House, Western Way, Bury St. Edmunds IP33 3EY ☎ 01285 757015
◌ karen.points@westsuffolk.gov.uk

Parking: Mr Darren Dixon, Car Parks Manager, West Suffolk House, Western Way, Bury St. Edmunds IP33 3EY ☎ 01284 757413
◌ darren.dixon@westsuffolk.gov.uk

Personnel / HR: Ms Wendy Canham, Service Manager - HR & OD, West Suffolk House, Western Way, Bury St. Edmunds IP33 3YB ☎ 01284 757006 ◌ wendy.canham@westsuffolk.gov.uk

Planning: Ms Rachel Almond, Service Manager - Planning & Development, Forest Heath District Council, College Heath Road, Mildenhall IP28 7EY ☎ 01638 719455
◌ rachel.almond@westsuffolk.gov.uk

Planning: Ms Marie Smith, Service Manager - Planning Strategy, Forest Heath District Council, College Heath Road, Mildenhall IP29 7EY ☎ 01638 719260 ◌ marie.smith@westsuffolk.gov.uk

Procurement: Mr Zia Quader, Procurement Manager, West Suffolk House, Western Way, Bury St. Edmunds IP33 3YB ☎ 01284 757310 ◌ zia.quader@westsuffolk.gov.uk

Recycling & Waste Minimisation: Mr Mark Christie, Service Manager - Business, West Suffolk House, Western Way, Bury St. Edmunds IP33 3YB ☎ 01638 719220
◌ mark.christie@westsuffolk.gov.uk

Regeneration: Mrs Andrea Mayley, Service Manager - Economic Development & Growth, West Suffolk House, Western Way, Bury St. Edmunds IP33 3YU ☎ 01284 757343
◌ andrea.mayley@westsuffolk.gov.uk

Staff Training: Ms Juliet Fulford, Learning & Development Advisor, Forest Heath District Council, College Heath Road, Mildenhall IP28 7EY ☎ 01284 757047
◌ juliet.fulford@westsuffolk.gov.uk

Street Scene: Mr Chris Silverwood, Service Manager - Operations, Waste & Street Scene, West Suffolk House, Western Way, Bury St. Edmunds IP33 3YB ☎ 01284 757472
◌ chris.silverwood@westsuffolk.gov.uk

Waste Collection and Disposal: Mr Chris Silverwood, Service Manager - Operations, Waste & Street Scene, West Suffolk House, Western Way, Bury St. Edmunds IP33 3YB ☎ 01284 757472
◌ chris.silverwood@westsuffolk.gov.uk

Waste Management: Mr Mark Walsh, Head of Operations, West Suffolk House, Western Way, Bury St. Edmunds IP33 3YU
☎ 01284 757300 ◌ mark.walsh@westsuffolk.gov.uk

Children's Play Areas: Mr Timothy McGee, Playground Inspector, West Suffolk House, Western Way, Bury St. Edmunds IP33 3YB
☎ 01284 757063 ◌ timothy.mcgee@westsuffolk.gov.uk

COUNCILLORS

Chair Lynch, Carol (CON - Red Lodge)
carol.lynch@forest-heath.gov.uk

Vice-Chair Anderson, Michael (CON - Severals)
michael.anderson@forest-heath.gov.uk

Leader of the Council: Waters, James (CON - Eriswell & The Rows)
james.waters@forest-heath.gov.uk

Deputy Leader of the Council: Millar, Robin (CON - All Saints)
robin.millar@forest-heath.gov.uk

Allen, Ruth (IND - Severals)
ruth.allen@forest-heath.gov.uk

Appleby, Andrew (IND - Severals)
andrew.appleby@forest-heath.gov.uk

Barker, Chris (CON - St Mary's)
chris.barker@forest-heath.gov.uk

Bloodworth, John (CON - Market)
john.bloodworth@forest-heath.gov.uk

Bowman, David (CON - Eriswell & The Rows)
david.bowman@forest-heath.gov.uk

Bowman, Ruth (CON - Market)
ruth.bowman@forest-heath.gov.uk

Burt, Rona (CON - Iceni)
rona.burt@forest-heath.gov.uk

Busuttil, Louis (CON - Great Heath)
louis.busuttil@forest-heath.gov.uk

Cole, Simon (IND - Exning)
simon.cole@forest-heath.gov.uk

Dicker, Roger (UKIP - South)
roger.dicker@forest-heath.gov.uk

Drummond, Andy (CON - St Mary's)
andy.drummond@forest-heath.gov.uk

Edwards, Stephen (CON - All Saints)
stephen.edwards@forest-heath.gov.uk

Harvey, Brian (CON - Manor)
brian.harvey@forest-heath.gov.uk

Lukaniuk, Victor (IND - Brandon West)
victor.lukaniuk@forest-heath.gov.uk

Marston, Louise (CON - Lakenheath)
louise.marston@forest-heath.gov.uk

Mason, Christine (CON - Brandon East)
christine.mason@forest-heath.gov.uk

Noble, Colin (CON - Lakenheath)
colin.noble@forest-heath.gov.uk

Palmer, David (IND - Brandon West)
david.palmer@forest-heath.gov.uk

Ridgwell, Peter (UKIP - Brandon East)
peter.ridgwell@forest-heath.gov.uk

Roman, Nigel (CON - Great Heath)
nigel.roman@forest-heath.gov.uk

Sadler, Bill (IND - St Mary's)
bill.sadler@forest-heath.gov.uk

Silvester, Reg (UKIP - Brandon East)
reg.silvester@forest-heath.gov.uk

Stanbury, Lance (CON - Red Lodge)
lance.stanbury@forest-heath.gov.uk

POLITICAL COMPOSITION
CON: 18, IND: 6, UKIP: 3

COMMITTEE CHAIRS

Audit: Mr Louis Busuttil

Development Control: Ms Rona Burt

Licensing: Mr Michael Anderson

Forest of Dean   D

Forest of Dean District Council, Council Offices, High Street, Coleford GL16 8HG
☎ 01594 810000 🖷 01594 812590 ⌂ council@fdean.gov.uk
🖳 www.fdean.gov.uk

FACTS AND FIGURES
Parliamentary Constituencies: Forest of Dean
EU Constituencies: South West
Election Frequency: Elections are of whole council

PRINCIPAL OFFICERS

Chief Executive: Ms Sue Pangbourne, Head of Paid Service, Council Offices, High Street, Coleford GL16 8HG ☎ 01594 812501
⌂ sue.pangborne@fdean.gov.uk

Senior Management: Mr David Neudegg, Managing Director, Council Offices, Trinity Road, Cirencester GL7 1PX ☎ 01285 623101
⌂ david.neudegg@2020partnership.uk

Senior Management: Mr Ralph Young, Programme Director, Council Offices, Trinity Road, Cirencester GL7 1PX ☎ 01285 623600 ⌂ ralph.young@cotswold.gov.uk

Building Control: Mr Peter Williams, Strategic Group Manager, Council Offices, Coleford GL16 8HG ☎ 01594 812300
⌂ peter.williams@fdean.gov.uk

PR / Communications: Miss Michaela Lee, Communications Officer, Council Offices, High Street, Coleford GL16 8HG
☎ 01594 812622 ⌂ michaela.lee@fdean.gov.uk

Community Safety: Ms Nicola Mclean, Community Engagement Officer, Council Offices, High Street, Coleford GL16 8HG
☎ 01594 812372 ⌂ nicola.mclean@fdean.gov.uk

Computer Management: Mrs Rachel McKinnon, ICT Manager, Council Offices, High Street, Coleford GL16 8HG ☎ 01242 264128
⌂ rachel.mckinnon@cheltenham.gov.uk

Corporate Services: Mrs Karen Rushworth, Corporate Support Manager, Council Offices, High Street, Coleford GL16 8HG
☎ 01594 812524 ⌂ karen.rushworth@fdean.gov.uk

E-Government: Mrs Rachel McKinnon, ICT Manager, Council Offices, High Street, Coleford GL16 8HG ☎ 01242 264128
⌂ rachel.mckinnon@cheltenham.gov.uk

Electoral Registration: Mrs Geraldine Randall-Wilce, Electoral Services Officer, Council Offices, Coleford GL16 8HG
☎ 01594 812626 ⌂ geraldine.randall-wilce@fdean.gov.uk

Emergency Planning: Mrs Karen Rushworth, Corporate Support Manager, Forest of Dean District Council, Council Offices, High Street, Coleford GL16 8HG ☎ 01594 812524
⌂ karen.rushworth@fdean.gov.uk

Environmental / Technical Services: Mr Matt Kirby, Service Leader - Business Support, Council Offices, High Street, Coleford GL16 8HG ☎ 07580 113230 ⌂ matthew.kirby@2020partnership.uk

Environmental Health: Mr Matt Kirby, Service Leader - Business Support, Council Offices, High Street, Coleford GL16 8HG
☎ 07580 113230 ⌂ matthew.kirby@2020partnership.uk

Estates, Property & Valuation: Mr Chris Johns, Land & Property Manager, Council Offices, Gloucester Road, Tewkesbury GL20 5TT
☎ 01594 812261 ⌂ chris.johns@fdean.gov.uk

Finance: Mr Paul Jones, GOSS Head of Finance, Council Offices, High Street, Coleford GL16 8HG ☎ 01242 775154
⌂ paul.jones@cheltenham.gov.uk

Grounds Maintenance: Mr Chris Johns, Land & Property Manager, Council Offices, Gloucester Road, Tewkesbury GL20 5TT
☎ 01594 812261 ⌂ chris.johns@fdean.gov.uk

Health and Safety: Mr Ian Badham, GO Shared Services, Municipal Offices, Promenade, Cheltenham GL50 9SA
☎ 01242 264356 ⌂ ian.badham@cheltenham.gov.uk

Housing: Mr Peter Williams, Strategic Group Manager, Council Offices, Coleford GL16 8HG ☎ 01594 812300
⌂ peter.williams@fdean.gov.uk

Legal: Ms Claire Hughes, Legal Team Manager, Council Offices, High Street, Coleford GL16 8HG ☎ 01594 812515
⌂ claire.hughes@fdean.gov.uk

Leisure and Cultural Services: Mr Andy Barge, Group Manager - Customer Services, Council Offices, Coleford GL16 8HG
☎ 01594 812383 ⌂ andy.barge@fdean.gov.uk

Licensing: Mr Matt Kirby, Service Leader - Business Support, Council Offices, High Street, Coleford GL16 8HG
☎ 07580 113230 ⌂ matthew.kirby@2020partnership.uk

Member Services: Mrs Julie Jones, Democratic Services Manager, Council Offices, High Street, Coleford GL16 8HG
☎ 01594 812623 ⌂ julie.jones@fdean.gov.uk

FOREST OF DEAN

Personnel / HR: Ms Deborah Bainbridge, Head of Human Resources, Council Offices, Woodgreen, Witney OX28 1NB
☎ 01285 623148 ^ deborah.bainbridge@cotswold.gov.uk

Planning: Mr Peter Williams, Strategic Group Manager, Council Offices, Coleford GL16 8HG ☎ 01594 812300
^ peter.williams@fdean.gov.uk

Procurement: Mr Dave Baker, Business Partner - Procurement, Council Offices, High Street, Coleford GL16 8HG ☎ 01242 775055
^ dave.baker@fdean.gov.uk

Recycling & Waste Minimisation: Ms Rachel Capon, Environmental Contracts Team Leader, Council Offices, High Street, Coleford GL16 8HG ☎ 01594 812431 ^ rachel.capon@fdean.gov.uk

Staff Training: Mrs Jan Bridges, Learning & Organisational Development Manager, Municipal Offices, Promenade, Cheltenham GL50 9SA ☎ 01242 775189 ^ jan.bridges@cheltenham.gov.uk

Street Scene: Mr Andy Barge, Group Manager - Customer Services, Council Offices, Coleford GL16 8HG ☎ 01594 812383
^ andy.barge@fdean.gov.uk

Sustainable Communities: Mr Alastair Chapman, Sustainability Team Leader, Council Offices, High Street, Coleford GL16 8HG
☎ 01594 812329 ^ alastair.chapman@fdean.gov.uk

Sustainable Development: Mr Alastair Chapman, Sustainability Team Leader, Council Offices, High Street, Coleford GL16 8HG
☎ 01594 812329 ^ alastair.chapman@fdean.gov.uk

Tourism: Ms Paula Burrows, Manager - Commercial Services, Council Offices, High Street, Coleford GL16 8HG ☎ 01594 812389
^ paula.burrows@fdean.gov.uk

Waste Collection and Disposal: Ms Rachel Capon, Environmental Contracts Team Leader, Council Offices, High Street, Coleford GL16 8HG ☎ 01594 812431 ^ rachel.capon@fdean.gov.uk

Waste Management: Ms Rachel Capon, Environmental Contracts Team Leader, Council Offices, High Street, Coleford GL16 8HG
☎ 01594 812431 ^ rachel.capon@fdean.gov.uk

COUNCILLORS

ChairHorne, Jane (CON - Tibberton)
jane.horne@fdean.gov.uk

Vice-ChairBevan, James (CON - Lydney East)
james.bevan@fdean.gov.uk

Leader of the Council: Molyneux, Patrick (CON - Hewelsfield & Woolaston)
patrick.molyneux@fdean.gov.uk

Deputy Leader of the Council: Robinson, Brian (CON - Mitcheldean & Drybrook)
brian.robinson@fdean.gov.uk

Allaway Martin, Carole (CON - Coleford Central)
carole.allawaymartin@fdean.gov.uk

Boyles, Richard (CON - Newnham & Westbury)
richard.boyles@fdean.gov.uk

Burford, Philip (IND - Hartpury)
philip.burford@fdean.gov.uk

Coborn, Max (LAB - Cinderford East)
max.coborn@fdean.gov.uk

Davies, Gethyn (CON - Tidenham)
gethyn.davies@fdean.gov.uk

East, David (INDNA - Blaisdon & Longhope)
david.east@fdean.gov.uk

Easton, David (CON - Coleford East)
david.easton@fdean.gov.uk

Edwards, Diana (CON - Pillowell)
diana.edwards@fdean.gov.uk

Edwards, Maria (CON - Tidenham)
maria.edwards@fdean.gov.uk

Elsmore, Clive (IND - Coleford Central)
clive.elsmore@fdean.gov.uk

Evans, Frankie (CON - Alvington, Aylburton & West Lydney)
frankie.evans@fdean.gov.uk

Fraser, Jackie (LAB - Mitcheldean & Drybrook)
jackie.fraser@fdean.gov.uk

Gardiner, Andrew (INDNA - Lydbrook & Ruardean)
andrew.gardiner@fdean.gov.uk

Gooch, Julia (INDNA - Newent Central)
julia.gooch@fdean.gov.uk

Grant, Alan (UKIP - Pillowell)
Alan.grant@fdean.gov.uk

Guyton, Colin (UKIP - Lydbrook & Ruardean)
colin.guyton@fdean.gov.uk

Gwilliam, Timothy (LAB - Berry Hill)
tim.gwilliam@fdean.gov.uk

Hale, Terry (CON - Newland & St Briavels)
terry.hale@fdean.gov.uk

Harris, Carol (UKIP - Lydney East)
carol.harris@fdean.gov.uk

Hawthorne, Dave (CON - Littledean & Ruspidge)
dave.hawthorne@fdean.gov.uk

Hiett, Paul (LAB - Bream)
paul.hiett@fdean.gov.uk

Hill, Martin (UKIP - Coleford East)
martin.hill@fdean.gov.uk

Hogan, Bruce (LAB - Lydbrook & Ruardean)
bruce.hogan@fdean.gov.uk

Hughes, Gareth (CON - Awre)
gareth.hughes@fdean.gov.uk

James, Roger (LAB - Coleford East)
roger.james@fdean.gov.uk

Jones, Brian (CON - Churcham & Huntley)
brian.jones@fdean.gov.uk

Lawton, Craig (CON - Oxenhall & Newent North East)
craig.lawton@fdean.gov.uk

Lawton, Len (CON - Newent Central)
len.lawton@fdean.gov.uk

Leppington, Richard (UKIP - Bream)
richard.leppington@fdean.gov.uk

Martin, Di (LAB - Cinderford East)
di.martin@fdean.gov.uk

McFarling, Chris (INDNA - Newland & St. Briavels)
chris.mcfarling@fdean.gov.uk

Molyneux, Helen (CON - Tidenham)
helen.molyneux@fdean.gov.uk

Morgan, Graham (LAB - Cinderford West)
graham.morgan@fdean.gov.uk

O'Neill, Bernie (LAB - Littledean & Ruspidge)
bernie.oneill@fdean.gov.uk

Osborne, Bill (LAB - Lydney East)
bill.osborne@fdean.gov.uk

Phelps, Simon (IND - Newnham & Westbury)
simon.phelps@fdean.gov.uk

Preest, Alan (UKIP - Lydney North)
alan.preest@fdean.gov.uk

Scott, Douglas (LAB - Mitcheldean & Drybrook)
douglas.scott@fdean.gov.uk

Simpson, Jim (UKIP - Alvington, Aylburton & West Lydney)
jim.simpson@fdean.gov.uk

Smart, Marrilyn (CON - Christchurch & English Bicknor)
marrilyn.smart@fdean.gov.uk

Sterry, Lynn (LAB - Cinderford West)
lynn.sterry@fdean.gov.uk

Sterry, Roger (LAB - Cinderford West)
roger.sterry@fdean.gov.uk

Williams, Clayton (CON - Redmarley)
clayton.williams@fdean.gov.uk

Yeates, Roger (CON - Bromsberrow & Dymock)
roger.yeates@fdean.gov.uk

POLITICAL COMPOSITION
CON: 21, LAB: 13, UKIP: 7, INDNA: 4, IND: 3

COMMITTEE CHAIRS

Audit: Mr Brian Jones

Licensing: Ms Lynn Sterry

Planning: Mr Philip Burford

Fylde   D

Fylde Borough Council, Town Hall, St. Annes Road West, St. Annes-on-Sea FY8 1LW
☎ 01253 658658 🖷 01253 713113 ⁀ listening@fylde.gov.uk
🖳 www.fylde.gov.uk

FACTS AND FIGURES
Parliamentary Constituencies: Fylde
EU Constituencies: North West
Election Frequency: Elections are of whole council

PRINCIPAL OFFICERS

Chief Executive: Mr Allan Oldfield, Chief Executive, Town Hall, St. Annes Road West, St. Annes-on-Sea FY8 1LW ☎ 01253 658500 ⁀ allan.oldfield@fylde.gov.uk

Senior Management: Mr Mark Evans, Head of Planning & Regeneration, Town Hall, St. Annes Road West, St. Annes-on-Sea FY8 1LW ☎ 01253 658460 ⁀ mark.evans@fylde.gov.uk

Senior Management: Ms Tracy Morrison, Director - Resources & Council Monitoring Officer, Town Hall, St. Annes Road West, St. Annes-on-Sea FY8 1LW ☎ 01253 658521 ⁀ tracy.morrison@fylde.gov.uk

Senior Management: Mr Paul O'Donoghue, Chief Finance & S151 Officer, Town Hall, St. Annes Road West, St. Annes-on-Sea FY8 1LW ☎ 01253 658658 ⁀ paul.o'donoghue@fylde.gov.uk

Senior Management: Mr Paul Walker, Director - Development Services, Town Hall, St. Annes Road West, St. Annes-on-Sea FY8 1LW ☎ 01253 658658 ⁀ paul.walker@fylde.gov.uk

Architect, Building / Property Services: Mr Andrew Dickson, Head - Technical Services, Town Hall, Lytham St. Annes FY8 1LW ☎ 01253 658675 ⁀ andrew.dickson@fylde.gov.uk

Building Control: Mr Andrew Dickson, Head - Technical Services, Town Hall, Lytham St. Annes FY8 1LW ☎ 01253 658675 ⁀ andrew.dickson@fylde.gov.uk

PR / Communications: Miss Erin Harkin, Communications & Consultations Officer, Town Hall, St. Annes Road West, St. Annes-on-Sea FY8 1LW ☎ 01253 658499 ⁀ erin.harkin@fylde.gov.uk

Community Planning: Mr Mark Evans, Head of Planning & Regeneration, Town Hall, St. Annes Road West, St. Annes-on-Sea FY8 1LW ☎ 01253 658460 ⁀ mark.evans@fylde.gov.uk

Community Safety: Ms Tracy Morrison, Director - Resources & Council Monitoring Officer, Town Hall, St. Annes Road West, St. Annes-on-Sea FY8 1LW ☎ 01253 658521 ⁀ tracy.morrison@fylde.gov.uk

Computer Management: Mr Dean Atherton, ICT Service Team Leader, Town Hall, St. Annes Road West, St. Annes-on-Sea FY8 1LW ☎ 01253 658580 ⁀ dean.atherton@fylde.gov.uk

Customer Service: Mr William Fisher, Customer Services Manager, Town Hall, St. Annes Road West, St. Annes-on-Sea FY8 1LW ☎ 01253 658450 ⁀ william.fisher@fylde.gov.uk

Economic Development: Mr Stephen Smith, Economic Development Officer, Town Hall, St. Annes Road West, St. Annes-on-Sea FY8 1LW ☎ 01253 658445 ⁀ stephen.smith@fylde.gov.uk

Electoral Registration: Mrs Hazel McNicoll, Electoral Services Manager, Town Hall, St. Annes Road West, St. Annes-on-Sea FY8 1LW ☎ 01253 658516 ⁀ hazel.mcnicoll@fylde.gov.uk

Emergency Planning: Ms Chris Hambly, Environmental Services Manager, Town Hall, St. Annes Road West, St. Annes-on-Sea FY8 1LW ☎ 01253 658422 ⁀ chris.hambly@fylde.gov.uk

Energy Management: Mr Andrew Loynd, Parking & Energy Officer, Town Hall, St. Annes Road West, St. Annes-on-Sea FY8 1LW ☎ 01253658527 ⁀ andrew.loynd@fylde.gov.uk

FYLDE

Environmental / Technical Services: Mr Andrew Dickson, Head - Technical Services, Town Hall, Lytham St. Annes FY8 1LW ☎ 01253 658675 🖂 andrew.dickson@fylde.gov.uk

Environmental Health: Ms Sara Carrington, Principal Officer - Commercial, Town Hall, St. Annes Road West, St. Annes-on-Sea FY8 1LW ☎ 01253 658627 🖂 sara.carrington@fylde.gov.uk

Estates, Property & Valuation: Mr Gary Sams, Principal Estates Surveyor, Town Hall, St. Annes Road West, St. Annes-on-Sea FY8 1LW ☎ 01253 658462 🖂 gary.sams@fylde.gov.uk

Finance: Mr Paul O'Donoghue, Chief Finance & S151 Officer, Town Hall, St. Annes Road West, St. Annes-on-Sea FY8 1LW ☎ 01253 658658 🖂 paul.o'donoghue@fylde.gov.uk

Grounds Maintenance: Mr Peter Graveson, Grounds Maintenance Officer, Town Hall, Lytham St. Annes FY8 1LW ☎ 01253 658471 🖂 peterg@fylde.gov.uk

Health and Safety: Ms Chris Hambly, Environmental Services Manager, Town Hall, St. Annes Road West, St. Annes-on-Sea FY8 1LW ☎ 01253 658422 🖂 chris.hambly@fylde.gov.uk

Housing: Ms Kristine Riding, Housing Manager, Town Hall, St. Annes Road West, St. Annes-on-Sea FY8 1LW ☎ 01253 658669 🖂 kristine.riding@fylde.gov.uk

Legal: Mr Ian Curtis, Head of Governance, Town Hall, St. Annes Road West, St. Annes-on-Sea FY8 1LW ☎ 01253 658506 🖂 ian.curtis@fylde.gov.uk

Leisure and Cultural Services: Mr Mark Wilde, Head of Parks, Leisure & Cultural Services, Town Hall, St. Annes Road West, St. Annes-on-Sea FY8 1LW ☎ 01253 658475 🖂 mark.wilde@fylde.gov.uk

Licensing: Ms Chris Hambly, Environmental Services Manager, Town Hall, St. Annes Road West, St. Annes-on-Sea FY8 1LW ☎ 01253 658422 🖂 chris.hambly@fylde.gov.uk

Member Services: Mr Ian Curtis, Head of Governance, Town Hall, St. Annes Road West, St. Annes-on-Sea FY8 1LW ☎ 01253 658506 🖂 ian.curtis@fylde.gov.uk

Parking: Mr Andrew Loynd, Parking & Energy Officer, Town Hall, St. Annes Road West, St. Annes-on-Sea FY8 1LW ☎ 01253658527 🖂 andrew.loynd@fylde.gov.uk

Personnel / HR: Mr Allan Oldfield, Chief Executive, Town Hall, St. Annes Road West, St. Annes-on-Sea FY8 1LW ☎ 01253 658500 🖂 allan.oldfield@fylde.gov.uk

Planning: Mr Mark Evans, Head of Planning & Regeneration, Town Hall, St. Annes Road West, St. Annes-on-Sea FY8 1LW ☎ 01253 658460 🖂 mark.evans@fylde.gov.uk

Recycling & Waste Minimisation: Ms Kathy Winstanley, Waste & Fleet Services Manager, Town Hall, St. Annes Road West, St. Annes-on-Sea FY8 1LW ☎ 01253 658576 🖂 kathy.winstanley@fylde.gov.uk

Regeneration: Mr Paul Drinnan, Regeneration Manager, Town Hall, St. Annes Road West, St. Annes-on-Sea FY8 1LW ☎ 01253 658434 🖂 paul.drinnan@fylde.gov.uk

Tourism: Mrs Vivien Wood, Tourism Officer, Town Hall, Lytham St. Annes FY8 1LW ☎ 01253 658436 🖂 viv.wood@fylde.gov.uk

Transport: Ms Kathy Winstanley, Waste & Fleet Services Manager, Town Hall, St. Annes Road West, St. Annes-on-Sea FY8 1LW ☎ 01253 658576 🖂 kathy.winstanley@fylde.gov.uk

Waste Collection and Disposal: Ms Kathy Winstanley, Waste & Fleet Services Manager, Town Hall, St. Annes Road West, St. Annes-on-Sea FY8 1LW ☎ 01253 658576 🖂 kathy.winstanley@fylde.gov.uk

Waste Management: Ms Kathy Winstanley, Waste & Fleet Services Manager, Town Hall, St. Annes Road West, St. Annes-on-Sea FY8 1LW ☎ 01253 658576 🖂 kathy.winstanley@fylde.gov.uk

Children's Play Areas: Mr Mark Wilde, Head of Parks, Leisure & Cultural Services, Town Hall, St. Annes Road West, St. Annes-on-Sea FY8 1LW ☎ 01253 658475 🖂 mark.wilde@fylde.gov.uk

COUNCILLORS

Mayor: Akeroyd, Christine (CON - Kilnhouse)
cllr.cakeroyd@fylde.gov.uk

Deputy Mayor: Jacques, Angela (CON - St Leonards)
cllr.ajacques@fylde.gov.uk

Leader of the Council: Fazackerley, Susan (CON - Central)
cllr.sfazackerley@fylde.gov.uk

Deputy Leader of the Council: Buckley, Karen (CON - St Leonards)
cllr.kbuckley@fylde.gov.uk

Aitken, Ben (CON - Ansdell)
cllr.baitken@fylde.gov.uk

Andrews, Frank (CON - Ribby-with-Wrea)
cllr.fandrews@fylde.gov.uk

Anthony, Peter (CON - Clifton)
peter.anthony@fylde.gov.uk

Ashton, Timothy (CON - St Johns)
tim.ashton@lancashire.gov.uk

Bamforth, Mark (R - St Johns)
cllr.mbamforth@fylde.gov.uk

Barker, Jan (LAB - Central)
cllr.jbarker@fylde.gov.uk

Beckett, Keith (IND - Kirkham North)
cllr.kbeckett@fylde.gov.uk

Blackshaw, Brenda (CON - Fairhaven)
cllr.bblackshaw@fylde.gov.uk

Brickles, Julie (IND - Warton & Westby)
cllr.jbrickles@fylde.gov.uk

Chew, Maxine (IND - Singleton & Greenhalgh)
cllr.mchew@fylde.gov.uk

Clayton, Alan (IND - Medlar-with-Wesham)
cllr.aclayton@fylde.gov.uk

Collins, Peter (IND - Newton & Treales)
petercollins4568@aol.com

Collins, Delma (CON - St Leonards)
cllr.dcollins@fylde.gov.uk

Cornah, Michael (CON - Warton & Westby)
cllr.mcornah@fylde.gov.uk

Donaldson, David (CON - Fairhaven)
cllr.ddonaldson@fylde.gov.uk

Eaves, David (CON - Ansdell)
cllr.deaves@fylde.gov.uk

Fiddler, Trevor (CON - Freckleton West)
cllr.tfiddler@fylde.gov.uk

Ford, Tony (LD - Ashton)
cllr.tford@fylde.gov.uk

Fradley, Richard (CON - Clifton)
cllr.rfradley@flyde.gov.uk

Goodman, Gill (CON - Ashton)
cllr.ggoodman@fylde.gov.uk

Green, Shirley (CON - Park)
cllr.sgreen@fylde.gov.uk

Hardy, Peter (IND - Kirkham South)
cllr.phardy@fylde.gov.uk

Harvey, Neil (CON - Park)
cllr.nharvey@fylde.gov.uk

Hayhurst, Paul (INDNA - Elswick & Little Eccleston)
cllr.phayhurst@fylde.gov.uk

Henshaw, Karen (LD - Kilnhouse)
cllr.khenshaw@fylde.gov.uk

Hodgson, Paul (IND - Kirkham North)
cllr.phodgson@fylde.gov.uk

Little, Cheryl (CON - Fairhaven)
cllr.clittle@fylde.gov.uk

Lloyd, Roger (R - St Johns)
cllr.rlloyd@fylde.gov.uk

Mulholland, James (INDNA - Freckleton East)
kiranmul@dsl.pipex.com

Nash, Edward (CON - Central)
cllr.enash@fylde.gov.uk

Nash, Barbara Ann (CON - Heyhouses)
cllr.bnash@fylde.gov.uk

Neale, Graeme (CON - Ashton)
cllr.gneale@fylde.gov.uk

Nulty, Linda (IND - Medlar-with-Wesham)
cllr.lnulty@fylde.gov.uk

Oades, Elizabeth (IND - Kirkham South)
cllr.eoades@fylde.gov.uk

Pitman, Sandra (CON - Park)
cllr.spitman@fylde.gov.uk

Pounder, Albert (CON - Staining & Weeton)
cllr.apounder@fylde.gov.uk

Redcliffe, Richard (CON - Ansdell)
cllr.rredcliffe@fylde.gov.uk

Rigby, Louis (IND - Freckleton West)
cllr.lrigby@fylde.gov.uk

Settle, Vince (CON - Heyhouses)
cllr.vsettle@fylde.gov.uk

Silverwood, Elaine (IND - Kirkham North)
cllr.esilverwood@fylde.gov.uk

Singleton, John (CON - Staining & Weeton)
cllr.jsingleton@fylde.gov.uk

Small, Roger (CON - Kilnhouse)
cllr.rsmall@fylde.gov.uk

Speak, Heather (IND - Newton & Treales)
cllr.hspeak@fylde.gov.uk

Taylor, Richard (CON - Warton & Westby)
cllr.rtaylor@fylde.gov.uk

Thomas, Raymond (CON - Clifton)
cllr.rthomas@fylde.gov.uk

Threlfall, Thomas (CON - Freckleton East)
cllr.tthrelfall@fylde.gov.uk

Willder, Vivienne (CON - Heyhouses)
cllr.vwillder@fylde.gov.uk

POLITICAL COMPOSITION
CON: 32, IND: 12, INDNA: 2, LD: 2, R: 2, LAB: 1

COMMITTEE CHAIRS

Audit: Mr John Singleton

Development Management: Mr Trevor Fiddler

Environment, Health & Housing: Mr Ben Aitken

Finance & Democracy: Ms Karen Buckley

Licensing: Ms Angela Jacques

Gateshead   M

Gateshead Council, Civic Centre, Regent Street, Gateshead
NE8 1HH
☎ 0191 433 3000 ✆ enquiries@gateshead.gov.uk
🖥 www.gateshead.gov.uk

FACTS AND FIGURES
Parliamentary Constituencies: Blaydon, Gateshead, Jarrow, Tyne Bridge
EU Constituencies: North East
Election Frequency: Elections are by thirds

PRINCIPAL OFFICERS

Chief Executive: Mr Mike Barker, Acting Chief Executive, Civic Centre, Regent Street, Gateshead NE8 1HH ☎ 0191 433 2102 ✆ mikebarker@gateshead.gov.uk

Senior Management: Mr Mike Barker, Acting Chief Executive, Civic Centre, Regent Street, Gateshead NE8 1HH ☎ 0191 433 2102 ✆ mikebarker@gateshead.gov.uk

Senior Management: Mr Darren Collins, Strategic Director - Corporate Resources, Civic Centre, Regent Street, Gateshead NE8 1HH ☎ 0191 433 3581 ✆ enwallis@gateshead.gov.uk

GATESHEAD

Senior Management: Mr Paul Dowling, Strategic Director - Communities & Environment, Civic Centre, Regent Street, Gateshead NE8 1HH ☎ 0191 433 3402 ⌂ gwengowland@gateshead.gov.uk

Access Officer / Social Services (Disability): Ms Clare Ault, Service Manager - Disabilities, Civic Centre, Regent Street, Gateshead NE8 1HH ☎ 0191 433 2613 ⌂ clareault@gateshead.gov.uk

Architect, Building / Property Services: Ms Victoria Beattie, Service Director - Construction, Civic Centre, Regent Street, Gateshead NE8 1HH ☎ 0191 433 7311 ⌂ victoriabeattie@gateshead.gov.uk

Architect, Building / Property Services: Mr Chris Tearney, Service Manager - Construction Services, Civic Centre, Regent Street, Gateshead NE8 1HH ☎ 0191 433 7201 ⌂ christearney@gateshead.gov.uk

Architect, Building / Property Services: Mr Peter Udall, Service Director - Design & Technical Services, Civic Centre, Regent Street, Gateshead NE8 1HH ☎ 0191 433 2901 ⌂ peterudall@gateshead.gov.uk

Best Value: Ms Marisa Jobling, Service Director - Policy, Performance & Communications, Civic Centre, Regent Street, Gateshead NE8 1HH ☎ 0191 433 3000 ⌂ marisajobling@gateshead.gov.uk

Building Control: Mrs Anneliese Hutchinson, Service Director - Development & Public Protection, Civic Centre, Regent Street, Gateshead NE8 1HH ☎ 0191 433 3881 ⌂ anneliesehutchinson@gateshead.gov.uk

Building Control: Ms Emma Lucas, Development Manager, Civic Centre, Regent Street, Gateshead NE8 1HH ☎ 0191 433 3000 ⌂ emmalucas@gateshead.gov.uk

Catering Services: Mr Dale Robson, Service Director - Facilities Management, Civic Centre, Regent Street, Gateshead NE8 1HH ☎ 0191 433 5510 ⌂ dalerobson@gateshead.gov.uk

Children / Youth Services: Ms Elaine Devaney, Service Manager - Looked After Children, Civic Centre, Regent Street, Gateshead NE8 1HH ☎ 0191 433 3000 ⌂ elainedevaney@gateshead.gov.uk

Children / Youth Services: Ms Val Hall, Service Director - Children & Families Support, Civic Centre, Regent Street, Gateshead NE8 1HH ☎ 0191 433 3000 ⌂ valhall@gateshead.gov.uk

Civil Registration: Ms Deborah Hill, Service Director - Human Resources & Litigation, Civic Centre, Regent Street, Gateshead NE8 1HH ☎ 0191 433 2110 ⌂ deborahhill@gateshead.gov.uk

PR / Communications: Ms Elaine Barclay, Policy & Communications Team Leader, Civic Centre, Regent Street, Gateshead NE8 1HH ☎ 0191 433 3544 ⌂ elainebarclay@gateshead.gov.uk

PR / Communications: Ms Marisa Jobling, Service Director - Policy, Performance & Communications, Civic Centre, Regent Street, Gateshead NE8 1HH ☎ 0191 433 3000 ⌂ marisajobling@gateshead.gov.uk

Community Planning: Mrs Lindsay Murray, Service Director - Culture, Communities, Leisure & Volunteering, Civic Centre, Regent Street, Gateshead NE8 1HH ☎ 0191 433 3000 ⌂ lindsaymurray@gateshead.gov.uk

Community Safety: Mrs Anneliese Hutchinson, Service Director - Development & Public Protection, Civic Centre, Regent Street, Gateshead NE8 1HH ☎ 0191 433 3881 ⌂ anneliesehutchinson@gateshead.gov.uk

Computer Management: Mr Roy Sheehan, Service Director - ICT, Civic Centre, Regent Street, Gateshead NE8 1HH ☎ 0191 433 3000 ⌂ roysheehan@gateshead.gov.uk

Consumer Protection and Trading Standards: Mr Peter Wright, Manager - Environmental Health & Trading Standards, Civic Centre, Regent Street, Gateshead NE8 1HH ☎ 0191 433 3910 ⌂ peterwright@gateshead.gov.uk

Contracts: Mrs Andrea Tickner, Service Director - Corporate Commissioning & Procurement, Civic Centre, Regent Street, Gateshead NE8 1HH ☎ 0191 438 5995 ⌂ andreatickner@gateshead.gov.uk

Corporate Services: Mr Martin Harrison, Service Director - Legal, Democratic & Property Services, Civic Centre, Regent Street, Gateshead NE8 1HH ☎ 0191 433 2101 ⌂ martinharrison@gateshead.gov.uk

Customer Service: Mr John Jopling, Service Director - Customer & Financial Services, Civic Centre, Regent Street, Gateshead NE8 1HH ☎ 0191 433 3000 ⌂ johnjopling@gateshead.gov.uk

Economic Development: Mr Andrew Marshall, Service Director - Economic & Housing Growth, Civic Centre, Regent Street, Gateshead NE8 1HH ☎ 0191 433 3422 ⌂ andrewmarshall@gateshead.gov.uk

Education: Mr Steve Horne, Service Director - Learning & Schools, Dryden Centre, Evistones Road, Low Fell, Gateshead NE9 5UR ☎ 0191 433 3000 ⌂ stevehorne@gateshead.gov.uk

E-Government: Mr Roy Sheehan, Service Director - ICT, Civic Centre, Regent Street, Gateshead NE8 1HH ☎ 0191 433 3000 ⌂ roysheehan@gateshead.gov.uk

Electoral Registration: Ms Christine Thomas, Electoral Services Manager, Civic Centre, Regent Street, Gateshead NE8 1HH ☎ 0191 433 2152 ⌂ christinethomas@gateshead.gov.uk

Emergency Planning: Mr Anthony Alder, Service Director - Commissioning & Business Support, Civic Centre, Regent Street, Gateshead NE8 1HH ☎ 0191 433 3000 ⌂ anthonyalder@gateshead.gov.uk

Energy Management: Mr Jim Gillon, Team Leader - Energy Services, Civic Centre, Regent Street, Gateshead NE8 1HH ☎ 0191 433 3000 ⌂ jimgillon@gateshead.gov.uk

Environmental / Technical Services: Mr Anthony Alder, Service Director - Commissioning & Business Support, Civic Centre, Regent Street, Gateshead NE8 1HH ☎ 0191 433 3000 ⏁ anthonyalder@gateshead.gov.uk

Environmental Health: Mrs Anneliese Hutchinson, Service Director - Development & Public Protection, Civic Centre, Regent Street, Gateshead NE8 1HH ☎ 0191 433 3881 ⏁ anneliesehutchinson@gateshead.gov.uk

Estates, Property & Valuation: Mr Peter Udall, Service Director - Design & Technical Services, Civic Centre, Regent Street, Gateshead NE8 1HH ☎ 0191 433 2901 ⏁ peterudall@gateshead.gov.uk

European Liaison: Ms Marisa Jobling, Service Director - Policy, Performance & Communications, Civic Centre, Regent Street, Gateshead NE8 1HH ☎ 0191 433 3000 ⏁ marisajobling@gateshead.gov.uk

Events Manager: Ms Jenny Allinson, Service Manager - Culture, Civic Centre, Regent Street, Gateshead NE8 1HH ☎ 0191 433 3000 ⏁ jennyallinson@gateshead.gov.uk

Facilities: Mr Dale Robson, Service Director - Facilities Management, Civic Centre, Regent Street, Gateshead NE8 1HH ☎ 0191 433 5510 ⏁ dalerobson@gateshead.gov.uk

Finance: Mr Darren Collins, Strategic Director - Corporate Resources, Civic Centre, Regent Street, Gateshead NE8 1HH ☎ 0191 433 3581 ⏁ enwallis@gateshead.gov.uk

Finance: Mr John Jopling, Service Director - Customer & Financial Services, Civic Centre, Regent Street, Gateshead NE8 1HH ☎ 0191 433 3000 ⏁ johnjopling@gateshead.gov.uk

Finance: Mr Keith Purvis, Service Director - Corporate Finance, Civic Centre, Regent Street, Gateshead NE8 1HH ☎ 0191 433 3000 ⏁ keithpurvis@gateshead.gov.uk

Fleet Management: Mr Graham Telfer, Fleet Manager, Civic Centre, Regent Street, Gateshead NE8 1HH ☎ 0191 433 7443 ⏁ grahamtelfer@gateshead.gov.uk

Grounds Maintenance: Mr Colin Huntington, Service Director - Waste Service, Grounds Maintenance & Fleet Manager, Civic Centre, Regent Street, Gateshead NE8 1HH ☎ 0191 433 7402 ⏁ colinhuntington@gateshead.gov.uk

Health and Safety: Ms Susan Smith, Occupational Health & Safety Manager, Civic Centre, Regent Street, Gateshead NE8 1HH ☎ 0191 433 3000 ⏁ susansmith@gateshead.gov.uk

Highways: Mrs Anneliese Hutchinson, Service Director - Development & Public Protection, Civic Centre, Regent Street, Gateshead NE8 1HH ☎ 0191 433 3881 ⏁ anneliesehutchinson@gateshead.gov.uk

Housing: Mr Andrew Marshall, Service Director - Economic & Housing Growth, Civic Centre, Regent Street, Gateshead NE8 1HH ☎ 0191 433 3422 ⏁ andrewmarshall@gateshead.gov.uk

Legal: Mr Mike Barker, Acting Chief Executive, Civic Centre, Regent Street, Gateshead NE8 1HH ☎ 0191 433 2102 ⏁ mikebarker@gateshead.gov.uk

Legal: Ms Deborah Hill, Service Director - Human Resources & Litigation, Civic Centre, Regent Street, Gateshead NE8 1HH ☎ 0191 433 2110 ⏁ deborahhill@gateshead.gov.uk

Leisure and Cultural Services: Mrs Lindsay Murray, Service Director - Culture, Communities, Leisure & Volunteering, Civic Centre, Regent Street, Gateshead NE8 1HH ☎ 0191 433 3000 ⏁ lindsaymurray@gateshead.gov.uk

Licensing: Ms Elaine Rudman, Environmental Health, Licensing & Enforcement Manager, Civic Centre, Regent Street, Gateshead NE8 1HH ☎ 0191 433 3911 ⏁ licensing@gateshead.gov.uk

Lifelong Learning: Mr Steve Horne, Service Director - Learning & Schools, Dryden Centre, Evistones Road, Low Fell, Gateshead NE9 5UR ☎ 0191 433 3000 ⏁ stevehorne@gateshead.gov.uk

Lifelong Learning: Mr Kevin Pearson, Principal Learning Skills Manager, Dryden Centre, Evistones Road, Low Fell, Gateshead NE9 5UR ☎ 0191 433 8652 ⏁ kevinpearson@gateshead.gov.uk

Lighting: Ms Victoria Beattie, Service Director - Construction, Civic Centre, Regent Street, Gateshead NE8 1HH ☎ 0191 433 7311 ⏁ victoriabeattie@gateshead.gov.uk

Lottery Funding, Charity and Voluntary: Mrs Lindsay Murray, Service Director - Culture, Communities, Leisure & Volunteering, Civic Centre, Regent Street, Gateshead NE8 1HH ☎ 0191 433 3000 ⏁ lindsaymurray@gateshead.gov.uk

Member Services: Mr Martin Harrison, Service Director - Legal, Democratic & Property Services, Civic Centre, Regent Street, Gateshead NE8 1HH ☎ 0191 433 2101 ⏁ martinharrison@gateshead.gov.uk

Parking: Mr Steve Donaldson, Parking Services Manager, Civic Centre, Regent Street, Gateshead NE8 1HH ☎ 0191 433 3000 ⏁ stevedonaldson@gateshead.gov.uk

Partnerships: Ms Marisa Jobling, Service Director - Policy, Performance & Communications, Civic Centre, Regent Street, Gateshead NE8 1HH ☎ 0191 433 3000 ⏁ marisajobling@gateshead.gov.uk

Personnel / HR: Ms Deborah Hill, Service Director - Human Resources & Litigation, Civic Centre, Regent Street, Gateshead NE8 1HH ☎ 0191 433 2110 ⏁ deborahhill@gateshead.gov.uk

Planning: Ms Emma Lucas, Development Manager, Civic Centre, Regent Street, Gateshead NE8 1HH ☎ 0191 433 3000 ⏁ emmalucas@gateshead.gov.uk

Procurement: Mrs Andrea Tickner, Service Director - Corporate Commissioning & Procurement, Civic Centre, Regent Street, Gateshead NE8 1HH ☎ 0191 438 5995 ⏁ andreatickner@gateshead.gov.uk

GATESHEAD

Public Libraries: Mrs Lindsay Murray, Service Director - Culture, Communities, Leisure & Volunteering, Civic Centre, Regent Street, Gateshead NE8 1HH ☎ 0191 433 3000 ⌕ lindsaymurray@gateshead.gov.uk

Public Libraries: Mr Stephen Walters, Principal Library Manager, Civic Centre, Regent Street, Gateshead NE8 1HH ☎ 0191 433 8400 ⌕ stephenwalters@gateshead.gov.uk

Recycling & Waste Minimisation: Mr Marc Morley, Waste, Recycling & Contract Manager, Civic Centre, Regent Street, Gateshead NE8 1HH ☎ 0191 433 7420 ⌕ marcmorley@gateshead.gov.uk

Regeneration: Mr Andrew Marshall, Service Director - Economic & Housing Growth, Civic Centre, Regent Street, Gateshead NE8 1HH ☎ 0191 433 3422 ⌕ andrewmarshall@gateshead.gov.uk

Road Safety: Mr Ian Gibson, Traffic Planning Manager, Civic Centre, Regent Street, Gateshead NE8 1HH ☎ 0191 433 3100 ⌕ iangibson@gateshead.gov.uk

Social Services (Adult): Mr Paul Grubic, Interim Service Director - Adult Social Care & Independent Living, Civic Centre, Regent Street, Gateshead NE8 1HH ☎ 0191 433 3919 ⌕ paulgrubic@gateshead.gov.uk

Social Services (Children): Ms Elaine Devaney, Service Manager - Looked After Children, Civic Centre, Regent Street, Gateshead NE8 1HH ☎ 0191 433 3000 ⌕ elainedevaney@gateshead.gov.uk

Public Health: Ms Alice Wiseman, Director - Public Health, Civic Centre, Regent Street, Gateshead NE8 1HH ☎ 0191 443 2777 ⌕ alicewiseman@gateshead.gov.uk

Street Scene: Mr Philip Hindmarsh, Street Scene Manager, Civic Centre, Regent Street, Gateshead NE8 1HH ☎ 0191 433 7445 ⌕ philiphindmarsh@gateshead.gov.uk

Sustainable Development: Mr Jim Gillon, Team Leader - Energy Services, Civic Centre, Regent Street, Gateshead NE8 1HH ☎ 0191 433 3000 ⌕ jimgillon@gateshead.gov.uk

Town Centre: Mr Andrew Marshall, Service Director - Economic & Housing Growth, Civic Centre, Regent Street, Gateshead NE8 1HH ☎ 0191 433 3422 ⌕ andrewmarshall@gateshead.gov.uk

Traffic Management: Mr Ian Gibson, Traffic Planning Manager, Civic Centre, Regent Street, Gateshead NE8 1HH ☎ 0191 433 3100 ⌕ iangibson@gateshead.gov.uk

Traffic Management: Mrs Anneliese Hutchinson, Service Director - Development & Public Protection, Civic Centre, Regent Street, Gateshead NE8 1HH ☎ 0191 433 3881 ⌕ anneliesehutchinson@gateshead.gov.uk

Transport: Mr Andrew Haysey, Transport Planning Manager, Civic Centre, Regent Street, Gateshead NE8 1HH ☎ 0191 433 3124 ⌕ andrewhaysey@gateshead.gov.uk

Transport: Mr Colin Huntington, Service Director - Waste Service, Grounds Maintenance & Fleet Manager, Civic Centre, Regent Street, Gateshead NE8 1HH ☎ 0191 433 7402 ⌕ colinhuntington@gateshead.gov.uk

Transport: Mrs Anneliese Hutchinson, Service Director - Development & Public Protection, Civic Centre, Regent Street, Gateshead NE8 1HH ☎ 0191 433 3881 ⌕ anneliesehutchinson@gateshead.gov.uk

Waste Collection and Disposal: Mr Colin Huntington, Service Director - Waste Service, Grounds Maintenance & Fleet Manager, Civic Centre, Regent Street, Gateshead NE8 1HH ☎ 0191 433 7402 ⌕ colinhuntington@gateshead.gov.uk

Waste Management: Mr Colin Huntington, Service Director - Waste Service, Grounds Maintenance & Fleet Manager, Civic Centre, Regent Street, Gateshead NE8 1HH ☎ 0191 433 7402 ⌕ colinhuntington@gateshead.gov.uk

Waste Management: Mr Marc Morley, Waste, Recycling & Contract Manager, Civic Centre, Regent Street, Gateshead NE8 1HH ☎ 0191 433 7420 ⌕ marcmorley@gateshead.gov.uk

Children's Play Areas: Mr Colin Huntington, Service Director - Waste Service, Grounds Maintenance & Fleet Manager, Civic Centre, Regent Street, Gateshead NE8 1HH ☎ 0191 433 7402 ⌕ colinhuntington@gateshead.gov.uk

COUNCILLORS

Leader of the Council: Gannon, Martin (LAB - Deckham) cllr.mgannon@gateshead.gov.uk

Deputy Leader of the Council: Donovan, Catherine (LAB - Lobley Hill & Bensham) cllr.cdonovan@gateshead.gov.uk

Adams, John (LAB - Saltwell) cllr.jadams@gateshead.gov.uk

Beadle, Ron (LD - Low Fell) cllr.rbeadle@gateshead.gov.uk

Bradley, Christine (LAB - Lamesley) cllr.cbradley@gateshead.gov.uk

Brain, Malcolm (LAB - Blaydon) cllr.mbrain@gateshead.gov.uk

Caffrey, Lynne (LAB - Chopwell & Rowlands Gill) cllr.lcaffrey@gateshead.gov.uk

Charlton, Marilyn (LAB - Winlaton & High Spen) cllr.mcharlton@gateshead.gov.uk

Clelland, Brenda (LAB - Dunston & Teams) cllr.bclelland@gateshead.gov.uk

Craig, Peter (LD - Whickham North) cllr.ptcraig@gateshead.gov.uk

Craig, Susan (LD - Low Fell) cllr.scraig@gateshead.gov.uk

Davidson, Doreen (LAB - High Fell) cllr.ddavidson@gateshead.gov.uk

Dick, Bill (LAB - Felling) cllr.wdick@gateshead.gov.uk

Dickie, Sonya (LAB - Felling) cllr.sdickie@gateshead.gov.uk

Dillon, Pauline (LAB - Dunston & Teams) cllr.pdillon@gateshead.gov.uk

Dodds, Kevin (LAB - Lobley Hill & Bensham)
cllr.k.dodds@gateshead.gov.uk

Douglas, Angela (LAB - Bridges)
cllr.aarmstrong@gateshead.gov.uk

Duggan, Daniel (LD - Low Fell)
cllr.dduggan@gateshead.gov.uk

Eagle, John (LAB - Bridges)
cllr.jeagle@gateshead.gov.uk

Ferdinand, Kathryn (LAB - Blaydon)
cllr.k.ferdinand@gateshead.gov.uk

Foy, Paul (LAB - Birtley)
cllr.pfoy@gateshead.gov.uk

Foy, Mary (LAB - Lamesley)
cllr.mfoy@gateshead.gov.uk

Geddes, Alex (LAB - Ryton, Crookhill & Stella)
cllr.ageddes@gateshead.gov.uk

Goldsworthy, Bob (LAB - Bridges)
cllr.bgoldsworthy@gateshead.gov.uk

Goldsworthy, Maureen (LAB - Chowdene)
cllr.mgoldsworthy@gateshead.gov.uk

Graham, Malcolm (LAB - High Fell)
cllr.mgraham@gateshead.gov.uk

Graham, Thomas (LAB - Windy Nook & Whitehills)
cllr.tgraham@gateshead.gov.uk

Graham, Jack (LAB - Crawcrook & Greenside)
cllr.jgraham@gateshead.gov.uk

Green, Linda (LAB - Wardley & Leam Lane)
cllr.lgreen@gateshead.gov.uk

Green, Stuart (LAB - Wardley & Leam Lane)
cllr.sgreen@gateshead.gov.uk

Green, Jill (LAB - Pelaw & Heworth)
cllr.jgreen@gateshead.gov.uk

Haley, Gary (LAB - Dunston & Teams)
cllr.ghaley@gateshead.gov.uk

Hall, Maria (LAB - Winlaton & High Spen)
cllr.mhall@gateshead.gov.uk

Hawkins, Sonya (LD - Whickham North)
cllr.shawkins@gateshead.gov.uk

Henry, Mick (LAB - Saltwell)
cllr.m.henry@gateshead.gov.uk

Hood, Michael (LAB - Lamesley)
cllr.mhood@gateshead.gov.uk

Hughes, Helen (LAB - Crawcrook & Greenside)
cllr.hhughes@gateshead.gov.uk

Ilderton-Thompson, Allison (LAB - Dunston Hill & Whickham East)
cllr.achatto@gateshead.gov.uk

Kielty, Jeannie (LAB - Saltwell)
cllr.jkielty@gateshead.gov.uk

Kirton, Leigh (LAB - Deckham)
cllr.lkirton@gateshead.gov.uk

Lee, Jean (LAB - High Fell)
cllr.jlee@gateshead.gov.uk

Maughan, Peter (LD - Dunston Hill & Whickham East)
cllr.pmaughan@gateshead.gov.uk

McCartney, Kathleen (LAB - Crawcrook & Greenside)
cllr.kmccartney@gateshead.gov.uk

McClurey, John (LD - Whickham South & Sunniside)
cllr.jmcclurey@gateshead.gov.uk

McElroy, John (LAB - Chowdene)
cllr.jmcelroy@gateshead.gov.uk

McHatton, Christine (LD - Ryton, Crookhill & Stella)
cllr.cmchatton@gateshead.gov.uk

McHugh, Chris (LAB - Dunston Hll & Whickham East)
cllr.cmhugh@gateshead.gov.uk

McMaster, Eileen (LAB - Lobley Hill & Bensham)
cllr.emcmaster@gateshead.gov.uk

McNally, Paul (LAB - Felling)
cllr.pmcnally@gateshead.gov.uk

McNestry, Michael (LAB - Chopwell & Rowlands Gill)
cllr.mmcnestry@gateshead.gov.uk

Mole, Peter (LAB - Wardley & Leam Lane)
cllr.pmole@gateshead.gov.uk

Mullen, Rachel (LAB - Windy Nook & Whitehills)
cllr.rmullen@gateshead.gov.uk

Oliphant, Bernadette (LAB - Deckham)
cllr.boliphant@gateshead.gov.uk

Ord, Christopher (LD - Whickham North)
cllr.cord@gateshead.gov.uk

Ord, Marilynn (LD - Whickham South & Sunniside)
cllr.mord@gateshead.gov.uk

Patterson, Ian (LD - Pelaw & Heworth)
cllr.ipatterson@gateshead.gov.uk

Ronchetti, Stephen (LAB - Blaydon)
cllr.sronchetti@gateshead.gov.uk

Simcox, Catherine (LAB - Birtley)
cllr.csimcox@gateshead.gov.uk

Simpson, Julie (LAB - Winlaton & High Spen)
cllr.jsimpson@gateshead.gov.uk

Turnbull, Jim (LAB - Windy Nook & Whitehills)
cllr.jturnbull@gateshead.gov.uk

Twist, Liz (LAB - Ryton, Crookhill & Stella)
cllr.ltwist@gateshead.gov.uk

Wallace, Jonathan (LD - Whickham South & Sunniside)
cllr.jwallace@gateshead.gov.uk

Weatherley, Neil (LAB - Birtley)
cllr.nweatherley@gateshead.gov.uk

Wheeler, Anne (LAB - Pelaw & Heworth)
cllr.awheeler@gateshead.gov.uk

Wood, Keith (LAB - Chowdene)
cllr.kwood@gateshead.gov.uk

POLITICAL COMPOSITION
LAB: 53, LD: 12, Vacant: 1

COMMITTEE CHAIRS
Health & Wellbeing: Ms Lynne Caffrey

GEDLING

Gedling Borough Council, Civic Centre, Arnot Hill Park, Nottingham NG5 6LU

☎ 0115 901 3901 ⌁ enquiries@gedling.gov.uk 🖥 www.gedling.gov.uk

FACTS AND FIGURES
Parliamentary Constituencies: Gedling, Sherwood
EU Constituencies: East Midlands
Election Frequency: Elections are of whole council

PRINCIPAL OFFICERS

Chief Executive: Mr John Robinson, Chief Executive, Civic Centre, Arnot Hill Park, Nottingham NG5 6LU ☎ 0115 901 3915 ⌁ john.robinson@gedling.gov.uk

Deputy Chief Executive: Mr Mike Hill, Deputy Chief Executive & Director - Finance, Civic Centre, Arnot Hill Park, Nottingham NG5 6LU ☎ 0115 901 3990 ⌁ mike.hill@gedling.gov.uk

Senior Management: Mrs Helen Barrington, Director - Organisational Development & Democratic Services, Civic Centre, Arnot Hill Park, Nottingham NG5 6LU ☎ 0115 901 3896 ⌁ helen.barrington@gedling.gov.uk

Senior Management: Mr David Wakelin, Director - Health & Community Wellbeing, Civic Centre, Arnot Hill Park, Nottingham NG5 6LU ☎ 0115 901 3952 ⌁ david.wakelin@gedling.gov.uk

Architect, Building / Property Services: Mr Vince Rimmington, Service Manager - Audit & Asset Management, Civic Centre, Arnot Hill Park, Nottingham NG5 6LU ☎ 0115 901 3850 ⌁ vince.rimmington@gedling.gov.uk

Building Control: Mr Mike Avery, Planning Delivery Manager, Civic Centre, Arnot Hill Park, Nottingham NG5 6LU ☎ 0115 901 3751 ⌁ mike.avery@gedling.gov.uk

PR / Communications: Miss Rosie Caddy, Service Manager - Customer Services & Communications, Civic Centre, Arnot Hill Park, Nottingham NG5 6LU ☎ 0115 901 3683 ⌁ rosie.caddy@gedling.gov.uk

Computer Management: Miss Rosie Caddy, Service Manager - Customer Services & Communications, Civic Centre, Arnot Hill Park, Nottingham NG5 6LU ☎ 0115 901 3683 ⌁ rosie.caddy@gedling.gov.uk

Corporate Services: Mr Mike Hill, Deputy Chief Executive & Director - Finance, Civic Centre, Arnot Hill Park, Nottingham NG5 6LU ☎ 0115 901 3990 ⌁ mike.hill@gedling.gov.uk

Customer Service: Miss Rosie Caddy, Service Manager - Customer Services & Communications, Civic Centre, Arnot Hill Park, Nottingham NG5 6LU ☎ 0115 901 3683 ⌁ rosie.caddy@gedling.gov.uk

Economic Development: Mrs Louise Ashby, Economic Development Officer, Civic Centre, Arnot Hill Park, Nottingham NG5 6LU ☎ 0115 901 3729 ⌁ louise.ashby@gedling.gov.uk

Economic Development: Ms Julie Beresford, Economic Development Officer, Civic Centre, Arnot Hill Park, Nottingham NG5 6LU ⌁ julie.beresford@gedling.gov.uk

E-Government: Miss Rosie Caddy, Service Manager - Customer Services & Communications, Civic Centre, Arnot Hill Park, Nottingham NG5 6LU ☎ 0115 901 3683 ⌁ rosie.caddy@gedling.gov.uk

Emergency Planning: Mr Vince Rimmington, Service Manager - Audit & Asset Management, Civic Centre, Arnot Hill Park, Nottingham NG5 6LU ☎ 0115 901 3850 ⌁ vince.rimmington@gedling.gov.uk

Energy Management: Mr Steve Wiseman, Architectural & Buildings Services Manager, Civic Centre, Arnot Hill Park, Arnold, Nottingham NG5 6LU ☎ 0115 901 3779 ⌁ steve.wiseman@gedling.gov.uk

Environmental / Technical Services: Mr Andy Callingham, Service Manager - Public Protection, Civic Centre, Arnot Hill Park, Nottingham NG5 6LU ☎ 0115 901 3834 ⌁ andy.callingham@gedling.gov.uk

Environmental Health: Mr Andy Callingham, Service Manager - Public Protection, Civic Centre, Arnot Hill Park, Nottingham NG5 6LU ☎ 0115 901 3834 ⌁ andy.callingham@gedling.gov.uk

Estates, Property & Valuation: Mr Vince Rimmington, Service Manager - Audit & Asset Management, Civic Centre, Arnot Hill Park, Nottingham NG5 6LU ☎ 0115 901 3850 ⌁ vince.rimmington@gedling.gov.uk

Events Manager: Ms Lorraine Brown, Events & Play Officer, Civic Centre, Arnot Hill Park, Nottingham NG5 6LU ☎ 015 901 3602 ⌁ lorraine.brown@gedling.gov.uk

Facilities: Mr Steve Wiseman, Architectural & Buildings Services Manager, Civic Centre, Arnot Hill Park, Arnold, Nottingham NG5 6LU ☎ 0115 901 3779 ⌁ steve.wiseman@gedling.gov.uk

Finance: Mr Mike Hill, Deputy Chief Executive & Director - Finance, Civic Centre, Arnot Hill Park, Nottingham NG5 6LU ☎ 0115 901 3990 ⌁ mike.hill@gedling.gov.uk

Treasury: Mr Mike Hill, Deputy Chief Executive & Director - Finance, Civic Centre, Arnot Hill Park, Nottingham NG5 6LU ☎ 0115 901 3990 ⌁ mike.hill@gedling.gov.uk

Fleet Management: Mr Mark Hurst, Transport Services Manager, Civic Centre, Arnot Hill Park, Nottingham NG5 6LU ☎ 0115 901 3612 ⌁ mark.hurst@gedling.gov.uk

Grounds Maintenance: Mr Melvyn Cryer, Service Manager - Parks & Street Care, Civic Centre, Arnot Hill Park, Nottingham NG5 6LU ☎ 0115 901 3788 ⌁ melvyn.cryer@gedling.gov.uk

Health and Safety: Mr Grant Illett, Safety Officer, Civic Centre, Arnot Hill Park, Arnold, Nottingham NG5 6LU ☎ 0115 901 3940 ⌁ grant.illett@gedling.gov.uk

Housing: Ms Alison Bennett, Service Manager - Housing & Localities, Civic Centre, Arnot Hill Park, Nottingham NG5 6LU
☎ 0115 901 3696 ✆ alison.bennett@gedling.gov.uk

Legal: Ms Francesca Whyley, Service Manager - Legal Services, Civic Centre, Arnot Hill Park, Nottingham NG5 6LU
☎ 0115 901 3907 ✆ francesca.whyley@gedling.gov.uk

Leisure and Cultural Services: Mr David Wakelin, Director - Health & Community Wellbeing, Civic Centre, Arnot Hill Park, Nottingham NG5 6LU ☎ 0115 901 3952 ✆ david.wakelin@gedling.gov.uk

Licensing: Mr Andy Callingham, Service Manager - Public Protection, Civic Centre, Arnot Hill Park, Nottingham NG5 6LU
☎ 0115 901 3834 ✆ andy.callingham@gedling.gov.uk

Member Services: Mr Alec Dubberley, Service Manager - Elections & Member Services, Civic Centre, Arnot Hill Park, Nottingham NG5 6LU ☎ 0115 901 3906
✆ alec.dubberley@gedling.gov.uk

Parking: Mr John Evens, Car Parks & Engineering Officer, Civic Centre, Arnot Hill Park, Nottingham NG5 6LU ☎ 0115 901 3767
✆ john.evens@gedling.gov.uk

Personnel / HR: Mr David Archer, Service Manager - Organisational Development, Civic Centre, Arnot Hill Park, Arnold, Nottingham NG5 6LU ☎ 0115 901 3937
✆ david.archer@gedling.gov.uk

Procurement: Mr David Hayes, Procurement Officer, Civic Centre, Arnot Hill Park, Nottingham NG5 6LU ☎ 0115 901 3911
✆ david.hayes@gedling.gov.uk

Recycling & Waste Minimisation: Mrs Caroline McKenzie, Service Manager - Waste Services, Civic Centre, Arnot Hill Park, Nottingham NG5 6LU ☎ 0115 901 3611
✆ caroline.mckenzie@gedling.gov.uk

Staff Training: Mr Mike Calladine, Training Officer, Civic Centre, Arnot Hill Park, Nottingham NG5 6LU ☎ 0115 901 3941
✆ mike.calladine@gedling.gov.uk

Tourism: Mr Andy Hardy, Service Manager - Leisure & Culture, Civic Centre, Arnot Hill Park, Nottingham NG5 6LU
☎ 0115 901 3703 ✆ andy.hardy@gedling.gov.uk

Transport: Mr Mark Hurst, Transport Services Manager, Civic Centre, Arnot Hill Park, Nottingham NG5 6LU ☎ 0115 901 3612
✆ mark.hurst@gedling.gov.uk

Waste Collection and Disposal: Mrs Caroline McKenzie, Service Manager - Waste Services, Civic Centre, Arnot Hill Park, Nottingham NG5 6LU ☎ 0115 901 3611
✆ caroline.mckenzie@gedling.gov.uk

Waste Management: Mrs Caroline McKenzie, Service Manager - Waste Services, Civic Centre, Arnot Hill Park, Nottingham NG5 6LU
☎ 0115 901 3611 ✆ caroline.mckenzie@gedling.gov.uk

Children's Play Areas: Mr Melvyn Cryer, Service Manager - Parks & Street Care, Civic Centre, Arnot Hill Park, Nottingham NG5 6LU
☎ 0115 901 3788 ✆ melvyn.cryer@gedling.gov.uk

COUNCILLORS

Mayor: Lawrence, Meredith (LAB - Colwick)
cllr.meredith.lawrence@gedling.gov.uk

Deputy Mayor: Barnes, Sandra (LAB - Daybrook)

Leader of the Council: Clarke, John (LAB - Netherfield)
cllr.john.clarke@gedling.gov.uk

Deputy Leader of the Council: Payne, Michael (LAB - Redhill)
cllr.michael.payne@gedling.gov.uk

Group LeaderBarnfather, Chris (CON - Newstead Abbey)
cllr.chirs.barnfather@gedling.gov.uk

Adams, Michael (CON - Woodthorpe)
cllr.michael.adams@gedling.gov.uk

Allan, Pauline (LAB - Redhill)
cllr.pauline.allan@gedling.gov.uk

Andrews, Bruce (CON - Newstead Abbey)
bruce@nodnol.org

Bailey, Emily (LAB - Cavendish)
cllr.emily.bailey@gedling.gov.uk

Barnes, Peter (LAB - Daybrook)

Beeston, Denis (LAB - Bestwood St. Albans)
cllr.denis.beeston@gedling.gov.uk

Bexon, Alan (CON - Gedling)
cllr.alan.bexon@gedling.gov.uk

Bisset, Tammy (CON - Bestwood St. Albans)
cllr.tammy.bisset@gedling.gov.uk

Brooks, Nicki (LAB - Carlton)
cllr.nicki.brooks@gedling.gov.uk

Collis, Bob (LAB - Porchester)
cllr.bob.collis@gedling.gov.uk

Creamer, Jim (LAB - Carlton Hill)
cllr.seamus.creamer@gedling.gov.uk

Doyle, Kevin (CON - Trent Valley)
cllr.kevin.doyle@gedling.gov.uk

Elliott, Boyd (CON - Calverton)
cllr.boyd.elliot@gedling.gov.uk

Ellis, David (LAB - Ernehale)
cllr.david.ellis@gedling.gov.uk

Ellis, Roxanne (LAB - Ernehale)
cllr.roxanne.ellis@gedling.gov.uk

Ellwood, Andrew (LD - Phoenix)
cllr.andrew.ellwood@gedling.gov.uk

Feeney, Paul (LAB - Carlton Hill)
cllr.paul.feeney@gedling.gov.uk

Fox, Kathryn (LAB - Phoenix)
cllr.kathryn.fox@gedling.gov.uk

Greensmith, Helen (CON - Dumbles)
cllr.helen.greensmith@gedling.gov.uk

Gregory, Gary (LAB - Cavendish)
cllr.gary.gregory@gedling.gov.uk

GEDLING

Hewson, Sarah (CON - Plains)
sarah.hewson2@ntlworld.com

Hollingsworth, Jenny (LAB - Gedling)
cllr.jenny.hollingsworth@gedling.gov.uk

McCrossen, Viv (LAB - Woodthorpe)
viv.mccrossen@gedling.gov.uk

Miller, Barbara (LAB - Netherfield)
cllr.barbara.miller@gedling.gov.uk

Paling, Marje (LAB - Coppice)
cllr.marje.paling@gedling.gov.uk

Parr, John (CON - Plains)
cllr.john.parr@gedling.gov.uk

Pepper, Carol (CON - Plains)
cllr.carol.pepper@gedling.gov.uk

Poole, Stephen (CON - Trent Valley)
cllr.stephen.poole@gedling.gov.uk

Powell, Colin (CON - Newstead Abbey)
cllr.colin.powell@gedling.gov.uk

Scroggie, Alex (LAB - Carlton Hill)
cllr.alex.scroggie@gedling.gov.uk

Stirland, Paul (CON - Calverton)
cllr.paul.stirland@gedling.gov.uk

Truscott, John (LAB - Porchester)
cllr.john.truscott@gedling.gov.uk

Walker, Jane (CON - Calverton)
cllr.jane.walker@gedling.gov.uk

Weisz, Muriel (LAB - Porchester)
cllr.muriel.weisz@gedling.gov.uk

Wheeler, Henry (LAB - Coppice)
cllr.henry.wheeler@gedling.gov.uk

Wilkinson, Paul (LAB - Carlton)
cllr.paul.wilkinson@gedling.gov.uk

POLITICAL COMPOSITION
LAB: 25, CON: 15, LD: 1

COMMITTEE CHAIRS

Audit: Mr Paul Feeney

Environment & Licensing: Ms Marje Paling

Planning: Mr John Truscott

Glasgow, City of   S

Glasgow City Council, City Chambers, George Square,
Glasgow G2 1DU
☎ 0141 287 2000 🖷 0141 287 5666 ⁂ pr@glasgow.gov.uk
🖥 www.glasgow.gov.uk

FACTS AND FIGURES
Parliamentary Constituencies: Glasgow Central, Glasgow East,
Glasgow North, Glasgow North East, Glasgow North West, Glasgow
South, Glasgow South West
EU Constituencies: Scotland
Election Frequency: Elections are of whole council

PRINCIPAL OFFICERS

Chief Executive: Ms Anne Marie O'Donnell, Chief Executive, City
Chambers, George Square, Glasgow G2 1DU ☎ 0141 287 4522
⁂ annemarie.o'donnell@ced.glasgow.gov.uk

Senior Management: Mr Brian Devlin, Executive Director - Land
& Environmental Services, Exchange House, 231 George Street,
Glasgow G1 1RX ☎ 0141 287 9100 ⁂ brian.devlin@glasgow.gov.uk

Senior Management: Ms Carole Forrest, Head of Governance
& Solicitor to the Council, City Chambers, George Square, Glasgow
G2 1DU ☎ 0141 287 0467 ⁂ carole.forrest@glasgow.gov.uk

Senior Management: Ms Morag Johnston, Interim Executive
Director - Financial Services, City Chambers, George Square,
Glasgow G2 1DU ☎ 0141 287 3837
⁂ morag.johnston@glasgow.gov.uk

Senior Management: Ms Maureen McKenna, Executive Director
- Education Services, 40 John Street, Glasgow G1 1JL ☎ 0141 287
4551 ⁂ maureen.mckenna@education.glasgow.gov.uk

Senior Management: Mr Hugh Munro, City Assessor & Electoral
Registration Officer, 220 High Street, Glasgow G4 0QW ☎ 0141 287
7518 ⁂ hugh.munro@fs.glasgow.gov.uk

Senior Management: Mr David Williams, Executive Director -
Social Work Services, 40 John Street, Glasgow G1 1JL ☎ 0141 287
8853 ⁂ david.williams@glasgow.gov.uk

Access Officer / Social Services (Disability): Ms Liz Oswald,
Policy Officer, City Chambers, George Square, Glasgow G2 1DU
☎ 0141 287 3840 ⁂ liz.oswald@glasgow.gov.uk

Architect, Building / Property Services: Mr Richard Brown,
Executive Director - Development & Regeneration Services,
Exchange House, 231 George Street, Glasgow G1 1RX
☎ 0141 287 6000 ⁂ lynn.brown@fs.glasgow.gov.uk

Architect, Building / Property Services: Mr Tom Turley,
Assistant Director - Development & Regeneration Services,
Exchange House, 229 George Street, Glasgow G1 1QU
☎ 0141 287 8571 ⁂ tom.turley@glasgow.gov.uk

Building Control: Mr Forbes Barron, Head of Planning & Building
Control, Exchange House, 231 George Street, Glasgow G1 1RX
☎ 0141 287 6064 ⁂ forbes.barron@glasgow.gov.uk

Children / Youth Services: Ms Jill Miller, Director - Cultural
Services, Glasgow Life, 220 High Street, Glasgow G4 0QW
☎ 0141 287 8900 ⁂ jill.miller@glasgow.gov.uk

Civil Registration: Ms Fiona English, Chief Registrar, 23
Montrose Street, Glasgow G1 1RG ☎ 0141 287 7653
⁂ fiona.english@glasgow.gov.uk

PR / Communications: Mr Chris Starrs, PR Manager, City
Chambers, George Square, Glasgow G2 1DU ☎ 0141 287 5742
⁂ chris.starrs@glasgow.gov.uk

Community Safety: Mr Phil Walker, Managing Director - Glasgow Community & Safety Services, Eastgate, 727 London Road, Glasgow G40 3AP ☎ 0141 276 7627 ⏁ phil.walker@glasgow.gov.uk

Computer Management: Ms Faye Shaw, Head of Information Technology, 220 High Street, Glasgow G4 0QW ☎ 0141 287 2381 ⏁ faye.shaw@access.uk.com

Corporate Services: Mr Jim Wilson, Head of Quality Improvement, 40 John Street, Glasgow G1 1JL ☎ 0141 287 4573 ⏁ jim.wilson@education.glasgow.gov.uk

Economic Development: Mr Alan Vesey, Head of City Deal, City Chambers, George Square, Glasgow G2 1DU ☎ 0141 287 6786 ⏁ alan.vesey@glasgow.gov.uk

Education: Ms Maureen McKenna, Executive Director - Education Services, City Chambers, George Square, Glasgow G2 1DU ☎ 0141 287 4551 ⏁ maureen.mckenna@education.glasgow.gov.uk

Electoral Registration: Mr Hugh Munro, City Assessor & Electoral Registration Officer, 220 High Street, Glasgow G4 0QW ☎ 0141 287 7518 ⏁ hugh.munro@fs.glasgow.gov.uk

Events Manager: Mr Colin Hartley, Head of Events, 220 High Street, Glasgow G4 0QW ☎ 0141 287 9863 ⏁ colin.hartley@glasgow.gov.uk

Events Manager: Mr Keith Russell, Head of Sport, Glasgow Life, 220 High Street, Glasgow G4 0QW ☎ 0141 287 5975 ⏁ keith.russell@glasgow.gov.uk

Finance: Ms Morag Johnston, Interim Executive Director - Financial Services, City Chambers, George Square, Glasgow G2 1DU ☎ 0141 287 3837 ⏁ morag.johnston@glasgow.gov.uk

Treasury: Mr Phillip Braat, City Treasurer, City Chambers, George Square, Glasgow G2 1DU ☎ 0141 287 5788 ⏁ phillip.braat@glasgow.gov.uk

Pensions: Ms Jacqueline Gillies, Assistant Pension Investments Officer, Capella Building, 6th Floor, York Street, Glasgow G2 8JX ☎ 0141 287 5786 ⏁ jacqueline.gilles@fs.glasgow.gov.uk

Pensions: Mr Richard Keery, Pension Investments Manager, Capella Building, 6th Floor, York Street, Glasgow G2 8JX ☎ 0141 287 7398 ⏁ richard.keery@fs.glasgow.gov.uk

Pensions: Mr Richard McIndoe, Head of Pensions, Capella Building, 6th Floor, York Street, Glasgow G2 8JX ☎ 0141 287 7383 ⏁ richard.mcindoe@glasgow.gov.uk

Highways: Mr Brian Devlin, Executive Director - Land & Environmental Services, Exchange House, 231 George Street, Glasgow G1 1RX ☎ 0141 287 9100 ⏁ brian.devlin@glasgow.gov.uk

Housing: Mr Patrick Flynn, Head of Housing Investment, Exchange House, 231 George Street, Glasgow G1 1QU ☎ 0141 287 8467 ⏁ patrick.flynn@glasgow.gov.uk

Housing Maintenance: Mr Graham Paterson, Executive Director, 350 Darnick Street, Glasgow G21 4BA ☎ 0141 287 1786 ⏁ graham.paterson@citybuildingglasgow.gov.uk

Legal: Ms Anne Marie O'Donnell, Chief Executive, City Chambers, George Square, Glasgow G2 1DU ☎ 0141 287 4522 ⏁ annemarie.o'donnell@ced.glasgow.gov.uk

Leisure and Cultural Services: Dr Bridget McConnell, Chief Executive - Glasgow Life, Glasgow Life, 220 High Street, Glasgow G4 0QW ☎ 0141 287 5058 ⏁ bridget.mcconnell@csglasgow.org

Leisure and Cultural Services: Mr Mark O'Neill, Director - Policy & Research, Glasgow Life, 220 High Street, Glasgow G4 0QW ☎ 0141 287 0446 ⏁ mark.o'neill@csglasgow.org

Leisure and Cultural Services: Mr Keith Russell, Head of Sport, Glasgow Life, 220 High Street, Glasgow G4 0QW ☎ 0141 287 5975 ⏁ keith.russell@glasgow.gov.uk

Lifelong Learning: Mrs Jane Edgar, Head of Learning, Glasgow Life, 220 High Street, Glasgow G4 0QW ☎ 0141 287 8937 ⏁ jane.edgar@glasgowlife.org.uk

Lighting: Mr George Gillespie, Assistant Director - Land & Environmental Services, 231 George Street, Glasgow G1 1RX ☎ 0141 287 9106 ⏁ george.gillespie@glasgow.gov.uk

Lottery Funding, Charity and Voluntary: Ms Morag Johnston, Interim Executive Director - Financial Services, City Chambers, George Square, Glasgow G2 1DU ☎ 0141 287 3837 ⏁ morag.johnston@glasgow.gov.uk

Member Services: Ms Carole Forrest, Head of Governance & Solicitor to the Council, City Chambers, George Square, Glasgow G2 1DU ☎ 0141 287 0467 ⏁ carole.forrest@glasgow.gov.uk

Parking: Mr Willie Taggart, Managing Director - City Parking, 3rd Floor, Cadogan Square, Glasgow G2 7PH ☎ 0141 276 1835 ⏁ willie.taggart@cityparkingglasgow.co.uk

Personnel / HR: Mr Robert Anderson, Executive HR Manager, 40 John Street, Glasgow G1 1JL ☎ 0141 287 5719 ⏁ robert.anderson@glasgow.gov.uk

Planning: Mr Forbes Barron, Head of Planning & Building Control, Exchange House, 231 George Street, Glasgow G1 1RX ☎ 0141 287 6064 ⏁ forbes.barron@glasgow.gov.uk

Planning: Mr Ian Manson, Chief Executive of Clyde Gateway, Clyde Gateway, 15 Bridgeton Cross, Glasgow G40 1BN ☎ 0141 276 1567 ⏁ ian.manson@glasgow.gov.uk

Procurement: Ms Elaine Galletly, Executive Legal Manager, 40 John Street, Glasgow G1 1JL ☎ 0141 287 4653 ⏁ elaine.galletly@glasgow.gov.uk

Public Libraries: Mr Gordon Anderson, Cultural Venues Manager, Glasgow Life, 220 High Street, Glasgow G4 0QW ☎ 0141 287 2949 ⏁ gordon.anderson@glasgow.gov.uk

GLASGOW, CITY OF

Recycling & Waste Minimisation: Mr Rolf Matthews, Waste Disposal Manager, Exchange House, 231 George Street, Glasgow G1 1RX ☎ 0141 287 2082 ✆ rolf.matthews@glasgow.gov.uk

Regeneration: Mr Richard Brown, Executive Director - Development & Regeneration Services, Exchange House, 231 George Street, Glasgow G1 1RX ☎ 0141 287 6000 ✆ lynn.brown@fs.glasgow.gov.uk

Road Safety: Mr George Cairns, Engineering Officer, Exchange House, 231 George Street, Glasgow G1 1JL ☎ 0141 287 9043 ✆ george.cairns@land.glasgow.gov.uk

Social Services: Mr David Williams, Executive Director - Social Work Services, 40 John Street, Glasgow G1 1JL ☎ 0141 287 8853 ✆ david.williams@glasgow.gov.uk

Waste Collection and Disposal: Mr Brian Devlin, Executive Director - Land & Environmental Services, Exchange House, 231 George Street, Glasgow G1 1RX ☎ 0141 287 9100 ✆ brian.devlin@glasgow.gov.uk

COUNCILLORS

Leader of the Council: McAveety, Frank (LAB - Shettleston)
frank.mcaveety@councillors.glasgow.gov.uk

Adams, James (LAB - Govan)
james.adams2@councillors.glasgow.gov.uk

Aitken, Susan (SNP - Langside)
susan.aitken@councillors.glasgow.gov.uk

Andrew, Ken (SNP - Hillhead)
ken.andrew@councillors.glasgow.gov.uk

Baker, Nina (SGP - Anderston/City)
nina.baker@councillors.glasgow.gov.uk

Balfour, Malcolm (SNP - Drumchapel/Anniesland)
malcolm.balfour@councillors.glasgow.gov.uk

Bartos, Martin (SGP - Patrick West)
martin.bartos@councillors.glasgow.gov.uk

Bolander, Eva (SNP - Anderston/City)
eva.bolander@glasgow.gov.uk

Boyle, Gerry (SNP - North East)
gerry.boyle2@councillors.glasgow.gov.uk

Braat, Philip (LAB - Anderston/City)
philip.braat@councillors.glasgow.gov.uk

Burke, Maureen (LAB - North East)
maureen.burke@councillors.glasgow.gov.uk

Butler, Bill (LAB - Greater Pollok)
bill.butler@councillors.glasgow.gov.uk

Cameron, Liz (LAB - Garscadden/Scotstounhill)
liz.cameron@councillors.glasgow.gov.uk

Carey, Paul (LAB - Drumchapel/Anniesland)
paul.carey@councillors.glasgow.gov.uk

Clark, Margot (LD - Linn)
margot.clark@councillors.glasgow.gov.uk

Coleman, James (LAB - Baillieston)
james.coleman@councillors.glasgow.gov.uk

Colleran, Aileen (LAB - Patrick West)
aileen.colleran@councillors.glasgow.gov.uk

Cunning, Malcolm (LAB - Linn)
malcolm.cunning@councillors.glasgow.gov.uk

Curran, Stephen (LAB - Newlands/Auldburn)
stephen.curran@councillors.glasgow.gov.uk

Dalton, Feargal (SNP - Patrick West)
feargal.dalton@councillors.glasgow.gov.uk

Davidson, Gilbert (LAB - Springburn)
gilbert.davidson@councillors.glasgow.gov.uk

Docherty, Josephine (SNP - Newlands/Auldburn)
josephine.docherty@councillors.glasgow.gov.uk

Docherty, Sadie (LAB - Linn)
sadie.docherty@councillors.glasgow.gov.uk

Docherty, Frank (LAB - East Centre)
frank.docherty@councillors.glasgow.gov.uk

Dornan, Stephen (LAB - Govan)
stephen.dornan@councillors.glasgow.gov.uk

Dunn, Jennifer (SNP - East Centre)
jennifer.dunn@councillors.glasgow.gov.uk

Elder, Glenn (SNP - Linn)
glenn.elder@councillors.glasgow.gov.uk

Findlay, Jonathan (LAB - Drumchapel/Anniesland)
jonathan.findlay@councillors.glasgow.gov.uk

Fisher, Judith (LAB - Drumchapel/Anniesland)
judith.fisher@councillors.glasgow.gov.uk

Garrity, Marie (LAB - Baillieston)
marie.garrity@councillors.glasgow.gov.uk

Gillan, Emma (LAB - Newlands/Auldburn)
emma.gillan@councillors.glasgow.gov.uk

Graham, Archie (LAB - Langside)
archie.graham@councillors.glasgow.gov.uk

Greene, Phil (SNP - Springburn)
phil.greene@councillors.glasgow.gov.uk

Hanif, Jahangir (SNP - Southside Central)
jahangir.hanif@councillors.glasgow.gov.uk

Hendry, Graeme (SNP - Garscadden/Scotstounhill)
graeme.hendry@councillors.glasgow.gov.uk

Hepburn, Greg (SNP - Calton)
greg.hepburn@glasgow.gov.uk

Hunter, Mhairi (SNP - Southside Central)
mhairi.hunter@councillors.glasgow.gov.uk

Hussain, Rashid (LAB - Greater Pollok)
rashid.hussain@councillors.glasgow.gov.uk

Jaffri, Shabbar (SNP - Greater Pollok)
shabbar.jaffri@councillors.glasgow.gov.uk

Kane, John (LAB - Govan)
john.kane@councillors.glasgow.gov.uk

Kelly, Chris (LAB - Canal)
chris.kelly@councillors.glasgow.gov.uk

Kelly, John (LAB - Garscadden/Scotstounhill)
john.kelly2@councillors.glasgow.gov.uk

Kerr, Matthew (LAB - Craigton)
matthew.kerr@councillors.glasgow.gov.uk

Kucuk, Yvonne (LAB - Calton)
yvonne.kucuk@councillors.glasgow.gov.uk

Leonard, Gerald (LAB - North East)
gerald.leonard@councillors.glasgow.gov.uk

Letford, John (SNP - Maryhill/Kelvin)
john.letford@councillors.glasgow.gov.uk

MacLeod, Norman (SNP - Pollokshields)
norman.macleod@councillors.glasgow.gov.uk

McAllister, Billy (SNP - Canal)
billy.mcallister@councillors.glasgow.gov.uk

McDonald, David (SNP - Greater Pollok)
david.mcdonald@councillors.glasgow.gov.uk

McDougall, Elaine (LAB - East Centre)
elaine.mcdougall@councillors.glasgow.gov.uk

McElroy, Martin (SNP - Hillhead)
martin.mcelroy@councillors.glasgow.gov.uk

McKeever, Pauline (LAB - Hillhead)
paulineann.mckeever@councillors.glasgow.gov.uk

McLaughlin, John (SNP - Shettleston)
john.mclaughlin@councillors.glasgow.gov.uk

McLean, Kenny (SNP - Patrick West)
kenny.mclean@councillors.glasgow.gov.uk

Meikle, David (CON - Pollokshields)
david.meikle@councillors.glasgow.gov.uk

Millar, Angus (SNP - Anderston/City)
angus.millar@glasgow.gov.uk

Neill, Martin (LAB - Shettleston)
martin.neill@councillors.glasgow.gov.uk

Raja, Hanif (LAB - Pollokshields)
hanif.raja@councillors.glasgow.gov.uk

Razaq, Mohammed (LAB - Maryhill/Kelvin)
mohammed.razaq@councillors.glasgow.gov.uk

Redmond, George (LAB - Calton)
george.redmond@councillors.glasgow.gov.uk

Rhodes, Martin (LAB - Maryhill/Kelvin)
martin.rhodes@councillors.glasgow.gov.uk

Richardson, Anna (SNP - Langside)
anna.richardson@glasgow.gov.uk

Robertson, Russell (LAB - East Centre)
russell.robertson@councillors.glasgow.gov.uk

Rooney, Paul (LAB - Garscadden/Scotstounhill)
paul.rooney@councillors.glasgow.gov.uk

Scally, Franny (SNP - Maryhill/Kelvin)
franny.scally@councillors.glasgow.gov.uk

Scanlon, James (LAB - Southside Central)
james.scanlon@councillors.glasgow.gov.uk

Sheridan, Austin (SNP - Baillieston)
austin.sheridan@councillors.glasgow.gov.uk

Siddique, Soryia (LAB - Southside Central)
soryia.siddique@councillors.glasgow.gov.uk

Simpson, Anne (LAB - Shettleston)
anne.simpson@councillors.glasgow.gov.uk

Singh, Sohan (LAB - North East)
sohan.singh@councillors.glasgow.gov.uk

Stephen, Helen (LAB - Canal)
helen.stephen@councillors.glasgow.gov.uk

Stewart, Allan (LAB - Springburn)
allan.stewart@councillors.glasgow.gov.uk

Thomas, Fariha (LAB - Govan)
fariha.thomas@councillors.glasgow.gov.uk

Torrance, Jim (SNP - Craigton)
jim.torrance@councillors.glasgow.gov.uk

Turner, David (SNP - Baillieston)
david.turner@councillors.glasgow.gov.uk

Wardrop, Martha (SGP - Hillhead)
martha.wordrop@councillors.glasgow.gov.uk

Watson, Alistair (LAB - Craigton)
alistair.watson@councillors.glasgow.gov.uk

Wild, Kieran (GRN - Canal)
kieran.wild@councillors.glasgow.gov.uk

Wilson, Alex (SNP - Craigton)
alex.wilson@glasgow.gov.uk

POLITICAL COMPOSITION
LAB: 44, SNP: 29, SGP: 3, CON: 1, LD: 1, GRN: 1

COMMITTEE CHAIRS

Audit & Finance: Mr Kenny McLean

Children & Young People: Mr Malcolm Cunning

Health & Social Care: Ms Emma Gillan

Licensing: Mr Frank Docherty

Planning: Mr James Scanlon

Regeneration & Economy: Ms Maureen Burke

Gloucester City   D

Gloucester City Council, c/o Gloucester City Council, Herbert Warehouse, The Docks, Gloucester GL1 2EQ
☎ 01452 396396 ⌨ heretohelp@gloucester.gov.uk
🖳 www.gloucester.gov.uk

FACTS AND FIGURES
Parliamentary Constituencies: Gloucester
EU Constituencies: South West
Election Frequency: Elections are by thirds

PRINCIPAL OFFICERS

Chief Executive: Mr Jon McGinty, Managing Director (Gloucester City) & Director - Commissioning (Gloucestershire CC), c/o Gloucester City Council, Herbert Warehouse, The Docks, Gloucester GL1 2EQ ⌨ jon.mcginty@gloucester.gov.uk

Senior Management: Ms Anne Brinkhoff, Corporate Director - Partnerships, c/o Gloucester City Council, Herbert Warehouse, The Docks, Gloucester GL1 2EQ ⌨ anne.brinkhoff@gloucester.gov.uk

Senior Management: Mr Jonathan Lund, Corporate Director - Service Transformation, c/o Gloucester City Council, Herbert Warehouse, The Docks, Gloucester GL1 2EQ
⌨ jonathan.lund@gloucester.gov.uk

GLOUCESTER CITY

Architect, Building / Property Services: Mr Mark Foyn, Asset Manager, c/o Gloucester City Council, Herbert Warehouse, The Docks, Gloucester GL1 2EQ ☎ 01452 396271 ⌨ mark.foyn@gloucester.gov.uk

Catering Services: Mr David Baldwin, Senior Custodian, Herbert Warehouse, The Docks, Gloucester GL1 2EQ ☎ 01452 396185 ⌨ david.baldwin@gloucester.gov.uk

Community Safety: Mr Edward Pomfret, Health & Safety Service Manager, Herbert Warehouse, The Docks, Gloucester GL1 2EQ ☎ 01452 396069 ⌨ edward.pomfret@gloucester.gov.uk

Contracts: Ms Diana Mumford, Procurement Officer, Herbert Warehouse, The Docks, Gloucester GL1 2EQ ☎ 01452 396419 ⌨ diana.mumford@gloucester.gov.uk

Customer Service: Ms Wendy Jones, Customer Service Manager, Herbert Warehouse, The Docks, Gloucester GL1 2EQ ☎ 01452 396101 ⌨ wendy.jones@gloucester.gov.uk

Economic Development: Mr Anthony Hodge, Head of Regeneration & Economic Development, Herbert Warehouse, The Docks, Gloucester GL1 2EQ ☎ 01452 396034 ⌨ anthony.hodge@gloucester.gov.uk

Electoral Registration: Mrs Kirsty Cox, Senior Electoral Services Officer, Legal and Democratic Services, Herbert Warehouse, The Docks, Gloucester GL1 2EP ☎ 01452 396203 ⌨ kirsty.cox@gloucester.gov.uk

Emergency Planning: Ms Gill Ragon, Head of Public Protection, Herbert Warehouse, The Docks, Gloucester GL1 2EP ☎ 01452 396321 ⌨ gill.ragon@gloucester.gov.uk

Environmental / Technical Services: Ms Gill Ragon, Head of Public Protection, Herbert Warehouse, The Docks, Gloucester GL1 2EP ☎ 01452 396321 ⌨ gill.ragon@gloucester.gov.uk

Environmental Health: Ms Gill Ragon, Head of Public Protection, Herbert Warehouse, The Docks, Gloucester GL1 2EP ☎ 01452 396321 ⌨ gill.ragon@gloucester.gov.uk

Estates, Property & Valuation: Mr Mark Foyn, Asset Manager, c/o Gloucester City Council, Herbert Warehouse, The Docks, Gloucester GL1 2EQ ☎ 01452 396271 ⌨ mark.foyn@gloucester.gov.uk

Events Manager: Ms Sarah Gilbert, Guildhall Manager, c/o Gloucester City Council, Herbert Warehouse, The Docks, Gloucester GL1 2EQ ☎ 01452 396372 ⌨ sarah.gilbert@gloucester.gov.uk

Facilities: Mr Anthony Hodge, Head of Regeneration & Economic Development, Herbert Warehouse, The Docks, Gloucester GL1 2EQ ☎ 01452 396034 ⌨ anthony.hodge@gloucester.gov.uk

Finance: Mr Jon Topping, Head of Finance, Herbert Warehouse, The Docks, Gloucester GL1 2EQ ☎ 01452 396242 ⌨ jon.topping@gloucester.gov.uk

Health and Safety: Mr Edward Pomfret, Health & Safety Service Manager, Herbert Warehouse, The Docks, Gloucester GL1 2EQ ☎ 01452 396069 ⌨ edward.pomfret@gloucester.gov.uk

Housing: Ms Helen Chard, Housing Strategy & Enabling Service Manager, Herbert Warehouse, The Docks, Gloucester GL1 2EQ ☎ 01452 396534 ⌨ helen.chard@gloucester.gov.uk

Housing Maintenance: Mr Ashley Green, Chief Executive of Gloucester City Homes, Railway House, Bruton Way, Gloucester GL1 1DG ☎ 01452 396471 ⌨ ashleyg@gloucester.gov.uk

Licensing: Ms Gill Ragon, Head of Public Protection, Herbert Warehouse, The Docks, Gloucester GL1 2EP ☎ 01452 396321 ⌨ gill.ragon@gloucester.gov.uk

Member Services: Mrs Tanya Davies, Democratic & Electoral Services Manager, Herbert Warehouse, The Docks, Gloucester GL1 2EQ ☎ 01452 396127 ⌨ tanya.davies@gloucester.gov.uk

Planning: Mr Jon Sutcliffe, Development Control Service Manager, Herbert Warehouse, The Docks, Gloucester GL1 2EQ ☎ 01452 396783 ⌨ jon.sutcliffe@gloucester.gov.uk

Procurement: Ms Diana Mumford, Procurement Officer, Herbert Warehouse, The Docks, Gloucester GL1 2EQ ☎ 01452 396419 ⌨ diana.mumford@gloucester.gov.uk

Regeneration: Mr Anthony Hodge, Head of Regeneration & Economic Development, Herbert Warehouse, The Docks, Gloucester GL1 2EQ ☎ 01452 396034 ⌨ anthony.hodge@gloucester.gov.uk

Street Scene: Mr Lloyd Griffiths, Head of Neighbourhood Services, Herbert Warehouse, The Docks, Gloucester GL1 2EQ ☎ 01452 396355 ⌨ lloyd.griffiths@gloucester.gov.uk

Waste Collection and Disposal: Mr Lloyd Griffiths, Head of Neighbourhood Services, Herbert Warehouse, The Docks, Gloucester GL1 2EQ ☎ 01452 396355 ⌨ lloyd.griffiths@gloucester.gov.uk

COUNCILLORS

Mayor: Hampson, Neil (LAB - Moreland)
neil.hampsom@gloucester.gov.uj

Deputy Mayor: Hansdot, Said (LAB - Barton & Tredworth)
ahmed.hansdot@gloucester.gov.uk

Leader of the Council: James, Paul (CON - Longlevens)

Deputy Leader of the Council: Dallimore, Jennie (CON - Kingsway)
jennie.dallimore@gloucester.gov.uk

Group Leader: Haigh, Katie (LAB - Matson & Robinswood)
kate.haigh@gloucester.gov.uk

Group Leader: Hilton, Jeremy (LD - Kingsholm & Wotton)
jeremy.hilton@gloucester.gov.uk

Bhaimia, Usman (LD - Barton & Tredworth)
usman.bhaimia@gloucester.gov.uk

Brazil, Isabel (LD - Kingsholm & Wotton)
isabel.brazil@gloucester.gov.uk

Brown, Joanne (LD - Barnwood)
joanne.brown@glouester.gov.uk

Brown, David (LD - Hucclecote)
david.brown@glouester.gov.uk

Cook, Richard (CON - Kingsway)
richard.cook@glouester.gov.uk

Coole, Tom (LAB - Matson & Robinswood)
tom.coole@glouester.gov.uk

Dee, Gerald (CON - Tuffley)
gerald.dee@glouester.gov.uk

Fearn, Lauren (LAB - Coney Hill)
lauren.fearn@glouester.gov.uk

Finnegan, Collette (CON - Abbeydale)
collette.finnegan@glouester.gov.uk

Gravells, Andrew (CON - Abbeydale)
andrew.gravells@glouester.gov.uk

Hanman, Nigel (CON - Grange)
nigel.hanman@glouester.gov.uk

Hawthorne, Lee (CON - Quedgeley Fieldcourt)
lee.hawthorne@glouester.gov.uk

Hyman, Howard (LD - Elmbridge)
howard.hyman@glouester.gov.uk

Lewis, Andrew (CON - Quedgeley Severn Vale)
anddrew.lewis@glouester.gov.uk

Lugg, Janet (LAB - Matson & Robinswood)
janet.lugg@glouester.gov.uk

Melvin, Dawn (CON - Westgate)
dawn.melvin@glouester.gov.uk

Morgan, Steve (CON - Grange)
steve.morgan@glouester.gov.uk

Noakes, Lise (CON - Barnwood)
lise.noakes@glouester.gov.uk

Norman, David (CON - Quedgeley Fieldcourt)

Norman, Hannah (CON - Quedgeley Severn Vale)
hannah.norman@glouester.gov.uk

Organ, Colin (CON - Tuffley)
colin.organ@glouester.gov.uk

Patel, Sajid (CON - Barton & Tredworth)
sajid.patel@glouester.gov.uk

Pearsall, Laura (CON - Abbeymead)
laura.pearsall@glouester.gov.uk

Porter, Jim (CON - Longlevens)
kim.porter@glouester.gov.uk

Pullen, Terry (LAB - Moreland)
terry.pullen@glouester.gov.uk

Ryall, Emily (LD - Elmbridge)
emily.ryall@glouester.gov.uk

Smith, Deborah (LAB - Podsmead)
deborah.smith@glouester.gov.uk

Stephens, Kevin (LAB - Moreland)
kevin.stephens@glouester.gov.uk

Taylor, Gordon (CON - Abbeymead)
gordon.taylor@glouester.gov.uk

Toleman, Paul (CON - Westgate)
paul.toleman@glouester.gov.uk

Tracey, Pam (CON - Westgate)
pam.tracey@glouester.gov.uk

Williams, Kathy (CON - Longlevens)
kathy.williams@glouester.gov.uk

Wilson, Declan (LD - Hucclecote)
declan.wilson@glouester.gov.uk

POLITICAL COMPOSITION
CON: 22, LAB: 9, LD: 8

COMMITTEE CHAIRS

Licensing: Ms Hannah Norman

Planning: Mr Gordon Taylor

Gloucestershire   C

Gloucestershire County Council, Shire Hall, Westgate Street,
Gloucester GL1 2TG
☎ 01452 425000 ✆ customerservices@gloucestershire.gov.uk
🖥 www.gloucestershire.gov.uk

FACTS AND FIGURES
Parliamentary Constituencies:
EU Constituencies: South West
Election Frequency: Elections are of whole council

PRINCIPAL OFFICERS

Chief Executive: Mr Peter Bungard, Chief Executive, Shire Hall,
Westgate Street, Gloucester GL1 2TG ☎ 01452 583444
✆ peter.bungard@gloucestershire.gov.uk

Senior Management: Ms Jane Burns, Director - Strategy &
Challenge, Shire Hall, Westgate Street, Gloucester GL1 2TG
☎ 01452 328472 ✆ jane.burns@gloucestershire.gov.uk

Senior Management: Mr Jon McGinty, Managing Director
(Gloucester City) & Director - Commissioning (Gloucestershire
CC), c/o Gloucester City Council, Herbert Warehouse, The Docks,
Gloucester GL1 2EQ ✆ jon.mcginty@gloucester.gov.uk

Senior Management: Mr Nigel Riglar, Commissioning Director
- Communities & Infrastructure, Shire Hall, Westgate Street,
Gloucester GL1 2TG ✆ nigel.riglar@gloucestershire.gov.uk

Senior Management: Ms Sarah Scott, Interim Director - Public
Health, Shire Hall, Westgate Street, Gloucester GL1 2TG
☎ 01452 328497 ✆ sarah.scott@gloucestershire.gov.uk

Senior Management: Ms Linda Uren, Commissioning Director -
Children, Shire Hall, Westgate Street, Gloucester GL1 2TG
☎ 01452 328471 ✆ linda.uren@gloucestershire.gov.uk

Senior Management: Ms Jo Walker, Director - Strategic Finance,
Shire Hall, Westgate Street, Gloucester GL1 2TG ☎ 01453 328469
✆ jo.walker@gloucestershire.gov.uk

Senior Management: Ms Margaret Willcox, Commissioning
Director - Adults, Shire Hall, Westgate Street, Gloucester GL1 2TG
☎ 01452 328468 ✆ margaret.willcox@gloucestershire.gov.uk

GLOUCESTERSHIRE

Architect, Building / Property Services: Mr Neil Corbett, Head of Corporate Property Services, Shire Hall, Westgate Street, Gloucester GL1 2TG ☎ 01452 328813 ✆ neil.corbett@gloucestershire.gov.uk

Best Value: Mr Rob Ayliffe, Head of Policy & Performance, Shire Hall, Westgate Street, Gloucester GL1 2TG ☎ 01452 426613 ✆ rob.ayliffe@gloucestershire.gov.uk

Building Control: Mr Neil Corbett, Head of Corporate Property Services, Shire Hall, Westgate Street, Gloucester GL1 2TG ☎ 01452 328813 ✆ neil.corbett@gloucestershire.gov.uk

Building Control: Mr Stephen Hetenyi, Support Services Manager, Shire Hall, Gloucester GL1 2TG ☎ 01452 328827 ✆ stephen.hetenyi@gloucestershire.gov.uk

Children / Youth Services: Mr Tim Browne, Head of Special Educational Needs, Shire Hall, Westgate Street, Gloucester GL1 2TG ☎ 01452 328693 ✆ tim.browne@gloucestershire.gov.uk

Children / Youth Services: Mr Ian Godfrey, Children In Care Service Manager, Shire Hall, Westgate Street, Block 1, Gloucester GL2 5GH ☎ 01452 427650 ✆ ian.godfrey@gloucestershire.gov.uk

Children / Youth Services: Mr Eugene O'Kane, Programme Manager, Shire Hall, Westgate Street, Gloucester GL1 2TG ☎ 01452 583591 ✆ eugene.okane@gloucestershire.gov.uk

Children / Youth Services: Ms Lynne Speak, Operations Manager, 92-96 Westgate Street, Gloucester GL1 2PF ☎ 01452 583791 ✆ lynne.speak@gloucestershire.gov.uk

Civil Registration: Ms Sally Bye, Registration & Coroner Services Manager, Hillfield House, Denmark Road, Gloucester GL1 3LD ☎ 01242 532451 ✆ sally.bye@gloucestershire.gov.uk

Computer Management: Mr Andrew Gilbert, ICT Manager, Shire Hall, Westgate Street, Gloucester GL1 2TG ☎ 01452 583706 ✆ andrew.gilbert@gloucestershire.gov.uk

Consumer Protection and Trading Standards: Mr Eddie Coventry, Head of Trading Standards, Registration & Coroners, Hillfield House, Denmark Road, Gloucester GL1 3LD ☎ 01452 426786 ✆ eddie.coventry@gloucestershire.gov.uk

Contracts: Mr Simon Bilous, Head of Commissioning, Shire Hall, Westgate Street, Gloucester GL1 2TG ☎ 01452 328489 ✆ simon.bilous@gloucestershire.gov.uk

Corporate Services: Ms Jane Burns, Director - Strategy & Challenge, Shire Hall, Gloucester GL1 2TG ☎ 01452 328472 ✆ jane.burns@gloucestershire.gov.uk

Corporate Services: Mr Stewart King, Head of Business Development, Shire Hall, Westgate Street, Gloucester GL1 2TG ☎ 01452 328488 ✆ stewart.king@gloucestershire.gov.uk

Customer Service: Ms Tricia Gallagher, Customer Service Team Operations Manager, Shire Hall, Westgate Street, Gloucester GL1 2TG ☎ 01452 427339 ✆ tricia.gallagher@gloucestershire.gov.uk

Customer Service: Ms Margaret Willcox, Commissioning Director - Adults, Shire Hall, Westgate Street, Gloucester GL1 2TG ☎ 01452 328468 ✆ margaret.willcox@gloucestershire.gov.uk

Education: Ms Jo Grills, Operations Director - Education, Learning & Libraries, Shire Hall, Gloucester GL1 2TG ☎ 01452 583559 ✆ jo.grills@gloucestershire.gov.uk

Environmental / Technical Services: Ms Jo Walker, Director - Strategic Finance, Shire Hall, Westgate Street, Gloucester GL1 2TG ☎ 01453 328469 ✆ jo.walker@gloucestershire.gov.uk

Environmental Health: Mr Paul Cobb, Safety Health & Environment Manager, Shire Hall, Westgate Street, Gloucester GL1 2TG ☎ 01452 426762 ✆ paul.cobb@gloucestershire.gov.uk

Estates, Property & Valuation: Mr Neil Corbett, Head of Corporate Property Services, Shire Hall, Westgate Street, Gloucester GL1 2TG ☎ 01452 328813 ✆ neil.corbett@gloucestershire.gov.uk

Facilities: Mr Neil Corbett, Head of Corporate Property Services, Shire Hall, Westgate Street, Gloucester GL1 2TG ☎ 01452 328813 ✆ neil.corbett@gloucestershire.gov.uk

Facilities: Mr Stephen Hetenyi, Support Services Manager, Shire Hall, Gloucester GL1 2TG ☎ 01452 328827 ✆ stephen.hetenyi@gloucestershire.gov.uk

Finance: Mr Graham Burrow, Head of Finance & Exchequer, Shire Hall, Westgate Street, Gloucester GL1 2TG ☎ 01452 328944 ✆ graham.burrow@gloucestershire.gov.uk

Finance: Mr Mark Spilsbury, Head of Finance for Financial Management, Shire Hall, Westgate Street, Gloucester GL1 2TG ☎ 01452 328920 ✆ mark.spilsbury@gloucestershire.gov.uk

Pensions: Mr Alan Marshall, Pensions Administration Manager, Shire Hall, Westgate Street, Gloucester GL1 2TG ☎ 01452 328866 ✆ alan.marshall@gloucestershire.gov.uk

Pensions: Ms Jenny Pitcher, Investment Manager, Llanthony Warehouse, The Docks, Gloucester GL1 2EH ☎ 01452 328308 ✆ jenny.pitcher@gloucestershire.gov.uk

Health and Safety: Mr Paul Cobb, Safety Health & Environment Manager, Shire Hall, Westgate Street, Gloucester GL1 2TG ☎ 01452 426762 ✆ paul.cobb@gloucestershire.gov.uk

Local Area Agreement: Mr Rob Ayliffe, Head of Performance & Need, Shire Hall, Westgate Street, Gloucester GL1 2TG ☎ 01452 328506 ✆ rob.ayliffe@gloucestershire.gov.uk

Local Area Agreement: Ms Jane Burns, Director - Strategy & Challenge, Shire Hall, Westgate Street, Gloucester GL1 2TG ☎ 01452 328472 ✆ jane.burns@gloucestershire.gov.uk

Legal: Ms Christine Wray, Head of Legal Services, Shire Hall, Westgate Street, Gloucester GL1 2TG ☎ 01452 328730 ✆ christine.wray@gloucestershire.gov.uk

Leisure and Cultural Services: Mr Chris Dee, Marketing Manager, Llanthony Warehouse, The Docks, Gloucester GL1 2EH
☎ 01452 328302 ⌁ chris.dee@gloucestershire.gov.uk

Lifelong Learning: Mr Jim Austin, Head of Adult Education, Llanthony Warehouse, The Docks, Gloucester GL1 2EH
☎ 01452 583810 ⌁ jim.austin@gloucestershire.gov.uk

Lottery Funding, Charity and Voluntary: Mrs Rachel Wright, Voluntary Sector Manager, Shire Hall, Westgate Street, Gloucester GL1 2TG ☎ 01452 427615 ⌁ rachel.wright@gloucestershire.gov.uk

Member Services: Mr Simon Harper, Lead Democratic Services Advisor, Shire Hall, Westgate Street, Gloucester GL1 2TG
☎ 01452 324202 ⌁ simon.harper@gloucestershire.gov.uk

Member Services: Mr Nigel Roberts, Head of Legal Services, Quayside House, First Floor, Gloucester GL1 2TG
☎ 01452 425201 ⌁ nigel.roberts@gloucestershire.gov.uk

Parking: Mr Jim Daniels, Parking Manager, Shire Hall, Westgate Street, Gloucester GL1 2TG ☎ 01452 425610
⌁ jim.daniels@gloucestershire.gov.uk

Partnerships: Ms Jane Burns, Director - Strategy & Challenge, Shire Hall, Westgate Street, Gloucester GL1 2TG ☎ 01452 328472
⌁ jane.burns@gloucestershire.gov.uk

Partnerships: Ms Linda Uren, Commissioning Director - Children, Shire Hall, Westgate Street, Gloucester GL1 2TG ☎ 01452 328471
⌁ linda.uren@gloucestershire.gov.uk

Personnel / HR: Ms Karen Grave, Interim Head of HR, Shire Hall, Westgate Street, Gloucester GL1 2TG ☎ 01452 324303
⌁ karen.grave@gloucestershire.gov.uk

Personnel / HR: Ms Susan Scrivens, Change Management Advisor, Shire Hall, Gloucester GL1 2TG ☎ 01452 427683
⌁ sue.scrivens@gloucestershire.gov.uk

Procurement: Mr Graham Collins, Procurement Consultant, Shire Hall, Westgate Street, Gloucester GL1 2TG ☎ 01452 328124
⌁ graham.collins@gloucestershire.gov.uk

Public Libraries: Ms Margaret Willcox, Commissioning Director - Adults, Shire Hall, Westgate Street, Gloucester GL1 2TG
☎ 01452 328468 ⌁ margaret.willcox@gloucestershire.gov.uk

Social Services: Mr Ian Godfrey, Children In Care Service Manager, Shire Hall, Westgate Street, Block 1, Gloucester GL2 5GH
☎ 01452 427650 ⌁ ian.godfrey@gloucestershire.gov.uk

Social Services: Ms Tina Reid, Operations Lead: Adult Social Care & Business Development, Shire Hall, Westgate Street, Gloucester GL1 2TG ☎ 01452 427300
⌁ tina.reid@gloucestershire.gov.uk

Social Services: Ms Margaret Willcox, Commissioning Director - Adults, Shire Hall, Westgate Street, Gloucester GL1 2TG
☎ 01452 328468 ⌁ margaret.willcox@gloucestershire.gov.uk

Social Services (Adult): Ms Margaret Willcox, Commissioning Director - Adults, Shire Hall, Westgate Street, Gloucester GL1 2TG
☎ 01452 328468 ⌁ margaret.willcox@gloucestershire.gov.uk

Public Health: Ms Sarah Scott, Interim Director - Public Health, Shire Hall, Westgate Street, Gloucester GL1 2TG ☎ 01452 328497
⌁ sarah.scott@gloucestershire.gov.uk

Sustainable Communities: Mr Peter Wiggins, Outcome Manager, Environment Directorate, Shire Hall, Westgate Street, Gloucester GL1 2TG ☎ 01452 328536
⌁ peter.wiggins@gloucestershire.gov.uk

Tourism: Mr Chris Dee, Marketing Manager, Llanthony Warehouse, The Docks, Gloucester GL1 2EH ☎ 01452 328302
⌁ chris.dee@gloucestershire.gov.uk

Waste Collection and Disposal: Mr Tony Childs, Waste Services & Sustainability Manager, Shire Hall, Westgate Street, Gloucester GL1 2TG ☎ 01452 425448 ⌁ tony.childs@gloucestershire.gov.uk

Waste Management: Mr Tony Childs, Waste Services & Sustainability Manager, Shire Hall, Westgate Street, Gloucester GL1 2TG ☎ 01452 425448 ⌁ tony.childs@gloucestershire.gov.uk

Waste Management: Mr Ian Mawdsley, Project Lead of Residual Waste Management, Shire Hall, Gloucester GL1 2TH
☎ 01452 425835 ⌁ ian.mawdsley@gloucestershire.gov.uk

COUNCILLORS

ChairHay, Colin (LD - All Saints & Oakley)
colin.hay@gloucestershire.gov.uk

Vice-ChairParsons, Shaun (CON - South Cerney)
shaun.parsons@gloucestershire.gov.uk

Leader of the Council: Hawthorne, Mark (CON - Quedgeley)
mark.hawthorne@gloucestershire.gov.uk

Deputy Leader of the Council: Theodoulou, Raymond (CON - Fairford & Lechdale on Thames)
raymond.theodoulou@gloucestershire.gov.uk

Group LeaderHilton, Jeremy (LD - Kingsholm & Wotton)
jeremy.hilton@gloucestershire.gov.uk

Group LeaderHodgkinson, Paul (LD - Bourton-on-the-Water & Northleach)
paul.hodgkinson@gloucestershire.gov.uk

Group LeaderPrince, David (IND - Pittville & Prestbury)
david.prince@gloucestershire.gov.uk

Awford, Phil (CON - Highnam)
philip.awford@gloucestershire.gov.uk

Binns, Dorcas (CON - Nailsworth)
dorcas.binns@gloucestershire.gov.uk

Bird, Robert (CON - Bishop's Cleeve)
robert.bird@gloucestershire.gov.uk

Blackburn, Anthony (CON - Hardwicke & Severn)
anthony.blackburn@gloucestershire.gov.uk

Brown, David (LD - Barnwood & Hucclecote)
cllrdavid.brown@gloucestershire.gov.uk

Bullingham, Jason (CON - Bisley & Painswick)
jason.bullingham@gloucestershire.gov.uk

GLOUCESTERSHIRE

Coleman, Christopher (LD - St Mark's & St Peter's)
christopher.coleman@gloucestershire.gov.uk

Cordwell, John (LD - Wotton-under-Edge)
john.cordwell@gloucestershire.gov.uk

Dobie, Iain (LD - Leckhampton & Warden Hill)
iain.dobie@gloucestershire.gov.uk

Fisher, Bernard (LD - St Paul's & Swindon)
bernard.fisher@gloucestershire.gov.uk

Gill, Jasminder (LAB - Barton & Tredworth)
jasminder.gill@gloucestershire.gov.uk

Gravells, Andrew (CON - Abbey)
andrew.gravells@gloucestershire.gov.uk

Guyton, Colin (IND - Drybrook & Lydbrook)
colin.guyton@gloucestershire.gov.uk

Harman, Tim (CON - Landsown & Park)
tim.harman@gloucestershire.gov.uk

Harris, Joe (LD - Cirencester Park)
joe.harris@gloucestershire.gov.uk

Hicks, Anthony (CON - Tetbury)
tony.hicks@gloucestershire.gov.uk

Kirby, Barry (LAB - Grange & Kingsway)
barry.kirby@gloucestershire.gov.uk

Leppington, Richard (UKIP - Blakeney & Bream)
richard.leppington@gloucestershire.gov.uk

Lunnon, Sarah (GRN - Stroud Central)
sarah.lunnon@gloucestershire.gov.uk

Lydon, Stephen (LAB - Dursley)
stephen.lydon@gloucestershire.gov.uk

McHale, Stephen (LAB - Coney Hill & Matson)
steve.mchale@gloucestershire.gov.uk

McLain, Paul (CON - Battledown & Carlton Kings)
paul.mclain@gloucestershire.gov.uk

McMahon, Paul (LAB - Coleford)
paul.mcmahon@gloucestershire.gov.uk

Millard, Tracy (LAB - Tuffley)
tracy.millard@gloucestershire.gov.uk

Molyneux, Patrick (CON - Sedbury)
patrick.molyneux@gloucestershire.gov.uk

Moor, Nigel (CON - Stow-on-the-Wold)
nigel.moor@gloucestershire.gov.uk

Morgan, Graham (LAB - Cinderford)
graham.morgan@gloucestershire.gov.uk

Oosthuysen, Brian (LAB - Rodborough)
brian.oosthuysen@gloucestershire.gov.uk

Preest, Alan (UKIP - Lydney)
alan.preest@gloucestershire.gov.uk

Robbins, Nigel (LD - Cirencester Beeches)
nigel.robbins@gloucestershire.gov.uk

Robinson, Brian (CON - Mitcheldean)
brian.robinson@gloucestershire.gov.uk

Smith, Vernon (CON - Tewkesbury East)
vernon.smith@gloucestershire.gov.uk

Stowe, Lynden (CON - Campden-Vale)
lynden.stowe@gloucestershire.gov.uk

Sudbury, Klara (LD - Charlton Park & College)
klara.sudbury@gloucestershire.gov.uk

Sztymiak, Mike (IND - Tewkesbury)
mike.sztymiak@gloucestershire.gov.uk

Tipper, Brian (CON - Cam Valley)
brian.tipper@gloucestershire.gov.uk

Tracey, Pam (CON - Hempsted & Westgate)
pam.tracey@gloucestershire.gov.uk

Vines, Robert (CON - Brockworth)
robert.vines@gloucestershire.gov.uk

Waddington, Stan (CON - Minchinhampton)
stan.waddington@gloucestershire.gov.uk

Wheeler, Simon (LD - Benhall & Up Hatherley)
simon.wheeler@gloucestershire.gov.uk

Williams, Jack (LD - Churchdown)
jack.williams@gloucestershire.gov.uk

Williams, Lesley (LAB - Stonehouse)
lesley.williams@gloucestershire.gov.uk

Williams, Suzanne (LD - Hesters Way & Springbank)
suzanne.williams@gloucestershire.gov.uk

Williams, Kathy (CON - Longlevens)
kathy.williams@gloucestershire.gov.uk

Wilson, Roger (CON - Winchcombe & Woodmancote)
roger.wilson@gloucestershire.gov.uk

Windsor-Clive, Will (CON - Newent)
will.windsor-clive@gloucestershire.gov.uk

POLITICAL COMPOSITION
CON: 24, LD: 14, LAB: 9, IND: 3, UKIP: 2, GRN: 1

COMMITTEE CHAIRS

Audit: Mr Nigel Robbins

Children & Families: Mr Tim Harman

Environment & Communities: Mr Robert Bird

Health & Wellbeing: Ms Dorcas Binns

Planning: Mr John Cordwell

Gosport
D

Gosport Borough Council, Town Hall, High Street, Gosport
PO12 1EB
☎ 023 9258 4242 📠 023 9254 5587 ✆ enquiries@gosport.gov.uk
💻 www.gosport.gov.uk

FACTS AND FIGURES
Parliamentary Constituencies: Gosport
EU Constituencies: South East
Election Frequency: Elections are biennial

PRINCIPAL OFFICERS

Chief Executive: Mr Ian Lycett, Chief Executive, Town Hall, High
Street, Gosport PO12 1EB ☎ 023 9251 5201
✆ ian.lycett@gosport.gov.uk

Deputy Chief Executive: Ms Linda Edwards, Deputy Chief Executive & Borough Solicitor, Town Hall, High Street, Gosport PO12 1EB ☎ 023 9254 5401 ◌ linda.edwards@gosport.gov.uk

Access Officer / Social Services (Disability): Mr John Shaw, Head of Building Control, Town Hall, High Street, Gosport PO12 1EB ☎ 01329 824450 ◌ jshaw@fareham.gov.uk

Architect, Building / Property Services: Mr Mark Johnson, Head of Property Services, Town Hall, High Street, Gosport PO12 1EB ☎ 023 9254 5563 ◌ mark.johnson@gosport.gov.uk

Best Value: Mrs Julie Petty, Head of Corporate Policy & Performance, Town Hall, High Street, Gosport PO12 1EB ☎ 023 9254 5381 ◌ julie.petty@gosport.gov.uk

Building Control: Mr John Shaw, Head of Building Control, Town Hall, High Street, Gosport PO12 1EB ☎ 01329 824450 ◌ jshaw@fareham.gov.uk

PR / Communications: Mrs Brenda Brooker, Press Officer, Town Hall, High Street, Gosport PO12 1EB ☎ 023 9254 5255 ◌ brenda.brooker@gosport.gov.uk

Community Planning: Mrs Julie Petty, Head of Corporate Policy & Performance, Town Hall, High Street, Gosport PO12 1EB ☎ 023 9254 5381 ◌ julie.petty@gosport.gov.uk

Community Safety: Mrs Julie Petty, Head of Corporate Policy & Performance, Town Hall, High Street, Gosport PO12 1EB ☎ 023 9254 5381 ◌ julie.petty@gosport.gov.uk

Computer Management: Mr David Eland, Head of IT, Town Hall, High Street, Gosport PO12 1EB ☎ 023 9254 5309 ◌ david.eland@gosport.gov.uk

Contracts: Mr Stevyn Ricketts, Head of Streetscene, Town Hall, High Street, Gosport PO12 1EB ☎ 023 9254 5282 ◌ stevyn.ricketts@gosport.gov.uk

E-Government: Mr David Eland, Head of IT, Town Hall, High Street, Gosport PO12 1EB ☎ 023 9254 5309 ◌ david.eland@gosport.gov.uk

Electoral Registration: Mr Graeme Jesty, Head of Election Services & Emergency Planning Officer, Town Hall, High Street, Gosport PO12 1EB ☎ 023 9254 5580 ◌ graeme.jesty@gosport.gov.uk

Emergency Planning: Mr Graeme Jesty, Head of Election Services & Emergency Planning Officer, Town Hall, High Street, Gosport PO12 1EB ☎ 023 9254 5580 ◌ graeme.jesty@gosport.gov.uk

Environmental Health: Mr Ian Rickman, Head of Environmental Health, Civic Offices, Civic Way, Fareham PO16 7AZ ☎ 01329 824773 ◌ irickman@fareham.gov.uk

Estates, Property & Valuation: Mr Mark Johnson, Head of Property Services, Town Hall, High Street, Gosport PO12 1EB ☎ 023 9254 5563 ◌ mark.johnson@gosport.gov.uk

Finance: Mr Julian Bowcher, Borough Treasurer, Town Hall, High Street, Gosport PO12 1EB ☎ 023 9254 5301 ◌ julian.bowcher@gosport.gov.uk

Treasury: Mr Julian Bowcher, Borough Treasurer, Town Hall, High Street, Gosport PO12 1EB ☎ 023 9254 5301 ◌ julian.bowcher@gosport.gov.uk

Grounds Maintenance: Ms Caroline Smith, Landscape Management Officer, Town Hall, High Street, Gosport PO12 1EB ☎ 023 9258 4566 ◌ caroline.smith@gosport.gov.uk

Health and Safety: Mr Keith Perkins, Health & Safety Officer, Civic Offices, Civic Way, Fareham PO16 7AZ ☎ 01329 236100 ◌ kperkins@fareham.gov.uk

Housing: Mr James Hill, Housing Services Manager, Town Hall, High Street, Gosport PO12 1EB ☎ 023 9254 5327 ◌ james.hill@gosport.gov.uk

Legal: Ms Linda Edwards, Deputy Chief Executive & Borough Solicitor, Town Hall, High Street, Gosport PO12 1EB ☎ 023 9254 5401 ◌ linda.edwards@gosport.gov.uk

Licensing: Mr Ian Rickman, Head of Environmental Health, Town Hall, High Street, Gosport PO12 1EB ☎ 023 9258 5517 ◌ irickman@fareham.gov.uk

Member Services: Mr Mark Simmonds, Head of Legal Services, Town Hall, High Street, Gosport PO12 1EB ☎ 023 9254 5653 ◌ mark.simmonds@gosport.gov.uk

Parking: Mr Graeme Mudge, Enforcement Officer, Town Hall, High Street, Gosport PO12 1EB ☎ 023 9254 5569 ◌ graeme.mudge@gosport.gov.uk

Personnel / HR: Mrs Kathy Inch, Head of Personnel, Town Hall, High Street, Gosport PO12 1EB ☎ 023 9251 5524 ◌ kathy.inch@gosport.gov.uk

Planning: Ms Linda Edwards, Deputy Chief Executive & Borough Solicitor, Town Hall, High Street, Gosport PO12 1EB ☎ 023 9254 5401 ◌ linda.edwards@gosport.gov.uk

Procurement: Mrs Maree Hall, Senior Procurement Officer, Town Hall, High Street, Gosport PO12 1EB ☎ 023 9254 5379 ◌ maree.hall@gosport.gov.uk

Recycling & Waste Minimisation: Mrs Angela Benneworth, Principal Contracts Officer, Town Hall, High Street, Gosport PO12 1EB ☎ 023 9254 8053 ◌ angela.benneworth@gosport.gov.uk

Road Safety: Mr David Duckett, Head of Traffic Management, Town Hall, High Street, Gosport PO12 1EB ☎ 023 9254 5424 ◌ david.duckett@gosport.gov.uk

Staff Training: Mrs Kathy Inch, Head of Personnel, Town Hall, High Street, Gosport PO12 1EB ☎ 023 9251 5524 ◌ kathy.inch@gosport.gov.uk

GOSPORT

Street Scene: Mr Stevyn Ricketts, Head of Streetscene, Town Hall, High Street, Gosport PO12 1EB ☎ 023 9254 5282
⌂ stevyn.ricketts@gosport.gov.uk

Sustainable Communities: Mrs Julie Petty, Head of Corporate Policy & Performance, Town Hall, High Street, Gosport PO12 1EB
☎ 023 9254 5381 ⌂ julie.petty@gosport.gov.uk

Traffic Management: Mr David Duckett, Head of Traffic Management, Town Hall, High Street, Gosport PO12 1EB
☎ 023 9254 5424 ⌂ david.duckett@gosport.gov.uk

Transport: Mr David Duckett, Head of Traffic Management, Town Hall, High Street, Gosport PO12 1EB ☎ 023 9254 5424
⌂ david.duckett@gosport.gov.uk

Transport Planner: Mr David Duckett, Head of Traffic Management, Town Hall, High Street, Gosport PO12 1EB
☎ 023 9254 5424 ⌂ david.duckett@gosport.gov.uk

Waste Collection and Disposal: Mr Stevyn Ricketts, Head of Streetscene, Town Hall, High Street, Gosport PO12 1EB
☎ 023 9254 5282 ⌂ stevyn.ricketts@gosport.gov.uk

COUNCILLORS

Mayor: Hook, Lynn (CON - Peel Common)
lynn.hook@gosport.gov.uk

Deputy Mayor: Batty, Linda (LAB - Bridgemary South)
linda.batty@gosport.gov.uk

Leader of the Council: Hook, Mark (CON - Alverstoke)
mark.hook@gosport.gov.uk

Deputy Leader of the Council: Burgess, Graham (CON - Lee East)

Allen, Roger (CON - Hardway)
roger.allen@gosport.gov.uk

Ballard, Susan (LD - Elson)
susan.ballard@gosport.gov.uk

Bateman, Piers (CON - Lee East)
piers.bateman@gosport.gov.uk

Beavis, John (CON - Lee West)
john.beavis@gosport.gov.uk

Bergin, Patrick (UKIP - Rowner & Holbrook)
patrick.bergin@gosport.gov.uk

Carter, Chris (CON - Lee West)
chris.carter@gosport.gov.uk

Chegwyn, Peter (LD - Leesland)
peter.chegwyn@gosport.gov.uk

Cully, June (LAB - Town)
june.cully@gosport.gov.uk

Diffey, Maria (LD - Leesland)
maria.diffey@gosport.gov.uk

Earle, Richard (LD - Elson)
richard.earle@gosport.gov.uk

Edgar, Peter (CON - Alverstoke)
peter.edgar@gosport.gov.uk

Farr, Keith (LAB - Forton)
keith.farr@gosport.gov.uk

Forder, Ingeborg (CON - Privett)

Foster-Reed, Clive (LD - Forton)
clive.foster-reed@gosport.gov.uk

Furlong, Diane (CON - Hardway)
diane.furlong@gosport.gov.uk

Hicks, Austin (LD - Brockhurst)
austin.hicks@gosport.gov.uk

Huggins, Zoe (CON - Privett)
zoe.huggins@gosport.gov.uk

Hylands, Robert (LD - Brockhurst)
robert.hylands@gosport.gov.uk

Jessop, Tony (CON - Grange)
tony.jessop@gosport.gov.uk

Jones, Kathleen (CON - Bridgemary South)
kathleen.jones@gosport.gov.uk

Kelly, Dawn (LD - Christchurch)
dawn.kelly@gosport.gov.uk

Morgan, Margaret (CON - Grange)
margaret.morgan@gosport.gov.uk

Murphy, Marcus (CON - Rowner & Holbrook)
marcus.murphy@gosport.gov.uk

Philpott, Stephen (CON - Peel Common)
stephen.philpott@gosport.gov.uk

Prickett, Angela (LD - Forton)
angela.prickett@gosport.gov.uk

Raffaelli, Philip (CON - Anglesey)
philip.raffaelli@gosport.gov.uk

Ronayne, Wayne (CON - Christchurch)
wayne.ronayne@gosport.gov.uk

Scard, Alan (CON - Anglesey)
alan.scard@gosport.gov.uk

Wright, Jill (LAB - Bridgemary North)
jill.wright@gosport.gov.uk

Wright, Dennis (LAB - Bridgemary North)

POLITICAL COMPOSITION
CON: 19, LD: 9, LAB: 5, UKIP: 1

COMMITTEE CHAIRS

Economic Development: Mr Stephen Philpott

Gravesham   D

Gravesham Borough Council, Civic Centre, Windmill Street, Gravesend DA12 1AU
☎ 01474 564422 🖷 01474 337453
⌂ forename.surname@gravesham.gov.uk ▢ www.gravesham.gov.uk

FACTS AND FIGURES
Parliamentary Constituencies: Gravesham
EU Constituencies: South East
Election Frequency: Elections are of whole council

PRINCIPAL OFFICERS

Chief Executive: Mr David Hughes, Chief Executive, Civic Centre, Windmill Street, Gravesend DA12 1AU ☎ 01474 337380
⌂ david.hughes@gravesham.gov.uk

Senior Management: Mr Nick Brown, Director - Environment & Operations, Brookvale, Springhead Road, Northfleet DA11 8HW
☎ 01474 337319 ✐ nick.brown@gravesham.gov.uk

Senior Management: Mr Kevin Burbidge, Director - Housing & Regeneration, Civic Centre, Windmill Street, Gravesend DA12 1BQ
☎ 01474 337585 ✐ kevin.burbidge@gravesham.gov.uk

Senior Management: Mrs Melanie Norris, Director - Communities, Civic Centre, Windmill Street, Gravesend DA12 1AU
☎ 01474 337324 ✐ melanie.norris@gravesham.gov.uk

Architect, Building / Property Services: Mrs Elizabeth Thornton, Property Services Manager, Civic Centre, Windmill Street, Gravesend DA12 1AU ☎ 01474 337522
✐ elizabeth.thornton@gravesham.gov.uk

Best Value: Mr Stuart Bobby, Director - Corporate Services, Civic Centre, Windmill Street, Gravesend DA12 1AU ☎ 01474 337431
✐ stuart.bobby@gravesham.gov.uk

PR / Communications: Mr Graham Cole, Communications Manager, Civic Centre, Windmill Street, Gravesend DA12 1AU
☎ 01474 337304 ✐ graham.cole@gravesham.gov.uk

Community Safety: Mr Simon Hookway, Service Manager - Economic Development, Civic Centre, Windmill Street, Gravesend DA12 1BQ ☎ 01474 337238 ✐ simon.hookway@gravesham.gov.uk

Computer Management: Mr Darren Everden, Service Manager - IT Services, Civic Centre, Windmill Street, Gravesend DA12 1AU
☎ 01474 337240 ✐ darren.everden@gravesham.gov.uk

Corporate Services: Mr Stuart Bobby, Director - Corporate Services, Civic Centre, Windmill Street, Gravesend DA12 1AU
☎ 01474 337431 ✐ stuart.bobby@gravesham.gov.uk

Customer Service: Ms Anita Tysoe, Service Manager - Customer & Theatre Services, Civic Centre, Windmill Street, Gravesend DA12 1AU ☎ 01474 337360 ✐ anita.tysoe@gravesham.gov.uk

Direct Labour: Mr Nick Brown, Director - Environment & Operations, Brookvale, Springhead Road, Northfleet DA11 8HW
☎ 01474 337319 ✐ nick.brown@gravesham.gov.uk

Economic Development: Mr Simon Hookway, Service Manager - Economic Development, Civic Centre, Windmill Street, Gravesend DA12 1BQ ☎ 01474 337238 ✐ simon.hookway@gravesham.gov.uk

E-Government: Mr Darren Everden, Service Manager - IT Services, Civic Centre, Windmill Street, Gravesend DA12 1AU
☎ 01474 337240 ✐ darren.everden@gravesham.gov.uk

Electoral Registration: Mrs Sarah Kilkie, Assistant Director - Communities, Civic Centre, Windmill Street, Gravesend DA12 1BQ
☎ 01474 337235 ✐ sarah.kilkie@gravesham.gov.uk

Emergency Planning: Mr Nick Brown, Director - Environment & Operations, Brookvale, Springhead Road, Northfleet DA11 8HW
☎ 01474 337319 ✐ nick.brown@gravesham.gov.uk

Environmental / Technical Services: Mrs Sarah Kilkie, Assistant Director - Communities, Civic Centre, Windmill Street, Gravesend DA12 1BQ ☎ 01474 337235
✐ sarah.kilkie@gravesham.gov.uk

Environmental Health: Mrs Sarah Kilkie, Assistant Director - Communities, Civic Centre, Windmill Street, Gravesend DA12 1BQ
☎ 01474 337235 ✐ sarah.kilkie@gravesham.gov.uk

Estates, Property & Valuation: Mrs Elizabeth Thornton, Property Services Manager, Civic Centre, Windmill Street, Gravesend DA12 1AU ☎ 01474 337522 ✐ elizabeth.thornton@gravesham.gov.uk

European Liaison: Mr Kevin Burbidge, Director - Housing & Regeneration, Civic Centre, Windmill Street, Gravesend DA12 1BQ
☎ 01474 337585 ✐ kevin.burbidge@gravesham.gov.uk

Events Manager: Mr Adrian Hickmott, Sport & Recreation Manager, Civic Centre, Windmill Street, Gravesend DA12 1AU
☎ 01474 337322 ✐ adrian.hickmott@gravesham.gov.uk

Facilities: Mrs Melanie Norris, Director - Communities, Civic Centre, Windmill Street, Gravesend DA12 1AU ☎ 01474 337324
✐ melanie.norris@gravesham.gov.uk

Finance: Mr Stuart Bobby, Director - Corporate Services, Civic Centre, Windmill Street, Gravesend DA12 1AU ☎ 01474 337431
✐ stuart.bobby@gravesham.gov.uk

Fleet Management: Mr Nick Brown, Director - Environment & Operations, Brookvale, Springhead Road, Northfleet DA11 8HW
☎ 01474 337319 ✐ nick.brown@gravesham.gov.uk

Grounds Maintenance: Mr Nick Brown, Director - Environment & Operations, Brookvale, Springhead Road, Northfleet DA11 8HW
☎ 01474 337319 ✐ nick.brown@gravesham.gov.uk

Health and Safety: Mrs Sarah Kilkie, Assistant Director - Communities, Civic Centre, Windmill Street, Gravesend DA12 1BQ
☎ 01474 337235 ✐ sarah.kilkie@gravesham.gov.uk

Housing: Mr Wale Adetoro, Assistant Director - Housing, Civic Centre, Windmill Street, Gravesend DA12 1AU ☎ 01474 337816
✐ wale.adetoro@gravesham.gov.uk

Housing Maintenance: Mr Wale Adetoro, Assistant Director - Housing, Civic Centre, Windmill Street, Gravesend DA12 1AU
☎ 01474 337816 ✐ wale.adetoro@gravesham.gov.uk

Legal: Mr Mike Hayley, Assistant Director - Governance & Law, Civic Centre, Windmill Street, Gravesend DA12 1AU
☎ 01474 337256 ✐ mike.hayley@gravesham.gov.uk

Leisure and Cultural Services: Mr Adrian Hickmott, Sport & Recreation Manager, Civic Centre, Windmill Street, Gravesend DA12 1AU ☎ 01474 337322 ✐ adrian.hickmott@gravesham.gov.uk

Licensing: Mrs Sarah Kilkie, Assistant Director - Communities, Civic Centre, Windmill Street, Gravesend DA12 1BQ
☎ 01474 337235 ✐ sarah.kilkie@gravesham.gov.uk

GRAVESHAM

Member Services: Mrs Sarah Kilkie, Assistant Director - Communities, Civic Centre, Windmill Street, Gravesend DA12 1BQ
☎ 01474 337235 ◌ sarah.kilkie@gravesham.gov.uk

Parking: Mr Daniel Killian, Service Manager - DSO, Civic Centre, Windmill Street, Gravesend DA12 1AU ☎ 01474 337820
◌ paul.gibbons@gravesham.gov.uk

Partnerships: Mr Stuart Bobby, Director - Corporate Services, Civic Centre, Windmill Street, Gravesend DA12 1AU
☎ 01474 337431 ◌ stuart.bobby@gravesham.gov.uk

Personnel / HR: Mrs Melanie Norris, Director - Communities, Civic Centre, Windmill Street, Gravesend DA12 1AU
☎ 01474 337324 ◌ melanie.norris@gravesham.gov.uk

Planning: Mr Kevin Burbidge, Director - Housing & Regeneration, Civic Centre, Windmill Street, Gravesend DA12 1BQ
☎ 01474 337585 ◌ kevin.burbidge@gravesham.gov.uk

Procurement: Mr Stuart Bobby, Director - Corporate Services, Civic Centre, Windmill Street, Gravesend DA12 1AU
☎ 01474 337431 ◌ stuart.bobby@gravesham.gov.uk

Recycling & Waste Minimisation: Mr Nick Brown, Director - Environment & Operations, Brookvale, Springhead Road, Northfleet DA11 8HW ☎ 01474 337319 ◌ nick.brown@gravesham.gov.uk

Regeneration: Mr Kevin Burbidge, Director - Housing & Regeneration, Civic Centre, Windmill Street, Gravesend DA12 1BQ
☎ 01474 337585 ◌ kevin.burbidge@gravesham.gov.uk

Staff Training: Mrs Melanie Norris, Director - Communities, Civic Centre, Windmill Street, Gravesend DA12 1AU ☎ 01474 337324
◌ melanie.norris@gravesham.gov.uk

Sustainable Communities: Mr David Hughes, Chief Executive, Civic Centre, Windmill Street, Gravesend DA12 1AU
☎ 01474 337380 ◌ david.hughes@gravesham.gov.uk

Sustainable Development: Mrs Sarah Kilkie, Assistant Director - Communities, Civic Centre, Windmill Street, Gravesend DA12 1BQ
☎ 01474 337235 ◌ sarah.kilkie@gravesham.gov.uk

Tourism: Mr Simon Hookway, Service Manager - Economic Development, Civic Centre, Windmill Street, Gravesend DA12 1BQ
☎ 01474 337238 ◌ simon.hookway@gravesham.gov.uk

Town Centre: Mr Simon Hookway, Service Manager - Economic Development, Civic Centre, Windmill Street, Gravesend DA12 1BQ
☎ 01474 337238 ◌ simon.hookway@gravesham.gov.uk

Traffic Management: Mr Rob Bright, Senior Engineer, Civic Centre, Windmill Street, Gravesend DA12 1AU ☎ 01474 337580
◌ rob.bright@gravesham.gov.uk

Transport Planner: Mr Tony Chadwick, Principal Planning Officer, Civic Centre, Windmill Street, Gravesend DA12 1AU
☎ 01474 337404 ◌ tony.chadwick@gravesham.gov.uk

Waste Collection and Disposal: Mr Nick Brown, Director - Environment & Operations, Brookvale, Springhead Road, Northfleet DA11 8HW ☎ 01474 337319 ◌ nick.brown@gravesham.gov.uk

Waste Management: Mr Nick Brown, Director - Environment & Operations, Brookvale, Springhead Road, Northfleet DA11 8HW
☎ 01474 337319 ◌ nick.brown@gravesham.gov.uk

COUNCILLORS

Mayor: Goatley, Greta (CON - Central)
greta.goatley@gravesham.gov.uk

Deputy Mayor: Craske, Harold (CON - Higham)
harold.craske@gravesham.gov.uk

Leader of the Council: Cubitt, John (CON - Meopham North)
john.cubitt@gravesham.gov.uk

Deputy Leader of the Council: Turner, David (CON - Istead Rise)
david.turner@gravesham.gov.uk

Group LeaderBurden, John (LAB - Northfleet South)
john.burden@gravesham.gov.uk

Ashenden, Valerie (LAB - Westcourt)
valerie.ashenden@gravesham.gov.uk

Bains, Gurjit (CON - Whitehill)
gurjit.bains@gravesham.gov.uk

Boycott, Lesley (CON - Meopham South & Vigo)
lesley.boycott@gravesham.gov.uk

Bungar, Gurdip Ram (LAB - Central)
gurdip.bungar@gravesham.gov.uk

Burgoyne, Julia (CON - Meopham North)
julia.burgoyne@gravesham.gov.uk

Caller, Colin (LAB - Westcourt)
colin.caller@gravesham.gov.uk

Caller, John (LAB - Westcourt)
john.caller@gravesham.gov.uk

Croxton, Lee (LAB - Riverside)
lee.croxton@gravesham.gov.uk

Francis, Brian (LAB - Singlewell)
brian.francis@gravesham.gov.uk

Garside, Sandra (CON - Painters Ash)
sandra.garside@gravesham.gov.uk

Halpin, Rob (LAB - Singlewell)
robert.halpin@gravesham.gov.uk

Hills, Leslie (CON - Chalk)
leslie.hills@gravesham.gov.uk

Howes, Les (LAB - Painters Ash)
les.howes@gravesham.gov.uk

Howes, Susan (LAB - Coldharbour)
susan.howes@gravesham.gov.uk

Hurdle, Karen (CON - Whitehill)
karen.hurdle@gravesham.gov.uk

Hurley, David (CON - Riverview)
david.hurley@gravesham.gov.uk

Jassal, Samir (CON - Shorne, Cobham & Luddesdown)
samir.jassal@gravesham.gov.uk

Knight, John (CON - Istead Riase)
John.knight@gravesham.gov.uk

Lambert, William (CON - Riverview)
william.lambert@gravesham.gov.uk

Langdale, Sara (CON - Woodlands)
sara.langdale@gravesham.gov.uk

Loughlin, John (LAB - Northfleet South)
john.loughlin@gravesham.gov.uk

McGarrity, Bronwen (CON - Coldharbour)
bronwen.mcgarrity@gravesham.gov.uk

Meade, Jordan (CON - Singlewell)
jordan.meade@gravesham.gov.uk

Milner, Lyn (LAB - Riverside)
lyn.milner@gravesham.gov.uk

Pearton, Leslie (CON - Higham)
leslie.pearton@graveshem.gov.uk

Pritchard, Anthony (CON - Woodlands)
anthony.pritchard@gravesham.gov.uk

Rayner, Peter (LAB - Northfleet North)
peter.rayner@gravesham.gov.uk

Ridgers, Alan (CON - Painters Ash)
alan.ridgers@gravesham.gov.uk

Rolles, Lenny (LAB - Riverside)
lenny.rolles@gravesham.gov.uk

Sangha, Brian (LAB - Pelham)
brian.sangha@gravesham.gov.uk

Scollard, Peter (LAB - Northfleet North)
peter.scollard@gravesham.gov.uk

Shelbrooke, Derek (CON - Meopham South & Vigo)
derek.shelbrooke@gravesham.gov.uk

Singh, Makhan (LAB - Pelham)
makhan.singh@gravesham.gov.uk

Singh-Thandi, Narinderjit (LAB - Northfleet South)
narinderjit.singh.thandi@gravesham.gov.uk

Sullivan, Lauren (LAB - Northfleet North)
lauren.sullivan@gravesham.gov.uk

Theobald, Robin (CON - Shorne, Cobham & Luddesdown)
robin.theobald@gravesham.gov.uk

Thomas, Steve (LAB - Central)
steve.thomas@gravesham.gov.uk

Wenban, Michael (CON - Woodlands)
michael.wenban@gravesham.gov.uk

POLITICAL COMPOSITION
CON: 23, LAB: 20

COMMITTEE CHAIRS

Audit & Finance: Mr Derek Shelbrooke

Licensing: Mr Harold Craske

Great Yarmouth   D

Great Yarmouth Borough Council, Town Hall, Hall Plain, Great Yarmouth NR30 2QF
☎ 01493 856100 ✆ enquiries@great-yarmouth.gov.uk
💻 www.great-yarmouth.gov.uk

FACTS AND FIGURES
Parliamentary Constituencies: Great Yarmouth
EU Constituencies: Eastern
Election Frequency: Elections are by thirds

PRINCIPAL OFFICERS

Chief Executive: Mrs Sheila Oxtoby, Chief Executive, Council Offices, Holt Road, Cromer NR27 9EN ☎ 01263 516000 ✆ sheila.oxtoby@north-norfolk.gov.uk

Senior Management: Mrs Jane Beck, Director - Customer Services, Town Hall, Hall Plain, Great Yarmouth NR30 2QF ☎ 01493 846418 ✆ jeb@great-yarmouth.gov.uk

Senior Management: Mr Robert Read, Director - Housing & Neighbourhoods, Greyfriars House, Greyfriars Way, Great Yarmouth NR30 2QE ☎ 01493 846278 ✆ rr@great-yarmouth.gov.uk

Senior Management: Miss Karen Sly, Director - Finance & S151 Officer, Council Offices, Holt Road, Cromer NR27 9EN ☎ 01263 516243 ✆ karen.sly@north-norfolk.gov.uk

Senior Management: Ms Kate Watts, Transformation Programme Manager, Town Hall, Hall Plain, Great Yarmouth NR30 2QF ☎ 01493 846547 ✆ kaw@great-yarmouth.gov.uk

Building Control: Mr Dean Minns, Group Manager - Planning, Town Hall, Hall Plain, Great Yarmouth NR30 2QF ☎ 01493 856100

PR / Communications: Mr Alan Carr, Group Manager - Tourism & Communications, Maritime House, 25 Marine Parade, Great Yarmouth NR30 2EN ☎ 01493 846341 ✆ aac@great-yarmouth.gov.uk

Community Planning: Mr Robert Gregory, Group Manager - Neighbourhoods & Communities, Town Hall, Hall Plain, Great Yarmouth NR30 2QF

Computer Management: Mrs Miranda Lee, Group Manager - Customer Services, Town Hall, Hall Plain, Great Yarmouth NR30 2QF ☎ 01493 846536 ✆ mvl@great-yarmouth.gov.uk

Customer Service: Mrs Miranda Lee, Group Manager - Customer Services, Town Hall, Hall Plain, Great Yarmouth NR30 2QF ☎ 01493 846536 ✆ mvl@great-yarmouth.gov.uk

Economic Development: Mr David Glason, Group Manager - Growth, Town Hall, Hall Plain, Great Yarmouth NR30 2QF ✆ dcg@great-yarmouth.gov.uk

Electoral Registration: Ms Denise Harvey, Acting Group Manager - Licensing & Elections, Town Hall, Hall Plain, Great Yarmouth NR30 2QF ☎ 01493 846100 ✆ dgh@great-yarmouth.gov.uk

Environmental Health: Mr Glenn Buck, Group Manager - Environmental Services, Town Hall, Hall Plain, Great Yarmouth NR30 2QF ☎ 01493 856100 ✆ gb@great-yarmouth.gov.uk

Estates, Property & Valuation: Mr Andy Dyson, Group Manager - Property & Construction, Town Hall, Hall Plain, Great Yarmouth NR30 2QF ☎ 01493 846440

GREAT YARMOUTH

Finance: Mr Andy Radford, Finance Officer, Town Hall, Hall Plain, Great Yarmouth NR30 2QF ☎ 01493 846132 ✆ aradford@great-yarmouth.gov.uk

Finance: Ms Donna Summers, Group Manager - Resources, Town Hall, Hall Plain, Great Yarmouth NR30 2QF ☎ 01493 846339 ✆ dsummers@great-yarmouth.gov.uk

Housing: Mr Robert Read, Director - Housing & Neighbourhoods, Greyfriars House, Greyfriars Way, Great Yarmouth NR30 2QE ☎ 01493 846278 ✆ rr@great-yarmouth.gov.uk

Licensing: Ms Denise Harvey, Acting Group Manager - Licensing & Elections, Town Hall, Hall Plain, Great Yarmouth NR30 2QF ☎ 01493 846100 ✆ dgh@great-yarmouth.gov.uk

Member Services: Mr Robin Hodds, Cabinet Secretary - Governance, Town Hall, Hall Plain, Great Yarmouth NR30 2QF ☎ 01493 856100 ✆ rh@great-yarmouth.gov.uk

Parking: Mrs Miranda Lee, Group Manager - Customer Services, Town Hall, Hall Plain, Great Yarmouth NR30 2QF ☎ 01493 846536 ✆ mvl@great-yarmouth.gov.uk

Personnel / HR: Ms Kate Watts, Transformation Programme Manager, Town Hall, Hall Plain, Great Yarmouth NR30 2QF ☎ 01493 846547 ✆ kaw@great-yarmouth.gov.uk

Planning: Mr Dean Minns, Group Manager - Planning, Town Hall, Hall Plain, Great Yarmouth NR30 2QF ☎ 01493 856100

Staff Training: Ms Kate Watts, Transformation Programme Manager, Town Hall, Hall Plain, Great Yarmouth NR30 2QF ☎ 01493 846547 ✆ kaw@great-yarmouth.gov.uk

Street Scene: Mr Jonathan Newman, Town Centre Manager, Unit 5, Wilkinsons Yard, Marketgates, Great Yarmouth NR30 2AX ☎ 01493 745828

Tourism: Mr Alan Carr, Group Manager - Tourism & Communications, Maritime House, 25 Marine Parade, Great Yarmouth NR30 2EN ☎ 01493 846341 ✆ aac@great-yarmouth.gov.uk

Town Centre: Mr Jonathan Newman, Town Centre Manager, Unit 5, Wilkinsons Yard, Marketgates, Great Yarmouth NR30 2AX ☎ 01493 745828

Transport Planner: Mr Jonathan Newman, Town Centre Manager, Unit 5, Wilkinsons Yard, Marketgates, Great Yarmouth NR30 2AX ☎ 01493 745828

COUNCILLORS

Leader of the Council: Plant, Graham (CON - Bradwell North)
cllr.graham.plant@great-yarmouth.gov.uk

Deputy Leader of the Council: Coleman, Barry (CON - West Flegg)
cllr.barry.coleman@great-yarmouth.gov.uk

Andrews, Tom (UKIP - Caister South)
cllr.tom.andrews@great-yarmouth.gov.uk

Annison, Carl (UKIP - Bradwell South & Hopton)
cllr.carl.annison@great-yarmouth.gov.uk

Bensly, James (CON - East Flegg)
cllr.james.bensly@great-yarmouth.gov.uk

Bird, Malcolm (UKIP - Central & Northgate)
cllr.malcolm.bird@great-yarmouth.gov.uk

Borg, Carol (LAB - Claydon)
cllr.carol.borg@great-yarmouth.gov.uk

Carpenter, Penny (CON - Caister North)
cllr.penny.carpenter@great-yarmouth.gov.uk

Coleman, Mary (CON - West Flegg)
cllr.mary.coleman@great-yarmouth.gov.uk

Connell, Robert (IND - Southtown & Cobholm)
cllr.robert.connell@great-yarmouth.gov.uk

Cutting, Jack (UKIP - Caister North)
cllr.jack.cutting@great-yarmouth.gov.uk

Davis, Lea (LAB - Central & Northgate)
cllr.lea.davis@great-yarmouth.gov.uk

Fairhead, Marlene (LAB - St Andrews)
cllr.marlene.fairhead@great-yarmouth.gov.uk

Flaxman-Taylor, Emma (CON - Gorleston)
cllr.emma.flaxman-taylor@great-yarmouth.gov.uk

Grant, Andy (CON - Bradwell South & Hopton)
cllr.andy.grant@great-yartmouth.gov.uk

Grey, Kay (UKIP - Gorleston)
cllr.kay.grey@great-yarmouth.gov.uk

Grey, Alan (UKIP - Bradwell North)
cllr.alan.gray@great-yarmouth.gov.uk

Hacon, Sue (UKIP - Bradwell South & Hopton)
cllr.sue.hacon@great-yarmouth.gov.uk

Hammond, Paul (UKIP - Yarmouth North)
cllr.paul.hammond@great-yarmouth.gov.uk

Hanton, Ronald (CON - Ormesby)
cllr.ronald.hanton@great-yarmouth.gov.uk

Jeal, Michael (LAB - Nelson)
cllr.michael.jeal@great-yarmouth.gov.uk

Jones, Rachel (UKIP - Yarmouth North)
cllr.rachel.jones@great-yarmouth.gov.uk

Lawn, Brian (CON - Lothingland)
cllr.brian.lawn@great-yarmouth.gov.uk

Mavroudis, Demetris (CON - Caister South)
cllr.demetris.mavroudis@great-yarmouth.gov.uk

Myers, Adrian (UKIP - Lothingland)
cllr.adrian.myers@great-yarmouth.gov.uk

Pratt, Sylvia (LAB - Magdalen)
cllr.sylvia.pratt@great-yarmouth.gov.uk

Reynolds, Charles (CON - Ormesby)
cllr.charles.reynolds@great-yarmouth.gov.uk

Robinson-Payne, Kerry (LAB - Nelson)
cllr.kelly.payne@great-yarmouth.gov.uk

Rodwell, Tabitha (UKIP - Claydon)
cllr.tabitha.rodwell@great-yarmouth.gov.uk

Smith, Carl (CON - Bradwell North)
cllr.carl.smith@great-yarmouth.gov.uk

Stenhouse, Katy (UKIP - Nelson)
cllr.katy.stenhouse@great-yarmouth.gov.uk

Thirtle, Haydn (CON - Fleggburgh)
cllr.haydn.thirtle@great-yarmouth.gov.uk

Wainwright, Trevor (LAB - Magdalen)
cllr.trevor.wainwright@great-yarmouth.gov.uk

Walch, Chris (UKIP - Central & Northgate)
cllr.chris.walch@great-yarmouth.gov.uk

Walker, Brian (LAB - Magdalen)
cllr.brian.walker@great-yarmouth.gov.uk

Waters-Bunn, Paula (LAB - Southtown & Cobholm)
cllr.paula.waters-bunn@great-yarmouth.gov.uk

Weymouth, Shirley (CON - East Flegg)
cllr.shirley.weymouth@great-yarmouth.gov.uk

Williamson, Bernard (LAB - Claydon)
cllr.bernard.williamson@great-yarmouth.gov.uk

Wright, Barbara (LAB - St Andrews)
cllr.barbara.wright@great-yarmouth.gov.uk

POLITICAL COMPOSITION
CON: 14, UKIP: 13, LAB: 11, IND: 1

Greenwich   L

Greenwich London Borough Council, The Woolwich Centre, 35 Wellington Street, Woolwich, London SE18 6HQ
☎ 020 8854 8888 🖷 020 8921 5074 🖳 www.greenwich.gov.uk

FACTS AND FIGURES
Parliamentary Constituencies: Eltham, Erith and Thamesmead, Greenwich and Woolwich
EU Constituencies: London
Election Frequency: Elections are of whole council

PRINCIPAL OFFICERS

Chief Executive: Mr John Comber, Chief Executive, Town Hall, Wellington Street, Woolwich, London SE18 6PW ☎ 020 8921 5000
🖰 chief.executives@royalgreenwich.gov.uk

Senior Management: Ms Katrina Delaney, Director - Central Services, The Woolwich Centre, 35 Wellington Street, Woolwich, London SE18 6HQ ☎ 020 8921 6101
🖰 katrina.delaney@greenwich.gov.uk

Senior Management: Ms Pippa Hack, Director - Regeneration Enterprise & Skills, The Woolwich Centre, 35 Wellington Street, Woolwich, London SE18 6HQ ☎ 020 8921 5519
🖰 pippa.hack@royalgreenwich.gov.uk

Senior Management: Ms Florence Kroll, Director - Children's Services, The Woolwich Centre, 35 Wellington Street, Woolwich, London SE18 6HQ 🖰 florence.kroll@royalgreenwich.gov.uk

Senior Management: Mr Matthew Norwell, Director - Community Safety & Environment, The Woolwich Centre, 35 Wellington Street, Woolwich, London SE18 6HQ ☎ 020 8921 8291
🖰 matthew.norwell@royalgreenwich.gov.uk

Senior Management: Mr Simon Pearce, Director - Health & Adult Social Care, The Woolwich Centre, 35 Wellington Street, Woolwich, London SE18 6HQ ☎ 020 8921 3000
🖰 simon.pearce@royalgreenwich.gov.uk

Senior Management: Ms Debbie Warren, Director - Finance, The Woolwich Centre, 35 Wellington Street, Woolwich, London SE18 6HQ ☎ 020 8921 5201 🖰 debbie.warren@royalgreenwich.gov.uk

Senior Management: Mr Steve Whiteman, Director - Public Health, The Woolwich Centre, 35 Wellington Street, Woolwich, London SE18 6HQ ☎ 020 8921 5514
🖰 steve.whiteman@royalgreenwich.gov.uk

Building Control: Mr Chris Stevens, Head - Building Control, The Woolwich Centre, 35 Wellington Street, Woolwich, London SE18 6HQ ☎ 020 8921 5414 🖰 chris.stevens@royalgreenwich.gov.uk

Children / Youth Services: Ms Jenny Kavanagh, IYSS Manager - Health & Integrated Support, The Woolwich Centre, 35 Wellington Street, Woolwich, London SE18 6HQ ☎ 020 8921 8249
🖰 jenny.kavanagh@royalgreenwich.gov.uk

PR / Communications: Ms Katrina Delaney, Director - Culture, Sport & Media, The Woolwich Centre, 35 Wellington Street, Woolwich, London SE18 6HQ ☎ 020 8921 6101
🖰 katrina.delaney@royalgreenwich.gov.uk

Community Planning: Mr Mike Hows, Assistant Director - Planning, The Woolwich Centre, 35 Wellington Street, Woolwich, London SE18 6HQ ☎ 020 8921 5363
🖰 mike.hows@royalgreenwich.gov.uk

Community Safety: Mr Matthew Norwell, Director - Community Safety & Environment, The Woolwich Centre, 35 Wellington Street, Woolwich, London SE18 6HQ ☎ 020 8921 8291
🖰 matthew.norwell@royalgreenwich.gov.uk

Computer Management: Mr Kevin Gibbs, Assistant Director - Customer Contact, The Woolwich Centre, 35 Wellington Street, Woolwich, London SE18 6HQ ☎ 020 8921 5244
🖰 kevin.gibbs@royalgreenwich.gov.uk

Consumer Protection and Trading Standards: Mr Ray Seabrook, Assistant Director - Community Safety, The Woolwich Centre, 35 Wellington Street, Woolwich, London SE18 6HQ
☎ 020 8921 3131 🖰 ray.seabrook@royalgreenwich.gov.uk

Contracts: Mr Ian Tasker, Head - Financial Operations, The Woolwich Centre, 35 Wellington Street, Woolwich, London SE18 6HQ ☎ 020 8921 6189 🖰 ian.tasker@royalgreenwich.gov.uk

Customer Service: Mr Kevin Gibbs, Assistant Director - Customer Contact, The Woolwich Centre, 35 Wellington Street, Woolwich, London SE18 6HQ ☎ 020 8921 5244
🖰 kevin.gibbs@royalgreenwich.gov.uk

Economic Development: Ms Michelle Rankin, Head - Employment & Skills, The Woolwich Centre, 35 Wellington Street, Woolwich, London SE18 6HQ ☎ 020 8921 3906
🖰 michelle.rankin@royalgreenwich.gov.uk

Education: Ms Florence Kroll, Director - Children's Services, The Woolwich Centre, 35 Wellington Street, Woolwich, London SE18 6HQ 🖰 florence.kroll@royalgreenwich.gov.uk

GREENWICH

E-Government: Mr Kevin Gibbs, Assistant Director - Customer Contact, The Woolwich Centre, 35 Wellington Street, Woolwich, London SE18 6HQ ☎ 020 8921 5244
🖰 kevin.gibbs@royalgreenwich.gov.uk

Electoral Registration: Mr James Pack, Electoral Support Manager, The Woolwich Centre, 35 Wellington Street, Woolwich, London SE18 6HQ ☎ 020 8921 6658
🖰 james.pack@royalgreenwich.gov.uk

Emergency Planning: Mr Ian Cheshire, Head - Emergency Planning & Business Continuity, The Woolwich Centre, 35 Wellington Street, Woolwich, London SE18 6HQ ☎ 020 8921 5868
🖰 ian.cheshire@royalgreenwich.gov.uk

Energy Management: Ms Pippa Hack, Director - Regeneration Enterprise & Skills, The Woolwich Centre, 35 Wellington Street, Woolwich, London SE18 6HQ ☎ 020 8921 5519
🖰 pippa.hack@royalgreenwich.gov.uk

Environmental Health: Mr Ray Seabrook, Assistant Director - Community Safety, The Woolwich Centre, 35 Wellington Street, Woolwich, London SE18 6HQ ☎ 020 8921 3131
🖰 ray.seabrook@royalgreenwich.gov.uk

Estates, Property & Valuation: Ms Pippa Hack, Director - Regeneration Enterprise & Skills, The Woolwich Centre, 35 Wellington Street, Woolwich, London SE18 6HQ ☎ 020 8921 5519
🖰 pippa.hack@royalgreenwich.gov.uk

Events Manager: Mr Bob Hills, Principal Communications Officer, The Woolwich Centre, 35 Wellington Street, Woolwich, London SE18 6HQ ☎ 020 8921 5077 🖰 bob.hills@royalgreenwich.gov.uk

Finance: Ms Debbie Warren, Director - Finance, The Woolwich Centre, 35 Wellington Street, Woolwich, London SE18 6HQ ☎ 020 8921 5201 🖰 debbie.warren@royalgreenwich.gov.uk

Treasury: Ms Debbie Warren, Director - Finance, The Woolwich Centre, 35 Wellington Street, Woolwich, London SE18 6HQ ☎ 020 8921 5201 🖰 debbie.warren@royalgreenwich.gov.uk

Pensions: Ms Kelly Scotford, Pensions & Operations Manager, The Woolwich Centre, 35 Wellington Street, Woolwich, London SE18 6HQ ☎ 020 8921 6949
🖰 kelly.scotford@royalgreenwich.gov.uk

Grounds Maintenance: Ms Dawn Squires, Head of Parks & Open Spaces, The Woolwich Centre, 35 Wellington Street, Woolwich, London SE18 6HQ ☎ 020 8921 4133
🖰 dawn.squires@royalgreenwich.gov.uk

Health and Safety: Mr Al Parry, Manager - Health, Safety & Wellbeing, The Woolwich Centre, 35 Wellington Street, Woolwich, London SE18 6HQ ☎ 020 8921 5196
🖰 al.parry@royalgreenwich.gov.uk

Highways: Mr Tim Jackson, Assistant Director - Strategic Transportation, The Woolwich Centre, 35 Wellington Street, Woolwich, London SE18 6HQ ☎ 020 8921 5453
🖰 tim.jackson@royalgreenwich.gov.uk

Home Energy Conservation: Ms Pippa Hack, Director - Regeneration Enterprise & Skills, The Woolwich Centre, 35 Wellington Street, Woolwich, London SE18 6HQ ☎ 020 8921 5519
🖰 pippa.hack@royalgreenwich.gov.uk

Housing: Mr Matthew Norwell, Director - Community Safety & Environment, The Woolwich Centre, 35 Wellington Street, Woolwich, London SE18 6HQ ☎ 020 8921 8291
🖰 matthew.norwell@royalgreenwich.gov.uk

Housing Maintenance: Mr Tim Derrik, Project Manager - Technical Services, The Woolwich Centre, 35 Wellington Street, Woolwich, London SE18 6HQ ☎ 020 8921 4275
🖰 tim.derrik@royalgreenwich.gov.uk

Legal: Mr John Scarborough, Head of Legal Services, The Woolwich Centre, 35 Wellington Street, Woolwich, London SE18 6HQ 🖰 john.swale@royalgreenwich.gov.uk

Leisure and Cultural Services: Ms Katrina Delaney, Director - Culture, Sport & Media, The Woolwich Centre, 35 Wellington Street, Woolwich, London SE18 6HQ ☎ 020 8921 6101
🖰 katrina.delaney@royalgreenwich.gov.uk

Licensing: Mr Des Campbell, Manager - Trading Standards & Licensing, The Woolwich Centre, 35 Wellington Street, Woolwich, London SE18 6HQ ☎ 020 8921 8137
🖰 des.campbell@royalgreenwich.gov.uk

Member Services: Ms Katrina Delaney, Director - Culture, Sport & Media, The Woolwich Centre, 35 Wellington Street, Woolwich, London SE18 6HQ ☎ 020 8921 6101
🖰 katrina.delaney@royalgreenwich.gov.uk

Parking: Mr Ollie Miller, Acting Head of Parking Services, The Woolwich Centre, 35 Wellington Street, Woolwich, London SE18 6HQ ☎ 020 8921 5877 🖰 ollie.miller@royalgreenwich.gov.uk

Partnerships: Ms Katrina Delaney, Director - Culture, Sport & Media, The Woolwich Centre, 35 Wellington Street, Woolwich, London SE18 6HQ ☎ 020 8921 6101
🖰 katrina.delaney@royalgreenwich.gov.uk

Planning: Mr Mike Hows, Assistant Director - Planning, The Woolwich Centre, 35 Wellington Street, Woolwich, London SE18 6HQ ☎ 020 8921 5363 🖰 mike.hows@royalgreenwich.gov.uk

Procurement: Mr Ian Tasker, Head - Financial Operations, The Woolwich Centre, 35 Wellington Street, Woolwich, London SE18 6HQ ☎ 020 8921 6189 🖰 ian.tasker@royalgreenwich.gov.uk

Public Libraries: Mr Gareth Edmunson, Head of Sport & Commissioning, The Woolwich Centre, 35 Wellington Street, Woolwich, London SE18 6HQ ☎ 020 8921 8006
🖰 gareth.edmunson@royalgreenwich.gov.uk

Recycling & Waste Minimisation: Mr Peter Dalley, Waste Services Operations Manager, The Woolwich Centre, 35 Wellington Street, Woolwich, London SE18 6HQ ☎ 020 8921 4641
🖰 peter.dalley@royalgreenwich.gov.uk

Regeneration: Mr John Comber, Chief Executive, The Woolwich Centre, 35 Wellington Street, Woolwich, London SE18 6HQ
☎ 020 8921 5000 ✆ chief.executives@royalgreenwich.gov.uk

Road Safety: Ms Raj Shukla, Road Safety Manager, The Woolwich Centre, 35 Wellington Street, Woolwich, London SE18 6HQ
☎ 020 8921 8082 ✆ raj.shukla@royalgreenwich.gov.uk

Social Services (Adult): Mr Simon Pearce, Director - Health & Adult Social Care, The Woolwich Centre, 35 Wellington Street, Woolwich, London SE18 6HQ ☎ 020 8921 3000
✆ simon.pearce@royalgreenwich.gov.uk

Social Services (Children): Ms Florence Kroll, Director - Children's Services, The Woolwich Centre, 35 Wellington Street, Woolwich, London SE18 6HQ
✆ florence.kroll@royalgreenwich.gov.uk

Public Health: Mr Steve Whiteman, Director - Public Health, The Woolwich Centre, 35 Wellington Street, Woolwich, London SE18 6HQ ☎ 020 8921 5514 ✆ steve.whiteman@royalgreenwich.gov.uk

Staff Training: Ms Lee Lucas, Learning & Development Officer, The Woolwich Centre, 35 Wellington Street, Woolwich, London SE18 6HQ ☎ 020 8921 4981 ✆ lee.lucas@royalgreenwich.gov.uk

Sustainable Communities: Ms Pippa Hack, Director - Regeneration Enterprise & Skills, The Woolwich Centre, 35 Wellington Street, Woolwich, London SE18 6HQ ☎ 020 8921 5519 ✆ pippa.hack@royalgreenwich.gov.uk

Sustainable Development: Ms Pippa Hack, Director - Regeneration Enterprise & Skills, The Woolwich Centre, 35 Wellington Street, Woolwich, London SE18 6HQ ☎ 020 8921 5519 ✆ pippa.hack@royalgreenwich.gov.uk

Tourism: Ms Katrina Delaney, Director - Culture, Sport & Media, The Woolwich Centre, 35 Wellington Street, Woolwich, London SE18 6HQ ☎ 020 8921 6101 ✆ katrina.delaney@royalgreenwich.gov.uk

Town Centre: Ms Pippa Hack, Director - Regeneration Enterprise & Skills, The Woolwich Centre, 35 Wellington Street, Woolwich, London SE18 6HQ ☎ 020 8921 5519
✆ pippa.hack@royalgreenwich.gov.uk

Traffic Management: Mr Tim Jackson, Assistant Director - Strategic Transportation, The Woolwich Centre, 35 Wellington Street, Woolwich, London SE18 6HQ ☎ 020 8921 5453
✆ tim.jackson@royalgreenwich.gov.uk

Transport Planner: Mr Tim Jackson, Assistant Director - Strategic Transportation, The Woolwich Centre, 35 Wellington Street, Woolwich, London SE18 6HQ ☎ 020 8921 5453
✆ tim.jackson@royalgreenwich.gov.uk

Waste Collection and Disposal: Mr Peter Dalley, Waste Services Operations Manager, The Woolwich Centre, 35 Wellington Street, Woolwich, London SE18 6HQ ☎ 020 8921 4641
✆ peter.dalley@royalgreenwich.gov.uk

Waste Management: Mr Peter Dalley, Waste Services Operations Manager, The Woolwich Centre, 35 Wellington Street, Woolwich, London SE18 6HQ ☎ 020 8921 4641
✆ peter.dalley@royalgreenwich.gov.uk

Children's Play Areas: Ms Dawn Squires, Head of Parks & Open Spaces, The Woolwich Centre, 35 Wellington Street, Woolwich, London SE18 6HQ ☎ 020 8921 4133
✆ dawn.squires@royalgreenwich.gov.uk

COUNCILLORS

Mayor: Babatola, Olu (LAB - Thamesmead Moorings)
olu.babatola@royalgreenwich.gov.uk

Leader of the Council: Hyland, Denise (LAB - Abbey Wood)
denise.hyland@royalgreenwich.gov.uk

Deputy Leader of the Council: Thorpe, Danny (LAB - Shooters Hill)
danny.thorpe@royalgreenwich.gov.uk

Group LeaderHartley, Matt (CON - Coldharbour & New Eltham)
matt.hartley@royalgreenwich.gov.uk

Adams, Norman (LAB - Kidbrooke & Hornfair)
norman.adams@royalgreenwich.gov.uk

Ashikodi, Tonia (LAB - Glyndon)
tonia.ashikodi@royalgreenwich.gov.uk

Austen, Don (LAB - Glyndon)
don.austen@royalgreenwich.gov.uk

Barwick, Barbara (LAB - Woolwich Riverside)
barbara.barwick@royalgreenwich.gov.uk

Bird, Linda (LAB - Eltham North)
linda.bird@royalgreenwich.gov.uk

Brain, Stephen (LAB - Peninsula)
stephen.brain@royalgreenwich.gov.uk

Brighty, Geoffrey (CON - Blackheath Westcombe)
geoffrey.brighty@royalgreenwich.gov.uk

Brinkhurst, Mandy (CON - Coldharbour & New Eltham)
mandy.brinkhurst@royalgreenwich.gov.uk

Brooks, Peter (LAB - Thamesmead Moorings)
peter.brooks@royalgreenwich.gov.uk

Clare, Matt (CON - Eltham South)
matt.clare@royalgreenwich.gov.uk

Cornforth, Angela (LAB - Plumstead)
angela.cornforth@royalgreenwich.gov.uk

Davies, Wynn (LAB - Eltham North)
wynn.davies@royalgreenwich.gov.uk

Drury, Spencer (CON - Eltham North)
spencer.drury@royalgreenwich.gov.uk

Elliott, Mark (CON - Eltham South)
mark.elliott@royalgreenwich.gov.uk

Fahy, John (LAB - Woolwich Riverside)
john.fahy@royalgreenwich.gov.uk

Freeman, Bill (LAB - Eltham West)
bill.freeman@royalgreenwich.gov.uk

Gardner, David (LAB - Woolwich Common)
david.gardner@royalgreenwich.gov.uk

Geary, Nuala (CON - Eltham South)
nuala.geary@royalgreenwich.gov.uk

GREENWICH

Grice, Christine (LAB - Kidbrooke with Hornfair)
christine.grice@royalgreenwich.gov.uk

Hayes, Mick (LAB - Eltham West)
mick.hayes@royalgreenwich.gov.uk

Hills, John (CON - Coldharbour & New Eltham)
john.hills@royalgreenwich.gov.uk

Hisbani, Ambreen (LAB - Woolwich Common)
ambreen.hisbani@royalgreenwich.gov.uk

James, Swize (LAB - Thamesmead Moorings)
swize.james@royalgreenwich.gov.uk

James, Mark (LAB - Middle Park & Sutcliffe)
mark.james@royalgreenwich.gov.uk

James, Rajinder (LAB - Plumstead)
rajinder.sehmar@royalgreenwich.gov.uk

Khan, Mehboob (LAB - Greenwich West)
mehboob.khan@royalgreenwich.gov.uk

Kirby, Chris (LAB - Shooters Hill)
chris.kirby@royalgreenwich.gov.uk

Lekau, Averil (LAB - Thameshead Moorings)
averil.lekau@royalgreenwich.gov.uk

Lloyd, Chris (LAB - Peninsula)
chris.lloyd@royalgreenwich.gov.uk

MacCarthy, Allan (LAB - Charlton)
allan.maccarthy@royalgreenwich.gov.uk

Mardner, Clive (LAB - Abbey Wood)
clive.mardner@royalgreenwich.gov.uk

May, Christine (LAB - Middle Park & Sutcliffe)
christine.may@royalgreenwich.gov.uk

Merrill, Sarah (LAB - Shooters Hill)
sarah.merrill@royalgreenwich.gov.uk

Morris, Clare (LAB - Middle Park & Sutcliffe)
clare.morris@royalgreenwich.gov.uk

Morrisey, Paul (LAB - Blackheat Westcombe)
paul.morrissey@royalgreenwich.gov.uk

Morrow, Matthew (LAB - Plumstead)
matthew.morrow@royalgreenwich.gov.uk

Offord, Steve (LAB - Abbey Wood)
steve.offord@royalgreenwich.gov.uk

O'Mara, Maureen (LAB - Greenwich West)
maureen.omara@royalgreenwich.gov.uk

Parker, Cherry (LAB - Blackheath Westcombe)
cherry.parker@royalgreenwich.gov.uk

Parker, Gary (LAB - Charlton)
gary.parker@royalgreenwich.gov.uk

Scott-McDonald, Denise (LAB - Peninsula)
denise.scott-mcdonald@royalgreenwich.gov.uk

Singh, Harry (LAB - Woolwich Common)
harpinder.singh@royalgreenwich.gov.uk

Smith, Jackie (LAB - Thamesmead Moorings)
jackie.smith@royalgreenwich.gov.uk

Smith, Aidan (LAB - Greenwich West)
aidan.smith@royalgreenwich.gov.uk

Stanley, David (LAB - Kidbrooke with Hornfair)
david.stanley@royalgreenwich.gov.uk

Walker, Ray (LAB - Eltham West)
ray.walker@royalgreenwich.gov.uk

Williams, Miranda (LAB - Charlton)
miranda.williams@royalgreenwich.gov.uk

POLITICAL COMPOSITION
LAB: 43, CON: 8

COMMITTEE CHAIRS

Audit: Mr David Stanley

Community Safety & Environment: Mr Gary Parker

Health & Wellbeing: Ms Denise Hyland

Licensing: Ms Jackie Smith

Pensions: Mr Don Austen

Planning: Mr Mark James

Sustainable Communities & Transport: Ms Christine May

Guildford   D

Guildford Borough Council, Millmead House, Millmead,
Guildford GU2 4BB
☎ 01483 505050 ▤ 01483 444444 ✆ customerservices@guildford.gov.uk
▢ www.guildford.gov.uk

FACTS AND FIGURES
Parliamentary Constituencies: Guildford
EU Constituencies: South East
Election Frequency: Elections are of whole council

PRINCIPAL OFFICERS

Chief Executive: Ms Sue Sturgeon, Managing Director, Millmead
House, Millmead, Guildford GU2 4BB ☎ 01483 505050
✆ sue.sturgeon@guildford.gov.uk

Deputy Chief Executive: Mr Satish Mistry, Director - Corporate
Services, Millmead House, Millmead, Guildford GU2 4BB
☎ 01483 505050 ✆ satish.mistry@guildford.gov.uk

Senior Management: Mr Satish Mistry, Director - Corporate
Services, Millmead House, Millmead, Guildford GU2 4BB
☎ 01483 505050 ✆ satish.mistry@guildford.gov.uk

Senior Management: Mr Philip O'Dwyer, Director - Community
Services, Millmead House, Millmead, Guildford GU2 4BB
☎ 01483 444318

Senior Management: Mr Steve White, Director - Resources,
Millmead House, Millmead, Guildford GU2 4BB ☎ 01483 444920

Senior Management: Mr James Whiteman, Director -
Environment, Cleansing Department, Woking Road Depot, Woking
Road, Guildford GU1 1QE ☎ 01483 445030
✆ james.whiteman@guildford.gov.uk

Architect, Building / Property Services: Ms Marieke van der
Reijden, Asset Development Manager, Guildford Borough Council,
Millmead House, Millmead, Guildford GU2 4BB ☎ 01483 444995

Building Control: Ms Jacqui Barr, Building Control Manager, Millmead House, Millmead, Guildford GU2 4BB ☎ 01483 444680

Community Safety: Mr John Martin, Head of Health & Community Care Services, Millmead House, Millmead, Guildford GU2 4BB ☎ 01483 444350

Computer Management: Mr Adrian Hudson, Head of Business Systems, Millmead House, Millmead, Guildford GU2 4BB ☎ 01483 444900 ✆ adrian.hudson@guildford.gov.uk

Direct Labour: Mr James Whiteman, Director - Environment, Cleansing Department, Woking Road Depot, Woking Road, Guildford GU1 1QE ☎ 01483 445030 ✆ james.whiteman@guildford.gov.uk

E-Government: Ms Claire Morris, Head of Financial Services, Millmead House, Millmead, Guildford GU2 4BB ☎ 01483 44827

Energy Management: Mr Kevin Handley, Facilities Manager, Millmead House, Millmead, Guildford GU2 5BB ☎ 01483 444447 ✆ kevin.handley@guildford.gov.uk

Environmental Health: Mr Chris Woodhatch, Principal Environmental Health Officer, Millmead House, Millmead, Guildford GU2 4BB ☎ 01483 444370; 01483 444370

Facilities: Mr Kevin Handley, Facilities Manager, Millmead House, Millmead, Guildford GU2 5BB ☎ 01483 444447 ✆ kevin.handley@guildford.gov.uk

Finance: Mr Steve White, Director - Resources, Millmead House, Millmead, Guildford GU2 4BB ☎ 01483 444920

Fleet Management: Mr Paul Wells, Waste & Fleet Operations Manager, Woking Road Depot, Woking Road, Guildford GU1 1QE ☎ 01483 445011

Health and Safety: Mr Paul Osborn, Occupational Health & Safety Officer, Millmead House, Millmead, Guildford GU2 4BB ☎ 01483 444025

Housing: Ms Kim Rippett, Head of Housing Advice, Millmead House, Millmead, Guildford GU2 4BB ☎ 01483 444240 ✆ kim.rippett@guildford.gov.uk

Housing Maintenance: Mr Philip O'Dwyer, Director - Community Services, Millmead House, Millmead, Guildford GU2 4BB ☎ 01483 444318

Legal: Ms Glynis Mancini, Principal Solicitor, Millmead House, Millmead, Guildford GU2 4BB ☎ 01483 444060

Licensing: Mr David Curtis-Botting, Licensing Services Manager, Millmead House, Millmead, Guildford GU2 4BB ☎ 01483 444387

Planning: Mr Barry Fagg, Head of Planning Services, Millmead House, Millmead, Guildford GU2 4BB ☎ 01483 444620

Procurement: Mr Simon Gregory, Procurement Officer, Millmead House, Millmead, Guildford GU2 4BB ☎ 01483 444421

Recycling & Waste Minimisation: Mr James Whiteman, Director - Environment, Cleansing Department, Woking Road Depot, Woking Road, Guildford GU1 1QE ☎ 01483 445030 ✆ james.whiteman@guildford.gov.uk

Social Services: Mr John Martin, Head of Health & Community Care Services, Millmead House, Millmead, Guildford GU2 4BB ☎ 01483 444350

Staff Training: Ms Hannah Cornick, Training Officer, Millmead House, Millmead, Guildford GU2 4BB ☎ 01483 505050

Transport: Mr Tim Pilsbury, Transportation Projects Manager, Millmead House, Millmead, Guildford GU2 4BB ☎ 01483 444521

Waste Collection and Disposal: Mr James Whiteman, Director - Environment, Cleansing Department, Woking Road Depot, Woking Road, Guildford GU1 1QE ☎ 01483 445030 ✆ james.whiteman@guildford.gov.uk

Waste Management: Mr James Whiteman, Director - Environment, Cleansing Department, Woking Road Depot, Woking Road, Guildford GU1 1QE ☎ 01483 445030 ✆ james.whiteman@guildford.gov.uk

COUNCILLORS

Mayor: Jackson, Gordon (CON - Pirbright) gordon.jackson@guildford.gov.uk

Deputy Mayor: Manning, Nigel (CON - Ash Vale) Nigel.Manning@guildford.gov.uk

Leader of the Council: Spooner, Paul (CON - Ash South & Tongham) paul.spooner@guildford.gov.uk

Deputy Leader of the Council: Furniss, Matt (CON - Christchurch) matt.furniss@guildford.gov.uk

Group LeaderReeves, Caroline (LD - Friary & St Nicolas) Caroline.Reeves@guildford.gov.uk

Bilbe, David (CON - Normandy) david.bilbe@guildford.gov.uk

Billington, Richard (CON - Tillingbourne) richard.billington@guildford.gov.uk

Brooker, Philip (CON - Merrow) philip.brooker@guildford.gov.uk

Chandler, Adrian (CON - Onslow) adrian.chandler@guildford.gov.uk

Chesterfield, Alexandra (CON - Friary & St Nicolas) alexanddra.chesterfield@guildford.gov.uk

Christiansen, Nils (CON - Holy Trinity) nils.christiansen@guildford.gov.uk

Cross, Colin (LD - Lovelace) colin.cross@guilford.gov.uk

Davis, Geoff (CON - Holy Trinity) geoff.davis@guildford.gov.uk

Ellwood, Graham (CON - Merrow) graham.ellwood@guildford.gov.uk

GUILDFORD

Elms, David (CON - Worplesdon)
david.elms@guildford.gov.uk

Gomm, Andrew (CON - Ash South & Tongham)
andrew.gomm@guildford.gov.uk

Goodwin, Angela (LD - Friary & St Nicolas)
angela.goodwin@guildford.gov.uk

Goodwin, David (LD - Onslow)
david.goodwin@guildford.gov.uk

Grubb Jnr, Murray (CON - Ash Wharf)
murray.grubb@guildford.gov.uk

Gunning, Angela (LAB - Stoke)
angela.gunning@guildford.gov.uk

Harwood, Gillian (LD - Stoughton)
gillian.harwood@guildford.gov.uk

Hogger, Liz (LD - Effingham)
liz.hogger@guildford.gov.uk

Holliday, Christian (CON - Burpham)
christian.holliday@guildford.gov.uk

Hooper, Liz (CON - Westborough)
liz.hooper@guildford.gov.uk

Hurdle, Mike (O - Send)
mike.hurdle@guildford.gov.uk

Illman, Michael (CON - Shalford)
michael.illman@guildford.gov.uk

Jordan, Jennifer (CON - Merrow)
jennifer.jordan@guildford.gov.uk

Kearse, Nigel (CON - Ash South & Tongham)
nigel.kearse@guildford.gov.uk

Kirkland, Sheila (CON - Westborough)
sheila.kirkland@guildford.gov.uk

McShane, Julia (LD - Westborough)
julia.mcshane@guildford.gov.uk

McShee, Bob (CON - Worplesdon)
bob.mcshee@guildford.gov.uk

Moseley, Marsha (CON - Ash Vale)
Marsha.Moseley@guildford.gov.uk

Nelson-Smith, Nikki (CON - Christchurch)
nikki.nelson-smith@guildford.gov.uk

Parker, Susan (O - Send)
susan.parker@guildford.gov.uk

Parsons, Mike (CON - Shalford)
mike.parsons@guildford.gov.uk

Paul, Dennis (CON - Holy Trinity)
dennis.oaul@guildford.gov.uk

Phillips, Tony (LD - Onslow)
tony.philips@guildford.gov.uk

Piper, Mike (CON - Burpham)
mike.piper@guildford@gov.uk

Quelch, David (CON - Stoughton)
david.quelch@guildford.gov.uk

Randall, Jo (CON - Ash Wharf)
jo.randall@guildford.gov.uk

Reeve, David (GRN - Clandon & Horsley)
david.reeve@guildford.gov.uk

Roche, Iseult (CON - Worplesdon)
iseult.roche@guildford.gov.uk

Rooth, Tony (CON - Pilgrims)
tony.rooth@guildford.gov.uk

Sarti, Matthew (CON - Clandon & Horsley)
mathew.sarti@guildford.gov.uk

Searle, Pauline (LD - Stoughton)
pauline.searle@guildford.gov.uk

Walsh, James (LAB - Stoke)
james.walsh@guildford.gov.uk

Wicks, Jenny (CON - Clandon & Horsley)
jenny.wicks@guildford.gov.uk

Wright, David (CON - Tillingbourne)
david.wright@guildford.gov.uk

POLITICAL COMPOSITION
CON: 34, LD: 9, O: 2, LAB: 2, GRN: 1

COMMITTEE CHAIRS

Licensing: Mr David Elms

Planning: Mrs Marsha Moseley

Gwynedd   W

Gwynedd Council, Swyddfa'r Cyngor, Stryd Y Jel, Caernarfon LL55 1SH
☎ 01286 672255 🖷 01286 673993 ◌ enquiries@gwynedd.gov.uk
🖳 www.gwynedd.gov.uk

FACTS AND FIGURES
Parliamentary Constituencies: Arfon, Dwyfor Meirionnydd
EU Constituencies: Wales
Election Frequency: Elections are of whole council

PRINCIPAL OFFICERS

Chief Executive: Mr Dilwyn Owen Williams, Chief Executive, Swyddfa'r Cyngor, Stryd Y Jel, Caernarfon LL55 1SH ☎ 01286 679514 ◌ dilwynowenwilliams@gwynedd.llyw.cymru

Senior Management: Mrs Morwena Edwards, Corporate Director, Swyddfa'r Cyngor, Stryd Y Jel, Caernarfon LL55 1SH
☎ 01286 679468 ◌ awenmorwenaedwards@gwynedd.llyw.cymru

Senior Management: Mr Iwan Trefor Jones, Corporate Director, Swyddfa'r Cyngor, Stryd Y Jel, Caernarfon LL55 1SH
☎ 01286 679162 ◌ iwantreforjones@gwynedd.llyw.cymru

Access Officer / Social Services (Disability): Mr Aled Davies, Head of Adults, Health & Wellbeing, Swyddfa'r Cyngor, Stryd Y Jel, Caernarfon LL55 1SH ☎ 01268 679954
◌ aled@gwynedd.llyw.cymru

Architect, Building / Property Services: Mr Huw Williams, Head of Gwynedd Consultancy, Swyddfa'r Cyngor, Stryd Y Jel, Caernarfon LL55 1SH ☎ 01286 679426
◌ huwwilliams@gwynedd.llyw.cymru

Best Value: Mr Geraint Owen, Head of Corporate Support, Swyddfa'r Cyngor, Stryd Y Jel, Caernarfon LL55 1SH
☎ 01286 679335 ⓔ geraintowen@gwynedd.llyw.cymru

Building Control: Mr Huw Williams, Head of Gwynedd Consultancy, Swyddfa'r Cyngor, Stryd Y Jel, Caernarfon LL55 1SH
☎ 01286 679426 ⓔ huwwilliams@gwynedd.llyw.cymru

Catering Services: Mr Arwyn Thomas, Head of Education, Swyddfa'r Cyngor, Stryd Y Jel, Caernarfon LL55 1SH
☎ 01286 679467 ⓔ arwynlloydthomas@gwynedd.llyw.cymru

Children / Youth Services: Mrs Marian Parry Hughes, Head of Children & Supporting Families, Swyddfa'r Cyngor, Stryd Y Jel, Caernarfon LL55 1SH ☎ 01286 679228
ⓔ marianparryhughes@gwynedd.llyw.cymru

Civil Registration: Mr Geraint Owen, Head of Corporate Support, Swyddfa'r Cyngor, Stryd Y Jel, Caernarfon LL55 1SH
☎ 01286 679335 ⓔ geraintowen@gwynedd.llyw.cymru

PR / Communications: Mr Sion Gwynfryn Williams, Communications & Engagement Manager, Swyddfa'r Cyngor, Stryd Y Jel, Caernarfon LL55 1SH ☎ 01286 679310
ⓔ siongwynfrynwilliams@gwynedd.llyw.cymru

Community Planning: Mrs Sioned Williams, Head of Economy & Community, Swyddfa'r Cyngor, Stryd Y Jel, Caernarfon LL55 1SH
☎ 01286 679547 ⓔ sionedewilliams@gwynedd.llyw.cymru

Community Safety: Ms Catherine Roberts, Senior Community Safety Officer, Swyddfa'r Cyngor, Stryd Y Jel, Caernarfon LL55 1SH
☎ 01286 679047 ⓔ catherineeirlysroberts@gwynedd.llyw.cymru

Computer Management: Mr Huw Ynyr, Senior Manager - IT & Business Transformation, Swyddfa'r Cyngor, Stryd Y Jel, Caernarfon LL55 1SH ☎ 01286 679302 ⓔ huwynyr@gwynedd.llyw.cymru

Consumer Protection and Trading Standards: Mr Dafydd Wyn Williams, Head of Regulatory, Swyddfa'r Cyngor, Stryd Y Jel, Caernarfon LL55 1SH ☎ 01286 679370
ⓔ dafyddwynwilliams@gwynedd.gov.uk

Contracts: Mr Geraint Owen, Head of Corporate Support, Swyddfa'r Cyngor, Stryd Y Jel, Caernarfon LL55 1SH
☎ 01286 679335 ⓔ geraintowen@gwynedd.llyw.cymru

Corporate Services: Mr Dilwyn Owen Williams, Chief Executive, Swyddfa'r Cyngor, Stryd Y Jel, Caernarfon LL55 1SH
☎ 01286 679514 ⓔ dilwynowenwilliams@gwynedd.llyw.cymru

Direct Labour: Mr Gwyn Morris Jones, Head of Highways & Municipal Services, Swyddfa'r Cyngor, Stryd Y Jel, Caernarfon LL55 1SH ☎ 01286 679402 ⓔ gwynmorrisjones@gwynedd.llyw.cymru

Economic Development: Mrs Sioned Williams, Head of Economy & Community, Swyddfa'r Cyngor, Stryd Y Jel, Caernarfon LL55 1SH
☎ 01286 679547 ⓔ sionedewilliams@gwynedd.llyw.cymru

Education: Mr Arwyn Thomas, Head of Education, Swyddfa'r Cyngor, Stryd Y Jel, Caernarfon LL55 1SH ☎ 01286 679467
ⓔ arwynlloydthomas@gwynedd.llyw.cymru

Electoral Registration: Mr Iwan Evans, Head of Legal Services, Swyddfa'r Cyngor, Stryd Y Jel, Caernarfon LL55 1SH
☎ 01286 679015 ⓔ iwangdevans@gwynedd.llyw.cymru

Emergency Planning: Mrs Morwena Edwards, Corporate Director, Swyddfa'r Cyngor, Stryd Y Jel, Caernarfon LL55 1SH
☎ 01286 679468 ⓔ awenmorwenaedwards@gwynedd.llyw.cymru

Energy Management: Mr David Mark Lewis, Energy Conservation Manager, Swyddfa'r Cyngor, Stryd Y Jel, Caernarfon LL55 1SH ☎ 01286 679307
ⓔ davidmarklewis@gwynedd.llyw.cmyru

Environmental Health: Mr Dafydd Wyn Williams, Head of Regulatory, Swyddfa'r Cyngor, Stryd Y Jel, Caernarfon LL55 1SH
☎ 01286 679370 ⓔ dafyddwynwilliams@gwynedd.gov.uk

Estates, Property & Valuation: Mr Dafydd Gibbard, Corporate Property - Senior Manager, Swyddfa'r Cyngor, Stryd Y Jel, Caernarfon LL55 1SH ☎ 01286 679957
ⓔ dafyddgibbard@gwynedd.llyw.cyrmu

European Liaison: Mrs Vivienne Pritchard, Europe Officer, Swyddfa'r Cyngor, Stryd Y Jel, Caernarfon LL55 1SH
☎ 01286 679487 ⓔ viviennepritchard@gwynedd.llyw.cymru

Events Manager: Mr Hugh Edwin Jones, Events Manager, Swyddfa'r Cyngor, Stryd Y Jel, Caernarfon LL55 1SH
☎ 01286 679398 ⓔ hughedwinjones@gwynedd.llyw.cymru

Finance: Mr Dafydd Edwards, Head of Finance, Swyddfa'r Cyngor, Stryd Y Jel, Caernarfon LL55 1SH ☎ 01286 682682
ⓔ dafyddedwards@gwynedd.llyw.cymru

Treasury: Mr Dafydd Edwards, Head of Finance, Swyddfa'r Cyngor, Stryd Y Jel, Caernarfon LL55 1SH ☎ 01286 682682
ⓔ dafyddedwards@gwynedd.llyw.cymru

Pensions: Mr Dafydd Edwards, Head of Finance, Swyddfa'r Cyngor, Stryd Y Jel, Caernarfon LL55 1SH ☎ 01286 682682
ⓔ dafyddedwards@gwynedd.llyw.cymru

Fleet Management: Mr Gwyn Morris Jones, Head of Highways & Municipal Services, Swyddfa'r Cyngor, Stryd Y Jel, Caernarfon LL55 1SH ☎ 01286 679402 ⓔ gwynmorrisjones@gwynedd.llyw.cymru

Grounds Maintenance: Mr Gwyn Morris Jones, Head of Highways & Municipal Services, Swyddfa'r Cyngor, Stryd Y Jel, Caernarfon LL55 1SH ☎ 01286 679402
ⓔ gwynmorrisjones@gwynedd.llyw.cymru

Health and Safety: Mr Geraint Owen, Head of Corporate Support, Swyddfa'r Cyngor, Stryd Y Jel, Caernarfon LL55 1SH
☎ 01286 679335 ⓔ geraintowen@gwynedd.llyw.cymru

Highways: Mr Gwyn Morris Jones, Head of Highways & Municipal Services, Swyddfa'r Cyngor, Stryd Y Jel, Caernarfon LL55 1SH
☎ 01286 679402 ⓔ gwynmorrisjones@gwynedd.llyw.cymru

Housing: Mr Aled Davies, Head of Adults, Health & Wellbeing, Swyddfa'r Cyngor, Stryd Y Jel, Caernarfon LL55 1SH ☎ 01268 679954 ⓔ aled@gwynedd.llyw.cymru

GWYNEDD

Legal: Mr Iwan Evans, Head of Legal Services, Swyddfa'r Cyngor, Stryd Y Jel, Caernarfon LL55 1SH ☎ 01286 679015 ⌁ iwangdevans@gwynedd.llyw.cymru

Leisure and Cultural Services: Mrs Sioned Williams, Head of Economy & Community, Swyddfa'r Cyngor, Stryd Y Jel, Caernarfon LL55 1SH ☎ 01286 679547 ⌁ sionedewilliams@gwynedd.llyw.cymru

Licensing: Mr Dafydd Wyn Williams, Head of Regulatory, Swyddfa'r Cyngor, Stryd Y Jel, Caernarfon LL55 1SH ☎ 01286 679370 ⌁ dafyddwynwilliams@gwynedd.gov.uk

Lighting: Mr Gwyn Morris Jones, Head of Highways & Municipal Services, Swyddfa'r Cyngor, Stryd Y Jel, Caernarfon LL55 1SH ☎ 01286 679402 ⌁ gwynmorrisjones@gwynedd.llyw.cymru

Lottery Funding, Charity and Voluntary: Ms Heather Wyn Williams, Senior Gwynedd Cist Officer, Plas Llanwnda, Castle Street, Caernarfon LL55 1SH ☎ 01286 679153 ⌁ heatherwynwilliams@gwynedd.llyw.cymru

Member Services: Mr Geraint Owen, Head of Corporate Support, Swyddfa'r Cyngor, Stryd Y Jel, Caernarfon LL55 1SH ☎ 01286 679335 ⌁ geraintowen@gwynedd.llyw.cymru

Parking: Mr Dafydd Wyn Williams, Head of Regulatory, Swyddfa'r Cyngor, Stryd Y Jel, Caernarfon LL55 1SH ☎ 01286 679370 ⌁ dafyddwynwilliams@gwynedd.gov.uk

Partnerships: Mr Geraint Owen, Head of Corporate Support, Swyddfa'r Cyngor, Stryd Y Jel, Caernarfon LL55 1SH ☎ 01286 679335 ⌁ geraintowen@gwynedd.llyw.cymru

Personnel / HR: Mr Geraint Owen, Head of Corporate Support, Swyddfa'r Cyngor, Stryd Y Jel, Caernarfon LL55 1SH ☎ 01286 679335 ⌁ geraintowen@gwynedd.llyw.cymru

Planning: Mr Dafydd Wyn Williams, Head of Regulatory, Swyddfa'r Cyngor, Stryd Y Jel, Caernarfon LL55 1SH ☎ 01286 679370 ⌁ dafyddwynwilliams@gwynedd.gov.uk

Procurement: Mr Geraint Owen, Head of Corporate Support, Swyddfa'r Cyngor, Stryd Y Jel, Caernarfon LL55 1SH ☎ 01286 679335 ⌁ geraintowen@gwynedd.llyw.cymru

Public Libraries: Mr Hywel James, Principal Librarian, Swyddfa'r Cyngor, Stryd Y Jel, Caernarfon LL55 1SH ☎ 01286 679463 ⌁ hyweljames@gwynedd.llyw.cymru

Recycling & Waste Minimisation: Mr Gwyn Morris Jones, Head of Highways & Municipal Services, Swyddfa'r Cyngor, Stryd Y Jel, Caernarfon LL55 1SH ☎ 01286 679402 ⌁ gwynmorrisjones@gwynedd.llyw.cymru

Regeneration: Mrs Sioned Williams, Head of Economy & Community, Swyddfa'r Cyngor, Stryd Y Jel, Caernarfon LL55 1SH ☎ 01286 679547 ⌁ sionedewilliams@gwynedd.llyw.cymru

Road Safety: Mr Colin Jones, Parking & Road Safety Manager, Swyddfa'r Cyngor, Stryd Y Jel, Caernarfon LL55 1SH ☎ 01286 679753 ⌁ colinjones@gwynedd.llyw.cymru

Social Services: Mrs Morwena Edwards, Corporate Director, Swyddfa'r Cyngor, Stryd Y Jel, Caernarfon LL55 1SH ☎ 01286 679468 ⌁ awenmorwenaedwards@gwynedd.llyw.cymru

Social Services (Adult): Mr Aled Davies, Head of Adults, Health & Wellbeing, Swyddfa'r Cyngor, Stryd Y Jel, Caernarfon LL55 1SH ☎ 01268 679954 ⌁ aled@gwynedd.llyw.cymru

Social Services (Children): Mrs Marian Parry Hughes, Head of Children & Supporting Families, Swyddfa'r Cyngor, Stryd Y Jel, Caernarfon LL55 1SH ☎ 01286 679228 ⌁ marianparryhughes@gwynedd.llyw.cymru

Staff Training: Mr Geraint Owen, Head of Corporate Support, Swyddfa'r Cyngor, Stryd Y Jel, Caernarfon LL55 1SH ☎ 01286 679335 ⌁ geraintowen@gwynedd.llyw.cymru

Street Scene: Mr Dafydd Wyn Williams, Head of Regulatory, Swyddfa'r Cyngor, Stryd Y Jel, Caernarfon LL55 1SH ☎ 01286 679370 ⌁ dafyddwynwilliams@gwynedd.gov.uk

Sustainable Communities: Mrs Sioned Williams, Head of Economy & Community, Swyddfa'r Cyngor, Stryd Y Jel, Caernarfon LL55 1SH ☎ 01286 679547 ⌁ sionedewilliams@gwynedd.llyw.cymru

Sustainable Development: Mr Dafydd Wyn Williams, Head of Regulatory, Swyddfa'r Cyngor, Stryd Y Jel, Caernarfon LL55 1SH ☎ 01286 679370 ⌁ dafyddwynwilliams@gwynedd.gov.uk

Tourism: Mrs Sian Pennant Jones, Marketing & Customer Care Manager, Swyddfa'r Cyngor, Stryd Y Jel, Caernarfon LL55 1SH ☎ 01286 679963 ⌁ sianjones@gwynedd.llyw.cymru

Town Centre: Mr Dafydd Wyn Williams, Head of Regulatory, Swyddfa'r Cyngor, Stryd Y Jel, Caernarfon LL55 1SH ☎ 01286 679370 ⌁ dafyddwynwilliams@gwynedd.gov.uk

Traffic Management: Mr Dafydd Wyn Williams, Head of Regulatory, Swyddfa'r Cyngor, Stryd Y Jel, Caernarfon LL55 1SH ☎ 01286 679370 ⌁ dafyddwynwilliams@gwynedd.gov.uk

Transport: Mr Dafydd Wyn Williams, Head of Regulatory, Swyddfa'r Cyngor, Stryd Y Jel, Caernarfon LL55 1SH ☎ 01286 679370 ⌁ dafyddwynwilliams@gwynedd.gov.uk

Transport Planner: Mr Dafydd Wyn Williams, Head of Regulatory, Swyddfa'r Cyngor, Stryd Y Jel, Caernarfon LL55 1SH ☎ 01286 679370 ⌁ dafyddwynwilliams@gwynedd.gov.uk

Total Place: Mr Iwan Trefor Jones, Corporate Director, Swyddfa'r Cyngor, Stryd Y Jel, Caernarfon LL55 1SH ☎ 01286 679162 ⌁ iwantreforjones@gwynedd.llyw.cymru

Waste Collection and Disposal: Mr Gwyn Morris Jones, Head of Highways & Municipal Services, Swyddfa'r Cyngor, Stryd Y Jel, Caernarfon LL55 1SH ☎ 01286 679402 ⌁ gwynmorrisjones@gwynedd.llyw.cymru

Waste Management: Mr Gwyn Morris Jones, Head of Highways & Municipal Services, Swyddfa'r Cyngor, Stryd Y Jel, Caernarfon LL55 1SH ☎ 01286 679402 🖰 gwynmorrisjones@gwynedd.llyw.cymru

Children's Play Areas: Mr Gwyn Morris Jones, Head of Highways & Municipal Services, Swyddfa'r Cyngor, Stryd Y Jel, Caernarfon LL55 1SH ☎ 01286 679402 🖰 gwynmorrisjones@gwynedd.llyw.cymru

COUNCILLORS

Leader of the Council: Edwards, Dyfed (PC - Penygroes)
cynghorydd.dyfededwards@gwynedd.gov.uk

Deputy Leader of the Council: Siencyn, Dyfrig (PC - Dolgellau (North))
cynghorydd.dyfriglewissiencyn@gwynedd.gov.uk

Ab Iago, Craig (PC - Llanllyfni)
cynghorydd.craigabiago@gwynedd.gov.uk

Churchman, Stephen (LD - Dolbenmaen)
cynghorydd.stephenchurchman@gwynedd.gov.uk

Cooke, Endaf (O - Seiont (1))
cynghorydd.endafcooke@gwynedd.gov.uk

Davies, Anwen (O - Efailnewydd/Buan)
cynghorydd.anwenjanedavies@gwynedd.gov.uk

Day, Lesley (IND - Garth)
cynghorydd@gwynedd.gov.uk

Dogan, Edward (PC - Dewi)

Edwards, Huw (PC - Cadnant)

Edwards, Trefor (IND - Llanberis)

Edwards, Gwynfor (LAB - Deiniol)
cynghorryd.gwynforedwards@gwynedd.gov.uk

Edwards, Elwyn (PC - Llandderfel)
cynghorydd.elwynedwards@gwynedd.gov.uk

Ellis, Thomas (IND - Trawsfynydd)
cynghorydd.tomellis@gwynedd.gov.uk

Evans, Alan (PC - Llanuwchllyn)
cynghorydd.alanjonesevans@gwynedd.gov.uk

Evans, Aled (PC - Llanystumdwy)
cynghorydd.aledevans@gwynedd.gov.uk

Forsyth, Jean (IND - Hirael)
cynghorydd.jeanforsyth@gwynedd.gov.uk

Glyn, Simon (O - Tudweiliog)
cynghorydd.simonglyn@gwynedd.gov.uk

Glyn, Gweno (O - Botwnnog)
cynghorydd.gwenoglyn@gwynedd.gov.uk

Griffith, Gwen (LAB - Tregarth and Mynydd Llandygai)
cynghorydd.gwengriffith@gwynedd.gov.uk

Griffiths, Selwyn (PC - Porthmadog (West))
cynghorydd.selwyngriffiths@gwynedd.gov.uk

Gruffydd, Alwyn (O - Porthmadog/Tremadog)
cynghorydd.alwyngruffydd@gwynedd.gov.uk

Gwenllian, Sian (PC - Y Felinheli)
cynghorydd.siangwenllian.gov.uk

Hughes, John (IND - Llanengan)
cynghorydd.johnhughes@gwynedd.gov.uk

Hughes, Christopher (PC - Bontnewydd)
cynghorydd.christopherhughes@gwynedd.gov.uk

Hughes, Louise (O - Llangelynnin)
cynghorydd.louisehughes@gwynedd.gov.uk

Hughes, Annwen (PC - Llanbedr)
cynghorydd.anwenhughes@gwynedd.gov.uk

Humphreys, Jason (O - Porthmadog (East))
cynghorydd.jasonhumphreys@gwynedd.gov.uk

Jenkins, Peredur (PC - Brithdir + Llanfachreth)
cynghorydd.peredurjenkins@gwynedd.gov.uk

Jones, Linda (PC - Teigl)
cynghorydd.lindaannjones@gwynedd.gov.uk

Jones, Aeron (O - Llanwnda)
cynghorydd.aeronjones@gwynedd.gov.uk

Jones, Dyfrig (PC - Gerlan)
cynghorydd.dyfrigjones@gwynedd.gov.uk

Jones, John Wynn (PC - Hendre)
cynghorydd.johnwynnjones@gwynedd.gov.uk

Jones, Llywarch (O - Llanaelhaearn)
cynghoryddllywarchwarchbowenjones@gwynedd.gov.uk

Jones, Elin (PC - Glyder)
cynghorydd.elinwjones@gwynedd.gov.uk

Jones, Eric (IND - Groeslon)
cynghorydd.ericmerfynjones@gwynedd.gov.uk

Jones, Sion (LAB - Bethel)
cynghorydd.sionjones@gwynedd.gov.uk

Jones, Brian (LAB - Cwm y Glo)
cynghorydd.brianjones@gwynedd.gov.uk

Jones, Charles (O - Llanrug)
cynghorydd.charleswynjones@gwynedd.gov.uk

Jones-Williams, Eryl (IND - Dyffryn Ardudwy)
cynghorydd.eryljoneswilliams@gwynedd.gov.uk

Lawton, Beth (IND - Bryncrug/Llanfihangel)
cynhorydd.bethlawton@gwnedd.gov.uk

Lloyd, Ifor (O - Talysarn)
cynghorydd.dilwynlloyd@gwynedd.gov.uk

Lloyd-Jones, Anne (IND - Tywyn (1))
cynghorydd.annelloyd-jones@gwynedd.gov.uk

Marshall, June (LD - Menai (Bangor) (1))
cynghorydd.junemarshall@gwynedd.gov.uk

Meurig, Dafydd (PC - Arllechwedd)
cynghorydd.dafyddmeurig@gwynedd.gov.uk

Morgan, Dilwyn (PC - Y Bala)
cynghordd.dilwynmorgan@gwynedd.gov.uk

Morgan, Linda (PC - Dolgellau (South))
cynghorydd.lindamorgan@gwynedd.gov.uk

O'Neal, Christopher (IND - Marchog (1))
cynghorydd.oneal@gwynedd.gov.uk

Owen, William Tudor (PC - Peblig)
cynghorydd.tudorowen@gwynedd.gov.uk

Owen, William (IND - Seiont (2))
cynghorydd.williamroyowen@gwynedd.gov.uk

Owen, Michael (PC - Pwllheli (North))
cynghorydd.michaelsolowen@gwynedd.gov.uk

GWYNEDD

Owen, Dewi (IND - Aberdyfi)
cynghorydd.dewiowen@gwynedd.gov.uk

Pickavance, Nigel (IND - Marchog (2))
cynghorydd.nigelpickavance@gwynedd.gov.uk

Read, Peter (O - Abererch)
cynghorydd.peterread@gwynedd.gov.uk

Roberts, Gareth (PC - Aberdaron)
cynghorydd.garethroberts@gwynedd.gov.uk

Roberts, Liz (PC - Morfa Nefyn)
cynghorydd.lizsavilleroberts@gwynedd.gov.uk

Roberts, John (IND - Corris/ Mawddwy)
cynghorydd.johnpugheroberts@gwynedd.gov.uk

Roberts, Caerwyn (PC - Harlech/Talsarnau)
cynghorydd.caerwynroberts@gwynedd.gov.uk

Rowlands, Mair (PC - Menai (Bangor) (2))
cynghorydd.mairrowlands@gwymedd.gov.uk

Russell, Angela (IND - Llanbedrog)
cynghorydd.angelarussell@gwynedd.gov.uk

Stevens, Mike (IND - Tywyn (2))
cynghorydd.mikestevens@gwynedd.gov.uk

Thomas, Gareth (PC - Penrhyndeudraeth)
cynghorydd.gareththomas@gwynedd.gov.uk

Thomas, Ioan (PC - Menai (Caernarfon))
cynghorydd.ioanthomas@gwynedd.gov.uk

Thomas, Paul (PC - Bowydd + Rhiw)
cynghorydd.paulthomas@gwynedd.gov.uk

Williams, Gruffydd (O - Nefyn)
cynghorydd.gruffyddwilliams@gwynedd.gov.uk

Williams, Gethin (PC - Abermaw)
cynghorydd.gethinglynwilliams@gwynedd.gov.uk

Williams, Elfed (IND - Deiniolen)
cynghorydd.elfedwilliams@gwynedd.gov.uk

Williams, Owain (O - Clynnog Fawr)
cynghorydd.owainwilliams@gwynedd.gov.uk

Williams, Eirwyn (IND - Cricieth)
cynghorydd.eirwynwilliams@gwynedd.gov.uk

Williams, Hywel (PC - Abersoch)
cynghorydd.RHywellWynWilliams@gwynedd.gov.uk

Williams, John (PC - Pentir)
cynghorydd.johnwynnwilliams@gwynedd.gov.uk

Williams, Ann (PC - Ogwen)
cynghorydd.annwilliams@gwynedd.gov.uk

Williams, Hefin (PC - Penisarwaun)
cynghorydd.hefinwilliams@gwynedd.gov.uk

Williams-Davies, Mandy (PC - Diffwys + Maenofferen)
cynghordd.mandywdavies@gwynedd.gov.uk

Wright, Bob (O - Pwllheli (South))
cynghorydd.bobwright@gwynedd.gov.uk

Wyn, Eurig (PC - Waunfawr)
cynghorydd.eurigwyn@gwynedd.gov.uk

POLITICAL COMPOSITION
PC: 36, IND: 18, O: 15, LAB: 4, LD: 2

Hackney   L

Hackney London Borough Council, Town Hall, Mare Street, London E8 1EA

☎ 020 8356 3000 ✆ info@hackney.gov.uk 🖳 www.hackney.gov.uk

FACTS AND FIGURES
Parliamentary Constituencies: Hackney North and Stoke Newington, Hackney South and Shoreditch
EU Constituencies: London
Election Frequency: Elections are of whole council

PRINCIPAL OFFICERS

Chief Executive: Mr Tim Shields, Chief Executive, Town Hall, Mare Street, London E8 1EA ☎ 020 8356 3210; 020 8356 3047 ✆ tim.shields@hackney.gov.uk

Senior Management: Dr Penny Bevan, Director - Public Health, Town Hall, Mare Street, London E8 1EA ✆ penny.bevan@hackney.gov.uk

Senior Management: Mr Ian Williams, Group Director - Finance & Resources, Town Hall, Mare Street, London E8 1EA ☎ 020 8356 3003 ✆ ian.williams@hackney.gov.uk

Senior Management: Ms Kim Wright, Group Director - Neighbourhoods & Housing, Town Hall, Mare Street, London E8 1EA ☎ 020 8356 7347; 020 8356 7544 ✆ kim.wright@hackney.gov.uk

Access Officer / Social Services (Disability): Mr Rob Blackstone, Assistant Director - Adult Social Care, 1 Hillman Street, London E8 1DY ☎ 020 8356 4282

Architect, Building / Property Services: Mr Chris Pritchard, Interim Assistant Director - Strategic Property Services, 1 Hillman Street, London E8 1DY ☎ 020 8356 3700 ✆ chris.pritchard@hackney.gov.uk

Building Control: Mr John Wheatley, Head of Environmental Operations, Millfields Depot, London E5 0AR ☎ 0208 356 6690 ✆ john.wheatley@hackney.gov.uk

Children / Youth Services: Ms Pauline Adams, Head of Young Hackney, 1 Hillman Street, London E8 1DY ☎ 020 8356 2709 ✆ pauline.adams@hackney.gov.uk

Civil Registration: Ms Lezma Allison, Ceremony Services Manager, Town Hall, Mare Street, London E8 1EA ☎ 020 8356 7402 ✆ lezma.allison@hackney.gov.uk

PR / Communications: Ms Polly Cziok, Head of Communications & Consultation, Town Hall, Mare Street, London E8 1EA ☎ 020 8356 3323 ✆ polly.cziok@hackney.gov.uk

Community Safety: Mr Steve Bending, Head of Safer Communities, Maurice Bishop House, 17 Reading Lane, London E8 1HH ☎ 020 8356 2070 ✆ steve.bending@hackney.gov.uk

Computer Management: Mr Rob Miller, Director - ICT, 6 - 15 Florfield Road, London E8 1DT ☎ 020 8356 2600 ✆ rob.miller@hackney.gov.uk

Consumer Protection and Trading Standards: Mr Robin Jones, Team Leader - Trading Standards, 2 Hillman Street, London E8 1DY ☎ 020 8356 4909 ⌨ robin.jones@hackney.gov.uk

Contracts: Mr Michael Robson, Head of Strategic Procurement, 3rd Floor Keltan House, 89 - 115 Mare Street, Hackney, London E8 4RU ☎ 0208 356 3821 ⌨ michael.robson@hackney.gov.uk

Customer Service: Ms Lisa Cook, Customer Services Operations Manager, 1 Hillman Street, London E8 1DY ☎ 020 8356 6501 ⌨ lisa.cook@hackney.gov.uk

Education: Ms Anne Canning, Acting Group Director - Children, Adults & Community Health, Town Hall, Mare Street, London E8 1EA ☎ 020 8356 7631 ⌨ anne.canning@hackney.gov.uk

Electoral Registration: Mr John Jones, Head of Electoral Services, Town Hall, Mare Street, London E8 1EA ☎ 020 8356 3234 ⌨ john.jones@hackney.gov.uk

Emergency Planning: Mr Roy Hitching, Head of Service of CCTV & Emergency Planning, Stoke Newington Municipal Offices, Stoke Newington Church Street, London N16 0JR ☎ 020 8356 2182 ⌨ roy.hitching@hackney.gov.uk

Energy Management: Mr Kamar Zaman, Head of Energy Management, 2 Hillman Street, London E8 1FB ☎ 020 8356 2764 ⌨ kamar.zaman@hackney.gov.uk

Environmental / Technical Services: Mr Aled Richards, Director - Public Realm, 2 Hillman Street, London E8 1FB ☎ 020 8356 7988 ⌨ aled.richards@hackney.gov.uk

Environmental Health: Ms Aleyne Fontenelle, Environmental Health Manager, Town Hall, Mare Street, London E8 1EA ☎ 020 8356 4918; 020 8356 4740 ⌨ aleyne.fontenelle@hackney.gov.uk

Estates, Property & Valuation: Mr Jonathan Angell, Head of Commercial Estates, Keltan House, 89 - 115 Mare Street, Hackney, London E8 4RU ☎ 020 8536 4034; 020 8536 8261 ⌨ jonathan.angell@hackney.gov.uk

Events Manager: Ms Christine Rupprecht, Venue Sales & Marketing Manager, 1st Floor, Maurice Bishop House, 17 Reading Lane, London E8 1HH ☎ 020 8356 2577

Facilities: Mr Gary Sherman, Facilities Operations Manager, Hackney Service Centre, 1 Hillman Street, Hackney, London E8 1DY ☎ 020 8356 4647 ⌨ gary.sherman@hackney.gov.uk

Finance: Ms Jill Davys, Head of Financial Services, Keltan House, 89-155 Mare Street, Hackney, London E8 4RU ☎ 020 8356 2646 ⌨ jill.davys@hackney.gov.uk

Finance: Mr Ian Williams, Group Director - Finance & Resources, Town Hall, Mare Street, London E8 1EA ☎ 020 8356 3003 ⌨ ian.williams@hackney.gov.uk

Pensions: Mr Gary Nash, Pensions Liaison Officer, Keltan House, 89-115 Mare Street, London E8 4RU ☎ 020 8356 2745 ⌨ gary.nash@hackney.gov.uk

Fleet Management: Mr Norman Harding, Corporate Fleet Manager, Fleet Mangement Unit, Hackney Service Centre, 1 Hillman Street, Hackney, London E8 1DY ☎ 020 8356 3613 ⌨ norman.harding@hackney.gov.uk

Health and Safety: Ms Lynne Thornburn, Health & Safety Adviser, 280 Mare Street, London E8 1EA ☎ 020 8356 4659 ⌨ lynne.thornburn@hackney.gov.uk

Highways: Mr Mark Pinnock, Group Engineer - Highways & Maintenance, Keltan House, 89 - 115 Mare Street, Hackney, London E8 4RU ☎ 020 8256 8312; 020 8356 2863 ⌨ mark.pinnock@hackney.gov.uk

Housing: Mr Michael Scorer, Interim Director - Housing, Christopher Addison House, 72 Wilton Way, London E8 1BJ ☎ 020 8356 3670 ⌨ michael.scorer@hackney.gov.uk

Local Area Agreement: Mr Bruce Devile, Head of Business Analysis, Town Hall, Mare Street, London E8 1EA ☎ 020 8356 3418 ⌨ bruce.devile@hackney.gov.uk

Legal: Ms Yinka Owa, Director - Legal, Town Hall, Mare Street, London E8 1EA ☎ 020 8356 6234 ⌨ yinka.owa@hackney.gov.uk

Leisure and Cultural Services: Mr Ian Holland, Head of Leisure & Open Spaces, Hackney Service Centre, 1 Hillman Street, Hackney, London E8 1DY ☎ 020 8356 3810 ⌨ ian.holland@hackney.gov.uk

Licensing: Mr Mike Smith, Senior Licensing Officer, 1 Hillman Street, London E8 1DY ☎ 020 8356 4973 ⌨ mike.smith@hackney.gov.uk

Parking: Mr Seamus Adams, Head of Parking Services, 2 Hillman Street, London E8 1FB ☎ 020 8356 8333 ⌨ seamus.adams@hackney.gov.uk

Partnerships: Ms Joanne Sumner, Assistant Chief Officer, Town Hall, Mare Street, London E8 1EA ☎ 020 8356 3135 ⌨ joanna.sumner@hackney.gov.uk

Personnel / HR: Mr Dan Paul, Head of HR & OD, 280 Mare Street, London E8 1FB ☎ 020 8356 3110 ⌨ dan.paul@hackney.gov.uk

Planning: Ms Cathy Gallagher, Assistant Director - Planning & Regulatory Services, 2 Hillman Street, London E8 1DY ☎ 020 8356 8134 ⌨ cathy.gallagher@hackney.gov.uk

Procurement: Mr Chris Hudson, Assistant Director - Procurement & Fleet, 3rd Floor Keltan House, E8 4RU ☎ 020 8356 2725; 020 8356 3037 ⌨ chris.hudson@hackney.gov.uk

Public Libraries: Mr Ted Rogers, Head of Libraries, Heritage & Culture, Hackney Service Centre, 1 Hillman Street, Hackney, London E8 1DY ☎ 020 8356 4782 ⌨ edward.rogers@hackney.gov.uk

Recycling & Waste Minimisation: Mr Richard Gilbert, Project Manager, Keltan House, 89-115 Mare Street, London E8 4RU ☎ 020 8356 4946; 020 8356 4740 ⌨ richard.gilbert@hackney.gov.uk

HACKNEY

Road Safety: Ms Maryann Allen, Transport & Sustainable Engagement Manager, Hackney Service Centre, 1 Hillman Street, Hackney, London E8 1DY ☎ 020 8356 8184; 020 8356 8263 ✒ maryann.allen@hackney.gov.uk

Social Services (Adult): Ms Anne Canning, Acting Group Director - Children, Adults & Community Health, Town Hall, Mare Street, London E8 1EA ☎ 020 8356 7631 ✒ anne.canning@hackney.gov.uk

Social Services (Children): Ms Sarah Wright, Director - Children & Families, Hackney Service Centre, 1 Hillman Street, Hackney, London E8 1DY ☎ 020 8356 6824 ✒ sarah.wright@hackney.gov.uk

Public Health: Dr Penny Bevan, Director - Public Health, Town Hall, Mare Street, London E8 1EA ✒ penny.bevan@hackney.gov.uk

Street Scene: Mr Andy Cunningham, Head of Streetscene, Keltan House, 89-115 Mare Street, London E8 4RU ☎ 020 8356 6657 ✒ andy.cunningham@hackney.gov.uk

Traffic Management: Mr Suresh Prajapati, Senior Enginner, Keltan House, 89 - 115 Mare Street, Hackney, London E8 4RU ☎ 020 8356 8374 ✒ suresh.prajapati@hackney.gov.uk

Transport: Mr Andy Cunningham, Head of Streetscene, Keltan House, 89-115 Mare Street, London E8 4RU ☎ 020 8356 6657 ✒ andy.cunningham@hackney.gov.uk

Transport: Mr Aled Richards, Director - Public Realm, 2 Hillman Street, London E8 1FB ☎ 020 8356 7988 ✒ aled.richards@hackney.gov.uk

Transport Planner: Mr Paul Bowker, Transport Planner, 300 Mare Street, London E8 3HE ☎ 020 8356 8123 ✒ paul.bowker@hackney.gov.uk

Waste Management: Mr John Wheatley, Head of Environmental Operations, Millfields Depot, London E5 0AR ☎ 0208 356 6690 ✒ john.wheatley@hackney.gov.uk

COUNCILLORS

Directly Elected Mayor: Pipe, Jules (LAB - London Borough of Hackney)

Deputy Mayor: Glanville, Philip (LAB - Hoxton West) philip.glanville@hackney.gov.uk

Adams, Kam (LAB - Hoxton East & Shoreditch)

Adejare, Soraya (LAB - Dalston) soraya.adejare@hackney.gov.uk

Akhoon, Dawood (LD - Cazenove) dawood.akhoon@hackney.gov.uk

Bell, Brian (LAB - Brownswood) brian.bell@hackney.gov.uk

Bramble, Anntoinette (LAB - London Fields) anntoinette.bramble@hackney.gov.uk

Brett, Will (LAB - Victoria) will.brett@hackney.gov.uk

Buitekant, Barry (LAB - Haggerston) barry.buitekant@hackney.gov.uk

Bunt, Laura (LAB - De Beauvoir) laura.bunt@hackney.gov.uk

Burke, Jon (LAB - Woodberry Down) jonburke@hackney.gov.uk

Cameron, Sophie (LAB - Clissold) sophie.cameron@hackney.gov.uk

Chapman, Robert (LAB - Homerton) robert.chapman@hackney.gov.uk

Coban, Mete (LAB - Stoke Newington) mete.coban@hackney.gov.uk

Demirci, Feryal (LAB - Hoxton East & Shoreditch) feryal.demirci@hackney.gov.uk

Desmond, Michael (LAB - Hackney Downs) michael@desm.new.labour.org.uk

Ebbutt, Tom (LAB - Hoxton East & Shoreditch) tom.ebbutt@hackney.gov.uk

Etti, Sade (LAB - Clissold) sade.etti@hackney.gov.uk

Fajana-Thomas, Susan (LAB - Stoke Newington) susan.fajanathomas@hackney.gov.uk

Gordon, Margaret (LAB - Leabridge) margaret.gordon@hackney.gov.uk

Gregory, Michelle (LAB - Shacklewell) michelle.gregory@hackney.gov.uk

Hanson, Katie (LAB - Victoria) katie.hanson@hackney.gov.uk

Hayhurst, Ben (LAB - Hackney Central) ben.hayhurst@hackney.gov.uk

Hercock, Ned (LAB - Clissold) ned.hercock@hackney.gov.uk

Jacobson, Abraham (LD - Cazenove) abraham.jacobson@hackney.gov.uk

Kennedy, Christopher (LAB - Hackney Wick) christopher.kennedy@hackney.gov.uk

Levy, Michael (CON - Springfield)

Lufkin, Richard (LAB - Shacklewell) richard.lufkin@hackney.gov.uk

McKenzie, Clayeon (LAB - Hoxton West) clayeon.mckenzie@hackney.gov.uk

McShane, Jonathan (LAB - Haggerston) jonathan.mcshane@hackney.gov.uk

Moema, Sem (LAB - Hackney Downs) sem.moema@hackney.gov.uk

Moule, Patrick (LAB - Stoke Newington) patrick.moule@hackney.gov.uk

Mulready, Sally (LAB - Homerton) sally.mulready@hackney.gov.uk

Munn, Ann (LAB - Haggerston) ann.munn@hackney.gov.uk

Nicholson, Guy (LAB - Homerton) guy.nicholson@hackney.gov.uk

Odze, Harvey (CON - Springfield) harvey.odze@hackney.gov.uk

Oguzkanli, Deniz (LAB - Leabridge) deniz.oguzkanli@hackney.gov.uk

---

Ozsen, M Can (LAB - London Fields)
mcan.ozsen@hackney.gov.uk

Papier, Benzion (CON - Stamford Hill West)
benzion.papier@hackney.gov.uk

Patrick, Sharon (LAB - Kings Park)
sharon.patrick@hackney.gov.uk

Peters, James (LAB - De Beauvoir)
james.peters@hackney.gov.uk

Plouviez, Emma (LAB - London Fields)
emma.plouviez@hackney.gov.uk

Potter, Clare (LAB - Brownswood)
clare.potter@hackney.gov.uk

Rahilly, Tom (LAB - Kings Park)
tom.rahilly@hackney.gov.uk

Rathbone, Ian (LAB - Leabridge)
ian.rathbone@hackney.gov.uk

Rennison, Rebecca (LAB - Kings Park)
rebecca.rennison@hackney.gov.uk

Rickard, Anna-Joy (LAB - Hackney Downs)
anna-joy.rickard@hackney.gov.uk

Sales, Rosemary (LAB - Stamford Hill West)
rosemary.sales@hackney.gov.uk

Selman, Caroline (LAB - Woodberry Down)
caroline.selman@hackney.gov.uk

Sharer, Ian (LD - Cazenove)
ian.sharer@hackney.gov.uk

Sharman, Nick (LAB - Hackney Wick)
nick.sharman@hackney.gov.uk

Snell, Peter (LAB - Dalston)
peter.snell@hackney.gov.uk

Steinberger, Simche (CON - Springfield)
simche.steinberger@hackney.gov.uk

Stops, Vincent (LAB - Hackney Central)
vincent.stops@hackney.gov.uk

Taylor, Geoffrey (LAB - Victoria)
geoffrey.taylor@hackney.gov.uk

Webb, Jessica (LAB - Hackney Wick)
jessica.webb@hackney.gov.uk

Williams, Carole (LAB - Hoxton West)
carole.williams@hackney.gov.uk

POLITICAL COMPOSITION
LAB: 50, CON: 4, LD: 3

COMMITTEE CHAIRS

Audit: Mr Nick Sharman

Pensions: Mr Robert Chapman

Halton   U

Halton Borough Council, Municipal Building, Kingsway, Widnes WA8 7QF
☎ 0303 333 4300 🖷 0151 471 7301 ✆ hdl@halton.gov.uk 🖳 www. halton.gov.uk

FACTS AND FIGURES
Parliamentary Constituencies: Halton
EU Constituencies: North West
Election Frequency: Elections are by thirds

PRINCIPAL OFFICERS

Chief Executive: Mr David Parr, Chief Executive, Municipal Building, Kingsway, Widnes WA8 7QF ☎ 0151 511 6000
✆ david.parr@halton.gov.uk

Senior Management: Mr Ian Leivesley, Strategic Director - Enterprise, Community & Resources, Municipal Building, Kingsway, Widnes WA8 7QF ☎ 0151 511 6002 ✆ ian.leivesley@halton.gov.uk

Senior Management: Mr Gerald Meehan, Strategic Director - Environment, Municipal Building, Kingsway, Widnes WA8 7QF
☎ 0151 511 6004; 0151 471 7304

Senior Management: Ms Eileen O'Meara, Director - Public Health, Municipal Building, Kingsway, Widnes WA8 7QF
✆ eileen.omeara@halton.gov.uk

Architect, Building / Property Services: Mr Wesley Rourke, Operational Director - Employment, Enterprise & Property, Corporate & Policy Directorate, Municipal Building, Kingsway, Widnes WA8 7QF ☎ 0151 511 8645 ✆ wesley.rourke@halton.gov.uk

Best Value: Mr Mike Foy, Senior Performance Management Officer, Corporate & Policy Directorate, Municipal Building, Kingsway, Widnes WA8 7QF ☎ 0151 511 8081; 0151 471 7301
✆ mike.foy@halton.gov.uk

Building Control: Mr Mick Noone, Operational Director - Policy, Planning & Transportation, Municipal Building, Kingsway, Widnes WA8 7QF ☎ 0151 511 7604 ✆ mick.noone@halton.gov.uk

Catering Services: Mr Chris Patino, Operational Director - Communities & Environment, Select Security Stadium, Lowerhouse Lane, Widnes WA8 7DZ ☎ 0151 510 6000
✆ chris.patino@halton.gov.uk

Children / Youth Services: Mr Gareth Jones, Head of Service - Youth Offenders, Grosvenor House, Halton Lea, Runcorn WA7 2WD ☎ 0151 511 7499 ✆ gareth.jones@halton.gov.uk

Children / Youth Services: Mr Gerald Meehan, Strategic Director - Children & Young People, Municipal Building, Kingsway, Widnes WA8 7QF ☎ 0151 511 6004 ✆ gerald.meehan@halton.gov.uk

Children / Youth Services: Mr Steve Nyakatawa, Operational Director - Children & Young People, Grosvenor House, Halton Lea, Runcorn WA7 2WD ☎ 0151 511 7344
✆ steve.nyakatawa@halton.gov.uk

PR / Communications: Mrs Michelle Osborne, Operational Director - Communications & Marketing, Municipal Building, Kingsway, Widnes WA8 7QF ☎ 0151 511 7723
✆ michelle.osborne@halton.gov.uk

Community Safety: Mr Mick Andrews, Community Safety Officer, 6-8 Church Street, Runcorn WA8 7LT ☎ 0151 511 7695

HALTON

Computer Management: Mr Simon Riley, Operational Director - ICT Services, Municipal Building, Kingsway, Widnes WA8 7QF
☎ 0151 511 7000; 0151 471 7302 ⏚ simon.riley@halton.gov.uk

Contracts: Ms Lorraine Cox, Head of Procurement, Municipal Building, Kingsway, Widnes WA8 7QF ☎ 0151 511 7925
⏚ lorraine.cox@halton.gov.uk

Corporate Services: Mr Ian Leivesley, Strategic Director - Enterprise, Community & Resources, Municipal Building, Kingsway, Widnes WA8 7QF ☎ 0151 511 6002 ⏚ ian.leivesley@halton.gov.uk

Education: Mr Gerald Meehan, Strategic Director - Children & Young People, Municipal Building, Kingsway, Widnes WA8 7QF
☎ 0151 511 6004 ⏚ gerald.meehan@halton.gov.uk

E-Government: Mr Patrick Oliver, E-Government Development Team Leader, Municipal Building, Kingsway, Widnes WA8 7QF
☎ 0151 511 7001 ⏚ pat.oliver@halton.gov.uk

Electoral Registration: Mrs Christine Lawley, Divisional Manager - Democratic Services, Corporate & Policy Directorate, Municipal Building, Kingsway, Widnes WA8 7QF ☎ 0151 511 8328; 0151 471 7301 ⏚ christine.lawley@halton.gov.uk

Emergency Planning: Mr Stephen Rimmer, Head - Traffic Risk & Emergency Planning, Municipal Building, Kingsway, Widnes WA8 7QF ☎ 0151 511 7401; 0151 471 7301 ⏚ stephen.rimmer@halton.gov.uk

Environmental Health: Mr Ian Leivesley, Strategic Director - Enterprise, Community & Resources, Municipal Building, Kingsway, Widnes WA8 7QF ☎ 0151 511 6002 ⏚ ian.leivesley@halton.gov.uk

Estates, Property & Valuation: Mr Wesley Rourke, Operational Director - Employment, Enterprise & Property, Corporate & Policy Directorate, Municipal Building, Kingsway, Widnes WA8 7QF
☎ 0151 511 8645 ⏚ wesley.rourke@halton.gov.uk

Facilities: Mr Simon Webb, Facilities Manager, Municipal Building, Kingsway, Widnes WA8 7QF ☎ 0151 511 8838
⏚ simon.webb@halton.gov.uk

Finance: Mr Ed Dawson, Operational Director - Financial Services, Municipal Building, Kingsway, Widnes WA8 7QF ☎ 0151 511 7965
⏚ ed.dawson@halton.gov.uk

Finance: Mr Peter McCann, Revenue, Benefits & Customer Services Manager, Municipal Building, Kingsway, Widnes WA8 7QF
☎ 0151 511 8411 ⏚ peter.mccann@halton.gov.uk

Fleet Management: Mr Chris Cullen, Head - Operational Support Services, Lowerhouse Lane Depot, Lowerhouse Lane, Widnes WA8 7AW ☎ 0151 511 7937 ⏚ chris.cullen@halton.gov.uk

Grounds Maintenance: Mr Tim Ward-Dutton, Operational Spaces Manager, Municipal Building, Kingsway, Widnes WA8 7QF
⏚ tim.ward-dutton@halton.gov.uk

Health and Safety: Mr Tony Dean, Principal Health & Safety Advisor, Municipal Building, Kingsway, Widnes WA8 7QF
☎ 0151 511 7967 ⏚ tony.dean@halton.gov.uk

Highways: Mr Mick Noone, Operational Director - Policy, Planning & Transportation, Municipal Building, Kingsway, Widnes WA8 7QF
☎ 0151 511 7604 ⏚ mick.noone@halton.gov.uk

Local Area Agreement: Ms Shelah Semoff, Partnership Officer, Municipal Building, Kingsway, Widnes WA8 7QF ☎ 0151 511 8677
⏚ shelah.semoff@halton.gov.uk

Legal: Mr Mark Reaney, Operational Director - Legal & Democratic Services, Municipal Building, Kingsway, Widnes WA8 7QF
☎ 0151 907 8300; 0151 471 7301 ⏚ mark.reaney@halton.gov.uk

Leisure and Cultural Services: Mr Chris Patino, Operational Director - Communities & Environment, Halton Stadium, Lowerhouse Lane, Widnes WA8 7DZ ☎ 0151 510 6000
⏚ chris.patino@halton.gov.uk

Licensing: Mr Mark Reaney, Operational Director - Legal & Democratic Services, Municipal Building, Kingsway, Widnes WA8 7QF ☎ 0151 511 6006 ⏚ mark.reaney@halton.gov.uk

Lighting: Mr Stephen Rimmer, Head - Traffic Risk & Emergency Planning, Municipal Building, Kingsway, Widnes WA8 7QF
☎ 0151 511 7401; 0151 471 7301 ⏚ stephen.rimmer@halton.gov.uk

Lottery Funding, Charity and Voluntary: Mr Wesley Rourke, Operational Director - Employment, Enterprise & Property, Corporate & Policy Directorate, Municipal Building, Kingsway, Widnes WA8 7QF ☎ 0151 511 8645 ⏚ wesley.rourke@halton.gov.uk

Member Services: Mrs Christine Lawley, Divisional Manager - Democratic Services, Corporate & Policy Directorate, Municipal Building, Kingsway, Widnes WA8 7QF ☎ 0151 511 8328; 0151 471 7301 ⏚ christine.lawley@halton.gov.uk

Personnel / HR: Mr Richard Rout, Divisional Manager - Policy, People, Performance & Efficiency, Municipal Building, Kingsway, Widnes WA8 7QF ⏚ richard.rout@halton.gov.uk

Planning: Mr Mick Noone, Operational Director - Policy, Planning & Transportation, Municipal Building, Kingsway, Widnes WA8 7QF
☎ 0151 511 7604 ⏚ mick.noone@halton.gov.uk

Procurement: Ms Lorraine Cox, Head of Procurement, Municipal Building, Kingsway, Widnes WA8 7QF ☎ 0151 511 7925
⏚ lorraine.cox@halton.gov.uk

Public Libraries: Ms Paula Reilly-Cooper, Library Services Manager, Town Hall, Heath Road, Runcorn WA7 5TD
⏚ paula.reilly-cooper@halton.gov.uk

Recycling & Waste Minimisation: Ms Cath Unsworth, Principal Officer - Waste & Recycling, Municipal Building, Kingsway, Widnes WA8 7QF ⏚ cath.unsworth@halton.gov.uk

Road Safety: Mr Stephen Rimmer, Head - Traffic Risk & Emergency Planning, Municipal Building, Kingsway, Widnes WA8 7QF ☎ 0151 511 7401; 0151 471 7301 ⏚ stephen.rimmer@halton.gov.uk

Social Services: Mr Ian Leivesley, Strategic Director - Enterprise, Community & Resources, Municipal Building, Kingsway, Widnes WA8 7QF ☎ 0151 511 6002 ⏚ ian.leivesley@halton.gov.uk

Public Health: Ms Eileen O'Meara, Director - Public Health, Municipal Building, Kingsway, Widnes WA8 7QF ✆ eileen.omeara@halton.gov.uk

Staff Training: Mr Richard Rout, Divisional Manager - Policy, People, Performance & Efficiency, Municipal Building, Kingsway, Widnes WA8 7QF ✆ richard.rout@halton.gov.uk

Traffic Management: Mr Stephen Rimmer, Head - Traffic Risk & Emergency Planning, Municipal Building, Kingsway, Widnes WA8 7QF ☎ 0151 511 7401; 0151 471 7301 ✆ stephen.rimmer@halton.gov.uk

Transport: Mr Mick Noone, Operational Director - Policy, Planning & Transportation, Municipal Building, Kingsway, Widnes WA8 7QF ☎ 0151 511 7604 ✆ mick.noone@halton.gov.uk

Transport Planner: Mr Mick Noone, Operational Director - Policy, Planning & Transportation, Municipal Building, Kingsway, Widnes WA8 7QF ☎ 0151 511 7604 ✆ mick.noone@halton.gov.uk

Waste Collection and Disposal: Mr Jimmy Unsworth, Head - Waste Management, Lowerhouse Lane Depot, Lowerhouse Lane, Widnes WA8 7AW ☎ 0151 511 7625 ✆ jimmy.Unsworth@halton.gov.uk

Waste Management: Mr Jimmy Unsworth, Head - Waste Management, Lowerhouse Lane Depot, Lowerhouse Lane, Widnes WA8 7AW ☎ 0151 511 7625 ✆ jimmy.Unsworth@halton.gov.uk

COUNCILLORS

Mayor: Philbin, Ged (LAB - Appleton)
ged.philbin@halton.gov.uk

Deputy Mayor: Lowe, Alan (LAB - Halton Lea)
alan.lowe@halton.gov.uk

Leader of the Council: Polhill, Rob (LAB - Halton View)
rob.polhill@halton.gov.uk

Deputy Leader of the Council: Wharton, Mike (LAB - Hale)
mike.wharton@halton.gov.uk

Abbott, John (LAB - Grange)
john.abbott@halton.gov.uk

Baker, Sandra (LAB - Birchfield)
sandra.baker@halton.gov.uk

Bradshaw, Marjorie (CON - Daresbury)
marjorie.bradshaw@halton.gov.uk

Bradshaw, John (CON - Daresbury)
john.bradshaw@halton.gov.uk

Cargill, Dave (LAB - Norton South)
dave.cargill@halton.gov.uk

Cargill, Ellen (LAB - Halton Castle)
ellen.cargill@halton.gov.uk

Cassidy, Lauren (LAB - Norton North)
lauren.cassidy@halton.gov.uk

Cole, Arthur (LAB - Halton Castle)
arthur.cole@halton.gov.uk

Dennett, Mark (LAB - Grange)
mark.dennett@halton.gov.uk

Edge, Susan (LAB - Appleton)
sue.edge@halton.gov.uk

Fry, Mike (LAB - Birchfield)
michael.fry@halton.gov.uk

Gerrard, John (LAB - Mersey)
john.gerrard@halton.gov.uk

Gerrard, Charlotte (LAB - Heath)
charlotte.gerrard@halton.gov.uk

Gilligan, Robert (LAB - Broadheath)
robert.gilligan@halton.gov.uk

Harris, Phil (LAB - Hough Green)
phil.harris@halton.gov.uk

Hignett, Pauline (LAB - Windmill House)
pauline.hignett2@halton.gov.uk

Hignett, Ron (LAB - Norton South)
ron.hignett@halton.gov.uk

Hill, Valerie (LAB - Farnworth)
valerie.hill@halton.gov.uk

Hill, Stan (LAB - Riverside)
stan.hill@halton.gov.uk

Horabin, Margaret (LAB - Kingsway)
margaret.horabin@halton.gov.uk

Howard, Harry (LAB - Halton Castle)
harry.howard@halton.gov.uk

Jones, Eddie (LAB - Appleton)
eddie.jones@halton.gov.uk

Lloyd-Jones, Martha (LAB - Norton South)
martha.lloydjones@halton.gov.uk

Lloyd-Jones, Peter (LAB - Norton North)
peter.lloydjones@halton.gov.uk

Loftus, Kath (LAB - Halton Lea)
kath.loftus@halton.gov.uk

Loftus, Chris (LAB - Beechwood)
chris.loftus@halton.gov.uk

Logan, Geoffrey (LAB - Beechwood)
geoffrey.logan@halton.gov.uk

Lowe, Joan (LAB - Grange)
joan.lowe@halton.gov.uk

MacManus, Andrew (LAB - Farnworth)
andrew.macmanus@halton.gov.uk

McDermott, Tony (LAB - Broadheath)
tony.mcdermott@halton.gov.uk

McInerney, Angela (LAB - Farnworth)
angela.mcinerney@halton.gov.uk

McInerney, Tom (LAB - Halton View)
tom.mcinerney@halton.gov.uk

Morley, Keith (LAB - Broadheath)
keith.morley@halton.gov.uk

Nelson, Stef (LAB - Halton Brook)
stef.nelson@halton.gov.uk

Nolan, Paul (LAB - Hough Green)
paul.nolan@halton.gov.uk

Osborne, Shaun (LAB - Ditton)
shaun.osborne@halton.gov.uk

Parker, Stan (LAB - Halton View)
stan.parker@halton.gov.uk

HALTON

Plumpton-Walsh, Carol (LAB - Halton Brook)
carol.plumptonwalsh@halton.gov.uk

Pumpton-Walsh, Norman (LAB - Mersey)
norman.plumptonwalsh@halton.gov.uk

Roberts, June (LAB - Kingsway)
june.roberts@halton.gov.uk

Roberts, Joe (LAB - Ditton)
joe.roberts@halton.gov.uk

Rowe, Christopher (LD - Heath)
christopher.rowe@halton.gov.uk

Sinnott, Pauline (LAB - Mersey)
pauline.sinnott2@halton.gov.uk

Stockton, John (LAB - Halton Brook)
john.stockton@halton.gov.uk

Stockton, Gareth (LD - Heath)
gareth.stockton@halton.gov.uk

Thompson, Dave (LAB - Halton Lea)
dave.thompson@halton.gov.uk

Wainwright, Kevan (LAB - Hough Green)
kevan.wainwright@halton.gov.uk

Wall, Andrea (LAB - Kingsway)
andrea.wall@halton.gov.uk

Wallace, Pamela (LAB - Riverside)
pamela.wallace@halton.gov.uk

Woolfall, Bill (LAB - Birchfield)
bill.woolfall2@halton.gov.uk

Wright, Marie (LAB - Ditton)
marie.wright@halton.gov.uk

Zygadllo, Geoff (LAB - Norton North)
geoff.zygadllo@halton.gov.uk

POLITICAL COMPOSITION
LAB: 52, LD: 2, CON: 2

COMMITTEE CHAIRS

Children, Young People & Families: Mr Mark Dennett

Development Control: Mr Paul Nolan

Hambleton   D

Hambleton District Council, Civic Centre, Stone Cross,
Northallerton DL6 2UU
☎ 01609 779977 ⌁ info@hambleton.gov.uk ▣ www.hambleton.gov.uk

FACTS AND FIGURES
Parliamentary Constituencies: Richmond (Yorks)
EU Constituencies: Yorkshire and the Humber
Election Frequency: Elections are of whole council

PRINCIPAL OFFICERS

Chief Executive: Dr Justin Ives, Chief Executive, Civic Centre,
Stone Cross, Northallerton DL6 2UU ☎ 01609 779977
⌁ justin.ives@hambleton.gov.uk

Senior Management: Mr Dave Goodwin, Executive Director, Civic
Centre, Stone Cross, Northallerton DL6 2UU ☎ 01609 779977
⌁ dave.goodwin@hambleton.gov.uk

Senior Management: Dr Justin Ives, Chief Executive, Civic
Centre, Stone Cross, Northallerton DL6 2UU ☎ 01609 779977
⌁ justin.ives@hambleton.gov.uk

Senior Management: Mr Michael Jewitt, Executive Director, Civic
Centre, Stone Cross, Northallerton DL6 2UU ☎ 01609 779977
⌁ mick.jewitt@hambleton.gov.uk

Building Control: Mr Mark Harbottle, Head of Service - Planning
& Housing, Civic Centre, Stone Cross, Northallerton DL6 2UU
☎ 01609 779977 ⌁ mark.harbottle@hambleton.gov.uk

PR / Communications: Mrs Aly Thompson, Senior
Communications & Media Manager, Civic Centre, Stone Cross,
Northallerton DL6 2UU ☎ 01609 767063
⌁ aly.thompson@hambleton.gov.uk

Community Safety: Ms Helen Kemp, Head of Service - Customer
& Economy, Civic Centre, Stone Cross, Northallerton DL6 2UU
☎ 01609 779977 ⌁ helen.kemp@hambleton.gov.uk

Customer Service: Ms Sandra Hall, Customer & Communications
Manager, Civic Centre, Stone Cross, Northallerton DL6 2UU
☎ 01609 779977 ⌁ sandra.hall@hambleton.gov.uk

Environmental Health: Mr Philip Mepham, Environmental Health
Manager, Swale House, Frenchgate, Richmond DL10 4JE ☎ 01748
829100; 01748 826186 ⌁ philip.mepham@richmondshire.gov.uk

Finance: Dr Justin Ives, Chief Executive, Civic Centre, Stone Cross,
Northallerton DL6 2UU ☎ 01609 779977
⌁ justin.ives@hambleton.gov.uk

Treasury: Dr Justin Ives, Chief Executive, Civic Centre, Stone
Cross, Northallerton DL6 2UU ☎ 01609 779977
⌁ justin.ives@hambleton.gov.uk

Legal: Mr Gary Nelson, Head of Service - Legal & Information,
Civic Centre, Stone Cross, Northallerton DL6 2UU ☎ 01609 779977
⌁ gary.nelson@hambleton.gov.uk

Leisure and Cultural Services: Mr Steve Lister, Head of Leisure
Services, Civic Centre, Stone Cross, Northallerton DL6 2UU
☎ 01609 779977 ⌁ steve.lister@hambleton.gov.uk

Member Services: Mr Gary Nelson, Head of Service - Legal &
Information, Civic Centre, Stone Cross, Northallerton DL6 2UU
☎ 01609 779977 ⌁ gary.nelson@hambleton.gov.uk

Planning: Mr Mark Harbottle, Head of Service - Planning &
Housing, Civic Centre, Stone Cross, Northallerton DL6 2UU
☎ 01609 779977 ⌁ mark.harbottle@hambleton.gov.uk

Recycling & Waste Minimisation: Mr Paul Staines, Head of
Service - Environment, Civic Centre, Stone Cross, Northallerton
DL6 2UU ☎ 0845 121 1555 ⌁ paul.staines@hambleton.gov.uk

Waste Collection and Disposal: Mr Paul Staines, Head of
Service - Environment, Civic Centre, Stone Cross, Northallerton
DL6 2UU ☎ 0845 121 1555 ⌁ paul.staines@hambleton.gov.uk

Waste Management: Mr Paul Staines, Head of Service -
Environment, Civic Centre, Stone Cross, Northallerton DL6 2UU
☎ 0845 121 1555 ⁐ paul.staines@hambleton.gov.uk

COUNCILLORS

Chair: Noone, John (CON - Bedale)
cllr.john.noone@hambleton.gov.uk

Leader of the Council: Robson, Mark (CON - Sowerby & Topcliffe)
cllr.mark.robson@hambleton.gov.uk

Deputy Leader of the Council: Wilkinson, Peter (CON - Romanby)
cllr.peter.wilkinson@hambleton.gov.uk

Baker, Robert (CON - Bagby & Thorntons)
cllr.bob.baker@hambleton.gov.uk

Bardon, Peter (CON - Sowerby & Topcliffe)
cllr.peter.bardon@hambleton.gov.uk

Barningham, Michael (CON - Bedale)
cllr.michael.barningham@hambleton.gov.uk

Blades, David (CON - Northallerton North & Brompton)
cllr.david.blades@hambleton.gov.uk

Cookman, Christine (CON - Huby)
cllr.christine.cookman@hambleton.gov.uk

Dadd, Gareth (CON - Thirsk)
cllr.gareth.dadd@hambleton.gov.uk

Dickins, Stephen (CON - Stokesley)
cllr.stephen.dickins@hambleton.gov.uk

Dickinson, Caroline (CON - Northallerton South)
cllr.caroline.dickinson@hambleton.gov.uk

Ellis, Geoff (CON - Easingwold)
cllr.geoff.ellis@hambleton.gov.uk

Fortune, Bridget (CON - Hutton Rudby)
cllr.bridget.fortune@hambleton.gov.uk

Hardisty, Kevin (CON - Romanby)
cllr.kevin.hardisty@hambleton.gov.uk

Hudson, Richard (CON - Great Ayton)
cllr.richard.hudson@hambleton.gov.uk

Hugill, David (CON - Osmotherley & Swainby)
cllr.david.hugill@hambleton.gov.uk

Kirk, Ron (CON - Great Ayton)
cllr.ron.kirk@hambleton.gov.uk

Knapton, Nigel (CON - Easingwold)
cllr.nigel.knapton@hambleton.gov.uk

Les, Carl (CON - Bedale)
cllr.carl.les@hambleton.gov.uk

Palmer, Claire (UKIP - Northallerton South)
cllr.claire.palmer@hambleton.gov.uk

Patmore, Caroline (CON - Raskelf & White Horse)
cllr.caroline.patmore@hambleton.gov.uk

Phillips, Brian (CON - Morton-on-Swale)
cllr.brian.phillips@hambleton.gov.uk

Rooke, Chris (CON - Easingwold)
cllr.chris.rooke@hambleton.gov.uk

Sanderson, Isobel (CON - Northallerton North & Brompton)
cllr.isobel.sanderson@hambleton.gov.uk

Wake, Andy (CON - Stokesley)
cllr.andy.wake@hambleton.gov.uk

Watson, Janet (CON - Thirsk)
cllr.janet.watson@hambleton.gov.uk

Watson, Stephen (CON - Appleton Wiske & Smeatons)
cllr.stephen.watson@hambleton.gov.uk

Webster, David (CON - Tanfield)
cllr.david.webster@hambleton.gov.uk

POLITICAL COMPOSITION
CON: 27, UKIP: 1

COMMITTEE CHAIRS

Audit, Governance & Standards: Mr Richard Hudson

Licensing: Ms Isobel Sanderson

Planning: Mr David Webster

Hammersmith & Fulham   L

Hammersmith & Fulham London Borough Council,
Hammersmith Town Hall, 7 King Street, London W6 9JU
☎ 020 8748 3020 ⎙ 020 8741 0307 ⁐ information@lbhf.gov.uk
🖳 www.lbhf.gov.uk

FACTS AND FIGURES
Parliamentary Constituencies: Hammersmith
EU Constituencies: London
Election Frequency: Elections are of whole council

PRINCIPAL OFFICERS

Chief Executive: Mr Nigel Pallace, Chief Executive, Town Hall
Extension, King Street, London W6 9JU ☎ 020 8753 3000
⁐ nigel.pallace@lbhf.gov.uk

Senior Management: Ms Liz Bruce, Tri-Borough Executive
Director - Adult Social Care, Town Hall, King Street, London W6
9JU ☎ 020 8753 5166 ⁐ liz.bruce@lbhf.gov.uk

Senior Management: Mrs Clare Chamberlain, Tri-Borough
Executive Director - Children's Services, Town Hall, Hornton Street,
London W8 7NX ⁐ clare.chamberlain@rbkc.gov.uk

Senior Management: Mr Ed Garcez, Tri-Borough Chief
Information Officer, Hammersmith Town Hall, 7 King Street, London
W6 9JU ☎ 020 8753 2900 ⁐ ed.garcez@lbhf.gov.uk

Senior Management: Mr Michael Hainge, Director - Commercial
& Procurement, Hammersmith Town Hall, 7 King Street, London
W6 9JU ☎ 020 8753 6992 ⁐ michael.hainge@lbhf.gov.uk

Senior Management: Mr Hitesh Jolapara, Strategic Director
- Financial Corporate Services, Hammersmith Town Hall, 7 King
Street, London W6 9JU ☎ 020 7361 2316
⁐ hitesh.jolapara@rbkc.gov.uk

Senior Management: Ms Debbie Morris, Director - Human
Resources, Hammersmith Town Hall, 7 King Street, London
W6 9JU ☎ 020 8753 3068 ⁐ debbie.morris@lbhf.gov.uk

HAMMERSMITH & FULHAM

Best Value: Ms Kim Dero, Director - Delivery & Value, Hammersmith Town Hall, 7 King Street, London W6 9JU ☎ 020 8748 3020 ⁂ kim.dero@lbhf.gov.uk

Building Control: Mr Jay Jayaweera, Head of Building Control, Hammersmith Town Hall, 7 King Street, London W6 9JU ☎ 020 8753 3424 ⁂ jay.jayaweera@lbhf.gov.uk

Building Control: Ms Maureen McDonald-Khan, Director - Building & Property Management, Hammersmith Town Hall, 7 King Street, London W6 9JU ☎ 020 8753 4701 ⁂ maureen.mcdonald-khan@lbhf.gov.uk

Children / Youth Services: Mrs Clare Chamberlain, Tri-Borough Executive Director - Children's Services, Town Hall, Hornton Street, London W8 7NX ⁂ clare.chamberlain@rbkc.gov.uk

Children / Youth Services: Ms Alison Farmer, Assistant Director - Special Educational Needs & Vulnerable Children, Hammersmith Town Hall, 7 King Street, London W6 9JU ☎ 020 7745 6457 ⁂ alison.farmer@rbkc.gov.uk

Children / Youth Services: Ms Betty McDonald, Head of Youth Offending Service, Hammersmith Town Hall, 7 King Street, London W6 9JU ☎ 020 7361 2725 ⁂ betty.mcdonald@rbkc.gov.uk

Children / Youth Services: Ms Fiona Phelps, Head of Service - SEN, Casework & Commissioning, Hammersmith Town Hall, 7 King Street, London W6 9JU ⁂ fiona.phelps@rbkc.gov.uk

PR / Communications: Ms Louise Raisey, Head of Communications, Hammersmith Town Hall, 7 King Street, London W6 9JU ☎ 020 8753 2012 ⁂ louise.raisey@lbhf.gov.uk

Community Planning: Ms Sue Spiller, Head of Community Investment, Hammersmith Town Hall, 7 King Street, London W6 9JU ☎ 020 8753 2483 ⁂ sue.spiller@lbhf.gov.uk

Community Safety: Mr David Page, Bi-Borough Director - Safer Neighbourhoods, Hammersmith Town Hall, 7 King Street, London W6 9JU ☎ 020 8753 2125 ⁂ david.page@lbhf.gov.uk

Community Safety: Ms Claire Rai, Head of Community Safety, Hammersmith Town Hall, 7 King Street, London W6 9JU ☎ 020 8753 3154 ⁂ claire.rai@lbhf.gov.uk

Computer Management: Mr Ed Garcez, Tri-Borough Chief Information Officer, Hammersmith Town Hall, 7 King Street, London W6 9JU ☎ 020 8753 2900 ⁂ ed.garcez@lbhf.gov.uk

Computer Management: Mr Ben Goward, Head of Digital, Westminster City Hall, 64 Victoria Street, London SW1E 6QP ☎ 020 7641 5504 ⁂ bgoward@westminster.gov.uk

Computer Management: Ms Ciara Shimidzu, Head of Information Management, Hammersmith Town Hall, 7 King Street, London W6 9JU ☎ 020 8753 3895 ⁂ ciara.shimidzu@lbhf.gov.uk

Consumer Protection and Trading Standards: Ms Valerie Simpson, Head of Environmental Health - Licensing & Trading Standards, Hammersmith Town Hall, 7 King Street, London W6 9JU ☎ 020 8753 3905 ⁂ valerie.simpson@lbhf.gov.uk

Corporate Services: Mr Zakki Ghauri, Head of Portfolio Management, Hammersmith Town Hall, 7 King Street, London W6 9JU ☎ 020 8753 5588 ⁂ zakki.ghauri@lbhf.gov.uk

Corporate Services: Mr Michael Hainge, Director - Commercial & Procurement, Hammersmith Town Hall, 7 King Street, London W6 9JU ☎ 020 8753 6992 ⁂ michael.hainge@lbhf.gov.uk

Corporate Services: Ms Moyra McGarvey, Director - Audit, Fraud, Risk & Insurance, Hammersmith Town Hall, 7 King Street, London W6 9JU ☎ 020 7361 2389 ⁂ moyra.mcgarvey@rbkc.gov.uk

Corporate Services: Ms Debbie Morris, Director - Human Resources, Hammersmith Town Hall, 7 King Street, London W6 9JU ☎ 020 8753 3068 ⁂ debbie.morris@lbhf.gov.uk

Corporate Services: Mr Martin Nottage, Director - Innovation & Change Management, Hammersmith Town Hall, 7 King Street, London W6 9JU ☎ 020 8753 3542 ⁂ martin.nottage@lbhf.gov.uk

Customer Service: Mr Steve Barrett, Head of Revenues & Benefits, Hammersmith Town Hall, 7 King Street, London W6 9JU ☎ 020 8753 1053 ⁂ steve.barrett@lbhf.gov.uk

Customer Service: Mr John Cordani, Head of Customer Services, Hammersmith Town Hall, 7 King Street, London W6 9JU ☎ 020 8753 1318 ⁂ john.cordani@lbhf.gov.uk

Education: Ms Wendy Anthony, Head of Schools Admissions, Hammersmith Town Hall, 7 King Street, London W6 9JU ☎ 020 7745 6640 ⁂ wendy.anthony@rbkc.gov.uk

Education: Mr Ian Heggs, Tri-Borough Director - Schools, Hammersmith Town Hall, 7 King Street, London W6 9JU ☎ 020 7745 6465 ⁂ ian.heggs@lbhf.gov.uk

Education: Mr Richard Stanley, Assistant Director - Schools Standards, Hammersmith Town Hall, 7 King Street, London W6 9JU ☎ 020 7745 6457 ⁂ richard.stanley@rbkc.gov.uk

Emergency Planning: Mr Alistair Ayres, Head of Emergency Services, Hammersmith Town Hall, 7 King Street, London W6 9JU ☎ 020 8753 3994 ⁂ alistair.ayres@lbhf.gov.uk

Environmental Health: Mr Nick Austin, Bi-Borough Director - Environmental Health, Hammersmith Town Hall, 7 King Street, London W6 9JU ☎ 020 8753 3904 ⁂ nick.austin@lbhf.gov.uk

Environmental Health: Mr Richard Buckley, Head of Environmental Health - Residential, Hammersmith Town Hall, 7 King Street, London W6 9JU ☎ 020 8753 3971 ⁂ richard.buckley@lbhf.gov.uk

Environmental Health: Ms Sue Harris, Director - Cleaner, Greener & Cultural Services, Hammersmith Town Hall, 7 King Street, London W6 9JU ☎ 020 8753 4295 ⁂ sue.harris@lbhf.gov.uk

Environmental Health: Ms Ann Ramage, Head of Environmental Health - Commercial, Hammersmith Town Hall, 7 King Street, London W6 9JU ☎ 020 7341 5612 ⁂ ann.ramage@rbkc.gov.uk

Environmental Health: Ms Valerie Simpson, Head of Environmental Health - Licensing & Trading Standards, Hammersmith Town Hall, 7 King Street, London W6 9JU ☎ 020 8753 3905 ✆ valerie.simpson@lbhf.gov.uk

Estates, Property & Valuation: Mr Stephen Kirrage, Director - Asset Management & Property Services, Hammersmith Town Hall, 7 King Street, London W6 9JU ☎ 020 8753 3064 ✆ stephen.kirrage@lbhf.gov.uk

Estates, Property & Valuation: Ms Sharon Schaaf, Head of Estate Services, Hammersmith Town Hall, 7 King Street, London W6 9JU ☎ 020 8753 2570 ✆ sharon.schaaf@lbhf.gov.uk

Finance: Mr Christopher Harris, Head of Finance - Corporate Accountancy & Capital, Hammersmith Town Hall, 7 King Street, London W6 9JU ☎ 020 8753 6440 ✆ christopher.harris@lbhf.gov.uk

Finance: Mr Hitesh Jolapara, Strategic Director - Financial Corporate Services, Hammersmith Town Hall, 7 King Street, London W6 9JU ☎ 020 7361 2316 ✆ hitesh.jolapara@rbkc.gov.uk

Finance: Mr Andrew Lord, Head of Strategic Planning & Monitoring Corporate Finance, Hammersmith Town Hall, 7 King Street, London W6 9JU ☎ 020 8753 2531 ✆ andrew.lord@lbhf.gov.uk

Health and Safety: Mr Norman Whyte, Head of Health & Safety, Hammersmith Town Hall, 7 King Street, London W6 9JU ☎ 020 8753 3647 ✆ norman.whyte@lbhf.gov.uk

Highways: Mr Ian Hawthorn, Head of Highway Maintenance & Projects, Hammersmith Town Hall, 7 King Street, London W6 9JU ☎ 020 8753 3058 ✆ ian.hawthorn.lbhf.gov.uk

Highways: Mr Mahmood Siddiqi, Bi-Borough Director - Transport & Highways, Hammersmith Town Hall, 7 King Street, London W6 9JU ☎ 020 7361 3589; 020 8748 3020 ✆ mahmood.siddiqi@rbkc.gov.uk

Housing: Mr Mike England, Director - Housing Strategy & Options, Hammersmith Town Hall, 7 King Street, London W6 9JU ☎ 020 8753 5344 ✆ mike.england@lbhf.gov.uk

Housing: Mr Nilavra Mukerji, Director - Housing Services, Hammersmith Town Hall, 7 King Street, London W6 9JU ☎ 020 8753 1313 ✆ nilavra.mukerji@lbhf.gov.uk

Housing: Ms Glendine Shepherd, Head of Allocations, Home Buy & Property Solutions, Hammersmith Town Hall, 7 King Street, London W6 9JU ☎ 020 8753 5813 ✆ glendine.shepherd@lbhf.gov.uk

Legal: Ms Rhian Davies, Chief Solicitor - Litigation & Social Care, Westminster City Hall, 64 Victoria Street, London SW1E 6QP ☎ 020 7641 2729 ✆ rdavies@westminster.gov.uk

Legal: Ms LeVerne Parker, Chief Solicitor - Planning & Property, Hammersmith Town Hall, 7 King Street, London W6 9JU ☎ 020 7361 2180 ✆ leverne.parker@rbkc.gov.uk

Legal: Mrs Tasnim Shawkat, Tri-Borough Director - Law, Hammersmith Town Hall, 7 King Street, London W6 9JU ☎ 020 8753 2700 ✆ tasnim.shawkat@lbhf.gov.uk

Legal: Mr Keith Simkins, Chief Solicitor - Contracts & Employment, Hammersmith Town Hall, 7 King Street, London W6 9JU ☎ 020 7361 2194 ✆ keith.simkins@rbkc.gov.uk

Leisure and Cultural Services: Mr Ullash Karia, Head of Leisure & Parks, The Stableyard, Holland Park, Ilchester Place, London W8 6LU ☎ 020 7938 8171 ✆ ullash.karia@rbkc.gov.uk

Leisure and Cultural Services: Ms Donna Pentelow, Bi-Borough Head of Culture, Hammersmith Town Hall, 7 King Street, London W6 9JU ☎ 020 8752 2358 ✆ donna.pentelow@lbhf.gov.uk

Licensing: Ms Valerie Simpson, Head of Environmental Health - Licensing & Trading Standards, Hammersmith Town Hall, 7 King Street, London W6 9JU ☎ 020 8753 3905 ✆ valerie.simpson@lbhf.gov.uk

Parking: Mr David Taylor, Bi-Borough Head of Parking Services, Hammersmith Town Hall, 7 King Street, London W6 9JU ☎ 020 8753 3251 ✆ david.taylor@lbhf.gov.uk

Personnel / HR: Ms Mary-Ann Lord, Head of HR Strategy & OD, Hammersmith Town Hall, 7 King Street, London W6 9JU ☎ 020 7361 2347 ✆ mary-ann.lord@rbkc.gov.uk

Personnel / HR: Ms Debbie Morris, Director - Human Resources, Hammersmith Town Hall, 7 King Street, London W6 9JU ☎ 020 8753 3068 ✆ debbie.morris@lbhf.gov.uk

Planning: Ms Juliemma McLoughlin, Director - Planning & Growth, Hammersmith Town Hall, 7 King Street, London W6 9JU ☎ 020 8753 3565 ✆ juliemma.mcloughlin@lbhf.gov.uk

Planning: Ms Ellen Whitchurch, Head of Development Management, Hammersmith Town Hall, 7 King Street, London W6 9JU ☎ 020 8753 3484 ✆ ellen.whitchurch@lbhf.gov.uk

Procurement: Mr John Francis, Joint Head of Procurement, Hammersmith Town Hall, 7 King Street, London W6 9JU ☎ 020 8753 2582 ✆ john.francis@lbhf.gov.uk

Procurement: Mr Michael Hainge, Director - Commercial & Procurement, Hammersmith Town Hall, 7 King Street, London W6 9JU ☎ 020 8753 6992 ✆ michael.hainge@lbhf.gov.uk

Procurement: Mr Alan Parry, Joint Head of Procurement, Hammersmith Town Hall, 7 King Street, London W6 9JU ☎ 020 8753 2581 ✆ alan.parry@lbhf.gov.uk

Public Libraries: Mr Mike Clarke, Tri-Borough Director - Libraries & Archives, Hammersmith Town Hall, 7 King Street, London W6 9JU ☎ 020 7641 2199 ✆ mclarke1@westminster.gov.uk

Regeneration: Mr John Finlayson, Head of Planning & Regeneration, Hammersmith Town Hall, 7 King Street, London W6 9JU ☎ 020 8753 674 ✆ john.finlayson@lbhf.gov.uk

HAMMERSMITH & FULHAM

Social Services (Adult): Ms Stella Baillie, Tri-Borough Director - Integrated Care, Hammersmith Town Hall, 7 King Street, London W6 9JU ☎ 020 7361 2398 ✒ stella.baillie2@lbhf.gov.uk

Social Services (Adult): Ms Helen Banham, Strategic Lead - Safeguarding & Professional Standards, Westminster City Hall, 64 Victoria Street, London SW1E 6QP ☎ 020 7641 4196 ✒ hbanham@westminster.gov.uk

Social Services (Adult): Ms Liz Bruce, Tri-Borough Executive Director - Adult Social Care, Town Hall, King Street, London W6 9JU ☎ 020 8753 5166 ✒ liz.bruce@lbhf.gov.uk

Social Services (Adult): Ms Mary Dalton, Head of Complex Needs Commissioning, Westminster City Hall, 64 Victoria Street, London SW1E 6QP ☎ 020 7641 6615 ✒ mdalton@westminster.gov.uk

Social Services (Children): Mrs Clare Chamberlain, Tri-Borough Executive Director - Children's Services, Town Hall, Hornton Street, London W8 7NX ✒ clare.chamberlain@rbkc.gov.uk

Social Services (Children): Ms Mandy Lawson, Head of Disabled Children's Services, Hammersmith Town Hall, 7 King Street, London W6 9JU ☎ 020 7641 2740 ✒ mandy.lawson@rbkc.gov.uk

Social Services (Children): Mr Stephen Miley, Director - Family Services, Hammersmith Town Hall, 7 King Street, London W6 9JU ☎ 020 8753 2300 ✒ steve.miley@lbhf.gov.uk

Fostering & Adoption: Ms Sally Pillay, Head of Fostering & Adoption Service, Hammersmith Town Hall, 7 King Street, London W6 9JU ☎ 020 8753 2320 ✒ sally.pillay@rbkc.gov.uk

Families: Mr Stephen Miley, Director - Family Services, Hammersmith Town Hall, 7 King Street, London W6 9JU ☎ 020 8753 2300 ✒ steve.miley@lbhf.gov.uk

Looked after Children: Ms Sara Scholey, Head of Looked After Children, Hammersmith Town Hall, 7 King Street, London W6 9JU ☎ 020 8753 5525 ✒ sara.scholey@lbhf.gov.uk

Public Health: Dr Mike Robinson, Director - Public Health, Hammersmith Town Hall, 7 King Street, London W6 9JU ☎ 020 7641 4590 ✒ mrobinson4@westminster.gov.uk

Transport: Mr Mahmood Siddiqi, Bi-Borough Director - Transport & Highways, Hammersmith Town Hall, 7 King Street, London W6 9JU ☎ 020 7361 3589; 020 8748 3020 ✒ mahmood.siddiqi@rbkc.gov.uk

Transport Planner: Mr Nick Boyle, Chief Transport Planner, Hammersmith Town Hall, 7 King Street, London W6 9JU ☎ 020 8753 3069 ✒ nick.boyle@lbhf.gov.uk

Transport Planner: Mr Mahmood Siddiqi, Bi-Borough Director - Transport & Highways, Hammersmith Town Hall, 7 King Street, London W6 9JU ☎ 020 7361 3589; 020 8748 3020 ✒ mahmood.siddiqi@rbkc.gov.uk

Waste Management: Ms Kathy May, Bi-Borough Head of Waste & Street Enforcement, Hammersmith Town Hall, 7 King Street, London W6 9JU ☎ 020 7341 5616 ✒ kathy.may@rbkc.gov.uk

COUNCILLORS

Mayor: Umeh, Mercy (LAB - Shepherds Bush Green) mercy.umeh@lbhf.gov.uk

Deputy Mayor: Brown, Daryl (LAB - North End) daryl.brown@lbhf.gov.uk

Leader of the Council: Cowan, Stephen (LAB - Hammersmith Broadway) stephen.cowan@lbhf.gov.uk

Deputy Leader of the Council: Cartwright, Michael (LAB - Hammersmith Broadway) michael.cartwright@lbhf.gov.uk

Group LeaderSmith, Gregg (CON - Town) greg.smith@lbhf.gov.uk

Adam, Michael (CON - Munster) michael.adam@lbhf.gov.uk

Aherne, Colin (LAB - Wormholt & White City) colin.aherne@lbhf.gov.uk

Alford, Adronie (CON - Munster) adronie.alford@lbhf.gov.uk

Barlow, Hannah (LAB - Avonmore & Brook Green) hannah.barlow@lbhf.gov.uk

Botterill, Nicholas (CON - Parsons Green & Walham) nicholas.botterill@lbhf.gov.uk

Brown, Andrew (CON - Town) andrew.brown@lbhf.gov.uk

Carlebach, Joe (CON - Avonmore & Brook Green) joe.carlebach@lbhf.gov.uk

Cassidy, Iain (LAB - Fulham Reach) Iain.Cassidy@lbhf.gov.uk

Chumnery, Elaine (LAB - College Park & Old Oak) elaine.chumnery@lbhf.gov.uk

Coleman, Ben (LAB - Fulham Broadway) ben.coleman@lbhf.gov.uk

Connell, Adam (LAB - Addison) adam.connell@lbhf.gov.uk

Culhane, Larry (LAB - North End) larry.culhane@lbhf.gov.uk

De'Ath, Alan (LAB - Fulham Broadway) alan.de'ath@lbhf.gov.uk

Dewhirst, Charlie (CON - Ravenscourt Park) charlie.dewhirst@lbhf.gov.uk

Donovan, Belinda (CON - Addison) belinda.donovan@lbhf.gov.uk

Fennimore, Sue (LAB - Addison) sue.fennimore@lbhf.gov.uk

Ffiske, Caroline (CON - Avonmore & Brook Green) caroline.ffiske@lbhf.gov.uk

Ginn, Marcus (CON - Palace Riverside) marcus.ginn@lbhf.gov.uk

Hamilton, Steve (CON - Sands End)
steve.hamilton@lbhf.gov.uk

Harcourt, Wesley (LAB - College Park & Old Oak)
wesley.harcourt@lbhf.gov.uk

Hashem, Ali (LAB - North End)
Ali.Hashem@lbhf.gov.uk

Holder, Sharon (LAB - Fulham Broadway)
sharon.holder@lbhf.gov.uk

Homan, Lisa (LAB - Askew)
lisa.homan@lbhf.gov.uk

Ivimy, Lucy (CON - Ravenscourt Park)
lucy.ivimy@lbhf.gov.uk

Johnson, Donald (CON - Palace Riverside)
donald.johnson@lbhf.gov.uk

Jones, Andrew (LAB - Shepherds Bush Green)
andrew.jones@lbhf.gov.uk

Karmel, Alex (CON - Munster)
alex.karmel@lbhf.gov.uk

Largan, Robert (CON - Sands End)
robert.largan@lbhf.gov.uk

Law, Jane (CON - Sands End)
jane.law@lbhf.gov.uk

Loveday, Mark (CON - Parsons Green & Walham)
mark.loveday@lbhf.gov.uk

Lukey, Vivienne (LAB - Fulham Reach)
vivienne.lukey@lbhf.gov.uk

Macmillan, Sue (LAB - Wormholt & White City)
sue.macmillan@lbhf.gov.uk

Murphy, PJ (LAB - Hammersmith Broadway)
pj.murphy@lbhf.gov.uk

Needham, Caroline (LAB - Askew)
caroline.needham@lbhf.gov.uk

Nsumbu, Viya (CON - Town)
viya.nsumbu@lbhf.gov.uk

Perez, Natalia (LAB - Shepherds Bush Green)
natalia.perez@lbhf.gov.uk

Phibbs, Harry (CON - Ravenscourt Park)
harry.phibbs@lbhf.gov.uk

Schmid, Max (LAB - Wormholt & White City)
max.schmid@lbhf.gov.uk

Stainton, Frances (CON - Parsons Green & Walham)
frances.stainton@lbhf.gov.uk

Vaughan, Rory (LAB - Askew)
rory.vaughan@lbhf.gov.uk

Vincent, Guy (LAB - Fulham Reach)
guy.vincent@lbhf.gov.uk

POLITICAL COMPOSITION
LAB: 26, CON: 20

COMMITTEE CHAIRS

Audit, Pensions & Standards: Mr Iain Cassidy

Children & Education: Ms Caroline Needham

Health & Wellbeing: Ms Vivienne Lukey

Health, Adult Social Care & Inclusion: Mr Rory Vaughan

Licensing: Ms Natalia Perez

Planning & Development Control: Mr Adam Connell

Hampshire   C

Hampshire County Council, The Castle, Winchester SO23 8UJ
☎ 0300 555 1375 ☐ info@hants.gov.uk ☐ www.hants.gov.uk

FACTS AND FIGURES
Parliamentary Constituencies: Aldershot, Basingstoke, Eastleigh, Fareham, Gosport, Havant, Meon Valley, New Forest East, New Forest West, Southampton, Test, Winchester
EU Constituencies: South East
Election Frequency: Elections are of whole council

PRINCIPAL OFFICERS

Chief Executive: Mr John Coughlan, Chief Executive, Elizabeth II Court, Winchester SO23 8UG ☎ 01962 846400
☐ john.coughlan@hants.gov.uk

Assistant Chief Executive: Ms Deborah Harkin, Assistant Chief Executive, Elizabeth II Court, Winchester SO23 8UJ
☎ 01962 846699 ☐ deborah.harkin@hants.gov.uk

Senior Management: Mr Graham Allen, Director - Adults' Health & Care, Elizabeth II Court, Winchester SO23 8UG ☎ 01962 845875
☐ graham.allen@hants.gov.uk

Senior Management: Mr Paul Archer, Director - Transformation & Governance, Elizabeth II Court South, Winchester SO23 8UJ
☎ 01962 846124 ☐ paul.archer@hants.gov.uk

Senior Management: Dr Sallie Bacon, Interim Director - Public Health, The Castle, Winchester SO23 8UJ ☎ 023 8038 3389
☐ sallie.bacon@hants.gov.uk

Senior Management: Mr Steve Crocker, Director - Children's Services, Elizabeth II Court, Winchester SO23 8UG ☎ 01962 847991
☐ steve.crocker@hants.gov.uk

Senior Management: Mr Stuart Jarvis, Director - Economy, Transport & Environment, Elizabeth II Court, Winchester SO23 8UD
☎ 01962 845260 ☐ stuart.jarvis@hants.gov.uk

Senior Management: Ms Karen Murray, Director - Culture, Communities & Business Services, Three Minsters House, 76 High Street, Winchester SO23 8UL ☎ 01962 847876
☐ karen.murray@hants.gov.uk

Senior Management: Mrs Carolyn Williamson, Director - Corporate Resources, Elizabeth II Court, Winchester SO23 8UJ
☎ 01962 847400 ☐ carolyn.williamson@hants.gov.uk

Access Officer / Social Services (Disability): Mr Graham Allen, Director - Adults' Health & Care, Elizabeth II Court, Winchester SO23 8UG ☎ 01962 845875
☐ graham.allen@hants.gov.uk

HAMPSHIRE

Architect, Building / Property Services: Mr Steve Clow, Assistant Director - Property Services, Three Minsters House, 76 High Street, Winchester SO23 8UL ☎ 01962 847858 ⌨ steve.clow@hants.gov.uk

Building Control: Mr Steve Clow, Assistant Director - Property Services, Three Minsters House, 76 High Street, Winchester SO23 8UL ☎ 01962 847858 ⌨ steve.clow@hants.gov.uk

Catering Services: Ms Carole Stebbing, Head of Catering Services, 27 - 29 Market Street, Eastleigh SO53 5RG ☎ 023 8062 9388 ⌨ carole.stebbing@hants.gov.uk

Children / Youth Services: Mr Steve Crocker, Director - Children's Services, Elizabeth II Court, Winchester SO23 8UG ☎ 01962 847991 ⌨ steve.crocker@hants.gov.uk

Civil Registration: Mrs Nicola Horsey, Assistant Director - Community & Regulatory Services, Three Ministers House, 76 High Street, Winchester SO23 8UL ☎ 01962 845423 ⌨ nicola.horsey@hants.gov.uk

PR / Communications: Ms Kate Ball, Communications Manager - Media, Elizabeth II Court South, Winchester SO23 8ZF ☎ 01962 847317 ⌨ kate.ball@hants.gov.uk

PR / Communications: Ms Helen Gregory, Communications Manager, Elizabeth II Court, Winchester SO23 8UJ ☎ 01962 847135 ⌨ helen.gregory2@hants.gov.uk

Community Planning: Mr Robert Ormerod, Community Strategy Manager, Elizabeth II Court, Winchester SO23 8UJ ☎ 01962 845122 ⌨ robert.ormerod@hants.gov.uk

Community Safety: Mrs Nicola Horsey, Assistant Director - Community & Regulatory Services, Three Ministers House, 76 High Street, Winchester SO23 8UL ☎ 01962 845423 ⌨ nicola.horsey@hants.gov.uk

Computer Management: Mr Chris Jackson, Head of Programmes & Solutions, Elizabeth II Court South, Winchester SO23 8UJ ☎ 01962 847103 ⌨ chris.jackson@hants.gov.uk

Consumer Protection and Trading Standards: Mrs Nicola Horsey, Assistant Director - Community & Regulatory Services, Three Minsters House, 76 High Street, Winchester SO23 8UL ☎ 01962 845423 ⌨ nicola.horsey@hants.gov.uk

Contracts: Ms Karen Murray, Director - Culture, Communities & Business Services, Three Minsters House, 76 High Street, Winchester SO23 8UL ☎ 01962 847876 ⌨ karen.murray@hants.gov.uk

Corporate Services: Mrs Barbara Beardwell, Head of Law & Governance / Monitoring Officer, Elizabeth II Court South, The Castle, Winchester SO23 8UJ ☎ 01962 845157 ⌨ barbara.beardwell@hants.gov.uk

Corporate Services: Mr Richard White, Head of Integrated Business Centre, Athelstan House, St. Clement Street, Winchester SO23 9DR ☎ 01962 813951 ⌨ richard.white@hants.gov.uk

Customer Service: Mr Bob Wild, Head of Corporate Customer Services, Parkway Offices, Wickham Road, Fareham PO16 7JL ☎ 01329 225335 ⌨ bob.wild@hants.gov.uk

Economic Development: Mr David Fletcher, Assistant Director - Economic Development, Elizabeth II Court West, Winchester SO23 8UG ☎ 01962 846125 ⌨ david.fletcher@hants.gov.uk

Education: Mr Steve Crocker, Director - Children's Services, Elizabeth II Court, Winchester SO23 8UG ☎ 01962 847991 ⌨ steve.crocker@hants.gov.uk

Emergency Planning: Mr Ian Hoult, Head of Emergency Planning & Resilience, Elizabeth II Court South, Winchester SO23 8UJ ☎ 01962 846840; 01962 834525 ⌨ ian.hoult@hants.gov.uk

Environmental / Technical Services: Mr Stuart Jarvis, Director - Economy, Transport & Environment, Elizabeth II Court, Winchester SO23 8UD ☎ 01962 845260 ⌨ stuart.jarvis@hants.gov.uk

Estates, Property & Valuation: Mr Steve Clow, Assistant Director - Property Services, Three Minsters House, 76 High Street, Winchester SO23 8UL ☎ 01962 847858 ⌨ steve.clow@hants.gov.uk

Events Manager: Ms Kathie Lock, Head of Facilities Management, Three Ministers House, 76 High Street, Winchester SO23 8UG ☎ 01962 847779 ⌨ kathie.lock@hants.gov.uk

Facilities: Ms Kathie Lock, Head of Facilities Management, Three Ministers House, 76 High Street, Winchester SO23 8UG ☎ 01962 847779 ⌨ kathie.lock@hants.gov.uk

Finance: Mr Rob Carr, Head of Finance, Elizabeth II Court, Winchester SO23 8UJ ☎ 01962 847508 ⌨ rob.carr@hants.gov.uk

Finance: Mr Nick Weaver, Head of Pension Services & Transactions, Elizabeth II Court, Winchester SO23 8UB ☎ 01962 847584 ⌨ nick.weaver@hants.gov.uk

Finance: Mrs Carolyn Williamson, Director - Corporate Resources, Elizabeth II Court, Winchester SO23 8UJ ☎ 01962 847400 ⌨ carolyn.williamson@hants.gov.uk

Grounds Maintenance: Mr Steve Clow, Assistant Director - Property Services, Three Minsters House, 76 High Street, Winchester SO23 8UL ☎ 01962 847858 ⌨ steve.clow@hants.gov.uk

Health and Safety: Mr Peter Andrews, Corporate Risk Manager, Elizabeth II Court South, Winchester SO23 8UJ ☎ 01962 847309 ⌨ peter.andrews@hants.gov.uk

Highways: Mr Colin Taylor, Interim Deputy Director - Highways, Traffic & Transport, Elizabeth II Court, Winchester SO23 8UD ☎ 01962 846753 ⌨ colin.taylor@hants.gov.uk

Legal: Mr David Kelly, Head of Legal Services & Deputy Monitoring Officer, Elizabeth II Court South, Winchester SO23 8UJ ☎ 01962 847381 ⌨ david.kelly@hants.gov.uk

Leisure and Cultural Services: Ms Jo Heath, Head of Countryside Service, Castle Avenue, Winchester SO23 8UJ ☎ 01962 847717 ⌨ jo.heath@hants.gov.uk

Leisure and Cultural Services: Mrs Nicola Horsey, Assistant Director - Community & Regulatory Services, Three Ministers House, 76 High Street, Winchester SO23 8UL ☎ 01962 845423 ✆ nicola.horsey@hants.gov.uk

Leisure and Cultural Services: Ms Karen Murray, Director - Culture, Communities & Business Services, Three Minsters House, 76 High Street, Winchester SO23 8UL ☎ 01962 847876 ✆ karen.murray@hants.gov.uk

Leisure and Cultural Services: Mr John Tickle, Assistant Director - Culture & Heritage, Three Ministers House, 76 High Street, Winchester SO23 8UL ☎ 01962 846000 ✆ john.tickle@hants.gov.uk

Lighting: Mr Julian Higgins, Assistant Highways Manager (ITS), HCC Street Lighting, PFI Office, Unit 1 Royal London Park, Flanders Road, Hedge End, Southampton SO30 2LG ☎ 01489 771772 ✆ julian.higgins@hants.gov.uk

Member Services: Mrs Debbie Vaughan, Head of Democratic & Member Services, Elizabeth II Court South, Winchester SO23 8UJ ☎ 01962 847330 ✆ debbie.vaughan@hants.gov.uk

Personnel / HR: Ms Jenny Lewis, Head of HR & Workforce Development, Elizabeth Court II, Winchester SO23 8UJ ☎ 01962 841841 ✆ jenny.lewis@hants.gov.uk

Planning: Mr Chris Murray, Head of Strategic Planning, Elizabeth II Court West, Winchester SO23 0UD ☎ 01962 846728 ✆ chris.murray@hants.gov.uk

Procurement: Ms Karen Murray, Director - Culture, Communities & Business Services, Three Minsters House, 76 High Street, Winchester SO23 8UL ☎ 01962 847876 ✆ karen.murray@hants.gov.uk

Public Libraries: Mrs Nicola Horsey, Assistant Director - Community & Regulatory Services, Three Ministers House, 76 High Street, Winchester SO23 8UL ☎ 01962 845423 ✆ nicola.horsey@hants.gov.uk

Recycling & Waste Minimisation: Mr James Potter, Head of Waste & Resource Management, Elizabeth Court II, Winchester SO23 8UD ☎ 01962 832275 ✆ james.potter@hants.gov.uk

Regeneration: Mr James Potter, Head of Waste & Resource Management, Elizabeth Court II, Winchester SO23 8UD ☎ 01962 832275 ✆ james.potter@hants.gov.uk

Road Safety: Mr Marc Samways, Traffic Management & Safety Manager, Elizabeth II Court West, Winchester SO23 8UD ☎ 01962 832238 ✆ marc.samways@hants.gov.uk

Social Services (Adult): Mr Graham Allen, Director - Adults' Health & Care, Elizabeth II Court, Winchester SO23 8UG ☎ 01962 845875 ✆ graham.allen@hants.gov.uk

Social Services (Children): Mr Steve Crocker, Director - Children's Services, Elizabeth II Court, Winchester SO23 8UG ☎ 01962 847991 ✆ steve.crocker@hants.gov.uk

Social Services (Children): Mrs Felicity Roe, Assistant Director - Access, Performance & Resources, Elizabeth II Court, Winchester SO23 8UG ☎ 01962 846374 ✆ felicity.roe@hants.gov.uk

Public Health: Dr Sallie Bacon, Interim Director - Public Health, The Castle, Winchester SO23 8UJ ☎ 023 8038 3389 ✆ sallie.bacon@hants.gov.uk

Tourism: Mr Andrew Bateman, Tourism Manager, ElizabethII Court, Winchester SO23 8UD ☎ 01962 845478 ✆ andrew.bateman@hants.gov.uk

Traffic Management: Mr Adrian Gray, Head of Highways (Traffic Management), Elizabeth II Court, Winchester SO23 8UD ☎ 01256 382409 ✆ adrian.gray@hants.gov.uk

Traffic Management: Mr Colin Taylor, Interim Deputy Director - Highways, Traffic & Transport, Elizabeth II Court, Winchester SO23 8UD ☎ 01962 846753 ✆ colin.taylor@hants.gov.uk

Transport: Mr Tim Lawton, Head of Highways for the South & West Areas, Jacobs Gutter Lane, Totton, Southampton SO40 9QT ☎ 023 8042 7001 ✆ tim.lawton@hants.gov.uk

Transport: Mr Peter Shelley, Head of Passenger Transport, Capital House, 48 Andover Road, Winchester SO22 6AG ☎ 01962 847212 ✆ peter.shelley@hants.gov.uk

Transport Planner: Mr Keith Willcox, Assistant Director - Strategic Transport, Elizabeth II Court West, Winchester SO23 8UD ☎ 01962 846997 ✆ keith.willcox@hants.gov.uk

Waste Collection and Disposal: Mr James Potter, Head of Waste & Resource Management, Elizabeth Court II, Winchester SO23 8UD ☎ 01962 832275 ✆ james.potter@hants.gov.uk

Waste Management: Mr James Potter, Head of Waste & Resource Management, Elizabeth Court II, Winchester SO23 8UD ☎ 01962 832275 ✆ james.potter@hants.gov.uk

COUNCILLORS

Chair: Chapman, Keith (CON - Calleva & Kingsclere) keith.chapman@hants.gov.uk

Leader of the Council: Perry, Roy (CON - Romsey Extra) roy.perry@hants.gov.uk

Deputy Leader of the Council: Mans, Keith (CON - Lyndhurst) keith.mans@hants.gov.uk

Bailey, Phil (LD - Winchester Downlands) phil.bailey@hants.gov.uk

Bennison, John (O - Church Crookham & Ewshot) john.bennison@hants.gov.uk

Bolton, Ray (CON - Emsworth & St Faith's) ray.bolton@hants.gov.uk

Briggs, Ann (CON - Waterloo & Stakes North) ann.briggs@hants.gov.uk

Brooks, Zilliah (CON - Andover West)

Burgess, Rita (CON - Basingstoke South West) rita.burgess@hants.gov.uk

HAMPSHIRE

Burgess, Graham (CON - Lee)
graham.burgess@hants.gov.uk

Carew, Adam (LD - Bordon, Whitehill & Lindford)
adam.carew@hants.gov.uk

Carter, Christopher (CON - Leesland and Town)
christopher.carter@hants.gov.uk

Chadd, Roz (CON - Farnborough North)
roz.chadd@hants.gov.uk

Chegwyn, Peter (LD - Hardway)
peter.chegwyn@hants.gov.uk

Choudhary, Charles (CON - Aldershot West)
charles.choudhary@hants.gov.uk

Clarke, Vaughan (CON - Petersfield Hangars)
vaughan.clarke@hants.gov.uk

Collett, Adrian (LD - Yateley East, Blackwater & Ancells)
adrian.collett@hants.gov.uk

Connor, Criss (LAB - Basingstoke Central)
criss.connor@hants.gov.uk

Cooper, Mark (LD - Romsey Town)
cllr.mark.cooper@hants.gov.uk

Cully, Shaun (LAB - Bridgemary)
shaun.cully@hants.gov.uk

Dowden, Alan (LD - Baddesley)
alan.dowden@hants.gov.uk

Edgar, Peter (CON - Leesland and Town)
peter.edgar@hants.gov.uk

England, Jacqui (IND - Lymington)
jacqui.england@hants.gov.uk

Evans, Keith (CON - Fareham Warsash)
keith.evans@hants.gov.uk

Fairhurst, Liz (CON - Bedhampton & Leigh Park)
liz.fairhurst@hants.gov.uk

Fawkes, Philip (UKIP - South Waterside)
philip.fawkes@hants.gov.uk

Finch, Ray (UKIP - Bedhampton & Leigh Park)
ray.finch@hants.gov.uk

Frankum, Jane (LAB - Basingstoke North)
jane.frankum@hants.gov.uk

Gibson, Andrew (CON - Test Valley Central)
andrew.gibson@hants.gov.uk

Glen, Jonathan (CON - Odiham)
jonathan.glen@hants.gov.uk

Grajewski, Judith (CON - Chandlers Ford)

Greenwood, Chris (UKIP - Eastleigh West)
chris.greenwood@hants.gov.uk

Gurden, Brian (LD - Basingstoke South East)
brian.gurden@hants.gov.uk

Harrison, David (LD - Totton South & Marchwood)
david.harrison@hants.gov.uk

Harvey, Marge (CON - Catherington)
marge.harvey@hants.gov.uk

Heron, Edward (CON - Fordingbridge)
edward.heron@hants.gov.uk

Hockley, Geoffrey (CON - Fareham Titchfield)
geoff.hockley@hants.gov.uk

Hooke, Tony (UKIP - Andover South)
tony.hooke@hants.gov.uk

House, Keith (LD - Hamble)
keith.house@hants.gov.uk

Humby, Rob (CON - Bishops Waltham)
rob.humby@hants.gov.uk

Huxstep, Roger (CON - Meon Valley)
roger.huxstep@hants.gov.uk

Joy, Andrew (CON - Alton Town)
andrew.joy@hants.gov.uk

Keast, David (CON - Cowplain & Hart Plain)
david.keast@hants.gov.uk

Kemp-Gee, Mark (CON - Alton Rural)
mark.kemp-gee@hants.gov.uk

Kendal, Mel (CON - New Milton)
mel.kendal@hants.gov.uk

Kryle, Rupert (LD - Botley & Hedge End)
rupert.kryle@hants.gov.uk

Lagdon, Chris (UKIP - Totton North)
chris.lagdon@hants.gov.uk

Latham, Peter (CON - Fareham Town)
peter.latham@hants.gov.uk

Lovegrove, Warwick (LD - Tadley & Baughurst)
warwick.lovegrove@hants.gov.uk

Lyon, Martin (UKIP - Bishopstoke & Fair Oak)
martin.lyon@hants.gov.uk

Mather, Fiona (CON - Winchester Eastgate)
fiona.mather@hants.gov.uk

Matthews, Chris (CON - Fareham Town)
chris.matthews@hants.gov.uk

McIntosh, Robin (CON - Purbrook & Stakes South)
robin.mcintosh@hants.gov.uk

McNair Scott, Anna (CON - Candovers)
anna.mcnairscott@hants.gov.uk

Mitchell, Floss (CON - Headley)
floss.mitchell@hants.gov.uk

Moon, Ken (CON - Petersfield Butser)
ken.moon@hants.gov.uk

Moore, Andy (UKIP - Eastleigh East)
andy.moore@hants.gov.uk

Pearce, Frank (CON - Hayling Island)
frank.pearce@hants.gov.uk

Porter, Jacqueline (LD - Itchen Valley)
jackie.porter@hants.gov.uk

Price, Roger (LD - Fareham Portchester)
roger.price@hants.gov.uk

Reid, Stephen (CON - Basingstoke North West)
stephen.reid@hants.gov.uk

Rice, Alan (CON - Milford & Hordle)
alan.rice@hants.gov.uk

Rippon-Swaine, Steve (CON - Ringwood)
steve.rippon-swaine@hants.gov.uk

Rolt, Timothy (UKIP - Andover North)
timothy.rolt@hants.gov.uk

Rust, Frank (LAB - Aldershot East)
frank.rust@hants.gov.uk

Simpson, David (LD - Hartley Wintney, Eversley & Yateley West)
david.simpson@hants.gov.uk

Stallard, Patricia (CON - Winchester Southern Parishes)
members.support@hants.gov.uk

Staplehurst, Mark (UKIP - Farnborough West)
mark.staplehurst@hants.gov.uk

Still, Elaine (CON - Loddon)
elaine.still@hants.gov.uk

Tennent, Bruce (LD - West End & Hedge End Grange Park)
bruce.tennent@hants.gov.uk

Thacker, Tom (CON - Whitchurch & Clere)
tom.thacker@hants.gov.uk

Thornber, Ken (CON - Brockenhurst)
ken.thornber@hants.gov.uk

Tod, Martin (LD - Winchester Westgate)
martin.tod@hants.gov.uk

Wade, Malcolm (LD - Dibden & Hythe)
malcolm.wade@hants.gov.uk

Wall, John (CON - Farnborough South)
john.wall@hants.gov.uk

Wheale, Sharyn (CON - Fleet)
sharyn.wheale@hants.gov.uk

Wood, Christopher (UKIP - Fareham Crofton)
christopher.wood@hants.gov.uk

Woodward, Seán (CON - Fareham Sarisbury)
sean.woodward@hants.gov.uk

POLITICAL COMPOSITION
CON: 45, LD: 17, UKIP: 10, LAB: 4, O: 1, IND: 1

Harborough   D

Harborough District Council, The Symington Building, Adam & Eve Street, Market Harborough LE16 7AG
☎ 01858 828282 ✆ customer.services@harborough.gov.uk
🖥 www.harborough.gov.uk

FACTS AND FIGURES
Parliamentary Constituencies: Harborough, Leicestershire South, Rutland and Melton
EU Constituencies: East Midlands
Election Frequency: Elections are of whole council

PRINCIPAL OFFICERS

Senior Management: Mr David Atkinson, Head of Planning & Regeneration, The Symington Building, Adam & Eve Street, Market Harborough LE16 7AG

Senior Management: Mrs Ann Marie Hawkins, Head of Community, Wellbeing & Partnerships, The Symington Building, Adam & Eve Street, Market Harborough LE16 7AG
☎ 01858 828282 ✆ a.hawkins@harborough.gov.uk

Senior Management: Mrs Beverley Jolly, Corporate Director - Resources, The Symington Building, Adam & Eve Street, Market Harborough LE16 7AG ☎ 01858 828282
✆ b.jolly@harborough.gov.uk

Senior Management: Mr Norman Proudfoot, Corporate Director - Community Resources, The Symington Building, Adam & Eve Street, Market Harborough LE16 7AG ☎ 01858 828282
✆ n.proudfoot@harborough.gov.uk

Senior Management: Mr Simon Riley, Head of Financial Services & S151 Officer, The Symington Building, Adam & Eve Street, Market Harborough LE16 7AG ☎ 01858 828282
✆ d.atkinson@harborough.gov.uk

Senior Management: Mrs Verina Wenham, Head of Legal & Democratic Services, The Symington Building, Adam & Eve Street, Market Harborough LE16 7AG ☎ 01858 821258
✆ v.wenham@harborough.gov.uk

Building Control: Mr Simon Costall, Principal Building Control Officer, The Symington Building, Adam & Eve Street, Market Harborough LE16 7AG ☎ 01858 821142
✆ s.costall@harborough.gov.uk

Children / Youth Services: Ms Mel Gould, Projects Manager - Harborough Children & Young People's Charity, The Symington Building, Adam & Eve Street, Market Harborough LE16 7AG
☎ 07502 365379 ✆ mel@hcyc@org.uk

PR / Communications: Mrs Rachael Felts, Communications & Customer Services Manager, The Symington Building, Adam & Eve Street, Market Harborough LE16 7AG ☎ 01858 821217
✆ r.felts@harborough.gov.uk

Community Safety: Mr Thomas Day, Community Safety Officer, The Symington Building, Adam & Eve Street, Market Harborough LE16 7AG ☎ 01858 828282 ✆ t.day@harborough.gov.uk

Computer Management: Mr Chris James, ICT Services Manager, The Symington Building, Adam & Eve Street, Market Harborough LE16 7AG ☎ 01858 821311; 01858 821311
✆ c.james@harborough.gov.uk

Contracts: Mr Jonathan Ward-Langman, Service Manager - Commissioning, The Symington Building, Adam & Eve Street, Market Harborough LE16 7AG ☎ 01858 828282
✆ j.ward-langman@harborough.gov.uk

Corporate Services: Mr Richard Ellis, Service Manager - Corporate Services, The Symington Building, Adam & Eve Street, Market Harborough LE16 7AG ☎ 01858 821370; 01858 821000
✆ r.ellis@harborough.gov.uk

Customer Service: Mrs Rachael Felts, Communications & Customer Services Manager, The Symington Building, Adam & Eve Street, Market Harborough LE16 7AG ☎ 01858 821217
✆ r.felts@harborough.gov.uk

Economic Development: Mrs Heather Wakefield, Planning Enforcement Officer, The Symington Building, Adam & Eve Street, Market Harborough LE16 7AG ☎ 01858 828282
✆ h.wakefield@harborough.gov.uk

HARBOROUGH

E-Government: Mr Chris James, ICT Services Manager, The Symington Building, Adam & Eve Street, Market Harborough LE16 7AG ☎ 01858 821311; 01858 821311 ᐧᕯ c.james@harborough.gov.uk

Electoral Registration: Ms Sheena Mortimer, Electoral Services Manager, The Symington Building, Adam & Eve Street, Market Harborough LE16 7AG ☎ 01858 828282 01858 821311 ᐧᕯ s.mortimer@harborough.gov.uk

Emergency Planning: Ms Elaine Bird, Regulatory Services Manager, The Symington Building, Adam & Eve Street, Market Harborough LE16 7AG ☎ 01858 821130; 01858 821100 ᐧᕯ e.bird@harborough.gov.uk

Energy Management: Mr Graham Ladds, Energy Manager & Technical Officer, The Symington Building, Adam & Eve Street, Market Harborough LE16 7AG ☎ 01858 821328; 01858 821002 ᐧᕯ g.ladds@harborough.gov.uk

Environmental / Technical Services: Ms Elaine Bird, Regulatory Services Manager, The Symington Building, Adam & Eve Street, Market Harborough LE16 7AG ☎ 01858 821130; 01858 821100 ᐧᕯ e.bird@harborough.gov.uk

Estates, Property & Valuation: Mr Mark Perris, Corporate Asset Manager, The Symington Building, Adam & Eve Street, Market Harborough LE16 7AG ᐧᕯ m.perris@harborough.gov.uk

Facilities: Mrs Michaela Barton, Assistant Buildings & Facilities Officer, The Symington Building, Adam & Eve Street, Market Harborough LE16 7AG ☎ 01858 828282 ᐧᕯ m.barton@harborough.gov.uk

Finance: Mr Simon Riley, Head of Financial Services & S151 Officer, The Symington Building, Adam & Eve Street, Market Harborough LE16 7AG ☎ 01858 828282 ᐧᕯ d.atkinson@harborough.gov.uk

Grounds Maintenance: Mr John Kemp, Senior Cleansing Officer, The Symington Building, Adam & Eve Street, Market Harborough LE16 7AG ☎ 01858 828282 ᐧᕯ j.kemp@harborough.gov.uk

Home Energy Conservation: Mr Graham Ladds, Energy Manager & Technical Officer, The Symington Building, Adam & Eve Street, Market Harborough LE16 7AG ☎ 01858 821328; 01858 821002 ᐧᕯ g.ladds@harborough.gov.uk

Legal: Mrs Verina Wenham, Head of Legal & Democratic Services, The Symington Building, Adam & Eve Street, Market Harborough LE16 7AG ☎ 01858 821258 ᐧᕯ v.wenham@harborough.gov.uk

Licensing: Mrs Sarah Greenway, Senior Licensing Officer, The Symington Building, Adam & Eve Street, Market Harborough LE16 7AG ☎ 01858 828282 ᐧᕯ s.greenway@harborough.gov.uk

Member Services: Ms Beth Murgatroyd, Principal Democratic Officer, The Symington Building, Adam & Eve Street, Market Harborough LE16 7AG ☎ 01858 821370 ᐧᕯ b.murgatroyd@harborough.gov.uk

Parking: Mr Phil Grant, Parking Services Manager, The Symington Building, Adam & Eve Street, Market Harborough LE16 7AG ᐧᕯ p.grant@harborough.gov.uk

Partnerships: Mrs Ann Marie Hawkins, Head of Community, Wellbeing & Partnerships, The Symington Building, Adam & Eve Street, Market Harborough LE16 7AG ☎ 01858 828282 ᐧᕯ a.hawkins@harborough.gov.uk

Personnel / HR: Mrs Rebecca Jenner, Human Resources Manager, The Symington Building, Adam & Eve Street, Market Harborough LE16 7AG ☎ 01858 828282 ᐧᕯ r.jenner@harborough.gov.uk

Planning: Mr Adrian Eastwood, Development Control Service Manager, The Symington Building, Adam & Eve Street, Market Harborough LE16 7AG ☎ 01858 821142; 01858 821097 ᐧᕯ a.eastwood@harborough.gov.uk

Recycling & Waste Minimisation: Mr Russell Smith, Senior Waste Management Officer, The Symington Building, Adam & Eve Street, Market Harborough LE16 7AG ☎ 01858 821177 ᐧᕯ r.smith@harborough.gov.uk

Regeneration: Mr Stephen Pointer, Strategic Planning Services Manager, The Symington Building, Adam & Eve Street, Market Harborough LE16 7AG ☎ 01858 821168 ᐧᕯ s.pointer@harborough.gov.uk

Staff Training: Mrs Rebecca Jenner, Human Resources Manager, The Symington Building, Adam & Eve Street, Market Harborough LE16 7AG ☎ 01858 828282 ᐧᕯ r.jenner@harborough.gov.uk

Street Scene: Mr Stephen Pointer, Strategic Planning Services Manager, The Symington Building, Adam & Eve Street, Market Harborough LE16 7AG ☎ 01858 821168 ᐧᕯ s.pointer@harborough.gov.uk

Tourism: Mr Stephen Pointer, Strategic Planning Services Manager, The Symington Building, Adam & Eve Street, Market Harborough LE16 7AG ☎ 01858 821168 ᐧᕯ s.pointer@harborough.gov.uk

Town Centre: Mrs Helen Nicholls, Town Centre Co-ordinator, The Symington Building, Adam & Eve Street, Market Harborough LE16 7AG ᐧᕯ h.nicholls@harborough.gov.uk

Waste Collection and Disposal: Mr Russell Smith, Senior Waste Management Officer, The Symington Building, Adam & Eve Street, Market Harborough LE16 7AG ☎ 01858 821177 ᐧᕯ r.smith@harborough.gov.uk

Waste Management: Mr Russell Smith, Senior Waste Management Officer, The Symington Building, Adam & Eve Street, Market Harborough LE16 7AG ☎ 01858 821177 ᐧᕯ r.smith@harborough.gov.uk

COUNCILLORS

Leader of the Council: Pain, Blake (CON - Lubenham) b.pain@harborough.gov.uk

Deputy Leader of the Council: King, Phillip (CON - Kibworth) p.king@harborough.gov.uk

Ackerley, Janette (CON - Lutterworth - Swift) j.ackerley@harborough.gov.uk

Bannister, Neil (CON - Dunton)
n.bannister@harborough.gov.uk

Beesley-Reynolds, Lynne (CON - Kibworth)
l.beesley-reynolds@harborough.gov.uk

Bilbie, Stephen (CON - Fleckney)
S.Bilbie@harborough.gov.uk

Bowles, Lesley (CON - Bosworth)
L.Bowles@harborough.gov.uk

Brodrick, Jo (CON - Market Harborough Welland)
j.brodrick@harborough.gov.uk

Burrell, Amanda (LD - Thurnby & Houghton)
a.burrell@harborough.gov.uk

Champion, Barry (CON - Market Harborough Great Bowden & Arden)
b.champion@harborough.gov.uk

Chapman, Elaine (CON - Lutterworth - Brookfield)
e.chapman@harborough.gov.uk

Dann, Paul (CON - Astley - Primethorpe)
p.dann@harborough.gov.uk

Dunton, Roger (LD - Market Harborough Welland)
r.dunton@harborough.gov.uk

Elliott, Peter (LD - Thurnby & Houghton)
p.elliott@harbourough.gov.uk

Evans, Derek (CON - Market Harborough - Little Bowden)
d.evans@harborough.gov.uk

Everett, John (CON - Misterton)
j.everett@harborough.gov.uk

Galton, Simon (LD - Thurnby & Houghton)
s.galton@harborough.gov.uk

Graves, Mark (CON - Astley - Astley)
m.graves@harborough.gov.uk

Hadkiss, Richard (CON - Market Harborough - Logan)
r.hadkiss@harborough.gov.uk

Hall, Neville (CON - Peatling)
npthall.knaptoft@gmail.com

Hallam, James (CON - Glen)
j.hallam@harborough.gov.uk

Hammond, Matthew (CON - Lutterworth - Springs)
m.hammond@harborough.gov.uk

Hill, Sarah (LD - Market Harborough Great Bowden & Arden)
s.hill@harborough.gov.uk

Holyoak, Christopher (CON - Kibworth)
c.holyoak@harborough.gov.uk

Johnson, Barbara (LD - Market Harborough - Logan)
b.johnson@harborough.gov.uk

Knowles, Phil (LD - Market Harborough Great Bowden & Arden)
p.knowles@harborough.gov.uk

Liquorish, Bill (CON - Astley - Sutton)
w.liquorish@harborough.gov.uk

Modha, Sindy (CON - Billesdon)
S.Modha@harborough.gov.uk

Nunn, Amanda (CON - Market Harborough - Little Bowden)
A.Nunn@harborough.gov.uk

Page, Rosita (CON - Ullesthorpe)
r.page@harborough.gov.uk

Rickman, Michael (CON - Nevill)
M.Rickman@harborough.gov.uk

Robinson, Geraldine (CON - Lutterworth - Orchard)
g.robinson@harborough.gov.uk

Rook, Michael (CON - Tilton)
m.rook@harborough.gov.uk

Simpson, Julie (LD - Market Harborough Welland)
j.simpson@harborough.gov.uk

Spendlove-Mason, Grahame (CON - Glen)
g.spendlove-mason@harborough.gov.uk

Tomlin, Richard (CON - Astley - Broughton)
r.tomlin@harborough.gov.uk

Wood, Charmaine (CON - Fleckney)
c.wood@harborough.gov.uk

POLITICAL COMPOSITION
CON: 29, LD: 8

COMMITTEE CHAIRS

Licensing: Mrs Geraldine Robinson

Planning: Mr Christopher Holyoak

Haringey   L

Haringey London Borough Council, River Park House, 225 High Road, London N22 8HQ
☎ 020 8489 0000 ✎ customer.services@haringey.gov.uk
🖥 www.haringey.gov.uk

FACTS AND FIGURES
Parliamentary Constituencies: Hornsey and Wood Green, Tottenham
EU Constituencies: London
Election Frequency: Elections are of whole council

PRINCIPAL OFFICERS

Chief Executive: Mr Nick Walkley, Chief Executive, 5th Floor, River Park House, 225 High Road, London N22 8HQ ☎ 020 8489 2648 ✎ nick.walkley@haringey.gov.uk

Deputy Chief Executive: Ms Zina Etheridge, Deputy Chief Executive, Level 5, River Park House, 225 High Road, London N22 8HQ ☎ 020 8489 8690 ✎ zina.etheridge@haringey.gov.uk

Senior Management: Dr Jeanelle de Gruchy, Director - Public Health, 4th Floor, River Park House, 225 Station Road, London N22 8HQ ☎ 020 8489 5119 ✎ jeanelle.degruchy@haringey.gov.uk

Senior Management: Ms Tracie Evans, Chief Operating Officer, Level 5, River Park House, 225 High Road, London N22 8HQ ☎ 020 8489 2688 ✎ tracie.evans@haringey.gov.uk

Senior Management: Ms Lyn Garner, Director - Regeneration, Planning & Development, Level 4, River Park House, 225 High Road, London N22 8HQ ☎ 020 8489 4523 ✎ lyn.garner@haringey.gov.uk

HARINGEY

Building Control: Mr Malcolm Greaves, Head of Asset Management, 6th Floor, Level ♿ Alexandra House, 10 Station Road, London N22 7TR ☎ 020 8489 2900
🖑 malcolm.greaves@haringey.gov.uk

Catering Services: Ms Marianna Clune-Georgiou, Head of Catering, Lea Valley Techno Park, London N17 9LN ☎ 020 8489 4643 🖑 marianna.clune-georgiou@haringey.gov.uk

Children / Youth Services: Mr Jon Abbey, Director - Children's Services, River Park House, 225 High Road, London N22 8HQ ☎ 020 8489 3206 🖑 jon.abbey@haringey.gov.uk

Children / Youth Services: Ms Gill Gibson, Assistant Director - Early Help & Prevention, River Park House, 225 High Road, London N22 8HQ ☎ 020 8489 1114 🖑 gill.gibson@haringey.gov.uk

PR / Communications: Mr Simon Jones, Assistant Director - Communications, River Park House, 225 High Road, London N22 8HQ ☎ 020 8489 2901 🖑 simon.jones@haringey.gov.uk

Community Planning: Ms Claire Kowalska, Community Safety Strategic Manager, 4th Floor, River Park House, 225 Station Road, London N22 8HQ ☎ 020 8489 6949
🖑 claire.kowlaska@haringey.gov.uk

Community Safety: Mr Steve McDonnell, Assistant Director - Environmental Services & Community Safety, Alexandra House, 5th Floor, 10 Station Road, London N22 7TR ☎ 020 8489 2485
🖑 steve.mcdonnell@haringey.gov.uk

Computer Management: Mr David Airey, Head of IT, 3rd Floor, River Park House, 225 High Road, London N22 8HQ ☎ 020 8489 4673; 020 8489 3998 🖑 david.airey@haringey.gov.uk

Consumer Protection and Trading Standards: Mr Keith Betts, Service Manager - Commercial Enforcement, 1st Floor, Ashley Road, London N17 9LN ☎ 020 8849 5525

Contracts: Mr Barry Phelps, Head of Procurement, 1st Floor, Alexandra House, 10 Station Road, London N22 7TR
☎ 020 8489 2744 🖑 barry.phelps@haringey.gov.uk

Corporate Services: Ms Helen Constantine, Strategic Lead - Government & Business Improvement, 7th Floor, River Park House, 225 High Road, London N22 7SG ☎ 020 8489 3905
🖑 helen.constantine@haringey.gov.uk

Corporate Services: Mr Sanjay Mackintosh, Head of Strategic Commissioning, River Park House, 225 High Road, London N22 8HQ ☎ 020 8489 5704 🖑 sanjay.mackintosh@haringey.gov.uk

Corporate Services: Ms Charlotte Pomery, Assistant Director - Commissioning, River Park House, 225 High Road, London N22 8HQ ☎ 020 8489 3751 🖑 charlotte.pomery@haringey.gov.uk

Corporate Services: Mr Bernie Ryan, Assistant Director - Corporate Governance, River Park House, 225 High Road, London N22 8HQ ☎ 020 8489 3974 🖑 bernie.ryan@haringey.gov.uk

Customer Service: Mr Sergio Sgambellone, Assistant Director - Customer Services, Alexandra House, 4th Floor, 10 Station Road, London N22 7TR ☎ 020 8489 1771
🖑 sergio.sgambellone@haringey.gov.uk

Electoral Registration: Mr George Cooper, Electoral Registration Manager, Civic Centre, Wood Green, High Road, London N22 8LE ☎ 020 8489 2976

Emergency Planning: Mr Andrew Meek, Emergency Planning Officer, Level 4, River Park House, 225 High Road, London N22 8HQ ☎ 020 8489 1171 🖑 andrew.meek@haringey.gov.uk

Events Manager: Ms Elena Pippou, Arts, Culture & Marketing Officer, Level 2, River Park House, 225 High Road, London N22 8HQ ☎ 020 8489 1419 🖑 elena.pippou@haringey.gov.uk

Pensions: Ms Janet Richards, Pensions Manager, 5th Floor, Alexandra House, 10 Station Road, London N22 8HQ ☎ 020 8489 3824 🖑 janet.richards@haringey.gov.uk

Fleet Management: Mr Darren Butterfield, Contract Waste Manager, Level 2, River Park House, 225 High Road, London N22 8HQ ☎ 020 8489 5786 🖑 darren.butterfield@haringey.gov.uk

Highways: Mr Peter Boddy, Sustainable Transport Manager, 5th Floor, Alexandra House, London N22 7TR ☎ 020 8489 1765
🖑 peter.boddy@haringey.gov.uk

Highways: Ms Ann Cunningham, Head of Traffic Management, Level 2, River Park House, 225 High Road, London N22 8HQ ☎ 020 8489 1355 🖑 ann.cunningham@haringey.gov.uk

Housing: Mr Andrew Billany, Managing Director - Homes for Haringey, 48 Station Road, 4th Floor, London N22 7TY ☎ 020 8489 4260 🖑 andrew.billany@homesforharingey.org

Housing: Mr David Sherrington, Director - Asset Management, Broadwater Farm Depot, 108C Gloucester Road, London N17 6GZ ☎ 020 8489 4487260 🖑 david.sherrington@haringey.gov.uk

Housing Maintenance: Mr Malcolm Greaves, Head of Asset Management, 6th Floor, Level ♿ Alexandra House, 10 Station Road, London N22 7TR ☎ 020 8489 2900
🖑 malcolm.greaves@haringey.gov.uk

Local Area Agreement: Ms Claire Kowalska, Community Safety Strategic Manager, 4th Floor, River Park House, 225 Station Road, London N22 8HQ ☎ 020 8489 6949
🖑 claire.kowlaska@haringey.gov.uk

Leisure and Cultural Services: Mr Simon Farrow, Head of Client Services, Alexandra House, 6th Floor, 10 Station Road, London N22 7TR ☎ 020 8489 3639 🖑 simon.farrow@haringey.gov.uk

Lighting: Ms Wendy Thorgood, Sustainable Transport Officer, 6th Floor, Alexandra House, 10 Station Road, London N22 7TR ☎ 020 8489 5351 🖑 wendy.thorgood@haringey.gov.uk

Lottery Funding, Charity and Voluntary: Ms Elena Pippou, Arts, Culture & Marketing Officer, Ground Floor, Hornsey Library, London N22 9JA ☎ 020 8489 1419 🖑 elena.pippou@haringey.gov.uk

Member Services: Mr Michael Kay, Cabinet Committees Manager, River Park House, 225 High Road, London N22 8HQ ☎ 020 8489 2920 ⌨ michael.kay@haringey.gov.uk

Personnel / HR: Ms Jacquie McGeachie, Assistant Director - Transformation & Resources, 5th Floor, Alexandra House, London N22 7TR ☎ 020 8489 3172 ⌨ jacquie.mcgeachie@haringey.gov.uk

Planning: Ms Lyn Garner, Director - Regeneration, Planning & Development, Level 4, River Park House, 225 High Road, London N22 8HQ ☎ 020 8489 4523 ⌨ lyn.garner@haringey.gov.uk

Planning: Mr Stephen Kelly, Assistant Director - Planning, River Park House, 225 High Road, London N22 8HQ ☎ 020 8489 5538 ⌨ stephen.kelly@haringey.gov.uk

Recycling & Waste Minimisation: Mr Stephen McDonnell, Assistant Director - Environmental Services & Community Safety, Level 2, River Park House, 225 High Road, London N22 8HQ ☎ 020 8489 2485 ⌨ stephen.mcdonnell@haringey.gov.uk

Regeneration: Ms Lyn Garner, Director - Regeneration, Planning & Development, Level 4, River Park House, 225 High Road, London N22 8HQ ☎ 020 8489 4523 ⌨ lyn.garner@haringey.gov.uk

Regeneration: Mr Dan Hawthorn, Assistant Director - Regeneration, River Park House, 225 High Road, London N22 8HQ ☎ 020 8489 2247 ⌨ dan.hawthorn@haringey.gov.uk

Road Safety: Ms Denise Adolphe, Smarter Travel Manager, Level 2, River Park House, 225 High Road, London N22 8HQ ☎ 020 8489 1128 ⌨ denise.adolphe@haringey.gov.uk

Social Services: Ms Neelam Bhardwaja, Assistant Director - Safeguarding & Social Care, River Park House, 225 High Road, London N22 8HQ ☎ 020 8489 4676 ⌨ neelam.bhardwaja@haringey.gov.uk

Social Services (Adult): Mr John Everson, Assistant Director - Adult Social Services, River Park House, 225 High Road, London N22 8HQ ☎ 020 8489 4433 ⌨ john.everson@haringey.gov.uk

Social Services (Adult): Ms Beverley Tarka, Director - Adult Social Services, River Park House, 225 High Road, London N22 8HQ ☎ 020 8489 2324 ⌨ beverley.tarka@haringey.gov.uk

Social Services (Children): Mr Jon Abbey, Director - Children's Services, River Park House, 225 High Road, London N22 8HQ ☎ 020 8489 3206 ⌨ jon.abbey@haringey.gov.uk

Social Services (Children): Ms Gill Gibson, Assistant Director - Early Help & Prevention, River Park House, 225 High Road, London N22 8HQ ☎ 020 8489 1114 ⌨ gill.gibson@haringey.gov.uk

Public Health: Dr Jeanelle de Gruchy, Director - Public Health, River Park House, 225 High Road, London N22 8HQ ☎ 020 8489 5119 ⌨ jeanelle.degruchy@haringey.gov.uk

Public Health: Ms Tamara Djuretic, Assistant Director - Public Health, River Park House, 225 High Road, London N22 8HQ ☎ 020 8489 3265 ⌨ tamara.djuretic@haringey.gov.uk

Public Health: Ms Susan Otiti, Assistant Director - Public Health, River Park House, 225 High Road, London N22 8HQ ☎ 020 8489 2629 ⌨ susan.otiti@haringey.gov.uk

Tourism: Ms Elena Pippou, Arts, Culture & Marketing Officer, River Park House, 225 High Road, London N22 8HQ ☎ 020 8489 1419 ⌨ elena.pippou@haringey.gov.uk

Traffic Management: Mr Anthony Kennedy, Sustainable Transport Manager, 1st Floor, River Park House, 225 High Road, London N22 8HQ ☎ 020 8489 5351 ⌨ tony.kennedy@haringey.gov.uk

Transport: Mr Pembe Hipolyte, Assistant Escort Team Manager, Alexandra House, 6th Floor, 10 Station Road, London N22 7TR ☎ 020 8489 5629; 020 8489 5647

Waste Collection and Disposal: Mr Stephen McDonnell, Assistant Director - Environmental Services & Community Safety, Level 2, River Park House, 225 High Road, London N22 8HQ ☎ 020 8489 2485 ⌨ stephen.mcdonnell@haringey.gov.uk

Waste Management: Mr Stephen McDonnell, Assistant Director - Environmental Services & Community Safety, Level 2, River Park House, 225 High Road, London N22 8HQ ☎ 020 8489 2485 ⌨ stephen.mcdonnell@haringey.gov.uk

COUNCILLORS

Mayor: Ozbek, Ali Gul (LAB - St Ann's)
aligul.ozbek@haringey.gov.uk

Deputy Mayor: Mann, Stephen (LAB - Noel Park)
stephen.mann@haringey.gov.uk

Leader of the Council: Kober, Claire (LAB - Seven Sisters)
claire.kober@haringey.gov.uk

Deputy Leader of the Council: Vanier, Bernice (LAB - Tottenham Green)
bernice.vanier@haringey.gov.uk

Group LeaderEngert, Gail (LD - Muswell Hill)
gail.engert@haringey.gov.uk

Adamou, Gina (LAB - Harringay)
gina.adamou@haringey.gov.uk

Adje, Charles (LAB - White Hart Lane)
charles.adje@haringey.gov.uk

Ahmet, Peray (LAB - Noel Park)
peray.ahmet@haringey.gov.uk

Akwasi-Ayisi, Eugene (LAB - West Green)
eugene.akwasi-ayisi@haringey.gov.uk

Amin, Kaushika (LAB - Northumberland Park)
kaushika.amin@haringey.gov.uk

Arthur, Jason (LAB - Crouch End)
jason.arthur@haringey.gov.uk

Basu, Dhiren (LAB - Seven Sisters)
dhiren.basu@haringey.gov.uk

Beacham, David (LD - Alexandra)
david.beacham@haringey.gov.uk

Berryman, Patrick (LAB - Fortis Green)
patrick.berryman@haringey.gov.uk

HARINGEY

Bevan, John (LAB - Northumberland Park)
john.bevan@haringey.gov.uk

Blake, Barbara (LAB - St Ann's)
barbara.blake@haringey.gov.uk

Blake, Mark (LAB - Muswell Hill)
mark.blake@haringey.gov.uk

Bull, Gideon (LAB - White Hart Lane)
gideon.bull@haringey.gov.uk

Bull, Clare (LAB - Bounds Green)
clare.bull@haringey.gov.uk

Carroll, Vincent (LAB - Tottenham Hale)
vincent.carroll@haringey.gov.uk

Carter, Clive (LD - Highgate)
clive.carter@haringey.gov.uk

Christophides, Joanna (LAB - Bounds Green)
joanna.christophides@haringey.gov.uk

Connor, Pippa (LD - Muswell Hill)
pippa.connor@haringey.gov.uk

Demirci, Ali (LAB - Bounds Green)
ali.demirci@haringey.gov.uk

Diakides, Isidoros (LAB - Tottenham Green)
isidoros.dialides@haringey.gov.uk

Doron, Natan (LAB - Crouch End)
natan.doron@haringey.gov.uk

Ejiofer, Joseph (LAB - Bruce Grove)
joseph.ejiofer@haringey.gov.uk

Elliot, Sarah (LD - Crouch End)
sarah.elliott@haringey.gov.uk

Gallagher, Tim (LAB - Stroud Green)
tim.gallagher@haringey.gov.uk

Goldberg, Joe (LAB - Seven Sisters)
joe.goldberg@haringey.gov.uk

Griffith, Eddie (LAB - West Green)
eddie.griffith@haringey.gov.uk

Gunes, Makbule (LAB - Tottenham Green)
makbule.gunes@haringey.gov.uk

Hare, Bob (LD - Highgate)
bob.hare@haringey.gov.uk

Hearn, Kirsten (LAB - Stroud Green)
kirsten.hearn@haringey.gov.uk

Ibrahim, Emine (LAB - Harringay)
emine.ibrahim@haringey.gov.uk

Jogee, Adam (LAB - Hornsey)
adam.jogee@haringey.gov.uk

Mallett, Toni (LAB - West Green)
toni.mallett@haringey.gov.uk

Mann, Jennifer (LAB - Hornsey)
jennifer.mann@haringey.gov.uk

McNamara, Stuart (LAB - Bruce Grove)
stuart.mcnamara@haringey.gov.uk

McShane, Liz (LAB - Alexandra)
liz.mcshane@haringey.gov.uk

Mitchell, Peter (LAB - Woodside)
peter.mitchell@haringey.gov.uk

Morris, Liz (LD - Highgate)
liz.morris@haringey.gov.uk

Morton, Peter (LAB - St Ann's)
peter.morton@haringey.gov.uk

Newton, Martin (LD - Fortis Green)
martin.newton@haringey.gov.uk

Opoku, Felicia (LAB - Bruce Grove)
felicia.opoku@haringey.gov.uk

Patterson, James (LAB - Alexandra)
james.patterson@haringey.gov.uk

Peacock, Sheila (LAB - Northumberland Park)
sheila.peacock@haringey.gov.uk

Reith, Lorna (LAB - Tottenham Hale)
lorna.reith@haringey.gov.uk

Rice, Reg (LAB - Tottenham Hale)
reg.rice@haringey.gov.uk

Ross, Viv (LD - Fortis Green)
viv.ross@haringey.gov.uk

Sahota, Raj (LAB - Stroud Green)
raj.sahota@haringey.gov.uk

Stennett, Anne (LAB - White Hart Lane)
anne.stennett@haringey.gov.uk

Strickland, Alan (LAB - Noel Park)
alan.strickland@haringey.gov.uk

Waters, Ann (LAB - Woodside)
ann.waters@haringey.gov.uk

Weston, Elin (LAB - Hornsey)
elin.weston@haringey.gov.uk

Wright, Charles (LAB - Woodside)
charles.wright@haringey.gov.uk

POLITICAL COMPOSITION
LAB: 47, LD: 9

COMMITTEE CHAIRS

Adults & Health: Ms Pippa Connor

Children & Young People: Ms Kirsten Hearn

Health & Wellbeing: Ms Claire Kober

Housing & Regeneration: Ms Emine Ibrahim

Harlow   D

Harlow District Council, Civic Centre, The Water Gardens, Harlow CM20 1WG

☎ 01279 446655 ◌ contact@harlow.gov.uk ⌨ www.harlow.gov.uk

FACTS AND FIGURES
Parliamentary Constituencies: Harlow
EU Constituencies: Eastern
Election Frequency: Elections are by thirds

PRINCIPAL OFFICERS

Chief Executive: Mr Malcolm Morley, Chief Executive, Civic Centre, The Water Gardens, Harlow CM20 1WG ☎ 01279 446611
◌ malcolm.morley@harlow.gov.uk

Senior Management: Mr Graham Branchett, Chief Operating Officer, Civic Centre, The Water Gardens, Harlow CM20 1WG ☎ 01279 446611 ⌁ graham.branchett@harlow.gov.uk

Architect, Building / Property Services: Mr Graeme Bloomer, Head of Place, Civic Centre, The Water Gardens, Harlow CM20 1WG ☎ 01276 446270 ⌁ graeme.bloomer@harlow.gov.uk

Building Control: Mr Graeme Bloomer, Head of Place, Civic Centre, The Water Gardens, Harlow CM20 1WG ☎ 01276 446270 ⌁ graeme.bloomer@harlow.gov.uk

Children / Youth Services: Ms Jane Greer, Head of Community Wellbeing, Civic Centre, The Water Gardens, Harlow CM20 1WG ☎ 01279 446410 ⌁ jane.greer@harlow.gov.uk

PR / Communications: Ms Jane Greer, Head of Community Wellbeing, Civic Centre, The Water Gardens, Harlow CM20 1WG ☎ 01279 446410 ⌁ jane.greer@harlow.gov.uk

Community Safety: Ms Jane Greer, Head of Community Wellbeing, Civic Centre, The Water Gardens, Harlow CM20 1WG ☎ 01279 446410 ⌁ jane.greer@harlow.gov.uk

Computer Management: Mr Simon Freeman, Head of Finance, Civic Centre, The Water Gardens, Harlow CM20 1WG ☎ 01279 446228 ⌁ simon.freeman@harlow.gov.uk

Contracts: Mr Brian Keane, Head of Governance, Civic Centre, The Water Gardens, Harlow CM20 1WG ☎ 01279 446037 ⌁ brian.keane@harlow.gov.uk

Corporate Services: Mr Brian Keane, Head of Governance, Civic Centre, The Water Gardens, Harlow CM20 1WG ☎ 01279 446037 ⌁ brian.keane@harlow.gov.uk

Customer Service: Ms Jane Greer, Head of Community Wellbeing, Civic Centre, The Water Gardens, Harlow CM20 1WG ☎ 01279 446410 ⌁ jane.greer@harlow.gov.uk

Economic Development: Ms Jane Greer, Head of Community Wellbeing, Civic Centre, The Water Gardens, Harlow CM20 1WG ☎ 01279 446410 ⌁ jane.greer@harlow.gov.uk

Electoral Registration: Mr Brian Keane, Head of Governance, Civic Centre, The Water Gardens, Harlow CM20 1WG ☎ 01279 446037 ⌁ brian.keane@harlow.gov.uk

Emergency Planning: Mr Graeme Bloomer, Head of Place, Civic Centre, The Water Gardens, Harlow CM20 1WG ☎ 01276 446270 ⌁ graeme.bloomer@harlow.gov.uk

Energy Management: Mr Graeme Bloomer, Head of Place, Civic Centre, The Water Gardens, Harlow CM20 1WG ☎ 01276 446270 ⌁ graeme.bloomer@harlow.gov.uk

Environmental / Technical Services: Mr Graeme Bloomer, Head of Place, Civic Centre, The Water Gardens, Harlow CM20 1WG ☎ 01276 446270 ⌁ graeme.bloomer@harlow.gov.uk

Environmental Health: Mr Graeme Bloomer, Head of Place, Civic Centre, The Water Gardens, Harlow CM20 1WG ☎ 01276 446270 ⌁ graeme.bloomer@harlow.gov.uk

Estates, Property & Valuation: Mr Graeme Bloomer, Head of Place, Civic Centre, The Water Gardens, Harlow CM20 1WG ☎ 01276 446270 ⌁ graeme.bloomer@harlow.gov.uk

Facilities: Mr Graeme Bloomer, Head of Place, Civic Centre, The Water Gardens, Harlow CM20 1WG ☎ 01276 446270 ⌁ graeme.bloomer@harlow.gov.uk

Grounds Maintenance: Mr Graeme Bloomer, Head of Place, Civic Centre, The Water Gardens, Harlow CM20 1WG ☎ 01276 446270 ⌁ graeme.bloomer@harlow.gov.uk

Health and Safety: Mr Brian Keane, Head of Governance, Civic Centre, The Water Gardens, Harlow CM20 1WG ☎ 01279 446037 ⌁ brian.keane@harlow.gov.uk

Highways: Mr Graeme Bloomer, Head of Place, Civic Centre, The Water Gardens, Harlow CM20 1WG ☎ 01276 446270 ⌁ graeme.bloomer@harlow.gov.uk

Home Energy Conservation: Mr Graeme Bloomer, Head of Place, Civic Centre, The Water Gardens, Harlow CM20 1WG ☎ 01276 446270 ⌁ graeme.bloomer@harlow.gov.uk

Housing: Mr Andrew Murray, Head of Housing, Civic Centre, The Water Gardens, Harlow SM20 1WG ☎ 01279 446676 ⌁ andrew.murray@harlow.gov.uk

Housing Maintenance: Mr Andrew Murray, Head of Housing, Civic Centre, The Water Gardens, Harlow SM20 1WG ☎ 01279 446676 ⌁ andrew.murray@harlow.gov.uk

Legal: Mr Brian Keane, Head of Governance, Civic Centre, The Water Gardens, Harlow CM20 1WG ☎ 01279 446037 ⌁ brian.keane@harlow.gov.uk

Leisure and Cultural Services: Ms Jane Greer, Head of Community Wellbeing, Civic Centre, The Water Gardens, Harlow CM20 1WG ☎ 01279 446410 ⌁ jane.greer@harlow.gov.uk

Licensing: Mr Graeme Bloomer, Head of Place, Civic Centre, The Water Gardens, Harlow CM20 1WG ☎ 01276 446270 ⌁ graeme.bloomer@harlow.gov.uk

Member Services: Mr Brian Keane, Head of Governance, Civic Centre, The Water Gardens, Harlow CM20 1WG ☎ 01279 446037 ⌁ brian.keane@harlow.gov.uk

Parking: Mr Graeme Bloomer, Head of Place, Civic Centre, The Water Gardens, Harlow CM20 1WG ☎ 01276 446270 ⌁ graeme.bloomer@harlow.gov.uk

Personnel / HR: Mr Brian Keane, Head of Governance, Civic Centre, The Water Gardens, Harlow CM20 1WG ☎ 01279 446037 ⌁ brian.keane@harlow.gov.uk

HARLOW

Planning: Mr Graeme Bloomer, Head of Place, Civic Centre, The Water Gardens, Harlow CM20 1WG ☎ 01276 446270
✆ graeme.bloomer@harlow.gov.uk

Procurement: Mr Brian Keane, Head of Governance, Civic Centre, The Water Gardens, Harlow CM20 1WG ☎ 01279 446037
✆ brian.keane@harlow.gov.uk

Recycling & Waste Minimisation: Mr Graeme Bloomer, Head of Place, Civic Centre, The Water Gardens, Harlow CM20 1WG
☎ 01276 446270 ✆ graeme.bloomer@harlow.gov.uk

Regeneration: Ms Jane Greer, Head of Community Wellbeing, Civic Centre, The Water Gardens, Harlow CM20 1WG
☎ 01279 446410 ✆ jane.greer@harlow.gov.uk

Staff Training: Mr Brian Keane, Head of Governance, Civic Centre, The Water Gardens, Harlow CM20 1WG ☎ 01279 446037
✆ brian.keane@harlow.gov.uk

Street Scene: Mr Graeme Bloomer, Head of Place, Civic Centre, The Water Gardens, Harlow CM20 1WG ☎ 01276 446270
✆ graeme.bloomer@harlow.gov.uk

Town Centre: Ms Jane Greer, Head of Community Wellbeing, Civic Centre, The Water Gardens, Harlow CM20 1WG
☎ 01279 446410 ✆ jane.greer@harlow.gov.uk

Waste Collection and Disposal: Mr Graeme Bloomer, Head of Place, Civic Centre, The Water Gardens, Harlow CM20 1WG
☎ 01276 446270 ✆ graeme.bloomer@harlow.gov.uk

Waste Management: Mr Graeme Bloomer, Head of Place, Civic Centre, The Water Gardens, Harlow CM20 1WG ☎ 01276 446270
✆ graeme.bloomer@harlow.gov.uk

COUNCILLORS

ChairStevens, Edna (LAB - Netteswell)
edna.stevens@harlow.gov.uk

Vice-ChairLivings, Sue (CON - Old Harlow)
sue.livings@harlow.gov.uk

Leader of the Council: Clempner, Jon (LAB - Little Parndon & Hare Street)
jon.clempner@harlow.gov.uk

Deputy Leader of the Council: Toal, Emma (LAB - Harlow Common)
emma.toal@harlow.gov.uk

Beckett, Ian (LAB - Bush Fair)
ian.beckett@harlow.gov.uk

Carter, David (CON - Great Parndon)
david.carter@harlow.gov.uk

Carter, Simon (CON - Church Langley)
simon.carter@harlow.gov.uk

Charles, Joel (CON - Old Harlow)
joel.charles@harlow.gov.uk

Churchill, Nick (CON - Sumners & Kingsmoor)
nick.churchill@harlow.gov.uk

Clark, Jean (LAB - Little Parndon & Hare Street)
jean.clark@harlow.gov.uk

Clempner, Karen (LAB - Toddbrook)
karen.clempner@harlow.gov.uk

Danvers, Mike (LAB - Netteswell)
mike.danvers@harlow.gov.uk

Davis, Bob (LAB - Mark Hall)
bob.davis@harlow.gov.uk

Durcan, Tony (LAB - Little Parndon & Hare Street)
anthony.durcan@harlow.gov.uk

Forman, Waida (LAB - Netteswell)
waida.forman@harlow.gov.uk

Garnett, Michael (CON - Old Harlow)
michael.garnett@harlow.gov.uk

Hall, Tony (CON - Church Langley)
tony.hall@harlow.gov.uk

Hulcoop, Maggie (LAB - Harlow Common)
maggie.hulcoop@harlow.gov.uk

Ingall, Mark (LAB - Bush Fair)
mark.ingall@harlow.gov.uk

Johnson, Shona (CON - Great Parndon)
Shona.johnson@harlow.gov.uk

Johnson, Eddie (CON - Great Parndon)
eddie.johnson@harlow.gov.uk

Johnson, Andrew (CON - Church Langley)
andrew.johnson@harlow.gov.uk

Long, Dan (UKIP - Bush Fair)
dan.long@harlow.gov.uk

Mullard, Stefan (LAB - Staple Tye)
stefan.mullard@harlow.gov.uk

Perrin, Russell (CON - Sumners & Kingsmoor)
russell.perrin@harlow.gov.uk

Pryor, Bill (UKIP - Staple Tye)
bill.pryor@harlow.gov.uk

Purton, Danny (LAB - Mark Hall)
danny.purton@harlow.gov.uk

Shears, Lanie (LAB - Mark Hall)
lanie.shears@harlow.gov.uk

Souter, Clive (CON - Sumners & Kingsmoor)
clive.souter@harlow.gov.uk

Strachan, John (LAB - Staple Tye)
john.strachan@harlow.gov.uk

Truan, Rod (LAB - Toddbrook)
rod.truan@harlow.gov.uk

Waite, Phil (LAB - Toddbrook)
phil.waite@harlow.gov.uk

Wilkinson, Mark (LAB - Harlow Common)
mark.wilkinson@harlow.gov.uk

POLITICAL COMPOSITION
LAB: 19, CON: 12, UKIP: 2

COMMITTEE CHAIRS

Audit: Ms Karen Clempner

Development Management: Mr Phil Waite

Licensing: Ms Maggie Hulcoop

Harrogate   D

Harrogate Borough Council, Council Offices, Crescent
Gardens, Harrogate HG1 2SG
☎ 01423 500600 🖷 01423 556100
🖳 customerservices@harrogate.gov.uk 🖳 www.harrogate.gov.uk

FACTS AND FIGURES
Parliamentary Constituencies: Harrogate and Knaresborough
EU Constituencies: Yorkshire and the Humber
Election Frequency: Elections are by thirds

PRINCIPAL OFFICERS

Chief Executive: Mr Wallace Sampson, Chief Executive, PO Box
787, Harrogate HG1 9RW ☎ 01423 500600 ext. 56081
🖑 wallace.sampson@harrogate.gov.uk

Senior Management: Mr Nigel Avison, Director - Economy &
Culture, PO Box 787, Harrogate HG1 9RW ☎ 01423 500600 ext.
58170 🖑 nigel.avison@harrogate.gov.uk

Senior Management: Mrs Rachel Bowles, Director - Corporate
Affairs, PO Box 787, Harrogate HG1 9RW ☎ 01423 500600 ext.
56705 🖑 rachel.bowles@harrogate.gov.uk

Senior Management: Mr Alan Jenks, Director - Community, PO
Box 787, Harrogate HG1 9RW ☎ 01423 500600 ext. 56849
🖑 alan.jenks@harrogate.gov.uk

Senior Management: Mr Simon Kent, Director - Harrogate
International Centre, Harrogate International Centre, Kings Road,
Harrogate HG1 5LA ☎ 01423 537237
🖑 simon.kent@harrogate.gov.uk

Architect, Building / Property Services: Mrs Madeleine Bell,
Head of Housing & Property, PO Box 787, Harrogate HG1 9RW
☎ 01423 500600 ext. 58352 🖑 madeleine.bell@harrogate.gov.uk

Building Control: Mr John Fowler, CYC Chief Building Control
Officer, PO Box 787, Harrogate HG1 9RW ☎ 01423 500600 ext.
56597 🖑 john.fowler@harrogate.gov.uk

PR / Communications: Mr Giles Latham, Communications &
Marketing Manager, PO Box 787, Harrogate HG1 9RW
☎ 01423 500600 ext. 58448 🖑 giles.latham@harrogate.gov.uk

Community Planning: Mr Alan Jenks, Director - Community, PO
Box 787, Harrogate HG1 9RW ☎ 01423 500600 ext. 56849
🖑 alan.jenks@harrogate.gov.uk

Community Safety: Mr Dean Richardson, Head of Safer
Communities, PO Box 787, Harrogate HG1 9RW ☎ 01423 500600
ext. 58522 🖑 dean.richardson@harrogate.gov.uk

Community Safety: Mrs Julia Stack, Community Safety & CCTV
Manager, PO Box 787, Harrogate HG1 9RW ☎ 01423 500600 ext.
58190 🖑 julia.stack@harrogate.gov.uk

Computer Management: Mr Roy Grant, Shared Head of ICT, PO
Box 787, Harrogate HG1 9RW ☎ 01423 500600 ext. 58560
🖑 roy.grant@harrogate.gov.uk

Corporate Services: Mr Simon Kent, Director - Harrogate
International Centre, Harrogate International Centre, Kings Road,
Harrogate HG1 5LA ☎ 01423 537237
🖑 simon.kent@harrogate.gov.uk

Customer Service: Mrs Christine Pyatt, Corporate Customer
Services Manager, PO Box 787, Harrogate HG1 9RW
☎ 01423 500600 ext. 51638 🖑 christine.pyatt@harrogate.gov.uk

Direct Labour: Mr Patrick Kilburn, Head of Parks & Environmental
Services, PO Box 787, Harrogate HG1 9RW ☎ 01423 500600 ext.
51106 🖑 patrick.kilburn@harrogate.gov.uk

Economic Development: Mr Nigel Avison, Director - Economy
& Culture, PO Box 787, Harrogate HG1 9RW ☎ 01423 500600 ext.
58170 🖑 nigel.avison@harrogate.gov.uk

E-Government: Mr Roy Grant, Shared Head of ICT, PO Box 787,
Harrogate HG1 9RW ☎ 01423 500600 ext. 58560
🖑 roy.grant@harrogate.gov.uk

Electoral Registration: Mrs Jennifer Norton, Head of Legal &
Governance, PO Box 787, Harrogate HG1 9RW ☎ 01423 500600
ext. 56036 🖑 jennifer.norton@harrogate.gov.uk

Emergency Planning: Mr Ian Speirs, Civil Contingencies Officer,
PO Box 787, Harrogate HG1 9RW ☎ 01423 500600 ext. 56014
🖑 ian.speirs@harrogate.gov.uk

Energy Management: Mr Nigel Avison, Director - Economy &
Culture, PO Box 787, Harrogate HG1 9RW ☎ 01423 500600 ext.
58170 🖑 nigel.avison@harrogate.gov.uk

Environmental / Technical Services: Mr Patrick Kilburn, Head of
Parks & Environmental Services, PO Box 787, Harrogate HG1 9RW
☎ 01423 500600 ext. 51106 🖑 patrick.kilburn@harrogate.gov.uk

Environmental Health: Mr Alan Jenks, Director - Community, PO
Box 787, Harrogate HG1 9RW ☎ 01423 500600 ext. 56849
🖑 alan.jenks@harrogate.gov.uk

Environmental Health: Mr Dean Richardson, Head of Safer
Communities, PO Box 787, Harrogate HG1 9RW ☎ 01423 500600
ext. 58522 🖑 dean.richardson@harrogate.gov.uk

Estates, Property & Valuation: Mr Nigel Avison, Director -
Economy & Culture, PO Box 787, Harrogate HG1 9RW
☎ 01423 500600 ext. 58170 🖑 nigel.avison@harrogate.gov.uk

European Liaison: Ms Genevieve Gillies, Economic Development
Officer, PO Box 787, Harrogate HG1 9RW ☎ 01423 500600 ext.
56079 🖑 genevieve.gillies@harrogate.gov.uk

Finance: Mr Andrew Crookham, Head of Finance, PO Box 787,
Harrogate HG1 9RW ☎ 01423 500600 ext. 58473
🖑 andrew.crookham@harrogate.gov.uk

HARROGATE

Fleet Management: Mr David Dumbleton, Transport Manager, PO Box 787, Harrogate HG1 9RW ☎ 01423 500600 ext. 58177 ✆ david.dumbleton@harrogate.gov.uk

Grounds Maintenance: Mr Patrick Kilburn, Head of Parks & Environmental Services, PO Box 787, Harrogate HG1 9RW ☎ 01423 500600 ext. 51106 ✆ patrick.kilburn@harrogate.gov.uk

Health and Safety: Mrs Sarah Young, Health & Safety Manager, PO Box 787, Harrogate HG1 9RW ☎ 01423 500600 ext. 58115 ✆ sarah.young@harrogate.gov.uk

Home Energy Conservation: Mr John Ward-Campbell, Sustainability Officer, PO Box 787, Harrogate HG1 9RW ☎ 01423 500600 ext. 56909 ✆ john.ward-campbell@harrogate.gov.uk

Housing: Mrs Madeleine Bell, Head of Housing & Property, PO Box 787, Harrogate HG1 9RW ☎ 01423 500600 ext. 58352 ✆ madeleine.bell@harrogate.gov.uk

Housing: Mr Alan Jenks, Director - Community, PO Box 787, Harrogate HG1 9RW ☎ 01423 500600 ext. 56849 ✆ alan.jenks@harrogate.gov.uk

Housing Maintenance: Mr Stephen Hargreaves, Executive Officer - Property Services, PO Box 787, Harrogate HG1 9RW ☎ 01423 500600 ext. 56907 ✆ stephen.hargreaves@harrogate.gov.uk

Legal: Mrs Jennifer Norton, Head of Legal & Governance, PO Box 787, Harrogate HG1 9RW ☎ 01423 500600 ext. 56036 ✆ jennifer.norton@harrogate.gov.uk

Leisure and Cultural Services: Ms Lois Toyne, Head of Culture, Tourism & Sports, PO Box 787, Harrogate HG1 9RW ☎ 01423 500600 ext. 58617 ✆ lois.toyne@harrogate.gov.uk

Licensing: Mr Gareth Bentley, Food, Licensing & Occupational Safety Manager, PO Box 787, Harrogate HG1 9RW ☎ 01423 500600 ext. 58501 ✆ gareth.bentley@harrogate.gov.uk

Lighting: Mr David Oliver, Street Lighting Engineer, PO Box 787, Harrogate HG1 9RW ☎ 01423 500600 ext. 56544 ✆ david.oliver@harrogate.gov.uk

Lottery Funding, Charity and Voluntary: Mrs Jennifer Norton, Head of Legal & Governance, PO Box 787, Harrogate HG1 9RW ☎ 01423 500600 ext. 56036 ✆ jennifer.norton@harrogate.gov.uk

Member Services: Mrs Jennifer Norton, Head of Legal & Governance, PO Box 787, Harrogate HG1 9RW ☎ 01423 500600 ext. 56036 ✆ jennifer.norton@harrogate.gov.uk

Parking: Ms Susan McGarry, Parking Services Manager, PO Box 787, Harrogate HG1 9RW ☎ 01423 500600 ext. 58350 ✆ susan.mcgarry@harrogate.gov.uk

Partnerships: Mrs Ann Byrne, Partnerships & Engagement Manager, PO Box 787, Harrogate HG1 9RW ☎ 01423 500600 ext. 56067 ✆ ann.byrne@harrogate.gov.uk

Personnel / HR: Ms Kay Atherton, Head of Organisational Development & Improvement, PO Box 787, Harrogate HG1 9RW ☎ 01423 500600 ext. 58472 ✆ kay.atherton@harrogate.gov.uk

Planning: Mrs Kathryn Daly, Head of Planning & Development, PO Box 787, Harrogate HG1 9RW ☎ 01423 500600 ext. 56054 ✆ kathryn.daly@harrogate.gov.uk

Procurement: Mrs Marion Wrightson, Procurement Manager, PO Box 787, Harrogate HG1 9RW ☎ 01423 500600 ext. 58609 ✆ marion.wrightson@harrogate.gov.uk

Recycling & Waste Minimisation: Mrs Kate Dawson, Strategic Development Manager, PO Box 787, Harrogate HG1 9RW ☎ 01423 500600 ext. 51097 ✆ kate.dawson@harrogate.gov.uk

Regeneration: Ms Genevieve Gillies, Economic Development Officer, PO Box 787, Harrogate HG1 9RW ☎ 01423 500600 ext. 56079 ✆ genevieve.gillies@harrogate.gov.uk

Tourism: Mr Simon Kent, Director - Harrogate International Centre, Harrogate International Centre, Kings Road, Harrogate HG1 5LA ☎ 01423 537237 ✆ simon.kent@harrogate.gov.uk

Tourism: Ms Helen Suckling, Visitor Services Manager, PO Box 787, Harrogate HG1 9RW ☎ 01423 500600 ext. 37306 ✆ helen.suckling@harrogate.gov.uk

Transport Planner: Mr Thomas Horner, Strategic Transport Planner, PO Box 787, Harrogate HG1 9RW ☎ 01423 500600 ext. 58332 ✆ thomas.horner@harrogate.gov.uk

Waste Collection and Disposal: Mr Patrick Kilburn, Head of Parks & Environmental Services, PO Box 787, Harrogate HG1 9RW ☎ 01423 500600 ext. 51106 ✆ patrick.kilburn@harrogate.gov.uk

Waste Management: Mr Patrick Kilburn, Head of Parks & Environmental Services, PO Box 787, Harrogate HG1 9RW ☎ 01423 500600 ext. 51106 ✆ patrick.kilburn@harrogate.gov.uk

Children's Play Areas: Mrs Jennifer Love, Technical Officer - District & Play, PO Box 787, Harrogate HG1 9RW ☎ 01423 500600 ext. 51072 ✆ jennifer.love@harrogate.gov.uk

COUNCILLORS

Mayor: Brown, Nick (CON - Newby)
nick.brown@harrogate.gov.uk

Deputy Mayor: Ryder, Christine (CON - Washburn)
christine.ryder@harrogate.gov.uk

Leader of the Council: Cooper, Richard (CON - High Harrogate)
richard.cooper@harrogate.gov.uk

Deputy Leader of the Council: Harrison, Michael (CON - Killinghall)
michael.harrison@harrogate.gov.uk

Atkinson, Margaret (CON - Kirkby Malzeard)
margaret.atkinson@harrogate.gov.uk

Bateman, Bernard (CON - Wathvale)
bernard.bateman@harrogate.gov.uk

Batt, John (CON - Knaresborough East)
john.batt@harrogate.gov.uk

Broadbank, Philip (LD - Starbeck)
philip.broadbank@harrogate.gov.uk

Burnett, Rebecca (CON - Rossett)
rebecca.burnett@harrogate.gov.uk

Butterfield, Jean (CON - Low Harrogate)
jean.butterfield@harrogate.gov.uk

Chambers, Michael (CON - Ripon Spa)
mike.chambers@harrogate.gov.uk

Chapman, Trevor (LD - New Park)
trevor.chapman@harrogate.gov.uk

Clark, Jim (CON - Rossett)
jim.clark@harrogate.gov.uk

Duxbury, Nick (CON - Claro)
nicholas.duxbury@harrogate.gov.uk

Ennis, John (CON - Low Harrogate)
john.ennis@harrogate.gov.uk

Fawcett, Shirley (CON - Spofforth with Lower Wharfedale)

Fox, Ivor (CON - Knaresborough Scriven Park)
ivor.fox@harrogate.gov.uk

Fox, John (LD - Granby)
john.fox@harrogate.gov.uk

Galloway, Ian (CON - Bishop Monkton)
ian.galloway@harrogate.gov.uk

Goode, David (LD - Knaresborough King James)
david.goode@harrogate.gov.uk

Goss, Andrew (LD - Woodfield)
andrew.goss@harrogate.gov.uk

Haslam, Paul (CON - Bilton)
paul.haslam@harrogate.gov.uk

Hawke, Sid (IND - Ripon Minster)
sid.hawke@harrogate.gov.uk

Hill, Matthew (CON - Pannal)
matt.hill@harrogate.gov.uk

Hull, Nathan (CON - Lower Nidderdale)
nathan.hull@harrogate.gov.uk

Ireland, Philip (CON - Knaresborough King James)
phil.ireland@harrogate.gov.uk

Jackson, Steven (CON - Saltergate)
steven.jackson@harrogate.gov.uk

Johnson, Ben (CON - High Harrogate)
ben.johnson@harrogate.gov.uk

Jones, Pat (CON - Stray)
Pat.Jones@harrogate.gov.uk

Jones, Anne (LD - Knaresborough Scriven Park)
anne.jones@harrogate.gov.uk

Law, Janet (LD - Starbeck)
janet.law@harrogate.gov.uk

Lumley, Stanley (CON - Pateley Bridge)
stanley.lumley@harrogate.gov.uk

Mackenzie, Don (CON - Harlow Moor)
don.mackenzie@harrogate.gov.uk

Mann, John (CON - Pannal)
john.mann@harrogate.gov.uk

Marsh, Pat (LD - Hookstone)
pat.marsh@harrogate.gov.uk

Martin, Stuart (CON - Ripon Moorside)
stuart.martin@harrogate.gov.uk

McHardy, Pauline (IND - Ripon Moorside)
pauline.mchardy@harrogate.gov.uk

Metcalfe, Zoe (CON - Ripon Minster)
zoe.metcalfe@harrogate.gov.uk

Myatt, Tim (CON - Marston Moor)
timothy.myatt@harrogate.gov.uk

O'Neill, Robert (LD - Woodfield)
robert.oneill@harrogate.gov.uk

Paraskos, Andrew (CON - Ribston)
andrew.paraskos@harrogate.gov.uk

Rodgers, Val (LD - Bilton)
val.rodgers@harrogate.gov.uk

Simms, Nigel (CON - Mashamshire)
nigel.simms@harrogate.gov.uk

Skardon, Clare (LD - Hookstone)
membserv@harrogate.gov.uk

Skidmore, Alan (CON - Ripon Spa)
alan.skidmore@harrogate.gov.uk

Swift, Graham (CON - Saltergate)
graham.swift@harrogate.gov.uk

Teague, Ashley (CON - Ouseburn)
ashley.teague@harrogate.gov.uk

Theakston, Simon (CON - Harlow Moor)
simon.theakston@theakstons.co.uk

Travena, Jennifer (LD - Granby)
jennifer.travena@harrogate.gov.uk

Trotter, Clifford (CON - Stray)
cliff.trotter@harrogate.gov.uk

Watson, Tom (LD - Nidd Valley)
thomas.watson@harrogate.gov.uk

Webber, Matthew (LD - New Park)
matthew.webber@harrogate.gov.uk

Willoughby, Christine (LD - Knaresborough East)
christine.willoughby@harrogate.gov.uk

Windass, Robert (CON - Boroughbridge)
cllr.windass@harrogate.gov.uk

POLITICAL COMPOSITION
CON: 37, LD: 15, IND: 2

COMMITTEE CHAIRS

Audit: Mr Simon Theakston

Licensing: Mr John Ennis

Planning: Mr John Mann

Harrow
L

Harrow London Borough Council, Civic Centre, Station Road, Harrow HA1 2XF
☎ 020 8863 5611 📠 020 8424 1134 ✆ info@harrow.gov.uk
💻 www.harrow.gov.uk

HARROW

FACTS AND FIGURES
Parliamentary Constituencies: Harrow East, Harrow West, Uxbridge and Ruislip South
EU Constituencies: London
Election Frequency: Elections are of whole council

PRINCIPAL OFFICERS

Chief Executive: Mr Michael Lockwood, Chief Executive, Civic Centre, Station Road, Harrow HA1 2XF ☎ 020 8424 1001 ⏚ michael.lockwood@harrow.gov.uk

Senior Management: Mr Tom McCourt, Corporate Director - Communities, Civic Centre, Station Road, Harrow HA1 2XF ⏚ tom.mccourt@harrow.gov.uk

Senior Management: Mr Chris Spencer, Corporate Director - People Services, Civic Centre, Station Road, Harrow HA1 2XF ⏚ chris.spencer@harrow.gov.uk

Senior Management: Mr Tom Whiting, Corporate Director - Resources & Commercial, Civic Centre, Station Road, Harrow HA1 2XF ☎ 020 8863 5611 ⏚ tom.whiting@harrow.gov.uk

Senior Management: Mr Paul Nichols, Divisional Director - Regeneration & Planning, Civic Centre, Station Road, Harrow HA1 2XF ☎ 020 8736 6149 ⏚ paul.nichols@harrow.gov.uk

Children / Youth Services: Mr Paul Hewitt, Divisional Director - Children & Young People's Services, Civic Centre, Station Road, Harrow HA1 2XF ☎ 020 8416 8830 ⏚ paul.hewitt@harrow.gov.uk

Children / Youth Services: Ms Johanna Morgan, Divisional Director - People's Services Strategy: Commercialisation & Regeneration, Civic Centre, Station Road, Harrow HA1 2XF ☎ 020 8424 1356 ⏚ johanna.morgan@harrow.gov.uk

Children / Youth Services: Mr Patrick O'Dwyer, Divisional Director - Education Services, Civic Centre, Station Road, Harrow HA1 2XF ☎ 020 8420 9344 ⏚ patrick.o'dwyer@harrow.gov.uk

Civil Registration: Ms Elaine McEachron, Registration & Support Services Manager, Civic Centre, Station Road, Harrow HA1 2XF ☎ 020 8424 1097 ⏚ elaine.mceachron@harrow.gov.uk

PR / Communications: Mr Daniel Lester, Head - Communications, Civic Centre, Station Road, Harrow HA1 2XF ☎ 020 8424 1292 ⏚ daniel.lester@harrow.gov.uk

Community Safety: Dr Andrew Howe, Director - Public Health, Civic Centre, Station Road, Harrow HA1 2XF ☎ 020 8359 3970 ⏚ andrew.howe@harrow.gov.uk

Customer Service: Ms Carol Cutler, Director - Business Transformation & Customer Service, Civic Centre, Station Road, Harrow HA1 2XF ☎ 020 8424 6701 ⏚ carol.cutler@harrow.gov.uk

Economic Development: Mr Mark Billington, Head of Service - Economic Development & Research, Civic Centre, Station Road, Harrow HA1 2XF ☎ 020 8736 6533 ⏚ mark.billington@harrow.gov.uk

Electoral Registration: Ms Elaine McEachron, Registration & Support Services Manager, Civic Centre, Station Road, Harrow HA1 2XF ☎ 020 8424 1097 ⏚ elaine.mceachron@harrow.gov.uk

Emergency Planning: Mr Kan Grover, Service Manager - Emergency Planning & Business Continuity, Civic Centre, Station Road, Harrow HA1 2XF ☎ 020 8420 9319 ⏚ kan.grover@harrow.gov.uk

Environmental / Technical Services: Mr Simon Baxter, Divisional Director - Environmental & Culture, Civic Centre, Station Road, Harrow HA1 2XF ☎ 020 8736 6799 ⏚ simon.baxter@harrow.gov.uk

Environmental Health: Mr Richard Lebrun, Environmental Services Manager, Civic Centre, Station Road, Harrow HA1 2XF ⏚ richard.lebrun@harrow.gov.uk

Finance: Ms Dawn Calvert, Finance Director, Civic Centre, Station Road, Harrow HA1 2XF ☎ 020 8420 9269 ⏚ dawn.calvert@harrow.gov.uk

Housing: Ms Lynne Pennington, Divisional Director - Housing Services, Civic Centre, Station Road, Harrow HA1 2XF ☎ 020 8424 1998 ⏚ lynne.pennington@harrow.gov.uk

Legal: Ms Jessica Farmer, Head - Legal Practice, Civic Centre, Station Road, Harrow HA1 2XF ☎ 020 8424 1889 ⏚ jessica.farmer@harrow.gov.uk

Legal: Mr Hugh Peart, Director - Legal & Governance Services, Civic Centre, Station Road, Harrow HA1 2XF ☎ 020 8424 1272 ⏚ hugh.peart@harrow.gov.uk

Leisure and Cultural Services: Ms Marianne Locke, Programme Director - Cultural Regeneration, Civic Centre, Station Road, Harrow HA1 2XF ☎ 020 8736 6530 ⏚ marianne.locke@harrow.gov.uk

Member Services: Ms Elaine McEachron, Registration & Support Services Manager, Civic Centre, Station Road, Harrow HA1 2XF ☎ 020 8424 1097 ⏚ elaine.mceachron@harrow.gov.uk

Partnerships: Mr Alex Dewsnap, Divisional Director - Strategic Commissioning, Civic Centre, Station Road, Harrow HA1 2XF ☎ 020 8416 8250 ⏚ alex.dewsnap@harrow.gov.uk

Personnel / HR: Mr Jon Turner, Divisional Director - HRD & Shared Services, Civic Centre, Station Road, Harrow HA1 2XF ☎ 020 8424 1225 ⏚ jon.turner@harrow.gov.uk

Planning: Mr Paul Nichols, Divisional Director - Regeneration & Planning, Civic Centre, Station Road, Harrow HA1 2XF ☎ 020 8736 6149 ⏚ paul.nichols@harrow.gov.uk

Planning: Mr Sunil Sahadevon, Head - Development Management & Planning, Civic Centre, Station Road, Harrow HA1 2XF ☎ 020 8424 1166 ⏚ sunil.sahadevon@harrow.gov.uk

Procurement: Mr Terry Brewer, Divisional Director - Commercial, Contracts & Procurement, Civic Centre, Station Road, Harrow HA1 2XF ☎ 020 8736 6799 ⏚ terry.brewer@harrow.gov.uk

Social Services (Adult): Ms Bernie Flaherty, Director - Adult Social Services, Civic Centre, Station Road, Harrow HA1 2XF ☎ 020 8863 5611 ⏚ bernie.flaherty@harrow.gov.uk

Public Health: Dr Andrew Howe, Director - Public Health, 27 Carnarvon Road, Barnet EN5 4LX ☎ 020 8359 3970
🖰 andrew.howe@harrow.gov.uk

COUNCILLORS

Mayor: Shah, Rekha (LAB - Wealdstone)
rekha.shah@harrow.gov.uk

Deputy Mayor: Davine, Margaret (LAB - Roxeth)
margaret.davine@harrow.gov.uk

Leader of the Council: Shah, Sachin (LAB - Queensbury)
sachin.shah@harrow.gov.uk

Deputy Leader of the Council: Ferry, Keith (LAB - Greenhill)
keith.ferry@harrow.gov.uk

Group LeaderHall, Susan (CON - Hatch End)
susan.hall@harrow.gov.uk

Ali, Ghazanfar (LAB - Greenhill)
ghazanfar.ali@harrow.gov.uk

Almond, Richard (CON - Pinner South)
richard.almond@harrow.gov.uk

Amadi, Chika (LAB - Edgware)
chika.amadi@harrow.gov.uk

Anderson, Jeff (LAB - Rayners Lane)
jeff.anderson@harrow.gov.uk

Anderson, Susan (LAB - Greenhill)
sue.anderson@harrow.gov.uk

Ashton, Marilyn (CON - Stanmore Park)
marilyn.ashton@harrow.gov.uk

Bath, Camilla (CON - Stanmore Park)
camilla.bath@harrow.gov.uk

Baxter, June (CON - Harrow on the Hill)
june.baxter@harrow.gov.uk

Bednell, Christine (CON - Stanmore Park)
christine.bednell@harrow.gov.uk

Bond, James (IND - Headstone North)
james.bond@harrow.gov.uk

Borio, Michael (LAB - Queensbury)
michael.borio@harrow.gov.uk

Brown, Simon (LAB - Headstone South)
simon.brown@harrow.gov.uk

Chana, Kamaljit (CON - Pinner South)
kamaljit.chana@harrow.gov.uk

Chauhan, Ramji (CON - Harrow Weald)
ramji.chauhan@harrow.gov.uk

Currie, Bob (LAB - Roxbourne)
bob.currie@harrow.gov.uk

Dattani, Niraj (LAB - Kenton East)
niraj.dattani@harrow.gov.uk

Dooley, Josephine (LAB - Roxbourne)
josephine.dooley@harrow.gov.uk

Fitzpatrick, Pamela (LAB - Headstone South)
pamela.fitzpatrick@harrow.gov.uk

Greek, Stephen (CON - Harrow Weald)
stephen.greek@harrow.gov.uk

Green, Mitzi (LAB - Kenton East)
mitzi.green@harrow.gov.uk

Hearnden, Glen (LAB - Harrow on the Hill)
glen.hearnden@harrow.gov.uk

Henson, Graham (LAB - Roxbourne)
graham.henson@harrow.gov.uk

Hinkley, John (CON - Hatch End)
john.hinkley@harrow.gov.uk

Jogia, Ameet (CON - Canons)
ameet.jogia@harrow.gov.uk

Kara, Manji (CON - Belmont)
maji.kara@harrow.gov.uk

Kendler, Barry (LAB - Edgware)
barry.kendler@harrow.gov.uk

Lammiman, Jean (CON - Hatch End)
jean.lammiman@harrow.gov.uk

Macleod, Barry (CON - Harrow on the Hill)
barry.macloed@harrow.gov.uk

Marikar, Kairul (LAB - West Harrow)
kairul.marikar@harrow.gov.uk

Maru, Ajay (LAB - Kenton West)
ajay.maru@harrow.gov.uk

Miles, Jerry (LAB - Roxeth)
jerry.miles@harrow.gov.uk

Mithanl, Vina (CON - Kenton West)
vina.mithani@harrow.gov.uk

Moshenson, Amir (CON - Canons)
amir.moshenson@harrow.gov.uk

Mote, Chris (CON - Pinner South)
chris.mote@harrow.gov.uk

Mote, Janet (CON - Headstone North)
janet.mote@harrow.gov.uk

Noyce, Chris (LD - Rayners Lane)
chris.noyce@harrow.gov.uk

O'Dell, Phillip (LAB - Wealdstone)
phillip.odell@harrow.gov.uk

Osborn, Paul (CON - Pinner)
paul.osborn@harrow.gov.uk

Parekh, Nitin (LAB - Edgware)
nitin.parekh@harrow.gov.uk

Parmar, Varsha (LAB - Marlborough)
varsha.parmar@harrow.gov.uk

Parmar, Mina (CON - Belmont)
mina.parmar@harrow.gov.uk

Patel, Primesh (LAB - Roxeth)
primesh.patel@harrow.gov.uk

Patel, Pritesh (CON - Harrow Weald)
pritesh.patel@harrow.gov.uk

Perry, David (LAB - Marlborough)
david.perry@harrow.gov.uk

Rabadia, Kantilal (CON - Kenton West)
kanti.rabadia@harrow.gov.uk

Ramchandani, Kiran (LAB - Queensbury)
kiran.ramchandani@harrow.gov.uk

Robson, Christine (LAB - West Harrow)
christine.robson@harrow.gov.uk

Seymour, Lynda (CON - Belmont)
lynda.seymour@harrow.gov.uk

Shah-Levy, Aneka (LAB - Kenton East)
aneka.shah@harrow.gov.uk

Stevenson, Norman (CON - Pinner)
norman.stevenson@harrow.gov.uk

Suresh, Krishna (LAB - Rayners Lane)
krishna.suresh@harrow.gov.uk

Suresh, Sasikala (LAB - Headstone South)
sasikala.suresh@harrow.gov.uk

Swersky, Adam (LAB - West Harrow)
adam.swersky@harrow.gov.uk

Thakker, Bharat (CON - Canons)
bharat.thakker@harrow.gov.uk

Weiss, Antonio (LAB - Marlborough)
antonio.weiss@harrow.gov.uk

Weston, Georgia (IND - Headstone North)
georgia.weston@harrow.gov.uk

Whitehead, Anne (LAB - Wealdstone)
anne.whitehead@harrow.gov.uk

Wright, Stephen (CON - Pinner)
stephen.wright@harrow.gov.uk

POLITICAL COMPOSITION
LAB: 34, CON: 26, IND: 2, LD: 1

COMMITTEE CHAIRS

Audit, Governance & Risk Management: Mr Antonio Weiss

Health & Wellbeing: Mr Sachin Shah

Licensing: Mr Krishna Suresh

Pensions: Mr Nitin Parekh

Planning: Mr Keith Ferry

Hart   D

Hart District Council, Civic Offices, Harlington Way, Fleet
GU51 4AE
☎ 01252 622122 🖨 01252 626886 ✆ enquiries@hart.gov.uk
🖳 www.hart.gov.uk

FACTS AND FIGURES
Parliamentary Constituencies: Hampshire North East
EU Constituencies: South East
Election Frequency: Elections are by thirds

PRINCIPAL OFFICERS

Chief Executive: Ms Patricia Hughes, Joint Chief Executive, Civic
Offices, Harlington Way, Fleet GU51 4AE ☎ 01252 622122
✆ patricia.hughes@hart.gov.uk

Chief Executive: Mr Daryl Phillips, Joint Chief Executive, Civic
Offices, Harlington Way, Fleet GU51 4AE ☎ 01252 622122
✆ daryl.phillips@hart.gov.uk

Senior Management: Mr John Elson, Head of Environment &
Technical Services, Civic Offices, Harlington Way, Fleet GU51 4AE
☎ 01252 622122 ✆ john.elson@hart.gov.uk

Senior Management: Mr Phil Turner, Head of Housing, Civic
Offices, Harlington Way, Fleet GU51 4AE ☎ 01252 774488
✆ phil.turner@hart.gov.uk

Senior Management: Mr Andrew Vallance, Head of Corporate
Services, Civic Offices, Harlington Way, Fleet GU51 4AE
✆ andrew.vallance@hart.gov.uk

Senior Management: Mr Nick Steevens, Head of Regulatory
Services, Civic Offices, Harlington Way, Fleet GU51 4AE
☎ 01252 774296 ✆ nick.steevens@hart.gov.uk

Architect, Building / Property Services: Mr John Elson, Head
of Environment & Technical Services, Civic Offices, Harlington Way,
Fleet GU51 4AE ☎ 01252 622122 ✆ john.elson@hart.gov.uk

Community Safety: Ms Caroline Ryan, Community Safety
Manager, Civic Offices, Harlington Way, Fleet GU51 4AE
☎ 01252 622122

Contracts: Mr John Elson, Head of Environment & Technical
Services, Civic Offices, Harlington Way, Fleet GU51 4AE
☎ 01252 622122 ✆ john.elson@hart.gov.uk

Corporate Services: Mr Andrew Vallance, Head of Corporate
Services, Civic Offices, Harlington Way, Fleet GU51 4AE
✆ andrew.vallance@hart.gov.uk

Customer Service: Mrs Liz Squires, Head of Revenues &
Benefits, Civic Offices, Harlington Way, Fleet GU51 4AE
☎ 01252 622122 ✆ liz.squires@hart.gov.uk

Direct Labour: Ms Sarah Robinson, Waste & Recycling Manager,
Springwell Lane Depot, Hartley Wintney RG27 8BW
☎ 01252 622122 ✆ sarah.robinson@hart.gov.uk

Electoral Registration: Mr Andy Tiffin, Elections & Information
Manager, Civic Offices, Harlington Way, Fleet GU51 4AE
☎ 01252 622122 ✆ andrew.tiffin@hart.gov.uk

Emergency Planning: Mr John Elson, Head of Environment &
Technical Services, Civic Offices, Harlington Way, Fleet GU51 4AE
☎ 01252 622122 ✆ john.elson@hart.gov.uk

Energy Management: Mr John Elson, Head of Environment &
Technical Services, Civic Offices, Harlington Way, Fleet GU51 4AE
☎ 01252 622122 ✆ john.elson@hart.gov.uk

Environmental / Technical Services: Mr John Elson, Head of
Environment & Technical Services, Civic Offices, Harlington Way,
Fleet GU51 4AE ☎ 01252 622122 ✆ john.elson@hart.gov.uk

Environmental Health: Mr Nick Steevens, Head of Regulatory
Services, Civic Offices, Harlington Way, Fleet GU51 4AE
☎ 01252 774296 ✆ nick.steevens@hart.gov.uk

Estates, Property & Valuation: Mr John Elson, Head of Environment & Technical Services, Civic Offices, Harlington Way, Fleet GU51 4AE ☎ 01252 622122 ⌨ john.elson@hart.gov.uk

Facilities: Mr Matt Saunders, Business Support & Facilities Manager, Civic Offices, Harlington Way, Fleet GU51 4AE ☎ 01252 622122; 01252 774408 ⌨ matt.saunders@hart.gov.uk

Finance: Mr Tony Higgins, Head of Finance & S151 Officer, Civic Offices, Harlington Way, Fleet GU51 4AE ☎ 01252 622122 ⌨ tony.higgins@hart.gov.uk

Treasury: Mr Tony Higgins, Head of Finance & S151 Officer, Civic Offices, Harlington Way, Fleet GU51 4AE ☎ 01252 622122 ⌨ tony.higgins@hart.gov.uk

Grounds Maintenance: Mr John Elson, Head of Environment & Technical Services, Civic Offices, Harlington Way, Fleet GU51 4AE ☎ 01252 622122 ⌨ john.elson@hart.gov.uk

Health and Safety: Mr Paul Beaumont, Corporate Health & Safety Officer, Civic Offices, Harlington Way, Fleet GU51 4AE ☎ 01252 622122 ⌨ paul.beaumont@hart.gov.uk

Highways: Mr John Elson, Head of Environment & Technical Services, Civic Offices, Harlington Way, Fleet GU51 4AE ☎ 01252 622122 ⌨ john.elson@hart.gov.uk

Housing: Mr Phil Turner, Head of Housing, Civic Offices, Harlington Way, Fleet GU51 4AE ☎ 01252 774488 ⌨ phil.turner@hart.gov.uk

Legal: Ms Melanie O'Sullivan, Legal Services Manager (Shared), Civic Offices, Harlington Way, Fleet GU51 4AE ☎ 01256 845402 ⌨ melanie.o'sullivan@basingstoke.gov.uk

Leisure and Cultural Services: Mr Carl Westby, Head of Leisure & Environmental Protection, Civic Offices, Harlington Way, Fleet GU51 4AE ☎ 01252 622122 ⌨ carl.westby@hart.gov.uk

Licensing: Ms Angela Semowa, Licensing & Technical Officer, Civic Offices, Harlington Way, Fleet GU51 4AE ☎ 01252 622122 ⌨ angela.semowa@hart.gov.uk

Member Services: Ms Gill Chapman, Committee Clerk, Civic Offices, Harlington Way, Fleet GU51 4AE ☎ 01252 622122 ⌨ gill.chapman@hart.gov.uk

Planning: Mr Daryl Phillips, Joint Chief Executive, Civic Offices, Harlington Way, Fleet GU51 4AE ☎ 01252 622122 ⌨ daryl.phillips@hart.gov.uk

Recycling & Waste Minimisation: Mr John Elson, Head of Environment & Technical Services, Civic Offices, Harlington Way, Fleet GU51 4AE ☎ 01252 622122 ⌨ john.elson@hart.gov.uk

Recycling & Waste Minimisation: Mrs Sarah Robinson, Waste & Recycling Manager, Civic Offices, London Road, Basingstoke RG21 4AH ☎ 01252 774426; 01256 845200 ⌨ sarah.robinson@hart.gov.uk

Road Safety: Mr John Elson, Head of Environment & Technical Services, Civic Offices, Harlington Way, Fleet GU51 4AE ☎ 01252 622122 ⌨ john.elson@hart.gov.uk

Street Scene: Ms Sarah Robinson, Waste & Recycling Manager, Springwell Lane Depot, Hartley Wintney RG27 8BW ☎ 01252 622122 ⌨ sarah.robinson@hart.gov.uk

Traffic Management: Mr John Elson, Head of Environment & Technical Services, Civic Offices, Harlington Way, Fleet GU51 4AE ☎ 01252 622122 ⌨ john.elson@hart.gov.uk

Waste Collection and Disposal: Mr John Elson, Head of Environment & Technical Services, Civic Offices, Harlington Way, Fleet GU51 4AE ☎ 01252 622122 ⌨ john.elson@hart.gov.uk

Waste Management: Ms Sarah Robinson, Waste & Recycling Manager, Springwell Lane Depot, Hartley Wintney RG27 8BW ☎ 01252 622122 ⌨ sarah.robinson@hart.gov.uk

Children's Play Areas: Mr Adam Green, Ecology & Countryside Manager, Civic Offices, Harlington Way, Fleet GU51 4AE ☎ 01252 622122 ⌨ adam.green@hart.gov.uk

COUNCILLORS

Chair: Southern, Tim (CON - Hartley Wintney) tim.southern@hart.gov.uk

Leader of the Council: Parker, Stephen (CON - Fleet East) stephen.parker@hart.gov.uk

Deputy Leader of the Council: Burchfield, Brian (CON - Hook) brian.burchfield@hart.gov.uk

Ambler, Simon (O - Crookham West & Ewshot) simon.ambler@hart.gov.uk

Axam, Chris (R - Crookham East) chris.axam@hart.gov.uk

Bailey, Stuart (LD - Yateley East) stuart.bailey@hart.gov.uk

Billings, Myra (LD - Yateley West) myra.billings@hart.gov.uk

Blewett, Brian (LD - Blackwater & Hawley) brian.blewett@hart.gov.uk

Butler, Gill (O - Crookham East) gill.butler@hart.gov.uk

Clarke, Tony (O - Crookham West & Ewshot) tony.clarke@hart.gov.uk

Cockarill, Graham (LD - Yateley East) graham.cockarill@hart.gov.uk

Collett, Adrian (LD - Blackwater & Hawley) adrian.collett@hart.gov.uk

Crampton, Anne (CON - Hartley Wintney) anne.crampton@hart.gov.uk

Crisp, Gerry (LD - Yateley West) enquiries@hart.gov.uk

Crookes, Kenneth (CON - Odiham) kenneth.crookes@hart.gov.uk

Dickens, Shawn (CON - Yateley West) shawn.dickens@hart.gov.uk

HART

Forster, Steve (CON - Fleet West)
steve.forster@hart.gov.uk

Gorys, Stephen (CON - Odiham)
stephen.gorys@hart.gov.uk

Gray, Alexander (CON - Fleet Central)
alex.gray@hart.gov.uk

Harward, Robert (LD - Blackwater & Hawley)
robert.harward@hart.gov.uk

Kennett, John (CON - Odiham)
john.kennett@hart.gov.uk

Kinnell, Sara (CON - Fleet West)
sara.kinnell@hart.gov.uk

Leeson, Robert (IND - Hook)
rob.leeson@hart.gov.uk

Makepeace-Browne, Wendy (O - Fleet Central)
wendy.makepeace-brown@hart.gov.uk

Morris, Mike (CON - Hook)
mike.morris@hart.gov.uk

Neighbour, David (LD - Yateley East)
david.neighbour@hart.gov.uk

Oliver, Alan (IND - Fleet Central)
alan.oliver@hart.gov.uk

Radley, James (O - Crookham East)
james.radley@hart.gov.uk

Radley, Jenny (O - Crookham West & Ewshot)
jenny.radley@hart.gov.uk

Renshaw, Andrew (CON - Hartley Wintney)
andrew.renshaw@hart.gov.uk

Wheale, Sharyn (CON - Fleet East)
sharyn.wheale@hart.gov.uk

Woods, Richard (CON - Fleet West)
richard.woods@hart.gov.uk

Wright, Jonathan (CON - Fleet East)

POLITICAL COMPOSITION
CON: 16, LD: 8, O: 6, IND: 2, R: 1

Hartlepool   U

Hartlepool Borough Council, Civic Centre, Victoria Road,
Hartlepool TS24 8AY
☎ 01429 266522 📠 01429 523005
📧 customer.service@hartlepool.gov.uk 🖥 www.hartlepool.gov.uk

FACTS AND FIGURES
Parliamentary Constituencies: Hartlepool
EU Constituencies: North East
Election Frequency: Elections are by thirds

PRINCIPAL OFFICERS

Chief Executive: Ms Gill Alexander, Chief Executive, Civic Centre,
Victoria Road, Hartlepool TS24 8AY ☎ 01429 523001
📧 gill.alexander@hartlepool.gov.uk

Assistant Chief Executive: Mr Andrew Atkin, Assistant Chief
Executive, Civic Centre, Victoria Road, Hartlepool TS24 8AY
☎ 01429 523003 📧 andrew.atkin@hartlepool.gov.uk

Senior Management: Mr Peter Devlin, Chief Solicitor, Civic
Centre, Victoria Road, Hartlepool TS24 8AY ☎ 01429 523003;
01429 523856 📧 peter.devlin@hartlepool.gov.uk

Senior Management: Mr Chris Little, Chief Finance Officer, Civic
Centre, Victoria Road, Hartlepool TS24 8AY ☎ 01429 523003
📧 chris.little@hartlepool.gov.uk

Senior Management: Mrs Denise Ogden, Director -
Regeneration & Neighbourhood Services, Civic Centre, Victoria
Road, Hartlepool TS24 8AY ☎ 01429 523808
📧 denise.ogden@hartlepool.gov.uk

Senior Management: Ms Louise Wallace, Director - Public
Health, Civic Centre, Victoria Road, Hartlepool TS24 8AY
☎ 01429 284030 📧 louise.wallace@hartlepool.gov.uk

Best Value: Mr Andrew Atkin, Assistant Chief Executive, Civic
Centre, Victoria Road, Hartlepool TS24 8AY ☎ 01429 523003
📧 andrew.atkin@hartlepool.gov.uk

Children / Youth Services: Mr Mark Smith, Head of Integrated
Youth Support Services, Civic Centre, Victoria Road, Hartlepool
TS24 8AY ☎ 01429 523901 📧 mark.smith@hartlepool.gov.uk

Civil Registration: Ms Julie Howard, Customer & Business
Manager, Civic Centre, Victoria Road, Hartlepool TS24 8AY
☎ 01429 284354 📧 julie.howard@hartlepool.gov.uk

PR / Communications: Mr Alastair Rae, Public Relations Officer,
Civic Centre, Victoria Road, Hartlepool TS24 8AY ☎ 01429 523510
📧 alastair.rae@hartlepool.gov.uk

Community Safety: Mrs Denise Ogden, Director - Regeneration
& Neighbourhood Services, Civic Centre, Victoria Road, Hartlepool
TS24 8AY ☎ 01429 523808 📧 denise.ogden@hartlepool.gov.uk

Computer Management: Mr Andrew Atkin, Assistant Chief
Executive, Civic Centre, Victoria Road, Hartlepool TS24 8AY
☎ 01429 523003 📧 andrew.atkin@hartlepool.gov.uk

Consumer Protection and Trading Standards: Mr Ian
Harrison, Principal Trading Standards & Licensing Officer, Bryan
Hanson House, Lynn Street, Hartlepool TS24 7BT ☎ 01429 523349
📧 ian.harrison@hartlepool.gov.uk

Contracts: Mr David Hart, Strategic Procurement Manager, Civic
Centre, Victoria Road, Hartlepool TS24 8AY ☎ 01429 523495
📧 david.hart@hartlepool.gov.uk

Corporate Services: Ms Julie Howard, Customer & Business
Manager, Civic Centre, Victoria Road, Hartlepool TS24 8AY
☎ 01429 284354 📧 julie.howard@hartlepool.gov.uk

Customer Service: Ms Julie Howard, Customer & Business
Manager, Civic Centre, Victoria Road, Hartlepool TS24 8AY
☎ 01429 284354 📧 julie.howard@hartlepool.gov.uk

Direct Labour: Ms Gill Alexander, Chief Executive, Civic Centre, Victoria Road, Hartlepool TS24 8AY ☎ 01429 523001 ✆ gill.alexander@hartlepool.gov.uk

Education: Mr Mark Patton, Assistant Director - Education, Learning & Skills 0-19, Civic Centre, Victoria Road, Hartlepool TS24 8AY ☎ 01426 523736 ✆ mark.patton@hartlepool.gov.uk

E-Government: Mr Andrew Atkin, Assistant Chief Executive, Civic Centre, Victoria Road, Hartlepool TS24 8AY ☎ 01429 523003 ✆ andrew.atkin@hartlepool.gov.uk

Electoral Registration: Mr Peter Devlin, Chief Solicitor, Civic Centre, Victoria Road, Hartlepool TS24 8AY ☎ 01429 523003 ✆ peter.devlin@hartlepool.gov.uk

Emergency Planning: Mr Robin Beech, Emergency Planning Officer, Emergency Planning Unit, Aurora Court, Barton Road, Riverside Park, Middlesbrough TS2 1RY ☎ 01642 232442; 01642 224926 ✆ robin.beech@hartlepool.gov.uk

Environmental Health: Mr Adrian Hurst, Principal Environmental Health Officer, Civic Centre, Victoria Road, Hartlepool TS24 8AY ☎ 01429 523323 ✆ adrian.hurst@hartlepool.gov.uk

Estates, Property & Valuation: Mr Dale Clarke, Estates & Regeneration Manager, Civic Centre, Victoria Road, Hartlepool TS24 8AY ☎ 01429 523386 ✆ dale.clarke@hartlepool.gov.uk

Finance: Mr Chris Little, Chief Finance Officer, Civic Centre, Victoria Road, Hartlepool TS24 8AY ☎ 01429 523003 ✆ chris.little@hartlepool.gov.uk

Grounds Maintenance: Mrs Denise Ogden, Director - Regeneration & Neighbourhood Services, Civic Centre, Victoria Road, Hartlepool TS24 8AY ☎ 01429 523808 ✆ denise.ogden@hartlepool.gov.uk

Health and Safety: Ms Rachel Price, Health, Safety & Wellbeing Manager, Civic Centre, Victoria Road, Hartlepool TS24 8AY ☎ 01429 523560 ✆ rachel.price2@hartlepool.gov.uk

Legal: Mr Peter Devlin, Chief Solicitor, Civic Centre, Victoria Road, Hartlepool TS24 8AY ☎ 01429 523003; 01429 523856 ✆ peter.devlin@hartlepool.gov.uk

Licensing: Mr Ian Harrison, Principal Trading Standards & Licensing Officer, Bryan Hanson House, Lynn Street, Hartlepool TS24 7BT ☎ 01429 523349 ✆ ian.harrison@hartlepool.gov.uk

Lighting: Mr Rob Daley, Public Lighting Officer, Civic Centre, Victoria Road, Hartlepool TS24 8AY ☎ 01429 523593 ✆ rob.daley@hartlepool.gov.uk

Member Services: Mrs Lorraine Bennison, Principal Registration & Members Services Officer, Civic Centre, Victoria Road, Hartlepool TS24 8AY ☎ 01429 523017 ✆ lorraine.bennison@hartlepool.gov.uk

Parking: Mr Phil Hepburn, Parking Services Manager, Civic Centre, Victoria Road, Hartlepool TS24 8AY ☎ 01429 523258 ✆ philip.hepburn@hartlepool.gov.uk

Partnerships: Mrs Catherine Grimwood, Performance & Partnerships Manager, Civic Centre, Victoria Road, Hartlepool TS24 8AY ☎ 01429 284322 ✆ catherine.grimwood@hartlepool.gov.uk

Procurement: Mr David Hart, Strategic Procurement Manager, Civic Centre, Victoria Road, Hartlepool TS24 8AY ☎ 01429 523495 ✆ david.hart@hartlepool.gov.uk

Recycling & Waste Minimisation: Mrs Denise Ogden, Director - Regeneration & Neighbourhood Services, Civic Centre, Victoria Road, Hartlepool TS24 8AY ☎ 01429 523808 ✆ denise.ogden@hartlepool.gov.uk

Recycling & Waste Minimisation: Ms Fiona Srogi, Waste Services Officer, Church Street, Lynn Street Depot, Hartlepool TS24 7BT ☎ 01429 523829 ✆ fiona.srogi@hartlepool.gov.uk

Regeneration: Mrs Denise Ogden, Director - Regeneration & Neighbourhood Services, Civic Centre, Victoria Road, Hartlepool TS24 8AY ☎ 01429 523808 ✆ denise.ogden@hartlepool.gov.uk

Road Safety: Mr Paul Watson, Road Safety Officer, Church Street, Lynn Street Depot, Hartlepool TS24 7BT ☎ 01429 523590; 01429 860830 ✆ paul.watson@hartlepool.gov.uk

Social Services (Adult): Ms Jill Harrison, Assistant Director - Adult Services, Civic Centre, Victoria Road, Hartlepool TS24 8AY ☎ 01429 523911 ✆ jill.harrison@hartlepool.gov.uk

Social Services (Children): Mr Mark Smith, Head of Integrated Youth Support Services, Civic Centre, Victoria Road, Hartlepool TS24 8AY ☎ 01429 523901 ✆ mark.smith@hartlepool.gov.uk

Public Health: Ms Louise Wallace, Director - Public Health, Civic Centre, Victoria Road, Hartlepool TS24 8AY ☎ 01429 284030 ✆ louise.wallace@hartlepool.gov.uk

Street Scene: Mrs Denise Ogden, Director - Regeneration & Neighbourhood Services, Civic Centre, Victoria Road, Hartlepool TS24 8AY ☎ 01429 523808 ✆ denise.ogden@hartlepool.gov.uk

Town Centre: Mrs Denise Ogden, Director - Regeneration & Neighbourhood Services, Civic Centre, Victoria Road, Hartlepool TS24 8AY ☎ 01429 523808 ✆ denise.ogden@hartlepool.gov.uk

Traffic Management: Mr Peter Frost, Highways, Traffic & Transport Team Leader, Civic Centre, Victoria Road, Hartlepool TS24 8AY ☎ 01429 523200 ✆ peter.frost@hartlepool.gov.uk

Transport Planner: Mr Peter Frost, Highways, Traffic & Transport Team Leader, Civic Centre, Victoria Road, Hartlepool TS24 8AY ☎ 01429 523200 ✆ peter.frost@hartlepool.gov.uk

Waste Collection and Disposal: Mrs Denise Ogden, Director - Regeneration & Neighbourhood Services, Civic Centre, Victoria Road, Hartlepool TS24 8AY ☎ 01429 523808 ✆ denise.ogden@hartlepool.gov.uk

Waste Management: Mrs Denise Ogden, Director - Regeneration & Neighbourhood Services, Civic Centre, Victoria Road, Hartlepool TS24 8AY ☎ 01429 523808 ✆ denise.ogden@hartlepool.gov.uk

HARTLEPOOL

COUNCILLORS

Ceremonial Mayor: Cook, Rob (LAB - De Bruce)
rob.cook@hartlepool.gov.uk

Ceremonial Deputy Mayor: Beck, Paul (LAB - Hart)
paul.beck@hartlepool.gov.uk

Leader of the Council: Akers-Belcher, Christopher (LAB - Foggy Furze)
christopher.akers-belcher@hartlepool.gov.uk

Deputy Leader of the Council: Richardson, Carl (LAB - Victoria)
carl.richardson@hartlepool.gov.uk

Akers-Belcher, Stephen (LAB - Manor House)
stephen.akers-belcher@hartlepool.gov.uk

Barclay, Allan (LAB - Manor House)
allan.barclay@hartlepool.gov.uk

Belcher, Sandra (LAB - Jesmond)
sandra.belcher@hartlepool.gov.uk

Black, James (O - Seaton)
james.black@hartlepool.gov.uk

Buchan, Bob (UKIP - Fens & Rossmere)
robert.buchan@hartlepool.gov.uk

Clark, Alan (LAB - Fens & Rossmere)
alan.clark@hartlepool.gov.uk

Cranney, Kevin (LAB - Foggy Furze)
kevin.cranney@hartlepool.gov.uk

Hall, Gerald (LAB - Burn Valley)
gerard.hall@hartlepool.gov.uk

Hamilton, Lesley (LAB - Victoria)
lesley.hamilton@hartlepool.gov.uk

Harrison, Brenda (LAB - De Bruce)
brenda.harrison@hartlepool.gov.uk

Hind, Thomas (UKIP - Seaton)
tom.hind@hartlepool.gov.uk

Hunter, Dave (LAB - Burn Valley)
dave.hunter@hartlepool.gov.uk

Jackson, Peter (LAB - Headland & Harbour)
peter.jackson@hartlepool.gov.uk

James, Marjorie (LAB - Manor House)
marjoriejames45@yahoo.co.uk

Lauderdale, John (IND - Burn Valley)
john.lauderdale@hartlepool.gov.uk

Lawton, Trisha (LAB - Victoria)
patirica.lawton@ntlworld.com

Lindridge, James (LAB - Fens & Rossmere)
jim.lindridge@hartlepool.gov.uk

Lyons, Brenda (CON - Rural West)
brenda.lyons@hartlepool.gov.uk

Martin-Wells, Ray (CON - Rural West)
ray.martin-wells@hartlepool.gov.uk

Moore, Shane (UKIP - Headland & Harbour)
shane.moore@hartlepool.gov.uk

Morris, George (CON - Rural West)
george.morris@hartlepool.gov.uk

Riddle, David (IND - Hart)
david.riddle@hartlepool.gov.uk

Robinson, Jean (LAB - Hart)
jean.robinson@hartlepool.gov.uk

Sirs, Kaylee (LAB - Foggy Furze)
kaylee.sirs@hartlepool.gov.uk

Springer, George (UKIP - Jesmond)
george.springer@hartlepool.gov.uk

Tempest, Sylvia (LAB - Headland & Harbour)
sylvia.tempest@hartlepool.gov.uk

Tennant, John (UKIP - Jesmond)
john.tennant@hartlepool.gov.uk

Thomas, Stephen (LAB - De Bruce)
stephen.thomas@hartlepool.gov.uk

Thompson, Paul (IND - Seaton)
paul.thompson@hartlepool.gov.uk

POLITICAL COMPOSITION
LAB: 21, UKIP: 5, CON: 3, IND: 3, O: 1

COMMITTEE CHAIRS

Adult Services: Mr Stephen Thomas

Audit: Mr Ray Martin-Wells

Children's Services: Mr Alan Clark

Licensing: Ms Brenda Lyons

Planning: Mr Stephen Akers-Belcher

Hastings   D

Hastings Borough Council, Town Hall, Queen's Road, Hastings TN34 1QR
☎ 01424 451066 🖶 01424 781743 🖥 www.hastings.gov.uk

FACTS AND FIGURES
Parliamentary Constituencies: Hastings and Rye
EU Constituencies: South East
Election Frequency: Elections are biennial

PRINCIPAL OFFICERS

Chief Executive: Ms Jane Hartnell, Director - Corporate Services & Governance (Head of Paide Service), Aquila House, Breeds Place, Hastings TB34 3UY ☎ 01424 451482; 01424 451732 ⌨ jhartnell@hastings.gov.uk

Senior Management: Ms Monica Adams-Acton, Assistant Director - Regeneration & Culture, Aquila House, Breeds Place, Hastings TN34 3UY ☎ 01424 451749; 01424 451749 ⌨ madams-acton@hastings.gov.uk

Senior Management: Ms Christine Barkshire-Jones, Chief Legal Officer & Monitoring Officer, Aquila House, Breeds Place, Hastings TN34 3UY ☎ 01424 451731; 01424 781732 ⌨ cbarkshire-jones@hastings.gov.uk

Senior Management: Mrs Verna Connolly, Executive Manager - People & Business Support, Town Hall, Queen's Road, Hastings TN34 1QR ☎ 01424 451707; 01424 451769 ⌨ vconnolly@hastings.gov.uk

Senior Management: Mr Peter Grace, Assistant Director - Financial Services & Revenues, Aquila House, Breeds Place, Hastings TN34 3UY ☎ 01424 451503; 01424 781515 ⌂ pgrace@hastings.gov.uk

Senior Management: Mr Mike Hepworth, Assistant Director - Environment & Place, Aquila House, Breeds Place, Hastings TN34 3UY ☎ 01424 783332 ⌂ mhepworth@hastings.gov.uk

Senior Management: Mr Simon Hubbard, Director - Operational Services, Aquila House, Breeds Place, Hastings TN34 3UY ☎ 01424 451753 ⌂ shubbard@hastings.gov.uk

Senior Management: Mr Andrew Palmer, Assistant Director - Housing & Built Environment, Aquila House, Breeds Place, Hastings TN34 3UY ☎ 01424 451316; 01424 781305 ⌂ apalmer@hastings.gov.uk

Architect, Building / Property Services: Mrs Amy Terry, Estates Manager, Aquila House, Breeds Place, Hastings TN34 3UY ☎ 01424 451640; 01424 451515 ⌂ aterry@hastings.gov.uk

Best Value: Mr Tom Davies, Chief Auditor, Town Hall, Queen's Road, Hastings TN34 1QR ☎ 01424 451524 ⌂ tdavies@hastings.gov.uk

Building Control: Mr Brian Bristow, Building Control Manager, Bexhill Town Hall, Bexhill-on-Sea TN39 3JX ☎ 01424 787680 ⌂ brian.bristow@rother.gov.uk

Children / Youth Services: Mr Emile Tambeh, Youth & Senior's Participation Officer, Town Hall, Queen's Road, Hastings TN34 1QR ☎ 01424 451760 ⌂ etambeh@hastings.gov.uk

PR / Communications: Mr Kevin Boorman, Marketing & Major Projects Manager, Aquila House, Breeds Place, Hastings TN34 3UY ☎ 01424 451123; 01424 781743 ⌂ kboorman@hastings.gov.uk

Community Safety: Mr Mike Fagan, Community Safety Manager, Aquila House, Breeds Place, Hastings TN34 3UY ☎ 01424 451438 ⌂ mfagan@hastings.gov.uk

Computer Management: Mr Mark Bourne, Head of Information Technology, Aquila House, Breeds Place, Hastings TN34 3UY ☎ 01424 451414; 01424 781401 ⌂ mbourne@hastings.gov.uk

Corporate Services: Mr Stephen Dodson, Accommodation & Transformation Manager, Town Hall, Queen's Road, Hastings TN34 1QR ☎ 01424 783326 ⌂ sdodson@hastings.gov.uk

Customer Service: Ms Natasha Tewkesbury, Corporate Customer Services Manager, Town Hall, Queen's Road, Hastings TN34 1QR ☎ 01424 451709 ⌂ ntewkesbury@hastings.gov.uk

Economic Development: Ms Monica Adams-Acton, Assistant Director - Regeneration & Culture, Aquila House, Breeds Place, Hastings TN34 3UY ☎ 01424 451749; 01424 451749 ⌂ madams-acton@hastings.gov.uk

E-Government: Mr Mark Bourne, Head of Information Technology, Aquila House, Breeds Place, Hastings TN34 3UY ☎ 01424 451414; 01424 781401 ⌂ mbourne@hastings.gov.uk

Electoral Registration: Mrs Katrina Silverson, Electoral Services Manager, Aquila House, Breeds Place, Hastings TN34 3UY ☎ 01424 451747; 01424 451732 ⌂ ksilverson@hastings.gov.uk

Emergency Planning: Mr Mike Hepworth, Assistant Director - Environment & Place, Aquila House, Breeds Place, Hastings TN34 3UY ☎ 01424 783332 ⌂ mhepworth@hastings.gov.uk

Environmental / Technical Services: Mr Mike Hepworth, Assistant Director - Environment & Place, Aquila House, Breeds Place, Hastings TN34 3UY ☎ 01424 783332 ⌂ mhepworth@hastings.gov.uk

Estates, Property & Valuation: Mrs Amy Terry, Estates Manager, Aquila House, Breeds Place, Hastings TN34 3UY ☎ 01424 451640; 01424 451515 ⌂ aterry@hastings.gov.uk

Events Manager: Mr Kevin Boorman, Marketing & Major Projects Manager, Aquila House, Breeds Place, Hastings TN34 3UY ☎ 01424 451123; 01424 781743 ⌂ kboorman@hastings.gov.uk

Facilities: Mr Mike Hepworth, Assistant Director - Environment & Place, Aquila House, Breeds Place, Hastings TN34 3UY ☎ 01424 783332 ⌂ mhepworth@hastings.gov.uk

Finance: Mr Peter Grace, Assistant Director - Financial Services & Revenues, Aquila House, Breeds Place, Hastings TN34 3UY ☎ 01424 451503; 01424 781515 ⌂ pgrace@hastings.gov.uk

Finance: Mr Alan Mitchell, Chief Accountant, Town Hall, Queen's Road, Hastings TN34 1QR ☎ 01424 451520; 01424 451515 ⌂ amitchell@hastings.gov.uk

Treasury: Mr Alan Mitchell, Chief Accountant, Town Hall, Queen's Road, Hastings TN34 1QR ☎ 01424 451520; 01424 451515 ⌂ amitchell@hastings.gov.uk

Grounds Maintenance: Mrs Virginia Gilbert, Head of Amenities, Resorts & Leisure, Aquila House, Breeds Place, Hastings TN34 3UY ☎ 01424 451066 ⌂ vgilbert@hastings.gov.uk

Health and Safety: Mr Mike Hepworth, Assistant Director - Environment & Place, Aquila House, Breeds Place, Hastings TN34 3UY ☎ 01424 783332 ⌂ mhepworth@hastings.gov.uk

Highways: Mr Mike Hepworth, Assistant Director - Environment & Place, Aquila House, Breeds Place, Hastings TN34 3UY ☎ 01424 783332 ⌂ mhepworth@hastings.gov.uk

Housing: Mr Andrew Palmer, Assistant Director - Housing & Built Environment, Aqulia House, Breeds Place, Hastings TN34 3UY ☎ 01424 451316; 01424 781305 ⌂ apalmer@hastings.gov.uk

Legal: Ms Christine Barkshire-Jones, Chief Legal Officer & Monitoring Officer, Aquila House, Breeds Place, Hastings TN34 3UY ☎ 01424 451731; 01424 781732 ⌂ cbarkshire-jones@hastings.gov.uk

Leisure and Cultural Services: Ms Monica Adams-Acton, Assistant Director - Regeneration & Culture, Aquila House, Breeds Place, Hastings TN34 3UY ☎ 01424 451749; 01424 451749 ⌂ madams-acton@hastings.gov.uk

HASTINGS

Licensing: Mr Bob Brown, Licensing Manager, Aquila House, Breeds Place, Hastings TN34 3UY ☎ 01424 783249 🖂 bbrown@hastings.gov.uk

Member Services: Mr Mark Horan, Continuous Improvement & Democratic Services Officer, Aquila House, Breeds Place, Hastings TB34 3UY ☎ 01424 451485 🖂 mhoran@hastings.gov.uk

Parking: Mr Mike Hepworth, Assistant Director - Environment & Place, Aquila House, Breeds Place, Hastings TN34 3UY ☎ 01424 783332 🖂 mhepworth@hastings.gov.uk

Personnel / HR: Mrs Verna Connolly, Executive Manager - People & Business Support, Town Hall, Queen's Road, Hastings TN34 1QR ☎ 01424 451707; 01424 451769 🖂 vconnolly@hastings.gov.uk

Planning: Mr Andrew Palmer, Assistant Director - Housing & Built Environment, Aqulia House, Breeds Place, Hastings TN34 3UY ☎ 01424 451316; 01424 781305 🖂 apalmer@hastings.gov.uk

Recycling & Waste Minimisation: Mr Mike Hepworth, Assistant Director - Environment & Place, Aquila House, Breeds Place, Hastings TN34 3UY ☎ 01424 783332 🖂 mhepworth@hastings.gov.uk

Regeneration: Ms Monica Adams-Acton, Assistant Director - Regeneration & Culture, Aquila House, Breeds Place, Hastings TN34 3UY ☎ 01424 451749; 01424 451749 🖂 madams-acton@hastings.gov.uk

Staff Training: Mrs Verna Connolly, Executive Manager - People & Business Support, Town Hall, Queen's Road, Hastings TN34 1QR ☎ 01424 451707; 01424 451769 🖂 vconnolly@hastings.gov.uk

Street Scene: Mr Mike Hepworth, Assistant Director - Environment & Place, Aquila House, Breeds Place, Hastings TN34 3UY ☎ 01424 783332 🖂 mhepworth@hastings.gov.uk

Tourism: Mr Kevin Boorman, Marketing & Major Projects Manager, Aquila House, Breeds Place, Hastings TN34 3UY ☎ 01424 451123; 01424 781743 🖂 kboorman@hastings.gov.uk

Town Centre: Mr Robert Woods, Town Centre Manager, Summerfields Business Centre, Bohemia Road, Hastings TN34 1UT ☎ 01424 205516 🖂 rwoods@hastings.gov.uk

Waste Collection and Disposal: Mr Mike Hepworth, Assistant Director - Environment & Place, Aquila House, Breeds Place, Hastings TN34 3UY ☎ 01424 783332 🖂 mhepworth@hastings.gov.uk

Waste Management: Mr Richard Homewood, Director - Environmental Services, Aquila House, Breeds Place, Hastings TN34 3UY ☎ 01424 783200 🖂 rhomewood@hastings.gov.uk

Children's Play Areas: Mr Mike Hepworth, Assistant Director - Environment & Place, Aquila House, Breeds Place, Hastings TN34 3UY ☎ 01424 783332 🖂 mhepworth@hastings.gov.uk

COUNCILLORS

Chair: Rogers, Judy (LAB - Castle)
cllr.judy.rogers@hastings.gov.uk

Leader of the Council: Chowney, Peter (LAB - Tressell)
cllr.peter.chowney@hastings.gov.uk

Deputy Leader of the Council: Forward, Kim (LAB - Gensing)
cllr.kim.forward@hastings.gov.uk

Atkins, Liam (CON - Conquest)
cllr.liam.atkins@hastings.gov.uk

Bacon, James (O - Old Hastings)
cllr.james.bacon@hastings.gov.uk

Batsford, Andy (LAB - St Helens)
cllr.andy.batsford@hastings.gov.uk

Beaney, Sue (LAB - Braybrooke)
cllr.sue.beaney@hastings.gov.uk

Beaver, Matthew (CON - West St Leonards)
cllr.matthew.beaver@hastings.gov.uk

Cartwright, Andrew (LAB - Gensing)
cllr.andrew.cartwright@hastings.gov.uk

Charman, Tania (LAB - Tressell)
cllr.tania.charman@hastings.gov.uk

Clark, Lee (LAB - Castle)
cllr.lee.clark@hastings.gov.uk

Clarke, Martin (CON - St Helens)
cllr.martin.clarke@hastings.gov.uk

Cooke, Robert (CON - Ashdown)
cllr.robert.cooke@hastings.gov.uk

Davies, Warren (LAB - Baird)
cllr.warren.davies@hastings.gov.uk

Dowling, Terri (LAB - Central St Leonards)
cllr.terri.dowling@hastings.gov.uk

Dowling, Bruce (LAB - Hollington)
cllr.bruce.dowling@hastings.gov.uk

Edwards, Michael (CON - Ashdown)
cllr.mike.edwards@hastings.gov.uk

Fitzgerald, Colin (LAB - Silverhill)
cllr.colin.fitzgerald@hastings.gov.uk

Howard, Mike (LAB - West St Leonards)
cllr.mike.howard@hastings.gov.uk

Lee, Rob (CON - Maze Hill)
cllr.rob.lee@hastings.gov.uk

Patmore, Andy (CON - Maze Hill)
cllr.andy.patmore@hastings.gov.uk

Poole, Dawn (LAB - Old Hastings)
cllr.dawn.poole@hastings.gov.uk

Rankin, John (CON - Conquest)
cllr.john.rankin@hastings.gov.uk

Roberts, Alan (LAB - Wishing Tree)
cllr.alan.roberts@hastings.gov.uk

Sabetian, Dominic (LAB - Braybrooke)
cllr.dominic.sabetian@hastings.gov.uk

Scott, Philip (LAB - Wishing Tree)
cllr.philip.scott@hastings.gov.uk

Sinden, Nigel (LAB - Silverhill)
cllr.nigel.sinden@hastings.gov.uk

Street, Richard (LAB - Ore)
cllr.richard.street@hastings.gov.uk

Turner, Mike (LAB - Baird)
cllr.mike.turner@hastings.gov.uk

Webb, Trevor (LAB - Central St Leonards)
cllr.trevor.webb@hastings.gov.uk

Westley, Emily (LAB - Hollington)
cllr.emily.westley@hastings.gov.uk

Wincott, Michael (LAB - Ore)
cllr.michael.wincott@hastings.gov.uk

POLITICAL COMPOSITION
LAB: 23, CON: 8, O: 1

COMMITTEE CHAIRS

Audit: Mr Matthew Beaver

Environment & Safety: Mr Bruce Dowling

Licensing: Mr Dominic Sabetian

Planning: Mr Richard Street

Havant	D

Havant Borough Council, Public Service Plaza, Civic Centre Road, Havant PO9 2AX
☎ 023 9244 6019 🖶 023 9248 0263 🖳 www.havant.gov.uk

FACTS AND FIGURES
Parliamentary Constituencies: Havant
EU Constituencies: South East
Election Frequency: Elections are by thirds

PRINCIPAL OFFICERS

Chief Executive: Ms Sandy Hopkins, Joint Chief Executive, Public Service Plaza, Civic Centre Road, Havant PO9 2AX ☎ 023 9244 6150 ✆ sandy.hopkins@havant.gov.uk

Senior Management: Mr Tom Horwood, Executive Director - Strategy & Governance, Public Service Plaza, Civic Centre Road, Havant PO9 2AX ☎ 01730 234025; 023 9244 6151 ✆ tom.horwood@easthants.gov.uk

Senior Management: Ms Gill Kneller, Executive Director - Commercial, Public Service Plaza, Civic Centre Road, Havant PO9 2AX ☎ 01730 234004; 023 9244 6151 ✆ gill.kneller@easthants.gov.uk

Senior Management: Ms Natalie Mether, Head of Neighbourhood Support, Public Service Plaza, Civic Centre Road, Havant PO9 2AX ☎ 023 9244 6019 ✆ natalie.mether@havant.gov.uk

Building Control: Mr Robin Seamer, Building Control Team Leader, Public Service Plaza, Civic Centre Road, Havant PO9 2AX ☎ 023 9244 6578 ✆ robin.seamer@ehavant.gov.uk

PR / Communications: Mrs Dawn Adey, Head of Research & Marketing, Public Service Plaza, Civic Centre Road, Havant PO9 2AX ☎ 023 9244 6392 ✆ dawn.adey@havant.gov.uk

Community Safety: Mr Tim Pointer, Neighbourhood Support Leader, Public Service Plaza, Civic Centre Road, Havant PO9 2AX ☎ 023 9244 6606; 023 8248 0263 ✆ tim.pointer@havant.gov.uk

Computer Management: Mr Craig Richards, IT Partnerships Manager, Public Service Plaza, Civic Centre Road, Havant PO9 2AX ☎ 023 9244 6391; 023 8248 0263 ✆ craig.richards@havant.gov.uk

Corporate Services: Ms Sandy Hopkins, Joint Chief Executive, Public Service Plaza, Civic Centre Road, Havant PO9 2AX ☎ 023 9244 6150 ✆ sandy.hopkins@havant.gov.uk

Customer Service: Mrs Janice Newman, Customer Services Manager, Public Service Plaza, Civic Centre Road, Havant PO9 2AX ☎ 023 9244 6040; 023 9248 0263 ✆ janice.newman@havant.gov.uk

Customer Service: Mr Brian Wood, Head of Customer Services, Penns Place, Petersfield GU31 4EX ☎ 01730 234026 ✆ brian.wood@easthants.gov.uk

Direct Labour: Mr Peter Vince, Operational Services Manager, Southmoor Depot, 2 Penner Road, Havant PO9 1QH ☎ 023 9244 6019 ✆ peter.vince@havant.gov.uk

Economic Development: Mr Jeff Crate, Economic Development Officer, Public Service Plaza, Civic Centre Road, Havant PO9 2AX ☎ 023 9244 6615; 023 9244 6545 ✆ jeff.crate@havant.gov.uk

E-Government: Mrs Susan Parker, Head of Programmes Redesign & Quality, Public Service Plaza, Civic Centre Road, Havant PO9 2AX ☎ 023 9244 6493 ✆ susan.parker@havant.gov.uk

Electoral Registration: Mrs Jayne Day, Electoral Services Manager, Public Service Plaza, Civic Centre Road, Havant PO9 2AX ☎ 023 9244 6226; 023 9248 0263 ✆ jayne.day@havant.gov.uk

Emergency Planning: Mr Stuart Pinkney, Safety & Emergency Planning Officer, Public Service Plaza, Civic Centre Road, Havant PO9 2AX ☎ 023 9244 6675 ✆ stuart.pinkney@havant.gov.uk

Energy Management: Mr Peter Gammage, Building Services Officer, Public Service Plaza, Civic Centre Road, Havant PO9 2AX ☎ 023 9244 6019 ✆ peter.gammage@havant.gov.uk

Environmental / Technical Services: Mr Steve Perkins, Executive Head - Environmental Services, Southmoor Depot, 2 Penner Road, Havant PO9 2AX ☎ 023 9244 6520 ✆ steve.perkins@havant.gov.uk

Environmental / Technical Services: Mr Peter Vince, Operational Services Manager, Southmoor Depot, 2 Penner Road, Havant PO9 1QH ☎ 023 9244 6019 ✆ peter.vince@havant.gov.uk

Environmental Health: Mrs Lorna Read, Interim Service Manager - Environmental Health, Public Service Plaza, Civic Centre Road, Havant PO9 1QH ☎ 023 9244 6665 ✆ lorna.read@havant.gov.uk

Estates, Property & Valuation: Mr Jon Sanders, Service Manager - Facilities, Public Service Plaza, Civic Centre Road, Havant PO9 2AX ☎ 023 9244 6566 ✆ jon.sanders@easthants.gov.uk

European Liaison: Miss Hannah Newbury, Senior Solicitor, Public Service Plaza, Civic Centre Road, Havant PO9 2AX ☎ 023 9244 6213; 023 9248 0263 ✆ hannah.newbury@havant.gov.uk

HAVANT

Facilities: Mr Neil Payne, Facilities Manager, Public Service Plaza, Civic Centre Road, Havant PO9 2AX ☎ 023 9244 6646; 023 9244 6240 ⌁ neil.payne@havant.gov.uk

Finance: Mrs Jane Eaton, Director - Corporate Resources, Public Service Plaza, Civic Centre Road, Havant PO9 2AX ☎ 01730 234035; 023 9244 6151 ⌁ jane.eaton@havant.gov.uk

Treasury: Mrs Jane Eaton, Director - Corporate Resources, Public Service Plaza, Civic Centre Road, Havant PO9 2AX ☎ 01730 234035; 023 9244 6151 ⌁ jane.eaton@havant.gov.uk

Fleet Management: Mr Peter Vince, Operational Services Manager, Southmoor Depot, 2 Penner Road, Havant PO9 1QH ☎ 023 9244 6019 ⌁ peter.vince@havant.gov.uk

Grounds Maintenance: Mr Peter Vince, Operational Services Manager, Southmoor Depot, 2 Penner Road, Havant PO9 1QH ☎ 023 9244 6019 ⌁ peter.vince@havant.gov.uk

Highways: Ms Michelle Green, Parking & Traffic Management Team Leader, Public Service Plaza, Civic Centre Road, Havant Po9 2AX ☎ 023 9244 6462; 023 9244 6455 ⌁ michelle.green@havan.gov.uk

Home Energy Conservation: Mrs Pennie Brown, Sustainability Adviser, Public Service Plaza, Civic Centre Road, Havant PO9 2AX ☎ 023 9244 6554; 023 9248 0263 ⌁ pennie.smith@havant.gov.uk

Housing: Ms Tracey Wood, Head of Housing, Public Service Plaza, Civic Centre Road, Havant PO9 2AX ☎ 023 9244 6020 ⌁ tracey.wood@easthants.gov.uk

Legal: Mr Abe Ezekiel, Head of Legal Services, Penns Place, Petersfield GU31 4EX ⌁ abe.ezekiel@easthants.gov.uk

Leisure and Cultural Services: Mr Tim Slater, Executive Head of Organisational Development & Programmes, Public Service Plaza, Civic Centre Road, Havant PO9 2AX ☎ 01730 234613 ⌁ tim.slater@havant.gov.uk

Licensing: Mrs Lorna Read, Interim Service Manager - Environmental Health, Public Service Plaza, Civic Centre Road, Havant PO9 1QH ☎ 023 9244 6665 ⌁ lorna.read@havant.gov.uk

Lottery Funding, Charity and Voluntary: Mr Dan Grindey, Business, Economy & Town Services Manager, Public Service Plaza, Civic Centre Road, Havant PO9 2AX ☎ 023 9244 6177 ⌁ dan.grindley@easthants.gov.uk

Member Services: Mrs Penny Milne, Democratic Services Team Leader, Public Service Plaza, Civic Centre Road, Havant PO9 2AX ☎ 023 9244 6230 ⌁ penny.milne@havant.gov.uk

Parking: Ms Michelle Green, Parking & Traffic Management Team Leader, Public Service Plaza, Civic Centre Road, Havant PO9 2AX ☎ 023 9244 6462; 023 9244 6455 ⌁ michelle.green@havant.gov.uk

Partnerships: Mrs Nicki Conyard, Community Regeneration Team Leader, Public Service Plaza, Civic Centre Road, Havant PO9 2AX ☎ 023 9244 6114 ⌁ nicki.conyard@havant.gov.uk

Personnel / HR: Ms Caroline Tickner, Service Manager of Human Resources, Public Service Plaza, Civic Centre Road, Havant PO9 2AX ☎ 023 9244 6160; 023 9244 6684 ⌁ caroline.tickner@havant.gov.uk

Planning: Mrs Julia Potter, Head of Development, Public Service Plaza, Civic Centre Road, Havant PO9 2AX ☎ 01730 234376; 023 9244 6520 ⌁ julia.potter@easthants.gov.uk

Procurement: Ms Hilda Jackson, Procurement Team Manager, Public Service Plaza, Civic Centre Road, Havant PO9 2AX ☎ 023 9244 6396; 023 9244 6240 ⌁ hilda.jackson@havant.gov.uk

Recycling & Waste Minimisation: Mr Peter Vince, Operational Services Manager, Southmoor Depot, 2 Penner Road, Havant PO9 1QH ☎ 023 9244 6019 ⌁ peter.vince@havant.gov.uk

Regeneration: Mrs Claire Hughes, Economic Development & Community Manager, Public Service Plaza, Civic Centre Road, Havant PO9 2AX ☎ 023 9244 5235; 023 9249 8031 ⌁ claire.hughes@havant.gov.uk

Staff Training: Ms Caroline Tickner, Service Manager of Human Resources, Public Service Plaza, Civic Centre Road, Havant PO9 2AX ☎ 023 9244 6160; 023 9244 6684 ⌁ caroline.tickner@havant.gov.uk

Sustainable Communities: Mrs Claire Hughes, Economic Development & Community Manager, Public Service Plaza, Civic Centre Road, Havant PO9 2AX ☎ 023 9244 5235; 023 9249 8031 ⌁ claire.hughes@havant.gov.uk

Tourism: Mr Jeff Crate, Economic Development Officer, Public Service Plaza, Civic Centre Road, Havant PO9 2AX ☎ 023 9244 6615; 023 9244 6545 ⌁ jeff.crate@havant.gov.uk

Town Centre: Mr Jeff Crate, Economic Development Officer, Public Service Plaza, Civic Centre Road, Havant PO9 2AX ☎ 023 9244 6615; 023 9244 6545 ⌁ jeff.crate@havant.gov.uk

Traffic Management: Ms Michelle Green, Parking & Traffic Management Team Leader, Public Service Plaza, Civic Centre Road, Havant PO9 2AX ☎ 023 9244 6462; 023 9244 6455 ⌁ michelle.green@havant.gov.uk

Transport: Mr Peter Vince, Operational Services Manager, Southmoor Depot, 2 Penner Road, Havant PO9 1QH ☎ 023 9244 6019 ⌁ peter.vince@havant.gov.uk

Waste Collection and Disposal: Mr Peter Vince, Operational Services Manager, Southmoor Depot, 2 Penner Road, Havant PO9 1QH ☎ 023 9244 6019 ⌁ peter.vince@havant.gov.uk

Waste Management: Mr Peter Vince, Operational Services Manager, Southmoor Depot, 2 Penner Road, Havant PO9 1QH ☎ 023 9244 6019 ⌁ peter.vince@havant.gov.uk

COUNCILLORS

Mayor: Ponsonby, Faith (LD - Battins)
faith.ponsonby@havant.gov.uk

Deputy Mayor: Shimbart, Elaine (IND - Hart Plain)
elaine.shimbart@havant.gov.uk

Leader of the Council: Cheshire, Michael (CON - Hart Plain)
michael.cheshire@havant.gov.uk

Deputy Leader of the Council: Briggs, Anthony (CON - Cowplain)
tony.briggs@havant.gov.uk

Group Leader: Hart, Terence (LAB - Bondfields)
terry.hart@havant.gov.uk

Group Leader: Perry, John (UKIP - Hayling East)
john.perry@havant.gov.uk

Bains, Narinda (CON - Cowplain)
Narinder./Baines@havant.gov.uk

Blackett, Gwendoline (CON - Purbrook)
gwen.blackett@havant.gov.uk

Bowerman, Lulu (CON - Emsworth)
lulu.bowerman@havant.gov.uk

Branson, Jackie (CON - St Faith's)
jackie.branson@havant.gov.uk

Buckley, Paul (CON - Waterloo)
paul.buckley@havant.gov.uk

Carpenter, Malc (UKIP - Battins)
malc.carpenter@havant.gov.uk

Cresswell, Rivka (CON - Emsworth)
Rivka.Cresswell@havant.gov.uk

Davis, John (UKIP - Warren Park)
john.davis@havant.gov.uk

Fairhurst, Michael (CON - Barncroft)
mike.fairhurst@havant.gov.uk

Francis, Beryl (LAB - Warren Park)
beryl.francis@havant.gov.uk

Guest, David (CON - St Faith's)
david.guest@havant.gov.uk

Howard, Caren (CON - Purbrook)
caren.howard@havant.gov.uk

Hughes, Gary (CON - Purbrook)
Gary.Hughes@havant.gov.uk

Keast, David (CON - Cowplain)
david.keast@havant.gov.uk

Kerrin, Garry (UKIP - Stakes)
garry.kerrin@havant.gov.uk

Lenaghan, Andrew (CON - Hayling West)
andrew.lenaghan@havant.gov.uk

Lloyd, Dianne (CON - Stakes)
dianne.lloyd@havant.gov.uk

Mackey, Colin (CON - Emsworth)
colin.mackey@havant.gov.uk

Patrick, Diana (CON - Stakes)
diana.patrick@havant.gov.uk

Pike, Tim (CON - St Faith's)
Tim.Pike@havant.gov.uk

Quantrill, Lance (CON - Bondfields)
lance.quantrill@havant.gov.uk

Rees, Edward (CON - Bedhampton)
Edward.Rees@havant.gov.uk

Satchwell, Clare (CON - Hayling East)
Clare.Satchwell@Havant.gov.uk

Sceal, Mike (CON - Waterloo)
michael.sceal@havant.gov.uk

Shimbart, Gerald (IND - Hart Plain)
gerald.shimbart@havant.gov.uk

Smith, Kenneth (CON - Bedhampton)
ken.smith@havant.gov.uk

Smith, David (CON - Bedhampton)
david.smith@havant.gov.uk

Thomas, Joanna (CON - Hayling West)
joanne.thomas@havant.gov.uk

Turner, Leah (CON - Hayling East)
leah.turner@havant.gov.uk

Wade, Peter (CON - Waterloo)
peter.wade@havant.gov.uk

Weeks, Yvonne (CON - Barncroft)
yvonne.weeks@havant.gov.uk

Wilson, Michael (CON - Hayling West)
michael.wilson@havant.gov.uk

POLITICAL COMPOSITION
CON: 29, UKIP: 4, IND: 2, LAB: 2, LD: 1

COMMITTEE CHAIRS

Audit & Governance: Mr Kenneth Smith

Licensing: Mr David Smith

Havering   L

Havering London Borough Council, Town Hall, Main Road,
Romford RM1 3BD
☎ 01708 434343 🖨 01708 432424 📧 info@havering.gov.uk
🖥 www.havering.gov.uk

FACTS AND FIGURES
Parliamentary Constituencies: Hornchurch and Upminster,
Romford
EU Constituencies: London
Election Frequency: Elections are of whole council

PRINCIPAL OFFICERS

Chief Executive: Mr Andrew Blake-Herbert, Chief Executive,
Town Hall, Main Road, Romford RM1 3BD ☎ 01708 432062
📧 andrew.blake-herbert@havering.gov.uk

Senior Management: Mr Tim Aldridge, Acting Director -
Children's Services, Town Hall, Main Road, Romford RM1 3BD
☎ 01708 434343 📧 tim.aldridge@havering.gov.uk

Senior Management: Ms Sarah Homer, Interim Chief Operating
Officer & S151 Officer, Town Hall, Main Road, Romford RM1 3BD
☎ 01708 434343 📧 sarah.homer@havering.gov.uk

Senior Management: Dr Sue Milner, Interim Director - Public
Health, Town Hall, Main Road, Romford RM1 3BD
📧 sue.milner@havering.gov.uk

HAVERING

Senior Management: Mr Steve Moore, Interim Director - Neighbourhoods & Head of Environment, Town Hall, Main Road, Romford RM1 3BD ☎ 01708 434343 ◌ steve.moore@havering.gov.uk

Senior Management: Mr Neil Stubbings, Director - Housing, Mercury House, Mercury Gardens, Romford RM1 3RX ◌ neil.stubbings@havering.gov.uk

Senior Management: Ms Barbara Nicholls, Director - Adult Services, Mercury House, Mercury Gardens, Romford RM1 3RX ☎ 01708 433069 ◌ barbara.nicholls@havering.gov.uk

Architect, Building / Property Services: Mr Garry Green, Head of Property, Tollgate House, 96 - 98 Market Place, Romford RM1 3ER ☎ 01708 432566 ◌ garry.green@havering.gov.uk

Architect, Building / Property Services: Mr Andrew Skeggs, Technical & Facilities Group Manager, River Chambers, 36 High Street, Romford RM1 1HR ☎ 01708 433600 ◌ andy.skeggs@havering.gov.uk

Best Value: Ms Claire Thompson, Corporate Policy & Community Manager, Town Hall, Main Road, Romford RM1 3BD ☎ 01708 431003 ◌ claire.thompson@havering.gov.uk

Building Control: Mr Ronald Adams, Building Control Team Leader, Town Hall, Main Road, Romford RM1 3BD ☎ 01708 432710 ◌ ron.adams@havering.gov.uk

Building Control: Mr Peter Berry, Building Control Team Leader, Town Hall, Main Road, Romford RM1 3BD ☎ 01708 432707 ◌ peter.berry@havering.gov.uk

Catering Services: Mr Dennis Brewin, Catering & Traded Services Manager, 7th Floor, Mercury House, Mercury Garden, Romford RM1 3AH ☎ 01708 433211 ◌ dennis.brewin@havering.gov.uk

Children / Youth Services: Ms Kathy Bundred, Head of Children & Young People, Mercury House, Mercury Gardens, Romford RM1 3SL ☎ 01708 434343 ◌ kathy.bundred@havering.gov.uk

Civil Registration: Ms Louise Edmonds, Registration & Bereavement Services Manager, Langtons House, Billte Land, Hornchurch RM1 1XL ☎ 01708 434343 ◌ louise.edmonds@havering.gov.uk

PR / Communications: Mr Mark Leech, Head of Communications, Town Hall, Main Road, Romford RM1 3BD ☎ 01708 434343 ◌ mark.leech@havering.gov.uk

Community Planning: Mr Patrick Keyes, Head of Regulatory Services, Town Hall, Main Road, Romford RM1 3BD ☎ 01708 432720 ◌ patrick.keyes@havering.gov.uk

Community Safety: Ms Diane Egan, Community Safety & Development Manager, Town Hall, Main Road, Romford RM1 3BD ☎ 01708 432927 ◌ diane.eagan@havering.gov.uk

Computer Management: Mr Geoff Connell, Director - ICT Services, Town Hall, Main Road, Romford RM1 3BD ☎ 01708 432226 ◌ geoff.connell@havering.gov.uk

Consumer Protection and Trading Standards: Mr John Wade, Public Protection Manager, Mercury House, Mercury Gardens, Romford RM1 3SL ☎ 01708 432748 ◌ john.wade@havering.gov.uk

Contracts: Mr Hassan Iqbal, Strategic Procurement Partner, Central Library, St Edwards Way, Romford RM1 3AR ☎ 01708 432541 ◌ hassan.iqbal@havering.gov.uk

Corporate Services: Mr Mark Butler, Director - Asset Management, River Chambers, High Street, Romford RM1 1JD ☎ 01708 432947 ◌ mark.butler@havering.gov.uk

Corporate Services: Ms Nikki Richardson, Corporate Support Manager, Town Hall, Main Road, Romford RM1 3BD ☎ 01708 432170 ◌ nikki.richardson@havering.gov.uk

Customer Service: Ms Penny Nugent, Customer Services Operations Manager, Mercury House, Mercury Gardens, Romford RM1 3SL ☎ 01708 434225 ◌ penny.nugent@havering.gov.uk

Economic Development: Mr Tom Dobrashian, Head of Economic Development, Town Hall, Main Road, Romford RM1 3BD ☎ 01708 432583 ◌ tom.dobrashian@havering.gov.uk

Education: Ms Mary Pattinson, Head of Learning & Achievement, Mercury House, Mercury Gardens, Romford RM1 3SL ☎ 01708 433808 ◌ mary.pattinson@havering.gov.uk

E-Government: Mr Geoff Connell, Director - ICT Services, Town Hall, Main Road, Romford RM1 3BD ☎ 020 8430 2000; 020 8430 2000 ◌ geoff.connell@havering.gov.uk

Electoral Registration: Mr Ronald Adams, Building Control Team Leader, Town Hall, Main Road, Romford RM1 3BD ☎ 01708 432710 ◌ ron.adams@havering.gov.uk

Emergency Planning: Mr Alan Clark, Emergency Planning & Business Continuity Manager, Mercury House, Mercury Gardens, Romford RM1 3SL ☎ 01708 433206 ◌ alan.clark@havering.gov.uk

Energy Management: Mr Mark Lowers, Energy Strategy Team Leader, Mercury House, Mercury Gardens, Romford RM1 3SL ☎ 01708 432884 ◌ mark.lowers@havering.gov.uk

Environmental / Technical Services: Mr John Wade, Public Protection Manager, Mercury House, Mercury Gardens, Romford RM1 3SL ☎ 01708 432748 ◌ john.wade@havering.gov.uk

Environmental Health: Mr John Wade, Public Protection Manager, Mercury House, Mercury Gardens, Romford RM1 3SL ☎ 01708 432748 ◌ john.wade@havering.gov.uk

Estates, Property & Valuation: Mr Garry Green, Head of Property, Mercury House, Mercury Gardens, Romford RM1 3SL ☎ 01708 432566 ◌ garry.green@havering.gov.uk

Events Manager: Mr Michael Thomas, Principal Elections Officer, Town Hall, Main Road, Romford RM1 3BD ☎ 01708 434343 ◌ michael.thomas@havering.gov.uk

Facilities: Mr Andrew Skeggs, Technical & Facilities Group Manager, River Chambers, 36 High Street, Romford RM1 1HR
☎ 01708 433600 ◌ andy.skeggs@havering.gov.uk

Finance: Mr Andrew Blake-Herbert, Chief Executive, Town Hall, Main Road, Romford RM1 3BD ☎ 01708 432062
◌ andrew.blake-herbert@havering.gov.uk

Finance: Ms Gillian Clelland, Chief Operating Officer, 4th Floor, Eastside, Newham, London E16 2QU ☎ 01708 434343
◌ gillian.cleland@onesource.co.uk

Pensions: Ms Tara Philpott, Head of Transactional People Services, Central Library, St Edwards Way, Romford RM1 3AR
◌ tara.philpott@havering.gov.uk

Fleet Management: Mr Mark Butler, Director - Asset Management, River Chambers, High Street, Romford RM1 1JD
☎ 01708 432947 ◌ mark.butler@havering.gov.uk

Health and Safety: Mrs Susan Wilks, Head of Health & Safety, Mercury House, Mercury Gardens, Romford RM1 3SL
☎ 01708 432903 ◌ susan.wilks@havering.gov.uk

Highways: Mr Bob Wenman, Head of Street Care, Mercury House, Mercury Gardens, Romford RM1 3RX ☎ 01708 432898
◌ bob.wenman@havering.gov.uk

Home Energy Conservation: Mr Mark Lowers, Energy Strategy Team Leader, Mercury House, Mercury Gardens, Romford RM1 3SL
☎ 01708 432884 ◌ mark.lowers@havering.gov.uk

Housing: Mr Brian Partridge, Interim Corporate Policy & Community Manager, 2nd Floor, Mercury House, Mercury Garden, Romford RM1 3SL ◌ brian.partridge@havering.gov.uk

Housing: Mr Neil Stubbings, Director - Housing, Mercury House, Mercury Gardens, Romford RM1 3RX
◌ neil.stubbings@havering.gov.uk

Housing Maintenance: Mr Kevin Hazelwood, Property & Land Manager, Homes and Housing Office, Chippenham Road, Harold Hill, Romford RM3 8YQ ☎ 01708 434091
◌ kevin.hazelwood@havering.gov.uk

Local Area Agreement: Mr Brian Partridge, Interim Corporate Policy & Community Manager, 2nd Floor, Mercury House, Mercury Garden, Romford RM1 3SL ◌ brian.partridge@havering.gov.uk

Legal: Mr Graham White, Acting Monitoring Officer, Third Floor Estates, Newham Dockside, London E16 2QU
◌ graham.white@havering.gov.uk

Leisure and Cultural Services: Mr Simon Parkinson, Head of Culture & Customer Access, Stable Block, Langtons House, Billet Lane, Hornchurch RM11 1XJ ☎ 01708 434014
◌ simon.parkinson@havering.gov.uk

Licensing: Ms Trudi Penman, Licensing & Health & Safety Manager, Mercury House, Mercury Gardens, Romford RM1 3SL
☎ 01708 432718 ◌ trudi.penman@havering.gov.uk

Lifelong Learning: Ms Barbara Nicholls, Director - Adult Services, Town Hall, Main Road, Romford RM1 3BD ☎ 01708 433069
◌ barbara.nicholls@havering.gov.uk

Lifelong Learning: Mrs Mary Pattinson, Head of Learning & Achievement, Mercury House, Mercury Gardens, Romford RM1 3SL
☎ 01708 433808 ◌ mary.pattinson@havering.gov.uk

Lighting: Mr Bob Wenman, Head of Street Care, Mercury House, Mercury Gardens, Romford RM1 3RX ☎ 01708 432898
◌ bob.wenman@havering.gov.uk

Lottery Funding, Charity and Voluntary: Mr Tom Dobrashian, Head of Economic Development, Town Hall, Main Road, Romford RM1 3BD ☎ 01708 432583 ◌ tom.dobrashian@havering.gov.uk

Member Services: Mr Andrew Beesley, Head of Democratic Services, Town Hall, Main Road, Romford RM1 3BD
☎ 01708 432437 ◌ andrew.beesley@havering.gov.uk

Personnel / HR: Mrs Caroline Nugent, Director - HR & Organisational Development, Central Library, St Edwards Way, Romford RM1 3AR ☎ 01708 432181
◌ caroline.nugent@havering.gov.uk

Planning: Ms Helen Oakerbee, Planning Manager - Planning Control, Town Hall, Main Road, Romford RM1 3BD
☎ 01708 432800 ◌ helen.oakerbees@havering.gov.uk

Public Libraries: Ms Ann Rennie, Library Service Manager, Central Library, St Edwards Way, Romford RM1 3AR
☎ 01708 434343 ◌ ann.rennie@havering.gov.uk

Recycling & Waste Minimisation: Mr Paul Ellis, Group Manager - Waste Environment Services, Mercury House, Mercury Gardens, Romford RM1 3SL ☎ 01708 432966 ◌ paul.ellis@havering.gov.uk

Social Services: Ms Barbara Nicholls, Director - Adult Services, Town Hall, Main Road, Romford RM1 3BD ☎ 01708 433069
◌ barbara.nicholls@havering.gov.uk

Social Services (Adult): Ms Barbara Nicholls, Director - Adult Services, Town Hall, Main Road, Romford RM1 3BD
☎ 01708 433069 ◌ barbara.nicholls@havering.gov.uk

Social Services (Children): Mr Tim Aldridge, Acting Director - Children's Services, Town Hall, Main Road, Romford RM1 3BD
☎ 01708 434343 ◌ tim.aldridge@havering.gov.uk

Social Services (Children): Ms Kathy Bundred, Head of Children & Young People, Mercury House, Mercury Gardens, Romford RM1 3SL ☎ 01708 434343 ◌ kathy.bundred@havering.gov.uk

Public Health: Dr Sue Milner, Interim Director - Public Health, Town Hall, Main Road, Romford RM1 3BD
◌ sue.milner@havering.gov.uk

Staff Training: Mr Mark Porter, Operational HR Team Leader, Central Library, St Edwards Way, Romford RM1 3AR
☎ 01708 432989 ◌ mark.porter@havering.gov.uk

HAVERING

Street Scene: Mr Bob Wenman, Head of Street Care, Mercury House, Mercury Gardens, Romford RM1 3RX ☎ 01708 432898
-🖰 bob.wenman@havering.gov.uk

Sustainable Development: Ms Sheri Lim, Sustainability Officer, Mercury House, Mercury Gardens, Romford RM1 3SL
☎ 01708 434343 -🖰 sheri.lim@havering.gov.uk

Tourism: Mr Tom Dobrashian, Head of Economic Development, Town Hall, Main Road, Romford RM1 3BD ☎ 01708 432583
-🖰 tom.dobrashian@havering.gov.uk

Town Centre: Mr Perry Brooker, Town Centres Officer, Town Hall, Main Road, Romford RM1 3BD ☎ 01708 432577
-🖰 perry.brooker@havering.gov.uk

Traffic Management: Mr Martyn Thomas, Development & Transport Manager, Town Hall, Main Road, Romford RM1 3BD
☎ 01708 434343 -🖰 martyn.thomas@havering.gov.uk

Transport Planner: Mr Martyn Thomas, Development & Transport Manager, Town Hall, Main Road, Romford RM1 3BD
☎ 01708 434343 -🖰 martyn.thomas@havering.gov.uk

Waste Collection and Disposal: Mr Paul Ellis, Group Manager - Waste Environment Services, Mercury House, Mercury Gardens, Romford RM1 3SL ☎ 01708 432966 -🖰 paul.ellis@havering.gov.uk

Waste Management: Mr Paul Ellis, Group Manager - Waste Environment Services, Mercury House, Mercury Gardens, Romford RM1 3SL ☎ 01708 432966 -🖰 paul.ellis@havering.gov.uk

Waste Management: Mr Bob Wenman, Head of Street Care, Mercury House, Mercury Gardens, Romford RM1 3RX
☎ 01708 432898 -🖰 bob.wenman@havering.gov.uk

Children's Play Areas: Mr Simon Parkinson, Head of Culture & Customer Access, Stable Block, Langtons House, Billet Lane, Hornchurch RM11 1XJ ☎ 01708 434014
-🖰 simon.parkinson@havering.gov.uk

COUNCILLORS

Mayor: Eagling, Brian (R - Harold Wood)
councillorbrian.eagling@havering.gov.uk

Deputy Mayor: Crowder, Philippa (CON - Pettits)
councillorphilippa.crowder@havering.gov.uk

Leader of the Council: Ramsey, Roger (CON - Emerson Park)
councillorroger.ramsey@havering.gov.uk

Deputy Leader of the Council: White, Damian (CON - Squirrel's Heath)
councillordamian.white@havering.gov.uk

Group LeaderBarrett, Clarence (R - Cranham)
councillorclarence.barrett@havering.gov.uk

Group LeaderMorgon, Ray (R - Hacton)
councillorraymond.morgan@havering.gov.uk

Group LeaderTucker, Jeffrey (R - Rainham & Wennington)
councillorjeffrey.tucker@havering.gov.uk

Alexander, June (R - Cranham)
councillorjune.alexander@havering.gov.uk

Benham, Robert (CON - Brooklands)
councillorrobert.benham@havering.gov.uk

Best, Ray (CON - Havering Park)
ray.best@havering.gov.uk

Brice-Thompson, Wendy (CON - Romford Town)
councillorwendy.bricethompson@havering.gov.uk

Burton, Michael Deon (R - South Hornchurch)
councillormichaeldeon.burton@havering.gov.uk

Chapman, Joshua (CON - Romford Town)
councillorjoshua.chapman@havering.gov.uk

Crowder, John (CON - Havering Park)
councillorjohn.crowder@havering.gov.uk

Darvill, Keith (LAB - Heaton)
councillorkeith.darvill@havering.gov.uk

Davis, Meg (CON - Havering Park)
councillormeg.davis@havering.gov.uk

de Wulverton, Ian (UKIP - Heaton)
councillorian.dewulverton@havering.gov.uk

Dervish, Osman (CON - Pettits)
councillorosman.dervish@havering.gov.uk

Dodin, Nic (R - Hacton)
councillornic.dodin@havering.gov.uk

Donald, Alex (R - Harold Wood)
councilloralex.donald@havering.gov.uk

Durant, David (R - Rainham & Wennington)
councillordavid.durant@havering.gov.uk

Ford, Gillian (R - Cranham)
councillorgillian.ford@havering.gov.uk

Frost, Jason (CON - Mawneys)
councillorjason.frost@havering.gov.uk

Ganly, Jody (R - Hylands)
councillorjody.ganly@havering.gov.uk

Glanville, John (UKIP - Emerson Park)
councillorjohn.glanville@havering.gov.uk

Hawthorn, Linda (R - Upminster)
councillorlinda.hawthorn@havering.gov.uk

Johnson, David (UKIP - Gooshays)
councillordavid.johnson@havering.gov.uk

Kelly, Steven (CON - Emerson Park)
councillorsteven.kelly@havering.gov.uk

Martin, Phil (UKIP - South Hornchurch)
councillorphil.martin@havering.gov.uk

Matthews, Barbara (R - Hacton)
councillorbarbara.matthews@havering.gov.uk

Misir, Robby (CON - Pettits)
councillorrobby.misir@havering.gov.uk

Mugglestone, Barry (R - Elm Park)
councillorbarry.mugglestone@havering.gov.uk

Mylod, John (R - Saint Andrews)
councillorjohn.mylod@havering.gov.uk

Nunn, Stephanie (R - Elm Park)
councillorstephanie.nunn@havering.gov.uk

O'Flynn, Denis (LAB - Heaton)
councillordenis.o'flynn@havering.gov.uk

Ower, Ron (R - Upminster)
councillorron.ower@havering.gov.uk

Pain, Gary (CON - Hylands)
councillorgary.pain@havering.gov.uk

Patel, Dilip (CON - Mawneys)
councillordilip.patel@havering.gov.uk

Persaud, Viddy (CON - Brooklands)
councillorviddy.persaud@havering.gov.uk

Roberts, Keith (R - Rainham & Wennington)
councillorkeith.roberts@havering.gov.uk

Rumble, Patricia (UKIP - Gooshays)
councillorpatricia.rumble@havering.gov.uk

Smith, Carol (CON - Hylands)
councillorcarol.smith@havering.gov.uk

Thompson, Frederick (CON - Romford Town)
councillorfrederick.thompson@havering.gov.uk

Trew, Linda (CON - Mawneys)
councillorlinda.trew@havering.gov.uk

Van den Hende, Linda (R - Upminster)
councillorlinda.vandenhende@havering.gov.uk

Wallace, Melvin (CON - Squirrel's Heath)
councillormelvin.wallace@havering.gov.uk

Webb, Lawrence (UKIP - Gooshays)
councillorlawrence.webb@havering.gov.uk

Westwood, Roger (CON - Brooklands)
councillorrobert.westwood@havering.gov.uk

White, Michael (CON - Squirrel's Heath)
councillormichael.white@havering.gov.uk

Whitney, Reg (R - Saint Andrews)
councillorreginald.whitney@havering.gov.uk

Wilkes, Julie (R - Elm Park)
councillorjulie.wilkes@havering.gov.uk

Williamson, Graham (R - South Hornchurch)
councillorgraham.williamson@havering.gov.uk

Wise, Darren (R - Harold Wood)
councillordarren.wise@havering.gov.uk

Wood, John (R - Saint Andrews)
councillorjohn.wood@havering.gov.uk

POLITICAL COMPOSITION
R: 24, CON: 22, UKIP: 6, LAB: 2

COMMITTEE CHAIRS

Audit: Ms Viddy Persaud

Health & Wellbeing: Ms Wendy Brice-Thompson

Licensing: Mr Dilip Patel

Pensions: Mr John Crowder

Herefordshire   U

Herefordshire Council, Plough Lane, Hereford HR4 0LE
☎ 01432 260000 🖷 01432 260286 🖑 info@herefordshire.gov.uk
🖳 www.herefordshire.gov.uk

HEREFORDSHIRE

FACTS AND FIGURES
Parliamentary Constituencies: Hereford and Herefordshire South, Herefordshire North
EU Constituencies: West Midlands
Election Frequency: Elections are by thirds

PRINCIPAL OFFICERS

Chief Executive: Mr Alistair Neill, Chief Executive, Plough Lane, Hereford HR4 0LE ☎ 01432 260044
🖑 alistair.neill@herefordshire.gov.uk

Senior Management: Ms Jo Davidson, Director - Children's Wellbeing, Plough Lane, Hereford HR4 0LE ☎ 01432 260039
🖑 jdavidson@herefordshire.gov.uk

Senior Management: Mr Geoff Hughes, Director - Economy, Communities & Corporate, Plough Lane, Hereford HR4 0LE
☎ 01432 260695 🖑 ghughes@herefordshire.gov.uk

Senior Management: Mr Martin Samuels, Director - Adults & Wellbeing, Plough Lane, Hereford HR4 0LE ☎ 01432 260339
🖑 martin.samuels@herefordshire.gov.uk

Senior Management: Prof Rod Thomson, Director - Public Health, Plough Lane, Hereford HR4 0LE ☎ 01432 383783
🖑 rod.thomson@herefordshire.gov.uk

Children / Youth Services: Ms Jo Davidson, Director - Children's Wellbeing, Plough Lane, Hereford HR4 0LE ☎ 01432 260039
🖑 jdavidson@herefordshire.gov.uk

PR / Communications: Ms Alex Floyd, Head of Communications & Engagement, Plough Lane, Hereford HR4 0LE ☎ 01432 383510
🖑 alexandra.floyd@herefordshire.gov.uk

Community Safety: Ms Nina Bridges, Sustainable Communities Manager, Plough Lane, Hereford HR4 0LE ☎ 01432 260624
🖑 nbridges@herefordshire.gov.uk

Consumer Protection and Trading Standards: Mr Marc Willimont, Head of Regulatory & Development Management Services, Blue School House, Blue School Street, Hereford HR1 2ZB ☎ 01432 261986 🖑 mwillimont@herefordshire.gov.uk

Customer Service: Mr Roger Horton, Customer Services Area Manager, Franklin House, 4 Commercial Road, Hereford HR1 2BB ☎ 01432 383828 🖑 roger.horton@herefordshire.gov.uk

Economic Development: Mr Richard Ball, Assistant Director - Environment & Place, Plough Lane, Hereford HR4 0LE
☎ 01432 260965; 01432 383031 🖑 rball@herefordshire.gov.uk

Education: Ms Lisa Fraser, Head of Learning Achievement, Plough Lane, Hereford HR4 0LE ☎ 01432 383043
🖑 lfraser@herefordshire.gov.uk

Electoral Registration: Ms Colette Maund, Electoral Services Manager, Town Hall, St Owens Street, Hereford HR1 2PJ
☎ 01432 260696; 01432 260114 🖑 cmaund@herefordshire.gov.uk

HEREFORDSHIRE

Emergency Planning: Mrs Carol Trachonitis, Equality & Compliance Manager, Plough Lane, Hereford HR4 0LE
☎ 01432 260616 ⌨ ct1@herefordshire.gov.uk

Environmental / Technical Services: Mr Chris Jenner, Environmental Services Manager, Blue School House, Blue School Street, Hereford HR1 2ZB ☎ 01432 261941
⌨ cjenner@herefordshire.gov.uk

Environmental Health: Mr Marc Willimont, Head of Regulatory & Development Management Services, Blue School House, Blue School Street, Hereford HR1 2ZB ☎ 01432 261986
⌨ mwillimont@herefordshire.gov.uk

Estates, Property & Valuation: Mr Tony Featherstone, Strategic Asset Manager, Plough Lane, Hereford HR4 0LE ☎ 01432 383368
⌨ afeatherstone@herefordshire.gov.uk

European Liaison: Ms Vinia Abesamis, Senior Policy & Funding Officer, Plough Lane, Hereford HR4 0LE ☎ 01432 383031; 01432 610677 ⌨ vabesamis@herefordshire.gov.uk

Facilities: Mr Geoffrey Jones, Property Operations Manager, Plough Lane, Hereford HR4 0LE ☎ 01432 261532
⌨ gjones@herefordshire.gov.uk

Finance: Mr Peter Robinson, Director - Resources, Plough Lane, Hereford HR4 0LE ☎ 01432 383519
⌨ dpowell@herefordshire.gov.uk

Health and Safety: Mr Phil Chandler, Health & Safety Advisor, Shirehall, St. Peter's Square, Hereford HR1 2HY ☎ 01432 260240
⌨ phil.chandler@herefordshire.gov.uk

Highways: Mr Richard Ball, Assistant Director - Environment & Place, Plough Lane, PO Box 236, Hereford HR4 0WZ ☎ 01432 260965; 01432 383031 ⌨ rball@herefordshire.gov.uk

Housing: Mr Sukhdev Dosanjhu, Assistant Director - Commissioning Adults' Wellbeing, Plough Lane, Hereford HR4 0LE
☎ 01432 383783 ⌨ sukhdev.dosanjhu@herefordshire.gov.uk

Legal: Ms Erica Hermon, Head of Law & Governance, Shirehall, St Peter's Square, Hereford HR1 2HY ☎ 01432 261906
⌨ ehermon@herefordshire.gov.uk

Leisure and Cultural Services: Mr Mick Ligema, Cultural Services Manager, Plough Lane, Hereford HR4 0LE
☎ 01432 260631 ⌨ mligema@herefordshire.gov.uk

Licensing: Ms Claire Corfield, Licensing & Gypsy Traveller Manager, Plough Lane, Hereford HR4 0LE ☎ 01432 383324
⌨ clcorfield@herefordshire.gov.uk

Lifelong Learning: Ms Susan Cobourne, Adult & Community Learning, Plough Lane, Hereford HR4 0LE ☎ 01432 383639
⌨ scobourne@herefordshire.gov.uk

Personnel / HR: Ms Tracey Sampson, Head of HR & OD, Plough Lane, Hereford HR4 0LE ☎ 01432 261855
⌨ tracey.sampson@herefordshire.gov.uk

Planning: Mr Marc Willimont, Head of Regulatory & Development Management Services, Blue School House, Blue School Street, Hereford HR1 2ZB ☎ 01432 261986
⌨ mwillimont@herefordshire.gov.uk

Procurement: Ms Erica Hermon, Head of Law & Governance, Shirehall, St Peter's Square, Hereford HR1 2HY ☎ 01432 261906
⌨ ehermon@herefordshire.gov.uk

Public Libraries: Mr Jonathan Chedgzoy, Libraries Manager, Plough Lane, Hereford HR4 0LE ☎ 01432 260557
⌨ jchedgzoy@herefordshire.gov.uk

Recycling & Waste Minimisation: Mr Kenton Vigus, Waste Disposal Team Leader, Plough Lane, Hereford HR4 0LE
☎ 01432 260169 ⌨ kvigus@herefordshire.gov.uk

Regeneration: Mr Nick Webster, Economic Development Manager, Plough Lane, Hereford HR4 0LE ☎ 01432 260601
⌨ nwebster@herefordshire.gov.uk

Road Safety: Mr Jeremy Callard, Team Leader Transport Strategy, Plough Lane, Hereford HR4 0LE ☎ 01432 383437
⌨ amann@herefordshire.gov.uk

Social Services (Adult): Mr Martin Samuels, Director - Adults & Wellbeing, Plough Lane, Hereford HR4 0LE ☎ 01432 260339
⌨ martin.samuels@herefordshire.gov.uk

Social Services (Children): Ms Jo Davidson, Director - Children's Wellbeing, Plough Lane, Hereford HR4 0LE ☎ 01432 260039
⌨ jdavidson@herefordshire.gov.uk

Public Health: Prof Rod Thomson, Director - Public Health, Plough Lane, Hereford HR4 0LE ☎ 01432 383783
⌨ rod.thomson@herefordshire.gov.uk

Staff Training: Ms Tracey Sampson, Head of HR & OD, Plough Lane, Hereford HR4 0LE ☎ 01432 261855
⌨ tracey.sampson@herefordshire.gov.uk

Transport: Mr Steve Burgess, Head of Transport & Access Services, Plough Lane, Hereford HR4 0LE ☎ 01432 260968
⌨ sburgess@herefordshire.gov.uk

Waste Management: Mr Richard Wood, Waste Services Manager, Plough Lane, Hereford HR4 0LE ☎ 01432 383009
⌨ rnwood@hereford.gov.uk

COUNCILLORS

Chair: Wilcox, DB (CON - College)
bwilcox@herefordshire.gov.uk

Vice-Chair: McCaull, PJ (IND - Leominster South)
pmccaull@herefordshire.gov.uk

Leader of the Council: Johnson, AW (CON - Hope End)
ajohnson@herefordshire.gov.uk

Deputy Leader of the Council: Morgan, PM (CON - Bishops Frome & Cradley)
pmorgan@herefordshire.gov.uk

Group Leader: Bartlett, Jenny (GRN - Leominster East)
jenny.bartlett@herefordshire.gov.uk

Group Leader: James, TM (LD - Kington)
tjames@herefordshire.gov.uk

Group Leader: Matthews, R (IND - Credenhill)
rmatthews@herefordshire.gov.uk

Andrews, PA (LD - Widemarsh)
paandrews@herefordshire.gov.uk

Baker, Bruce (CON - Hampton)
bruce.baker@herefordshire.gov.uk

Bowen, WLS (IND - Bircher)
sbowen@herefordshire.gov.uk

Bowes, Tracy (IND - Belmont Rural)
tracy.bowes@herefordshire.gov.uk

Bramer, H (CON - Penyard)
hbramer@herefordshire.gov.uk

Butler, Clive (CON - Bobblestock)
clive.butler@herefordshire.gov.uk

Chappell, ACR (IND - Hinton & Hunderton)
cchappell@herefordshire.gov.uk

Cooper, MJK (CON - Weobley)
mcooper2@herefordshire.gov.uk

Crockett, Pauline (IND - Queenswood)
pauline.crockett@herefordshire.gov.uk

Cutter, PGH (CON - Ross East)
pcutter@herefordshire.gov.uk

Durkin, BA (CON - Old Gore)
bdurkin@herefordshire.gov.uk

Edwards, PJ (IND - Newton Farm)
pjedwards@herefordshire.gov.uk

Gandy, Carole (CON - Mortimer)
carole.gandy@herefordshire.gov.uk

Greenow, DW (CON - Hagley)
dgreenow@herefordshire.gov.uk

Guthrie, KS (CON - Sutton Walls)
kguthrie@herefordshire.gov.uk

Hardwick, J (IND - Backbury)
jhardwick1@herefordshire.gov.uk

Harlow, David (CON - Birch)
david.harlow@herefordshire.gov.uk

Harvey, EPJ (IND - Ledbury North)
epjharvey@herefordshire.gov.uk

Holton, Emma (CON - Ledbury South)
emma.holton@herefordshire.gov.uk

Hyde, JA (CON - Ross North)
jhyde@herefordshire.gov.uk

Johnson, Jon (CON - Wormside)
jon.johnson@herefordshire.gov.uk

Kenyon, JLV (IND - Tupsley)
jkenyon@herefordshire.gov.uk

Lester, JG (CON - Three Crosses)
jlester@herefordshire.gov.uk

Lloyd-Hayes, MD (IND - Aylestone Hill)
mlloyd-hayes@herefordshire.gov.uk

Mansell, Mark (IND - Kings Acre)
mark.mansell@herefordshire.gov.uk

Mayo, RL (CON - Ross West)
rmayo@herefordshire.gov.uk

McEvilly, Mark (CON - Saxon Gate)
mark.mcevilly@herefordshire.gov.uk

Michael, SM (IND - Whitecross)
smichael@herefordshire.gov.uk

Newman, Paul (CON - Kerne Bridge)
paul.newman@herefordshire.gov.uk

Norman, FM (GRN - Leominster West)
fnorman@herefordshire.gov.uk

North, Cath (INDNA - Eign Hill)
cath.north@herefordshire.gov.uk

Phillips, RJ (CON - Arrow)
rjphillips@herefordshire.gov.uk

Powell, Graham (CON - Golden Valley South)
grahampowell@herefordshire.gov.uk

Powers, Anthony (IND - Greyfriars)
anthony.powers@herefordshire.gov.uk

Price, PD (CON - Golden Valley North)
pprice@herefordshire.gov.uk

Rone, P (CON - Redhill)
prone@herefordshire.gov.uk

Round, Andrew (IND - Holmer)
andrew.round@herefordshire.gov.uk

Seldon, A (IND - Bromyard West)
aseldon@herefordshire.gov.uk

Shaw, Nigel (CON - Bromyard Bringsty)
nigel.shaw@herefordshire.gov.uk

Skelton, Clive (CON - Castle)
clive.skelton@herefordshire.gov.uk

Stone, J (CON - Leominster North & Rural)
jstone@herefordshire.gov.uk

Summers, David (IND - Dinedor Hill)
david.summers@herefordshire.gov.uk

Swinglehurst, Elissa (CON - Llangarron)
elissawinglehurst@tiscali.co.uk

Tawn, Len (IND - Central)
len.tawn@herefordshire.gov.uk

West, Andrew (IND - Ledbury West)
andrew.warmington@herefordshire.gov.uk

Williams, Steve (CON - Stoney Street)
steve.williams@herefordshire.gov.uk

POLITICAL COMPOSITION
CON: 29, IND: 19, LD: 2, GRN: 2, INDNA: 1

COMMITTEE CHAIRS

Audit & Governance: Mr Paul Newman

Health & Social Care: Ms PA Andrews

Health & Wellbeing: Ms PM Morgan

Planning: Mr PGH Cutter

HERTFORDSHIRE

Hertfordshire County Council, County Hall, Pegs Lane, Hertford SG13 8DE
☎ 0300 123 4040 ⌨ www.hertsdirect.org

FACTS AND FIGURES
Parliamentary Constituencies: Hertfordshire South West
EU Constituencies: Eastern
Election Frequency: Elections are of whole council

PRINCIPAL OFFICERS

Chief Executive: Mr John Wood, Chief Executive & Director - Environment, County Hall, Pegs Lane, Hertford SG13 8DF ☎ 01992 555601; 01992 555505 ⌂ john.wood@hertfordshire.gov.uk

Senior Management: Ms Jenny Coles, Director - Children's Services, County Hall, Pegs Lane, Hertford SG13 8DE ☎ 01992 555755; 01992 555719 ⌂ jenny.coles@hertfordshire.gov.uk

Senior Management: Mr Iain MacBeath, Director - Health & Community Services, County Hall, Pegs Lane, Hertford SG13 8DE ☎ 01992 556363; 01992 556323 ⌂ iain.macbeath@hertfordshire.gov.uk

Senior Management: Mr Owen Mapley, Director - Resources, County Hall, Pegs Lane, Hertford SG13 8DE ☎ 01992 555601 ⌂ owen.mapley@hertfordshire.gov.uk

Senior Management: Mr Jim McManus, Director - Public Health, County Hall, Pegs Lane, Hertford SG13 8DE ☎ 01438 845389 ⌂ jim.mcmanus@hertfordshire.gov.uk

Senior Management: Mr Roy Wilsher, Director - Community Protection & Chief Fire Officer, Service HQ, Old London Road, Hertford SG13 7LD ☎ 01992 507501; 01992 503048 ⌂ roy.wilsher@hertfordshire.gov.uk

Best Value: Ms Rebecca Price, Head of Performance & Improvement, County Hall, Pegs Lane, Hertford SG13 8DE ☎ 01992 588746; 01992 555930 ⌂ rebecca.price@hertfordshire.gov.uk

Building Control: Ms Angela Bucksey, Assistant Director - Property, County Hall, Pegs Lane, Hertford SG13 8DE ☎ 01992 556397; 01992 555505 ⌂ angela.bucksey@hertfordshire.gov.uk

Catering Services: Ms Lin O'Brien, Chief Executive of Hertfordshire Catering Ltd, Hertfordshire Business Services, The Mundells, Welwyn Garden City, Hertford AL7 1FT ☎ 01707 293510 ⌂ lin.obrien@hertfordshire.gov.uk

Children / Youth Services: Mr Andrew Simmons, Deputy Director - Children's Services & Education, County Hall, Pegs Lane, Hertford SG13 8DE ☎ 01992 555503 ⌂ andrew.simmons@hertfordshire.gov.uk

Civil Registration: Mr Steve Charteris, Head of Democratic & Statutory Services, The Old Courthouse, St Albans Road East, Hatfield AL10 0ES ☎ 01707 897375; 01707 897379 ⌂ steve.charteris@hertfordshire.gov.uk

PR / Communications: Ms Lindsay Coulson, Head of Communications & Strategic Engagement, County Hall, Pegs Lane, Hertford SG13 8DE ☎ 01992 556655; 01992 555647 ⌂ lindsay.coulson@hertfordshire.gov.uk

Computer Management: Mr Stuart Bannerman-Campbell, Assistant Director - Improvement & Technology, County Hall, Pegs Lane, Hertford SG13 8DE ☎ 01992 588397; 01992 555505 ⌂ stuart.campbell@hertfordshire.gov.uk

Consumer Protection and Trading Standards: Mr Guy Pratt, Assistant Director - Community Protection, Service HQ, Old London Road, Hertford SG13 7LD ☎ 01727 813849; 01727 813829 ⌂ guy.pratt@hertfordshire.gov.uk

Contracts: Mr Stuart Bannerman-Campbell, Assistant Director - Improvement & Technology, County Hall, Pegs Lane, Hertford SG13 8DE ☎ 01992 588397; 01992 555505 ⌂ stuart.campbell@hertfordshire.gov.uk

Customer Service: Mr Michael Francis, Head of Customer Service, County Hall, Pegs Lane, Hertford SG13 8DE ☎ 01992 556994; 01992 588550 ⌂ michael.francis@hertfordshire.gov.uk

Economic Development: Ms Jan Hayes-Griffin, Assistant Director - Planning & Economy, County Hall, Pegs Lane, Hertford SG13 8DE ☎ 01992 555203; 01992 555505 ⌂ jan.hayes-griffin@hertfordshire.gov.uk

Education: Mr Andrew Simmons, Deputy Director - Children's Services & Education, County Hall, Pegs Lane, Hertford SG13 8DE ☎ 01992 555503 ⌂ andrew.simmons@hertfordshire.gov.uk

E-Government: Mr Michael Francis, Head of Customer Service, County Hall, Pegs Lane, Hertford SG13 8DE ☎ 01992 556994; 01992 588550 ⌂ michael.francis@hertfordshire.gov.uk

Electoral Registration: Mr Steve Charteris, Head of Democratic & Statutory Services, The Old Courthouse, St Albans Road East, Hatfield AL10 0ES ☎ 01707 897375; 01707 897379 ⌂ steve.charteris@hertfordshire.gov.uk

Emergency Planning: Mr John Boulter, Head of Protection (Business), County Hall, Pegs Lane, Hertford SG13 8DE ☎ 01992 555951 ⌂ john.boulter@hertfordshire.gov.uk

Estates, Property & Valuation: Ms Angela Bucksey, Assistant Director - Property, County Hall, Pegs Lane, Hertford SG13 8DE ☎ 01992 556397; 01992 555505 ⌂ angela.bucksey@hertfordshire.gov.uk

Facilities: Ms Angela Bucksey, Assistant Director - Property, County Hall, Pegs Lane, Hertford SG13 8DE ☎ 01992 556397; 01992 555505 ⌂ angela.bucksey@hertfordshire.gov.uk

Finance: Ms Claire Cook, Assistant Director - Finance, County Hall, Pegs Lane, Hertford SG13 8DE ☎ 01992 555555 ⌂ claire.cook@hertfordshire.gov.uk

Treasury: Ms Claire Cook, Assistant Director - Finance, County Hall, Pegs Lane, Hertford SG13 8DE ☎ 01992 555555 ⌂ claire.cook@hertfordshire.gov.uk

Fleet Management: Ms Angela Bucksey, Assistant Director - Property, County Hall, Pegs Lane, Hertford SG13 8DE ☎ 01992 556397; 01992 555505 ⌨ angela.bucksey@hertfordshire.gov.uk

Health and Safety: Mr James Ottery, Health & Safety Manager, County Hall, Pegs Lane, Hertford SG13 8DE ☎ 01992 556677; 01992 555962 ⌨ james.ottery@hertfordshire.gov.uk

Highways: Mr Rob Smith, Deputy Director - Environment, County Hall, Pegs Lane, Hertford SG13 8DE ☎ 01992 556121; 01992 556106 ⌨ rob.smith@hertfordshire.gov.uk

Legal: Ms Kathryn Pettitt, Chief Legal Officer, County Hall, Pegs Lane, Hertford SG13 8DE ☎ 01992 555527 ⌨ kathryn.pettitt@hertfordshire.gov.uk

Lifelong Learning: Mr Andrew Bignell, Head of Libraries, Culture & Learning, County Hall, Pegs Lane, Hertford SG13 8DE ☎ 01992 588309; 01707 281589 ⌨ andrew.bignell@hertfordshire.gov.uk

Member Services: Mr Alex James, Head of Corporate Policy & Business Support, County Hall, Pegs Lane, Hertford SG13 8DE ☎ 01992 588259 ⌨ alex.james@hertfordshire.gov.uk

Partnerships: Ms Jan Hayes-Griffin, Assistant Director - Planning & Economy, County Hall, Pegs Lane, Hertford SG13 8DE ☎ 01992 555203; 01992 555505 ⌨ jan.hayes-griffin@hertfordshire.gov.uk

Personnel / HR: Ms Sally Hopper, Assistant Director - Human Resources Services, County Hall, Pegs Lane, Hertford SG13 8DE ☎ 01992 556651 ⌨ sally.hopper@hertfordshire.gov.uk

Planning: Ms Jan Hayes-Griffin, Assistant Director - Planning & Economy, County Hall, Pegs Lane, Hertford SG13 8DE ☎ 01992 555203; 01992 555505 ⌨ jan.hayes-griffin@hertfordshire.gov.uk

Procurement: Mr Stuart Bannerman-Campbell, Assistant Director - Improvement & Technology, County Hall, Pegs Lane, Hertford SG13 8DE ☎ 01992 588397; 01992 555505 ⌨ stuart.campbell@hertfordshire.gov.uk

Public Libraries: Mrs Taryn Pearson-Rose, Assistant Director of Customer Services & Libraries, County Hall, Pegs Lane, Hertford SG13 8DE ☎ 01992 556351 ⌨ taryn.pearson-rose@hertfordshire.gov.uk

Recycling & Waste Minimisation: Mr Matthew King, Head of Waste Management, County Hall, Pegs Lane, Hertford SG13 8DE ☎ 01992 556160; 01992 556180 ⌨ matthew.king@hertfordshire.gov.uk

Regeneration: Mr Jon Tiley, Business Manager - Spatial Planning & Economy, County Hall, Pegs Lane, Hertford SG13 8DE ☎ 01992 556292; 01992 556290 ⌨ jonathan.tiley@hertfordshire.gov.uk

Road Safety: Mr Trevor Mason, Team Leader - Rail Strategy & Liason, County Hall, Pegs Lane, Hertford SG13 8DE ☎ 01992 556804; 01992 556820 ⌨ trevor.mason@hertfordshire.gov.uk

Social Services (Adult): Mr Chris Badger, Operation Director - Older People & Physical Disabilities, County Hall, Pegs Lane, Hertford SG13 8DE ☎ 01992 556301 ⌨ chris.badger@hertfordshire.gov.uk

Social Services (Adult): Mr Iain MacBeath, Director - Health & Community Services, County Hall, Pegs Lane, Hertford SG13 8DE ☎ 01992 556363; 01992 556323 ⌨ iain.macbeath@hertfordshire.gov.uk

Social Services (Children): Ms Jenny Coles, Director - Children's Services, County Hall, Pegs Lane, Hertford SG13 8DE ☎ 01992 555755; 01992 555719 ⌨ jenny.coles@hertfordshire.gov.uk

Staff Training: Ms Samantha Holliday, Head of HR Learning & Organisational Development, County Hall, Pegs Lane, Hertford SG13 8DE ☎ 01438 845105 ⌨ samantha.holliday@hertscc.gov.uk

Sustainable Communities: Mr John Rumble, Head - Environmental Resource Planning, County Hall, Pegs Lane, Hertford SG13 8DE ☎ 01992 556296; 01992 556290 ⌨ john.rumble@hertfordshire.gov.uk

Sustainable Development: Mr Jon Tiley, Business Manager - Spatial Planning & Economy, County Hall, Pegs Lane, Hertford SG13 8DE ☎ 01992 556292; 01992 556290 ⌨ jonathan.tiley@hertfordshire.gov.uk

Transport: Mr Rob Smith, Deputy Director - Environment, County Hall, Pegs Lane, Hertford SG13 8DE ☎ 01992 556121; 01992 556106 ⌨ rob.smith@hertfordshire.gov.uk

Transport Planner: Ms Glenda Hardy, Head of Admissions & Transport, County Hall, Pegs Lane, Hertford SG13 8DE ☎ 01438 737500 ⌨ glenda.hardy@hertfordshire.gov.uk

Transport Planner: Mr Tom Hennessey, Business Manager - Transport, Access & Safety, County Hall, Pegs Lane, Hertford SG13 8DE ☎ 01992 588385 ⌨ tom.hennessey@hertfordshire.gov.uk

Waste Management: Mr Matthew King, Head of Waste Management, County Hall, Pegs Lane, Hertford SG13 8DE ☎ 01992 556160; 01992 556180 ⌨ matthew.king@hertfordshire.gov.uk

COUNCILLORS

ChairButton, Frances (CON - Oxhey Park)
frances.button@hertscc.gov.uk

Leader of the Council: Gordon, Robert (CON - Goffs Oak & Bury Green)
robert.gordon@hertscc.gov.uk

Andrews, David (CON - Ware North)
david.andrews@hertscc.gov.uk

Ashley, Derrick (CON - Hitchin South)
derrick.ashley@hertscc.gov.uk

Barfoot, John (CON - Bishop's Stortford East)
john.barfoot@hertscc.gov.uk

Barnard, David (CON - Hitchin Rural)
david.barnard@hertfordshire.gov.uk

HERTFORDSHIRE

Batson, Sherma (LAB - Broadwater)
sherma.batson@hertfordshire.gov.uk

Bedford, Sara (LD - Abbots Langley)
sara.bedford@hertfordshire.gov.uk

Beeching, Roger (CON - Sawbridgeworth)
roger.beeching@hertscc.gov.uk

Bell, Nigel (LAB - Vicarage Holywell)
nigel.bell@hertscc.gov.uk

Billing, Judi (LAB - Hitchin North)
judi.billing@hertfordshire.gov.uk

Bright, Morris (CON - Potters Bar West & Shenley)
morris.bright@hertfordshire.gov.uk

Chesterman, Lynn (LAB - Welwyn Garden City South)
lynn.chesterman@sky.com

Cheswright, Rosemary (CON - Braughing)
rose.cheswright@hertfordshire.gov.uk

Churchard, Geoff (LD - Sandridge)
geoff.churchard@hertscc.gov.uk

Clapper, Caroline (CON - Watling)
caroline.clapper@hertscc.gov.uk

Cook, Maureen (LAB - Hatfield North)
maureen.cook@hertfordshire.gov.uk

Cowan, Malcolm (LD - Handside & Peartree)
malcolm.cowan@hertscc.gov.uk

Crawley, Maxine (CON - St Albans Rural)
maxine.crawley@hertscc.gov.uk

Crofton, Ken (CON - Hertford Rural)
ken.crofton@hertfordshire.gov.uk

Douris, Terry (CON - Hemel Hempstead North West)
terry.douris@hertscc.gov.uk

Drury, Steve (LD - Croxley)
david.drury@hertscc.gov.uk

Giles-Medhurst, Stephen (LD - Central Oxhey)
sgm@cix.co.uk

Gordon, Dreda (LAB - The Colneys)
dreda.gordon@hertfordshire.gov.uk

Hart, Dee (CON - Waltham Cross)
dee.hart@hertscc.gov.uk

Hastrick, Kareen (LD - Meriden Tudor)
kareen.hastrick@hertfordshire.gov.uk

Hayward, Chris (CON - Chorleywood)
christopher.hayward@hertscc.gov.uk

Henry, Richard (LAB - St Nicholas)
richard.henry@hertfordshire.gov.uk

Heritage, Teresa (CON - Harpenden South West)
teresa.heritage@hertscc.gov.uk

Hewitt, David (CON - Cheshunt Central)
david.hewitt@hertscc.gov.uk

Hill, Fiona (CON - Royston)
fiona.hill@hertscc.gov.uk

Hollinghurst, Nicholas (LD - Tring)
nicholas.hollinghurst@hertscc.gov.uk

Hone, Terry (CON - Letchworth South)
terry.hone@hertfordshire.gov.uk

Hunter, Tony (CON - North Herts Rural)
tony.hunter@hertscc.gov.uk

Hutchings, Tim (CON - Hoddesdon North)
tim.hutchings@hertfordshire.gov.uk

Johnston, Sara (CON - Haldens)
sara.johnston@hertscc.gov.uk

Joynes, Anne (LAB - Callowland Leggatts)
acj276@btinternet.com

Kercher, Lorna (LAB - Letchworth North West)
lorna.kercher@sky.com

King, Amanda (LAB - Old Stevenage)
amanda.king@hertfordshire.gov.uk

King, Joan (LAB - South Oxhey)
joan.king@hertfordshire.gov.uk

Knell, Peter (CON - Potters Bar East)
peter.knell@hertfordshire.gov.uk

Lee, Aislinn (LD - St Stephen's)
aislinn.lee@hertscc.gov.uk

Lloyd, David (CON - Bridgewater)
david.lloyd@hertscc.gov.uk

Lloyd, John (LAB - Shephall)
john.lloyd@hertscc.gov.uk

Mason, Paul (CON - Flamstead End & Turnford)
paul.mason@hertfordshire.gov.uk

McAndrew, Graham (CON - Bishop's Stortford Rural)
graham.mcandrew@hertfordshire.gov.uk

McKay, Anthony (CON - Hemel Hempstead South East)
anthony.mckay@hertfordshire.gov.uk

Mills, Roma (LAB - St Albans North)
roma.mills@btinternet.com

Mills-Bishop, Mark (CON - Hatfield Rural)
mark.mills-bishop@hertfordshire.gov.uk

Muir, Michael (CON - Letchworth East & Baldock)
michael.muir@hertscc.gov.uk

Parker, Robin (LD - Chells)
robin.parker@hertscc.gov.uk

Plancey, Alan (CON - Borehamwood South)
alan.plancey@hertfordshire.gov.uk

Prowse, Robert (LD - St Albans East)
robert.prowse@hertscc.gov.uk

Quilty, Seamus (CON - Bushey South)
seamus.quilty@hertscc.gov.uk

Reay, Ian (CON - Berkhamsted)
ian.reay@hertscc.gov.uk

Reefe, Leon (LAB - Borehamwood North)
leon.reefe@hertfordshire.gov.uk

Roberts, Richard (CON - Kings Langley)
richard.roberts@hertscc.gov.uk

Ruffles, Peter (CON - St Andrew's)
peter.ruffles@hertscc.gov.uk

Sangster, Ralph (CON - Rickmansworth)
ralph.sangster@hertfordshire.gov.uk

Scudder, Derek (LD - Woodside Stanborough)
derek.scudder@hertscc.gov.uk

Searing, Alan (CON - Hoddesdon South)
alan.searing@hertscc.gov.uk

Smith, Richard (CON - Welwyn)
richard.smith@hertscc.gov.uk

Stevenson, Andrew (CON - All Saints)
andrew.stevenson@hertfordshire.gov.uk

Taylor, Sharon (LAB - Bedwell)
sharon.taylor@stevenage.gov.uk

Taylor, Jeanette (CON - Ware South)
jeanette.taylor@hertfordshire.gov.uk

Thake, Richard (CON - Knebworth & Codicote)
richard.thake@hertscc.gov.uk

Tindell, Ron (LD - Hemel Hempstead St Paul's)
ron.tindall@hertscc.gov.uk

Walkington, Sandy (LD - St Albans South)
sandy.walkington@hertfordshire.gov.uk

Watkin, Mark (LD - Nascot Park)
mark.watkin@hertscc.gov.uk

West, Jane (CON - Bushey North)
jane.west@hertfordshire.gov.uk

White, Chris (LD - St Albans Central)
chriswhite@cix.co.uk

Williams, Andrew (CON - Hemel Hempstead East)
andrew.williams@hertscc.gov.uk

Williams, David (CON - Harpenden North East)
david.williams@hertfordshire.gov.uk

Woodward, Colin (CON - Bishop's Stortford West)
colin.woodward@hertscc.gov.uk

Wyatt-Lowe, William (CON - Hemel Hempstead Town)
william.wyatt-lowe@hertfordshire.gov.uk

Wyatt-Lowe, Colette (CON - Hemel Hempstead North East)
colette.wyatt-lowe@hertscc.gov.uk

Zukowskyj, Paul (LD - Hatfield South)
paul.zukowskyj@hertfordshire.gov.uk

POLITICAL COMPOSITION
CON: 46, LD: 16, LAB: 15

COMMITTEE CHAIRS
Audit: Mr Andrew Williams

Development Control: Mr Ian Reay

Health & Wellbeing: Ms Colette Wyatt-Lowe

Pensions: Mr Chris Hayward

Hertsmere   D

Hertsmere Borough Council, Civic Office, Elstree Way, Borehamwood WD6 1WA
☎ 020 8207 2277 🖶 020 8207 7441
customer.services@hertsmere.gov.uk 🖳 www.hertsmere.gov.uk

FACTS AND FIGURES
Parliamentary Constituencies: Hertsmere
EU Constituencies: Eastern
Election Frequency: Elections are by thirds

PRINCIPAL OFFICERS

Chief Executive: Mr Donald Graham, Chief Executive, Civic Office, Elstree Way, Borehamwood WD6 1WA ☎ 020 8207 2277; 020 8207 7441 donald.graham@hertsmere.gov.uk

Senior Management: Ms Sajida Bijle, Director - Resources, Civic Offices, Elstree Way, Borehamwood WD6 1WA ☎ 020 8207 2277; 020 8207 7487 sajida.bijle@hertsmere.gov.uk

Senior Management: Mr Glen Wooldrige, Director - Environment, Civic Office, Elstree Way, Borehamwood WD6 1WA ☎ 020 8207 2277 environment@hertsmere.gov.uk

Architect, Building / Property Services: Mr Richard Stubbs, Asset Manager, Civic Office, Elstree Way, Borehamwood WD6 1WA ☎ 020 8207 2277; 020 8207 7441

PR / Communications: Ms Catherine Shepherd, Corporate Communications Manager, Civic Offices, Elstree Way, Borehamwood WD6 1WA ☎ 020 8207 2277 corporate.communications@hertsmere.gov.uk

Community Safety: Ms Valerie Kane, Community Safety Manager, Civic Offices, Elstree Way, Borehamwood WD6 1WA ☎ 020 8207 7462; 020 8207 7478 community.services@hertsmere.gov.uk

Computer Management: Ms Sajida Bijle, Director - Resources, Civic Office, Elstree Way, Borehamwood WD6 1WA ☎ 020 8207 2277; 020 8207 7487 sajida.bijle@hertsmere.gov.uk

Contracts: Mr Andrew Harper, Procurement Manager, Civic Offices, Elstree Way, Borehamwood WD6 1WA ☎ 020 8207 2277; 01707 357371 a.harper@welhat.gov.uk

Corporate Services: Ms Hilary Shade, Head of Partnerships & Community Engagement, Civic Office, Elstree Way, Borehamwood WD6 1WA ☎ 020 8207 7519; 020 8207 7499 corporate.support@hertsmere.gov.uk

Customer Service: Ms Judith Fear, Head of HR & Customer Services, Civic Offices, Elstree Way, Borehamwood WD6 1WA ☎ 020 8207 7475; 020 8207 7550 human.resources@hertsmere.gov.uk

Customer Service: Mr Lee Gallagher, Customer Service Operation Manager, Civic Offices, Elstree Way, Borehamwood WD6 1WA ☎ 020 8207 2277; 020 8207 7424 customer.services@hertsmere.gov.uk

Economic Development: Mr Glen Wooldrige, Director - Environment, Civic Office, Elstree Way, Borehamwood WD6 1WA ☎ 020 8207 2277 environment@hertsmere.gov.uk

Electoral Registration: Ms Jo Bateman, Electoral Services Manager, Civic Office, Elstree Way, Borehamwood WD6 1WA ☎ 020 8207 7481; 020 8207 7555 jo.bateman@hertsmere.gov.uk

Emergency Planning: Mr Chris Gascoine, Chief Environmental Health Officer, Civic Offices, Elstree Way, Borehamwood WD6 1WA ☎ 020 8207 7433; 020 8207 7441 environmental.health@hertsmere.gov.uk

HERTSMERE

Emergency Planning: Mr Glen Wooldrige, Director - Environment, Civic Office, Elstree Way, Borehamwood WD6 1WA
☎ 020 8207 2277 📧 environment@hertsmere.gov.uk

Environmental / Technical Services: Mr Simon Payton, Head of Engineering, Civic Offices, Elstree Way, Borehamwood WD6 1WA
☎ 020 8207 2277; 020 8207 7441
📧 engineering.services@hertsmere.gov.uk

Environmental Health: Mr Chris Gascoine, Chief Environmental Health Officer, Civic Offices, Elstree Way, Borehamwood WD6 1WA
☎ 020 8207 7433; 020 8207 7441
📧 environmental.health@hertsmere.gov.uk

Environmental Health: Mr Glen Wooldrige, Director - Environment, Civic Office, Elstree Way, Borehamwood WD6 1WA
☎ 020 8207 2277 📧 environment@hertsmere.gov.uk

Estates, Property & Valuation: Mr Richard Stubbs, Asset Manager, Civic Office, Elstree Way, Borehamwood WD6 1WA
☎ 020 8207 2277; 020 8207 7441

Finance: Ms Sajida Bijle, Director - Resources, Civic Office, Elstree Way, Borehamwood WD6 1WA ☎ 020 8207 2277; 020 8207 7487
📧 sajida.bijle@hertsmere.gov.uk

Finance: Mr M Bunyon, Head of Finance, Revenues, Benefits & IS, Civic Office, Elstree Way, Borehamwood WD6 1WA
☎ 020 8207 2277

Treasury: Mr James Woodward, S151 Officer, Civic Office, Elstree Way, Borehamwood WD6 1WA ☎ 020 8207 2277
📧 james.woodward@hertsmere.gov.uk

Fleet Management: Mr Steve Burton, Head of Waste & Street Scene, Civic Offices, Elstree Way, Borehamwood WD6 1WA
☎ 020 8207 2277 📧 waste.management@hertsmere.gov.uk

Grounds Maintenance: Mr Steve Burton, Head of Waste & Street Scene, Civic Office, Elstree Way, Borehamwood WD6 1WA
☎ 020 8207 2277 📧 waste.management@hertsmere.gov.uk

Housing: Mr Glen Wooldrige, Director - Environment, Civic Office, Elstree Way, Borehamwood WD6 1WA ☎ 020 8207 2277
📧 environment@hertsmere.gov.uk

Legal: Ms Sajida Bijle, Director - Resources, Civic Office, Elstree Way, Borehamwood WD6 1WA ☎ 020 8207 2277; 020 8207 7487
📧 sajida.bijle@hertsmere.gov.uk

Licensing: Ms Sue Hardy, Principal Licensing Officer, Civic Office, Elstree Way, Borehamwood WD6 1WA ☎ 020 8207 7441; 020 8207 7436 📧 licensing.services@hertsmere.gov.uk

Licensing: Mr Glen Wooldrige, Director - Environment, Civic Office, Elstree Way, Borehamwood WD6 1WA ☎ 020 8207 2277
📧 environment@hertsmere.gov.uk

Member Services: Ms Sajida Bijle, Director - Resources, Civic Office, Elstree Way, Borehamwood WD6 1WA ☎ 020 8207 2277; 020 8207 7487 📧 sajida.bijle@hertsmere.gov.uk

Parking: Mrs Clare Fensome, Parking Operations Manager, Civic Office, Elstree Way, Borehamwood WD6 1WA ☎ 020 7208 2277
📧 cpz.department@hertsmere.gov.uk

Parking: Mr Glen Wooldrige, Director - Environment, Civic Office, Elstree Way, Borehamwood WD6 1WA ☎ 020 8207 2277
📧 environment@hertsmere.gov.uk

Partnerships: Ms Hilary Shade, Head of Partnerships & Community Engagement, Civic Office, Elstree Way, Borehamwood WD6 1WA ☎ 020 8207 7519; 020 8207 7499
📧 corporate.support@hertsmere.gov.uk

Personnel / HR: Ms Sajida Bijle, Director - Resources, Civic Office, Elstree Way, Borehamwood WD6 1WA ☎ 020 8207 2277; 020 8207 7487 📧 sajida.bijle@hertsmere.gov.uk

Personnel / HR: Ms Judith Fear, Head of HR & Customer Services, Civic Offices, Elstree Way, Borehamwood WD6 1WA
☎ 020 8207 7475; 020 8207 7550
📧 human.resources@hertsmere.gov.uk

Planning: Mr Glen Wooldrige, Director - Environment, Civic Office, Elstree Way, Borehamwood WD6 1WA ☎ 020 8207 2277
📧 environment@hertsmere.gov.uk

Procurement: Mr Andrew Harper, Procurement Manager, Civic Offices, Elstree Way, Borehamwood WD6 1WA ☎ 020 8207 2277; 01707 357371 📧 a.harper@welhat.gov.uk

Recycling & Waste Minimisation: Mr Steve Burton, Head of Waste & Street Scene, Civic Offices, Elstree Way, Borehamwood WD6 1WA ☎ 020 8207 2277
📧 waste.management@hertsmere.gov.uk

Recycling & Waste Minimisation: Mr Glen Wooldrige, Director - Environment, Civic Office, Elstree Way, Borehamwood WD6 1WA
☎ 020 8207 2277 📧 environment@hertsmere.gov.uk

Staff Training: Ms Judith Fear, Head of HR & Customer Services, Civic Offices, Elstree Way, Borehamwood WD6 1WA ☎ 020 8207 7475; 020 8207 7550 📧 human.resources@hertsmere.gov.uk

Street Scene: Mr Steve Burton, Head of Waste & Street Scene, Civic Office, Elstree Way, Borehamwood WD6 1WA ☎ 020 8207 2277 📧 waste.management@hertsmere.gov.uk

Street Scene: Mr Glen Wooldrige, Director - Environment, Civic Office, Elstree Way, Borehamwood WD6 1WA ☎ 020 8207 2277
📧 environment@hertsmere.gov.uk

Sustainable Communities: Mr Chris Gascoine, Chief Environmental Health Officer, Civic Offices, Elstree Way, Borehamwood WD6 1WA ☎ 020 8207 7433; 020 8207 7441
📧 environmental.health@hertsmere.gov.uk

Tourism: Mr Lee Gallagher, Customer Service Operation Manager, Civic Offices, Elstree Way, Borehamwood WD6 1WA ☎ 020 8207 2277; 020 8207 7424 📧 customer.services@hertsmere.gov.uk

Waste Collection and Disposal: Mr Steve Burton, Head of Waste & Street Scene, Civic Offices, Elstree Way, Borehamwood WD6 1WA ☎ 020 8207 2277 ✆ waste.management@hertsmere.gov.uk

Waste Collection and Disposal: Mr Glen Wooldrige, Director - Environment, Civic Office, Elstree Way, Borehamwood WD6 1WA ☎ 020 8207 2277 ✆ environment@hertsmere.gov.uk

Waste Management: Mr Steve Burton, Head of Waste & Street Scene, Civic Offices, Elstree Way, Borehamwood WD6 1WA ☎ 020 8207 2277 ✆ waste.management@hertsmere.gov.uk

COUNCILLORS

Mayor: Rutledge, Peter (CON - Bushey St James) cllr.pete.rutledge@hertsmere.gov.uk

Deputy Mayor: Goldstein, Charles (CON - Aldenham East) cllr.charles.goldstein@hertsmere.gov.uk

Leader of the Council: Bright, Morris (CON - Elstree) cllr.morris.bright@hertsmere.gov.uk

Deputy Leader of the Council: Graham, John (CON - Aldenham East) cllr.john.graham@hertsmere.gov.uk

Ash, Thomas (CON - Borehamwood Kenilworth) cllr.thomas.ash@hertsmere.gov.uk

Barker, Cynthia (CON - Potters Bar Furzefield) cllr.cynthia.barker@hertsmere.gov.uk

Batten, Brenda (CON - Bushey Heath) cllr.brenda.batten@hertsmere.gov.uk

Brown, Susan (CON - Borehamwood Brookmeadow) cllr.susan.brown@hertsmere.gov.uk

Burcombe, David (IND - Borehamwood Cowley Hill) Cllr.David.Burcombe@hertsmere.gov.uk

Butler, Richard (LAB - Borehamwood Cowley Hill) cllr.richard.butler@hertsmere.gov.uk

Choudhury, Pervez (CON - Bushey St James) cllr.pervez.choudhury@hertsmere.gov.uk

Clapper, Caroline (CON - Aldenham West) cllr.caroline.clapper@hertsmere.gov.uk

Cohen, Harvey (CON - Elstree) cllr.harvey.cohen@hertsmere.gov.uk

Davis, Lawrence (CON - Bushey North) cllr.lawrence.davis@hertsmere.gov.uk

Donne, John (CON - Potters Bar Parkfield) cllr.john.donne@hertsmere.gov.uk

Eni, Victor (CON - Borehamwood Kenilworth) Cllr.Victor.Eni@hertsmere.gov.uk

Heywood, Jean (CON - Potters Bar Oakmere) cllr.jean.heywood@hertsmere.gov.uk

Hodgson-Jones, Paul (CON - Potters Bar Parkfield) cllr.paul.hodgson-jones@hertsmere.gov.uk

Keates, Carey (CON - Bushey St James) cllr.carey.keates@hertsmere.gov.uk

Kelly, Charles (CON - Borehamwood Hillside) cllr.charles.kelly@hertsmere.gov.uk

Knell, Peter (CON - Potters Bar Furzefield) cllr.peter.knell@hertsmere.gov.uk

Lambert, David (CON - Aldenham West) cllr.david.lambert@hertsmere.gov.uk

Lyon, Ruth (CON - Potters Bar Oakmere) cllr.ruth.lyon@hertsmere.gov.uk

Merchant, Kashif (CON - Bushey North) cllr.kashif.merchant@hertsmere.gov.uk

Morris, Paul (CON - Bushey Heath) cllr.paul.morris@hertsmere.gov.uk

Plancey, Alan (CON - Borehamwood Brookmeadow) Cllr.Alan.Plancey@hertsmere.gov.uk

Quilty, Seamus (CON - Bushey Heath) cllr.seamus.quilty@hertsmere.gov.uk

Sachdev, Abhishek (CON - Potters Bar Parkfield) cllr.abhishek.sachdev@hertsmere.gov.uk

Sachdev, Meenal (CON - Borehamwood Hillside) Cllr.Meenal.Sachdev@hertsmere.gov.uk

Silver, Gary (CON - Borehamwood Brookmeadow) cllr.gary.silver@hertsmere.gov.uk

Silver, Linda (CON - Bushey Park) cllr.linda.silver@hertsmere.gov.uk

Spencer, Anthony (CON - Shenley) cllr.anthony.spencer@hertsmere.gov.uk

Swallow, Penny (CON - Potters Bar Oakmere) cllr.penny.swallow@hertsmere.gov.uk

Swerling, Anne (CON - Bushey Park) cllr.anne.swerling@hertsmere.gov.uk

Turner, Farida (CON - Borehamwood Hillside) cllr.fardia.turner@hertsmere.gov.uk

Vince, Michelle (LAB - Borehamwood Cowley Hill) cllr.michelle.vince@hertsmere.gov.uk

Wayne, Peter (CON - Shenley) cllr.peter.wayne@hertsmere.gov.uk

West, Jane (CON - Bushey North) jane.west@hertsmere.gov.uk

Worster, Martin (CON - Potters Bar Furzefield) cllr.martin.worster@hertsmere.gov.uk

POLITICAL COMPOSITION
CON: 36, LAB: 2, IND: 1

COMMITTEE CHAIRS

Audit: Mr Charles Goldstein

Licensing: Mr John Donne

Planning: Ms Linda Silver

High Peak   D

High Peak Borough Council, Town Hall, Market Place, Buxton SK17 6EL ☎ 0345 129 7777 🖥 www.highpeak.gov.uk

FACTS AND FIGURES
Parliamentary Constituencies: High Peak

HIGH PEAK

EU Constituencies: East Midlands
Election Frequency: Elections are of whole council

PRINCIPAL OFFICERS

Chief Executive: Mr Simon Baker, Chief Executive, Town Hall, Market Place, Buxton SK17 6EL ☎ 01538 395400
✆ simon.baker@staffsmoorlands.gov.uk; simon.baker@highpeak.gov.uk

Senior Management: Mr Dai Larner, Executive Director - Place, Town Hall, Market Place, Buxton SK17 6EL ☎ 01538 395400
✆ dai.larner@highpeak.gov.uk

Senior Management: Mr Andrew Stokes, Executive Director - Transformation, Town Hall, Market Place, Buxton SK17 6EL
☎ 01538 395622 ✆ andrew.stokes@staffsmoorlands.gov.uk

Senior Management: Mr Mark Trillo, Executive Director - People, Moorlands House, Stockwell Street, Leek ST13 6HQ
☎ 01538 395623 ✆ mark.trillo@staffsmoorlands.gov.uk

Architect, Building / Property Services: Mr Paul Hare, Assets Manager, Moorlands House, Stockwell Street, Leek ST13 6HQ
☎ 01538 395400 ✆ paul.hare@highpeak.gov.uk

Building Control: Mr Robert Weaver, Head of Regulatory Services, Moorlands House, Stockwell Street, Leek ST13 6HQ
☎ 01538 395400 ✆ robert.weaver@highpeak.gov.uk

PR / Communications: Miss Carolyn Sanders, Press & Promotions Officer, Moorlands House, Stockwell Street, Leek ST13 6HQ ☎ 01538 395400 ✆ carolyn.sanders@highpeak.gov.uk

Community Planning: Mr Mark Forrester, Democratic & Community Services Manager, Moorlands House, Stockwell Street, Leek ST13 6HQ ☎ 01538 395768
✆ mark.forrester@staffsmoorlands.gov.uk

Community Safety: Mr David Smith, Principal Officer - Community & Partnerships, Moorlands House, Stockwell Street, Leek ST13 6HQ ☎ 01538 395692
✆ david.smith@staffsmoorlands.gov.uk

Computer Management: Ms Mary Walker, Organisational Development & Transformation Manager, Town Hall, Market Place, Buxton SK17 6EL ☎ 01538 395400 ✆ mary.walker@highpeak.gov.uk

Customer Service: Mr Roger Burnett, Head of Customer Services, Town Hall, Market Place, Buxton SK17 6EL
☎ 01538 395400 ✆ roger.burnett@highpeak.gov.uk

Economic Development: Ms Pranali Parikh, Regeneration Manager, Moorlands House, Stockwell Street, Leek ST13 6HQ
☎ 01538 395400 ✆ pranali.parikh@highpeak.gov.uk

Electoral Registration: Mr Paul Rushworth, Legal & Elections Manager, Moorlands House, Stockwell Street, Leek ST13 6HQ
☎ 01538 395400 ✆ paul.rushworth@highpeak.gov.uk

Emergency Planning: Mr David Owen, Corporate Health & Safety Advisor, Moorlands House, Stockwell Street, Leek ST13 6HQ
☎ 01538 395595 ✆ david.owen@staffsmoorlands.gov.uk

Environmental Health: Mr Robert Weaver, Head of Regulatory Services, Town Hall, Market Place, Buxton SK17 6EL
☎ 01538 395400 ✆ robert.weaver@highpeak.gov.uk

Estates, Property & Valuation: Mr Paul Hare, Assets Manager, Moorlands House, Stockwell Street, Leek ST13 6HQ
☎ 01538 395400 ✆ paul.hare@highpeak.gov.uk

Facilities: Mr Paul Hare, Assets Manager, Moorlands House, Stockwell Street, Leek ST13 6HQ ☎ 01538 395400
✆ paul.hare@highpeak.gov.uk

Finance: Mr Andrew Stokes, Executive Director - Transformation, Moorlands House, Stockwell Street, Leek ST13 6HQ
☎ 01538 395622 ✆ andrew.stokes@staffsmoorlands.gov.uk

Fleet Management: Mr Martin Sollis, Operations Manager, Town Hall, Market Place, Buxton SK17 6EL ☎ 01538 395400
✆ martin.sollis@highpeak.gov.uk

Grounds Maintenance: Mr Keith Parker, Head of Operational Services, Moorlands House, Stockwell Street, Leek ST13 6HQ
☎ 01538 395400 ✆ keith.parker@staffsmoorlands.gov.uk

Health and Safety: Mr David Owen, Corporate Health & Safety Advisor, Moorlands House, Stockwell Street, Leek ST13 6HQ
☎ 01538 395595 ✆ david.owen@staffsmoorlands.gov.uk

Housing: Mr Dai Larner, Executive Director - Place, Moorlands House, Stockwell Street, Leek ST13 6HQ ☎ 01538 395400
✆ dai.larner@highpeak.gov.uk

Housing Maintenance: Mr Paul Hare, Assets Manager, Moorlands House, Stockwell Street, Leek ST13 6HQ
☎ 01538 395400 ✆ paul.hare@highpeak.gov.uk

Local Area Agreement: Mr Mark Forrester, Democratic & Community Services Manager, Moorlands House, Stockwell Street, Leek ST13 6HQ ☎ 01538 395768
✆ mark.forrester@staffsmoorlands.gov.uk

Legal: Mr Mark Trillo, Executive Director - People, Moorlands House, Stockwell Street, Leek ST13 6HQ ☎ 01538 395623
✆ mark.trillo@highpeak.gov.uk

Leisure and Cultural Services: Mr Terry Crawford, Visitor Services Manager, Pavilion Gardens, Buxton SK17 6BE
☎ 01298 28400 Ext 4224 ✆ terry.crawford@highpeak.gov.uk

Licensing: Mr Robert Weaver, Head of Regulatory Services, Moorlands House, Stockwell Street, Leek ST13 6HQ
☎ 01538 395400 ✆ robert.weaver@highpeak.gov.uk

Member Services: Mr Mark Forrester, Democratic & Community Services Manager, Moorlands House, Stockwell Street, Leek ST13 6HQ ☎ 01538 395768 ✆ mark.forrester@staffsmoorlands.gov.uk

Member Services: Mr Linden Vernon, Member Services Manager, Moorlands House, Stockwell Street, Leek ST13 6HQ
☎ 01538 395400 ✆ linden.vernon@highpeak.gov.uk

Partnerships: Mr Mark Forrester, Democratic & Community Services Manager, Moorlands House, Stockwell Street, Leek ST13 6HQ ☎ 01538 395768 ⌨ mark.forrester@staffsmoorlands.gov.uk

Personnel / HR: Ms Mary Walker, Organisational Development & Transformation Manager, Town Hall, Market Place, Buxton SK17 6EL ☎ 01538 395400 ⌨ mary.walker@highpeak.gov.uk

Planning: Mr Dai Larner, Executive Director - Place, Town Hall, Market Place, Buxton SK17 6EL ☎ 01538 395400 ⌨ dai.larner@highpeak.gov.uk

Procurement: Ms Claire Hazeldene, Finance & Procurement Manager, Moorlands House, Stockwell Street, Leek ST13 6HQ ☎ 01538 395400 ⌨ claire.hazeldene@highpeak.gov.uk

Recycling & Waste Minimisation: Mr Keith Parker, Head of Operational Services, Moorlands House, Stockwell Street, Leek ST13 6HQ ☎ 01538 395400 ⌨ keith.parker@staffsmoorlands.gov.uk

Regeneration: Ms Pranali Parikh, Regeneration Manager, Moorlands House, Stockwell Street, Leek ST13 6HQ ☎ 01538 395400 ⌨ pranali.parikh@highpeak.gov.uk

Staff Training: Ms Mary Walker, Organisational Development & Transformation Manager, Town Hall, Market Place, Buxton SK17 6EL ☎ 01538 395400 ⌨ mary.walker@highpeak.gov.uk

Street Scene: Mrs Joy Redfern, Street Scene Manager, Town Hall, Market Place, Buxton SK17 6EL ☎ 0845 129 7777 ⌨ joy.redfern@highpeak.gov.uk

Sustainable Communities: Mr Mark Forrester, Democratic & Community Services Manager, Moorlands House, Stockwell Street, Leek ST13 6HQ ☎ 01538 395768 ⌨ mark.forrester@staffsmoorlands.gov.uk

Tourism: Mr Terry Crawford, Visitor Services Manager, Pavilion Gardens, Buxton SK17 6BE ☎ 01298 28400 Ext 4224 ⌨ terry.crawford@highpeak.gov.uk

Town Centre: Mr Dai Larner, Executive Director - Place, Moorlands House, Stockwell Street, Leek ST13 6HQ ☎ 01538 395400 ⌨ dai.larner@highpeak.gov.uk

Total Place: Mr Mark Forrester, Democratic & Community Services Manager, Moorlands House, Stockwell Street, Leek ST13 6HQ ☎ 01538 395768 ⌨ mark.forrester@staffsmoorlands.gov.uk

Waste Collection and Disposal: Mr Keith Parker, Head of Operational Services, Town Hall, Market Place, Buxton SK17 6EL ☎ 01538 395400 ⌨ keith.parker@staffsmoorlands.gov.uk

Waste Management: Mr Keith Parker, Head of Operational Services, Town Hall, Market Place, Buxton SK17 6EL ☎ 01538 395400 ⌨ keith.parker@staffsmoorlands.gov.uk

COUNCILLORS

Mayor: Wharmby, Jean (CON - Dinting)
jean.wharmby@highpeak.gov.uk

Deputy Mayor: Stone, Matthew (LAB - Buxton Central)
matthew.stone@highpeak.gov.uk

Leader of the Council: Ashton, Tony (CON - Sett)
tony.ashton@highpeak.gov.uk

Deputy Leader of the Council: Kemp, Tony (CON - Corbar)
tony.kemp@highpeak.gov.uk

Group LeaderLomax, David (LD - Whaley Bridge)
david.lomax@highpeak.gov.uk

Atkins, Ray (LD - New Mills West)
raymond.atkins@highpeak.gov.uk

Barrow, Alan (LAB - New Mills East)
alan.barrow@highpeak.gov.uk

Boynton, Colin (CON - Cote Heath)
colin.boynton@highpeak.gov.uk

Claff, Godfrey (LAB - Howard Town)
godfrey.claff@highpeak.gov.uk

Douglas, Jamie (CON - Old Glossop)
jamie.douglas@highpeak.gov.uk

Dowson, Lance (LAB - New Mills West)
lance.dowson@highpeak.gov.uk

Easter, Peter (CON - Hayfield)
peter.easter@highpeak.gov.uk

Flower, Samantha (CON - Burbage)
samantha.flower@highpeak.gov.uk

Fox, Andrew (CON - Whaley Bridge)
andrew.fox@highpeak.gov.uk

Greenhalgh, Damien (LAB - Howard Town)
damien.greenalgh@highpeak.gov.uk

Grooby, Linda (CON - Cote Heath)
linda.grooby@highpeak.gov.uk

Haken, John (CON - Simmondley)
john.haken@highpeak.gov.uk

Hardy, Paul (CON - Old Glossop)
paul.hardy@highpeak.gov.uk

Helliwell, Sarah (CON - Hope Valley)
sarah.helliwell@highpeak.gov.uk

Howe, Caroline (CON - Blackbrook)
caroline.howe@highpeak.gov.uk

Huddlestone, Ian (LAB - New Mills East)
ian.huddlestone@highpeak.gov.uk

Jenner, Pat (LAB - Tintwistle)
pat.jenner@highpeak.gov.uk

Johnson, Clive (CON - Corbar)
clive.johnson@highpeak.gov.uk

Kappes, John (CON - Blackbrook)
john.kappes@highpeak.gov.uk

Kelly, Ed (LAB - Hadfield North)
edward.kelly@highpeak/gov.uk

Kerr, David (LAB - Stone Bench)
david.kerr@hhighpeak.gov.uk

Longos, Nick (LAB - Padfield)
nicholas.longos@highpeak.gov.uk

McCabe, Julie Ann (CON - Simmondley)
julie.mccabe@highpeak.gov.uk

HIGH PEAK

McKeown, Anthony (LAB - Gamesley)
anthony.mckeown@highpeak.gov.uk

McKeown, Robert (LAB - Hadfield South)
robert.mckeown@highpeak.gov.uk

Oakley, Graham (LAB - Whitfield)
graham.oakley@highpeak.gov.uk

Perkins, Jim (CON - Chapel East)
jim.perkins@highpeak.gov.uk

Pritchard, John (IND - Whaley Bridge)
john.pritchard@highpeak.gov.uk

Quinn, Rachael (LAB - Barms)
rachael.quinn@highpeak.gov.uk

Robins, Daren (CON - Limestone Peak)
daren.robins@highpeak.gov.uk

Siddall, Edward (LAB - Hadfield South)
edward.siddall@highpeak.gov.uk

Sizeland, Kath (CON - Chapel West)
kathleen.sizeland@highpeaks.gov.uk

Sloman, Fiona (LAB - Stone Bench)
fiona.sloman@highpeak.gov.uk

Thrane, Emily (CON - Temple)
emily.thrane@highpeak.gov.uk

Todd, Jean (LAB - Buxton Central)
jean.todd@highpeak.gov.uk

Walton, John (CON - Hope Valley)
john.walton@highpeak.gov.uk

Young, Stewart (CON - Chapel West)
stewart.young@highpeak.gov.uk

POLITICAL COMPOSITION
CON: 22, LAB: 17, LD: 2, Vacant: 1, IND: 1

COMMITTEE CHAIRS

Audit: Mr John Pritchard

Development Control: Mr David Lomax

Licensing: Mr Jim Perkins

Highland   S

Highland Council, Council Offices, Glenurquhart Road,
Inverness IV3 5NX
☎ 01349 886606 🖳 www.highland.gov.uk

FACTS AND FIGURES
Parliamentary Constituencies: Caithness, Sutherland and Easter
Ross, Inverness, Nairn, Badenoch and Strathspey, Ross, Skye and
Lochaber
EU Constituencies: Scotland
Election Frequency: Elections are of whole council

PRINCIPAL OFFICERS

Chief Executive: Mr Steve Barron, Chief Executive, Council
Offices, Glenurquhart Road, Inverness IV3 5NX ☎ 01463 702837;
01463 702879 🖰 steve.barron@highland.gov.uk

Assistant Chief Executive: Ms Michelle Morris, Depute Chief
Executive / Director - Corporate Development, Council Offices,
Glenurquhart Road, Inverness IV3 5NX ☎ 01463 702845; 01463
702879 🖰 michelle.morris@highland.gov.uk

Senior Management: Mr Bill Alexander, Director - Care &
Learning, Council Offices, Glenurquhart Road, Inverness IV3 5NX
☎ 01463 702860 🖰 bill.alexander@highland.gov.uk

Senior Management: Mr Stuart Black, Director - Development
& Infrastructure, Council Offices, Glenurquhart Road, Inverness IV3
5NX ☎ 01463 702251; 01463 702298 🖰 stuart.black@highland.gov.
uk

Senior Management: Mr William Gilfillan, Director - Community
Services, Council Offices, Glenurquhart Road, Inverness IV3 5NX
☎ 01463 252920 🖰 william.gilfillan@highland.gov.uk

Senior Management: Mr Derek Yule, Director - Finance, Council
Offices, Glenurquhart Road, Inverness IV3 5NX ☎ 01463 702301;
01463 702310 🖰 derek.yule@highland.gov.uk

Architect, Building / Property Services: Mr David Goldie, Head
of Housing & Building Maintenance, Council Offices, Glenurquhart
Road, Inverness IV3 5NX ☎ 01463 702864
🖰 david.goldie@highland.gov.uk

Building Control: Mr Glenn Campbell, Building Standards
Manager, Council Offices, Glenurquhart Road, Inverness IV3 5NX
☎ 01463 702561 🖰 glenn.campbell@highland.gov.uk

Children / Youth Services: Ms Sandra Campbell, Head of
Children's Services, Council Offices, Glenurquhart Road, Inverness
IV3 5NX ☎ 01463 702819 🖰 sandra.campbell@highland.gov.uk

Civil Registration: Ms Diane Minty, Chief Registrar, Highland
Archive & Registration Office, Bught Road, Inverness IV3 5SS
☎ 01463 256402 🖰 diane.minty@highland.gov.uk

PR / Communications: Ms Alison MacNeill, Acting Public
Relations Manager, Council Offices, Glenurquhart Road, Inverness
IV3 5NX ☎ 01463 702071; 01463 702025
🖰 alison.macneill@highland.gov.uk

Community Planning: Ms Carron McDiarmid, Head of Policy &
Reform, Council Offices, Glenurquhart Road, Inverness IV3 5NX
☎ 01349 886606 🖰 carron.mcdiarmid@highland.gov.uk

Community Safety: Ms Isabelle Baikie, Community Safety Officer,
Council Offices, Glenurquhart Road, Inverness IV3 5NX
☎ 01463 702246; 01463 702830 🖰 isabelle.baikie@highland.gov.uk

Computer Management: Mr John Grieve, Corporate ICT
Manager, Council Offices, Glenurquhart Road, Inverness IV3 5NX
☎ 01463 702741 🖰 john.grieve@highland.gov.uk

Contracts: Mr Finlay Macdonald, Head of Property, Council
Offices, Glenurquhart Road, Inverness IV3 5NX ☎ 01463 702211
🖰 finlay.macdonald@highland.gov.uk

Corporate Services: Ms Michelle Morris, Depute Chief Executive / Director - Corporate Development, Council Offices, Glenurquhart Road, Inverness IV3 5NX ☎ 01463 702845; 01463 702879 ◦ michelle.morris@highland.gov.uk

Customer Service: Ms Tina Page, Customer Services Manager, Council Offices, Glenurquhart Road, Inverness IV3 5NX ☎ 01463 702707 ◦ tina.page@highland.gov.uk

Economic Development: Mr Stuart Black, Director - Development & Infrastructure, Council Offices, Glenurquhart Road, Inverness IV3 5NX ☎ 01463 702251; 01463 702298 ◦ stuart.black@highland.gov.uk

Education: Mr Jim Steven, Head of Education, Council Offices, Glenurquhart Road, Inverness IV3 5NX ☎ 01463 702804 ◦ jim.steven@highland.gov.uk

E-Government: Ms Vicki Nairn, Head of Digital Transformation, Council Offices, Glenurquhart Road, Inverness IV3 5NX ☎ 01463 702848 ◦ vicki.nairn@highland.gov.uk

Electoral Registration: Mr David Sutherland, Elections Manager, Council Offices, Glenurquhart Road, Inverness IV3 5NX ☎ 01349 886606 ◦ david.sutherland.gov.uk

Emergency Planning: Mr Donald Norrie, Emergency Planning & Business Continuity Manager, Council Offices, Glenurquhart Road, Inverness IV3 5NX ☎ 01349 886606; 01463 243583 ◦ donald.norrie@highland.gov.uk

Energy Management: Mr Eddie Boyd, Principal Engineer, Council Offices, Glenurquhart Road, Inverness IV3 5NX ☎ 01463 255270 ◦ eddie.boyd@highland.gov.uk

Environmental Health: Dr Colin Clark, Head of Environmental & Regulatory Services, Council Offices, Glenurquhart Road, Inverness IV3 5NX ☎ 01463 702527 ◦ colin.clark@highland.gov.uk

Estates, Property & Valuation: Mr Allan Maguire, Head of Property Partnerships, Council Offices, Glenurquhart Road, Inverness IV3 5NX ☎ 01463 702528; 01463 702885 ◦ allan.maguire@highland.gov.uk

European Liaison: Mr Gordon Summers, Principal European Officer, Council Offices, Glenurquhart Road, Inverness IV3 5NX ☎ 01463 702508; 01463 702830 ◦ gordon.summers@highland.gov.uk

Events Manager: Mr Gerry Reynolds, Inverness Events Manager, Town House, Inverness IV2 4SF ☎ 01463 785006 ◦ gerry.reynolds@highlands.gov.uk

Finance: Mr Derek Yule, Director - Finance, Council Offices, Glenurquhart Road, Inverness IV3 5NX ☎ 01463 702301; 01463 702310 ◦ derek.yule@highland.gov.uk

Pensions: Mr Charlie McCallum, Payroll & Pensions Manager, Council Offices, Glenurquhart Road, Inverness IV3 5NX ☎ 01463 702000 ◦ charlie.mccallum@highland.gov.uk

Fleet Management: Mr Richard Evans, Head of Roads & Transport, Council Offices, Glenurquhart Road, Inverness IV3 5NX ☎ 01463 252922 ◦ richard.evans@highland.gov.uk

Grounds Maintenance: Mr Richard Evans, Head of Roads & Transport, Council Offices, Glenurquhart Road, Inverness IV3 5NX ☎ 01463 252922 ◦ richard.evans@highland.gov.uk

Health and Safety: Ms Gena Falconer, Occupational Health, Safety & Wellbeing Manager, Dochfour Drive, Inverness IV3 5EB ☎ 01463 703094; 01463 703090 ◦ gena.falconer@highland.gov.uk

Highways: Mr Richard Evans, Head of Roads & Transport, Council Offices, Glenurquhart Road, Inverness IV3 5NX ☎ 01463 252922 ◦ richard.evans@highland.gov.uk

Home Energy Conservation: Mr Eddie Boyd, Principal Engineer, Council Offices, Glenurquhart Road, Inverness IV3 5NX ☎ 01463 255270 ◦ eddie.boyd@highland.gov.uk

Housing: Mr David Goldie, Head of Housing & Building Maintenance, Council Offices, Glenurquhart Road, Inverness IV3 5NX ☎ 01463 702864 ◦ david.goldie@highland.gov.uk

Housing Maintenance: Mrs Caroline Campbell, Performance & Building Maintenance Manager, Council Offices, Glenurquhart Road, Inverness IV3 5NX ☎ 01463 702610 ◦ caroline.campbell@highland.gov.uk

Legal: Mr Stewart Fraser, Head of Corporate Governance, Council Offices, Glenurquhart Road, Inverness IV3 5NX ☎ 01463 702112 ◦ stewart.fraser@highland.gov.uk

Leisure and Cultural Services: Mr Ian Murray, Chief Executive - High Life Highland, 12/13 Ardross Street, Inverness IV3 5NS ☎ 01463 663824; 01463 663809 ◦ ian.murray@highland.gov.uk

Licensing: Mr Michael Elsey, Senior Licensing Officer, Town House, High Street, Inverness IV1 1JJ ☎ 01349 886606 ◦ michael.elsey@highland.gov.uk

Lottery Funding, Charity and Voluntary: Mrs Carron McDiarmid, Head of Policy & Reform, Council Offices, Glenurquhart Road, Inverness IV3 5NX ☎ 01463 702852 ◦ carron.mcdiarmid@highland.gov.uk

Member Services: Ms Julie MacLennan, Democratic Services Manager, Council Offices, Glenurquhart Road, Inverness IV3 5NX ☎ 01463 702118; 01463 702182 ◦ julie.maclennan@highland.gov.uk

Parking: Mr Richard Evans, Head of Roads & Transport, Council Offices, Glenurquhart Road, Inverness IV3 5NX ☎ 01463 252922 ◦ richard.evans@highland.gov.uk

Personnel / HR: Mr Steve Walsh, Head of People & Transformation, Council Offices, Glenurquhart Road, Inverness IV3 5NX ☎ 01349 886606 ◦ steve.walsh@highland.gov.uk

Planning: Mr Stuart Black, Director - Development & Infrastructure, Council Offices, Glenurquhart Road, Inverness IV3 5NX ☎ 01463 702251; 01463 702298 ◦ stuart.black@highland.gov.uk

HIGHLAND

Public Libraries: Mr Douglas Wilby, Head of Performance - High Life Highland, High Life Highland, 12 - 13 Ardross Street, Inverness IV3 5NS ☎ 01463 663800 🖰 douglas.wilby@highlifehighland.com

Recycling & Waste Minimisation: Dr Colin Clark, Head of Environmental & Regulatory Services, Council Offices, Glenurquhart Road, Inverness IV3 5NX ☎ 01463 702527 🖰 colin.clark@highland.gov.uk

Regeneration: Mr Andy McCann, Economy & Regeneration Manager, Council Offices, Glenurquhart Road, Inverness IV3 5NX ☎ 01463 702260 🖰 andy.mccann@highland.gov.uk

Road Safety: Mr Richard Evans, Head of Roads & Transport, Council Offices, Glenurquhart Road, Inverness IV3 5NX ☎ 01463 252922 🖰 richard.evans@highland.gov.uk

Social Services: Ms Sandra Campbell, Head of Children's Services, Council Offices, Glenurquhart Road, Inverness IV3 5NX ☎ 01463 702819 🖰 sandra.campbell@highland.gov.uk

Social Services (Children): Ms Sandra Campbell, Head of Children's Services, Council Offices, Glenurquhart Road, Inverness IV3 5NX ☎ 01463 702819 🖰 sandra.campbell@highland.gov.uk

Staff Training: Mr Murdo MacDonald, HR Manager, Council Offices, Glenurquhart Road, Inverness IV3 5NX ☎ 01349 886606 🖰 murdo.macdonald@highland.gov.uk

Sustainable Development: Ms Carron McDiarmid, Head of Policy & Reform, Council Offices, Glenurquhart Road, Inverness IV3 5NX ☎ 01349 886606 🖰 carron.mcdiarmid@highland.gov.uk

Tourism: Mr Colin Simpson, Principal Tourism & Film Co-ordinator, Council Offices, Glenurquhart Road, Inverness IV3 5NX ☎ 01463 702957 🖰 colin.simpson@highland.gov.uk

Town Centre: Mr David Haas, City Manager, Town House, High Street, Inverness IV1 1JJ ☎ 01463 724201 🖰 david.haas@highland.gov.uk

Traffic Management: Mr Richard Evans, Head of Roads & Transport, Council Offices, Glenurquhart Road, Inverness IV3 5NX ☎ 01463 252922 🖰 richard.evans@highland.gov.uk

Waste Collection and Disposal: Dr Colin Clark, Head of Environmental & Regulatory Services, Council Offices, Glenurquhart Road, Inverness IV3 5NX ☎ 01463 702527 🖰 colin.clark@highland.gov.uk

Waste Management: Dr Colin Clark, Head of Environmental & Regulatory Services, Council Offices, Glenurquhart Road, Inverness IV3 5NX ☎ 01463 702527 🖰 colin.clark@highland.gov.uk

COUNCILLORS

Convener: McCallum, Isobel (IND - Black Isle)
isobel.mccallum.cllr@highland.gov.uk

Leader of the Council: Davidson, Margaret (IND - Aird & Loch Ness)
margaret.davidson.cllr@highland.gov.uk

Deputy Leader of the Council: Rhind, Alasdair (IND - Tain & Easter Ross)
alasdair.rhind.cllr@highland.gov.uk

Group Leader Smith, Maxine (SNP - Cromarty Firth)
maxine.smith.cllr@highland.gov.uk

Alston, David (LD - Black Isle)
david.alston.cllr@highland.gov.uk

Balfour, Roddy (IND - Culloden & Ardersier)
roderick.balfour.cllr@highland.gov.uk

Barclay, Jennifer (IND - Black Isle)
jennifer.barclay.cllr@highland.gov.uk

Baxter, Andrew (IND - Fort William & Ardnamurchan)
andrew.baxter.cllr@highland.gov.uk

Bremner, David (IND - Landward Caithness)
david.bremner.cllr@highland.gov.uk

Brown, Ian (SNP - Inverness Millburn)
ian.brown.cllr@highland.gov.uk

Caddick, Carolyn (LD - Inverness South)
carolyn.caddick.cllr@highland.gov.uk

Campbell, Janet (IND - Inverness Central)
janet.campbell.cllr@highland.gov.uk

Campbell, Isabelle (IND - Wester Ross, Strathpeffer & Lochalsh)
isabelle.campbell.cllr@highland.gov.uk

Carmichael, Helen (IND - Aird & Loch Ness)
helen.carmichael.cllr@highland.gov.uk

Christie, Alasdair (LD - Inverness Ness-side)
alasdair.christie.cllr@highland.gov.uk

Clark, Bill (SNP - Caol & Mallaig)
bill.clark.cllr@highland.gov.uk

Cockburn, Ian (SNP - Wester Ross, Strathpeffer & Lochalsh)
ian.cockburn.cllr@highland.gov.uk

Coghill, Gillian (IND - Landward Caithness)
gillian.coghill.cllr@highland.gov.uk

Crawford, Jim (IND - Inverness South)
jim.crawford.cllr@highland.gov.uk

Davis, Jean (LD - Aird & Loch Ness)
jean.davis@highland.gov.uk

Donald, Norrie (IND - Inverness Ness-side)
norrie.donald.cllr@highland.gov.uk

Douglas, Jaci (IND - Badenoch & Strathspey)
jaci.douglas.cllr@highland.gov.uk

Duffy, Allan (SNP - Inverness West)
allan.duffy.cllr@highland.gov.uk

Fallows, David (SNP - Badenoch & Strathspey)
bill.fallows.cllr@highland.gov.uk

Farlow, George (SNP - North, West & Central Sutherland)
george.farlow.cllr@highland.gov.uk

Fernie, Bill (IND - Wick)
bill.fernie.cllr@highland.gov.uk

Finlayson, Mike (IND - Cromarty Firth)
michael.finlayson.cllr@highland.gov.uk

Fraser, Hamish (IND - Eilean a' Cheò)
hamish.fraser.cllr@highland.gov.uk

Fraser, Laurie (IND - Nairn)
laurie.fraser.cllr@highland.gov.uk

Fraser, Craig (SNP - Black Isle)
craig.fraser.cllr@highland.gov.uk

Fuller, Stephen (SNP - Nairn)
stephen.fuller.cllr@highland.gov.uk

Gordon, John (IND - Eilean a' Cheò)
john.gordon.cllr@highland.gov.uk

Gormley, Bren (SNP - Fort William & Ardnamurchan)
bren.gormley.cllr@highland.gov.uk

Gowans, Ken (SNP - Inverness South)
ken.gowans.cllr@highland.gov.uk

Graham, Alex (LD - Inverness West)
alex.graham.cllr@highland.gov.uk

Gray, Jimmy (LAB - Inverness Millburn)
jimmy.gray.cllr@highland.gov.uk

Green, Michael (IND - Nairn)
michael.green.cllr@highland.gov.uk

Greene, Richard (IND - Wester Ross, Strathpeffer & Lochalsh)
richard.greene.cllr@highland.gov.uk

Henderson, Allan (IND - Caol & Mallaig)
allan.henderson.cllr@highland.gov.uk

Kerr, Donnie (IND - Inverness Central)
donnie.kerr.cllr@highland.gov.uk

Laird, Richard (SNP - Inverness Central)
richard.laird.cllr@highland.gov.uk

Lobban, Bill (SNP - Badenoch & Strathspey)
bill.loban.cllr@highland.gov.uk

MacDonald, Neil (LAB - Wick)
neil.macdonald.cllr@highland.gov.uk

MacDonald, Liz (SNP - Nairn)
liz.macdonald.cllr@highland.gov.uk

Mackay, Donnie (IND - Thurso)
donnie.mackay.cllr@highland.gov.uk

MacKay, Deirdre (LAB - East Sutherland & Edderton)
deirdre.mackay.cllr@highland.gov.uk

MacKay, Willie (IND - Landward Caithness)
willie.mackay.cllr@highland.gov.uk

MacKenzie, Graham (SNP - Dingwall & Seaforth)
graham.mackenzie.cllr@highland.gov.uk

MacKinnon, Alister (IND - Dingwall & Seaforth)
alister.mackinnon.cllr@highland.gov.uk

MacLean, Angela (LD - Dingwall & Seaforth)
angela.maclean.cllr@highland.gov.uk

MacLennan, Thomas (IND - Fort William & Ardnamurchan)
thomas.maclennan.cllr@highland.gov.uk

MacLeod, Kenneth (LD - Inverness Millburn)
kenneth.macleod.cllr@highland.gov.uk

McAlister, Bet (LAB - Inverness Central)
elizabeth.mcallister.cllr@highland.gov.uk

McGillivray, Jim (IND - East Sutherland & Edderton)
jim.mcgillivray.cllr@highland.gov.uk

Millar, Drew (LD - Eilean a' Cheò)
drew.millar.cllr@highland.gov.uk

Morrison, Hugh (IND - North, West & Central Sutherland)
hugh.morrison.cllr@highland.gov.uk

Munro, Linda (INDNA - North, West & Central Sutherland)
linda.munro.cllr@highland.gov.uk

Murphy, Brian (LAB - Fort William & Ardnamurchan)
brian.murphy.cllr@highland.gov.uk

Parr, Fraser (LAB - Inverness Ness-side)
fraser.parr.cllr@highland.gov.uk

Paterson, Margaret (IND - Dingwall & Seaforth)
margaret.paterson.cllr@highland.gov.uk

Phillips, Graham (SNP - East Sutherland & Edderton)
graham.phillips.cllr@highland.gov.uk

Prag, Thomas (LD - Inverness South)
thomas.prag.cllr@highland.gov.uk

Rattray, Martin (LD - Cromarty Firth)
martin.rattray.cllr@highland.gov.uk

Reiss, Matthew (IND - Landward Caithness)
matthew.reiss.cllr@highland.gov.uk

Renwick, Ian (SNP - Eilean a' Cheò)
ian.renwick.cllr@highland.gov.uk

Rimell, Gregor (SNP - Badenoch & Strathspey)
gregor.rimmel.cllr@highland.gov.uk

Robertson, Fiona (IND - Tain & Easter Ross)
fiona.robertson.cllr@highland.gov.uk

Rosie, John (IND - Thurso)
john.rosie2.cllr@highland.gov.uk

Ross, Graham (IND - Inverness West)
graham.ross.cllr@highland.gov.uk

Ross, Gail (SNP - Wick)
gail.ross.cllr@highland.gov.uk

Saxon, Roger (LAB - Thurso)
roger.saxon.cllr@highland.gov.uk

Sinclair, Glynis (SNP - Culloden & Ardersier)
glynis.sinclair.cllr@highland.gov.uk

Sinclair, Audrey (IND - Wester Ross, Strathpeffer & Lochalsh)
audrey.sinclair.cllr@highland.gov.uk

Slater, Jean (SNP - Inverness Ness-side)
jean.slater.cllr@highland.gov.uk

Stephen, Kate (LD - Culloden & Ardersier)
kate.stephen.cllr@highland.gov.uk

Stone, Jamie (LD - Tain & Easter Ross)
jamie.stone.cllr@highland.gov.uk

Thompson, Ben (IND - Caol & Mallaig)
ben.thompson.cllr@highland.gov.uk

Wilson, Carolyn (IND - Cromarty Firth)
carolyn.wilson.cllr@highland.gov.uk

Wood, Hamish (LD - Aird & Loch Ness)
hamish.wood.cllr@highland.gov.uk

POLITICAL COMPOSITION
IND: 37, SNP: 21, LD: 13, LAB: 7, INDNA: 1

COMMITTEE CHAIRS

Audit: Mr Richard Laird

Communities & Partnerships: Mr Hamish Fraser

Education, Children & Adult Services: Mr Drew Millar

HIGHLAND

Licensing: Mr Ian Cockburn

Planning, Development & Infrastructure: Dr Audrey Sinclair

Hillingdon   L

Hillingdon London Borough Council, Civic Centre, High Street, Uxbridge UB8 1UW

☎ 01895 250111 ✆ contact@hillingdon.gov.uk ▭ www.hillingdon.gov.uk

FACTS AND FIGURES
Parliamentary Constituencies: Hayes and Harlington, Ruislip-Northwood, Uxbridge and Ruislip South
EU Constituencies: London
Election Frequency: Elections are of whole council

PRINCIPAL OFFICERS

Chief Executive: Ms Fran Beasley, Chief Executive & Corporate Director - Administration, Civic Centre, High Street, Uxbridge UB8 1UW ☎ 01895 250569; 01895 277047 ✆ fbeasley@hillingdon.gov.uk

Deputy Chief Executive: Ms Jean Palmer, Deputy Chief Executive & Director - Residents' Services, Civic Centre, Uxbridge UB8 1UW ☎ 01895 250622; 01895 250223 ✆ jean.palmer@hillingdon.gov.uk

Senior Management: Mr Steve Hajioff, Director - Public Health, Civic Centre, High Street, Uxbridge UB8 1UW ☎ 01895 277574 ✆ shajioff@hillingdon.gov.uk

Senior Management: Mr Paul Whaymand, Director - Finance, Civic Centre, High Street, Uxbridge UB8 1UW ☎ 01895 250725; 01895 277047 ✆ pwhaymand@hillingdon.gov.uk

Senior Management: Mr Tony Zaman, Director - Adult & Young People's Services, Civic Centre, High Street, Uxbridge UB8 1UW ☎ 01895 250506 ✆ tzaman@hillingdon.gov.uk

Access Officer / Social Services (Disability): Ms Clare Harris, SEN Category Lead, Civic Centre, High Street, Uxbridge UB8 1UW ☎ 01895 277051 ✆ charris@hillingdon.gov.uk

Architect, Building / Property Services: Mr John Gill, Estate Service Manager, Civic Centre, High Street, Uxbridge UB8 1UW ☎ 01895 277036 ✆ jgill3@hillingdon.gov.uk

Building Control: Mr James Rodger, Head of Planning & Enforcement, Civic Centre, High Street, Uxbridge UB8 1UW ☎ 01895 220049 ✆ jrodger2@hillingdon.gov.uk

Catering Services: Ms Gwen Terry, Contract Manager of FM Soft Services, Civic Centre, High Street, Uxbridge UB8 1UW ☎ 01895 250221 ✆ gterry@hillingdon.gov.uk

Children / Youth Services: Mr Tom Murphy, Head - Early Intervention & Prevention Services, Civic Centre, High Street, Uxbridge UB8 1UW ☎ 01895 558273; 01895 250493 ✆ tmurphy@hillingdon.gov.uk

Civil Registration: Mr Mike Liddiard, Electoral & Registration Services Manager, Civic Centre, High Street, Uxbridge UB8 1UW ☎ 01895 250962; 01805 250812 ✆ mliddiard@hillingdon.gov.uk

PR / Communications: Mr Mark Purvis, Deputy Director - Digital Strategy & Communication, Civic Centre, High Street, Uxbridge UB8 1UW ☎ 01895 558179 ✆ mpurvis@hillingdon.gov.uk

Community Safety: Mr Mark Wolski, Community Safety Team Service Manager, Civic Centre, High Street, Uxbridge UB8 1UW ☎ 01895 277532 ✆ mwolski@hillingdon.gov.uk

Computer Management: Ms Shirley Clipp, ICT Service Manager, Civic Centre, High Street, Uxbridge UB8 1UW ☎ 01895 250759 ✆ sclipp@hillingdon.gov.uk

Consumer Protection and Trading Standards: Miss Sue Pollitt, Trading Standards Manager, Civic Centre, Uxbridge UB8 1UW ☎ 01895 277425; 01895 277443 ✆ spollitt@hillingdon.gov.uk

Contracts: Mr Perry Scott, Deputy Director - Development, Assets & Procurement, Civic Centre, High Street, Uxbridge UB8 1UW ☎ 01895 277240 ✆ pscott@hillingdon.gov.uk

Customer Service: Ms Louise Forster, Access Channel Manager, Civic Centre, High Street, Uxbridge UB8 1UW ☎ 01895 556021; 01895 250869 ✆ lforster@hillingdon.gov.uk

Economic Development: Ms Inga Spencer, Senior Economic Development Officer, Civic Centre, High Street, Uxbridge UB8 1UW ☎ 01895 250580; 01895 250823 ✆ ispencer@hillingdon.gov.uk

Education: Mr Dan Kennedy, Head of Business Performance, Policy & Standards, Education, Housing & Public Health, Civic Centre, High Street, Uxbridge UB8 1UW ☎ 01895 250495 ✆ dkennedy@hillingdon.gov.uk

Electoral Registration: Mr Mike Liddiard, Electoral & Registration Services Manager, Civic Centre, High Street, Uxbridge UB8 1UW ☎ 01895 250962; 01805 250812 ✆ mliddiard@hillingdon.gov.uk

Emergency Planning: Ms Jill Covill, Head - Business & Technical Support, Civic Centre, High Street, Uxbridge UB8 1UW ☎ 01895 277418 ✆ jcovill@hillingdon.gov.uk

Energy Management: Mr Richard Coomber, Energy Officer, Civic Centre, High Street, Uxbridge UB8 1UW ☎ 01895 556478 ✆ rcoomber@hillingdon.gov.uk

Estates, Property & Valuation: Mr John Gill, Estate Service Manager, Civic Centre, High Street, Uxbridge UB8 1UW ☎ 01895 277036 ✆ jgill3@hillingdon.gov.uk

Events Manager: Ms Lyn Summers, Project & Events Officer, Civic Centre, High Street, Uxbridge UB8 1UW ☎ 01895 556640 ✆ lsummers@hillingdon.gov.uk

Facilities: Mr Lee Rooke, Soft Services Manager, Civic Centre, High Street, Uxbridge UB8 1UW ☎ 01895 250062 ✆ lrooke@hillingdon.gov.uk

Finance: Mr Paul Whaymand, Director - Finance, Civic Centre, High Street, Uxbridge UB8 1UW ☎ 01895 250725; 01895 277047 ✆ pwhaymand@hillingdon.gov.uk

Pensions: Mr Ken Chisholm, Corporate Pensions Manager, Civic Centre, High Street, Uxbridge UB8 1UW ☎ 01895 250847 ⌂ ken.chisholm@hillingdon.gov.uk

Fleet Management: Mr Colin Russell, Waste Division Manager, Harlington Road Depot, Harlington Road, Hillingdon UB8 3EY ☎ 01895 556217; 01895 2500103 ⌂ crussell@hillingdon.gov.uk

Grounds Maintenance: Mr Paul Richards, Head of Green Spaces, Sport & Culture, Civic Centre, High Street, Uxbridge UB8 1UW ☎ 01895 250814 ⌂ prichards@hillingdon.gov.uk

Health and Safety: Ms Christine Barker, Corporate Health & Safety Manager, Civic Centre, High Street, Uxbridge UB8 1UW ☎ 01895 277377; 01895 250217 ⌂ cbarker@hillingdon.gov.uk

Highways: Mr Chris Tasker, Team Manager, Civic Centre, High Street, Uxbridge UB8 1UW ☎ 01895 250564; 01895 277086 ⌂ ctasker@hillingdon.gov.uk

Home Energy Conservation: Mr Richard Coomber, Energy Officer, Civic Centre, High Street, Uxbridge UB8 1UW ☎ 01895 556478 ⌂ rcoomber@hillingdon.gov.uk

Housing: Mr Nigel Dicker, Deputy Director - Residents' Services, Civic Centre, High Street, Uxbridge UB8 1UW ☎ 01895 250566 ⌂ ndicker@hillingdon.gov.uk

Housing Maintenance: Mr Graham Ross, Maintenance Contracts Officer, Civic Centre, High Street, Uxbridge UB8 1UW ☎ 01895 556642 ⌂ gross@hillingdon.gov.uk

Legal: Mr Rajesh Alagh, Borough Solicitor, Civic Centre, Uxbridge UB8 1UW ☎ 01895 250617; 01895 277373 ⌂ ralagh@hillingdon.gov.uk

Leisure and Cultural Services: Mr Nigel Dicker, Deputy Director - Residents' Services, Civic Centre, High Street, Uxbridge UB8 1UW ☎ 01895 250566 ⌂ ndicker@hillingdon.gov.uk

Leisure and Cultural Services: Mr James Rodger, Head of Planning & Enforcement, Civic Centre, High Street, Uxbridge UB8 1UW ☎ 01895 220049 ⌂ jrodger2@hillingdon.gov.uk

Licensing: Ms Stephanie Waterford, Licensing Services Manager, Civic Centre, High Street, Uxbridge UB8 1UW ☎ 01895 277232; 01895 250223 ⌂ swaterford@hillingdon.gov.uk

Lifelong Learning: Ms Gill McLean, Corporate Learning & Development Manager, Civic Centre, High Street, Uxbridge UB8 1UW ☎ 01895 277338 ⌂ gmclean@hillingdon.gov.uk

Lighting: Mr Tim Edwards, Public Lighting Manager, Civic Centre, High Street, Uxbridge UB8 1UW ☎ 01895 277511; 01895 277508 ⌂ tedwards@hillingdon.gov.uk

Lottery Funding, Charity and Voluntary: Mr Nigel Cramb, Partnerships, Business & Community Engagement Manager, Civic Centre, Uxbridge UB8 1UW ☎ 01895 250394; 01895 250823 ⌂ ncramb@hillingdon.gov.uk

Member Services: Mr Lloyd White, Head of Democratic Services, Civic Centre, High Street, Uxbridge UB8 1UW ☎ 01895 250636; 01895 277373 ⌂ lwhite@hillingdon.gov.uk

Parking: Mr Roy Clark, Parking Services Manager, Civic Centre, High Street, Uxbridge UB8 1UW ☎ 01895 277776 ⌂ rclark@hillingdon.gov.uk

Partnerships: Mr Kevin Byrne, Head of Policy & Partnerships, Civic Centre, High Street, Uxbridge UB8 1UW ☎ 01895 556063 ⌂ kbyrne2@hillingdon.gov.uk

Personnel / HR: Ms Pauline Moore, Head of Business Improvement & HR, Civic Centre, High Street, Uxbridge UB8 1UW ☎ 01895 556719 ⌂ pmoore2@hillingdon.gov.uk

Planning: Mr James Rodger, Head of Planning & Enforcement, Civic Centre, High Street, Uxbridge UB8 1UW ☎ 01895 220049 ⌂ jrodger2@hillingdon.gov.uk

Procurement: Mr Perry Scott, Deputy Director - Development, Assets & Procurement, Civic Centre, High Street, Uxbridge UB8 1UW ☎ 01895 277240 ⌂ pscott@hillingdon.gov.uk

Public Libraries: Mr Nigel Dicker, Deputy Director - Residents' Services, Civic Centre, High Street, Uxbridge UB8 1UW ☎ 01895 250566 ⌂ ndicker@hillingdon.gov.uk

Recycling & Waste Minimisation: Mr Colin Russell, Waste Division Manager, Harlington Road Depot, Harlington Road, Hillingdon UB8 3EY ☎ 01895 556217; 01895 2500103 ⌂ crussell@hillingdon.gov.uk

Road Safety: Mrs Mhairi Mansi, Road Safety & School Travel Manager, Civic Centre, High Street, Uxbridge UB8 1UW ☎ 01895 250484; 01895 277208 ⌂ mstephens@hillingdon.gov.uk

Social Services: Mr Tony Zaman, Director - Adult & Young People's Services, Civic Centre, High Street, Uxbridge UB8 1UW ☎ 01895 250506 ⌂ tzaman@hillingdon.gov.uk

Social Services (Adult): Mr Tony Zaman, Director - Adult & Young People's Services, Civic Centre, High Street, Uxbridge UB8 1UW ☎ 01895 250506 ⌂ tzaman@hillingdon.gov.uk

Social Services (Children): Ms Lynne Adams, Service Manager - Children's Resources, Civic Centre, High Street, Uxbridge UB8 1UW ☎ 01895 277867 ⌂ ladams@hillingdon.gov.uk

Public Health: Mr Steve Hajioff, Director - Public Health, Civic Centre, High Street, Uxbridge UB8 1UW ☎ 01895 277574 ⌂ shajioff@hillingdon.gov.uk

Staff Training: Ms Gill McLean, Corporate Learning & Development Manager, Civic Centre, High Street, Uxbridge UB8 1UW ☎ 01895 277338 ⌂ gmclean@hillingdon.gov.uk

Sustainable Communities: Mr Kevin Byrne, Head of Policy & Partnerships, Civic Centre, High Street, Uxbridge UB8 1UW ☎ 01895 556063 ⌂ kbyrne2@hillingdon.gov.uk

HILLINGDON

Town Centre: Mr David Knowles, Transport & Projects Senior Manager, Civic Centre, High Street, Uxbridge UB8 1UW ☎ 01895 277598 ◌ dknowles@hillingdon.gov.uk

Traffic Management: Mr Colin Rider, Highways Inspector, Civic Centre, High Street, Uxbridge UB8 1UW ☎ 01895 556133 ◌ crider@hillingdon.gov.uk

Transport: Mr Colin Russell, Waste Division Manager, Harlington Road Depot, Harlington Road, Hillingdon UB8 3EY ☎ 01895 556217; 01895 2500103 ◌ crussell@hillingdon.gov.uk

Total Place: Mr Kevin Byrne, Head of Policy & Partnerships, Civic Centre, High Street, Uxbridge UB8 1UW ☎ 01895 556063 ◌ kbyrne2@hillingdon.gov.uk

Waste Collection and Disposal: Mr Colin Russell, Waste Division Manager, Harlington Road Depot, Harlington Road, Hillingdon UB8 3EY ☎ 01895 556217; 01895 2500103 ◌ crussell@hillingdon.gov.uk

Waste Management: Mr Colin Russell, Waste Division Manager, Harlington Road Depot, Harlington Road, Hillingdon UB8 3EY ☎ 01895 556217; 01895 2500103 ◌ crussell@hillingdon.gov.uk

Children's Play Areas: Mr Paul Richards, Head of Green Spaces, Sport & Culture, Civic Centre, High Street, Uxbridge UB8 1UW ☎ 01895 250814 ◌ prichards@hillingdon.gov.uk

COUNCILLORS

Mayor: Hensley, John (CON - Ickenham) jhensley@hillingdon.gov.uk

Deputy Mayor: Melvin, Carol (CON - Northwood) cmelvin@hillingdon.gov.uk

Leader of the Council: Puddifoot, Ray (CON - Ickenham) leader@hillingdon.gov.uk

Deputy Leader of the Council: Simmonds, David (CON - Ickenham) dsimmonds@hillingdon.gov.uk

Group Leader: Khursheed, Mo (LAB - Botwell) mkhursheed@hillingdon.gov.uk

Ahmad-Wallana, Shehryar (CON - Yiewsley) sahmed-wallana@hillingdon.gov.uk

Allen, Lynne (LAB - Townfield) lallen@hillingdon.gov.uk

Barnes, Teji (CON - Cavendish) tbarnes@hillingdon.gov.uk

Bianco, Jonathan (CON - Northwood Hills) jbianco@hillingdon.gov.uk

Birah, Mohinder (LAB - Yeading) mbirah@hillingdon.gov.uk

Bridges, Wayne (CON - Hillingdon East) wbridges@hillingdon.gov.uk

Burles, Tony (LAB - Uxbridge South) anthonyburles@hotmail.co.uk

Burrows, Keith (CON - Uxbridge South) kburrows@hillingdon.gov.uk

Chamdal, Roy (CON - Brunel) rchamdal@hillingdon.gov.uk

Chapman, Alan (CON - Hillingdon East) achapman@hillingdon.gov.uk

Cooper, George (CON - Uxbridge North) gcooper@hillingdon.gov.uk

Cooper, Judith (CON - Uxbridge South) jcooper@hillingdon.gov.uk

Corthorne, Philip (CON - West Ruislip) pcorthorne@hillingdon.gov.uk

Crowe, Brian (CON - West Ruislip) bcrowe@hillingdon.gov.uk

Curling, Peter (LAB - Townfield) pcurling@hillingdon.gov.uk

Dann, Catherine (CON - Eastcote & East Ruislip) cdann@hillingdon.gov.uk

Davis, Peter (CON - Yiewsley) pdavis@hillingdon.gov.uk

Denys, Nick (CON - Eastcote & East Ruislip) ndenys@hillingdon.gov.uk

Dheer, Kanwal (LAB - Barnhill) kdheer@hillingdon.gov.uk

Dhillon, Jazz (LAB - Pinkwell) jdhillon@hillingdon.gov.uk

Dhot, Jas (LAB - Barnhill) jdhot@hillingdon.gov.uk

Duducu, Jem (CON - South Ruislip) jduducu@hillingdon.gov.uk

Duncan, Janet (LAB - West Drayton) jduncan2@hillingdon.gov.uk

East, Beulah (LAB - Charville) beulaheast@hillingdon.gov.uk

Edwards, Ian (CON - Yiewsley) iedwards@hillingdon.gov.uk

Eginton, Tony (LAB - Barnhill) teginton@hillingdon.gov.uk

Flynn, Duncan (CON - Northwood Hills) dflynn@hillingdon.gov.uk

Fyfe, Neil (CON - Charville) nfyfe@hillingdon.gov.uk

Gardner, Janet (LAB - Botwell) jgardner@hillingdon.gov.uk

Garg, Narinder (LAB - Yeading) ngarg@hillingdon.gov.uk

Gilham, Dominic (CON - West Drayton) dgilham@hillingdon.gov.uk

Graham, Raymond (CON - Uxbridge North) rgraham@hillingdon.gov.uk

Haggar, Becky (CON - Eastcote & East Ruislip) bhaggar@hillingdon.gov.uk

Higgins, Henry (CON - Harefield) hhiggins@hillingdon.gov.uk

Jackson, Pat (CON - Hillingdon East) pjackson@hillingdon.gov.uk

Jarjussey, Phoday (LAB - Botwell)
pjarjussey@hillingdon.gov.uk

Kauffman, Allan (CON - South Ruislip)
akauffman2@hillingdon.gov.uk

Kelly, Judy (CON - South Ruislip)
jkelly@hillingdon.gov.uk

Khatra, Manjit (LAB - Heathrow Villages)
mkhatra@hillingdon.gov.uk

Lakhmana, Kuldeep (LAB - Pinkwell)
klakhmana@hillingdon.gov.uk

Lavery, Edward (CON - Cavendish)
elavery@hillingdon.gov.uk

Lewis, Richard (CON - Northwood)
rlewis@hillingdon.gov.uk

Markham, Michael (CON - Manor)
mmarkham@hillingdon.gov.uk

Mills, Douglas (CON - Manor)
dmills@hillingdon.gov.uk

Mills, Richard (CON - Brunel)
rmills2@hillingdon.gov.uk

Money, Peter (LAB - Heathrow Villages)
pmoney@hillingdon.gov.uk

Morgan, John (CON - Northwood Hills)
jmorgan2@hillingdon.gov.uk

Morse, John (LAB - Pinkwell)
jmorse2@hillingdon.gov.uk

Nelson, June (LAB - Heathrow Villages)
jnelson@hillingdon.gov.uk

O'Brien, Susan (CON - Manor)
so'brien@hillingdon.gov.uk

Oswell, John (LAB - Charville)
joswell@hillingdon.gov.uk

Palmer, Jane (CON - Harefield)
jpalmer3@hillingdon.gov.uk

Riley, John (CON - West Ruislip)
jriley@hillingdon.gov.uk

Sansarpuri, Robin (LAB - Townfield)
rsansarpuri@hillingdon.gov.uk

Seaman-Digby, Scott (CON - Northwood)
scott@seaman-digby.com

Singh, Jagjit (LAB - Yeading)
jsingh2@hillingdon.gov.uk

Stead, Brian (CON - Brunel)
bstead@hillingdon.gov.uk

Sweeting, Jan (LAB - West Drayton)
jsweeting@hillingdon.gov.uk

White, Michael (CON - Cavendish)
mrwhite@hillingdon.gov.uk

Yarrow, David (CON - Uxbridge North)
dyarrow@hillingdon.gov.uk

POLITICAL COMPOSITION
CON: 42, LAB: 23

COMMITTEE CHAIRS

Children, Young People & Learning: Ms Jane Palmer

Health & Wellbeing: Mr Ray Puddifoot

Licensing: Mr Dominic Gilham

Pensions: Mr Philip Corthorne

Pensions: Mr David Simmonds

Social Services, Housing & Public Health: Mr Wayne Bridges

Hinckley & Bosworth   D

Hinckley & Bosworth Borough Council, Council Offices, Hinckley Hub, Rugby Road, Hinckley LE10 0FR
☎ 01455 238141 📠 01455 251172 🖥 www.hinckley-bosworth.gov.uk

FACTS AND FIGURES
Parliamentary Constituencies: Bosworth
EU Constituencies: East Midlands
Election Frequency: Elections are of whole council

PRINCIPAL OFFICERS

Chief Executive: Mr Steve Atkinson, Chief Executive, Council Offices, Hinckley Hub, Rugby Road, Hinckley LE10 0FR ☎ 01455 255606; 01455 251172 📧 steve.atkinson@hinckley-bosworth.gov.uk

Deputy Chief Executive: Mr Bill Cullen, Deputy Chief Executive - Community Direction, Council Offices, Hinckley Hub, Rugby Road, Hinckley LE10 0FR ☎ 01455 255676; 01455 251172 📧 bill.cullen@hinckley-bosworth.gov.uk

Senior Management: Ms Julie Kenny, Chief Officer - Corporate Governance & Housing Repairs, Council Offices, Hinckley Hub, Rugby Road, Hinckley LE10 0FR ☎ 01455 255985 📧 julie.kenny@hinckley-bosworth.gov.uk

Senior Management: Mr Rob Parkinson, Chief Officer - Environmental Health, Council Offices, Hinckley Hub, Rugby Road, Hinckley LE10 0FR ☎ 01455 255641; 01455 234590 📧 rob.parkinson@hinckley-bosworth.gov.uk

Senior Management: Ms Katherine Plummer, Chief Officer - Finance, Customer Services & Compliance, Council Offices, Hinckley Hub, Rugby Road, Hinckley LE10 0FR 📧 katherine.plummer@hinckley-bosworth.gov.uk

Senior Management: Ms Sharon Stacey, Chief Officer - Housing, Community Safety & Partnerships, Council Offices, St Mary's Road, Hinckley LE10 1EQ ☎ 01455 255636; 01455 251172 📧 sharon.stacey@hinckley-bosworth.gov.uk

Senior Management: Mr Nic Thomas, Chief Planning & Development Officer, Council Offices, Hinckley Hub, Rugby Road, Hinckley LE10 0FR ☎ 01455 255692 📧 nic.thomas@hinckley-bosworth.gov.uk

Building Control: Mr Nic Thomas, Chief Planning & Development Officer, Council Offices, Hinckley Hub, Rugby Road, Hinckley LE10 0FR ☎ 01455 255692 📧 nic.thomas@hinckley-bosworth.gov.uk

HINCKLEY & BOSWORTH

Children / Youth Services: Ms Rebecca Ball, Children & Young People's Strategic Co-ordinator, Council Offices, Hinckley Hub, Rugby Road, Hinckley LE10 0FR; 01455 255937; 01455 891505
✆ rebecca.ball@hinckley-bosworth.gov.uk

PR / Communications: Mrs Jacqueline Puffett, Communications & Promotions Officer, Council Offices, Hinckley Hub, Rugby Road, Hinckley LE10 0FR ☎ 01455 255630; 01455 635692
✆ jacqueline.puffett@hinckley-bosworth.gov.uk

Community Planning: Ms Edwina Grant, Strategic & Community Planning Officer, Council Offices, Hinckley Hub, Rugby Road, Hinckley LE10 0FR ☎ 01455 255629; 01455 255997
✆ edwina.grant@hinckley-bosworth.gov.uk

Community Safety: Ms Sharon Stacey, Chief Officer - Housing, Community Safety & Partnerships, Council Offices, Hinckley Hub, Rugby Road, Hinckley LE10 0FR ☎ 01455 255636; 01455 251172
✆ sharon.stacey@hinckley-bosworth.gov.uk

Contracts: Mrs Julie Kenny, Chief Officer - Corporate Governance & Housing Repair, Council Offices, Hinckley Hub, Rugby Road, Hinckley LE10 0FR ☎ 01455 255985; 01455 251172
✆ julie.kenny@hinckley-bosworth.gov.uk

Customer Service: Ms Laura Blain, Customer Services Manager, Council Offices, Hinckley Hub, Rugby Road, Hinckley LE10 0FR
☎ 01455 255987 ✆ laura.blain@hinckley-bosworth.gov.uk

Customer Service: Ms Denise Courteney, Customer Services Manager, Council Offices, Hinckley Hub, Rugby Road, Hinckley LE10 0FR ☎ 01455 255921
✆ denise.courteney@hinckley-bosworth.gov.uk

Economic Development: Mrs Judith Sturley, Senior Economic Regeneration Officer, Council Offices, Hinckley Hub, Rugby Road, Hinckley LE10 0FR ☎ 01455 255855; 01455 251172
✆ judith.sturley@hinckley-bosworth.gov.uk

Environmental / Technical Services: Mr Rob Parkinson, Chief Officer - Environmental Health, Council Offices, Hinckley Hub, Rugby Road, Hinckley LE10 0FR ☎ 01455 255641; 01455 234590
✆ rob.parkinson@hinckley-bosworth.gov.uk

Environmental Health: Mr Steven Merry, Commercial Environmental Health Manager, Council Offices, Hinckley Hub, Rugby Road, Hinckley LE10 0FR ☎ 01455 255735; 01455 234590
✆ steven.merry@hinckley-bosworth.gov.uk

Environmental Health: Mr Rob Parkinson, Chief Officer - Environmental Health, Council Offices, St Mary's Road, Hinckley LE10 1EQ ☎ 01455 255641; 01455 234590
✆ rob.parkinson@hinckley-bosworth.gov.uk

Estates, Property & Valuation: Mr Malcolm Evans, Estates & Assets Manager, Council Offices, Hinckley Hub, Rugby Road, Hinckley LE10 0FR ☎ 01455 255614; 01455 251172
✆ malcolm.evans@hinckley-bosworth.gov.uk

Events Manager: Ms Sarah Underwood, Events Assistant, Council Offices, Hinckley Hub, Rugby Road, Hinckley LE10 0FR
☎ 01455 255784 ✆ sarah.underwood@hinckley-bosworth.gov.uk

Finance: Ms Katherine Plummer, Chief Officer - Finance, Customer Services & Compliance, Council Offices, Hinckley Hub, Rugby Road, Hinckley LE10 0FR
✆ katherine.plummer@hinckley-bosworth.gov.uk

Grounds Maintenance: Mrs Caroline Roffey, Public Space Manager, The Depot, Middlefield Lane, Hinckley LE10 0RA ☎ 01455 255782; 01455 891428 ✆ caroline.roffey@hinckley-bosworth.gov.uk

Health and Safety: Mr Adrian Wykes, Principal Safety, Health & Resilience Officer for Environmental Health, Council Offices, Hinckley Hub, Rugby Road, Hinckley LE10 0FR
☎ 01455 234590 ✆ adrian.wykes@hinckley-bosworth.gov.uk

Housing: Ms Sharon Stacey, Chief Officer - Housing, Community Safety & Partnerships, Council Offices, St Mary's Road, Hinckley LE10 1EQ ☎ 01455 255636; 01455 251172
✆ sharon.stacey@hinckley-bosworth.gov.uk

Housing Maintenance: Ms Sharon Stacey, Chief Officer - Housing, Community Safety & Partnerships, Council Offices, St Mary's Road, Hinckley LE10 1EQ ☎ 01455 255636; 01455 251172
✆ sharon.stacey@hinckley-bosworth.gov.uk

Legal: Ms Aftab Razzaq, Legal Services Manager, Council Offices, Hinckley Hub, Rugby Road, Hinckley LE10 0FR ☎ 01455 255621
✆ aftab.razzaq@hinckley-bosworth.gov.uk

Leisure and Cultural Services: Mr Simon Jones, Cultural Services Manager, Council Offices, Hinckley Hub, Rugby Road, Hinckley LE10 0FR ☎ 01455 255699; 01455 891505
✆ simon.jones@hinckley-bosworth.gov.uk

Licensing: Mr Mark Brymer, Principal Licensing Officer, Council Offices, Hinckley Hub, Rugby Road, Hinckley LE10 0FR ☎ 01455 255645; 01455 234590 ✆ mark.brymer@hinckley-bosworth.gov.uk

Member Services: Miss Rebecca Owen, Democratic Services Officer, Council Offices, Hinckley Hub, Rugby Road, Hinckley LE10 0FR ☎ 01455 255879; 01455 635692
✆ rebecca.owen@hinckley-bosworth.gov.uk

Parking: Ms Jackie Lee, Public Space Officer, Council Offices, Hinckley Hub, Rugby Road, Hinckley LE10 0FR ☎ 01455 255626
✆ jackie.lee@hinckley-bosworth.gov.uk

Personnel / HR: Mrs Julie Stay, Human Resources & Transformation Manager, Council Offices, Hinckley Hub, Rugby Road, Hinckley LE10 0FR ☎ 01455 255688; 01455 255997
✆ julie.stay@hinckley-bosworth.gov.uk

Planning: Mr Nic Thomas, Chief Planning & Development Officer, Council Offices, Hinckley Hub, Rugby Road, Hinckley LE10 0FR
☎ 01455 255692 ✆ nic.thomas@hinckley-bosworth.gov.uk

Procurement: Mrs Julie Kenny, Chief Officer - Corporate Governance & Housing Repair, Council Offices, St Mary's Road, Hinckley LE10 1EQ ☎ 01455 255985; 01455 251172
✆ julie.kenny@hinckley-bosworth.gov.uk

Regeneration: Mr Nic Thomas, Chief Planning & Development Officer, Council Offices, Hinckley Hub, Rugby Road, Hinckley LE10 0FR ☎ 01455 255692 ⌀ nic.thomas@hinckley-bosworth.gov.uk

Staff Training: Mrs Julie Stay, Human Resources & Transformation Manager, Council Offices, St Mary's Road, Hinckley LE10 1EQ ☎ 01455 255688; 01455 255997 ⌀ julie.stay@hinckley-bosworth.gov.uk

Street Scene: Mr Darren Moore, Business Development & Waste Manager, Council Offices, Hinckley Hub, Rugby Road, Hinckley LE10 0FR ☎ 01455 255976 ⌀ darren.moore@hinckley-bosworth.gov.uk

Tourism: Ms Lindsay Orton, Creative Communites & Tourism Officer, Council Offices, Hinckley Hub, Rugby Road, Hinckley LE10 0FR ☎ 01455 255805; 01455 891505 ⌀ linday.orton@hinckley-bosworth.gov.uk

Town Centre: Mr Mark Hyrniw, Town Centre Manager, Council Offices, Hinckley Hub, Rugby Road, Hinckley LE10 0FR ☎ 01455 255755; 01455 891505 ⌀ mark.hryniw@hinckley-bosworth.gov.uk

COUNCILLORS

Mayor: Allen, Richard (CON - Earl Shilton)
richard.allen@hinckley-bosworth.gov.uk

Deputy Mayor: O'Shea, Ozzy (CON - Ratby, Bagworth & Thornton)
ozzy.oshea@hinckley-bosworth.gov.uk

Leader of the Council: Hall, Mike (CON - Burbage Sketchley & Stretton)
mike.hall@hinckley-bosworth.gov.uk

Deputy Leader of the Council: Morrell, K (CON - Twycross & Witherley with Sheepy)
kevin.morrell@hinckley-bosworth.gov.uk

Group Leader: Bray, Stuart (LD - Hinckley Castle)
stuart.bray@hinckley-bosworth.gov.uk

Bessant, Paul (CON - Markfield, Stanton & Field Head)
paul.bessant@hinckley-bosworth.gov.uk

Bill, David (LD - Hinckley Clarendon)
david.bill@hinckley-bosworth.gov.uk

Boothby, Chris (CON - Ratby, Bagworth & Thornton)
chris.boothby@hinckley-bosworth.gov.uk

Camamile, Ruth (CON - NewboldVerdon with Desford & Peckleton)
ruth.camamile@hinckley-bosworth.gov.uk

Cartwright, Martin (LD - Groby)
martin.cartwright@hinckley-bosworth.gov.uk

Cook, Maureen (CON - Cadeby, Carlton & Market Bosworth with Shackerstone)
maureen.cook@hinckley-bosworth.gov.uk

Cope, Genesta (LD - Hinckley Trinity)
genesta.cope@hinckley-bosworth.gov.uk

Cope, David (LD - Hinckley Trinity)
david.cope@hinckley-bosworth.gov.uk

Crooks, William (LD - Barlestone, Nailstone & Obaston)
bill.crooks@hinckley-bosworth.gov.uk

Hodgkins, Lynda (LD - Hinckley De Montfort)
lynda.hodgkins@hinckley-bosworth.gov.uk

Hollick, Ted (LD - Groby)
ted.hollick@hinckley-bosworth.gov.uk

Kirby, Jan (CON - Hinckley De Montfort)
jan.kirby@hinckley-bosworth.gov.uk

Ladkin, Chris (CON - Earl Shilton)
chris.ladkin@hinckley-bosworth.gov.uk

Lay, Matthew (LAB - Markfield, Stanton & Field Head)
matthew.lay@hinckley-bosworth.gov.uk

Lynch, Keith (LD - Hinckley Clarendon)
keith.lynch@hinckley-bosworth.gov.uk

Nichols, Keith (LD - Hinckley De Montfort)
keith.nichols@hinckley-bosworth.gov.uk

Nickerson, Mark (CON - Burbage St Catherines & Lash Hill)
mark.nickerson@hinckley-bosworth.gov.uk

Richards, Janice (CON - Earl Shilton)
janice.richards@hinckley-bosworth.gov.uk

Roberts, RB (CON - Barwell)
russel.roberts@hinckley-bosworth.gov.uk

Rooney, Stanley (CON - Burbage Sketchley & Stretton)
stanley.rooney@hinclkey_bosworth.gov.uk

Smith, Hazel (CON - Barwell)
hazel.smith@hinckley-bosworth.gov.uk

Surtees, Miriam (CON - Newbold Verdon with Desford & Peckleton)
miriam.surtees@hinckley-bosworth.gov.uk

Sutton, Brian (CON - Newbold Verdon with Desford & Peckleton)
brian.sutton@hinckley-bosworth.gov.uk

Taylor, Diane (LD - Hinckley Clarendon)
diane.taylor@hinckley-bosworth.gov.uk

Wallace, Peter (CON - Burbage St Catherines & Lash Hill)
peter.wallace@hinckley-bosworth.gov.uk

Ward, R (CON - Ambien)
reg.ward@hinckley-bosworth.gov.uk

Williams, Huw (CON - Barwell)
huw.williams@hinckley-bosworthuk

Witherford, Bronwen (LD - Hinckley Castle)
bron.witherford@hinckley-bosworth.gov.uk

Wright, Amanda (CON - Burbage Sketchley & Stretton)
amanda.wright@hinckley-bosworth.gov.uk

POLITICAL COMPOSITION
CON: 21, LD: 12, LAB: 1

COMMITTEE CHAIRS

Audit: Mrs Ruth Camamile

Finance & Performance: Mr Keith Lynch

Licensing: Ms Hazel Smith

Planning: Mr R Ward

Horsham   D

Horsham District Council, Parkside, Chart Way, Horsham RH12 1RL
☎ 01403 215100 🖶 01403 262985 ⌀ contact@horsham.gov.uk
🖳 www.horsham.gov.uk

HORSHAM

FACTS AND FIGURES
Parliamentary Constituencies: Arundel and South Downs, Horsham
EU Constituencies: South East
Election Frequency: Elections are of whole council

PRINCIPAL OFFICERS

Chief Executive: Mr Tom Crowley, Chief Executive, Parkside, Chart Way, Horsham RH12 1RL ☎ 01403 215102; 01403 215145 ✆ tom.crowley@horsham.gov.uk

Senior Management: Mrs Natalie Brahma-Pearl, Director - Community Services, Parkside, Chart Way, Horsham RH12 1RL ☎ 01403 215250 ✆ natalie.brahma-pearl@horsham.gov.uk

Senior Management: Ms Jane Eaton, Director - Corporate Resources, Parkside, Chart Way, Horsham RH12 1RL ☎ 01403 215300 ✆ jane.eaton@horsham.gov.uk

Senior Management: Mr Chris Lyons, Director - Planning, Economic Development & Property, Parkside, Chart Way, Horsham RH12 1RL ☎ 01403 215401 ✆ chris.lyons@horsham.gov.uk

Access Officer / Social Services (Disability): Mr Stephen Shorrocks, Building Control Manager, Parkside, Chart Way, Horsham RH12 1RL ☎ 01403 215500; 01403 215198 ✆ stephen.shorrocks@horsham.gov.uk

Architect, Building / Property Services: Mr Brian Elliott, Property & Facilities Manager, Parkside, Chart Way, Horsham RH12 1RL ✆ brian.elliott@horsham.gov.uk

Best Value: Mr Mark Pritchard, Commissioning & Performance Manager, Parkside, Chart Way, Horsham RH12 1RL ☎ 01403 215110 ✆ mark.pritchard@horsham.gov.uk

Building Control: Mr Stephen Shorrocks, Building Control Manager, Parkside, Chart Way, Horsham RH12 1RL ☎ 01403 215500; 01403 215198 ✆ stephen.shorrocks@horsham.gov.uk

PR / Communications: Mrs Alison Turner, Communications Manager, Parkside, Chart Way, Horsham RH12 1RL ☎ 01403 215549; 01403 262985 ✆ alison.turner@horsham.gov.uk

Community Planning: Mrs Barbara Childs, Spatial Planning Manager, Parkside, Chart Way, Horsham RH12 1RL ☎ 01403 215181

Community Safety: Mr Trevor Beadle, Head of Community & Culture, Parkside, Chart Way, Horsham RH12 1RL ☎ 01403 215493; 01403 262985 ✆ trevor.beadle@horsham.gov.uk

Community Safety: Mr Greg Charman, Community Safety Manager, Parkside, Chart Way, Horsham RH12 1RL ☎ 01403 215124 ✆ greg.charman@horsham.gov.uk

Contracts: Mrs Katharine Eberhart, Director - Corporate Resources, Parkside, Chart Way, Horsham RH12 1RL ☎ 01403 215301; 01403 215371 ✆ katharine.eberhart@horsham.gov.uk

Customer Service: Mr David Plank, Customer Services Manager, Parkside, Chart Way, Horsham RH12 1RL ☎ 01403 215371 ✆ david.plank@horsham.gov.uk

Economic Development: Ms Lynda Spain, Economic Development Officer, Parkside, Chart Way, Horsham RH12 1RL ☎ 01403 215137 ✆ lynda.spain@horsham.gov.uk

Electoral Registration: Mrs Maxine Mears, Elections Services Officer, Parkside, Chart Way, Horsham RH12 1RL ☎ 01403 215126; 01403 262985 ✆ maxine.mears@horsham.gov.uk

Emergency Planning: Mr Greg Charman, Community Safety Manager, Parkside, Chart Way, Horsham RH12 1RL ☎ 01403 215124 ✆ greg.charman@horsham.gov.uk

Environmental Health: Mr John Batchelor, Environmental Health, Parkside, Chart Way, Horsham RH12 1RL ☎ 01403 215417 ✆ john.batchelor@horsham.gov.uk

Estates, Property & Valuation: Mr Brian Elliott, Property & Facilities Manager, Parkside, Chart Way, Horsham RH12 1RL ✆ brian.elliott@horsham.gov.uk

Estates, Property & Valuation: Mr John Loxley, Estates Management & Valuation Surveyor, Parkside, Chart Way, Horsham RH12 1RL ☎ 01403 215483; 01403 215487 ✆ john.loxley@horsham.gov.uk

Facilities: Mr Brian Elliott, Property & Facilities Manager, Parkside, Chart Way, Horsham RH12 1RL ✆ brian.elliott@horsham.gov.uk

Finance: Ms Jane Eaton, Director - Corporate Resources, Parkside, Chart Way, Horsham RH12 1RL ☎ 01403 215300 ✆ jane.eaton@horsham.gov.uk

Fleet Management: Mr John McArthur, Head of Waste, Street Scene & Fleet, Parkside, Chart Way, Horsham RH12 1RL ☎ 01403 739388 ✆ john.mcarthur@horsham.gov.uk

Grounds Maintenance: Mr Evan Giles, Parks Services Manager, Parkside, Chart Way, Horsham RH12 1RL ☎ 01403 215257; 01403 215268 ✆ evan.giles@horsham.gov.uk

Health and Safety: Mr Michael Marchant, Corporate Safety Officer, Parkside, Chart Way, Horsham RH12 1RL ☎ 01403 215211 ✆ michael.marchant@horsham.gov.uk

Home Energy Conservation: Miss Gill Daniel, Environmental Co-ordination Officer, Parkside, Chart Way, Horsham RH12 1RL ☎ 01403 215281; 01403 215467 ✆ gill.daniel@horsham.gov.uk

Legal: Mr Paul Cummins, Head of Legal & Democratic Services, Parkside, Chart Way, Horsham RH12 1RL ☎ 01403 215435 ✆ paul.cummins@horsham.gov.uk

Leisure and Cultural Services: Mr Trevor Beadle, Head of Community & Culture, Parkside, Chart Way, Horsham RH12 1RL ☎ 01403 215493; 01403 262985 ✆ trevor.beadle@horsham.gov.uk

Licensing: Mr John Batchelor, Environmental Health, Parkside, Chart Way, Horsham RH12 1RL ☎ 01403 215417 ✆ john.batchelor@horsham.gov.uk

Member Services: Mr Paul Cummins, Head of Legal & Democratic Services, Parkside, Chart Way, Horsham RH12 1RL ☎ 01403 215435 ⏻ paul.cummins@horsham.gov.uk

Parking: Mr Ben Golds, Parking Services Manager, Parkside, Chart Way, Horsham RH12 1RL ☎ 01403 215055 ⏻ ben.golds@horsham.gov.uk

Personnel / HR: Mr Robert Laban, Human Resources & Organisational Development Manager, Parkside, Chart Way, Horsham RH12 1RL ☎ 01403 215406 ⏻ robert.laban@horsham.gov.uk

Planning: Mr Aidan Thatcher, Development Manager, Parkside, Chart Way, Horsham RH12 1RL ☎ 01403 215167 ⏻ aidan.thatcher@horsham.gov.uk

Procurement: Mr Roger Dennis, Joint Procurement Officer, Parkside, Chart Way, Horsham RH12 1RL ☎ 01444 477254 ⏻ rogerd@horsham.gov.uk

Recycling & Waste Minimisation: Mr Colin Mee, Waste & Recycling Manager, Parkside, Chart Way, Horsham RH12 1RL ☎ 01403 739940 ⏻ colin.mee@horsham.gov.uk

Staff Training: Mr Robert Laban, Human Resources & Organisational Development Manager, Parkside, Chart Way, Horsham RH12 1RL ☎ 01403 215406 ⏻ robert.laban@horsham.gov.uk

Street Scene: Mr John McArthur, Head of Waste, Street Scene & Fleet, Parkside, Chart Way, Horsham RH12 1RL ☎ 01403 739388 ⏻ john.mcarthur@horsham.gov.uk

Sustainable Communities: Mr Trevor Beadle, Head of Community & Culture, Parkside, Chart Way, Horsham RH12 1RL ☎ 01403 215493; 01403 262985 ⏻ trevor.beadle@horsham.gov.uk

Sustainable Development: Mrs Barbara Childs, Spatial Planning Manager, Parkside, Chart Way, Horsham RH12 1RL ☎ 01403 215181

Tourism: Mr Trevor Beadle, Head of Community & Culture, Parkside, Chart Way, Horsham RH12 1RL ☎ 01403 215493; 01403 262985 ⏻ trevor.beadle@horsham.gov.uk

Town Centre: Mr Garry Mortimer-Cook, Town Centres Manager, Parkside, Chart Way, Horsham RH12 1RL ☎ 01403 215386 ⏻ garry.mortimer-cook@horsham.gov.uk

Waste Collection and Disposal: Mr John McArthur, Head of Waste, Street Scene & Fleet, Parkside, Chart Way, Horsham RH12 1RL ☎ 01403 739388 ⏻ john.mcarthur@horsham.gov.uk

Children's Play Areas: Mr Evan Giles, Parks Services Manager, Parkside, Chart Way, Horsham RH12 1RL ☎ 01403 215257; 01403 215268 ⏻ evan.giles@horsham.gov.uk

COUNCILLORS

Leader of the Council: Dawe, Ray (CON - Chantry) ray.dawe@horsham.gov.uk

Deputy Leader of the Council: Chowen, Jonathan (CON - Cowfold, Shermanbury & West Grinstead) jonathan.chowen@horsham.gov.uk

Bailey, John (CON - Rudgwick) john.bailey@horsham.gov.uk

Baldwin, Andrew (CON - Holbrook East) andrew.baldwin@horsham.gov.uk

Blackall, John (CON - Chanctonbury) john.blackall@horsham.gov.uk

Bradnum, Toni (CON - Nuthurst) toni.bradnum@horsham.gov.uk

Britten, Alan (CON - Roffey North) alan.britten@horsham.gov.uk

Burgess, Peter (CON - Holbrook West) peter.burgess@horsham.gov.uk

Burgess, Karen (CON - Holbrook East) karen.burgess@horsham.gov.uk

Chidlow, John (CON - Southwater) john.chidlow@horsham.gov.uk

Circus, Philip (CON - Chanctonbury) philip.circus@horsham.gov.uk

Clarke, Roger (CON - Cowfold, Shermanbury & West Grinstead) roger.clarke@horsham.gov.uk

Clarke, Paul (CON - Pulborough & Coldwaltham) paul.clarke@horsham.gov.uk

Coldwell, David (CON - Bramber, Upper Beeding & Woodmancote) david.coldwell@horsham.gov.uk

Cornell, Roy (CON - Roffey South) roy.cornell@horsham.gov.uk

Costin, Christine (LD - Trafalgar) christine.costin@horsham.gov.uk

Crosbie, Leonard (LD - Trafalgar) leonard.crosbie@horsham.gov.uk

Dancer, Jonathan (LD - Roffey North) jonathan.dancer@horsham.gov.uk

Donnelly, Brian (CON - Pulborough & Coldwaltham) brian.donnelly@horsham.gov.uk

French, Matthew (CON - Broadbridge Heath) matthew.french@horsham.gov.uk

Hogben, Tony (CON - Denne) anthony.hogben@horsham.gov.uk

Howard, Ian (CON - Southwater) ian.howard@horsham.gov.uk

Jenkins, David (CON - Chanctonbury) david.jenkins@horsham.gov.uk

Jupp, Nigel (CON - Billingshurst & Shipley) nigel.jupp@horsham.gov.uk

Kitchen, Liz (CON - Rusper & Colgate) elizabeth.kitchen@horsham.gov.uk

Lee, Adrian (CON - Denne) adrian.lee@horsham.gov.uk

Lindsay, Gordon (CON - Billingshurst & Shipley) gordon.lindsay@horsham.gov.uk

Lloyd, Tim (CON - Steyning) timothy.lloyd@horsham.gov.uk

HORSHAM

Marshall, Paul (CON - Chantry)
paul.marshall@horsham.gov.uk

Mitchell, Christian (CON - Holbrook West)
christian.mitchell@horsham.gov.uk

Morgan, Mike (IND - Henfield)
mike.morgan@horsham.gov.uk

Murphy, Josh (CON - Horsham Park)
josh.murphy@horsham.gov.uk

Newman, Godfrey (LD - Forest)
godfrey.newman@horsham.gov.uk

O'Connell, Brian (CON - Henfield)
brian.o'connell@horsham.gov.uk

Relleen, Connor (IND - Horsham Park)
connor.relleen@horsham.gov.uk

Ritchie, Stuart (CON - Itchingfield, Slinfold & Warnham)
stuart.ritchie@horsham.gov.uk

Rowbottom, Kate (CON - Billingshurst & Shipley)
kate.rowbottom@horsham.gov.uk

Sanson, Jim (CON - Chantry)
jim.sanson@horsham.gov.uk

Skipp, David (LD - Horsham Park)
david.skipp@horsham.gov.uk

Staines, Ben (CON - Bramber, Upper Beeding & Woodmancote)
ben.staines@horsham.gov.uk

Torn, Simon (CON - Roffey South)
simon.torn@horsham.gov.uk

Vickers, Claire (CON - Southwater)
claire.vickers@horsham.gov.uk

Willett, Michael (CON - Steyning)
michael.willett@horsham.gov.uk

Youtan, Tricia (CON - Itchingfield, Slinfold & Warnham)
tricia.youtan@horsham.gov.uk

POLITICAL COMPOSITION
CON: 37, LD: 5, IND: 2

COMMITTEE CHAIRS

Licensing: Mr Jim Sanson

Hounslow   L

Hounslow London Borough Council, Civic Centre, Lampton
Road, Hounslow TW3 4DN
☎ 020 8583 2000 🖷 020 8583 2592 🖳 www.hounslow.gov.uk

FACTS AND FIGURES
Parliamentary Constituencies: Brentford and Isleworth, Feltham
and Heston
EU Constituencies: London
Election Frequency: Elections are of whole council

PRINCIPAL OFFICERS

Chief Executive: Ms Mary Harpley, Chief Executive, Civic Centre,
Lampton Road, Hounslow TW3 4DN ☎ 020 8583 2012 202 8583
2013 ⌁ mary.harpley@hounslow.gov.uk

Deputy Chief Executive: Mr Alan Adams, Deputy CEO &
Executive Director - Housing, Children's & Adults' Services, Civic
Centre, Lampton Road, Hounslow TW3 4DN ☎ 020 8583 3500
⌁ alan.adams@hounslow.gov.uk

Senior Management: Mr Alan Adams, Deputy CEO & Executive
Director - Housing, Children's & Adults' Services, Civic Centre,
Lampton Road, Hounslow TW3 4DN ☎ 020 8583 3500
⌁ alan.adams@hounslow.gov.uk

Senior Management: Mr Brendon Walsh, Executive Director -
Regeneration, Economic Development & Environment, Civic Centre,
Lampton Road, Hounslow TW3 4DN ☎ 020 8583 5331
⌁ brendon.walsh@hounslow.gov.uk

Best Value: Mr David Allum, Director - Corporate Services,
Hounslow Homes, St Catherines House, 2 Hanworth Road, Feltham
TW13 5AB ☎ 020 8583 3938; 020 8583 3730
⌁ david.allum@hounslowhomes.org.uk

Building Control: Mr Paul Johnston, Head of Building Control,
Civic Centre, Lampton Road, Hounslow TW3 4DN
☎ 020 8583 5402 ⌁ paul.johnston@hounslow.gov.uk

Children / Youth Services: Mr Michael Marks, Assistant Director
- Early Intervention & Education, Civic Centre, Lampton Road,
Hounslow TW3 4DN ☎ 020 8583 2903
⌁ michael.marks@hounslow.gov.uk

Civil Registration: Ms Susan Hayter, Registration & Nationality
Service Manager Superintendent Registrar, Civic Centre, Lampton
Road, Hounslow TW3 4DN ☎ 020 8583 2086
⌁ susan.hayter@hounslow.gov.uk

PR / Communications: Ms Victoria Lawson, Director - Customer
Relations, Communications & Engagement, Civic Centre, Lampton
Road, Hounslow TW3 4DN ☎ 020 8583 4463
⌁ victoria.lawson@hounslow.gov.uk

Community Planning: Ms Merle Abbott, Head of Inclusion, Civic
Centre, Lampton Road, Hounslow TW3 4DN ☎ 020 8583 2788
⌁ merle.abbott@hounslow.gov.uk

Community Safety: Mr Gerry McCarthy, Head of Enforcement,
Community Safety & Commercial, Civic Centre, Lampton Road,
Hounslow TW3 4DN ☎ 020 8583 5183
⌁ gerry.mccarthy@hounslow.gov.uk

Computer Management: Ms Balvinder Heran, Director - ICT,
Civic Centre, Lampton Road, Hounslow TW3 4DN
☎ 020 8583 2214 ⌁ balvinder.heran@hounslow.gov.uk

Consumer Protection and Trading Standards: Mr Gerry
McCarthy, Head of Enforcement, Community Safety & Commercial,
Civic Centre, Lampton Road, Hounslow TW3 4DN
☎ 020 8583 5183 ⌁ gerry.mccarthy@hounslow.gov.uk

Corporate Services: Mr Peter Morris, Interim Deputy Head of
Corporate Communications, Civic Centre, Lampton Road, Hounslow
TW3 4DN ☎ 020 8583 2186 ⌁ peter.morris@hounslow.gov.uk

Corporate Services: Ms Sarah Rayner, Assistant Director - Supply Chain Management, Civic Centre, Lampton Road, Hounslow TW3 4DN ☎ 020 8583 5018 ◌ sarah.rayner@hounslow.gov.uk

Customer Service: Ms Susan Austin, Customer Services Manager, Civic Centre, Lampton Road, Hounslow TW3 4DN ☎ 020 8583 3391 ◌ susan.austin@hounslow.gov.uk

Customer Service: Mr David Palmer, Head of Business Support, Civic Centre, Lampton Road, Hounslow TW3 4DN ☎ 020 8583 5300 ◌ david.palmer@hounslow.gov.uk

Customer Service: Ms Majella Sharma, Customer Satisfaction Manager, Civic Centre, Lampton Road, Hounslow TW3 4DN ☎ 020 8583 3415 ◌ majella.sharma@hounslow.gov.uk

Direct Labour: Mr Sayeed Kadir, Director - Property Services for Hounslow Homes, Hounslow Homes, Civic Centre, Lampton Road, Hounslow TW3 4DN ☎ 020 8583 4301; 020 8583 3709 ◌ sayeed.kadir@hounslowhomes.org.uk

Economic Development: Mr Alan Hesketh, Interim Principal Economic Development Officer, Civic Centre, Lampton Road, Hounslow TW3 4DN ☎ 020 8583 2420 ◌ alan.hesketh@hounslow.gov.uk

Economic Development: Mr Peter Learner, Interim Director - Economy, Environment & Enforcement, Civic Centre, Lampton Road, Hounslow TW3 4DN ☎ 020 8583 4769 ◌ peter.learner@hounslow.gov.uk

Economic Development: Mr Brendon Walsh, Executive Director - Regeneration, Economic Development & Environment, Civic Centre, Lampton Road, Hounslow TW3 4DN ☎ 020 8583 5331 ◌ brendon.walsh@hounslow.gov.uk

Education: Mr Michael Marks, Assistant Director - Early Intervention & Education, Civic Centre, Lampton Road, Hounslow TW3 4DN ☎ 020 8583 2903 ◌ michael.marks@hounslow.gov.uk

E-Government: Ms Barbara Munden, Head of ICT, Civic Centre, Lampton Road, Hounslow TW3 4DN ☎ 020 8583 5950 ◌ barbara.munden@hounslow.gov.uk

Electoral Registration: Ms Cassie Triggs, Electoral Manager, Civic Centre, Lampton Road, Hounslow TW3 4DN ☎ 020 8583 2095; 020 8583 2055 ◌ cassie.triggs@hounslow.gov.uk

Emergency Planning: Mr Twm Palmer, Interim Head of Emergency Planning, Civic Centre, Lampton Road, Hounslow TW3 4DN ☎ 020 8583 5019 ◌ twm.palmer@hounslow.gov.uk

Energy Management: Mr Charles Pipe, Energy Manager, Civic Centre, Lampton Road, Hounslow TW3 4DN ☎ 020 8583 3963; 020 8583 3990 ◌ charles.pipe@hounslow.gov.uk

Environmental / Technical Services: Mr Brendon Walsh, Executive Director - Regeneration, Economic Development & Environment, Civic Centre, Lampton Road, Hounslow TW3 4DN ☎ 020 8583 5331 ◌ brendon.walsh@hounslow.gov.uk

Environmental Health: Mr Gerry McCarthy, Head of Enforcement, Community Safety & Commercial, Civic Centre, Lampton Road, Hounslow TW3 4DN ☎ 020 8583 5183 ◌ gerry.mccarthy@hounslow.gov.uk

Estates, Property & Valuation: Mr Ed Palmieri, Interim Head of Property Management in Corporate Property, Civic Centre, Lampton Road, Hounslow TW3 4DN ☎ 020 8583 2500 ◌ ed.palmieri@hounslow.gov.uk

Events Manager: Ms Anita Bhangoo, Events Manager, Civic Centre, Lampton Road, Hounslow TW3 4DN ☎ 020 8583 2547 ◌ anita.bhangoo@hounslow.gov.uk

Facilities: Ms Anna Harries, Head of Facilities, Civic Centre, Lampton Road, Hounslow TW3 4DN ☎ 020 8583 4079; 020 8583 2488 ◌ anna.harries@hounslow.gov.uk

Finance: Ms Christine Holland, Head of Central Finance (CED), Civic Centre, Lampton Road, Hounslow TW3 4DN ☎ 020 8583 2380 ◌ christine.holland@hounslow.gov.uk

Finance: Mr Robert Meldrum, Head of Finance for Environment, Civic Centre, Lampton Road, Hounslow TW3 4DN ☎ 020 8583 5311 ◌ robert.meldrum@hounslow.gov.uk

Finance: Mr Clive Palfreyman, Director - Finance & Corporate Services, Civic Centre, Lampton Road, Hounslow TW3 4DN ☎ 020 8583 2430 ◌ clive.palfreyman@hounslow.gov.uk

Finance: Mr Alex Taylor, Head of Finance & Accountancy (CSLL), Civic Centre, Lampton Road, Hounslow TW3 4DN ☎ 020 8583 2836 ◌ alex.taylor@hounslow.gov.uk

Pensions: Ms L Lorelei, Chief Technical Officer - Pensions & Investment, Civic Centre, Lampton Road, Hounslow TW3 4DN ☎ 020 8583 2310 ◌ lorelei.watson@hounslow.gov.uk

Pensions: Mr Neil Mason, Pensions Officer, Civic Centre, Lampton Road, Hounslow TW3 4DN ☎ 020 8583 5635 ◌ neil.mason@hounslow.gov.uk

Fleet Management: Ms Sarah Rayner, Assistant Director - Supply Chain Management, Civic Centre, Lampton Road, Hounslow TW3 4DN ☎ 020 8583 5018 ◌ sarah.rayner@hounslow.gov.uk

Grounds Maintenance: Mr Paul Bassi, Leisure & Cultural Services Manager, Civic Centre, Lampton Road, Hounslow TW3 4DN ☎ 020 8583 6794 ◌ paul.bassi@hounslow.gov.uk

Health and Safety: Ms Melanie Fontinelle, Head of Health & Safety, Civic Centre, Lampton Road, Hounslow TW3 4DN ☎ 020 8583 2164 ◌ melanie.fontinelle@hounslow.gov.uk

Health and Safety: Mr Peter Matthew, Assistant Director - Housing, Civic Centre, Lampton Road, Hounslow TW3 4DN ☎ 020 8583 2504 ◌ peter.matthew@hounslow.gov.uk

Health and Safety: Mr Aled Richards, Assistant Director - Community Safety, Environment & Regulatory Services, Civic Centre, Lampton Road, Hounslow TW3 4DN ☎ 020 8583 4961 ◌ aled.richards@hounslow.gov.uk

HOUNSLOW

Home Energy Conservation: Mr Charles Pipe, Energy Manager, Civic Centre, Lampton Road, Hounslow TW3 4DN ☎ 020 8583 3963; 020 8583 3990 ⌂ charles.pipe@hounslow.gov.uk

Housing: Mr Peter Matthew, Assistant Director - Housing, Civic Centre, Lampton Road, Hounslow TW3 4DN ☎ 020 8583 2504 ⌂ peter.matthew@hounslow.gov.uk

Housing: Ms Alison Simmons, Assistant Director - Housing Strategy Services, Civic Centre, Lampton Road, Hounslow TW3 4DN ☎ 020 8583 3500 ⌂ alison.simmons@hounslow.gov.uk

Housing Maintenance: Ms Orla Gallagher, Interim Chief Executive - Houslow Housing, Civic Centre, Lampton Road, Hounslow TW3 4DN ☎ 020 8583 3707; 020 8583 2592 ⌂ orla.gallagher@hounslow.gov.uk

Local Area Agreement: Ms Helen Wilson, Policy Officer, Civic Centre, Lampton Road, Hounslow TW3 4DN ☎ 020 8583 2461 ⌂ helen.wilson@hounslow.gov.uk

Legal: Mr Peter Large, Head of Governance, Civic Centre, Lampton Road, Hounslow TW3 4DN ☎ 020 8583 1974 ⌂ peter.large@hounslow.gov.uk

Leisure and Cultural Services: Dr Imran Choudhury, Director - Public Health & Leisure, Civic Centre, Lampton Road, Hounslow TW3 4DN ☎ 0208583 5239 ⌂ imran.choudhury@hounslow.gov.uk

Leisure and Cultural Services: Mr Hamish Pringle, Assistant Director - Leisure & Cultural Services, Civic Centre, Lampton Road, Hounslow TW3 4DN ☎ 202 8583 4647 ⌂ Hamish.pringle@hounslow.gov.uk

Licensing: Mr Gerry McCarthy, Head of Enforcement, Community Safety & Commercial, Civic Centre, Lampton Road, Hounslow TW3 4DN ☎ 020 8583 5183 ⌂ gerry.mccarthy@hounslow.gov.uk

Lifelong Learning: Mr Alan Adams, Deputy CEO & Executive Director - Housing, Children's & Adults' Services, Civic Centre, Lampton Road, Hounslow TW3 4DN ☎ 020 8583 3500 ⌂ alan.adams@hounslow.gov.uk

Lottery Funding, Charity and Voluntary: Ms Uttam Gujral, Head of Community Partnerships Unit, Civic Centre, Lampton Road, Hounslow TW3 4DN ☎ 020 8583 2455; 020 8583 2466 ⌂ uttam.gujral@hounslow.gov.uk

Member Services: Mr Ian Duke, Head of Policy & Scrutiny, Civic Centre, Lampton Road, Hounslow TW3 4DN ☎ 020 8583 2191 ⌂ ian.duke@hounslow.gov.uk

Member Services: Mr Thomas Ribbits, Head of Democratic Services, Civic Centre, Lampton Road, Hounslow TW3 4DN ☎ 020 8583 2251; 020 8583 2252 ⌂ thomas.ribbits@hounslow.gov.uk

Parking: Mr Steve Stearn, Interim Head of Parking, Civic Centre, Lampton Road, Hounslow TW3 4DN ☎ 020 8583 2000 ⌂ steve.stearn@hounslow.gov.uk

Personnel / HR: Mr John Walsh, Director - Transformation, Civic Centre, Lampton Road, Hounslow TW3 4DN ☎ 020 8583 2100 ⌂ john.walsh@hounslow.gov.uk

Personnel / HR: Mr Steve Williams, Head of Human Resources, Civic Centre, Lampton Road, Hounslow TW3 4DN ☎ 020 8583 3539 ⌂ steve.williams@hounslow.gov.uk

Planning: Ms Marilyn Smith, Head of Strategic Planning, Civic Centre, Lampton Road, Hounslow TW3 4DN ☎ 020 8583 4994 ⌂ marilyn.smith@hounslow.gov.uk

Planning: Mr Brendon Walsh, Executive Director - Regeneration, Economic Development & Environment, Civic Centre, Lampton Road, Hounslow TW3 4DN ☎ 020 8583 5331 ⌂ brendon.walsh@hounslow.gov.uk

Procurement: Mr Mark Pearson, Head of Procurement, Civic Centre, Lampton Road, Hounslow TW3 4DN ☎ 020 8583 5763 ⌂ mark.pearson@hounslow.gov.uk

Public Libraries: Dr Imran Choudhury, Director - Public Health & Leisure, Civic Centre, Lampton Road, Hounslow TW3 4DN ☎ 0208583 5239 ⌂ imran.choudhury@hounslow.gov.uk

Recycling & Waste Minimisation: Mr Andrew Baker, Interim Head of Waste & Recycling, Civic Centre, Lampton Road, Hounslow TW3 4DN ☎ 020 8583 5065 ⌂ andrew.baker@hounslow.gov.uk

Regeneration: Ms Heather Cheesbrough, Assistant Director - Strategic Planning, Regeneration & Economic Development, Civic Centre, Lampton Road, Hounslow TW3 4DN ☎ 020 8583 5328 ⌂ heather.cheesbrough@hounslow.gov.uk

Regeneration: Mr Brendon Walsh, Executive Director - Regeneration, Economic Development & Environment, Civic Centre, Lampton Road, Hounslow TW3 4DN ☎ 020 8583 5331 ⌂ brendon.walsh@hounslow.gov.uk

Road Safety: Mr Mark Frost, Road Safety Manager, Civic Centre, Lampton Road, Hounslow TW3 4DN ☎ 020 8583 5037 ⌂ mark.frost@hounslow.gov.uk

Social Services: Mr Mun Thong Phung, Assistant Director - Adult Safeguarding, Social Care & Health, Civic Centre, Lampton Road, Hounslow TW3 4DN ☎ 020 8583 3593 ⌂ mun-thong.phung@hounslow.gov.uk

Social Services (Adult): Mr Alan Adams, Deputy CEO & Executive Director - Housing, Children's & Adults' Services, Civic Centre, Lampton Road, Hounslow TW3 4DN ☎ 020 8583 3500 ⌂ alan.adams@hounslow.gov.uk

Social Services (Adult): Ms Rachel Egan, Assistant Director - Strategy, Planning & Transformation, Civic Centre, Lampton Road, Hounslow TW3 4DN ☎ 020 8583 3001 ⌂ rachel.egan@hounslow.gov.uk

Social Services (Adult): Ms Mimi Konigsberg, Director - Community Services, Civic Centre, Lampton Road, Hounslow TW3 4DN ☎ 020 8583 3500; 020 8583 3077 ⌂ mimi.konigsberg@hounslow.gov.uk

Social Services (Children): Ms Jacqui McShannon, Director - Children's Safeguarding & Specialist Services, Civic Centre, Lampton Road, Hounslow TW3 4DN ☎ 020 8583 3002 ⌂ jacqui.mcshannon@hounslow.gov.uk

Safeguarding: Mr Mun Thong Phung, Assistant Director - Adult Safeguarding, Social Care & Health, Civic Centre, Lampton Road, Hounslow TW3 4DN ☎ 020 8583 3593 ⏱ mun-thong.phung@hounslow.gov.uk

Public Health: Dr Imran Choudhury, Director - Public Health & Leisure, Civic Centre, Lampton Road, Hounslow TW3 4DN ☎ 0208583 5239 ⏱ imran.choudhury@hounslow.gov.uk

Sustainable Development: Mr Rob Gibson, Head of Environmental Strategy, Civic Centre, Lampton Road, Hounslow TW3 4DN ☎ 020 8583 5217; 020 8583 5233 ⏱ rob.gibson@hounslow.gov.uk

Traffic Management: Mr Mark Frost, Road Safety Manager, Civic Centre, Lampton Road, Hounslow TW3 4DN ☎ 020 8583 5037 ⏱ mark.frost@hounslow.gov.uk

Transport: Mr Mark Frost, Road Safety Manager, Civic Centre, Lampton Road, Hounslow TW3 4DN ☎ 020 8583 5037 ⏱ mark.frost@hounslow.gov.uk

Waste Collection and Disposal: Mr Andrew Baker, Interim Head of Waste & Recycling, Civic Centre, Lampton Road, Hounslow TW3 4DN ☎ 020 8583 5065 ⏱ andrew.baker@hounslow.gov.uk

Waste Management: Mr Andrew Baker, Interim Head of Waste & Recycling, Civic Centre, Lampton Road, Hounslow TW3 4DN ☎ 020 8583 5065 ⏱ andrew.baker@hounslow.gov.uk

COUNCILLORS

Chair: Grewal, Ajmer (LAB - Hounslow Central)
ajmer.grewal@hounslow.gov.uk

Leader of the Council: Curran, Steve (LAB - Syon)
steve.curran@hounslow.gov.uk

Deputy Leader of the Council: Mann, Amritpal (LAB - Heston East)
amrit.mann@hounslow.gov.uk

Anderson, Keith (LAB - Bedfont)
keith.anderson@hounslow.gov.uk

Atterton, Candice (LAB - Hanworth)
candice.atterton@hounslow.gov.uk

Atwal Hear, Harleen (LAB - Heston Central)
harleen.atwalhear@hounslow.gov.uk

Barwood, Felicity (CON - Chiswick Riverside)
felicity.barwood@hounslow.gov.uk

Bath, Lily (LAB - Heston West)
lily.bath@hounslow.gov.uk

Bath, Rajinder (LAB - Heston West)
rajinder.bath@hounslow.gov.uk

Bruce, Tom (LAB - Hounslow South)
tom.bruce@hounslow.gov.uk

Buttar, Manjit (LAB - Heston Central)
manjit.buttar@hounslow.gov.uk

Chatt, John (LAB - Feltham North)
john.chatt@hounslow.gov.uk

Chaudhary, Samia (LAB - Hanworth)
samia.chaudhary@hounslow.gov.uk

Chopra, Bandna (LAB - Hounslow West)
bandna.chopra@hounslow.gov.uk

Christie, Sam (LAB - Bedfont)
sam.christie@hounslow.gov.uk

Collins, Mel (LAB - Brentford)
mel.collins@hounslow.gov.uk

Davies, Samantha (CON - Turnham Green)
samantha.davies@hounslow.gov.uk

De Vic Carey, Peter (CON - Osterley & Spring Grove)
peter.carey@hounslow.gov.uk

Dennison, Theo (LAB - Syon)
theo.dennison@hounslow.gov.uk

Dhaliwal, Sukhbir (LAB - Cranford)
sukhbir.dhaliwal@hounslow.gov.uk

Dunne, Katherine (LAB - Syon)
katherine.dunne@hounslow.gov.uk

Ellar, Colin (LAB - Hounslow Heath)
colin.ellar@hounslow.gov.uk

Foote, Richard (LAB - Hanworth)
richard.foote@hounslow.gov.uk

Green, Linda (LAB - Isleworth)
linda.green@hounslow.gov.uk

Grewal, Pritam (LAB - Hounslow Central)
pritam.grewal@hounslow.gov.uk

Grewal, Puneet (LAB - Hounslow West)
puneet.grewal@hounslow.gov.uk

Gupta, Sachin (LAB - Bedfont)
sachin.gupta@hounslow.gov.uk

Gurung, Bishnu Bahadur (LAB - Hanworth Park)
bishnu.gurung@hounslow.gov.uk

Hearn, Sam (CON - Chiswick Riverside)
sam.hearn@hounslow.gov.uk

Howe, Tina (LAB - Hanworth Park)
tina.howe@hounslow.gov.uk

Hughes, Elizabeth (LAB - Feltham West)
elizabeth.hughes@hounslow.gov.uk

Hughes, David (LAB - Feltham West)
david.hughes@hounslow.gov.uk

Kaur, Kamaljit (LAB - Heston East)
kamaljit.kaur@hounslow.gov.uk

Khan, Hanif (LAB - Hanworth Park)
hanif.khan@hounslow.gov.uk

Lal, Gurmail (LAB - Heston East)
gurmail.lal@hounslow.gov.uk

Lambert, Guy (LAB - Brentford)
guy.lambert@hounslow.gov.uk

Lee, Adrian (CON - Turnham Green)
adrian.lee@hounslow.gov.uk

Louki, Tony (LAB - Osterley & Spring Grove)
tony.louki@hounslow.gov.uk

Lynch, Paul (CON - Chiswick Riverside)
paul.lynch@hounslow.gov.uk

Malhotra, Mukesh (LAB - Hounslow Heath)
mukesh.malhotra@hounslow.gov.uk

Malik, Khulique (LAB - Feltham North)
khulique.malik@hounslow.gov.uk

Malik, Nisar (LAB - Hounslow Central)
nisar.malik@hounslow.gov.uk

Mayne, Ed (LAB - Isleworth)
ed.mayne@hounslow.gov.uk

McGregor, Gerald (CON - Chiswick Homefields)
gerald.mcgregor@hounslow.gov.uk

Mehrban, Shaida (LAB - Hounslow South)
shaida.mehrban@hounslow.gov.uk

Mir, Hina (LAB - Feltham North)
hina.mir@hounslow.gov.uk

Mitchell, Alan (LAB - Feltham West)
alan.mitchell@hounslow.gov.uk

O'Reilly, Sheila (CON - Osterley & Spring Grove)
sheila.o'reilly@hounslow.gov.uk

Oulds, Robert (CON - Chiswick Homefields)
robert.oulds@hounslow.gov.uk

Purewal, Surinder (LAB - Heston Central)
surinder.purewal@hounslow.gov.uk

Rajawat, Shantanu (LAB - Heston West)
Shantanu.Rajawat@hounslow.gov.uk

Saeed, Daanish (LAB - Cranford)
daanish.saeed@hounslow.gov.uk

Sampson, Sue (LAB - Isleworth)
sue.sampson@hounslow.gov.uk

Savin, Myra (LAB - Brentford)
myra.savin@hounslow.gov.uk

Sharma, Jagdish (LAB - Hounslow West)
jagdish.sharma@hounslow.gov.uk

Smart, Corinna (LAB - Hounslow Heath)
corinna.smart@hounslow.gov.uk

Thompson, Peter (CON - Turnham Green)
peter.thompson@hounslow.gov.uk

Todd, John (CON - Chiswick Homefields)
john.todd@hounslow.gov.uk

Virdi, Gurpal (IND - Cranford)
gurpal.virdi1@hounslow.gov.uk

Whatley, Bob (LAB - Hounslow South)
bob.whatley@hounslow.gov.uk

POLITICAL COMPOSITION
LAB: 48, CON: 11, IND: 1

COMMITTEE CHAIRS

Audit: Mr Surinder Purewal

Children & Young People: Ms Samia Chaudhary

Health & Adults: Ms Lily Bath

Health & Wellbeing: Mr Steve Curran

Housing & Environment: Mr Colin Ellar

Licensing: Mr David Hughes

Pensions: Mr Mukesh Malhotra

Planning: Mr Bob Whatley

Huntingdonshire   D

Huntingdonshire District Council, Pathfinder House, St. Mary's Street, Huntingdon PE29 3TN
☎ 01480 388388 ◌ mail@huntingdonshire.gov.uk
▢ www.huntingdonshire.gov.uk

FACTS AND FIGURES
Parliamentary Constituencies: Cambridgeshire North West, Huntingdon
EU Constituencies: Eastern
Election Frequency: Elections are by thirds

PRINCIPAL OFFICERS

Chief Executive: Ms Jo Lancaster, Managing Director, Pathfinder House, St. Mary's Street, Huntingdon PE29 3TN ☎ 01480 388300 ◌ jo.lancaster@huntingdonshire.gov.uk

Senior Management: Mr Nigel McCurdy, Corporate Director - Delivery, Pathfinder House, St. Mary's Street, Huntingdon PE29 3TN ☎ 01480 388332; 01480 388099 ◌ nigel.mccurdy@huntingdonshire.gov.uk

Senior Management: Mr Anthony Kemp, Interim Corporate Director - Services, Pathfinder House, St. Mary's Street, Huntingdon PE29 3TN ◌ anthony.kemp@huntingdonshire.gov.uk

Architect, Building / Property Services: Mr Chris Stopford, Head of Community Services, Pathfinder House, St. Mary's Street, Huntingdon PE29 3TN ☎ 01480 388280; 01480 388099 ◌ chris.stopford@huntingdonshire.gov.uk

Building Control: Mr Chris Knights, Building Control Officer, Pathfinder House, St. Mary's Street, Huntingdon PE29 3TN ☎ 01480 388449; 01480 388099 ◌ chris.knights@huntingdonshire.gov.uk

Building Control: Mr John Thompson, Building Control Manager, The Guildhall, Cambridge CB2 3QJ ☎ 01223 457111 ◌ john.thompson@3csharedservices.org

PR / Communications: Mrs Donna Rockett, Communications Officer, Pathfinder House, St. Mary's Street, Huntingdon PE29 3TN ☎ 01480 388239; 01480 388099 ◌ donna.rocket@huntingdonshire.gov.uk

Community Planning: Mr Chris Stopford, Head of Community Services, Pathfinder House, St. Mary's Street, Huntingdon PE29 3TN ☎ 01480 388280; 01480 388099 ◌ chris.stopford@huntingdonshire.gov.uk

Community Safety: Mrs Claudia Deeth, Team Leader - Community Safety, Pathfinder House, St. Mary's Street, Huntingdon PE29 3TN ☎ 01480 388233; 01480 388099 ◌ claudia.deeth@huntingdonshire.gov.uk

Computer Management: Mr David Lawrence, Interim Service Director - ICT, Pathfinder House, St. Mary's Street, Huntingdon PE29 3TN ☎ 01480 388055 ◌ david.lawrence@huntingdonshire.gov.uk

Contracts: Mr Nigel Arkle, Procurement Manager, Pathfinder House, St. Mary's Street, Huntingdon PE29 3TN ☎ 01480 388104; 01480 388099 ✆ nigel.arkle@huntingdonshire.gov.uk

Corporate Services: Mr Adrian Dobbyne, Corporate Team Manager, Pathfinder House, St. Mary's Street, Huntingdon PE29 3TN ☎ 01480 388100; 01480 388099 ✆ adrian.dobbyne@huntingdonshire.gov.uk

Customer Service: Mr John Taylor, Head of Customer Services, Pathfinder House, St. Mary's Street, Huntingdon PE29 3TN ☎ 01480 388119; 01480 388099 ✆ john.taylor@huntingdonshire.gov.uk

Economic Development: Mrs Sue Bedlow, Economic Development Manager, Pathfinder House, St. Mary's Street, Huntingdon PE29 3TN ☎ 01480 387096; 01480 388099 ✆ susan.bedlow@huntingdonshire.gov.uk

E-Government: Mr Joe Bedingfield, Digital Manager, Pathfinder House, St. Mary's Street, Huntingdon PE29 3TN ☎ 01480 388235; 01480 388099 ✆ joe.bedingfield@huntingdonshire.gov.uk

Electoral Registration: Mrs Lisa Jablonska, Elections & Democratic Services Manager, Pathfinder House, St. Mary's Street, Huntingdon PE29 3TN ☎ 01480 388004; 01480 388099 ✆ lisa.jablonska@huntingdonshire.gov.uk

Emergency Planning: Mr Chris Stopford, Head of Community Services, Pathfinder House, St. Mary's Street, Huntingdon PE29 3TN ☎ 01480 388280; 01480 388099 ✆ chris.stopford@huntingdonshire.gov.uk

Energy Management: Mr Chris Jablonski, Business Development Manager, Pathfinder House, St. Mary's Street, Huntingdon PE29 3TN ☎ 01480 388368; 01480 388099 ✆ chris.jablonski@huntingdonshire.gov.uk

Environmental Health: Mr Chris Stopford, Head of Community Services, Pathfinder House, St. Mary's Street, Huntingdon PE29 3TN ☎ 01480 388280; 01480 388099 ✆ chris.stopford@huntingdonshire.gov.uk

Estates, Property & Valuation: Mr Clive Mason, Head of Resources, Pathfinder House, St. Mary's Street, Huntingdon PE29 3TN ☎ 01480 388103; 01480 388099 ✆ clive.mason@huntingdonshire.gov.uk

Facilities: Mr Chris Jablonski, Business Development Manager, Pathfinder House, St. Mary's Street, Huntingdon PE29 3TN ☎ 01480 388368; 01480 388099 ✆ chris.jablonski@huntingdonshire.gov.uk

Finance: Mr Clive Mason, Head of Resources, Pathfinder House, St. Mary's Street, Huntingdon PE29 3TN ☎ 01480 388103; 01480 388099 ✆ clive.mason@huntingdonshire.gov.uk

Fleet Management: Mrs Beth Gordon, Operations Manager - Commercial Services, Pathfinder House, St. Mary's Street, Huntingdon PE29 3TN ☎ 01480 388368 ✆ beth.gordon@huntingdonshire.gov.uk

Grounds Maintenance: Mr Matthew Chudley, Operations Manager - Environmental Services, Pathfinder House, St. Mary's Street, Huntingdon PE29 3TN ☎ 01480 388648 ✆ matthew.chudley@huntingdonshire.gov.uk

Health and Safety: Mr Chris Stopford, Head of Community Services, Pathfinder House, St. Mary's Street, Huntingdon PE29 3TN ☎ 01480 388280; 01480 388099 ✆ chris.stopford@huntingdonshire.gov.uk

Home Energy Conservation: Ms Julia Blackwell, Energy Efficiency Officer, Pathfinder House, St. Mary's Street, Huntingdon PE29 3TN ☎ 01480 388527; 01480 388099 ✆ julia.blackwell@huntingdonshire.gov.uk

Housing: Mr John Taylor, Head of Customer Services, Pathfinder House, St. Mary's Street, Huntingdon PE29 3TN ☎ 01480 388119; 01480 388099 ✆ john.taylor@huntingdonshire.gov.uk

Housing Maintenance: Mr John Taylor, Head of Customer Services, Pathfinder House, St. Mary's Street, Huntingdon PE29 3TN ☎ 01480 388119; 01480 388099 ✆ john.taylor@huntingdonshire.gov.uk

Legal: Mr Tom Lewis, Head of Legal Practice, The Guildhall, Cambridge CB2 3QJ ☎ 01223 457401 ✆ tom.lewis@cambridge.gov.uk

Leisure and Cultural Services: Ms Jayne Wisely, Head of Leisure & Health, Pathfinder House, St. Mary's Street, Huntingdon PE29 3TN ☎ 01480 388049; 01480 388099 ✆ simon.bell@huntingdonshire.gov.uk

Licensing: Mrs Christine Allison, Licensing Manager, Pathfinder House, St. Mary's Street, Huntingdon PE29 3TN ☎ 01480 388010; 01480 388099 ✆ christine.allison@huntingdonshire.gov.uk

Lottery Funding, Charity and Voluntary: Mr Chris Stopford, Head of Community Services, Pathfinder House, St. Mary's Street, Huntingdon PE29 3TN ☎ 01480 388280; 01480 388099 ✆ chris.stopford@huntingdonshire.gov.uk

Member Services: Mrs Lisa Jablonska, Elections & Democratic Services Manager, Pathfinder House, St. Mary's Street, Huntingdon PE29 3TN ☎ 01480 388004; 01480 388099 ✆ lisa.jablonska@huntingdonshire.gov.uk

Parking: Mr George McDowell, Parking Services Manager, Pathfinder House, St. Mary's Street, Huntingdon PE29 3TN ☎ 01480 388386 ✆ george.mcdowell@huntingdonshire.gov.uk

Partnerships: Mr Adrian Dobbyne, Corporate Team Manager, Pathfinder House, St. Mary's Street, Huntingdon PE29 3TN ☎ 01480 388100; 01480 388099 ✆ adrian.dobbyne@ huntingdonshire.gov.uk

Personnel / HR: Mr Adrian Dobbyne, Corporate Team Manager, Pathfinder House, St. Mary's Street, Huntingdon PE29 3TN ☎ 01480 388100; 01480 388099 ✆ adrian.dobbyne@huntingdonshire.gov.uk

HUNTINGDONSHIRE

Planning: Mr Andy Moffat, Head of Development, Pathfinder House, St. Mary's Street, Huntingdon PE29 3TN ☎ 01480 388400; 01480 388099 📠 andy.moffatt@huntingdonshire.gov.uk

Procurement: Mr Nigel Arkle, Procurement Manager, Pathfinder House, St. Mary's Street, Huntingdon PE29 3TN ☎ 01480 388104; 01480 388099 📠 nigel.arkle@huntingdonshire.gov.uk

Recycling & Waste Minimisation: Mrs Beth Gordon, Operations Manager - Commercial Services, Pathfinder House, St. Mary's Street, Huntingdon PE29 3TN ☎ 01480 388368 📠 beth.gordon@huntingdonshire.gov.uk

Regeneration: Mr Andy Moffat, Head of Development, Pathfinder House, St. Mary's Street, Huntingdon PE29 3TN ☎ 01480 388400; 01480 388099 📠 andy.moffatt@huntingdonshire.gov.uk

Staff Training: Ms Laura Lock, Programme & Project Manager, Pathfinder House, St. Mary's Street, Huntingdon PE29 3TN ☎ 01480 388086 📠 laura.lock@huntingdonshire.gov.uk

Street Scene: Mr Matthew Chudley, Operations Manager - Environmental Services, Pathfinder House, St. Mary's Street, Huntingdon PE29 3TN ☎ 01480 388648 📠 matthew.chudley@huntingdonshire.gov.uk

Sustainable Communities: Mr Chris Stopford, Head of Community Services, Pathfinder House, St. Mary's Street, Huntingdon PE29 3TN ☎ 01480 388280; 01480 388099 📠 chris.stopford@huntingdonshire.gov.uk

Sustainable Development: Mr Andy Moffat, Head of Development, Pathfinder House, St. Mary's Street, Huntingdon PE29 3TN ☎ 01480 388400; 01480 388099 📠 andy.moffatt@huntingdonshire.gov.uk

Town Centre: Mrs Sue Bedlow, Economic Development Manager, Pathfinder House, St. Mary's Street, Huntingdon PE29 3TN ☎ 01480 387096; 01480 388099 📠 susan.bedlow@huntingdonshire.gov.uk

Transport: Mr Stuart Bell, Transportation Officer, Pathfinder House, St. Mary's Street, Huntingdon PE29 3TN ☎ 01480 388387; 01480 388099 📠 stuart.bell@huntingdonshire.gov.uk

Transport Planner: Mr Stuart Bell, Transportation Officer, Pathfinder House, St. Mary's Street, Huntingdon PE29 3TN ☎ 01480 388387; 01480 388099 📠 stuart.bell@huntingdonshire.gov.uk

Waste Collection and Disposal: Mrs Beth Gordon, Operations Manager - Commercial Services, Pathfinder House, St. Mary's Street, Huntingdon PE29 3TN ☎ 01480 388368 📠 beth.gordon@huntingdonshire.gov.uk

Waste Management: Mrs Beth Gordon, Operations Manager - Commercial Services, Pathfinder House, St. Mary's Street, Huntingdon PE29 3TN ☎ 01480 388368 📠 beth.gordon@huntingdonshire.gov.uk

Children's Play Areas: Mr Matthew Chudley, Operations Manager - Environmental Services, Pathfinder House, St. Mary's Street, Huntingdon PE29 3TN ☎ 01480 388648 📠 matthew.chudley@huntingdonshire.gov.uk

COUNCILLORS

Chair: Bucknell, Peter (CON - Warboys & Bury)
peter.bucknell@huntingdonshire.gov.uk

Vice-Chair: West, Richard (CON - Gransden & The Offords)
richard.west@huntingdonshire.gov.uk

Leader of the Council: Howe, Robin (CON - Upwood & The Raveleys)
robin.howe@huntingdonshire.gov.uk

Deputy Leader of the Council: Gray, Jonathan (CON - Kimbolton & Staughton)
jonathan.gray@huntingdonshire.gov.uk

Group Leader: Conboy, Sarah (LD - Godmanchester)
sarah.conboy@huntingdonshire.gov.uk

Group Leader: Duffy, Lisa (UKIP - Ramsey)
lisa.duffy@huntingdonshire.gov.uk

Ablewhite, Jason (CON - St Ives - East)
jason.ablewhite@huntingdonshire.gov.uk

Alban, Timothy (CON - Stilton)
tim.alban@huntingdonshire.gov.uk

Baker, Keith (CON - Alconbury & The Stukeleys)
keith.baker@huntingdonshire.gov.uk

Boddington, Barbara (CON - Gransden & The Offords)
barbara.boddington@huntingdonshire.gov.uk

Brown, Daryl (CON - Huntingdon East)
daryl.brown@huntingdonshire.gov.uk

Bull, Graham (CON - Somersham)
Graham.Bull@huntingdonshire.gov.uk

Butler, Eric (CON - Yaxley & Farcet)
eric.butler@huntsdc.gov.uk

Carter, Robin (CON - Earith)
roboin.carter@huntingdonshire.gov.uk

Cawley, Stephen (CON - Huntingdon West)
stephen.cawley@huntingdonshire.gov.uk

Chapman, Barry (CON - St Neots - Priory Park)
barry.chapman@huntingdonshire.gov.uk

Corley, James (IND - St Neots - Eynesbury)
james.corley@huntingdonshire.gov.uk

Criswell, Steve (CON - Somersham)
steve.criswell@huntingdonshire.gov.uk

Davies, John (CON - St Ives - South)
john.davies@huntingdonshire.gov.uk

Dew, Douglas (CON - The Hemingfords)
douglas.dew@huntingdonshire.gov.uk

Dickinson, Angie (CON - St Ives - South)
angie.dickinson@huntingdonshire.gov.uk

Donaldson, Alison (CON - The Hemingfords)

Francis, Mike (CON - Earith)
mike.francis@huntingdonshire.gov.uk

Fuller, Ryan (CON - St Ives - West)
ryan.fuller@huntingdonshire.gov.uk

Gardener, Ian (CON - St Neots - Priory Park)
ian.gardener@huntingdonshire.gov.uk

George, Leedo (LAB - Huntingdon North)
leedo.george@huntingdonshire.gov.uk

Giles, Sandra (IND - St Neots - Eaton Ford)
sandie.giles@huntingdonshire.gov.uk

Giles, Derek (IND - St Neots - Eaton Socon)
derek.giles@huntingdonshire.gov.uk

Greenall, Stephen (LD - Huntingdon East)
ste.greenall@huntingdonshire.gov.uk

Harrison, Roger (CON - St Neots - Eaton Socon)
roger.harrison@huntingdonshire.gov.uk

Harty, David (CON - St Neots - Eaton Ford)
david.harty@huntingdonshire.gov.uk

Hayward, Terry (IND - Buckden)
terry.hayward@huntingdonshire.gov.uk

Hyland, Barry (UKIP - Yaxley & Farcet)
barry.hyland@huntingdonshire.gov.uk

Jordan, Patricia (LD - Brampton)
patricia.jordan@huntingdonshire.gov.uk

Kadewere, Patrick (LAB - Huntingdon North)
patrick.kadewere@huntingdonshire.gov.uk

Matthews, Rita (CON - Elton & Folksworth)
rita.matthews@huntingdonshire.gov.uk

Mead, David (CON - Fenstanton)
david.mead@huntingdonshire.gov.uk

Morris, John (LD - Brampton)
john.morris@huntingdonshire.gov.uk

Palmer, John (CON - Ramsey)
john.palmer@huntingdonshire.gov.uk

Reeve, Peter (UKIP - Ramsey)
reeve@ukip.org

Reynolds, Deborah (CON - St Ives - East)
deborah.reynolds@huntingdonshire.gov.uk

Sanderson, Tom (IND - Huntingdon West)
tom.sanderson@huntingdonshire.gov.uk

Shellens, Michael (LD - Huntingdon East)
mike.shellens@huntingdonshire.gov.uk

Swain, Laurence (CON - Little Paxton)

Tavener, Jill (CON - Warboys & Bury)
jill.tavener@huntingdonshire.gov.uk

Taylor, Simone (IND - St Neots - Eynesbury)
simone.taylor@huntingdonshire.gov.uk

Tuplin, Dick (IND - Sawtry)
dick.tuplin@huntingdonshire.gov.uk

Tysoe, Darren (CON - Sawtry)
darren.tysoe@huntingdonshire.gov.uk

Underwood, David (LD - Godmanchester)
david.underwood@huntingdonshire.gov.uk

Wainwright, Karl (CON - St Neots - Eynesbury)
karl.wainwright@huntingdonshire.gov.uk

Watt, Des (CON - Yaxley & Farcet)
des.watt@huntingdonshire.gov.uk

White, Jim (CON - Ellington) jim.white@huntingdonshire.gov.uk

POLITICAL COMPOSITION
CON: 34, IND: 7, LD: 6, UKIP: 3, LAB: 2

COMMITTEE CHAIRS

Development Management: Mrs Barbara Boddington

Development Management: Mr Ian Gardener

Development Management: Mr Eric Butler

Licensing: Mr Ryan Fuller

Hyndburn   D

Hyndburn Borough Council, Scaitcliffe House, Ormerod Street, Accrington BB5 0PF
☎ 01254 388111 🖷 01254 392597 ⌁ enquiries@hyndburnbc.gov.uk
🖵 www.hyndburnbc.gov.uk

FACTS AND FIGURES
Parliamentary Constituencies: Hyndburn
EU Constituencies: North West
Election Frequency: Elections are by thirds

PRINCIPAL OFFICERS

Chief Executive: Mr David Welsby, Chief Executive, Scaitcliffe House, Ormerod Street, Accrington BB5 0PF ☎ 01254 388111; 01254 380637 ⌁ dave.welsby@hyndburnbc.gov.uk

Deputy Chief Executive: Mr Joe McIntyre, Deputy Chief Executive, Scaitcliffe House, Ormerod Street, Accrington BB5 0PF ☎ 01254 388111; 01254 380637 ⌁ joe.mcintyre@hyndburnbc.gov.uk

Senior Management: Ms Jane Ellis, Executive Director - Legal & Democratic Services, Scaitcliffe House, Ormerod Street, Accrington BB5 0PF ☎ 01254 388111; 01254 380637 ⌁ jane.ellis@hyndburnbc.gov.uk

Architect, Building / Property Services: Mrs Helen McCue-Melling, Regeneration & Property Manager, Scaitcliffe House, Ormerod Street, Accrington BB5 0PF ☎ 01254 388111; 01254 380122 ⌁ helen.mccue-melling@hyndburnbc.gov.uk

Best Value: Mr Michael Walker, Corporate Performance Manager, Scaitcliffe House, Ormerod Street, Accrington BB5 0PF ☎ 01254 388111; 01254 380637 ⌁ michael.walker@hyndburnbc.gov.uk

Building Control: Mr Simon Prideaux, Chief Planning & Transportation Officer, Scaitcliffe House, Ormerod Street, Accrington BB5 0PF ☎ 01254 388111; 01254 391625 ⌁ simon.prideaux@hyndburnbc.gov.uk

PR / Communications: Mrs Cathy Kierans, Senior Marketing & Communications Officer, Scaitcliffe House, Ormerod Street, Accrington BB5 0PF ☎ 01254 388111; 01254 380637 ⌁ cathy.kierans@hyndburnbc.gov.uk

Community Planning: Mrs Karen Hall, Town Centre Manager, Accrington Market Office, Market Hall, Peel Street, Accrington BB5 1ER ☎ 01254 388111 ⌁ karen.hall@hyndburn.gov.uk

HYNDBURN

Community Safety: Mr Michael Walker, Corporate Performance Manager, Scaitcliffe House, Ormerod Street, Accrington BB5 0PF ☎ 01254 388111; 01254 380637 ⌨ michael.walker@hyndburnbc.gov.uk

Computer Management: Mr Scott Gardner, ICT Manager, Scaitcliffe House, Ormerod Street, Accrington BB5 0PF ☎ 01254 388111; 01254 380272 ⌨ scott.gardner@hyndburnbc.gov.uk

Corporate Services: Mr David Welsby, Chief Executive, Scaitcliffe House, Ormerod Street, Accrington BB5 0PF ☎ 01254 388111; 01254 380637 ⌨ dave.welsby@hyndburnbc.gov.uk

Customer Service: Mrs Pauline Duckworth, Head of Customer Services & Benefits, Town Hall, Blackburn Road, Accrington BB5 1LA ☎ 01254 388111 ⌨ pauline.duckworth@hyndburnbc.gov.uk

Customer Service: Mr Lee Middlehurst, Revenues Manager, Town Hall, Blackburn Road, Accrington BB5 1LA ☎ 01254 388111; 01254 392597 ⌨ lee.middlehurst@hyndburnbc.gov.uk

E-Government: Mr Scott Gardner, ICT Manager, Scaitcliffe House, Ormerod Street, Accrington BB5 0PF ☎ 01254 388111; 01254 380272 ⌨ scott.gardner@hyndburnbc.gov.uk

Electoral Registration: Ms Karina Bilham, Elections Officer, Scaitcliffe House, Ormerod Street, Accrington BB5 0PF ☎ 01254 388111; 01254 392597 ⌨ karina.billham@hyndburnbc.gov.uk

Emergency Planning: Mr Paul Fleck, Safety & Emergency Planning Officer, Willows Lane Depot, Willows Lane, Accrington BB5 0RT ☎ 01254 388111; 01254 872250 ⌨ paul.fleck@hyndburnbc.gov.uk

Energy Management: Mrs Helen McCue-Melling, Regeneration & Property Manager, Scaitcliffe House, Ormerod Street, Accrington BB5 0PF ☎ 01254 388111; 01254 380122 ⌨ helen.mccue-melling@hyndburnbc.gov.uk

Environmental Health: Mr Tony Akrigg, Head of Environmental Partnership, Willows Lane Depot, Willows Lane, Accrington BB5 0RT ☎ 01254 388111; 01254 872250 ⌨ tony.akrigg@hyndburnbc.gov.uk

Estates, Property & Valuation: Mrs Helen McCue-Melling, Regeneration & Property Manager, Scaitcliffe House, Ormerod Street, Accrington BB5 0PF ☎ 01254 388111; 01254 380122 ⌨ helen.mccue-melling@hyndburnbc.gov.uk

Facilities: Mrs Helen McCue-Melling, Regeneration & Property Manager, Scaitcliffe House, Ormerod Street, Accrington BB5 0PF ☎ 01254 388111; 01254 380122 ⌨ helen.mccue-melling@hyndburnbc.gov.uk

Finance: Mr Joe McIntyre, Deputy Chief Executive, Scaitcliffe House, Ormerod Street, Accrington BB5 0PF ☎ 01254 388111; 01254 380637 ⌨ joe.mcintyre@hyndburnbc.gov.uk

Fleet Management: Mr Steve Riley, Head of Community Services, Willows Lane Depot, Willows Lane, Accrington BB5 0RT ☎ 01254 388111; 01254 872250 ⌨ steve.riley@hyndburnbc.gov.uk

Grounds Maintenance: Mr Craig Haraben, Head of Parks & Cemeteries, Willows Lane Depot, Willows Lane, Accrington BB5 0RT ☎ 01254 388111; 01254 872250 ⌨ craig.haraben@hyndburndc.gov.uk

Health and Safety: Mr Paul Fleck, Safety & Emergency Planning Officer, Willows Lane Depot, Willows Lane, Accrington BB5 0RT ☎ 01254 388111; 01254 872250 ⌨ paul.fleck@hyndburnbc.gov.uk

Housing: Mr Denis Aldridge, Housing Advice & Homeslessness Manager, Scaitcliffe House, Ormerod Street, Accrington BB5 0PF ☎ 01254 388111; 01254 391625 ⌨ denis.aldridge@hyndburnbc.gov.uk

Legal: Ms Jane Ellis, Executive Director - Legal & Democratic Services, Scaitcliffe House, Ormerod Street, Accrington BB5 0PF ☎ 01254 388111; 01254 380637 ⌨ jane.ellis@hyndburnbc.gov.uk

Leisure and Cultural Services: Mr Joe McIntyre, Deputy Chief Executive, Scaitcliffe House, Ormerod Street, Accrington BB5 0PF ☎ 01254 388111; 01254 380637 ⌨ joe.mcintyre@hyndburnbc.gov.uk

Licensing: Mr Howard Bee, Licensing Manager, Scaitcliffe House, Ormerod Street, Accrington BB5 0PF ☎ 01254 388111; 01254 386711 ⌨ howard.bee@hyndburnbc.gov.uk

Member Services: Mrs Helen Gee, Member Services Manager, Scaitcliffe House, Ormerod Street, Accrington BB5 0PF ☎ 01254 388111; 01254 380122 ⌨ helen.gee@hyndburnbc.gov.uk

Partnerships: Mr Michael Walker, Corporate Performance Manager, Scaitcliffe House, Ormerod Street, Accrington BB5 0PF ☎ 01254 388111; 01254 380637 ⌨ michael.walker@hyndburnbc.gov.uk

Personnel / HR: Mrs Kirsten Burnett, Head of Human Resources, Scaitcliffe House, Ormerod Street, Accrington BB5 0PF ☎ 01254 388111; 01254 392597 ⌨ kirsten.burnett@hyndburnbc.gov.uk

Planning: Mr Simon Prideaux, Chief Planning & Transportation Officer, Scaitcliffe House, Ormerod Street, Accrington BB5 0PF ☎ 01254 388111; 01254 391625 ⌨ simon.prideaux@hyndburnbc.gov.uk

Procurement: Mr Derek Rydeheard, Administration Services Manager, Scaitcliffe House, Ormerod Street, Accrington BB5 0PF ☎ 01254 388111; 01254 392597 ⌨ derek.rydeheard@hyndburnbc.gov.uk

Recycling & Waste Minimisation: Mr Steve Riley, Head of Community Services, Willows Lane Depot, Willows Lane, Accrington BB5 0RT ☎ 01254 388111; 01254 872250 ⌨ steve.riley@hyndburnbc.gov.uk

Regeneration: Mr Mark Hoyle, Head of Regeneration & Housing, Scaitcliffe House, Ormerod Street, Accrington BB5 0PF ☎ 01254 388111; 01254 380122 ⌨ mark.hoyle@hyndburnbc.gov.uk

Staff Training: Mrs Kirsten Burnett, Head of Human Resources, Scaitcliffe House, Ormerod Street, Accrington BB5 0PF ☎ 01254 388111; 01254 392597 ⌨ kirsten.burnett@hyndburnbc.gov.uk

Street Scene: Mr Steve Riley, Head of Community Services, Willows Lane Depot, Willows Lane, Accrington BB5 0RT ☎ 01254 388111; 01254 872250 ✆ steve.riley@hyndburnbc.gov.uk

Sustainable Communities: Mr Simon Prideaux, Chief Planning & Transportation Officer, Scaitcliffe House, Ormerod Street, Accrington BB5 0PF ☎ 01254 388111; 01254 391625 ✆ simon.prideaux@hyndburnbc.gov.uk

Sustainable Development: Ms Anne Hourican, Senior Environmental Initiatives Officer, Scaitcliffe House, Ormerod Street, Accrington BB5 0PF ☎ 01254 388111; 01254 391625 ✆ anne.hourican@hyndburnbc.gov.uk

Town Centre: Mrs Karen Hall, Town Centre Manager, Accrington Market Office, Market Hall, Peel Street, Accrington BB5 1ER ☎ 01254 388111 ✆ karen.hall@hyndburn.gov.uk

Waste Collection and Disposal: Mr Steve Riley, Head of Community Services, Willows Lane Depot, Willows Lane, Accrington BB5 0RT ☎ 01254 388111; 01254 872250 ✆ steve.riley@hyndburnbc.gov.uk

Waste Management: Mr Steve Riley, Head of Community Services, Willows Lane Depot, Willows Lane, Accrington BB5 0RT ☎ 01254 388111; 01254 872250 ✆ steve.riley@hyndburnbc.gov.uk

Children's Play Areas: Mr Craig Haraben, Head of Parks & Cemeteries, Willows Lane Depot, Willows Lane, Accrington BB5 0RT ☎ 01254 388111; 01254 872250 ✆ craig.haraben@hyndburndc.gov.uk

COUNCILLORS

Mayor: O'Kane, Tim (LAB - Clayton-le-Moors)
tim.okane@hyndburnbc.gov.uk

Deputy Mayor: Britcliffe, Peter (CON - St. Andrew's)
peter.britcliffe@hyndburnbc.gov.uk

Leader of the Council: Parkinson, Miles (LAB - Altham)
miles.parkinson@hyndburnbc.gov.uk

Deputy Leader of the Council: Cox, Paul (LAB - Milnshaw)
paul.cox@hyndburnbc.gov.uk

Group LeaderDobson, Tony (CON - Barnfield)
tdob@aol.com

Group LeaderThompson, Paul (UKIP - St. Oswald's)
paul.thompson@hyndburnbc.gov.uk

Addison, Judith (CON - Immanuel)
judith.addison@hyndburnfc.gov.uk

Allen, Lisa (CON - St. Oswald's)
lisa.allen@hyndburnbc.gov.uk

Ayub, Mohammad (LAB - Central)
mohammad.ayub@hyndburnbc.gov.uk

Aziz, Noordad (LAB - Netherton)
noordad.aziz@hyndburnbc.gov.uk

Battle, Jean (LAB - Church)
jean.battle@hyndburnbc.gov.uk

Button, Stephen (LAB - Altham)
stephen.button@hyndburnbc.gov.uk

Cleary, Clare (LAB - Rishton)
clare.cleary@hyndburnbc.gov.uk

Cox, Loraine (LAB - Church)
loraine.cox@hyndburnbc.gov.uk

Dad, Munsif (LAB - Spring Hill)
munsif.dad@hyndburnbc.gov.uk

Dawson, Bernard (LAB - Huncoat)
b.dawson453@btinternet.com

Eaves, Stewart (LAB - St. Andrew's)
stewart.eaves@hyndburnbc.gov.uk

Fielding, Diane (LAB - Spring Hill)
enquiries@hyndburnbc.gov.uk

Fisher, Melissa (LAB - Clayton-le-Moors)
melissa.fisher@hyndburnbc.gov.uk

Harrison, Glen (LAB - St. Oswald's)
glen.harrison@hyndburnbc.gov.uk

Harrison, June (LAB - Barnfield)
june.harrison@hyndburnbc.gov.uk

Haworth, Stephanie (LAB - Overton)
stephanie.haworth@hyndburnbc.gov.uk

Higgins, Eamonn (LAB - Huncoat)
eamonn.higgins@hyndburnbc.gov.uk

Hurn, Terry (CON - Baxenden)
terry.hurn@hyndburnbc.gov.uk

Khan, Abdul (LAB - Central)
abdul.khan@hyndburnbc.gov.uk

Livesey, Julie (CON - Immanuel)
julie.livesey@hyndburnbc.gov.uk

Molineux, Gareth (LAB - Overton)
gareth.molineux@hyndburnbc.gov.uk

Moss, Ken (LAB - Rishton)
ken.moss@hyndburnfc.gov.uk

Nedwell, Jenny (LAB - Overton)
jenny.nedwell@hyndburnbc.gov.uk

Parkinson, Bernadette (LAB - Netherton)
bernadette.parkinson@hyndburnbc.gov.uk

Plummer, Joyce (LAB - Peel)
joyce.plummer@hyndburnbc.gov.uk

Pratt, Kath (CON - Baxenden)
kathleen.pratt@hyndburnbc.gov.uk

Pritchard, Malcolm (UKIP - Milnshaw)
malcolm.pritchard@hyndburnbc.gov.uk

Scales, Jeff (LAB - Rishton)
jeff.scales@hyndburnbc.gov.uk

Short, Paddy (LAB - Peel)
paddy.short@hyndburnbc.gov.uk

POLITICAL COMPOSITION
LAB: 26, CON: 7, UKIP: 2

Inverclyde   S

Inverclyde Council, Municipal Buildings, Clyde Square, Greenock PA15 1LY
☎ 01475 717171 🖷 01475 712777 🖳 www.inverclyde.gov.uk

INVERCLYDE

FACTS AND FIGURES
Parliamentary Constituencies: Inverclyde
EU Constituencies: Scotland
Election Frequency: Elections are of whole council

PRINCIPAL OFFICERS

Chief Executive: Mr Aubrey Fawcett, Chief Executive, Municipal Buildings, Clyde Square, Greenock PA15 1LY ☎ 01475 712701
✆ aubrey.fawcett@inverclyde.gov.uk

Senior Management: Mr Brian Moore, Corporate Director - Community Health & Care Partnership, Dalrymple House, Dalrymple Street, Greenock PA15 1HT ☎ 01475 717171
✆ brian.moore@inverclyde.gov.uk

Access Officer / Social Services (Disability): Mr Stuart Jamieson, Head of Regeneration & Planning, 6 Cathcart Square, Greenock PA15 1LS ☎ 01475 712402; 01475 712468
✆ stuart.jamieson@inverclyde.gov.uk

Building Control: Mr Nicolas McLaren, Building Control Manager, Municipal Buildings, Clyde Square, Greenock PA15 1LY
☎ 01475 717171 ✆ nicolas.mclaren@inverclyde.gov.uk

Catering Services: Ms Elspeth Tierney, Service Manager, Municipal Buildings, Greenock PA15 1LY ☎ 01475 712449
✆ elspeth.tierney@inverclyde.gov.uk

Civil Registration: Mr Ian Kearns, Registration Manager, 40 West Stewart Street, Greenock PA15 1YA ☎ 01475 714256
✆ ian.kearns@inverclyde.gov.uk

PR / Communications: Mr George Barbour, Corporate Communications Manager, Municipal Buildings, Clyde Square, Greenock PA15 1LY ☎ 01475 712385
✆ george.barbour@inverclyde.gov.uk

Community Planning: Ms Miriam McKenna, Corporate Policy & Partnership Manager, Municipal Buildings, Clyde Square, Greenock PA15 1LY ☎ 01475 712042 ✆ miriam.mckenna@inverclyde.gov.uk

Computer Management: Mr Allan McDonald, Operations Manager, Municipal Buildings, Clyde Square, Greenock PA15 1LY
☎ 01475 717171 ✆ allan.mcdonald@inverclyde.gov.uk

Consumer Protection and Trading Standards: Mr John Arthur, Head of Safer & Inclusive Communities, West Stewart Street, Greenock PA15 1SN ☎ 01475 714263; 01475 714253
✆ john.arthur@inverclyde.gov.uk

Economic Development: Mr Stuart Jamieson, Head of Regeneration & Planning, 6 Cathcart Square, Greenock PA15 1LS
☎ 01475 712402; 01475 712468 ✆ stuart.jamieson@inverclyde.gov.uk

Education: Ms Ruth Binks, Head of Education, Municipal Buildings, Clyde Square, Greenock PA15 1LY ☎ 01475 712850
✆ ruth.binks@inverclyde.gov.uk

Education: Ms Angela Edwards, Head of Educational Planning & Culture, 105 Dalrymple Street, Greenock PA15 1LS
✆ angela.edwards@inverclyde.gov.uk

Emergency Planning: Mr Colin Pearson, Civil Contingencies Officer, West Stewart Street, Greenock PA15 1SN ☎ 01475 714222
✆ colin.pearson@inverclyde.gov.uk

Environmental Health: Mr John Arthur, Head of Safer & Inclusive Communities, West Stewart Street, Greenock PA15 1SN
☎ 01475 714263; 01475 714253 ✆ john.arthur@inverclyde.gov.uk

Estates, Property & Valuation: Mrs Audrey Galloway, Asset Management Planning Manager, Cathcart House, Cathcart Sqaure, Greenock PA15 1LS ☎ 01475 717171
✆ audrey.greenwood@inverclyde.gov.uk

European Liaison: Mr Stuart Jamieson, Head of Regeneration & Planning, 6 Cathcart Square, Greenock PA15 1LS ☎ 01475 712402; 01475 712468 ✆ stuart.jamieson@inverclyde.gov.uk

Events Manager: Mr Stuart Jamieson, Head of Regeneration & Planning, 6 Cathcart Square, Greenock PA15 1LS ☎ 01475 712402; 01475 712468 ✆ stuart.jamieson@inverclyde.gov.uk

Finance: Mr Alan Puckrin, Chief Financial Officer, Municipal Buildings, Clyde Square, Greenock PA15 1LY ☎ 01475 712223; 01475 712288 ✆ alan.puckrin@inverclyde.gov.uk

Fleet Management: Mr John Williams, Transport Manager, Municipal Buildings, Clyde Square, Greenock PA15 1LY
☎ 01475 717171

Grounds Maintenance: Mr William Rennie, Grounds Services Manager, Pottery Street, Greenock PA15 2UD ☎ 01475 714761
✆ willie.rennie@inverclyde.gov.uk

Health and Safety: Ms Pauline Ramsay, Senior Health & Safety Officer, Personnel Services, Municipal Buildings, Clyde Square, Greenock PA15 1LY ☎ 01475 717171
✆ pauline.ramsay@inverclyde.gov.uk

Highways: Mr Robert Graham, Environmental Services Manager Roads, Transport & Waste Services, 71 East Hamilton Street, Greenock PA15 2UA ☎ 01475 714800; 01475 714825
✆ robert.graham@inverclyde.gov.uk

Legal: Mr Gerard Malone, Head of Legal & Property Services, Municipal Buildings, Clyde Square, Greenock PA15 1LY
☎ 01475 712139 ✆ gerard.malone@inverclyde.gov.uk

Leisure and Cultural Services: Mr Stuart Jamieson, Head of Regeneration & Planning, 6 Cathcart Square, Greenock PA15 1LS
☎ 01475 712402; 01475 712468 ✆ stuart.jamieson@inverclyde.gov.uk

Lighting: Mr Robert Graham, Environmental Services Manager Roads, Transport & Waste Services, 71 East Hamilton Street, Greenock PA15 2UA ☎ 01475 714800; 01475 714825
✆ robert.graham@inverclyde.gov.uk

Lottery Funding, Charity and Voluntary: Mr Stuart Jamieson, Head of Regeneration & Planning, 6 Cathcart Square, Greenock PA15 1LS ☎ 01475 712402; 01475 712468
✆ stuart.jamieson@inverclyde.gov.uk

Personnel / HR: Mr Steven McNab, Head of Organisational Development & Human Resources, Municipal Buildings, Clyde Square, Greenock PA15 1LY ☎ 01475 712015 ✆ steven.mcnab@inverclyde.gov.uk

Planning: Mr Stuart Jamieson, Head of Regeneration & Planning, 6 Cathcart Square, Greenock PA15 1LS ☎ 01475 712402; 01475 712468 ✆ stuart.jamieson@inverclyde.gov.uk

Public Libraries: Mr Stuart Jamieson, Head of Regeneration & Planning, 6 Cathcart Sqaure, Greenock PA15 1LS ☎ 01475 712402; 01475 712468 ✆ stuart.jamieson@inverclyde.gov.uk

Public Libraries: Ms Alana Ward, Libraries, Museums & Archives Manager, Central Library, Clyde Square, Greenock PA15 1NB ☎ 01475 712347 ✆ alana.ward@inverclyde.gov.uk

Recycling & Waste Minimisation: Mr Drew Hall, Service Manager, Environmental & Consumer Services, 40 West Stewart Street, Greenock PA15 1SN ☎ 01475 714272; 01475 714216 ✆ drew.hall@inverclyde.gov.uk

Road Safety: Ms Margaret Dickson, Road Safety Training Officer, 71 East Hamilton Street, Greenock PA15 2UA ☎ 01475 717171 ✆ margaret.dickson@inverclyde.gov.uk

Social Services: Mr Brian Moore, Corporate Director - Community Health & Care Partnership, Dalrymple House, Dalrymple Street, Greenock PA15 1HT ☎ 01475 717171 ✆ brian.moore@inverclyde.gov.uk

Social Services (Adult): Mr Brian Moore, Corporate Director - Community Health & Care Partnership, Dalrymple House, Dalrymple Street, Greenock PA15 1HT ☎ 01475 717171 ✆ brian.moore@inverclyde.gov.uk

Social Services (Children): Ms Sharon McAlees, Head of Children & Criminal Justic Services, Dalrymple House, Dalrymple Street, Greenock PA15 1UN ☎ 01475 717171 ✆ robert.murphy@inverclyde.gov.uk

Staff Training: Mrs Carol Reid, Project Manager, Municipal Buildings, Clyde Square, Greenock PA15 1LY ☎ 01475 712027; 01475 712726 ✆ carol.reid@inverclyde.gov.uk

Street Scene: Mr William Rennie, Grounds Services Manager, Pottery Street, Greenock PA15 2UD ☎ 01475 714761 ✆ willie.rennie@inverclyde.gov.uk

Sustainable Development: Mr Drew Hall, Service Manager, Environmental & Consumer Services, 40 West Stewart Street, Greenock PA15 1SN ☎ 01475 714272; 01475 714216 ✆ drew.hall@inverclyde.gov.uk

Tourism: Mr Stuart Jamieson, Head of Regeneration & Planning, Business Store, Greenock PA15 1DE ☎ 01475 712402; 01475 712468 ✆ stuart.jamieson@inverclyde.gov.uk

Traffic Management: Mr Robert Graham, Environmental Services Manager Roads, Transport & Waste Services, 71 East Hamilton Street, Greenock PA15 2UA ☎ 01475 714800; 01475 714825 ✆ robert.graham@inverclyde.gov.uk

Transport: Mr John Williams, Transport Manager, Pottery Street, Greenock PA15 2UH ☎ 01475 717171

Waste Collection and Disposal: Mr Ian Moffat, Head of Environmental & Commercial Services, Pottery Street, Greenock PA15 2UH ☎ 01475 717171 ✆ ian.moffat@inverclyde.gov.uk

Waste Management: Mr Ian Moffat, Head of Environmental & Commercial Services, Pottery Street, Greenock PA15 2UH ☎ 01475 717171 ✆ ian.moffat@inverclyde.gov.uk

COUNCILLORS

Leader of the Council: McCabe, Stephen (LAB - Inverclyde East)
stephen.mccabe@inverclyde.gov.uk

Deputy Leader of the Council: Clocherty, Jim (LAB - Inverclyde North)
jim.clocherty@inverclyde.gov.uk

Group LeaderMcEleny, Chris (SNP - Inverclyde West)
chris.mceleny@inverclyde.gov.uk

Ahlfeld, Ronnie (IND - Inverclyde West)
ronnie.ahlfeld@inverclyde.gov.uk

Brennan, Martin (LAB - Inverclyde North)
martin.brennan@inverclyde.gov.uk

Brooks, Keith (SNP - Inverclyde South)
keith.brooks@inverclyde.gov.uk

Campbell-Sturgess, Math (SNP - Inverclyde North)
math.campbell@inverclyde.gov.uk

Dorrian, Gerry (LAB - Inverclyde South West)
gerry.dorrian@inverclyde.gov.uk

Grieve, Jim (SNP - Inverclyde East Central)
jim.grieve@inverclyde.gov.uk

Jones, Vaughan (IND - Inverclyde South)
vaughan.jones@inverclyde.gov.uk

Loughran, Terry (LAB - Inverclyde West)
terry.loughran@linverclyde.gov.uk

MacLeod, Jim (SNP - Inverclyde East)
jim.macleod@inverclyde.gov.uk

McColgan, James (LAB - Inverclyde East)
james.mccolgan@inverclyde.gov.uk

McCormick, Michael (LAB - Inverclyde East Central)
michael.mccormick@inverclyde.gov.uk

McIlwee, Joe (LAB - Inverclyde South)
joe.mcilwee@inverclyde.gov.uk

Moran, Robert (LAB - Inverclyde East Central)
robert.moran@inverclyde.gov.uk

Nelson, Innes (SNP - Inverclyde South West)
innes.nelson@inverclyde.gov.uk

Rebecchi, Luciano (LD - Inverclyde South West)
luciano.rebecchi@inverclyde.gov.uk

Shepherd, Kenny (LD - Inverclyde North)
kenny.shepherd@inverclyde.gov.uk

Wilson, David (CON - Inverclyde East)
david.wilson@inverclyde.gov.uk

POLITICAL COMPOSITION
LAB: 9, SNP: 6, LD: 2, IND: 2, CON: 1

INVERCLYDE

COMMITTEE CHAIRS

Audit: Mr Luciano Rebecchi

Environment & Regeneration: Mr Michael McCormick

Health & Social Care: Mr Joe McIlwee

Planning: Mr David Wilson

Ipswich   D

Ipswich Borough Council, Grafton House, 15 - 17 Russell Road, Ipswich IP1 2DE
☎ 01473 432000 🖶 01473 432522 ᐧᵈ enquiries@ipswich.gov.uk
🖳 www.ipswich.gov.uk

FACTS AND FIGURES
Parliamentary Constituencies: Ipswich
EU Constituencies: Eastern
Election Frequency: Elections are by thirds

PRINCIPAL OFFICERS

Chief Executive: Mr Russell Williams, Chief Executive, Grafton House, 15 - 17 Russell Road, Ipswich IP1 2DE ☎ 01473 433501 ᐧᵈ russell.williams@ipswich.gov.uk

Deputy Chief Executive: Ms Helen Pluck, Chief Operating Officer / Deputy Chief Executive, Grafton House, 15 - 17 Russell Road, Ipswich IP1 2DE ☎ 01473 432002 ᐧᵈ helen.pluck@ipswich.gov.uk

Senior Management: Mr Ian Blofield, Head - Housing & Community Services, Grafton House, 15-17 Russell Road, Ipswich IP1 2DE ☎ 01473 433710 ᐧᵈ ian.blofield@ipswich.gov.uk

Senior Management: Ms Evelyn Crossland, Head - Shared Revenues Partnership, Grafton House, 15 - 17 Russell Road, Ipswich IP1 2DE ☎ 01473 433782 ᐧᵈ evelyn.cross@ipswich.gov.uk

Senior Management: Mr David Field, Head - Resource Management, Grafton House, 15 - 17 Russell Road, Ipswich IP1 2DE ☎ 01473 433859 ᐧᵈ david.field@ipswich.gov.uk

Senior Management: Mr Peter Thompson, Head - Development, Grafton House, 15 - 17 Russell Road, Ipswich IP1 2DE ᐧᵈ peter.thompson@ipswich.gov.uk

Access Officer / Social Services (Disability): Mr Malcolm Brown, Principal Building Control Surveyor, Grafton House, 15 - 17 Russell Road, Ipswich IP1 2DE ☎ 01473 432957 ᐧᵈ malcolm.brown@ipswich.gov.uk

Architect, Building / Property Services: Ms Emily Atack, Operations Manager - Asset, Property & Economic Development, Grafton House, 15 - 17 Russell Road, Ipswich IP1 2DE ☎ 01473 432200 ᐧᵈ emily.atack@ipswich.gov.uk

Best Value: Mrs Vicky Moseley, Senior Performance & Projects Officer, Grafton House, 15-17 Russell Road, Ipswich IP1 2DE ☎ 01473 432044 ᐧᵈ vicky.moseley@ipswich.gov.uk

Building Control: Mr Malcolm Brown, Principal Building Control Surveyor, Grafton House, 15 - 17 Russell Road, Ipswich IP1 2DE ☎ 01473 432957 ᐧᵈ malcolm.brown@ipswich.gov.uk

PR / Communications: Mr Max Stocker, Head - Communications & Design, Grafton House, 15-17 Russell Road, Ipswich IP1 2DE ☎ 01473 432035 ᐧᵈ max.stocker@ipswich.gov.uk

Community Planning: Ms Janice Robinson, Community Development & Democratic Operations Manager, Grafton House, 15 - 17 Russell Road, Ipswich IP1 2DE ☎ 01473 432510 ᐧᵈ janice.robinson@ipswich.gov.uk

Community Safety: Mr Mike Grimwood, Operations Manager - Community Protection, Grafton House, 15-17 Russell Road, Ipswich IP1 2DE ☎ 01473 433052 ᐧᵈ mike.grimwood@ipswich.gov.uk

Computer Management: Mr Howard Gaskin, IT Infrastructure Manager, Grafton House, 15 - 17 Russell Road, Ipswich IP1 2DE ☎ 01473 433891 ᐧᵈ howard.gaskin@ipswich.gov.uk

Contracts: Mr Kevin Oxborrow, Operations Manager - Maintenance & Contracts, Gipping House, 7 Whittle Road, Hadleigh Road Industrial Estate, Ipswich IP1 2DE ☎ 01473 432414 ᐧᵈ kevin.oxborrow@ipswich.gov.uk

Corporate Services: Mr David Field, Head - Resource Management, Grafton House, 15 - 17 Russell Road, Ipswich IP1 2DE ☎ 01473 433859 ᐧᵈ david.field@ipswich.gov.uk

Customer Service: Ms Janine Last, Customer Services Operations Manager, Grafton House, 15 - 17 Russell Road, Ipswich IP1 2DE ☎ 01473 432360 ᐧᵈ janine.last@ipswich.gov.uk

Economic Development: Ms Maxine Narburgh, Economic Development Project Manager, Grafton House, 15 - 17 Russell Road, Ipswich IP1 2DE ☎ 01473 432918 ᐧᵈ maxine.narburgh@ipswich.gov.uk

Electoral Registration: Mr John Stebbings, Corporate Support Operations Manager, Grafton House, 15 - 17 Russell Road, Ipswich IP1 2DE ☎ 01473 432208 ᐧᵈ john.stebbings@ipswich.gov.uk

Estates, Property & Valuation: Mr Simon Unthank, Principal Valuation Surveyor, Grafton House, 15 - 17 Russell Road, Ipswich IP1 2DE ☎ 01473 432212 ᐧᵈ simon.unthank@ipswich.gov.uk

Events Manager: Mr Mark Whiting, Operations Manager - Arts & Entertainment, Grafton House, 15 - 17 Russell Road, Ipswich IP1 2DE ☎ 01473 433726 ᐧᵈ mark.whiting@ipswich.gov.uk

Facilities: Mr Colin Moffat, Facilities Manager, Grafton House, 15 - 17 Russell Road, Ipswich IP1 2DE ☎ 01473 432008 ᐧᵈ colin.moffat@ipswich.gov.uk

Finance: Mr Ian Blofield, Head - Housing & Community Services, Grafton House, 15-17 Russell Road, Ipswich IP1 2DE ☎ 01473 433710 ᐧᵈ ian.blofield@ipswich.gov.uk

Finance: Mr Jon Hudson, Operations Manager - Finance, Grafton House, 15 - 17 Russell Road, Ipswich IP1 2DE ☎ 01473 433740 ᐧᵈ jon.hudson@ipswich.gov.uk

Fleet Management: Ms Ondraya Plowman, Vehicle Fleet Manager, Grafton House, 15 - 17 Russell Road, Ipswich IP1 2DE ☎ 01473 432430 ⁰ ondraya.plowman@ipswich.gov.uk

Home Energy Conservation: Mr Ian Blofield, Head - Housing & Community Services, Grafton House, 15-17 Russell Road, Ipswich IP1 2DE ☎ 01473 433710 ⁰ ian.blofield@ipswich.gov.uk

Housing: Mr Ian Blofield, Head - Housing & Community Services, Grafton House, 15-17 Russell Road, Ipswich IP1 2DE ☎ 01473 433710 ⁰ ian.blofield@ipswich.gov.uk

Housing Maintenance: Mr Ian Blofield, Head - Housing & Community Services, Grafton House, 15-17 Russell Road, Ipswich IP1 2DE ☎ 01473 433710 ⁰ ian.blofield@ipswich.gov.uk

Legal: Ms Pauline McBride, Head - Legal & Democratic Services Manager, Grafton House, 15 - 17 Russell Road, Ipswich IP1 2DE ☎ 01473 4332323 ⁰ pauline.mcbride@ipswich.gov.uk

Licensing: Mr Mike Grimwood, Operations Manager - Community Protection, Grafton House, 15-17 Russell Road, Ipswich IP1 2DE ☎ 01473 433052 ⁰ mike.grimwood@ipswich.gov.uk

Member Services: Ms Janice Robinson, Community Development & Democratic Operations Manager, Grafton House, 15 - 17 Russell Road, Ipswich IP1 2DE ☎ 01473 432510 ⁰ janice.robinson@ipswich.gov.uk

Parking: Ms Mandy Chapman, Assistant Manager - Car Parks, Gipping House, 7 Whittle Road, Hadleigh Road Industrial Estate, Ipswich IP2 0UH ☎ 01473 432849 ⁰ mandy.chapman@ipswich.gov.uk

Planning: Mr Steve Miller, Operations Manager - Development Control, Grafton House, 15 - 17 Russell Road, Ipswich IP1 2DE ☎ 01473 432903 ⁰ steve.miller@ipswich.gov.uk

Procurement: Mr Andrew Beschizza, Procurement Manager, Grafton House, 15-17 Russell Road, Ipswich IP1 2DE ☎ 01473 433906 ⁰ andrew.beschizza@ipswich.gov.uk

Staff Training: Ms Katie Coupe, Employee Development Advisor, Grafton House, 15-17 Russell Road, Ipswich IP1 2DE ☎ 01473 433425 ⁰ katie.coupe@ipswich.gov.uk

Street Scene: Ms Ondraya Plowman, Vehicle Fleet Manager, Gipping House, 7 Whittle Road, Hadleigh Road Industrial Estate, Ipswich IP2 0UH ☎ 01473 432430 ⁰ ondraya.plowman@ipswich.gov.uk

Sustainable Communities: Ms Janice Robinson, Community Development & Democratic Operations Manager, Grafton House, 15 - 17 Russell Road, Ipswich IP1 2DE ☎ 01473 432510 ⁰ janice.robinson@ipswich.gov.uk

Sustainable Development: Mr Robert Hobbs, Planning Policy Team Leader, Grafton House, 15 - 17 Russell Road, Ipswich IP1 2DE ☎ 01473 432931 ⁰ robert.hobbs@ipswich.gov.uk

Tourism: Mr David Stainer, Tourist Centre Manager, Tourist Information Centre, St Stephens Church, St Stephens Lane, Ipswich IP1 1DP ☎ 01473 43078

Town Centre: Ms Maxine Narburgh, Economic Development Project Manager, Grafton House, 15 - 17 Russell Road, Ipswich IP1 2DE ☎ 01473 432918 ⁰ maxine.narburgh@ipswich.gov.uk

Waste Collection and Disposal: Mr James Fairclough, Waste & Fleet Operations Manager, Grafton House, 15 - 17 Russell Road, Ipswich IP1 2DE ☎ 01473 432060 ⁰ james.fairclough@ipswich.gov.uk

Waste Management: Mr James Fairclough, Waste & Fleet Operations Manager, Grafton House, 15 - 17 Russell Road, Ipswich IP1 2DE ☎ 01473 432060 ⁰ james.fairclough@ipswich.gov.uk

Children's Play Areas: Mr Steve Kemp, Parks & Cemeteries Services Operations Manager, Grafton House, 15 - 17 Russell Road, Ipswich IP1 2DE ☎ 01473 433584 ⁰ steve.kemp@ipswich.gov.uk

COUNCILLORS

Leader of the Council: Ellesmere, David (LAB - Gipping) david.ellesmere@councillors.ipswich.gov.uk

Deputy Leader of the Council: Rudkin, Bryony (LAB - Bridge) bryony.rudkin@councillors.ipswich.gov.uk

Barber, Sarah (LAB - Priory Heath) sarah.barber@councillors.ipswich.gov.uk

Carnall, John (CON - Bixley) john.carnall@councillors.ipswich.gov.uk

Cenci, Nadia (CON - Stoke Park) nadia.cenci@councillors.ipswich.gov.uk

Chisolm, Glen (LAB - Whitehouse) glen.chisolm@councillors.ipswich.gov.uk

Clarke, Hamil (LAB - Sprites) hamil.clarke@councillors.ipswich.gov.uk

Connelly, Stephen (LAB - Gainsborough) stephen.connelly@councillors.ipswich.gov.uk

Cook, Martin (LAB - Gainsborough) martin.cook@councillors.ipswich.gov.uk

Cook, John (LAB - Alexandra) john.cook@councillors.ipswich.gov.uk

Darwin, Shelley (LAB - St John's) shelley.darwin@councillors.ipswich.gov.uk

Debman, George (CON - Holywells) george.debman@councillors.ipswich.gov.uk

Elavalakan, Elango (LAB - St John's) elango.elavalakan@councillors.ipswich.gov.uk

Fern, Roger (LAB - Sprites) roger.fern@councillors.ipswich.gov.uk

Fisher, Ian (CON - Castle Hill) ian.fisher@councillors.ipswich.gov.uk

Gage, Sandra (LAB - Rushmere) sandra.gage@councillors.ipswich.gov.uk

Gardiner, Peter (LAB - Gipping) peter.gardiner@councillors.ipswich.gov.uk

Gibbs, Julian (LAB - Westgate) julian.gibbs@councillors.ipswich.gov.uk

Goldsmith, David (CON - Castle Hill) david.goldsmith@councillors.ipswich.gov.uk

IPSWICH

Goonan, Martin (LAB - Whitehouse)
martin.goonan@councillors.ipswich.gov.uk

Grant, Tracy (LAB - Stoke Park)
tracy.grant@councillors.ipswich.gov.uk

Harsant, Elizabeth (CON - Holywells)
elizabeth.harsant@councillors.ipswich.gov.uk

Holmes, Oliver (LD - St Margaret's)
oliver.holmes@councillors.ipwich.gov.uk

Hopgood, Andi (LAB - Gainsborough)
andi.hopgood@coucillors.ipswich.gov.uk

Hyde-Chambers, Robin (CON - Stoke Park)
robin.hyde-chambers@councillors.ipswich.gov.uk

Ion, Stephen (CON - Rushmere)
stephen.ion@councillors.ipswich gov.uk

Jones, Carole (LAB - Westgate)
carole.jones@councillors.ipswich.gov.uk

Knowles, Bill (LAB - Priory Heath)
bill.knowles@councillors.ipswich.gov.uk

Kreidewolf, Colin (LAB - Westgate)
colin.kreidewolf@councillors.ipswich.gov.uk

Leeder, Adam (LAB - Alexandra)
adam.leeder@councillors.ipswich.gov.uk

Lockington, Inga (LD - St Margaret's)
inga.lockington@councillors.ipswich.gov.uk

Macartney, Jeanette (LAB - Gipping)
jeanette.macartney@councillors.ipswich.gov.uk

Macdonald, Neil (LAB - St John's)
neil.macdonald@councillors.ipswich.gov.uk

Maguire, Daniel (LAB - Priory Heath)
daniel.maguire@councillors.ipswich.gov.uk

Meudec, Sophie (LAB - Whitton)
sophie.meudec@councillors.ipswich.gov.uk

Phillips, Edward (CON - Bixley)
edward.phillips@councillors.ipswich.gov.uk

Pope, Richard (CON - Bixley)
richard.pope@councillors.ipswich.gov.uk

Powell, Jim (LAB - Bridge)
jim.powell@councillors.ipswich.gov.uk

Reynolds, Lee (DUP - St Margaret's)
lee.reynolds@councillors.ipswich.gov.uk

Riley, Jane (LAB - Alexandra)
jane.riley@coucillors.ipswich.gov.uk

Ross, Alasdair (LAB - Rushmere)
alasdair.ross@councillors.ipswich.gov.uk

Smart, Phil (LAB - Bridge)
phil.smart@councillors.ipswich.gov.uk

Smart, Colin (LAB - Sprites)
colin.smart@councillors.ipswich.gov.uk

Studd, Barry (LAB - Holywells)
barry.studd@councillors.ipswich.gov.uk

Vickery, Robin (CON - Castle Hill)
robin.vickery@councillors.ipswich.gov.uk

Whittal, Hugh (LAB - Whitton)
hugh.whittall@councillors.ipswich.gov.uk

Wright, Colin (LAB - Whitehouse)
colin.wright@councillors.ipswich.gov.uk

Xhaferaj, Erion (CON - Whitton)
erion.xhaferaj@councillors.ipswich.gov.uk

POLITICAL COMPOSITION
LAB: 33, CON: 12, LD: 2, DUP: 1

COMMITTEE CHAIRS

Planning & Development: Mr Peter Gardiner

Isle of Anglesey   W

Isle of Anglesey County Council, Swyddfa'r Sir, Llangefni
LL77 7TW
☎ 01248 750057 🖷 01248 750839 🖳 www.anglesey.gov.uk

FACTS AND FIGURES
Parliamentary Constituencies: Ynys Mon
EU Constituencies: Wales
Election Frequency: Elections are of whole council

PRINCIPAL OFFICERS

Chief Executive: Dr Gwynne Jones, Chief Executive, Swyddfa'r
Sir, Llangefni LL77 7TW ☎ 01248 752102

Assistant Chief Executive: Mrs Annwen Morgan, Assistant Chief
Executive, Swyddfa'r Sir, Llangefni LL77 7TW
🖑 annwenmorgan@ynysmon.gov.uk

Assistant Chief Executive: Dr Caroline Turner, Assistant Chief
Executive, Swyddfa'r Sir, Llangefni LL77 7TW ☎ 01248 751919
🖑 carolineturner@ynysmon.gov.uk

Access Officer / Social Services (Disability): Mrs Glenys
Williams, Team Leader - Disability Service, Swyddfa'r Sir, Llangefni
LL7 7TW ☎ 01248 752771 🖑 gwxss@ynysmon.gov.uk

Architect, Building / Property Services: Mr Rhys Griffiths,
Principal Surveyor, Swyddfa'r Sir, Llangefni LL77 7TW
☎ 01248 752161 🖑 rhghp@ynysmon.gov.uk

Best Value: Mr Gethin Morgan, Business Planning & Programme
Manager, Swyddfa'r Sir, Llangefni LL77 7TW ☎ 01248 752111
🖑 grmce@ynysmon.gov.uk

Building Control: Mr Alun Rowlands, Team Leader - Building
Control, Swyddfa'r Sir, Llangefni LL77 7TW ☎ 01248 752220
🖑 alunrowlands@ynysmon.gov.uk

Children / Youth Services: Mrs Anwen Huws, Head of
Children's Services, Swyddfa'r Sir, Llangefni LL77 7TW
☎ 01248 752797 🖑 anwenhuws@ynysmon.gov.uk

Civil Registration: Ms Marian Wyn Griffiths, Superintendent
Registrar, Shire Hall, Llangefni LL77 7TW ☎ 01248 752564
🖑 mariangriffiths@ynysmon.gov.uk

PR / Communications: Mr Gethin Jones, Communication Officer,
Swyddfa'r Sir, Llangefni LL77 7TW ☎ 01248 752130
🖑 gethinjones@ynysmon.gov.uk

Community Safety: Mrs Catherine Roberts, Community Safety Delivery Manager for Gwynedd and Anglesey, Adeilad Mona, Swyddfa'r Cyngor, Caernarfon LL55 1SH ☎ 01286 679047
⌁ CatherineERoberts@gwynedd.gov.uk

Computer Management: Mr John Thomas, Business Transformation Manager, County Offices, Llangefni LL77 7TW ☎ 01248 7519591 ⌁ johnthomas@ynysmon.gov.uk

Consumer Protection and Trading Standards: Mr David Riley, Chief Public Protection Officer, Swyddfa'r Sir, Llangefni LL77 7TW ☎ 01248 752841; 01248 752880 ⌁ daveriley@ynysmon.gov.uk

Corporate Services: Ms Carys Edwards, Head of Profession - Human Resources, Swyddfa'r Sir, Llangefni LL77 7TW ☎ 01248 752502; 01248 752583 ⌁ cexcs@ynysmon.gov.uk

Economic Development: Mr Dylan Williams, Head of Economic & Community Regeneration, Anglesey Business Centre, Bryn Cefni Business Park, Llangefni LL77 7XA ☎ 01248 752499; 01248 752192 ⌁ dwxpl@ynysmon.gov.uk

Education: Mrs Delyth Molyneux, Head of Service - Education, Parc Mount, Glanhwfa Road, Llangefni LL77 7EY ☎ 01248 752916 ⌁ delythmolyneux@ynysmon.gov.uk

E-Government: Mr John Thomas, Business Transformation Manager, County Offices, Llangefni LL77 7TW ☎ 01248 7519591 ⌁ johnthomas@ynysmon.gov.uk

Electoral Registration: Ms Haulwen Ann Hughes, Electoral Services Officer, Anglesey Business Centre, Bryn Cefni Business Park, Llangefni LL77 7XA ☎ 01248 752519
⌁ haulwenhughes@ynysmon.gov.uk

Energy Management: Mr Adrian Williams, Energy Manager, Swyddfa'r Sir, Llangefni LL77 7TW ☎ 01248 752249; 01248 724839 ⌁ awxht@ynysmon.gov.uk

Environmental / Technical Services: Mr Dewi Williams, Director - Sustainable Development, Swyddfa'r Sir, Llangefni LL77 7TW ☎ 01248 752303 ⌁ dewiwilliams@ynysmon.gov.uk

Environmental Health: Mr David Riley, Chief Public Protection Officer, Swyddfa'r Sir, Llangefni LL77 7TW ☎ 01248 752841; 01248 752880 ⌁ daveriley@ynysmon.gov.uk

Estates, Property & Valuation: Mr Dylan Edwards, Principal Valuation Officer, Swyddfa'r Sir, Llangefni LL77 7TW ☎ 01248 752277 ⌁ tedwards@ynysmon.gov.uk

European Liaison: Mr Aled Prys Davies, Principal Development Officer (Support & Funding), Anglesey Business Centre, Bryn Cefni Business Park, Llangefni LL77 7XA ☎ 01248 752479; 01248 752192 ⌁ apdpl@ynysmon.gov.uk

Events Manager: Mr Michael Thomas, Senior Development Officer - Tourism & Marketing, Anglesey Business Centre, Bryn Cefni Business Park, Llangefni LL77 7XA ☎ 01248 752492 ⌁ mptpl@ynysmon.gov.uk

Finance: Mr Marc Jones, Head of Function - Resources, Swyddfa'r Sir, Llangefni LL77 7TW ☎ 01248 752601
⌁ marcjones@ynysmon.gov.uk

Fleet Management: Mr Gareth Owens, Fleet & Driver Manager, Swyddfa'r Sir, Llangefni LL77 7TW ☎ 01248 752126 ⌁ garethowens@ynysmon.gov.uk

Grounds Maintenance: Mr Huw Percy, Chief Engineer (Maintenance), Swyddfa'r Sir, Llangefni LL77 7TW ☎ 01248 752371; 01248 724839 ⌁ hmpht@ynysmon.gov.uk

Health and Safety: Mr Stephen Nicol, Health & Safety Team Leader, Swyddfa'r Sir, Llangefni LL77 7TW ☎ 01248 751884; 01248 752880 ⌁ snxpp@anglesey.gov.uk

Highways: Mr Huw Percy, Chief Engineer (Maintenance), Swyddfa'r Sir, Llangefni LL77 7TW ☎ 01248 752371; 01248 724839 ⌁ hmpht@ynysmon.gov.uk

Housing: Ms Shan Williams, Head of Housing, Swyddfa'r Sir, Llangefni LL77 7TW ☎ 01248 725201; 01248 752243; 01248 752233 ⌁ slwhp@ynysmon.gov.uk

Legal: Ms Lynn Ball, Head of Function: Legal & Administration / Monitoring Officer, Swyddfa'r Sir, Llangefni LL77 7TW ☎ 01248 752586; 01248 752132 ⌁ lbxcs@ynysmon.gov.uk

Leisure and Cultural Services: Mrs Delyth Molyneux, Head of Service - Education, Parc Mount, Glanhwfa Road, Llangefni LL77 7EY ☎ 01248 752916 ⌁ delythmolyneux@ynysmon.gov.uk

Leisure and Cultural Services: Mr Dylan Williams, Head of Economic & Community Regeneration, Anglesey Business Centre, Bryn Cefni Business Park, Llangefni LL77 7XA ☎ 01248 752499; 01248 752192 ⌁ dwxpl@ynysmon.gov.uk

Licensing: Mr John Lloyd, Senior Enforcement Officer (Licensing), Swyddfa'r Sir, Llangefni LL77 7TW ☎ 01248 752852; 01248 752884 ⌁ jelpp@ynysmon.gov.uk

Licensing: Mr Sion Lloyd Jones, Operations Manager, Swyddfa'r Sir, Llangefni LL77 7EY ☎ 01248 752843 ⌁ slhpp@ynysmon.gov.uk

Lifelong Learning: Mrs Delyth Molyneux, Head of Service - Education, Parc Mount, Glanhwfa Road, Llangefni LL77 7EY ☎ 01248 752916 ⌁ delythmolyneux@ynysmon.gov.uk

Lighting: Mr Eryl Davies, Senior Engineer (Lighting), Swyddfa'r Sir, Llangefni LL77 7TW ☎ 01248 752393 ⌁ ecdxht@ynysmon.gov.uk

Member Services: Mr Huw Jones, Head of Democratic Services, Swyddfa'r Sir, Llangefni LL77 7TW ☎ 01248 752108; 01248 750839 ⌁ jhjce@ynysmon.gov.uk

Parking: Mr Alun Roberts, Decriminalised Parking Officer, Swyddfa'r Sir, Llangefni LL77 7TW ☎ 01248 752244 ⌁ jarht@ynysmon.gov.uk

ISLE OF ANGLESEY

Personnel / HR: Ms Carys Edwards, Head of Profession - Human Resources, Swyddfa'r Sir, Llangefni LL77 7TW ☎ 01248 752502; 01248 752583 ⊕ cexcs@ynysmon.gov.uk

Planning: Mr Dewi Jones, Planning Development Manager, Swyddfa'r Sir, Llangefni LL77 7TW ☎ 01248 752420 ⊕ dewijones@ynysmon.gov.uk

Procurement: Mrs Sioned Rowlands, Procurement Officer, Swyddfa'r Sir, Llangefni LL77 7TW ☎ 01248 752136 ⊕ sionedrowlands@ynysmon.gov.uk

Public Libraries: Mrs Delyth Molyneux, Head of Service - Education, Parc Mount, Glanhwfa Road, Llangefni LL77 7EY ☎ 01248 752916 ⊕ delythmolyneux@ynysmon.gov.uk

Recycling & Waste Minimisation: Mr Meirion Edwards, Principal Waste Management Officer, Swyddfa'r Sir, Llangefni LL77 7TW ☎ 01248 752818 ⊕ mpepp@ynysmon.gov.uk

Regeneration: Mr Dylan Williams, Head of Economic & Community Regeneration, Anglesey Business Centre, Bryn Cefni Business Park, Llangefni LL77 7XA ☎ 01248 752499; 01248 752192 ⊕ dwxpl@ynysmon.gov.uk

Road Safety: Mr Huw Percy, Chief Engineer (Maintenance), Swyddfa'r Sir, Llangefni LL77 7TW ☎ 01248 752371; 01248 724839 ⊕ hmpht@ynysmon.gov.uk

Social Services (Adult): Mr Alwyn Rhys Jones, Head of Adult Services, County Offices, Llangefni LL77 7TW ☎ 01248 752707 ⊕ alwynrhys-jones@ynysmon.gov.uk

Social Services (Children): Mrs Anwen Huws, Head of Children's Services, Swyddfa'r Sir, Llangefni LL77 7TW ☎ 01248 752797 ⊕ anwenhuws@ynysmon.gov.uk

Staff Training: Ms Carys Edwards, Head of Profession - Human Resources, Swyddfa'r Sir, Llangefni LL77 7TW ☎ 01248 752502; 01248 752583 ⊕ cexcs@ynysmon.gov.uk

Tourism: Mr Iwan Huws, Tourism & Maritime Manager, Anglesey Business Centre, Bryn Cefni Business Park, Llangefni LL77 7TW ☎ 01248 752493 ⊕ gihpl@anglesey.gov.uk

Traffic Management: Mr Huw Percy, Chief Engineer (Maintenance), Swyddfa'r Sir, Llangefni LL77 7TW ☎ 01248 752371; 01248 724839 ⊕ hmpht@ynysmon.gov.uk

Transport Planner: Mr Huw Percy, Chief Engineer (Maintenance), Swyddfa'r Sir, Llangefni LL77 7TW ☎ 01248 752371; 01248 724839 ⊕ hmpht@ynysmon.gov.uk

Waste Collection and Disposal: Mr Meirion Edwards, Principal Waste Management Officer, Swyddfa'r Sir, Llangefni LL77 7TW ☎ 01248 752860; 01248 752880 ⊕ mpepp@ynysmon.gov.uk

Waste Collection and Disposal: Ms Carys Wyn Roberts, Contract Supervisor, Swyddfa'r Sir, Llangefni LL77 7TW ☎ 01248 752860; 01248 752880 ⊕ cwrpp@anglesey.gov.uk

Waste Management: Mr Meirion Edwards, Principal Waste Management Officer, Swyddfa'r Sir, Llangefni LL77 7TW ☎ 01248 752860; 01248 752880 ⊕ mpepp@ynysmon.gov.uk

COUNCILLORS

Chair: Parry, Robert (PC - Canolbarth Môn)
bobparry@anglesey.gov.uk

Vice-Chair: Jones, Richard (IND - Twrcelyn)
richardowainjones@anglesey.gov.uk

Leader of the Council: Williams, Ieuan (IND - Lligwy)
ieuanwilliams@anglesey.gov.uk

Deputy Leader of the Council: Roberts, J Arwel (LAB - Caergybi)
johnarwelroberts@anglesey.gov.uk

Davies, Lewis (PC - Seiriol)
lewisdavies@anglesey.gov.uk

Dew, Richard (IND - Llifon)
richarddew@anglesey.gov.uk

Evans, Jim (IND - Aethwy)
jimevans@anglesey.gov.uk

Evans, Jeffrey (IND - Ynys Gybi)
jeffreyevans@anglesey.gov.uk

Griffith, Ann (PC - Bro Aberffraw)
anngriffith@anglesey.gov.uk

Griffith, John (PC - Talybolion)
johngriffith@anglesey.gov.uk

Hughes, Kenneth (IND - Talybolion)
kennethphughes@anglesey.gov.uk

Hughes, Derlwyn Rees (IND - Lligwy)
derlwynrhughes@anglesey.gov.uk

Hughes, Vaughan (PC - Lligwy)
vaughanhughes@anglesey.gov.uk

Hughes, Victor (IND - Bro Rhosyr)
tvictor.hughes@anglesey.gov.uk

Hughes, Williams (IND - Twrcelyn)
wthau@anglesey.gov.uk

Hughes, Trefor (PC - Ynys Gybi)
treforlloydhughes@anglesey.gov.uk

Huws, Llinos Medi (PC - Talybolion)
llinosmedihuws@anglesey.gov.uk

Jones, Carwyn (PC - Seiriol)
carwyneliasjones@anglesey.gov.uk

Jones, Gwilym (IND - Llifon)
gwilymojones@anglesey.gov.uk

Jones, Hywel Eifion (IND - Bro Rhosyr)
hyweleifionjones@anglesey.gov.uk

Jones, Robert Llewelyn (INDNA - Caergybi)
robertljones@anglesey.gov.uk

Jones, Raymond (IND - Caergybi)
raymondjones@anglesey.gov.uk

Jones, R.Meirion (PC - Aethwy)
rmeirionjones@anglesey.gov.uk

Jones, Aled (INDNA - Twrcelyn)
aledmjones@anglesey.gov.uk

Mummery, Alun (PC - Aethwy)
alunwmummery@anglesey.gov.uk

Rees, Dylan (PC - Canolbarth Môn)
dylanrees@anglesey.gov.uk

Roberts, Nicola (PC - Canolbarth Môn)
nicolaroberts@anglesey.gov.uk

Rogers, Peter (IND - Bro Aberffraw)
peterrogers@anglesey.gov.uk

Rowlands, Alwyn (LAB - Seiriol)
alwynrowlands@anglesey.gov.uk

Thomas, Dafydd (IND - Ynys Gybi)
dafyddrhysthomas@anglesey.gov.uk

POLITICAL COMPOSITION
IND: 14, PC: 12, INDNA: 2, LAB: 2

COMMITTEE CHAIRS

Audit: Mr Robert Llewelyn Jones

Licensing: Ms Ann Griffith

Planning: Ms Ann Griffith

Isle of Wight   U

Isle of Wight Council, County Hall, High Street, Newport PO30 1UD
☎ 01983 821000 🖨 01983 823333 ⌨ customer.services@iow.gov.uk
💻 www.iwight.com

FACTS AND FIGURES
Parliamentary Constituencies: Isle of Wight
EU Constituencies: South East
Election Frequency: Elections are of whole council

PRINCIPAL OFFICERS

Chief Executive: Mr John Metcalfe, Chief Executive, County Hall, High Street, Newport PO30 1UD ☎ 01983 821000 ⌨ john.metcalf@iow.gov.uk

Architect, Building / Property Services: Mr Ashley Curzon, Strategic Manager - Economic Development & Asset Management, County Hall, High Street, Newport PO30 1UD ☎ 01983 821000 ext 6210 ⌨ ashley.curzon@iow.gov.uk

Building Control: Mr John Lutas, Building Control Manager, Seaclose, Fairlee Road, Newport PO30 2QS ☎ 01983 821000 ⌨ john.lutas@iow.gov.uk

Civil Registration: Mrs Sharon Crews, Celebratory & Registration Service Manager, Seaclose Offices, Fairlee Road, Newport PO30 2QS ☎ 01983 821000 ⌨ janice.lord@iow.gov.uk

PR / Communications: Mrs Helen Wheller, Media Team Leader, County Hall, High Street, Newport PO30 1UD ☎ 01983 821000 ⌨ helen.wheller@iow.gov.uk

Community Planning: Dr Carol Tozer, Director - Adult Social Care, County Hall, High Street, Newport PO30 1UD ☎ 01983 821000 ⌨ carol.tozer@iow.gov.uk

Computer Management: Mr Gavin Muncaster, Strategic Manager - ICT & Digital Services, Bugle House, High Street, Newport PO30 1UD ☎ 01983 821000 ⌨ gavin.muncaster@iow.gov.uk

Consumer Protection and Trading Standards: Mr Mike Cleary, Senior Trading Standards Manager, Jubilee Stores, The Quay, Newport PO30 2EH ☎ 01983 821000 ⌨ mike.cleary@iow.gov.uk

Contracts: Mrs Sue Dasant, Strategic Manager - Procurement & Contract, County Hall, High Street, Newport PO30 1UD ☎ 01983 821000 ⌨ sue.dasant@iow.gov.uk

Customer Service: Mrs Sharon Betts, Shared Service Manager, Westbridge Centre, Brading Road, Ryde PO33 1QS ☎ 01983 821000 ⌨ sharon.betts@iow.gov.uk

Economic Development: Mr John Metcalfe, Chief Executive, County Hall, High Street, Newport PO30 1UD ☎ 01983 821000 ⌨ john.metcalf@iow.gov.uk

E-Government: Mr Gavin Muncaster, Strategic Manager - ICT & Digital Services, Bugle House, High Street, Newport PO30 1UD ☎ 01983 821000 ⌨ gavin.muncaster@iow.gov.uk

Electoral Registration: Mr Clive Joynes, Election & Land Charges Manager, County Hall, High Street, Newport PO30 1UD ☎ 01983 823341 ⌨ clive.joynes@iow.gov.uk

Emergency Planning: Mr Darren Steed, Resilience Manager, County Hall, High Street, Newport PO30 1UD ☎ 01983 823314 ⌨ darren.steed@iow.gov.uk

Energy Management: Mr Timothy Watson, Energy Manager, County Hall, High Street, Newport PO30 1UD ☎ 01983 821000 ⌨ timothy.watson@iow.gov.uk

Estates, Property & Valuation: Miss Andrea Jenkins, Senior Estates Manager, County Hall, High Street, Newport PO30 1UD ☎ 01983 823263 ⌨ andrea.jenkins@iow.gov.uk

Events Manager: Miss Elaine Cesar, Senior Events Officer, County Hall, High Street, Newport PO30 1UD ☎ 01983 821000 ⌨ elaine.cesar@iow.gov.uk

Facilities: Mrs Ruth Jones, Facilities Manager, County Hall, High Street, Newport PO30 1UD ☎ 01983 821000 ⌨ ruth.jones@iow.gov.uk

Finance: Mr Stuart Fraser, Head of Finance & Section 151, County Hall, High Street, Newport PO30 1UD ☎ 01983 821000 ⌨ stuart.fraser@iow.gov.uk

Treasury: Mrs Jo Thistlewood, Technical Finance Officer, County Hall, High Street, Newport PO30 1UD ☎ 01983 821000 ⌨ jo.thistlewood@iow.gov.uk

Pensions: Mr Graham Fahy, HR Support & Pensions Manager, Westbridge Centre, Brading Road, Ryde PO33 1QS ☎ 01983 821000 ⌨ graham.fahy@iow.gov.uk

ISLE OF WIGHT

Fleet Management: Mr Nick Symes, Fleet Manager, Cemetery Hill, Carisbrooke, Newport PO30 1YS ☎ 01983 823786 ◌ nick.symes@iow.gov.uk

Grounds Maintenance: Mr Matthew Chatfield, Parks & Countryside Manager, County Hall, High Street, Newport PO30 1UD ☎ 01983 821000 ◌ matthew.chatfield@iow.gov.uk

Health and Safety: Mr Anthony Thorn, Strategic Lead - People Management Service, County Hall, High Street, Newport PO30 1UD ☎ 01983 821000 ◌ anthony.thorn@iow.gov.uk

Highways: Mr Antony Cooke, Highways PFI Contract Programme Manager, Enterprise House, St Cross Buisness Park, Newport PO30 5WB ☎ 01983 821000 ◌ antony.cook@iow.gov.uk

Housing: Mrs Wendy Perera, Head - Planning & Regulatory Services, County Hall, High Street, Newport PO30 1UD ☎ 01983 821000 ◌ wendy.perera@iow.gov.uk

Legal: Mrs Helen Miles, Strategic Manager & Deputy Monitoring Officer, County Hall, High Street, Newport PO30 1UD ☎ 01983 821000 ◌ helen.miles@iow.gov.uk

Leisure and Cultural Services: Mr Lee Matthews, Recreation & Public Spaces Manager, County Hall, High Street, Newport PO30 1UD ☎ 01983 823815 ◌ lee.matthews@iow.gov.uk

Licensing: Mr Kevin Winchcombe, Principal Licensing Officer, Jubilee Stores, The Quay, Newport PO30 2EH ☎ 01983 821000 ◌ kevin.winchcombe@iow.gov.uk

Lifelong Learning: Mrs Sarah Teague, Commissioner - Learning & Development, Carnival Learning Centre, Westridge, PO33 1QS ☎ 01983 817280 ◌ sarah.teague@iow.gov.uk

Member Services: Mrs Jo Cooke, Business Hub Manager - Members & Governance, County Hall, High Street, Newport PO30 1UD ☎ 01983 821000 ◌ jo.cooke@iow.gov.uk

Parking: Mr Mark Downer, Parking Operations Manager, Enterprise House, Newport PO30 5WB ☎ 01983 821000 ◌ mark.downer@iow.gov.uk

Partnerships: Ms Astrid Davies, Commissioning Manager, County Hall, High Street, Newport PO30 1UD ☎ 01983 823804 ◌ astrid.davies@iow.gov.uk

Personnel / HR: Mrs Claire Shand, Head - Human Resources & Organisational Change, County Hall, High Street, Newport PO30 1UD ☎ 01983 823120 ◌ claire.shand@iow.gov.uk

Planning: Mrs Wendy Perera, Head - Planning & Regulatory Services, County Hall, High Street, Newport PO30 1UD ☎ 01983 821000 ◌ wendy.perera@iow.gov.uk

Procurement: Mrs Sue Dasant, Strategic Manager - Procurement & Contract, County Hall, High Street, Newport PO30 1UD ☎ 01983 821000 ◌ sue.dasant@iow.gov.uk

Public Libraries: Mr Rob Jones, Libraries Officer, 5 Mariners Way, Somerton Industrial Estate, Cowes PO31 8PD ☎ 01983 203885 ◌ rob.jones@iow.gov.uk

Recycling & Waste Minimisation: Ms Laura Kay, Principal Waste Policy & Delivery Manager, County Hall, High Street, Newport PO30 1UD ☎ 01983 823777 ◌ laura.kay@iow.gov.uk

Road Safety: Mrs Tracey Webb, Senior Road Safety Officer, Sandown Fire Station, East Yar Road, Newport PO36 9AX ☎ 01983 408263 ◌ tracey.webb@iow.gov.uk

Social Services: Mr Martin Elliott, Director - Adult Social Care, County Hall, High Street, Newport PO30 1UD ☎ 01983 821000 ◌ martin.elliott@iow.gov.uk

Public Health: Prof Rida Elkheir, Director - Public Health, County Hall, High Street, Newport PO30 1UD ◌ rida.elkheir@iow.gov.uk

Staff Training: Mr Charles Charalambous, Commissioning Manager, The Carnival Learning Centre, Westridge, Brading Road, Ryde PO33 1QS ☎ 01983 821000 ◌ charles.charalambous@iow.gov.uk

Sustainable Development: Mr Jim Fawcett, Principal Officer - Environment, County Hall, High Street, Newport PO30 1UD ☎ 01983 821000 ◌ ashley.curzon@iow.gov.uk

Tourism: Mr Ashley Curzon, Strategic Manager - Economic Development & Asset Management, County Hall, High Street, Newport PO30 1UD ☎ 01983 821000 ext 6210 ◌ ashley.curzon@iow.gov.uk

Transport Planner: Mr Chris Wells, Principal Policy Planning Officer - Highways & Transport, Enterprise House, St Cross Business Park, Newport PO30 5WB ☎ 01983 821000 ◌ chris.wells@iow.gov.uk

Waste Collection and Disposal: Mr Mike Ackrill, Principal Waste & Contracts Officer, County Hall, High Street, Newport PO30 1UD ☎ 01983 821000 ◌ mike.ackrill@iow.gov.uk

Waste Management: Mr Mike Ackrill, Principal Waste & Contracts Officer, County Hall, High Street, Newport PO30 1UD ☎ 01983 821000 ◌ mike.ackrill@iow.gov.uk

COUNCILLORS

Leader of the Council: Bacon, Jonathan (IND - Brading, St.Helens & Bembridge)
jonathan.bacon@iow.gov.uk

Deputy Leader of the Council: Stubbings, Stephen (IND - Ventnor West)
stephen.stubbings@iow.gov.uk

Baker-Smith, Julia (IND - Whippingham & Osborne)
julia.baker-smith@iow.gov.uk

Barry, Reginald (LD - Nettlestone and Seaview)
regbarry@outlook.com

Bertie, Paul (CON - Cowes North)
paul.bertie@iow.gov.uk

Blezzard, Robert (IND - Sandown North)
bob.blezzard@iow.gov.uk

Bloomfield, Raymond (CON - Lake South)
ray.bloomfield@iow.gov.uk

Chapman, Charles (IND - Ryde South)
charles.chapman@iow.gov.uk

Downer, Rodney (IND - Godshill and Wroxhall)
rodney.downer@iow.gov.uk

Eccles, David (CON - Freshwater North)
david.eccles@iow.gov.uk

Fuller, Paul (IND - Cowes West and Gurnard)
paulfulleriw@gmail.com

Gauntlett, Conrad (CON - Havenstreet, Ashey & Haylands)

Gilbey, Jonathan (IND - Shanklin Central)
jonathan.gilbey@iow.gov.uk

Hillard, Luisa (IND - East Cowes)
luisa.hillard@iow.gov.uk

Hobart, John (CON - Carisbrooke)
john.hobart@iow.gov.uk

Hollands, Alan (LAB - Lake North)
alan.hollands@btinternet.com

Hollis, Richard (CON - Parkhurst)
richard.hollis@iow.gov.uk

Howe, John (LD - Totland)
john.howe@iow.gov.uk

Hutchinson, Stuart (CON - West Wight)
stu.hutch@btinternet.com

Jones-Evans, Julie (CON - Newport Central)
julie.jones-evans@iow.gov.uk

Jordan, Philip (IND - Ryde North West)
phil.jordan@iow.gov.uk

Kendall, Gordon (IND - Brading, St Helens & Bembridge)
gordon.kendall@tiscali.co.uk

Lumley, Geoff (LAB - Newport East)
geofflumley2@gmail.com

Medland, John (IND - Freshwater South)
john.medland@iow.gov.uk

Nicholson, John (CON - Cowes South & Northwood)
cllr.john.nicholson@btconnect.com

Peacey-Wilcox, Lora (CON - Cowes Medina)
lora@onwight.net

Perks, Graham (UKIP - Ventnor East)
graham.perks@iow.gov.uk

Pitcher, Daryll (UKIP - Wootton Bridge)
daryll.pitcher@iow.gov.uk

Price, Matthew (CON - Newport North)
matthew.price@iow.gov.uk

Priest, Richard (IND - Shanklin South)
richard.priest@iow.gov.uk

Richards, Colin (IND - Arreton & Newchurch)
colin.richards@iow.gov.uk

Seely, Robert (CON - Central Wight)
bob.seely@iow.gov.uk

Smart, Shirley (IND - Newport South)
shirley.smart@iow.gov.uk

Stephens, Ian (IND - Ryde West)
ian.stephens@iow.gov.uk

Stewart, David (CON - Chale Niton & Whitwell)
david.stewart@iow.gov.uk

Ward, Ian (CON - Sandown South)
ian.ward@iow.gov.uk

Warlow, Ivor (IND - Binstead and Fishbourne)
ivor.warlow@iow.gov.uk

Whitby-Smith, Roger (IND - Ryde East)
roger.whitbysmith@iow.gov.uk

Whitehouse, Christopher (CON - Newport West)
chris.whitehouse@iow.gov.uk

Whittle, Wayne (CON - Ryde North East)
wayne.whittle@iow.gov.uk

POLITICAL COMPOSITION
IND: 18, CON: 16, LAB: 2, LD: 2, UKIP: 2

Islington   L

Islington London Borough Council, Town Hall, Upper Street,
London N1 2UD
☎ 020 7527 2000 ⌀ contact@islington.gov.uk ⌨ www.islington.gov.uk

FACTS AND FIGURES
Parliamentary Constituencies: Islington North, Islington South and
Finsbury
EU Constituencies: London
Election Frequency: Elections are of whole council

PRINCIPAL OFFICERS

Chief Executive: Ms Lesley Seary, Chief Executive, Town Hall,
Upper Street, London N1 2UD ☎ 020 7527 3062
⌀ lesley.seary@islington.gov.uk

Assistant Chief Executive: Ms Lela Kogbara, ACE - Strategy &
Partnerships, Room G16, Town Hall, Upper Street, London N1 2UD
☎ 020 7527 3120; 020 7527 3013 ⌀ lela.kogbara@islington.gov.uk

Assistant Chief Executive: Ms Debra Norman, ACE -
Governance & HR, Town Hall, Upper Street, London N1 2UD
☎ 020 7527 6096; 020 7527 3267 ⌀ debra.norman@islington.gov.uk

Senior Management: Ms Julie Billett, Director - Public Health,
Town Hall, Upper Street, London N1 2UD ☎ 020 7527 1221
⌀ julie.billett@camden.gov.uk

Senior Management: Mr Mike Curtis, Corporate Director -
Finance & Resources, 7 Newington Barrow Way, London N7 7EP
☎ 020 7527 2294; 020 7527 2407 ⌀ mike.curtis@islington.gov.uk

Senior Management: Ms Carmel Littleton, Corporate Director -
Children's Services, Town Hall, Upper Street, London N1 2UD
⌀ carmel.littleton@islington.gov.uk

Senior Management: Mr Sean McLaughlin, Corporate Director
- Housing & Adult Social Services, 338-346 Goswell Road, London
EC1V 7LQ ☎ 020 7527 8178; 020 7527 8362
⌀ sean.mclaughlin@islington.gov.uk

ISLINGTON

Senior Management: Mr Kevin O'Leary, Corporate Director - Environment & Regeneration, 222 Upper Street, London N1 1XR ☎ 020 7527 2350; 020 7527 2731 ✆ kevin.oleary@islington.gov.uk

Access Officer / Social Services (Disability): Mr Sean McLaughlin, Corporate Director - Housing & Adult Social Services, 338-346 Goswell Road, London EC1V 7LQ ☎ 020 7527 8178; 020 7527 8362 ✆ sean.mclaughlin@islington.gov.uk

Building Control: Ms Jan Hart, Service Director - Public Protection & Development Management, 222 Upper Street, London N1 1XR ☎ 020 7527 3193; 020 7527 3375 ✆ jan.hart@islington.gov.uk

Civil Registration: Mr Besserat Atsehaba, Superintendent Registrar, Town Hall, Upper Street, London N1 2UD ☎ 020 7527 6357; 020 7527 6308 ✆ besserat.atsehaba@islington.gov.uk

PR / Communications: Ms Lela Kogbara, ACE - Strategy & Partnerships, Room G16, Town Hall, Upper Street, London N1 2UD ☎ 020 7527 3120; 020 7527 3013 ✆ lela.kogbara@islington.gov.uk

Community Safety: Mr Alva Bailey, Head of Service - Community Safety, Room 116, 222 Upper Street, London N1 1XR ☎ 020 7527 3135; 020 7527 3098 ✆ alva.bailey@islington.gov.uk

Computer Management: Mr Ian Adams, Director - Digital & Processing Services, 7 Newington Barrow Way, London N7 7EP ☎ 020 7527 4796 ✆ ian.adams@islington.gov.uk

Consumer Protection and Trading Standards: Ms Jan Hart, Service Director - Public Protection & Development Management, 222 Upper Street, London N1 1XR ☎ 020 7527 3193; 020 7527 3375 ✆ jan.hart@islington.gov.uk

Contracts: Mr Peter Hurlock, Head of Strategic Procurement, 7 Newington Barrow Way, Finsbury Park, London N7 7EP ☎ 020 7257 3131 ✆ peter.hurlock@islington.gov.uk

Customer Service: Mr Martin Bevis, Director - Revenues & Customer Service, 222 Upper Street, London N1 7XR ☎ 07825 098691 ✆ martin.bevis@islington.gov.uk

Economic Development: Ms Lela Kogbara, ACE - Strategy & Partnerships, Room G16, Town Hall, Upper Street, London N1 2UD ☎ 020 7527 3120; 020 7527 3013 ✆ lela.kogbara@islington.gov.uk

E-Government: Mr Ian Adams, Director - Digital & Processing Services, 7 Newington Barrow Way, London N7 7EP ☎ 020 7527 4796 ✆ ian.adams@islington.gov.uk

Electoral Registration: Mr Andrew Smith, Electoral Services Manager, Town Hall, Upper Street, London N1 2UD ☎ 020 7527 3085; 020 7527 3289 ✆ andrew.smith@islington.gov.uk

Emergency Planning: Mr Dan Lawson, Emergency Planning Officer, 222 Upper Street, London N1 1XE ☎ 020 7527 2690 ✆ daniel.lawson@islington.gov.uk

Environmental / Technical Services: Mr Kevin O'Leary, Corporate Director - Environment & Regeneration, 222 Upper Street, London N1 1XR ☎ 020 7527 2350; 020 7527 2731 ✆ kevin.oleary@islington.gov.uk

Environmental Health: Ms Jan Hart, Service Director - Public Protection & Development Management, 222 Upper Street, London N1 1XE ☎ 020 7527 3193; 020 7527 3375 ✆ jan.hart@islington.gov.uk

Facilities: Mr Martin Bevis, Director - Revenues & Customer Service, 222 Upper Street, London N1 7XR ☎ 07825 098691 ✆ martin.bevis@islington.gov.uk

Finance: Mr Mike Curtis, Corporate Director - Finance & Resources, 222 Upper Street, London N1 1XR ☎ 020 7527 2294; 020 7527 2407 ✆ mike.curtis@islington.gov.uk

Finance: Mr Alan Layton, Director - Financial Management, 222 Upper Street, London N1 1XR ☎ 020 7527 2835; 020 7527 2407 ✆ alan.layton@islington.gov.uk

Treasury: Mr Mike Curtis, Corporate Director - Finance & Resources, 7 Newington Barrow Way, London N7 7EP ☎ 020 7527 2294; 020 7527 2407 ✆ mike.curtis@islington.gov.uk

Pensions: Mr Stephen Rogers, Pensions Manager, 7 Newington Barrow Way, Finsbury Park, London N7 7EP ☎ 020 7527 2028 ✆ stephen.rogers@islington.gov.uk

Fleet Management: Mr Martin Holland, Head of Highway Services, 222 Upper Street, London N1 1XR ☎ 020 7527 2434 ✆ martin.holland@islington.gov.uk

Grounds Maintenance: Mr Andrew Bedford, Parks & Open Spaces Manager, Clocktower Office, 36 North Road, London N7 9TU ☎ 020 7527 3287 ✆ andrew.bedford@islington.gov.uk

Health and Safety: Ms Donna Lewis, Head of Health & Safety, 7 Newington Barrow Way, Finsbury Park, London N7 7EP ☎ 020 7527 2230 ✆ donna.lewis@islington.gov.uk

Highways: Mr Bram Kainth, Director - Public Realm, 222 Upper Street, London N1 1XR ☎ 020 7527 2949; 020 7527 2145 ✆ bram.kainth@islington.gov.uk

Home Energy Conservation: Ms Lucy Padfield, Energy Services Manager, Energy Centre, 222 Upper Street, London N1 1RE ☎ 020 7527 2501; 020 7527 2332 ✆ lucy.padfield@islington.gov.uk

Housing: Mr Sean McLaughlin, Corporate Director - Housing & Adult Social Services, 338-346 Goswell Road, London EC1V 7LQ ☎ 020 7527 8178 ✆ sean.mclaughlin@islington.gov.uk

Local Area Agreement: Ms Anette Hobart, Corporate Partnership & Performance Manager, Town Hall, Upper Street, London N1 2UD ☎ 020 7527 3244 ✆ annette.hobart@islington.gov.uk

Legal: Ms Debra Norman, ACE - Governance & HR, Town Hall, Upper Street, London N1 2UD ☎ 020 7527 6096; 020 7527 3267 ✆ debra.norman@islington.gov.uk

Licensing: Ms Jan Hart, Service Director - Public Protection & Development Management, 222 Upper Street, London N1 1RE ☎ 020 7527 3193; 020 7527 3375 ✆ jan.hart@islington.gov.uk

Lighting: Mr Bram Kainth, Director - Public Realm, 222 Upper Street, London N1 1XR ☎ 020 7527 2949; 020 7527 2145 ⏱ bram.kainth@islington.gov.uk

Member Services: Mr John Lynch, Head - Democratic Services, Town Hall, Upper Street, London N1 2UD ☎ 020 7527 3002; 020 7527 3092 ⏱ john.lynch@islington.gov.uk

Parking: Mr Bram Kainth, Director - Public Realm, 222 Upper Street, London N1 1XR ☎ 020 7527 2949; 020 7527 2145 ⏱ bram.kainth@islington.gov.uk

Personnel / HR: Ms Debra Norman, ACE - Governance & HR, Town Hall, Upper Street, London N1 2UD ☎ 020 7527 6096; 020 7527 3267 ⏱ debra.norman@islington.gov.uk

Planning: Ms Karen Sullivan, Service Director - Planning & Development, 222 Upper Street, London N1 1XR ☎ 020 7527 2730 ⏱ karen.sullivan@islington.gov.uk

Public Libraries: Ms Rosemary Doyle, Head of Library & Cultural Services, Fieldway Crescent, London N5 1PF ☎ 020 7619 6903; 020 7619 6906 ⏱ rosemary.doyle@islington.gov.uk

Recycling & Waste Minimisation: Mr Bram Kainth, Director - Public Realm, 222 Upper Street, London N1 1XR ☎ 020 7527 2949; 020 7527 2145 ⏱ bram.kainth@islington.gov.uk

Road Safety: Mr Bram Kainth, Director - Public Realm, 222 Upper Street, London N1 1XR ☎ 020 7527 2949; 020 7527 2145 ⏱ bram.kainth@islington.gov.uk

Social Services (Adult): Mr Sean McLaughlin, Corporate Director - Housing & Adult Social Services, 338-346 Goswell Road, London EC1V 7LQ ☎ 020 7527 8178; 020 7527 8362 ⏱ sean.mclaughlin@islington.gov.uk

Public Health: Ms Julie Billett, Director - Public Health, Town Hall, Upper Street, London N1 2UD ☎ 020 7527 1221 ⏱ julie.billett@camden.gov.uk

Street Scene: Mr Bram Kainth, Director - Public Realm, 222 Upper Street, London N1 1XR ☎ 020 7527 2949; 020 7527 2145 ⏱ bram.kainth@islington.gov.uk

Traffic Management: Mr Bram Kainth, Director - Public Realm, 222 Upper Street, London N1 1XR ☎ 020 7527 2949; 020 7527 2145 ⏱ bram.kainth@islington.gov.uk

Transport: Mr Bram Kainth, Director - Public Realm, 222 Upper Street, London N1 1XR ☎ 020 7527 2949; 020 7527 2145 ⏱ bram.kainth@islington.gov.uk

Transport Planner: Ms Karen Sullivan, Service Director - Planning & Development, 222 Upper Street, London N1 1XR ☎ 020 7527 2730 ⏱ karen.sullivan@islington.gov.uk

Waste Collection and Disposal: Mr Bram Kainth, Director - Public Realm, 222 Upper Street, London N1 1XR ☎ 020 7527 2949; 020 7527 2145 ⏱ bram.kainth@islington.gov.uk

Waste Management: Mr Bram Kainth, Director - Public Realm, 222 Upper Street, London N1 1XR ☎ 020 7527 2949; 020 7527 2145 ⏱ bram.kainth@islington.gov.uk

COUNCILLORS

Mayor: Fletcher, Kat (LAB - St. George's) kat.fletcher@islington.gov.uk

Deputy Mayor: O'Halloran, Una (LAB - Caledonian) una.o'halloran@islington.gov.uk

Leader of the Council: Watts, Richard (LAB - Tollington) richard.watts@islington.gov.uk

Deputy Leader of the Council: Burgess, Janet (LAB - Junction) janet.burgess@islington.gov.uk

Andrews, Raphael (LAB - Clerkenwell) raphael.andrews@islington.gov.uk

Caluori, Joe (LAB - Mildmay) joe.caluori@islington.gov.uk

Champion, Rowena (LAB - Barnsbury)

Chowdhury, Jilani (LAB - Barnsbury) jilani.chowdhury@islington.gov.uk

Comer- Schwartz, Kaya (LAB - Junction) kaya.comerschwartz@islington.gov.uk

Convery, Paul (LAB - Caledonian) paul.convery@islington.gov.uk

Court, James (LAB - Clerkenwell) james.court@islington.gov.uk

Debono, Theresa (LAB - Highbury West) theresa.debono@islington.gov.uk

Diner, Alex (LAB - Canonbury) alex.diner@islington.gov.uk

Donovan, Alice (LAB - Clerkenwell) alice.donovan@islington.gov.uk

Doolan, Gary (LAB - St. Peter's) gary.doolan@islington.gov.uk

Erdogan, Aysegul (LAB - Highbury East) aysegul.erdogan@islington.gov.uk

Gallagher, Troy (LAB - Bunhill) troy.gallagher@islington.gov.uk

Gantly, Osh (LAB - Highbury East) osh.gantly@islington.gov.uk

Gill, Satnam (LAB - St. George's) satnam.gill@islington.gov.uk

Greening, Richard (LAB - Highbury West) richard.greening@islington.gov.uk

Hamitouche, Mouna (LAB - Barnsbury) mouna.hamitouche@islington.gov.uk

Heather, Gary (LAB - Finsbury Park) gary.heather@islington.gov.uk

Hull, Andy (LAB - Highbury West) andy.hull@islington.gov.uk

Ismail, Rakhia (LAB - Holloway) rakhia.ismail@islington.gov.uk

Jeapes, Clare (LAB - Canonbury) clare.jeapes@islington.gov.uk

ISLINGTON

Kaseki, Jean Roger (LAB - Tollington)
jean.kaseki@islington.gov.uk

Kay, Jenny (LAB - Mildmay)
jenny.kay@islington.gov.uk

Khan, Robert (LAB - Bunhill)
robert.khan@islington.gov.uk

Klute, Martin (LAB - St. Peter's)
martin.klute@islington.gov.uk

Nicholls, Tim (LAB - Junction)
tim.nicholls@islington.gov.uk

O'Sullivan, Michael (LAB - Finsbury Park)
mick.o'sullivan@islington.gov.uk

Parker, Olly (LAB - Mildmay)
olly.parker@islington.gov.uk

Perry, Alice (LAB - St. Peter's)
alice.perry@islington.gov.uk

Perry, Rupert (LAB - Caledonian)
rupert.perry@islington.gov.uk

Picknell, Angela (LAB - St. Mary's)
angela.picknell@islington.gov.uk

Poole, Gary (LAB - St. Mary's)
gary.poole@islington.gov.uk

Poyser, Dave (LAB - Hillrise)
dave.poyser@islington.gov.uk

Russell, Caroline (GRN - Highbury East)
caroline.russell@islington.gov.uk

Safi Ngongo, Micheline (LAB - Hillrise)
michelline.ngongo@islington.gov.uk

Shaikh, Asima (LAB - Finsbury Park)
asima.shaikh@islington.gov.uk

Smith, Paul (LAB - Holloway)
paul.smith@islington.gov.uk

Spall, Marian (LAB - Hillrise)
marian.spall@islington.gov.uk

Turan, Nurullah (LAB - St. Mary's)
nurullah.turan@islington.gov.uk

Ward, Nick (LAB - St. George's)
nick.ward@islington.gov.uk

Ward, Diarmaid (LAB - Holloway)
diarmaid.ward@islington.gov.uk

Wayne, Nick (LAB - Canonbury)
nick.wayne@islington.gov.uk

Webbe, Claudia (LAB - Bunhill)
claudia.webbe@islington.gov.uk

Williamson, Flora (LAB - Tollington)
flora.williamson@islington.gov.uk

POLITICAL COMPOSITION
LAB: 47, GRN: 1

COMMITTEE CHAIRS

Audit: Mr Satnam Gill

Environment & Regeneration: Mr James Court

Health & Care: Mr Martin Klute

Health & Wellbeing: Mr Richard Watts

Housing: Mr Michael O'Sullivan

Licensing: Ms Flora Williamson

Planning: Mr Robert Khan

Kensington & Chelsea   L

The Royal Borough of Kensington & Chelsea Council, Town Hall, Hornton Street, London W8 7NX
☎ 020 7361 3000 📠 020 7938 1445 🖥 www.rbkc.gov.uk

FACTS AND FIGURES
Parliamentary Constituencies: Chelsea and Fulham, Kensington
EU Constituencies: London
Election Frequency: Elections are of whole council

PRINCIPAL OFFICERS

Chief Executive: Mr Nicholas Holgate, Town Clerk, Town Hall, Hornton Street, London W8 7NX ☎ 020 8753 2001; 020 7361 2299; 020 8741 0307; 020 7361 2764 📧 nicholas.holgate@rbkc.gov.uk

Senior Management: Ms Liz Bruce, Tri-Borough Executive Director - Adult Social Care, Town Hall, King Street, London W6 9JU ☎ 020 8753 5166 📧 liz.bruce@lbhf.gov.uk

Senior Management: Mrs Clare Chamberlain, Tri-Borough Executive Director - Children's Services, Town Hall, Hornton Street, London W8 7NX 📧 clare.chamberlain@rbkc.gov.uk

Senior Management: Ms Sue Harris, Director - Cleaner, Greener & Cultural Services, Town Hall, King Street, London W6 0LJ ☎ 020 8753 4295 📧 sue.harris@lbhf.gov.uk

Senior Management: Mr Tony Redpath, Director - Strategy & Local Services, Town Hall, Hornton Street, London W8 7NX ☎ 020 7361 3174 📧 tony.redpath@rbkc.gov.uk

Senior Management: Dr Mike Robinson, Director - Public Health, Hammersmith Town Hall, 7 King Street, London W6 9JU ☎ 020 7641 4590 📧 mrobinson4@westminster.gov.uk

Senior Management: Mr Graham Stallwood, Executive Director - Planning & Borough Development, Town Hall, Hornton Street, London W8 7NX ☎ 020 7361 2075 📧 graham.stallwood@brkc.gov.uk

Building Control: Mr John Allen, Building Control Manager, Town Hall, Hornton Street, London W8 7NX ☎ 020 7361 3802 📧 john.allen@rbkc.gov.uk

Building Control: Mr Graham Stallwood, Executive Director - Planning & Borough Development, Town Hall, Hornton Street, London W8 7NX ☎ 020 7361 2075 📧 graham.stallwood@brkc.gov.uk

Children / Youth Services: Mrs Clare Chamberlain, Tri-Borough Executive Director - Children's Services, Town Hall, Hornton Street, London W8 7NX 📧 clare.chamberlain@rbkc.gov.uk

Children / Youth Services: Ms Rachel Wright-Turner, Tri-Borough Director - Strategic Commissioning for Children & Families, Town Hall, Hornton Street, London W8 7NX ⏱ rachel.wright-turner@rbkc.gov.uk

Civil Registration: Mr Steven Lord, Superintendent Registrar, Chelsea Registrar Office, Kings Road, London SW3 5EE ☎ 020 7361 4107 ⏱ steven.lord@rbkc.gov.uk

PR / Communications: Mr Martin Fitzpatrick, Head of Media & Communications, Town Hall, Hornton Street, London W8 7NX ☎ 020 7361 3585; 020 7937 9670 ⏱ martin.fitzpatrick@rbkc.gov.uk

Community Safety: Mr David Page, Bi-Borough Director - Safer Neighbourhoods, Town Hall, King Street, London W6 9JU ☎ 020 8753 2125 ⏱ david.page@lbhf.gov.uk

Computer Management: Mr Ed Garcez, Tri-Borough Chief Information Officer, Town Hall, King Street, London W6 9JU ☎ 020 8753 2900 ⏱ ed.garcez@lbhf.gov.uk

Contracts: Mr Roger van Goethem, Procurement & Commercial Manager, Town Hall, Hornton Street, London W8 7NX ☎ 020 7361 3345 ⏱ roger.vangoethem@rbkc.gov.uk

Corporate Services: Ms Debbie Morris, Director - Human Resources, Town Hall, Hornton Street, London W8 7NX ☎ 020 8753 3068 ⏱ debbie.morris@lbhf.gov.uk

Customer Service: Mr Ray Brown, Director - Customer Access, Town Hall, Hornton Street, London W8 7NX ☎ 020 7361 3291; 020 7368 0246 ⏱ ray.brown@rbkc.gov.uk

Economic Development: Mr Graham Hart, Regeneration Manager, Town Hall, Hornton Street, London W8 7NX ☎ 020 7631 3336; 020 7361 2764 ⏱ graham.hart@rbkc.gov.uk

Education: Mrs Clare Chamberlain, Tri-Borough Executive Director - Children's Services, Town Hall, Hornton Street, London W8 7NX ⏱ clare.chamberlain@rbkc.gov.uk

Education: Mr Ian Heggs, Tri-Borough Director - Schools, Town Hall, Hornton Street, London W8 7NX ☎ 020 7745 6465 ⏱ ian.heggs@lbhf.gov.uk

Electoral Registration: Mrs Susan Loynes, Electoral Services Manager, Town Hall, Hornton Street, London W8 7NX ☎ 020 7361 3931 ⏱ susan.loynes@rbkc.gov.uk

Emergency Planning: Mr David Kerry, Contingency Planning Manager, Town Hall, Hornton Street, London W8 7NX ☎ 020 7361 2139; 020 7361 2573 ⏱ david.kerry@rbkc.gov.uk

Energy Management: Ms Debbie Morris, Director - Human Resources, Town Hall, King Street, London W6 9JU ☎ 020 8753 3068 ⏱ debbie.morris@lbhf.gov.uk

Environmental Health: Mr Nick Austin, Bi-Borough Director - Environmental Health, Council Offices, 37 Pembroke Road, London W6 6PW ☎ 020 8753 3904 ⏱ nick.austin@lbhf.gov.uk

Estates, Property & Valuation: Mr Richard Egan, Interim Director - Corporate Property & Customer Services, Town Hall, Hornton Street, London W8 7NX ⏱ richard.egan@rbkc.gov.uk

Facilities: Ms Debbie Morris, Director - Human Resources, Town Hall, King Street, London W6 9JU ☎ 020 8753 3068 ⏱ debbie.morris@lbhf.gov.uk

Finance: Mr Nicholas Holgate, Town Clerk, Town Hall, Hornton Street, London W8 7NX ☎ 020 7361 2384; 020 7361 3716 ⏱ nicholas.holgate@rbkc.gov.uk

Finance: Mr Hitesh Jolapara, Strategic Director - Financial Corporate Services, Town Hall, Hornton Street, London W8 7NX ☎ 020 7361 2316 ⏱ hitesh.jolapara@rbkc.gov.uk

Pensions: Mrs Maria Bailey, Pensions Manager, Town Hall, Hornton Street, London W8 7NX ☎ 020 7361 3000 ⏱ maria.bailey@rbkc.gov.uk

Pensions: Mr George Bruce, Tri-Borough Director - Pensions & Treasury, Westminster City Hall, 64 Victoria Street, London SW1E 6QP ⏱ g.bruce@westminster.gov.uk

Health and Safety: Mr Gary Mann, Health & Safety Officer, Town Hall, Hornton Street, London W8 7NX ☎ 020 7361 3733; 020 7361 2676 ⏱ gary.mann@rbkc.gov.uk

Highways: Mr Mahmood Siddiqi, Bi-Borough Director - Transport & Highways, Town Hall, Hornton Street, London W8 7NX ☎ 020 7361 3589; 020 8748 3020 ⏱ mahmood.siddiqi@rbkc.gov.uk

Housing: Ms Laura Johnson, Director - Housing, Town Hall, Hornton Street, London W8 7NX ☎ 020 7361 2362 ⏱ laura.johnson@rbkc.gov.uk

Housing Maintenance: Mr Nick Austin, Bi-Borough Director - Environmental Health, Council Offices, 37 Pembroke Road, London W6 6PW ☎ 020 8753 3904 ⏱ nick.austin@lbhf.gov.uk

Legal: Mrs Tasnim Shawkat, Tri-Borough Director - Law, Town Hall, Hornton Street, London W8 7NX ☎ 020 8753 2700 ⏱ tasnim.shawkat@lbhf.gov.uk

Leisure and Cultural Services: Mr Ullash Karia, Head of Leisure & Parks, The Stableyard, Holland Park, Ilchester Place, London W8 6LU ☎ 020 7938 8171 ⏱ ullash.karia@rbkc.gov.uk

Leisure and Cultural Services: Ms Donna Pentelow, Bi-Borough Head of Culture, Town Hall, King Street, London W6 0LJ ☎ 020 8752 2358 ⏱ donna.pentelow@lbhf.gov.uk

Licensing: Mr Patrick Crowley, Licensing Team Manager, Council Offices, 37 Pembroke Road, London W8 6PW ☎ 020 7341 5601; 020 7368 0231 ⏱ patrick.crowley@rbkc.gov.uk

Lighting: Mr Derek Mahon, Senior Lighting Engineer, Council Offices, 37 Pembroke Road, London W8 6PW ☎ 020 7341 5254 ⏱ derek.mahon@rbkc.gov.uk

KENSINGTON & CHELSEA

Lottery Funding, Charity and Voluntary: Mrs Lucy Ashdown, Funding & Partnerships Officer, Town Hall, Hornton Street, London W8 7NX ☎ 020 7361 2509 ⏚ lucy.ashdown@rbkc.gov.uk

Parking: Mr David Taylor, Bi-Borough Head of Parking Services, PO Box 3387, London SW6 2QF ☎ 020 8753 3251 ⏚ david.taylor@lbhf.gov.uk

Partnerships: Mrs Mel Marshman, Community Engagement Manager, Town Hall, Hornton Street, London W8 7NX ☎ 020 7361 2262 ⏚ melanie.marshman@rbkc.gov.uk

Personnel / HR: Ms Debbie Morris, Director - Human Resources, Town Hall, Hornton Street, London W8 7NX ☎ 020 8753 3068 ⏚ debbie.morris@lbhf.gov.uk

Planning: Mr Graham Stallwood, Executive Director - Planning & Borough Development, Town Hall, Hornton Street, London W8 7NX ☎ 020 7361 2075 ⏚ graham.stallwood@brkc.gov.uk

Procurement: Mr Andrew Lee, Head of Strategic Procurement, Town Hall, Hornton Street, London W8 7NX ☎ 020 7361 2674 ⏚ andrew.lee@rbkc.gov.uk

Public Libraries: Mr Mike Clarke, Tri-Borough Director - Libraries & Archives, Westminster City Hall, 64 Victoria Street, London SW1E 6QP ☎ 020 7641 2199 ⏚ mclarke1@westminster.gov.uk

Recycling & Waste Minimisation: Ms Sue Harris, Director - Cleaner, Greener & Cultural Services, Town Hall, King Street, London W6 0LJ ☎ 020 8753 4295 ⏚ sue.harris@lbhf.gov.uk

Regeneration: Mr Graham Hart, Regeneration Manager, Town Hall, Hornton Street, London W8 7NX ☎ 020 7631 3336; 020 7361 2764 ⏚ graham.hart@rbkc.gov.uk

Road Safety: Mr Neil Simpson, Road Safety Manager, Council Offices, 37 Pembroke Road, London W8 6PW ☎ 020 7361 3628 ⏚ neil.simpson@rbkc.gov.uk

Social Services: Ms Stella Baillie, Tri-Borough Director - Integrated Care, Town Hall, Hornton Street, London W8 7NX ☎ 020 7361 2398 ⏚ stella.baillie2@lbhf.gov.uk

Social Services: Ms Gaynor Driscoll, Joint Commissioning Manager - Sexual Health, Westminster City Hall, 64 Victoria Street, London SW1E 6QP ☎ 020 7641 4000 ⏚ gdriscoll@westminster.gov.uk

Social Services (Children): Mrs Clare Chamberlain, Tri-Borough Executive Director - Children's Services, Town Hall, Hornton Street, London W8 7NX ⏚ clare.chamberlain@rbkc.gov.uk

Public Health: Dr Mike Robinson, Director - Public Health, Hammersmith Town Hall, 7 King Street, London W6 9JU ☎ 020 7641 4590 ⏚ mrobinson4@westminster.gov.uk

Staff Training: Mr Nick Alcock, Corporate Learning & Development Manager, Council Offices, 37 Pembroke Road, London W8 6PW ☎ 020 7341 5130 ⏚ nick.alcock@rbkc.gov.uk

Sustainable Communities: Mr Tony Redpath, Director - Strategy & Local Services, Town Hall, Hornton Street, London W8 7NX ☎ 020 7361 3174 ⏚ tony.redpath@rbkc.gov.uk

Sustainable Development: Ms Joan McGarvey, Bi-Borough Senior Policy Officer, Transport, Environment and Leisure Services, Council Offices, 37 Pembroke Road, London W8 6PW ☎ 020 7341 5173 ⏚ joan.mcgarvey@rbkc.gov.uk

Town Centre: Ms Joanna Hammond, Neighbourhood Planning Manager, Town Hall, Hornton Street, London W8 7NX ☎ 020 7361 2061 ⏚ joanna.hammond@rbkc.gov.uk

Transport Planner: Mr Mark Chetwynd, Chief Transport Policy Officer, Town Hall, Hornton Street, London W8 7NX ☎ 020 7361 3747 ⏚ mark.chetwynd@rbkc.gov.uk

Waste Management: Ms Kathy May, Bi-Borough Head of Waste & Street Enforcement, Council Offices, 37 Pembroke Road, London W8 6PW ☎ 020 7341 5616 ⏚ kathy.may@rbkc.gov.uk

COUNCILLORS

Mayor: Rutherford, Elizabeth (CON - Courtfield) cllr.rutherford@rbkc.gov.uk

Deputy Mayor: Pascall, Will (CON - Stanley) cllr.pascall@rbkc.gov.uk

Leader of the Council: Paget-Brown, Nicholas (CON - Brompton & Hans Town) cllr.paget-brown@rbkc.gov.uk

Deputy Leader of the Council: Feilding-Mellen, Rock (CON - Holland) cllr.feilding-mellen@rbkc.gov.uk

Addenbrooke, Sarah (CON - Abingdon) cllr.addenbrooke@rbkc.gov.uk

Ahern, Tim (CON - Campden) cllr.ahern@rbkc.gov.uk

Allison, Eve (CON - St Helen's) cllr.allison@rbkc.gov.uk

Aouane, Fenella (CON - Earl's Court) cllr.aouane@rbkc.gov.uk

Atkinson, Robert (LAB - Notting Dale) cllr.r.atkinson@rbkc.gov.uk

Bakhtiar, Mohammed (LAB - St Helen's) cllr.bakhtiar@rbkc.gov.uk

Berrill-Cox, Adrian (CON - Chelsea Riverside) cllr.berrill-cox@rbkc.gov.uk

Blakeman, Judith (LAB - Notting Dale) cllr.blakeman@rbkc.gov.uk

Campbell, Elizabeth (CON - Royal Hospital) cllr.e.campbell@rbkc.gov.uk

Campbell, Barbara (CON - Pembridge) cllr.campbell@rbkc.gov.uk

Campion, David (CON - Pembridge) cllr.campion@rbkc.gov.uk

Coates, Anthony (CON - Courtfield) cllr.coates@rbkc.gov.uk

Coleridge, Timothy (CON - Brompton & Hans Town)
cllr.colleridge@rbkc.gov.uk

Collinson, Deborah (CON - Holland)
cllr.collinson@rbkc.gov.uk

Condon-Simmonds, Maighread (CON - Chelsea Riverside)
cllr.condon-simmonds@rbkc.gov.uk

Cyron, Anne (CON - Abingdon)
cllr.cyron@rbkc.gov.uk

Dent Coad, Emma (LAB - Golborne)
cllr.dentcoad@rbkc.gov.uk

Faulks, Catherine (CON - Campden)
cllr.faulks@rbkc.gov.uk

Freeman, Robert (CON - Campden)
mayor@rbkc.gov.uk

Hargreaves, Gerard (CON - Chelsea Riverside)
cllr.hargreaves@rbkc.gov.uk

Healy, Pat (LAB - Dalgarno)
cllr.healy@rbkc.gov.uk

Husband, James (CON - Abingdon)
cllr.husband@rbkc.gov.uk

Lasharie, Beinazir (LAB - Notting Dale)
cllr.lasharie@rbkc.gov.uk

Lightfoot, Warwick (CON - Holland)
cllr.lightfoot@rbkc.gov.uk

Lindsay, David (CON - Norland)
cllr.lindsay@rbkc.gov.uk

Littler, Harrison (LAB - Colville)
cllr.littler@rbkc.gov.uk

Lomas, Andrew (LAB - Colville)
cllr.lomas@rbkc.gov.uk

Mackover, Sam (CON - Queen's Gate)
Cllr.mackover@rbkc.gov.uk

Marshall, Quentin (CON - Courtfield)
cllr.marshall@rbkc.gov.uk

Mason, Pat (LAB - Golborne)
cllr.mason@rbkc.gov.uk

Mills, Julie (CON - Norland)
cllr.mills@rbkc.gov.uk

Moylan, Daniel (CON - Queen's Gate)
cllr.moylan@rbkc.gov.uk

Nicholls, David (CON - Redcliffe)
cllr.nicholls@rbkc.gov.uk

Palmer, Matthew (CON - Queen's Gate)
cllr.palmer@rbkc.gov.uk

Powell, Bevan (LAB - Golborne)
cllr.powell@rbkc.gov.uk

Press, Monica (LAB - Colville)
cllr.press@rbkc.gov.uk

Rinker, Andrew (CON - Royal Hospital)
cllr.rinker@rbkc.gov.uk

Rossi, Marie-Therese (CON - Redcliffe)
cllr.rossi@rbkc.gov.uk

Spalding, Malcolm (CON - Earl's Court)
cllr.spalding@rbkc.gov.uk

Taylor-Smith, Kim (CON - Stanley)
cllr.taylor-smith@rbkc.gov.uk

Thompson, Robert (LAB - Dalgarno)
cllr.thompson@rbkc.gov.uk

Wade, Linda (LD - Earl's Court)
cllr.wade@rbkc.gov.uk

Warrick, Paul (CON - Stanley)
cllr.warrick@rbkc.gov.uk

Weale, Mary (CON - Brompton & Hans Town)
cllr.weale@rbkc.gov.uk

Will, Emma (CON - Royal Hospital)
cllr.will@rbkc.gov.uk

Williams, Charles (CON - Redcliffe)
cllr.williams@rbkc.gov.uk

POLITICAL COMPOSITION
CON: 37, LAB: 12, LD: 1

COMMITTEE CHAIRS

Adult Social Care & Health: Mr Charles Williams

Family & Children's Services: Mr David Lindsay

Licensing: Ms Julie Mills

Planning: Mr Quentin Marshall

Kent   C

Kent County Council, Sessions House, County Hall, Maidstone ME14 1XQ
☎ 0845 824 7247 ⎙ 01622 759905 🖥 www.kent.gov.uk

FACTS AND FIGURES
Parliamentary Constituencies: Thanet North, Thanet South
EU Constituencies: South East
Election Frequency: Elections are of whole council

PRINCIPAL OFFICERS

Chief Executive: Mr David Cockburn, Head of Paid Service & Corporate Director, Sessions House, County Hall, Maidstone ME14 1XQ ☎ 03000 410001 ✑ david.cockburn@kent.gov.uk

Senior Management: Ms Amanda Beer, Corporate Director - Engagement, Organisation, Development & Design, Sessions House, County Hall, Maidstone ME14 1XQ ☎ 03000 415835 ✑ amanda.beer@kent.gov.uk

Senior Management: Ms Barbara Cooper, Corporate Director - Growth, Environment & Transport, Sessions House, County Hall, Maidstone ME14 1XQ ☎ 03000 415981 ✑ barbara.cooper@kent.gov.uk

Senior Management: Mr Andrew Ireland, Corporate Director - Social Care, Health & Wellbeing, Sessions House, County Hall, Maidstone ME14 1XQ ☎ 03000 416297 ✑ andrew.ireland@kent.gov.uk

Senior Management: Mr Patrick Leeson, Corporate Director - Education & Young People's Services, Sessions House, County Hall, Maidstone ME14 1XQ ☎ 03000 416384 ✑ patrick.leeson@kent.gov.uk

KENT

Senior Management: Mr Andrew Scott-Clark, Director - Public Health, Sessions House, County Hall, Maidstone ME14 1XQ ☎ 03000 416659 ⌁ andrew.scott-clark@kent.gov.uk

Senior Management: Mr Geoff Wild, Director - Governance & Law, Sessions House, County Hall, Maidstone ME14 1XQ ☎ 03000 416840 ⌁ geoff.wild@kent.gov.uk

Senior Management: Mr Andy Wood, Corporate Director - Finance & Procurement, Sessions House, County Hall, Maidstone ME14 1XQ ☎ 03000 416854 ⌁ andy.wood@kent.gov.uk

Architect, Building / Property Services: Ms Rebecca Spore, Director - Infrastructure, Sessions House, County Hall, Maidstone ME14 1XQ ☎ 03000 416716 ⌁ rebecca.spore@kent.gov.uk

Building Control: Ms Rebecca Spore, Director - Infrastructure, Sessions House, County Hall, Maidstone ME14 1XQ ☎ 03000 416716 ⌁ rebecca.spore@kent.gov.uk

Children / Youth Services: Mr Patrick Leeson, Corporate Director - Education & Young People's Services, Sessions House, County Hall, Maidstone ME14 1XQ ☎ 03000 416384 ⌁ patrick.leeson@kent.gov.uk

Civil Registration: Mr Andrew Stephens, Head of Libraries, Registration & Archives, Sessions House, County Hall, Maidstone ME14 1XQ ☎ 03000 414906 ⌁ andrew.stephens@kent.gov.uk

Community Safety: Mr Shafick Peerbux, Community Safety & Partnership Manager, Sessions House, County Hall, Maidstone ME14 1XQ ☎ 03000 413431 ⌁ shafick.peerbux@kent.gov.uk

Computer Management: Mr Michael Lloyd, Head of Technology, Strategy & Commissioning, Sessions House, County Hall, Maidstone ME14 1XQ ☎ 03000 410341 ⌁ michael.lloyd@kent.gov.uk

Consumer Protection and Trading Standards: Mr Mike Overbeke, Head of Public Protection, 8 Abbey Wood Road, Kingshill, West Malling ME19 4YT ☎ 03000 413427 ⌁ mike.overbeke@kent.gov.uk

Customer Service: Ms Diane Trollope, Head of Engagement & Consultation, Sessions House, County Hall, Maidstone ME14 1XQ ☎ 03000 416781 ⌁ diane.trollope@kent.gov.uk

Economic Development: Mr David Smith, Director - Economic Development, Invicta House, County Hall, Maidstone ME14 1XX ☎ 03000 417176 ⌁ david.smith2@kent.gov.uk

Education: Mr Scott Bagshaw, Head of Admissions & Transport, Sessions House, County Hall, Maidstone ME14 1XQ ☎ 03000 415798 ⌁ scott.bagshaw@kent.gov.uk

Education: Mr Patrick Leeson, Corporate Director - Education & Young People's Services, Sessions House, County Hall, Maidstone ME14 1XQ ☎ 03000 416384 ⌁ patrick.leeson@kent.gov.uk

Emergency Planning: Mrs Katie Stewart, Director - Environment Planning & Enforcement, Invicta House, County Hall, Maidstone ME14 1XX ☎ 0300 418827 ⌁ katie.stewart@kent.gov.uk

European Liaison: Mr Dafydd Pugh, Head of Brussels Office, Kent Brussels Office, International House, 45 Rue du Commerce, Brussels, B- 1000 ☎ 00322 504 0750 ⌁ dafydd.pugh@kent.gov.uk

Events Manager: Mrs Deborah Malthouse, Events Manager, Sessions House, County Hall, Maidstone ME14 1XQ ☎ 03000 416426 ⌁ deborah.malthouse@kent.gov.uk

Facilities: Ms Diane Woodcock, Kent Facilities (Amey), Sessions House, County Hall, Maidstone ME14 1XQ ☎ 03000 416772 ⌁ dianne.woodcock@kent.gov.uk

Pensions: Ms Barbara Cheatle, Pensions Manager, Brenchley House, Week Street, Maidstone ME14 1RF ☎ 03000 415270 ⌁ barbara.cheatle@kent.gov.uk

Grounds Maintenance: Mr Richard Kilvington, Business Manager, Aylesford Depot, Aylesford ME20 7HB ☎ 01622 605025 ⌁ richard.kilvington@kent.gov.uk

Health and Safety: Ms Helen Bale, Corporate Health & Safety Manager, Sessions House, County Hall, Maidstone ME14 1XQ ☎ 03000 417239 ⌁ helen.bale@kent.gov.uk

Highways: Mr Roger Wilkin, Director - Highways, Transportation & Waste, Invicta House, County Hall, Maidstone ME14 1XX ☎ 0300 413479 ⌁ roger.wilkin@kent.gov.uk

Legal: Mr Ben Watts, Interim General Counsel, Sessions House, County Hall, Maidstone ME14 1XQ ☎ 03000 416814 ⌁ benjamin.watts@kent.gov.uk

Member Services: Mr Paul Wickenden, Democratic Services Manager, Sessions House, County Hall, Maidstone ME14 1XQ ☎ 03000 416836 ⌁ paul.wickenden@kent.gov.uk

Personnel / HR: Ms Amanda Beer, Corporate Director - Engagement, Organisation, Development & Design, Sessions House, County Hall, Maidstone ME14 1XQ ☎ 03000 415835 ⌁ amanda.beer@kent.gov.uk

Planning: Mrs Katie Stewart, Director - Environment Planning & Enforcement, Invicta House, County Hall, Maidstone ME14 1XX ☎ 0300 418827 ⌁ katie.stewart@kent.gov.uk

Planning: Mrs Sharon Thompson, Head of Planning Applications, Invicta House, County Hall, Maidstone ME14 1XX ☎ 03000 413468 ⌁ sharon.thompson@kent.gov.uk

Procurement: Mr Henry Swan, Head of Procurement, Sessions House, County Hall, Maidstone ME14 1XQ ☎ 03000 416742 ⌁ henry.swan@kent.gov.uk

Public Libraries: Mr Andrew Stephens, Head of Libraries, Registration & Archives, Sessions House, County Hall, Maidstone ME14 1XQ ☎ 03000 414906 ⌁ andrew.stephens@kent.gov.uk

Social Services: Mr Andrew Ireland, Corporate Director - Social Care, Health & Wellbeing, Sessions House, County Hall, Maidstone ME14 1XQ ☎ 03000 416297 ⌁ andrew.ireland@kent.gov.uk

Social Services: Mr Mark Lobban, Director - Strategic Commissioning, Sessions House, County Hall, Maidstone ME14 1XQ ☎ 03000 415393 ✆ mark.lobban@kent.gov.uk

Social Services: Ms Penny Southern, Director - Learning Disability & Mental Health FSC, Sessions House, County Hall, Maidstone ME14 1XQ ☎ 03000 415505 ✆ penny.southern@kent.gov.uk

Social Services (Adult): Ms Anne Tidmarsh, Director - Older People & Physical Disability, Sessions House, County Hall, Maidstone ME14 1XQ ✆ anne.tidmarsh@kent.gov.uk

Social Services (Children): Mr Philip Segurola, Director - Specialist Children's Services, Sessions House, County Hall, Maidstone ME14 1XQ ☎ 03000 413120 ✆ philip.segurola@kent.gov.uk

Public Health: Mr Andrew Scott-Clark, Director - Public Health, Sessions House, County Hall, Maidstone ME14 1XQ ☎ 03000 416659 ✆ andrew.scott-clark@kent.gov.uk

Staff Training: Ms Julie Cudmore, Head of Organisation Development, Sessions House, County Hall, Maidstone ME14 1XQ ☎ 03000 417212 ✆ julie.cudmore@kent.gov.uk

Transport: Mr Philip Lightowler, Head of Public Transport, 1st Floor, Invicta House, County Hall, Maidstone ME14 1XX ☎ 03000 414073 ✆ philip.lightowler@kent.gov.uk

Waste Management: Mr Roger Wilkin, Director - Highways, Transportation & Waste, Invicta House, County Hall, Maidstone ME14 1XX ☎ 0300 413479 ✆ roger.wilkin@kent.gov.uk

COUNCILLORS

Chair: Gates, Tom (CON - Faversham)
tom.gates@kent.gov.uk

Vice-Chair: Brazier, David (CON - Sevenoaks North East)
david.brazier@kent.gov.uk

Leader of the Council: Carter, Paul (CON - Maidstone Rural North)
paul.carter@kent.gov.uk

Deputy Leader of the Council: Simmonds, John (CON - Canterbury West)
john.simmonds@kent.gov.uk

Group LeaderLatchford, Roger (UKIP - Birchington & Villages)
roger.latchford@kent.gov.uk

Allen, Ann (CON - Wilmington)
ann.allen@kent.gov.uk

Angell, Mike (CON - Ashford Rural South)
mike.angell@kent.gov.uk

Baldock, Mike (UKIP - Swale West)
mike.baldock@kent.gov.uk

Balfour, Matthew (CON - Malling Rural East)
matthew.balfour@kent.gov.uk

Bird, Rob (LD - Maidstone Central)
rob.bird@kent.gov.uk

Birkby, Hod (UKIP - Folkestone West)
hod.birkby@kent.gov.uk

Bond, Nicholas (UKIP - Herne Bay)
nicholas.bond@kent.gov.uk

Bowles, Andrew (CON - Swale East)
andrew.bowles@kent.gov.uk

Brivio, Pam (LAB - Dover Town)
pam.brivio@kent.gov.uk

Burgess, Lee (UKIP - Swale Central)
lee.burgess@kent.gov.uk

Caller, Colin (LAB - Gravesham East)
colin.caller@kent.gov.uk

Carey, Susan (CON - Elham Valley)
susan.carey@kent.gov.uk

Chard, Nick (CON - Sevenoaks East)
nick.chard@kent.gov.uk

Chittenden, Ian (LD - Maidstone North East)
ian.chittenden@kent.gov.uk

Clark, Brian (LD - Maidstone South)
brian.clark@kent.gov.uk

Cole, Penny (CON - Dartford East)
penny.cole@kent.gov.uk

Cooke, Gary (CON - Maidstone South East)
gary.cooke@kent.gov.uk

Cowan, Gordon (LAB - Dover Town)
gordon.cowan@kent.gov.uk

Crabtree, Margaret (CON - Sevenoaks Central)
margaret.crabtree@kent.gov.uk

Crowther, Adrian (UKIP - Sheppey)
adrian.crowther@kent.gov.uk

Dagger, Valerie (CON - Malling West)
valerie.dagger@kent.gov.uk

Daley, Dan (LD - Maidstone Central)
dan.daley@kent.gov.uk

Dance, Mark (CON - Whitstable)
mark.dance@kent.gov.uk

Davies, John (CON - Tunbridge Wells West)
john.davies@kent.gov.uk

Dean, Trudy (LD - Malling Central)
trudy.dean@kent.gov.uk

Eddy, Mike (LAB - Deal)
mike.eddy@kent.gov.uk

Elenor, Mo (UKIP - Margate & Cliftonville)
mo.elenor@kent.gov.uk

Elenor, Jeff (IND - Margate West)
jeffrey.elenor@kent.gov.uk

Gibbens, Graham (CON - Canterbury City North East)
graham.gibbens@kent.gov.uk

Gough, Roger (CON - Darent Valley)
roger.gough@kent.gov.uk

Harman, Peter (R - Swanscombe & Greenhithe)
peter.harman@kent.gov.uk

Harrison, Mike (CON - Whitstable)
mike.harrison@kent.gov.uk

Harrison, Angela (LAB - Sheerness)
angela.harrison@kent.gov.uk

Heale, Martyn (UKIP - Ramsgate)
martyn.heale@kent.gov.uk

KENT

Hill, Michael (CON - Tenterden)
michael.hill@kent.gov.uk

Hoare, Chris (UKIP - Tunbridge Wells East)
christopher.hoare@kent.gov.uk

Hohler, Sarah (CON - Malling North)
sarah.hohler@kent.gov.uk

Holden, Seán (CON - Cranbrook)
sean.holden@kent.gov.uk

Homewood, Peter (CON - Malling Rural North East)
peter.homewood@kent.gov.uk

Hotson, Eric (CON - Maidstone Rural South)
eric.hotson@kent.gov.uk

Howes, Sue (LAB - Northfleet & Gravesend West)
sue.howes@kent.gov.uk

King, Alex (CON - Tunbridge Wells Rural)
alex.king@kent.gov.uk

Kite, Jeremy (CON - Dartford Rural)
jeremy.kite@kent.gov.uk

Koowaree, George (LD - Ashford East)
george.koowaree@kent.gov.uk

Long, Richard (CON - Tonbridge)
richard.long1@kent.gov.uk

Lymer, Geoff (CON - Dover West)
geoff.lymer@kent.gov.uk

MacDowall, Brian (UKIP - Herne Bay)
brian.macdowall@kent.gov.uk

Maddison, Tom (LAB - Dartford North East)
tom.maddison@kent.gov.uk

Manion, Steve (CON - Dover North)
steve.manion@kent.gov.uk

Marsh, Alan (CON - Herne & Sturry)
alan.marsh@kent.gov.uk

McKenna, Frank (UKIP - Folkestone North East)
frank.mckenna@kent.gov.uk

Neaves, Bob (UKIP - Folkestone South)
bob.neaves@kent.gov.uk

Northey, Michael (CON - Canterbury South East)
michael.northey@kent.gov.uk

Oakford, Peter (CON - Tunbridge Wells North)
peter.oakford@kent.gov.uk

Ozog, Jan (CON - Dartford West)
jan.ozog@kent.gov.uk

Parry, Richard (CON - Sevenoaks West)
richard.parry@kent.gov.uk

Pearman, Clive (CON - Sevenoaks South)
clive.pearman@kent.gov.uk

Ridings, Leyland (CON - Sandwich)
leyland.ridings@kent.gov.uk

Rowbotham, Eileen (LAB - Deal)
eileen.rowbotham@kent.gov.uk

Scholes, James (CON - Tunbridge Wells South)
james.scholes@kent.gov.uk

Scobie, William (LAB - Margate & Cliftonville)
william.scobie@kent.gov.uk

Shonk, Trevor (UKIP - Ramsgate)
trevor.shonk@kent.gov.uk

Simkins, Charlie (CON - Ashford Rural West)
charlie.simkins@kent.ac.uk

Smith, Christopher (CON - Tonbridge)
chris.smith@kent.gov.uk

Smyth, Derek (LAB - Ashford South)
derek.smyth@kent.gov.uk

Stockell, Paulina (CON - Maidstone Rural West)
paulina.stockell@kent.gov.uk

Sweetland, Bryan (CON - Gravesham Rural)
bryan.sweetland@kent.gov.uk

Terry, Alan (UKIP - Broadstairs & Sir Moses Montefiore)
alan.terry@kent.gov.uk

Thandi, Narinderjit (LAB - Northfleet & Gravesend West)
narinderjit.thandi@kent.gov.uk

Truelove, Roger (LAB - Swale Central)
roger.truelove@kent.gov.uk

Vye, Martin (LD - Canterbury City South West)
martin.vye@kent.gov.uk

Waters, Carole (CON - Romney Marsh)
carole.waters@kent.gov.uk

Wedgebury, Jim (CON - Ashford Central)
jim.wedgebury@kent.gov.uk

Whittle, Jenny (CON - Maidstone Rural East)
jenny.whittle2@kent.gov.uk

Whybrow, Martin (GRN - Hythe)
martin.whybrow@kent.gov.uk

Wickham, Andrew (CON - Ashford Rural East)
andrew.wickham@kent.gov.uk

Wiltshire, Zita (UKIP - Broadstairs & Sir Moses Montefiore)
zita.wiltshire@kent.gov.uk

POLITICAL COMPOSITION
CON: 45, UKIP: 15, LAB: 12, LD: 7, R: 1, GRN: 1, Vacant: 1, IND: 1

COMMITTEE CHAIRS

Adult Social Care & Health: Mr Christopher Smith

Audit: Mr Richard Long

Children's Social Care & Health: Ms Jenny Whittle

Economic Development & Communities: Mr Andrew Wickham

Education & Young People's Services: Mr Leyland Ridings

Environment & Transport: Mrs Paulina Stockell

Health & Wellbeing: Mr Roger Gough

Planning: Mr John Davies

Kettering   D

Kettering Borough Council, Municipal Offices, Bowling Green Road, Kettering NN15 7QX
☎ 01536 410333 🖨 01536 410795
📧 customerservices@kettering.gov.uk
🖥 www.kettering.gov.uk

FACTS AND FIGURES
Parliamentary Constituencies: Kettering
EU Constituencies: East Midlands
Election Frequency: Elections are of whole council

PRINCIPAL OFFICERS

Chief Executive: Mr Graham Soulsby, Managing Director, Municipal Offices, Bowling Green Road, Kettering NN15 7QX
☎ 01536 532413 ⁂ grahamsoulsby@kettering.gov.uk

Deputy Chief Executive: Mr Martin Hammond, Deputy Chief Executive, Municipal Offices, Bowling Green Road, Kettering NN15 7QX ☎ 01536 534210 ⁂ martinhammond@kettering.gov.uk

Assistant Chief Executive: Ms Lisa Hyde, Assistant Chief Executive, Municipal Offices, Bowling Green Road, Kettering NN15 7QX ☎ 01536 534342 ⁂ lisahyde@kettering.gov.uk

Senior Management: Mr Guy Holloway, Head - Corporate & Cultural, Municipal Offices, Bowling Green Road, Kettering NN15 7QX ☎ 01536 534243 ⁂ guyholloway@kettering.gov.uk

Senior Management: Ms Sue Lyons, Head - Democratic & Legal Services, Municipal Offices, Bowling Green Road, Kettering NN15 7QX ☎ 01536 534209; 01536 543209 ⁂ suelyons@kettering.gov.uk

Best Value: Mr Guy Holloway, Head - Corporate & Cultural, Municipal Offices, Bowling Green Road, Kettering NN15 7QX
☎ 01536 534243 ⁂ guyholloway@kettering.gov.uk

Building Control: Mr Robert Harbour, Head - Development Services, Municipal Offices, Bowling Green Road, Kettering NN15 7QX ☎ 01536 534126 ⁂ robertharbour@kettering.gov.uk

PR / Communications: Mr Guy Holloway, Head - Corporate & Cultural, Municipal Offices, Bowling Green Road, Kettering NN15 7QX ☎ 01536 534243 ⁂ guyholloway@kettering.gov.uk

Community Planning: Mr Robert Harbour, Head - Development Services, Municipal Offices, Bowling Green Road, Kettering NN15 7QX ☎ 01536 534126 ⁂ robertharbour@kettering.gov.uk

Community Safety: Mrs Shirley Plenderleith, Head - Public Services, Municipal Offices, Bowling Green Road, Kettering NN15 7QX ☎ 01536 535696 ⁂ shirleyplenderleith@kettering.gov.uk

Computer Management: Mr Guy Holloway, Head - Corporate & Cultural, Municipal Offices, Bowling Green Road, Kettering NN15 7QX ☎ 01536 534243 ⁂ guyholloway@kettering.gov.uk

Corporate Services: Mr Guy Holloway, Head - Corporate & Cultural, Municipal Offices, Bowling Green Road, Kettering NN15 7QX ☎ 01536 534243 ⁂ guyholloway@kettering.gov.uk

Customer Service: Mrs Julie Trahern, Head - Customer Services, Municipal Offices, Bowling Green Road, Kettering NN15 7QX
☎ 01536 532428 ⁂ julietrahern@kettering.gov.uk

E-Government: Mr Guy Holloway, Head - Corporate & Cultural, Municipal Offices, Bowling Green Road, Kettering NN15 7QX
☎ 01536 534243 ⁂ guyholloway@kettering.gov.uk

Electoral Registration: Ms Sue Lyons, Head - Democratic & Legal Services, Municipal Offices, Bowling Green Road, Kettering NN15 7QX ☎ 01536 534209; 01536 543209 ⁂ suelyons@kettering.gov.uk

Emergency Planning: Mr Brendan Coleman, Head - Environmental Care Services, 4 Robinson Way, Telford Way Industrial Estate, Kettering NN16 8PP ☎ 01536 534460 ⁂ brendancoleman@kettering.gov.uk

Environmental Health: Mrs Shirley Plenderleith, Head - Public Services, Municipal Offices, Bowling Green Road, Kettering NN15 7QX ☎ 01536 535696 ⁂ shirleyplenderleith@kettering.gov.uk

Estates, Property & Valuation: Mr Mark Dickenson, Head - Resources, Municipal Offices, Bowling Green Road, Kettering NN15 7QX ☎ 01536 534303 ⁂ markdickenson@kettering.gov.uk

Facilities: Mr Guy Holloway, Head - Corporate & Cultural, Municipal Offices, Bowling Green Road, Kettering NN15 7QX
☎ 01536 534243 ⁂ guyholloway@kettering.gov.uk

Finance: Mr Mark Dickenson, Head - Resources, Municipal Offices, Bowling Green Road, Kettering NN15 7QX
☎ 01536 534303 ⁂ markdickenson@kettering.gov.uk

Finance: Mr Graham Soulsby, Managing Director, Municipal Offices, Bowling Green Road, Kettering NN15 7QX
☎ 01536 532413 ⁂ grahamsoulsby@kettering.gov.uk

Fleet Management: Mr Brendan Coleman, Head - Environmental Care Services, 4 Robinson Way, Telford Way Industrial Estate, Kettering NN16 8PP ☎ 01536 534460
⁂ brendancoleman@kettering.gov.uk

Grounds Maintenance: Mr Brendan Coleman, Head - Environmental Care Services, 4 Robinson Way, Telford Way Industrial Estate, Kettering NN16 8PP ☎ 01536 534460
⁂ brendancoleman@kettering.gov.uk

Health and Safety: Mr Brendan Coleman, Head - Environmental Care Services, 4 Robinson Way, Telford Way Industrial Estate, Kettering NN16 8PP ☎ 01536 534460
⁂ brendancoleman@kettering.gov.uk

Home Energy Conservation: Mrs Shirley Plenderleith, Head - Public Services, Municipal Offices, Bowling Green Road, Kettering NN15 7QX ☎ 01536 535696 ⁂ shirleyplenderleith@kettering.gov.uk

Housing: Mr John Conway, Head - Housing, Municipal Offices, Bowling Green Road, Kettering NN15 7QX ☎ 01536 534288
⁂ johnconway@kettering.gov.uk

Housing Maintenance: Mr John Conway, Head - Housing, Municipal Offices, Bowling Green Road, Kettering NN15 7QX
☎ 01536 534288 ⁂ johnconway@kettering.gov.uk

Legal: Ms Sue Lyons, Head - Democratic & Legal Services, Municipal Offices, Bowling Green Road, Kettering NN15 7QX
☎ 01536 534209; 01536 543209 ⁂ suelyons@kettering.gov.uk

KETTERING

Leisure and Cultural Services: Mr Guy Holloway, Head - Corporate & Cultural, Municipal Offices, Bowling Green Road, Kettering NN15 7QX ☎ 01536 534243 ⏱ guyholloway@kettering.gov.uk

Licensing: Mrs Shirley Plenderleith, Head - Public Services, Municipal Offices, Bowling Green Road, Kettering NN15 7QX ☎ 01536 535696 ⏱ shirleyplenderleith@kettering.gov.uk

Lighting: Mr Brendan Coleman, Head - Environmental Care Services, 4 Robinson Way, Telford Way Industrial Estate, Kettering NN16 8PP ☎ 01536 534460 ⏱ brendancoleman@kettering.gov.uk

Lottery Funding, Charity and Voluntary: Mrs Shirley Plenderleith, Head - Public Services, Municipal Offices, Bowling Green Road, Kettering NN15 7QX ☎ 01536 535696 ⏱ shirleyplenderleith@kettering.gov.uk

Member Services: Ms Sue Lyons, Head - Democratic & Legal Services, Municipal Offices, Bowling Green Road, Kettering NN15 7QX ☎ 01536 534209; 01536 543209 ⏱ suelyons@kettering.gov.uk

Parking: Mrs Shirley Plenderleith, Head - Public Services, Municipal Offices, Bowling Green Road, Kettering NN15 7QX ☎ 01536 535696 ⏱ shirleyplenderleith@kettering.gov.uk

Personnel / HR: Mr Mark Dickenson, Head - Resources, Municipal Offices, Bowling Green Road, Kettering NN15 7QX ☎ 01536 534303 ⏱ markdickenson@kettering.gov.uk

Planning: Mr Robert Harbour, Head - Development Services, Municipal Offices, Bowling Green Road, Kettering NN15 7QX ☎ 01536 534126 ⏱ robertharbour@kettering.gov.uk

Procurement: Mr Mark Dickenson, Head - Resources, Municipal Offices, Bowling Green Road, Kettering NN15 7QX ☎ 01536 534303 ⏱ markdickenson@kettering.gov.uk

Recycling & Waste Minimisation: Mr Brendan Coleman, Head - Environmental Care Services, 4 Robinson Way, Telford Way Industrial Estate, Kettering NN16 8PP ☎ 01536 534460 ⏱ brendancoleman@kettering.gov.uk

Staff Training: Mr Mark Dickenson, Head - Resources, Municipal Offices, Bowling Green Road, Kettering NN15 7QX ☎ 01536 534303 ⏱ markdickenson@kettering.gov.uk

Street Scene: Mr Brendan Coleman, Head - Environmental Care Services, 4 Robinson Way, Telford Way Industrial Estate, Kettering NN16 8PP ☎ 01536 534460 ⏱ brendancoleman@kettering.gov.uk

Sustainable Communities: Mr Robert Harbour, Head - Development Services, Municipal Offices, Bowling Green Road, Kettering NN15 7QX ☎ 01536 534126 ⏱ robertharbour@kettering.gov.uk

Sustainable Development: Mr Robert Harbour, Head - Development Services, Municipal Offices, Bowling Green Road, Kettering NN15 7QX ☎ 01536 534126 ⏱ robertharbour@kettering.gov.uk

Waste Collection and Disposal: Mr Brendan Coleman, Head - Environmental Care Services, 4 Robinson Way, Telford Way Industrial Estate, Kettering NN16 8PP ☎ 01536 534460 ⏱ brendancoleman@kettering.gov.uk

Waste Management: Mr Brendan Coleman, Head - Environmental Care Services, 4 Robinson Way, Telford Way Industrial Estate, Kettering NN16 8PP ☎ 01536 534460 ⏱ brendancoleman@kettering.gov.uk

COUNCILLORS

Mayor: Edwards, Scott (CON - St. Michael's & Wicksteed) scottedwards@kettering.gov.uk

Deputy Mayor: Zanger, Derek (CON - Burton Latimer) derekzanger@kettering.gov.uk

Leader of the Council: Roberts, Russell (CON - Barton) russellroberts@kettering.gov.uk

Deputy Leader of the Council: Bunday, Lloyd (CON - Ise Lodge) lloydbunday@kettering.gov.uk

Adams, Linda (LAB - Avondale Grange) lindaadams@kettering.gov.uk

Bain, Duncan (CON - Pipers Hill) duncanbain@kettering.gov.uk

Bellamy, Steve (CON - Barton) stevebellamy@kettering.gov.uk

Brown, Michael (CON - Brambleside) michaelbrown@kettering.gov.uk

Burton, James (CON - All Saint) jamesburton@kettering.gov.uk

Davies, Ashely (CON - Brambleside) ashdavies@kettering.gov.uk

Dearing, Mark (CON - Desborough Loatland) markdearing@kettering.gov.uk

Derbyshire, June (CON - Desborough Loatland) junederbyshire@kettering.gov.uk

Don, Maggie (LAB - St. Michael's & Wicksteed) maggiedon2@kettering.gov.uk

Groome, Ruth (IND - Burton Latimer) ruthgroome@kettering.gov.uk

Hakewill, Jim (CON - Slade) jimhakewill@kettering.gov.uk

Henson, Jenny (CON - St. Michael's & Wicksteed) jennyhenson@kettering.gov.uk

Hollobone, Philip (CON - Ise Lodge) philip.hollobone.mp@parliament.uk

Howes, David (CON - Welland) davidhowes@kettering.gov.uk

Jelley, Ian (CON - St. Peter's) ianjelley@kettering.gov.uk

Lee, Anne (LAB - Pipers Hill) annelee@kettering.gov.uk

Lynch, Shirley (CON - Ise Lodge) shirleylynch@kettering.gov.uk

Malin, Mary (CON - St. Peter's) marymalin@kettering.gov.uk

Mitchell, Clark (LAB - Avondale Grange)
clarkmitchell@kettering.gov.uk

Moreton, Cliff (CON - Slade)
cliffmoreton@kettering.gov.uk

Rowley, Mark (CON - Queen Eleanor & Buccleuch)
markrowley@kettering.gov.uk

Scrimshaw, Mike (LAB - William Knibb)
mikescrimshaw@kettering.gov.uk

Smith, Jan (CON - Burton Latimer)
jansmith@kettering.gov.uk

Soans, Dave (CON - Desborough St. Giles)
davesoans@kettering.gov.uk

Sumpter, Karl (CON - Rothwell)

Talbot, Margaret (CON - Rothwell)
margarettalbot@kettering.gov.uk

Tebbutt, Mike (CON - Desborough St. Giles)
miketebbutt@kettering.gov.uk

Thurland, Lesley (CON - All Saints)
lesleythurland@kettering.gov.uk

Titcombe, Gregory (CON - All Saints)
gregtitcombe@kettering.gov.uk

Watts, Keli (LAB - William Knibb)
keliwatts@kettering.gov.uk

West, Johnathon (LAB - Northfield)
jonathanwest@kettering.gov.uk

POLITICAL COMPOSITION
CON: 27, LAB: 7, IND: 1

COMMITTEE CHAIRS

Audit: Mr Johnathon West

Licensing: Mrs Margaret Talbot

Planning: Mrs Shirley Lynch

King's Lynn & West Norfolk   D

Borough Council of King's Lynn & West Norfolk, Chapel Street, King's Lynn PE30 1EX
☎ 01553 616200 🖷 01553 691663 ⌧ contact@west-norfolk.gov.uk
🖳 www.west-norfolk.gov.uk

FACTS AND FIGURES
Parliamentary Constituencies: Norfolk North West, Norfolk South West
EU Constituencies: Eastern
Election Frequency: Elections are of whole council

PRINCIPAL OFFICERS

Chief Executive: Mr Ray Harding, Chief Executive, King's Court, Chapel Street, King's Lynn PE30 1EX ☎ 01553 616245; 01553 616736 ⌧ ray.harding@west-norfolk.gov.uk

Senior Management: Mr Chris Bamfield, Executive Director - Commercial Services, King's Court, Chapel Street, King's Lynn PE30 1EX ☎ 01553 616648; 01553 616640 ⌧ chris.bamfield@west-norfolk.gov.uk

Senior Management: Mrs Debbie Gates, Executive Director - Central Services, King's Court, Chapel Street, King's Lynn PE30 1EX ☎ 01553 616605; 01553 616728 ⌧ debbie.gates@west-norfolk.gov.uk

Senior Management: Ms Lorraine Gore, Assistant Director - Finance, King's Court, Chapel Street, King's Lynn PE30 1EX ☎ 01553 616432 ⌧ lorraine.gore@west-norfolk.gov.uk

Senior Management: Mr Geoff Hall, Executive Director - Environment & Planning, King's Court, Chapel Street, King's Lynn PE30 1EX ☎ 01553 616618; 01553 616652 ⌧ geoff.hall@west-norfolk.gov.uk

Access Officer / Social Services (Disability): Mrs Allison Bingham, Building Technician, King's Court, Chapel Street, King's Lynn PE30 1EX ☎ 01553 616743 ⌧ allison.bingham@west-norfolk.gov.uk

Architect, Building / Property Services: Mr Matthew Henry, Property Services Manager, King's Court, Chapel Street, King's Lynn PE30 1EX ☎ 01553 616272; 01553 616682 ⌧ matthew.henry@west-norfolk.gov.uk

Best Value: Ms Sarah Dennis, Partnerships & Funding Officer, King's Court, Chapel Street, King's Lynn PE30 1EX ☎ 01553 616 256 ⌧ sarah.dennis@west-norfolk.gov.uk

Building Control: Mr Geoff Hall, Executive Director - Environment & Planning, King's Court, Chapel Street, King's Lynn PE30 1EX ☎ 01553 616618; 01553 616652 ⌧ geoff.hall@west-norfolk.gov.uk

PR / Communications: Mrs Sharon Clifton, Communications Manager, King's Court, Chapel Street, King's Lynn PE30 1EX ☎ 01553 616711 ⌧ sharon.clifton@west-norfolk.gov.uk

Community Planning: Mrs Debbie Gates, Executive Director - Central Services, King's Court, Chapel Street, King's Lynn PE30 1EX ☎ 01553 616605; 01553 616728 ⌧ debbie.gates@west-norfolk.gov.uk

Computer Management: Mrs Debbie Gates, Executive Director - Central Services, King's Court, Chapel Street, King's Lynn PE30 1EX ☎ 01553 616605; 01553 616728 ⌧ debbie.gates@west-norfolk.gov.uk

Contracts: Ms Lorraine Gore, Assistant Director - Finance, King's Court, Chapel Street, King's Lynn PE30 1EX ☎ 01553 616432 ⌧ lorraine.gore@west-norfolk.gov.uk

Corporate Services: Mr Ray Harding, Chief Executive, King's Court, Chapel Street, King's Lynn PE30 1EX ☎ 01553 616245; 01553 616736 ⌧ ray.harding@west-norfolk.gov.uk

Customer Service: Mrs Debbie Gates, Executive Director - Central Services, King's Court, Chapel Street, King's Lynn PE30 1EX ☎ 01553 616605; 01553 616728 ⌧ debbie.gates@west-norfolk.gov.uk

Economic Development: Mr Geoff Hall, Executive Director - Environment & Planning, King's Court, Chapel Street, King's Lynn PE30 1EX ☎ 01553 616618; 01553 616652 ⌧ geoff.hall@west-norfolk.gov.uk

KING'S LYNN & WEST NORFOLK

E-Government: Mrs Debbie Gates, Executive Director - Central Services, King's Court, Chapel Street, King's Lynn PE30 1EX ☎ 01553 616605; 01553 616728 ⌂ debbie.gates@west-norfolk.gov.uk

Electoral Registration: Mrs Sam Winter, Democratic Services Manager, King's Court, Chapel Street, King's Lynn PE30 1EX ☎ 01553 616327; 01553 616758 ⌂ sam.winter@west-norfolk.gov.uk

Emergency Planning: Mr Geoff Hall, Executive Director - Environment & Planning, King's Court, Chapel Street, King's Lynn PE30 1EX ☎ 01553 616618; 01553 616652 ⌂ geoff.hall@west-norfolk.gov.uk

Environmental Health: Mr Geoff Hall, Executive Director - Environment & Planning, King's Court, Chapel Street, King's Lynn PE30 1EX ☎ 01553 616618; 01553 616652 ⌂ geoff.hall@west-norfolk.gov.uk

Estates, Property & Valuation: Mr Matthew Henry, Property Services Manager, King's Court, Chapel Street, King's Lynn PE30 1EX ☎ 01553 616272; 01553 616682 ⌂ matthew.henry@west-norfolk.gov.uk

European Liaison: Mr Ostap Paparega, Regeneration & Economic Development Manager, King's Court, Chapel Street, King's Lynn PE30 1EX ☎ 01553 616890; 01553 775726 ⌂ ostap.paparega@west-norfolk.gov.uk

Events Manager: Mr Chris Bamfield, Executive Director - Commercial Services, King's Court, Chapel Street, King's Lynn PE30 1EX ☎ 01553 616648; 01553 616640 ⌂ chris.bamfield@west-norfolk.gov.uk

Finance: Ms Lorraine Gore, Assistant Director - Finance, King's Court, Chapel Street, King's Lynn PE30 1EX ☎ 01553 616432 ⌂ lorraine.gore@west-norfolk.gov.uk

Treasury: Mr Geoff Hall, Executive Director - Environment & Planning, King's Court, Chapel Street, King's Lynn PE30 1EX ☎ 01553 616618; 01553 616652 ⌂ geoff.hall@west-norfolk.gov.uk

Fleet Management: Mr Nathan Johnson, Public & Open Space Manager, King's Court, Chapel Street, King's Lynn PE30 1EX ☎ 01553 780780; 01553 771657 ⌂ nathan.johnson@west-norfolk.gov.uk

Grounds Maintenance: Mr Nathan Johnson, Public & Open Space Manager, King's Court, Chapel Street, King's Lynn PE30 1EX ☎ 01553 780780; 01553 771657 ⌂ nathan.johnson@west-norfolk.gov.uk

Health and Safety: Mr Dave Clack, Safety & Welfare Adviser, King's Court, Chapel Street, King's Lynn PE30 1EX ☎ 01553 616368; 01553 616680 ⌂ dave.clack@west-norfolk.gov.uk

Home Energy Conservation: Mr Tony Howell, Housing Officer, King's Court, Chapel Street, King's Lynn PE30 1EX ☎ 01553 616469; 01553 775142 ⌂ tony.howell@west-norfolk.gov.uk

Housing: Mr Duncan Hall, Strategic Housing & Community Safety Manager, King's Court, Chapel Street, King's Lynn PE30 1EX ☎ 01553 616445 ⌂ duncan.hall@west-norfolk.gov.uk

Legal: Ms Emma Duncan, Legal Services Manager, King's Court, Chapel Street, King's Lynn PE30 1EX ☎ 01553 616270 ⌂ emma.duncan@west-norfolk.gov.uk

Leisure and Cultural Services: Mr Chris Bamfield, Executive Director - Commercial Services, King's Court, Chapel Street, King's Lynn PE30 1EX ☎ 01553 616648; 01553 616640 ⌂ chris.bamfield@west-norfolk.gov.uk

Lottery Funding, Charity and Voluntary: Ms Sarah Dennis, Partnerships & Funding Officer, King's Court, Chapel Street, King's Lynn PE30 1EX ☎ 01553 616 256 ⌂ sarah.dennis@west-norfolk.gov.uk

Member Services: Mrs Sam Winter, Democratic Services Manager, King's Court, Chapel Street, King's Lynn PE30 1EX ☎ 01553 616327; 01553 616758 ⌂ sam.winter@west-norfolk.gov.uk

Parking: Mr Martin Chisholm, Business Manager - Commercial Services, King's Court, Chapel Street, King's Lynn PE30 1EX ☎ 01553 616650 ⌂ martin.chisholm@west-norfolk.gov.uk

Partnerships: Ms Sarah Dennis, Partnerships & Funding Officer, King's Court, Chapel Street, King's Lynn PE30 1EX ☎ 01553 616 256 ⌂ sarah.dennis@west-norfolk.gov.uk

Personnel / HR: Mrs Debbie Gates, Executive Director - Central Services, King's Court, Chapel Street, King's Lynn PE30 1EX ☎ 01553 616605; 01553 616728 ⌂ debbie.gates@west-norfolk.gov.uk

Planning: Mr Geoff Hall, Executive Director - Environment & Planning, King's Court, Chapel Street, King's Lynn PE30 1EX ☎ 01553 616618; 01553 616652 ⌂ geoff.hall@west-norfolk.gov.uk

Procurement: Mr Toby Cowper, Principal Accountant, King's Court, Chapel Street, King's Lynn PE30 1EX ☎ 01553 616248; 01553 616565 ⌂ toby.cowper@west-norfolk.gov.uk

Recycling & Waste Minimisation: Mr Chris Bamfield, Executive Director - Commercial Services, King's Court, Chapel Street, King's Lynn PE30 1EX ☎ 01553 616648; 01553 616640 ⌂ chris.bamfield@west-norfolk.gov.uk

Recycling & Waste Minimisation: Mr Nathan Johnson, Public & Open Space Manager, King's Court, Chapel Street, King's Lynn PE30 1EX ☎ 01553 780780; 01553 771657 ⌂ nathan.johnson@west-norfolk.gov.uk

Regeneration: Mr Ostap Paparega, Regeneration & Economic Development Manager, King's Court, Chapel Street, King's Lynn PE30 1EX ☎ 01553 616890; 01553 775726 ⌂ ostap.paparega@west-norfolk.gov.uk

Staff Training: Miss Becky Box, Personnel Manager, King's Court, Chapel Street, King's Lynn PE30 1EX ☎ 01553 616502; 01553 616680 ⌂ becky.box@west-norfolk.gov.uk

Street Scene: Mr Nathan Johnson, Public & Open Space Manager, King's Court, Chapel Street, King's Lynn PE30 1EX ☎ 01553 780780; 01553 771657 ⌂ nathan.johnson@west-norfolk.gov.uk

Sustainable Communities: Mr Geoff Hall, Executive Director - Environment & Planning, King's Court, Chapel Street, King's Lynn PE30 1EX ☎ 01553 616618; 01553 616652
⌐ geoff.hall@west-norfolk.gov.uk

Sustainable Development: Mr Geoff Hall, Executive Director - Environment & Planning, King's Court, Chapel Street, King's Lynn PE30 1EX ☎ 01553 616618; 01553 616652
⌐ geoff.hall@west-norfolk.gov.uk

Tourism: Mr Tim Humphreys, Tourism Manager, King's Court, Chapel Street, King's Lynn PE30 1EX ☎ 01553 616643; 01553 775726 ⌐ tim.humphreys@west-norfolk.gov.uk

Town Centre: Mr Alistair Cox, Town Centre Manager, King's Court, Chapel Street, King's Lynn PE30 1EX ☎ 01553 616739; 01553 775726 ⌐ alistair.cox@west-norfolk.gov.uk

Waste Collection and Disposal: Mr Nathan Johnson, Public & Open Space Manager, King's Court, Chapel Street, King's Lynn PE30 1EX ☎ 01553 780780; 01553 771657
⌐ nathan.johnson@west-norfolk.gov.uk

Waste Management: Mr Chris Bamfield, Executive Director - Commercial Services, King's Court, Chapel Street, King's Lynn PE30 1EX ☎ 01553 616648; 01553 616640
⌐ chris.bamfield@west-norfolk.gov.uk

COUNCILLORS

Mayor: Whitby, David (CON - Clenchwarton)
cllr.david.whitby@west-norfolk.gov.uk

Deputy Mayor: Bower, Carol (CON - Hunstanton)
cllr.carol.bower@west-norfolk.gov.uk

Leader of the Council: Long, Brian (CON - Mershe Land)
cllr.brian.long@west-norfolk.gov.uk

Deputy Leader of the Council: Beales, Alistair (CON - Gayton)
cllr.alistair.beales@west-norfolk.gov.uk

Anota, Baljinder (CON - West Winch)
cllr.baljinder.anota@west-norfolk.gov.uk

Ayres, Barry (CON - St. Lawrence)
cllr.barry.ayres@west-norfolk.gov.uk

Bambridge, Lesley (CON - St. Margaret's with St. Nicholas)
cllr.lesley.bambridge@west-norfolk.gov.uk

Beal, Paul (CON - Hunstanton)
cllr.paul.beal@west-norfolk.gov.uk

Bird, Richard (IND - Hunstanton)
cllr.richard.bird@west-norfolk.gov.uk

Blunt, Richard (CON - Walpole)
cllr.richard.blunt@west-norfolk.gov.uk

Bubb, Anthony (LD - Dersingham)
cllr.tony.bubb@west-norfolk.gov.uk

Buck, Sandra (LAB - North Lynn)
cllr.sandra.buck@west-norfolk.gov.uk

Collingham, Judy (CON - Dersingham)
cllr.judith.collingham@west-norfolk.gov.uk

Collop, Sandra (LAB - Gaywood Chase)
cllr.sandra.collop@west-norfolk.gov.uk

Collop, John (LAB - Gaywood Chase)
cllr.john.collop@west-norfolk.gov.uk

Crofts, Chris (CON - Emneth with Outwell)
cllr.chris.crofts@west-norfolk.gov.uk

Daubney, Nick (CON - South Wootton)
cllr.nick.daubney@west-norfolk.gov.uk

Devereux, Ian (CON - Snettisham)
cllr.ian.devereux@west-norfolk.gov.uk

Fraser, Susan (CON - Grimston)
cllr.susan.fraser@west-norfolk.gov.uk

Gidney, Peter (CON - West Winch)
cllr.peter.gidney@west-norfolk.gov.uk

Gourlay, Ian (LAB - Fairstead)
cllr.ian.gourlay@west-norfolk.gov.uk

Groom, Roy (CON - Walton)
cllr.roy.groom@west-norfolk.gov.uk

Hipperson, Geoffrey (CON - Airfield)
cllr.geoffrey.hipperson@west-norfolk.gov.uk

Hodson, Peter (CON - Watlington)
cllr.peter.hodson@west-norfolk.gov.uk

Hopkins, Marcus (CON - Wiggenhall)
cllr.marcus.hopkins@west-norfolk.gov.uk

Howard, Greville (CON - North Wootton)
cllr.greville.howard@west-norfolk.gov.uk

Howland, Michael (CON - Airfield)
cllr.michael.howland@west-norfolk.gov.uk

Humphrey, Harry (CON - Emneth with Outwell)
cllr.harry.humphrey@west-norfolk.gov.uk

Joyce, Charles (LAB - South & West Lynn)
cllr.charles.joyce@west-norfolk.gov.uk

Kittow, Claire (LAB - St. Margaret's with St. Nicholas)
cllr.claire.kittow@west-norfolk.gov.uk

Kunes, Paul (CON - Spellowfields)
cllr.paul.kunes@west-norfolk.gov.uk

Lawrence, Adrian (CON - Denton)
cllr.adrian.lawrence@west-norfolk.gov.uk

Manning, Colin (CON - Heacham)
cllr.colin.manning@west-norfolk.gov.uk

McGuinness, Gary (LAB - South & West Lynn)
cllr.gary.mcguinness@west-norfolk.gov.uk

Mellish, Kathy (CON - Downham Old Town)
cllr.kathy.mellish@west-norfolk.gov.uk

Middleton, Graham (CON - Old Gaywood)
cllr.graham.middleton@west-norfolk.gov.uk

Moriarty, Jim (IND - Priory)
cllr.james.moriarty@west-norfolk.gov.uk

Morrison, Andrew (CON - Docking)
cllr.andrew.morrison@west-norfolk.gov.uk

Nockolds, Elizabeth (CON - South Wootton)
cllr.elizabeth.nockolds@west-norfolk.gov.uk

of Horsbrugh, Chenery (CON - Rudham)
cllr.baron.horsbrugh@west-norfolk.gov.uk

Peake, Mick (CON - Denton)
cllr.mick.peake@west-norfolk.gov.uk

KING'S LYNN & WEST NORFOLK

Pope, David (CON - Upwell & Delph)
cllr.david.pope@west-norfolk.gov.uk

Rochford, Patrick (CON - Gaywood North Bank)
cllr.patrick.rochford@west-norfolk.gov.uk

Sampson, Colin (CON - Wissey)
cllr.colin.sampson@west-norfolk.gov.uk

Sandell, Sam (CON - Burnham)
cllr.sam.sandell@west-norfolk.gov.uk

Shorting, Mark (CON - Gaywood North Bank)
cllr.mark.shorting@west-norfolk.gov.uk

Smith, Thomas (CON - Gaywood North Bank)
cllr.thomas.smith@west-norfolk.gov.uk

Spikings, Vivienne (CON - Upwell & Delph)
cllr.vivienne.spikings@west-norfolk.gov.uk

Squire, Sandra (CON - Wimbotsham with Fincham)
cllr.sandra.squire@west-norfolk.gov.uk

Storey, Martin (CON - Denton)
cllr.martin.storey@west-norfolk.gov.uk

Tilbrook, Tim (CON - Valley Hill)
cllr.tim.tilbrook@west-norfolk.gov.uk

Tyler, Don (CON - South Downham)
cllr.donald.tyler@west-norfolk.gov.uk

Tyler, Andy (LAB - North Lynn)
cllr.andy.tyler@west-norfolk.gov.uk

Wareham, Geoffrey (CON - Downham North)
cllr.geoff.wareham@west-norfolk.gov.uk

Watson, Elizabeth (CON - Brancaster)
cllr.elizabeth.watson@west-norfolk.gov.uk

Westrop, Jacqueline (CON - Downham East)
cllr.jackqueline.westrop@west-norfolk.gov.uk

White, Anthony (CON - Hilgay with Denver)
cllr.tony.white@west-norfolk.gov.uk

Wilkinson, Margaret (LAB - Fairstead)
cllr.margaret.wilkinson@west-norfolk.gov.uk

Wing-Pentelow, Toby (CON - Springwood)
cllr.toby.wing-pentelow@west-norfolk.gov.uk

Wright, Avril (CON - Snettisham)
cllr.avril.wright@west-norfolk.gov.uk

Young, Sheila (CON - Spellowfields)
cllr.sheila.young@west-norfolk.gov.uk

POLITICAL COMPOSITION
CON: 49, LAB: 9, IND: 2, LD: 1, Vacant: 1

COMMITTEE CHAIRS
Environment & Community: Mr Colin Sampson

Planning: Mrs Vivienne Spikings

Kingston upon Hull City   U

Kingston upon Hull City Council, The Guildhall, Alfred Gelder Street, Hull HU1 2AA
☎ 01482 609100 ⏚ info@hullcc.gov.uk
🖳 www.hullcc.gov.uk

FACTS AND FIGURES
Parliamentary Constituencies: Hull East, Hull North, Hull West and Hessle
EU Constituencies: Yorkshire and the Humber
Election Frequency: Elections are by thirds

PRINCIPAL OFFICERS

Chief Executive: Mr Matt Jukes, Chief Executive, The Guildhall, Alfred Gelder Street, Hull HU1 2AA ☎ 01482 616328 ⏚ matt.jukes@hullcc.gov.uk

Deputy Chief Executive: Miss Trish Dalby, Deputy Chief Executive, The Guildhall, Alfred Gelder Street, Hull HU1 2AA ☎ 01482 615000 ⏚ trish.dalby@hullcc.gov.uk

Senior Management: Mr Mark Jones, Director - Regeneration, The Guildhall, Alfred Gelder Street, Hull HU1 2AA ☎ 01482 615128; 01482 612160 ⏚ mark.jones@hullcc.gov.uk

Senior Management: Mr Milorad Vasic, Director - Young People & Family Services, The Guildhall, Alfred Gelder Street, Hull HU1 2AA ☎ 01482 613232 ⏚ milorad.vasic@hullcc.gov.uk

Senior Management: Mrs Julia Weldon, Director - Public Health & Adult Services, The Guildhall, Alfred Gelder Street, Hull HU1 2AA ☎ 01482 616324 ⏚ julia.weldon@hullcc.gov.uk

Access Officer / Social Services (Disability): Ms Alison Barker, City Adults Social Care Manager, Brunswick Huse, Strand Close, Beverley Road, Hull HU2 9DB ☎ 01482 616308; 01483 616162 ⏚ alison.barker@hullcc.gov.uk

Access Officer / Social Services (Disability): Ms Tracy Harsley, CitySafe & Early Intervention Manager, Brunswick House, Strand Close, Bevereley Road, Hull HU2 9DB ☎ 01482 616039 ⏚ tracy.harsley@hullcc.go.uk

Architect, Building / Property Services: Mr Nick Howbridge, City Property & Assets Manager, The Myton Centre, William Street, Hull HU1 2SP ☎ 01482 331038 ⏚ nick.howbridge@hullcc.gov.uk

Building Control: Mr Nick Howbridge, City Property & Assets Manager, The Myton Centre, William Street, Hull HU1 2SP ☎ 01482 331038 ⏚ nick.howbridge@hullcc.gov.uk

Children / Youth Services: Mr Graham Talbot, City Education, Learning & Skills Manager, Brunswick House, Strand Close, Bevereley Road, Hull HU2 9DB ☎ 01482 616094 ⏚ graham.talbot@hullcc.gov.uk

Children / Youth Services: Mr Milorad Vasic, Director - Young People & Family Services, The Guildhall, Alfred Gelder Street, Hull HU1 2AA ☎ 01482 613232 ⏚ milorad.vasic@hullcc.gov.uk

Civil Registration: Mr Andy Brown, City Customer Services Manager, The Guildhall, Alfred Gelder Street, Hull HU1 2AA ☎ 01482 613444; 01482 613562 ⏚ andy.brown@hullcc.gov.uk

PR / Communications: Mr Nathan Turner, Assistant City Manager - Regeneration & Policy, The Guildhall, Alfred Gelder Street, Hull HU1 2AA ☎ 01482 613175 ⏚ nathan.turner@hullcc.gov.uk

Community Safety: Ms Tracy Harsley, CitySafe & Early Intervention Manager, Brunswick House, Strand Close, Bevereley Road, Hull HU2 9DB ☎ 01482 616039 ⌁ tracy.harsley@hullcc.go.uk

Consumer Protection and Trading Standards: Ms Tracy Harsley, CitySafe & Early Intervention Manager, Brunswick House, Strand Close, Bevereley Road, Hull HU2 9DB ☎ 01482 616039 ⌁ tracy.harsley@hullcc.go.uk

Customer Service: Mr Andy Brown, City Customer Services Manager, The Guildhall, Alfred Gelder Street, Hull HU1 2AA ☎ 01482 613444; 01482 613562 ⌁ andy.brown@hullcc.gov.uk

Economic Development: Mr Mark Jones, Director - Regeneration, The Guildhall, Alfred Gelder Street, Hull HU1 2AA ☎ 01482 615128; 01482 612160 ⌁ mark.jones@hullcc.gov.uk

Education: Mr Graham Talbot, City Education, Learning & Skills Manager, Brunswick House, Strand Close, Bevereley Road, Hull HU2 9DB ☎ 01482 616094 ⌁ graham.talbot@hullcc.gov.uk

Education: Mr Milorad Vasic, Director - Young People & Family Services, The Guildhall, Alfred Gelder Street, Hull HU1 2AA ☎ 01482 613232 ⌁ milorad.vasic@hullcc.gov.uk

Electoral Registration: Mr Ian Anderson, Town Clerk, Guildhall, Alfred Gelder Street, Hull HU1 2AA ☎ 01482 613233; 01482 613081 ⌁ ian.anderson@hullcc.gov.uk

Emergency Planning: Mrs Julia Weldon, Director - Public Health & Adult Services, The Guildhall, Alfred Gelder Street, Hull HU1 2AA ☎ 01482 616324 ⌁ julia.weldon@hullcc.gov.uk

Environmental / Technical Services: Mr Andy Burton, City Streetscene Manager, Staveley House, Stockholm Road Depot, Hull HU7 0XW ☎ 01482 614002 ⌁ andy.burton@hullcc.gov.uk

Environmental / Technical Services: Ms Tracy Harsley, CitySafe & Early Intervention Manager, Brunswick House, Strand Close, Bevereley Road, Hull HU2 9DB ☎ 01482 616039 ⌁ tracy.harsley@hullcc.go.uk

Environmental Health: Mr Tim Fielding, City Health & Wellbeing Manager, The Guildhall, Alfred Gelder Street, Hull HU1 2AA ☎ 01482 615169 ⌁ tim.fielding@hullcc.gov.uk

Estates, Property & Valuation: Mr Nick Howbridge, City Property & Assets Manager, The Myton Centre, William Street, Hull HU1 2SP ☎ 01482 331038 ⌁ nick.howbridge@hullcc.gov.uk

European Liaison: Mr Mark Jones, Director - Regeneration, The Guildhall, Alfred Gelder Street, Hull HU1 2AA ☎ 01482 615128; 01482 612160 ⌁ mark.jones@hullcc.gov.uk

Events Manager: Mr Mark Jones, Director - Regeneration, The Guildhall, Alfred Gelder Street, Hull HU1 2AA ☎ 01482 615128; 01482 612160 ⌁ mark.jones@hullcc.gov.uk

Fleet Management: Mr Andy Burton, City Streetscene Manager, Staveley House, Stockholm Road Depot, Hull HU7 0XW ☎ 01482 614002 ⌁ andy.burton@hullcc.gov.uk

Grounds Maintenance: Mr Andy Burton, City Streetscene Manager, Staveley House, Stockholm Road Depot, Hull HU7 0XW ☎ 01482 614002 ⌁ andy.burton@hullcc.gov.uk

Highways: Mr Andy Burton, City Streetscene Manager, Staveley House, Stockholm Road Depot, Hull HU7 0XW ☎ 01482 614002 ⌁ andy.burton@hullcc.gov.uk

Housing: Mr David Richmond, City Neighbourhoods & Housing Manager, Warehouse 9, 1 Guildhall Road, Hull HU1 1HJ ☎ 01482 616860 ⌁ dave.richmond@hullcc.gov.uk

Housing Maintenance: Mr David Richmond, City Neighbourhoods & Housing Manager, Warehouse 9, 1 Guildhall Road, Hull HU1 1HJ ☎ 01482 616860 ⌁ dave.richmond@hullcc.gov.uk

Legal: Mr Ian Anderson, Town Clerk, The Guildhall, Alfred Gelder Street, Hull HU1 2AA ☎ 01482 613233; 01482 613081 ⌁ ian.anderson@hullcc.gov.uk

Leisure and Cultural Services: Mr Mitch Upfold, Hull Culture & Leisure Services Managing Director, Dock Office Chambers, New Cross Street, Hull HU1 3DU ☎ 01482 614778 ⌁ mitch.upfold@hcandl.co.uk

Licensing: Ms Tracy Harsley, CitySafe & Early Intervention Manager, Brunswick House, Strand Close, Bevereley Road, Hull HU2 9DB ☎ 01482 616039 ⌁ tracy.harsley@hullcc.go.uk

Lifelong Learning: Mr Graham Talbot, City Education, Learning & Skills Manager, Brunswick House, Strand Close, Bevereley Road, Hull HU2 9DB ☎ 01482 616094 ⌁ graham.talbot@hullcc.gov.uk

Lifelong Learning: Mr Milorad Vasic, Director - Young People & Family Services, The Guildhall, Alfred Gelder Street, Hull HU1 2AA ☎ 01482 613232 ⌁ milorad.vasic@hullcc.gov.uk

Lighting: Mr Andy Burton, City Streetscene Manager, Staveley House, Stockholm Road Depot, Hull HU7 0XW ☎ 01482 614002 ⌁ andy.burton@hullcc.gov.uk

Member Services: Mr Ian Anderson, Town Clerk, The Guildhall, Alfred Gelder Street, Hull HU1 2AA ☎ 01482 613233; 01482 613081 ⌁ ian.anderson@hullcc.gov.uk

Parking: Mr Andy Burton, City Streetscene Manager, Staveley House, Stockholm Road Depot, Hull HU7 0XW ☎ 01482 614002 ⌁ andy.burton@hullcc.gov.uk

Personnel / HR: Mrs Jacqui Blesic, City Human Resources Manager, The Guildhall, Alfred Gelder Street, Hull HU1 2AA ☎ 01482 613044 ⌁ jacqui.blesic@hullcc.gov.uk

Planning: Mr Mark Jones, Director - Regeneration, The Guildhall, Alfred Gelder Street, Hull HU1 2AA ☎ 01482 615128; 01482 612160 ⌁ mark.jones@hullcc.gov.uk

Procurement: Mr Ian Anderson, Town Clerk, The Guildhall, Alfred Gelder Street, Hull HU1 2AA ☎ 01482 613233; 01482 613081 ⌁ ian.anderson@hullcc.gov.uk

KINGSTON UPON HULL CITY

Public Libraries: Mr Mitch Upfold, Hull Culture & Leisure Services Managing Director, Dock Office Chambers, New Cross Street, Hull HU1 3DU ☎ 01482 614778 ◌ mitch.upfold@hcandl.co.uk

Recycling & Waste Minimisation: Mr Andy Burton, City Streetscene Manager, Staveley House, Stockholm Road Depot, Hull HU7 0XW ☎ 01482 614002 ◌ andy.burton@hullcc.gov.uk

Regeneration: Mr Mark Jones, Director - Regeneration, The Guildhall, Alfred Gelder Street, Hull HU1 2AA ☎ 01482 615128; 01482 612160 ◌ mark.jones@hullcc.gov.uk

Road Safety: Mr Andy Burton, City Streetscene Manager, Staveley House, Stockholm Road Depot, Hull HU7 0XW ☎ 01482 614002 ◌ andy.burton@hullcc.gov.uk

Social Services: Mr Milorad Vasic, Director - Young People & Family Services, The Guildhall, Alfred Gelder Street, Hull HU1 2AA ☎ 01482 613232 ◌ milorad.vasic@hullcc.gov.uk

Social Services (Adult): Ms Alison Barker, City Adults Social Care Manager, Brunswick Huse, Strand Close, Beverley Road, Hull HU2 9DB ☎ 01482 616308; 01483 616162 ◌ alison.barker@hullcc.gov.uk

Social Services (Children): Mr Jon Plant, City Safeguarding Manager, Brunswick House, Strand Close, Bevereley Road, Hull HU2 9DB ☎ 01482 616004; 01482 616107 ◌ jon.plant@hullcc.gov.uk

Social Services (Children): Mr Milorad Vasic, Director - Young People & Family Services, The Guildhall, Alfred Gelder Street, Hull HU1 2AA ☎ 01482 613232 ◌ milorad.vasic@hullcc.gov.uk

Public Health: Mrs Julia Weldon, Director - Public Health & Adult Services, The Guildhall, Alfred Gelder Street, Hull HU1 2AA ☎ 01482 616324 ◌ julia.weldon@hullcc.gov.uk

Staff Training: Mrs Jacqui Blesic, City Human Resources Manager, The Guildhall, Alfred Gelder Street, Hull HU1 2AA ☎ 01482 613044 ◌ jacqui.blesic@hullcc.gov.uk

Street Scene: Mr Andy Burton, City Streetscene Manager, Staveley House, Stockholm Road Depot, Hull HU7 0XW ☎ 01482 614002 ◌ andy.burton@hullcc.gov.uk

Sustainable Communities: Mr Mark Jones, Director - Regeneration, The Guildhall, Alfred Gelder Street, Hull HU1 2AA ☎ 01482 615128; 01482 612160 ◌ mark.jones@hullcc.gov.uk

Sustainable Development: Mr Mark Jones, Director - Regeneration, The Guildhall, Alfred Gelder Street, Hull HU1 2AA ☎ 01482 615128; 01482 612160 ◌ mark.jones@hullcc.gov.uk

Tourism: Mr Mark Jones, Director - Regeneration, The Guildhall, Alfred Gelder Street, Hull HU1 2AA ☎ 01482 615128; 01482 612160 ◌ mark.jones@hullcc.gov.uk

Town Centre: Mr Mark Jones, Director - Regeneration, The Guildhall, Alfred Gelder Street, Hull HU1 2AA ☎ 01482 615128; 01482 612160 ◌ mark.jones@hullcc.gov.uk

Traffic Management: Mr Andy Burton, City Streetscene Manager, Staveley House, Stockholm Road Depot, Hull HU7 0XW ☎ 01482 614002 ◌ andy.burton@hullcc.gov.uk

Waste Collection and Disposal: Mr Andy Burton, City Streetscene Manager, Staveley House, Stockholm Road Depot, Hull HU7 0XW ☎ 01482 614002 ◌ andy.burton@hullcc.gov.uk

Waste Management: Mr Andy Burton, City Streetscene Manager, Staveley House, Stockholm Road Depot, Hull HU7 0XW ☎ 01482 614002 ◌ andy.burton@hullcc.gov.uk

COUNCILLORS

The Lord Mayor: Chaytor, Sean (LAB - Marfleet) councillor.chaytor@hullcc.gov.uk

Deputy Lord Mayor: Hewitt, John (LAB - Longhill) councillor.j.hewitt@hullcc.gov.uk

Leader of the Council: Brady, Stephen (LAB - Southcoates West) councillor.brady@hullcc.gov.uk

Deputy Leader of the Council: Hale, Daren (LAB - St Andrews) councillor.hale@hullcc.gov.uk

Group Leader: Fareham, John (CON - Bricknell) councillor.fareham@hullcc.gov.uk

Group Leader: Ross, Michael (LD - Newland) councillor.ross@hullcc.gov.uk

Abbott, John (CON - Bricknell) councillor.abbott@hullcc.gov.uk

Allen, Pete (LAB - Pickering) councillor.allen@hullcc.gov.uk

Barrett, Richard (IND - Southcoates East) councillor.barrett@hullcc.gov.uk

Bayes, Steven (LAB - Orchard Park & Greenwood) steven.bayes@hullcc.gov.uk

Belcher, Sharon (LAB - Marfleet) councillor.belcher@hullcc.gov.uk

Bell, Abigail (LD - Pickering) councillor.bell@hullcc.gov.uk

Black, John (LAB - Longhill) councillor.black@hullcc.gov.uk

Brabazon, Marjorie (LAB - Avenue) councillor.brabazon@hullcc.gov.uk

Bridges, Hester (LAB - Southcoates East) councillor.bridges@hullcc.gov.uk

Brown, Danny (LAB - Kings Park) councillor.brown@hullcc.gov.uk

Chambers, Linda (LD - Drypool) councillor.chambers@hullcc.gov.uk

Clark, Peter (LAB - Bransholme East) councillor.p.clark@hullcc.gov.uk

Clark, Alan (LAB - Newington) councillor.clark@hullcc.gov.uk

Clarkson, Carol (LAB - Longhill) councillor.clarkson@hullcc.gov.uk

Conner, Julia (LAB - Orchard Park & Greenwood) councillor.conner@hullcc.gov.uk

Coward, Maria (LD - Boothferry)
councillor.coward@hullcc.gov.uk

Craker, Dave (LAB - Sutton)
councillor.craker@hullcc.gov.uk

Dad, Jackie (LD - Holderness)
councillor.dad@hullcc.gov.uk

Dorton, Andy (LAB - Avenue)
councillor.dorton@hullcc.gov.uk

Fudge, Leanne (LAB - Derringham)
councillor.fudge2@hullcc.gov.uk

Fudge, Nadine (LAB - St Andrews)
councillor.fudge@hullcc.gov.uk

Gardiner, Alan (LAB - Ings)
councillor.gardiner@hullcc.gov.uk

Geraghty, Terry (LAB - Orchard Park & Greenwood)
councillor.geraghty@hullcc.gov.uk

Glew, Mary (LAB - Southcoates West)
councillor.glew@hullcc.gov.uk

Harrison, Anita (LAB - Bransholme East)
councillor.harrison@hullcc.gov.uk

Hatcher, Diana (LD - Drypool)
councillor.hatcher@hullcc.gov.uk

Herrera-Richmond, Haraldo (LAB - Boothferry)
councillor.herrara-richmond@hullcc.gov.uk

Inglis, Colin (LAB - Myton)
councillor.inglis@hullcc.gov.uk

Jones, Rilba (LAB - Myton)
councillor.jones@hullcc.gov.uk

Keal, Terry (LD - Sutton)
councillor.keal@hullcc.gov.uk

Korczak Fields, Joyce (LAB - University)
councillor.KorczakFields@hullcc.gov.uk

Langley, Ryan (LD - Derringham)
cllr.ryanlangley@gmail.com

Lunn, Gwen (LAB - Newland)
councillor.lunn@hullcc.gov.uk

Mancey, Martin (LAB - Myton)
councillor.mancey@hullcc.gov.uk

Mathieson, Karen (LD - Beverely)
councillor.mathieson@hullcc.gov.uk

McCobb, David (LD - Beverley)
councillor.mccobb@hullcc.gov.uk

O'Mullane, Helene (LAB - Bransholme West)
councillor.o'mullane@hullcc.gov.uk

Pantelakis, Rosemary (LAB - Marfleet)
councillor.pantelakis@hullcc.gov.uk

Payne, Cheryl (LD - Derringham)
councillor.c.payne@hullcc.gov.uk

Payne, Ruth (LD - Boothferry)
councillor.r.payne@hullcc.gov.uk

Petrini, Lynn (LAB - Newington)
councillor.petrini@hullcc.gov.uk

Quinn, Charles (LD - Kings Park)
councillor.quinn@hullcc.gov.uk

Robinson, John (LD - Avenue)
councillor.robinson@yahoo.com

Spencer, Helena (LAB - Newington)
councillor.spencer@hullcc.gov.uk

Sumpton, Christopher (LAB - Holderness)
councillor.sumpton@hullcc.gov.uk

Thomas, Claire (LD - Pickering)
councillor.thomas@hullcc.gov.uk

Thompson, Mike (LAB - Ings)
councillor.thompson@hullcc.gov.uk

Thompson, Denise (LAB - Ings)
councillor.d.thompson@hullcc.gov.uk

Tock, Linda (LD - Holderness)
councillor.tock@hullcc.gov.uk

Turner, Ken (LAB - Sutton)
councillor.turner@hullcc.gov.uk

Webster, Phil (LAB - Bransholme West)
councillor.webster@hullcc.gov.uk

Williams, Adam (LD - Drypool)
councillor.williams@hullcc.gov.uk

Wilson, Steve (LAB - University)
councillor.wilson@hullcc.gov.uk

POLITICAL COMPOSITION
LAB: 39, LD: 17, CON: 2, IND: 1

COMMITTEE CHAIRS

Economy & Regeneration: Ms Claire Thomas

Health & Social Wellbeing: Mr Danny Brown

Health & Wellbeing: Mr Colin Inglis

Licensing: Mrs Nadine Fudge

People & Communities: Mr Dave Craker

Planning: Mr Sean Chaytor

Kingston upon Thames   L

Royal Borough of Kingston upon Thames Council, Guildhall 1,
High Street, Kingston upon Thames KT1 1EU
☎ 020 8547 5757 ▣ www.kingston.gov.uk

FACTS AND FIGURES
Parliamentary Constituencies: Kingston and Surbiton, Richmond Park
EU Constituencies: London
Election Frequency: Elections are of whole council

PRINCIPAL OFFICERS

Chief Executive: Ms Charlie Adan, Chief Executive, Guildhall 1,
High Street, Kingston upon Thames KT1 1EU ☎ 020 8547 4774
⌖ charlie.adan@kingston.gov.uk

Senior Management: Dr Jonathan Hildebrand, Director - Public
Health, Guildhall 1, High Street, Kingston upon Thames KT1 1EU
☎ 020 8547 6800 ⌖ jonathan.hildebrand@rbk.kingston.gov.uk

KINGSTON UPON THAMES

Senior Management: Mr Roy Thompson, Director - Place, Guildhall 1, High Street, Kingston upon Thames KT1 1EU ☎ 020 8547 5343 ✆ roy.thompson@rbk.kingston.gov.uk

Senior Management: Mrs Sheila West, Executive Head - Organisational Development & Strategic Business, Guildhall 2, Kingston upon Thames KT1 1EU ☎ 020 8547 5153 ✆ sheila.west@rbk.kingston.gov.uk

Senior Management: Mr Leigh Whitehouse, Director - Finance, Guildhall 2, Kingston upon Thames KT1 1EU ☎ 020 8547 5570 ✆ leigh.whitehouse@rbk.kingston.gov.uk

Architect, Building / Property Services: Mr Karl Limbert, Head of Property, Guildhall 1, High Street, Kingston upon Thames KT1 1EU ☎ 020 8547 5155 ✆ karl.limbert@kingston.gov.uk

Best Value: Mr Chris Morgan, Capability Lead - Commissioning, Guildhall 1, High Street, Kingston upon Thames KT1 1EU ☎ 020 8547 5300 ✆ chris.morgan@rbk.kingston.gov.uk

Building Control: Mr Alex Chaplin, Lead Officer - Building Control, Guildhall 1, High Street, Kingston upon Thames KT1 1EU ☎ 020 8547 5357 ✆ alex.chaplin@kingston.gov.uk

Children / Youth Services: Ms Alison Twynam, Director - Children's Social Care (Achieving for Children), Civic Centre, 44 York Street, Twickenham TW1 3BZ ☎ 020 8891 6137 ✆ alison.twyman@achievingforchildren.org.uk

Civil Registration: Mr Dennis Mulligan, Registration Manager & Superintendent Registrar, The Register Office, 35 Coombe Road, Kingston upon Thames KT2 7BA ☎ 020 8547 6191; 020 8547 6188 ✆ dennis.mulligan@rbk.kingston.gov.uk

PR / Communications: Ms Kerry Middleton, Head of Communications, Guildhall 1, High Street, Kingston upon Thames KT1 1EU ☎ 020 8547 6935 ✆ kerry.middleton@kingston.gov.uk

Community Planning: Mr Gary Walsh, Capability Lead - Community, Guildhall 1, High Street, Kingston upon Thames KT1 1EU ☎ 020 8547 4698 ✆ gary.walsh@rbk.kingston.gov.uk

Community Safety: Ms Marion Todd, Safer Kingston Partnership Manager, Guildhall 1, High Street, Kingston upon Thames KT1 1EU ☎ 020 8547 5039 ✆ marion.todd@rbk.kingston.gov.uk

Computer Management: Mr Matthew Taylor, Interim Head of Shared ICT Service, Guildhall 1, High Street, Kingston upon Thames KT1 1EU ✆ matthew.taylor@kingston.gov.uk

Consumer Protection and Trading Standards: Mr Mark Reed, Interim Service Manager - Environmental Health & Trading Standards, Guildhall 1, High Street, Kingston upon Thames KT1 1EU ☎ 020 8547 5513; 020 8547 5515 ✆ markreed@kingston.gov.uk

Contracts: Mr Chris Morgan, Capability Lead - Commissioning, Guildhall 1, High Street, Kingston upon Thames KT1 1EU ☎ 020 8547 5300 ✆ chris.morgan@rbk.kingston.gov.uk

Customer Service: Ms Monika Singh, Head of Customer Experience, Guildhall 1, High Street, Kingston upon Thames KT1 1EU ✆ monika.singh@kingston.gov.uk

Economic Development: Mr Andrew Sherville, Team Leader - Business Community Sector, Guildhall 1, High Street, Kingston upon Thames KT1 1EU ☎ 020 8547 5025 ✆ andrew.sherville@kingston.gov.uk

Electoral Registration: Mr Andrew Bessant, Head - Corporate Governance, Guildhall 1, High Street, Kingston upon Thames KT1 1EU ☎ 020 8547 4628; 020 8547 5125 ✆ andrew.bessant@rbk.kingston.gov.uk

Electoral Registration: Mr Gareth Harrington, Manager - Electoral Services, Guildhall, High Street, Kingston upon Thames KT1 1EU ☎ 020 8547 5035; 020 8547 5099 ✆ gareth.harrington@rbk.kingston.gov.uk

Emergency Planning: Mr Chris Begley, Contingency Planning Manager, Guildhall 1, High Street, Kingston upon Thames KT1 1EU ☎ 020 8547 5400; 020 8547 6224 ✆ chris.begley@kingston.gov.uk

Environmental / Technical Services: Mrs Rachel Lewis, Head of Environment Services, Guildhall 1, High Street, Kingston upon Thames KT1 1EU ☎ 020 8547 4705 ✆ rachel.lewis@kingston.gov.uk

Environmental / Technical Services: Mrs Shifa Mustafa, Interim Head of Kingston & Sutton Shared Environment Service, Guildhall 1, High Street, Kingston upon Thames KT1 1EU ☎ 020 8547 4705 ✆ shifa.mustafa@kingston.gov.uk

Environmental Health: Mrs Jan Gransden, Group Manager - Enforcement Services, 24 Denmark Road, Carshalton SM5 2JG ☎ 020 8770 5550 ✆ jan.gransden@sutton.gov.uk

Estates, Property & Valuation: Mr Karl Limbert, Head of Property, Guildhall 1, High Street, Kingston upon Thames KT1 1EU ☎ 020 8547 5155 ✆ karl.limbert@kingston.gov.uk

Finance: Mr Jeremy Randall, Head of Finance - Strategy & Accounting, Guildhall 1, High Street, Kingston upon Thames KT1 1EU ☎ 020 8547 5572 ✆ jeremy.randall@rbk.kingston.gov.uk

Finance: Mr Leigh Whitehouse, Director - Finance, Guildhall 2, Kingston upon Thames KT1 1EU ☎ 020 8547 5570 ✆ leigh.whitehouse@rbk.kingston.gov.uk

Treasury: Mrs Rachel Howard, Capability Lead - Finance Strategy, Guildhall 1, High Street, Kingston upon Thames KT1 1EU ☎ 020 8547 5625 ✆ rachel.howard@kingston.gov.uk

Pensions: Mr Paul Godfrey, Senior Finance Analyst, Guildhall 1, High Street, Kingston upon Thames KT1 1EU ☎ 020 8547 5621 ✆ paul.godfrey@kingston.gov.uk

Grounds Maintenance: Ms Marie-Claire Edwards, Service Manager - Green Spaces, Guildhall 2, Kingston upon Thames KT1 1EU ☎ 020 8547 5372 ✆ marie-claire.edwards@rbk.kingston.gov.uk

Health and Safety: Ms Lorna Mansell, Occupational Health & Safety Manager, Guildhall, Kingston upon Thames KT1 1EU ☎ 020 8547 5187; 020 8547 5186 ✆ lorna.mansell@rbk.kingston.gov.uk

Highways: Mr Roger Archer-Reeves, Interim Group Manager - Highways & Transport, Guildhall 1, High Street, Kingston upon Thames KT1 1EU ☎ 020 8547 5760
⊘ roger.archer-reeves@kingston.gov.uk

Housing: Mr Darren Walsh, Head of Housing, Guildhall 2, Kingston upon Thames KT1 1EU ☎ 020 8547 5430
⊘ darren.welsh@kingston.gov.uk

Local Area Agreement: Mr Kevin Mitchell, Capability Lead - Strategy, Guildhall 1, High Street, Kingston upon Thames KT1 1EU ☎ 020 8547 5982 ⊘ kevin.mitchell@rbk.kingston.gov.uk

Legal: Mr Nick Bishop, Corporate Solicitor, Guildhall, Kingston upon Thames KT1 1EU ☎ 020 8547 5110; 020 8547 5127
⊘ nick.bishop@rbk.kingston.gov.uk

Leisure and Cultural Services: Ms Colette Kelly, Head of Culture, Guildhall 1, High Street, Kingston upon Thames KT1 1EU ☎ 020 8547 5267 ⊘ colette.kelly@kingston.gov.uk

Lifelong Learning: Mr Ian Dodds, Director - Standards & Improvements, Achieving for Children, Regal House, London Road, Twickenham TW1 3BQ ☎ 020 8831 6116; 020 8891 7714
⊘ ian.dodds@achievingforchildren.org.uk

Lottery Funding, Charity and Voluntary: Ms Jill Darling, Team Leader - Voluntary Sector & Business Community, Guildhall, High Street, Kingston upon Thames KT1 1EU ☎ 020 8547 5124
⊘ jill.darling@rbk.kingston.gov.uk

Member Services: Mr Andrew Bessant, Head - Corporate Governance, Guildhall, Kingston upon Thames KT1 1EU ☎ 020 8547 4628 ⊘ andrew.bessant@rbk.kingston.gov.uk

Parking: Mr Phillip Hoare, Parking Services Manager, Guildhall 1, High Street, Kingston upon Thames KT1 1EU ☎ 020 8547 5969
⊘ phillip.hoare@kingston.gov.uk

Personnel / HR: Mrs Sheila West, Executive Head - Organisational Development & Strategic Business, Guildhall 2, Kingston upon Thames KT1 1EU ☎ 020 8547 5153; 020 8547 5188
⊘ sheila.west@rbk.kingston.gov.uk

Planning: Mr Viv Evans, Head of Planning & Transportation, Guildhall 1, High Street, Kingston upon Thames KT1 1EU ☎ 020 8547 5933 ⊘ viv.evans@kingston.gov.uk

Procurement: Mr Chris Morgan, Capability Lead - Commissioning, Guildhall 1, High Street, Kingston upon Thames KT1 1EU ☎ 020 8547 5300 ⊘ chris.morgan@rbk.kingston.gov.uk

Public Libraries: Ms Joanne Moulton, Head of Libraries, Museums & Archives, Kingston Library, Fairfield Road, Kingston upon Thames KT1 2PS ☎ 020 8547 6754 ⊘ joanne.moulton@kingston.gov.uk

Recycling & Waste Minimisation: Mrs Deborah Flintoff, Waste Services Manager, Guildhall 1, High Street, Kingston upon Thames KT1 1EU ☎ 020 8547 5559 ⊘ deborah.flintoff@kingston.gov.uk

Road Safety: Mr Roger Archer-Reeves, Interim Group Manager - Highways & Transport, Guildhall 1, High Street, Kingston upon Thames KT1 1EU ☎ 020 8547 5760
⊘ roger.archer-reeves@kingston.gov.uk

Social Services (Adult): Mr Stephen Taylor, Director - Adults & Social Services, Guildhall 1, High Street, Kingston upon Thames KT1 1EU ☎ 020 8547 6052 ⊘ stephen.taylor@kingston.gov.uk

Public Health: Dr Jonathan Hildebrand, Director - Public Health, Guildhall 1, High Street, Kingston upon Thames KT1 1EU ☎ 020 8547 6800 ⊘ jonathan.hildebrand@rbk.kingston.gov.uk

Staff Training: Mr James Taylor, Lead Consultant - Planning & Development, Council Chamber, Royal Borough of Kingston, 1st Floor, Guildhall, High Street, Kingston upon Thames KT1 1EU ☎ 020 8547 5174 ⊘ james.taylor@kingston.gov.uk

Staff Training: Mrs Sheila West, Executive Head - Organisational Development & Strategic Business, Guildhall 2, Kingston upon Thames KT1 1EU ☎ 020 8547 5153; 020 8547 5188
⊘ sheila.west@rbk.kingston.gov.uk

Street Scene: Mr Roger Archer-Reeves, Interim Group Manager - Highways & Transport, Guildhall 1, High Street, Kingston upon Thames KT1 1EU ☎ 020 8547 5760
⊘ roger.archer-reeves@kingston.gov.uk

Sustainable Communities: Ms Paula Tribe, Relationship Manager - Place, Guildhall, High Street, Kingston upon Thames KT1 1EU ☎ 020 8547 5421 ⊘ paula.tribe@kingston.gov.uk

Town Centre: Ms Ros Morgan, Kingston Town Centre Manager, 3rd Floor, Neville House, 55 Eden Street, Kingston upon Thames KT1 1EU ☎ 020 8547 1221

Traffic Management: Mr Roger Archer-Reeves, Interim Group Manager - Highways & Transport, Guildhall 1, High Street, Kingston upon Thames KT1 1EU ☎ 020 8547 5760
⊘ roger.archer-reeves@kingston.gov.uk

Waste Collection and Disposal: Mrs Deborah Flintoff, Waste Services Manager, Guildhall 1, High Street, Kingston upon Thames KT1 1EU ☎ 020 8547 5559 ⊘ deborah.flintoff@kingston.gov.uk

COUNCILLORS

Mayor: Austin, Geoff (CON - Canbury)
geoffrey.Austin@councillors.kingston.gov.uk

Deputy Mayor: Bass, Rowena (CON - Coombe Hill)
rowena.bass@kingston.gov.uk

Leader of the Council: Davis, Kevin (CON - Old Malden)
kevin.davis@kingston.gov.uk

Deputy Leader of the Council: Paton, Terry (CON - Beverley)
terry.paton@councillors.kingston.gov.uk

Group Leader: Cottington, Linsey (LAB - Norbiton)
linsey.cottington@kingston.gov.uk

Group Leader: Green, Elizabeth (LD - St Mark's)
liz.green@councillors.kingston.gov.uk

KINGSTON UPON THAMES

Abraham, Sushila (LD - Berrylands)
sushila.abraham@councillors.kingston.gov.uk

Arora, Roy (CON - Coombe Vale)
roy.arora@kingston.gov.uk

Ayles, John (LD - Surbiton Hill)
john.ayles@councillors.kingston.gov.uk

Bamford, Patricia (LD - Chessington South)
patricia.bamford@councillors.kingston.gov.uk

Bedforth, Paul (CON - Beverley)
paul.bedforth@kingston.gov.uk

Brisbane, Bill (LD - Norbiton)
bill.brisbane@kingston.gov.uk

Chase, Clive (LD - Chessington North & Hook)
clive.chase@kingston.gov.uk

Cheetham, Jack (CON - St James)
jack.cheetham@kingston.gov.uk

Clark, Mary (CON - Old Malden)
mary.clark@kingston.gov.uk

Craig, Andrea (CON - Canbury)
andrea.craig@councillors.kingston.gov.uk

Cunningham, David (CON - Tudor)
david.cunningham@councillors.kingston.gov.uk

Davies, Tom (LD - Tolworth & Hook Rise)
tom.davies@kingston.gov.uk

Day, Andrew (CON - Chessington North & Hook)
andrew.day@councillors.kingston.gov.uk

Doyle, Phil (CON - Grove)
phil.doyle@kingston.gov.uk

Fraser, David (CON - Old Malden)
david.fraser@councillors.kingston.gov.uk

Gander, Hilary (LD - Surbiton Hill)
hilary.gander@kingston.gov.uk

George, Ian (CON - Alexandra)
ian.george@kingston.gov.uk

Glasspool, David (CON - Canbury)
david.glasspool@kingston.gov.uk

Griffin, Sheila (LAB - Norbiton)
sheila.griffin@kingston.gov.uk

Hayes, Chris (CON - Alexandra)
chris.hayes@kingston.gov.uk

Head, Mike (CON - Berrylands)
mike.head@kingston.gov.uk

Hudson, Richard (CON - Alexandra)
richard.hudson@councillors.kingston.gov.uk

Humphrey, Eric (CON - Coombe Hill)
eric.humphrey@councillors.kingston.gov.uk

Johnson, Andy (CON - Berrylands)
andy.johnson@kingston.gov.uk

Mirza, Shiraz (LD - Chessington South)
shiraz.mirza@councillors.kingston.gov.uk

Moll, Rebekah (LD - Grove)
rebekah.moll@kingston.gov.uk

Netley, Maria (CON - Tudor)
maria.netley@kingston.gov.uk

Pandya, Raju (CON - Beverley)
raju.pandya@kingston.gov.uk

Patel, Priyen (CON - St James)
priyen.patel@councillors.kingston.gov.uk

Pickering, Julie (CON - Coombe Vale)
julie.pickering@councillors.kingston.gov.uk

Reid, Rachel (LD - Chessington South)
rachel.reid@councillors.kingston.gov.uk

Roberts, Cathy (CON - Coombe Vale)
cathy.roberts@kingston.gov.uk

Rolfe, Lorraine (LD - Tolworth & Hook Rise)
lorraine.rolfe@kingston.gov.uk

Scantlebury, Hugh (CON - Tudor)
hugh.scantlebury@kingston.gov.uk

Self, Malcolm (LD - Surbiton Hill)
malcolm.self@councillors.kingston.gov.uk

Smith, Ken (CON - St James)
ken.smith@councillors.kingston.gov.uk

Thayalan, Thay (LD - Tolworth & Hook Rise)
thay.thayalan@kingston.gov.uk

Thompson, Margaret (LD - Chessington North & Hook)
margaret.thompson@councillors.kingston.gov.uk

Tolley, Jon (LD - Grove)
jon.tolley@kingston.gov.uk

Wallooppillai, Gaj (CON - Coombe Hill)
gaj.wallooppillai@councillors.kingston.gov.uk

White, Diane (LD - St Mark's)
diane.white@kingston.gov.uk

Yoganathan, Yogan (LD - St Mark's)
yogan.yoganathan@councillors.kingston.gov.uk

POLITICAL COMPOSITION
CON: 28, LD: 18, LAB: 2

COMMITTEE CHAIRS

Adults & Children: Mr Richard Hudson

Audit, Governance & Standards: Mr Chris Hayes

Development Control: Mr Hugh Scantlebury

Licensing: Mr Mike Head

Pensions: Mr Eric Humphrey

Kirklees   M

Kirklees Metropolitan Council, Civic Centre 3, Market Street, Huddersfield HD1 1WG
☎ 01484 221000 🖷 01484 221777
🖥 www.kirklees.gov.uk

FACTS AND FIGURES
Parliamentary Constituencies: Batley and Spen, Colne Valley, Dewsbury, Huddersfield, Wakefield
EU Constituencies: Yorkshire and the Humber
Election Frequency: Elections are by thirds

PRINCIPAL OFFICERS

Chief Executive: Mr Adrian Lythgo, Chief Executive, 1st Floor, Civic Centre 3, Market Street, Huddersfield HD1 2TG
☎ 01484 221000 ⌁ adrian.lythgo@kirklees.gov.uk

Senior Management: Ms Sarah Callaghan, Director - Children & Adults, Civic Centre 3, Market Street, Huddersfield HD1 1WG
☎ 01484 221000 ⌁ sarah.callaghan@kirklees.gov.uk

Senior Management: Ms Jacqui Gedman, Director - Place, Civic Centre 3, Market Street, Huddersfield HD1 1WG ☎ 01484 221000 ⌁ jacqui.gedman@kirklees.gov.uk

Senior Management: Ms Ruth Redfern, Director - Communities, Transformation & Change, Civic Centre 3, Market Street, Huddersfield HD1 1WG

Senior Management: Mr David Smith, Director - Resources, Civic Centre 3, Market Street, Huddersfield HD1 1WG ☎ 01484 221000 ⌁ david.smith@kirklees.gov.uk

Senior Management: Ms Rachel Spencer-Henshall, Director - Public Health, Civic Centre 3, Market Street, Huddersfield HD1 1WG ⌁ rachael.spencer-henshall@kirklees.gov.uk

Catering Services: Ms Jenny Frear, Schools Facilities Manager, Safety House, Whitestone Lane, Fartown, Huddersfield HD1 6JY
☎ 01484 221000 ⌁ jenny.frear@kirklees.gov.uk

Children / Youth Services: Ms Carly Speechley, Interim Assistant Director - Family Support & Child Protection, Civic Centre 3, Market Street, Huddersfield HD1 1WG
⌁ carly.speechley@kirklees.gov.uk

Civil Registration: Ms Chantal Nolan, Deputy Superintendent Registrar, Civic Centre 3, Market Street, Huddersfield HD1 1WG
☎ 01484 221000 ⌁ chantal.nolan@kirklees.gov.uk

PR / Communications: Mr Alun Ireland, Publicity & Media Manager, Civic Centre 3, Market Street, Huddersfield HD1 1WG
☎ 01484 221000

Community Safety: Ms Carol Gilchrist, Head of Safe & Cohesive Communities, Civic Centre 3, Market Street, Huddersfield HD1 1WG
☎ 01484 221000 ⌁ carol.gilchrist@kirklees.gov.uk

Computer Management: Mr Andy Bramall, Head of IT & Change, Civic Centre 3, Market Street, Huddersfield HD1 1WG
☎ 01484 221000 ⌁ andy.bramall@kirklees.gov.uk

Consumer Protection and Trading Standards: Mr Graham Hebblethwaite, Chief Officer - West Yorkshire Joint Services, West Yorkshire Joint Services, PO Box 5, Nepshaw Lane South, Morley LS27 0QP ☎ 0113 253 0241

Contracts: Mr Keith Smith, Assistant Director - Personalisation & Commissioning, Gateway to Care, 3rd Floor, Market Street, Huddersfield HD1 2HG ☎ 01484 221000
⌁ keith.smith@kirklees.gov.uk

Corporate Services: Ms Julie Fothergill, Policy Unit Manager, Civic Centre 3, Market Street, Huddersfield HD1 1WG
☎ 01484 221783 ⌁ julie.fothergill@kirklees.gov.uk

Corporate Services: Mr John Heneghan, Policy Unit Manager, Civic Centre 3, Market Street, Huddersfield HD1 1WG
☎ 01484 221779 ⌁ john.henegham@kirklees.gov.uk

Customer Service: Ms Jane Brady, Assistant Director - Resources, Civic Centre 1, High Street, Huddersfield HD1 2NF
☎ 01484 221000 ⌁ jane.brady@kirklees.gov.uk

Electoral Registration: Ms Susan Hutson, Electoral Services Manager, 49-51 Huddersfield Road, Holmfirth HD9 3ER
☎ 01484 222403 ⌁ susan.hutson@kirklees.gov.uk

Emergency Planning: Mr Sean Westerby, Corporate Safety / Resilience Team Manager, Emergency Planning, Kirkgate Buildings, Byram Street, Huddersfield HD1 1BY ☎ 01484 226414
⌁ sean.westerby@kirklees.gov.uk

Environmental / Technical Services: Mr Rob Dalby, Environmental Protection Manager, Flint Street, Fartown, Huddersfield HD1 6LG ☎ 01484 226403
⌁ rob.dalby@kirkless.gov.uk

Environmental Health: Mr Rob Dalby, Environmental Protection Manager, Flint Street, Fartown, Huddersfield HD1 6LG
☎ 01484 226403 ⌁ rob.dalby@kirkless.gov.uk

Estates, Property & Valuation: Ms Joanne Bartholomew, Assistant Director - Physical Resources & Procurement, Design & Property Service, Kirkgate Buildings, Byram street, Huddersfield HD1 4SA ☎ 01484 226052 ⌁ joanne.bartholomew@kirklees.gov.uk

European Liaison: Mr Chris Rowe, Policy Officer, Civic Centre 3, Market Street, Huddersfield HD1 1WG ☎ 01484 221000
⌁ chris.rowe@kirklees.gov.uk

Facilities: Ms Joanne Bartholomew, Assistant Director - Physical Resources & Procurement, Design & Property Service, Kirkgate Buildings, Byram street, Huddersfield HD1 4SA ☎ 01484 226052
⌁ joanne.bartholomew@kirklees.gov.uk

Finance: Mr David Smith, Director - Resources, Civic Centre 3, Market Street, Huddersfield HD1 1WG ☎ 01484 221000
⌁ david.smith@kirklees.gov.uk

Fleet Management: Mr Darren Fletcher, Fleet Manager, Civic Centre 3, Market Street, Huddersfield HD1 1WG ☎ 01484 221000
⌁ darren.fletcher@kirklees.gov.uk

Grounds Maintenance: Mr John Fletcher, Assistant Head of Service - Parks & Open Spaces, Culture & Leisure Services, The Stadium Business and Leisure Complex, Stadium Way, Huddersfield HD1 6PG ☎ 01484 221000
⌁ john.fletcher@kirklees.gov.uk

Highways: Ms Jacqui Gedman, Director - Place, E & T Highways & Transportation, Flint Street, Huddersfield HD1 6LG
☎ 01484 221000 ⌁ jacqui.gedman@kirklees.gov.uk

KIRKLEES

Housing: Ms Kim Brear, Assistant Director - Streetscene & Housing, Civic Centre 1, 4th Floor South, High Street, Huddersfield HD1 2NF ☎ 01484 221487 ⌁ kim.brear@kirklees.gov.uk

Local Area Agreement: Ms Julie Fothergill, Policy Unit Manager, Civic Centre 3, Market Street, Huddersfield HD1 1WG ☎ 01484 221783 ⌁ julie.fothergill@kirklees.gov.uk

Legal: Ms Julie Muscroft, Assistant Director - Legal Governance & Monitoring, Civic Centre 3, Market Street, Huddersfield HD1 1WG ☎ 01484 221720 ⌁ julie.muscroft@kirklees.gov.uk

Leisure and Cultural Services: Ms Kimiyo Rickett, Assistant Director - Communities & Leisure, The Stadium Business and Leisure Complex, Stadium Way, Huddersfield HD1 6PG ☎ 01484 234002 ⌁ kimiyo.rickett@kirklees.gov.uk

Licensing: Ms Catherine Walter, Licensing Manager, Flint Street Depot, Flint Street, Fartown, Huddersfield HD1 6LG ☎ 01484 221000 ⌁ catherine.walter@kirklees.gov.uk

Parking: Mr Neil Tootill, Operational Manager, Corporation Yard, Mayman Lane, Batley WF17 7TA ☎ 01484 222858 ⌁ neil.tootill@kirklees.gov.uk

Personnel / HR: Ms Rosemary Gibson, Head of HR, Civic Centre 3, Market Street, Huddersfield HD1 1WG ☎ 01484 221000 ⌁ rosemary.gibson@kirklees.gov.uk

Planning: Mr Paul Kemp, Assistant Director - Commissioning & Safeguarding Assurance, Ground Floor, Civic Centre 1, High Street, Huddersfield HD1 2NF ☎ 01484 221000 ⌁ paul.kemp@kirklees.gov.uk

Planning: Mr Keith Smith, Assistant Director - Personalisation & Commissioning, Gateway to Care, 3rd Floor, Market Street, Huddersfield HD1 2HG ☎ 01484 221000 ⌁ keith.smith@kirklees.gov.uk

Procurement: Ms Joanne Bartholomew, Assistant Director - Physical Resources & Procurement, Kirkgate Buildings, Byram Street, Huddersfield HD1 1BY ☎ 01484 226052 ⌁ joanne.bartholomew@kirklees.gov.uk

Public Libraries: Ms Jane Brady, Assistant Director - Resources, Civic Centre 1, High Street, Huddersfield HD1 2NF ☎ 01484 221000 ⌁ jane.brady@kirklees.gov.uk

Recycling & Waste Minimisation: Mr Dave McMahon, Environmental Projects Manager, Vine Street Depot, Leeds Road, Huddersfield HD1 6NT ☎ 01484 223116 ⌁ dave.mcmahon@kirklees.gov.uk

Regeneration: Ms Jacqui Gedman, Director - Place, Civic Centre 3, Market Street, Huddersfield HD1 1WG ☎ 01484 221000 ⌁ jacqui.gedman@kirklees.gov.uk

Road Safety: Ms Cath Bottomley, Unit Manager - Business Support, Flint Street, Fartown, Huddersfield HD1 6LG ☎ 01484 225552 ⌁ cath.bottomley@kirklees.gov.uk

Social Services: Ms Carly Speechley, Interim Assistant Director - Family Support & Child Protection, Civic Centre 3, Market Street, Huddersfield HD1 1WG ⌁ carly.speechley@kirklees.gov.uk

Social Services (Adult): Mr Keith Smith, Assistant Director - Personalisation & Commissioning, Gateway to Care, 3rd Floor, Market Street, Huddersfield HD1 2HG ☎ 01484 221000 ⌁ keith.smith@kirklees.gov.uk

Social Services (Children): Mrs Alison O'Sullivan, Director - Children & Adults, Ground Floor, Civic Centre 1, High Street, Huddersfield HD1 2NF ☎ 01484 221000 ⌁ alison.o'sullivan@kirklees.gov.uk

Public Health: Ms Rachel Spencer-Henshall, Director - Public Health, Civic Centre 3, Market Street, Huddersfield HD1 1WG ⌁ rachael.spencer-henshall@kirklees.gov.uk

Street Scene: Ms Kim Brear, Assistant Director - Streetscene & Housing, Civic Centre 1, 4th Floor South, High Street, Huddersfield HD1 2NF ☎ 01484 221487 ⌁ kim.brear@kirklees.gov.uk

Tourism: Ms Jess Newbould, Senior Tourism Officer, Economic Development Service, Civic Centre 3, Huddersfield HD1 2EY ☎ 01484 221675 ⌁ jess.newbould@kirklees.gov.uk

Town Centre: Ms Jayne Pearson, Town Centre Manager, Queensgate Market, Princess Alexandra Walk, Huddersfield HD1 2SU ☎ 01484 223357 ⌁ jayne.pearson@kirklees.gov.uk

Waste Collection and Disposal: Mr Will Acornley, Head of Waste, Recycling & Transport, Riverbank Court, Wakefield Road, Huddersfield HD5 9AA ☎ 01484 223146 ⌁ will.acornley@kirklees.gov.uk

COUNCILLORS

Mayor: Kane, Paul (LAB - Dewsbury East)
paul.kane@kirklees.gov.uk

Deputy Mayor: Dodds, Jim (CON - Denby Dale)
jim.dodds@kirklees.gov.uk

Leader of the Council: Sheard, David (LAB - Heckmondwike)
david.sheard@kirklees.gov.uk

Deputy Leader of the Council: Pandor, Shabir (LAB - Batley West)
shabir.pandor@kirklees.gov.uk

Group Leader: Cooper, Andrew (GRN - Newsome)
andrew.cooper@kirklees.gov.uk

Group Leader: Greaves, Charles (IND - Holme Valley North)
charles.greaves@kirklees.gov.uk

Group Leader: Hall, David (CON - Liversedge & Gomersal)
david.hall@kirklees.gov.uk

Group Leader: Turner, Nicola (LD - Colne Valley)
nicola.turner@kirklees.gov.uk

Ahmed, Masood (LAB - Dewsbury South)
masoodg.ahmed@kirklees.gov.uk

Akhtar, Mahmood (LAB - Batley East)
mahmood.akhtar@kirklees.gov.uk

Allison, Karen (GRN - Newsome)
karen.allison@kirklees.gov.uk

Armer, Bill (CON - Kirkburton)
bill.armer@kirklees.gov.uk

Asif, Gulfam (LAB - Dewsbury South)
gulfam.asif@kirklees.gov.uk

Bellamy, Donna (CON - Colne Valley)
donna.bellamy@kirklees.gov.uk

Bolt, Martyn (CON - Mirfield)
martyn.bolt@kirklees.gov.uk

Burke, Cahal (LD - Lindley)
cahal.burke@kirklees.gov.uk

Calvert, Jean (LAB - Ashbrow)
jean.calvert@kirklees.gov.uk

Dad, Nosheen (LAB - Dewsbury South)
nosheen.dad@kirklees.gov.uk

Eastwood, Richard (LD - Lindley)
richard.eastwood@kirklees.gov.uk

Fadia, Fazila (LAB - Batley East)
fazila.fadia@kirklees.gov.uk

Firth, Eric (LAB - Dewsbury East)
eric.firth@kirklees.gov.uk

Firth, Donald (CON - Holme Valley South)
donald.firth@kirklees.gov.uk

Grainger-Mead, Michelle (CON - Liversedge & Gomersal)
michelle.grainger@kirklees.gov.uk

Hall, Steve (LAB - Heckmondwike)
steve.hall@kirklees.gov.uk

Hill, Erin (LAB - Crosland Moor & Netherton)
erin.hill@kirklees.gov.uk

Holmes, Lisa (CON - Liversedge & Gomersal)
lisa.holmes@kirklees.gov.uk

Holroyd-Doveton, Edgar (IND - Holme Valley North)
edgar.holroyd-doveton@kirklees.gov.uk

Homewood, James (LAB - Ashbrow)
james.homewood@kirklees.gov.uk

Hughes, Judith (LAB - Almondbury)
judith.hughes@kirklees.gov.uk

Hussain, Mumtaz (LAB - Dewsbury West)
mumtaz.hussain@kirklees.gov.uk

Iredale, Christine (LD - Golcar)
christine.iredale@kirklees.gov.uk

Kaushik, Manisha (LAB - Crosland Moor & Netherton)
manisha.kaushik@kirklees.gov.uk

Kendrick, Viv (LAB - Heckmondwike)
viv.kendrick@kirklees.gov.uk

Khan, Murarrat (LAB - Dalton)
mussarat.khan@kirklees.gov.uk

Lawson, John Craig (LD - Cleckheaton)
john.lawson@kirklees.gov.uk

Lees-Hamilton, Vivien (CON - Mirfield)
vivien.lees-hamilton@kirklees.gov.uk

Light, Robert (CON - Birstall & Birkenshaw)
robert.light@kirklees.gov.uk

Lowe, Gwen (LAB - Batley West)
gwen.lowe@kirklees.gov.uk

Lyons, Terry (IND - Holme Valley North)
terry.lyons@kirklees.gov.uk

Marchington, Andrew (LD - Golcar)
andrew.marchington@kirklees.gov.uk

Mather, Naheed (LAB - Dalton)
naheed.mather@kirklees.gov.uk

McBride, Peter (LAB - Dalton)
peter.mcbride@kirklees.gov.uk

McGuin, Bernard (CON - Almondbury)
bernard.mcguin@kirklees.gov.uk

O'Donovan, Darren (LAB - Dewsbury West)
darren.odonovan@kirklees.gov.uk

O'Neill, Peter (LAB - Batley West)
peter.o'neill@kirklees.gov.uk

Palfreeman, Andrew (CON - Birstall & Birkenshaw)
andrew.palfreeman@kirklees.gov.uk

Patrick, Nigel (CON - Holme Valley South)
nigel.patrick@kirklees.gov.uk

Pattison, Carole (LAB - Greenhead)
carole.pattison@kirklees.gov.uk

Pervaiz, Mussarat (LAB - Dewsbury West)
mussarat.pervaiz@kirklees.gov.uk

Pinnock, Andrew (LD - Cleckheaton)
andrew.pinnock@kirklees.gov.uk

Pinnock, Kath (LD - Cleckheaton)
kath.pinnock@kirklees.gov.uk

Pinnock, Amanda (LAB - Ashbrow)
amanda.pinnock@kirklees.gov.uk

Richards, Hilary (LAB - Golcar)
hilary.richards@kirklees.gov.uk

Sarwar, Mohammad (LAB - Crosland Moor & Netherton)
mohammad.sarwar@kirklees.gov.uk

Scott, Cathy (LAB - Dewsbury East)
cathy.scott@kirklees.gov.uk

Sims, Ken (CON - Holme Valley South)
kenneth.sims@kirklees.gov.uk

Smaje, Liz (CON - Birstall & Birkenshaw)
elizabeth.smaje@kirklees.gov.uk

Smith, Richard (CON - Kirkburton)
richard.smith@kirklees.gov.uk

Sokhal, Mohan (LAB - Greenhead)
mohan.sokhal@kirklees.gov.uk

Stewart-Turner, Julie (GRN - Newsome)
julie.stewart-turner@kirklees.gov.uk

Stubley, Amanda (LAB - Batley East)
amanda.stubley@kirklees.gov.uk

Taylor, Kathleen (CON - Mirfield)
kath.taylor@kirklees.gov.uk

Taylor, John (CON - Kirkburton)
johnj.taylor@kirklees.gov.uk

Turner, Graham (LAB - Denby Dale)
graham.turner@kirklees.gov.uk

Ullah, Sheikh (LAB - Greenhead)
sheikh.ullah@kirklees.gov.uk

KIRKLEES

Walker, Rob (LAB - Colne Valley)
rob.walker@kirklees.gov.uk

Watson, Michael (CON - Denby Dale)
michael.watson@kirklees.gov.uk

Wilkinson, Linda (LD - Almondbury)
linda.wilkinson@kirklees.gov.uk

Wilson, Gemma (CON - Lindley)
gemma.wilson@kirklees.gov.uk

POLITICAL COMPOSITION
LAB: 34, CON: 20, LD: 9, GRN: 3, IND: 3

COMMITTEE CHAIRS

Audit & Governance: Ms Hilary Richards

Health & Wellbeing: Ms Viv Kendrick

Licensing: Ms Cathy Scott

Planning: Mr Steve Hall

Knowsley   M

Knowsley Metropolitan Borough Council, Municipal Buildings, Archway Road, Huyton L36 9UX
☎ 0151 489 6000 📠 0151 443 3507 🖥 www.knowsley.gov.uk

FACTS AND FIGURES
Parliamentary Constituencies: Garston and Halewood, Knowsley
EU Constituencies: North West
Election Frequency: Elections are by thirds

PRINCIPAL OFFICERS

Chief Executive: Mr Mike Harden, Chief Executive, PO Box 24, Municipal Buildings, Archway Road, Huyton L36 9UX
☎ 0151 443 3772 ✆ mike.harden@knowsley.gov.uk

Assistant Chief Executive: Mr Mark Butterworth, Assistant Chief Executive, PO Box 24, Municipal Buildings, Archway Road, Huyton L36 9UX ☎ 0151 443 3849 ✆ mark.butterworth@knowsley.gov.uk

Senior Management: Mr Matthew Ashton, Assistant Executive Director - Public Health & Wellbeing, Municipal Buildings, Archway Road, Huyton L36 9UX ☎ 0151 443 4844 ✆ matthew.ashton@knowsley.gov.uk

Architect, Building / Property Services: Mr Ian Capper, Head of Property & Development, Municipal Buildings, Archway Road, Huyton L36 9UX ☎ 0151 443 2220 ✆ ian.capper@knowsley.gov.uk

Architect, Building / Property Services: Mr Mark Cawood, Head of Planning, PO Box 26, Municipal Buildings, Archway Road, Huyton L36 9UX ☎ 0151 443 2303 ✆ mark.cawood@knowsley.gov.uk

Catering Services: Mr Jon Dyson, Head of Commercial Services, Yorkon Building, Archway Road, Huyton L36 9YX ☎ 0151 443 2407 ✆ jon.dyson@knowsley.gov.uk

Civil Registration: Ms Pauline Douglas, Superintendent Registrar, Council Offices, High Street, Prescot L34 3LH ☎ 0151 443 5299 ✆ pauline.douglas@knowsley.gov.uk

Community Safety: Ms Jemma Jones, Head of Safer Communities, Yorkon Building, Archway Road, Huyton L36 9UX
☎ 0151 443 4683 ✆ jemma.jones@knowsley.gov.uk

Computer Management: Mr Andrew Garden, Head of IT, Civic Way, Westmoreland Road, Huyton L36 9GD ☎ 0151 443 3487 ✆ andrew.garden@knowsley.gov.uk

Consumer Protection and Trading Standards: Mr Mike Leyden, Better Regulations & Compliance Manager, Yorkon Buildings, Archway Road, Huyton L36 9UX ☎ 0151 443 4744 ✆ mike.leyden@knowsley.gov.uk

Contracts: Ms Deborah Lee, Head of Exchequer Services, Kirkby Municipal Buildings, Cherryfield Drive, Kirkby L32 1TX ☎ 0151 443 4163 ✆ deborah.lee@knowsley.gov.uk

Corporate Services: Mrs Dawn Boyer, Head of Corporate Services, Nutgrove Villa, Westmorland Road, Huyton, Liverpool L36 6GA ☎ 0151 443 4165 ✆ dawn.boyer@knowsley.gov.uk

Customer Service: Mr Phil Aspinall, Head of Customer Services, Municipal Buildings, Archway Road, Huyton L36 9UX ☎ 0151 443 3378 ✆ phil.aspinall@knowsley.gov.uk

Economic Development: Mr Barry Fawcett, Head of Housing & Economic Development, Yorkon Building, Archway Road, Huyton L36 9UX ☎ 0151 443 2251 ✆ barry.fawcett@knowsley.gov.uk

Education: Ms Maria Taylor, Head of Schools & Educational Attainment, Municipal Buildings, Archway Road, Huyton L36 9UX
☎ 0151 443 5614 ✆ maria.taylor@knowsley.gov.uk

E-Government: Mr Andrew Garden, Head of IT, Civic Way, Westmoreland Road, Huyton L36 9GD ☎ 0151 443 3487 ✆ andrew.garden@knowsley.gov.uk

Electoral Registration: Ms Cheryl Ryder, Elections Manager, Democratic Services, Municipal Buildings, Archway Road, Huyton L36 9UX ☎ 0151 489 6000 ✆ cheryl.ryder@knowsley.gov.uk

Emergency Planning: Mr Brian Toolan, Head of Risk & Resilience, Civic Way, Westmorland Road, Huyton L36 9GD
☎ 0151 443 3601 ✆ brian.toolan@knowsley.gov.uk

Energy Management: Mr John Burns, Senior Energy Officer, Municipal Buildings, Archway Road, Huyton L36 9UX
☎ 0151 443 2612 ✆ john.burns@knowsley.gov.uk

Environmental / Technical Services: Mr John Flaherty, Executive Director - Place, Municipal Buildings, Archway Road, Huyton L36 9UX ☎ 0151 443 2410 ✆ john.flaherty@knowsley.gov.uk

Environmental Health: Ms Tracy Dickinson, Head of Environmental Health & Consumer Protection, 2nd Floor, Yorkon Building, Archway Road, Huyton L36 9FB ☎ 0151 443 4732 ✆ tracy.dickinson@knowsley.gov.uk

Estates, Property & Valuation: Mr Ian Capper, Head of Property & Development, Municipal Buildings, Archway Road, Huyton L36 9UX ☎ 0151 443 2220 ✆ ian.capper@knowsley.gov.uk

Facilities: Mr Jon Dyson, Head of Commercial Services, Yorkon Building, Archway Road, Huyton L36 9YX ☎ 0151 443 2407 ⌨ jon.dyson@knowsley.gov.uk

Finance: Mr James Duncan, Executive Director - Resources, PO Box 24, Municipal Buildings, Archway Road, Huyton L36 9YZ ☎ 0151 443 3407 ⌨ james.duncan@knowsley.gov.uk

Fleet Management: Mrs Julie Mallon, Head of Streetscene, Fleet & Logistics Services, Stretton Way, Huyton L36 6JF ☎ 0151 443 2412 ⌨ julie.mallon@knowsley.gov.uk

Fleet Management: Mr Keith Simpson, Fleet Operations Manager, Stretton Way, Huyton L36 6JF ☎ 0151 443 2416 ⌨ keith.simpson@knowsley.gov.uk

Grounds Maintenance: Ms Denise Best, Operations Manager (Streetscene), Stretton Way, Huyton L36 6JF ☎ 0151 443 2427 ⌨ denise.best@knowsley.gov.uk

Highways: Mr Jon Robinson, Group Manager - Highways, Yorkon Building, Archway Way, Huyton L36 9FB ☎ 0151 443 5962 ⌨ jon.robinson@knowsley.gov.uk

Home Energy Conservation: Mr Dale Milburn, Assistant Executive Director - Economic Development, Yorkon Building, Archway Road, Huyton L36 9FB ☎ 0151 443 2290 ⌨ dale.milburn@knowsley.gov.uk

Housing: Ms Lisa Harris, Assistant Executive Director - Regeneration & Housing, Yorkon Building, Archway Road, Huyton L36 9FB ☎ 0151 443 2377 ⌨ lisa.harris@knowsley.gov.uk

Local Area Agreement: Mr Justin Thompson, Assistant Executive Director - Neighbourhoods, PO Box 21, Municipal Buildings, Archway Road, Huyton L36 9YU ☎ 0151 443 3397 ⌨ justin.thompson@knowsley.gov.uk

Legal: Mr Mike Dearing, Head of Legal Services, PO Box 21, Municipal Buildings, Archway Road, Huyton L36 9YU ☎ 0151 443 3762 ⌨ mike.dearing@knowsley.gov.uk

Leisure and Cultural Services: Ms Paula Williams, Head of Culture & Libraries, Municipal Buildings, Archway Road, Huyton L36 9UX ☎ 0151 443 3468 ⌨ paula.williams@knowsley.gov.uk

Licensing: Mr Alan Shone, Consumer Protection Manager, Yorkon Building, Archway Road, Huyton L36 9YU ☎ 0151 443 2798 ⌨ alan.shone@knowsley.gov.uk

Lighting: Ms Michele Grey, Street Lighting Contract Manager (PFI), PO Box 26, Municipal Buildings, Archway Road, Huyton L36 9FB ☎ 0151 443 3170 ⌨ michele.grey@knowlsey.gov.uk

Member Services: Ms Yvonne Ledgerton, Assistant Executive Director - Governance, PO Box 21, Municipal Buildings, Archway Road, Huyton L36 9UX ☎ 0151 443 3609 ⌨ yvonne.ledgerton@knowsley.gov.uk

Parking: Mr Steve Myers, Town Centres Investment Manager, York Building, Archway Road, Huyton L36 9FB ☎ 0151 443 2298 ⌨ steve.myers@knowsley.gov.uk

Partnerships: Mr Justin Thompson, Assistant Executive Director - Neighbourhoods, Yorkon Building, Archway Road, Huyton L36 9YU ☎ 0151 443 3397 ⌨ justin.thompson@knowsley.gov.uk

Personnel / HR: Mr Dave Turner, Head of Human Resources, Civic Way, Westmorland Road, Huyton L36 9GD ☎ 0151 443 2951 ⌨ dave.turner@knowsley.gov.uk

Planning: Mr Mark Cawood, Head of Planning, PO Box 26, Municipal Buildings, Archway Road, Huyton L36 9UX ☎ 0151 443 2303 ⌨ mark.cawood@knowsley.gov.uk

Procurement: Mr Liam Power, Procurement Manager, Municipal Buildings, Archway Road, Huyton L36 9UX ☎ 0151 443 4169 ⌨ liam.power@knowsley.gov.uk

Public Libraries: Ms Paula Williams, Head of Culture & Libraries, Municipal Buildings, Archway Road, Huyton L36 9UX ☎ 0151 443 3468 ⌨ paula.williams@knowsley.gov.uk

Recycling & Waste Minimisation: Mr Jon Dyson, Head of Commercial Services, Yorkon Buildings, Archway Road, Huyton L36 9YU ☎ 0151 443 2407 ⌨ jon.dyson@knowsley.gov.uk

Regeneration: Ms Lisa Harris, Assistant Executive Director - Regeneration & Housing, Yorkon Building, Archway Road, Huyton L36 9FB ☎ 0151 443 2377 ⌨ lisa.harris@knowsley.gov.uk

Road Safety: Ms Sarah Vose, Road Safety Advisor, PO Box 26, Municipal Buildings, Archway Road, Huyton L36 9FB ☎ 0151 443 2030 ⌨ sarah.vose@knowsley.gov.uk

Social Services (Adult): Ms Julie Moss, Assistant Executive Director - Adult Social Care, Municipal Buildings, Archway Road, Huyton L36 9UX ☎ 0151 443 4486 ⌨ julie.moss@knowsley.gov.uk

Social Services (Children): Mr Peter Murphy, Assistant Executive Director - Children's Social Care, Municipal Buildings, Archway Road, Huyton L36 9UX ☎ 0151 443 3024 ⌨ peter.murphy@knowsley.gov.uk

Public Health: Mr Matthew Ashton, Assistant Executive Director - Public Health & Wellbeing, Municipal Buildings, Archway Road, Huyton L36 9UX ☎ 0151 443 4844 ⌨ matthew.ashton@knowsley.gov.uk

Street Scene: Mrs Julie Mallon, Head of Streetscene, Fleet & Logistics Services, Municipal Buildings, Archway Road, Huyton L36 9UX ☎ 0151 443 2412 ⌨ julie.mallon@knowsley.gov.uk

Sustainable Development: Mr Rupert Casey, Head of Sustainable Resources, Stretton Way, Archway Road, Huyton L36 6JF ☎ 0151 443 2411 ⌨ rupert.casey@knowsley.gov.uk

Town Centre: Ms Lisa Harris, Assistant Executive Director - Regeneration & Housing, Yorkon Building, Archway Road, Huyton L36 9FB ☎ 0151 443 2377 ⌨ lisa.harris@knowsley.gov.uk

Transport: Mr Andy Millar, Transportation, Road Safety & Travel Plans Manager, PO Box 26, Municipal Buildings, Archway Road, Huyton L36 9FB ☎ 0151 443 2235 ⌨ andy.millar@knowsley.gov.uk

KNOWSLEY

Waste Management: Mr Jon Dyson, Head of Commercial Services, Yorkon Building, Archway Road, Huyton L36 9YU ☎ 0151 443 2407 📠 jon.dyson@knowsley.gov.uk

COUNCILLORS

Mayor: Walsh, Frank (LAB - St. Gabriel's)
frank.walsh@knowsley.gov.uk

Leader of the Council: Moorhead, Andy (LAB - Page Moss)
andy.moorhead@knowsley.gov.uk

Deputy Leader of the Council: Murphy, Michael (LAB - Northwood)
michael.murphy@knowsley.gov.uk

Allen, Denise (LAB - Prescot South)
denise.allen@knowsley.gov.uk

Aston, Jayne (LAB - Cherryfield)
jayne.aston@knowsley.gov.uk

Bannon, Christine (LAB - Swanside)
christine.bannon@knowsley.gov.uk

Baum, Dennis (LAB - Stockbridge)
dennis.baum@knowsley.gov.uk

Brennan, Tony (LAB - Shevington)
tony.brennan@knowsley.gov.uk

Byron, Terry (LAB - Whiston & Cronton)
terry.byron@knowsley.gov.uk

Cashman, Carl (LD - Prescot North)
carl.cashman@knowsley.gov.uk

Connor, Edward (LAB - Northwood)
eddie.connor@knowsley.gov.uk

Denver, Colin (LAB - Swanside)
colin.denver@knowsley.gov.uk

Donnelly, John (LAB - Stockbridge)
john.donnelly@knowsley.gov.uk

Donnelly, Sean (LAB - Whitefield)
sean.donnelly@knowsley.gov.uk

Finneran, Edna (LAB - Halewood South)
edna.finneran@knowsley.gov.uk

Flatley, Gillian (LAB - Whiston & Cronton)
gillian.flatley@knowsley.gov.uk

Flute, Alan (LAB - Halewood North)
alan.flute@knowsley.gov.uk

Halpin, Ray (LAB - Shevington)
ray.halpin@knowsley.gov.uk

Harris, Tina (LAB - Halewood South)
tina.harris@knowsley.gov.uk

Harris, Jackie (LAB - Cherryfield)
jackie.harris@knowsley.gov.uk

Harvey, Margaret (LAB - Roby)
margaret.harvey@knowsley.gov.uk

Keats, Norman (LAB - Whitefield)
norman.keats@knowsley.gov.uk

Lamb, Victoria (LAB - St. Michael's)
vickie.lamb@knowsley.gov.uk

Lilly, Joan (LAB - St. Michael's)
joan.lilly@knowsley.gov.uk

Lonergan, David (LAB - Cherryfield)
david.lonergan@knowsley.gov.uk

McGlashan, Ken (LAB - Page Moss)
ken.mcglashan@knowsley.gov.uk

McNeill, Veronica (LAB - Page Moss)
veronica.mcneill@knowsley.gov.uk

Mooney, Linda (LAB - Shevington)
linda.mooney@knowsley.gov.uk

Moorhead, Kay (LAB - St. Michael's)
kay.moorhead@knowsley.gov.uk

Morgan, Graham (LAB - Swanside)
graham.morgan@knowsley.gov.uk

Newman, Tony (LAB - Whiston & Cronton)
tony.newman@knowsley.gov.uk

O'Hare, Brian (LAB - St. Gabriel's)
brian.o'hare@knowsley.gov.uk

O'Hare, Christina (LAB - St. Gabriel's)
christina.ohare@knowsley.gov.uk

O'Keeffe, Steff (LAB - Prescot South)
steff.o'keeffe@knowsley.gov.uk

O'Mara, Margi (LAB - Stockbridge)
margi.o'mara@knowsley.gov.uk

Powell, Terry (LAB - Halewood North)
terry.powell@knowsley.gov.uk

Powell, Shelley (LAB - Halewood North)
shelley.powell@knowsley.gov.uk

See, Gary (LAB - Halewood South)
gary.see@knowsley.gov.uk

Smith, Ian (LD - Prescot North)
ian.smith@knowsley.gov.uk

Smith, Ros (LAB - Whitefield)
ros.smith@knowsley.gov.uk

Spall, Pam (LAB - Roby)
pam.spall@knowsley.gov.uk

Spall, Sarah (LAB - Roby)
sarah.spall@knowsley.gov.uk

Stuart, Marie (LAB - Northwood)
marie.stuart@knowsley.gov.uk

Williams, David (LAB - Prescot South)
david.williams@knowsley.gov.uk

Wynn, Mike (LD - Prescot North)
mike.wynn@knowsley.gov.uk

POLITICAL COMPOSITION
LAB: 42, LD: 3

COMMITTEE CHAIRS

Licensing: Mr Terry Powell

Planning: Ms Margaret Harvey

Lambeth   L

London Borough of Lambeth, Lambeth Town Hall, Brixton Hill, London SW2 1RW
☎ 020 7926 1000 ☝ infoservice@lambeth.gov.uk
🖳 www.lambeth.gov.uk

FACTS AND FIGURES
Parliamentary Constituencies: Dulwich and West Norwood, Streatham, Vauxhall
EU Constituencies: London
Election Frequency: Elections are of whole council

PRINCIPAL OFFICERS

Chief Executive: Mr Sean Harriss, Chief Executive, Lambeth Town Hall, Brixton Hill, London SW2 1RW ☎ 020 7926 1000 ☝ sharriss@lambeth.gov.uk

Senior Management: Ms Jackie Belton, Strategic Director - Corporate Resources, Lambeth Town Hall, Brixton Hill, London SW2 1RW ☎ 020 7926 9673 ☝ jbelton@lambeth.gov.uk

Senior Management: Ms Helen Charlesworth-May, Strategic Director - Children, Adults & Health, Phoenix House, 40 Wandsworth Road, London SW8 2LL ☎ 020 7926 1000 ☝ hcharlesworth@lambeth.gov.uk

Senior Management: Ms Sue Foster, Strategic Director - Neighbourhoods & Growth, Hambrook House, Porden Road, London SW2 5RW ☎ 020 7926 3426 ☝ sfoster1@lambeth.gov.uk

Senior Management: Ms Annie Hudson, Interim Strategic Director - Children's Services & Statutory DCS, Lambeth Town Hall, Brixton Hill, London SW2 1RW ahudson@lambeth.gov.uk

Senior Management: Dr Ruth Wallis, Director - Public Health, 160 Tooley Street, London SE1 2QH ruth.wallis@southwark.gov.uk

Access Officer / Social Services (Disability): Ms Fiona Connolly, Service Director - Adult Social Care, Lambeth Town Hall, Brixton Hill, London SW2 1RW ☎ 020 7926 1000 ☝ fconnolly@lambeth.gov.uk

PR / Communications: Mr Julian Ellerby, Director - Corporate Business & Development, Lambeth Town Hall, Brixton Hill, London SW2 1RW ☎ 020 7926 1273 ☝ jellerby@lambeth.gov.uk

Community Planning: Mr David Joyce, Assistant Director - Planning & Development, Phoenix House, 10 Wandsworth Road, London SW8 2LL ☎ 020 7926 1109 ☝ djoyce@lambeth.gov.uk

Community Safety: Ms Ann Corbett, Assistant Director - Community Safety, 205 Stockwell Road, Brixton, London SW9 9SL ☎ 020 7926 2898 ☝ acorbett@lambeth.gov.uk

Consumer Protection and Trading Standards: Mr Robert Gardner, Head of Trading Standards, 2 Herne Hill Road, Brixton, London SE24 0AU ☎ 020 7926 6122

Corporate Services: Mr Julian Ellerby, Director - Corporate Business & Development, Lambeth Town Hall, Brixton Hill, London SW2 1RW ☎ 020 7926 1273 ☝ jellerby@lambeth.gov.uk

Electoral Registration: Mr Jamie Baker, Electoral & Civic Services Manager, Lambeth Town Hall, Brixton Hill, London SW2 1RW ☎ 020 7926 2307 ☝ jbaker1@lambeth.gov.uk

Emergency Planning: Mr Jo Couzens, Emergency Response Planning Officer, Lambeth Town Hall, Brixton Hill, London SW2 1RW ☎ 020 7926 6162 ☝ jcouzens@lambeth.gov.uk

Environmental / Technical Services: Ms Sue Foster, Strategic Director - Neighbourhoods & Growth, Hambrook House, Porden Road, London SW2 5RW ☎ 020 7926 3426 ☝ sfoster1@lambeth.gov.uk

Estates, Property & Valuation: Ms Sophie Linton, Head of Variation & Strategic Property Services, Lambeth Town Hall, Brixton Hill, London SW2 1RW ☎ 020 7926 1000 ☝ slinton@lambeth.gov.uk

Pensions: Mrs Linda Osborne, Pensions Manager, Phoenix House, 10 Wandsworth Road, London SW8 2LL ☎ 020 7926 1000 ☝ losborne1@lambeth.gov.uk

Highways: Mr Raj Mistry, Head of Parking Services, 234 - 244 Stockwell Road, Brixton, London SW9 9SP ☎ 020 7926 6263 ☝ rmistry@lambeth.gov.uk

Housing: Ms Sue Foster, Strategic Director - Neighbourhoods & Growth, Hambrook House, Porden Road, London SW2 5RW ☎ 020 7926 3426 ☝ sfoster1@lambeth.gov.uk

Legal: Mr Mark Hynes, Director - Corporate Affairs, Lambeth Town Hall, Brixton Hill, London SW2 1RW ☎ 020 7926 2433

Member Services: Mr Wayne Chandai, Democratic Services Manager, Lambeth Town Hall, Brixton Hill, London SW2 1RW ☎ 020 7926 1000 ☝ wchandai@lambeth.gov.uk

Parking: Mr Raj Mistry, Head of Parking Services, 234 - 244 Stockwell Road, Brixton, London SW9 9SP ☎ 020 7926 6263 ☝ rmistry@lambeth.gov.uk

Personnel / HR: Mr Steve Jonathan, Director - HR & Transformation, Lambeth Town Hall, Brixton Hill, London SW2 1RW ☎ 020 7926 1000 ☝ sjonathan@lambeth.gov.uk

Regeneration: Ms Sue Foster, Strategic Director - Neighbourhoods & Growth, Hambrook House, Porden Road, London SW2 5RW ☎ 020 7926 3426 ☝ sfoster1@lambeth.gov.uk

Social Services (Adult): Ms Fiona Connolly, Service Director - Adult Social Care, Lambeth Town Hall, Brixton Hill, London SW2 1RW ☎ 020 7926 1000 ☝ fconnolly@lambeth.gov.uk

Social Services (Children): Ms Helen Charlesworth-May, Strategic Director - Children, Adults & Health, Phoenix House, 40 Wandsworth Road, London SW8 2LL ☎ 020 7926 1000 ☝ hcharlesworth@lambeth.gov.uk

Social Services (Children): Ms Annie Hudson, Interim Strategic Director - Children's Services & Statutory DCS, Lambeth Town Hall, Brixton Hill, London SW2 1RW ahudson@lambeth.gov.uk

LAMBETH

Public Health: Dr Ruth Wallis, Director - Public Health, 160 Tooley Street, London SE1 2QH ruth.wallis@southwark.gov.uk

Street Scene: Mr Raj Mistry, Head of Parking Services, 234 - 244 Stockwell Road, Brixton, London SW9 9SP ☎ 020 7926 6263 ✒ rmistry@lambeth.gov.uk

COUNCILLORS

Mayor: Jaffer, Saleha (LAB - St. Leonard's)
sjaffer@lambeth.gov.uk

Deputy Mayor: Cameron, Marcia (LAB - Tulse Hill)
mcameron@lambeth.gov.uk

Leader of the Council: Peck, Lib (LAB - Thornton)
lpeck@lambeth.gov.uk

Deputy Leader of the Council: McGlone, Paul (LAB - Ferndale)
pmcglone@lambeth.gov.uk

Deputy Leader of the Council: Walker, Imogen (LAB - Stockwell)
iwalker@lambeth.gov.uk

Group Leader: Briggs, Tim (CON - Clapham Common)
tbriggs@lambeth.gov.uk

Adilypour, Danial (LAB - Streatham South)
dadilypour@lambeth.gov.uk

Agdomar, Michelle (LAB - Herne Hill)
magdomar@lambeth.gov.uk

Ainslie, Scott (GRN - St. Leonard's)
streathamgreenparty@gmail.com

Aminu, Adedamola (LAB - Tulse Hill)
aaminu@lambeth.gov.uk

Amos, David (LAB - Prince's)
damos@lambeth.gov.uk

Anyanwu, Donatus (LAB - Coldharbour)
danyanwu@lambeth.gov.uk

Atkins, Mary (LAB - Tulse Hill)
matkins@lambeth.gov.uk

Atkins, Liz (LAB - Streatham Hill)
latkins@lambeth.gov.uk

Bennett, Matthew (LAB - Gipsy Hill)
mpbennett@lambeth.gov.uk

Bigham, Alex (LAB - Stockwell)
abigham@lambeth.gov.uk

Birley, Anna (LAB - Thurlow Park)
abirley@lambeth.gov.uk

Brathwaite, Jennifer (LAB - Gipsy Hill)
jbrathwaite@lambeth.gov.uk

Bray, Linda (LAB - Clapham Town)
lbray@lambeth.gov.uk

Chowdhury, Rezina (LAB - Streatham Hill)
rchowdhury@lambeth.gov.uk

Clark, Malcolm (LAB - Streatham Wells)
mclark@lambeth.gov.uk

Cowell, Fred (LAB - Thurlow Park)
fcowell@lambeth.gov.uk

Craig, Kevin (LAB - Bishop's)
kcraigh@lambeth.gov.uk

Davie, Edward (LAB - Thornton)
edavie@lambeth.gov.uk

de Cordova, Marsha (LAB - Larkhall)
mdecordova@lambeth.gov.uk

Deckers Dowber, Max (LAB - Thurlow Park)
mdeckersdowber@lambeth.gov.uk

Dickson, Jim (LAB - Herne Hill)
jdickson@lambeth.gov.uk

Dyer, Jacqui (LAB - Vassall)
jdyer3@lambeth.gov.uk

Edbrooke, Jane (LAB - Oval)
jedbrooke@lambeth.gov.uk

Eshalomi, Florence (LAB - Brixton Hill)
feshalomi@lambeth.gov.uk

Gadsby, Paul (LAB - Vassall)
pgadsby@lambeth.gov.uk

Gallop, Annie (LAB - Vassall)
agallop@lambeth.gov.uk

Garden, Adrian (LAB - Brixton Hill)
agarden@lambeth.gov.uk

Gentry, Bernard (CON - Clapham Common)
bgentry@lambeth.gov.uk

Haselden, Nigel (LAB - Clapham Town)
nhaselden@lambeth.gov.uk

Heywood, Rachel (LAB - Coldharbour)
rheywood@lambeth.gov.uk

Hill, Robert (LAB - St. Leonard's)
rhill@lambeth.gov.uk

Holborn, Jack (LAB - Herne Hill)
jholborn@lambeth.gov.uk

Holland, Claire (LAB - Oval)
cholland@lambeth.gov.uk

Hopkins, Jack (LAB - Oval)
jhopkins@lambeth.gov.uk

Kazantzis, John (LAB - Streatham South)
jkazantzis@lambeth.gov.uk

Kind, Ben (LAB - Bishop's)
bkind@lambeth.gov.uk

McClure, Vaila (LAB - Prince's)
vmcclure@lambeth.gov.uk

Meldrum, Jackie (LAB - Knight's Hill)
jmeldrum@lambeth.gov.uk

Morris, Diana (LAB - Thornton)
dmmorris@lambeth.gov.uk

Mosley, Jennie (LAB - Bishop's)
jmosley@lambeth.gov.uk

Murphy, Luk (LAB - Gipsy Hill)
lmurphy1@lambeth.gov.uk

Nathanson, Louise (CON - Clapham Common)
lnathanson@lambeth.gov.uk

Parr, Matt (LAB - Coldharbour)
mparr1@lambeth.gov.uk

Pickard, Jane (LAB - Knight's Hill)
jpickard@lambeth.gov.uk

Prentice, Sally (LAB - Ferndale)
sprentice@lambeth.gov.uk

Rosa, Guilherme (LAB - Stockwell)
grosa@lambeth.gov.uk

Sabharwal, Neil (LAB - Ferndale)
nsabharwal@lambeth.gov.uk

Seedat, Mohammed (LAB - Streatham Wells)
mseedat@lambeth.gov.uk

Simpson, Joanne (LAB - Prince's)
jsimpson2@lambeth.gov.uk

Simpson, Iain (LAB - Streatham Hill)
isimpson@lambeth.gov.uk

Tiedemann, Martin (LAB - Brixton Hill)
mtiedemann@lambeth.gov.uk

Treppass, Amélie (LAB - Streatham Wells)
atreppass@lambeth.gov.uk

Valcarcel, Christiana (LAB - Larkhall)
cvalcarcel@lambeth.gov.uk

Wellbelove, Christopher (LAB - Clapham Town)
cllrwellbelove@gmail.com

Wilcox, Clair (LAB - Streatham South)
cwilcox@lambeth.gov.uk

Wilson, Andrew (LAB - Larkhall)
awilson5@lambeth.gov.uk

Winifred, Sonia (LAB - Knight's Hill)
swinifred@lambeth.gov.uk

POLITICAL COMPOSITION
LAB: 59, CON: 3, GRN: 1

COMMITTEE CHAIRS

Health & Wellbeing: Mr Jim Dickson

Health & Wellbeing: Mr Mohammed Seedat

Licensing: Ms Michelle Agdomar

Pensions: Mr Iain Simpson

Planning: Ms Clair Wilcox

Lancashire   C

Lancashire County Council, PO Box 78, County Hall, Preston PR1 8XJ

☎ 0300 123 6701 📠 01722 533553 ✆ enquiries@lancashire.gov.uk
🖥 www.lancashire.gov.uk

FACTS AND FIGURES
Parliamentary Constituencies: Burnley, Chorley, Fylde, Hyndburn, Morecambe and Lunesdale, Pendle, Preston, Ribble Valley, Rossendale and Darwen, South Ribble
EU Constituencies: North West
Election Frequency: Elections are of whole council

PRINCIPAL OFFICERS

Chief Executive: Ms Jo Turton, Chief Executive, PO Box 61, County Hall, Preston PR1 0LD ☎ 01772 536260
✆ jo.turton@lancashire.gov.uk

Assistant Chief Executive: Mr Steve Browne, Corporate Director - Commissioning & Deputy Chief Executive, PO Box 78, County Hall, Preston PR1 8XJ ✆ 01772 534121 ✆ steve.browne@lancashire.gov.uk

Senior Management: Mr Phil Barrett, Director - Community Services, PO Box 78, County Hall, Preston PR1 8XJ ☎ 01772 538222 ✆ phil.barrett@lancashire.gov.uk

Senior Management: Ms Linda Clegg, Interim Director - Children's Services, PO Box 78, County Hall, Preston PR1 8XJ ☎ 01772 531652 ✆ linda.clegg@lancashire.gov.uk

Senior Management: Mr George Graham, Director - Pension Fund, PO Box 78, County Hall, Preston PR1 8XJ ☎ 01772 538102 ✆ george.graham@lancashire.gov.uk

Senior Management: Mr Mike Jenson, Chief Investment Officer, PO Box 78, County Hall, Preston PR1 8XJ ☎ 01772 534742 ✆ mike.jenson@lancashire.gov.uk

Senior Management: Dr Sakthi Karunanithi, Director - Public Health & Wellbeing, PO Box 78, County Hall, Preston PR1 8XJ ☎ 01772 536287 ✆ sakthi.karunanithi@lancashire.gov.uk

Senior Management: Mr Martin Kelly, Director - Economic Development, PO Box 78, County Hall, Preston PR1 8XJ ☎ 01772 536197 ✆ martin.kelly@lancashire.gov.uk

Senior Management: Mr Mike Kirby, Director - Corporate Commissioning, PO Box 78, County Hall, Preston PR1 8XJ ☎ 01772 534660 ✆ mike.kirby@lancashire.gov.uk

Senior Management: Mr Neil Kissock, Director - Financial Resources, PO Box 78, County Hall, Preston PR1 8XJ ☎ 01772 534715 ✆ neil.kissock@lancashire.gov.uk

Senior Management: Ms Lisa Kitto, Director - Corporate Services, PO Box 78, County Hall, Preston PR1 8XJ ☎ 01772 534757 ✆ lisa.kitto@lancashire.gov.uk

Senior Management: Mr Tony Pounder, Director - Adult Services, PO Box 78, County Hall, Preston PR1 8XJ ☎ 01772 531553 ✆ tony.pounder@lancashire.gov.uk

Senior Management: Ms Sue Procter, Director - Programmes & Project Management, PO Box 78, County Hall, Preston PR1 8XJ ☎ 01772 539493 ✆ sue.procter@lancashire.gov.uk

Senior Management: Ms Laura Sales, Director - Legal, Democratic & Governance, PO Box 78, County Hall, Preston PR1 8XJ ☎ 01772 533375 ✆ laura.sales@lancashire.gov.uk

Senior Management: Mr Eddie Sutton, Director - Development & Corporate Services, PO Box 78, County Hall, Preston PR1 8XJ ☎ 01772 533475 ✆ eddie.sutton@lancashire.gov.uk

Senior Management: Ms Louise Taylor, Corporate Director - Operations & Delivery, PO Box 78, County Hall, Preston PR1 8XJ ☎ 01772 534121 ✆ louise.taylor@lancashire.gov.uk

LANCASHIRE

Senior Management: Mr Ian Young, Director - Governance, Finance & Public Services, PO Box 78, County Hall, Preston PR1 8XJ ☎ 01772 533531 ⌂ ian.young@lancashire.gov.uk

Architect, Building / Property Services: Mr Shaun Capper, Head of Service - Design & Construction, Cuerdan Way, Bamber Bridge, Preston PR5 6BF ☎ 01772 530251 ⌂ shaun.capper@lancashire.gov.uk

Children / Youth Services: Ms Diane Booth, Head of Service - Children's Social Care, PO Box 78, County Hall, Preston PR1 8XJ ☎ 01282 470129 ⌂ diane.booth@lancashire.gov.uk

Children / Youth Services: Mr Bob Stott, Director - Education, Schools & Care, PO Box 78, County Hall, Preston PR1 8XJ ☎ 01772 531652 ⌂ bob.stott@lancashire.gov.uk

Children / Youth Services: Ms Louise Taylor, Corporate Director - Operations & Delivery, PO Box 78, County Hall, Preston PR1 8XJ ☎ 01772 534121 ⌂ louise.taylor@lancashire.gov.uk

Civil Registration: Ms Julie Bell, Head of Service - Libraries, Museums, Culture & Registrars, Park Hotel, East Cliff, Preston PR1 3EA ☎ 01772 536727 ⌂ julie.bell@lancashire.gov.uk

PR / Communications: Mr Tim Seamans, Head of Service - Communications, Corporate Communications Group, County Hall, Preston PR1 8XJ ☎ 01772 530760 ⌂ tim.seamans@lancashire.gov.uk

Community Planning: Mr Phil Barrett, Director - Community Services, PO Box 78, County Hall, Preston PR1 8XJ ☎ 01772 538222 ⌂ phil.barrett@lancashire.gov.uk

Consumer Protection and Trading Standards: Mr Paul Noone, Head of Trading Standards Service, County Hall, Preston PR1 0LD ☎ 01772 534123 ⌂ paul.noone@lancashire.gov.uk

Corporate Services: Ms Lisa Kitto, Director - Corporate Services, PO Box 78, County Hall, Preston PR1 8XJ ☎ 01772 534757 ⌂ lisa.kitto@lancashire.gov.uk

Corporate Services: Ms Ruth Lowry, Head of Service - Internal Audit, PO Box 78, County Hall, Preston PR1 8XJ ☎ 01772 534898 ⌂ ruth.lowry@lancashire.gov.uk

Corporate Services: Ms Sue Procter, Director - Programmes & Project Management, PO Box 78, County Hall, Preston PR1 8XJ ☎ 01772 539493 ⌂ sue.procter@lancashire.gov.uk

Customer Service: Ms Sarah Jenkins, Head of Customer Access, PO Box 78, County Hall, Preston PR1 8XJ ☎ 01772 537401 ⌂ sarah.jenkins@lancashire.gov.uk

Economic Development: Mr Martin Kelly, Director - Economic Development, PO Box 78, County Hall, Preston PR1 8XJ ☎ 01772 536197 ⌂ martin.kelly@lancashire.gov.uk

Education: Mr Brendan Lee, Head of Service - Special Educational Needs & Disabilty, PO Box 78, County Hall, Preston PR1 8XJ ☎ 01772 538323 ⌂ brendan.lee@lancashire.gov.uk

Emergency Planning: Mr Alan Wilton, Head of Service - Emergency Planning & Resilience, PO Box 78, County Hall, Preston PR1 8XJ ☎ 01772 537902 ⌂ alan.wilton@lancashire.gov.uk

Environmental / Technical Services: Mr Andrew Mullaney, Head of Service - Planning & Environment, PO Box 78, County Hall, Preston PR1 8XJ ☎ 01772 534190 ⌂ andrew.mullaney@lancashire.gov.uk

Environmental Health: Mr Paul Noone, Head of Service - Trading Standards & Scientific Services, PO Box 78, County Hall, Preston PR1 8XJ ☎ 01772 534123 ⌂ steve.scott@lancashire.gov.uk

Estates, Property & Valuation: Mr Gary Pearse, Head of Service - Estates, PO Box 78, County Hall, Preston PR1 8XJ ☎ 01772 533903 ⌂ gary.pearse@lancashire.gov.uk

Finance: Mr Ian Young, Director - Governance, Finance & Public Services, PO Box 78, County Hall, Preston PR1 8XJ ☎ 01772 533531 ⌂ ian.young@lancashire.gov.uk

Pensions: Mr George Graham, Director - Pension Fund, PO Box 78, County Hall, Preston PR1 8XJ ☎ 01772 538102 ⌂ george.graham@lancashire.gov.uk

Highways: Mr Shaun Capper, Head of Service - Design & Construction, Cuerdan Way, Bamber Bridge, Preston PR5 6BF ☎ 01772 530251 ⌂ shaun.capper@lancashire.gov.uk

Highways: Mr Phil Durnell, Head of Service - Highways, PO Box 78, County Hall, Preston PR1 8XJ ☎ 01772 538502 ⌂ phil.durnell@lancashire.gov.uk

Legal: Mr Paul Bond, Head of Legal & Democratic Services, PO Box 78, County Hall, Preston PR1 8XJ ☎ 01772 534676 ⌂ paul.bond@lancashire.gov.uk

Leisure and Cultural Services: Ms Julie Bell, Head of Service - Libraries, Museums, Culture & Registrars, Park Hotel, East Cliff, Preston PR1 3EA ☎ 01772 536727 ⌂ julie.bell@lancashire.gov.uk

Member Services: Mr Paul Bond, Head of Legal & Democratic Services, PO Box 78, County Hall, Preston PR1 8XJ ☎ 01772 534676 ⌂ paul.bond@lancashire.gov.uk

Partnerships: Ms Clare Platt, Head of Partnerships, PO Box 78, County Hall, Preston PR1 8XJ ☎ 07876 844627 ⌂ clare.platt@lancashire.gov.uk

Personnel / HR: Ms Deborah Barrow, Head of Service - Human Resources, PO Box 78, County Hall, Preston PR1 8XJ ☎ 01772 535805 ⌂ deborah.burrows@lancashire.gov.uk

Planning: Mr Andrew Mullaney, Head of Service - Planning & Environment, PO Box 78, County Hall, Preston PR1 8XJ ☎ 01772 534190 ⌂ andrew.mullaney@lancashire.gov.uk

Public Libraries: Ms Julie Bell, Head of Service - Libraries, Museums, Culture & Registrars, Park Hotel, East Cliff, Preston PR1 3EA ☎ 01772 536727 ⌂ julie.bell@lancashire.gov.uk

Recycling & Waste Minimisation: Ms Sue Procter, Assistant Director - Environmental Services (Area East), LCC Highways Office, Highways Depot, Willows Lane, Accrington BB5 oRT
☎ 01254 770985 ◌ susan.procter@lancashire.gov.uk

Recycling & Waste Minimisation: Mr Steve Scott, Head of Service - Trading Standards & Scientific Services, PO Box 78, County Hall, Preston PR1 8XJ ☎ 01772 533755
◌ steve.scott@lancashire.gov.uk

Social Services: Mr Brendan Lee, Head of Service - Special Educational Needs & Disabilty, PO Box 78, County Hall, Preston PR1 8XJ ☎ 01772 538323 ◌ brendan.lee@lancashire.gov.uk

Social Services: Ms Catherine Whalley, Head of Service - Social Care, PO Box 78, County Hall, Preston PR1 8XJ ☎ 07816 971177
◌ catherine.whalley@lancashire.gov.uk

Social Services (Adult): Mr Tony Pounder, Director - Adult Services, PO Box 78, County Hall, Preston PR1 8XJ
☎ 01772 531553 ◌ tony.pounder@lancashire.gov.uk

Social Services (Adult): Ms Liz Wilde, Head of Service - Older People, PO Box 78, County Hall, Preston PR1 8XJ ☎ 07887 831031
◌ liz.wilde@lancashire.gov.uk

Social Services (Children): Ms Diane Booth, Head of Service - Children's Social Care, PO Box 78, County Hall, Preston PR1 8XJ
☎ 01282 470129 ◌ diane.booth@lancashire.gov.uk

Fostering & Adoption: Ms Barbara Bath, Head of Service - Adoption, Fostering & Residential, PO Box 78, County Hall, Preston PR1 8XJ ☎ 01772 535491 ◌ barbara.bath@lancashire.gov.uk

Safeguarding: Ms Charlotte Hammond, Head of Service - Safeguarding, PO Box 78, County Hall, Preston PR1 8XJ
☎ 0777 133 8882 ◌ charlotte.hammond@lancashire.gov.uk

Public Health: Dr Sakthi Karunanithi, Director - Public Health & Wellbeing, PO Box 78, County Hall, Preston PR1 8XJ
☎ 01772 536287 ◌ sakthi.karunanithi@lancashire.gov.uk

Transport: Mr Oliver Starkey, Head of Service - Public & Integrated Transport, PO Box 78, County Hall, Preston PR1 8XJ
☎ 01772 534619 ◌ oliver.starkey@lancashire.gov.uk

Transport Planner: Mr Oliver Starkey, Head of Service - Public & Integrated Transport, PO Box 78, County Hall, Preston PR1 8XJ ☎ 01772 534619 ◌ oliver.starkey@lancashire.gov.uk

Waste Collection and Disposal: Mr Steve Scott, Head of Service - Trading Standards & Scientific Services, PO Box 78, County Hall, Preston PR1 8XJ ☎ 01772 533755 ◌ steve.scott@lancashire.gov.uk

COUNCILLORS

Chair: Hanson, Janice (LAB - Morecambe West)
janice.hanson@lancashire.gov.uk

Vice-Chair: Aldridge, Terence (LAB - Skelmersdale Central)
terry.aldridge@lancashire.gov.uk

Leader of the Council: Mein, Jennifer (LAB - Preston South East)
jennifer.mein@lancashire.gov.uk

Deputy Leader of the Council: Borrow, David (LAB - Preston North West)
david.borrow@lancashire.gov.uk

Ali, Azhar (LAB - Nelson South)
azhar.ali@lancashire.gov.uk

Ashton, Timothy (CON - Lytham)
tim.ashton@lancashire.gov.uk

Atkinson, Albert (CON - Ribble Valley North East)
albert.atkinson@lancashire.gov.uk

Barnes, Alyson (LAB - Rossendale North)
alyson.barnes@lancashire.gov.uk

Barron, Malcolm (CON - West Lancashire North)
malcolm.barron@lancashire.gov.uk

Beavers, Lorraine (LAB - Fleetwood West)
lorraine.beavers@lancashire.gov.uk

Brindle, Margaret (LD - Burnley Rural)
margaret.brindle@lancashire.gov.uk

Britcliffe, Peter (CON - Oswaldtwistle)
peter.britcliffe@lancashire.gov.uk

Brown, Terry (LAB - Chorley East)
terry.brown@lancashire.gov.uk

Brown, Ian (CON - Clitheroe)
ian.brown2@lancashire.gov.uk

Brown, Ken (CON - Heysham)
ken.brown@lancashire.gov.uk

Buckley, Peter (CON - St Annes North)
peter.buckley@lancashire.gov.uk

Burns, Terry (LAB - Burnley North East)
terry.burns@lancashire.gov.uk

Charles, Susie (CON - Lancaster Rural East)
susie.charles@lancashire.gov.uk

Cheetham, Anne (CON - Rossendale South)
anne.cheetham@lancashire.gov.uk

Clempson, Alf (CON - Poulton-le-Fylde)
alf.clempson@lancashire.gov.uk

Clifford, Darren (LAB - Morecambe South)
darren.clifford@lancashire.gov.uk

Collinge, Lizzi (LAB - Lancaster East)
lizzi.collinge@lancashire.gov.uk

Craig-Wilson, Fabian (CON - St Annes South)
fabian.craig-wilson@lancashire.gov.uk

Crompton, Carl (LAB - Preston Central South)
carl.crompton@lancashire.gov.uk

Cullens, Alan (CON - Chorley Rural North)
alan.cullens@lancashire.gov.uk

Dad, Munsif (LAB - Accrington West)
munsif.dad@lancashire.gov.uk

Dawson, Bernard (LAB - Accrington South)
bernard.dawson@lancashire.gov.uk

De Molfetta, Francesco (LAB - Preston Central North)
francesco.demolfetta@lancashire.gov.uk

Dereli, Cynthia (LAB - West Lancashire West)
cynthia.dereli@lancashire.gov.uk

LANCASHIRE

Dowding, Gina (GRN - Lancaster Central)
gina.dowding@lancashire.gov.uk

Driver, Geoff (CON - Preston North)
geoff.driver@lancashire.gov.uk

Ellard, Kevin (LAB - Preston East)
kevin.ellard@lancashire.gov.uk

Fillis, John (LAB - Skelmersdale East)
john.fillis@lancashire.gov.uk

Gibson, Julie (LAB - Skelmersdale West)
julie.gibson@lancashire.gov.uk

Gooch, Graham (CON - South Ribble Rural West)
graham.gooch@lancashire.gov.uk

Green, Michael (CON - Leyland South West)
mike.france@lancashire.gov.uk

Hassan, Misfar (LAB - Burnley Central East)
misfar.hassan@lancashire.gov.uk

Hayhurst, Paul (IND - Fylde West)
paul.hayhurst@lancashire.gov.uk

Henig, Chris (LAB - Lancaster South East)
chris.henig@lancashire.gov.uk

Hennessy, Nikki (LAB - Ormskirk West)
nikki.hennessy2@lancashire.gov.uk

Holgate, Steven (LAB - Chorley West)
steve.holgate@lancashire.gov.uk

Howarth, David (LD - Penwortham North)
david.howarth2@lancashire.gov.uk

Iddon, Keith (CON - Chorley Rural West)
keith.iddon@lancashire.gov.uk

Iqbal, Mohammed (LAB - Brierfield & Nelson North)
mohammed.iqbal@lancashire.gov.uk

James, Alycia (CON - Lancaster Rural North)
alycia.james@lancashire.gov.uk

Johnstone, Marcus (LAB - Padiham & Burnley West)
marcus.johnstone@lancashire.gov.uk

Jones, Anthony (CON - Morecambe North)
anthony.jones@lancashire.gov.uk

Kay, Andrea (CON - Thornton Cleveleys North)
andrea.kay@lancashire.gov.uk

Lawrenson, Jim (CON - Thornton Cleveleys Central)
jim.lawrenson@lancashire.co.uk

Lord, Dorothy (LD - Pendle Central)
dorothy.lord@lancashire.gov.uk

Martin, Tony (LAB - Burnley Central West)
tony.martin@lancashire.gov.uk

Molineux, Gareth (LAB - Great Harwood)
gareth.molineux@lancashire.gov.uk

Motala, Yousuf (LAB - Preston City)
yousuf.motala@lancashire.gov.uk

Murray, Bev (LAB - Chorley South)
bev.murray@lancashire.gov.uk

Oades, Liz (IND - Fylde East)
liz.oades@lancashire.gov.uk

Oakes, Jackie (LAB - Rossendale East)
jackie.oakes@lancashire.gov.uk

O'Toole, David (CON - West Lancashire South)
david.o'toole@lancashire.gov.uk

Otter, Mike (CON - Farington)
mike.otter@lancashire.gov.uk

Parkinson, Miles (LAB - Rishton & Clayton-Le-Moors)
miles.parkinson@lancashire.gov.uk

Penney, Nicola (LAB - Skerton)
niki.penney@lancashire.gov.uk

Perkins, Sandra (IND - Garstang)
sandra.perkins@lancashire.gov.uk

Perks, Mark (CON - Chorley North)
mark.perks@lancashire.gov.uk

Pritchard, Clare (LAB - Accrington North)
clare.pritchard@lancashire.gov.uk

Prynn, Sue (LAB - Penwortham South)
sue.prynn@lancashire.gov.uk

Rigby, Paul (CON - Fylde South)
paul.rigby@lancashire.gov.uk

Schofield, Alan (CON - Ribble Valley South West)
alan.schofield@lancashire.gov.uk

Sedgewick, Keith (CON - Preston North East)
keith.sedgewick@lancashire.gov.uk

Serridge, Sean (LAB - Whitworth)
sean.serridge@lancashire.gov.uk

Shedwick, John (CON - Amounderness)
john.shedwick@lancashire.gov.uk

Shewan, Ron (LAB - Fleetwood East)
ron.shewan@lancashire.gov.uk

Smith, David (CON - Longridge with Bowland)
david.smith@lancashire.gov.uk

Snape, Kim (LAB - Chorley Rural East)
kim.snape@lancashire.gov.uk

Stansfield, David (CON - Rossendale West)
dave.stansfield@lancashire.gov.uk

Sumner, Jeff (LD - Burnley South West)
jeff.sumner@lancashire.gov.uk

Taylor, Vivien (CON - Wyreside)
vivien.taylor@lancashire.gov.uk

Tomlinson, Matthew (LAB - Leyland Central)
matthew.tomlinson@lancashire.gov.uk

Wakeford, Christian (CON - Pendle West)
christian.wakeford@lancashire.gov.uk

Watts, David (LAB - Bamber Bridge & Walton le Dale)
dave.watts@lancashire.gov.uk

Westley, David (CON - West Lancashire East)
david.westley@lancashire.gov.uk

Whipp, David (LD - West Craven)
david.whipp@lancashire.gov.uk

White, Paul (CON - Pendle East)
paul.white@lancashire.gov.uk

Wilkins, George (CON - Preston Rural)
george.wilkins@lancashire.gov.uk

Winlow, Bill (LD - Preston West)
bill.winlow@lancashire.gov.uk

Yates, Barrie (CON - South Ribble Rural East)
barrie.yates2@lancashire.gov.uk

POLITICAL COMPOSITION
LAB: 39, CON: 35, LD: 6, IND: 3, GRN: 1

COMMITTEE CHAIRS

Audit: Mr Terry Brown

Children's Services: Ms Gina Dowding

Development Control: Mr Munsif Dad

Health & Wellbeing: Mrs Jennifer Mein

Pensions: Mr Kevin Ellard

Lancaster City   D

Lancaster City Council, Town Hall, Dalton Square, Lancaster LA1 1PJ
☎ 01524 582000 🖷 01524 582979
🖰 customerservices@lancaster.gov.uk 🖳 www.lancaster.gov.uk

FACTS AND FIGURES
Parliamentary Constituencies: Lancaster and Fleetwood
EU Constituencies: North West
Election Frequency: Elections are of whole council

PRINCIPAL OFFICERS

Chief Executive: Ms Susan Parsonage, Chief Executive, Town Hall, Dalton Square, Lancaster LA1 1PJ ☎ 01524 582011
🖰 chiefexecutive@lancaster.gov.uk

Senior Management: Mr Mark Davies, Chief Officer - Environment, White Lund Depot, White Lund Industrial Estate, Morecambe LA3 3DT ☎ 01524 582401 🖰 mdavies@lancaster.gov.uk

Senior Management: Mr Andrew Dobson, Chief Officer - Regeneration & Planning, Town Hall, Marine Road, Morecambe LA4 4AF ☎ 01524 582303 🖰 adobson@lancaster.gov.uk

Senior Management: Ms Suzanne Lodge, Chief Officer - Health & Housing, Town Hall, Marine Road, Morecambe LA4 4AF ☎ 01524 582709 🖰 slodge@lancaster.gov.uk

Senior Management: Ms Nadine Muschamp, Chief Officer - Resources (S151 Officer), Town Hall, Dalton Square, Lancaster LA1 1PJ ☎ 01524 582117 🖰 nmuschamp@lancaster.gov.uk

Architect, Building / Property Services: Ms Nadine Muschamp, Chief Officer - Resources (S151 Officer), Town Hall, Dalton Square, Lancaster LA1 1PJ ☎ 01524 582117 🖰 nmuschamp@lancaster.gov.uk

Building Control: Mr Andrew Dobson, Chief Officer - Regeneration & Planning, Town Hall, Marine Road, Morecambe LA4 4AF ☎ 01524 582303 🖰 adobson@lancaster.gov.uk

PR / Communications: Mr Michael Hill, Communications & Marketing Team Leader, Town Hall, Dalton Square, Lancaster LA1 1PJ ☎ 0524 582041 🖰 mhill@lancaster.gov.uk

Community Planning: Mr Andrew Dobson, Chief Officer - Regeneration & Planning, Town Hall, Marine Road, Morecambe LA4 4AF ☎ 01524 582303 🖰 adobson@lancaster.gov.uk

Community Safety: Mr Mark Davies, Chief Officer - Environment, White Lund Depot, White Lund Industrial Estate, Morecambe LA3 3DT ☎ 01524 582401 🖰 mdavies@lancaster.gov.uk

Computer Management: Mr Chris Riley, Applications Manager for ICT Services, Town Hall, Dalton Square, Lancaster LA1 1PJ ☎ 01524 582106 🖰 cjriley@lancaster.gov.uk

Consumer Protection and Trading Standards: Ms Suzanne Lodge, Chief Officer - Health & Housing, Town Hall, Marine Road, Morecambe LA4 4AF ☎ 01524 582709 🖰 slodge@lancaster.gov.uk

Contracts: Mr Mark Davies, Chief Officer - Environment, White Lund Depot, White Lund Industrial Estate, Morecambe LA3 3DT ☎ 01524 582401 🖰 mdavies@lancaster.gov.uk

Corporate Services: Mr Mark Cullinan, Chief Executive, Town Hall, Dalton Square, Lancaster LA1 1PJ ☎ 01524 582011 🖰 chiefexecutive@lancaster.gov.uk

Customer Service: Ms Alison McGurk, Customer Service & Visitor Information Centre Manager, Town Hall, Dalton Square, Lancaster LA1 1PJ ☎ 01524 582399 🖰 amcgurk@lancaster.gov.uk

Direct Labour: Mr Mark Davies, Chief Officer - Environment, White Lund Depot, White Lund Industrial Estate, Morecambe LA3 3DT ☎ 01524 582401 🖰 mdavies@lancaster.gov.uk

Economic Development: Mr Andrew Dobson, Chief Officer - Regeneration & Planning, Town Hall, Marine Road, Morecambe LA4 4AF ☎ 01524 582303 🖰 adobson@lancaster.gov.uk

Electoral Registration: Mrs Lisa Vines, Election Manager, Town Hall, Dalton Square, Lancaster LA1 1PJ ☎ 01524 582070 🖰 lvines@lancaster.gov.uk

Emergency Planning: Mr Mark Bartlett, Civil Contingencies Officer, Town Hall, Marine Road, Morecambe LA4 4AF ☎ 01524 582680 🖰 mbartlett@lancaster.gov.uk

Energy Management: Ms Suzanne Lodge, Chief Officer - Health & Housing, Town Hall, Marine Road, Morecambe LA4 4AF ☎ 01524 582709 🖰 slodge@lancaster.gov.uk

Environmental / Technical Services: Mr Mark Davies, Chief Officer - Environment, White Lund Depot, White Lund Industrial Estate, Morecambe LA3 3DT ☎ 01524 582401 🖰 mdavies@lancaster.gov.uk

Environmental Health: Ms Suzanne Lodge, Chief Officer - Health & Housing, Town Hall, Marine Road, Morecambe LA4 4AF ☎ 01524 582709 🖰 slodge@lancaster.gov.uk

Estates, Property & Valuation: Mr Andrew Dobson, Chief Officer - Regeneration & Planning, Town Hall, Marine Road, Morecambe LA4 4AF ☎ 01524 582303 🖰 adobson@lancaster.gov.uk

LANCASTER CITY

Events Manager: Mr Andrew Dobson, Chief Officer - Regeneration & Planning, Town Hall, Marine Road, Morecambe LA4 4AF ☎ 01524 582303 ⌂ adobson@lancaster.gov.uk

Facilities: Ms Nadine Muschamp, Chief Officer - Resources (S151 Officer), Town Hall, Dalton Square, Lancaster LA1 1PJ ☎ 01524 582117 ⌂ nmuschamp@lancaster.gov.uk

Finance: Ms Nadine Muschamp, Chief Officer - Resources (S151 Officer), Town Hall, Dalton Square, Lancaster LA1 1PJ ☎ 01524 582117 ⌂ nmuschamp@lancaster.gov.uk

Fleet Management: Mr Mark Davies, Chief Officer - Environment, White Lund Depot, White Lund Industrial Estate, Morecambe LA3 3DT ☎ 01524 582401 ⌂ mdavies@lancaster.gov.uk

Grounds Maintenance: Mr Mark Davies, Chief Officer - Environment, White Lund Depot, White Lund Industrial Estate, Morecambe LA3 3DT ☎ 01524 582401 ⌂ mdavies@lancaster.gov.uk

Health and Safety: Ms Suzanne Lodge, Chief Officer - Health & Housing, Town Hall, Marine Road, Morecambe LA4 4AF ☎ 01524 582709 ⌂ slodge@lancaster.gov.uk

Highways: Mr Mark Davies, Chief Officer - Environment, White Lund Depot, White Lund Industrial Estate, Morecambe LA3 3DT ☎ 01524 582401 ⌂ mdavies@lancaster.gov.uk

Housing: Ms Suzanne Lodge, Chief Officer - Health & Housing, Town Hall, Marine Road, Morecambe LA4 4AF ☎ 01524 582709 ⌂ slodge@lancaster.gov.uk

Housing Maintenance: Ms Suzanne Lodge, Chief Officer - Health & Housing, Town Hall, Marine Road, Morecambe LA4 4AF ☎ 01524 582709 ⌂ slodge@lancaster.gov.uk

Legal: Mrs Angela Parkinson, Senior Solicitor, Town Hall, Dalton Square, Lancaster LA1 1PJ ☎ 01524 582318 ⌂ aparkinson@lancaster.gov.uk

Leisure and Cultural Services: Ms Suzanne Lodge, Chief Officer - Health & Housing, Town Hall, Marine Road, Morecambe LA4 4AF ☎ 01524 582709 ⌂ slodge@lancaster.gov.uk

Licensing: Mrs Wendy Peck, Licensing Manager, Town Hall, Dalton Square, Lancaster LA1 1PJ ☎ 01524 582317 ⌂ wpeck@lancaster.gov.uk

Lighting: Mr Mark Davies, Chief Officer - Environment, White Lund Depot, White Lund Industrial Estate, Morecambe LA3 3DT ☎ 01524 582401 ⌂ mdavies@lancaster.gov.uk

Parking: Mr Mark Davies, Chief Officer - Environment, White Lund Depot, White Lund Industrial Estate, Morecambe LA3 3DT ☎ 01524 582401 ⌂ mdavies@lancaster.gov.uk

Personnel / HR: Mrs Angela Jackson, HR Services Manager, Town Hall, Dalton Square, Lancaster LA1 1PJ ☎ 01524 582179 ⌂ ajackson@lancaster.gov.uk

Planning: Mr Andrew Dobson, Chief Officer - Regeneration & Planning, Town Hall, Marine Road, Morecambe LA4 4AF ☎ 01524 582303 ⌂ adobson@lancaster.gov.uk

Procurement: Ms Nadine Muschamp, Chief Officer - Resources (S151 Officer), Town Hall, Dalton Square, Lancaster LA1 1PJ ☎ 01524 582117 ⌂ nmuschamp@lancaster.gov.uk

Recycling & Waste Minimisation: Mr Mark Davies, Chief Officer - Environment, White Lund Depot, White Lund Industrial Estate, Morecambe LA3 3DT ☎ 01524 582401 ⌂ mdavies@lancaster.gov.uk

Regeneration: Mr Andrew Dobson, Chief Officer - Regeneration & Planning, Town Hall, Marine Road, Morecambe LA4 4AF ☎ 01524 582303 ⌂ adobson@lancaster.gov.uk

Staff Training: Mrs Angela Jackson, HR Services Manager, Town Hall, Dalton Square, Lancaster LA1 1PJ ☎ 01524 582179 ⌂ ajackson@lancaster.gov.uk

Street Scene: Mr Mark Davies, Chief Officer - Environment, White Lund Depot, White Lund Industrial Estate, Morecambe LA3 3DT ☎ 01524 582401 ⌂ mdavies@lancaster.gov.uk

Sustainable Development: Mr Andrew Dobson, Chief Officer - Regeneration & Planning, Town Hall, Marine Road, Morecambe LA4 4AF ☎ 01524 582303 ⌂ adobson@lancaster.gov.uk

Tourism: Mr Andrew Dobson, Chief Officer - Regeneration & Planning, Town Hall, Marine Road, Morecambe LA4 4AF ☎ 01524 582303 ⌂ adobson@lancaster.gov.uk

Town Centre: Mr Andrew Dobson, Chief Officer - Regeneration & Planning, Town Hall, Marine Road, Morecambe LA4 4AF ☎ 01524 582303 ⌂ adobson@lancaster.gov.uk

Waste Collection and Disposal: Mr Mark Davies, Chief Officer - Environment, White Lund Depot, White Lund Industrial Estate, Morecambe LA3 3DT ☎ 01524 582401 ⌂ mdavies@lancaster.gov.uk

Waste Management: Mr Mark Davies, Chief Officer - Environment, White Lund Depot, White Lund Industrial Estate, Morecambe LA3 3DT ☎ 01524 582401 ⌂ mdavies@lancaster.gov.uk

COUNCILLORS

Mayor: Redfern, Robert (LAB - Skerton East) rredfern@lancaster.gov.uk

Deputy Mayor: Jackson, Caroline (GRN - Bulk) cjackson@lancaster.gov.uk

Leader of the Council: Blamire, Eileen (LAB - John O'Gaunt) eblamire@lancaster.gov.uk

Deputy Leader of the Council: Hanson, Janice (LAB - Harbour) jhanson@lancaster.gov.uk

Armstrong, Sam (GRN - University & Scotforth) starmstrong@lancaster.gov.uk

Ashworth, June (IND - Bare) jashworth@lancaster.gov.uk

Atkinson, Lucy (LAB - University & Scotforth) latkinson@lancaster.gov.uk

Barry, Jon (GRN - Marsh)
jbarry@lancaster.gov.uk

Bateson, Stuart (CON - Heysham South)
sbateson@lancaster.gov.uk

Biddulph, Alan (LAB - Heysham South)
abiddulph@lancaster.gov.uk

Brayshaw, Carla (LAB - Heysham Central)
cbrayshaw@lancaster.gov.uk

Brookes, Dave (GRN - Castle)
dbrookes@lancaster.gov.uk

Brown, Tracy (LAB - Westgate)
tmbrown@lancaster.gov.uk

Bryning, Abbott (LAB - Skerton East)
abryning@lancaster.gov.uk

Charles, Susie (CON - Ellel)
scharles@lancaster.gov.uk

Clifford, Darren (LAB - Harbour)
dclifford@lancaster.gov.uk

Cooper, Brett (CON - Bare)
bcooper@lancaster.gov.uk

Cozler, Claire (LAB - Westgate)
ccozler@lancaster.gov.uk

Denwood, Sheila (LAB - Scotforth West)
sdenwood@lancaster.gov.uk

Devey, Rob (LAB - Skerton West)
rdevey@lancaster.gov.uk

Edwards, Charlie (CON - Bare)
cedwards@lancaster.gov.uk

Gardiner, Andrew (CON - Overton)
agardiner@lancaster.gov.uk

Goodrich, Nigel (CON - Silverdale)
ngoodrich@lancaster.gov.uk

Guilding, Melanie (CON - Carnforth & Millhead)
mguilding@lancaster.gov.uk

Hall, Janet (LAB - Skerton East)
jhall@lancaster.gov.uk

Hamilton-Cox, Tim (GRN - Bulk)
thamiltoncox@lancaster.gov.uk

Hartley, Colin (LAB - Heysham South)
chartley@lancaster.gov.uk

Helme, Helen (CON - Ellel)
hhelme@lancaster.gov.uk

Hughes, Brendan (LAB - Poulton)
bhughes@lancaster.gov.uk

Jackson, Joan (CON - Lower Lune Valley)
jjackson@lancaster.gov.uk

Kay, Andrew (GRN - Bulk)
akay@lancaster.gov.uk

Kershaw, Ronnie (LAB - Scotforth West)
rkershaw@lancaster.gov.uk

Knight, Geoff (IND - Heysham Central)
gknight@lancaster.gov.uk

Leyshon, James (LAB - Scotforth East)
jleyshon@lancaster.gov.uk

Leytham, Karen (LAB - Skerton West)
kleytham@lancaster.gov.uk

Mace, Roger (CON - Kellet)
rmace@lancaster.gov.uk

Mann, Matt (LAB - University & Scotforth)
mmann@lancaster.gov.uk

Metcalfe, Terrie (LAB - Poulton)
tmetcalfe@lancaster.gov.uk

Mills, Abi (GRN - Scotforth West)
amills@lancaster.gov.uk

Novell, Rebecca (GRN - Marsh)
rnovell@lancaster.gov.uk

Parkinson, Jane (CON - Lower Lune Valley)
japarkinson@lancaster.gov.uk

Pattison, Margaret (LAB - Heysham North)
mpattison@lancaster.gov.uk

Reynolds, John (LAB - Carnforth & Millhead)

Rogerson, Sylvia (CON - Bolton & Slyne)
srogerson@lancaster.gov.uk

Sands, Ron (LAB - Heysham North)
rsands@lancaster.gov.uk

Scott, Elizabeth (LAB - John O'Gaunt)
lscott@lancaster.gov.uk

Sherlock, Roger (LAB - Skerton West)
rsherlock@lancaster.gov.uk

Smith, David (LAB - Westgate)
dasmith@lancaster.gov.uk

Sykes, Susan (CON - Warton)
ssykes@lancaster.gov.uk

Thomas, Malcolm (CON - Bolton & Slyne)
jthomas@lancaster.gov.uk

Thynne, Oscar (LAB - John O'Gaunt)

Warriner, Andrew (LAB - Torrisholme)
awarriner@lancaster.gov.uk

Whitaker, David (LAB - Harbour)
dwhitaker@lancaster.gov.uk

Whitehead, Anne (LAB - Scotforth East)
pawhitehead@lancaster.gov.uk

Wild, John (CON - Bolton & Slyne)
jwild@lancaster.gov.uk

Wilkinson, Nicholas (GRN - Castle)
nwilkinson@lancaster.gov.uk

Williamson, Phillippa (CON - Torrisholme)
phwilliamson@lancaster.gov.uk

Williamson, Peter (CON - Upper Lune Valley)
pwilliamson@lancaster.gov.uk

Woodruff, Paul (IND - Halton-with-Aughton)
pwoodruff@lancaster.gov.uk

Yates, Peter (CON - Carnforth & Millhead)
pyates@lancaster.gov.uk

POLITICAL COMPOSITION
LAB: 30, CON: 18, GRN: 9, IND: 3

LANCASTER CITY

COMMITTEE CHAIRS

Audit: Mr Matt Mann

Licensing: Mr Colin Hartley

Planning & Highways: Ms Carla Brayshaw

Leeds City   M

Leeds City Council, Civic Hall, Leeds LS1 1UR
☎ 0113 222 4444 ⌁ general.enquiries@leeds.gov.uk
🖳 www.leeds.gov.uk

FACTS AND FIGURES
Parliamentary Constituencies: Elmet and Rothwell, Leeds Central, Leeds East, Leeds North East, Leeds North West, Leeds West, Morley and Outwood, Normanton, Pontefract and Castleford, Pudsey
EU Constituencies: Yorkshire and the Humber
Election Frequency: Elections are by thirds

PRINCIPAL OFFICERS

Chief Executive: Mr Tom Riordan, Chief Executive, Chief Executive's Office, 3rd Floor East, Civic Hall, Leeds LS1 1UR
☎ 0113 247 4554 ⌁ tom.riordan@leeds.gov.uk

Deputy Chief Executive: Mr Alan Gay, Deputy Chief Executive & Director - Resources, Civic Hall, Calverley Street, Leeds LS1 1UR
☎ 0113 247 4226 ⌁ alan.gay@leeds.gov.uk

Assistant Chief Executive: Mr James Rogers, Assistant Chief Executive - Citizens & Communities, 3rd Floor East, Civic Hall, Calverley Street, Leeds LS1 1UR ☎ 0113 224 3579
⌁ james.rogers@leeds.gov.uk

Senior Management: Dr Ian Cameron, Executive Director - Public Health, 3rd Floor East, Civic Hall, Calverley Street, Leeds LS1 1UR ☎ 0113 395 2810 ⌁ ian.cameron@leeds.gov.uk

Senior Management: Mr Neil Evans, Director - Environment & Housing, 4th Floor West, Merrion House, Leeds LS1 1UR
☎ 0113 247 4721 ⌁ neil.evans@leeds.gov.uk

Senior Management: Mr Martin Farrington, Director - City Development, The Leonardo Building, 2 Rossington Street, Leeds LS2 8HB ☎ 0113 224 3816 ⌁ martin.farrington@leeds.gov.uk

Senior Management: Mr Nigel Richardson, Director - Children's Services, 3rd Floor, St. Georges House, Leeds LS1 3DL
☎ 0113 222 4444 ⌁ nigel.richardson@leeds.gov.uk

Senior Management: Ms Cath Roff, Director - Adult Social Care, Civic Hall, Leeds LS1 1UR cath.roff@ledds.gov.uk

Senior Management: Ms Catherine Witham, City Solicitor, Civic Hall, Leeds LS1 1UR ☎ 0113 247 4537
⌁ catherine.witham@leeds.gov.uk

Architect, Building / Property Services: Mr Martin Farrington, Director - City Development, The Leonardo Building, 2 Rossington Street, Leeds LS2 8HB ☎ 0113 224 3816
⌁ martin.farrington@leeds.gov.uk

Best Value: Mr Alan Gay, Deputy Chief Executive & Director - Resources, Civic Hall, Calverley Street, Leeds LS1 1UR
☎ 0113 247 4226 ⌁ alan.gay@leeds.gov.uk

Building Control: Mr Martin Farrington, Director - City Development, The Leonardo Building, 2 Rossington Street, Leeds LS2 8HB ☎ 0113 224 3816 ⌁ martin.farrington@leeds.gov.uk

Catering Services: Ms Sarah Martin, Head of Property & Fleet Services, Commercial Services, Seacroft Ring Road Depot, Ring Road, Seacroft, Leeds LS14 1NZ ☎ 0113 378 2358
⌁ sarah.martin@leeds.gov.uk

Children / Youth Services: Mr Jim Hopkinson, Head of Service - Targetted Services, 3rd Floor, St. Georges House, Leeds LS1 3DL
☎ 0113 222 4444 ⌁ jim.hopkinson@leeds.gov.uk

Children / Youth Services: Mr Nigel Richardson, Director - Children's Services, 3rd Floor, St. Georges House, Leeds LS1 3DL
☎ 0113 222 4444 ⌁ nigel.richardson@leeds.gov.uk

Civil Registration: Mr James Rogers, Assistant Chief Executive - Citizens & Communities, Civic Hall, Leeds LS1 1UR
☎ 0113 224 3579 ⌁ james.rogers@leeds.gov.uk

PR / Communications: Ms Dee Reid, Head of Communications & Marketing, Communications Team, 4th Floor West, Civic Hall, Leeds LS1 1UR ☎ 0113 247 5427; 0113 247 5427
⌁ dee.reid@leeds.gov.uk; dee.reid@leeds.gov.uk

Community Planning: Mr James Rogers, Assistant Chief Executive - Citizens & Communities, 3rd Floor East, Civic Hall, Calverley Street, Leeds LS1 1UR ☎ 0113 224 3579
⌁ james.rogers@leeds.gov.uk

Community Safety: Mr Neil Evans, Director - Environment & Housing, 4th Floor West, Merrion House, Leeds LS1 1UR
☎ 0113 247 4721 ⌁ neil.evans@leeds.gov.uk

Computer Management: Mr Alan Gay, Deputy Chief Executive & Director - Resources, Civic Hall, Calverley Street, Leeds LS1 1UR
☎ 0113 247 4226 ⌁ alan.gay@leeds.gov.uk

Computer Management: Mr Dylan Roberts, Chief ICT Officer, Apex Centre, Apex Way, Leeds LS11 5LT ☎ 0113 395 1515 ⌁ dylan.roberts@leeds.gov.uk

Contracts: Mr David Outram, Chief Officer - Strategy & Resources, St George House, 40 Great George Street, Leeds LS1 3DL
☎ 0113 395 2463 ⌁ david.outram@leeds.gov.uk

Corporate Services: Mr Alan Gay, Deputy Chief Executive & Director - Resources, Civic Hall, Calverley Street, Leeds LS1 1UR
☎ 0113 247 4226 ⌁ alan.gay@leeds.gov.uk

Corporate Services: Ms Mariana Pexton, Chief Officer - Strategy & Improvement, 3rd Floor East, Civic Hall, Calverley Street, Leeds LS1 1UR ☎ 0113 376 0001 ⌁ mariana.pexton@leeds.gov.uk

Customer Service: Mr Lee Hemsworth, Chief Officer - Customer Access, West Gate, Ground Floor, 🖳 Grace Street, Leeds LS1 2RP
☎ 0113 376002 ⌁ lee.hemsworth@leeds.gov.uk

Customer Service: Ms Susan Murray, Head of Customer Contact, Westgate, ⛫ Grace Street, Leeds LS1 2RP ☎ 0113 222 4444 ⬦ susan.murray@leeds.gov.uk

Customer Service: Mr James Rogers, Assistant Chief Executive - Citizens & Communities, 3rd Floor East, Civic Hall, Calverley Street, Leeds LS1 1UR ☎ 0113 224 3579 ⬦ james.rogers@leeds.gov.uk

Economic Development: Mr Tom Bridges, Chief Officer - Economy & Regeneration, The Leonardo Building, Level 6, 2 Rossington Street, Leeds LS2 8HD ☎ 0113 224 3735 ⬦ tom.bridges@leeds.gov.uk

Economic Development: Ms Sue Burgess, Head of Markets Service, Kirkgate Market, 34 George Street, Leeds LS2 7HY ☎ 0113 378 1950

Education: Mr Nigel Richardson, Director - Children's Services, Childrens Services, 6th Floor East, Civic Hall, Leeds LS2 8DT ☎ 0113 222 4444 ⬦ nigel.richardson@leeds.gov.uk

E-Government: Mr James Rogers, Assistant Chief Executive - Citizens & Communities, 3rd Floor East, Civic Hall, Calverley Street, Leeds LS1 1UR ☎ 0113 224 3579 ⬦ james.rogers@leeds.gov.uk

Electoral Registration: Ms Susanna Benton, Electoral Services Manager, Town Hall, The Headrow, Leeds LS1 3AD ☎ 0113 247 6727 ⬦ susanna.benton@leeds.gov.uk

Emergency Planning: Mr Nigel Street, Principal Officer - Resilience & Emergencies, Civic Hall, Leeds LS1 1UR ☎ 0113 247 4341 ⬦ nigel.street@leeds.gov.uk

Energy Management: Mr Peter Lynes, Senior Asset Management Officer, Thoresby House, Level 5SE, 2 Rossington Street, Leeds LS2 8HD ☎ 0113 247 5536 ⬦ peter.lynes@leeds.gov.uk

Environmental / Technical Services: Ms Helen Freeman, Chief Officer - Environmental Action, Level 2 Southside, Thoresby House, Rossington Street, Leeds LS2 8HD ☎ 0113 247 8888 ⬦ helen.freeman@leeds.gov.uk

Environmental Health: Ms Helen Freeman, Chief Officer - Environmental Action, Level 2 Southside, Thoresby House, Rossington Street, Leeds LS2 8HD ☎ 0113 247 8888 ⬦ helen.freeman@leeds.gov.uk

Estates, Property & Valuation: Mr Martin Farrington, Director - City Development, The Leonardo Building, 2 Rossington Street, Leeds LS2 8HB ☎ 0113 224 3816 ⬦ martin.farrington@leeds.gov.uk

Events Manager: Mr Paul Footitt, Events Manager, 1st Floor, Town Hall, Headrow, Leeds LS1 3AD ☎ 0113 224 3600 ⬦ paul.footitt@leeds.gov.uk

Facilities: Ms Sarah Martin, Head of Property & Fleet Services, Commercial Services, Seacroft Ring Road Depot, Ring Road, Seacroft, Leeds LS14 1NZ ☎ 0113 378 2358 ⬦ sarah.martin@leeds.gov.uk

Finance: Mr Alan Gay, Deputy Chief Executive & Director - Resources, Civic Hall, Calverley Street, Leeds LS1 1UR ☎ 0113 247 4226 ⬦ alan.gay@leeds.gov.uk

Fleet Management: Mr Terence Pycroft, Head of Fleet Services, 255a York Road, Leeds LS9 7QQ ☎ 0113 378 1440 ⬦ terry.pycroft@leeds.gov.uk

Grounds Maintenance: Mr Neil Evans, Director - Environment & Housing, 4th Floor West, Merrion House, Leeds LS1 1UR ☎ 0113 247 4721 ⬦ neil.evans@leeds.gov.uk

Grounds Maintenance: Ms Sarah Martin, Head of Property & Fleet Services, Commercial Services, Seacroft Ring Road Depot, Ring Road, Seacroft, Leeds LS14 1NZ ☎ 0113 378 2358 ⬦ sarah.martin@leeds.gov.uk

Health and Safety: Ms Lorraine Hallam, Chief Officer - Human Resources, Civic Hall, Calverley Street, Leeds LS1 1UR ☎ 0113 395 1600 ⬦ lorraine.hallam@leeds.gov.uk

Highways: Mr Gary Bartlett, Chief Highways Officer, Civic Hall, Leeds LS1 1UR ☎ 0113 247 5319 ⬦ gary.bartlett@leeds.gov.uk

Highways: Mr Martin Farrington, Director - City Development, The Leonardo Building, 2 Rossington Street, Leeds LS2 8HB ☎ 0113 224 3816 ⬦ martin.farrington@leeds.gov.uk

Home Energy Conservation: Mr George Munson, Senior Programme Leader (Environment & Housing), 2nd Floor, St. Georges Hall, Leeds LS1 3DL ☎ 0113 395 1767 ⬦ george.munson@leeds.gov.uk

Housing: Mr Neil Evans, Director - Environment & Housing, 4th Floor West, Merrion House, Leeds LS1 1UR ☎ 0113 247 4721 ⬦ neil.evans@leeds.gov.uk

Housing Maintenance: Mr Simon Costigan, Chief Officer - Property & Contract, Civic Hall, Leeds LS1 1UR ☎ 0113 222 4444 ⬦ simon.costigan@leeds.gov.uk

Local Area Agreement: Ms Mariana Pexton, Chief Officer - Strategy & Improvement, 3rd Floor East, Civic Hall, Calverley Street, Leeds LS1 1UR ☎ 0113 376 0001 ⬦ mariana.pexton@leeds.gov.uk

Legal: Ms Catherine Witham, City Solicitor, Civic Hall, Leeds LS1 1UR ☎ 0113 247 4537 ⬦ catherine.witham@leeds.gov.uk

Leisure and Cultural Services: Mr Martin Farrington, Director - City Development, The Leonardo Building, 2 Rossington Street, Leeds LS2 8HB ☎ 0113 224 3816 ⬦ martin.farrington@leeds.gov.uk

Leisure and Cultural Services: Mr Cluny Macpherson, Chief Officer - Culture & Sport, Leonardo Building, 6th Floor, 2 Rossington Street, Leeds LS2 8HD cluny.macpherson@leeds.gov.uk

Licensing: Mr James Rogers, Assistant Chief Executive - Citizens & Communities, 3rd Floor East, Civic Hall, Calverley Street, Leeds LS1 1UR ☎ 0113 224 3579 ⬦ james.rogers@leeds.gov.uk

Lifelong Learning: Mr Nigel Richardson, Director - Children's Services, 3rd Floor, St. Georges House, Leeds LS1 3DL ☎ 0113 222 4444 ⬦ nigel.richardson@leeds.gov.uk

LEEDS CITY

Lighting: Mr Martin Farrington, Director - City Development, The Leonardo Building, 2 Rossington Street, Leeds LS2 8HB ☎ 0113 224 3816 ⏧ martin.farrington@leeds.gov.uk

Lottery Funding, Charity and Voluntary: Mr James Rogers, Assistant Chief Executive - Citizens & Communities, 3rd Floor East, Civic Hall, Calverley Street, Leeds LS1 1UR ☎ 0113 224 3579 ⏧ james.rogers@leeds.gov.uk

Member Services: Mr Ian Cornick, Head of Civic & Member Support, Civic Hall, Leeds LS1 1UR ☎ 0113 224 3206 ⏧ ian.cornick@leeds.gov.uk

Member Services: Mr Andy Hodson, Head of Governance Services, Corporate Governance, 4th Floor West, Civic Hall, Leeds LS1 1UR ☎ 0113 224 3208 ⏧ andy.hodson@leeds.gov.uk

Member Services: Mr Peter Marrington, Head of Scrutiny, Civic Hall, Leeds LS1 1UR ☎ 0113 395 1151 ⏧ peter.marrington@leeds.gov.uk

Member Services: Ms Catherine Witham, City Solicitor, Civic Hall, Leeds LS1 1UR ☎ 0113 247 4537 ⏧ catherine.witham@leeds.gov.uk

Parking: Mr Neil Evans, Director - Environment & Housing, 4th Floor West, Merrion House, Leeds LS1 1UR ☎ 0113 247 4721 ⏧ neil.evans@leeds.gov.uk

Partnerships: Mr Alan Gay, Deputy Chief Executive & Director - Resources, Civic Hall, Calverley Street, Leeds LS1 1UR ☎ 0113 247 4226 ⏧ alan.gay@leeds.gov.uk

Partnerships: Mr James Rogers, Assistant Chief Executive - Citizens & Communities, 3rd Floor East, Civic Hall, Calverley Street, Leeds LS1 1UR ☎ 0113 224 3579 ⏧ james.rogers@leeds.gov.uk

Personnel / HR: Mr Alan Gay, Deputy Chief Executive & Director - Resources, Civic Hall, Calverley Street, Leeds LS1 1UR ☎ 0113 247 4226 ⏧ alan.gay@leeds.gov.uk

Personnel / HR: Ms Lorraine Hallam, Chief Officer - Human Resources, Civic Hall, Calverley Street, Leeds LS1 1UR ☎ 0113 395 1600 ⏧ lorraine.hallam@leeds.gov.uk

Planning: Mr Martin Farrington, Director - City Development, The Leonardo Building, 2 Rossington Street, Leeds LS2 8HB ☎ 0113 224 3816 ⏧ martin.farrington@leeds.gov.uk

Procurement: Mr Alan Gay, Deputy Chief Executive & Director - Resources, Civic Hall, Calverley Street, Leeds LS1 1UR ☎ 0113 247 4226 ⏧ alan.gay@leeds.gov.uk

Procurement: Mr David Outram, Chief Officer - Strategy & Resources, St George House, 40 Great George Street, Leeds LS1 3DL ☎ 0113 395 2463 ⏧ david.outram@leeds.gov.uk

Public Libraries: Mr Martin Farrington, Director - City Development, The Leonardo Building, 2 Rossington Street, Leeds LS2 8HB ☎ 0113 224 3816 ⏧ martin.farrington@leeds.gov.uk

Public Libraries: Mr Cluny Macpherson, Chief Officer - Culture & Sport, Leonardo Building, 6th Floor, 2 Rossington Street, Leeds LS2 8HD ⏧ cluny.macpherson@leeds.gov.uk

Recycling & Waste Minimisation: Mrs Susan Upton, Chief Officer - Waste Management, Level 2 Southside, Thoresby House, Rossington Street, Leeds LS2 8HD ☎ 0113 247 8888 ⏧ susan.upton@leeds.gov.uk

Regeneration: Mr Tom Bridges, Chief Officer - Economy & Regeneration, The Leonardo Building, Level 6, 2 Rossington Street, Leeds LS2 8HD ☎ 0113 224 3735 ⏧ tom.bridges@leeds.gov.uk

Road Safety: Mr Gary Bartlett, Chief Highways Officer, Civic Hall, Leeds LS1 1UR ☎ 0113 247 5319 ⏧ gary.bartlett@leeds.gov.uk

Social Services: Ms Cath Roff, Director - Adult Social Care, Civic Hall, Leeds LS1 1UR ⏧ cath.roff@ledds.gov.uk

Social Services (Adult): Ms Cath Roff, Director - Adult Social Care, Civic Hall, Leeds LS1 1UR ⏧ cath.roff@ledds.gov.uk

Social Services (Children): Mr Nigel Richardson, Director - Children's Services, 3rd Floor, St. Georges House, Leeds LS1 3DL ☎ 0113 222 4444 ⏧ nigel.richardson@leeds.gov.uk

Public Health: Dr Ian Cameron, Executive Director - Public Health, Civic Hall, Leeds LS1 1UR ☎ 0113 395 2810 ⏧ ian.cameron@leeds.gov.uk

Staff Training: Ms Lorraine Hallam, Chief Officer - Human Resources, Civic Hall, Calverley Street, Leeds LS1 1UR ☎ 0113 395 1600 ⏧ lorraine.hallam@leeds.gov.uk

Street Scene: Mr Neil Evans, Director - Environment & Housing, 4th Floor West, Merrion House, Leeds LS1 1UR ☎ 0113 247 4721 ⏧ neil.evans@leeds.gov.uk

Street Scene: Ms Helen Freeman, Chief Officer - Environmental Action, Level 2 Southside, Thoresby House, Rossington Street, Leeds LS2 8HD ☎ 0113 247 8888 ⏧ helen.freeman@leeds.gov.uk

Sustainable Communities: Mr James Rogers, Assistant Chief Executive - Citizens & Communities, 3rd Floor East, Civic Hall, Calverley Street, Leeds LS1 1UR ☎ 0113 224 3579 ⏧ james.rogers@leeds.gov.uk

Sustainable Development: Mr Tim Hill, Chief Planning Officer, The Leonardo Building, 2 Rossington Street, Leeds LS2 8HD ☎ 0113 247 8177 ⏧ tim.hill@leeds.gov.uk

Tourism: Mr Tom Bridges, Chief Officer - Economy & Regeneration, The Leonardo Building, Level 6, 2 Rossington Street, Leeds LS2 8HD ☎ 0113 224 3735 ⏧ tom.bridges@leeds.gov.uk

Town Centre: Mr John Ebo, City Centre Manager, Leonardo Buidling, 2 Rossington Street, Leeds LS2 8HD ☎ 0113 247 4714 ⏧ john.ebo@leeds.gov.uk

Traffic Management: Mr Gary Bartlett, Chief Highways Officer, Civic Hall, Leeds LS1 1UR ☎ 0113 247 5319 ✆ gary.bartlett@leeds.gov.uk

Transport: Ms Julie Meakin, Chief Commercial Services Officer, Seacroft Ring Road Depot, Ring Road, Seacroft, Leeds LS14 1NZ ☎ 0113 222 4444 ✆ julie.meakin@leeds.gov.uk

Transport Planner: Mr Gary Bartlett, Chief Highways Officer, Civic Hall, Leeds LS1 1UR ☎ 0113 247 5319 ✆ gary.bartlett@leeds.gov.uk

Waste Collection and Disposal: Mrs Susan Upton, Chief Officer - Waste Management, Level 2 Southside, Thoresby House, Rossington Street, Leeds LS2 8HD ☎ 0113 247 8888 ✆ susan.upton@leeds.gov.uk

Waste Management: Mr Tom Smith, Head of Environmental Services, 1st Floor, Dewsbury Road One Stop, 190 Dewsbury Road, Leeds LS11 6PF ☎ 0113 395 1395 ✆ tom.smith@leeds.gov.uk

COUNCILLORS

The Lord Mayor: Harper, Gerry (LAB - Hyde Park & Woodhouse) gerald.harper@leeds.gov.uk

Leader of the Council: Blake, Judith (LAB - Middleton Park) judith.blake@leeds.gov.uk

Deputy Leader of the Council: Lewis, James (LAB - Kippax & Methley) james.lewis@leeds.gov.uk

Deputy Leader of the Council: Yeadon, Lucinda (LAB - Kirkstall) lucinda.yeadon@leeds.gov.uk

Group Leader: Blackburn, David (GRN - Farnley & Wortley) cllr.david.blackburn@leeds.gov.uk

Group Leader: Carter, Andrew (CON - Calverley & Farsley) andrew.carter@leeds.gov.uk

Group Leader: Finnigan, Robert (IND - Morley North) robert.finnigan@leeds.gov.uk

Group Leader: Golton, Stewart (LD - Rothwell) stewart.golton@leeds.gov.uk

Akhtar, Javaid (LAB - Hyde Park & Woodhouse) javaid.akhtar@leeds.gov.uk

Anderson, Barry (CON - Adel & Wharfedale) barry.anderson@leeds.gov.uk

Anderson, Caroline (CON - Adel & Wharfedale) caroline.anderson@leeds.gov.uk

Arif, Salma (LAB - Gipton & Harehills) salma.arif@leeds.gov.uk

Bentley, Sue (LD - Weetwood) sue.bentley@leeds.gov.uk

Bentley, Jonathan (LD - Weetwood) jonathan.bentley@leeds.gov.uk

Blackburn, Ann (GRN - Farnley & Wortley) ann.blackburn@leeds.gov.uk

Bruce, Karen (LAB - Rothwell) karen.bruce@leeds.gov.uk

Buckley, Neil (CON - Alwoodley) neil.buckley@leeds.gov.uk

Campbell, Colin (LD - Otley & Yeadon) colin.campbell@leeds.gov.uk

Carter, Amanda (CON - Calverley & Farsley)

Chapman, Judith (LD - Weetwood) judith.m.chapman@leeds.gov.uk

Charlwood, Rebecca (LAB - Moortown) rebecca.charlwood@leeds.gov.uk

Cleasby, Brian (LD – Horsforth) brian.cleasby@leeds.gov.uk

Cohen, Daniel (CON - Alwoodley) daniel.cohen@leeds.gov.uk

Collins, Dawn (CON - Horsforth) dawn.collins2@leeds.gov.uk

Congreve, David (LAB - Beeston & Holbeck) david.congreve@leeds.gov.uk

Coulson, Mick (LAB - Pudsey) mick.coulson@leeds.gov.uk

Coupar, Debra (LAB - Temple Newsam) debra.coupar@leeds.gov.uk

Davey, Patrick (LAB - City & Hunslet) patrick.davey@leeds.gov.uk

Dawson, Neil (LAB - Morley South) neil.dawson@leeds.gov.uk

Dobson, Mark (LAB - Garforth & Swillington) mark.dobson@leeds.gov.uk

Dobson, Catherine (LAB - Killingbeck & Seacroft)

Downes, Ryk (LD - Otley & Yeadon) ryk.downes@leeds.gov.uk

Dowson, Jane (LAB - Chapel Allerton) jane.dowson@leeds.gov.uk

Dunn, Jack (LAB - Ardsley & Robin Hood) jack.dunn@leeds.gov.uk

Elliott, Judith (IND - Morley South) judith.elliott@leeds.gov.uk

Field, Sarah (LAB - Garforth & Swillington) sarah.field@leeds.gov.uk

Flynn, Billy (CON - Adel & Wharfedale) billy.flynn@leeds.gov.uk

Gabriel, Angela (LAB - Beeston & Holbeck) angela.gabriel@leeds.gov.uk

Garthwaite, Al (LAB - Headingley) al.garthwaite@leeds.gov.uk

Gettings, Bob (IND - Morley North) robert.gettings@leeds.gov.uk

Grahame, Ronald (LAB - Burmantofts & Richmond Hill) ronald.grahame@leeds.gov.uk

Grahame, Pauleen (LAB - Cross Gates & Whinmoor) pauleen.grahame@leeds.gov.uk

Groves, Kim (LAB - Middleton Park) kim.groves@leeds.gov.uk

Gruen, Peter (LAB - Cross Gates & Whinmoor) peter.gruen@leeds.gov.uk

Gruen, Caroline (LAB - Bramley & Stanningley) caroline.gruen@leeds.gov.uk

LEEDS CITY

Hamilton, Sharon (LAB - Moortown)
sharon.hamilton@leeds.gov.uk

Harland, Mary (LAB - Kippax & Methley)
mary.harland@leeds.gov.uk

Harrand, Peter (CON - Alwoodley)
peter.harrand@leeds.gov.uk

Hayden, Helen (LAB - Temple Newsam)

Heselwood, Julie (LAB - Bramley & Stanningley)
julie.heselwood@leeds.gov.uk

Hussain, Arif (LAB - Gipton & Harehills)
arif.hussain@leeds.gov.uk

Hussain, Ghulam (LAB - Roundhay)
ghulam.hussain@leeds.gov.uk

Hyde, Graham (LAB - Killingbeck & Seacroft)
graham.hyde@leeds.gov.uk

Illingworth, John (LAB - Kirkstall)
john.illingworth@leeds.gov.uk

Iqbal, Mohammed (LAB - City & Hunslet)
mohammed.iqbal@leeds.gov.uk

Jarosz, Josephine (LAB - Pudsey)
josephine.jarosz@leeds.gov.uk

Khan, Asghar (LAB - Burmantofts & Richmond Hill)
asghar.khan@leeds.gov.uk

Lamb, Alan (CON - Wetherby)
alan.lamb@leeds.gov.uk

Latty, Pat (CON - Guiseley & Rawdon)
patricia.latty@leeds.gov.uk

Latty, Graham (CON - Guiseley & Rawdon)
graham.latty@leeds.gov.uk

Lay, Sandy (LD - Otley & Yeadon)
sandy.lay@leeds.gov.uk

Leadley, Tom (IND - Morley North)
thomas.leadley@leeds.gov.uk

Lewis, Richard (LAB - Pudsey)
richard.lewis@leeds.gov.uk

Lowe, Alison (LAB - Armley)
alison.lowe@leeds.gov.uk

Lyons, Michael (LAB - Temple Newsam)
michael.lyons@leeds.gov.uk

Macniven, Christine (LAB - Roundhay)
christine.macniven@leeds.gov.uk

Maqsood, Kamila (LAB - Gipton & Harehills)
kamila.maqsood@leeds.gov.uk

McKenna, James (LAB - Armley)
james.mckenna@leeds.gov.uk

McKenna, Stuart (LAB - Garforth & Swillington)
stuart.mckenna@leeds.gov.uk

Mulherin, Lisa (LAB - Ardsley & Robin Hood)
lisa.mulherin@leeds.gov.uk

Nagle, David (LAB - Rothwell)
david.nagle@leeds.gov.uk

Nash, Elizabeth (LAB - City & Hunslet)
elizabeth.nash@leeds.gov.uk

Ogilvie, Adam (LAB - Beeston & Holbeck)
adam.ogilvie@leeds.gov.uk

Procter, John (CON - Wetherby)
john.procter@leeds.gov.uk

Procter, Rachael (CON - Harewood)
rachael.procter@leeds.gov.uk

Pryor, Jonathan (LAB - Headingley)
jonathan.pryor@leeds.gov.uk

Rafique, Mohammed (LAB - Chapel Allerton)
cllr.mohammed.rafique@leeds.gov.uk

Ragan, Denise (LAB - Burmantofts & Richmond Hill)
denise.ragan@leeds.gov.uk

Renshaw, Karen (LAB - Ardsley & Robin Hood)
karen.renshaw@leeds.gov.uk

Ritchie, Kevin (LAB - Bramley & Stanningley)
kevin.ritchie@leeds.gov.uk

Robinson, Matthew (CON - Harewood)
matthew.robinson@leeds.gov.uk

Selby, Brian (LAB - Killingbeck & Seacroft)
brian.selby@leeds.gov.uk

Smart, Alice (LAB - Armley)
alice.smart@leeds.gov.uk

Sobel, Alex (LAB - Moortown)
alex.sobel@leeds.gov.uk

Stephenson, Ryan (CON - Harewood)
ryan.stephenson@leeds.gov.uk

Taylor, Eileen (LAB - Chapel Allerton)
eileen.taylor@leeds.gov.uk

Towler, Christine (LAB - Hyde Park & Woodhouse)
christine.towler@leeds.gov.uk

Townsley, Christopher (LD - Horsforth)
christopher.townsley@leeds.gov.uk

Truswell, Paul (LAB - Middleton Park)
paul.truswell@leeds.gov.uk

Tunnicliffe, Eleanor (LAB - Roundhay)
eleanor.tunnicliffe@leeds.gov.uk

Varley, Shirley (IND - Morley South)
shirley.varley@leeds.gov.uk

Venner, Fiona (LAB - Kirkstall)
fiona.venner@leeds.gov.uk

Wadsworth, Paul (CON - Guiseley & Rawdon)
paul.wadsworth@leeds.gov.uk

Wakefield, Keith (LAB - Kippax & Methley)
keith.wakefield@leeds.gov.uk

Walker, Janette (LAB - Cross Gates & Whinmoor)
janette.walker@leeds.gov.uk

Walshaw, Neil (LAB - Headingley)
neil.walshaw@leeds.gov.uk

Wilford, Terry (GRN - Farnley & Wortley)
terry.wilford@leeds.gov.uk

Wilkinson, Gerald (CON - Wetherby)
gerald.wilkinson@leeds.gov.uk

Wood, Rod (CON - Calverley & Farsley)
roderic.wood@leeds.gov.uk

POLITICAL COMPOSITION
LAB: 63, CON: 19, LD: 9, IND: 5, GRN: 3

COMMITTEE CHAIRS

Adult Social Services, Public Health & NHS: Mr Peter Gruen

Audit: Mrs Pauleen Grahame

Children's Services: Ms Sue Bentley

Environment & Housing: Mr John Procter

Health & Wellbeing: Mr Rebecca Charlwood

Licensing: Mr Brian Selby

Leicester City   U

Leicester City Council, City Hall, 115 Charles Street, Leicester LE1 1FZ

☎ 0116 454 1000 🖷 0116 454 1011 🖵 www.leicester.gov.uk

FACTS AND FIGURES
Parliamentary Constituencies: Leicester East, Leicester South, Leicester West
EU Constituencies: East Midlands
Election Frequency: Elections are of whole council

PRINCIPAL OFFICERS

Chief Executive: Mr Andy Keeling, Chief Operating Officer, City Hall, 115 Charles Street, Leicester LE1 1FZ ☎ 0116 454 0112
🖑 andy.keeling@leicester.gov.uk

Senior Management: Ms Frances Craven, Strategic Director - Education & Children's Services, City Hall, 115 Charles Street, Leicester LE1 1FZ ☎ 0116 454 0124
🖑 frances.craven@leicester.gov.uk

Senior Management: Mr Steven Forbes, Strategic Director - Adult Social Care & Health, City Hall, 115 Charles Street, Leicester LE1 1FZ ☎ 0116 454 2206 🖑 steven.forbes@leicester.gov.uk

Senior Management: Mr Frank Jordan, Strategic Director - City Development & Neighbourhoods, City Hall, 115 Charles Street, Leicester LE1 1FZ ☎ 0116 454 0104 🖑 frank.jordan@leicester.gov.uk

Senior Management: Ms Ruth Tennant, Director - Public Health, City Hall, 115 Charles Street, Leicester LE1 1FZ ☎ 0116 454 0237
🖑 ruth.tennant@leicester.gov.uk

Access Officer / Social Services (Disability): Ms Tracie Rees, Director - Care Services & Commissioning, City Hall, 115 Charles Street, Leicester LE1 1FZ ☎ 0116 454 2301
🖑 tracie.rees@leicester.gov.uk

Architect, Building / Property Services: Mr Andrew Smith, Director - Planning, Transport & Economic Development, City Hall, 115 Charles Street, Leicester LE1 1FZ ☎ 0116 454 2801
🖑 andrewl.smith@leicester.gov.uk

Catering Services: Ms Jane Faulks, Education Catering Manager, 90 Leycroft Road, Leicester LE4 1BZ ☎ 0116 454 5067
🖑 jane.faulk@leicester.gov.uk

Children / Youth Services: Mr Ian Bailey, Interim Director - Learning Services, City Hall, 115 Charles Street, Leicester LE1 1FZ
☎ 0116 454 6212 🖑 ian.bailey@leicester.gov.uk

Children / Youth Services: Ms Frances Craven, Strategic Director - Education & Children's Services, City Hall, 115 Charles Street, Leicester LE1 1FZ ☎ 0116 454 0124
🖑 frances.craven@leicester.gov.uk

Civil Registration: Mr Kevin Lewis, Registration Service Manager, Town Hall, Town Hall Square, Leicester LE1 9BG ☎ 0845 045 0901
🖑 lewk001@leicester.gov.uk

PR / Communications: Ms Deborah Reynolds, Media & PR Manager, City Hall, 115 Charles Street, Leicester LE1 1FZ
☎ 0116 454 4151 🖑 debra.reynolds@leicester.gov.uk

Community Safety: Ms Daxa Pancholi, Head of Community Safety, City Hall, 115 Charles Street, Leicester LE1 1FZ
☎ 0116 454 0203 🖑 daxa.pancholi@leicester.gov.uk

Computer Management: Mr Carl Skidmore, City Information Officer, City Hall, 115 Charles Street, Leicester LE1 1FZ
☎ 0116 454 1166 🖑 carl.skidmore@leicester.gov.uk

Consumer Protection and Trading Standards: Mr Roman Leszczyszyn, Head of Regulatory Services, New Walk Centre, Welford Place, Leicester LE1 6ZG ☎ 0116 454 3191
🖑 roman.leszczyszyn@leicester.gov.uk

Corporate Services: Ms Miranda Cannon, Director - Delivery, Communications & Political Governance, City Hall, 115 Charles Street, Leicester LE1 1FZ ☎ 0116 454 0102
🖑 miranda.cannon@leicester.gov.uk

Customer Service: Mrs Caroline Jackson, Head of Revenues & Customer Support, City Hall, 115 Charles Street, Leicester LE1 1FZ
☎ 0116 454 2501 🖑 caroline.jackson@leicester.gov.uk

Economic Development: Mr Andrew Smith, Director - Planning, Transport & Economic Development, City Hall, 115 Charles Street, Leicester LE1 1FZ ☎ 0116 454 2801
🖑 andrewl.smith@leicester.gov.uk

E-Government: Mr Carl Skidmore, City Information Officer, City Hall, 115 Charles Street, Leicester LE1 1FZ ☎ 0116 454 1166
🖑 carl.skidmore@leicester.gov.uk

Electoral Registration: Ms Alison Saxby, Electoral Services Manager, York House, Granby Street, Leicester LE1 6FB
☎ 0116 299 5965 🖑 alison.saxby@leicester.gov.uk

Emergency Planning: Mr Martin Halse, Resilience Manager, City Hall, 115 Charles Street, Leicester LE1 1FZ ☎ 0116 238 5001
🖑 martin.halse@leicester.gov.uk

Energy Management: Mr Nicholas Morris, Head of Energy Services, 2 - 4 Market Place South, Leicester LE1 5HB
☎ 0116 454 2229 🖑 nicholas.morris@leicester.gov.uk

Environmental Health: Mr John Leach, Director - Local Services, City Hall, 115 Charles Street, Leicester LE1 1FZ ☎ 0116 454 1828
🖑 john.leach@leicester.gov.uk

Estates, Property & Valuation: Mr Neil Gamble, Head of Property, City Hall, 115 Charles Street, Leicester LE1 1FZ ☎ 0116 454 2104 🖑 neil.gamble@leicester.gov.uk

LEICESTER CITY

European Liaison: Mrs Joanne Ives, Policy, Partnerships & Programmes Manager, City Hall, 115 Charles Street, Leicester LE1 1FZ ☎ 0116 454 2934 ◦⌂ joanne.ives@leicester.gov.uk

Events Manager: Ms Maggie Shutt, Festivals & Events Manager, Wellington House, Wellington Street, Leicester LE1 6HL ☎ 0116 454 3601 ◦⌂ maggie.shutt@leicester.gov.uk

Facilities: Mr Wyndham Price, Corporate Premises Manager, City Hall, 115 Charles Street, Leicester LE1 1FZ ☎ 0116 454 2189 ◦⌂ wyndham.price@leicester.gov.uk

Finance: Ms Alison Greenhill, Director - Finance, City Hall, 115 Charles Street, Leicester LE1 1FZ ☎ 0116 454 4001 ◦⌂ alison.greenhill@leicester.gov.uk

Grounds Maintenance: Mr Stewart Doughty, Head of Parks & Open Space, Abbey Park, Abbey Park Road, Leicester LE4 5AQ ☎ 0116 233 3020 ◦⌂ stewart.doughty@leicester.gov.uk

Health and Safety: Mr Martin Southam, Head of Health & Safety, City Hall, 115 Charles Street, Leicester LE1 1FZ ☎ 0116 454 4307 ◦⌂ martin.southam@leicester.gov.uk

Highways: Mr Martin Fletcher, Head of Highways, Leycroft Road, Leicester LE4 1BZ ☎ 0116 454 4965 ◦⌂ martin.fletcher@leicester.gov.uk

Home Energy Conservation: Mr Mike Richardson, Home Energy Team Leader, 35 Rowsley Street, Leicester LE5 5JP ☎ 0116 454 3781 ◦⌂ richm002@leicester.gov.uk

Housing: Mr Chris Burgin, Director - Housing, Ian Marlow Centre, Blackbird Road, Leicester LE4 0AR ☎ 0116 454 5143 ◦⌂ chris.burgin@leicester.gov.uk

Housing Maintenance: Mr Chris Burgin, Director - Housing, Ian Marlow Centre, Blackbird Road, Leicester LE4 0AR ☎ 0116 454 5143 ◦⌂ chris.burgin@leicester.gov.uk

Housing Maintenance: Mr Ian Craig, Head of Direct Services, Housing Department, Blackbird Road, Leicester LE4 0AR ☎ 0116 454 5211 ◦⌂ craii001@leicester.gov.uk

Legal: Mr Kamal Adatia, City Barrister & Head of Standards, 16 New Walk, Leicester LE1 6UB ☎ 0116 454 1401 ◦⌂ kamal.adatia@leicester.gov.uk

Leisure and Cultural Services: Mr Andrew Beddow, Head of Sports Services, City Hall, 115 Charles Street, Leicester LE1 1FZ ☎ 0116 454 5036 ◦⌂ andrew.beddow@leicester.gov.uk

Leisure and Cultural Services: Ms Sarah Levitt, Head of Arts & Museums, City Hall, 115 Charles Street, Leicester LE1 1FZ ☎ 0116 454 3521 ◦⌂ sarah.levitt@leicester.gov.uk

Licensing: Mr Mike Broster, Head of Licensing & Pollution Control, New Walk Centre, Welford Place, Leicester LE1 6ZG ☎ 0116 454 3041 ◦⌂ mike.broster@leicester.gov.uk

Personnel / HR: Ms Joanne Jackson, Head of HR, Sovereign House, Princess Road West, Leicester LE1 6TR ☎ 0116 454 5710 ◦⌂ joanne.jackson@leicester.gov.uk

Planning: Mr Andrew Smith, Director - Planning, Transport & Economic Development, City Hall, 115 Charles Street, Leicester LE1 1FZ ☎ 0116 454 2801 ◦⌂ andrewl.smith@leicester.gov.uk

Procurement: Mr Neil Bayliss, Head of Procurement, City Hall, 115 Charles Street, Leicester LE1 1FZ ☎ 0116 454 4021 ◦⌂ neil.bayliss@leicester.gov.uk

Public Libraries: Mr Adrian Wills, Head of Libraries & Information Services, City Hall, 115 Charles Street, Leicester LE1 1FZ ☎ 0116 454 3541 ◦⌂ adrian.wills@leicester.gov.uk

Recycling & Waste Minimisation: Mr Geoff Soden, Waste Services Manager, City Hall, 115 Charles Street, Leicester LE1 1FZ ☎ 0116 454 6732 ◦⌂ geoff.soden@leicester.gov.uk

Social Services: Ms Ruth Tennant, Director - Public Health, City Hall, 115 Charles Street, Leicester LE1 1FZ ☎ 0116 454 0237 ◦⌂ ruth.tennant@leicester.gov.uk

Social Services: Mrs Caroline Tote, Director - Social Care & Early Help, City Hall, 115 Charles Street, Leicester LE1 1FZ ☎ 0116 454 0125 ◦⌂ caroline.tote@leicester.gov.uk

Social Services (Adult): Ms Ruth Lake, Director - Adult Social Care & Safeguarding, City Hall, 115 Charles Street, Leicester LE1 1FZ ☎ 0116 454 5551 ◦⌂ ruth.lake@leicester.gov.uk

Social Services (Children): Mrs Caroline Tote, Director - Social Care & Early Help, City Hall, 115 Charles Street, Leicester LE1 1FZ ☎ 0116 454 0125 ◦⌂ caroline.tote@leicester.gov.uk

Public Health: Ms Ruth Tennant, Director - Public Health, City Hall, 115 Charles Street, Leicester LE1 1FZ ☎ 0116 454 0237 ◦⌂ ruth.tennant@leicester.gov.uk

Street Scene: Mr John Leach, Director - Local Services, City Hall, 115 Charles Street, Leicester LE1 1FZ ☎ 0116 454 1828 ◦⌂ john.leach@leicester.gov.uk

Sustainable Communities: Ms Carol Brass, Team Leader - Environment Team, 16 New Walk, Leicester LE1 6UB ☎ 0116 252 6732 ◦⌂ carol.brass@leicester.gov.uk

Sustainable Communities: Ms Anna Dodd, Team Leader - Environment Team, 16 New Walk, Leicester LE1 6UB ☎ 0116 252 6732 ◦⌂ anna.dodd@leicester.gov.uk

Tourism: Mr Mike Dalzell, Director - Tourism, Culture & Inward Investment, City Hall, 115 Charles Street, Leicester LE1 1FZ ☎ 0116 454 2931 ◦⌂ mike.dalzell@leicester.gov.uk

Town Centre: Ms Sarah Harrison, Director - City Centre, York House, Granby Street, Leicester LE1 6FB ☎ 0116 222 3329 ◦⌂ sarahmharrison@leicester.gov.uk

Waste Management: Mr Geoff Soden, Waste Services Manager, City Hall, 115 Charles Street, Leicester LE1 1FZ ☎ 0116 454 6732 ✆ geoff.soden@leicester.gov.uk

COUNCILLORS

Mayor: Soulsby, Peter (LAB - Citywide)
peter.soulsby@leicester.gov.uk

Deputy Mayor: Palmer, Rory (LAB - Eyres Monsell)
rory.palmer@leicester.gov.uk

Aldred, Teresa (LAB - Thurncourt)
teresa.aldred@leicester.gov.uk

Alfonso, Dawn (LAB - Fosse)
dawn.alfonso@leicester.gov.uk

Aqbany, Hanif (LAB - Wycliffe)
hanif.aqbany@leicester.gov.uk

Bajaj, Deepak (LAB - Evington)
deepak.bajaj@leicester.gov.uk

Barton, Susan (LAB - Western)
susan.barton@leicester.gov.uk

Bhavsar, Harshad (LAB - Abbey)
harshad.bhavsar@leicester.gov.uk

Byrne, Annette (LAB - Abbey)
annette.byrne@leicester.gov.uk

Cank, Diane (LAB - Troon)
diane.cank@leicester.gov.uk

Cassidy, Ted (LAB - Fosse)

Chaplin, Lucy (LAB - Stoneygate)

Chohan, Mansukhlal (LAB - Belgrave)
mo.chohan@leicester.gov.uk

Chowdhury, Shofiqul (LAB - Spinney Hills)
shofiqul.chowdhury@leicester.gov.uk

Clair, Piara (LAB - Rushey Mead)
piara.singhclair@leicester.gov.uk

Clarke, Adam (LAB - Aylestone)
adam.clarke@leicester.gov.uk

Cleaver, Virginia (LAB - Eyres Monsell)
virginia.cleaver@leicester.gov.uk

Cole, George (LAB - Western)
george.cole@leicester.gov.uk

Connelly, Andrew (LAB - Westcotes)
andy.connelly@leicester.gov.uk

Corrall, Stephen (LAB - Braunston Park & Rowley Fields)
stephen.corrall@leicester.gov.uk

Cutkelvin, Elly (LAB - Saffron)
elly.cutkelvin@leicester.gov.uk

Dawood, Mohammed (LAB - Wycliffe)
councillor.mohammed.dawood@leicester.gov.uk

Dempster, Vi (LAB - Humberstone & Hamilton)
vi.dempster@leicester.gov.uk

Fonseca, Luis (LAB - North Evington)
luis.fonseca@leicester.gov.uk

Govind, Ratilal (LAB - Evington)
ratilal.govind@leicester.gov.uk

Grant, Ross (CON - Knighton)
ross.grant@leicester.gov.uk

Gugnani, Inderjit (LAB - Knighton)
inderjit.gugnani@leicester.gov.uk

Halford, Elaine (LAB - Braunston Park & Rowley Fields)
elaine.halford@leicester.gov.uk

Hunter, Sue (LAB - Evington)
councillor.sue.hunter@leicester.gov.uk

Joshi, Rashmikant (LAB - Humberstone & Hamilton)
rashmikant.joshi@leicester.gov.uk

Khote, Jean (LAB - North Evington)
jean.khote@leicester.gov.uk

Kitterick, Patrick (LAB - Castle)
patrick.kitterick@btinternet.com

Malik, Mustafa (LAB - Spinney Hills)

Master, Kirk (LAB - Stoneygate)
kirk.master@leicester.gov.uk

Moore, Lynn (LAB - Knighton)
councillor.lynn.moore@leicester.gov.uk

Newcombe, Paul (LAB - Thurncourt)
paul.newcombe@leicester.gov.uk

Osman, Abdul Razak (LAB - North Evington)
abdul.osman@leicester.gov.uk

Patel, Rita (LAB - Rushey Mead)
councillor.rita.patel@leicester.gov.uk

Porter, Nigel (LD - Aylestone)
nigel.porter@leicester.gov.uk

Rae Bhatia, Hemant (LAB - Beaumont Leys)
hemant.raebhatia@leicester.gov.uk

Riyait, Vijay Singh (LAB - Abbey)
vijay.rayait@leicester.gov.uk

Russell, Sarah (LAB - Westcotes)
sarah.russell@leicester.gov.uk

Sandhu, Gurinder Singh (LAB - Humberstone & Hamilton)

Sangster, Deborah (LAB - Castle)
deborah.sangster@leicester.gov.uk

Senior, Lynn (LAB - Castle)
lynn.senior@leicester.gov.uk

Shelton, Bill (LAB - Saffron)
bill.shelton@leicester.gov.uk

Singh, Baljit (LAB - Troon)
baljit.singh@leicester.gov.uk

Singh Johal, Kulwinder (LAB - Braunston Park & Rowley Fields)
kulwinder.singhjoha.@leicester.gov.uk

Sood, Manjula (LAB - Belgrave)
manjula.sood@leicester.gov.uk

Thalukdar, Aminur (LAB - Stoneygate)
aminur.thalukdar@leicester.gov.uk

Thomas, John (LAB - Belgrave)
john.thomas@leicester.gov.uk

Unsworth, Malcolm (LAB - Western)
malcolm.unsworth@leicester.gov.uk

Waddington, Susan (LAB - Beaumont Leys)
sue.waddington@leicester.gov.uk

LEICESTER CITY

Westley, Paul (LAB - Beaumont Leys)
paul.westley@leicester.gov.uk

Willmott, Ross (LAB - Rushey Mead)
members.services@leicester.gov.uk

POLITICAL COMPOSITION
LAB: 53, LD: 1, CON: 1

COMMITTEE CHAIRS

Adult Social Care: Ms Virginia Cleaver

Audit: Ms Rita Patel

Children, Young People & Schools: Dr Lynn Moore

Economic Development, Transport & Tourism: Ms Jean Khote

Health & Wellbeing: Ms Vi Dempster

Licensing: Mr John Thomas

Planning & Development: Mr Ted Cassidy

Leicestershire   C

Leicestershire County Council, County Hall, Glenfield,
Leicester LE3 8RA
☎ 0116 232 3232 ᐃ 0116 305 6260; 0116 265 6260
ᐧ information@leics.gov.uk 🖳 www.leics.gov.uk

FACTS AND FIGURES
EU Constituencies: East Midlands
Election Frequency: Elections are of whole council

PRINCIPAL OFFICERS

Chief Executive: Mr John Sinnott, Chief Executive, County Hall,
Glenfield, Leicester LE3 8RA ☎ 0116 305 6001
ᐧ john.sinnott@leics.gov.uk

Assistant Chief Executive: Mr Tom Purnell, Assistant Chief
Executive, County Hall, Glenfield, Leicester LE3 8RA ☎ 0116 305
7019 ᐧ tom.purnell@leics.gov.uk

Senior Management: Mr Phil Crossland, Director - Environment
& Transport, County Hall, Glenfield, Leicester LE3 8TF
☎ 0116 305 7000 ᐧ phil.crossland@leics.gov.uk

Senior Management: Mr Paul Meredith, Interim Director -
Children & Family Services, County Hall, Glenfield, Leicester
LE3 8RA ☎ 0116 305 6340 ᐧ paul.meredith@leics.gov.uk

Senior Management: Mr Brian Roberts, Director - Corporate
Resources, County Hall, Glenfield, Leicester LE3 8RA
☎ 0116 305 7830 ᐧ brian.roberts@leic.gov.uk

Senior Management: Mr Mike Sandys, Director - Public Health,
County Hall, Glenfield, Leicester LE3 8TF ☎ 0116 305 4239
ᐧ mike.sandys@leics.gov.uk

Access Officer / Social Services (Disability): Ms Heather
Pick, Head of Personal Care & Support, County Hall, Glenfield,
Leicester LE3 8TF ☎ 0116 305 7458 ᐧ heather.pick@leics.gov.uk

Architect, Building / Property Services: Mr Richard Tebbatt,
Technical Manager, County Hall, Glenfield, Leicester LE3 8TF
☎ 0116 305 6886 ᐧ richard.tebbatt@leics.gov.uk

Catering Services: Mr Tim Brackenbury, Catering Manager,
County Hall, Glenfield, Leicester LE3 8RA ☎ 0116 305 6115
ᐧ tim.brackenbury@leics.gov.uk

Catering Services: Ms Carol Harris, Food & Nutrition Manager,
County Hall, Glenfield, Leicester LE3 8TF ☎ 0116 305 9242
ᐧ carol.harris@leics.gov.uk

Catering Services: Ms Wendy Philp, School Food Service
Manager, County Hall, Glenfield, Leicester LE3 8TF
☎ 0116 305 5770 ᐧ wendy.philp@leics.gov.uk

Children / Youth Services: Ms Sharon Cooke, Assistant Director
- Children & Family Services, County Hall, Glenfield, Leicester LE3
8RA ☎ 0116 305 7441 ᐧ sharon.cooke@leics.gov.uk

Children / Youth Services: Mr Paul Meredith, Interim Director
- Children & Family Services, County Hall, Glenfield, Leicester LE3
8RA ☎ 0116 305 6340 ᐧ paul.meredith@leics.gov.uk

Children / Youth Services: Mrs Jane Moore, Head of Youth
Justice & Safer Communities, County Hall, Glenfield, Leicester LE3
8TF ☎ 0116 305 2649 ᐧ jane.moore@leics.gov.uk

Civil Registration: Mrs Amanda Bettany, County Superintendent
Registrar, County Hall, Glenfield, Leicester LE3 8TF
☎ 0116 605 6585 ᐧ amanda.bettany@leics.gov.uk

PR / Communications: Ms Joanna Morrison, Head of
Communications & Digital Services, County Hall, Glenfield, Leicester
LE3 8TF ☎ 0116 305 5850 ᐧ joanna.morrison@leics.gov.uk

Community Planning: Mr Tom Purnell, Assistant Chief Executive,
County Hall, Glenfield, Leicester LE3 8RA ☎ 0116 305 7019
ᐧ tom.purnell@leics.gov.uk

Community Safety: Mrs Gurjit Samra-Rai, Community Safety
Manager, County Hall, Glenfield, Leicester LE3 8RA ☎ 0116 305
6056 ᐧ grai@leics.gov.uk

Computer Management: Mr Manjit Saroya, Head of ICT
Services, County Hall, Glenfield, Leicester LE3 8TF ☎ 0116 305
7780 ᐧ manjit.saroya@leics.gov.uk

Consumer Protection and Trading Standards: Mr Gary
Connors, Head of Regulatory Services, County Hall, Glenfield,
Leicester LE3 8RA ☎ 0116 305 6536 ᐧ gary.connors@leics.gov.uk

Corporate Services: Mr Roderick O'Connor, Assistant Director -
Commercial & Customer Services, County Hall, Glenfield, Leicester
LE3 8RA ☎ 0116 305 5846 ᐧ roderick.o'connor@leics.gov.uk

Customer Service: Mrs Rachael Stone-Browning, Customer
Services Manager, County Hall, Glenfield, Leicester LE3 8RA
☎ 0116 305 6227 ᐧ rachael.stone-browning@leics.gov.uk

Economic Development: Mr Nev Wilkinson, Head of Commercial Services, County Hall, Glenfield, Leicester LE3 8TF
☏ nev.wilkinson@leics.gov.uk

Education: Mr David Atterbury, Education Officer - Strategic Services, County Hall, Glenfield, Leicester LE3 8TF
☎ 0116 305 7729 ☏ david.atterbury@leics.gov.uk

Education: Mr Paul Meredith, Interim Director - Children & Family Services, County Hall, Glenfield, Leicester LE3 8RA
☎ 0116 305 6340 ☏ paul.meredith@leics.gov.uk

E-Government: Mr Manjit Saroya, Head of ICT Services, County Hall, Glenfield, Leicester LE3 8TF ☎ 0116 305 7780
☏ manjit.saroya@leics.gov.uk

Electoral Registration: Mr Mohammed Seedat, Head of Democratic Services & Administration, County Hall, Glenfield, Leicester LE3 8TF ☎ 0116 305 6037 ☏ mo.seedat@leics.gov.uk

Emergency Planning: Ms Fiona Holbourn, Head of Procurement & Resilience, County Hall, Glenfield, Leicester LE3 8RB
☎ 0116 305 6185 ☏ fiona.holbourn@leics.gov.uk

Energy Management: Mr Graham Read, Corporate Facilities Manager, County Hall, Glenfield, Leicester LE3 8TF
☎ 0116 305 6278 ☏ graham.read@leics.gov.uk

Environmental / Technical Services: Ms Jo Guyll, Assistant Director - Environment & Waste, County Hall, Glenfield, Leicester LE3 8RA ☎ 0116 305 8101 ☏ jo.guyll@leics.gov.uk

Estates, Property & Valuation: Mr Graham Read, Corporate Facilities Manager, County Hall, Glenfield, Leicester LE3 8TF
☎ 0116 305 6278 ☏ graham.read@leics.gov.uk

Facilities: Mr Graham Read, Corporate Facilities Manager, County Hall, Glenfield, Leicester LE3 8TF ☎ 0116 305 6278
☏ graham.read@leics.gov.uk

Finance: Mr Chris Tambini, Assistant Director - Strategic Finance & Procurement, County Hall, Glenfield, Leicester LE3 8TF
☎ 0116 305 6199 ☏ chris.tambini@leics.gov.uk

Pensions: Mr Ian Howe, Pensions Manager, County Hall, Glenfield, Leicester LE3 8TF ☎ 0116 305 6945 ☏ ian.howe@leics.gov.uk

Pensions: Mr Colin Pratt, Pension Investments Officer, County Hall, Glenfield, Leicester LE3 8TF ☎ 0116 305 7656
☏ colin.pratt@leics.gov.uk

Fleet Management: Mr David Atterbury, Education Officer - Strategic Services, County Hall, Glenfield, Leicester LE3 8TF
☎ 0116 305 7729 ☏ david.atterbury@leics.gov.uk

Fleet Management: Mr Tony Kirk, Group Manager - Passenger Transport Unit, County Hall, Glenfield, Leicester LE3 8TF
☎ 0116 305 6270 ☏ tony.kirk@leics.gov.uk

Grounds Maintenance: Mr Graham Read, Corporate Facilities Manager, County Hall, Glenfield, Leicester LE3 8TF
☎ 0116 305 6278 ☏ graham.read@leics.gov.uk

Health and Safety: Mr Colin Jones, Health, Safety & Wellbeing Manager, County Hall, Glenfield, Leicester LE3 8TF
☎ 0116 305 7552 ☏ colin.jones@leics.gov.uk

Highways: Mr Phil Crossland, Director - Environment & Transport, County Hall, Glenfield, Leicester LE3 8TF ☎ 0116 305 7000
☏ phil.crossland@leics.gov.uk

Local Area Agreement: Mr John Wright, Senior Policy & Performance Officer, County Hall, Glenfield, Leicester LE3 8TF
☎ 0116 305 7041 ☏ john.r.wright@leics.gov.uk

Legal: Ms Lauren Haslam, Head of Law & Governance, County Hall, Glenfield, Leicester LE3 8RA ☎ 0116 305 6240
☏ lauren.haslam@leics.gov.uk

Leisure and Cultural Services: Mr John Byrne, Sports Co-ordinator, County Hall, Glenfield, Leicester LE3 8RA
☎ 01509 564852 ☏ j.byrne2@lboro.ac.uk

Leisure and Cultural Services: Ms Franne Wills, Assistant Director - Communities, County Hall, Glenfield, Leicester LE3 8TF
☎ 0116 305 0692 ☏ franne.wills@leics.gov.uk

Lifelong Learning: Ms Franne Wills, Assistant Director - Communities, County Hall, Glenfield, Leicester LE3 8TF
☎ 0116 305 0692 ☏ franne.wills@leics.gov.uk

Lighting: Ms Ann Carruthers, Assistant Director - Highways & Transportation, County Hall, Glenfield, Leicester LE3 8RA
☎ 0116 305 7966 ☏ ann.carruthers@leics.gov.uk

Member Services: Mr Mohammed Seedat, Head of Democratic Services & Administration, County Hall, Glenfield, Leicester LE3 8TF ☎ 0116 305 6037 ☏ mo.seedat@leics.gov.uk

Partnerships: Mr Tom Purnell, Assistant Chief Executive, County Hall, Glenfield, Leicester LE3 8RA ☎ 0116 305 7019
☏ tom.purnell@leics.gov.uk

Personnel / HR: Mr Gordon McFarlane, Assistant Director - Corporate Services & Transformation, County Hall, Glenfield, Leicester LE3 8TF ☎ 0116 305 6123 ☏ gordon.mcfarlane@leics.gov.uk

Planning: Mr Lonek Wojtulewicz, Head of Planning Historic & Natural Environment, County Hall, Glenfield, Leicester LE3 8TE
☎ 0116 305 7040 ☏ lonek.wojtulewicz@leics.gov.uk

Procurement: Ms Fiona Holbourn, Head of Procurement & Resilience, County Hall, Glenfield, Leicester LE3 8RB ☎ 0116 305 6185 ☏ fiona.holbourn@leics.gov.uk

Public Libraries: Mr Nigel Thomas, Service Delivery Manager, County Hall, Glenfield, Leicester LE3 8TF ☎ 0116 305 7379
☏ nigel.thomas@leics.gov.uk

Recycling & Waste Minimisation: Ms Jo Guyll, Assistant Director - Environment & Waste, County Hall, Glenfield, Leicester LE3 8RA ☎ 0116 305 8101 ☏ jo.guyll@leics.gov.uk

LEICESTERSHIRE

Regeneration: Mr Derk Van Der Wardt, Group Manager of Communities & Places, County Hall, Glenfield, Leicester LE3 8TF ☎ 0116 305 7581 🖷 derk.vanderwardt@leics.gov.uk

Road Safety: Mr Nigel Horsley, Team Manager, Road Safety & Travel Awareness, County Hall, Glenfield, Leicester LE3 8TF ☎ 0116 305 7227 🖷 nigel.horsley@leics.gov.uk

Social Services: Mr Jon Wilson, Director - Adults & Communities, County Hall, Glenfield, Leicester LE3 8RA ☎ 0116 305 7454 🖷 jon.wilson@leics.gov.uk

Social Services (Children): Ms Sharon Cooke, Assistant Director - Children & Family Services, County Hall, Glenfield, Leicester LE3 8RA ☎ 0116 305 7441 🖷 sharon.cooke@leics.gov.uk

Public Health: Mr Mike Sandys, Director - Public Health, County Hall, Glenfield, Leicester LE3 8TF ☎ 0116 305 4239 🖷 mike.sandys@leics.gov.uk

Staff Training: Ms Nicola Houwayek, Head of Organisational Development, County Hall, Glenfield, Leicester LE3 8RA ☎ 0116 305 5615 🖷 nicola.houwayek@leics.gov.uk

Transport: Mr Phil Crossland, Director - Environment & Transport, County Hall, Glenfield, Leicester LE3 8TF ☎ 0116 305 7000 🖷 phil.crossland@leics.gov.uk

Transport Planner: Mr Paul Sheard, Group Manager of Transport Planning, County Hall, Glenfield, Leicester LE3 8RJ ☎ 0116 305 7191 🖷 paul.sheard@leics.gov.uk

Waste Collection and Disposal: Ms Jo Guyll, Assistant Director - Environment & Waste, County Hall, Glenfield, Leicester LE3 8RA ☎ 0116 305 8101 🖷 jo.guyll@leics.gov.uk

Waste Management: Mr Phil Crossland, Director - Environment & Transport, County Hall, Glenfield, Leicester LE3 8TF ☎ 0116 305 7000 🖷 phil.crossland@leics.gov.uk

Waste Management: Ms Jo Guyll, Assistant Director - Environment & Waste, County Hall, Glenfield, Leicester LE3 8RA ☎ 0116 305 8101 🖷 jo.guyll@leics.gov.uk

COUNCILLORS

Chair: Liquorish, Bill (CON - Broughton Astley)
bill.liquorish@leics.gov.uk

Leader of the Council: Rushton, Nicholas (CON - Valley)
nicholas.rushton@leics.gov.uk

Deputy Leader of the Council: Rhodes, Byron (CON - Belvoir)
byron.rhodes@leics.gov.uk

Bently, Iain (CON - Birstall)
iain.bentley@leics.gov.uk

Bill, David (LD - Hinckley)
david.bill@leics.gov.uk

Blunt, Richard (CON - Kirby Muxloe & Leicester Forest)
richard.blunt@leics.gov.uk

Boulter, Bill (LD - Wigston South)
bill.boulter@leics.gov.uk

Bray, Stuart (LD - Burbage Castle)
stuart.bray@leics.gov.uk

Camamile, Ruth (CON - Mallory)
ruth.camamile@leics.gov.uk

Charlesworth, Michael (LD - Wigston Busloe)
michael.charlesworth@leics.gov.uk

Coxon, John (CON - Ashby de la Zouch)
john.coxon@leics.gov.uk

Dickinson, Jackie (CON - Enderby Meridian)
jackie.dickinson@leics.gov.uk

Enynon, Terri (LAB - Coalville)
terri.enyon@leics.gov.uk

Feltham, Kevin (CON - Gartree)
kevin.feltham@leics.gov.uk

Fox, Jo (LAB - Braunstone Town)
jo.fox@leics.gov.uk

Galton, Simon (LD - Launde)
simon.galton@leics.gov.uk

Gamble, Dean (LD - Oadby)
dean.gamble@leics.gov.uk

Hampson, Stephen (CON - Syston Ridgeway)
stephen.hampson@leics.gov.uk

Hart, Graham (CON - Bruntingthorpe)
graham.hart@leics.gov.uk

Hill, Sarah (LD - Market Harborough East)
sarah.hill@leics.gov.uk

Houseman, David (CON - Syston Fosse)
dave.houseman@leics.gov.uk

Hunt, Max (LAB - Loughborough North West)
max.hunt@leics.gov.uk

Jennings, David (CON - Cosby & Countesthorpe)
david.jennings@leics.gov.uk

Kaufman, Jeffrey (LD - Oadby)
jeffrey.kaufman@leics.gov.uk

Kershaw, Tony (CON - Quorn & Barrow)
tony.kershaw@leics.gov.uk

Knaggs, Kate (LAB - Thurmaston)
kate.knaggs@leics.gov.uk

Lewis, Peter (CON - Loughborough South West)
peter.lewis@leics.gov.uk

Lloydall, Helen (LD - Wigston Poplars)
helen.lloydall@leics.gov.uk

Lynch, Keith (LD - Burbage Castle)
keith.lynch@leics.gov.uk

Miah, Jewel (LAB - Loughborough East)
jewel.miah@leics.gov.uk

Mullaney, Michael (LD - Hinckley)
michael.mullaney@leics.gov.uk

Newton, Betty (LAB - Loughborough North)
betty.newton@leics.gov.uk

Orson, Joseph (CON - Asfordby)
joe.orson@leics.gov.uk

Osborne, Peter (CON - Rothley & Mountsorrel)
peter.osborne@leics.gov.uk

O'Shea, Ozzy (CON - Groby & Ratby)
ozzy.o'shea@leics.gov.uk

Ould, Ivan (CON - Market Bosworth)
ivan.ould@leics.gov.uk

Page, Rosita (CON - Lutterworth)
rosita.page@leics.gov.uk

Pain, Blake (CON - Market Harborough West & Foxton)
blake.pain@leics.gov.uk

Pearson, Alan (CON - Melton South)
alan.pearson@leics.gov.uk

Pendleton, Trevor (CON - Castle Donington)
trevor.pendleton@leics.gov.uk

Posnett, Pam (CON - Melton North)
pam.posnett@leics.gov.uk

Radford, Christine (CON - Shepshed)
christine.radford@leics.gov.uk

Richards, Janice (CON - Earl Shilton)
janice.richards@leics.gov.uk

Richardson, Terry (CON - Narborough & Whetstone)
terry.richardson@leics.gov.uk

Sharp, Robert (LAB - Loughborough South)
robert.sharp@leics.gov.uk

Sheahan, Sean (LAB - Forest & Measham)
sean.sheahan@leics.gov.uk

Shepherd, Richard (CON - Sileby & The Wolds)
richard.shepherd@leics.gov.uk

Snartt, David (CON - Bradgate)
david.snartt@leics.gov.uk

Spence, Leon (LAB - Whitwick)
leon.spence@leics.gov.uk

Sprason, David (UKIP - Markfield Desford & Thornton)
david.sprason@leics.gov.uk

Walsh, Geoff (LD - Blaby & Glen Parva)
geoff.walsh@leics.gov.uk

White, Ernie (CON - Stanton Croft & Normanton)
ernie.white@leics.gov.uk

Worman, Heather (LAB - Ibstock & Appleby)
heather.worman@leics.gov.uk

Wyatt, Michael (LD - Warren Hills)
michael.wyatt@leics.gov.uk

Yates, Lynton (UKIP - Glenfields)
lynton.yates@leics.gov.uk

POLITICAL COMPOSITION
CON: 30, LD: 13, LAB: 10, UKIP: 2

COMMITTEE CHAIRS

Children & Families: Mr Leon Spence

Development Control: Mr Trevor Pendleton

Environment & Transport: Mr David Jennings

Health & Wellbeing: Mr Ernie White

Pensions: Mr Graham Hart

Lewes D

Lewes District Council, Lewes House, 32 High Street, Lewes BN7 2LX
☎ 01273 471600 ⌨ www.lewes.gov.uk

FACTS AND FIGURES
Parliamentary Constituencies: Lewes
EU Constituencies: South East
Election Frequency: Elections are of whole council

PRINCIPAL OFFICERS

Chief Executive: Mr Robert Cottrill, Chief Executive, 1 Grove Road, Eastbourne BN21 4TW ☎ 01323 415046 robert.cottrill@eastbourne.gov.uk

Senior Management: Mr Alan Osborne, Director - Corporate Services, Southover House, Southover Road, Lewes BN7 1AB ☎ 01273 484112 alan.osborne@lewes.gov.uk

Access Officer / Social Services (Disability): Ms Ioni Sullivan, Performance Officer - Equalities, Southover House, Southover Road, Lewes BN7 1AB ☎ 01273 471600 ioni.sullivan@lewes.gov.uk

Architect, Building / Property Services: Mr Ian Morris, Head - Planning & Revenue, Lewes House, 32 High Street, Lewes BN7 2LX ☎ 01273 471600 ian.morris@lewes.gov.uk

Best Value: Mr David Heath, Head - Audit & Performance, 4 Fisher Street, Lewes BN7 2DQ ☎ 01273 471600 david.heath@lewes.gov.uk

Building Control: Mr Roger Carsons, Head - Building Control, Planning & Environment Services, PO Box 2707, Southover House, Southover Road, Lewes BN7 1AB ☎ 01273 481120 roger.carsons@lewes.gov.uk

PR / Communications: Ms Liz Lacon, Press Officer, Southover House, Southover Road, Lewes BN7 1AB ☎ 01273 484141 liz.lacon@lewes.gov.uk

Computer Management: Ms Kalpna Dice, Head of IT Department, Southover House, Southover Road, Lewes BN7 1AB ☎ 01273 471600 kalpna.dice@lewes.gov.uk

Contracts: Mr Alan Osborne, Director - Corporate Services, Southover House, Southover Road, Lewes BN7 1AB ☎ 01273 484112 alan.osborne@lewes.gov.uk

Corporate Services: Mr Alan Osborne, Director - Corporate Services, Southover House, Southover Road, Lewes BN7 1AB ☎ 01273 484112 alan.osborne@lewes.gov.uk

Customer Service: Mr David Parry, Senior Customer Services Assistant, Southover House, Southover Road, Lewes BN7 1AB ☎ 01273 486031 david.parry@lewes.gov.uk

Economic Development: Ms Nazeya Hussain, Director - Business Strategy & Development, Southover House, Southover Road, Lewes BN7 1AB ☎ 01273 471600 nazeya.hussain@lewes.gov.uk

LEWES

Electoral Registration: Mr Steven Andrews, Electoral Services Manager, Lewes House, 32 High Street, Lewes BN7 2LX
☎ 01273 484117 ✆ steven.andrews@lewes.gov.uk

Emergency Planning: Mr Ian Hodgson, Emergency Planning Officer, Southover House, Southover Road, Lewes BN7 1AB
☎ 01273 486334 ✆ ian.hodgson@lewes.gov.uk

Environmental Health: Mr Ed Hele, Principal Environmental Health Officer - Public Health & Licensing, Southover House, Southover Road, Lewes BN7 1AB ☎ 01273 471600
✆ ed.hele@lewes.gov.uk

Estates, Property & Valuation: Ms Bee Lewis, Head - Property & Facilities, Lewes House, 32 High Street, Lewes BN7 2LX
☎ 01273 661101 ✆ bee.lewis@lewes.gov.uk

Facilities: Ms Bee Lewis, Head - Property & Facilities, Lewes House, 32 High Street, Lewes BN7 2LX ☎ 01273 661101
✆ bee.lewis@lewes.gov.uk

Finance: Mr Ian Morris, Head - Planning & Revenue, Lewes House, 32 High Street, Lewes BN7 2LX ☎ 01273 471600
✆ ian.morris@lewes.gov.uk

Finance: Mr Alan Osborne, Director - Corporate Services, Southover House, Southover Road, Lewes BN7 1AB
☎ 01273 484112 ✆ alan.osborne@lewes.gov.uk

Grounds Maintenance: Mr Andy Frost, Parks Manager, Southover House, Southover Road, Lewes BN7 1AB
☎ 01273 484398 ✆ andy.frost@lewes.gov.uk

Health and Safety: Ms Jill Yeates, Health & Safety Officer, Lewes House, 32 High Street, Lewes BN7 2LX
☎ 01273 486276 ✆ jill.yeates@lewes.gov.uk

Housing: Mr Andy Chequers, Head - Housing & Environment, Lewes House, 32 High Street, Lewes BN7 2LX ☎ 01273 484380
✆ andy.chequers@lewes.gov.uk

Housing: Ms Karen Sedgwick, Temporary Services Manager - Housing Needs & Private Sector, Southover House, Southover Road, Lewes BN7 1AB ☎ 01272 471600 ✆ karen.sedgwick@lewes.gov.uk

Housing Maintenance: Mr Andy Chequers, Head - Housing & Environment, Lewes House, 32 High Street, Lewes BN7 2LX
☎ 01273 484380 ✆ andy.chequers@lewes.gov.uk

Legal: Ms Celia Cullen, Director - Shared Legal Services Unit, Southover House, Southover Road, Lewes BN7 1AB
☎ 01273 471600 ✆ celia.cullen@lewes.gov.uk

Legal: Ms Catherine Knight, Assistant Director - Corporate Services, Southover House, Southover Road, Lewes BN7 1AB
☎ 01273 481116 ✆ catherine.knight@lewes.gov.uk

Leisure and Cultural Services: Ms Jackie Blackwell, Regeneration Project Manager, Southover House, Southover Road, Lewes BN7 1AB ☎ 01273 471600 ✆ jackie.blackwell@lewes.gov.uk

Licensing: Ms Sue Lindsey, Licensing Officer, Southover House, Southover Road, Lewes BN7 1AB ☎ 01273 471600
✆ sue.lindsey@lewes.gov.uk

Member Services: Ms Caroline Hanlon, Civic & Member Services Officer, Southover House, Southover Road, Lewes BN7 1AB
☎ 01273 471600 ✆ caroline.hanlon@lewes.gov.uk

Parking: Ms Bee Lewis, Head - Property & Facilities, Lewes House, 32 High Street, Lewes BN7 2LX ☎ 01273 661101
✆ bee.lewis@lewes.gov.uk

Personnel / HR: Ms Becky Cooke, Head of Organisational Development, Lewes House, 32 High Street, Lewes BN7 2LX
becky.cooke@lewes.gov.uk

Planning: Ms Nazeya Hussain, Director - Business Strategy & Development, Southover House, Southover Road, Lewes BN7 1AB
☎ 01273 471600 ✆ nazeya.hussain@lewes.gov.uk

Procurement: Mr David Heath, Head - Audit & Performance, 4 Fisher Street, Lewes BN7 2DQ ☎ 01273 471600
✆ david.heath@lewes.gov.uk

Recycling & Waste Minimisation: Ms Julia Black, Community Recycling Officer, Community Recycling Centre, 20 North Street, Lewes BN7 2PE ☎ 01273 486268 ✆ julia.black@lewes.gov.uk

Regeneration: Mr Max Woodford, Head of Regeneration & Investment, Lewes House, 32 High Street, Lewes BN7 2LX
☎ 07966 645037 ✆ max.woodford@lewes.gov.uk

Staff Training: Ms Helen Knight, HR Manager, Lewes House, 32 High Street, Lewes BN7 2LX ☎ 01273 481365
✆ helen.knight@lewes.gov.uk

Waste Collection and Disposal: Mr Greg Martin, Waste Operations Manager, Community Recycling Centre, 20 North Street, Lewes BN7 2PE ☎ 01273 486423 ✆ greg.martin@lewes.gov.uk

Waste Management: Mr Greg Martin, Waste Operations Manager, Community Recycling Centre, 20 North Street, Lewes BN7 2PE ☎ 01273 486423 ✆ greg.martin@lewes.gov.uk

COUNCILLORS

Leader of the Council: Smith, Andy (CON - East Saltdean & Telscombe Cliffs)
cllr.andysmith.ldc@gmail.com

Deputy Leader of the Council: Merry, Elayne (CON - Peacehaven North)
elayne.merry@lewes.gov.uk

Group Leader: Osborne, Sarah (LD - Plumpton Streat East Chiltington & St John Without)
sarah.osborne2@lewes.gov.uk

Adeniji, Sam (CON - Seaford South)
sam.adeniji@lewes.gov.uk

Amy, Graham (LD - Newhaven Denton & Meeching)
graham.amy@lewes.gov.uk

Barnes, Simon (UKIP - Newhaven Denton & Meeching)
simon.barnes@lewes.gov.uk

Blackman, Rob (CON - Seaford West)
rob.blackman@lewes.gov.uk

Botting, Wayne (CON - East Saltdean & Telscombe Cliffs)
wayne.botting@lewes.gov.uk

Bovington, Bill (CON - Seaford Central)
bill.bovington@lewes.gov.uk

Carr, Julie (LD - Newhaven Valley)
julie.carr@lewes.gov.uk

Carter, Joanna (GRN - Lewes Bridge)
joanna.carter@lewes.gov.uk

Catlin, Stephen (IND - Lewes Priory)
stephen.catlin@lewes.gov.uk

Chartier, Michael (LD - Lewes Castle)
michael.cartier@lewes.gov.uk

Davy, Sharon (CON - Chailey & Wivelsfield)
sharon.davy@lewes.gov.uk

Elliott, Will (LD - Lewes Bridge)
will.elliott@lewes.gov.uk

Enever, Nigel (CON - Peacehaven East)
nigel.enever@lewes.gov.uk

Franklin, Paul (CON - Seaford North)
paul.franklin@lewes.gov.uk

Gander, Paul (CON - Ouse Valley & Ringmer)
paul.gander@lewes.gov.uk

Gardiner, Peter (LD - Ouse Valley & Ringmer)
peter.gardiner@lewes.gov.uk

Gauntlett, Stephen (LD - Seaford Central)
stephen.gauntlett@lewes.gov.uk

Giles, Bill (CON - Newhaven Denton & Meeching)
bill.giles@lewes.gov.uk

Harrison-Hicks, Jacqueline (CON - Peacehaven East)
jmharricks@btinternet.com

Honeyman, Olivia (LD - Seaford South)
olivia.honeyman@lewes.gov.uk

Ient, Vic (LD - Kingston)
vic.ient@lewes.gov.uk

Jones, Tom (CON - Ditchling & Westmerton)
tom.jones@lewes.gov.uk

Lambert, Alex (LD - Seaford North)
alex.lambert@lewes.gov.uk

Linington, Isabelle (CON - Barcombe & Hamsey)
isabelle.linington@lewes.gov.uk

Lorraine, Andy (CON - Peacehaven North)
andy.lorraine@lewes.gov.uk

Maskell, Ron (CON - East Saltdean & Telscombe Cliffs)
cllr.ronmaskell@gmail.com

Murray, Susan (GRN - Lewes Castle)
susan.murray@lewes.gov.uk

Neave, Dave (CON - Peacehaven West)
david.neave@lewes.gov.uk

Nicholson, Tony (CON - Seaford East)
tony.angela@btinternet.com

O'Keeffe, Ruth (IND - Lewes Priory)
rok@supanet.com

Peterson, Julian (CON - Seaford East)
julian.peterson@lewes.gov.uk

Robertson, Robbie (CON - Peacehaven West)
robbie.robertson@lewes.gov.uk

Rowell, Tony (GRN - Lewes Priory)
tony.rowell@lewes.gov.uk

Saunders, Steve (LD - Newhaven Valley)
steve.saunders@lewes.gov.uk

Sheppard, Jim (CON - Newick)
j.sheppard3@btinternet.com

Sugarman, Cyril (CON - Chailey & Wivelsfield)
cyril.sugarman@lewes.gov.uk

Turner, Richard (CON - Ouse Valley & Ringmer)
richard.turner@lewes.gov.uk

Wallraven, Linda (CON - Seaford West)
linda.wallraven@lewes.gov.uk

POLITICAL COMPOSITION
CON: 24, LD: 11, GRN: 3, IND: 2, UKIP: 1

COMMITTEE CHAIRS

Audit: Mr Michael Chartier

Licensing: Mr Sam Adeniji

Planning: Ms Sharon Davy

Lewisham   L

Lewisham London Borough Council, Civic Suite, Town Hall, London SE6 4RU

☎ 020 8314 6000 🖳 www.lewisham.gov.uk

FACTS AND FIGURES
Parliamentary Constituencies: Lewisham Deptford, Lewisham East, Lewisham West and Penge
EU Constituencies: London
Election Frequency: Elections are of whole council

PRINCIPAL OFFICERS

Chief Executive: Mr Barry Quirk, Chief Executive, 5th Floor, Laurence House, 1 Catford Road, London SE6 4RU
☎ 020 8314 6445 ✆ barry.quirk@lewisham.gov.uk

Senior Management: Ms Aileen Buckton, Executive Director - Community Services, 5th Floor, Laurence House, 1 Catford Road, London SE6 4RU ☎ 020 8314 8107
✆ aileen.buckton@lewisham.gov.uk

Senior Management: Dr Danny Ruta, Director - Public Health, Laurence House, 1 Catford Road, London SE6 4RU
☎ 020 8314 9094 ✆ danny.ruta@lewisham.gov.uk

Senior Management: Ms Janet Senior, Executive Director - Resources & Regeneration, 5th Floor, Laurence House, 1 Catford Road, London SE6 4RU ☎ 020 8314 8013
✆ janet.senior@lewisham.gov.uk

LEWISHAM

Senior Management: Mr Kevin Sheehan, Executive Director - Customer Services, 5th Floor, Laurence House, 1 Catford Road, London SE6 4RU ☎ 020 8314 6800 ✆ kevin.sheehan@lewisham. gov.uk

Senior Management: Ms Sara Williams, Executive Director - Children & Young People, Laurence House, 1 Catford Road, London SE6 4RU ☎ 020 8314 8527 ✆ sara.williams@lewisham.gov.uk

Architect, Building / Property Services: Ms Annnettal Crossley, Head of Property Services, 2nd Floor, Laurence House, 1 Catford Road, London SE6 4RU ☎ 020 8314 9222 ✆ annettal.crossley@lewisham.gov.uk

Best Value: Mr Barrie Neal, Head of Corporate Policy & Governance, 5th Floor, Laurence House, 1 Catford Road, London SE6 4RU ☎ 020 8314 9852 ✆ barrie.neal@lewisham.gov.uk

Building Control: Mr Thiru Moolan, Civil & Structural Engineering Manager, 4th Floor, Laurence House, 1 Catford Road, London SE6 4RU building.control@lewisham.gov.uk

Children / Youth Services: Mr Alan Docksey, Head of Resources CYP, 3rd Floor, Laurence House, 1 Catford Road, London SE6 4RU ☎ 020 8314 3582 ✆ alan.docksey@lewisham.gov.uk

Children / Youth Services: Ms Sara Williams, Executive Director - Children & Young People, Laurence House, 1 Catford Road, London SE6 4RU ☎ 020 8314 8527 ✆ sara.williams@lewisham.gov.uk

Civil Registration: Mr Glynne Harris, Superintendent Registrar, Registrar Office, Lewisham High Street, London SE13 4RU ☎ 020 8690 2128 ✆ glynne.harris@lewisham.gov.uk

Civil Registration: Ms Renee Hayles, Head of Land Charges, 5th Floor, Laurence House, 1 Catford Road, London SE6 4RU ☎ 020 8314 6078 ✆ renee.hayles@lewisham.gov.uk

PR / Communications: Mr Adrian Wardle, Head of Communications, Civic Suite, Town Hall, London SE6 4RU ☎ 020 8314 6087 ✆ adrian.wardle@lewisham.gov.uk

Community Planning: Ms Liz Dart, Head of Culture & Community Development, Laurence House, 1 Catford Road, London SE6 4RU ☎ 020 8314 6000 ✆ liz.dart@lewisham.gov.uk

Community Safety: Mr Gary Connors, Crime Enforcement Regulation Team Service Manager, Mercia Grove, Lewisham, London SE13 7EZ ☎ 020 8314 9773 ✆ gary.connors@lewisham.gov.uk

Community Safety: Ms Geeta Subramaniam, Head of Crime Reduction & Supporting People, 5th Floor, Laurence House, 1 Catford Road, London SE6 4RU ☎ 020 8314 9509 ✆ geeta.subramaniam@lewisham.gov.uk

Computer Management: Mr Duncan Dewhurst, Head of Service Change & Technology, 5th Floor, Laurence House, 1 Catford Road, London SE6 4RU ☎ 07875 082430 ✆ duncan.dewhurst@lewisham.gov.uk

Consumer Protection and Trading Standards: Mr Gary Connors, Crime Enforcement Regulation Team Service Manager, Mercia Grove, Lewisham, London SE13 7EZ ☎ 020 8314 9773 ✆ gary.connors@lewisham.gov.uk

Customer Service: Mr Kevin Sheehan, Executive Director - Customer Services, 5th Floor, Laurence House, 1 Catford Road, London SE6 4RU ☎ 020 8314 6800 ✆ kevin.sheehan@lewisham.gov.uk

Economic Development: Mr Kevin Turner, Economic Development Manager, Laurence House, 1 Catford Road, London SE6 4RU ☎ 020 8314 8229 ✆ kevin.turner@lewisham.gov.uk

Education: Ms Louise Comely, Head of Inclusion Service, Kaleidoscope, 4th Floor, 32 Rushey Green, London SE6 4JF ☎ 020 7138 1432 ✆ louise.comely@lewisham.gov.uk

Education: Ms Sara Williams, Executive Director - Children & Young People, Laurence House, 1 Catford Road, London SE6 4RU ☎ 020 8314 8527 ✆ sara.williams@lewisham.gov.uk

Electoral Registration: Ms Kath Nicholson, Head of Law, 5th Floor, Laurence House, 1 Catford Road, London SE6 4RU ☎ 020 8314 7648 ✆ kath.nicholson@lewisham.gov.uk

Emergency Planning: Mr James Cook, Prinicpal Emergency Planning Officer, 5th Floor, Laurence House, 1 Catford Road, London SE6 4RU ☎ 020 8314 8579 ✆ james.cook@lewisham.gov.uk

Energy Management: Mr Martin O'Brien, Sustainability Officer, Laurence House, 1 Catford Road, London SE6 4RU ☎ 020 8314 6605 ✆ martin.o'brien@lewisham.gov.uk

Environmental / Technical Services: Mr Nigel Tyrell, Head of Environment, Wearside Service Centre, Wearside Road, London SE13 7EZ ☎ 020 8314 6000 ✆ nigel.tyrell@lewisham.gov.uk

Estates, Property & Valuation: Mr Rob Holmans, Head of Programme Management & Property, Laurence House, 1 Catford Road, London SE6 4RU ☎ 020 8314 6000 ✆ rob.holmes@lewisham.gov.uk

European Liaison: Ms Nicola Marven, International Partnerships & Projects Officer, Civic Suite, Town Hall, London SE6 4RU ☎ 020 8324 7227 ✆ nicola.marven@lewisham.gov.uk

Events Manager: Ms Carmel Langstaff, Head of Arts & Entertainment, 5th Floor, Laurence House, 1 Catford Road, London SE6 4RU ☎ 020 8314 7729 ✆ carmel.langstaff@lewisham.gov.uk

Events Manager: Mr Andy Thomas, Cultural Development Manager, 5th Floor, Laurence House, 1 Catford Road, London SE6 4RU ☎ 020 8314 6000 ✆ andy.thomas@lewisham.gov.uk

Facilities: Ms Annettal Crossley, Head of Property Services, 2nd Floor, Laurence House, 1 Catford Road, London SE6 4RU ☎ 020 8314 9222 ✆ annettal.crossley@lewisham.gov.uk

Finance: Ms Janet Senior, Executive Director - Resources & Regeneration, 5th Floor, Laurence House, 1 Catford Road, London SE6 4RU ☎ 020 8314 8013 ✆ janet.senior@lewisham.gov.uk

Pensions: Mr Tim O'Connor, Pensions Manager, 5th Floor, Laurence House, 1 Catford Road, London SE6 4RU
☎ 020 8314 7142 ⏚ tim.o'connor@lewisham.gov.uk

Pensions: Mr Selwyn Thompson, Pension Investment Manager, 5th Floor, Laurence House, 1 Catford Road, London SE6 4RU
☎ 020 8314 6932 ⏚ selwyn.thompson@lewisham.gov.uk

Fleet Management: Mr Martin Champkins, Service Unit Manager of Lewisham Door to Door, Lewisham Town Hall, London SE6 4RU
☎ 020 8314 0991 ⏚ martin.champkins@lewisham.gov.uk

Health and Safety: Mr David Austin, Head of Corporate Resources, 3rd Floor, Town Hall, London SE6 4RU
☎ 020 8314 8914 ⏚ david.austin@lewisham.gov.uk

Housing: Ms Genevieve Macklin, Head of Strategic Housing, 5th Floor, Laurence House, 1 Catford Road, London SE6 4RU
☎ 020 8314 6057 ⏚ genevieve.macklin@lewisham.gov.uk

Local Area Agreement: Ms Fenella Beckman, Strategic Partnership Manager, Civic Suite, Town Hall, London SE6 4RU
☎ 020 8314 8632 ⏚ Fenella.Beckman@lewisham.gov.uk

Legal: Ms Kath Nicholson, Head of Law, 5th Floor, Laurence House, 1 Catford Road, London SE6 4RU ☎ 020 8314 7648
⏚ kath.nicholson@lewisham.gov.uk

Leisure and Cultural Services: Mr Andy Thomas, Cultural Development Manager, 5th Floor, Laurence House, 1 Catford Road, London SE6 4RU ☎ 020 8314 6000
⏚ andy.thomas@lewisham.gov.uk

Licensing: Mr Gary Connors, Crime Enforcement Regulation Team Service Manager, Mercia Grove, Lewisham, London SE13 7EZ
☎ 020 8314 9773 ⏚ gary.connors@lewisham.gov.uk

Lottery Funding, Charity and Voluntary: Mr Paul Hadfield, Enterprise Development Manager, 5th Floor, Laurence House, 1 Catford Road, London SE6 4RU ☎ 020 8314 8022
⏚ paul.hadfield@lewisham.gov.uk

Member Services: Mr Kevin Flaherty, Head of Business & Committee, Civic Suite, Town Hall, London SE6 4RU
☎ 020 8314 8824 ⏚ kevin.flaherty@lewisham.gov.uk

Member Services: Mr Derek Johnson, Business & Civic Co-ordinator, Civic Suite, Town Hall, London SE6 4RU
☎ 020 8314 8636 ⏚ derek.johnson@lewisham.gov.uk

Parking: Ms Lesley Brooks, Service Group Manager of Travel Demand, Wearside Depot, Lewisham, London SE13 7EZ
☎ 020 8314 6000 ⏚ lesley.brooks@lewisham.gov.uk

Partnerships: Mr Paul Aladenika, Head of Policy & Partnerships, 5th Floor, Laurence House, 1 Catford Road, London SE6 4RU
☎ 020 8314 7148 ⏚ paul.aladenika@lewisham.gov.uk

Personnel / HR: Mr Andreas Ghosh, Head of Personnel & Development, 5th Floor, Laurence House, 1 Catford Road, London SE6 4RU ☎ 020 8314 7519 ⏚ andreas.ghosh@lewisham.gov.uk

Planning: Ms Emma Talbot, Head of Planning Services, Civic Suite, Town Hall, London SE6 4RU ☎ 020 8314 8706
⏚ emma.talbot@lewisham.gov.uk

Public Libraries: Mr Gerald Jones, Head of Community Education, 2nd Floor, Laurence House, 1 Catford Road, London SE5 4RU ☎ 020 8314 6189 ⏚ gerald.jones@lewisham.gov.uk

Public Libraries: Mr Antonio Rizzo, Head of Libraries, 2nd Floor, Laurence House, 1 Catford Road, London SE13 6LG
☎ 020 8314 8025 ⏚ antonio.rizzo@lewisham.gov.uk

Recycling & Waste Minimisation: Ms Sam Kirk, Strategic Waste & Environment Manager, Wearside Service Centre, Wearside Road, London SE13 7EZ ☎ 020 8314 2076
⏚ sam.kirk@lewisham.gov.uk

Road Safety: Ms Lesley Brooks, Service Group Manager of Travel Demand, Wearside Depot, Lewisham, London SE13 7EZ
☎ 020 8314 6000 ⏚ lesley.brooks@lewisham.gov.uk

Social Services: Ms Alison Beck, Head of Bereavement Services, Lewisham Crematorium, Verdant Lane, London SE16 1TP
☎ 020 8314 6000 ⏚ alison.beck@lewisham.gov.uk

Social Services: Ms Aileen Buckton, Executive Director - Community Services, 5th Floor, Laurence House, 1 Catford Road, London SE6 4RU
☎ 020 8314 8107 ⏚ aileen.buckton@lewisham.gov.uk

Social Services: Mr Alan Docksey, Head of Resources - Social Care, 3rd Floor, Laurence House, 1 Cartford Road, London SE6 4RU
☎ 020 8314 3582 ⏚ alan.docksey@lewisham.gov.uk

Social Services: Ms Sarah Wainer, Head of Performance & Strategy in Adult Care & Health, 5th Floor, Laurence House, 1 Catford Road, London SE6 4RU ☎ 020 8314 9611
⏚ sarah.wainer@lewisham.gov.uk

Social Services (Children): Mr Stephen Kitchman, Interim Director - Children's Social Care, Civic Suite, Town Hall, London SE6 4RU ☎ 020 8314 8140 ⏚ stephen.kitchman@lewisham.gov.uk

Public Health: Dr Danny Ruta, Director - Public Health, Civic Suite, Town Hall, London SE6 4RU ☎ 020 8314 9094
⏚ danny.ruta@lewisham.gov.uk

Staff Training: Mr Andrew Jacobs, Organisational Learning & Talent Manager, Lewisham Town Hall, London SE6 4RU
☎ 020 8314 6035 ⏚ andrew.jacobs@lewisham.gov.uk

Street Scene: Mr Noel Everest, Transport Service Group Manager, Wearside Service Centre, Wearside Road, London SE13 7EZ
☎ 020 8314 6000 ⏚ noel.everest@lewisham.gov.uk

Sustainable Communities: Mr Martin O'Brien, Sustainability Officer, 5th Floor, Laurence House, 1 Catford Road, London SE6 4RU ☎ 020 8314 6605 ⏚ martin.o'brien@lewisham.gov.uk

Sustainable Development: Mr Martin O'Brien, Sustainability Officer, 5th Floor, Laurence House, 1 Catford Road, London SE6 4RU ☎ 020 8314 6605 ⏚ martin.o'brien@lewisham.gov.uk

LEWISHAM

Tourism: Mr Kevin Turner, Economic Development Manager, Laurence House, 1 Catford Road, London SE6 4RU
☎ 020 8314 8229 🖑 kevin.turner@lewisham.gov.uk

Waste Collection and Disposal: Mr Michael Bryan, Group Service Manager - Refuse, Wearside Service Centre, Wearside Road, London SE13 7EZ ☎ 020 8314 2113
🖑 michael.bryan@lewisham.gov.uk

Waste Collection and Disposal: Ms Sam Kirk, Strategic Waste & Environment Manager, Wearside Service Centre, Wearside Road, London SE13 7EZ ☎ 020 8314 2076 🖑 sam.kirk@lewisham.gov.uk

Waste Management: Ms Sam Kirk, Strategic Waste & Environment Manager, Wearside Service Centre, Wearside Road, London SE13 7EZ ☎ 020 8314 2076 🖑 sam.kirk@lewisham.gov.uk

COUNCILLORS

Chair: Adefiranye, Obajimi (LAB - Brockley)
cllr_obajimi.adefiranye@lewisham.gov.uk

Vice-Chair: Till, Alan (LAB - Perry Vale)
cllr_alan.till@lewisham.gov.uk

Mayor: Bullock, Steve (LAB - London Borough of Lewisham)
steve.bullock@lewisham.gov.uk

Deputy Mayor: Smith, Alan (LAB - Catford South)
cllr_alan.smith@lewisham.gov.uk

Amrani, Abdeslam (LAB - Catford South)
cllr_abdeslam.amrani@lewisham.gov.uk

Barnham, Chris (LAB - Crofton Park)
cllr_chris.barnham@lewisham.gov.uk

Bell, Paul (LAB - Telegraph Hill)
cllr_paul.bell@lewisham.gov.uk

Bernards, Peter (LAB - Forest Hill)
cllr_peter.bernards@lewisham.gov.uk

Best, Chris (LAB - Sydenham)
cllr_chris.best@lewisham.gov.uk

Bonavia, Kevin (LAB - Blackheath)
cllr_kevin.bonavia@lewisham.gov.uk

Bourne, Andre (LAB - Downham)
cllr_andre.bourne@lewisham.gov.uk

Britton, David (LAB - Downham)
david.britton17@hotmail.com

Brown, Bill (LAB - Ladywell)
cllr_bill.brown@lewisham.gov.uk

Clarke, Suzannah (LAB - Grove Park)
cllr_suzannah.clarke@lewisham.gov.uk

Coughlin, John (GRN - Brockley)
cllr_john.coughlin@lewisham.gov.uk

Curran, Liam (LAB - Sydenham)
cllr_liam.curran@lewisham.gov.uk

Daby, Janet (LAB - Whitefoot)
cllr_janet.daby@lewisham.gov.uk

Dacres, Brenda (LAB - New Cross)
cllr_brenda.dacres@lewisham.gov.uk

De Ryk, Amanda (LD - Blackheath)
cllr_amanda.deryk@lewisham.gov.uk

Dromey, Joe (LAB - New Cross)
cllr_joe.dromey@lewisham.gov.uk

Egan, Damien (LAB - Lewisham Central)
damien.egan@lewisham.gov.uk

Elliott, Colin (LAB - Grove Park)
cllr_colin.elliott@lewisham.gov.uk

Hall, Alan (LAB - Bellingham)
cllr_alan.hall@lewisham.gov.uk

Handley, Carl (LAB - Ladywell)
cllr_carlrichard.handley@lewisham.gov.uk

Hilton, Maja (LAB - Forest Hill)
cllr_maja.hilton@lewisham.gov.uk

Hooks, Simon (LAB - Lee Green)
cllr_simon.hooks@lewisham.gov.uk

Hordijenko, Sue (LAB - Bellingham)

Ingleby, Mark (LAB - Whitefoot)
cllr_mark.ingleby@lewisham.gov.uk

Jeffrey, Stella (LAB - Lewisham Central)
cllr_stella.jeffrey@lewisham.gov.uk

Johnston-Franklin, Liz (LAB - Ladywell)
cllr_liz.johnston-franklin@lewisham.gov.uk

Kennedy, Alicia (LAB - Brockley)
cllr_alicia.kennedy@lewisham.gov.uk

Kennedy, Roy (LAB - Crofton Park)
cllr_roy.kennedy@lewisham.gov.uk

Klier, Helen (LAB - Rushey Green)
cllr_helen.klier@lewisham.gov.uk

Mallory, Jim (LAB - Lee Green)
cllr_jim.mallory@lewisham.gov.uk

Maslin, Paul (LAB - New Cross)
cllr_paul.maslin@lewisham.gov.uk

Michael, David (LAB - Evelyn)
cllr_david.michael@lewisham.gov.uk

Millbank, Joan (LAB - Telegraph Hill)
cllr_joan.millbank@lewisham.gov.uk

Milne, Jamie (LAB - Evelyn)
cllr_jamie.milne@lewisham.gov.uk

Moore, Hilary (LAB - Grove Park)
cllr_hilary.moore@lewisham.gov.uk

Morrison, Pauline (LAB - Crofton Park)
cllr_pauline.morrison@lewisham.gov.uk

Muldoon, John (LAB - Rushey Green)
cllr_john.muldoon@lewisham.gov.uk

Ogunbadewa, Olurotimi (LAB - Downham)
cllr_olurotimi.ogunbadewa@lewisham.gov.uk

Onikosi, Rachel (LAB - Sydenham)
cllr_rachel.onikosi@lewisham.gov.uk

Onuegbu, Crada (LAB - Evelyn)
cllr_crada.onuegbu@lewisham.gov.uk

Paschoud, Jacq (LAB - Bellingham)
cllr_jacq.paschoud@lewisham.gov.uk

Paschoud, John (LAB - Perry Vale)
cllr_john.paschoud@lewisham.gov.uk

Raven, Pat (LAB - Lee Green)
cllr_pat.raven@lewisham.gov.uk

Reid, Joan (LAB - Lewisham Central)
cllr_joan.reid@lewisham.gov.uk

Siddorn, Gareth (LAB - Blackheath)
cllr_gareth.siddorn@lewisham.gov.uk

Slater, Jonathan (LAB - Whitefoot)
cllr_jonathan.slater@lewisham.gov.uk

Sorba, Luke (LAB - Telegraph Hill)
cllr_luke.sorba@lewisham.gov.uk

Stamirowski, Eva (LAB - Catford South)
cllr_eva.stamirowski@lewisham.gov.uk

Upex, Paul (LAB - Forest Hill)
cllr_paul.upex@lewisham.gov.uk

Walsh, James-J (LAB - Rushey Green)
cllr_james-j.walsh@lewisham.gov.uk

Wise, Susan (LAB - Perry Vale)
cllr_susan.wise@lewisham.gov.uk

POLITICAL COMPOSITION
LAB: 53, LD: 1, GRN: 1

COMMITTEE CHAIRS

Audit: Ms Helen Klier

Children & Young People: Ms Hilary Moore

Health & Wellbeing: Sir Steve Bullock

Licensing: Ms Eva Stamirowski

Pensions: Mr Mark Ingleby

Planning: Ms Amanda De Ryk

Lichfield   D

Lichfield District Council, District Council House, Frog Lane, Lichfield WS13 6ZB
☎ 01543 308000 🖷 01543 309899 ⊕ enquiries@lichfielddc.gov.uk
🖳 www.lichfielddc.gov.uk

FACTS AND FIGURES
Parliamentary Constituencies: Lichfield, Tamworth
EU Constituencies: West Midlands
Election Frequency: Elections are of whole council

PRINCIPAL OFFICERS

Chief Executive: Ms Diane Tilley, Chief Executive, District Council House, Frog Lane, Lichfield WS13 6ZB ☎ 01543 308001
⊕ diane.tilley@lichfielddc.gov.uk

Senior Management: Mr Richard King, Director - Place & Community, District Council House, Frog Lane, Lichfield WS13 6YU
☎ 01543 308060 ⊕ richard.king@lichfielddc.gov.uk

Senior Management: Mr Neil Turner, Director - Transformation & Resources, District Council House, Frog Lane, Lichfield WS13 6ZD
☎ 01543 308761

Architect, Building / Property Services: Mr Richard King, Director - Place & Community, District Council House, Frog Lane, Lichfield WS13 6YU ☎ 01543 308060 ⊕ richard.king@lichfielddc.gov.uk

Architect, Building / Property Services: Mr Bryn Owen, Surveyor, District Council House, Frog Lane, Lichfield WS13 6ZB
☎ 01543 308061 ⊕ bryn.owen@lichfielddc.gov.uk

Building Control: Mr Ged Cooper, Partnership Manager, District Council House, Frog Lane, Lichfield WS13 6YZ ☎ 01543 308155
⊕ ged.cooper@lichfielddc.gov.uk

Building Control: Mr Richard King, Director - Place & Community, District Council House, Frog Lane, Lichfield WS13 6YU
☎ 01543 308060 ⊕ richard.king@lichfielddc.gov.uk

PR / Communications: Mr Richard King, Director - Place & Community, District Council House, Frog Lane, Lichfield WS13 6YU
☎ 01543 308060 ⊕ richard.king@lichfielddc.gov.uk

PR / Communications: Ms Elizabeth Thatcher, Communications & Tourism Manager, District Council House, Frog Lane, Lichfield WS13 6ZD ☎ 01543 308781 ⊕ elizabeth.thatcher@lichfielddc.gov.uk

Community Planning: Mr Richard King, Director - Place & Community, District Council House, Frog Lane, Lichfield WS13 6YU
☎ 01543 308060 ⊕ richard.king@lichfielddc.gov.uk

Community Planning: Mr Richard King, Director - Place & Community, District Council House, Frog Lane, Lichfield WS13 6YU
☎ 01543 308060 ⊕ richard.king@lichfielddc.gov.uk

Community Safety: Ms Jenni Coleman, Community Safety Officer, Donegal House, Bore Street, Lichfield WS13 6NE
☎ 01543 308005 ⊕ jenni.coleman@lichfielddc.gov.uk

Community Safety: Mr Richard King, Director - Place & Community, District Council House, Frog Lane, Lichfield WS13 6YU
☎ 01543 308060 ⊕ richard.king@lichfielddc.gov.uk

Computer Management: Mr Kevin Sleeman, Information Systems & Strategy Manager, District Council House, Frog Lane, Lichfield WS13 6ZF ☎ 01543 308120 ⊕ kevin.sleeman@lichfield.gov.uk

Contracts: Ms Bal Nahal, Head of Legal, Property & Democratic Services (Monitoring Officer), District Council House, Frog Lane, Lichfield WS13 6ZB ☎ 01543 308062 ⊕ bal.nahal@lichfielddc.gov.uk

Corporate Services: Mr Richard King, Director - Place & Community, District Council House, Frog Lane, Lichfield WS13 6YU
☎ 01543 308060 ⊕ richard.king@lichfielddc.gov.uk

Customer Service: Mr Richard King, Director - Place & Community, District Council House, Frog Lane, Lichfield WS13 6YU
☎ 01543 308060 ⊕ richard.king@lichfielddc.gov.uk

Customer Service: Ms Pat Leybourne, Head of Revenues, Benefits & Customer Services, District Council House, Frog Lane, Lichfield WS13 6ZB pat.leybourne@lichfielddc.gov.uk

LICHFIELD

Customer Service: Mrs Ysanne Williams, Customer Services Manager, District Council House, Frog Lane, Lichfield WS13 6ZF ☎ 01543 308738 ⏚ ysanne.williams@lichfielddc.gov.uk

Economic Development: Mr Craig Jordan, Head of Economic Growth, District Council House, Frog Lane, Lichfield WS13 6ZB ☎ 01543 308202 ⏚ craig.jordan@lichfielddc.gov.uk

Economic Development: Mr Richard King, Director - Place & Community, District Council House, Frog Lane, Lichfield WS13 6YU ☎ 01543 308060 ⏚ richard.king@lichfielddc.gov.uk

E-Government: Mr Kevin Sleeman, Information Systems & Strategy Manager, District Council House, Frog Lane, Lichfield WS13 6ZF ☎ 01543 308120 ⏚ kevin.sleeman@lichfield.gov.uk

Electoral Registration: Mr Richard King, Director - Place & Community, District Council House, Frog Lane, Lichfield WS13 6YU ☎ 01543 308060 ⏚ richard.king@lichfielddc.gov.uk

Electoral Registration: Ms Sarah Pearce, Licensing & Electoral Services Manager, District Council House, Frog Lane, Lichfield WS13 6YU ☎ 01543 308008 ⏚ sarah.pearce@lichfielddc.gov.uk

Emergency Planning: Mr Steve Berry, Civil Contingencies Officer, District Council House, Frog Lane, Lichfield WS13 6ZB ☎ 01543 308070 ⏚ steve.berry@lichfielddc.gov.uk

Energy Management: Mr Richard King, Director - Place & Community, District Council House, Frog Lane, Lichfield WS13 6YU ☎ 01543 308060 ⏚ richard.king@lichfielddc.gov.uk

Energy Management: Mr Richard King, Director - Place & Community, District Council House, Frog Lane, Lichfield WS13 6YU ☎ 01543 308060 ⏚ richard.king@lichfielddc.gov.uk

Environmental / Technical Services: Mr Richard King, Director - Place & Community, District Council House, Frog Lane, Lichfield WS13 6YU ☎ 01543 308060 ⏚ richard.king@lichfielddc.gov.uk

Environmental Health: Mr Gareth Davies, Head of Regulatory Services, District Council House, Frog Lane, Lichfield WS13 6ZB ☎ 01543 308741 ⏚ gareth.davies@lichfielddc.gov.uk

Environmental Health: Mr Richard King, Director - Place & Community, District Council House, Frog Lane, Lichfield WS13 6YU ☎ 01543 308060 ⏚ richard.king@lichfielddc.gov.uk

Estates, Property & Valuation: Mr Richard Haigh, Facilities Management, District Council House, Frog Lane, Lichfield WS13 6ZB ☎ 01543 308061 ⏚ richard.haigh@lichfielddc.gov.uk

Estates, Property & Valuation: Mr Richard King, Director - Place & Community, District Council House, Frog Lane, Lichfield WS13 6YU ☎ 01543 308060 ⏚ richard.king@lichfielddc.gov.uk

Finance: Ms Pat Leybourne, Head of Revenues, Benefits & Customer Services, District Council House, Frog Lane, Lichfield WS13 6ZB pat.leybourne@lichfielddc.gov.uk

Fleet Management: Mr Gary Brownridge, Streetscene & Fleet Manager, Lichfield District Council, Reliant Way, Burntwood Business Park, Zone 2, Burntwood WS7 3JH ☎ 01543 687572 ⏚ gary.brownridge@lichfielddc.gov.uk

Grounds Maintenance: Mr Gary Brownridge, Streetscene & Fleet Manager, Lichfield District Council, Reliant Way, Burntwood Business Park, Zone 2, Burntwood WS7 3JH ☎ 01543 687572 ⏚ gary.brownridge@lichfielddc.gov.uk

Health and Safety: Mr Richard King, Director - Place & Community, District Council House, Frog Lane, Lichfield WS13 6YU ☎ 01543 308060 ⏚ richard.king@lichfielddc.gov.uk

Health and Safety: Mr Steve Langston, Health & Safety Manager, District Council House, Frog Lane, Lichfield WS13 6ZF ☎ 01543 308107; 01827 709224 ⏚ steven.langston@lichfielddc.gov.uk

Health and Safety: Mr Neil Turner, Director - Transformation & Resources, District Council House, Frog Lane, Lichfield WS13 6ZD ☎ 01543 308761

Home Energy Conservation: Mr Richard King, Director - Place & Community, District Council House, Frog Lane, Lichfield WS13 6YU ☎ 01543 308060 ⏚ richard.king@lichfielddc.gov.uk

Housing: Mr Richard King, Director - Place & Community, District Council House, Frog Lane, Lichfield WS13 6YU ☎ 01543 308060 ⏚ richard.king@lichfielddc.gov.uk

Legal: Mr Richard King, Director - Place & Community, District Council House, Frog Lane, Lichfield WS13 6YU ☎ 01543 308060 ⏚ richard.king@lichfielddc.gov.uk

Legal: Ms Bal Nahal, Head of Legal, Property & Democratic Services (Monitoring Officer), District Council House, Frog Lane, Lichfield WS13 6ZB ☎ 01543 308062 ⏚ bal.nahal@lichfielddc.gov.uk

Leisure and Cultural Services: Mr Neil Turner, Director - Transformation & Resources, District Council House, Frog Lane, Lichfield WS13 6ZD ☎ 01543 308761

Licensing: Mr Richard King, Director - Place & Community, District Council House, Frog Lane, Lichfield WS13 6YU ☎ 01543 308060 ⏚ richard.king@lichfielddc.gov.uk

Licensing: Ms Sarah Pearce, Licensing & Electoral Services Manager, District Council House, Frog Lane, Lichfield WS13 6YU ☎ 01543 308008 ⏚ sarah.pearce@lichfieddc.gov.uk

Lottery Funding, Charity and Voluntary: Mr Clive Gibbons, Housing Services Manager, District Council House, Frog Lane, Lichfield WS13 6ZB ☎ 01543 308702 ⏚ clive.gibbons@lichfielddc.gov.uk

Member Services: Mr Richard King, Director - Place & Community, District Council House, Frog Lane, Lichfield WS13 6YU ☎ 01543 308060 ⏚ richard.king@lichfielddc.gov.uk

Member Services: Ms Bal Nahal, Head of Legal, Property & Democratic Services (Monitoring Officer), District Council House, Frog Lane, Lichfield WS13 6ZB ☎ 01543 308062 ⏚ bal.nahal@lichfielddc.gov.uk

Parking: Mr Craig Jordan, Head of Economic Growth, District Council House, Frog Lane, Lichfield WS13 6ZB ☎ 01543 308202 ⏚ craig.jordan@lichfielddc.gov.uk

Personnel / HR: Mrs Cathy Pepper, Personnel Manager, District Council House, Frog Lane, Lichfield WS13 6ZF ☎ 01543 308112 ⏚ cathy.pepper@lichfielddc.gov.uk

Personnel / HR: Ms Diane Tilley, Chief Executive, District Council House, Frog Lane, Lichfield WS13 6ZB ☎ 01543 308001 ⏚ diane.tilley@lichfielddc.gov.uk

Planning: Mr Richard King, Director - Place & Community, District Council House, Frog Lane, Lichfield WS13 6YU ☎ 01543 308060 ⏚ richard.king@lichfielddc.gov.uk

Procurement: Ms Pat Leybourne, Head of Revenues, Benefits & Customer Services, District Council House, Frog Lane, Lichfield WS13 6ZB pat.leybourne@lichfielddc.gov.uk

Procurement: Mr Kevin Sleeman, Information Systems & Strategy Manager, District Council House, Frog Lane, Lichfield WS13 6ZF ☎ 01543 308120 ⏚ kevin.sleeman@lichfield.gov.uk

Recycling & Waste Minimisation: Mr Nigel Harris, Waste & Environmental Protection Manager, Lichfield District Council, Reliant Way, Burntwood Business Park, Zone 2, Burntwood WS7 3JH ☎ 01543 687549 ⏚ nigel.harris@lichfielddc.gov.uk

Regeneration: Mr Richard King, Director - Place & Community, District Council House, Frog Lane, Lichfield WS13 6YU ☎ 01543 308060 ⏚ richard.king@lichfielddc.gov.uk

Street Scene: Mr Gary Brownridge, Streetscene & Fleet Manager, Lichfield District Council, Reliant Way, Burntwood Business Park, Zone 2, Burntwood WS7 3JH ☎ 01543 687572 ⏚ gary.brownridge@lichfielddc.gov.uk

Sustainable Communities: Mr Richard King, Director - Place & Community, District Council House, Frog Lane, Lichfield WS13 6YU ☎ 01543 308060 ⏚ richard.king@lichfielddc.gov.uk

Sustainable Development: Mr Richard King, Director - Place & Community, District Council House, Frog Lane, Lichfield WS13 6YU ☎ 01543 308060 ⏚ richard.king@lichfielddc.gov.uk

Tourism: Ms Elizabeth Thatcher, Communications & Tourism Manager, District Council House, Frog Lane, Lichfield WS13 6ZD ☎ 01543 308781 ⏚ elizabeth.thatcher@lichfielddc.gov.uk

Waste Collection and Disposal: Mr Nigel Harris, Waste & Environmental Protection Manager, Lichfield District Council, Reliant Way, Burntwood Business Park, Zone 2, Burntwood WS7 3JH ☎ 01543 687549 ⏚ nigel.harris@lichfielddc.gov.uk

Waste Management: Mr Nigel Harris, Waste & Environmental Protection Manager, Lichfield District Council, Reliant Way, Burntwood Business Park, Zone 2, Burntwood WS7 3JH ☎ 01543 687549 ⏚ nigel.harris@lichfielddc.gov.uk

Children's Play Areas: Mr Neil Turner, Director - Transformation & Resources, District Council House, Frog Lane, Lichfield WS13 6ZD ☎ 01543 308761

COUNCILLORS

Leader of the Council: Wilcox, Michael (CON - Alrewas & Fradley) michael.wilcox@lichfielddc.gov.uk

Deputy Leader of the Council: Pritchard, Ian (CON - Longdon) ian.pritchard@lichfielddc.gov.uk

Allsopp, Jeanette (CON - Curborough) jeanette.allsopp@lichfielddc.gov.uk

Awty, Bob (CON - Leomansley) bob.awty@lichfielddc.gov.uk

Bacon, Norma (CON - Curborough) norma.bacon@lichfielddc.gov.uk

Baker, Deb (CON - St. John's) deb.baker@lichfielddc.gov.uk

Bamborough, Richard (CON - Boney Hay & Central) richard.bamborough@licfielddc.gov.uk

Banevicius, Sharon (LAB - Chasetown) sharon.banevicius@lichfielddc.gov.uk

Barnett, Shirley Ann (CON - Colton & The Ridwares) shirley.barnett@lichfielddc.gov.uk

Boyle, Gwyneth (CON - Chadsmead) gwyneth.boyle@lichfielddc.gov.uk

Constable, Douglas (CON - Highfield) douglas.constable@lichfielddc.gov.uk

Constable, Brenda (CON - Summerfield & All Saints) brenda.constable@lichfielddc.gov.uk

Cox, Richard (CON - Armitage with Handsacre) richard.cox@lichfielddc.gov.uk

Drinkwater, Eric (LAB - Chase Terrace) eric.drinkwater@lichfielddc.gov.uk

Eadie, Iain (CON - Leomansley) iain.eadie@lichfielddc.gov.uk

Eagland, Janet (CON - Boley Park) janet.eagland@lichfielddc.gov.uk

Evans, Diane (LAB - Boney Hay & Central) diane.evans@lichfielddc.gov.uk

Fisher, Helen (CON - Highfield) helen.fisher@lichfielddc.gov.uk

Fisher, Beth (CON - Chasetown) beth.fisher@lichfielddc.gov.uk

Greatorex, Colin (CON - Stowe) colin.greatorex@lichfielddc.gov.uk

Hassall, Elizabeth (CON - Little Aston & Stonnall) elizabeth.hassall@lichfielddc.gov.uk

Humphreys, Ken (CON - Hammerwich & Wall) kenneth.humphreys@lichfielddc.gov.uk

Inez Pullen, Natasha (CON - Boney Hay & Central) natasha.pullen@lichfielddc.gov.uk

Leytham, David (CON - Whittington & Streethay) david.leytham@lichfielddc.gov.uk

Marshall, Thomas (CON - Armitage with Handsacre) thomas.marshall@lichfielddc.gov.uk

LICHFIELD

Matthews, Tim (CON - St. John's)
tim.matthews@lichfielddc.gov.uk

Mills, John (UKIP - Fazeley)
john.mills@lichfielddc.gov.uk

Mosson, Richard (CON - Summerfield & All Saints)
richard.mosson@lichfielddc.gov.uk

O'Hagan, Jon (CON - Stowe)
jon.ohagan@lichfielddc.gov.uk

Powell, Joseph (CON - Little Aston & Stonnall)
joseph.powell@lichfielddc.gov.uk

Pullen, Doug (CON - Hammerwich & Wall)
doug.pullen@lichfielddc.gov.uk

Ray, Paul (LD - Chadsmead)
paul.ray@lichfielddc.gov.uk

Rayner, Ben (CON - Alrewas & Fradley)
ben.rayner@lichfielddc.gov.uk

Salter, David (CON - Shenstone)
david.salter@lichfielddc.gov.uk

Shepherd, Olivia (CON - Fazeley)
olivia.shepherd@lichfielddc.gov.uk

Smedley, David (CON - Stowe)
david.smedley@lichfielddc.gov.uk

Smith, Andrew (CON - Leomansley)
andrew.smith@lichfielddc.gov.uk

Spruce, Christopher (CON - St. John's)
christopher.spruce@lichfielddc.gov.uk

Stanhope, Margaret (CON - Alrewas & Fradley)
margaret.stanhope@lichfielddc.gov.uk

Strachan, Robert (CON - Whittington & Streethay)
rob.strachan@lichfield.gov.uk

Tittley, Martyn (CON - Armitage with Handsacre)
martyn.tittley@lichfielddc.gov.uk

Tranter, Heather (CON - Summerfield & All Saints)
heather.tranter@lichfielddc.gov.uk

Warfield, Mark (CON - Boley Park)
mark.warfield@lichfielddc.gov.uk

White, Alan (CON - Whittington & Streethay)
alan.white@lichfielddc.gov.uk

Woodward, Susan (LAB - Chase Terrace)
susan.woodward@lichfielddc.gov.uk

Yeates, Brian (CON - Bourne Vale)
brian.yeates@lichfielddc.gov.uk

Yeates, Ashley (CON - Mease Valley)
ashley.yeates@lichfielddc.gov.uk

POLITICAL COMPOSITION
CON: 41, LAB: 4, LD: 1, UKIP: 1

Lincoln City   D

Lincoln City Council, City Hall, Beaumont Fee, Lincoln
LN1 1DD
☎ 01522 881188
✆ customer.services@lincoln.gov.uk
🖳 www.lincoln.gov.uk

FACTS AND FIGURES
Parliamentary Constituencies: Lincoln
EU Constituencies: East Midlands
Election Frequency: Elections are by thirds

PRINCIPAL OFFICERS

Chief Executive: Mrs Angela Andrews, Chief Executive, City Hall,
Beaumont Fee, Lincoln LN1 1DD ☎ 01522 873292
✆ angela.andrews@lincoln.gov.uk

Senior Management: Mrs Angela Andrews, Chief Executive, City
Hall, Beaumont Fee, Lincoln LN1 1DD ☎ 01522 873292
✆ angela.andrews@lincoln.gov.uk

Senior Management: Mr Bob Ledger, Director - Housing &
Regeneration, City Hall, Beaumont Fee, Lincoln LN1 1DD
☎ 01522 873200 ✆ bob.ledger@lincoln.gov.uk

Senior Management: Mr Simon Walters, Director - Communities
& Environment, City Hall, Beaumont Fee, Lincoln LN1 1DD
☎ 01522 873866 ✆ simon.walters@lincoln.gov.uk

Building Control: Mr Marcus Tasker, Principal Building Control
Officer, City Hall, Beaumont Fee, Lincoln LN1 1DD ☎ 01522 873429
✆ marcus.tasker@lincoln.gov.uk

PR / Communications: Mr Steven Welsby, Communications
Manager, City Hall, Beaumont Fee, Lincoln LN1 1DD
☎ 01522 873318 ✆ steven.welsby@lincoln.gov.uk

Computer Management: Mr Matt Smith, Business Development
& IT Manager, City Hall, Beaumont Fee, Lincoln LN1 1DD
☎ 01522 873308 ✆ matt.smith@lincoln.gov.uk

Corporate Services: Mr Simon Walters, Director - Communities &
Environment, City Hall, Beaumont Fee, Lincoln LN1 1DD
☎ 01522 873866 ✆ simon.walters@lincoln.gov.uk

Corporate Services: Mrs Carolyn Wheater, City Solicitor, City Hall,
Beaumont Fee, Lincoln LN1 1DD ☎ 01522 873323
✆ carolyn.wheater@lincoln.gov.uk

Customer Service: Ms Joanne Crookes, Customer Services
Manager, City Hall, Beaumont Fee, Lincoln LN1 1DD
☎ 01522 873407 ✆ joanne.crookes@lincoln.gov.uk

Economic Development: Ms Kate Ellis, Assistant Director -
Growth & Regeneration, City Hall, Beaumont Fee, Lincoln LN1 1DD
☎ 01522 873824 ✆ kate.ellis@lincoln.gov.uk

E-Government: Mr Matt Smith, Business Development & IT
Manager, City Hall, Beaumont Fee, Lincoln LN1 1DD
☎ 01522 873308 ✆ matt.smith@lincoln.gov.uk

Electoral Registration: Mr Steve Swain, Principal Democratic
Services Officer, City Hall, Beaumont Fee, Lincoln LN1 1DD
☎ 01522 873439 ✆ steve.swain@lincoln.gov.uk

Emergency Planning: Mr Simon Colburn, Assistant Director -
Health & Environmental Services, City Hall, Beaumont Fee, Lincoln
LN1 1DD ☎ 01522 873241 ✆ simon.colburn@lincoln.gov.uk

Energy Management: Mr David Bowskill, Housing Energy Officer, City Hall, Beaumont Fee, Lincoln LN1 1DD ☎ 01522 873377 ⏱ david.bowskill@lincoln.gov.uk

Environmental Health: Ms Sara Boothright, Food, Health & Safety Manager, City Hall, Beaumont Fee, Lincoln LN1 1DD ☎ 01522 873314 ⏱ sara.boothright@lincoln.gov.uk

Estates, Property & Valuation: Mr Mark Wheater, Strategic Property Services Manager, City Hall, Beaumont Fee, Lincoln LN1 1DD ☎ 01522 873513 ⏱ mark.wheater@lincoln.gov.uk

European Liaison: Ms Michelle Smith, Senior Programme Managements Officer, City Hall, Beaumont Fee, Lincoln LN1 1DD ☎ 01522 873329 ⏱ michelle.smith@lincoln.gov.uk

Events Manager: Ms Claire McDowall, Principal Events & Culture Officer, City Hall, Beaumont Fee, Lincoln LN1 1DD ☎ 01522 873540 ⏱ claire.mcdowall@lincoln.gov.uk

Facilities: Mr Mark Wheater, Strategic Property Services Manager, City Hall, Beaumont Fee, Lincoln LN1 1DD ☎ 01522 873513 ⏱ mark.wheater@lincoln.gov.uk

Finance: Ms Jaclyn Gibson, Chief Finance Officer, City Hall, Beaumont Fee, Lincoln LN1 1DD ☎ 01522 873258 ⏱ jaclyn.gibson@lincoln.gov.uk

Fleet Management: Mr David Mason, Business Service Manager, City Hall, Beaumont Fee, Lincoln LN1 1DD ☎ 01522 873488 ⏱ david.mason@lincoln.gov.uk

Grounds Maintenance: Mr Dave Charysz, Open Spaces Officer, City Hall, Beaumont Fee, Lincoln LN1 1DE ☎ 01522 873414 ⏱ dave.charysz@lincoln.gov.uk

Health and Safety: Ms Sara Boothright, Food, Health & Safety Manager, City Hall, Beaumont Fee, Lincoln LN1 1DD ☎ 01522 873314 ⏱ sara.boothright@lincoln.gov.uk

Home Energy Conservation: Mr David Bowskill, Housing Energy Officer, City Hall, Beaumont Fee, Lincoln LN1 1DD ☎ 01522 873377 ⏱ david.bowskill@lincoln.gov.uk

Housing: Ms Karen Talbot, Assistant Director - Housing, City Hall, Beaumont Fee, Lincoln LN1 1DD ☎ 01522 873734 ⏱ karen.talbot@lincoln.gov.uk

Housing Maintenance: Mr Matthew Hillman, Maintenance Manager, City Hall, Beaumont Fee, Lincoln LN1 1DD ☎ 01522 873639 ⏱ matthew.hillman@lincoln.gov.uk

Legal: Ms Carolyn Wheater, City Solicitor, City Hall, Beaumont Fee, Lincoln LN1 1DD ☎ 01522 873323 ⏱ carolyn.wheater@lincoln.gov.uk

Leisure and Cultural Services: Mr Steve Bird, Assistant Director - Communities & Street Scene, City Hall, Beaumont Fee, Lincoln LN1 1DH ☎ 01522 873421 ⏱ steve.bird@lincoln.gov.uk

Leisure and Cultural Services: Mr Simon Colburn, Assistant Director - Health & Environmental Services, City Hall, Beaumont Fee, Lincoln LN1 1DD ☎ 01522 873241 ⏱ simon.colburn@lincoln.gov.uk

Licensing: Mr Kevin Barron, Licensing Manager, City Hall, Beaumont Fee, Lincoln LN1 1DD ☎ 01522 873564 ⏱ kevin.barron@lincoln.gov.uk

Lifelong Learning: Ms Claire Burroughs, HR & Work Based Learning Manager, City Hall, Beaumont Fee, Lincoln LN1 1DD ☎ 01522 873807 ⏱ claire.burroughs@lincoln.gov.uk

Lottery Funding, Charity and Voluntary: Ms Michelle Smith, Senior Programme Managements Officer, City Hall, Beaumont Fee, Lincoln LN1 1DD ☎ 01522 873329 ⏱ michelle.smith@lincoln.gov.uk

Member Services: Mr Steve Swain, Principal Democratic Services Officer, City Hall, Beaumont Fee, Lincoln LN1 1DD ☎ 01522 873439 ⏱ steve.swain@lincoln.gov.uk

Parking: Mr Steve Lockwood, Leisure, Sport & City Services Manager, City Hall, Beaumont Fee, Lincoln LN1 1DD ☎ 01522 873520 ⏱ steve.lockwood@lincoln.gov.uk

Partnerships: Mr Simon Walters, Director - Communities & Environment, City Hall, Beaumont Fee, Lincoln LN1 1DD ☎ 01522 873866 ⏱ simon.walters@lincoln.gov.uk

Personnel / HR: Ms Claire Burroughs, HR & Work Based Learning Manager, City Hall, Beaumont Fee, Lincoln LN1 1DD ☎ 01522 873807 ⏱ claire.burroughs@lincoln.gov.uk

Planning: Ms Kate Ellis, Assistant Director - Growth & Regeneration, City Hall, Beaumont Fee, Lincoln LN1 1DD ☎ 01522 873824 ⏱ kate.ellis@lincoln.gov.uk

Procurement: Mrs Heather Carmichael, Client Procurement Officer, City Hall, Beaumont Fee, Lincoln LN1 1DD ☎ 01522 873309 ⏱ heather.carmichael@lincoln.gov.uk

Recycling & Waste Minimisation: Mr Steve Bird, Assistant Director - Communities & Street Scene, City Hall, Beaumont Fee, Lincoln LN1 1DH ☎ 01522 873421 ⏱ steve.bird@lincoln.gov.uk

Staff Training: Ms Claire Burroughs, HR & Work Based Learning Manager, City Hall, Beaumont Fee, Lincoln LN1 1DD ☎ 01522 873807 ⏱ claire.burroughs@lincoln.gov.uk

Street Scene: Ms Caroline Bird, Community Services Manager, City Hall, Beaumont Fee, Lincoln LN1 1DD ☎ 01522 873405 ⏱ caroline.bird@lincoln.gov.uk

Waste Collection and Disposal: Mr Steve Bird, Assistant Director - Communities & Street Scene, City Hall, Beaumont Fee, Lincoln LN1 1DH ☎ 01522 873421 ⏱ steve.bird@lincoln.gov.uk

Waste Management: Ms Caroline Bird, Community Services Manager, City Hall, Beaumont Fee, Lincoln LN1 1DD ☎ 01522 873405 ⏱ caroline.bird@lincoln.gov.uk

LINCOLN CITY

Children's Play Areas: Mr Dave Charysz, Open Spaces Officer, City Hall, Beaumont Fee, Lincoln LN1 1DE ☎ 01522 873414
📧 dave.charysz@lincoln.gov.uk

COUNCILLORS

Mayor: Bodger, Yvonne (CON - Minster)
yvonne.bodger@lincoln.gov.uk

Leader of the Council: Metcalfe, Richard (LAB - Glebe)
richard.metcalfe@lincoln.gov.uk

Deputy Leader of the Council: Nannestad, Donald (LAB - Castle)
donald.nannestad@lincoln.gov.uk

Group Leader: Hills, Ronald (CON - Hartsolme)
ronald.hills@lincoln.gov.uk

Bean, Biff (LAB - Hartsolme)
biff.bean@lincoln.gov.uk

Brothwell, Kathleen (LAB - Abbey)
kathleen.brothwell@lincoln.gov.uk

Burke, Chris (LAB - Park)
chris.burke@lincoln.gov.uk

Bushell, Bob (LAB - Moorland)
bob.bushell@lincoln.gov.uk

Charlesworth, Brent (LAB - Park)
brent.charlesworth@lincoln.gov.uk

Clayton-Hewson, Gill (LAB - Boultham)
gill.clayton-hewson@lincoln.gov.uk

Dyer, Thomas (CON - Witham)
thomas.dyer@lincoln.gov.uk

Ellis, Geoff (LAB - Moorland)
geoff.ellis@lincoln.gov.uk

Gowan, Paul (LAB - Birchwood)
paul.gowan@lincoln.gov.uk

Hanrahan, Jim (LAB - Castle)
jim.hanrahan@lincoln.gov.uk

Hewson, Gary (LAB - Boultham)
gary.hewson@lincoln.gov.uk

Kerry, Andrew (CON - Hartsolme)
andrew.kerry@lincoln.gov.uk

Kirk, Rosanne (LAB - Birchwood)
rosanne.kirk@lincoln.gov.uk

Kirk, Jackie (LAB - Glebe)
jackie.kirk@lincoln.gov.uk

Lee, Karen (LAB - Carholme)
karen.lee@lincoln.gov.uk

Loffhagen, Jane (LAB - Witham)
jane.loffhagen@lincoln.gov.uk

Mair, Helena (LAB - Park)
helena.mair@lincoln.gov.uk

Maxwell, Liz (LAB - Minster)
liz.maxwell@lincoln.gov.uk

McNulty, Adrianna (LAB - Moorland)
adrianna.mcnulty@lincoln.gov.uk

Murray, Neil (LAB - Carholme)
neil.murray@lincoln.gov.uk

Smith, Fay (LAB - Abbey)
fay.smith@lincoln.gov.uk

Speakman, Tony (LAB - Carholme)
tony.speakman@lincoln.gov.uk

Strengiel, Edmund (CON - Birchwood)
edmund.strengiel@lincoln.gov.uk

Toofany, Ralph (LAB - Boultham)
ralph.toofany@lincoln.gov.uk

Tweddle, Naomi (LAB - Minster)
naomi.tweddle@lincoln.gov.uk

Vaughan, Patrick (LAB - Glebe)
pat.vaughan@lincoln.gov.uk

Weaver, Keith (CON - Witham)
keith.weaver@lincoln.gov.uk

West, Peter (LAB - Abbey)
peter.west@lincoln.gov.uk

Woolley, Loraine (LAB - Castle)
loraine.woolley@lincoln.gov.uk

POLITICAL COMPOSITION
LAB: 27, CON: 6

COMMITTEE CHAIRS

Audit: Mr Tony Speakman

Licensing: Ms Kathleen Brothwell

Planning: Mr Jim Hanrahan

Lincolnshire   C

Lincolnshire County Council, County Offices, Newland, Lincoln LN1 1YL
☎ 01522 552222 📠 01522 516137
📧 customer_services@lincolnshire.gov.uk 🖥 www.lincolnshire.gov.uk

FACTS AND FIGURES
EU Constituencies: East Midlands
Election Frequency: Elections are of whole council

PRINCIPAL OFFICERS

Chief Executive: Mr Tony McArdle, Chief Executive, County Offices, Newland, Lincoln LN1 1YL ☎ 01522 552001
📧 tony.mcardle@lincolnshire.gov.uk

Senior Management: Ms Debbie Barnes, Executive Director - Children's Services, County Offices, Newland, Lincoln LN1 1YL
☎ 01552 553201 📧 debbie.barnes@lincolnshire.gov.uk

Senior Management: Mr Glen Garrod, Executive Director - Adult Social Services, County Offices, Newland, Lincoln LN1 1YL
☎ 01522 550808 📧 glen.garrod@lincolnshire.gov.uk

Senior Management: Ms Judith Hetherington-Smith, Chief Information & Commissioning Officer, County Offices, Newland, Lincoln LN1 1YL ☎ 01522 553603
📧 judith.hetheringtonsmith@lincolnshire.gov.uk

Senior Management: Dr Tony Hill, Executive Director - Community Wellbeing & Public Health, County Offices, Newland, Lincoln LN1 1YL ☎ 01552 553960 ⌂ tony.hill@lincolnshire.gov.uk

Senior Management: Mr Pete Moore, Executive Director - Finance & Public Protection, County Offices, Newland, Lincoln LN1 1YL ☎ 01522 553602 ⌂ pete.moore@lincolnshire.gov.uk

Senior Management: Mr Richard Wills, Executive Director - Environment & Economy, County Offices, Newland, Lincoln LN1 1YL ☎ 01522 553000 ⌂ richard.wills@lincolnshire.gov.uk

Access Officer / Social Services (Disability): Mr Glen Garrod, Executive Director - Adult Social Services, County Offices, Newland, Lincoln LN1 1YL ☎ 01522 550808 ⌂ glen.garrod@lincolnshire.gov.uk

Architect, Building / Property Services: Mr Kevin Kendall, County Property Officer, County Offices, Newland, Lincoln LN1 1YL ☎ 01552 553099 ⌂ kevin.kendall@lincolnshire.gov.uk

Best Value: Mr George Spiteri, Strategic Commercial & Performance Manager, County Offices, Newland, Lincoln LN1 1YL ☎ 01522 552120 ⌂ george.spiteri@lincolnshire.gov.uk

Children / Youth Services: Mr Stuart Carlton, Assistant Director - Lead Early Help, County Offices, Newland, Lincoln LN1 1YL ☎ 01552 554051 ⌂ stuart.carlton@lincolnshire.gov.uk

Civil Registration: Ms Donna Sharp, County Services Manager, Lindum Road, Lincoln LN2 1NN ☎ 01522 554052 ⌂ donna.sharp@lincolnshire.gov.uk

PR / Communications: Ms Karen Spencer, Strategic Communications & Digital Engagement Manager, County Offices, Newland, Lincoln LN1 1YL ☎ 01522 552303 ⌂ karen.spencer@lincolnshire.gov.uk

Community Safety: Mr Mark Housley, County Officer - Public Protection, Room 35, Myle Cross Centre, Lincoln LN2 4EL ☎ 01522 554593 ⌂ mark.housley@lincolnshire.gov.uk

Computer Management: Mr Simon Oliver, Chief Technology Officer, Orchard House, Orchard Street, Lincoln LN2 4EL ☎ 01522 555596 ⌂ simon.oliver@lincolnshire.gov.uk

Consumer Protection and Trading Standards: Mrs Sara Barry, Safer Communities Manager, Myle Cross Centre, Lincoln LN2 4EL ☎ 01522 552499 ⌂ sara.barry@lincolnshire.gov.uk

Contracts: Ms Sophie Reeve, Chief Commercial Officer, County Offices, Newland, Lincoln LN1 1YL ☎ 01522 552578 ⌂ sophie.reeve@lincolnshire.gov.uk

Corporate Services: Mr Pete Moore, Executive Director - Finance & Public Protection, County Offices, Newland, Lincoln LN1 1YL ☎ 01522 553602 ⌂ pete.moore@lincolnshire.gov.uk

Customer Service: Ms Nicole Hilton, Commissioning Manager - Customer Services, Orchard House, Orchard Street, Lincoln LN1 1BA ☎ 01522 553786 ⌂ nicole.hilton@lincolnshire.gov.uk

Economic Development: Mr Justin Brown, Enterprise Commissioner, Witham Park House, Waterside South, Lincoln LN5 7JN ☎ 01522 550630 ⌂ justin.brown@lincolnshire.gov.uk

Education: Ms Debbie Barnes, Executive Director - Children's Services, County Offices, Newland, Lincoln LN1 1YL ☎ 01552 553201 ⌂ debbie.barnes@lincolnshire.gov.uk

E-Government: Ms Judith Hetherington-Smith, Chief Information & Commissioning Officer, County Offices, Newland, Lincoln LN1 1YL ☎ 01522 553603 ⌂ judith.hetheringtonsmith@lincolnshire.gov.uk

Emergency Planning: Mr Ian Reed, Head - Emergency Planning, Fire & Rescue Headquarters, South Park Avenue, Lincoln LN5 8EL ☎ 01522 582263 ⌂ ian.reed@lincoln.fire-uk.org

Energy Management: Mr Kevin Kendall, County Property Officer, County Offices, Newland, Lincoln LN1 1YL ☎ 01552 553099 ⌂ kevin.kendall@lincolnshire.gov.uk

Environmental / Technical Services: Mr Richard Wills, Executive Director - Environment & Economy, County Offices, Newland, Lincoln LN1 1YL ☎ 01522 553000 ⌂ richard.wills@lincolnshire.gov.uk

Environmental Health: Mr Sean Kent, Group Manager - Environmental Services, Witham Park House, Waterside South, Lincoln LN5 7JN ☎ 01522 554833 ⌂ sean.kent@lincolnshire.gov.uk

Estates, Property & Valuation: Mr Kevin Kendall, County Property Officer, County Offices, Newland, Lincoln LN1 1YL ☎ 01552 553099 ⌂ kevin.kendall@lincolnshire.gov.uk

European Liaison: Ms Susannah Lewis, Principal Commissioning Officer - Funding, Witham Park House, Waterside South, Lincoln LN5 7JN ☎ 01522 550638 ⌂ susannah.lewis@lincolnshire.gov.uk

Events Manager: Mr Mark Stoneham, Events Manager, County Offices, Newland, Lincoln LN1 1YL ☎ 01522 552118 ⌂ mark.stoneham@lincolnshire.gov.uk

Finance: Mr David Forbes, County Finance Officer, Orchard House, Orchard Street, Lincoln LN1 1YZ ☎ 01522 553642 ⌂ david.forbes@lincolnshire.gov.uk

Finance: Mr Pete Moore, Executive Director - Finance & Public Protection, County Offices, Newland, Lincoln LN1 1YL ☎ 01522 553602 ⌂ pete.moore@lincolnshire.gov.uk

Treasury: Mr Pete Moore, Executive Director - Finance & Public Protection, County Offices, Newland, Lincoln LN1 1YL ☎ 01522 553602 ⌂ pete.moore@lincolnshire.gov.uk

Pensions: Ms Jo Ray, Pensions Fund Manager, County Offices, Newland, Lincoln LN1 1YL ☎ 01522 553656 ⌂ jo.ray@lincolnshire.gov.uk

Fleet Management: Mr David J Davies, Principal Maintenance Engineer & County Fleet Manager, Unit 7, Witham Park House, Waterside South, Lincoln LN5 7JN ☎ 01522 553080 ⌂ davidj.davies@lincolnshire.gov.uk

LINCOLNSHIRE

Health and Safety: Mr Fraser Shooter, Corporate Health & Safety Team Leader, County Offices, Newland, Lincoln LN1 1YL
☎ 01522 554917 ⁀Ͽ fraser.shooter@lincolnshire.gov.uk

Highways: Mr Steve Willis, Chief Operating Officer - Development Services, Witham Park House, Waterside South, Lincoln LN5 7JN
☎ 01522 554848 ⁀Ͽ steve.willis@lincolnshire.gov.uk

Legal: Mr David Coleman, Chief Legal Officer, 45 - 49 Newland, Lincoln LN1 1XZ ☎ 01522 552542
⁀Ͽ david.coleman@lincolnshire.gov.uk

Lifelong Learning: Ms Thea Croxall, Principal Commissioning Officer - Learning, Sleaford Area Office, Office 2, Eastgate, Sleaford NG34 7EB ☎ 01522 550381 ⁀Ͽ thea.croxall@lincolnshire.gov.uk

Lighting: Mr Patrick Cant, Senior Lighting Engineer, Crown House, Grantham Street, Lincoln LN2 1BD ☎ 01522 555574
⁀Ͽ patrick.cant@lincolnshire.gov.uk

Lottery Funding, Charity and Voluntary: Ms Wendy Moore, Funding & Community Grants Officer, 15 - 17 The Avenue, Lincoln LN1 1PD ☎ 01522 552223 ⁀Ͽ wendy.moore@lincolnshire.gov.uk

Member Services: Mr Nigel West, Head - Democratic Services & Statutory Scrutiny Officer, County Offices, Newland, Lincoln LN1 1YL ☎ 01522 552840 ⁀Ͽ nigel.west@lincolnshire.gov.uk

Parking: Mr Matt Jones, Parking Services Manager, Unit 7, Witham Park House, Waterside South, Lincoln LN5 7JN ☎ 01522 552110
⁀Ͽ matt.jones@lincoln.gov.uk

Personnel / HR: Mrs Fiona Thompson, Service Manager - People, County Offices, Newland, Lincoln LN1 1YL ☎ 01522 552207
⁀Ͽ fiona.thompson@lincolnshire.gov.uk

Planning: Mr Andrew Gutherson, County Commissioner - Environment & Economy, Witham Park House, Waterside South, Lincoln LN5 7JN
☎ 01522 554827 ⁀Ͽ andy.gutherson@lincolnshire.gov.uk

Procurement: Ms Sophie Reeve, Chief Commercial Officer, County Offices, Newland, Lincoln LN1 1YL ☎ 01522 552578
⁀Ͽ sophie.reeve@lincolnshire.gov.uk

Recycling & Waste Minimisation: Mr Sean Kent, Group Manager - Environmental Services, Witham Park House, Waterside South, Lincoln LN5 7JN ☎ 01522 554833
⁀Ͽ sean.kent@lincolnshire.gov.uk

Regeneration: Mr Paul Wheatley, Group Manager - Economic Delivery, Witham Park House, Waterside South, Lincoln LN5 7JN
☎ 01522 550600 ⁀Ͽ paul.wheatley@lincolnshire.gov.uk

Road Safety: Mr Stephen Batchelor, LRSP Manager, Witham House, The Pelham Centre, Lincoln LN5 8HE ☎ 01522 805801
⁀Ͽ stephen.batchelor@lincolnshire.gov.uk

Social Services (Adult): Mr Justin Hackney, Assistant Director - Specialist Adult Services, County Offices, Newland, Lincoln LN1 1YL
☎ 01522 554259 ⁀Ͽ justin.hackney@lincolnshire.gov.uk

Social Services (Adult): Mr Pete Sidgewick, Assistant Director - Adult Care, Frailty & Long Term Conditions, Orchard House, Orchard Street, Lincoln LN1 1BA ☎ 01522 552211
⁀Ͽ pete.sidgewick@lincolnshire.gov.uk

Social Services (Children): Ms Debbie Barnes, Executive Director - Children's Services, County Offices, Newland, Lincoln LN1 1YL ☎ 01552 553201 ⁀Ͽ debbie.barnes@lincolnshire.gov.uk

Staff Training: Mrs Fiona Thompson, Service Manager - People, County Offices, Newland, Lincoln LN1 1YL ☎ 01522 552207
⁀Ͽ fiona.thompson@lincolnshire.gov.uk

Sustainable Development: Mr Douglas Robinson, Principal Sustainability Policy Officer, Witham Park House, Waterside South, Lincoln LN5 7JN ☎ 01522 554816
⁀Ͽ douglas.robinson@lincolnshire.gov.uk

Tourism: Ms Mary Powell, Tourism & Development Manager, Unit 4, Witham Park House, Waterside South, Lincoln LN5 7JN
☎ 01522 550612 ⁀Ͽ mary.powell@lincolnshire.gov.uk

Traffic Management: Mr Steve Willis, Chief Operating Officer - Development Services, Witham Park House, Waterside South, Lincoln LN5 7JN ☎ 01522 554848 ⁀Ͽ steve.willis@lincolnshire.gov.uk

Transport: Ms Anita Ruffle, Group Manager - Passenger Transport Unit, Crown House, Grantham Street, Lincoln LN2 1BD
☎ 01522 553147 ⁀Ͽ anita.ruffle@lincolnshire.gov.uk

Transport Planner: Ms Anita Ruffle, Group Manager - Passenger Transport Unit, Crown House, Grantham Street, Lincoln LN2 1BD
☎ 01522 553147 ⁀Ͽ anita.ruffle@lincolnshire.gov.uk

Waste Collection and Disposal: Mr Sean Kent, Group Manager - Environmental Services, Witham Park House, Waterside South, Lincoln LN5 7JN ☎ 01522 554833 ⁀Ͽ sean.kent@lincolnshire.gov.uk

Waste Management: Mr Sean Kent, Group Manager - Environmental Services, Witham Park House, Waterside South, Lincoln LN5 7JN ☎ 01522 554833 ⁀Ͽ sean.kent@lincolnshire.gov.uk

COUNCILLORS

Chair: Trollope-Bellew, Martin (CON - Stamford Rural)
cllrt.trollopebellew@lincolnshire.gov.uk

Vice-Chair: Hagues, Andrew (CON - Sleaford West & Leasingham)
cllra.hagues@lincolnshire.gov.uk

Leader of the Council: Hill, Martin (CON - Folkingham Rural)
cllrm.hill@lincolnshire.gov.uk

Deputy Leader of the Council: Bradwell, Patricia (CON - Billinghay & Metheringham)
cllrp.bradwell@lincolnshire.gov.uk

Adams, Bob (CON - Colsterworth Rural)
cllrb.adams@lincolnshire.gov.uk

Allan, Mark (IND - Sleaford)
cllrm.allan@lincolnshire.gov.uk

Aron, Bill (IND - Horncastle & Tetford)
cllrb.aron@lincolnshire.gov.uk

Austin, Alison (IND - Boston South)
cllra.austin@lincolnshire.gov.uk

Ayling, Victoria (UKIP - Spilsby Fen)
cllrv.ayling@lincolnshire.gov.uk

Beaver, John (IND - Gainsborough Hill)
cllrj.beaver@lincolnshire.gov.uk

Brailsford, David (CON - Stamford West)
cllrd.brailsford@lincolnshire.gov.uk

Brewis, Christopher (IND - Sutton Elloe)
cllrc.brewis@lincolnshire.gov.uk

Bridges, Anthony (CON - Louth Rural North)
cllrt.bridges@lincolnshire.gov.uk

Brockway, Jacqueline (CON - Nettleham & Saxilby)
cllrj.brockway@lincolnshire.gov.uk

Brookes, Michael (CON - Boston Rural)
cllrm.brookes@lincolnshire.gov.uk

Clarke, Kevin (LAB - Lincoln Boultham)
cllrk.clarke@lincolnshire.gov.uk

Davie, Colin (CON - Ingoldmells Rural)
cllrc.davie@lincolnshire.gov.uk

Davies, Richard (CON - Grantham North West)
cllrr.davies@lincolnshire.gov.uk

Dilks, Philip (LAB - Deeping St. James)
cllrp.dilks@lincolnshire.gov.uk

Dodds, Sarah (LAB - Louth North)
cllrs.dodds@lincolnshire.gov.uk

Ellis, Geoffrey (LAB - Lincoln Moorland)
cllrg.ellis@lincolnshire.gov.uk

Fairman, Richard (UKIP - Spalding East & Moulton)
cllrr.faiman@lincolnshire.gov.uk

Fleetwood, Ian (CON - Bardney & Cherry Willingham)
cllri.fleetwood@lincolnshire.gov.uk

Foulkes, Robert (UKIP - Stamford North)
cllrr.foulkes@lincolnshire.gov.uk

Hough, John (LAB - Louth South)
cllrj.hough@lincolnshire.gov.uk

Hoyes, Denis (CON - Woodhall Spa & Wragby)
cllrd.hoyes@lincolnshire.gov.uk

Hunter-Clarke, Dean (UKIP - Skegness North)
cllrd.hunter-clarke@lincolnshire.gov.uk

Hunter-Clarke, Robin (UKIP - Skegness South)
cllrr.hunter-clarke@lincolnshire.gov.uk

Jackson, Nev (LAB - Lincoln Park)
cllrn.jackson@lincolnshire.gov.uk

Jesson, Alan (UKIP - Spalding South)
cllra.jesson@lincolnshire.gov.uk

Jones, Marc (CON - Lincoln Bracebridge)
cllrm.jones@lincolnshire.gov.uk

Keimach, Burt (CON - Market Rasen Wolds)
cllrb.keimach@lincolnshire.gov.uk

Keywood-Wainwright, Tiggs (IND - Boston North West)
cllrt.keywood-wainwright@lincolnshire.gov.uk

Kinch, Stuart (CON - Gainsborough Rural South)
cllrs.kinch@lincolnshire.gov.uk

Kirk, Rosanne (LAB - Lincoln Birchwood)
cllrr.kirk@lincolnshire.gov.uk

Mair, Colin (UKIP - Tattershall Castle)
cllrc.mair@lincolnshire.gov.uk

Marfleet, Hugo (CON - Louth Wolds)
cllrh.marfleet@lincolnshire.gov.uk

Marriott, John (LD - Hykeham Forum)
cllrj.marriott@lincolnshire.gov.uk

McAuley, Robert (IND - Boston West)
cllrb.mcauley@lincolnshire.gov.uk

McNally, Daniel (UKIP - Louth Marsh)
cllrd.mcnally@lincolnshire.gov.uk

Morgan, Dawn (LAB - Grantham South)
cllrc.morgan@lincolnshire.gov.uk

Murray, Neil (LAB - Lincoln Glebe)
cllrn.murray@lincolnshire.gov.uk

Newton, Angela (IND - Spalding West)
cllra.newton@lincolnshire.gov.uk

O'Connor, Pat (LD - Gainsborough Trent)
cllrp.oconnor@lincolnshire.gov.uk

Overton, Marianne (IND - Branston & Navenby)
cllrm.overton@lincolnshire.gov.uk

Oxby, Ron (CON - Heighington & Washingborough)
cllrr.oxby@lincolnshire.gov.uk

Pain, Christopher (IND - Wainfleet & Burgh)
cllrc.pain@lincolnshire.gov.uk

Palmer, Stephen (IND - Alford & Sutton)
cllrs.palmer@lincolnshire.gov.uk

Parker, Robert (LAB - Lincoln West)
cllrs.parker@lincolnshire.gov.uk

Pepper, Nigel (CON - Crowland & Whaplode)
cllrn.pepper@lincolnshire.gov.uk

Phillips, Raymond (CON - Bassingham Rural)
cllrr.phillips@lincolnshire.gov.uk

Powell, Helen (IND - Bourne Castle)
cllrh.powell@lincolnshire.gov.uk

Ransome, Sue (UKIP - Boston East)
cllrs.ransome@lincolnshire.gov.uk

Ransome, Felicity (UKIP - Boston Coastal)
cllrf.ransome@lincolnshire.gov.uk

Ransome, Elizabeth (UKIP - Boston Fishtoft)
cllre.ransome@lincolnshire.gov.uk

Rawlins, Sue (CON - Welton Rural)
cllrs.rawlins@lincolnshire.gov.uk

Renshaw, Judith (LAB - Lincoln North)
cllrj.renshaw@lincolnshire.gov.uk

Renshaw, Robin (LAB - Lincoln East)
cllrr.renshaw@lincolnshire.gov.uk

Robinson, Peter (CON - Market Deeping & West Deeping)
cllrp.robinson@lincolnshire.gov.uk

Rollings, Lesley Anne (LD - Scotter Rural)

Shore, Reg (LD - Skellingthorpe & Hykeham South)
cllrr.shore@lincolnshire.gov.uk

Smith, Nicola (UKIP - Lincoln Hartsholme)
cllrj.smith@lincolnshire.gov.uk

LINCOLNSHIRE

Sneath, Elizabeth (CON - Spalding Elloe)
cllre.sneath@lincolnshire.gov.uk

Strange, Charles (CON - Ancholme Cliff)
cllrc.strange@lincolnshire.gov.uk

Talbot, Christine (CON - Bracebridge Heath & Waddington)
cllrc.talbot@lincolnshire.gov.uk

Turner, Tony (CON - North Wolds)
cllra.turner@lincolnshire.gov.uk

Tweedale, Stuart (CON - Ruskington & Cranwell)
cllrs.tweedale@lincolnshire.gov.uk

Webb, William (CON - Holbeach Rural)
cllrw.webb@lincolnshire.gov.uk

Whittington, Mark (CON - Grantham Barrowby)
cllrm.whittington@lincolnshire.gov.uk

Wood, Paul (IND - Hough)
cllrp.wood@lincolnshire.gov.uk

Woolley, Sue (CON - Bourne Abbey)
cllrs.woolley@lincolnshire.gov.uk

Wootten, Ray (CON - Grantham North)
cllrr.wootten@lincolnshire.gov.uk

Wootten, Linda (CON - Grantham East)
cllrl.wootten@lincolnshire.gov.uk

Worth, Charles (CON - Holbeach)
cllrn.worth@lincolnshire.gov.uk

Wray, Susan (CON - Donington Rural)
cllrs.wray@lincolnshire.gov.uk

Young, Barry (CON - Sleaford Rural South)
cllrb.young@lincolnshire.gov.uk

POLITICAL COMPOSITION
CON: 35, IND: 13, LAB: 12, UKIP: 12, LD: 4, Vacant: 1

COMMITTEE CHAIRS

Adults: Mr Hugo Marfleet

Audit: Mrs Sue Rawlins

Health & Wellbeing: Mrs Sue Woolley

Pensions: Mr Mark Allan

Planning: Mr Ian Fleetwood

Lisburn City & Castlereagh District   N

Lisburn City & Castlereagh District, Civic Headquarters,
Lagan Valley Island, Lisburn BT27 4RL
☎ 028 9250 9250 🖳 www.lisburncastlereagh.gov.uk

PRINCIPAL OFFICERS

Chief Executive: Dr Theresa Donaldson, Chief Executive, Civic
Headquarters, Lagan Valley Island, Lisburn BT27 4RL ☎ 028 9244
7207 ⏰ theresa.donaldson@lisburncastlereagh.gov.uk

Senior Management: Mr Adrian Donaldson, Director - Corporate
Services, Civic Headquarters, Lagan Valley Island, Lisburn
BT27 4RL ☎ 028 9244 7528 ⏰ adriand@lisburncastlereagh.gov.uk

Senior Management: Mr Paul McCormick, Lead Head -
Development, Civic Headquarters, Lagan Valley Island, Lisburn
BT27 4RL ☎ 028 9244 7350
⏰ paul.mccormick@lisburncastlereagh.gov.uk

Senior Management: Ms Heather Moore, Director -
Environmental Services, 1 Bradford Court, Upper Galwally,
Castlereagh, Belfast BT8 6RB ☎ 028 9049 4517
⏰ heather.moore@lisburncastlereagh.gov.uk

Senior Management: Mr Jim Rose, Director - Leisure &
Community Services, Civic Headquarters, Lagan Valley Island,
Lisburn BT27 4RL ☎ 028 9244 7203
⏰ jim.rose@lisburncastlereagh.gov.uk

Senior Management: Mr Ian Wilson, Lead Head - Planning &
Building Control, Civic Headquarters, Lagan Valley Island, Lisburn
BT27 4RL ☎ 028 9244 7806
⏰ ian.wilson@lisburncastlereagh.gov.uk

Building Control: Mr Colin Duff, Head of Building Control, Civic
Headquarters, Lagan Valley Island, Lisburn BT27 4RL
☎ 028 9244 7370 ⏰ colin.duff@lisburncastlereagh.gov.uk

Civil Registration: Mrs Carmel Connolly, Head of Central Support
Services, Civic Headquarters, Lagan Valley Island, Lisburn BT27 4RL
☎ 028 9244 7259 ⏰ carmel.connolly@lisburncastlereagh.gov.uk

PR / Communications: Mrs Claire Bethel, Head of Marketing &
Communications, Civic Headquarters, Lagan Valley Island, Lisburn
BT27 4RL ☎ 028 9244 9214
⏰ mcuheadofservice@lisburncastlereagh.gov.uk

PR / Communications: Ms Alison Goddard, Head of Marketing &
Communications, Civic Headquarters, Lagan Valley Island, Lisburn
BT27 4RL ☎ 028 9244 9215
⏰ mcuheadofservice@lisburncastlereagh.gov.uk

Community Planning: Mrs Catharine McWhirter, Community
Planning Manager, Civic Headquarters, Lagan Valley Island, Lisburn
BT27 4RL ☎ 028 9244 7513
⏰ catharine.mcwhirter@lisburncastlereagh.gov.uk

Computer Management: Mrs Leah Scott, Head of Finance & IT,
Civic Headquarters, Lagan Valley Island, Lisburn BT27 4RL
☎ 028 9244 7245 ⏰ leah.scott@lisburncastlereagh.gov.uk

Consumer Protection and Trading Standards: Mr Richard
Harvey, Head of Environmental Services, 1 Bradford Court, Upper
Galwally, Castlereagh, Belfast BT8 6RB ☎ 028 9049 4640
⏰ richard.harvey@lisburncastlereagh.gov.uk

Corporate Services: Mr Adrian Donaldson, Director - Corporate
Services, Island Civic Centre, The Island, Lisburn BT27 4RL
☎ 028 9244 7528 ⏰ adriand@lisburncastlereagh.gov.uk

Customer Service: Mrs Kerrie-Anne McKibbin, Performance
Development Officer, Civic Headquarters, Lagan Valley Island,
Lisburn BT27 4RL ☎ 028 9244 7559
⏰ kerrie-anne.mckibbin@lisburncastlereagh.gov.uk

Economic Development: Mr Paul McCormick, Lead Head - Development, Civic Headquarters, Lagan Valley Island, Lisburn BT27 4RL ☎ 028 9244 7350
☞ paul.mccormick@lisburncastlereagh.gov.uk

Emergency Planning: Mr Kieran Connolly, Health & Safety and Emergency Planning Officer, 1 Bradford Court, Upper Galwally, Castlereagh, Belfast BT8 6RB ☎ 028 9049 4675
☞ kieran.connolly@lisburncastlereagh.gov.uk

Environmental / Technical Services: Mr Albert Reynolds, Head of Technical & Estates Services, Civic Headquarters, Lagan Valley Island, Lisburn BT27 4RL ☎ 028 9244 7450
☞ albert.reynolds@lisburncastlereagh.gov.uk

Environmental Health: Mr Richard Harvey, Head of Environmental Services, 1 Bradford Court, Upper Galwally, Castlereagh, Belfast BT8 6RB ☎ 028 9049 4640
☞ richard.harvey@lisburncastlereagh.gov.uk

Finance: Mrs Leah Scott, Head of Finance & IT, Civic Headquarters, Lagan Valley Island, Lisburn BT27 4RL
☎ 028 9244 7245 ☞ leah.scott@lisburncastlereagh.gov.uk

Fleet Management: Mr Tom Cousins, Head of Operational Services, Central Services Depot, Unit 2, Blaris Industrial Estate, Altona Road, Lisburn BT27 5QB ☎ 028 9267 3417
☞ tom.cousins@lisburncastlereagh.gov.uk

Grounds Maintenance: Mr Tom Cousins, Head of Operational Services, Central Services Depot, Unit 2, Blaris Industrial Estate, Altona Road, Lisburn BT27 5QB ☎ 028 9267 3417
☞ tom.cousins@lisburncastlereagh.gov.uk

Health and Safety: Mr Richard Harvey, Head of Environmental Services, 1 Bradford Court, Upper Galwally, Castlereagh, Belfast BT8 6RB ☎ 028 9049 4640
☞ richard.harvey@lisburncastlereagh.gov.uk

Home Energy Conservation: Mr Colin Duff, Head of Building Control, Civic Headquarters, Lagan Valley Island, Lisburn BT27 4RL
☎ 028 9244 7370 ☞ colin.duff@lisburncastlereagh.gov.uk

Legal: Mrs Carmel Connolly, Head of Central Support Services, Civic Headquarters, Lagan Valley Island, Lisburn BT27 4RL
☎ 028 9244 7259 ☞ carmel.connolly@lisburncastlereagh.gov.uk

Leisure and Cultural Services: Mr Ryan Black, Head of Cultural & Community Services, 1 Bradford Court, Upper Galwally, Castlereagh, Belfast BT8 6RB ☎ 028 9049 4550
☞ ryan.black@lisburncastlereagh.gov.uk

Licensing: Mr Richard Harvey, Head of Environmental Services, 1 Bradford Court, Upper Galwally, Castlereagh, Belfast BT8 6RB
☎ 028 9049 4640 ☞ richard.harvey@lisburncastlereagh.gov.uk

Member Services: Mrs Carmel Connolly, Head of Central Support Services, Civic Headquarters, Lagan Valley Island, Lisburn BT27 4RL
☎ 028 9244 7259 ☞ carmel.connolly@lisburncastlereagh.gov.uk

Parking: Mr Richard Harvey, Head of Environmental Services, 1 Bradford Court, Upper Galwally, Castlereagh, Belfast BT8 6RB
☎ 028 9049 4640 ☞ richard.harvey@lisburncastlereagh.gov.uk

Personnel / HR: Miss Sinead Clarke, Head of Human Resources & Organisational Development, Civic Headquarters, Lagan Valley Island, Lisburn BT27 4RL ☎ 028 9244 7379
☞ sinead.clarke@lisburncastlereagh.gov.uk

Planning: Mr Ian Wilson, Lead Head - Planning & Building Control, Civic Headquarters, Lagan Valley Island, Lisburn BT27 4RL
☎ 028 9244 7806 ☞ ian.wilson@lisburncastlereagh.gov.uk

Procurement: Mrs Leah Scott, Head of Finance & IT, Civic Headquarters, Lagan Valley Island, Lisburn BT27 4RL
☎ 028 9244 7245 ☞ leah.scott@lisburncastlereagh.gov.uk

Recycling & Waste Minimisation: Mr Albert Reynolds, Head of Technical & Estates Services, Civic Headquarters, Lagan Valley Island, Lisburn BT27 4RL ☎ 028 9244 7450
☞ albert.reynolds@lisburncastlereagh.gov.uk

Regeneration: Mr Paul McCormick, Lead Head - Development, Civic Headquarters, Lagan Valley Island, Lisburn BT27 4RL
☎ 028 9244 7350 ☞ paul.mccormick@lisburncastlereagh.gov.uk

Staff Training: Miss Sinead Clarke, Head of Human Resources & Organisational Development, Civic Headquarters, Lagan Valley Island, Lisburn BT27 4RL ☎ 028 9244 7379
☞ sinead.clarke@lisburncastlereagh.gov.uk

Tourism: Mr Paul McCormick, Lead Head - Development, Civic Headquarters, Lagan Valley Island, Lisburn BT27 4RL
☎ 028 9244 7350 ☞ paul.mccormick@lisburncastlereagh.gov.uk

Town Centre: Mr Paul McCormick, Lead Head - Development, Civic Headquarters, Lagan Valley Island, Lisburn BT27 4RL
☎ 028 9244 7350 ☞ paul.mccormick@lisburncastlereagh.gov.uk

Waste Collection and Disposal: Mr Tom Cousins, Head of Operational Services, Central Services Depot, Unit 2, Blaris Industrial Estate, Altona Road, Lisburn BT27 5QB ☎ 028 9267 3417
☞ tom.cousins@lisburncastlereagh.gov.uk

Waste Management: Mr Albert Reynolds, Head of Technical & Estates Services, Civic Headquarters, Lagan Valley Island, Lisburn BT27 4RL ☎ 028 9244 7450
☞ albert.reynolds@lisburncastlereagh.gov.uk

COUNCILLORS

Anderson, Nathan (DUP - Castlereagh South)
nathan.anderson@lisburncastlereagh.gov.uk

Baird, James (UUP - Downshire East)
james.baird@lisburncastlereagh.gov.uk

Beckett, Thomas (DUP - Killultagh)
thomas.beckett@lisburncastlereagh.gov.uk

Bloomfield, Brian (UUP - Lisburn North)
brian.bloomfield@lisburncastlereagh.gov.uk

Butler, Robbie (UUP - Killultagh)
robbie.butler@lisburncastlereagh.gov.uk

Carson, Scott (DUP - Lisburn North)
scott.carson@lisburncastlereagh.gov.uk

Catney, Patrick (SDLP - Killultagh)
pat.catney@lisburncastlereagh.gov.uk

LISBURN CITY & CASTLEREAGH DISTRICT

Dillon, James (UUP - Downshire West)
jim.dillon@lisburncastlereagh.gov.uk

Drysdale, David (DUP - Castlereagh East)
david.drysdale@lisburncastlereagh.gov.uk

Ewart, Allan (DUP - Downshire West)
allan.ewart@lisburncastlereagh.gov.uk

Ewing, Andrew (DUP - Lisburn South)
andrew.ewing@lisburncastlereagh.gov.uk

Gallen, John (SDLP - Castlereagh South)
john.gallen@lisburncastlereagh.gov.uk

Gawaith, Owen (O - Downshire West)
owen.gawaith@lisburncastlereagh.gov.uk

Girvin, Andrew (O - Castlereagh East)
andrew.girvan@lisburncastlereagh.gov.uk

Givan, Alan (DUP - Lisburn South)
alan.givan@lisburncastlereagh.gov.uk

Gray, Janet (DUP - Downshire East)
janet.gray@lisburncastlereagh.gov.uk

Grehan, Amanda (O - Lisburn South)
amanda.grehan@lisburncastlereagh.gov.uk

Harvey, Brian (SDLP - Castlereagh South)
brian.harvey@lisburncastlereagh.gov.uk

Henderson, Michael (UUP - Castlereagh South)
michael.henderson@lisburncastlereagh.gov.uk

Jeffers, Tommy (DUP - Castlereagh East)
tommy.jeffers@lisburncastlereagh.gov.uk

Kamble, Vasundhara (O - Castlereagh South)
vasundhara.kamble@lisburncastlereagh.gov.uk

Leathem, William (DUP - Killultagh)
william.leathem@lisburncastlereagh.gov.uk

Legge, Hazel (UUP - Castlereagh East)
hazel.legge@lisburncastlereagh.gov.uk

Mackin, Uel (DUP - Downshire East)
uel.mackin@lisburncastlereagh.gov.uk

Mallon, Ben (DUP - Castlereagh South)
ben.mallon@lisburncastlereagh.gov.uk

Martin, Stephen (O - Lisburn North)
stephen.martin@lisburncastlereagh.gov.uk

McCarthy, Jonny (O - Lisburn North)
johnny.mccarthy@lisburncastlereagh.gov.uk

McIntyre, Aaron (O - Downshire East)
aaron.mcintyre@lisburncastlereagh.gov.uk

Mitchell, Tim (UUP - Lisburn South)
tim.mitchell@lisburncastlereagh.gov.uk

Morrow, Tim (O - Castlereagh East)
tim.morrow@lisburncastlereagh.gov.uk

Palmer, John (DUP - Downshire West)
john.palmer@lisburncastlereagh.gov.uk

Palmer, Jenny (DUP - Lisburn North)
jenny.palmer@lisburncastlereagh.gov.uk

Poots, Luke (DUP - Downshire East)
luke.poots@lisburncastlereagh.gov.uk

Porter, Paul (DUP - Lisburn South)
paul.porter@lisburncastlereagh.gov.uk

Redpath, Alexander (UUP - Downshire West)
alexander.redpath@lisburncastlereagh.gov.uk

Rice, Geraldine (O - Castlereagh South)
geraldine.rice@lisburncastlereagh.gov.uk

Skillen, Sharon (DUP - Castlereagh East)
sharon.skillen@lisburncastlereagh.gov.uk

Tinsley, James (DUP - Killultagh)
james.tinsley@lisburncastlereagh.gov.uk

Tolerton, Margaret (DUP - Lisburn North)
margaret.tolerton@lisburncastlereagh.gov.uk

Walker, Rhoda (DUP - Lisburn South)
rhoda.walker@lisburncastlereagh.gov.uk

POLITICAL COMPOSITION
DUP: 20, O: 9, UUP: 8, SDLP: 3

Liverpool City   M

Liverpool City Council, Municipal Buildings, Dale Street,
Liverpool L69 2DH
☎ 0151 233 3000 ✆ liverpool.direct@liverpool.gov.uk
🖳 www.liverpool.gov.uk

FACTS AND FIGURES
Parliamentary Constituencies: Liverpool, Riverside, Liverpool,
Walton, Liverpool, Wavertree, Liverpool, West Derby
EU Constituencies: North West
Election Frequency: Elections are by thirds

PRINCIPAL OFFICERS

Chief Executive: Mr Ged Fitzgerald, Chief Executive, Municipal
Buildings, Dale Street, Liverpool L69 2DH
✆ ged.fitzgerald@liverpool.gov.uk

Senior Management: Ms Sandra Davies, Director - Public Health,
Labour Group Office, Municipal Buildings, Dale Street, Liverpool
L69 2DH ☎ 0151 233 1106 ✆ sandra.davies@liverpool.gov.uk

Senior Management: Ms Becky Hellard, Director - Finance &
Resources, Room 14, Municipal Buildings, Dale Street, Liverpool L69
2DH ☎ 0151 233 3000 ✆ becky.hellard@liverpool.gov.uk

Senior Management: Mr Samih Kalakeche, Director - Adult
Services & Health, Municipal Buildings, Dale Street, Liverpool L69
2DH ☎ 0151 233 3800 ✆ samih.kalakeche@liverpool.gov.uk

Senior Management: Mr Nick Kavanagh, Director - Regeneration
& Employment, 3rd Floor, Millennium House, Victoria Street, Liverpool
L1 6LD ☎ 0151 233 6715 ✆ nick.kavanagh@liverpool.gov.uk

Senior Management: Ms Colette O'Brien, Director - Children &
Young People's Services, 2nd Floor, Millennium House, 60 Victoria
Street, Liverpool L1 6JF ☎ 0151 233 2799
✆ colette.o'brien@liverpool.gov.uk

Senior Management: Mr Ron Odunaiya, Director - Community
Services, 1st Floor, Management Suite, Millennium House, Victoria
Street, Liverpool L1 6LD ☎ 0151 233 4415
✆ ron.odunaiya@liverpool.gov.uk

Catering Services: Ms Suzanne Halsall, Catering Business Manager, Dyson Hall, Dyson Hall Drive, Liverpool L9 7HA ☎ 0151 233 3000 ✆ suzanne.halsall@liverpool.gov.uk

Children / Youth Services: Ms Colette O'Brien, Director - Children & Young People's Services, 2nd Floor, Millennium House, 60 Victoria Street, Liverpool L1 6JF ☎ 0151 233 2799 ✆ colette.o'brien@liverpool.gov.uk

Civil Registration: Ms Patricia Dobie, Superintendent Registrar, The Register Office, Heritage Entrance, St. George's Hall, St. George's Place, Liverpool L1 1JJ ☎ 0151 225 5719 ✆ patricia.dobie@liverpool.gov.uk

PR / Communications: Mr Paul Johnston, Communications Manager, Municipal Buildings, Dale Street, Liverpool LR 2DH ☎ 0151 233 3000 ✆ paul.johnston@liverpool.gov.uk

Community Planning: Mr Mark Kitts, Assistant Director - Regeneration, Municipal Buildings, Dale Street, Liverpool L2 2DH ☎ 0151 233 3000 ✆ mark.kitts@liverpool.gov.uk

Community Safety: Mr Ron Odunaiya, Director - Community Services, 1st Floor, Management Suite, Millennium House, Victoria Street, Liverpool L1 6LD ☎ 0151 233 4415 ✆ ron.odunaiya@liverpool.gov.uk

Consumer Protection and Trading Standards: Mr Dale Willis, Cemeteries, Crematoria & Mortuary Manager, 3rd Floor, Millennium House, Victoria Street, Liverpool L1 6LD ☎ 0151 233 3000 ✆ dale.willis@liverpool.gov.uk

Economic Development: Mr Nick Kavanagh, Director - Regeneration & Employment, 3rd Floor Millennium House, Victoria Street, Liverpool L1 6LD ☎ 0151 233 6715 ✆ nick.kavanagh@liverpool.gov.uk

Education: Ms Colette O'Brien, Director - Children & Young People's Services, 2nd Floor, Millennium House, 60 Victoria Street, Liverpool L1 6JF ☎ 0151 233 2799 ✆ colette.o'brien@liverpool.gov.uk

Electoral Registration: Mr Stephen Barker, Electoral Services Manager, Room 230, Municipal Buildings, Dale Street, Liverpool L2 2DH ☎ 0151 225 3519 ✆ stephen.barker@liverpool.gov.uk

Emergency Planning: Mr Jamie Riley, Emergency Planning Officer, Brougham Terrace, West Derby Road, Liverpool L6 1AE ☎ 0151 225 6017 ✆ jamie.riley@liverpool.gov.uk

Environmental Health: Mr Chris Lomas, Divisional Manager - Licensing & Public Protection, Municipal Buildings, Dale Street, Liverpool L2 2DH ☎ 0151 225 6056 ✆ chris.lomas@liverpool.gov.uk

European Liaison: Mr Martin Eyres, Head of European Programmes, Chief Executive's Office, Municipal Buildings, Dale Street, Liverpool L2 2DH ☎ 0151 233 3000 ✆ martin.eyres@liverpool.gov.uk

Events Manager: Mrs Judith Feather, Head of Events, The Capital Building, 10th Floor, 39 Old Hall Street, Liverpool L3 9PP ☎ 0151 600 2909 ✆ judith.feather@liverpool.gov.uk

Facilities: Mr Tony Wylie, Premises Manager, Ground Floor, Mucipal Buildings, Dale Street, Liverpool L2 2DH ☎ 0151 233 3000 ✆ tony.wylie@liverpool.gov.uk

Finance: Ms Becky Hellard, Director - Finance & Resources, Room 14, Municipal Buildings, Dale Street, Liverpool L69 2DH ☎ 0151 233 3000 ✆ becky.hellard@liverpool.gov.uk

Finance: Mr Tim Povall, Head of Finance, Ground Floor, Municipal Buildings, Dale Street, Liverpool L2 2DH ☎ 0151 233 3000 ✆ tim.povall@liverpool.gov.uk

Fleet Management: Mr John Carrington, Fleet Services Manager, Newton Road Depot, Liverpool L2 2DH ☎ 0151 233 6504 ✆ john.carrington@liverpool.gov.uk

Highways: Mr Steven Holcroft, Transportation Divisional Manager, 4th Floor, Millennium House, 60 Victoria Street, Liverpool L2 2DH ☎ 0151 233 3000 ✆ steven.holcroft@liverpool.gov.uk

Home Energy Conservation: Mr Brendan Peurcell, Head of Energy Management, Room 106, Municipal Buildings, Dale Street, Liverpool L69 2DH ☎ 0151 233 3000 ✆ brendan.purcell@liverpool.gov.uk

Housing: Mr Mark Kitts, Assistant Director - Regeneration, Municipal Buildings, Dale Street, Liverpool L2 2DH ☎ 0151 233 3000 ✆ mark.kitts@liverpool.gov.uk

Legal: Mrs Jeanette McLoughlin, City Solicitor & Monitoring Officer, Labour Group Office, Municipal Buildings, Dale Street, Liverpool L69 2DH ☎ 0151 233 3000 ✆ jeanette.mcloughlin@liverpool.gov.uk

Leisure and Cultural Services: Mrs Claire McColgan, Assistant Director - Culture & Tourism, The Capital Building, 10th Floor, 39 Old Hall Street, Liverpool L3 9PP ☎ 0151 600 2956 ✆ claire.mccolgan@liverpool.gov.uk

Licensing: Mr John McHale, Interim Director - Licensing, Room 216, Municipal Buildings, Dale Street, Liverpool L2 2DH ☎ 0151 233 4415 ✆ john.mchale@liverpool.gov.uk

Lighting: Mr Steven Holcroft, Transportation Divisional Manager, 4th Floor, Millennium House, 60 Victoria Street, Liverpool L2 2DH ☎ 0151 233 3000 ✆ steven.holcroft@liverpool.gov.uk

Member Services: Mr Chris Walsh, Head of Democratic Services, Municipal Buildings, Dale Street, Liverpool L2 2DH ☎ 0151 233 3000 ✆ chris.walsh@liverpool.gov.uk

Parking: Mr Roy Tunstall, Parking Services Manager, 5 Crosshall Street, Liverpool L2 2DH ☎ 0151 233 3011 ✆ roy.tunstall@liverpool.gov.uk

Partnerships: Ms Catherine Garnell, Assistant Chief Executive, Municipal Buildings, Dale Street, Liverpool L2 2DH ☎ 0151 225 2877 ✆ catherine.garnell@liverpool.gov.uk

LIVERPOOL CITY

Personnel / HR: Ms Colette Hannay, Head of Human Resources & Payroll Services, 6th Floor, Venture Place, 13 - 17 Sir Thomas Street, Liverpool L1 6BW ☎ 0151 233 3000 ✆ colette.hannay@liverpool.gov.uk

Planning: Mr Andy Barr, Interim Head of Planning, Municipal Buildings, Dale Street, Liverpool L69 2DH ☎ 0151 233 0317 ✆ andy.barr@liverpool.gov.uk

Public Libraries: Mr David Sharman, Manager - Library & Museum Services, Municipal Buildings, Dale Street, Liverpool L69 2DH ☎ 0151 233 3000 ✆ david.sharman@liverpool.gov.uk

Recycling & Waste Minimisation: Mr Andrew McCartan, Environmental Services Manager, 1st Floor, Millennium House, Victoria Street, Liverpool L69 1JB ☎ 0151 233 6380 ✆ andrew.mccartan@liverpool.gov.uk

Regeneration: Mr Nick Kavanagh, Director - Regeneration & Employment, 3rd Floor Millennium House, Victoria Street, Liverpool L1 6LD ☎ 0151 233 6715 ✆ nick.kavanagh@liverpool.gov.uk

Road Safety: Mr David Ng, Team Leader, PO Box 981, Municipal Buildings, Liverpool L69 1JB ☎ 0151 233 2386 ✆ david.ng@liverpool.gov.uk

Social Services: Mrs Bernie Brown, Assistant Director - Education & Children's Services, 2nd Floor, Millennium House, 60 Victoria Street, Liverpool L1 6JF bernie.brown@liverpool.gov.uk

Social Services (Adult): Mr Samih Kalakeche, Director - Adult Services & Health, Municipal Buildings, Dale Street, Liverpool L69 2DH ☎ 0151 233 3800 ✆ samih.kalakeche@liverpool.gov.uk

Social Services (Children): Ms Liz Mekki, Divisional Manager - Children's Safeguarding, Team 2, 2nd Floor, Millennium House, 60 Victoria Street, Liverpool L1 6JF ☎ 0151 233 4174 ✆ liz.mekki@liverpool.gov.uk

Public Health: Ms Sandra Davies, Director - Public Health, Labour Group Office, Municipal Buildings, Dale Street, Liverpool L69 2DH ☎ 0151 233 1106 ✆ sandra.davies@liverpool.gov.uk

Sustainable Development: Mr Mark Kitts, Assistant Director - Regeneration, Municipal Buildings, Dale Street, Liverpool L2 2DH ☎ 0151 233 3000 ✆ mark.kitts@liverpool.gov.uk

Tourism: Mr Keith Blundell, Director - Blue Chip Tourism & Liverpool Destination Services, The Capital Building, 39 Old Hall Street, Liverpool L3 9PP ☎ 0151 233 3000

Town Centre: Mr Mike Cockburn, City Centre Manager, 1st Floor, Millennium House, 60 Victoria Street, Liverpool L1 6JE ☎ 07739 703967 ✆ mike.cockburn@liverpool.gov.uk

Traffic Management: Mr Steven Holcroft, Transportation Divisional Manager, 4th Floor, Millennium House, 60 Victoria Street, Liverpool L2 2DH ☎ 0151 233 3000 ✆ steven.holcroft@liverpool.gov.uk

Transport: Mr Steven Holcroft, Transportation Divisional Manager, 4th Floor, Millennium House, 60 Victoria Street, Liverpool L2 2DH ☎ 0151 233 3000 ✆ steven.holcroft@liverpool.gov.uk

Transport Planner: Mr Steven Holcroft, Transportation Divisional Manager, 4th Floor, Millennium House, 60 Victoria Street, Liverpool L2 2DH ☎ 0151 233 3000 ✆ steven.holcroft@liverpool.gov.uk

Waste Collection and Disposal: Mr Chris Lomas, Divisional Manager - Licensing & Public Protection, Municipal Buildings, Dale Street, Liverpool L2 2DH ☎ 0151 225 6056 ✆ chris.lomas@liverpool.gov.uk

Waste Management: Mr Chris Lomas, Divisional Manager - Licensing & Public Protection, Municipal Buildings, Dale Street, Liverpool L2 2DH ☎ 0151 225 6056 ✆ chris.lomas@liverpool.gov.uk

COUNCILLORS

The Lord Mayor: Gladden, Roz (LAB - Clubmoor) roz.gladden@liverpool.gov.uk

Deputy Lord Mayor: Kennedy, Malcolm (LAB - Kirkdale) malcolm.kennedy@liverpool.gov.uk

Mayor: Anderson, Joe (LAB - No Ward) mayor@liverpool.gov.uk

Deputy Mayor: O'Byrne, Ann (LAB - Warbreck) ann.o'byrne@liverpool.gov.uk

Group Leader: Crone, Thomas (GRN - St Michael's) thomas.crone@liverpool.gov.uk

Group Leader: Kemp, Richard (LD - Church) richard.kemp@liverpool.gov.uk

Group Leader: Radford, Steve (LIB - Tuebrook & Stoneycroft) northwestliberalparty@hotmail.co.uk

Banks, Christine (LAB - Central) christine.banks2@liverpool.gov.uk

Barrington, Daniel (LAB - West Derby) daniel.barrington@liverpool.gov.uk

Beaumont, Tim (LAB - Picton) tim.beaumont@liverpool.gov.uk

Bennett, Alice (LAB - Woolton) alice.bennett@liverpool.gov.uk

Bennett, Ruth (LAB - Belle Vale) ruth.bennett@liverpool.gov.uk

Brant, Paul (LAB - Fazakerley) paul.brant@liverpool.gov.uk

Brennan, Peter (LAB - Old Swan) peter.brennan2@liverpool.gov.uk

Brown, Lawrence (GRN - Greenbank) lawrence.brown@liverpool.gov.uk

Calvert, Joanne (LAB - Old Swan) joanne.calvert@liverpool.gov.uk

Casstles, Helen (LAB - Wavertree) helen.casstles@liverpool.gov.uk

Clarke, Peter (LAB - Fazakerley) peter.clarke@liverpool.gov.uk

Concepcion, Tony (LAB - Yew Tree)

Connor, Sharon (LAB - Allerton & Hunts Cross)
sharon.connor@liverpool.gov.uk

Corbett, Jane (LAB - Everton)
jane.corbett@liverpool.gov.uk

Corrigan, Michelle (LAB - Riverside)
michelle.corrigan@liverpool.gov.uk

Crofts, Nick (LAB - Knotty Ash)
nick.crofts@liverpool.gov.uk

Cummings, Dave (LAB - Wavertree)
dave.cummings@liverpool.gov.uk

Davies, Kay (LAB - County)
kay.davies@liverpool.gov.uk

Dean, Alan (LAB - Princes Park)
alan.dean@liverpool.gov.uk

Dowling, Adele (LAB - Anfield)
adele.dowling@liverpool.gov.uk

Foxley, Andrew (LAB - Mossley Hill)
Andrew.Foxley@liverpool.gov.uk

Fraenkel, Beatrice (LAB - Kirkdale)
beatrice.fraenkel@liverpool.gov.uk

Francis, Ian (LAB - Anfield)
ian.francis@liverpool.gov.uk

Gladden, Roy (LAB - County)
roy.gladden@liverpool.gov.uk

Groves, Ros (LAB - Anfield)
ros.groves@liverpool.gov.uk

Hanratty, Dave (LAB - Fazakerley)
dave.hanratty@liverpool.gov.uk

Hanson, Joseph (LAB - Kirkdale)
joseph.hanson@liverpool.gov.uk

Harrison, Cheryl (LAB - Warbreck)
cheryl.harrison@liverpool.gov.uk

Heron, Sue (LAB - Kensington & Fairfield)
sue.heron@liverpool.gov.uk

Hinnigan, Lynnie (LAB - Cressington)
lynnie.hinnigan@liverpool.gov.uk

Hont, Frank (LAB - Childwall)
frank.hont@liverpool.gov.uk

Hurley, Patrick (LAB - Mossley Hill)
patrick.hurley@liverpool.gov.uk

Jennings, Sarah (GRN - St Michael's)
sarah.jennings@liverpool.gov.uk

Jolly, Rosie (LD - Wavertree)
rosie.jolly@liverpool.gov.uk

Jones, Bill (LAB - Cressington)
bill.jones@liverpool.gov.uk

Juarez, Mirna (LD - Allerton & Hunts Cross)
mirna.juarez@liverpool.gov.uk

Kelly, Malcolm (LD - Woolton)
malcolm.kelly@liverpool.gov.uk

Key, Anna (GRN - St Michael's)
anna.key@liverpool.gov.uk

Knight, Doreen (LAB - Speke-Garston)
doreen.knight@liverpool.gov.uk

Kushner, Barry (LAB - Norris Green)
barry.kushner@liverpool.gov.uk

Kushner, Joann (LAB - Croxteth)
joann.kushner@liverpool.gov.uk

Lavelle, Anthony (LAB - Croxteth)
anthony.lavelle@liverpool.gov.uk

Makinson, Andrew (LD - Church)
andrew.makinson@liverpool.gov.uk

McAlley, Colin (LAB - Woolton)
colin.mcalley@liverpool.gov.uk

McIntosh, John (LAB - Everton)
john.mcintosh@liverpool.gov.uk

McLinden, Richard (LAB - Warbreck)
richard.mclinden@liverpool.gov.uk

Millar, Gary (LD - Old Swan)
gary.millar@liverpool.gov.uk

Mitchell, Peter (LAB - Croxteth)
peter.mitchell@liverpool.gov.uk

Moore, Timothy (LAB - Princes Park)
timothy.moore@liverpool.gov.uk

Morrison, Kevin (LIB - Tuebrook & Stoneycroft)
kevin.morrison@liverpool.gov.uk

Munby, Steve (LAB - Riverside)
stephen.munby@liverpool.gov.uk

Murray, Barbara (LAB - Yew Tree)
barbara.murray@liverpool.gov.uk

Nicholas, Nathalie (LAB - Picton)
nathalie.nicholas@liverpool.gov.uk

Noakes, James (LAB - Clubmoor)
james.noakes@liverpool.gov.uk

O'Brien, Tricia (LAB - Cressington)
tricia.obrien@liverpool.gov.uk

O'Byrne, Rachael (LAB - Allerton & Hunts Cross)
rachael.o'byrne@liverpool.gov.uk

Orr, Lana (LAB - West Derby)
lana.orr@liverpool.gov.uk

Parsons, Liz (LAB - Childwall)
liz.parsons1@liverpool.gov.uk

Prendergast, Frank (LAB - Everton)
frank.prendergast@liverpool.gov.uk

Prince, John (LAB - Yew Tree)
john.prince@liverpool.gov.uk

Qadir, Abdul (LAB - Picton)
abdul.qadir@liverpool.gov.uk

Rainey, Irene (LAB - Clubmoor)
irene.rainey@liverpool.gov.uk

Rasmussen, Mary (LAB - Speke-Garston)
mary.rasmussen@liverpool.gov.uk

Roberts, James (LAB - Greenbank)
james.roberts2@liverpool.gov.uk

Robertson-Collins, Laura (LAB - Greenbank)
laura.robertson-collins@liverpool.gov.uk

Robinson, Liam (LAB - Kensington & Fairfield)
liam.robinson@liverpool.gov.uk

LIVERPOOL CITY

Ross, Sharon (LAB - Norris Green)
sharon.ross@liverpool.gov.uk

Rothery, Anna (LAB - Princes Park)
anna.rothery@liverpool.gov.uk

Simon, Wendy (LAB - Kensington & Fairfield)
wendy.simon@liverpool.gov.uk

Small, Nick (LAB - Central)
nick.small@liverpool.gov.uk

Spurrell, Emily (LAB - Mossley Hill)
emily.spurrell@liverpool.gov.uk

Sullivan, Sharon (LAB - Central)
sharon.sullivan@liverpool.gov.uk

Taylor, Ged (LAB - Knotty Ash)
ged.taylor@liverpool.gov.uk

Taylor, Jacqui (LAB - Knotty Ash)

Thomas, Pam (LAB - West Derby)
pamela.thomas@liverpool.gov.uk

Thompson, Helen (LAB - Belle Vale)
helen.thompson@liverpool.gov.uk

Tootle, Leon (LAB - Speke-Garston)
leon.tootle@liverpool.gov.uk

Walker, Alan (LAB - Norris Green)
alan.walker@liverpool.gov.uk

Walton, Pauline (LAB - Belle Vale)
pauline.walton@liverpool.gov.uk

Wenstone, Richard (LAB - Church)
richard.wenstone@liverpool.gov.uk

Williams, Hazel (LIB - Tuebrook & Stoneycroft)
hazel.williams@liverpool.gov.uk

Wolfson, Jeremy (LAB - Childwall)
jeremy.wolfson@liverpool.gov.uk

Wood, Hetty (LAB - Riverside)
hetty.wood@liverpool.gov.uk

Woodhouse, Gerard (LAB - County)
gerard.woodhouse@liverpool.gov.uk

POLITICAL COMPOSITION
LAB: 78, LD: 6, GRN: 4, LIB: 3

COMMITTEE CHAIRS

Audit: Mr Frank Prendergast

Education & Children's Services: Mr John Prince

Health & Wellbeing: Mr Joe Anderson

Licensing: Ms Christine Banks

Planning: Mr John McIntosh

Regeneration, Housing & Sustainability: Ms Hetty Wood

Luton   U

Luton Borough Council, Town Hall, Luton LU1 2BQ
☎ 01582 546000 🖷 01582 546680 ▭ www.luton.gov.uk

FACTS AND FIGURES
Parliamentary Constituencies: Luton North, Luton South

EU Constituencies: Eastern
Election Frequency: Elections are of whole council

PRINCIPAL OFFICERS

Chief Executive: Mr Trevor Holden, Chief Executive, Town Hall, Luton LU1 2BQ ☎ 01582 546015 ◌ chiefexec@luton.gov.uk

Senior Management: Ms Laura Church, Corporate Director - Place & Infrastructure, 2nd Floor, Town Hall, Luton LU1 2BQ ☎ 01582 546433 ◌ laura.church@luton.gov.uk

Senior Management: Ms Nicola Monk, Service Director - Policy, Communities & Engagement, Town Hall, Luton LU1 2BQ ◌ nicola.monk@luton.gov.uk

Senior Management: Mr Robin Porter, Corporate Director - Customer & Commercial, 3rd Floor, Town Hall, Luton LU1 2BQ ☎ 01582 548205 ◌ robin.porter@luton.gov.uk

Senior Management: Ms Jayne Robinson, Interim Service Director - Transformation & Technology, Town Hall, Luton LU1 2BQ ◌ jayne.robinson@luton.gov.uk

Senior Management: Ms Sally Rowe, Corporate Director - People, Town Hall, Luton LU1 2BQ ☎ 01582 547500 ◌ sally.rowe@luton.gov.uk

Senior Management: Ms Gerry Taylor, Corporate Director - Public Health, Commissioning & Procurement, 4th Floor, Unity House, 111 Stuart Street, Luton LU1 2NP ☎ 01582 548448 ◌ gerry.taylor@luton.gov.uk

Architect, Building / Property Services: Mr Roger Kirk, Head of Fixed Assets, 3rd Floor, Apex House, 30-34 Upper George Street, Luton LU1 2RD ☎ 01582 548268 ◌ roger.kirk@luton.gov.uk

Best Value: Ms Nicola Perry, Head of Policy & Performance, Ground Floor, Town Hall, Luton LU1 2BQ ☎ 01582 546073 ◌ HOPP@luton.gov.uk

Building Control: Mr Chris Pagdin, Head of Planning & Transport, Town Hall, Luton LU1 2BQ ☎ 01582 546329 ◌ chris.pagdin@luton.gov.uk

Catering Services: Mr Ferri Fassihi, General Catering Manager, Luton Learning and Resource Centre, Strangers Way, Luton LU1 ☎ 01582 538211 ◌ feraidoun.fassihi@luton.gov.uk

Children / Youth Services: Mr Nick Chamberlain, Early Intervention Service Manager, 1st Floor, Unity House, 111 Stuart Street, Luton LU1 5NP ☎ 01582 548057 ◌ nicholas.chamberlain@luton.gov.uk

Children / Youth Services: Ms Sally Rowe, Corporate Director - People, Town Hall, Luton LU1 2BQ ☎ 01582 547500 ◌ sally.rowe@luton.gov.uk

Civil Registration: Ms Angela Claridge, Head of HR & Monitoring Officer, 2nd Floor, Apex House, 30-34 Upper George Street, Luton LU1 2RD ☎ 01582 546291 ◌ angela.claridge@luton.gov.uk

PR / Communications: Mr Rob Leigh, Head of Communications, 1st Floor, Town Hall Annexe, Luton LU1 2BQ ☎ 01582 546000 ◌ rob.leigh@luton.gov.uk

Community Planning: Ms Laura Church, Corporate Director - Place & Infrastructure, 2nd Floor, Town Hall, Luton LU1 2BQ ☎ 01582 546433 ◌ laura.church@luton.gov.uk

Community Safety: Ms Vicky Hayes, Community Safety & Anti-Social Behaviour Officer, Luton Police Station, Buxton Road, Luton LU4 8AU ☎ 01582 394177 ◌ vicky.hayes@luton.gov.uk

Computer Management: Ms Jayne Robinson, Interim Service Director - Transformation & Technology, Town Hall, Luton LU1 2BQ jayne.robinson@luton.gov.uk

Contracts: Mr Chris Addey, Strategic Procurement Manager, 2nd Floor - Stuart House, Upper George Street, Luton LU1 2RD ☎ 01582 546867 ◌ addeyc@luton.gov.uk

Corporate Services: Mr Robin Porter, Corporate Director - Customer & Commercial, Ground Floor, Unity House, 111 Stuart Street, Luton LU1 2NP ☎ 01582 548205 ◌ robin.porter@luton.gov.uk

Customer Service: Ms Sue Nelson, Head of Revenues, Benefits & Customer Service, Ground Floor, Unity House, Town Hall, Luton LU1 2BQ ☎ 01582 547094 ◌ sue.nelson@luton.gov.uk

Customer Service: Mr Robin Porter, Corporate Director - Customer & Commercial, Ground Floor, Unity House, 111 Stuart Street, Luton LU1 2NP ☎ 01582 548205 ◌ robin.porter@luton.gov.uk

Direct Labour: Ms Mo Harkin, Head of Housing, 2nd Floor, Unity House, 111 Stuart Street, Luton LU1 5NP ☎ 01582 546202 ◌ HOHSG@luton.gov.uk

Economic Development: Ms Laura Church, Corporate Director - Place & Infrastructure, 1st Floor - Stuart House, Upper George Street, Luton LU1 2RD ☎ 01582 546433 ◌ laura.church@luton.gov.uk

Education: Ms Sally Rowe, Corporate Director - People, Town Hall, Luton LU1 2BQ ☎ 01582 547500 ◌ sally.rowe@luton.gov.uk

Electoral Registration: Mr Sam Freer, Electoral Services Manager, 1st Floor, Town Hall, Luton LU1 2BQ ☎ 01582 546088 ◌ sam.freer@luton.gov.uk

Emergency Planning: Mr Anthony Green, Civil Protection Officer, 1st Floor, Town Hall Annexe, Luton LU1 2BQ ☎ 01582 547240 ◌ anthony.green@luton.gov.uk

Environmental / Technical Services: Ms Laura Church, Corporate Director - Place & Infrastructure, 2nd Floor, Town Hall, Luton LU1 2BQ ☎ 01582 546433 ◌ laura.church@luton.gov.uk

Environmental Health: Ms Laura Church, Corporate Director - Place & Infrastructure, 1st Floor - Stuart House, Upper George Street, Luton LU1 2RD ☎ 01582 546433 ◌ laura.church@luton.gov.uk

Finance: Mr Dev Gopal, Service Director - Finance & Audit, Town Hall, Luton LU1 2BQ ☎ 01582 546000 ◌ dev.gopal@luton.gov.uk

Fleet Management: Mr Simon Smith, Transport Manager, Central Depot, Kingsway, Luton LU4 8AU ☎ 01582 546877 ◌ simon.smith@luton.gov.uk

Grounds Maintenance: Mr Barry Timms, Parks & Cemeteries Manager, Wardown Park Offices, Luton LU2 7HA ☎ 01582 546702 ◌ barry.timms@luton.gov.uk

Health and Safety: Ms Caron Owens, Corporate Health & Safety Manager, 2nd Floor, Clemiston House, 14 Upper George Street, Luton LU1 2RP ☎ 01582 546299 ◌ caron.owens@luton.gov.uk

Highways: Mr Alex Constantinides, Head of Engineering & Street Services, 2nd Floor, Town Hall, Luton LU1 2BQ ☎ 01582 546619 ◌ alex.constantinides@luton.gov.uk

Housing: Ms Mo Harkin, Head of Housing, 2nd Floor, Unity House, 111 Stuart Street, Luton LU1 5NP ☎ 01582 546202 ◌ HOHSG@luton.gov.uk

Local Area Agreement: Ms Nicola Perry, Head of Policy & Performance, Ground Floor, Town Hall, Luton LU1 2BQ ☎ 01582 546073 ◌ HOPP@luton.gov.uk

Legal: Ms Angela Claridge, Head of HR & Monitoring Officer, Apex House, Luton LU1 2RD ☎ 01582 546291 ◌ angela.claridge@luton.gov.uk

Leisure and Cultural Services: Ms Maggie Appleton, Leisure & Cultural Services Manager, Central Library, Luton LU1 2BQ ☎ 01582 546000 ◌ maggie.appleton@luton.gov.uk

Licensing: Ms Laura Church, Corporate Director - Place & Infrastructure, 1st Floor - Stuart House, Upper George Street, Luton LU1 2RD ☎ 01582 546433 ◌ laura.church@luton.gov.uk

Lifelong Learning: Ms Sally Rowe, Corporate Director - People, Town Hall, Luton LU1 2BQ ☎ 01582 547500 ◌ sally.rowe@luton.gov.uk

Lighting: Mr Alex Constantinides, Head of Engineering & Street Services, 2nd Floor, Town Hall, Luton LU1 2BQ ☎ 01582 546619 ◌ alex.constantinides@luton.gov.uk

Lighting: Mr Graham Turner, Highways Maintenance Services Manager, 4th Floor, Town Hall, Luton LU1 2BQ ☎ 01582 546000 ◌ graham.turner@luton.gov.uk

Member Services: Ms Debbie Janes, Democracy Manager, Town Hall, Luton LU1 2BQ ☎ 01582 546038 ◌ deborah.janes@luton.gov.uk

Parking: Mr Tony Stefano, Parking Operations Manager, Town Hall, Luton LU1 2BQ ☎ 01582 548521 ◌ tony.stefano@luton.gov.uk

Personnel / HR: Ms Angela Claridge, Head of HR & Monitoring Officer, 2nd Floor, Apex House, 30-34 Upper George Street, Luton LU1 2RD ☎ 01582 546291 ◌ angela.claridge@luton.gov.uk

LUTON

Planning: Mr Chris Pagdin, Head of Planning & Transport, Town Hall, Luton LU1 2BQ ☎ 01582 546329 ⌁ chris.pagdin@luton.gov.uk

Procurement: Mr William Clapp, Head of Procurement & Shared Services, Town Hall, Luton LU1 2BQ ☎ 01582 546867 ⌁ william.clapp@luton.gov.uk

Procurement: Ms Gerry Taylor, Corporate Director - Public Health, Commissioning & Procurement, 4th Floor, Unity House, 111 Stuart Street, Luton LU1 2NP ☎ 01582 548448 ⌁ gerry.taylor@luton.gov.uk

Regeneration: Ms Laura Church, Corporate Director - Place & Infrastructure, 2nd Floor, Town Hall, George Street, Luton LU1 2RD ☎ 01582 546433 ⌁ laura.church@luton.gov.uk

Road Safety: Mr Alex Constantinides, Head of Engineering & Street Services, 2nd Floor, Town Hall, Luton LU1 2BQ ☎ 01582 546619 ⌁ alex.constantinides@luton.gov.uk

Social Services (Adult): Ms Maud O'Leary, Head of Adult Social Care, 2nd Floor, Unity House, 111 Stuart Street, Luton LU1 5NP ☎ 01582 547503 ⌁ maud.oleary@luton.gov.uk

Social Services (Children): Ms Jo Fisher, Head of Prevention, 3rd Floor, Unity House, 111 Stuart Street, Luton LU1 5NP ☎ 01582 548006 ⌁ joanne.fisher@luton.gov.uk

Social Services (Children): Ms Sally Rowe, Corporate Director - People, Town Hall, Luton LU1 2BQ ☎ 01582 547500 ⌁ sally.rowe@luton.gov.uk

Public Health: Ms Gerry Taylor, Corporate Director - Public Health, Commissioning & Procurement, 4th Floor, Unity House, 111 Stuart Street, Luton LU1 2NP ☎ 01582 548448 ⌁ gerry.taylor@luton.gov.uk

Staff Training: Ms Lesley McNeill, Corporate Learning & Development Manager, Ground Floor, Apex House, 30 - 34 George Street, Luton LU1 2RD ☎ 01582 547556 ⌁ lesley.mcneill@luton.gov.uk

Street Scene: Mr Alex Constantinides, Head of Engineering & Street Services, 2nd Floor, Town Hall, Luton LU1 2BQ ☎ 01582 546619 ⌁ alex.constantinides@luton.gov.uk

Sustainable Communities: Ms Laura Church, Corporate Director - Place & Infrastructure, 2nd Floor, Town Hall, Luton LU1 2BQ ☎ 01582 546433 ⌁ laura.church@luton.gov.uk

Sustainable Development: Ms Laura Church, Corporate Director - Place & Infrastructure, 2nd Floor, Town Hall, Luton LU1 2BQ ☎ 01582 546433 ⌁ laura.church@luton.gov.uk

Tourism: Ms Laura Church, Corporate Director - Place & Infrastructure, 2nd Floor, Town Hall, Luton LU1 2BQ ☎ 01582 546433 ⌁ laura.church@luton.gov.uk

Town Centre: Mr Paul Adams, Acting Service Director - Business & Consumer Services, Town Hall, Luton LU1 2BQ ☎ 01582 546000 ⌁ paul.adams@luton.gov.uk

Traffic Management: Mr Jonathan Palmer, Traffic & Asset Manager, 4th Floor, Town Hall, Luton LU1 2BQ ☎ 01582 546000 ⌁ jonathan.palmer@luton.gov.uk

Transport: Mr Simon Smith, Transport Manager, Central Depot, Kingsway, Luton LU4 8AU ☎ 01582 546877 ⌁ simon.smith@luton.gov.uk

Transport Planner: Mr Alex Constantinides, Head of Engineering & Street Services, 2nd Floor, Town Hall, Luton LU1 2BQ ☎ 01582 546619 ⌁ alex.constantinides@luton.gov.uk

Total Place: Mr Robin Porter, Corporate Director - Customer & Commercial, Ground Floor, Unity House, 111 Stuart Street, Luton LU1 2NP ☎ 01582 548205 ⌁ robin.porter@luton.gov.uk

Waste Management: Mr Shaun Askins, Strategic Waste Manager, Central Depot, Luton LU4 8AU ☎ 01582 546807

COUNCILLORS

Mayor: Taylor, Dave (LAB - Farley)
dave.taylor@luton.gov.uk

Deputy Mayor: Saleem, Sameera (LAB - Leagrave)
sameera.saleem@luton.gov.uk

Leader of the Council: Simmons, Hazel (LAB - Lewsey)
hazel.simmons@luton.gov.uk

Deputy Leader of the Council: Timoney, Sian (LAB - Farley)
sian.timoney@luton.gov.uk

Agbley, David (LAB - South)
david.agbley@luton.gov.uk

Akbar, Waheed (LAB - Leagrave)
waheed.akbar@luton.gov.uk

Ashraf, Mohammed (LAB - Dallow)
mohammed.ashraf@luton.gov.uk

Ayub, Mohammad (LAB - Biscot)
mohammad.ayub@luton.gov.uk

Ayub, Naseem (LAB - Biscot)
naseem.ayub@luton.gov.uk

Baker, John (CON - Round Green)
john.baker@luton.gov.uk

Burnett, Jacqui (LAB - Lewsey)
jacqueline.burnett@luton.gov.uk

Campbell, Gilbert (CON - Bramingham)
gilbert.campbell@luton.gov.uk

Castleman, Paul (LAB - South)
paul.castleman@luton.gov.uk

Chapman, Peter (LD - Wigmore)
peter.chapman@luton.gov.uk

Chowdhury, Irak (LAB - Round Green)
irak.chowdhury@luton.gov.uk

Davis, Roy J (LAB - Northwell)
roy.davis@luton.gov.uk

Dolling, Michael (LD - Stopsley)
michael.dolling@luton.gov.uk

Dolling, Meryl (LD - Stopsley)
meryl.dolling@luton.gov.uk

Farooq, Mohammed (LAB - Dallow)
mohammed.farooq@luton.gov.uk

Franks, David (LD - Barnfield)
david.franks@luton.gov.uk

Garrett, Michael (CON - Icknield)
michael.garrett@luton.gov.uk

Green, Fiona (LAB - Sundon Park)
fiona.green@luton.gov.uk

Gurbuz, Aysegul (LAB - High Town)
aysegul.gurbuz@luton.gov.uk

Hopkins, Rachel (LAB - Barnfield)
rachel.hopkins@luton.gov.uk

Hussain, Mahmood (LAB - Farley)
mahmood.hussain@luton.gov.uk

Keens, Terry (LD - Crawley)
terry.keens@luton.gov.uk

Khan, Aslam (LAB - Lewsey)
aslam.khan@luton.gov.uk

Khan, Tahir (LAB - Biscot)
tahir.khan@luton.gov.uk

Lewis, Stephen (LAB - Limbury)
stephen.lewis@luton.gov.uk

Malcolm, Andrew (LAB - High Town)
andrew.malcolm@luton.gov.uk

Malik, Tahir (LAB - Challney)
tahir.malik@luton.gov.uk

Moles, Diane (LD - Wigmore)
diane.moles@luton.gov.uk

O'Callaghan, Amy (LAB - South)
amy.ocallaghan@luton.gov.uk

Pedersen, Anna (LD - Sundon Park)
anna.pedersen@luton.gov.uk

Petts, Jeff (CON - Icknield)
jeff.petts@luton.gov.uk

Rafiq, Nazia (LAB - Dallow)
nazia.rafiq@luton.gov.uk

Rathore, Asma (LAB - Saints)
asma.rathore@luton.gov.uk

Riaz, Mohammed (LAB - Saints)
mohammed.riaz@luton.gov.uk

Rivers, Mark (LAB - Round Green)
mark.rivers@luton.gov.uk

Roden, Sheila (LAB - Leagrave)
sheila.roden@luton.gov.uk

Rowlands, Jennifer (LAB - Limbury)
jennifer.rowlands@luton.gov.uk

Saleem, Raja (LAB - Saints)
raja.saleem@luton.gov.uk

Shaw, Tom (LAB - Challney)
tom.shaw@luton.gov.uk

Skepelhorn, Alan (LD - Wigmore)
alan.skepelhorn@luton.gov.uk

Taylor, James (LAB - Crawley)
james.taylor@luton.gov.uk

Waheed, Yasmin (LAB - Challney)
yasmin.waheed@luton.gov.uk

Worling, Don (LAB - Northwell)
don.worling@luton.gov.uk

Young, John (CON - Bramingham)
john.young@luton.gov.uk

POLITICAL COMPOSITION
LAB: 35, LD: 8, CON: 5

COMMITTEE CHAIRS

Audit & Governance: Mr David Agbley

Licensing: Mr Mark Rivers

Maidstone   D

Maidstone Borough Council, Maidstone House, King Street, Maidstone ME15 6JQ
☎ 01622 602000 ⌨ www.maidstone.gov.uk

FACTS AND FIGURES
Parliamentary Constituencies: Faversham & Mid Kent, Maidstone and the Weald
EU Constituencies: South East
Election Frequency: Elections are by thirds

PRINCIPAL OFFICERS

Chief Executive: Mrs Alison Broom, Chief Executive, Maidstone House, King Street, Maidstone ME15 6JQ ☎ 01622 602019
⌨ alisonbroom@maidstone.gov.uk

Senior Management: Mr William Cornall, Director - Regeneration & Place, Maidstone House, King Street, Maidstone ME15 6JQ
☎ 01622 602364 ⌨ williamcornll@maidstone.gov.uk

Senior Management: Mr Mark Green, Director - Finance & Business Improvement, Maidstone House, King Street, Maidstone ME15 6JQ ☎ 01622 602297 ⌨ markgreen@maidstone.gov.uk

Senior Management: Mr Paul Taylor, Mid Kent Services Director, Maidstone House, King Street, Maidstone ME15 6JQ
☎ 01622 602663 ⌨ paultaylor@maidstone.gov.uk

Architect, Building / Property Services: Mr David Tibbit, Property & Procurement Manager, Maidstone House, King Street, Maidstone ME15 6JQ ☎ 01622 602361
⌨ davidtibbit@maidstone.gov.uk

Best Value: Miss Georgia Hawkes, Service Improvement Manager, Maidstone House, King Street, Maidstone ME15 6JQ
☎ 01622 602168 ⌨ georgiahawkes@maidstone.gov.uk

Building Control: Mr David Harrison, Emergency Planning Officer, Maidstone House, King Street, Maidstone ME12 6JQ
☎ 01622 602034 ⌨ davidharrison@maidstone.gov.uk

PR / Communications: Mrs Angela Woodhouse, Head of Policy & Communications, Maidstone House, King Street, Maidstone ME15 6JQ ☎ 01622 602620 ⌨ angelawoodhouse@maidstone.gov.uk

MAIDSTONE

Community Safety: Mr John Littlemore, Head of Housing & Community Services, Maidstone House, King Street, Maidstone ME15 6JQ ☎ 01622 602207 ✆ johnlittlemore@maidstone.gov.uk

Computer Management: Mr Tony Bullock, Chief Technology Officer, Maidstone House, King Street, Maidstone ME15 6JQ ☎ 01622 602915 ✆ tonybullock@maidstone.gov.uk

Computer Management: Mr Andrew Cole, Head of ICT Shared Services, Maidstone House, King Street, Maidstone ME15 6JQ ☎ 01622 602662 ✆ andrew.cole@tunbridgewells.gov.uk

Computer Management: Mr Dave Lindsay, Chief Information Officer, Maidstone House, King Street, Maidstone ME15 6JQ ☎ 01622 602156 ✆ davelindsay@maidstone.gov.uk

Contracts: Mr David Tibbit, Property & Procurement Manager, Maidstone House, King Street, Maidstone ME15 6JQ ☎ 01622 602361 ✆ davidtibbit@maidstone.gov.uk

Corporate Services: Mr Mark Green, Director - Finance & Business Improvement, Maidstone House, King Street, Maidstone ME15 6JQ ☎ 01622 602297 ✆ markgreen@maidstone.gov.uk

Customer Service: Mrs Angela Woodhouse, Head of Policy & Communications, Maidstone House, King Street, Maidstone ME15 6JQ ☎ 01622 602620 ✆ angelawoodhouse@maidstone.gov.uk

Economic Development: Mrs Dawn Hudd, Head of Commercial & Economic Development, Maidstone House, King Street, Maidstone ME15 6JQ ☎ 01622 602336 ✆ dawnhudd@maidstone.gov.uk

E-Government: Mr Dave Lindsay, Chief Information Officer, Maidstone House, King Street, Maidstone ME15 6JQ ☎ 01622 602156 ✆ davelindsay@maidstone.gov.uk

Electoral Registration: Mrs Kathy Hildidge, Interim Electoral Services Manager, Maidstone House, King Street, Maidstone ME15 6JQ ☎ 01622 602023 ✆ kathyhildidge@maidstone.gov.uk

Emergency Planning: Mr David Harrison, Emergency Planning Officer, Maidstone House, King Street, Maidstone ME12 6JQ ☎ 01622 602034 ✆ davidharrison@maidstone.gov.uk

Energy Management: Mr David Tibbit, Property & Procurement Manager, Maidstone House, King Street, Maidstone ME15 6JQ ☎ 01622 602361 ✆ davidtibbit@maidstone.gov.uk

Environmental Health: Mr John Littlemore, Head of Housing & Community Services, Maidstone House, King Street, Maidstone ME15 6JQ ☎ 01622 602207 ✆ johnlittlemore@maidstone.gov.uk

Estates, Property & Valuation: Mr David Tibbit, Property & Procurement Manager, Maidstone House, King Street, Maidstone ME15 6JQ ☎ 01622 602361 ✆ davidtibbit@maidstone.gov.uk

Events Manager: Ms Michelle King, MCL Events Officer, Maidstone House, King Street, Maidstone ME15 6JQ ☎ 01622 602718 ✆ michelleking@maidstone.gov.uk

Facilities: Ms Lisa Cook, Facilities & Corporate Support Manager, Maidstone House, King Street, Maidstone ME15 6JQ ☎ 01622 602236 ✆ lisacook@maidstone.gov.uk

Finance: Mr Mark Green, Director - Finance & Business Improvement, Maidstone House, King Street, Maidstone ME15 6JQ ☎ 01622 602297 ✆ markgreen@maidstone.gov.uk

Fleet Management: Mrs Jennifer Shepherd, Waste & Street Scene Manager, Maidstone House, King Street, Maidstone ME15 6JQ ☎ 01622 602400 ✆ jennifershepherd@maidstone.gov.uk

Grounds Maintenance: Mrs Jennifer Shepherd, Waste & Street Scene Manager, Maidstone House, King Street, Maidstone ME15 6JQ ☎ 01622 602400 ✆ jennifershepherd@maidstone.gov.uk

Health and Safety: Mr Alistair Barker, Corporate Health & Safety Manager, Maidstone House, King Street, Maidstone ME15 6JQ ☎ 01622 605308 ✆ alastairbarker@maidstone.gov.uk

Housing: Mr John Littlemore, Head of Housing & Community Services, Maidstone House, King Street, Maidstone ME15 6JQ ☎ 01622 602207 ✆ johnlittlemore@maidstone.gov.uk

Leisure and Cultural Services: Mrs Dawn Hudd, Head of Commercial & Economic Development, Maidstone House, King Street, Maidstone ME15 6JQ ☎ 01622 602336 ✆ dawnhudd@maidstone.gov.uk

Licensing: Mr John Littlemore, Head of Housing & Community Services, Maidstone House, King Street, Maidstone ME15 6JQ ☎ 01622 602207 ✆ johnlittlemore@maidstone.gov.uk

Licensing: Mrs Claire Perry, Licensing Partnership Manager, Council Offices, Argyle Road, Sevenoaks TN13 1HG ☎ 01732 227325; 07970 731616 ✆ claire.perry@tunbridgewells.gov.uk

Member Services: Mrs Angela Woodhouse, Head of Policy & Communications, Maidstone House, King Street, Maidstone ME15 6JQ ☎ 01622 602620 ✆ angelawoodhouse@maidstone.gov.uk

Parking: Mr Jeff Kitson, Parking Services Manager, Maidstone House, King Street, Maidstone ME15 6JQ ☎ 01622 602376 ✆ jeffkitson@maidstone.gov.uk

Partnerships: Mr Paul Taylor, Mid Kent Services Director, Maidstone House, King Street, Maidstone ME15 6JQ ☎ 01622 602663 ✆ paultaylor@maidstone.gov.uk

Personnel / HR: Ms Dena Smart, Head of HR Shared Services, Maidstone House, King Street, Maidstone ME15 6JQ ☎ 01622 602712 ✆ denasmart@maidstone.gov.uk

Planning: Mr Rob Jarman, Head of Planning & Development, Maidstone House, King Street, Maidstone ME15 6JQ ☎ 01622 602214 ✆ robjarman@maidstone.gov.uk

Procurement: Mr Stephen Trigg, Procurement Manager, Maidstone House, King Street, Maidstone ME15 6JQ ☎ 01622 602811 ✆ stephentrigg@maidstone.gov.uk

Recycling & Waste Minimisation: Mrs Jennifer Shepherd, Waste & Street Scene Manager, Maidstone House, King Street, Maidstone ME15 6JQ ☎ 01622 602400
🖑 jennifershepherd@maidstone.gov.uk

Regeneration: Mrs Dawn Hudd, Head of Commercial & Economic Development, Maidstone House, King Street, Maidstone ME15 6JQ
☎ 01622 602336 🖑 dawnhudd@maidstone.gov.uk

Staff Training: Mrs Catherine Harrison, Learning & Development Manager, Maidstone House, King Street, Maidstone ME15 6JQ
☎ 01622 602349 🖑 catherineharrison@maidstone.gov.uk

Sustainable Communities: Mr John Littlemore, Head of Housing & Community Services, Maidstone House, King Street, Maidstone ME15 6JQ ☎ 01622 602207
🖑 johnlittlemore@maidstone.gov.uk

Sustainable Development: Mr Rob Jarman, Head of Planning & Development, Maidstone House, King Street, Maidstone ME15 6JQ
☎ 01622 602214 🖑 robjarman@maidstone.gov.uk

Tourism: Mrs Laura Dickson, Tourism Manager, Maidstone House, King Street, Maidstone ME15 6JQ ☎ 01622 602510
🖑 andrewdavy@maidstone.gov.uk

Town Centre: Mr Andrew Davy, Town Centre Manager, The Management Suite, Chequers Centre, Pads Hill, Maidstone ME15 6AL

Waste Collection and Disposal: Mrs Jennifer Shepherd, Waste & Street Scene Manager, Maidstone House, King Street, Maidstone ME15 6JQ ☎ 01622 602400 🖑 jennifershepherd@maidstone.gov.uk

COUNCILLORS

Mayor: Butler, Derek (CON - Boxley)
derekbutler@maidstone.gov.uk

Leader of the Council: Wilson, Fran (LD - High Street)
franwilson@maidstone.gov.uk

Adkinson, Keith (LAB - Fant)
keithadkinson@maidstone.gov.uk

Blackmore, Annabelle (CON - Marden & Yalding)
annabelleblackmore@maidstone.gov.uk

Boughton, Matt (CON - Fant)
mattboughton@maidstone.gov.uk

Brice, Louise (CON - Staplehurst)
louisebrice@maidstone.gov.uk

Burton, David (CON - Marden & Yalding)
david.burton@burtons.uk.com

Burton, Matthew (CON - Park Wood)
mattburton@maidstone.gov.uk

Clark, Brian (LD - South)
brianclark@maidstone.gov.uk

Cox, Martin (LD - East)
martincox@maidstone.gov.uk

Cuming, Mike (CON - Bearsted)
mikecuming@maidstone.gov.uk

Daley, Dan (LD - Allington)
dandaley@maidstone.gov.uk

de Wiggondene, Nick (CON - Detling & Thurnham)
nickdewiggondene@maidstone.gov.uk

Ells, Simon (UKIP - Shepway North)
simonells@maidstone.gov.uk

English, Clive (LD - High Street)
cliveenglish@maidstone.gov.uk

Fermor, Emily (LD - Coxheath & Hunton)
emily.fermor@maidstone.gov.uk

Fissenden, Nikki (LD - East)
nicolafissenden@maidstone.gov.uk

Fort, Gill (CON - Leeds)
gillfort@maidstone.gov.uk

Garland, Christopher (CON - Shepway North)
christophergarland@maidstone.gov.uk

Garten, Patrik (CON - North Downs)
patrikgarten@maidstone.gov.uk

Gooch, Fay (IND - Barming)
faygooch@maidstone.gov.uk

Greer, Malcolm (CON - Boxley)
malcolmgreer@hazelwoodbox.fsnet.co.uk

Grigg, Susan (LD - Loose)
susangrigg@maidstone.gov.uk

Harper, Paul (LAB - Fant)
paulharper@maidstone.gov.uk

Harvey, Georgia (LD - Bridge)
georgiaharvey@maidstone.gov.uk

Harwood, Tony (LD - North)
tonyharwood@maidstone.gov.uk

Hastie, Michelle (LD - North)
michellehastie@maidstone.gov.uk

Hemsley, Michael (CON - North)
michaelhemsley@maidstone.gov.uk

Hinder, Wendy (CON - Boxley)
wendyhinder@maidstone.gov.uk

Joy, Denise (LD - High Street)
denisejoy@maidstone.gov.uk

Lewis, Diana (LD - Allington)
dianalewis@maidstone.gov.uk

McLoughlin, Steve (CON - Marden & Yalding)
stevemcloughlin@maidstone.gov.uk

Mortimer, Derek (LD - South)
derekmortimer@maidstone.gov.uk

Mortimer, Brian (LD - Coxheath & Hunton)
brianmortimer@maidstone.gov.uk

Munford, Steve (IND - Boughton Monchelsea & Chart Sutton)
stevemunford@maidstone.gov.uk

Naghi, David (LD - East)
davidnaghi@maidstone.gov.uk

Newton, Gordon (IND - Downswood & Otham)
gordonnewton@maidstone.gov.uk

Perry, John (CON - Staplehurst)
johnperry@maidstone.gov.uk

MAIDSTONE

Pickett, David (LD - Bridge)
davidpickett@maidstone.gov.uk

Powell, Eddie (UKIP - Shepway South)
eddpow@hotmail.com

Prendergast, Shellina (CON - Headcorn)
shellinaprendergast@maidstone.gov.uk

Revell, Mike (CON - Bearsted)
mikerevell@maidstone.gov.uk

Ring, Marion (CON - Shepway North)
marionring@maidstone.gov.uk

Robertson, Cynthia (LD - Allington)
cynthiarobertson@maidstone.gov.uk

Round, Martin (CON - Headcorn)
martinround@maidstone.gov.uk

Sams, Janetta (IND - Harrietsham & Lenham)

Sams, Tom (IND - Harrietsham & Lenham)
tomsams@maidstone.gov.uk

Springett, Val (CON - Bearsted)
valspringett@maidstone.gov.uk

Stockell, Paulina (CON - Sutton Valence & Langley)
paulinastockell@maidstone.gov.uk

Vizzard, Bryan (LD - Heath)
bryanvizzard@maidstone.gov.uk

Webb, Richard (LD - Coxheath & Hunton)
richardwebb@maidstone.gov.uk

Webster, Jade (CON - Park Wood)
jadewebster@maidstone.gov.uk

Wilby, Paul (LD - South)
paulwilby@maidstone.gov.uk

Willis, James (LD - Heath)
jameswills@maidstone.gov.uk

POLITICAL COMPOSITION
CON: 23, LD: 22, IND: 5, LAB: 2, UKIP: 2, Vacant: 1

COMMITTEE CHAIRS

Audit: Mr Steve McLoughlin

Licensing: Mrs Denise Joy

Planning: Mr John Perry

Maldon   D

Maldon District Council, Council Offices, Princes Road,
Maldon CM9 5DL
☎ 01621 854477 🖨 01621 852575 ✆ contact@maldon.gov.uk
🖥 www.maldon.gov.uk

FACTS AND FIGURES
Parliamentary Constituencies: Maldon
EU Constituencies: Eastern
Election Frequency: Elections are of whole council

PRINCIPAL OFFICERS

Chief Executive: Ms Fiona Marshall, Chief Executive, Council
Offices, Princes Road, Maldon CM9 5DL ☎ 01621 854477
✆ fiona.marshall@maldon.gov.uk

Senior Management: Mr Nick Fenwick, Director - Planning &
Regulatory Services, District Council Offices, Princes Road, Maldon
CM9 7DL ☎ 01621 854477 ✆ nick.fenwick@maldon.gov.uk

Senior Management: Mr Richard Holmes, Director - Customers
& Community, District Council Offices, Princes Road, Maldon CM9
7DL ☎ 01621 875752 ✆ richard.holmes@maldon.gov.uk

Senior Management: Ms Ka Ng, Director - Resources, District
Council Offices, Princes Road, Maldon CM9 7DL

Access Officer / Social Services (Disability): Mr Norman
Wright, Part-Time Access Officer, Princes Road, Maldon CM9 5DL
☎ 01621 854477 ✆ norman.wright@maldon.gov.uk

Building Control: Mr Alan Taylor, Consultant Building Control
Team Leader, Council Offices, Princes Road, Maldon CM9 5DL
☎ 01621 854477 ✆ alan.taylor@maldon.gov.uk

PR / Communications: Mr Russell Dawes, Public Relations
Manager, Council Offices, Princes Road, Maldon CM9 5DL
☎ 01621 854477 ✆ russell.dawes@maldon.gov.uk

Community Safety: Mr Richard Holmes, Director - Customers
& Community, District Council Offices, Princes Road, Maldon CM9
7DL ☎ 01621 875752 ✆ richard.holmes@maldon.gov.uk

Community Safety: Mrs Chris Rust, Community Safety & LSP
Co-ordinator, District Council Offices, Princes Road, Maldon CM9
7DL ☎ 01621 854477 ✆ chris.rust@maldon.gov.uk

Contracts: Mr Jonathan Stevens, Contracts & Facilities Manager,
District Council Offices, Princes Road, Maldon CM9 7DL
☎ 01621 854477 ✆ jonathan.stevens@maldon.gov.uk

Customer Service: Mrs Sue Green, Customers Manager, District
Council Offices, Princes Road, Maldon CM9 7DL ☎ 01621 854477
✆ sue.green@maldon.gov.uk

Direct Labour: Mr Steve Krolzig, Maintenance Officer, District
Council Offices, Princes Road, Maldon CM9 7DL ☎ 01621 875826
✆ steve.krolzig@maldon.gov.uk

Economic Development: Mrs Kerry Martin, Economic
Development Manager, District Council Offices, Princes Road,
Maldon CM9 7DL ☎ 01621 875853 ✆ kerry.martin@maldon.gov.uk

E-Government: Mr Simon Mitchell, IT Team Leader, Council
Offices, Princes Road, Maldon CM9 5DL ☎ 01621 854477
✆ simon.mitchell@maldon.gov.uk

Electoral Registration: Ms Lynda Elsegood, Elections
Management Officer, Council Offices, Princes Road, Maldon CM9
5DL ☎ 01621 854477 ✆ lynda.elsegood@maldon.gov.uk

Electoral Registration: Mrs Melissa Kelly, Legal & Democratic
Services Manager, District Council Offices, Princes Road, Maldon
CM9 7DL ☎ 01621 854477 ✆ melissa.kelly@maldon.gov.uk

Emergency Planning: Mr Richard Holmes, Director - Customers & Community, District Council Offices, Princes Road, Maldon CM9 7DL ☎ 01621 875752 ⌨ richard.holmes@maldon.gov.uk

Energy Management: Mrs Shirley Hall, Environment Team Leader, Council Offices, Princes Road, Maldon CM9 7DL ☎ 01621 854477 ⌨ shirley.hall@maldon.gov.uk

Environmental / Technical Services: Mrs Gill Gibson, Commercial Environmental Health Team Leader, Council Offices, Princes Road, Maldon CM9 5DL ☎ 01621 854477 ⌨ gillian.gibson@maldon.gov.uk

Environmental / Technical Services: Mr Ian Haines, Environmental Manager, Council Offices, Princes Road, Maldon CM9 5DL ☎ 01621 854477 ⌨ ian.haines@maldon.gov.uk

Environmental Health: Mrs Gill Gibson, Commercial Environmental Health Team Leader, Council Offices, Princes Road, Maldon CM9 5DL ☎ 01621 854477 ⌨ gillian.gibson@maldon.gov.uk

Environmental Health: Mr Ian Haines, Environmental Manager, Council Offices, Princes Road, Maldon CM9 5DL ☎ 01621 854477 ⌨ ian.haines@maldon.gov.uk

Estates, Property & Valuation: Mr David Rust, Senior Technical Officer, District Council Offices, Princes Road, Maldon CM9 7DL ☎ 01621 854477 ⌨ david.rust@maldon.gov.uk

Events Manager: Miss Alexis Brown, Tourism & Events Manager, District Council Offices, Princes Road, Maldon CM9 7DL ☎ 01621 856503 ⌨ alexis.brown@maldon.gov.uk

Facilities: Mr Jonathan Stevens, Contracts & Facilities Manager, District Council Offices, Princes Road, Maldon CM9 7DL ☎ 01621 854477 ⌨ jonathan.stevens@maldon.gov.uk

Finance: Ms Ka Ng, Director - Resources, District Council Offices, Princes Road, Maldon CM9 7DL

Grounds Maintenance: Mr Ben Brown, Tourism, Countryside & Coast Manager, District Council Offices, Princes Road, Maldon CM9 7DL ☎ 01621 875752 ⌨ ben.brown@maldon.gov.uk

Grounds Maintenance: Mr Steve Krolzig, Maintenance Officer, District Council Offices, Princes Road, Maldon CM9 7DL ☎ 01621 875826 ⌨ steve.krolzig@maldon.gov.uk

Health and Safety: Mrs Gill Gibson, Commercial Environmental Health Team Leader, Council Offices, Princes Road, Maldon CM9 5DL ☎ 01621 854477 ⌨ gillian.gibson@maldon.gov.uk

Housing: Mr Paul Gayler, Strategic Housing Manager, District Council Offices, Princes Road, Maldon CM9 7DL ☎ 01621 854477 ⌨ paul.gayler@maldon.gov.uk

Legal: Mrs Melissa Kelly, Legal & Democratic Services Manager, District Council Offices, Princes Road, Maldon CM9 7DL ☎ 01621 854477 ⌨ melissa.kelly@maldon.gov.uk

Leisure and Cultural Services: Mr Richard Heard, Leisure & Community Team Leader, District Council Offices, Princes Road, Maldon CM9 7DL ☎ 01621 875838 ⌨ richard.heard@maldon.gov.uk

Leisure and Cultural Services: Mr Richard Holmes, Director - Customers & Community, District Council Offices, Princes Road, Maldon CM9 7DL ☎ 01621 875752 ⌨ richard.holmes@maldon.gov.uk

Lottery Funding, Charity and Voluntary: Ms Ka Ng, Director - Resources, District Council Offices, Princes Road, Maldon CM9 7DL

Member Services: Mrs Val Downes, PA to the Leader, Council Offices, Princes Road, Maldon CM9 7DL ☎ 01621 854477 ⌨ val.downes@maldon.gov.uk

Parking: Mr Richard Holmes, Director - Customers & Community, District Council Offices, Princes Road, Maldon CM9 7DL ☎ 01621 875752 ⌨ richard.holmes@maldon.gov.uk

Personnel / HR: Mrs Dawn Moyse, Group Manager - People, Policy & Performance, District Council Offices, Princes Road, Maldon CM9 7DL ☎ 01621 854477 ⌨ dawn.moyse@maldon.gov.uk

Planning: Mr Nick Fenwick, Director - Planning & Regulatory Services, District Council Offices, Princes Road, Maldon CM9 7DL ☎ 01621 854477 ⌨ nick.fenwick@maldon.gov.uk

Recycling & Waste Minimisation: Mrs Karen Bomford, Customers & Living Manager, District Council Offices, Princes Road, Maldon CM9 7DL ☎ 01621 854477 ⌨ karen.bomford@maldon.gov.uk

Staff Training: Mrs Dawn Moyse, Group Manager - People, Policy & Performance, District Council Offices, Princes Road, Maldon CM9 7DL ☎ 01621 854477 ⌨ dawn.moyse@maldon.gov.uk

Street Scene: Mrs Karen Bomford, Customers & Living Manager, District Council Offices, Princes Road, Maldon CM9 7DL ☎ 01621 854477 ⌨ karen.bomford@maldon.gov.uk

Sustainable Communities: Mr Richard Holmes, Director - Customers & Community, District Council Offices, Princes Road, Maldon CM9 7DL ☎ 01621 875752 ⌨ richard.holmes@maldon.gov.uk

Waste Collection and Disposal: Mrs Karen Bomford, Customers & Living Manager, District Council Offices, Princes Road, Maldon CM9 7DL ☎ 01621 854477 ⌨ karen.bomford@maldon.gov.uk

Waste Management: Mrs Karen Bomford, Customers & Living Manager, District Council Offices, Princes Road, Maldon CM9 7DL ☎ 01621 854477 ⌨ karen.bomford@maldon.gov.uk

COUNCILLORS

Chair: Elliott, Peter (CON - Burnham-on-Crouch South) cllr.peter.elliott@maldon.gov.uk

Leader of the Council: Lewis, Miriam (CON - Heybridge West) cllr.miriam.lewis@maldon.gov.uk

Deputy Leader of the Council: Durham, Mark (CON - Wickham Bishops & Woodham) cllr.mark.durham@maldon.gov.uk

MALDON

Group Leader: Beale, Brian (IND - Southminster)
cllr.brian.beale@maldon.gov.uk

Acevedo, Beverley (UKIP - Althorne)
cllr.beverley.acevedo@maldon.gov.uk

Archer, John (CON - Purleigh)
cllr.john.archer@maldon.gov.uk

Bamford, Elaine (CON - Tolleshunt D'Arcy)
cllr.elaine.bamford@maldon.gov.uk

Bass, Henry (CON - Wickham Bishops & Woodham)
cllr.henry.bass@maldon.gov.uk

Beale, Anne (CON - Heybridge East)
cllr.anne.beale@maldon.gov.uk

Boyce, Robert (CON - Althorne)
cllr.bob.boyce@maldon.gov.uk

Cain, Andrew (CON - Maldon South)
cllr.andrew.cain@maldon.gov.uk

Channer, Penny (CON - Mayland)
cllr.penny.channer@maldon.gov.uk

Dewick, Richard (CON - Tillingham)
cllr.richard.dewick@maldon.gov.uk

Dobson, Ian (CON - Heybridge West)
cllr.ian.dobson@maldon.gov.uk

Elliott, Helen (CON - Burnham-on-Crouch North)
cllr.helen.elliott@maldon.gov.uk

Fluker, Adrian (CON - Southminster)
cllr.adrian.fluker@maldon.gov.uk

Harker, Bryan (CON - Heybridge East)
cllr.bryan.harker@maldon.gov.uk

Harker, Brenda (CON - Maldon South)
cllr.brenda.harker@maldon.gov.uk

Heard, Mark (IND - Maldon West)
cllr.mark.heard@maldon.gov.uk

Helm, Michael (CON - Mayland)
cllr.michael.helm@maldon.gov.uk

Keys, John (CON - Great Totham)
cllr.john.keys@maldon.gov.uk

MacKenzie, Charles (CON - Maldon West)
cllr.charles.mackenzie@maldon.gov.uk

Pearlman, Michael (CON - Maldon North)
cllr.michael.pearlman@maldon.gov.uk

Pratt, Ron (CON - Burnham-on-Crouch South)
cllr.ron.pratt@maldon.gov.uk

Pudney, Neil (CON - Burnham-on-Crouch North)
cllr.neil.pudney@maldon.gov.uk

Savage, Stephen (CON - Maldon East)
cllr.stephen.savage@maldon.gov.uk

Shrimpton, Tony (CON - Maldon North)
cllr.tony.shrimpton@maldon.gov.uk

Sismey, David (CON - Great Totham)
cllr.david.sismey@maldon.gov.uk

St. Joseph, Andrew (CON - Tollesbury)
cllr.andrew.st.joseph@maldon.gov.uk

Thompson, Maddie (CON - Tolleshunt D'Arcy)
cllr.maddie.thompson@maldon.gov.uk

White, Sue (CON - Purleigh)
cllr.sue.white@maldon.gov.uk

POLITICAL COMPOSITION
CON: 28, IND: 2, UKIP: 1

COMMITTEE CHAIRS

Audit: Mr Bryan Harker

Planning & Licensing: Mrs Penny Channer

Malvern Hills   D

Malvern Hills District Council, Council House, Avenue Road, Malvern WR14 3AF
☎ 01684 862151 🖷 01684 862473 ✆ contactus@malvernhills.gov.uk
🖥 www.malvernhills.gov.uk

FACTS AND FIGURES
EU Constituencies: West Midlands
Election Frequency: Elections are of whole council

PRINCIPAL OFFICERS

Chief Executive: Mr Jack Hegarty, Chief Executive, Council House, Avenue Road, Malvern WR14 3AF ☎ 01684 862338

Deputy Chief Executive: Mr Andy Baldwin, Deputy Chief Executive - Head of Resources, Council House, Avenue Road, Malvern WR14 3AF ☎ 01684 862236 ✆ andy.baldwin@malvernhills.gov.uk

Senior Management: Mr Vic Allison, Deputy Managing Director, Civic Centre, Queen Elizabeth Drive, Pershore WR10 1PT ☎ 01386 565586 ✆ vic.allison@wychavon.gov.uk

Senior Management: Mr Phil Merrick, Joint Head of Economy & Community Services, Council House, Avenue Road, Malvern WR14 3AF ☎ 01386 565588 ✆ phil.merrick@wychavon.gov.uk

Senior Management: Ms Fiona Narburgh, Joint Head of Strategy, Democratic & Customer Services, Council House, Avenue Road, Malvern WR14 3AF ☎ 01386 565101 ✆ fiona.narburgh@wychavon.gov.uk

Senior Management: Mr Gary Williams, Joint Head of Planning & Housing Services, Council House, Avenue Road, Malvern WR14 2TB ☎ 01386 565279 ✆ gary.williams@wychavon.gov.uk

Best Value: Ms Fiona Narburgh, Joint Head of Strategy, Democratic & Customer Services, Council House, Avenue Road, Malvern WR14 3AF ☎ 01386 565101 ✆ fiona.narburgh@wychavon.gov.uk

PR / Communications: Ms Emma Wild, Joint Marketing & Communications Manager, Civic Centre, Queen Elizabeth Drive, Pershore WR10 1PT ☎ 01386 565102 ✆ emma.wild@wychavon.gov.uk

Community Planning: Mr Gary Williams, Joint Head of Planning & Housing Services, Council House, Avenue Road, Malvern WR14 2TB ☎ 01386 565279 ✆ gary.williams@wychavon.gov.uk

Computer Management: Mr Andy Baldwin, Deputy Chief Executive - Head of Resources, Council House, Avenue Road, Malvern WR14 3AF ☎ 01684 862236
🖅 andy.baldwin@malvernhills.gov.uk

Contracts: Mr John Williams, Head of Policy & Governance, Council House, Avenue Road, Malvern WR14 3AF ☎ 01684 862227
🖅 john.williams@malvernhills.gov.uk

Corporate Services: Mr John Williams, Head of Policy & Governance, Council House, Avenue Road, Malvern WR14 3AF ☎ 01684 862227 🖅 john.williams@malvernhills.gov.uk

Customer Service: Mr Ivor Pumfrey, Acting Head of Regulatory Services, Council House, Avenue Road, Malvern WR14 3AF ☎ 01684 862296 🖅 ivor.pumfrey@malvernhills.gov.uk

Economic Development: Mr Phil Merrick, Joint Head of Economy & Community Services, Council House, Avenue Road, Malvern WR14 3AF ☎ 01386 565588 🖅 phil.merrick@wychavon.gov.uk

Emergency Planning: Mr Phil Merrick, Joint Head of Economy & Community Services, Council House, Avenue Road, Malvern WR14 3AF ☎ 01386 565588 🖅 phil.merrick@wychavon.gov.uk

Emergency Planning: Mr John Williams, Head of Policy & Governance, Council House, Avenue Road, Malvern WR14 3AF ☎ 01684 862227 🖅 john.williams@malvernhills.gov.uk

Estates, Property & Valuation: Mr Andy Baldwin, Deputy Chief Executive - Head of Resources, Council House, Avenue Road, Malvern WR14 3AF ☎ 01684 862236
🖅 andy.baldwin@malvernhills.gov.uk

Events Manager: Ms Emma Wild, Joint Marketing & Communications Manager, Civic Centre, Queen Elizabeth Drive, Pershore WR10 1PT ☎ 01386 565102
🖅 emma.wild@wychavon.gov.uk

Facilities: Mr Andy Baldwin, Deputy Chief Executive - Head of Resources, Council House, Avenue Road, Malvern WR14 3AF ☎ 01684 862236 🖅 andy.baldwin@malvernhills.gov.uk

Finance: Mr Andy Baldwin, Deputy Chief Executive - Head of Resources, Council House, Avenue Road, Malvern WR14 3AF ☎ 01684 862236 🖅 andy.baldwin@malvernhills.gov.uk

Housing: Mr Gary Williams, Joint Head of Planning & Housing Services, Council House, Avenue Road, Malvern WR14 2TB ☎ 01386 565279 🖅 gary.williams@wychavon.gov.uk

Legal: Mr Andy Baldwin, Deputy Chief Executive - Head of Resources, Council House, Avenue Road, Malvern WR14 3AF ☎ 01684 862236 🖅 andy.baldwin@malvernhills.gov.uk

Leisure and Cultural Services: Mr Phil Merrick, Joint Head of Economy & Community Services, Council House, Avenue Road, Malvern WR14 3AF ☎ 01386 565588
🖅 phil.merrick@wychavon.gov.uk

Member Services: Ms Fiona Narburgh, Joint Head of Strategy, Democratic & Customer Services, Council House, Avenue Road, Malvern WR14 3AF ☎ 01386 565101
🖅 fiona.narburgh@wychavon.gov.uk

Personnel / HR: Mr Andy Baldwin, Deputy Chief Executive - Head of Resources, Council House, Avenue Road, Malvern WR14 3AF ☎ 01684 862236 🖅 andy.baldwin@malvernhills.gov.uk

Planning: Mr Gary Williams, Joint Head of Planning & Housing Services, Council House, Avenue Road, Malvern WR14 2TB ☎ 01386 565279 🖅 gary.williams@wychavon.gov.uk

Waste Collection and Disposal: Mr Phil Merrick, Joint Head of Economy & Community Services, Council House, Avenue Road, Malvern WR14 3AF ☎ 01386 565588
🖅 phil.merrick@wychavon.gov.uk

COUNCILLORS

Chair: Raine, John (GRN - West)
john.raine@malvernhillssdc.net

Vice-Chair: O'Donnell, Chris (CON - Wells)
chris.odonnell@malvernhillssdc.net

Leader of the Council: Grove, Phillip (CON - Tenbury)
phillip.grove@malvernhillssdc.net

Deputy Leader of the Council: Chambers, David (CON - Broadheath)
david.chambers@malvernhillssdc.net

Group Leader: Roskams, Julian (GRN - West)
julian.roskams@malvernhillssdc.net

Group Leader: Wells, Tom (LD - Powick)
talwells@btinernet.com

Baker, Melanie (CON - Chase)
melanie.baker@malvernhillssdc.net

Baker, Tony (CON - Dyson Perrins)
tony.baker@malvernhillssdc.net

Behan, Bronwen (CON - Longdon)
bronwen.behan@malvernhillssdc.net

Bovey, Caroline (LD - Pickersleigh)
caroline.bovey@malvernhillssdc.net

Campbell, Hannah (CON - Priory)
hannah.campbell@malvernhillssdc.net

Campbell, Jill (IND - Wells)
jill.campbell@malvernhillssdc.net

Clarke, Dean (IND - Hallow)
drcmhdc@gamil.com

Cumming, Pam (CON - Baldwin)
pam.cumming@malvernhillssdc.net

Cumming, Paul (CON - Woodbury)
paul.cumming@malvernhillssdc.net

Davies, Mick (IND - Morton)
mick.davies@malvernhillssdc.net

Dell, Chris (CON - Lindbridge)
chris.dell@malvernhillssdc.net

Godwin, Douglas (CON - Broadheath)
douglas.godwin@malvernhillssdc.net

Halling, Leanne (CON - Pickersleigh)
leanne.halling@malvernhillssdc.net

MALVERN HILLS

Hall-Jones, Roger (CON - Priory)
roger.hall-jones@malvernhillsdc.net

Harrison, David (IND - Kempsey)
david.harrison@malvernhillsdc.net

Hung Chan, Kwai (LD - Link)
kwai.hung.chang@malvernhillsdc.net

Kerby, Robert (CON - Link)
robert.kerby@malvernhillsdc.net

Massey, Rebecca (CON - Chase)
rebecca.massey@malvernhillsdc.net

Michael, John (IND - Kempsey)
john.michael@malvernhillsdc.net

Morgan, Mike (CON - Upton & Hanley)
mike.morgan@malvernhillsdc.net

Morgan, Andrea (CON - Upton & Hanley)
andrea.morgan@malvernhillsdc.net

Myatt, Val (LD - Pickersleigh)
val.myatt@malvernhillsdc.net

Newman, Elaine (LD - Powick)
elaine.newman@malvernhillsdc.net

O'Donnell, James (CON - Chase)
james.odonnell@malvernhillsdc.net

Owenson, Jeremy (CON - Ripple)
jeremy.owenson@malvernhillsdc.net

Palethorpe, Caroline (CON - Teme Valley)
caroline.palethorpe@malvernhillsdc.net

Penn, Tony (CON - Tenbury)
tony.penn@malvernhillsdc.net

Reed, Chris (GRN - Dyson Perrins)
chris.reed@malvernhillsdc.net

Rouse, Sarah (IND - Alfrick & Leigh)
sarah.rouse@malvernhillsdc.net

Warburton, Anthony (IND - Alfrick & Leigh)
anthony.warburton@malvernhillsdc.net

Watkins, David (CON - Link)
david.watkins@malvernhillsdc.net

Williams, Barbara (CON - Martley)
barbara.williams@malvernhillsdc.net

POLITICAL COMPOSITION
CON: 23, IND: 7, LD: 5, GRN: 3

COMMITTEE CHAIRS

Planning: Ms Melanie Baker

Manchester City   M

Manchester City Council, Manchester City Council, Town Hall, Albert Square, Manchester M60 2LA
☎ 0161 234 5000 ⌨ manchester@manchester.gov.uk
🖥 www.manchester.gov.uk

FACTS AND FIGURES
Parliamentary Constituencies: Blackley and Broughton, Manchester Central, Manchester, Gorton, Manchester, Withington, Wythenshawe and Sale East
EU Constituencies: North West

Election Frequency: Elections are by thirds

PRINCIPAL OFFICERS

Chief Executive: Sir Howard Bernstein, Chief Executive, Manchester City Council, Town Hall, Albert Square, Manchester M60 2LA ☎ 0161 234 3006 ⌨ h.bernstein@manchester.gov.uk

Deputy Chief Executive: Mr Geoff Little, Deputy Chief Executive - People, Policy & Reform, Manchester City Council, Town Hall, Albert Square, Manchester M60 2LA ☎ 0161 234 3280 ⌨ g.little@manchester.gov.uk

Deputy Chief Executive: Ms Sara Todd, Deputy Chief Executive - Growth & Neighbourhoods, Manchester City Council, Town Hall, Albert Square, Manchester M60 2LA ☎ 0161 234 3286 ⌨ s.todd@manchester.gov.uk

Assistant Chief Executive: Mr Sean McGonigle, Assistant Chief Executive - Growth, Manchester City Council, Town Hall, Albert Square, Manchester M60 2LA ☎ 0161 234 4821 ⌨ s.mcgonigle@manchester.gov.uk

Senior Management: Mr Bob Brown, Chief Information Officer, Manchester City Council, Town Hall, Albert Square, Manchester M60 2LA ☎ 0161 234 5998 ⌨ b.brown1@manchester.gov.uk

Senior Management: Mr Kenny Brown, Interim Director - HR & OD, Manchester City Council, Town Hall, Albert Square, Manchester M60 2LA ☎ 0161 600 8380 ⌨ k.brown@manchester.gov.uk

Senior Management: Ms Lorraine Butcher, Joint Director - Health & Social Care, Manchester City Council, Town Hall, Albert Square, Manchester M60 2LA l.butcher@manchester.gov.uk

Senior Management: Ms Carol Culley, City Treasurer, Manchester City Council, Town Hall, Albert Square, Manchester M60 2LA ☎ 0161 234 3406 ⌨ c.culley@manchester.gov.uk

Senior Management: Mr Kim Dorrington, Interim Director - Highways, Manchester City Council, Town Hall, Albert Square, Manchester M60 2LA k.dorrington@manchester.gov.uk

Senior Management: Mr John Edwards, Director - Education & Skills, Manchester City Council, Town Hall, Albert Square, Manchester M60 2LA ☎ 0161 234 4314 ⌨ j.edwards@manchester.gov.uk

Senior Management: Ms Janice Gotts, Deputy City Treasurer, Manchester City Council, Town Hall, Albert Square, Manchester M60 2LA ☎ 0161 234 3590 ⌨ j.gotts@manchester.gov.uk

Senior Management: Mr Paul Marshall, Strategic Director - Children's Commissioning, Manchester City Council, Town Hall, Albert Square, Manchester M60 2LA ☎ 0161 234 3804 ⌨ p.marshall1@manchester.gov.uk

Senior Management: Ms Carmel McKeogh, Interim Director - HR & OD, Manchester City Council, Town Hall, Albert Square, Manchester M60 2LA ☎ 0161 600 8380 ⌨ c.mckeogh@manchester.gov.uk

Senior Management: Mr David Regan, Director - Public Health, Manchester City Council, Town Hall, Albert Square, Manchester M60 2LA ☎ 0161 234 5000 ⊕ d.regan@manchester.gov.uk

Senior Management: Mr Eddie Smith, Strategic Director - Strategic Development, Manchester City Council, Town Hall, Albert Square, Manchester M60 2LA ☎ 0161 234 3030 ⊕ e.smith@manchester.gov.uk

Senior Management: Ms Hazel Summers, Strategic Director - Adult Services, Manchester City Council, Town Hall, Albert Square, Manchester M60 2LA ☎ 0161 234 4994 ⊕ h.summers@manchester.gov.uk

Senior Management: Ms Liz Treacy, City Solicitor, Manchester City Council, Town Hall, Albert Square, Manchester M60 2LA ☎ 0161 234 3339 ⊕ l.treacy@manchester.gov.uk

Senior Management: Ms Fiona Worrall, Director - Neighbourhoods, Manchester City Council, Town Hall, Albert Square, Manchester M60 2LA ☎ 0161 234 3926 ⊕ fiona.worrall@manchester.gov.uk

Access Officer / Social Services (Disability): Ms Kathleen Weaver, Head of Customer Access, Manchester City Council, Town Hall, Albert Square, Manchester M60 2LA ☎ 0161 234 3745 ⊕ k.weaver1@manchester.gov.uk

Architect, Building / Property Services: Ms Carol Culley, City Treasurer, Manchester City Council, Town Hall, Albert Square, Manchester M60 2LA ☎ 0161 234 3406 ⊕ c.culley@manchester.gov.uk

Best Value: Ms Sarah Henry, Head of Public Intelligence & Performance, Manchester City Council, Town Hall, Albert Square, Manchester M60 2LA ☎ 0161 234 1012 ⊕ s.henry@manchester.gov.uk

Building Control: Ms Julie Roscoe, Head of Planning, Licensing & Building Control, Manchester City Council, Town Hall, Albert Square, Manchester M60 2LA ☎ 0161 234 4552 ⊕ j.roscoe@manchester.gov.uk

Children / Youth Services: Ms Amanda Amesbury, Strategic Head of Children's Social Care, Manchester City Council, Town Hall, Albert Square, Manchester M60 2LA ☎ 0161 219 2442 ⊕ a.amesbury@manchester.gov.uk

Children / Youth Services: Mr Paul Marshall, Strategic Director - Children's Commissioning, Manchester City Council, Town Hall, Albert Square, Manchester M60 2LA ☎ 0161 234 3804 ⊕ p.marshall1@manchester.gov.uk

Civil Registration: Mr Jonathan Kershners, Registration & Coroners Service Manager, Manchester City Council, Town Hall, Albert Square, Manchester M60 2LA ☎ 0161 234 5566 ⊕ j.kershner@manchester.gov.uk

Community Safety: Ms Fiona Sharkey, Strategic Lead - Compliance / Community Safety, Manchester City Council, Town Hall, Albert Square, Manchester M60 2LA ☎ 0161 957 8379 ⊕ fiona.sharkey@manchester.gov.uk

Computer Management: Mr Bob Brown, Chief Information Officer, Manchester City Council, Town Hall, Albert Square, Manchester M60 2LA ☎ 0161 234 5998 ⊕ b.brown1@manchester.gov.uk

Consumer Protection and Trading Standards: Ms Fiona Sharkey, Strategic Lead - Compliance / Community Safety, Manchester City Council, Town Hall, Albert Square, Manchester M60 2LA ☎ 0161 957 8379 ⊕ fiona.sharkey@manchester.gov.uk

Contracts: Mr Ian Brown, Head of Corporate Procurement, Manchester City Council, Town Hall, Albert Square, Manchester M60 2LA ☎ 0161 234 3255 ⊕ i.brown@manchester.gov.uk

Corporate Services: Ms Carol Culley, City Treasurer, Manchester City Council, Town Hall, Albert Square, Manchester M60 2LA ☎ 0161 234 3406 ⊕ c.culley@manchester.gov.uk

Customer Service: Mr Lee Owen, Head of Customer Services, Manchester City Council, Town Hall, Albert Square, Manchester M60 2LA ☎ 0161 245 7525 ⊕ l.owen@manchester.gov.uk

Direct Labour: Mr Mike Brogan, Operations Manager, Manchester City Council, Hopper Street Depot, Ardwick, Manchester M12 6LA ☎ 0161 908 5800 ⊕ m.brogan@manchester.gov.uk

Economic Development: Ms Angela Harrington, Head of Work & Skills, Manchester City Council, Town Hall, Albert Square, Manchester M60 2LA ☎ 0161 234 1501 ⊕ a.harrington@manchester.gov.uk

E-Government: Ms Jennifer Green, Head of Strategic Communications, Manchester City Council, Town Hall, Albert Square, Manchester M60 2LA ☎ 0161 234 4420 ⊕ j.green1@manchester.gov.uk

Electoral Registration: Ms Emma Burnett, Head of Electoral Services, Manchester City Council, Town Hall, Albert Square, Manchester M60 2LA ☎ 0161 234 3146 ⊕ e.burnett@manchester.gov.uk

Emergency Planning: Ms Fiona Worrall, Director - Neighbourhoods, Manchester City Council, Town Hall, Albert Square, Manchester M60 2LA ☎ 0161 234 3926 ⊕ fiona.worrall@manchester.gov.uk

Energy Management: Mr Walter Dooley, Group Energy Manager, Manchester City Council, Town Hall, Albert Square, Manchester M60 2LA ☎ 0161 234 3633 ⊕ w.dooley@manchester.gov.uk

Environmental / Technical Services: Mr Richard Elliott, Head of Policy, Partnerships & Research, Manchester City Council, Town Hall, Albert Square, Manchester M60 2LA ☎ 0161 219 6494 ⊕ r.elliott@manchester.gov.uk

Environmental Health: Ms Janet Shaw, Citywide Support Team Lead, Manchester City Council, Town Hall, Albert Square, Manchester M60 2LA ☎ 0161 234 1587 ⊕ j.shaw@manchester.gov.uk

MANCHESTER CITY

Estates, Property & Valuation: Ms Julie McMurray, Head of Client Relationships, Manchester City Council, Town Hall, Albert Square, Manchester M60 2LA j.mcmurray@manchester.gov.uk

European Liaison: Mr Richard Elliott, Head of Policy, Partnerships & Research, Manchester City Council, Town Hall, Albert Square, Manchester M60 2LA ☎ 0161 219 6494 ⌨ r.elliott@manchester.gov.uk

Events Manager: Mr Mike Parrott, Head of Events, Manchester City Council, Town Hall, Albert Square, Manchester M60 2LA ☎ 0161 234 5242 ⌨ m.parrott@manchester.gov.uk

Facilities: Mr Steven Southern, Head of Facilities Management, New Smithfield Market, Whitworth Street East, Bradford, Manchester M11 2NQ ☎ 0161 234 5242 ⌨ s.southern@manchester.gov.uk

Finance: Ms Carol Culley, City Treasurer, Manchester City Council, Town Hall, Albert Square, Manchester M60 2LA ☎ 0161 234 3406 ⌨ c.culley@manchester.gov.uk

Treasury: Ms Carol Culley, City Treasurer, Manchester City Council, Town Hall, Albert Square, Manchester M60 2LA ☎ 0161 234 3406 ⌨ c.culley@manchester.gov.uk

Fleet Management: Ms Elaine Heggie, Head of Business Units, Manchester City Council, Town Hall, Albert Square, Manchester M60 2LA ☎ 0161 234 1290 ⌨ e.heggie@manchester.gov.uk

Grounds Maintenance: Mr Chaz Farghaly, Citywide Support Lead, Manchester City Council, Town Hall, Albert Square, Manchester M60 2LA ☎ 0161 953 8393 ⌨ c.farghaly@manchester.gov.uk

Health and Safety: Mr Simon Gardiner, Health & Safety Manager, Manchester City Council, Town Hall, Albert Square, Manchester M60 2LA ☎ 0161 234 5260 ⌨ s.gardiner@manchester.gov.uk

Highways: Mr Kevin Gillham, Citywide Highway Manager, Manchester City Council, Town Hall, Albert Square, Manchester M60 2LA ☎ 0161 234 5148 ⌨ k.gillham@manchester.gov.uk

Housing: Mr Paul Beardmore, Director - Housing, Manchester City Council, Town Hall, Albert Square, Manchester M60 2LA ☎ 0161 234 4811 ⌨ p.beardmore@manchester.gov.uk

Local Area Agreement: Mr Richard Elliott, Head of Policy, Partnerships & Research, Manchester City Council, Town Hall, Albert Square, Manchester M60 2LA ☎ 0161 219 6494 ⌨ r.elliott@manchester.gov.uk

Legal: Ms Jacqueline Dennis, Head of Legal Services, Manchester City Council, Town Hall, Albert Square, Manchester M60 2LA ☎ 0161 234 3053 ⌨ j.dennis@manchester.gov.uk

Legal: Ms Liz Treacy, City Solicitor, Manchester City Council, Town Hall, Albert Square, Manchester M60 2LA ☎ 0161 234 3339 ⌨ l.treacy@manchester.gov.uk

Leisure and Cultural Services: Mr Neil Fairlamb, Strategic Lead - Parks / Leisure / Events, Manchester City Council, Town Hall, Albert Square, Manchester M60 2LA ☎ 0161 219 2539 ⌨ n.fairlamb@manchester.gov.uk

Leisure and Cultural Services: Mr Neil MacInnes, Strategic Lead - Library / Galleries / Culture, Manchester City Council, Town Hall, Albert Square, Manchester M60 2LA ☎ 0161 234 1392 ⌨ n.macinnes@libraries.manchester.gov.uk

Licensing: Ms Julie Roscoe, Head of Planning, Licensing & Building Control, Manchester City Council, Town Hall, Albert Square, Manchester M60 2LA ☎ 0161 234 4552 ⌨ j.roscoe@manchester.gov.uk

Lifelong Learning: Ms Julie Rushton, Head of Manchester Adult Education Service, Manchester City Council, Town Hall, Albert Square, Manchester M60 2LA ☎ 0161 234 5679 ⌨ j.rushton@manchester.gov.uk

Lighting: Mr Kevin Gillham, Citywide Highway Manager, Manchester City Council, Town Hall, Albert Square, Manchester M60 2LA ☎ 0161 234 5148 ⌨ k.gillham@manchester.gov.uk

Lottery Funding, Charity and Voluntary: Ms Liz Goodger, Commissioning Manager, Manchester City Council, Town Hall, Albert Square, Manchester M60 2LA ☎ 0161 234 1285 ⌨ l.goodger@manchester.gov.uk

Member Services: Ms Patricia Wilkinson, Head of Member Services, Manchester City Council, Town Hall, Albert Square, Manchester M60 2LA ☎ 0161 234 4289 ⌨ p.wilkinson1@manchester.gov.uk

Partnerships: Mr Richard Elliott, Head of Policy, Partnerships & Research, Manchester City Council, Town Hall, Albert Square, Manchester M60 2LA ☎ 0161 219 6494 ⌨ r.elliott@manchester.gov.uk

Planning: Ms Julie Roscoe, Head of Planning, Licensing & Building Control, Manchester City Council, Town Hall, Albert Square, Manchester M60 2LA ☎ 0161 234 4552 ⌨ j.roscoe@manchester.gov.uk

Procurement: Mr Ian Brown, Head of Corporate Procurement, Manchester City Council, Town Hall, Albert Square, Manchester M60 2LA ☎ 0161 234 3255 ⌨ i.brown@manchester.gov.uk

Public Libraries: Mr Neil MacInnes, Strategic Lead - Library / Galleries / Culture, Manchester City Council, Town Hall, Albert Square, Manchester M60 2LA ☎ 0161 234 1392 ⌨ n.macinnes@libraries.manchester.gov.uk

Recycling & Waste Minimisation: Mr Mark Glynn, Strategic Lead - Waste / Recycling / Street Cleansing, Hammerstone Road Depot, Hammerstone Road, Manchester M18 8EQ ☎ 0161 234 5501 ⌨ m.glynn@manchester.gov.uk

Regeneration: Ms Fiona Worrall, Director - Neighbourhoods, Manchester City Council, Town Hall, Albert Square, Manchester M60 2LA ☎ 0161 234 3926 ⌨ fiona.worrall@manchester.gov.uk

Road Safety: Mr Kevin Gillham, Citywide Highway Manager, Manchester City Council, Town Hall, Albert Square, Manchester M60 2LA ☎ 0161 234 5148 ⌨ k.gillham@manchester.gov.uk

Road Safety: Mr Kent Wells, Service Manager, Manchester City Council, Town Hall, Albert Square, Manchester M60 2LA ☎ 0161 245 7440 ⊕ k.wells@manchester.gov.uk

Social Services (Adult): Ms Mary Smith, Head of Adult Social Care, Manchester City Council, Town Hall, Albert Square, Manchester M60 2LA mary.smith@manchester.gov.uk

Social Services (Adult): Ms Hazel Summers, Strategic Director - Adult Services, Manchester City Council, Town Hall, Albert Square, Manchester M60 2LA ☎ 0161 234 4994 ⊕ h.summers@manchester.gov.uk

Public Health: Mr David Regan, Director - Public Health, Manchester City Council, Town Hall, Albert Square, Manchester M60 2LA ☎ 0161 234 5000 ⊕ d.regan@manchester.gov.uk

Staff Training: Ms Caroline Powell, Strategic Business Partner, Manchester City Council, Town Hall, Albert Square, Manchester M60 2LA ☎ 0161 234 6522 ⊕ c.powell@manchester.gov.uk

Street Scene: Mr Chaz Farghaly, Citywide Support Lead, Manchester City Council, Town Hall, Albert Square, Manchester M60 2LA ☎ 0161 953 8393 ⊕ c.farghaly@manchester.gov.uk

Sustainable Communities: Ms Fiona Worrall, Director - Neighbourhoods, Manchester City Council, Town Hall, Albert Square, Manchester M60 2LA ☎ 0161 234 3926 ⊕ fiona.worrall@manchester.gov.uk

Town Centre: Mr Andy Wilson, Strategic Lead - Neighbourhood & City Centre, Manchester City Council, Town Hall, Albert Square, Manchester M60 2LA ☎ 0161 234 4067 ⊕ a.wilson@manchester.gov.uk

Traffic Management: Mr Kevin Gillham, Citywide Highway Manager, Manchester City Council, Town Hall, Albert Square, Manchester M60 2LA ☎ 0161 234 5148 ⊕ k.gillham@manchester.gov.uk

Transport: Mr Gary Campin, Fleet Services Manager, Hammerstone Road Depot, Hammerstone Road, Manchester M18 8EQ ☎ 0161 957 8419 ⊕ g.campin@manchester.gov.uk

Transport Planner: Mr Kevin Gillham, Citywide Highway Manager, Manchester City Council, Town Hall, Albert Square, Manchester M60 2LA ☎ 0161 234 5148 ⊕ k.gillham@manchester.gov.uk

Waste Collection and Disposal: Mr Mark Glynn, Strategic Lead - Waste / Recycling / Street Cleansing, Hammerstone Road Depot, Hammerstone Road, Manchester M18 8EQ ☎ 0161 234 5501 ⊕ m.glynn@manchester.gov.uk

Waste Management: Mr Kevin Gillham, Citywide Highway Manager, Manchester City Council, Town Hall, Albert Square, Manchester M60 2LA ☎ 0161 234 5148 ⊕ k.gillham@manchester.gov.uk

COUNCILLORS

The Lord Mayor: Austin-Behan, Carl (LAB - Burnage) cllr.c.austin-behan@manchester.gov.uk

Leader of the Council: Leese, Richard (LAB - Crumpsall) cllr.r.leese@manchester.gov.uk

Deputy Leader of the Council: Murphy, Sue (LAB - Brooklands) cllr.s.murphy@manchester.gov.uk

Deputy Leader of the Council: Priest, Bernard (LAB - Ardwick) cllr.b.priest@manchester.gov.uk

Akbar, Rabnawaz (LAB - Rusholme) cllr.r.akbar@manchester.gov.uk

Ali, Ahmed (LAB - Rusholme) cllr.a.ali@manchester.gov.uk

Ali, Azra (LAB - Burnage) cllr.azra.ali@manchester.gov.uk

Ali, Nasrin (LAB - Levenshulme) cllr.n.ali@manchester.gov.uk

Ali, Shaukat (LAB - Cheetham) cllr.shaukat.ali@manchester.gov.uk

Ali, Sameem (LAB - Moss Side) cllr.s.ali@manchester.gov.uk

Alijah, Zahra (LAB - Fallowfield) cllr.z.alijah@manchester.gov.uk

Amesbury, Michael Lee (LAB - Fallowfield) cllr.m.amesbury@manchester.gov.uk

Andrews, Paul (LAB - Baguley) cllr.p.andrews@manchester.gov.uk

Appleby, Paula (LAB - Moston) cllr.p.appleby@manchester.gov.uk

Barrett, Hugh (LAB - Sharston) cllr.h.barrett@manchester.gov.uk

Battle, Rosa (LAB - Bradford) cllr.r.battle@manchester.gov.uk

Bridges, Garry (LAB - Old Moat) cllr.g.bridges@manchester.gov.uk

Chappell, Kate (LAB - Rusholme) cllr.k.chappell@manchester.gov.uk

Chohan, Abid (LAB - Longsight) cllr.a.chohan@manchester.gov.uk

Collins, Sandra (LAB - Harpurhey) cllr.s.collins@manchester.gov.uk

Connolly, Julie (LAB - Cheetham) cllr.j.connolly@manchester.gov.uk

Cookson, Peter (LAB - Gorton South) cllr.p.cookson@manchester.gov.uk

Cooley, Susan (LAB - Brooklands) cllr.s.cooley@manchester.gov.uk

Craig, Bev (LAB - Burnage) cllr.b.craig@manchester.gov.uk

Curley, Basil (LAB - Charlestown) cllr.b.curley@manchester.gov.uk

Dar, Yasmine (LAB - Moston) cllr.y.dar@manchester.gov.uk

Davies, Joan (LAB - City Centre) cllr.j.davies@mamchester.gov.uk

Ellison, David (LAB - Didsbury West) cllr.d.ellison@manchester.gov.uk

Evans, Glynn (LAB - Brooklands) cllr.g.evans@manchester.gov.uk

MANCHESTER CITY

Farrell, John (LAB - Higher Blackley)
cllr.j.farrell@manchester.gov.uk

Fender, Andrew (LAB - Old Moat)
cllr.a.fender@manchester.gov.uk

Flanagan, John (LAB - Miles Platting & Newton Heath)
cll.j.flanagan@manchester.gov.uk

Fletcher-Hackwood, Grace (LAB - Fallowfield)
cllr.g.fletcher-hackwood@manchester.gov.uk

Green, Joanne (LAB - Harpurhey)
cllr.j.green@manchester.gov.uk

Grimshaw, Carmine (LAB - Miles Platting & Newton Heath)
cllr.c.grimshaw@manchester.gov.uk

Hacking, John (LAB - Chorlton)
cllr.j.hacking@manchester.gov.uk

Hassan, Naeem (LAB - Cheetham)
cllr.n.hassan@manchester.gov.uk

Hewitson, Tina (LAB - Ardwick)
cllr.t.hewitson@manchester.gov.uk

Hitchen, June (LAB - Miles Platting & Newton Heath)
cllr.j.hitchen@manchester.gov.uk

Hughes, Jon (LAB - Gorton North)
cllr.j.hughes@manchester.gov.uk

Igbon, Lee-Ann (LAB - Hulme)
cllr.l.igbon@manchester.gov.uk

Judge, Thomas (LAB - Sharston)
cllr.t.judge@manchester.gov.uk

Judge, Sarah (LAB - Woodhouse Park)
cllr.s.judge@manchester.gov.uk

Kamal, Afia (LAB - Gorton North)
cllr.a.kamal@manchester.gov.uk

Karney, Patrick (LAB - Harpurhey)
cllr.p.karney@manchester.gov.uk

Kirkpartick, Veronica (LAB - Charlestown)
cllr.v.kirkpatrick@manchester.gov.uk

Knowles, Beth (LAB - City Centre)
cllr.b.knowles@manchester.gov.uk

Lanchbury, Shelley (LAB - Higher Blackley)
cllr.s.lanchbury@manchester.gov.uk

Leech, John (LD - Didsbury West)
cllr.j.leech@manchester.gov.uk

Lone, Amina (LAB - Hulme)
cllr.a.lone@manchester.gov.uk

Longsden, John (LAB - Bradford)
cllr.j.longsden@manchester.gov.uk

Loughman, Mick (LAB - Ancoats & Clayton)
cllr.m.loughman@manchester.gov.uk

Ludford, Donna (LAB - Ancoats & Clayton)
cllr.d.ludford@manchester.gov.uk

Manco, Ollie (LAB - Ancoats & Clayton)
cllr.o.manco@manchester.gov.uk

Marshall, Beth (LAB - Crumpsall)
cllr.b.marshall@manchester.gov.uk

Midgley, Joanna (LAB - Chorlton Park)
cllr.j.midgley@manchester.gov.uk

Monaghan, Mary (LAB - Northenden)
cllr.mary.monaghan@manchester.gov.uk

Monaghan, Madeleine (LAB - Sharston)
cllr.m.monaghan@manchester.gov.uk

Moore, Rebecca (LAB - Withington)
cllr.r.moore@manchester.gov.uk

Murphy, Nigel (LAB - Hulme)
cllr.n.murphy@manchester.gov.uk

Newman, Eddy (LAB - Woodhouse Park)
cllr.e.newman@manchester.gov.uk

Newman, Sheila (LAB - Chorlton)
cllr.s.newman@manchester.gov.uk

Noor, Dzidra (LAB - Levenshulme)
cllr.d.noor@manchester.gov.uk

Ollerhead, Carl (LAB - Moston)
cllr.c.ollerhead@manchester.gov.uk

O'Neil, Brian (LAB - Woodhouse Park)
cllr.brian.oneil@manchester.gov.uk

Paul, Chris (LAB - Withington)
cllr.c.paul@manchester.gov.uk

Peel, Kevin (LAB - City Centre)
cllr.k.peel@manchester.gov.uk

Priest, Hannah (LAB - Charlestown)
cllr.h.priest@manchester.gov.uk

Pritchard, Jon-Leigh (LAB - Crumpsall)
cllr.j.pritchard@manchester.gov.uk

Rahman, Luthfur (LAB - Longsight)
cllr.l.rahman@manchester.gov.uk

Raikes, Luke (LAB - Baguley)
cllr.l.raikes@manchester.gov.uk

Rawlins, Tracey (LAB - Baguley)
cllr.t.rawlins@manchester.gov.uk

Rawson, Dave (LAB - Chorlton Park)
cllr.d.rawson@manchester.gov.uk

Razaq, Aftab (LAB - Whalley Range)
cllr.a.razaq@manchester.gov.uk

Reeves, Suzannah (LAB - Old Moat)
cllr.s.reeves@manchester.gov.uk

Reid, Julie (LAB - Gorton South)
cllr.j.reid@manchester.gov.uk

Richards, Suzanne (LAB - Longsight)
cllr.s.richards@manchester.gov.uk

Rowles, Emily (LAB - Moss Side)
cllr.e.rowles@manchester.gov.uk

Russell, Sarah (LAB - Northenden)
cllr.s.russell@manchester.gov.uk

Sadler, Paula (LAB - Higher Blackley)
cllr.p.sadler@manchester.gov.uk

Sharif-Mahamed, Mahadi (LAB - Moss Side)
cllr.m.sharif-mahamed@manchester.gov.uk

Sheikh, Basat (LAB - Levenshulme)
cllr.b.sheikh@manchester.gov.uk

Shilton-Godwin, Mandie (LAB - Chorlton Park)
cllr.m.shiltongodwin@manchester.gov.uk

Siddiqi, Nilofar (LAB - Gorton North)
cllr.n.siddiqi@manchester.gov.uk

Simcock, Andrew (LAB - Didsbury East)
cllr.a.simcock@manchester.gov.uk

Simcock, Kelly (LAB - Didsbury East)
cllr.k.simcock@manchester.gov.uk

Smitheman, Mavis (LAB - Ardwick)
mave@smitheman1.demon.co.uk

Stogia, Angeliki (LAB - Whalley Range)
cllr.a.stogia@manchester.gov.uk

Stone, Bernard (LAB - Gorton South)
cllr.b.stone@manchester.gov.uk

Strong, Matt (LAB - Chorlton)
cllr.m.strong@manchester.gov.uk

Taylor, Emma (LAB - Bradford)
cllr.e.taylor@manchester.gov.uk

Teubler, Josie (LAB - Didsbury West)
cllr.j.teubler@manchester.gov.uk

Watson, Mary (LAB - Whalley Range)
cllr.m.watson@manchester.gov.uk

Webb, Chris (LAB - Northenden)
cllr.c.webb@manchester.gov.uk

Wills, Chris (LAB - Withington)
cllr.c.wills@manchester.gov.uk

Wilson, James (LAB - Didsbury East)
cllr.j.wilson@manchester.gov.uk

POLITICAL COMPOSITION
LAB: 95, LD: 1

COMMITTEE CHAIRS

Audit: Ms Sarah Russell

Children & Young People: Ms Julie Reid

Licensing: Mr John Longsden

Neighbourhoods & Environment: Mr Kevin Peel

Mansfield   D

Mansfield District Council, Civic Centre, Chesterfield Road
South, Mansfield NG19 7BH
☎ 01623 463463 📠 01623 463900 ⁀ᵾ mdc@mansfield.gov.uk
🖳 www.mansfield.gov.uk

FACTS AND FIGURES
Parliamentary Constituencies: Mansfield
EU Constituencies: East Midlands
Election Frequency: Elections are of whole council

PRINCIPAL OFFICERS

Chief Executive: Mrs Bev Smith, Chief Executive, Civic Centre,
Chesterfield Road South, Mansfield NG19 7BH ☎ 01623 463036
⁀ᵾ bsmith@mansfield.gov.uk

Deputy Chief Executive: Mr Mick Andrews, Director - Commerce
& Customer Services & Deputy Chief Executive, Civic Centre,
Chesterfield Road South, Mansfield NG19 7BH ☎ 01623 463015
⁀ᵾ mandrews@mansfield.gov.uk

Senior Management: Mr Mick Andrews, Director - Commerce
& Customer Services & Deputy Chief Executive, Civic Centre,
Chesterfield Road South, Mansfield NG19 7BH ☎ 01623 463015
⁀ᵾ mandrews@mansfield.gov.uk

Senior Management: Ms Hayley Barsby, Director - Communities
& Deputy Chief Executive, Civic Centre, Chesterfield Road South,
Mansfield NG19 7BH ☎ 01623 463404 ⁀ᵾ hbarsby@mansfield.gov.uk

Senior Management: Ms Jacqueline Collins, Director -
Governance & Monitoring Officer, Civic Centre, Chesterfield Road
South, Mansfield NG19 7BH ☎ 01623 463075
⁀ᵾ collinssj@mansfield.gov.uk

Senior Management: Mr Michael Robinson, Director - Economic
Growth, Civic Centre, Chesterfield Road South, Mansfield NG19
7BH ☎ 01623 463370 ⁀ᵾ mrobinson@mansfield.gov.uk

Senior Management: Mr Martyn Saxton, Director - Place &
Wellbeing, Civic Centre, Chesterfield Road South, Mansfield NG19
7BH ☎ 01623 463024 ⁀ᵾ saxtonm@mansfield.gov.uk

Access Officer / Social Services (Disability): Ms Sharon
Allman, Equality & Diversity Research Officer, Mansfield District
Council, Civic Centre, Chesterfield Road South, Mansfield NG19
7BH ☎ 01623 463042 ⁀ᵾ sallman@mansfield.gov.uk

Architect, Building / Property Services: Mr Philip Colledge,
Principal General Practice Surveyor & Corporate Asset Manager,
Civic Centre, Chesterfield Road South, Mansfield NG19 7BH
☎ 01623 463463 ⁀ᵾ pcolledge@mansfield.gov.uk

Architect, Building / Property Services: Mr Brian Holmes,
Design Services Manager, Civic Centre, Chesterfield Road South,
Mansfield NG19 7BH ☎ 01623 463463
⁀ᵾ bholmes@mansfield.gov.uk

Architect, Building / Property Services: Mr Steve Melhuish,
Group Architect, Civic Centre, Chesterfield Road South, Mansfield
NG19 7BH ☎ 01623 463463 ⁀ᵾ smelhuish@mansfield.gov.uk

Building Control: Mr Martyn Saxton, Head of Planning,
Community Safety & Regulatory Services, Civic Centre, Chesterfield
Road South, Mansfield NG19 7BH ☎ 01623 463208
⁀ᵾ msaxton@mansfield.gov.uk

PR / Communications: Mrs Helen Sisson, Marketing &
Communications Manager, Civic Centre, Chesterfield Road South,
Mansfield NG19 7BH ☎ 01623 463463 ⁀ᵾ hsisson@mansfield.gov.uk

Community Planning: Mr Michael Robinson, Director - Economic
Growth, Civic Centre, Chesterfield Road South, Mansfield NG19
7BH ☎ 01623 463370 ⁀ᵾ mrobinson@mansfield.gov.uk

Computer Management: Mrs Christine Marsh, ICT Manager,
Civic Centre, Chesterfield Road South, Mansfield NG19 7BH
☎ 01623 463463 ⁀ᵾ cmarsh@mansfield.gov.uk

Contracts: Mr Mick Andrews, Director - Commerce & Customer
Services & Deputy Chief Executive, Civic Centre, Chesterfield Road
South, Mansfield NG19 7BH ☎ 01623 463015
⁀ᵾ mandrews@mansfield.gov.uk

MANSFIELD

Corporate Services: Ms Jacqueline Collins, Director - Governance & Monitoring Officer, Civic Centre, Chesterfield Road South, Mansfield NG19 7BH ☎ 01623 463075 ✆ collinssj@mansfield.gov.uk

Customer Service: Mr Mick Andrews, Director - Commerce & Customer Services & Deputy Chief Executive, Civic Centre, Chesterfield Road South, Mansfield NG19 7BH ☎ 01623 463015 ✆ mandrews@mansfield.gov.uk

Direct Labour: Mr Mick Andrews, Director - Commerce & Customer Services & Deputy Chief Executive, Civic Centre, Chesterfield Road South, Mansfield NG19 7BH ☎ 01623 463015 ✆ mandrews@mansfield.gov.uk

Economic Development: Mr Michael Robinson, Director - Economic Growth, Civic Centre, Chesterfield Road South, Mansfield NG19 7BH ☎ 01623 463370 ✆ mrobinson@mansfield.gov.uk

E-Government: Mrs Christine Marsh, ICT Manager, Civic Centre, Chesterfield Road South, Mansfield NG19 7BH ☎ 01623 463463 ✆ cmarsh@mansfield.gov.uk

Electoral Registration: Ms Julie Jevons, Electoral Services Manager, Civic Centre, Chesterfield Road South, Mansfield NG19 7BH ☎ 01623 463463 Extn 3394 ✆ jjevons@mansfield.gov.uk

Energy Management: Mr Michael Robinson, Director - Economic Growth, Civic Centre, Chesterfield Road South, Mansfield NG19 7BH ☎ 01623 463370 ✆ mrobinson@mansfield.gov.uk

Environmental / Technical Services: Mr Michael Robinson, Director - Economic Growth, Civic Centre, Chesterfield Road South, Mansfield NG19 7BH ☎ 01623 463370 ✆ mrobinson@mansfield.gov.uk

Environmental Health: Mrs Julia Beresford, Environmental Health Manager, Civic Centre, Chesterfield Road South, Mansfield NG19 7BH ☎ 01623 463038 ✆ jberesford@mansfield.gov.uk

Estates, Property & Valuation: Mr Philip Colledge, Principal General Practice Surveyor & Corporate Asset Manager, Civic Centre, Chesterfield Road South, Mansfield NG19 7BH ☎ 01623 463463 ✆ pcolledge@mansfield.gov.uk

Events Manager: Mr Kevan Poyntz, Town Centre Manager, Civic Centre, Chesterfield Road South, Mansfield NG19 7BH ☎ 01623 653350 ✆ kpoyntz@mansfield.gov.uk

Finance: Mr Mick Andrews, Director - Commerce & Customer Services & Deputy Chief Executive, Civic Centre, Chesterfield Road South, Mansfield NG19 7BH ☎ 01623 463015 ✆ mandrews@mansfield.gov.uk

Fleet Management: Mr George Farrell, Fleet Manager, Hermitage Lane Depot, Hermitage Lane, Mansfield NG18 5GU ☎ 01623 463093 ✆ gfarrell@mansfield.gov.uk

Grounds Maintenance: Mr Timothy Downs, Neighbourhood Services Manager, Civic Centre, Chesterfield Road South, Mansfield NG19 7BH ☎ 01623 463463 ✆ tdowns@mansfield.gov.uk

Home Energy Conservation: Mr Brian Holmes, Design Services Manager, Civic Centre, Chesterfield Road South, Mansfield NG19 7BH ☎ 01623 463463 ✆ bholmes@mansfield.gov.uk

Housing: Ms Hayley Barsby, Director - Communities & Deputy Chief Executive, Civic Centre, Chesterfield Road South, Mansfield NG19 7BH ☎ 01623 463404 ✆ hbarsby@mansfield.gov.uk

Housing Maintenance: Mr Andrew Johnson, Housing Repairs, Civic Centre, Chesterfield Road South, Mansfield NG19 7BH ☎ 01623 463463 (extn 1)

Legal: Ms Jacqueline Collins, Director - Governance & Monitoring Officer, Civic Centre, Chesterfield Road South, Mansfield NG19 7BH ☎ 01623 463075 ✆ collinssj@mansfield.gov.uk

Leisure and Cultural Services: Mr Martyn Saxton, Director - Place & Wellbeing, Civic Centre, Chesterfield Road South, Mansfield NG19 7BH ☎ 01623 463024 ✆ saxtonm@mansfield.gov.uk

Licensing: Ms Samantha Yates, Licensing Manager, Civic Centre, Chesterfield Road South, Mansfield NG19 7BH ☎ 01623 463463 ✆ syates@mansfield.gov.uk

Lighting: Mr Mick Andrews, Director - Commerce & Customer Services & Deputy Chief Executive, Civic Centre, Chesterfield Road South, Mansfield NG19 7BH ☎ 01623 463015 ✆ mandrews@mansfield.gov.uk

Member Services: Mr Mark Pemberton, Democratic Services Manager, Civic Centre, Chesterfield Road South, Mansfield NG19 7BH ☎ 01623 463463 ✆ mpemberton@mansfield.gov.uk

Parking: Mr Kevan Poyntz, Town Centre Manager, Civic Centre, Chesterfield Road South, Mansfield NG19 7BH ☎ 01623 653350 ✆ kpoyntz@mansfield.gov.uk

Personnel / HR: Mrs Mariam Amos, HR Manager, Council Offices, Urban Road, Kirkby-in-Ashfield NG17 8DA ☎ 01623 663032 ✆ mamos@mansfield.gov.uk

Planning: Mr Martyn Saxton, Head of Planning, Community Safety & Regulatory Services, Civic Centre, Chesterfield Road South, Mansfield NG19 7BH ☎ 01623 463208 ✆ msaxton@mansfield.gov.uk

Procurement: Mr Mick Andrews, Director - Commerce & Customer Services & Deputy Chief Executive, Civic Centre, Chesterfield Road South, Mansfield NG19 7BH ☎ 01623 463015 ✆ mandrews@mansfield.gov.uk

Recycling & Waste Minimisation: Ms Hayley Barsby, Director - Communities & Deputy Chief Executive, Civic Centre, Chesterfield Road South, Mansfield NG19 7BH ☎ 01623 463404 ✆ hbarsby@mansfield.gov.uk

Regeneration: Mr Michael Robinson, Director - Economic Growth, Civic Centre, Chesterfield Road South, Mansfield NG19 7BH ☎ 01623 463370 ✆ mrobinson@mansfield.gov.uk

Staff Training: Mrs Lorraine Powney, Principal Learning & Development Adviser, Civic Centre, Chesterfield Road South, Mansfield NG19 7BH ☎ 01623 463250 ✆ lpowney@mansfield.gov.uk

Street Scene: Mr Michael Robinson, Director - Economic Growth, Civic Centre, Chesterfield Road South, Mansfield NG19 7BH ☎ 01623 463370 ✆ mrobinson@mansfield.gov.uk

Sustainable Communities: Mrs Bev Smith, Chief Executive, Civic Centre, Chesterfield Road South, Mansfield NG19 7BH ☎ 01623 463036 ✆ bsmith@mansfield.gov.uk

Town Centre: Mr Kevan Poyntz, Town Centre Manager, Civic Centre, Chesterfield Road South, Mansfield NG19 7BH ☎ 01623 653350 ✆ kpoyntz@mansfield.gov.uk

Waste Collection and Disposal: Ms Hayley Barsby, Director - Communities & Deputy Chief Executive, Civic Centre, Chesterfield Road South, Mansfield NG19 7BH ☎ 01623 463404 ✆ hbarsby@mansfield.gov.uk

Waste Management: Ms Hayley Barsby, Director - Communities & Deputy Chief Executive, Civic Centre, Chesterfield Road South, Mansfield NG19 7BH ☎ 01623 463404 ✆ hbarsby@mansfield.gov.uk

COUNCILLORS

Mayor: Allsop, Kate (IND - Mayor's Ward) kallsop@mansfield.gov.uk

Deputy Mayor: Barton, Mick (IND - Maun Valley) mbarton@mansfield.gov.uk

Adey, Sharron (LAB - Netherfield) sadey@mansfield.gov.uk

Answer, Barry (UKIP - Abbott) banswer@mansfield.gov.uk

Atherton, Katrina (LAB - Manor) katherton@mansfield.gov.uk

Bennett, Nicholas (LAB - Kingsway) nbennett@mansfield.gov.uk

Bosnjak, Joyce (LAB - Hornby) jbosnjak@mansfield.gov.uk

Brown, Kevin (IND - Oakham) brownk@mansfield.gov.uk

Clay, Terry (LAB - Brick Kiln) tclay@mansfield.gov.uk

Crawford, Peter (LAB - Warsop Carrs) pcrawford@mansfield.gov.uk

Drewett, Bill (IND - Ling Forest) bdrewett@mansfield.gov.uk

Fisher, Amanda (LAB - Woodhouse) afisher@mansfield.gov.uk

Garner, Stephen (IND - Racecourse) sgarner@mansfield.gov.uk

Harvey, S (IND - Kingswalk) sharvey@mansfield.gov.uk

Higgins, Sally (LAB - Ladybrook) shiggins@mansfield.gov.uk

Hopewell, Vaughan (LAB - Oak Tree) vhopewell@mansfield.gov.uk

Jelley, Ron (IND - Grange Farm) rjelley@mansfield.gov.uk

Kerr, John (LAB - Market Warsop) jkerr@mansfield.gov.uk

Lohan, Brian (LAB - Portland) blohan@mansfield.gov.uk

McCallum, S (LAB - Sherwood) smccallum@mansfield.gov.uk

Norman, Ann (LAB - Park Hall) anorman@mansfield.gov.uk

Richardson, Stuart (LAB - Penniment) srichardson@mansfield.gov.uk

Rickersey, Stewart (IND - Eakring) srickersey@mansfield.gov.uk

Saunders, Dave (IND - Sandhurst) dsaunders@mansfield.gov.uk

Sheppard, Ian (IND - Broomhill) isheppard@mansfield.gov.uk

Sissons, Andy (IND - Newgate) asissons@mansfield.gov.uk

Smart, John (LAB - Ransom Wood) jsmart@mansfield.gov.uk

Smith, David (IND - Woodlands) dmsmith@mansfield.gov.uk

Sutcliffe, Roger (IND - Lindhurst) rsutcliffe@mansfield.gov.uk

Tristram, Andrew (IND - Berry Hill) atristram@mansfield.gov.uk

Walker, Sidney (UKIP - Newlands) swalker@mansfield.gov.uk

Wallace, Stuart (IND - Carr Bank) swallace@mansfield.gov.uk

Ward, Sonya (LAB - Bull Farm & Pleasley Hill) sward@mansfield.gov.uk

Wetton, Andy (LAB - Meden) jwetton@mansfield.gov.uk

Wright, Lesley (LAB - Peafields) lwright@mansfield.gov.uk

Wright, Martin (IND - Holly) mwright@mansfield.gov.uk

POLITICAL COMPOSITION
LAB: 18, IND: 16, UKIP: 2, Vacant: 1

Medway   U

Medway Council, Civic Headquarters, Gun Wharf, Dock Road, Chatham ME4 4TR
☎ 01634 306000 🖷 01634 332756 ✆ info@medway.gov.uk
🖳 www.medway.gov.uk

FACTS AND FIGURES
Parliamentary Constituencies: Chatham and Aylesford, Gillingham and Rainham, Rochester and Strood
EU Constituencies: South East

MEDWAY

Election Frequency: Elections are of whole council

PRINCIPAL OFFICERS

Chief Executive: Mr Neil Davies, Chief Executive, Civic Headquarters, Gun Wharf, Dock Road, Chatham ME4 4TR
☎ 01634 332705 ✆ neil.davies@medway.gov.uk

Senior Management: Mr Richard Hicks, Director - Regeneration, Culture, Environment & Transformation, Civic Headquarters, Gun Wharf, Dock Road, Chatham ME4 4TR ☎ 01634 338108
✆ richard.hicks@medway.gov.uk

Senior Management: Mr Ian Sutherland, Interim Director - Children & Adults, Civic Headquarters, Gun Wharf, Dock Road, Chatham ME4 4TR ☎ 01634 331212
✆ ian.sutherland@medway.gov.uk

Access Officer / Social Services (Disability): Ms Jackie Challis, Joint Physical Disability Manager, Civic Headquarters, Gun Wharf, Dock Road, Chatham ME4 4TR ☎ 01634 331272
✆ jackie.challis@medway.gov.uk

Access Officer / Social Services (Disability): Ms Amanda Dean, Joint Physical Disability Manager, Civic Headquarters, Gun Wharf, Dock Road, Chatham ME4 4TR ☎ 01634 331272
✆ amanda.dean@medway.gov.uk

Architect, Building / Property Services: Mr Rob Dennis, Head - Property & Capital Projects, Civic Headquarters, Gun Wharf, Dock Road, Chatham ME4 4TR ☎ 01634 332880
✆ rob.dennis@medway.gov.uk

Building Control: Mr Tony Van Veghel, South Thames Gateway Building Control Partnership Director, Compass Centre, Chatham Maritime, Chatham ME4 4YH ☎ 01634 331552
✆ tony.vanveghel@medway.gov.uk

Children / Youth Services: Ms Pauline Maddison, Interim Assistant Director - Inclusion & Improvement, Civic Headquarters, Gun Wharf, Dock Road, Chatham ME4 4TR ☎ 01634 331013
✆ pauline.maddison@medway.gov.uk

Civil Registration: Mr Paul Edwards, Bereavement & Registration Services Manager, Medway Crematorium, Upper Robin Hood Lane, Blue Bell Hill, Chatham ME5 9QU ☎ 01634 331352
✆ paul.edwards@medway.gov.uk

PR / Communications: Ms Cathy Collins, Marketing Communications Manager, Civic Headquarters, Gun Wharf, Dock Road, Chatham ME4 4TR ☎ 01634 332776
✆ cathy.collins@medway.gov.uk

PR / Communications: Ms Stephanie Goad, Assistant Director - Transformation, Civic Headquarters, Gun Wharf, Dock Road, Chatham ME4 4TR ☎ 01634 332737 ✆ stephanie.goad@medway.gov.uk

Community Safety: Mr Tim England, Head - Safer Communities & Greenspaces, Civic Headquarters, Gun Wharf, Dock Road, Chatham ME4 4TR ☎ 01634 333534 ✆ tim.england@medway.gov.uk

Computer Management: Mr Andrew Cole, Interim Head - ICT, Civic Headquarters, Gun Wharf, Dock Road, Chatham ME4 4TR
☎ 01634 332087 ✆ andrew.cole@medway.gov.uk

Consumer Protection and Trading Standards: Mr Tim England, Head - Safer Communities & Greenspaces, Civic Headquarters, Gun Wharf, Dock Road, Chatham ME4 4TR
☎ 01634 333534 ✆ tim.england@medway.gov.uk

Corporate Services: Mr Perry Holmes, Assistant Director, Civic Headquarters, Gun Wharf, Dock Road, Chatham ME4 4TR
☎ 01634 332133 ✆ perry.holmes@medway.gov.uk

Customer Service: Mr Martin Garlick, Head - Customer Contact, Community Hubs & Libraries, Civic Headquarters, Gun Wharf, Dock Road, Chatham ME4 4TR ☎ 01634 338771
✆ martin.garlick@medway.gov.uk

Economic Development: Mr Sunny Ee, Head - Regeneration Delivery, Civic Headquarters, Gun Wharf, Dock Road, Chatham ME4 4TR ☎ 01634 331030 ✆ sunny.ee@medway.gov.uk

Education: Ms Pauline Maddison, Interim Assistant Director - Inclusion & Improvement, Civic Headquarters, Gun Wharf, Dock Road, Chatham ME4 4TR ☎ 01634 331013
✆ pauline.maddison@medway.gov.uk

E-Government: Mr Andrew Cole, Interim Head - ICT, Civic Headquarters, Gun Wharf, Dock Road, Chatham ME4 4TR
☎ 01634 332087 ✆ andrew.cole@medway.gov.uk

Electoral Registration: Ms Jane Ringham, Head - Elections & Member Services, Civic Headquarters, Gun Wharf, Dock Road, Chatham ME4 4TR ☎ 01634 332864
✆ jane.ringham@medway.gov.uk

Emergency Planning: Ms Angela Wilkins, Emergency Planning Manager, Civic Headquarters, Gun Wharf, Dock Road, Chatham ME4 4TR ☎ 01634 333542 ✆ angela.wilkins@medway.gov.uk

Energy Management: Mr Rob Dennis, Head - Property & Capital Projects, Civic Headquarters, Gun Wharf, Dock Road, Chatham ME4 4TR ☎ 01634 332880 ✆ rob.dennis@medway.gov.uk

Environmental / Technical Services: Mr Andy McGrath, Assistant Director, Civic Headquarters, Gun Wharf, Dock Road, Chatham ME4 4TR ☎ 01634 331376 ✆ andy.mcgrath@medway.gov.uk

Environmental Health: Mr Andy McGrath, Assistant Director, Civic Headquarters, Gun Wharf, Dock Road, Chatham ME4 4TR
☎ 01634 331376 ✆ andy.mcgrath@medway.gov.uk

Estates, Property & Valuation: Mr Rob Dennis, Head - Property & Capital Projects, Civic Headquarters, Gun Wharf, Dock Road, Chatham ME4 4TR ☎ 01634 332880 ✆ rob.dennis@medway.gov.uk

Events Manager: Mr Carl Madjitey, Head - Festivals, Arts, Theatres & Events, Civic Headquarters, Gun Wharf, Dock Road, Chatham ME4 4TR ☎ 01634 338114 ✆ carl.madjitey@medway.gov.uk

Facilities: Mr Rob Dennis, Head - Property & Capital Projects, Civic Headquarters, Gun Wharf, Dock Road, Chatham ME4 4TR
☎ 01634 332880 ✆ rob.dennis@medway.gov.uk

Finance: Mr Phil Watts, Chief Finance Officer, Civic Headquarters, Gun Wharf, Dock Road, Chatham ME4 4TR ☎ 01634 332220 ✆ phil.watts@medway.gov.uk

Grounds Maintenance: Mr Tim England, Head - Safer Communities & Greenspaces, Civic Headquarters, Gun Wharf, Dock Road, Chatham ME4 4TR ☎ 01634 333534 ✆ tim.england@medway.gov.uk

Health and Safety: Ms Tracey Barefoot, Health & Safety Advisor, Civic Headquarters, Gun Wharf, Dock Road, Chatham ME4 4TR ☎ 01634 332160 ✆ tracey.barefoot@medway.gov.uk

Highways: Mr Simon Swift, Head - Highways, Maintenance & Parking, Civic Headquarters, Gun Wharf, Dock Road, Chatham ME4 4TR ☎ 01634 331276 ✆ simon.swift@medway.gov.uk

Housing: Mr Matthew Gough, Head - Strategic Housing, Civic Headquarters, Gun Wharf, Dock Road, Chatham ME4 4TR ☎ 01634 333177 ✆ matthew.gough@medway.gov.uk

Housing Maintenance: Mr Marc Blowers, Head - Housing Management, Civic Headquarters, Gun Wharf, Dock Road, Chatham ME4 4TR ☎ 01634 334382 ✆ marc.blowers@medway.gov.uk

Legal: Ms Jan Guyler, Head of Legal Services, Civic Headquarters, Gun Wharf, Dock Road, Chatham ME4 4TR ☎ 01634 332158 ✆ jan.guyler@medway.gov.uk

Leisure and Cultural Services: Mr Tomasz Kozlowski, Assistant Director - Physical & Cultural Regeneration, Civic Headquarters, Gun Wharf, Dock Road, Chatham ME4 4TR ☎ 01634 338121 ✆ tomasz.kozlowski@medway.gov.uk

Licensing: Ms Alison Poulson, Local Land Charges & Licensing Manager, Civic Headquarters, Gun Wharf, Dock Road, Chatham ME4 4TR ☎ 01634 332774 ✆ alison.poulson@medway.gov.uk

Lifelong Learning: Mr Martin Garlick, Head - Customer Contact, Community Hubs & Libraries, Civic Headquarters, Gun Wharf, Dock Road, Chatham ME4 4TR ☎ 01634 338771 ✆ martin.garlick@medway.gov.uk

Lighting: Mr Simon Swift, Head - Highways, Maintenance & Parking, Civic Headquarters, Gun Wharf, Dock Road, Chatham ME4 4TR ☎ 01634 331276 ✆ simon.swift@medway.gov.uk

Member Services: Ms Jane Ringham, Head - Elections & Member Services, Civic Headquarters, Gun Wharf, Dock Road, Chatham ME4 4TR ☎ 01634 332864 ✆ jane.ringham@medway.gov.uk

Parking: Ms Rubena Hafizi, Parking Manager, Civic Centre, Strood, Rochester ME2 4AU ☎ 01634 331725 ✆ rubena.hafizi@medway.gov.uk

Partnerships: Ms Stephanie Goad, Assistant Director - Transformation, Civic Headquarters, Gun Wharf, Dock Road, Chatham ME4 4TR ☎ 01634 332737 ✆ stephanie.goad@medway.gov.uk

Personnel / HR: Mrs Carrie McKenzie, Head - People, Civic Headquarters, Gun Wharf, Dock Road, Chatham ME4 4TR ☎ 01634 332261 ✆ carrie.mckenzie@medway.gov.uk

Planning: Mr Dave Harris, Development Control Manager, Civic Headquarters, Gun Wharf, Dock Road, Chatham ME4 4TR ☎ 01634 331575 ✆ dave.harris@medway.gov.uk

Procurement: Mr Perry Holmes, Assistant Director, Civic Headquarters, Gun Wharf, Dock Road, Chatham ME4 4TR ☎ 01634 332133 ✆ perry.holmes@medway.gov.uk

Public Libraries: Mr Martin Garlick, Head - Customer Contact, Community Hubs & Libraries, Civic Headquarters, Gun Wharf, Dock Road, Chatham ME4 4TR ☎ 01634 338771 ✆ martin.garlick@medway.gov.uk

Recycling & Waste Minimisation: Ms Sarah Dagwell, Head - Waste Services Operational, Civic Centre, Rochester ME2 4AU ☎ 01634 331597 ✆ sarah.dagwell@medway.gov.uk

Regeneration: Mr Sunny Ee, Head - Regeneration Delivery, Civic Headquarters, Gun Wharf, Dock Road, Chatham ME4 4TR ☎ 01634 331030 ✆ sunny.ee@medway.gov.uk

Social Services: Mr Ian Sutherland, Interim Director - Children & Adults, Civic Headquarters, Gun Wharf, Dock Road, Chatham ME4 4TR ☎ 01634 331212 ✆ ian.sutherland@medway.gov.uk

Social Services (Adult): Ms Linda Jackson, Interim Assistant Director - Adult Social Care, Civic Headquarters, Gun Wharf, Dock Road, Chatham ME4 4TR ☎ 01634 331212 ✆ linda.jackson@medway.gov.uk

Social Services (Children): Ms Ann Domeney, Assistant Director - Children's Social Care, Civic Headquarters, Gun Wharf, Dock Road, Chatham ME4 4TR ☎ 01634 331215 ✆ ann.domeney@medway.gov.uk

Public Health: Dr Andrew Burnett, Interim Director - Public Health, Civic Headquarters, Gun Wharf, Dock Road, Chatham ME4 4TR ☎ 01273 336032 ✆ andrew.burnett@medway.gov.uk

Staff Training: Mrs Carrie McKenzie, Head - People, Civic Headquarters, Gun Wharf, Dock Road, Chatham ME4 4TR ☎ 01634 332261 ✆ carrie.mckenzie@medway.gov.uk

Sustainable Communities: Mr Tomasz Kozlowski, Assistant Director - Physical & Cultural Regeneration, Civic Headquarters, Gun Wharf, Dock Road, Chatham ME4 4TR ☎ 01634 338121 ✆ tomasz.kozlowski@medway.gov.uk

Sustainable Development: Mr Tomasz Kozlowski, Assistant Director - Physical & Cultural Regeneration, Civic Headquarters, Gun Wharf, Dock Road, Chatham ME4 4TR ☎ 01634 338121 ✆ tomasz.kozlowski@medway.gov.uk

Tourism: Mr Bob Dimond, Head - Sport, Leisure, Tourism & Heritage, Civic Headquarters, Gun Wharf, Dock Road, Chatham ME4 4TR ☎ 01634 338238 ✆ bob.dimond@medway.gov.uk

Town Centre: Mr Sunny Ee, Head - Regeneration Delivery, Civic Headquarters, Gun Wharf, Dock Road, Chatham ME4 4TR ☎ 01634 331030 ✆ sunny.ee@medway.gov.uk

MEDWAY

Traffic Management: Mr Martin Morris, Traffic Management Manager, Civic Headquarters, Gun Wharf, Dock Road, Chatham ME4 4TR ☎ 01634 331148 ⌁ martin.morris@medway.gov.uk

Transport: Mr Steve Hewlett, Head - Integrated Transport, Civic Headquarters, Gun Wharf, Dock Road, Chatham ME4 4TR ☎ 01634 331103 ⌁ steve.hewlett@medway.gov.uk

Transport Planner: Mr Steve Hewlett, Head - Integrated Transport, Civic Headquarters, Gun Wharf, Dock Road, Chatham ME4 4TR ☎ 01634 331103 ⌁ steve.hewlett@medway.gov.uk

Waste Collection and Disposal: Ms Michelle Chambers, Contract Services Manager, Civic Centre, Rochester ME2 4AU ☎ 01634 333008 ⌁ michelle.chambers@medway.gov.uk

Waste Collection and Disposal: Ms Sarah Dagwell, Head - Waste Services Operational, Civic Centre, Rochester ME2 4AU ☎ 01634 331597 ⌁ sarah.dagwell@medway.gov.uk

Waste Management: Ms Sarah Dagwell, Head - Waste Services Operational, Civic Centre, Rochester ME2 4AU ☎ 01634 331597 ⌁ sarah.dagwell@medway.gov.uk

Children's Play Areas: Mr Tim England, Head - Safer Communities & Greenspaces, Civic Headquarters, Gun Wharf, Dock Road, Chatham ME4 4TR ☎ 01634 333534 ⌁ tim.england@medway.gov.uk

COUNCILLORS

Mayor: Tranter, Stuart (CON - Rochester West)
stuart-tranter@btconnect.com

Deputy Mayor: Opara, Gloria (CON - Princes Park)
gloria.opara@medway.gov.uk

Leader of the Council: Jarrett, Alan (CON - Lordswood & Capstone)
alan.jarrett@medway.gov.uk

Deputy Leader of the Council: Doe, Howard (CON - Rainham South)
howard.doe@blueyonder.co.uk

Group Leader: Freshwater, Roy (UKIP - Peninsula)
royfreshwater@hotmail.co.uk

Group Leader: Maple, Vince (LAB - Chatham Central)
vince.maple@medway.gov.uk

Avey, John (CON - Strood South)
johnavey838@btinternet.com

Bhutia, Tashi (CON - Princes Park)
tashi747@gmail.com

Bowler, Nicholas (LAB - Rochester East)
nickbowler89@btinternet.com

Brake, David (CON - Walderslade)
david.brake@medway.gov.uk

Brown-Reckless, Catriona (UKIP - Strood South)
catriona.reckless@medway.gov.uk

Carr, David (CON - Rainham North)
david-j-carr@hotmail.co.uk

Chambers, Rodney (CON - Hempstead & Wigmore)
rodney.chambers@medway.gov.uk

Chambers, Diane (CON - Hempstead & Wigmore)
diane.chambers@medway.gov.uk

Chishti, Rehman (CON - Rainham Central)
rehman.chishti.mp@parliament.uk

Chitty, Jane (CON - Strood North)
jane.chitty@medway.gov.uk

Clarke, Trevor (CON - Rochester South & Horsted)
trevorclarke@blueyonder.co.uk

Cooper, Pat (IND - Gillingham North)
patecooper@virginmedia.com

Craven, Sam (LAB - Luton & Wayfield)
samcraven2010@hotmail.co.uk

Etheridge, Gary (CON - Strood Rural)
medway48@yahoo.co.uk

Fearn, Matt (CON - Cuxton & Halling)
matt_fearn@hotmail.com

Filmer, Philip (CON - Peninsula)
phil.filmer@medway.gov.uk

Franklin, Michael (CON - Luton & Wayfield)
mikefranklin@blueyonder.co.uk

Gilry, Dorte (LAB - Twydall)
gilry.dorte@gmail.com

Godwin, Paul (LAB - Chatham Central)
paul.godwin@medway.gov.uk

Griffin, Sylvia (CON - Rochester South & Horsted)
sylvia_brian@btinternet.com

Griffiths, Glyn (LAB - Twydall)
glyngriff@blueyonder.co.uk

Gulvi, Adrian (CON - Walderslade)
avhgulvin@btinternet.com

Hall, Phil (CON - Strood North)
phil.hall@medway.gov.uk

Hicks, Peter (CON - Strood Rural)
peterhicks690@yahoo.co.uk

Howard, Anne-Claire (CON - Twydall)
anneclaire4twydall@gmail.com

Iles, Steve (CON - Strood North)
steve.iles@live.co.uk

Johnson, Clive (LAB - Gillingham South)
clive.johnson@medway.gov.uk

Joy, Mark (IND - Strood South)
mpjoystroodsouth@gmail.com

Kemp, Barry (CON - Rainham Central)
barryjkemp@hotmail.com

Khan, Naushabah (LAB - Gillingham South)
naushabah.khan@medway.gov.uk

Mackness, Andrew (CON - River)
andrewmackness@live.co.uk

McDonald, Dan (LAB - Gillingham South)
dan.mcdonald@medway.gov.uk

Murray, Teresa (LAB - Rochester East)
teresamurraytm@aol.com

O'Brien, Mike (CON - Rainham Central)
mikeobrien155@blueyonder.co.uk

Osborne, Tristan (LAB - Luton & Wayfield)
tris.osborne@gmail.com

Pendergast, Mick (UKIP - Peninsula)
mick.pendergast@medway.gov.uk

Potter, Martin (CON - Rainham North)
mpotter.rainham@gmail.com

Price, Adam (LAB - Gillingham North)
adam.price@medway.gov.uk

Purdy, Wendy (CON - Watling)
johnpurdy@btinternet.com

Royle, David (CON - Rainham South)
david.royle94@btinternet.com

Saroy, Asha (CON - Watling)
cllrsaroy@outlook.com

Shaw, Julie (LAB - Chatham Central)
shaw9089@btinternet.com

Stamp, Andy (LAB - Gillingham North)
andy.stamp@medway.gov.uk

Tejan, Habib (CON - River)
habibtejan@live.co.uk

Tolhurst, Kelly (CON - Rochester West)
kellytolhurst@hotmail.co.uk

Turpin, Rupert (CON - Rochester South & Horsted)
cllrturpin@gmail.com

Wicks, Les (CON - Rainham South)
les.wicks@hotmail.com

Wildey, David (CON - Lordswood & Capstone)
david.wiley@medway.gov.uk

Williams, John (CON - Strood Rural)
johnwilliams@freeavalon.co.uk

POLITICAL COMPOSITION
CON: 36, LAB: 14, UKIP: 3, IND: 2

COMMITTEE CHAIRS
Audit: Mr Barry Kemp

Children & Young People: Mr David Royle

Health & Adult Social Care: Mr David Wildey

Health & Wellbeing: Mr David Brake

Licensing: Mrs Diane Chambers

Planning: Mrs Diane Chambers

Regeneration, Culture & Environment: Mr Trevor Clarke

Melton   **D**

Melton Borough Council, Parkside, Station Approach, Burton Street, Melton Mowbray LE13 1GH
☎ 01664 502502 ✆ contactus@melton.gov.uk 🖥 www.melton.gov.uk

FACTS AND FIGURES
Parliamentary Constituencies: Rutland and Melton
EU Constituencies: East Midlands
Election Frequency: Elections are of whole council

PRINCIPAL OFFICERS
Chief Executive: Mrs Lynn Aisbett, Chief Executive, Parkside, Station Approach, Burton Street, Melton Mowbray LE13 1GH ☎ 01664 502502 ✆ laisbett@melton.gov.uk

Senior Management: Mr Keith Aubrey, Strategic Director, Parkside, Station Approach, Burton Street, Melton Mowbray LE13 1GH

Senior Management: Mrs Dawn Garton, Head of Central Services, Parkside, Station Approach, Burton Street, Melton Mowbray LE13 1GH ☎ 01664 502502 ✆ dgarton@melton.gov.uk

Senior Management: Ms Christine Marshall, Strategic Director, Parkside, Station Approach, Burton Street, Melton Mowbray LE13 1GH ☎ 01664 502502 ✆ cmarshall@melton.gov.uk

Senior Management: Mr Harrinder Rai, Head of Communities & Neighbourhoods, Parkside, Station Approach, Burton Street, Melton Mowbray LE13 1GH ☎ 01664 502502 ✆ hrai@melton.gov.uk

Senior Management: Mrs Angela Tebbutt, Head of Communications, Parkside, Station Approach, Burton Street, Melton Mowbray LE13 1GH ☎ 01664 502502 ✆ atebbutt@melton.gov.uk

Senior Management: Mr Jim Worley, Head of Regulatory Services, Parkside, Station Approach, Burton Street, Melton Mowbray LE13 1GH ☎ 01664 502502 ✆ jworley@melton.gov.uk

Architect, Building / Property Services: Mr David Blanchard, Corporate Property Officer, Parkside, Station Approach, Burton Street, Melton Mowbray LE13 1GH ☎ 01664 502502 ✆ dblanchard@melton.gov.uk

Building Control: Mr Jim Worley, Head of Regulatory Services, Parkside, Station Approach, Burton Street, Melton Mowbray LE13 1GH ☎ 01664 502502 ✆ jworley@melton.gov.uk

PR / Communications: Mrs Angela Tebbutt, Head of Communications, Parkside, Station Approach, Burton Street, Melton Mowbray LE13 1GH ☎ 01664 502502 ✆ atebbutt@melton.gov.uk

Community Planning: Mr Harrinder Rai, Head of Communities & Neighbourhoods, Parkside, Station Approach, Burton Street, Melton Mowbray LE13 1GH ☎ 01664 502502 ✆ hrai@melton.gov.uk

Community Safety: Mr Harrinder Rai, Head of Communities & Neighbourhoods, Parkside, Station Approach, Burton Street, Melton Mowbray LE13 1GH ☎ 01664 502502 ✆ hrai@melton.gov.uk

Computer Management: Mr Paul Langham, IT Client Manager, Parkside, Station Approach, Burton Street, Melton Mowbray LE13 1GH ☎ 01455 255995 ✆ plangham@melton.gov.uk

Contracts: Mr Tony Hall, Head of Welland Procurement, Parkside, Station Approach, Burton Street, Melton Mowbray LE13 1GH ☎ 01664 502502 ✆ thall@melton.gov.uk

Customer Service: Mrs Angela Tebbutt, Head of Communications, Parkside, Station Approach, Burton Street, Melton Mowbray LE13 1GH ☎ 01664 502502 ✆ atebbutt@melton.gov.uk

MELTON

Economic Development: Mr Harrinder Rai, Head of Communities & Neighbourhoods, Parkside, Station Approach, Burton Street, Melton Mowbray LE13 1GH ☎ 01664 502502 ⌨ hrai@melton.gov.uk

Electoral Registration: Ms Sally Renwick, Elections Officer, Parkside, Station Approach, Burton Street, Melton Mowbray LE13 1GH ☎ 01664 502502 ⌨ srenwick@melton.gov.uk

Emergency Planning: Mr Jim Worley, Head of Regulatory Services, Parkside, Station Approach, Burton Street, Melton Mowbray LE13 1GH ☎ 01664 502502 ⌨ jworley@melton.gov.uk

Environmental Health: Mrs Victoria Clarke, Environment Protection & Safety Manager, Parkside, Station Approach, Burton Street, Melton Mowbray LE13 1GH ☎ 01664 502502 ⌨ vclarke@melton.gov.uk

Estates, Property & Valuation: Mr David Blanchard, Corporate Property Officer, Parkside, Station Approach, Burton Street, Melton Mowbray LE13 1GH ☎ 01664 502502 ⌨ dblanchard@melton.gov.uk

Events Manager: Ms Lisa Hammond, Joint Town Centre Manager, Parkside, Station Approach, Burton Street, Melton Mowbray LE13 1GH ☎ 01664 502502 ⌨ lhammond@melton.gov.uk

Facilities: Mr Stephen Richardson, Facilities Manager, Parkside, Station Approach, Burton Street, Melton Mowbray LE13 1GH ☎ 01664 502502 ⌨ srichardson@melton.gov.uk

Finance: Mrs Dawn Garton, Head of Central Services, Parkside, Station Approach, Burton Street, Melton Mowbray LE13 1GH ☎ 01664 502502 ⌨ dgarton@melton.gov.uk

Grounds Maintenance: Mr Ramon Selvon, Waste & Grounds Maintenance Manager, Parkside, Station Approach, Burton Street, Melton Mowbray LE13 1GH ☎ 01664 502502 ⌨ rselvon@melton.gov.uk

Health and Safety: Mr Chris Morris, HR & Health & Safety Officer, Parkside, Station Approach, Burton Street, Melton Mowbray LE13 1GH ☎ 01664 502502 ⌨ sburton@melton.gov.uk

Home Energy Conservation: Mrs Victoria Clarke, Environment Protection & Safety Manager, Parkside, Station Approach, Burton Street, Melton Mowbray LE13 1GH ☎ 01664 502502 ⌨ vclarke@melton.gov.uk

Housing: Mr Harrinder Rai, Head of Communities & Neighbourhoods, Parkside, Station Approach, Burton Street, Melton Mowbray LE13 1GH ☎ 01664 502502 ⌨ hrai@melton.gov.uk

Housing Maintenance: Mr Harrinder Rai, Head of Communities & Neighbourhoods, Parkside, Station Approach, Burton Street, Melton Mowbray LE13 1GH ☎ 01664 502502 ⌨ hrai@melton.gov.uk

Legal: Ms Verina Wenham, Solicitor to the Council, Parkside, Station Approach, Burton Street, Melton Mowbray LE13 1GH ☎ 01664 502502 ⌨ vwenham@melton.gov.uk

Leisure and Cultural Services: Mr Ronan Browne, People Manager, Parkside, Station Approach, Burton Street, Melton Mowbray LE13 1GH ☎ 01664 502502 ⌨ rbrowne@melton.gov.uk

Licensing: Mrs E Holdsworth, Licensing Officer, Parkside, Station Approach, Burton Street, Melton Mowbray LE13 1GH ☎ 01664 502502 ⌨ eholdsworth@melton.gov.uk

Licensing: Mr Jim Worley, Head of Regulatory Services, Parkside, Station Approach, Burton Street, Melton Mowbray LE13 1GH ☎ 01664 502502 ⌨ jworley@melton.gov.uk

Lottery Funding, Charity and Voluntary: Mr Harrinder Rai, Head of Communities & Neighbourhoods, Parkside, Station Approach, Burton Street, Melton Mowbray LE13 1GH ☎ 01664 502502 ⌨ hrai@melton.gov.uk

Member Services: Mrs Angela Tebbutt, Head of Communications, Parkside, Station Approach, Burton Street, Melton Mowbray LE13 1GH ☎ 01664 502502 ⌨ atebbutt@melton.gov.uk

Parking: Mr David Blanchard, Corporate Property Officer, Parkside, Station Approach, Burton Street, Melton Mowbray LE13 1GH ☎ 01664 502502 ⌨ dblanchard@melton.gov.uk

Personnel / HR: Mrs Angela Tebbutt, Head of Communications, Parkside, Station Approach, Burton Street, Melton Mowbray LE13 1GH ☎ 01664 502502 ⌨ atebbutt@melton.gov.uk

Planning: Mr Jim Worley, Head of Regulatory Services, Parkside, Station Approach, Burton Street, Melton Mowbray LE13 1GH ☎ 01664 502502 ⌨ jworley@melton.gov.uk

Procurement: Mr Tony Hall, Head of Welland Procurement, Parkside, Station Approach, Burton Street, Melton Mowbray LE13 1GH ☎ 01664 502502 ⌨ thall@melton.gov.uk

Recycling & Waste Minimisation: Ms Amanda Hume, Environmental Services Officer, Parkside, Station Approach, Burton Street, Melton Mowbray LE13 1GH ☎ 01664 502502 ⌨ ahume@melton.gov.uk

Recycling & Waste Minimisation: Mr Ramon Selvon, Waste & Grounds Maintenance Manager, Parkside, Station Approach, Burton Street, Melton Mowbray LE13 1GH ☎ 01664 502502 ⌨ rselvon@melton.gov.uk

Regeneration: Mr Harrinder Rai, Head of Communities & Neighbourhoods, Parkside, Station Approach, Burton Street, Melton Mowbray LE13 1GH ☎ 01664 502502 ⌨ hrai@melton.gov.uk

Staff Training: Mrs Sarah-Jane O'Connor, HR & Communications Manager, Parkside, Station Approach, Burton Street, Melton Mowbray LE13 1GH ☎ 01664 502502 ⌨ soconnor@melton.gov.uk

Sustainable Communities: Mr Harrinder Rai, Head of Communities & Neighbourhoods, Parkside, Station Approach, Burton Street, Melton Mowbray LE13 1GH ☎ 01664 502502 ⌨ hrai@melton.gov.uk

Sustainable Development: Mr Harrinder Rai, Head of Communities & Neighbourhoods, Parkside, Station Approach, Burton Street, Melton Mowbray LE13 1GH ☎ 01664 502502 ⌁ hrai@melton.gov.uk

Tourism: Mr Harrinder Rai, Head of Communities & Neighbourhoods, Parkside, Station Approach, Burton Street, Melton Mowbray LE13 1GH ☎ 01664 502502 ⌁ hrai@melton.gov.uk

Town Centre: Ms Shelagh Core, Joint Town Centre Manager, Parkside, Station Approach, Burton Street, Melton Mowbray LE13 1GH ☎ 01664 502502 ⌁ score@melton.gov.uk

Town Centre: Ms Lisa Hammond, Joint Town Centre Manager, Parkside, Station Approach, Burton Street, Melton Mowbray LE13 1GH ☎ 01664 502502 ⌁ lhammond@melton.gov.uk

Transport: Mr Jim Worley, Head of Regulatory Services, Parkside, Station Approach, Burton Street, Melton Mowbray LE13 1GH ☎ 01664 502502 ⌁ jworley@melton.gov.uk

Waste Collection and Disposal: Mr Jim Worley, Head of Regulatory Services, Parkside, Station Approach, Burton Street, Melton Mowbray LE13 1GH ☎ 01664 502502 ⌁ jworley@melton.gov.uk

Waste Management: Mr Ramon Selvon, Waste & Grounds Maintenance Manager, Parkside, Station Approach, Burton Street, Melton Mowbray LE13 1GH ☎ 01664 502502 ⌁ rselvon@melton.gov.uk

Waste Management: Mr Jim Worley, Head of Regulatory Services, Parkside, Station Approach, Burton Street, Melton Mowbray LE13 1GH ☎ 01664 502502 ⌁ jworley@melton.gov.uk

COUNCILLORS

Mayor: Wright, David (CON - Bottesford)
dwright@melton.gov.uk

Deputy Mayor: Bains, Tejpal (CON - Melton Sysonby)
tbains@melton.gov.uk

Group Leader: Holmes, Elaine (IND - Waltham on the Wolds)
eholmes@melton.gov.uk

Baguley, Pam (CON - Long Clawson & Stathern)
pbaguley@melton.gov.uk

Blase, Michael (LAB - Melton Egerton)
mblase@melton.gov.uk

Botterill, Gerald (CON - Croxton Kerrial)
gbotterill@melton.gov.uk

Chandler, Pru (CON - Bottesford)
pchandler@melton.gov.uk

Culley, Tina (IND - Melton Egerton)
tculley@melton.gov.uk

Cumbers, Pat (CON - Melton Dorian)
pcumbers@melton.gov.uk

de Burle, Ronnie (CON - Ashfordby)
rdeburle@melton.gov.uk

Douglas, Jeanne (CON - Melton Craven)
jdouglas@melton.gov.uk

Glancy, Margaret (CON - Melton Newport)
mglancy@melton.gov.uk

Graham, Malise (CON - Wymondham)
mgraham@melton.gov.uk

Greenow, Tom (CON - Melton Warwick)
tgreenow@melton.gov.uk

Higgins, Leigh (CON - Somerby)
lhiggins@melton.gov.uk

Hurrell, Julia (CON - Melton Warwick)
jhurrell@melton.gov.uk

Hutchinson, Edward (IND - Frisby on the Wreake)
ehutchinson@melton.gov.uk

Illingworth, John (CON - Melton Sysonby)
jillingworth@melton.gov.uk

Lumley, Simon (CON - Melton Newport)
slumley@melton.gov.uk

Manderson, Val (CON - Melton Sysonby)
vmanderson@melton.gov.uk

Orson, Joe (CON - Old Dalby)
jorson@melton.gov.uk

Pearson, Alan (CON - Melton Dorian)
apearson@melton.gov.uk

Posnett, Pam (CON - Melton Newport)
pposnett@melton.gov.uk

Rhodes, Byron (CON - Long Clawson & Stathern)
brhodes@leics.gov.uk

Sheldon, Mal (CON - Ashfordby)
msheldon@melton.gov.uk

Simpson, Janet (CON - Gaddesby)
janetsimpson@melton.gov.uk

Wyatt, John (CON - Melton Dorian)
jwyatt@melton.gov.uk

POLITICAL COMPOSITION
CON: 23, IND: 3, LAB: 1, Vacant: 1

COMMITTEE CHAIRS

Licensing: Mr John Wyatt

Planning: Mr John Illingworth

Mendip   D

Mendip District Council, Council Offices, Cannards Grave Road, Shepton Mallet BA4 5BT
☎ 0300 303 8588 ⌁ customerservices@mendip.gov.uk
🖳 www.mendip.gov.uk

FACTS AND FIGURES
Parliamentary Constituencies: Wells
EU Constituencies: South West
Election Frequency: Elections are of whole council

PRINCIPAL OFFICERS

Chief Executive: Mr Stuart Brown, Chief Executive, Mendip District Council, Cannards Grave Road, Shepton Mallet BA4 5BT
☎ 0300 303 8588 ⌁ stuart.brown@mendip.gov.uk

MENDIP

Senior Management: Mrs Tracy Aarons, Corporate Manager - Built Environment, Council Offices, Cannards Grave Road, Shepton Mallet BA4 5BT ☎ 0300 303 8588 ◌ tracy.aarons@mendip.gov.uk

Senior Management: Mrs Chris Atkinson, Corporate Manager - Access to Services, Council Offices, Cannards Grave Road, Shepton Mallet BA4 5BT ☎ 0300 303 8588 ◌ chris.atkinson@mendip.gov.uk

Senior Management: Mr Stuart Cave, Corporate Manager - Regulatory Services, Mendip District Council, Cannards Grave Road, Shepton Mallet BA4 5BT ☎ 0300 303 8588 ◌ stuart.cave@mendip.gov.uk

Senior Management: Mrs Donna Nolan, Corporate Manager - Governance & Public Spaces, Mendip District Council, Cannards Grave Road, Shepton Mallet BA4 5BT ☎ 0300 303 8588 ◌ donna.nolan@mendip.gov.uk

Building Control: Mrs Tracy Aarons, Corporate Manager - Built Environment, Council Offices, Cannards Grave Road, Shepton Mallet BA4 5BT ☎ 0300 303 8588 ◌ tracy.aarons@mendip.gov.uk

Building Control: Mr Nigel Hunt, Somerset Building Control Partnership Manager, Bridgwater House, Kings Square, Bridgwater TA6 9ZY ☎ 01823 356473 ◌ nigel.hunt@mendip.gov.uk

PR / Communications: Mr Matt Smith, Senior Communications Officer, Council Offices, Cannards Grave Road, Shepton Mallet BA4 5BT ☎ 0300 303 8588 ◌ matthew.smith@mendip.gov.uk

Contracts: Mrs Chris Atkinson, Corporate Manager - Access to Services, Council Offices, Cannards Grave Road, Shepton Mallet BA4 5BT ☎ 0300 303 8588 ◌ chris.atkinson@mendip.gov.uk

Corporate Services: Mrs Chris Atkinson, Corporate Manager - Access to Services, Council Offices, Cannards Grave Road, Shepton Mallet BA4 5BT ☎ 0300 303 8588 ◌ chris.atkinson@mendip.gov.uk

Customer Service: Mrs Chris Atkinson, Corporate Manager - Access to Services, Council Offices, Cannards Grave Road, Shepton Mallet BA4 5BT ☎ 0300 303 8588 ◌ chris.atkinson@mendip.gov.uk

Economic Development: Mr Stuart Cave, Corporate Manager - Regulatory Services, Mendip District Council, Cannards Grave Road, Shepton Mallet BA4 5BT ☎ 0300 303 8588 ◌ stuart.cave@mendip.gov.uk

Electoral Registration: Mr Steve Lake, Electoral Services Manager, Mendip District Council, Cannards Grave Road, Shepton Mallet BA4 5BT ☎ 0300 303 8588 ◌ steven.lake@capita.co.uk

Environmental Health: Mrs Claire Malcolmson, Compliance Team Manager, Mendip District Council, Cannards Grave Road, Shepton Mallet BA4 5BT ☎ 0300 303 8588 ◌ claire.malcolmson@mendip.gov.uk

Finance: Mr Paul Deal, Section 151 Officer, Council Offices, Cannards Grave Road, Shepton Mallet BA4 5BT ☎ 0300 303 8588 ◌ paul.deal@mendip.gov.uk

Health and Safety: Mr Stuart Finney, Operational Assets Team Manager, Council Offices, Cannards Grave Road, Shepton Mallet BA4 5BT ☎ 0300 303 8588 ◌ stuart.finney@mendip.gov.uk

Housing: Mrs Tracy Aarons, Corporate Manager - Built Environment, Council Offices, Cannards Grave Road, Shepton Mallet BA4 5BT ☎ 0300 303 8588 ◌ tracy.aarons@mendip.gov.uk

Legal: Mrs Donna Nolan, Corporate Manager - Governance & Public Spaces, Mendip District Council, Cannards Grave Road, Shepton Mallet BA4 5BT ☎ 0300 303 8588 ◌ donna.nolan@mendip.gov.uk

Licensing: Mr Jason Kirkwood, Licensing Manager, Council Offices, Cannards Grave Road, Shepton Mallet BA4 5BT ☎ 0300 303 8588 ◌ jason.kirkwood@mendip.gov.uk

Member Services: Mrs Claire Dicken, Committee Support Officer, Council Offices, Cannards Grave Road, Shepton Mallet BA4 5BT ☎ 0300 303 8588 ◌ claire.dicken@mendip.gov.uk

Personnel / HR: Ms Tanya Shirt, HR, Training & Business Partner, Council Offices, Cannards Grave Road, Shepton Mallet BA4 5BT tanya.shirt@mendip.gov.uk

Planning: Mrs Tracy Aarons, Corporate Manager - Built Environment, Council Offices, Cannards Grave Road, Shepton Mallet BA4 5BT ☎ 0300 303 8588 ◌ tracy.aarons@mendip.gov.uk

Procurement: Mr Geoff Thompson, Corporate Services Team Manager, Council Offices, Cannards Grave Road, Shepton Mallet BA4 5BT ☎ 0300 303 8588 ◌ geoff.thompson@mendip.gov.uk

Staff Training: Ms Maureen Teasdale, HR Officer, Council Offices, Cannards Grave Road, Shepton Mallet BA4 5BT ◌ maureen.teasdale@mendip.gov.uk

COUNCILLORS

Chair: Marsh, Jeannette (CON - Shepton East) cllr.marsh@mendip.gov.uk

Vice-Chair: Drewe, Edward (CON - Ammerdown) cllr.drewe@mendip.gov.uk

Leader of the Council: Siggs, Harvey (CON - Wells St Cuthbert's) cllr.siggs@mendip.gov.uk

Deputy Leader of the Council: Killen, Tom (CON - Chewton Mendip & Ston Easton) cllr.killen@mendip.gov.uk

Group Leader: Sprawson-White, Helen (LD - Frome Oakfield) cllr.sprawson-white@mendip.gov.uk

Beale, Joanna (CON - Frome Berkley Down) cllr.beale@mendip.gov.uk

Beha, Bryan (LD - Street South) cllr.beha@mendip.gov.uk

Berry, Eve (CON - Frome Berkley Down) cllr.berry@mendip.gov.uk

Boyden, Adam (LD - Frome College) cllr.boyden@mendip.gov.uk

Bradshaw, Peter (CON - Creech)
cllr.bradshaw@mendip.gov.uk

Brunsdon, John (CON - Glastonbury St Mary's)
cllr.brunsdon@mendip.gov.uk

Carter, Rachel (CON - Ashwick, Chilcompton & Stratton)
cllr.rcarter@mendip.gov.uk

Carter, John (CON - Ashwick, Chilcompton & Stratton)
cllr.carter@mendip.gov.uk

Coles, John (CON - Glastonbury St John's)
cllr.coles@mendip.gov.uk

Collins, Shane (GRN - Frome Keyford)
cllr.collins@mendip.gov.uk

Cottle, Nick (LD - Glastonbury St Edmund's)
cllr.cottle@mendip.gov.uk

Davies, Simon (CON - Shepton West)
cllr.davies@mendip.gov.uk

Falle, Stina (GRN - Frome Market)
cllr.falle@mendip.gov.uk

Greenhalgh, John (CON - The Pennards & Ditcheat)
cllr.greenhalgh@mendip.gov.uk

Ham, Philip (CON - Coleford & Holcombe)
cllr.ham@mendip.gov.uk

Harris, Des (GRN - Frome Market)
cllr.harris@mendip.gov.uk

Height, Bente (IND - Shepton East)
cllr.height@mendip.gov.uk

Henderson, Steve (CON - Glastonbury St Benedict's)
cllr.henderson@mendip.gov.uk

Hewitt-Cooper, Nigel (CON - Croscombe & Pilton)
cllr.hewitt-cooper@mendip.gov.uk

Hooton, Damon (LD - Frome Park)
cllr.hooton@mendip.gov.uk

Horsfall, Alvin (LD - Frome Keyford)
cllr.horsfall@mendip.gov.uk

Hudson, Claire (LD - Frome Park)
cllr.hudson@mendip.gov.uk

Hughes, Lloyd (IND - Street South)
cllr.hughes@mendip.gov.uk

Mackenzie, Roy (LD - Wells St Thomas)
cllr.mackenzie@mendip.gov.uk

Mockford, Clive (CON - Beckington & Selwood)
cllr.mockford@mendip.gov.uk

Napper, Terry (CON - Street West)
cllr.napper@mendip.gov.uk

Noel, Graham (CON - Moor)
cllr.noel@mendip.gov.uk

North, John (CON - Wells Central)
cllr.north@mendip.gov.uk

Oliver, Linda (CON - Rode & Norton St Phillip)
cllr.loliver@mendip.gov.uk

Osman, John (CON - Wells St Cuthburt's)
cllr.osman@mendip.gov.uk

Parham, John (CON - Shepton West)
cllr.parham@mendip.gov.uk

Pullin, Mike (CON - St Cuthbert Out North)
cllr.pullin@mendip.gov.uk

Rice, Timothy (CON - Street North)
cllr.rice@mendip.gov.uk

Rideout, Mike (CON - Frome College)
cllr.rideout@mendip.gov.uk

Sen, Adam (LD - Street North)
cllr.sen@mendip.gov.uk

Skidmore, Dick (CON - No Ward)
cllr.skidmore@mendip.gov.uk

Taylor, Nigel (CON - Wookey & St Cuthbert Out West)
cllr.taylor@mendip.gov.uk

Townsend, Alan (CON - Coleford & Holcombe)
cllr.townsend@mendip.gov.uk

Unwin, Daniel (LD - Wells St Thomas)
cllr.unwin@mendip.gov.uk

van Dyk, David (CON - Cranmore, Doulting & Nunney)
cllr.vandyk@mendip.gov.uk

Woollcombe-Adams, Nigel (CON - Butleigh & Baltonsborough)
cllr.woollcombe-adams@mendip.gov.uk

Wyke, Ros (LD - Rodney & Westbury)

POLITICAL COMPOSITION
CON: 31, LD: 11, GRN: 3, IND: 2

COMMITTEE CHAIRS

Audit: Mr John North

Licensing: Mr Peter Bradshaw

Planning: Mr Nigel Hewitt-Cooper

Merthyr Tydfil   **W**

Merthyr Tydfil County Borough Council, Civic Centre, Castle Street, Merthyr Tydfil CF47 8AN
☎ 01685 725000 🖷 01685 722146 ✆ customer.care@merthyr.gov.uk
🖥 www.merthyr.gov.uk

FACTS AND FIGURES
Parliamentary Constituencies: Merthyr Tydfil and Rhymney
EU Constituencies: Wales
Election Frequency: Elections are of whole council

PRINCIPAL OFFICERS

Chief Executive: Mr Gareth Chapman, Chief Executive, Civic Centre, Castle Street, Merthyr Tydfil CF47 8AN ☎ 01685 725208 ✆ gareth.chapman@merthyr.gov.uk

Deputy Chief Executive: Mr Ellis Cooper, Deputy Chief Executive, Civic Centre, Castle Street, Merthyr Tydfil CF47 8AN ☎ 01685 726295 ✆ ellis.cooper@merthyr.gov.uk

Senior Management: Miss Lorraine Buck, Corporate Director, Civic Centre, Castle Street, Merthyr Tydfil CF47 8AN ☎ 01685 724621 ✆ lorraine.buck@merthyr.gov.uk

MERTHYR TYDFIL

Access Officer / Social Services (Disability): Ms Lisa Emerson, Asset Manager, Ty Keir Hardie, Riverside Court, Avenue de Clichy, Merthyr Tydfil CF47 8XD ☎ 01685 725000 ✆ lisa.emerson@merthyr.gov.uk

Architect, Building / Property Services: Ms Cheryllee Evans, Head of Property Services & Estates, Unit 5, Triangle Business Park, Pentrebach, Merthyr Tydfil CF48 4TQ ☎ 01685 725290 ✆ cheryllee.evans@merthyr.gov.uk

Building Control: Mr Ken Bateman, Group Leader - Building Control, Unit 5, Triangle Business Park, Pentrebach, Merthyr Tydfil CF4 4TQ ☎ 01685 726257 ✆ ken.bateman@merthyr.gov.uk

Catering Services: Ms Edwina Pickering, Acting Team Leader - Catering Service, Unit 5, Triangle Business Park, Pentrebach, Merthyr Tydfil CF48 4TQ ☎ 01685 725000 ✆ edwina.pickering@merthyr.gov.uk

Children / Youth Services: Mr Chris Hole, Head - Youth Service, Civic Centre, Castle Street, Merthyr Tydfil CF47 8AN ☎ 01685 725000 ✆ chris.hole@merthyr.gov.uk

Civil Registration: Mrs Dianne Green, Superintendent Registrar, Register Office, Ty Penderyn, 26 High Street, Merthyr Tydfil CF47 8DP ☎ 01685 725000 ✆ dianne.green@merthyr.gov.uk

PR / Communications: Mrs Ceri Dinham, Team Leader - Corporate Communications, Civic Centre, Castle Street, Merthyr Tydfil CF47 8AN ☎ 01685 725483 ✆ corporate.communications@merthyr.gov.uk

Community Planning: Ms Judith Jones, Head of Planning, Unit 5, Triangle Business Park, Pentrebach, Merthyr Tydfil CF48 4TQ ☎ 01685 725000 ✆ judith.jones@merthyr.gov.uk

Community Safety: Ms Judith Jones, Head of Planning, Unit 5, Triangle Business Park, Pentrebach, Merthyr Tydfil CF48 4TQ ☎ 01685 725000 ✆ judith.jones@merthyr.gov.uk

Computer Management: Mr Richard Evans, ICT Manager, Civic Centre, Castle Street, Merthyr Tydfil CF47 8AN ☎ 01685 725000 ✆ richard.evans@merthyr.gov.uk

Consumer Protection and Trading Standards: Mr Paul Lewis, Trading Standards Manager, Civic Centre, Castle Street, Merthyr Tydfil CF47 8AN ☎ 01685 725000 ✆ paul.lewis@merthyr.gov.uk

Consumer Protection and Trading Standards: Mr Steve Peters, Head of Public Protection, Civic Centre, Castle Street, Merthyr Tydfil CF47 8AN ☎ 01685 725030 ✆ steve.peters@merthyr.gov.uk

Contracts: Mr Ellis Cooper, Deputy Chief Executive, Civic Centre, Castle Street, Merthyr Tydfil CF47 8AN ☎ 01685 726295 ✆ ellis.cooper@merthyr.gov.uk

Contracts: Mr Paul Davies, Procurement & Efficiency Officer, Unit 5, Triangle Business Park, Pentrebach, Merthyr Tydfil CF48 4TQ ☎ 01685 724904 ✆ paul.davies@merthyr.gov.uk

Corporate Services: Mr Mark Thomas, Head of Corporate Services, Civic Centre, Castle Street, Merthyr Tydfil CF47 8AN ☎ 01685 725000 ✆ mark.thomas@merthyr.gov.uk

Customer Service: Mr Gregg Edwards, Customer & Corporate Support Manager, Civic Centre, Castle Street, Merthyr Tydfil CF47 8AN ☎ 01685 725000 ✆ gregg.edwards@merthyr.gov.uk

Direct Labour: Mrs Cherylee Evans, Chief Officer - Neighbourhood Services, Civic Centre, Castle Street, Merthyr Tydfil CF47 8AN ☎ 01685 725000 ✆ cherylee.evans@merthyr.gov.uk

Economic Development: Mr Chris Long, Business Support & Tourism Manager, Unit 5, Triangle Business Park, Pentrebach, Merthyr Tydfil CF48 4TQ ☎ 01685 725079 ✆ chris.long@merthyr.gov.uk

Economic Development: Mr Alyn Owen, Chief Officer - Regeneration, Unit 5, Triangle Business Park, Pentrebach, Merthyr Tydfil CF48 4QT ☎ 01625 725303 ✆ alyn.owen@merthyr.gov.uk

Education: Mrs Dorothy Haines, Chief Officer - Learning, Civic Centre, Castle Street, Merthyr Tydfil CF47 8AN ☎ 01685 724621 ✆ dorothy.haines@merthyr.gov.uk

E-Government: Mr Ellis Cooper, Deputy Chief Executive, Civic Centre, Castle Street, Merthyr Tydfil CF47 8AN ☎ 01685 726295 ✆ ellis.cooper@merthyr.gov.uk

Electoral Registration: Ms Ann Taylor, Democratic Services Manager, Civic Centre, Castle Street, Merthyr Tydfil CF47 8AN ☎ 01685 725202 ✆ ann.taylor@merthyr.gov.uk

Emergency Planning: Mr Robert Gough, Emergency Planning / Local Resilience Unit Manager, Unit 5, Triangle Business Park, Pentrebach, Merthyr Tydfil CF48 4TQ ☎ 01685 725162 ✆ robert.gough@merthyr.gov.uk

Energy Management: Mr James Edwards, Energy Officer, Unit 5, Triangle Business Park, Pentrebach, Merthyr Tydfil CF48 4TQ ☎ 01685 726208 ✆ james.edwards@merthyr.gov.uk

Energy Management: Mrs Cherylee Evans, Chief Officer - Neighbourhood Services, Civic Centre, Castle Street, Merthyr Tydfil CF47 8AN ☎ 01685 725000 ✆ cherylee.evans@merthyr.gov.uk

Environmental / Technical Services: Mrs Cherylee Evans, Chief Officer - Neighbourhood Services, Civic Centre, Castle Street, Merthyr Tydfil CF47 8AN ☎ 01685 725000 ✆ cherylee.evans@merthyr.gov.uk

Environmental Health: Mr Steve Peters, Head of Public Protection, Civic Centre, Castle Street, Merthyr Tydfil CF47 8AN ☎ 01685 725030 ✆ steve.peters@merthyr.gov.uk

Estates, Property & Valuation: Ms Lisa Emerson, Asset Manager, Unit 5, Triangle Business Park, Pentrebach, Merthyr Tydfil CF48 4TQ ☎ 01685 725000 ✆ lisa.emerson@merthyr.gov.uk

European Liaison: Mr Alyn Owen, Chief Officer - Regeneration, Unit 5, Triangle Business Park, Pentrebach, Merthyr Tydfil CF48 4QT ☎ 01625 725303 ✆ alyn.owen@merthyr.gov.uk

Finance: Mr Steve Jones, Head of Finance, Civic Centre, Castle Street, Merthyr Tydfil CF47 8AN ☎ 01685 725000
✆ steve.jones@merthyr.gov.uk

Fleet Management: Mr Paul Davies, Fleet Manager, Unit 20, Merthyr Industrial Estate, Pentrebach, Merthyr Tydfil CF48 4DR
☎ 01685 725000 ✆ paul.davies@merthyr.gov.uk

Grounds Maintenance: Mrs Cherylee Evans, Chief Officer - Neighbourhood Services, Civic Centre, Castle Street, Merthyr Tydfil CF47 8AN ☎ 01685 725000 ✆ cherylee.evans@merthyr.gov.uk

Health and Safety: Mr Alyn Dinham, Occupational Health & Safety Officer, Civic Centre, Castle Street, Merthyr Tydfil CF47 8AN ☎ 01685 724677 ✆ alyn.dinham@merthyr.gov.uk

Highways: Mrs Cherylee Evans, Chief Officer - Neighbourhood Services, Civic Centre, Castle Street, Merthyr Tydfil CF47 8AN ☎ 01685 725000 ✆ cherylee.evans@merthyr.gov.uk

Housing: Mr Steve Peters, Head of Public Protection, Civic Centre, Castle Street, Merthyr Tydfil CF47 8AN ☎ 01685 725030 ✆ steve.peters@merthyr.gov.uk

Legal: Mrs Carys Kennedy, Head - Legal Services, Civic Centre, Castle Street, Merthyr Tydfil CF47 8AN ☎ 01685 725454 ✆ carys.kennedy@merthyr.gov.uk

Leisure and Cultural Services: Mr Richard Marsh, Manager - Leisure, Culture & Environment, Civic Centre, Castle Street, Merthyr Tydfil CF47 8AN ☎ 01685 725273 ✆ richard.marsh@merthyr.gov.uk

Licensing: Mr Paul Lewis, Trading Standards Manager, Civic Centre, Castle Street, Merthyr Tydfil CF47 8AN ☎ 01685 725000 ✆ paul.lewis@merthyr.gov.uk

Lifelong Learning: Mrs Dorothy Haines, Chief Officer - Learning, Civic Centre, Castle Street, Merthyr Tydfil CF47 8AN ☎ 01685 724621 ✆ dorothy.haines@merthyr.gov.uk

Member Services: Ms Ann Taylor, Democratic Services Manager, Civic Centre, Castle Street, Merthyr Tydfil CF47 8AN ☎ 01685 725202 ✆ ann.taylor@merthyr.gov.uk

Parking: Mr Gregg Edwards, Customer & Corporate Support Manager, Civic Centre, Castle Street, Merthyr Tydfil CF47 8AN ☎ 01685 725000 ✆ gregg.edwards@merthyr.gov.uk

Partnerships: Mr Mark Thomas, Head of Corporate Services, Civic Centre, Castle Street, Merthyr Tydfil CF47 8AN ☎ 01685 725000 ✆ mark.thomas@merthyr.gov.uk

Personnel / HR: Mr David Jones, Payroll Officer, Unit 5, Triangle Business Park, Pentrebach, Merthyr Tydfil CF48 4TQ ☎ 01685 725325 ✆ david.jones@merthyr.gov.uk

Personnel / HR: Ms Lisa Jones, Head of HR, Civic Centre, Castle Street, Merthyr Tydfil CF47 8AN ☎ 01685 725000 ✆ lisa.jones@merthyr.gov.uk

Planning: Ms Judith Jones, Head of Planning, Unit 5, Triangle Business Park, Pentrebach, Merthyr Tydfil CF48 4TQ ☎ 01685 725000 ✆ judith.jones@merthyr.gov.uk

Procurement: Mr Paul Davies, Procurement & Efficiency Officer, Unit 5, Triangle Business Park, Pentrebach, Merthyr Tydfil CF48 4TQ ☎ 01685 724904 ✆ paul.davies@merthyr.gov.uk

Public Libraries: Ms Sian Antony, Libraries Manager, Central Library, High Street, Merthyr Tydfil CF47 8AF ☎ 01685 353480 ✆ sian.antony@merthyr.gov.uk

Public Libraries: Ms Jane Selwood, Libraries Manager, Central Library, High Street, Merthyr Tydfil CF47 8AF ☎ 01685 353480 ✆ jane.selwood@merthyr.gov.uk

Recycling & Waste Minimisation: Ms Valerie Steel, Waste Services Officer, Unit 4, Pentrebach Industrial Park, Pentrebach, Merthyr Tydfil CF48 4DR ☎ 01685 725478 ✆ val.steel@merthyr.gov.uk

Regeneration: Mr Alyn Owen, Chief Officer - Regeneration, Unit 5, Triangle Business Park, Pentrebach, Merthyr Tydfil CF48 4QT ☎ 01625 725303 ✆ alyn.owen@merthyr.gov.uk

Road Safety: Ms Lisa Clement-Williams, Road Safety Officer, Unit 20, Merthyr Industrial Estate, Pentrebach, Merthyr Tydfil CF48 4DR ☎ 01685 726286 ✆ lisa.clement-williams@merthyr.gov.uk

Social Services (Adult): Mr Mark Anderton, Head of Adult Social Services, Unit 20, Merthyr Industrial Estate, Pentrebach, Merthyr Tydfil CF48 4DR ☎ 01685 725000 ✆ mark.anderton@merthyr.gov.uk

Social Services (Children): Mrs Annabel Lloyd, Head of Children's Services, Unit 20, Merthyr Industrial Estate, Pentrebach, Merthyr Tydfil CF48 4DR ☎ 01685 725000 ✆ annabel.lloyd@merthyr.gov.uk

Town Centre: Mrs Rhian Prosser, Town Centre Manager, Unit 5, Triangle Business Park, Pentrebach, Merthyr Tydfil CF48 4TQ ☎ 01685 725106 ✆ rhian.prosser@merthyr.gov.uk

Traffic Management: Mr Martin Stark, Traffic Management Engineer, Unit 20, Merthyr Industrial Park, Pentrebach, Merthyr Tydfil CF48 4DR ☎ 01685 726287 ✆ martin.stark@merthyr.gov.uk

Transport: Mr Martin Stark, Traffic Management Engineer, Unit 20, Merthyr Industrial Park, Pentrebach, Merthyr Tydfil CF48 4DR ☎ 01685 726287 ✆ martin.stark@merthyr.gov.uk

COUNCILLORS

Mayor: Davies, Margaret (LAB - Cyfarthfa)
margaret.davies@merthyr.gov.uk

Deputy Mayor: Slater, Sian (LAB - Town)
sian.slater@hotmail.com

Leader of the Council: Toomey, Brendan (LAB - Park)
brendan.toomey@merthyr.gov.uk

Deputy Leader of the Council: Williams, Phil (LAB - Dowlais)
phil.williams@merthyr.gov.uk

MERTHYR TYDFIL

Group Leader: Thomas, Richard (IND - Treharris)
richard.thomas@merthyr.gov.uk

Barrett, Howard (IND - Vaynor)
howard.barrett@merthyr.gov.uk

Barry, Chris (LAB - Park)
chris.barry@merthyr.gov.uk

Braithwaite, Rhonda (LAB - Gurnos)
rhonda.braithwaite@merthyr.gov.uk

Brown, Paul (IND - Cyfarthfa)
paul.brown@merthyr.gov.uk

Carter, Brent (LAB - Plymouth)
brent.carter@merthyr.gov.uk

Chaplin, Tony (LAB - Cyfarthfa)
tony.chaplin@merthyr.gov.uk

Davies, David (LAB - Town)
david.davies3@merthyr.gov.uk

Galsworthy, Ernie (LAB - Treharris)
ernie.galsworthy@merthyr.gov.uk

Isaac, David (LAB - Penydarren)
david.isaac@merthyr.gov.uk

Jones, Harvey (LAB - Plymouth)
harvey.jones@merthyr.gov.uk

Jones, Allan (IND - Penydarren)
allan.jones@merthyr.gov.uk

Jones, David (LAB - Town)
david.jones2@merthyr.gov.uk

Jones, Clive (LAB - Park)
clive.jones@merthyr.gov.uk

Jones, Gareth (IND - Bedlinog)
gareth.jones1@merthyr.gov.uk

Lewis, Gareth (LAB - Plymouth)
gareth.lewis@merthyr.gov.uk

Lewis, Tom (LAB - Dowlais)
tom.lewis@merthyr.gov.uk

Mansbridge, Brian (LAB - Merthyr Vale)
brian.mansbridge@merthyr.gov.uk

Matthews, Linda (LAB - Town)
linda.matthews@merthyr.gov.uk

McCarthy, John (LAB - Penydarren)
john.mccarthy@merthyr.gov.uk

Moran, Kate (LAB - Treharris)
kate.moran@merthyr.gov.uk

Mytton, Lisa (IND - Vaynor)
lisa.mytton@merthyr.gov.uk

O'Neill, Mike (LAB - Gurnos)
mike.o'neill@merthyr.gov.uk

Roberts, Darren (LAB - Merthyr Vale)
darren.roberts@merthyr.gov.uk

Smart, Leighton (IND - Bedlinog)
leighton.smart@merthyr.gov.uk

Smith, Bill (LAB - Gurnos)
bill.smith@merthyr.gov.uk

Thomas, Raymond (LAB - Dowlais)
ray.thomas@merthyr.gov.uk

Tovey, Clive (IND - Gurnos)
clive.tovey@merthyr.gov.uk

Williams, Simon (LAB - Dowlais)
simon.williams@merthyr.gov.uk

POLITICAL COMPOSITION
LAB: 25, IND: 8

COMMITTEE CHAIRS

Audit: Mr Richard Thomas

Licensing: Mr Clive Jones

Regeneration, Planning & Countryside: Mr Gareth Jones

Merton   L

London Borough of Merton, Merton Civic Centre, London
Road, Morden SM4 5DX
☎ 020 8274 4901 🖷 020 8545 0446 ✆ communications@merton.gov.uk
🖥 www.merton.gov.uk

FACTS AND FIGURES
Parliamentary Constituencies: Mitcham and Morden, Wimbledon
EU Constituencies: London
Election Frequency: Elections are of whole council

PRINCIPAL OFFICERS

Chief Executive: Mr Ged Curran, Chief Executive, Merton Civic
Centre, London Road, Morden SM4 5DX ☎ 020 8545 3332
✆ ged.curran@merton.gov.uk

Senior Management: Ms Caroline Holland, Director - Corporate
Services, Merton Civic Centre, London Road, Morden SM4 5DX
☎ 020 8545 3450 ✆ caroline.holland@merton.gov.uk

Senior Management: Mr Chris Lee, Director - Environment &
Regeneration, Merton Civic Centre, London Road, Morden SM4
5DX ☎ 020 8545 3050 ✆ chris.lee@merton.gov.uk

Senior Management: Ms Yvette Stanley, Director - Children,
Schools & Families, Merton Civic Centre, London Road, Morden
SM4 5DX ☎ 020 8545 3251 ✆ yvette.stanley@merton.gov.uk

Senior Management: Mr Simon Williams, Director - Community
& Housing, Merton Civic Centre, London Road, Morden SM4 5DX
☎ 020 8545 3680 ✆ simon.williams@merton.gov.uk

Senior Management: Ms Dagmar Zeuner, Director - Public
Health, Merton Civic Centre, London Road, Morden SM4 5DX
☎ 020 8545 4836 ✆ dagmar.zeuner@merton.gov.uk

Architect, Building / Property Services: Mr Howard Joy,
Property Management & Review Manager, Merton Civic Centre,
London Road, Morden SM4 5DX ☎ 020 8545 3083
✆ howard.joy@merton.gov.uk

Architect, Building / Property Services: Mr James McGinlay,
Head - Sustainable Communities, Merton Civic Centre, London
Road, Morden SM4 5DX ☎ 020 8545 4154
✆ james.mcginlay@merton.gov.uk

Building Control: Mr John Hill, Head - Public Protection & Development, Merton Civic Centre, London Road, Morden SM4 5DX ☎ 020 8545 3052 ⏚ john.hill@merton.gov.uk

Building Control: Mr Chris Lee, Director - Environment & Regeneration, Merton Civic Centre, London Road, Morden SM4 5DX ☎ 020 8545 3050 ⏚ chris.lee@merton.gov.uk

Building Control: Mr Neil Milligan, Development Control Manager, Merton Civic Centre, London Road, Morden SM4 5DX ☎ 020 8545 3099 ⏚ neil.milligan@merton.gov.uk

Catering Services: Mrs Christine Humphries, Corporate Contracts & Technical Administration Manager, Merton Civic Centre, London Road, Morden SM4 5DX ☎ 020 8545 3510 ⏚ christine.humphries@merton.gov.uk

Children / Youth Services: Mr Paul Angeli, Assistant Director - Children's Social Care & Youth Inclusion, Merton Civic Centre, London Road, Morden SM4 5DX ☎ 020 8545 3376 ⏚ paul.angeli@merton.gov.uk

Children / Youth Services: Mr Paul Ballatt, Head - Commissioning, Strategy & Performance, Merton Civic Centre, London Road, Morden SM4 5DX ☎ 020 8545 4066 ⏚ paul.ballatt@merton.gov.uk

Children / Youth Services: Ms Allison Jones, Service Manager – Early Years, Merton Civic Centre, London Road, Morden SM4 5DX ☎ 020 8545 3796 ⏚ allison.jones@merton.gov.uk

Children / Youth Services: Ms Jane McSherry, Head - Education, Merton Civic Centre, London Road, Morden SM4 5DX ☎ 020 8545 4060 ⏚ jane.mcsherry@merton.gov.uk

Children / Youth Services: Ms Lisa Richardson, Service Support Manager - Permanence, LAC & Care Leavers, Merton Civic Centre, London Road, Morden SM4 5DX ☎ 020 8545 4288 ⏚ lisa.richardson@merton.gov.uk

Children / Youth Services: Ms Yvette Stanley, Director - Children, Schools & Families, Merton Civic Centre, London Road, Morden SM4 5DX ☎ 020 8545 3251 ⏚ yvette.stanley@merton.gov.uk

PR / Communications: Ms Sophie Poole, Head - Communications, Merton Civic Centre, London Road, Morden SM4 5DX ☎ 020 8545 3181 ⏚ sophie.poole@merton.gov.uk

Computer Management: Mr Mark Humphries, Assistant Director - Infrastructure & Transactions, Merton Civic Centre, London Road, Morden SM4 5DX ☎ 020 8545 3193 ⏚ mark.humphries@merton.gov.uk

Contracts: Mr Paul Ballatt, Head - Commissioning, Strategy & Performance, Merton Civic Centre, London Road, Morden SM4 5DX ☎ 020 8545 4066 ⏚ paul.ballatt@merton.gov.uk

Contracts: Mrs Christine Humphries, Corporate Contracts & Technical Administration Manager, Merton Civic Centre, London Road, Morden SM4 5DX ☎ 020 8545 3510 ⏚ christine.humphries@merton.gov.uk

Corporate Services: Ms Kim Brown, Joint Head of Human Resources, Merton Civic Centre, London Road, Morden SM4 5DX ☎ 020 8545 3152 ⏚ kim.brown@sutton.gov.uk

Corporate Services: Ms Caroline Holland, Director - Corporate Services, Merton Civic Centre, London Road, Morden SM4 5DX ☎ 020 8545 3450 ⏚ caroline.holland@merton.gov.uk

Customer Service: Mr Sean Cunniffe, Head - Customer Contact, Merton Civic Centre, London Road, Morden SM4 5DX ☎ 020 8274 4928 ⏚ sean.cunniffe@merton.gov.uk

Education: Ms Yvette Stanley, Director - Children, Schools & Families, Merton Civic Centre, London Road, Morden SM4 5DX ☎ 020 8545 3251 ⏚ yvette.stanley@merton.gov.uk

Education: Ms Yvonne Tomlin, Head - Community Education, Merton Civic Centre, London Road, Morden SM4 5DX ☎ 020 8274 5236 ⏚ yvonne.tomlin@merton.gov.uk

Electoral Registration: Mr Paul Evans, Assistant Director - Corporate Governance & Head of Shared Legal Services, Clifford House, 67C St Helier Avenue, Morden SM4 6HY ☎ 020 8545 3338 ⏚ paul.evans@merton.gov.uk

Emergency Planning: Mr Adam Viccari, Head - Corporate Safety Services, Merton Civic Centre, London Road, Morden SM4 5DX ☎ 020 8545 4803 ⏚ adam.viccari@merton.gov.uk

Environmental Health: Mr Chris Lee, Director - Environment & Regeneration, Merton Civic Centre, London Road, Morden SM4 5DX ☎ 020 8545 3050 ⏚ chris.lee@merton.gov.uk

Estates, Property & Valuation: Mr Howard Joy, Property Management & Review Manager, Merton Civic Centre, London Road, Morden SM4 5DX ☎ 020 8545 3083 ⏚ howard.joy@merton.gov.uk

Facilities: Mrs Christine Humphries, Corporate Contracts & Technical Administration Manager, Merton Civic Centre, London Road, Morden SM4 5DX ☎ 020 8545 3510 ⏚ christine.humphries@merton.gov.uk

Finance: Mr Paul Dale, Interim Assistant Director - Resources, Merton Civic Centre, London Road, Morden SM4 5DX ☎ 020 8545 3458 ⏚ paul.dale@merton.gov.uk

Fleet Management: Mr Cormac Stokes, Head - Street Scene & Waste, Merton Civic Centre, London Road, Morden SM4 5DX ☎ 020 8545 3190 ⏚ cormac.stokes@merton.gov.uk

Grounds Maintenance: Mr Doug Napier, Leisure & Culture Greenspaces Manager, Merton Civic Centre, London Road, Morden SM4 5DX ☎ 020 8545 3657 ⏚ doug.napier@merton.gov.uk

Highways: Mr Cormac Stokes, Head - Street Scene & Waste, Merton Civic Centre, London Road, Morden SM4 5DX ☎ 020 8545 3190 ⏚ cormac.stokes@merton.gov.uk

Housing: Mr Simon Williams, Director - Community & Housing, Merton Civic Centre, London Road, Morden SM4 5DX ☎ 020 8545 3680 ⏚ simon.williams@merton.gov.uk

MERTON

Legal: Mr Paul Evans, Assistant Director - Corporate Governance & Head of Shared Legal Services, Clifford House, 67C St Helier Avenue, Morden SM4 6HY ☎ 020 8545 3338
✆ paul.evans@merton.gov.uk

Leisure and Cultural Services: Mr Anthony Hopkins, Head - Libraries & Heritage Services, Merton Civic Centre, London Road, Morden SM4 5DX ☎ 020 8545 3770
✆ anthony.hopkins@merton.gov.uk

Leisure and Cultural Services: Ms Christine Parsloe, Manager - Culture Development, Merton Civic Centre, London Road, Morden SM4 5DX ☎ 020 8545 3669 ✆ christine.parsloe@merton.gov.uk

Licensing: Mr Ian Murrell, Environmental Health, Trading Standards & Licensing Manager, Merton Civic Centre, London Road, Morden SM4 5DX ☎ 020 8545 3859
✆ ian.murrell@merton.gov.uk

Lifelong Learning: Ms Yvonne Tomlin, Head - Community Education, Merton Civic Centre, London Road, Morden SM4 5DX ☎ 020 8274 5236 ✆ yvonne.tomlin@merton.gov.uk

Lighting: Mr Cormac Stokes, Head - Street Scene & Waste, Merton Civic Centre, London Road, Morden SM4 5DX ☎ 020 8545 3190 ✆ cormac.stokes@merton.gov.uk

Parking: Mr John Hill, Head - Public Protection & Development, Merton Civic Centre, London Road, Morden SM4 5DX ☎ 020 8545 3052 ✆ john.hill@merton.gov.uk

Procurement: Mr Tom Procter, Manager - Contracts & School Organisation, Merton Civic Centre, London Road, Morden SM4 5DX ☎ 020 8545 3306 ✆ tom.procter@merton.gov.uk

Public Libraries: Mr Anthony Hopkins, Head - Libraries & Heritage Services, Merton Civic Centre, London Road, Morden SM4 5DX ☎ 020 8545 3770 ✆ anthony.hopkins@merton.gov.uk

Recycling & Waste Minimisation: Mr Cormac Stokes, Head - Street Scene & Waste, Merton Civic Centre, London Road, Morden SM4 5DX ☎ 020 8545 3190 ✆ cormac.stokes@merton.gov.uk

Regeneration: Mr James McGinlay, Head - Sustainable Communities, Merton Civic Centre, London Road, Morden SM4 5DX ☎ 020 8545 4154 ✆ james.mcginlay@merton.gov.uk

Social Services (Children): Ms Naheed Chaudhry, Service Manager - Policy, Planning & Performance, Merton Civic Centre, London Road, Morden SM4 5DX ☎ 020 8545 4090 ✆ naheed.chaudhry@merton.gov.uk

Social Services (Children): Mr Keith Shipman, Manager - Education & Inclusion, Merton Civic Centre, London Road, Morden SM4 5DX ☎ 020 8545 3546 ✆ keith.shipman@merton.gov.uk

Social Services (Children): Ms Leanne Wallder, Joint Commissioning Manager - Children & Families, Merton Civic Centre, London Road, Morden SM4 5DX ☎ 020 8545 3591 ✆ leanne.wallder@merton.gov.uk

Street Scene: Mr Cormac Stokes, Head - Street Scene & Waste, Merton Civic Centre, London Road, Morden SM4 5DX ☎ 020 8545 3190 ✆ cormac.stokes@merton.gov.uk

Sustainable Communities: Mr James McGinlay, Head - Sustainable Communities, Merton Civic Centre, London Road, Morden SM4 5DX ☎ 020 8545 4154 ✆ james.mcginlay@merton.gov.uk

Sustainable Development: Mr John Hill, Head - Public Protection & Development, Merton Civic Centre, London Road, Morden SM4 5DX ☎ 020 8545 3052 ✆ john.hill@merton.gov.uk

Sustainable Development: Mr James McGinlay, Head - Sustainable Communities, Merton Civic Centre, London Road, Morden SM4 5DX ☎ 020 8545 4154 ✆ james.mcginlay@merton.gov.uk

Town Centre: Mr John Hill, Head - Public Protection & Development, Merton Civic Centre, London Road, Morden SM4 5DX ☎ 020 8545 3052 ✆ john.hill@merton.gov.uk

Traffic Management: Mr Cormac Stokes, Head - Street Scene & Waste, Merton Civic Centre, London Road, Morden SM4 5DX ☎ 020 8545 3190 ✆ cormac.stokes@merton.gov.uk

Transport: Mr Cormac Stokes, Head - Street Scene & Waste, Merton Civic Centre, London Road, Morden SM4 5DX ☎ 020 8545 3190 ✆ cormac.stokes@merton.gov.uk

Transport Planner: Mr Cormac Stokes, Head - Street Scene & Waste, Merton Civic Centre, London Road, Morden SM4 5DX ☎ 020 8545 3190 ✆ cormac.stokes@merton.gov.uk

Waste Collection and Disposal: Mr Brian McLoughlin, Waste Operations Manager, Merton Civic Centre, London Road, Morden SM4 5DX ☎ 020 8274 4936 ✆ brian.mcloughlin@merton.gov.uk

Waste Collection and Disposal: Mr Cormac Stokes, Head - Street Scene & Waste, Merton Civic Centre, London Road, Morden SM4 5DX ☎ 020 8545 3190 ✆ cormac.stokes@merton.gov.uk

Waste Management: Mr Brian McLoughlin, Waste Operations Manager, Merton Civic Centre, London Road, Morden SM4 5DX ☎ 020 8274 4936 ✆ brian.mcloughlin@merton.gov.uk

COUNCILLORS

Mayor: Fraser, Brenda (LAB - Longthornton)
brenda.fraser@merton.gov.uk

Deputy Mayor: Anderson, Stan (LAB - Lower Morden)
stan.anderson@merton.gov.uk

Leader of the Council: Alambritis, Stephen (LAB - Ravensbury)
stephen.alambritis@merton.gov.uk

Deputy Leader of the Council: Allison, Mark (LAB - Lavender Fields)
mark.allison@merton.gov.uk

Akyigyina, Agatha (LAB - Figge's Marsh)
agatha.akyigyina@merton.gov.uk

Attawar, Laxmi (LAB - Colliers Wood)
laxmi.attawar@merton.gov.uk

Badenoch, Hamish (CON - Village)
hamish.badenoch@merton.gov.uk

Bowcott, John (CON - Village)
john.bowcott@merton.gov.uk

Brunt, Mike (LAB - Figge's Marsh)
mike.brunt@merton.gov.uk

Bull, Michael (CON - Dundonald)
michael.bull@merton.gov.uk

Bush, Adam (CON - Raynes Park)
adam.bush@merton.gov.uk

Byers, Tobin (LAB - Cannon Hill)
tobin.byers@merton.gov.uk

Chirico, Charlie (CON - Trinity)
charlie.chirico@merton.gov.uk

Chung, David (LAB - Longthornton)
david.chung@merton.gov.uk

Cooper-Marbiah, Caroline (LAB - Colliers Wood)
caroline.cooper-marbiah@merton.gov.uk

Cowper, Pauline (LAB - Cannon Hill)
pauline.cowper@merton.gov.uk

Crowe, Stephen (CON - Raynes Park)
stephen.crowe@merton.gov.uk

Curtin, Mary (LAB - Lower Morden)
mary.curtin@merton.gov.uk

Dean, David (CON - Dundonald)
david.dean@merton.gov.uk

Dehaney, John (LAB - Graveney)
john.dehaney@merton.gov.uk

Draper, Nick (LAB - Colliers Wood)
nick.draper@merton.gov.uk

Foley, Edward (R - Merton Park)
edward.foley@merton.gov.uk

Gadzama, Fidelis (LAB - Cannon Hill)
fidelis.gadzama@merton.gov.uk

Garrod, Ross (LAB - Lavender Fields)
ross.garrod@merton.gov.uk

Grocott, Suzanne (CON - Dundonald)
suzanne.grocott@merton.gov.uk

Hanna, Jeff (LAB - Pollards Hill)
jeff.hanna@merton.gov.uk

Henry, Joan (LAB - Pollards Hill)
joan.henry@merton.gov.uk

Holden, Daniel (CON - Hillside)
daniel.holden@merton.gov.uk

Holmes, James (CON - Trinity)
james.holmes@merton.gov.uk

Howard, Janice (CON - Wimbledon Park)
janice.howard@merton.gov.uk

Jeanes, Mary-Jane (LD - West Barnes)
mary-jane.jeanes@merton.gov.uk

Jones, Philip (LAB - Ravensbury)
philip.jones@merton.gov.uk

Jones, Abigail (LAB - Abbey)
abigail.jones@merton.gov.uk

Judge, Andrew (LAB - Abbey)
andrew.judge@merton.gov.uk

Kenny, Sally (LAB - Lower Morden)
sally.kenny@labour.gov.uk

Kirby, Linda (LAB - Graveney)
linda.kirby@merton.gov.uk

Latif, Najeeb (CON - Village)
najeeb.latif@merton.gov.uk

Latif, Abdul (CON - Trinity)
abdul.latif@merton.gov.uk

Lewis-Lavender, Gilli (CON - West Barnes)
gilli.lewis-lavender@merton.gov.uk

Lewis-Lavender, Brian (CON - West Barnes)
brian.lewis-lavender@merton.gov.uk

Macauley, Edith (LAB - Lavender Fields)
edith.macauley@merton.gov.uk

Makin, Russell (LAB - Cricket Green)
russell.makin@merton.gov.uk

McCabe, Peter (LAB - Ravensbury)
peter.mccabe@merton.gov.uk

Moulton, Oonagh (CON - Wimbledon Park)
oonagh.moulton@merton.gov.uk

Munn, Ian (LAB - Cricket Green)
ian.munn@merton.gov.uk

Neep, Katy (LAB - Abbey)
katy.neep@merton.gov.uk

Neil, Jerome (LAB - St. Helier)

Pearce, Dennis (LAB - St. Helier)
dennis.pearce@merton.gov.uk

Sargeant, John (R - Merton Park)
john.sargeant@merton.gov.uk

Saunders, Judy (LAB - Cricket Green)
judy.saunders@merton.gov.uk

Simpson, David (CON - Hillside)
david.simpson@merton.gov.uk

Skeete, Marsie (LAB - Longthornton)
marsie.skeete@merton.gov.uk

Southgate, Peter (R - Merton Park)
peter.southgate@merton.gov.uk

Stanford, Geraldine (LAB - Figge's Marsh)
geraldine.stanord@merton.gov.uk

Taylor, Linda (CON - Wimbledon Park)
linda.taylor@merton.gov.uk

Uddin, Imran (LAB - St. Helier)
imran.uddin@merton.gov.uk

Udeh, Gregory (LAB - Graveney)
gregory.udeh@merton.gov.uk

West, Jill (CON - Raynes Park)
jill.west@merton.gov.uk

Whelton, Martin (LAB - Pollards Hill)
martin.whelton@merton.gov.uk

Williams, David (CON - Hillside)
david.williams@merton.gov.uk

MERTON

POLITICAL COMPOSITION
LAB: 36, CON: 20, R: 3, LD: 1

COMMITTEE CHAIRS

Children & Young People: Mr Dennis Pearce

Health & Wellbeing: Mr Tobin Byers

Licensing: Ms Agatha Akyigyina

Planning: Ms Linda Kirby

Mid & East Antrim District Council   N

Mid & East Antrim District Council, The Braid, 1 - 29 Bridge Street, Ballymena BT43 5EJ
☎ 0300 124 5000 ⏚ enquiries@midandeastantrim.gov.uk
💻 www.midandeastantrim.gov.uk

PRINCIPAL OFFICERS

Chief Executive: Ms Anne Donaghy, Chief Executive, The Braid, 1 - 29 Bridge Street, Ballymena BT43 5EJ
⏚ anne.donaghy@midandeastantrim.gov.uk

Senior Management: Mrs Sandra Cole, Director - Finance, ICT & Governance, The Braid, 1 - 29 Bridge Street, Ballymena BT43 5EJ
⏚ sandra.cole@midandeastantrim.gov.uk

Senior Management: Mrs Karen Hargan, Director - Organisation Development & Community Planning, The Braid, 1 - 29 Bridge Street, Ballymena BT43 5EJ
⏚ karen.hargan@midandeastantrim.gov.uk

Senior Management: Mr Philip Thompson, Director - Operations, The Braid, 1 - 29 Bridge Street, Ballymena BT43 5EJ
⏚ philip.thompson@midandeastantrim.gov.uk

Building Control: Ms Patricia Allen, Head of Regulatory Services, Ardeevin, 80 Galgorm Road, Ballymena BT42 1AB
⏚ patricia.allen@midandeastantrim.gov.uk

PR / Communications: Ms Victoria Law, Head of Communications, The Braid, 1 - 29 Bridge Street, Ballymena BT43 5EJ ⏚ victoria.law@midandeastantrim.gov.uk

Community Planning: Mrs Karen Hargan, Director - Organisation Development & Community Planning, The Braid, 1 - 29 Bridge Street, Ballymena BT43 5EJ
⏚ karen.hargan@midandeastantrim.gov.uk

Contracts: Mrs Sandra Cole, Director - Finance, ICT & Governance, The Braid, 1 - 29 Bridge Street, Ballymena BT43 5EJ
⏚ sandra.cole@midandeastantrim.gov.uk

Economic Development: Ms Linda Williams, Director - Economic Growth, Regeneration & Tourism, The Braid, 1 - 29 Bridge Street, Ballymena BT43 5EJ ⏚ linda.williams@midandeastantrim.gov.uk

Emergency Planning: Ms Patricia Allen, Head of Regulatory Services, Ardeevin, 80 Galgorm Road, Ballymena BT42 1AB
⏚ patricia.allen@midandeastantrim.gov.uk

Energy Management: Ms Patricia Allen, Head of Regulatory Services, Ardeevin, 80 Galgorm Road, Ballymena BT42 1AB
⏚ patricia.allen@midandeastantrim.gov.uk

Environmental Health: Ms Patricia Allen, Head of Regulatory Services, Ardeevin, 80 Galgorm Road, Ballymena BT42 1AB
⏚ patricia.allen@midandeastantrim.gov.uk

Estates, Property & Valuation: Ms Patricia Allen, Head of Regulatory Services, Ardeevin, 80 Galgorm Road, Ballymena BT42 1AB ⏚ patricia.allen@midandeastantrim.gov.uk

European Liaison: Ms Linda Williams, Director - Economic Growth, Regeneration & Tourism, The Braid, 1 - 29 Bridge Street, Ballymena BT43 5EJ ⏚ linda.williams@midandeastantrim.gov.uk

Facilities: Mr Trevor Kyle, Head of Assets & Facilities Management, Ardeevin, 80 Galgorm Road, Ballymena BT42 1AB
⏚ trevor.kyle@midandeastantrim.gov.uk

Finance: Mrs Sandra Cole, Director - Finance, ICT & Governance, The Braid, 1 - 29 Bridge Street, Ballymena BT43 5EJ
⏚ sandra.cole@midandeastantrim.gov.uk

Grounds Maintenance: Mr Stephen Daye, Head of Open Spaces, Museum & Civic Centre, 11 Antrim Street, Carrickfergus BT38 7DG
⏚ stephen.daye@midandeastantrim.gov.uk

Health and Safety: Ms Patricia Allen, Head of Regulatory Services, Ardeevin, 80 Galgorm Road, Ballymena BT42 1AB
⏚ patricia.allen@midandeastantrim.gov.uk

Home Energy Conservation: Ms Patricia Allen, Head of Regulatory Services, Ardeevin, 80 Galgorm Road, Ballymena BT42 1AB ⏚ patricia.allen@midandeastantrim.gov.uk

Legal: Mrs Sandra Cole, Director - Finance, ICT & Governance, The Braid, 1 - 29 Bridge Street, Ballymena BT43 5EJ
⏚ sandra.cole@midandeastantrim.gov.uk

Leisure and Cultural Services: Mrs Bernie Candlish, Head of Leisure, Arts & Culture, Ardeevin, 80 Galgorm Road, Ballymena BT42 1AB ⏚ bernie.candlish@midandeastantrim.gov.uk

Licensing: Ms Patricia Allen, Head of Regulatory Services, Ardeevin, 80 Galgorm Road, Ballymena BT42 1AB
⏚ patricia.allen@midandeastantrim.gov.uk

Lighting: Mr Trevor Kyle, Head of Assets & Facilities Management, Ardeevin, 80 Galgorm Road, Ballymena BT42 1AB
⏚ trevor.kyle@midandeastantrim.gov.uk

Lottery Funding, Charity and Voluntary: Ms Jackie Patton, Head of Community Planning, Ardeevin, 80 Galgorm Road, Ballymena BT42 1AB ⏚ jackie.patton@midandeastantrim.gov.uk

Member Services: Mrs Lorraine Hunter, Head of Members' Services, The Braid, 1 - 29 Bridge Street, Ballymena BT43 5EJ
⏚ lorraine.hunter@midandeastantrim.gov.uk

Partnerships: Ms Linda Williams, Director - Economic Growth, Regeneration & Tourism, The Braid, 1 - 29 Bridge Street, Ballymena BT43 5EJ ⌂ linda.williams@midandeastantrim.gov.uk

Personnel / HR: Mrs Karen Hargan, Director - Organisation Development & Community Planning, The Braid, 1 - 29 Bridge Street, Ballymena BT43 5EJ ⌂ karen.hargan@midandeastantrim.gov.uk

Planning: Mr Paul Duffy, Head of Planning, The Braid, 1 - 29 Bridge Street, Ballymena BT43 5EJ ⌂ paul.duffy@midandeastantrim.gov.uk

Procurement: Mr Sean Laverty, Head of ICT & Procurement, Ardeevin, 80 Galgorm Road, Ballymena BT42 1AB ⌂ sean.laverty@midandeastantrim.gov.uk

Recycling & Waste Minimisation: Mr Stephen Holgate, Head of Waste Management, The Braid, 1 - 29 Bridge Street, Ballymena BT43 5EJ ⌂ stephen.holgate@mideastandantrim.gov.uk

Regeneration: Ms Linda Williams, Director - Economic Growth, Regeneration & Tourism, The Braid, 1 - 29 Bridge Street, Ballymena BT43 5EJ ⌂ linda.williams@midandeastantrim.gov.uk

Staff Training: Ms Sinead McNicholl, Head of HR, Ardeevin, 80 Galgorm Road, Ballymena BT41 1AB ⌂ sinead.mcnicholl@midandeastantrim.gov.uk

Sustainable Communities: Ms Jackie Patton, Head of Community Planning, Ardeevin, 80 Galgorm Road, Ballymena BT42 1AB ⌂ jackie.patton@midandeastantrim.gov.uk

Sustainable Development: Ms Linda Williams, Director - Economic Growth, Regeneration & Tourism, The Braid, 1 - 29 Bridge Street, Ballymena BT43 5EJ ⌂ linda.williams@midandeastantrim.gov.uk

Tourism: Ms Linda Williams, Director - Economic Growth, Regeneration & Tourism, The Braid, 1 - 29 Bridge Street, Ballymena BT43 5EJ ⌂ linda.williams@midandeastantrim.gov.uk

Town Centre: Ms Linda Williams, Director - Economic Growth, Regeneration & Tourism, The Braid, 1 - 29 Bridge Street, Ballymena BT43 5EJ ⌂ linda.williams@midandeastantrim.gov.uk

Waste Collection and Disposal: Mr Stephen Holgate, Head of Waste Management, The Braid, 1 - 29 Bridge Street, Ballymena BT43 5EJ ⌂ stephen.holgate@mideastandantrim.gov.uk

Waste Management: Mr Stephen Holgate, Head of Waste Management, The Braid, 1 - 29 Bridge Street, Ballymena BT43 5EJ ⌂ stephen.holgate@mideastandantrim.gov.uk

COUNCILLORS

Mayor: Wales, Audrey (DUP - Ballymena)
cllr.wales@ballymena.gov.uk

Deputy Mayor: McNeilly, William (UUP - Bannside)
cr.mcneilly@ballymena.gov.uk

Adger, Beth (DUP - Braid)
cr.adger@ballymena.gov.uk

Anderson, Donna (O - Ballymena)
cllr.anderson@midandeastantrim.gov.uk

Ashe, Billy (DUP - Carrick Castle)
billy.ashe@carrickfergus.org

Beattie, May (DUP - Knockagh)
may.beattie@carrickfergus.org

Brown, James (IND - Carrick Castle)

Carson, John (DUP - Ballymena)
cllr.carson@ballymena.gov.uk

Cherry, Robin (UUP - Braid)
ald.cherry@ballymena.gov.uk

Clyde, Beth (DUP - Braid)
beth.clyde@ballymena.gov.uk

Gaston, Timothy (O - Bannside)
cr.gaston@ballymena.gov.uk

Glover, Reuben (DUP - Ballymena)
cllr.glover@midandeastantrim.gov.uk

Hanna, Sam (DUP - Braid)
ald.hanna@ballymena.gov.uk

Hardy, Patrice (SF - Bannside)
cllr.hardy@midandeastantrim.gov.uk

Henry, Billy (DUP - Bannside)
billy.henry@ballymena.gov.uk

Henry, James (IND - Ballymena)
cr.jhenry@ballymena.gov.uk

Johnston, Cheryl (DUP - Carrick Castle)
cllr.johnston@midandeastantrim.gov.uk

Jordan, Noel (UKIP - Carrick Castle)
cllr.jordan@midandeastantrim.gov.uk

Logan, Robert (ALL - Larne Lough)
cllr.logan@midandeastantrim.org

Lyons, Gordon (DUP - Coast Road)
cllr.lyons@midandeastantrim.gov.uk

Maguire, Paul (SF - Braid)
paul.maguire@ballymenacouncil.org

McCaughey, William (DUP - Braid)
clr.mccaughey@ballymena.gov.uk

McClurg, Lynn (DUP - Knockagh)
lynn.mcclurg@carrickfergus.org

McDonald, Stewart (O - Bannside)
cllr.mcdonald@midandeastantrim.gov.uk

McKeen, Gregg (DUP - Larne Lough)
gregg.mckeen@larne.gov.uk

McKeown, James (SF - Coast Road)
james.mckeown@larne.gov.uk

McKinty, Mark (UUP - Larne Lough)
mark.mckinty@larne.gov.uk

Millar, Lindsay (UUP - Knockagh)
cllr.millar@midandeastantrim.org

Morrow, Maureen (UUP - Coast Road)
maureen.morrow@larne.gov.uk

MID & EAST ANTRIM DISTRICT COUNCIL

Mulvenna, Geraldine (ALL - Coast Road)
geraldine.mulvenna@larne.gov.uk

Nicholl, Stephen (UUP - Ballymena)
cllr.snichol@midandeastantrim.gov.uk

Nicholl, Tommy (DUP - Bannside)
crt.nicholl@ballymena.gov.uk

O'Loan, Declan (SDLP - Ballymena)
cr.o'loan@ballymena.gov.uk

Reid, Paul (DUP - Larne Lough)
cllr.reid@midandeastantrim.gov.uk

Sinclair, Paul (ALL - Knockagh)
cllr.sinclair@midandeastantrim.org

Stewart, John (UUP - Carrick Castle)
john.stewart@carrickfergus.org

Wilson, Andrew (UUP - Knockagh)
andrew.wilson@carrickfergus.org

Wilson, Ruth (O - Coast Road)
cllr.rwilson@midandeastantrim.gov.uk

Wilson, Andrew (UUP - Larne Lough)
cllr.andyparkwilson@midandeastantrim.gov.uk

POLITICAL COMPOSITION
DUP: 16, UUP: 9, O: 4, SF: 3, ALL: 3, IND: 2, SDLP: 1, UKIP: 1

Mid Devon   D

Mid Devon District Council, Phoenix House, Phoenix Lane,
Tiverton EX16 6PP
☎ 01884 255255 🖷 01884 234318 ⏚ chiefexec@middevon.gov.uk
🖵 www.middevon.gov.uk

FACTS AND FIGURES
Parliamentary Constituencies: Devon Central, Tiverton and
Honiton
EU Constituencies: South West
Election Frequency: Elections are of whole council

PRINCIPAL OFFICERS

Chief Executive: Mr Stephen Walford, Chief Executive, Phoenix
House, Phoenix Lane, Tiverton EX16 6PP swalford@middevon.gov.
uk

Senior Management: Mrs Jenny Clifford, Head of Planning &
Regeneration, Phoenix House, Phoenix Lane, Tiverton EX16 6PP
☎ 01884 234346 ⏚ jclifford@middevon.gov.uk

Senior Management: Mr Andrew Jarrett, Head of Finance,
Phoenix House, Phoenix Lane, Tiverton EX16 6PP ☎ 01884 234242
⏚ ajarrett@middevon.gov.uk

Senior Management: Mrs Jill May, Head of HR & Development,
Phoenix House, Phoenix Lane, Tiverton EX16 6PP ☎ 01884 234381
⏚ jmay@middevon.gov.uk

Senior Management: Ms Liz Reeves, Head of Customer
Services, Phoenix House, Phoenix Lane, Tiverton EX16 6PP
☎ 01884 234371 ⏚ lreeves@middevon.gov.uk

Senior Management: Mr Nick Sanderson, Head of Housing &
Property Services, Phoenix House, Phoenix Lane, Tiverton EX16
6PP ☎ 01884 234960 ⏚ nsanderson@middevon.gov.uk

Senior Management: Mrs Amy Tregellas, Head of Communities
& Governance, Phoenix House, Phoenix Lane, Tiverton EX16 6PP
☎ 01884 234246 ⏚ atregellas@middevon.gov.uk

Architect, Building / Property Services: Mr Nick Sanderson,
Head of Housing & Property Services, Phoenix House, Phoenix
Lane, Tiverton EX16 6PP ☎ 01884 234960 ⏚ nsanderson@
middevon.gov.uk

Building Control: Mrs Jenny Clifford, Head of Planning &
Regeneration, Phoenix House, Phoenix Lane, Tiverton EX16 6PP
☎ 01884 234346 ⏚ jclifford@middevon.gov.uk

Children / Youth Services: Mr John Bodley-Scott, Community
Development Manager, Phoenix House, Phoenix Lane, Tiverton
EX16 6PP ☎ 01884 234363 ⏚ jbodleyscott@middevon.gov.uk

PR / Communications: Ms Liz Reeves, Head of Customer
Services, Phoenix House, Phoenix Lane, Tiverton EX16 6PP
☎ 01884 234371 ⏚ lreeves@middevon.gov.uk

Community Planning: Mr John Bodley-Scott, Community
Development Manager, Phoenix House, Phoenix Lane, Tiverton
EX16 6PP ☎ 01884 234363 ⏚ jbodleyscott@middevon.gov.uk

Community Safety: Mrs Julia Ryder, Community Safety &
Emergency Planning Officer, Phoenix House, Phoenix Lane,
Tiverton EX16 6PP ☎ 01884 234997 ⏚ jryder@middevon.gov.uk

Computer Management: Ms Liz Reeves, Head of Customer
Services, Phoenix House, Phoenix Lane, Tiverton EX16 6PP
☎ 01884 234371 ⏚ lreeves@middevon.gov.uk

Contracts: Mrs Chanelle Busby, Procurement Manager, Phoenix
House, Phoenix Lane, Tiverton EX16 6PP ☎ 01884 234228
⏚ cwhite@middevon.gov.uk

Corporate Services: Mr Stephen Walford, Chief Executive,
Phoenix House, Phoenix Lane, Tiverton EX16 6PP
⏚ swalford@middevon.gov.uk

Customer Service: Ms Liz Reeves, Head of Customer Services,
Phoenix House, Phoenix Lane, Tiverton EX16 6PP
☎ 01884 234371 ⏚ lreeves@middevon.gov.uk

Economic Development: Mr John Bodley-Scott, Community
Development Manager, Phoenix House, Phoenix Lane, Tiverton
EX16 6PP ☎ 01884 234363 ⏚ jbodleyscott@middevon.gov.uk

Electoral Registration: Miss Jackie Stoneman, Electoral Services
Manager, Phoenix House, Phoenix Lane, Tiverton EX16 6PP
☎ 01884 234214 ⏚ jstoneman@middevon.gov.uk

Emergency Planning: Mrs Julia Ryder, Community Safety
& Emergency Planning Officer, Phoenix House, Phoenix Lane,
Tiverton EX16 6PP ☎ 01884 234997 ⏚ jryder@middevon.gov.uk

Energy Management: Mr Andrew Busby, Estates Manager, Phoenix House, Phoenix Lane, Tiverton EX16 6PP ☎ 01884 234948 ✆ abusby@middevon.gov.uk

Environmental Health: Mr Simon Newcombe, Public Health Manager, Phoenix House, Phoenix Lane, Tiverton EX16 6PP ☎ 01884 244615 ✆ snewcombe@middevon.gov.uk

Estates, Property & Valuation: Mr Nick Sanderson, Head of Housing & Property Services, Phoenix House, Phoenix Lane, Tiverton EX16 6PP ☎ 01884 234960 ✆ nsanderson@middevon.gov.uk

European Liaison: Mr John Bodley-Scott, Community Development Manager, Phoenix House, Phoenix Lane, Tiverton EX16 6PP ☎ 01884 234363 ✆ jbodleyscott@middevon.gov.uk

Facilities: Mr Andrew Busby, Estates Manager, Phoenix House, Phoenix Lane, Tiverton EX16 6PP ☎ 01884 234948 ✆ abusby@middevon.gov.uk

Finance: Mr Andrew Jarrett, Head of Finance, Phoenix House, Phoenix Lane, Tiverton EX16 6PP ☎ 01884 234242 ✆ ajarrett@middevon.gov.uk

Fleet Management: Mr Stuart Noyce, Waste Services Manager, Phoenix House, Phoenix Lane, Tiverton EX16 6PP ☎ 01884 244635 ✆ snoyce@middevon.gov.uk

Grounds Maintenance: Mr Andrew Busby, Estates Manager, Phoenix House, Phoenix Lane, Tiverton EX16 6PP ☎ 01884 234948 ✆ abusby@middevon.gov.uk

Health and Safety: Mr Michael Lowe, Health & Safety Officer, Phoenix House, Phoenix Lane, Tiverton EX16 6PP ☎ 01884 234395 ✆ mlowe@middevon.gov.uk

Housing: Mrs Claire Fry, Housing Services Manager, Phoenix House, Phoenix Lane, Tiverton EX16 6PP ☎ 01884 234386 ✆ cfry@middevon.gov.uk

Housing Maintenance: Mr Mark Baglow, Housing Maintenance Manager, Phoenix House, Phoenix Lane, Tiverton EX16 6PP ☎ 01884 233011 ✆ mbaglow@middevon.gov.uk

Legal: Mr Simon Johnson, Legal Services Manager, Phoenix House, Phoenix Lane, Tiverton EX16 6PP ☎ 01884 234210 ✆ sjohnson@middevon.gov.uk

Leisure and Cultural Services: Mr Lee Chester, Leisure Services General Manager, Phoenix House, Phoenix Lane, Tiverton EX16 6PP ☎ 01884 234902 ✆ lchester@middevon.gov.uk

Licensing: Mr Tom Keating, Licensing Officer, Phoenix House, Phoenix Lane, Tiverton EX16 6PP ☎ 01884 244618 ✆ tkeating@middevon.gov.uk

Lottery Funding, Charity and Voluntary: Mr Paul Tucker, Grants Officer, Phoenix House, Phoenix Lane, Tiverton EX16 6PP ☎ 01884 234930 ✆ ptucker@middevon.gov.uk

Member Services: Mrs Amy Tregellas, Head of Communities & Governance, Phoenix House, Phoenix Lane, Tiverton EX16 6PP ☎ 01884 234246 ✆ atregellas@middevon.gov.uk

Parking: Mr Stuart Noyce, Waste Services Manager, Phoenix House, Phoenix Lane, Tiverton EX16 6PP ☎ 01884 244635 ✆ snoyce@middevon.gov.uk

Personnel / HR: Mrs Jill May, Head of HR & Development, Phoenix House, Phoenix Lane, Tiverton EX16 6PP ☎ 01884 234381 ✆ jmay@middevon.gov.uk

Planning: Mrs Jenny Clifford, Head of Planning & Regeneration, Phoenix House, Phoenix Lane, Tiverton EX16 6PP ☎ 01884 234346 ✆ jclifford@middevon.gov.uk

Procurement: Mrs Chanelle Busby, Procurement Manager, Phoenix House, Phoenix Lane, Tiverton EX16 6PP ☎ 01884 234228 ✆ cwhite@middevon.gov.uk

Recycling & Waste Minimisation: Mr Stuart Noyce, Waste Services Manager, Phoenix House, Phoenix Lane, Tiverton EX16 6PP ☎ 01884 244635 ✆ snoyce@middevon.gov.uk

Regeneration: Mr John Bodley-Scott, Community Development Manager, Phoenix House, Phoenix Lane, Tiverton EX16 6PP ☎ 01884 234363 ✆ jbodleyscott@middevon.gov.uk

Staff Training: Mrs Katie Furner, Learning & Development Manager, Phoenix House, Phoenix Lane, Tiverton EX16 6PP ☎ 01884 234381 ✆ kfurner@middevon.gov.uk

Street Scene: Mr Stuart Noyce, Waste Services Manager, Phoenix House, Phoenix Lane, Tiverton EX16 6PP ☎ 01884 244635 ✆ snoyce@middevon.gov.uk

Sustainable Communities: Mr John Bodley-Scott, Community Development Manager, Phoenix House, Phoenix Lane, Tiverton EX16 6PP ☎ 01884 234363 ✆ jbodleyscott@middevon.gov.uk

Tourism: Mr John Bodley-Scott, Community Development Manager, Phoenix House, Phoenix Lane, Tiverton EX16 6PP ☎ 01884 234363 ✆ jbodleyscott@middevon.gov.uk

Town Centre: Mrs Rachel Jenman, Town Centre Manager, Phoenix House, Phoenix Lane, Tiverton EX16 6PP ☎ 01884 234620 ✆ rjenman@middevon.gov.uk

Waste Collection and Disposal: Mr Stuart Noyce, Waste Services Manager, Phoenix House, Phoenix Lane, Tiverton EX16 6PP ☎ 01884 244635 ✆ snoyce@middevon.gov.uk

Waste Management: Mr Stuart Noyce, Waste Services Manager, Phoenix House, Phoenix Lane, Tiverton EX16 6PP ☎ 01884 244635 ✆ snoyce@middevon.gov.uk

Children's Play Areas: Mr Andrew Busby, Estates Manager, Phoenix House, Phoenix Lane, Tiverton EX16 6PP ☎ 01884 234948 ✆ abusby@middevon.gov.uk

MID DEVON

COUNCILLORS

Chair: Daw, John (CON - Taw)
jdaw@middevon.gov.uk

Vice-Chair: Hughes, Glanmor (CON - Upper Culm)
ghughes@middevon.gov.uk

Leader of the Council: Eginton, Clive (CON - Taw Vale)
ceginton@middevon.gov.uk

Andrews, Eileen (IND - Cullompton South)
eandrews@middevon.gov.uk

Bainbridge, Heather (CON - Canonsleigh)
hbainbridge@middevon.gov.uk

Berry, Rosemary (CON - Cullompton Outer)
rberry@middevon.gov.uk

Binks, Judi (CON - Sandford & Creedy)
jbink@middevon.gov.uk

Busch, Karl (CON - Cullompton North)
kbusch@middeveon.gov.uk

Chesterton, Richard (CON - Lower Culm)
rchesterton@middevon.gov.uk

Collis, Christine (CON - Canonsleigh)
ccollis@middevon.gov.uk

Colthorpe, Polly (CON - Way)
pcolthorpe@middevon.gov.uk

Coren, Derek (CON - Yeo)
dcoren@middevon.gov.uk

Davey, Neal (CON - Lowman)
ndavey@middevon.gov.uk

Daw, Chris (CON - Cranmore)
cdaw@middevon.gov.uk

Deed, Bob (IND - Cadbury)
bdeed@middevon.gov.uk

Doe, Jill (CON - Lower Culm)
jdoe@middevon.gov.uk

Dolley, Ron (UKIP - Westexe)
rdolley@middevon.gov.uk

Downes, John (LD - Boniface)
jdownes@middevon.gov.uk

Evans, Bob (CON - Lower Culm)
revans@middevon.gov.uk

Flaws, Steve (CON - Westexe)
sflaws@middevon.gov.uk

Griggs, Sue (CON - Cranmore)
sgriggs@middevon.gov.uk

Hare-Scott, Peter (CON - Newbrooke)
pharescott@middevon.gov.uk

Heal, Peter (CON - Yeo)
pheal@middevon.gov.uk

Hull, Brenda (CON - Castle)
bhull@middevon.gov.uk

Knowles, Dennis (IND - Lowman)
dknowles@middevon.gov.uk

Letch, Frank (LD - Lawrence)
fletch@middevon.gov.uk

Moore, Andrew (CON - Clare & Shuttern)
amoore@middevon.gov.uk

Radford, Ray (CON - Halberton)
rradford@middevon.gov.uk

Roach, Jenny (LIB - Silverton)
jroach@middevon.gov.uk

Rosamond, Frank (IND - Upper Culm)
frosamond@middevon.gov.uk

Slade, Colin (CON - Lowman)
cslade@middevon.gov.uk

Slade, Clarrisa (CON - Cranmore)
celslade@middevon.gov.uk

Slade, Elizabeth (CON - Castle)

Smith, Johnathan (UKIP - Westexe)
jsmith@middevon.gov.uk

Snow, Terry (IND - Cullompton South)
tsnow@middevon.gov.uk

Squire, John (CON - Upper Yeo)
jsquire@middevon.gov.uk

Squires, Margaret (CON - Sandford & Creedy)
msquires@middevon.gov.uk

Stanley, Raymond (CON - Clare & Shuttern)
rstanley@middevon.gov.uk

Taylor, Luke (LD - Bradninch)
ntaylor@middevon.gov.uk

Way, Nick (LD - Boniface)
nway@middevon.gov.uk

Woollatt, Nikki (IND - Cullompton North)
nwoollatt@middevon.gov.uk

Wright, Bob (LD - Lawrence)
bwright@middevon.gov.uk

POLITICAL COMPOSITION
CON: 28, IND: 6, LD: 5, UKIP: 2, LIB: 1

COMMITTEE CHAIRS

Audit: Mr Bob Evans

Mid Suffolk   D

Mid Suffolk District Council, Council Offices, 131 High Street, Needham Market IP6 8DL
☎ 01473 826622 ✆ customer.services@baberghmidsuffolk.gov.uk
🖥 www.midsuffolk.gov.uk

FACTS AND FIGURES
Parliamentary Constituencies: Bury St. Edmunds
EU Constituencies: Eastern
Election Frequency: Elections are of whole council

PRINCIPAL OFFICERS

Deputy Chief Executive: Ms Lindsay Barker, Deputy Chief Executive, Council Offices, 131 High Street, Needham Market IP6 8DL ☎ 01473 825844 ✆ lindsay.barker@midsuffolk.gov.uk; lindsay.barker@baberghmidsuffolk.gov.uk

Senior Management: Mr Tom Barker, Assistant Director - Planning for Growth, Council Offices, Corks Lane, Hadleigh, Ipswich IP7 6SJ ☎ 01449 724647 ✆ tom.barker@midsuffolk.gov.uk

Senior Management: Ms Suki Binjal, Interim Assistant Director - Law & Governance, Council Offices, Corks Lane, Hadleigh, Ipswich IP7 6SJ ☎ 01473 825811 ✆ suki.binjal@baberghmidsuffolk.gov.uk

Senior Management: Mr Paul Doe, ICT Strategic Lead, Council Offices, Corks Lane, Hadleigh, Ipswich IP7 6SJ ☎ 01473 825746 ✆ michael.evans@baberghmidsuffolk.gov.uk

Senior Management: Mr Mike Evans, Strategic Director, Council Offices, 131 High Street, Needham Market IP6 8DL ☎ 01473 825746 ✆ michael.evans@baberghmidsuffolk.gov.uk

Senior Management: Mr Jonathan Free, Assistant Director - Communities & Public Access, Council Offices, Corks Lane, Hadleigh, Ipswich IP7 6SJ ☎ 01449 724859 ✆ jonathan.free@baberghmidsuffolk.gov.uk

Senior Management: Mr Chris Fry, Assistant Director - Environment & Projects, Council Offices, Corks Lane, Hadleigh, Ipswich IP7 6SJ ☎ 01449 724805 ✆ chris.fry@baberghmidsuffolk.gov.uk

Senior Management: Mr Martin King, Assistant Director - Supported Living, Council Offices, 131 High Street, Needham Market IP6 8DL ☎ 01473 826649 ✆ martin.king@midsuffolk.gov.uk; martin.king@baberghmidsuffolk.gov.uk

Senior Management: Ms Lou Rawsthorne, Assistant Director - Investment & Commercial Delivery, Council Offices, Corks Lane, Hadleigh, Ipswich IP7 6SJ ☎ 01449 724772 ✆ lou.rawsthorne@baberghmidsuffolk.gov.uk

Senior Management: Ms Katherine Steel, Assistant Director - Corporate Resources, Council Offices, Corks Lane, Hadleigh, Ipswich IP7 6SJ ☎ 01449 724772 ✆ katherine.steel@baberghmidsuffolk.gov.uk

Architect, Building / Property Services: Mr Steve Clarke, Senior Surveyor - Building Services, Council Offices, 131 High Street, Needham Market IP6 8DL ☎ 01473 825774 ✆ stephen.clarke@baberghmidsuffolk.gov.uk

Best Value: Ms Karen Coll, Corporate Manager - Business Improvement, Council Offices, 131 High Street, Needham Market IP6 8DL ☎ 01449 724566 ✆ karen.coll@baberghmidsuffolk.gov.uk

Building Control: Mr Gary Starling, Corporate Manager - Building Control, Council Offices, 131 High Street, Needham Market IP6 8DL ☎ 01449 724502 ✆ gary.starling@baberghmidsuffolk.gov.uk

Community Planning: Mr Bill Newman, Corporate Manager - Strategic Planning, Council Offices, Corks Lane, Hadleigh, Ipswich IP7 6SJ ☎ 01473 825712 ✆ bill.newman@baberghmidsuffolk.gov.uk

Community Safety: Ms Sue Clements, Corporate Manager - Strong & Safe Communities, Council Offices, Corks Lane, Hadleigh, Ipswich IP7 6SJ ☎ 01449 724657 ✆ sue.clemments@baberghmidsuffolk.gov.uk

Computer Management: Mr Kevin Peck, Information & Technology Architect, Council Offices, Corks Lane, Hadleigh, Ipswich IP7 6SJ ☎ 01473 825824 ✆ kevin.peck@baberghmidsuffolk.gov.uk

Computer Management: Mr Carl Reeder, Corporate Manager - Information Management & ICT, Council Offices, Corks Lane, Hadleigh, Ipswich IP7 6SJ ☎ 01449 724862 ✆ carl.reeder@baberghmidsuffolk.gov.uk

Contracts: Ms Tracey Farthing, Senior Commissioning & Procurement Officer, Council Offices, Corks Lane, Hadleigh, Ipswich IP7 6SJ ☎ 01473 825715 ✆ tracey.farthing@baberghmidsuffolk.gov.uk

Corporate Services: Ms Suki Binjal, Interim Assistant Director - Law & Governance, Council Offices, Corks Lane, Hadleigh, Ipswich IP7 6SJ ☎ 01473 825811 ✆ suki.binjal@baberghmidsuffolk.gov.uk

Corporate Services: Ms Katherine Steel, Assistant Director - Corporate Resources, Council Offices, 131 High Street, Needham Market IP6 8DL ☎ 01449 724772 ✆ katherine.steel@baberghmidsuffolk.gov.uk

Customer Service: Mr Jonathan Free, Assistant Director - Communities & Public Access, Council Offices, Corks Lane, Hadleigh, Ipswich IP7 6SJ ☎ 01449 724859 ✆ jonathan.free@baberghmidsuffolk.gov.uk

Direct Labour: Mr Martin King, Assistant Director - Supported Living, Council Offices, 131 High Street, Needham Market IP6 8DL ☎ 01473 826649 ✆ martin.king@midsuffolk.gov.uk; martin.king@baberghmidsuffolk.gov.uk

Economic Development: Mr Lee Carvell, Corporate Manager - Open for Business, Council Offices, Corks Lane, Hadleigh, Ipswich IP7 6SJ ☎ 01473 825719 ✆ lee.carvell@baberghmidsuffolk.gov.uk

Economic Development: Ms Lou Rawsthorne, Assistant Director - Investment & Commercial Delivery, Council Offices, Corks Lane, Hadleigh, Ipswich IP7 6SJ ☎ 01449 724772 ✆ lou.rawsthorne@baberghmidsuffolk.gov.uk

E-Government: Mr Carl Reeder, Corporate Manager - Information Management & ICT, Council Offices, 131 High Street, Needham Market IP6 8DL ☎ 01449 724862 ✆ carl.reeder@baberghmidsuffolk.gov.uk

Electoral Registration: Mrs Emily Yule, Corporate Manager - Elections & Electoral Management, Council Offices, Corks Lane, Hadleigh, Ipswich IP7 6SJ ☎ 01473 825891 ✆ emily.yule@baberghmidsuffolk.gov.uk

Emergency Planning: Ms Sue Herne, Emergency Planning Responsive Officer, Council Offices, 131 High Street, Needham Market, Ipswich IP6 8DL ☎ 01449 724851 ✆ sue.herne@baberghmidsuffolk.gov.uk

Energy Management: Mr Steve Clarke, Senior Surveyor - Building Services, Council Offices, 131 High Street, Needham Market IP6 8DL ☎ 01473 825774 ✆ stephen.clarke@baberghmidsuffolk.gov.uk

Energy Management: Mr Iain Farquharson, Environmental Management Officer, Council Offices, 131 High Street, Needham Market IP6 8DL ☎ 01449 724878 ✆ iain.farquharson@baberghmidsuffolk.gov.uk

MID SUFFOLK

Environmental / Technical Services: Mr Martin King, Assistant Director - Supported Living, Council Offices, 131 High Street, Needham Market IP6 8DL ☎ 01473 826649
✆ martin.king@midsuffolk.gov.uk;
martin.king@baberghmidsuffolk.gov.uk

Environmental Health: Mr Chris Fry, Head - Environment, Council Offices, Corks Lane, Hadleigh, Ipswich IP7 6SJ ☎ 01473 826649 ✆ chris.fry@baberghmidsuffolk.gov.uk

Estates, Property & Valuation: Mr Steve Clarke, Senior Surveyor - Building Services, Council Offices, 131 High Street, Needham Market IP6 8DL ☎ 01473 825774
✆ stephen.clarke@baberghmidsuffolk.gov.uk

European Liaison: Mr Lee Carvell, Corporate Manager - Open for Business, Council Offices, 131 High Street, Needham Market IP6 8DL ☎ 01473 825719 ✆ lee.carvell@baberghmidsuffolk.gov.uk

Facilities: Ms Heather Worton, Corporate Manager, Council Offices, Corks Lane, Hadleigh, Ipswich IP7 6SJ ☎ 01473 825702
✆ heather.worton@baberghmidsuffolk.gov.uk

Finance: Ms Katherine Steel, Assistant Director - Corporate Resources, Council Offices, 131 High Street, Needham Market IP6 8DL ☎ 01449 724772 ✆ katherine.steel@baberghmidsuffolk.gov.uk

Grounds Maintenance: Mr Peter Garrett, Corporate Manager - Countryside & Public Realm, Council Offices, Corks Lane, Hadleigh, Ipswich IP7 6SJ ☎ 01449 724944
✆ peter.garrett@baberghmidsuffolk.gov.uk

Health and Safety: Mr John Grayling, Corporate Manager - Food & Safety, Council Offices, 131 High Street, Needham Market, Ipswich IP6 8DL ☎ 01449 724722
✆ john.grayling@baberghmidsuffolk.gov.uk

Health and Safety: Ms Eira Trafford, Health & Safety Business Partner, Council Offices, 131 High Street, Needham Market IP6 8DL ☎ 01473 825752 ✆ eira.trafford@baberghmidsuffolk.gov.uk

Home Energy Conservation: Ms Heather Worton, Corporate Manager, Council Offices, Corks Lane, Hadleigh, Ipswich IP7 6SJ ☎ 01473 825702 ✆ heather.worton@baberghmidsuffolk.gov.uk

Housing: Mr Martin King, Assistant Director - Supported Living, Council Offices, 131 High Street, Needham Market IP6 8DL ☎ 01473 826649 ✆ martin.king@midsuffolk.gov.uk;
martin.king@baberghmidsuffolk.gov.uk

Housing Maintenance: Mr Gavin Fisk, Interim Corporate Manager - Responsive Repairs, Council Offices, Corks Lane, Hadleigh, Ipswich IP7 6SJ ☎ 01449 724969
✆ gavin.fisk@baberghmidsuffolk.gov.uk

Legal: Ms Suki Binjal, Interim Assistant Director - Law & Governance, Council Offices, Corks Lane, Hadleigh, Ipswich IP7 6SJ ☎ 01473 825811 ✆ suki.binjal@baberghmidsuffolk.gov.uk

Leisure and Cultural Services: Mr Jonathan Free, Assistant Director - Communities & Public Access, Council Offices, 131 High Street, Needham Market IP6 8DL ☎ 01449 724859
✆ jonathan.free@baberghmidsuffolk.gov.uk

Leisure and Cultural Services: Mr Jonathan Seed, Corporate Manager - Health & Wellbeing, Council Offices, 131 High Street, Needham Market IP6 8DL ☎ 01449 724857 ✆ jonathan.seed@baberghmidsuffolk.gov.uk

Licensing: Mr Lee Carvell, Corporate Manager - Open for Business, Council Offices, 131 High Street, Needham Market IP6 8DL ☎ 01473 825719 ✆ lee.carvell@baberghmidsuffolk.gov.uk

Lottery Funding, Charity and Voluntary: Ms Sue Clements, Corporate Manager - Strong & Safe Communities, Council Offices, Corks Lane, Hadleigh, Ipswich IP7 6SJ ☎ 01449 724657
✆ sue.clemments@baberghmidsuffolk.gov.uk

Member Services: Ms Jeanette McGarry, Interim Head of Democratic Services, Council Offices, Corks Lane, Hadleigh, Ipswich IP7 6SJ ☎ 01473 825891
✆ jeanette.mcgarry@baberghmidsuffolk.gov.uk

Parking: Mr Jonathan Free, Assistant Director - Communities & Public Access, Council Offices, Corks Lane, Hadleigh, Ipswich IP7 6SJ ☎ 01449 724859 ✆ jonathan.free@baberghmidsuffolk.gov.uk

Partnerships: Ms Sue Clements, Corporate Manager - Strong & Safe Communities, Council Offices, Corks Lane, Hadleigh, Ipswich IP7 6SJ ☎ 01449 724657
✆ sue.clemments@baberghmidsuffolk.gov.uk

Personnel / HR: Ms Jackie Foglietta, Corporate Manager - Organisational Development, Council Offices, Corks Lane, Hadleigh, Ipswich IP7 6SJ ☎ 01449 724803
✆ jackie.foglietta@baberghmidsuffolk.gov.uk

Planning: Mr Tom Barker, Assistant Director - Planning for Growth, Council Offices, Corks Lane, Hadleigh, Ipswich IP7 6SJ ☎ 01449 724647 ✆ tom.barker@midsuffolk.gov.uk

Planning: Mr Philip Isbel, Professional Lead - Growth & Sustainable Planning, Council Offices, 131 High Street, Needham Market IP6 8DL ☎ 01449 724537
✆ philip.isbel@baberghmidsuffolk.gov.uk

Procurement: Ms Tracey Farthing, Senior Commissioning & Procurement Officer, Council Offices, Corks Lane, Hadleigh, Ipswich IP7 6SJ ☎ 01473 825715
✆ tracey.farthing@baberghmidsuffolk.gov.uk

Recycling & Waste Minimisation: Mr Oliver Faiers, Corporate Manager - Waste, Council Offices, Corks Lane, Hadleigh, Ipswich IP7 6SJ ☎ 01449 778621 ✆ oliver.faiers@baberghmidsuffolk.gov.uk

Recycling & Waste Minimisation: Mr Chris Fry, Assistant Director - Environment & Projects, Council Offices, Corks Lane, Hadleigh, Ipswich IP7 6SJ ☎ 01449 724805
✆ chris.fry@baberghmidsuffolk.gov.uk

Regeneration: Mr Lee Carvell, Corporate Manager - Open for Business, Council Offices, 131 High Street, Needham Market IP6 8DL ☎ 01473 825719 ✆ lee.carvell@baberghmidsuffolk.gov.uk

Staff Training: Mrs Jo Knight, Leadership & OD Business Partner, Council Offices, Corks Lane, Hadleigh, Ipswich IP7 6SJ ☎ 01473 825804 ✆ jo.knight@baberghmidsuffolk.gov.uk

Sustainable Communities: Mr Jonathan Free, Assistant Director - Communities & Public Access, Council Offices, Corks Lane, Hadleigh, Ipswich IP7 6SJ ☎ 01449 724859
✆ jonathan.free@baberghmidsuffolk.gov.uk

Sustainable Development: Mr Chris Fry, Assistant Director - Environment & Projects, Council Offices, 131 High Street, Needham Market IP6 8DL ☎ 01449 724805
✆ chris.fry@baberghmidsuffolk.gov.uk

Tourism: Mr Lee Carvell, Corporate Manager - Open for Business, Council Offices, 131 High Street, Needham Market IP6 8DL
☎ 01473 825719 ✆ lee.carvell@baberghmidsuffolk.gov.uk

Waste Collection and Disposal: Mr Oliver Faiers, Corporate Manager - Waste, Council Offices, Corks Lane, Hadleigh, Ipswich IP7 6SJ ☎ 01449 778621 ✆ oliver.faiers@baberghmidsuffolk.gov.uk

Waste Collection and Disposal: Mr Chris Fry, Assistant Director - Environment & Projects, Council Offices, Corks Lane, Hadleigh, Ipswich IP7 6SJ ☎ 01449 724805
✆ chris.fry@baberghmidsuffolk.gov.uk

Waste Management: Mr Oliver Faiers, Corporate Manager - Waste, Council Offices, Corks Lane, Hadleigh, Ipswich IP7 6SJ
☎ 01449 778621 ✆ oliver.faiers@baberghmidsuffolk.gov.uk

Waste Management: Mr Chris Fry, Assistant Director - Environment & Projects, Council Offices, Corks Lane, Hadleigh, Ipswich IP7 6SJ ☎ 01449 724805
✆ chris.fry@baberghmidsuffolk.gov.uk

Children's Play Areas: Mr Jonathan Free, Assistant Director - Communities & Public Access, Council Offices, Corks Lane, Hadleigh, Ipswich IP7 6SJ ☎ 01449 724859
✆ jonathan.free@baberghmidsuffolk.gov.uk

COUNCILLORS

Chair: Gibson-Harries, Elizabeth (CON - Hoxne)
elizabeth.gibson-harries@midsuffolk.gov.uk

Leader of the Council: Gowrley, Nick (CON - Stowmarket South)
nick.gowrley@midsuffolk.gov.uk

Deputy Leader of the Council: Horn, Glen (CON - Wetheringsett)
glen.horn@midsuffolk.gov.uk

Group Leader: Otton, Penny (LD - Rattlesden)
penny.otton@midsuffolk.gov.uk

Group Leader: Stringer, Andrew (GRN - Mendlesham)
andrew.stringer@midsuffolk.gov.uk

Barker, Roy (CON - Badwell Ash)
roy.barker@midsuffolk.gov.uk

Brewster, Gerard (IND - Stowmarket South)
gerard.brewster@midsuffolk.gov.uk

Burn, David (CON - Palgrave)
david.burn@midsuffolk.gov.uk

Card, David (CON - Barking & Somersham)
david.card@midsuffolk.gov.uk

Caston, James (CON - Claydon & Barham)
james.caston@midsuffolk.gov.uk

Eburne, Rachel (GRN - Haughley & Wetherden)
rachel.eburne@midsuffolk.gov.uk

Ekpenyong, Paul (CON - Stowmarket Central)
paul.ekpenyong@midsuffolk.gov.uk

Field, John (LD - Bramford & Blakenham)
john.field@midsuffolk.gov.uk

Flatman, Charles (IND - Eye)
charles.flatman@midsuffolk.gov.uk

Flatman, Julie (CON - Stradbroke & Laxfield)

Fleming, Jessica (CON - Rickinghall & Walsham)

Green, Gary (CON - Stowmarket North)
gary.green@midsuffolk.gov.uk

Guthrie, Kathie (CON - Debenham)
kathie.guthrie@midsuffolk.gov.uk

Hadingham, Lavinia (CON - Fressingfield)
lavinia.hadingham@midsuffolk.gov.uk

Haley, Derrick (CON - Thurston & Hessett)
derrick.haley@midsuffolk.gov.uk

Hicks, Matthew (CON - Worlingworth)
matthew.hicks@midsuffolk.gov.uk

Humphreys, Barry (CON - Stowmarket North)
barry.humphreys@midsuffolk.gov.uk

Jewson, Esther (CON - Thurston & Hessett)
esther.jewson@midsuffolk.gov.uk

Kearsley, Diana (CON - Gislingham)
diana.kearsley@midsuffolk.gov.uk

Killett, Anne-Marie (GRN - Barking & Somersham)
anne.killett@midsuffolk.gov.uk

Levantis, John (CON - Elmswell & Norton)
john.levantis@midsuffolk.gov.uk

Mansel, Sarah (GRN - Elmswell & Norton)
sarah.mansel@midsuffolk.gov.uk

Marchant, Wendy (LD - Needham Market)
wendy.marchant@midsuffolk.gov.uk

Matthissen, John (GRN - Onehouse)
john.matthissen@midsuffolk.gov.uk

Mayes, Lesley (CON - Stowmarket Central)

Morley, Suzie (CON - The Stonhams)
suzie.morley@midsuffolk.gov.uk

Muller, Dave (CON - Stowmarket North)
dave.muller@midsuffolk.gov.uk

Norris, Mike (LD - Needham Market)
mike.norris@midsuffolk.gov.uk

Osborne, Derek (CON - Rickinghall & Walsham)

Passmore, Tim (CON - Helmingham & Coddenham)
timothy.passmore@midsuffolk.gov.uk

Storey, Jane (CON - Woolpit)
jane.storey@midsuffolk.gov.uk

Welham, Keith (GRN - Stowupland)
keith.welham@midsuffolk.gov.uk

Welsby, Kevin (CON - Bramford & Blakenham)
kevin.welsby@midsuffolk.gov.uk

Whitehead, John (CON - Claydon & Barham)
john.whitehead@midsuffolk.gov.uk

MID SUFFOLK

Whybrow, David (CON - Ringshall)
david.whybrow@midsuffolk.gov.uk

Wilshaw, Jill (CON - Bacton & Old Newton)
jill.wilshaw@midsuffolk.gov.uk

POLITICAL COMPOSITION
CON: 29, GRN: 6, LD: 4, IND: 2

COMMITTEE CHAIRS

Audit: Ms Suzie Morley

Licensing: Mrs Kathie Guthrie

Planning: Mrs Kathie Guthrie

Mid Sussex   D

Mid Sussex District Council, Oaklands, Oaklands Road,
Haywards Heath RH16 1SS
☎ 01444 458166 🖷 01444 450027 📧 enquiries@midsussex.gov.uk
🖥 www.midsussex.gov.uk

FACTS AND FIGURES
EU Constituencies: South East
Election Frequency: Elections are of whole council

PRINCIPAL OFFICERS

Chief Executive: Ms Kathryn Hall, Chief Executive, Mid Sussex
District Council, Oaklands, Oaklands Road, Haywards Heath RH16
1SS ☎ 01444 477498 📧 kathryn.hall@midsussex.gov.uk

Assistant Chief Executive: Miss Judy Holmes, Assistant Chief
Executive, Oaklands, Oaklands Road, Haywards Heath RH16 1SS
☎ 0144 477015 📧 judy.holmes@midsussex.gov.uk

Senior Management: Mr Tom Clark, Head of Regulatory
Services, Mid Sussex District Council, Oaklands, Oaklands Road,
Haywards Heath RH16 1SS ☎ 01444 477459
📧 tom.clark@midsussex.gov.uk

Senior Management: Mr Simon Hughes, Head of Digital &
Customer Services, Oaklands, Oaklands Road, Haywards Heath
RH16 1SS simon.hughes@midsussex.gov.uk

Senior Management: Mr Peter Stuart, Head of Corporate
Resources, Oaklands, Oaklands Road, Haywards Heath RH16 1SS
☎ 01444 477315 📧 peter.stuart@midsussex.gov.uk

Building Control: Mrs Yvonne Leddy, Business Unit Leader -
Environmental Health & Building Control, Oaklands, Oaklands Road,
Haywards Heath RH16 1SS ☎ 01444 477300
📧 yvonne.leddy@midsussex.gov.uk

Children / Youth Services: Ms Regina Choudhury, Community
Development Officer, Oaklands, Oaklands Road, Haywards Heath
RH16 1SS ☎ 01444 458166 📧 regina.choudhury@midsussex.gov.uk

PR / Communications: Mr Mat Jarman, Business Unit Leader -
Customer Services & Communications, Oaklands, Oaklands Road,
Haywards Heath RH16 1SS ☎ 01444 477387
📧 mat.jarman@midsussex.gov.uk

Community Planning: Mr Tim Cusack, Business Unit Leader -
Performance & Partnerships, Oaklands, Oaklands Road, Haywards
Heath RH16 1SS ☎ 01444 477421 📧 tim.cusack@midsussex.gov.uk

Community Safety: Ms Nicola Jackson, Community Safety
Officer, Oaklands, Oaklands Road, Haywards Heath RH16 1SS
☎ 01444 477550 📧 nicolette.russell@midsussex.gov.uk

Computer Management: Mr Mark Gawley, CenSus IT Operations
Manager, Horsham DC, Parkside, Chart Way, Horsham RH12 1PL
☎ 01903 221477; 01903 221197
📧 mark.gawley@adur-worthing.gov.uk

Contracts: Mr Thuso Selelo, Acting Business Unit Leader -
Corporate Estates & Facilities, Oaklands, Oaklands Road, Haywards
Heath RH16 1SS ☎ 01444 477577 📧 thuso.selelo@midsussex.gov.uk

Corporate Services: Miss Judy Holmes, Assistant Chief
Executive, Oaklands, Oaklands Road, Haywards Heath RH16 1SS
☎ 0144 477015 📧 judy.holmes@midsussex.gov.uk

Customer Service: Mr Mat Jarman, Business Unit Leader -
Customer Services & Communications, Oaklands, Oaklands Road,
Haywards Heath RH16 1SS ☎ 01444 477387
📧 mat.jarman@midsussex.gov.uk

Customer Service: Ms Karen Speirs, Senior Customer Services
Officer, Oaklands, Oaklands Road, Haywards Heath RH16 1SS
☎ 01444 477510 📧 karen.speirs@midsussex.gov.uk

Electoral Registration: Mr Terry Stanley, Business Unit Leader
- Democratic Services, Oaklands, Oaklands Road, Haywards Heath
RH16 1SS ☎ 01444 477415 📧 terry.stanley@midsussex.gov.uk

Emergency Planning: Mr Ben Toogood, Emergency Planning &
Outdoor Services Manager, Oaklands, Oaklands Road, Haywards
Heath RH16 1SS ☎ 01444 477379
📧 ben.toogood@midsussex.gov.uk

Energy Management: Mr Thuso Selelo, Acting Business Unit
Leader - Corporate Estates & Facilities, Oaklands, Oaklands Road,
Haywards Heath RH16 1SS ☎ 01444 477577
📧 thuso.selelo@midsussex.gov.uk

Environmental Health: Mrs Yvonne Leddy, Business Unit Leader
- Environmental Health & Building Control, Oaklands, Oaklands
Road, Haywards Heath RH16 1SS ☎ 01444 477300
📧 yvonne.leddy@midsussex.gov.uk

Estates, Property & Valuation: Mr Thuso Selelo, Acting
Business Unit Leader - Corporate Estates & Facilities, Oaklands,
Oaklands Road, Haywards Heath RH16 1SS ☎ 01444 477577
📧 thuso.selelo@midsussex.gov.uk

Facilities: Mr David Harper, Business Unit Leader - Waste &
Outdoor Services, Oaklands, Oaklands Road, Haywards Heath RH16
1SS ☎ 01444 477487 📧 david.harper@midsussex.gov.uk

Finance: Ms Cathy Craigen, Business Unit Leader - Finance,
Oaklands, Oaklands Road, Haywards Heath RH16 1SS
☎ 01444 477384 📧 cathy.craigen@midsussex.gov.uk

Finance: Mr Peter Stuart, Head of Corporate Resources, Oaklands, Oaklands Road, Haywards Heath RH16 1SS ☎ 01444 477315 ✆ peter.stuart@midsussex.gov.uk

Grounds Maintenance: Mr David Harper, Business Unit Leader - Waste & Outdoor Services, Oaklands, Oaklands Road, Haywards Heath RH16 1SS ☎ 01444 477487 ✆ david.harper@midsussex.gov.uk

Health and Safety: Mr Scott Wakely, Corporate Safety & Technical Services Officer, Oaklands, Oaklands Road, Haywards Heath RH16 1SS ☎ 01444 477002 ✆ scott.wakely@midsussex.gov.uk

Home Energy Conservation: Ms Celia Austin, Sustainability Officer, Oaklands, Oaklands Road, Haywards Heath RH16 1SS ☎ 01444 477370 ✆ celia.austin@midsussex.gov.uk

Housing: Ms Emma Shuttleworth, Business Unit Leader - Housing Enabling, Oaklands, Oaklands Road, Haywards Heath RH16 1SS ☎ 01444 477431 ✆ emma.shuttleworth@midsussex.gov.uk

Legal: Mr Tom Clark, Head of Regulatory Services, Mid Sussex District Council, Oaklands, Oaklands Road, Haywards Heath RH16 1SS ☎ 01444 477459 ✆ tom.clark@midsussex.gov.uk

Licensing: Mr Paul Thornton, Senior Licensing Officer, Oaklands, Oaklands Road, Haywards Heath RH16 1SS ☎ 01444 477428 ✆ paul.thornton@midsussex.gov.uk

Member Services: Mr Terry Stanley, Business Unit Leader - Democratic Services, Oaklands, Oaklands Road, Haywards Heath RH16 1SS ☎ 01444 477415 ✆ terry.stanley@midsussex.gov.uk

Parking: Ms Claire Onslow, Business Unit Leader - Parking Services, Oaklands, Oaklands Road, Haywards Heath RH16 1SS ☎ 01444 477586 ✆ claire.onslow@midsussex.gov.uk

Partnerships: Mr Tim Cusack, Business Unit Leader - Performance & Partnerships, Oaklands, Oaklands Road, Haywards Heath RH16 1SS ☎ 01444 477421 ✆ tim.cusack@midsussex.gov.uk

Personnel / HR: Mr Tim Martland, Business Unit Leader - HR, Training & Payroll, Oaklands, Oaklands Road, Haywards Heath RH16 1SS ☎ 01444 477251 ✆ tim.martland@midsussex.gov.uk

Personnel / HR: Mr Peter Stuart, Head of Corporate Resources, Oaklands, Oaklands Road, Haywards Heath RH16 1SS ☎ 01444 477315 ✆ peter.stuart@midsussex.gov.uk

Planning: Mr Nick Rogers, Business Unit Leader - Development Management, Oaklands, Oaklands Road, Haywards Heath RH16 1SS ☎ 01444 477341 ✆ nick.rogers@midsussex.gov.uk

Procurement: Mr Roger Dennis, Joint Procurement Officer, Oaklands, Oaklands Road, Haywards Heath RH16 1SS ☎ 01444 477254 ✆ rogerd@horsham.gov.uk

Recycling & Waste Minimisation: Mr David Harper, Business Unit Leader - Waste & Outdoor Services, Oaklands, Oaklands Road, Haywards Heath RH16 1SS ☎ 01444 477487 ✆ david.harper@midsussex.gov.uk

Staff Training: Mr Tim Martland, Business Unit Leader - HR, Training & Payroll, Oaklands, Oaklands Road, Haywards Heath RH16 1SS ☎ 01444 477251 ✆ tim.martland@midsussex.gov.uk

Sustainable Communities: Mr Simon Hardy, Business Unit Leader - Community Services & Culture, Oaklands, Oaklands Road, Haywards Heath RH16 1SS ☎ 01444 477454 ✆ simon.hardy@midsussex.gov.uk

Sustainable Development: Ms Celia Austin, Sustainability Officer, Oaklands, Oaklands Road, Haywards Heath RH16 1SS ☎ 01444 477370 ✆ celia.austin@midsussex.gov.uk

Waste Collection and Disposal: Mr David Harper, Business Unit Leader - Waste & Outdoor Services, Oaklands, Oaklands Road, Haywards Heath RH16 1SS ☎ 01444 477487 ✆ david.harper@midsussex.gov.uk

Waste Management: Mr David Harper, Business Unit Leader - Waste & Outdoor Services, Oaklands, Oaklands Road, Haywards Heath RH16 1SS ☎ 01444 477487 ✆ david.harper@midsussex.gov.uk

Children's Play Areas: Mr David Harper, Business Unit Leader - Waste & Outdoor Services, Oaklands, Oaklands Road, Haywards Heath RH16 1SS ☎ 01444 477487 ✆ david.harper@midsussex.gov.uk

COUNCILLORS

Chair: Reed, Peter (CON - East Grinstead - Ashplats) peter.reed@midsussex.gov.uk

Leader of the Council: Wall, Garry (CON - Haywards Heath - Franklands) garry.wall@midsussex.gov.uk

Deputy Leader of the Council: Ash-Edwards, Jonathan (CON - Haywards Heath - Heath) jonathan.ash-edwards@midsussex.gov.uk

Allen, John (CON - Bolney) john.allen@midsussex.gov.uk

Barrett-Miles, Andrew (CON - Burgess Hill - Dunstall) andrew.barrett-miles@midsussex.gov.uk

Belsey, Margaret (CON - East Grinstead - Baldwins) margaret.belsey@midsussex.gov.uk

Belsey, John (CON - Ashurst Wood) john.belsey@midsussex.gov.uk

Belsey, Edward (CON - East Grinstead - Herontye) edward.belsey@midsussex.gov.uk

Bennett, Liz (CON - East Grinstead - Ashplats) liz.bennett@midsussex.gov.uk

Boutrup, Anne (CON - Haywards Heath - Ashenground) anne.boutrup@midsussex.gov.uk

Bradbury, Pete (CON - Cuckfield) pete.bradbury@midsussex.gov.uk

Brunsdon, Heidi (CON - East Grinstead - Imberhorne) heidi.brunsdon@midsussex.gov.uk

Burke, Kevin (CON - Hassocks) kevin.burke@midsussex.gov.uk

Catharine, Cherry (CON - Burgess Hill - Leylands) cherry.catharine@midsussex.gov.uk

MID SUSSEX

Cherry, Richard (CON - Burgess Hill - Meeds)
richard.cherry@midsussex.gov.uk

Clarke, Rod (CON - Haywards Heath - Franklands)
rod.clarke@midsussex.gov.uk

Coote, Philip (CON - Crawley Down & Turners Hill)
phillip.coote@midsussex.gov.uk

de Mierre, Ruth (CON - Haywards Heath - Bentswood)
ruth.demierre@midsussex.gov.uk

Dorey, Tony (CON - Copthorne & Worth)
tony.dorey@midsussex.gov.uk

Dorking, David (CON - Haywards Heath - Bentswood)
david.dorking@midsussex.gov.uk

Ellis, Sandy (CON - Haywards Heath - Heath)
sandra.ellis@midsussex.gov.uk

Forbes, Bruce (CON - Crawley Down & Turners Hill)
bruce.forbes@midsussex.gov.uk

Hansford, Steven (CON - Burgess Hill - Victoria)
steven.hansford@midsussex.gov.uk

Heard, Ginny (CON - Burgess Hill - Franklands)
ginny.heard@midsussex.gov.uk

Hersey, Margaret (CON - Lindfield)
margaret.hersey@midsussex.gov.uk

Hersey, Christopher (CON - High Weald)
chris.hersey@midsussex.gov.uk

Holden, Colin (CON - Burgess Hill - St Andrews)
colin.holden@midsussex.gov.uk

Jones, Anne (CON - Burgess Hill - Meeds)
anne.jones@midsussex.gov.uk

King, Chris (CON - Burgess Hill - Franklands)
chris.king@midsussex.gov.uk

Knight, Jim (CON - Haywards Heath - Lucastes)
jim.knight@midsussex.gov.uk

Landriani, Jacqui (CON - Burgess Hill - Dunstall)
jacqui.landriani@midsussex.gov.uk

Lea, Andrew (CON - Lindfield)
andrew.lea@midsussex.gov.uk

Lea, Anthea (CON - Lindfield)
anthea.lea@midsussex.gov.uk

MacNaughton, Andrew (CON - Ardingly & Balcombe)
andrew.macnaughton@midsussex.gov.uk

Mainstone, Bob (LD - East Grinstead - Imberhorne)
bob.mainstone@midsussex.gov.uk

Marples, Gordon (CON - Hassocks)
gordon.marples@midsussex.gov.uk

Marsh, Gary (CON - Ardingly & Balcombe)
gary.marsh@midsussex.gov.uk

Martin, Peter (CON - Hassocks)
peter.martin@midsussex.gov.uk

Matthews, Edward (CON - Copthorne & Worth)
edward.matthews@midsussex.gov.uk

Mockford, Norman (CON - East Grinstead - Town)
norman.mockford@midsussex.gov.uk

Moore, Pru (CON - Burgess Hill - Leylands)
pru.moore@midsussex.gov.uk

Mundin, Howard (CON - Haywards Heath - Ashenground)
howard.mundin@midsussex.gov.uk

Page, Kirsty (CON - Burgess Hill - St Andrews)
kirsty.page@midsussex.gov.uk

Rawlinson, Geoff (CON - Haywards Heath - Lucastes)
geoff.rawlinson@midsussex.gov.uk

Salisbury, Robert (CON - Cuckfield)
robert.salisbury@midsussex.gov.uk

Stockwell, Linda (CON - High Weald)
linda.stockwell@midsussex.gov.uk

Sweatman, Dick (CON - East Grinstead - Herontye)
dick.sweatman@midsussex.gov.uk

Thomas-Atkin, Mandy (CON - Burgess Hill - Victoria)
mandy.thomas-atkin@midsussex.gov.uk

Trumble, Colin (CON - Hurstpierpoint & Downs)
colin.trumble@midsussex.gov.uk

Walker, Neville (CON - Crawley Down & Turners Hill)
neville.walker@midsussex.gov.uk

Watts Williams, Anthony (CON - Hurstpierpoint & Downs)
anthonywattswilliams@midsussex.gov.uk

Webster, Norman (CON - East Grinstead - Baldwins)
norman.webster@midsussex.gov.uk

Wilkinson, John (CON - Hurstpierpoint & Downs)
john.wilkinson@midsussex.gov.uk

Wyan, Peter (CON - East Grinstead - Town)
peter.wyan@midsussex.gov.uk

POLITICAL COMPOSITION
CON: 53, LD: 1

COMMITTEE CHAIRS

Audit: Mr John Belsey

Licensing: Mr Jim Knight

Planning: Mr Robert Salisbury

Mid Ulster District   N

Mid Ulster District, Mid Ulster Transition Committee, Change Management Office, c/o Dungannon & South Tyrone Borough Council, Circular Road, Dungannon BT71 6DT
☎ 03000 132132 ⫟ info@midulstercouncil.org
🖥 www.midulstercouncil.org

PRINCIPAL OFFICERS

Chief Executive: Mr Anthony Tohill, Chief Executive, Mid Ulster Transition Committee, Change Management Office, c/o Dungannon & South Tyrone Borough Council, Circular Road, Dungannon BT71 6DT

Senior Management: Dr Chris Boomer, Planning Manager, Mid Ulster Transition Committee, Change Management Office, c/o Dungannon & South Tyrone Borough Council, Circular Road, Dungannon BT71 6DT ☎ 03000 132132
⫟ chris.boomer@midulstercouncil.org

Senior Management: Ms Anne-Marie Campbell, Director - Culture & Leisure, Mid Ulster Transition Committee, Change Management Office, c/o Dungannon & South Tyrone Borough Council, Circular Road, Dungannon BT71 6DT ☎ 03000 132132
✆ annemarie.campbell@midulstercouncil.org

Senior Management: Ms Marissa Canavan, Lead HR Officer, Mid Ulster Transition Committee, Change Management Office, c/o Dungannon & South Tyrone Borough Council, Circular Road, Dungannon BT71 6DT ☎ 03000 132132
✆ marissa.canavan@midulstercouncil.org

Senior Management: Mr Andrew Cassells, Director - Environment & Property, Mid Ulster Transition Committee, Change Management Office, c/o Dungannon & South Tyrone Borough Council, Circular Road, Dungannon BT71 6DT ☎ 03000 132132
✆ andrew.cassells@midulstercouncil.org

Senior Management: Mr Mark Kelso, Director - Public Health & Infrastructure, Mid Ulster Transition Committee, Change Management Office, c/o Dungannon & South Tyrone Borough Council, Circular Road, Dungannon BT71 6DT ☎ 03000 132132
✆ mark.kelso@midulstercouncil.org

Senior Management: Mr Adrian McCreesh, Director - Business & Communities, Mid Ulster Transition Committee, Change Management Office, c/o Dungannon & South Tyrone Borough Council, Circular Road, Dungannon BT71 6DT ☎ 03000 132132
✆ adrian.mccreesh@midulstercouncil.org

Senior Management: Mr JJ Tohill, Lead Finance Officer, Mid Ulster Transition Committee, Change Management Office, c/o Dungannon & South Tyrone Borough Council, Circular Road, Dungannon BT71 6DT ☎ 03000 132132 ✆ jj.tohill@midulstercouncil.org

Architect, Building / Property Services: Mr Terry Scullion, Head of Property Services, Mid Ulster Transition Committee, Change Management Office, c/o Dungannon & South Tyrone Borough Council, Circular Road, Dungannon BT71 6DT ☎ 03000 132132 ✆ terry.scullion@midulstercouncil.org

Building Control: Mr Willie Wilkinson, Head of Building Control, Mid Ulster Transition Committee, Change Management Office, c/o Dungannon & South Tyrone Borough Council, Circular Road, Dungannon BT71 6DT ☎ 03000 132132
✆ willie.wilkinson@midulstercouncil.org

Community Planning: Ms Claire Linney, Head of Community Development, Mid Ulster Transition Committee, Change Management Office, c/o Dungannon & South Tyrone Borough Council, Circular Road, Dungannon BT71 6DT ☎ 03000 132132
✆ claire.linney@midulstercouncil.org

Computer Management: Mr Barry O'Hagan, Head of ICT, Mid Ulster Transition Committee, Change Management Office, c/o Dungannon & South Tyrone Borough Council, Circular Road, Dungannon BT71 6DT ☎ 03000 132132
✆ barry.ohagan@midulstercouncil.org

Corporate Services: Mr Adrian McCreesh, Director - Business & Communities, Mid Ulster Transition Committee, Change Management Office, c/o Dungannon & South Tyrone Borough Council, Circular Road, Dungannon BT71 6DT ☎ 03000 132132
✆ adrian.mccreesh@midulstercouncil.org

Corporate Services: Mr Philip Moffett, Change Manager, Mid Ulster Transition Committee, Change Management Office, c/o Dungannon & South Tyrone Borough Council, Circular Road, Dungannon BT71 6DT

Economic Development: Ms Fiona McKeown, Head of Economic Development, Mid Ulster Transition Committee, Change Management Office, c/o Dungannon & South Tyrone Borough Council, Circular Road, Dungannon BT71 6DT ☎ 03000 132132
✆ fiona.mckeown@midulstercouncil.org

Environmental / Technical Services: Mr Andrew Cassells, Director - Environment & Property, Mid Ulster Transition Committee, Change Management Office, c/o Dungannon & South Tyrone Borough Council, Circular Road, Dungannon BT71 6DT
☎ 03000 132132 ✆ andrew.cassells@midulstercouncil.org

Environmental / Technical Services: Mr Raymond Lowry, Head of Technical Services, Mid Ulster Transition Committee, Change Management Office, c/o Dungannon & South Tyrone Borough Council, Circular Road, Dungannon BT71 6DT ☎ 03000 132132
✆ raymond.lowry@midulstercouncil.org

Environmental / Technical Services: Mr Mark McAdoo, Head of Environmental Services, Mid Ulster Transition Committee, Change Management Office, c/o Dungannon & South Tyrone Borough Council, Circular Road, Dungannon BT71 6DT
☎ 03000 132132 ✆ mark.mcadoo@midulstercouncil.org

Environmental Health: Mr Andrew Cassells, Director - Environment & Property, Mid Ulster Transition Committee, Change Management Office, c/o Dungannon & South Tyrone Borough Council, Circular Road, Dungannon BT71 6DT ☎ 03000 132132
✆ andrew.cassells@midulstercouncil.org

Environmental Health: Ms Fiona McClements, Head of Environmental Health, Mid Ulster Transition Committee, Change Management Office, c/o Dungannon & South Tyrone Borough Council, Circular Road, Dungannon BT71 6DT ☎ 03000 132132
✆ fiona.mcclements@midulstercouncil.org

Finance: Ms Paula Keer, Head of Finance, Mid Ulster Transition Committee, Change Management Office, c/o Dungannon & South Tyrone Borough Council, Circular Road, Dungannon BT71 6DT
☎ 03000 132132 ✆ paula.kerr@midulstercouncil.org

Finance: Mr JJ Tohill, Lead Finance Officer, Mid Ulster Transition Committee, Change Management Office, c/o Dungannon & South Tyrone Borough Council, Circular Road, Dungannon BT71 6DT
☎ 03000 132132 ✆ jj.tohill@midulstercouncil.org

Leisure and Cultural Services: Ms Anne-Marie Campbell, Director - Culture & Leisure, Mid Ulster Transition Committee, Change Management Office, c/o Dungannon & South Tyrone Borough Council, Circular Road, Dungannon BT71 6DT
☎ 03000 132132 ✆ annemarie.campbell@midulstercouncil.org

Personnel / HR: Ms Marissa Canavan, Lead HR Officer, Mid Ulster Transition Committee, Change Management Office, c/o Dungannon & South Tyrone Borough Council, Circular Road, Dungannon BT71 6DT ☎ 03000 132132
✆ marissa.canavan@midulstercouncil.org

MID ULSTER DISTRICT

Personnel / HR: Ms Geraldine Dyson, Head of HR, Mid Ulster Transition Committee, Change Management Office, c/o Dungannon & South Tyrone Borough Council, Circular Road, Dungannon BT71 6DT ☎ 03000 132132 ⌂ geraldine.dyson@midulstercouncil.org

Planning: Dr Chris Boomer, Planning Manager, Mid Ulster Transition Committee, Change Management Office, c/o Dungannon & South Tyrone Borough Council, Circular Road, Dungannon BT71 6DT ☎ 03000 132132 ⌂ chris.boomer@midulstercouncil.org

Planning: Mr Melvin Brown, Head of Development Management, Mid Ulster Transition Committee, Change Management Office, c/o Dungannon & South Tyrone Borough Council, Circular Road, Dungannon BT71 6DT ☎ 03000 132132 ⌂ melvin.brown@midulstercouncil.org

Public Health: Mr Mark Kelso, Director - Public Health & Infrastructure, Mid Ulster Transition Committee, Change Management Office, c/o Dungannon & South Tyrone Borough Council, Circular Road, Dungannon BT71 6DT ☎ 03000 132132 ⌂ mark.kelso@midulstercouncil.org

Tourism: Mr Michael Browne, Head of Tourism, Mid Ulster Transition Committee, Change Management Office, c/o Dungannon & South Tyrone Borough Council, Circular Road, Dungannon BT71 6DT ☎ 03000 132132 ⌂ michael.browne@midulstercouncil.org

COUNCILLORS

Chair: Wilson, Trevor (UUP - Cookstown)
trevor@8theash.freeserve.co.uk

Vice-Chair: McAleer, Sharon (SDLP - Clogher Valley)
sharonmcaleer.sdlp@gmail.com

Ashton, Kim (DUP - Dungannon)
kim.ashton@dstbc.org

Bateson, Peter (SF - Moyola)
peadardebath@gmail.com

Bell, Gavin (SF - Cookstown)
gavin.bell.sf@gmail.com

Buchanan, Wilbert (DUP - Cookstown)
william774@btinternet.com

Burton, Frances (DUP - Clogher Valley)
frances.burton@dstbc.org

Clarke, Sean (SF - Magherafelt)
clerke@hotmail.com

Cuddy, Walter (UUP - Dungannon)
walter.cuddy@dstbc.org

Cuthbertson, Clement (DUP - Dungannon)
clementcuthbertson@hotmail.co.uk

Dillon, Linda (SF - Torrent)
linda.dillon81@gmail.com

Elattar, Catherine (SF - Moyola)
celattar@yahoo.ie

Forde, Anne (DUP - Moyola)
cllr.forde@magherafelt.gov.uk

Gildernew, Phelim (SF - Clogher Valley)
phelim.gildernew@dstbc.org

Gillespie, Mickey (SF - Torrent)
michael.gillespie@dstbc.org

Glasgow, Mark (UUP - Cookstown)
mark814glasgow@btinternet.com

Kearney, Martin (SDLP - Carntogher)
kearney768@btinternet.com

Mallaghan, Cáthal (SF - Cookstown)
cathalmallaghan@hotmail.com

McEldowney, Kate (SF - Carntogher)
kate.mceldowney@yahoo.ie

McFlynn, Christine (SDLP - Magherafelt)
christine.mcflynn@cookstown.gov.uk

McGinley, Ronan (SF - Torrent)
ronanmcginley@ymail.com

McGuigan, Sean (SF - Clogher Valley)
sean.mcguigan@dstbc.org

McGuigan, Brian (SF - Carntogher)
bmcguigan52@yahoo.ie

McKinney, Derek (UUP - Moyola)
derekmckinney71@gmail.com

McLean, Paul (DUP - Magherafelt)
mcleanpaul@me.com

McNamee, John (SF - Cookstown)
john.mcnamee@cookstown.gov.uk

McPeake, Seán (SF - Carntogher)
seanmcpeake@hotmail.com

Molloy, Dominic (SF - Dungannon)
domonic.molloy@dstbc.org

Monteith, Barry (IND - Dungannon)
barry.monteith@dstbc.org

Mullen, Denise (SDLP - Dungannon)
denise.mullen.125@gmail.com

Mulligan, Robert (UUP - Clogher Valley)
robert.mulligan@dstbc.org

O'Neill, Caoimhe (SF - Moyola)
caoimheoneill01@yahoo.com

O'Neill, Joe (SF - Torrent)
joe.oneill@dstbc.org

Quinn, Malachy (SDLP - Torrent)
malachyquinn@hotmail.com

Quinn, Tony (SDLP - Cookstown)
tony.quinn@cookstown.gov.uk

Reid, Kenneth (UUP - Torrent)
kenneth.reid@dstbc.org

Robinson, Wills (DUP - Clogher Valley)
wills.robinson@dstbc.org

Shiels, George (UUP - Magherafelt)
g.shiels49@btinternet.com

Shiels, James (DUP - Carntogher)
jamesshiels817@gmail.com

Totten, Darren (SF - Magherafelt)
darrentotten34@gmail.com

POLITICAL COMPOSITION
SF: 18, DUP: 8, UUP: 7, SDLP: 6, IND: 1

Middlesbrough   U

Middlesbrough Council, Town Hall, Middlesbrough TS1 2QQ
☎ 01642 245432 ⏱ contactcentre@middlesbrough.gov.uk
💻 www.middlesbrough.gov.uk

FACTS AND FIGURES
Parliamentary Constituencies: Middlesbrough
EU Constituencies: North East
Election Frequency: Elections are of whole council

PRINCIPAL OFFICERS

Chief Executive: Mr Tony Parkinson, Interim Chief Executive, PO Box 500, Civic Centre, Middlesbrough TS1 9FZ ☎ 01642 729101 ⏱ tony_parkinson@middlesbrough.gov.uk

Senior Management: Mrs Richenda Broad, Executive Director - Wellbeing, Care & Learning, PO Box 151, Civic Centre, Middlesbrough TS1 9FU ☎ 01642 729500 ⏱ richenda_broad@middlesbrough.gov.uk

Senior Management: Mr James Bromiley, Strategic Director - Finance, Governance & Support, PO Box 505, Civic Centre, Middlesbrough TS1 9FZ ☎ 01642 729046 ⏱ james_bromiley@middlesbrough.gov.uk

Senior Management: Mr Kevin Parkes, Executive Director - Economic Development & Communities, PO Box 506, Civic Centre, Middlesbrough TS1 9FY ☎ 01642 729300 ⏱ kevin_parkes@middlesbrough.gov.uk

Access Officer / Social Services (Disability): Mr Eric Scollay, Executive Director - Social Care, PO Box 151, Civic Centre, Middlesbrough TS1 9FU ☎ 01642 728489 ⏱ eric_scollay@middlesbrough.gov.uk

Architect, Building / Property Services: Mr Kevin Paylor, Maintenance Officer - Building, PO Box 503, Civic Centre, Middlesbrough TS1 9FX ☎ 01642 729820 ⏱ kevin_paylor@middlesbrough.gov.uk

Building Control: Mr Kevin Wood, Building Control Group Leader, PO Box 506, Civic Centre, Middlesbrough TS1 9FY ☎ 01642 729473 ⏱ kevin_wood@middlesbrough.gov.uk

Catering Services: Mrs Angela Blower, Catering Manager, Central Depot, Cargo Fleet Lane, Middlesbrough TS3 8AL ☎ 01642 728030 ⏱ angela_blower@middlesbrough.gov.uk

Children / Youth Services: Mrs Richenda Broad, Executive Director - Wellbeing, Care & Learning, PO Box 151, Civic Centre, Middlesbrough TS1 9FU ☎ 01642 729500 ⏱ richenda_broad@middlesbrough.gov.uk

Civil Registration: Ms Christine Green, Registration Services Manager, Register Office, Corporation Road, Middlesbrough TS1 2DA ☎ 01642 729457 ⏱ christine_green@middlesbrough.gov.uk

PR / Communications: Ms Kim Flynn, Marketing & Communications Manager, PO Box 500, Civic Centre, Middlesbrough TS1 9FY ☎ 01642 729039 ⏱ kim_flynn@middlesbrough.gov.uk

Community Safety: Ms Jane Hill, Community Safety Manager, 3rd Floor, Vancouver House, Gurney Street, Middlesbrough TS1 9FU ☎ 01642 728112 ⏱ jane_hill@middlesbrough.gov.uk

Computer Management: Mr Andy Evans, ICT Manager (Infrastructure Services), Vancouver House, Middlesbrough TS1 9FY ☎ 01642 727801 ⏱ andy_evans@middlesbrough.gov.uk

Consumer Protection and Trading Standards: Mr John Wells, Public Protection Operations Manager, Vancouver House, Middlesbrough TS1 1LY ☎ 01642 728221 ⏱ john_wells@middlesbrough.gov.uk

Contracts: Ms Claire Walker, Procurement Manager, Civic Centre, Middlesbrough TS1 9FT ☎ 01642 728415 ⏱ claire_walker@middlesbrough.gov.uk

Corporate Services: Mr Tony Parkinson, Interim Chief Executive, PO Box 500, Civic Centre, Middlesbrough TS1 9FZ ☎ 01642 729101 ⏱ tony_parkinson@middlesbrough.gov.uk

Customer Service: Mr Andy Unsworth, Customer Services Manager, Vancouver House, 50 Corporation Road, Middlesbrough TS1 2RH ☎ 01642 726104 ⏱ andy_unsworth@middlesbrough.gov.uk

Economic Development: Mr Kevin Parkes, Executive Director - Economic Development & Communities, PO Box 506, Civic Centre, Middlesbrough TS1 9FY ☎ 01642 729300 ⏱ kevin_parkes@middlesbrough.gov.uk

Economic Development: Ms Sharon Thomas, Assistant Director - Economic Development, PO Box 506, Civic Centre, Middlesbrough TS1 9FY ☎ 01642 729600 ⏱ sharon_thomas@middlesbrough.gov.uk

Education: Mrs Richenda Broad, Executive Director - Wellbeing, Care & Learning, PO Box 151, Civic Centre, Middlesbrough TS1 9FU ☎ 01642 729500 ⏱ richenda_broad@middlesbrough.gov.uk

Education: Mr Paul Wilson, Head of Education ICT, Rede House, Middlesbrough TS1 1LY ☎ 01642 727609

E-Government: Mr Tim Whitehead, Principal Digital Media Officer, PO Box 500, Civic Centre, Middlesbrough TS1 9FX ☎ 01642 729311 ⏱ tim_whitehead@middlesbrough.gov.uk

Electoral Registration: Mr John Stuart, Senior Electoral Services Manager, PO Box 503, Civic Centre, Middlesbrough TS1 9FX ☎ 01642 729772 ⏱ john_stuart@middlesbrough.gov.uk

Emergency Planning: Mr Edward Kunonga, Assistant Director - Improving Public Health & Director - Public Health, PO Box 505, Town Hall, Middlesbrough TS1 9FZ ☎ 01642 728020 ⏱ edward_kunonga@middlesbrough.gov.uk

Energy Management: Mr Gareth Lonsbrough, Asset Manager, Civic Centre, Middlesbrough TS1 9FT ☎ 01642 729270 ⏱ gavin_lonsbrough@middlesbrough.gov.uk

Environmental / Technical Services: Mr Geoff Field, Assistant Director - Environment, Property & Commercial Services, PO Box 506, Civic Centre, Middlesbrough TS1 9FX ☎ 01642 728300 ⏱ geoff_field@middlesbrough.gov.uk

MIDDLESBROUGH

Environmental Health: Mrs Judith Hedgley, Environmental Health Manager, Vancouver House, Middlesbrough TS1 9FW
☎ 01642 728215 ◌ judith_hedgley@middlesbrough.gov.uk

Estates, Property & Valuation: Mr Tim Wake, Principal Estates Surveyor, PO Box 506, Civic Centre, Middlesbrough TS1 9FY
☎ 01642 729107 ◌ tim.wake@middlesbrough.gov.uk

Finance: Mr Mark Taylor, Interim Assistant Director - Finance & Investment, PO Box 506, Civic Centre, Middlesbrough TS1 9FX
☎ 01642 729032 ◌ markd_taylor@middlesbrough.gov.uk

Pensions: Mr Mike Hopwood, Head of Pensions, PO Box 340, Middlesbrough TS1 2XP ☎ 01642 727778
◌ mike_hopwood@middlesbrough.gov.uk

Fleet Management: Mr Geoff Field, Assistant Director - Environment, Property & Commercial Services, PO Box 506, Civic Centre, Middlesbrough TS1 9FX ☎ 01642 728300
◌ geoff_field@middlesbrough.gov.uk

Grounds Maintenance: Mr Geoff Field, Assistant Director - Environment, Property & Commercial Services, PO Box 506, Civic Centre, Middlesbrough TS1 9FX ☎ 01642 728300
◌ geoff_field@middlesbrough.gov.uk

Health and Safety: Ms Anne Pennock, Assistant Health & Safety Advisor, 4th Floor, Vancouver House, Gurney Street, Middlesbrough TS1 9FW ☎ 01642 727419 ◌ anne_pennock@middlesbrough.gov.uk

Highways: Mr David Carter, Head of Transport & Infrastructure, PO Box 502, Vancouver House, Gurney Street, Middlesbrough TS1 9FW ☎ 01642 728636 ◌ david_carter@middlesbrough.gov.uk

Housing: Ms Sharon Thomas, Assistant Director - Economic Development, PO Box 506, Civic Centre, Middlesbrough TS1 9FY
☎ 01642 729600 ◌ sharon_thomas@middlesbrough.gov.uk

Legal: Mr Bryn Roberts, Legal Services Manager, Town Hall, Middlesbrough TS1 2QQ ☎ 01642 729738
◌ bryn_roberts@middlesbrough.gov.uk

Leisure and Cultural Services: Ms Anne Besford, Cultural Services Manager, PO Box 504, Town Hall, Middlesbrough TS1 9FY
☎ 01642 729703 ◌ anne_besford@middlesbrough.gov.uk

Licensing: Mr Tim Hodgkinson, Principal Licensing Officer, PO Box 502, Vancouver House, Gurney Street, Middlesbrough TS1 9FW
☎ 01642 728720 ◌ tim_hodgkinson@middlesbrough.gov.uk

Lottery Funding, Charity and Voluntary: Mr Martin Harvey, Community Infrastructure Manager, PO Box 506, Civic Centre, Middlesbrough TS1 9FY ☎ 01642 729254
◌ martin_harvey@middlesbrough.gov.uk

Member Services: Mr Nigel Sayer, Head of Democratic Services, PO Box 503, Town Hall, Middlesbrough TS1 9FX ☎ 01642 729031
◌ nigel_sayer@middlesbrough.gov.uk

Parking: Mr David Carter, Head of Transport & Infrastructure, PO Box 502, Vancouver House, Gurney Street, Middlesbrough TS1 9FW
☎ 01642 728636 ◌ david_carter@middlesbrough.gov.uk

Partnerships: Mr Paul Stephens, Head of Performance & Partnerships, PO Box 500, Civic Centre, Middlesbrough TS1 9FT
☎ 01642 729223 ◌ paul_stephens@middlesbrough.gov.uk

Personnel / HR: Mrs Pip Schofield, Head of Human Resources, 4th Floor, Vancouver House, Gurney Street, Middlesbrough TS1 9FW ☎ 01642 729440 ◌ pip_schofield@middlesbrough.gov.uk

Planning: Mrs Sharon Thomas, Assistant Director - Economic Development, PO Box 506, Civic Centre, Middlesbrough TS1 9FY
☎ 01642 729600 ◌ sharon_thomas@middlesbrough.gov.uk

Procurement: Ms Claire Walker, Procurement Manager, Civic Centre, Middlesbrough TS1 9FT ☎ 01642 728415
◌ claire_walker@middlesbrough.gov.uk

Public Libraries: Mr Martin Harvey, Community Infrastructure Manager, PO Box 506, Civic Centre, Middlesbrough TS1 9FY
☎ 01642 729254 ◌ martin_harvey@middlesbrough.gov.uk

Recycling & Waste Minimisation: Mr Ken Sherwood, Waste & Environmental Strategy Manager, PO Box 502, Vancouver House, Gurney Street, Middlesbrough TS1 9FW ☎ 01642 728514
◌ ken_sherwood@middlesbrough.gov.uk

Regeneration: Mr Kevin Parkes, Executive Director - Economic Development & Communities, PO Box 506, Civic Centre, Middlesbrough TS1 9FY ☎ 01642 729300
◌ kevin_parkes@middlesbrough.gov.uk

Road Safety: Mr David Carter, Head of Transport & Infrastructure, PO Box 502, Vancouver House, Gurney Street, Middlesbrough TS1 9FW ☎ 01642 728636 ◌ david_carter@middlesbrough.gov.uk

Social Services: Mrs Richenda Broad, Executive Director - Wellbeing, Care & Learning, PO Box 151, Civic Centre, Middlesbrough TS1 9FU ☎ 01642 729500
◌ richenda_broad@middlesbrough.gov.uk

Social Services (Adult): Mrs Richenda Broad, Executive Director - Wellbeing, Care & Learning, PO Box 151, Civic Centre, Middlesbrough TS1 9FU ☎ 01642 729500
◌ richenda_broad@middlesbrough.gov.uk

Public Health: Mr Edward Kunonga, Assistant Director - Improving Public Health & Director - Public Health, PO Box 505, Town Hall, Middlesbrough TS1 9FZ ☎ 01642 728020
◌ edward_kunonga@middlesbrough.gov.uk

Staff Training: Ms Lisa Brett, Manager - Workforce & Engagement, Partnership Team, 3rd Floor, Vancouver House, Gurney Street, Middlesbrough TS1 9FW ☎ 01642 728727
◌ lisa_brett@middlesbrough.gov.uk

Street Scene: Mr Geoff Field, Assistant Director - Environment, Property & Commercial Services, PO Box 506, Civic Centre, Middlesbrough TS1 9FX ☎ 01642 728300
◌ geoff_field@middlesbrough.gov.uk

Sustainable Development: Mr Richard Horniman, Assistant Director - Supporting Communities, PO Box 504, Civic Centre, Middlesbrough TS1 9FY ☎ 01642 729538
◌ richard_horniman@middlebrough.gov.uk

Tourism: Mrs Yaffa Philips, Economic Development Officer, PO Box 506, Civic Centre, Middlesbrough TS1 9FY ☎ 01642 729139 ✆ yaffa_phillips@middlesbrough.gov.uk

Traffic Management: Mr David Carter, Head of Transport & Infrastructure, PO Box 502, Vancouver House, Gurney Street, Middlesbrough TS1 9FW ☎ 01642 728636 ✆ david_carter@middlesbrough.gov.uk

Transport: Mr David Carter, Head of Transport & Infrastructure, PO Box 502, Vancouver House, Gurney Street, Middlesbrough TS1 9FW ☎ 01642 728636 ✆ david_carter@middlesbrough.gov.uk

Transport Planner: Mr David Carter, Head of Transport & Infrastructure, PO Box 502, Vancouver House, Gurney Street, Middlesbrough TS1 9FW ☎ 01642 728636 ✆ david_carter@middlesbrough.gov.uk

Total Place: Mr Martin Harvey, Community Infrastructure Manager, PO Box 506, Civic Centre, Middlesbrough TS1 9FY ☎ 01642 729254 ✆ martin_harvey@middlesbrough.gov.uk

Waste Collection and Disposal: Mr Ken Sherwood, Waste & Environmental Strategy Manager, PO Box 502, Vancouver House, Gurney Street, Middlesbrough TS1 9FW ☎ 01642 728514 ✆ ken_sherwood@middlesbrough.gov.uk

Waste Management: Mr Ken Sherwood, Waste & Environmental Strategy Manager, PO Box 502, Vancouver House, Gurney Street, Middlesbrough TS1 9FW ☎ 01642 728514 ✆ ken_sherwood@middlesbrough.gov.uk

COUNCILLORS

Mayor: Budd, David (LAB - No Ward)
mayor@middlesbrough.gov.uk

Deputy Mayor: Rooney, Charles (LAB - Longlands & Beechwood)
charles_rooney@middlesbrough.gov.uk

Arundale, Ronald (CON - Kader)
ronald_arundale@middlesbrough.gov.uk

Biswas, Shamal (LAB - Acklam)
shamal_biswas@middlesbrough.gov.uk

Bloundele, Stephen (LAB - Linthorpe)
stephen_bloundele@middlesbrough.gov.uk

Blyth, Jordan (LAB - Kader)
jordan_blyth@middlesbrough.gov.uk

Brady, Bob (LAB - Newport)
bob_brady@middlesbrough.gov.uk

Branson, David (LAB - Coulby Newham)
david_branson@middlesbrough.gov.uk

Brunton, Janice (LAB - Coulby Newham)
janice_brunton@middlesbrough.gov.uk

Carr, Michael (LAB - Ladgate)
mike_carr@middlesbrough.gov.uk

Cole, John (LAB - Coulby Newham)
john_cole@middlesbrough.gov.uk

Coupe, David (CON - Stainton & Thornton)
david_coupe@middlesbrough.gov.uk

Cox, Peter (IND - Park End & Beckfield)
peter_cox@middlesbrough.gov.uk

Davison, Dorothy (IND - Marton East)
dorothy_davison@middlesbrough.gov.uk

Dean, Sheila (LAB - Acklam)
sheila_dean@middlesbrough.gov.uk

Dryden, Eddie (LAB - Berwick Hills & Pallister)
eddie_dryden@middlesbrough.gov.uk

Goodchild, June (LAB - Ladgate)
june_goodchild@middlesbrough.gov.uk

Harvey, Tracy (LAB - Newport)
cllrtracy_harvey@middlesbrough.gov.uk

Hellaoui, Alma (LAB - Newport)
alma_hellaoui@middlesbrough.gov.uk

Higgins, Teresa (LAB - Longlands & Beechwood)
teresa_higgins@middlesbrough.gov.uk

Hobson, Christine (CON - Marton West)
chris_hobson@middlesbrough.gov.uk

Hobson, John (CON - Marton West)
john_hobson@middlesbrough.gov.uk

Hubbard, Brian (IND - Park End & Beckfield)
brian_hubbard@middlesbrough.gov.uk

Hussain, Naweed (LAB - Linthorpe)
naweed_hussain@middlesbrough.gov.uk

Lawton, Terry (LAB - Brambles & Thorntree)
terence_lawton@middlesbrough.gov.uk

Lewis, Linda (LAB - Central)
linda_lewis@middlesbrough.gov.uk

Mawston, Tom (IND - Marton East)
tom_mawston@middlesbrough.gov.uk

McCabe, Dennis (IND - Trimdon)
dennis_mccabe@middlesbrough.gov.uk

McGee, Julie (LAB - Berwick Hills & Pallister)
julie_mcgee@middlesbrough.gov.uk

McGloin, Lesley (IND - Nunthorpe)
lesley_mcgloin@middlesbrough.gov.uk

McIntyre, Frances (LAB - Park)
fraces_mcintyre@middlesbrough.gov.uk

McTigue, Joan (IND - Longlands & Beechwood)
joan_mctigue@middlesbrough.gov.uk

Purvis, Peter (LAB - Brambles & Thorntree)
peter_purvis@middlesbrough.gov.uk

Purvis, Geraldine (LAB - Brambles & Thorntree)
geraldine_purvis@middlesbrough.gov.uk

Rathmell, Jon (IND - Nunthorpe)
jon_rathmell@middlesbrough.gov.uk

Rooney, Denise (LAB - Ayresome)
denise_rooney@middlesbrough.gov.uk

Rostron, Julia (LAB - Park)
julia_rostron@middlesbrough.gov.uk

Saunders, Michael (IND - Park End & Beckfield)
michael_saunders@middlesbrough.gov.uk

Sharrocks, Jean (LAB - Trimdon)
jean_sharrocks@middlesbrough.gov.uk

MIDDLESBROUGH

Taylor, Bernard (LAB - Ayresome)
bernard_taylor@middlesbrough.gov.uk

Thompson, Michael (LAB - Berwick Hills & Pallister)
mick_thompson@middlesbrough.gov.uk

Uddin, Zafar (LAB - Central)
zafar_uddin@middlesbrough.gov.uk

Walker, Nicola (LAB - Hemlington)
nicola_walker@middlesbrough.gov.uk

Walker, Jeanette (LAB - Hemlington)
jeanette_walker@middlesbrough.gov.uk

Walters, Margaret (LAB - Park)
margaret_walters@middlesbrough.gov.uk

Young, Lewis (LAB - North Ormesby)
lewis_young@middlesbrough.gov.uk

POLITICAL COMPOSITION
LAB: 33, IND: 9, CON: 4

COMMITTEE CHAIRS

Audit: Mr Peter Purvis

Children & Learning: Mr Jeanette Walker

Licensing: Mr Bernard Taylor

Planning & Development: Mr John Cole

Social Care & Adult Services: Ms Julie McGee

Midlothian   S

Midlothian Council, Midlothian House, 40-46 Buccleuch
Street, Dalkeith EH22 1DN
☎ 0131 270 7500 🖷 0131 271 3050 ⌂ enquiries@midlothian.gov.uk
🖳 www.midlothian.gov.uk

FACTS AND FIGURES
Parliamentary Constituencies: Midlothian
EU Constituencies: Scotland
Election Frequency: Elections are of whole council

PRINCIPAL OFFICERS

Chief Executive: Mr Kenneth Lawrie, Chief Executive, Midlothian
House, 40-46 Buccleuch Street, Dalkeith EH22 1DN ☎ 0131 271
3002 ⌂ kenneth.lawrie@midlothian.gov.uk

Senior Management: Mr John Blair, Director - Resources,
Midlothian House, Buccleuch Street, Dalkeith EH22 1DJ ☎ 0131 271
3102 ⌂ john.blair@midlothian.gov.uk

Senior Management: Ms Eibhlin McHugh, Joint Director - Health
& Social Care, Fairfield House 8 Lothian Road, Dalkeith EH22 3ZH
☎ 0131 271 3605 ⌂ eibhlin.mchugh@midlothian.gov.uk

Senior Management: Dr Mary Smith, Director - Education,
Communities & Economy, Fairfield House 8 Lothian Road, Dalkeith
EH22 3ZG ☎ 0131 271 3718 ⌂ mary.smith@midlothian.gov.uk

Access Officer / Social Services (Disability): Ms Jo Foley,
Service Manager - Resources, Fairfield House 8 Lothian Road,
Dalkeith EH22 3ZG ☎ 0131 271 3792 ⌂ jo.foley@midlothian.gov.uk

Access Officer / Social Services (Disability): Ms Alison White,
Head of Adult & Social Care, Fairfield House 8 Lothian Road,
Dalkeith EH22 3ZH ☎ 0131 271 3605
⌂ alison.white@midlothian.gov.uk

Architect, Building / Property Services: Mr Garry Sheret, Head
of Property & Facilities Management, Midlothian House, Buccleuch
Street, Dalkeith EH22 1DN ☎ 0131 561 5249
⌂ garry.sheret@midlothian.gov.uk

Best Value: Ms Nancy Brown, Transformation Programme
Manager, Midlothian House, 40-46 Buccleuch Street, Dalkeith
EH22 1DN ☎ 0131 271 3444 ⌂ nancy.brown@midlothian.gov.uk

Building Control: Mr John Delamar, Building Standards Manager,
Fairfield House 8 Lothian Road, Dalkeith EH22 1DJ ☎ 0131 271
3322 ⌂ john.delamar@midlothian.gov.uk

Building Control: Mr Ian Johnson, Head of Communities &
Economy, Fairfield House 8 Lothian Road, Dalkeith EH22 3ZQ
☎ 0131 271 3460 ⌂ ian.johnson@midlothian.gov.uk

Catering Services: Ms Margaret McKenzie, Catering Services
Manager, Midlothian House, 40-46 Buccleuch Street, Dalkeith EH22
1DN ☎ 0131 561 5314 ⌂ margaret.mckenzie@midlothian.gov.uk

Children / Youth Services: Ms Joan Tranent, Head of Children's
Services, Fairfield House 8 Lothian Road, Dalkeith EH22 3ZG
☎ 0131 271 3721 ⌂ joan.tranent@midlothian.gov.uk

Children / Youth Services: Ms Grace Vickers, Head of
Education, Fairfield House 8 Lothian Road, Dalkeith EH22 3ZG
☎ 0131 271 3719 ⌂ grace.vickers@midlothian.gov.uk

Civil Registration: Ms Jane Milne, Customer Service Manager,
Buccleuch House, 1 White Hart Street, Dalkeith EH22 1AE
☎ 0131 271 3971 ⌂ jane.milne@midlothian.gov.uk

PR / Communications: Ms Ranaa Ahmed, Public Relations
Officer, 29 Jarnac Court, Dalkeith EH22 1HU ☎ 0131 271 3423
⌂ ranaa.ahmed@midlothian.gov.uk

PR / Communications: Ms Lynn Cochrane, Senior Public
Relations Officer, 29 Jarnac Court, Dalkeith EH22 1HU ☎ 0131 271
3294 ⌂ lynn.cochrane@midlothian.gov.uk

Community Planning: Mr Alasdair Mathers, Communities &
Performance Manager, Fairfield House 8 Lothian Road, Dalkeith
EH22 3ZG ☎ 0131 271 3438 ⌂ alasdair.mathers@midlothian.gov.uk

Community Safety: Mr Kevin Anderson, Head of Customer &
Housing Services, Buccleuch House, 1 White Hart Street, Dalkeith
EH22 1AE ☎ 0131 271 3615 ⌂ kevin.anderson@midlothian.gov.uk

Community Safety: Ms Rosie Kendall, Community Safety
Manager, Fairfield House 8 Lothian Road, Dalkeith EH22 3ZG
☎ 0131 271 6654 ⌂ rosie.kendall@midlothian.gov.uk

Community Safety: Ms Eibhlin McHugh, Joint Director - Health &
Social Care, Fairfield House 8 Lothian Road, Dalkeith EH22 3ZH ☎
0131 271 3605 ⌂ eibhlin.mchugh@midlothian.gov.uk

Computer Management: Mr Phil Timoney, Digital Services Manager, Midlothian House, 40-46 Buccleuch Street, Dalkeith EH22 1DN ☎ 0131 271 3030 ⏁ phil.timoney@midlothian.gov.uk

Consumer Protection and Trading Standards: Mr Ian Johnson, Head of Communities & Economy, Fairfield House 8 Lothian Road, Dalkeith EH22 3ZQ ☎ 0131 271 3460 ⏁ ian.johnson@midlothian.gov.uk

Consumer Protection and Trading Standards: Mr Stephen Thomson, Principal Trading Standards & Laboratory Manager, Fairfield House 8 Lothian Road, Dalkeith EH22 3ZG ☎ 0131 271 3553 ⏁ stephen.thomson@midlothian.gov.uk

Contracts: Mr Iain Johnston, Procurement Manager, Midlothian House, 40-46 Buccleuch Street, Dalkeith EH22 1DN ☎ 0131 561 5385 ⏁ iain.johnston@midlothian.gov.uk

Corporate Services: Mr John Blair, Director - Resources, Midlothian House, Buccleuch Street, Dalkeith EH22 1DJ ☎ 0131 271 3102 ⏁ john.blair@midlothian.gov.uk

Customer Service: Ms Jane Milne, Customer Service Manager, Buccleuch House, 1 White Hart Street, Dalkeith EH22 1AE ☎ 0131 271 3971 ⏁ jane.milne@midlothian.gov.uk

Direct Labour: Mr Ricky Moffat, Head of Commercial Operations, Midlothian House, 40-46 Buccleuch Street, Dalkeith EH22 1DN ☎ 0131 561 5306 ⏁ ricky.moffat@midlothian.gov.uk

Direct Labour: Mr Garry Sheret, Head of Property & Facilities Management, Midlothian House, Buccleuch Street, Dalkeith EH22 1DN ☎ 0131 561 5249 ⏁ garry.sheret@midlothian.gov.uk

Economic Development: Mr Ian Johnson, Head of Communities & Economy, Fairfield House 8 Lothian Road, Dalkeith EH22 3ZQ ☎ 0131 271 3460 ⏁ ian.johnson@midlothian.gov.uk

Education: Ms Grace Vickers, Head of Education, Fairfield House ⏁ Lothian Road, Dalkeith EH22 3ZG ☎ 0131 271 3719 ⏁ grace.vickers@midlothian.gov.uk

E-Government: Mr Phil Timoney, Digital Services Manager, Midlothian House, 40-46 Buccleuch Street, Dalkeith EH22 1DN ☎ 0131 271 3030 ⏁ phil.timoney@midlothian.gov.uk

Electoral Registration: Mr John Blair, Director - Resources, Midlothian House, Buccleuch Street, Dalkeith EH22 1DJ ☎ 0131 271 3102 ⏁ john.blair@midlothian.gov.uk

Electoral Registration: Mr Allan Brown, Electoral Officer, Midlothian House, Buccleuch Street, Dalkeith EH22 1DN ☎ 0131 271 3255 ⏁ allan.brown@midlothian.gov.uk

Emergency Planning: Mr John Blair, Director - Resources, Midlothian House, Buccleuch Street, Dalkeith EH22 1DJ ☎ 0131 271 3102 ⏁ john.blair@midlothian.gov.uk

Emergency Planning: Mrs Jane Young, Contingency Planning Officer, Midlothian House, 40-46 Buccleuch Street, Dalkeith EH22 1DN ☎ 0131 271 3078 ⏁ jane.young@midlothian.gov.uk

Energy Management: Mr Garry Sheret, Head of Property & Facilities Management, Midlothian House, Buccleuch Street, Dalkeith EH22 1DN ☎ 0131 561 5249 ⏁ garry.sheret@midlothian.gov.uk

Environmental / Technical Services: Ms Edel Ryan, Group Manager - Environmental Health, Fairfield House 8 Lothian Street, Dalkeith EH22 3ZG ☎ 0131 271 3742 ⏁ edel.ryan@midlothian.gov.uk

Environmental Health: Mr Ian Johnson, Head of Communities & Economy, Fairfield House 8 Lothian Road, Dalkeith EH22 3ZQ ☎ 0131 271 3460 ⏁ ian.johnson@midlothian.gov.uk

Environmental Health: Ms Edel Ryan, Group Manager - Environmental Health, Fairfield House 8 Lothian Street, Dalkeith EH22 3ZH ☎ 0131 271 3742 ⏁ edel.ryan@midlothian.gov.uk

Estates, Property & Valuation: Mr Gareth Davies, Property Manager, Fairfield House 8 Lothian Road, Dalkeith EH22 3ZH ☎ 0131 271 3495 ⏁ gareth.davies@midlothian.gov.uk

Estates, Property & Valuation: Mr Garry Sheret, Head of Property & Facilities Management, Midlothian House, Buccleuch Street, Dalkeith EH22 1DN ☎ 0131 561 5249 ⏁ garry.sheret@midlothian.gov.uk

Events Manager: Mr Ricky Moffat, Head of Commercial Operations, Midlothian House, 40-46 Buccleuch Street, Dalkeith EH22 1DN ☎ 0131 561 5306 ⏁ ricky.moffat@midlothian.gov.uk

Facilities: Mr Garry Sheret, Head of Property & Facilities Management, Midlothian House, Buccleuch Street, Dalkeith EH22 1DN ☎ 0131 561 5249 ⏁ garry.sheret@midlothian.gov.uk

Finance: Mr Gary Fairley, Head of Finance & Integrated Service Support, Midlothian House, 40-46 Buccleuch Street, Dalkeith EH22 1DN ☎ 0131 271 3110 ⏁ gary.fairley@midlothian.gov.uk

Fleet Management: Mr Trevor Docherty, Business Manager - Travel & Fleet, Midlothian House, 40-46 Buccleuch Street, Dalkeith EH22 1DN ☎ 0131 561 5448 ⏁ trevor.docherty@midlothian.gov.uk

Grounds Maintenance: Mr Justin Venton, Land & Countryside Manager, Midlothian House, 40-46 Buccleuch Street, Dalkeith EH22 1DN ☎ 0131 561 5220 ⏁ justin.venton@midlothian.gov.uk

Health and Safety: Mr Chris Lawson, Risk Manager, Midlothian House, 40-46 Buccleuch Street, Dalkeith EH22 1DN ☎ 0131 271 3069 ⏁ chris.lawson@midlothian.gov.uk

Highways: Mr Neil Dougall, Road Services Manager, Midlothian House, 40-46 Buccleuch Street, Dalkeith EH22 1DN ☎ 0131 561 5215 ⏁ neil.dougall@midlothian.gov.uk

Home Energy Conservation: Mr William Jackson, Building Services Manager, Midlothian House, 40-46 Buccleuch Street, Dalkeith EH22 1DN ☎ 0131 561 5310 ⏁ billy.jackson@midlothian.gov.uk

Housing: Mr Kevin Anderson, Head of Customer & Housing Services, Buccleuch House, 1 White Hart Street, Dalkeith EH22 1AE ☎ 0131 271 3615 ⏁ kevin.anderson@midlothian.gov.uk

MIDLOTHIAN

Housing: Mr Stephen Clark, Group Manager - Performance & Housing Strategy, Buccleuch House, 1 White Hart Street, Dalkeith EH22 1AE ☎ 0131 271 3506 ⌁ stephen.clark@midlothian.gov.uk

Housing Maintenance: Mr William Jackson, Building Services Manager, Midlothian House, 40-46 Buccleuch Street, Dalkeith EH22 1DN ☎ 0131 561 5310 ⌁ billy.jackson@midlothian.gov.uk

Legal: Mr Alan Turpie, Legal Services Manager, Midlothian House, 40-46 Buccleuch Street, Dalkeith EH22 1DN ☎ 0131 271 3667 ⌁ alan.turpie@midlothian.gov.uk

Leisure and Cultural Services: Mr Garry Sheret, Head of Property & Facilities Management, Midlothian House, Buccleuch Street, Dalkeith EH22 1DN ☎ 0131 561 5249 ⌁ garry.sheret@midlothian.gov.uk

Licensing: Mr Alan Turpie, Legal Services Manager, Midlothian House, 40-46 Buccleuch Street, Dalkeith EH22 1DN ☎ 0131 271 3667 ⌁ alan.turpie@midlothian.gov.uk

Lifelong Learning: Ms Annette Lang, Manager - Lifelong Learning & Employability, Fairfield House 8 Lothian Street, Dalkeith EH22 3ZG ☎ 0131 271 3923 ⌁ annette.lang@midlothian.gov.uk

Lighting: Mr Keith Slight, Lighting Manager, Midlothian House, Buccleuch Street, Dalkeith EH22 1DN ☎ 0131 561 5222 ⌁ keith.slight@midlothian.gov.uk

Lottery Funding, Charity and Voluntary: Mr Alasdair Mathers, Communities & Performance Manager, Fairfield House 8 Lothian Street, Dalkeith EH22 3ZG ☎ 0131 271 3438 ⌁ alasdair.mathers@midlothian.gov.uk

Member Services: Mr Kyle Clark-Hay, Democratic & Document Services Manager, Midlothian House, 40-46 Buccleuch Street, Dalkeith EH22 1DN ☎ 0131 270 5796 ⌁ kyle.clark-hay@midlothian.gov.uk

Parking: Mr Neil Dougall, Road Services Manager, Midlothian House, 40-46 Buccleuch Street, Dalkeith EH22 1DN ☎ 0131 561 5215 ⌁ neil.dougall@midlothian.gov.uk

Partnerships: Mr John Blair, Director - Resources, Midlothian House, Buccleuch Street, Dalkeith EH22 1DJ ☎ 0131 271 3102 ⌁ john.blair@midlothian.gov.uk

Personnel / HR: Mr Gary Fairley, Head of Finance & Integrated Service Support, Midlothian House, 40-46 Buccleuch Street, Dalkeith EH22 1DN ☎ 0131 271 3110 ⌁ gary.fairley@midlothian.gov.uk

Personnel / HR: Ms Marina Naylor, Organisational Development HR Manager, Midlothian House, 40-46 Buccleuch Street, Dalkeith EH22 1DN ☎ 0131 271 3988 ⌁ marina.naylor@midlothian.gov.uk

Planning: Mr Ian Johnson, Head of Communities & Economy, Fairfield House 8 Lothian Road, Dalkeith EH22 3ZQ ☎ 0131 271 3460 ⌁ ian.johnson@midlothian.gov.uk

Procurement: Mr Iain Johnston, Procurement Manager, Midlothian House, 40-46 Buccleuch Street, Dalkeith EH22 1DN ☎ 0131 561 5385 ⌁ iain.johnston@midlothian.gov.uk

Public Libraries: Ms Jane Milne, Customer Service Manager, Buccleuch House, 1 White Hart Street, Dalkeith EH22 1AE ☎ 0131 271 3971 ⌁ jane.milne@midlothian.gov.uk

Recycling & Waste Minimisation: Mr Phil Riddell, Business Manager - Waste & Fleet Services, Stobhill Depot, 40a Stobhill Road, Newtongrange, Dalkeith EH22 4NU ☎ 0131 561 5300 ⌁ phil.riddell@midlothian.gov.uk

Regeneration: Mr Alasdair Mathers, Communities & Performance Manager, Fairfield House 8 Lothian Street, Dalkeith EH22 3ZG ☎ 0131 271 3438 ⌁ alasdair.mathers@midlothian.gov.uk

Road Safety: Mr Neil Dougall, Road Services Manager, Midlothian House, 40-46 Buccleuch Street, Dalkeith EH22 1DN ☎ 0131 561 5215 ⌁ neil.dougall@midlothian.gov.uk

Social Services: Ms Eibhlin McHugh, Joint Director - Health & Social Care, Fairfield House 8 Lothian Road, Dalkeith EH22 3ZH ☎ 0131 271 3605 ⌁ eibhlin.mchugh@midlothian.gov.uk

Social Services (Adult): Ms Alison White, Head of Adult & Social Care, Fairfield House 8 Lothian Road, Dalkeith EH22 3ZH ☎ 0131 271 3605 ⌁ alison.white@midlothian.gov.uk

Social Services (Children): Ms Joan Tranent, Head of Children's Services, Fairfield House 8 Lothian Road, Dalkeith EH22 3ZG ☎ 0131 271 3721 ⌁ joan.tranent@midlothian.gov.uk

Staff Training: Ms Marina Naylor, Organisational Development HR Manager, Midlothian House, 40-46 Buccleuch Street, Dalkeith EH22 1DN ☎ 0131 271 3988 ⌁ marina.naylor@midlothian.gov.uk

Sustainable Communities: Mr Alasdair Mathers, Communities & Performance Manager, Fairfield House 8 Lothian Street, Dalkeith EH22 3ZG ☎ 0131 271 3438 ⌁ alasdair.mathers@midlothian.gov.uk

Sustainable Development: Mr Ian Johnson, Head of Communities & Economy, Fairfield House 8 Lothian Road, Dalkeith EH22 3ZQ ☎ 0131 271 3460 ⌁ ian.johnson@midlothian.gov.uk

Tourism: Mr John Beveridge, Economic Development Manager, Fairfield House 8 Lothian Street, Dalkeith EH22 3ZG ☎ 0131 271 3431 ⌁ john.beveridge@midlothian.gov.uk

Town Centre: Mr Garry Sheret, Head of Property & Facilities Management, Midlothian House, Buccleuch Street, Dalkeith EH22 1DN ☎ 0131 561 5249 ⌁ garry.sheret@midlothian.gov.uk

Traffic Management: Mr Neil Dougall, Road Services Manager, Midlothian House, 40-46 Buccleuch Street, Dalkeith EH22 1DN ☎ 0131 561 5215 ⌁ neil.dougall@midlothian.gov.uk

Transport: Mr Trevor Docherty, Business Manager - Travel & Fleet, Midlothian House, 40-46 Buccleuch Street, Dalkeith EH22 1DN ☎ 0131 561 5448 ⌁ trevor.docherty@midlothian.gov.uk

Transport Planner: Mr Neil Dougall, Road Services Manager, Midlothian House, 40-46 Buccleuch Street, Dalkeith EH22 1DN ☎ 0131 561 5215 ⌁ neil.dougall@midlothian.gov.uk

Waste Collection and Disposal: Mr Ricky Moffat, Head of Commercial Operations, Midlothian House, 40-46 Buccleuch Street, Dalkeith EH22 1DN ☎ 0131 561 5306 ⏚ ricky.moffat@midlothian.gov.uk

Waste Management: Mr Phil Riddell, Business Manager - Waste & Fleet Services, Stobhill Depot, 40a Stobhill Road, Newtongrange, Dalkeith EH22 4NU ☎ 0131 561 5300 ⏚ phil.riddell@midlothian.gov.uk

Children's Play Areas: Mr Justin Venton, Land & Countryside Manager, Midlothian House, 40-46 Buccleuch Street, Dalkeith EH22 1DN ☎ 0131 561 5220 ⏚ justin.venton@midlothian.gov.uk

COUNCILLORS

Leader of the Council: Johnstone, Catherine (SNP - Midlothian South)
catherine.johnstone@midlothian.gov.uk

Deputy Leader of the Council: Constable, Bob (SNP - Bonnyrigg)
bob.constable@midlothian.gov.uk

Baxter, Ian (SGP - Bonnyrigg)
ian.baxter@midlothian.gov.uk

Beattie, Lisa (SNP - Midlothian East)
lisa.beattie@midlothian.gov.uk

Bennett, Alex (LAB - Dalkeith)
alex.bennett@midlothian.gov.uk

Bryant, Jim (SNP - Dalkeith)
jim.bryant@midlothian.gov.uk

Coventry, Andrew (SNP - Midlothian West)
andrew.coventry@midlothian.gov.uk

de Vink, Peter (IND - Midlothian East)
peter.devink@midlothian.gov.uk

Imrie, Russell (LAB - Midlothian West)
russell.imrie@midlothian.gov.uk

Milligan, Derek (LAB - Bonnyrigg)
derek.milligan@midlothian.gov.uk

Montgomery, Adam (LAB - Penicuik)
adam.montgomery@midlothian.gov.uk

Muirhead, Jim (LAB - Midlothian South)
jim.muirhead@midlothian.gov.uk

Parry, Kelly (SNP - Midlothian West)
kelly.parry@midlothian.gov.uk

Pottinger, Bryan (LAB - Midlothian South)
bryan.pottinger@midlothian.gov.uk

Rosie, Derek (SNP - Penicuik)
derek.rosie@midlothian.gov.uk

Russell, Margot (LAB - Dalkeith)
margot.russell@midlothian.gov.uk

Wallace, Joe (SNP - Penicuik)
joe.wallace@midlothian.gov.uk

Young, Kenny (LAB - Midlothian East)
kenny.young@midlothian.gov.uk

POLITICAL COMPOSITION
LAB: 8, SNP: 8, IND: 1, SGP: 1

COMMITTEE CHAIRS
Licensing: Mr Bob Constable

Milton Keynes   U

Milton Keynes Council, Civic Offices, 1 Saxon Gate East, Milton Keynes MK9 3EJ
☎ 01908 691691 ⏚ info@milton-keynes.gov.uk
🖥 www.milton-keynes.gov.uk

FACTS AND FIGURES
Parliamentary Constituencies: Milton Keynes North, Milton Keynes South
EU Constituencies: South East
Election Frequency: Elections are by thirds

PRINCIPAL OFFICERS

Chief Executive: Ms Carole Mills, Chief Executive, Civic Offices, 1 Saxon Gate East, Milton Keynes MK9 3EJ ☎ 01908 252200 ⏚ carole.mills@milton-keynes.gov.uk

Senior Management: Mr Michael Bracey, Corporate Director - People, Saxon Court, 502 Avebury Boulevard, Milton Keynes MK9 3HS ☎ 01908 258041 ⏚ michael.bracey@milton-keynes.gov.uk

Senior Management: Ms Nicole Jones, Corporate Director - Resources, Saxon Court, 502 Avebury Blvd, Milton Keynes MK9 3HS ☎ 01908 252079 ⏚ nicole.jones@milton-keynes.gov.uk

Senior Management: Mr Duncan Sharkey, Corporate Director - Place, Civic Offices, 1 Saxon Gate East, Milton Keynes MK9 3EJ duncan.sharkey@milton-keynes.gov.uk

Access Officer / Social Services (Disability): Ms Amanda Dade, Head of Learning Disability Services, Tower Drive Centre, Tower Drive, Neath Hill, Milton Keynes MK14 6NA ☎ 01908 253042 ⏚ amanda.dade@milton-keynes.gov.uk

Architect, Building / Property Services: Mr Kamram Rashid, Interim Capital Programme Director, Saxon Court, 502 Avebury Boulevard, Milton Keynes MK9 3HS ☎ 01908 253375 ⏚ kamran.rashid@milton-keynes.gov.uk

Building Control: Mr Neil Allen, Head of Regulatory Services, Civic Offices, 1 Saxon Gate East, Milton Keynes MK9 3EJ ☎ 01908 252365 ⏚ neil.allen@milton-keynes.gov.uk

Children / Youth Services: Mr Michael Bracey, Corporate Director - People, Saxon Court, 502 Avebury Boulevard, Milton Keynes MK9 3HS ☎ 01908 258041 ⏚ michael.bracey@milton-keynes.gov.uk

Children / Youth Services: Ms Nicky Rayner, Service Director - Children & Families, Saxon Court, 502 Avebury Boulevard, Milton Keynes MK9 3HS ☎ 01908 253121 ⏚ nicky.rayner@milton-keynes.gov.uk

Civil Registration: Ms Yvette Medri, Registration Services Manager, Bracknell House, Aylesbury Street, Bletchley MK2 2BE ☎ 01908 372101 ⏚ yvette.medri@milton-keynes.gov.uk

MILTON KEYNES

PR / Communications: Ms Kellie Evans, Corporate Communications Manager, Civic Offices, 1 Saxon Gate East, Milton Keynes MK9 3EJ ☎ 01908 252413 🖰 kellie.evans@milton-keynes.gov.uk

Community Planning: Mr Bob Wilson, Development Plans Manager, Civic Offices, 1 Saxon Gate East, Milton Keynes MK9 3EJ ☎ 01908 252480 🖰 bob.wilson@milton-keynes.gov.uk

Community Safety: Mr Colin Wilderspin, Head of Community Safety, Civic Offices, 1 Saxon Gate East, Milton Keynes MK9 3EJ ☎ 01908 254533 🖰 colin.wilderspin@milton-keynes.gov.uk

Computer Management: Ms Hazel Lewis, Service Delivery Manager, Saxon Court, 502 Avebury Blvd, Milton Keynes MK9 3HS ☎ 01908 254117 🖰 hazel.lewis@milton-keynes.gov.uk

Consumer Protection and Trading Standards: Mr Neil Allen, Head of Regulatory Services, Civic Offices, 1 Saxon Gate East, Milton Keynes MK9 3EJ ☎ 01908 252365 🖰 neil.allen@milton-keynes.gov.uk

Contracts: Mr Mick Hancock, Assistant Director - Joint Commissioning & Contracts, Civic Offices, 1 Saxon Gate East, Milton Keynes MK9 3EJ ☎ 01908 257967 🖰 mick.hancock@milton-keynes.gov.uk

Contracts: Mr Paul White, Head of LGSS Procurement, Civic Offices, 1 Saxon Gate East, Milton Keynes MK9 3EJ ☎ 01604 236465 🖰 pwhite@northamptonshire.gov.uk

Corporate Services: Ms Nicole Jones, Corporate Director - Resources, Saxon Court, 502 Avebury Blvd, Milton Keynes MK9 3HS ☎ 01908 252079 🖰 nicole.jones@milton-keynes.gov.uk

Customer Service: Ms Rebecca Peck, Head of Customer Service, Civic Offices, 1 Saxon Gate East, Milton Keynes MK9 3EJ ☎ 01908 253930 🖰 rebecca.peck@milton-keynes.gov.uk

Direct Labour: Mr Tom Blackburn-Maze, Service Director - Public Realm Service Group, Civic Offices, 1 Saxon Gate East, Milton Keynes MK9 3EJ ☎ 01908 252213 🖰 tom.blackburn-maze@milton-keynes.gov.uk

Economic Development: Ms Pam Gosal, Corporate Head of Economic Development, Civic Offices, 1 Saxon Gate East, Milton Keynes MK9 3EJ ☎ 01908 252192 🖰 pam.gosal@milton-keynes.gov.uk

Education: Mr Michael Bracey, Corporate Director - People, Saxon Court, 502 Avebury Boulevard, Milton Keynes MK9 3HS ☎ 01908 258041 🖰 michael.bracey@milton-keynes.gov.uk

E-Government: Mr Paul Wheeler, ICT Contracts & Compliance Manager, Saxon Court, 502 Avebury Blvd, Milton Keynes MK9 3HS ☎ 01908 254148 🖰 paul.wheeler@milton-keynes.gov.uk

Electoral Registration: Mr Simon Heap, Committee Services & Scrutiny Manager, Civic Offices, 1 Saxon Gate East, Milton Keynes MK9 3EJ ☎ 01908 252567 🖰 simon.heap@milton-keynes.gov.uk

Emergency Planning: Mr Neil Allen, Head of Regulatory Services, Civic Offices, 1 Saxon Gate East, Milton Keynes MK9 3EJ ☎ 01908 252365 🖰 neil.allen@milton-keynes.gov.uk

Energy Management: Mr Jeremy Draper, Senior Practitioner, Civic Offices, 1 Saxon Gate East, Milton Keynes MK9 3EJ ☎ 01908 252652 🖰 jeremy.draper@milton-keynes.gov.uk

Environmental / Technical Services: Mr Tom Blackburn-Maze, Service Director - Public Realm Service Group, Civic Offices, 1 Saxon Gate East, Milton Keynes MK9 3EJ ☎ 01908 252213 🖰 tom.blackburn-maze@milton-keynes.gov.uk

Environmental Health: Mr Neil Allen, Head of Regulatory Services, Civic Offices, 1 Saxon Gate East, Milton Keynes MK9 3EJ ☎ 01908 252365 🖰 neil.allen@milton-keynes.gov.uk

Estates, Property & Valuation: Mr Kamram Rashid, Interim Capital Programme Director, Saxon Court, 502 Avebury Boulevard, Milton Keynes MK9 3HS ☎ 01908 253375 🖰 kamran.rashid@milton-keynes.gov.uk

Facilities: Ms Yvonne Mullens, Facilities Manager, Saxon Court, 502 Avebury Boulevard, Milton Keynes MK9 3HS ☎ 01908 253627 🖰 yvonne.mullens@milton-keynes.gov.uk

Finance: Ms Nicole Jones, Corporate Director - Resources, Saxon Court, 502 Avebury Blvd, Milton Keynes MK9 3HS ☎ 01908 252079 🖰 nicole.jones@milton-keynes.gov.uk

Grounds Maintenance: Mr Andy Hudson, Head of Environment & Waste, Civic Offices, 1 Saxon Gate East, Milton Keynes MK9 3EJ ☎ 01908 252577 🖰 andy.hudson@milton-keynes.gov.uk

Health and Safety: Mr Neil Allen, Head of Regulatory Services, Civic Offices, 1 Saxon Gate East, Milton Keynes MK9 3EJ ☎ 01908 252365 🖰 neil.allen@milton-keynes.gov.uk

Highways: Mr Tony Toynton, Interim Head of Highways, Synergy Park, Chesney Wold, Bleak Hall, Milton Keynes NK6 1LY ☎ 01908 252994 🖰 tony.toynton@milton-keynes.gov.uk

Home Energy Conservation: Mr Jeremy Draper, Senior Practitioner, Civic Offices, 1 Saxon Gate East, Milton Keynes MK9 3EJ ☎ 01908 252652 🖰 jeremy.draper@milton-keynes.gov.uk

Housing: Ms Jane Reed, Service Director - Housing & Communities, Civic Offices, 1 Saxon Gate East, Milton Keynes MK9 3EJ ☎ 01908 252782 🖰 jane.reed@milton-keynes.gov.uk

Housing Maintenance: Mr David Gleeson, Managing Director - YourMK, Civic Offices, 1 Saxon Gate East, Milton Keynes MK9 3EJ ☎ 01908 253945 🖰 david.gleeson@milton-keynes.gov.uk

Legal: Ms Sharon Bridglalsingh, Service Director - Legal & Democratic Services, Civic Offices, 1 Saxon Gate East, Milton Keynes MK9 3EJ ☎ 01908 252095 🖰 sharon.bridglalsingh@milton-keynes.gov.uk

Leisure and Cultural Services: Mr Paul Sanders, Assistant Director - Community Facilities Unit, Civic Offices, 1 Saxon Gate East, Milton Keynes MK9 3EJ ☎ 01908 253639 ☙ paul.sanders@milton-keynes.gov.uk

Licensing: Mr Neil Allen, Head of Regulatory Services, Civic Offices, 1 Saxon Gate East, Milton Keynes MK9 3EJ ☎ 01908 252365 ☙ neil.allen@milton-keynes.gov.uk

Lifelong Learning: Mr Michael Bracey, Corporate Director - People, Saxon Court, 502 Avebury Boulevard, Milton Keynes MK9 3HS ☎ 01908 258041 ☙ michael.bracey@milton-keynes.gov.uk

Lighting: Mr Chris Hales, Street Lighting Engineer, Saxon Court, 502 Avebury Boulevard, Milton Keynes MK6 1HS ☎ 01908 252825 ☙ chris.hales@milton-keynes.gov.uk

Lottery Funding, Charity and Voluntary: Mr Paul Sanders, Assistant Director - Community Facilities Unit, Saxon Court, 502 Avebury Boulevard, Milton Keynes MK6 1NE ☎ 01908 253639 ☙ paul.sanders@milton-keynes.gov.uk

Member Services: Mr Simon Heap, Committee Services & Scrutiny Manager, Civic Offices, 1 Saxon Gate East, Milton Keynes MK9 3EJ ☎ 01908 252567 ☙ simon.heap@milton-keynes.gov.uk

Parking: Ms Sara Bailey, Parking Strategy Manager, Civic Offices, 1 Saxon Gate East, Milton Keynes MK9 3EJ ☎ 01908 252198 ☙ sara.bailey@milton-keynes.gov.uk

Partnerships: Ms Sarah Gonsalves, Head of Policy & Performance, Civic Offices, 1 Saxon Gate East, Milton Keynes MK9 3EJ ☎ 01908 253099 ☙ sarah.gonsalves@milton-keynes.gov.uk

Personnel / HR: Ms Marie Devlin-Hogg, Head of HR & Strategy, Saxon Court, 502 Avebury Boulevard, Milton Keynes MK9 3HS ☎ 01908 254278 ☙ marie.devlin-hogg@milton-keynes.gov.uk

Planning: Mr David Hackford, Interim Assistant Director - Planning & Transport, Civic Offices, 1 Saxon Gate East, Milton Keynes MK9 3EJ ☎ 01908 252492 ☙ david.hackford@milton-keynes.gov.uk

Procurement: Mr Paul White, Head of LGSS Procurement, Civic Offices, 1 Saxon Gate East, Milton Keynes MK9 3EJ ☎ 01604 236465 ☙ pwhite@northamptonshire.gov.uk

Public Libraries: Ms Helen Boult, Library Services Manager, CMK Library, 555 Silbury Blvd, Milton Keynes MK9 3HL ☎ 01908 254068 ☙ helen.boult@milton-keynes.gov.uk

Recycling & Waste Minimisation: Mr Andy Hudson, Head of Environment & Waste, Civic Offices, 1 Saxon Gate East, Milton Keynes MK9 3EJ ☎ 01908 252577 ☙ andy.hudson@milton-keynes.gov.uk

Regeneration: Ms Kathryn Eames, Head of Regeneration, Cedar House, Woodlands Business Park, Milton Keynes MK14 6EY ☎ 01908 254788 ☙ kathryn.eames@milton-keynes.gov.uk

Regeneration: Mr Duncan Sharkey, Corporate Director - Place, Civic Offices, 1 Saxon Gate East, Milton Keynes MK9 3EJ ☙ duncan.sharkey@milton-keynes.gov.uk

Road Safety: Mr Kevan Paradine, Road Safety Team Leader, Civic Offices, 1 Saxon Gate East, Milton Keynes MK9 3EJ ☎ 01908 252036 ☙ kevan.paradine@milton-keynes.gov.uk

Social Services: Mr Michael Bracey, Corporate Director - People, Saxon Court, 502 Avebury Boulevard, Milton Keynes MK9 3HS ☎ 01908 258041 ☙ michael.bracey@milton-keynes.gov.uk

Social Services (Adult): Ms Victoria Collins, Assistant Director - Adult Social Care, Saxon Court, 502 Avebury Boulevard, Milton Keynes MK9 3HS ☎ 01908 253508 ☙ victoria.collins@milton-keynes.gov.uk

Social Services (Children): Ms Nicky Rayner, Service Director - Children & Families, Saxon Court, 502 Avebury Boulevard, Milton Keynes MK9 3HS ☎ 01908 253121 ☙ nicky.rayner@milton-keynes.gov.uk

Public Health: Ms Muriel Scott, Director - Public Health, Saxon Court, 502 Avebury Boulevard, Milton Keynes MK9 3HS ☎ 0300 300 5616 ☙ muriel.scott@centralbedfordshire.gov.uk

Staff Training: Ms Marie Devlin-Hogg, Head of HR & Strategy, Saxon Court, 502 Avebury Boulevard, Milton Keynes MK9 3HS ☎ 01908 254278 ☙ marie.devlin-hogg@milton-keynes.gov.uk

Sustainable Communities: Mr Geoff Snelson, Director - Strategy, Civic Offices, 1 Saxon Gate East, Milton Keynes MK9 3EJ ☎ 01908 252665 ☙ geoff.snelson@milton-keynes.gov.uk

Sustainable Development: Mr Brett Leahy, Head of Development Management, Civic Offices, 1 Saxon Gate East, Milton Keynes MK9 3EJ ☎ 01908 252609 ☙ brett.leahy@milton-keynes.gov.uk

Traffic Management: Mr Tony Toynton, Interim Head of Highways, Synergy Park, Chesney Wold, Bleak Hall, Milton Keynes NK6 1LY ☎ 01908 252994 ☙ tony.toynton@milton-keynes.gov.uk

Transport: Mr Andrew Coleman, Passenger Transport Manager, Civic Offices, 1 Saxon Gate East, Milton Keynes MK9 3EJ ☎ 01908 254739 ☙ andrew.coleman@milton-keynes.gov.uk

Transport: Mr Andrew Moss, Interim Head of Transportation Services, Civic Offices, 1 Saxon Gate East, Milton Keynes MK9 3EJ ☎ 01175 894523 ☙ andrew.moss@milton-keynes.gov.uk

Transport Planner: Mr David Lawson, Transport Policy & Programme Manager, Civic Offices, 1 Saxon Gate East, Milton Keynes MK9 3EJ ☎ 01908 252510 ☙ david.lawson@milton-keynes.gov.uk

Waste Collection and Disposal: Mr Andy Hudson, Head of Environment & Waste, Civic Offices, 1 Saxon Gate East, Milton Keynes MK9 3EJ ☎ 01908 252577 ☙ andy.hudson@milton-keynes.gov.uk

Waste Management: Mr Andy Hudson, Head of Environment & Waste, Civic Offices, 1 Saxon Gate East, Milton Keynes MK9 3EJ ☎ 01908 252577 ☙ andy.hudson@milton-keynes.gov.uk

MILTON KEYNES

COUNCILLORS

Leader of the Council: Marland, Peter (LAB - Wolverton)
peter.marland@milton-keynes.gov.uk

Alexander, Paul (LD - Newport Pagnell South)
paul.alexander@milton-keynes.gov.uk

Bald, Edith (CON - Tattenhoe)
edith.bald@milton-keynes.gov.uk

Betteley, Sarah (LAB - Central Milton Keynes)
sarah.betteley@milton-keynes.gov.uk

Bint, John (CON - Broughton)
john.bint@milton-keynes.gov.uk

Brackenbury, Ric (LD - Campbell Park & Old Woughton)
ric.brackenbury@milton-keynes.gov.uk

Bradburn, Marie (LD - Bradwell)

Bradburn, Robin (LD - Bradwell)
robin.bradburn@milton-keynes.gov.uk

Brunning, Denise (CON - Stony Stratford)
denise.brunning@milton-keynes.gov.uk

Buckley, Andrew (CON - Monkston)
andrew.buckley@milton-keynes.gov.uk

Burke, Margaret (LAB - Stantonbury)
margaret.burke@milton-keynes.gov.uk

Cannon, Peter (LD - Shenley Brook End)
peter.cannon@milton-keynes.gov.uk

Clancy, Ann (CON - Bletchley Park)
ann.clancy@milton-keynes.gov.uk

Clifton, Matthew (LAB - Loughton & Shenley)
matthew.clifton@milton-keynes.gov.uk

Coventry, Stephen (LAB - Woughton & Fishermead)
cllrstevencoventry@talktalk.net

Crooks, Samuel (LD - Broughton)
sam.crooks@milton-keynes.gov.uk

Dransfield, Andrew (CON - Loughton & Shenley)
andy.dransfield@milton-keynes.gov.uk

Eastman, Derek (LD - Newport Pagnell South)
derek.eastman@milton-keynes.gov.uk

Exon, Robert (LD - Bradwell)
robert.exon@milton-keynes.gov.uk

Ferrans, Jennie (LD - Monkston)
jenni.ferans@milton-keynes.gov.uk

Ganatra, Hiten (CON - Shenley Brook End)
hiten.ganatra@milton-keynes.gov.uk

Geaney, Maggie (CON - Bletchley West)
maggie.geaney@milton-keynes.gov.uk

Geary, Peter (CON - Olney)
peter.geary@milton-keynes.gov.uk

Geary, Andrew (CON - Newport Pagnell North & Hanslope)
andrew.geary@milton-keynes.gov.uk

Gifford, Liz (LAB - Stony Stratford)
liz.gifford@milton-keynes.gov.uk

Gowans, Martin (LAB - Bletchley East)
martin.gowans@milton-keynes.gov.uk

Green, Jeanette (CON - Newport Pagnell North & Hanslope)
jeanette.green@milton-keynes.gov.uk

Hopkins, Victoria (CON - Danesborough & Walton)
victoria.hopkins@milton-keynes.gov.uk

Hopkins, David (CON - Danesborough & Walton)
david.hopkins@milton-keynes.gov.uk

Hosking, David (CON - Olney)
david.hosking@milton-keynes.gov.uk

Jenkins, Alice (CON - Danesborough & Walton)
alice.jenkins@milton-keynes.gov.uk

Khan, Mohammed (LAB - Bletchley East)
mohammed.khan@milton-keynes.gov.uk

Legg, Mick (LAB - Bletchley West)
michael.legg@yahoo.com

Long, Nigel (LAB - Bletchley West)
nigel.long@milton-keynes.gov.uk

McCall, Douglas (LD - Newport Pagnell South)
douglas.mccall@milton-keynes.gov.uk

McCall, Isobel (LD - Campbell Park & Old Woughton)
isobel.mccall@milton-keynes.gov.uk

McDonald, Peter (CON - Campbell Park & Old Woughton)
peter.mcdonald@milton-keynes.gov.uk

McKenzie, Gladstone (LAB - Bletchley Park)
gladstone.mckenzie@milton-keynes.gov.uk

McLean, Keith (CON - Olney)
keith.mclean@milton-keynes.gov.uk

McPake, Vanessa (LD - Monkston)
vanessa.mcpake@milton-keynes.gov.uk

Middleton, Robert (LAB - Wolverton)
robert.middleton@milton-keynes.gov.uk

Miles, Norman (LAB - Wolverton)
norman.miles@milton-keynes.gov.uk

Morla, Geetha (CON - Tattenhoe)
geetha.morla@milton-keynes.gov.uk

Morris, Catriona (CON - Broughton)
catriona.morris@milton-keynes.gov.uk

Nolan, Zoe (LAB - Loughton & Shenley)
zoe.nolan@milton-keynes.gov.uk

O'Neill, Hannah (LAB - Woughton & Fishermead)
hannah.o'neill@milton-keynes.gov.uk

Patey-Smith, Lynn (CON - Newport Pagnell North & Hanslope)
lynn.patey-smith@milton-keynes.gov.uk

Petchey, Martin (LAB - Stantonbury)

Small, Gerald (CON - Tattenhoe)
gerald.small@milton-keynes.gov.uk

Wales, Elaine (LAB - Bletchley Park)

Walker, Alex (CON - Stantonbury)
alex.walker@milton-keynes.gov.uk

Wallis, Pauline (LAB - Central Milton Keynes)
pauline.wallis@milton-keynes.gov.uk

Webb, Alan (LAB - Bletchley East)
alan.webb@milton-keynes.gov.uk

Williams, Chris (LD - Shenley Brook End)
chris.williams1@milton-keynes.gov.uk

Williams, Paul (LAB - Central Milton Keynes)
paul.williams@milton-keynes.gov.uk

Wilson, Charlie (LAB - Stony Stratford)

Wilson, Kevin (LAB - Woughton & Fishermead)
kevin.wilson@milton-keynes.gov.uk

POLITICAL COMPOSITION
CON: 22, LAB: 22, LD: 13

COMMITTEE CHAIRS

Audit: Mr Peter Geary

Children & Young People: Mr Samuel Crooks

Development Control: Mr Andrew Geary

Economy, Growth & Regeneration: Ms Isobel McCall

Environment & Transport: Mr Peter Geary

Health & Adult Social Care: Ms Alice Jenkins

Health & Wellbeing: Mr Peter Marland

Housing & Community: Mr Chris Williams

Licensing: Ms Catriona Morris

Mole Valley   D

Mole Valley District Council, Pippbrook, Dorking RH4 1SJ
☎ 01306 885001 🖨 01306 876821 🖂 info@molevalley.gov.uk
🖥 www.molevalley.gov.uk

FACTS AND FIGURES
Parliamentary Constituencies: Mole Valley
EU Constituencies: South East
Election Frequency: Elections are by thirds

PRINCIPAL OFFICERS

Chief Executive: Ms Yvonne Rees, Chief Executive (Mole Valley)
& Strategic Director - Customers & Communities (Surrey CC),
Pippbrook, Dorking RH4 1SJ ☎ 01306 879101
🖂 yvonne.rees@molevalley.gov.uk

Deputy Chief Executive: Mr Nick Gray, Deputy Chief Executive,
Pippbrook, Dorking RH4 1SJ ☎ 01306 879307
🖂 nick.gray@molevalley.gov.uk

Senior Management: Mr Richard Burrows, Corporate Head of
Service, Pippbrook, Dorking RH4 1SJ ☎ 01306 879156
🖂 richard.burrows@molevalley.gov.uk

Senior Management: Mrs Angela Griffiths, Corporate Head of
Service, Pippbrook, Dorking RH4 1SJ ☎ 01306 879133
🖂 angela.griffiths@molevalley.gov.uk

Senior Management: Mr Graeme Kane, Corporate Head of
Service, Pippbrook, Dorking RH4 1SJ ☎ 01306 870622
🖂 graeme.kane@molevalley.gov.uk

Senior Management: Mrs Rachel O'Reilly, Corporate Head of
Service, Pippbrook, Dorking RH4 1SJ ☎ 01306 879358
🖂 rachel.o'reilly@molevalley.gov.uk

Senior Management: Mr Steve Ruddy, Corporate Head of
Service, Pippbrook, Dorking RH4 1SJ ☎ 01306 879225
🖂 steve.ruddy@molevalley.gov.uk

Senior Management: Mr Jack Straw, Interim Corporate Head of
Service, Pippbrook, Dorking RH4 1SJ ☎ 01306 879246
🖂 jack.straw@molevalley.gov.uk

Architect, Building / Property Services: Mr Paul Brooks,
Property Manager, Pippbrook, Dorking RH4 1SJ ☎ 01306 879105
🖂 paul.brooks@molevalley.gov.uk

Building Control: Mr Andrew Winton, Building Control Manager,
Pippbrook, Dorking RH4 1SJ ☎ 01306 879252
🖂 andrew.winton@molevalley.gov.uk

PR / Communications: Mrs Louise Bircher, Customer Service &
Communications Manager, Pippbrook, Dorking RH4 1SJ
☎ 01306 879155 🖂 louise.bircher@molevalley.gov.uk

Community Safety: Mr Patrick McCord, Partnerships &
Development Manager, Pippbrook, Dorking RH4 1SJ
☎ 01306 870610 🖂 patrick.mccord@molevalley.gov.uk

Computer Management: Mr Robert Thomas, Head of
Information Technology, Pippbrook, Dorking RH4 1SJ
☎ 01306 879171 🖂 bob.thomas@molevalley.gov.uk

Contracts: Mr Chris Harris, Legal Services Manager, Pippbrook,
Dorking RH4 1SJ ☎ 01306 879130
🖂 christopher.harris@molevalley.gov.uk

Customer Service: Mrs Louise Bircher, Customer Service &
Communications Manager, Pippbrook, Dorking RH4 1SJ
☎ 01306 879155 🖂 louise.bircher@molevalley.gov.uk

Economic Development: Mr Robert Jolley, Economic
Development Manager, Pippbrook, Dorking RH4 1SJ
☎ 01306 879202 🖂 robert.jolley@molevalley.gov.uk

Electoral Registration: Mrs Arabella Davies, Democratic Services
Manager, Pippbrook, Dorking RH4 1SJ ☎ 01306 879137
🖂 arabella.davies@molevalley.gov.uk

Emergency Planning: Mrs Arabella Davies, Democratic Services
Manager, Pippbrook, Dorking RH4 1SJ ☎ 01306 879137
🖂 arabella.davies@molevalley.gov.uk

Environmental Health: Mr Richard Haddad, Environmental
Health Manager, Pippbrook, Dorking RH4 1SJ ☎ 01306 879226
🖂 richard.haddad@molevalley.gov.uk

Estates, Property & Valuation: Mr Paul Brooks, Property
Manager, Pippbrook, Dorking RH4 1SJ ☎ 01306 879105
🖂 paul.brooks@molevalley.gov.uk

Facilities: Mr Jason Hughes, Facilities & Engineering Manager,
Pippbrook, Dorking RH4 1SJ ☎ 01306 879184
🖂 jason.hughes@molevalley.gov.uk

Finance: Mr Nick Gray, Deputy Chief Executive, Pippbrook,
Dorking RH4 1SJ ☎ 01306 879307 🖂 nick.gray@molevalley.gov.uk

Grounds Maintenance: Mr Paul Anderson, Environmental
Services Manager, Pippbrook, Dorking RH4 1SJ ☎ 01306 870613
🖂 paul.anderson@molevalley.gov.uk

MOLE VALLEY

Health and Safety: Mrs Angela Griffiths, Corporate Head of Service, Pippbrook, Dorking RH4 1SJ ☎ 01306 879133 ✆ angela.griffiths@molevalley.gov.uk

Housing: Ms Alison Wilks, Strategic Housing Manager, Pippbrook, Dorking RH4 1SJ ☎ 01306 870645 ✆ alison.wilks@molevalley.gov.uk

Legal: Mr Chris Harris, Legal Services Manager, Pippbrook, Dorking RH4 1SJ ☎ 01306 879130 ✆ christopher.harris@molevalley.gov.uk

Leisure and Cultural Services: Mr Patrick McCord, Partnerships & Development Manager, Pippbrook, Dorking RH4 1SJ ☎ 01306 870610 ✆ patrick.mccord@molevalley.gov.uk

Licensing: Mr John Pleasance, Senior Licensing Officer, Pippbrook, Dorking RH4 1SJ ☎ 01306 879351 ✆ john.pleasance@molevalley.gov.uk

Member Services: Mrs Arabella Davies, Democratic Services Manager, Pippbrook, Dorking RH4 1SJ ☎ 01306 879137 ✆ arabella.davies@molevalley.gov.uk

Parking: Mr Paul Anderson, Environmental Services Manager, Pippbrook, Dorking RH4 1SJ ☎ 01306 870613 ✆ paul.anderson@molevalley.gov.uk

Partnerships: Mr Patrick McCord, Partnerships & Development Manager, Pippbrook, Dorking RH4 1SJ ☎ 01306 870610 ✆ patrick.mccord@molevalley.gov.uk

Personnel / HR: Ms Kate Ivackovic, Strategic HR & OD Manager, Pippbrook, Dorking RH4 1SJ ☎ 01306 879360 ✆ kate.ivackovic@molevalley.gov.uk

Planning: Mr Jack Straw, Interim Corporate Head of Service, Pippbrook, Dorking RH4 1SJ ☎ 01306 879246 ✆ jack.straw@molevalley.gov.uk

Procurement: Mrs Ellie Guinan, Procurement Officer, Pippbrook, Dorking RH4 1SJ ☎ 01306 870617 ✆ ellie.guinan@molevalley.gov.uk

Recycling & Waste Minimisation: Mr Josh Lambe, Recycling & Sustainability Manager, Pippbrook, Dorking RH4 1SJ ☎ 01306 879118 ✆ josh.lambe@molevalley.gov.uk

Staff Training: Ms Kate Ivackovic, Strategic HR & OD Manager, Pippbrook, Dorking RH4 1SJ ☎ 01306 879360 ✆ kate.ivackovic@molevalley.gov.uk

Street Scene: Mr Rod Shaw, Principal Conservation Officer, Pippbrook, Dorking RH4 1SJ ☎ 01306 879247 ✆ rod.shaw@molevalley.gov.uk

Sustainable Development: Mr Jack Straw, Interim Corporate Head of Service, Pippbrook, Dorking RH4 1SJ ☎ 01306 879246 ✆ jack.straw@molevalley.gov.uk

Waste Collection and Disposal: Mr Paul Anderson, Environmental Services Manager, Pippbrook, Dorking RH4 1SJ ☎ 01306 870613 ✆ paul.anderson@molevalley.gov.uk

Waste Management: Mr Paul Anderson, Environmental Services Manager, Pippbrook, Dorking RH4 1SJ ☎ 01306 870613 ✆ paul.anderson@molevalley.gov.uk

Children's Play Areas: Mr Paul Anderson, Environmental Services Manager, Pippbrook, Dorking RH4 1SJ ☎ 01306 870613 ✆ paul.anderson@molevalley.gov.uk

COUNCILLORS

Leader of the Council: Michael, Vivienne (CON - Okewood)
cllr.michael@molevalley.gov.uk

Deputy Leader of the Council: Yarwood, Charles (CON - Charlwood)
cllr.yarwood@molevalley.gov.uk

Ashton, Tim (CON - Leatherhead South)
cllr.ashton@molevalley.gov.uk

Botting, Lucy (CON - Bookham North)
cllr.botting@molevalley.gov.uk

Brooks, Lynne (CON - Fetcham East)
cllr.lynnebrooks@molevalley.gov.uk

Chandler, John (NP - Bookham South)
cllr.chandler@molevalley.gov.uk

Cooksey, Stephen (LD - Dorking South)
cllr.cooksey@molevalley.gov.uk

Cooksey, Margaret (LD - Dorking South)
cllr.margaretcooksey@molevalley.gov.uk

Cooper, Mary (IND - Ashtead Village)
cllr.cooper@molevalley.gov.uk

Crome, Joe (LD - Leatherhead North)
cllr.crome@molevalley.gov.uk

Dickson, Rosemary (CON - Leatherhead South)
cllr.dickson@molevalley.gov.uk

Draper, David (LD - Dorking North)
cllr.draper@molevalley.gov.uk

Edge, Simon (CON - Bookham South)
cllr.edge@molevalley.gov.uk

Elderton, Paul (LD - Dorking North)
paul.elderton@virgin.net

Friend, James (CON - Westcott)
cllr.friend@molevalley.gov.uk

Haque, Raj (LD - Fetcham West)
cllr.haque@molevalley.gov.uk

Harper, David (IND - Ashtead Park)
cllr.harper@molevalley.gov.uk

Hawksworth, David (IND - Ashtead Common)
cllr.hawksworth@molevalley.gov.uk

Huggins, Mary (CON - Capel, Leigh & Newdigate)
cllr.huggins@molevalley.gov.uk

Hunt, Chris (CON - Ashtead Village)
cllr.hunt@molevalley.gov.uk

Huseyin, Metin (CON - Bookham North)
cllr.huseyin@molevalley.gov.uk

Irvine, Duncan (CON - Mickleham, Westhumble & Pixham)
councillor.irvine@molevalley.gov.uk

Jones, Howard (CON - Leatherhead North)
cllr.jones@molevalley.gov.uk

Kendrick, Bridget (LD - Leatherhead North)
cllr.kendrick@molevalley.gov.uk

Kennedy, Paul (LD - Fetcham West)
cllr.kennedy@molevalley.gov.uk

Ladell, Malcolm (CON - Box Hill & Headley)
councillor.ladell@molevalley.gov.uk

Ling, Simon (IND - Ashtead Village)
cllr.ling@molevalley.gov.uk

Loretto, Tim (LD - Dorking South)
cllr.loretto@molevalley.gov.uk

Malcolmson, Claire (LD - Holmwoods)
cllr.malcolmson@molevalley.gov.uk

Mir, David (CON - Leith Hill)
cllr.mir@molevalley.gov.uk

Monkman, Wayne (LD - Holmwoods)
cllr.monkman@molevalley.gov.uk

Muggeridge, John (CON - Brockham, Betchwood & Buckland)
cllr.muggeridge@molevalley.gov.uk

Newman, Paul (CON - Bookham North)
cllr.newman@molevalley.gov.uk

Osborne-Patterson, Corinna (CON - Capel, Leigh & Newdigate)
cllr.osborne-patterson@molevalley.gov.uk

Patel, Jatin (CON - Bookham South)
cllr.patel@molevalley.gov.uk

Potter, Paul (LD - Brockham, Betchworth & Buckland)
cllr.potter@molevalley.gov.uk

Seed, Sarah (CON - Fetcham East)
cllr.seed@molevalley.gov.uk

Stanyard, Peter (IND - Ashtead Park)
cllr.stanyard@molevalley.gov.uk

Watson, Michelle (CON - Beare Green)
cllr.watson@molevalley.gov.uk

Wellman, Clayton (LD - Holmwoods) cllr.wellman@molevalley.gov.uk

Wiltshire, Patricia (IND - Ashtead Common)
cllr.wiltshire@molevalley.gov.uk

POLITICAL COMPOSITION
CON: 21, LD: 13, IND: 6, NP: 1

COMMITTEE CHAIRS

Audit: Mr Paul Kennedy

Development Control: Mr Chris Hunt

Licensing: Mr John Chandler

Monmouthshire   W

Monmouthshire County Council, County Hall, Rhadyr, Usk
NP15 1GA
☎ 01633 644644 ⌃ contact@monmouthshire.gov.uk
🖥 www.monmouthshire.gov.uk

FACTS AND FIGURES
Parliamentary Constituencies: Monmouth
EU Constituencies: Wales
Election Frequency: Elections are of whole council

PRINCIPAL OFFICERS

Chief Executive: Mr Paul Matthews, Chief Executive, County Hall, Rhadyr, Usk NP15 1GA ☎ 01633 644644
⌃ paulmatthews@monmouthshire.gov.uk

Deputy Chief Executive: Ms Kellie Beirne, Deputy Chief Executive & Chief Officer - Innovation & Enterprise, County Hall, Rhadyr, Usk NP15 1GA ☎ 01633 644468
⌃ kelliebeirne@monmouthshire.gov.uk

Senior Management: Ms Kellie Beirne, Deputy Chief Executive & Chief Officer - Innovation & Enterprise, County Hall, Rhadyr, Usk NP15 1GA ☎ 01633 644468 ⌃ kelliebeirne@monmouthshire.gov.uk

Senior Management: Mr Peter Davies, Chief Officer - Resources, County Hall, Rhadyr, Usk NP15 1GA ☎ 01633 644644
⌃ peterdavies@monmouthshire.gov.uk

Senior Management: Ms Tracey Harry, Head - HR, People & Information Governance, County Hall, Rhadyr, Usk NP15 1GA
☎ 01633 644644 ⌃ traceyharry@monmouthshire.gov.uk

Senior Management: Mr Roger Hoggins, Head - Operations, County Hall, Rhadyr, Usk NP15 1GA ☎ 01633 644134
⌃ rogerhoggins@monmouthshire.gov.uk

Senior Management: Ms Claire Marchant, Chief Officer - Health & Social Care, County Hall, Rhadyr, Usk NP15 1GA ☎ 01633 644601
⌃ clairemarchant@monmouthshire.gov.uk

Senior Management: Ms Sarah McGuiness, Chief Officer - Children & Young People, County Hall, Rhadyr, Usk NP15 1GA
☎ 01633 644644 ⌃ sarahmcguiness@monmouthshire.gov.uk

Senior Management: Mr Will McLean, Head - Governance, Engagement & Improvement, County Hall, Rhadyr, Usk NP15 1GA

Senior Management: Mrs Joy Robson, Head - Finance & Section 151 Officer, County Hall, Rhadyr, Usk NP15 1GA
☎ 01633 644644 ⌃ joyrobson@monmouthshire.gov.uk

Access Officer / Social Services (Disability): Mr Alan Burkitt, Policy Officer - Equalities & Welsh Language, County Hall, Rhadyr, Usk NP15 1GA ☎ 01633 644644
⌃ alanburkitt@monmouthshire.gov.uk

Architect, Building / Property Services: Mr Rob O'Dwyer, Head of Property Services & Facilities Manager, Innovation House, Wales 1 Business Park, Newport Road, Magor, Caldicot NP26 3DG
☎ 01633 644452 ⌃ roberto'dwyer@monmouthshire.gov.uk

Building Control: Mr Philip Thomas, Development Control Manager, County Hall, Rhadyr, Usk NP15 1GA ☎ 01633 644644
⌃ philipthomas@monmouthshire.gov.uk

Children / Youth Services: Ms Jane Rodgers, Head - Children's Services, County Hall, Rhadyr, Usk NP15 1GA ☎ 01633 644571
⌃ janerodgers@monmouthshire.gov.uk

Civil Registration: Ms Sally Morgan, Registration Service Manager, County Hall, Rhadyr, Usk NP15 1GA ☎ 01873 735468
⌃ sallymorgan@monmouthshire.gov.uk

PR / Communications: Ms Abigail le Barton, Communications & Engagement Manager, County Hall, Rhadyr, Usk NP15 1GA ☎ 01633 644644 ⌂ abigaillebarton@monmouthshire.gov.uk

Community Planning: Ms Deb Hill-Howells, Head - Community Led Delivery, County Hall, Rhadyr, Usk NP15 1GA ☎ 01633 644281 ⌂ debrahill-howells@monmouthshire.gov.uk

Computer Management: Ms Sian Hayward, Digital & Technology Manager, County Hall, Rhadyr, Usk NP15 1GA ☎ 01633 644309 ⌂ sianhayward@monmouthshire.gov.uk

Contracts: Mr Roger Hoggins, Head - Operations, County Hall, Rhadyr, Usk NP15 1GA ☎ 01633 644134 ⌂ rogerhoggins@monmouthshire.gov.uk

Direct Labour: Mr Roger Hoggins, Head - Operations, County Hall, Rhadyr, Usk NP15 1GA ☎ 01633 644134 ⌂ rogerhoggins@monmouthshire.gov.uk

Economic Development: Ms Cath Fallon, Head - Economy & Enterprise, County Hall, Rhadyr, Usk NP15 1GA ☎ 01633 748316 ⌂ cathfallon@monmouthshire.gov.uk

Education: Ms Sarah McGuiness, Chief Officer - Children & Young People, County Hall, Rhadyr, Usk NP15 1GA ☎ 01633 644644 ⌂ sarahmcguiness@monmouthshire.gov.uk

Energy Management: Mr Roger Hoggins, Head - Operations, County Hall, Rhadyr, Usk NP15 1GA ☎ 01633 644134 ⌂ rogerhoggins@monmouthshire.gov.uk

Events Manager: Mr Dan Davies, Enterprise Co-ordinator, County Hall, Rhadyr, Usk NP15 1GA ☎ 01633 644044 ⌂ dandavies@monmouthshire.gov.uk

Facilities: Mr Rob O'Dwyer, Head of Property Services & Facilities Manager, County Hall, Rhadyr, Usk NP15 1GA ☎ 01633 644452 ⌂ roberto'dwyer@monmouthshire.gov.uk

Finance: Mrs Joy Robson, Head - Finance & Section 151 Officer, County Hall, Rhadyr, Usk NP15 1GA ☎ 01633 644644 ⌂ joyrobson@monmouthshire.gov.uk

Fleet Management: Ms Deb Jackson, Transport Manager, County Hall, Rhadyr, Usk NP15 1GA ☎ 01291 691312 ⌂ debjackson@monmouthshire.gov.uk

Grounds Maintenance: Mr Roger Hoggins, Head - Operations, County Hall, Rhadyr, Usk NP15 1GA ☎ 01633 644134 ⌂ rogerhoggins@monmouthshire.gov.uk

Health and Safety: Mr Laurence Dawkins, Safety Manager, County Hall, Rhadyr, Usk NP15 1GA ☎ 01633 644196 ⌂ laurencedawkins@monmouthshire.gov.uk

Home Energy Conservation: Mr John Parfitt, Housing Renewals & Careline Manager, County Hall, Rhadyr, Usk NP15 1GA ☎ 01633 644681 ⌂ johnparfitt@monmouthshire.gov.uk

Housing: Mr Ian Bakewell, Housing & Regeneration Manager, County Hall, Rhadyr, Usk NP15 1GA ☎ 01633 644479 ⌂ ian.bakewell@monmouthshire.gov.uk

Housing Maintenance: Mr Ian Bakewell, Housing & Regeneration Manager, County Hall, Rhadyr, Usk NP15 1GA ☎ 01633 644479 ⌂ ian.bakewell@monmouthshire.gov.uk

Legal: Mr Rob Tranter, Monitoring Officer / Head of Legal Services, County Hall, Rhadyr, Usk NP15 1GA ☎ 01633 644064 ⌂ robtranter@monmouthshire.gov.uk

Leisure and Cultural Services: Mr Ian Saunders, Head of Tourism, Leisure & Culture, County Hall, Rhadyr, Usk NP15 1GA ☎ 01633 644499 ⌂ iansaunders@monmouthshire.gov.uk

Licensing: Ms Linda O'Gorman, Principal Licensing Officer, County Hall, Rhadyr, Usk NP15 1GA ☎ 01633 644214 ⌂ lindaogorman@monmouthshire.gov.uk

Lifelong Learning: Ms Sarah McGuiness, Chief Officer - Children & Young People, County Hall, Rhadyr, Usk NP15 1GA ☎ 01633 644644 ⌂ sarahmcguiness@monmouthshire.gov.uk

Member Services: Mr John Pearson, Local Democracy Manager, County Hall, Rhadyr, Usk NP15 1GA ☎ 01633 644978 ⌂ johnpearson@monmouthshire.gov.uk

Parking: Mr Roger Hoggins, Head - Operations, County Hall, Rhadyr, Usk NP15 1GA ☎ 01633 644134 ⌂ rogerhoggins@monmouthshire.gov.uk

Personnel / HR: Ms Tracey Harry, Head - HR, People & Information Governance, County Hall, Rhadyr, Usk NP15 1GA ☎ 01633 644644 ⌂ traceyharry@monmouthshire.gov.uk

Public Libraries: Ms Ann Jones, Libraries, Museums & Art Manager, County Hall, Rhadyr, Usk NP15 1GA ⌂ annjones@monmouthshire.gov.uk

Recycling & Waste Minimisation: Ms Rachel Jowitt, Head - Waste & Street Services, County Hall, Rhadyr, Usk NP15 1GA ☎ 01633 748326 ⌂ racheljowitt@monmouthshire.gov.uk

Regeneration: Ms Kellie Beirne, Deputy Chief Executive & Chief Officer - Innovation & Enterprise, County Hall, Rhadyr, Usk NP15 1GA ☎ 01633 644468 ⌂ kelliebeirne@monmouthshire.gov.uk

Road Safety: Mr Paul Keeble, Traffic & Network Manager, County Hall, Rhadyr, Usk NP15 1GA ☎ 01633 644644 ⌂ paulkeeble@monmouthshire.gov.uk

Social Services: Ms Claire Marchant, Chief Officer - Health & Social Care, County Hall, Rhadyr, Usk NP15 1GA ☎ 01633 644601 ⌂ clairemarchant@monmouthshire.gov.uk

Social Services (Adult): Ms Julie Boothroyd, Head - Adult Services, County Hall, Rhadyr, Usk NP15 1GA ☎ 01633 644601 ⌂ julieboothroyd@monmouthshire.gov.uk

Social Services (Children): Ms Jane Rodgers, Head - Children's Services, County Hall, Rhadyr, Usk NP15 1GA ☎ 01633 644571 ⌨ janerodgers@monmouthshire.gov.uk

Staff Training: Mr John McConnachie, Training Lead, County Hall, Rhadyr, Usk NP15 1GA ☎ 01873 735453 ⌨ johnmcconnachie@monmouthshire.gov.uk

Street Scene: Ms Rachel Jowitt, Head - Waste & Street Services, County Hall, Rhadyr, Usk NP15 1GA ☎ 01633 748326 ⌨ racheljowitt@monmouthshire.gov.uk

Sustainable Communities: Ms Kellie Beirne, Deputy Chief Executive & Chief Officer - Innovation & Enterprise, County Hall, Rhadyr, Usk NP15 1GA ☎ 01633 644468 ⌨ kelliebeirne@monmouthshire.gov.uk

Sustainable Development: Ms Hazel Clatworthy, Sustainable Community Officer, County Hall, Rhadyr, Usk NP15 1GA ☎ 01633 644843 ⌨ hazelclatworthy@monmouthshire.gov.uk

Tourism: Ms Nicola Smith, Tourism Officer, County Hall, Rhadyr, Usk NP15 1GA ☎ 01633 644847 ⌨ nicolasmith@monmouthshire.gov.uk

Traffic Management: Mr Paul Keeble, Traffic & Network Manager, County Hall, Rhadyr, Usk NP15 1GA ☎ 01633 644644 ⌨ paulkeeble@monmouthshire.gov.uk

Transport: Mr Richard Cope, Passenger Transport Unit Manager, County Hall, Rhadyr, Usk NP15 1GA ☎ 01633 644745 ⌨ richardcope@monmouthshire.gov.uk

Transport Planner: Mr Christian Schmidt, Transport Planning & Policy Officer, County Hall, Rhadyr, Usk NP15 1GA ☎ 01633 644727 ⌨ christianschmidt@monmouthshire.gov.uk

Total Place: Ms Deb Hill-Howells, Head - Community Led Delivery, County Hall, Rhadyr, Usk NP15 1GA ☎ 01633 644281 ⌨ debrahill-howells@monmouthshire.gov.uk

Waste Collection and Disposal: Ms Rachel Jowitt, Head - Waste & Street Services, County Hall, Rhadyr, Usk NP15 1GA ☎ 01633 748326 ⌨ racheljowitt@monmouthshire.gov.uk

Waste Management: Ms Rachel Jowitt, Head - Waste & Street Services, County Hall, Rhadyr, Usk NP15 1GA ☎ 01633 748326 ⌨ racheljowitt@monmouthshire.gov.uk

Children's Play Areas: Mr Tim Bradfield, Recreation Officer, County Hall, Rhadyr, Usk NP15 1GA ☎ 01633 644136 ⌨ timbradfield@monmouthshire.gov.uk

COUNCILLORS

Chair: Higginson, Jim (LAB - Severn)
ronhigginson@monmouthshire.gov.uk

Vice-Chair: Jordan, Paul (CON - Cantref)
pauljordan@monmouthshire.gov.uk

Leader of the Council: Fox, Peter (CON - Portskewett)
peterfox@monmouthshire.gov.uk

Batrouni, Dimitri (LAB - St. Christopher's)
dimitribatrouni@monmouthshire.gov.uk

Blakebrough, Debby (IND - Trellech United)
debbyblakebrough@monmouthshire.gov.uk

Burrows, Geoffrey (CON - Mitchel Troy)
geoffburrows@monmouthshire.gov.uk

Chapman, Ralph (IND - Mardy)
ralphchapman@monmouthshire.gov.uk

Clarke, Peter (CON - Llangybi Fawr)
peterclarke@monmouthshire.gov.uk

Crook, Jessica (LAB - The Elms)
jessicacrook@monmouthshire.gov.uk

Dovey, David (CON - St. Kingsmark)
daviddovey@monmouthshire.gov.uk

Down, Graham (IND - Shirenewton)
grahamdown@monmouthshire.gov.uk

Easson, Tony (LAB - Dewstow)
anthonyeasson@monmouthshire.gov.uk

Edwards, Douglas (LD - Grofield)
douglasedwards@monmouthshire.gov.uk

Edwards, Ruth (CON - Llantilio Crossenny)
ruthedwards@monmouthshire.gov.uk

Evans, David (LAB - West End)
davidevans2@monmouthshire.gov.uk

Farley, Peter (LAB - St. Mary's)
peterfarley@monmouthshire.gov.uk

George, James (LAB - Lansdown)
jamesgeorge@monmouthshire.gov.uk

Greenland, Robert (CON - Devauden)
robertgreenland@monmouthshire.gov.uk

Guppy, Linda (LD - Rogiet)
lindaguppy@monmouthshire.gov.uk

Hacket Pain, Liz (CON - Wyesham)
lizhacketpain@monmouthshire.gov.uk

Harris, Roger (LAB - Croesonen)
rogerharris@monmouthshire.gov.uk

Hayward, Robert (IND - Dixton with Osbaston)
bobhayward@monmouthshire.gov.uk

Hickman, Martin (CON - Llanfoist Fawr)
martinhickman@monmouthshire.gov.uk

Hobson, Phyl (LD - Larkfield)
phylhobson@monmouthshire.gov.uk

Howard, Giles (CON - Llanelly Hill)
gileshoward@monmouthshire.gov.uk

Howarth, Simon (IND - Llanelly Hill)
simonhowarth@monmouthshire.gov.uk

Jones, Bryan (CON - Goetre Fawr)
bryanjones@monmouthshire.gov.uk

Jones, Sara (CON - Llanover)
sarajones2@monmouthshire.gov.uk

Jones, Penny (CON - Raglan)
pennyjones@monmouthshire.gov.uk

Jones, David (IND - Crucorney)
davidhughesjones@monmouthshire.gov.uk

MONMOUTHSHIRE

Marshall, John (IND - Green Lane)
johnmarshall@monmouthshire.gov.uk

Murphy, Phil (CON - Caerwent)
philmurphy@monmouthshire.gov.uk

Powell, Maureen (CON - Castle)
maureenpowell@monmouthshire.gov.uk

Prosser, John (CON - Priory)
johnprosser@monmouthshire.gov.uk

Smith, Val (IND - Llanbadoc)
valsmith@monmouthshire.gov.uk

Strong, Brian (CON - Usk)
brianstrong@monmouthshire.gov.uk

Taylor, Frances (IND - Mill)
francestaylor@monmouthdhire.gov.uk

Watts, Pauline (LAB - Caldicot Castle)
paulinewatts@monmouthshire.gov.uk

Watts, Armand (LAB - Thornwell)
armandwatts@monmouthshire.gov.uk

Webb, Ann (CON - St. Arvans)
annwebb@monmouthshire.gov.uk

White, Susan (CON - Overmonnow)
susanwhite@monmouthshire.gov.uk

Williams, Kevin (LAB - Llanwenarth Ultra)
kevinwilliams@monmouthshire.gov.uk

Wintle, Alan (IND - Drybirdge)
alanwintle@monmouthshire.gov.uk

POLITICAL COMPOSITION
CON: 19, LAB: 11, IND: 10, LD: 3

COMMITTEE CHAIRS

Adults: Mr Peter Farley

Audit: Mr Jim Higginson

Children & Young People: Ms Penny Jones

Economy & Development: Ms Sara Jones

Licensing: Ms Linda Guppy

Planning: Ms Ruth Edwards

Moray   S

Moray Council, Council Offices, High Street, Elgin IV30 1BX
☎ 01343 543451 🖷 01343 540399 ⌨ www.moray.gov.uk

FACTS AND FIGURES
Parliamentary Constituencies: Moray
EU Constituencies: Scotland
Election Frequency: Elections are of whole council

PRINCIPAL OFFICERS

Chief Executive: Mr Roddy Burns, Chief Executive, Council
Offices, High Street, Elgin IV30 1BX ☎ 01343 563001
🕾 roddy.burns@moray.gov.uk

Senior Management: Mr Richard Anderson, Head of Housing &
Property, Council Offices, High Street, Elgin IV30 1BX
☎ 01343 563532 🕾 richard.anderson@moray.gov.uk

Senior Management: Mr Stephen Cooper, Head of Direct
Services, PO Box 6760, Elgin IV30 9BX ☎ 01343 563777
🕾 stephen.p.cooper@moray.gov.uk

Senior Management: Ms Vivienne Cross, Acting Head of
Schools & Curriculum Development, Council Offices, High Street,
Elgin IV30 1BX ☎ 01343 563411 🕾 vivienne.cross@moray.gov.uk

Senior Management: Mr Laurence Findlay, Corporate Director
- Education & Social Care, Council Office, High Street, Elgin IV30
1BX ☎ 01343 563530 🕾 laurence.findlay@moray.gov.uk

Senior Management: Ms Pam Gowans, Chief Officer - Moray
Health & Social Care Partnership, Council Offices, High Street,
Elgin IV30 1BX ☎ 01343 563552 🕾 pamela.gowans@moray.gov.uk

Senior Management: Mr Jim Grant, Head of Development
Services, Council Offices, High Street, Elgin IV30 1BX
☎ 01343 563262 🕾 jim.grant@moray.gov.uk

Senior Management: Mrs Rhona Gunn, Acting Corporate
Director - Economic Development, Planning & Infrastructure,
Council Offices, High Street, Elgin IV30 1BX ☎ 01343 563152
🕾 rhona.gunn@moray.gov.uk

Senior Management: Mr Graham Jarvis, Head of Lifelong
Learning, Culture & Sport, Council Offices, High Street, Elgin IV30
1BX ☎ 01343 563365 🕾 graham.jarvis@moray.gov.uk

Senior Management: Ms Susan Maclaren, Head of Integrated
Children's Services, Council Offices, High Street, Elgin IV30 1BX
☎ 01343 563584 🕾 susan.maclaren@moray.gov.uk

Senior Management: Mr Alasdair McEachan, Head of Legal &
Democratic Services, Council Offices, High Street, Elgin IV30 1BX
☎ 01343 563080 🕾 alasdair.mceachan@moray.gov.uk

Senior Management: Mr Mark Palmer, Corporate Director -
Corporate Services, Council Offices, High Street, Elgin IV30 1BX
☎ 01343 563103 🕾 mark.palmer@moray.gov.uk

Senior Management: Mrs Denise Whitworth, Head of Human
Resources & ICT, Council Offices, High Street, Elgin IV30 1BX
☎ 01343 563060 🕾 denise.whitworth@moray.gov.uk

Senior Management: Ms Margaret Wilson, Head of Financial
Services, Council Offices, High Street, Elgin IV30 1BX
🕾 margaret.wilson@moray.gov.uk

Architect, Building / Property Services: Mr Moray Mcleod,
Design Manager, Council Offices, High Street, Elgin IV30 1BX
☎ 01343 563727 🕾 moray.mcleod@moray.gov.uk

Architect, Building / Property Services: Mr Eddie Milne,
Property Resources Manager, Council Office, High Street, Elgin
IV30 1BX ☎ 01343 563708 🕾 eddie.milne@moray.gov.uk

Best Value: Mrs Bridget Mustard, Corporate Policy Unit Manager, Council Offices, High Street, Elgin IV30 1BX ☎ 01343 563048 bridget.mustard@moray.gov.uk

Building Control: Mr Kevan Sturgeon, Building Standards Manager, Council Offices, High Street, Elgin IV30 1BX ☎ 01343 563269 kevan.sturgeon@moray.gov.uk

Catering Services: Ms Pearl Gray, Catering Officer, PO Box 6760, Elgin IV30 9BX ☎ 01343 557086 pearl.gray@moray.gov.uk

Children / Youth Services: Ms Susan Maclaren, Head of Integrated Children's Services, Council Offices, High Street, Elgin IV30 1BX ☎ 01343 563584 susan.maclaren@moray.gov.uk

Civil Registration: Mrs Heather Greig, Senior Registrar, 240 High Street, Elgin IV30 1BA ☎ 01343 554600 heather.greig@moray.gov.uk

PR / Communications: Mr Peter Jones, PR & Communications Officer, Council Offices, High Street, Elgin IV30 1BX ☎ 01343 563601 peter.jones@moray.gov.uk

Community Planning: Mrs Bridget Mustard, Corporate Policy Unit Manager, Council Offices, High Street, Elgin IV30 1BX ☎ 01343 563048 bridget.mustard@moray.gov.uk

Community Safety: Mr Willie Findlay, Community Safety Officer, Council Offices, High Street, Elgin IV30 1BX ☎ 01343 563322 willie.findlay@moray.gov.uk

Community Safety: Mrs Jane Mackie, Head of Community Care, The Moray Council, Spynie Hospital, Elgin IV30 5PW ☎ 01343 567127 jane.mackie@moray.gov.uk

Computer Management: Ms Denise Whitworth, Head of Human Resources & ICT, Council Offices, High Street, Elgin IV30 1BX ☎ 01343 563060 denise.whitworth@moray.gov.uk

Consumer Protection and Trading Standards: Mr Peter Adamson, Trading Standards Manager, Council Offices, High Street, Elgin IV30 1BX ☎ 01343 563940 peter.adamson@moray.gov.uk

Contracts: Mr Colin Bell, Environmental Protection Manager, PO Box 6760, Elgin IV30 9BX ☎ 01353 577040 colin.bell@moray.gov.uk

Customer Service: Mr Eric Bell, Customer Services Manager, Council Offices, High Street, Elgin IV30 1BX ☎ 01343 563107 eric.bell@moray.gov.uk

Direct Labour: Mr Michael Rollo, Building Services Manager, Unit 6, Mosstodloch Industrial Estate, Elgin IV30 1TY ☎ 01343 823043 mike.rollo@moray.gov.uk

Economic Development: Mr Gordon Sutherland, Planning & Economic Development Manager, Council Offices, High Street, Elgin IV30 1BX ☎ 01343 563278 gordon.sutherland@moray.gov.uk

Education: Mr Laurence Findlay, Corporate Director - Education & Social Care, Council Office, High Street, Elgin IV30 1BX ☎ 01343 563530 laurence.findlay@moray.gov.uk

Electoral Registration: Mr Roddy Burns, Chief Executive, Council Offices, High Street, Elgin IV30 1BX ☎ 01343 563001 roddy.burns@moray.gov.uk

Emergency Planning: Mrs Donna McLean, Emergency Planning Officer, Council Offices, High Street, Elgin IV30 1BX ☎ 01343 563865 donna.mclean@moray.gov.uk

Energy Management: Mr Moray MacLeod, Design Manager, Council Offices, High Street, Elgin IV30 1BX ☎ 01343 563727 moray.macleod@moray.gov.uk

Environmental / Technical Services: Mr Jim Grant, Head of Development Services, Council Offices, High Street, Elgin IV30 1BX ☎ 01343 563262 jim.grant@moray.gov.uk

Environmental Health: Ms Karen Sievewright, Environmental Health Manager, Council Offices, High Street, Elgin IV30 1BX ☎ 01343 563356 karen.sievewright@moray.gov.uk

Estates, Property & Valuation: Mr Stuart Beveridge, Estates Manager, Council Offices, High Street, Elgin IV30 1BX ☎ 01343 563257 stuart.beveridge@moray.gov.uk

Facilities: Mrs Susan May, Operational Support Officer, PO Box 6760, Elgin IV30 9BX ☎ 01343 557088 susan.may@moray.gov.uk

Finance: Ms Margaret Wilson, Head of Financial Services, Council Offices, High Street, Elgin IV30 1BX ☎ 01343 563102 margaret.wilson@moray.gov.uk

Fleet Management: Mr Leslie Thomson, Fleet Services Manager, PO Box 6760, Elgin IV30 9BX ☎ 01343 557051 leslie.thomson@moray.gov.uk

Grounds Maintenance: Mr Ken Kennedy, Lands & Parks Officer, PO Box 6760, Elgin IV30 9BX ☎ 01343 557051 ken.kennedy@moray.gov.uk

Health and Safety: Mr Doug Reid, Health & Safety Manager, Council Offices, High Street, Elgin IV30 1BX ☎ 01343 563073 doug.reid@moray.gov.uk

Highways: Mr Stephen Cooper, Head of Direct Services, PO Box 6760, Elgin IV30 9BX ☎ 01343 563777 stephen.p.cooper@moray.gov.uk

Housing: Mr Richard Anderson, Head of Housing & Property, Council Offices, High Street, Elgin IV30 1BX ☎ 01343 563532 richard.anderson@moray.gov.uk

Housing Maintenance: Mr John MacDonald, Asset Manager, Council Offices, High Street, Elgin IV30 1BX ☎ 0343 563743 john.macdonald@moray.gov.uk

Legal: Mr Alasdair McEachan, Head of Legal & Democratic Services, Council Offices, High Street, Elgin IV30 1BX ☎ 01343 563080 alasdair.mceachan@moray.gov.uk

Leisure and Cultural Services: Mr Nick Goodchild, Educational Resources Manager, Council Offices, High Street, Elgin IV30 1BX ☎ 01343 563401 goodchn@moray.gov.uk

MORAY

Licensing: Mr Alasdair McEachan, Head of Legal & Democratic Services, Council Offices, High Street, Elgin IV30 1BX
☎ 01343 563080 ·⊕ alasdair.mceachan@moray.gov.uk

Lifelong Learning: Mr Graham Jarvis, Head of Lifelong Learning, Culture & Sport, Council Offices, High Street, Elgin IV30 1BX
☎ 01343 563365 ·⊕ graham.jarvis@moray.gov.uk

Lighting: Mr Mark Atherton, Roads Maintenance Manager, PO Box 6760, Elgin IV30 9BX ☎ 01343 577303
·⊕ mark.atherton@moray.gov.uk

Member Services: Mr Roddy Burns, Chief Executive, Council Offices, High Street, Elgin IV30 1BX ☎ 01343 563001
·⊕ roddy.burns@moray.gov.uk

Parking: Mrs Nicola Moss, Transportation Manager, PO Box 6760, Elgin IV30 9BX ☎ 01343 563785 ·⊕ nicola.moss@moray.gov.uk

Partnerships: Mr Peter Jones, PR & Communications Officer, Council Offices, High Street, Elgin IV30 1BX ☎ 01343 563601
·⊕ peter.jones@moray.gov.uk

Partnerships: Mrs Bridget Mustard, Corporate Policy Unit Manager, Council Offices, High Street, Elgin IV30 1BX
☎ 01343 563048 ·⊕ bridget.mustard@moray.gov.uk

Personnel / HR: Ms Denise Whitworth, Head of Human Resources & ICT, Council Offices, High Street, Elgin IV30 1BX
☎ 01343 563060 ·⊕ denise.whitworth@moray.gov.uk

Procurement: Mrs Diane Beattie, Payments Manager, Council Offices, High Street, Elgin IV30 1BX ☎ 01343 563136
·⊕ diane.beattie@moray.gov.uk

Public Libraries: Mrs Sheila Campbell, Principal Librarian, Council Offices, High Street, Elgin IV30 1BX ☎ 01343 562600
·⊕ sheila.campbell@moray.gov.uk

Recycling & Waste Minimisation: Mr Colin Bell, Environmental Protection Manager, PO Box 6760, Elgin IV30 9BX
☎ 01353 577040 ·⊕ colin.bell@moray.gov.uk

Recycling & Waste Minimisation: Mr Stephen Cooper, Head of Direct Services, PO Box 6760, Elgin IV30 9BX ☎ 01343 563777
·⊕ stephen.p.cooper@moray.gov.uk

Road Safety: Mr Dave Malpas, Senior Engineer - Traffic, PO Box 6760, Elgin IV30 9BX ☎ 01343 563780
·⊕ dave.malpas@moray.gov.uk

Social Services: Ms Susan Maclaren, Head of Integrated Children's Services, Council Offices, High Street, Elgin IV30 1BX
☎ 01343 563584 ·⊕ susan.maclaren@moray.gov.uk

Social Services (Adult): Mrs Jane Mackie, Head of Community Care, The Moray Council, Spynie Hospital, Elgin IV30 5PW
☎ 01343 567127 ·⊕ jane.mackie@moray.gov.uk

Social Services (Children): Ms Susan Maclaren, Head of Integrated Children's Services, Council Offices, High Street, Elgin IV30 1BX ☎ 01343 563584 ·⊕ susan.maclaren@moray.gov.uk

Staff Training: Ms Carol Sheridan, Employee Development Manager, Council Offices, 149 High Street, Elgin IV30 1BX
☎ 01343 563070 ·⊕ carol.sheridan@moray.gov.uk

Traffic Management: Mr Dave Malpas, Senior Engineer - Traffic, PO Box 6760, Elgin IV30 9BX ☎ 01343 563780
·⊕ dave.malpas@moray.gov.uk

Transport: Mr Stephen Cooper, Head of Direct Services, PO Box 6760, Elgin IV30 9BX ☎ 01343 563777
·⊕ stephen.p.cooper@moray.gov.uk

Transport: Mrs Nicola Moss, Transportation Manager, PO Box 6760, Elgin IV30 9BX ☎ 01343 563785 ·⊕ nicola.moss@moray.gov.uk

Waste Collection and Disposal: Mr Colin Bell, Environmental Protection Manager, PO Box 6760, Elgin IV30 9BX
☎ 01353 577040 ·⊕ colin.bell@moray.gov.uk

Waste Management: Mr Colin Bell, Environmental Protection Manager, PO Box 6760, Elgin IV30 9BX ☎ 01353 577040
·⊕ colin.bell@moray.gov.uk

Children's Play Areas: Mr Ken Kennedy, Lands & Parks Officer, PO Box 6760, Elgin IV30 9BX ☎ 01343 557051
·⊕ ken.kennedy@moray.gov.uk

COUNCILLORS

ConvenerWright, Allan (CON - Heldon & Laich)
allan.wright@moray.gov.uk

Leader of the Council: Cree, Stewart (IND - Keith & Cullen)
stewart.cree@moray.gov.uk

Alexander, George (IND - Forres)
george.alexander@moray.gov.uk

Allan, James (CON - Elgin City South)
james.allan@moray.gov.uk

Coull, Gary (SNP - Keith & Cullen)
gary.coull@moray.gov.uk

Cowe, John (IND - Heldon & Laich)
john.cowe@moray.gov.uk

Cowie, Gordon (IND - Buckie)
gordon.cowie@moray.gov.uk

Creswell, Lorna (IND - Forres)
lorna.creswell@moray.gov.uk

Divers, John (SNP - Elgin City South)
john.divers@moray.gov.uk

Gowans, Patsy (SNP - Elgin City North)
patsy.gowans@moray.gov.uk

Howe, Margo (SNP - Fochabers Lhanbryde)
margo.howe@moray.gov.uk

Leadbitter, Graham (SNP - Elgin City South)
graham.leadbitter@moray.gov.uk

McConachie, Michael (SNP - Speyside Glenlivet)
michael.mcconachie@moray.gov.uk

McDonald, Gordon (SNP - Buckie)
gordon.mcdonald@moray.gov.uk

McGillivray, Eric (IND - Heldon & Laich)
eric.mcgillivray@moray.gov.uk

McLean, Aaron (SNP - Forres)
aaron.mclean@moray.gov.uk

Morton, Sean (LAB - Fochabers Lhanbryde)
sean.morton@moray.gov.uk

Murdoch, Fiona (IND - Speyside Glenlivet)
fiona.murdoch@moray.gov.uk

Paul, Pearl (SNP - Speyside Glenlivet)
pearl.paul@moray.gov.uk

Reid, Kirsty (SNP - Elgin City North)
kirsty.reid@moray.gov.uk

Ross, Douglas (CON - Fochabers Lhanbryde)
douglas.ross@moray.gov.uk

Shand, Michael (SNP - Elgin City North)
mike.shand@moray.gov.uk

Shepherd, Ronald (IND - Keith & Cullen)
ronald.shepherd@moray.gov.uk

Skene, Anne (IND - Forres)
anne.skene@moray.gov.uk

Tuke, Chris (IND - Heldon & Laich)
chris.tuke@moray.gov.uk

Warren, Sonya (SNP - Buckie)
sonya.warren@moray.gov.uk

POLITICAL COMPOSITION
SNP: 12, IND: 10, CON: 3, LAB: 1

Neath Port Talbot   W

Neath Port Talbot County Borough Council, Civic Centre, Port Talbot SA13 1PJ
☎ 01639 686868 ⌁ contactus@npt.gov.uk 🖥 www.npt.gov.uk

FACTS AND FIGURES
Parliamentary Constituencies: Aberavon, Neath
EU Constituencies: Wales
Election Frequency: Elections are of whole council

PRINCIPAL OFFICERS

Chief Executive: Mr Steven Phillips, Chief Executive, Civic Centre, Port Talbot SA13 1PJ

Senior Management: Mr Aled Evans, Corporate Director - Education, Leisure & Lifelong Learning, Civic Centre, Port Talbot SA13 1PJ ☎ 01639 763298 ⌁ a.evans@npt.gov.uk

Senior Management: Mr Nick Jarman, Corporate Director - Social Services, Health & Housing, Port Talbot Civic Centre, Port Talbot SA13 1PJ ☎ 01639 763333; 01639 763279 ⌁ n.jarman@npt.gov.uk

Senior Management: Mr Hywel Jenkins, Corporate Director - Finance & Corporate Services, Civic Centre, Port Talbot SA13 1PJ ☎ 01639 763252 ⌁ h.jenkins@npt.gov.uk

Senior Management: Mr Gareth Nutt, Corporate Director - Environment, The Quays, Brunel Way, Baglan Energy Park, Neath SA11 2GG ☎ 01639 686668 ⌁ g.nutt@npt.gov.uk

Architect, Building / Property Services: Mr Simon Brennan, Head of Property & Regeneration, The Quays, Brunel Way, Baglan Energy Park, Neath SA11 2GG ☎ 01639 686370 ⌁ s.brennan@npt.gov.uk

Best Value: Mrs Karen Jones, Head of Corporate Strategy & Democratic Services, Civic Centre, Port Talbot SA13 1PJ ☎ 01639 763713 ⌁ k.jones3@npt.gov.uk

Building Control: Mrs Nicola Pearce, Head of Planning, The Quays, Brunel Way, Baglan Energy Park, Neath SA11 2GG ☎ 01639 686681 ⌁ n.pearce@npt.gov.uk

Catering Services: Mr Andrew Thomas, Head of Support Services & Commissioning Development, Civic Centre, Port Talbot SA13 1PJ ☎ 01639 686868 ⌁ a.d.thomas@npt.gov.uk

Children / Youth Services: Mr Aled Evans, Corporate Director - Education, Leisure & Lifelong Learning, Civic Centre, Port Talbot SA13 1PJ ☎ 01639 763298 ⌁ a.evans@npt.gov.uk

Civil Registration: Mr David Michael, Head of Legal & Monitoring Officer, Civic Centre, Port Talbot SA13 1PJ ☎ 01639 763368 ⌁ d.michael@npt.gov.uk

Community Planning: Mrs Karen Jones, Head of Corporate Strategy & Democratic Services, Civic Centre, Port Talbot SA13 1PJ ☎ 01639 763713 ⌁ k.jones3@npt.gov.uk

Computer Management: Mr Stephen John, Head of ICT, The Quays, Brunel Way, Baglan Energy Park, Neath SA11 2GG ☎ 01639 686218 ⌁ s.john@npt.gov.uk

Consumer Protection and Trading Standards: Ms Angela Thomas, Head of Business Strategy & Public Protection, Civic Centre, Port Talbot SA13 1PJ ☎ 01639 763794 ⌁ a.j.thomas@npt.gov.uk

Contracts: Mr David Rees, Head of Financial Services, Aberavon House, Port Talbot SA13 1PJ ☎ 01639 763646 ⌁ d.rees1@npt.gov.uk

Corporate Services: Mr Hywel Jenkins, Corporate Director - Finance & Corporate Services, Civic Centre, Port Talbot SA13 1PJ ☎ 01639 763252 ⌁ h.jenkins@npt.gov.uk

Corporate Services: Mrs Karen Jones, Head of Corporate Strategy & Democratic Services, Civic Centre, Port Talbot SA13 1PJ ☎ 01639 763713 ⌁ k.jones3@npt.gov.uk

Customer Service: Mrs Karen Jones, Head of Corporate Strategy & Democratic Services, Civic Centre, Port Talbot SA13 1PJ ☎ 01639 763713 ⌁ k.jones3@npt.gov.uk

Economic Development: Mr Simon Brennan, Head of Property & Regeneration, The Quays, Brunel Way, Baglan Energy Park, Neath SA11 2GG ☎ 01639 686370 ⌁ s.brennan@npt.gov.uk

NEATH PORT TALBOT

Education: Mr Aled Evans, Corporate Director - Education, Leisure & Lifelong Learning, Civic Centre, Port Talbot SA13 1PJ
☎ 01639 763298 ⁰ a.evans@npt.gov.uk

E-Government: Mr Hywel Jenkins, Corporate Director - Finance & Corporate Services, Civic Centre, Port Talbot SA13 1PJ
☎ 01639 763252 ⁰ h.jenkins@npt.gov.uk

Electoral Registration: Mr Rhys George, Electoral Registration Officer, Civic Centre, Port Talbot SA13 1PJ ☎ 01639 686868
⁰ r.j.george@npt.gov.uk

Emergency Planning: Mrs Sheenagh Rees, Head of Human Resources, Civic Centre, Port Talbot SA13 1PJ ☎ 01639 763315
⁰ s.rees5@npt.gov.uk

Energy Management: Mr Simon Brennan, Head of Property & Regeneration, The Quays, Brunel Way, Baglan Energy Park, Neath SA11 2GG ☎ 01639 686370 ⁰ s.brennan@npt.gov.uk

Environmental / Technical Services: Mr Simon Brennan, Head of Property & Regeneration, The Quays, Brunel Way, Baglan Energy Park, Neath SA11 2GG ☎ 01639 686370 ⁰ s.brennan@npt.gov.uk

Environmental Health: Ms Angela Thomas, Head of Business Strategy & Public Protection, Civic Centre, Port Talbot SA13 1PJ
☎ 01639 763794 ⁰ a.j.thomas@npt.gov.uk

Estates, Property & Valuation: Mr Simon Brennan, Head of Property & Regeneration, The Quays, Brunel Way, Baglan Energy Park, Neath SA11 2GG ☎ 01639 686370 ⁰ s.brennan@npt.gov.uk

European Liaison: Mr Gareth Nutt, Corporate Director - Environment, The Quays, Brunel Way, Baglan Energy Park, Neath SA11 2GG ☎ 01639 686668 ⁰ g.nutt@npt.gov.uk

Facilities: Mr Simon Brennan, Head of Property & Regeneration, The Quays, Brunel Way, Baglan Energy Park, Neath SA11 2GG
☎ 01639 686370 ⁰ s.brennan@npt.gov.uk

Finance: Mr Hywel Jenkins, Corporate Director - Finance & Corporate Services, Civic Centre, Port Talbot SA13 1PJ
☎ 01639 763252 ⁰ h.jenkins@npt.gov.uk

Fleet Management: Mr Mike Roberts, Head of Streetcare, The Quays, Brunel Way, Baglan Energy Park, Neath SA11 2GG
☎ 01639 686966 ⁰ m.roberts@npt.gov.uk

Grounds Maintenance: Mr Mike Roberts, Head of Streetcare, The Quays, Brunel Way, Baglan Energy Park, Neath SA11 2GG
☎ 01639 686966 ⁰ m.roberts@npt.gov.uk

Health and Safety: Mrs Sheenagh Rees, Head of Human Resources, Civic Centre, Port Talbot SA13 1PJ ☎ 01639 763315
⁰ s.rees5@npt.gov.uk

Highways: Mr David Griffiths, Head of Engineering & Transport, The Quays, Brunel Way, Baglan Energy Park, Neath SA11 2GG
☎ 01639 686340 ⁰ d.w.griffiths@npt.gov.uk

Legal: Mr David Michael, Head of Legal & Monitoring Officer, Civic Centre, Port Talbot SA13 1PJ ☎ 01639 763368
⁰ d.michael@npt.gov.uk

Leisure and Cultural Services: Mr Andrew Thomas, Head of Support Services & Commissioning Development, Civic Centre, Port Talbot SA13 1PJ ☎ 01639 686868 ⁰ a.d.thomas@npt.gov.uk

Licensing: Mr David Michael, Head of Legal & Monitoring Officer, Civic Centre, Port Talbot SA13 1PJ ☎ 01639 763368
⁰ d.michael@npt.gov.uk

Lifelong Learning: Mr Chris Millis, Head of Participation, Civic Centre, Port Talbot SA13 1PJ ☎ 01639 763226
⁰ c.d.millis@npt.gov.uk

Lighting: Mr Mike Roberts, Head of Streetcare, The Quays, Brunel Way, Baglan Energy Park, Neath SA11 2GG ☎ 01639 686966
⁰ m.roberts@npt.gov.uk

Member Services: Mrs Karen Jones, Head of Change Management and Innovation, Civic Centre, Port Talbot SA13 1PJ
☎ 01639 763713 ⁰ k.jones3@npt.gov.uk

Member Services: Mr David Michael, Head of Legal & Monitoring Officer, Civic Centre, Port Talbot SA13 1PJ ☎ 01639 763368
⁰ d.michael@npt.gov.uk

Parking: Mr David Griffiths, Head of Engineering & Transport, The Quays, Brunel Way, Baglan Energy Park, Neath SA11 2GG
☎ 01639 686340 ⁰ d.w.griffiths@npt.gov.uk

Partnerships: Mr Aled Evans, Corporate Director - Education, Leisure & Lifelong Learning, Civic Centre, Port Talbot SA13 1PJ
☎ 01639 763298 ⁰ a.evans@npt.gov.uk

Personnel / HR: Mrs Sheenagh Rees, Head of Human Resources, Civic Centre, Port Talbot SA13 1PJ ☎ 01639 763315
⁰ s.rees5@npt.gov.uk

Planning: Mrs Nicola Pearce, Head of Planning, The Quays, Brunel Way, Baglan Energy Park, Neath SA11 2GG ☎ 01639 686681
⁰ n.pearce@npt.gov.uk

Procurement: Mr David Rees, Head of Financial Services, Aberavon House, Port Talbot SA13 1PJ ☎ 01639 763646
⁰ d.rees1@npt.gov.uk

Public Libraries: Mr Andrew Thomas, Head of Support Services & Commissioning Development, Civic Centre, Port Talbot SA13 1PJ
☎ 01639 686868 ⁰ a.d.thomas@npt.gov.uk

Recycling & Waste Minimisation: Mr Mike Roberts, Head of Streetcare, The Quays, Brunel Way, Baglan Energy Park, Neath SA11 2GG ☎ 01639 686966 ⁰ m.roberts@npt.gov.uk

Regeneration: Mr Simon Brennan, Head of Property & Regeneration, The Quays, Brunel Way, Baglan Energy Park, Neath SA11 2GG ☎ 01639 686370 ⁰ s.brennan@npt.gov.uk

Road Safety: Mr David Griffiths, Head of Engineering & Transport, The Quays, Brunel Way, Baglan Energy Park, Neath SA11 2GG
☎ 01639 686340 ⏚ d.w.griffiths@npt.gov.uk

Social Services: Mr Nick Jarman, Corporate Director - Social Services, Health & Housing, Port Talbot Civic Centre, Port Talbot SA13 1PJ ☎ 01639 763333; 01639 763279 ⏚ n.jarman@npt.gov.uk

Social Services (Adult): Ms Claire Marchant, Head of Community Care & Housing Services, Civic Centre, Port Talbot SA13 1PJ
☎ 01639 763287 ⏚ c.marchant@npt.gov.uk

Social Services (Children): Mr Andrew Jarrett, Head of Children & Young People Services, Civic Centre, Port Talbot SA13 1PJ
☎ 01639 763283 ⏚ a.jarrett@npt.gov.uk

Staff Training: Mrs Sheenagh Rees, Head of Human Resources, Civic Centre, Port Talbot SA13 1PJ ☎ 01639 763315
⏚ s.rees5@npt.gov.uk

Street Scene: Mr Mike Roberts, Head of Streetcare, The Quays, Brunel Way, Baglan Energy Park, Neath SA11 2GG
☎ 01639 686966 ⏚ m.roberts@npt.gov.uk

Sustainable Communities: Ms Claire Marchant, Head of Community Care & Housing Services, Civic Centre, Port Talbot SA13 1PJ ☎ 01639 763287 ⏚ c.marchant@npt.gov.uk

Sustainable Communities: Mrs Nicola Pearce, Head of Planning, The Quays, Brunel Way, Baglan Energy Park, Neath SA11 2GG ☎ 01639 686681 ⏚ n.pearce@npt.gov.uk

Sustainable Development: Mrs Nicola Pearce, Head of Planning, The Quays, Brunel Way, Baglan Energy Park, Neath SA11 2GG ☎ 01639 686681 ⏚ n.pearce@npt.gov.uk

Town Centre: Mr Andrew Collins, Regeneration Manager, Civic Centre, Port Talbot SA13 1PJ ☎ 01639 686416
⏚ a.collins@npt.gov.uk

Traffic Management: Mr David Griffiths, Head of Engineering & Transport, The Quays, Brunel Way, Baglan Energy Park, Neath SA11 2GG ☎ 01639 686340 ⏚ d.w.griffiths@npt.gov.uk

Transport: Mr David Griffiths, Head of Engineering & Transport, The Quays, Brunel Way, Baglan Energy Park, Neath SA11 2GG
☎ 01639 686340 ⏚ d.w.griffiths@npt.gov.uk

Waste Collection and Disposal: Mr Mike Roberts, Head of Streetcare, The Quays, Brunel Way, Baglan Energy Park, Neath SA11 2GG ☎ 01639 686966 ⏚ m.roberts@npt.gov.uk

Waste Management: Mr Mike Roberts, Head of Streetcare, The Quays, Brunel Way, Baglan Energy Park, Neath SA11 2GG
☎ 01639 686966 ⏚ m.roberts@npt.gov.uk

COUNCILLORS

Mayor: Penry, Sheila (LAB - Neath East)
cllr.s.m.penry@npt.gov.uk

Deputy Mayor: Dudley, Janice (PC - Bryncoch South)
cllr.j.dudley@npt.gov.uk

Leader of the Council: Thomas, Alun (LAB - Onllwyn)
leader@npt.gov.uk

Deputy Leader of the Council: Rees, Peter (LAB - Neath South)
cllr.p.rees@npt.gov.uk

Bebell, Harry (LAB - Coedffranc West)
cllr.h.m.bebell@npt.gov.uk

Bebell, Paula (LAB - Coedffranc Central)
cllr.p.bebell@npt.gov.uk

Bryant, John (PC - Bryncoch North)
cllr.j.r.bryant@npt.gov.uk

Carter, Alan (LAB - Cimla)
cllr.a.carter@npt.gov.uk

Chaves, Audrey (LAB - Sandfields West)
cllr.a.chaves@npt.gov.uk

Clement-Williams, Carol (LAB - Baglan)
cllr.c.clement@npt.gov.uk

Crowley, Matthew (LAB - Sandfields East)
cllr.c.m.crowley@npt.gov.uk

Davies, Rosalyn (PC - Godre'rgraig)
cllr.r.davies@npt.gov.uk

Davies, Des (LAB - Resolven)
cllr.d.w.davies@npt.gov.uk

Davies, Arthur (LAB - Coedffranc Central)
cllr.a.p.h.davies@npt.gov.uk

Ellis, Martin (IND - Pelenna)
cllr.m.ellis@npt.gov.uk

Evans, James (LAB - Sandfields West)
cllr.j.s.evans@npt.gov.uk

Golding, Ceri (LAB - Aberavon)
cllr.c.p.golding@npt.gov.uk

Greenaway, Paul (LAB - Baglan)
cllr.p.greenaway@npt.gov.uk

Harvey, Mike (LAB - Coedffranc North)
cllr.m.harvey@npt.gov.uk

Hunt, Steve (IND - Seven Sisters)
cllr.s.k.hunt@npt.gov.uk

James, Ian (LAB - Port Talbot)
cllr.i.b.james@npt.gov.uk

James, Rob (LAB - Bryncoch South)
cllr.r.james@npt.gov.uk

James, Lella (IND - Sandfields East)
cllr.l.h.james@npt.gov.uk

James, Hugh (LAB - Briton Ferry West)
cllr.h.n.james@npt.gov.uk

James, Mike (LAB - Pontardawe)
cllr.m.l.james@npt.gov.uk

Jenkins, Andrew (LAB - Neath South)
cllr.a.jenkins@npt.gov.uk

Jones, Doreen (LAB - Aberdulais)
cllr.d.jones@npt.gov.uk

Jones, Eddie (LAB - Glynneath)
cllr.e.e.jones@npt.gov.uk

Jones, Mark (LAB - Aberavon)
cllr.m.jones@npt.gov.uk

NEATH PORT TALBOT

Jones, Rob (LAB - Margam)
cllr.r.g.jones@npt.gov.uk

Jones, Scott (LAB - Cymmer)
cllr.s.jones@npt.gov.uk

Keogh, Dennis (LAB - Port Talbot)
cllr.d.keogh@npt.gov.uk

Latham, Edward (LAB - Sandfields East)
cllr.e.v.latham@npt.gov.uk

Lewis, Marian (LAB - Bryn & Cwmavon)
cllr.m.a.lewis@npt.gov.uk

Lewis, David (INDNA - Allt-Wen)
cllr.d.lewis@npt.gov.uk

Llewellyn, Alun (PC - Ystalyfera)
cllr.a.llewellyn@npt.gov.uk

Lloyd, Kristine (LAB - Cwmllynfell)
cllr.k.lloyd@npt.gov.uk

Lockyer, Alan Richard (LAB - Neath North)
cllr.a.r.lockyer@npt.gov.uk

Miller, John (LAB - Neath East)
cllr.j.miller@npt.gov.uk

Miller, Sandra (LAB - Neath East)
cllr.s.miller@npt.gov.uk

Morgan, Del (PC - Glynneath)
cllr.j.d.morgan@npt.gov.uk

Morgan, Colin (LAB - Briton Ferry East)
cllr.c.morgan@npt.gov.uk

Morgans, Cari (LAB - Tonna)
cllr.c.morgans@npt.gov.uk

Paddison, Suzanne (LAB - Sandfields West)
cllr.s.paddison@npt.gov.uk

Pearson, Karen (LAB - Crynant)
cllr.k.pearson@npt.gov.uk

Peters, Martin (PC - Dyffryn)
cllr.d.m.peters@npt.gov.uk

Phillips, Rebecca (PC - Trebanos)
cllr.r.phillips@npt.gov.uk

Protheroe, Mark (LAB - Neath North)
cllr.m.protheroe@npt.gov.uk

Purcell, Linet (PC - Pontardawe)
cllr.l.purcell@npt.gov.uk

Rahaman, Saifur (LAB - Port Talbot)
cllr.s.rahaman@npt.gov.uk

Rawlings, Glyn (LAB - Glyncorrwg)
cllr.h.g.rawlings@npt.gov.uk

Richards, Peter (LAB - Baglan)
cllr.p.d.richards@npt.gov.uk

Rogers, John (LAB - Tai-Bach)
cllr.j.rogers@npt.gov.uk

Taylor, Anthony (IND - Aberavon)
cllr.a.taylor@npt.gov.uk

Taylor, Anthony J (LAB - Tai-Bach)
cllr.a.j.taylor@npt.gov.uk

Thomas, Alex (LAB - Rhos)
cllr.a.l.thomas@npt.gov.uk

Thomas, Ralph (LAB - Gwynfi)
cllr.r.thomas@npt.gov.uk

Warman, John (LD - Cimla)
cllr.j.warman@npt.gov.uk

Whitelock, Dave (LAB - Bryn & Cwmavon)
cllr.d.whitelock@npt.gov.uk

Williams, David (LAB - Bryn & Cwmavon)
cllr.i.d.williams@npt.gov.uk

Williams, Lynda (LAB - Gwaun-Cae-Gurwen)
cllr.l.g.williams@npt.gov.uk

Wingrave, Annette (LAB - Cadoxton)
cllr.a.wingrave@npt.gov.uk

Woolcock, Arwyn (LAB - Lower Brynamman)
cllr.a.n.woolcock@npt.gov.uk

POLITICAL COMPOSITION
LAB: 49, PC: 8, IND: 4, INDNA: 1, LD: 1, Vacant: 1

COMMITTEE CHAIRS

Audit: Mrs Lella James

Children, Young People & Education: Mr Alan Richard Lockyer

Economic & Community Regeneration: Mr Alun Llewellyn

Licensing: Mr Eddie Jones

Planning: Mr Rob Jones

Social Care, Health & Housing: Mrs Doreen Jones

New Forest   D

New Forest District Council, Appletree Court, Beaulieu Road, Lyndhurst SO43 7PA
☎ 023 8028 5000 ✆ contact@nfdc.gov.uk ⌨ www.newforest.gov.uk

FACTS AND FIGURES
Parliamentary Constituencies: New Forest East, New Forest West
EU Constituencies: South East
Election Frequency: Elections are of whole council

PRINCIPAL OFFICERS

Chief Executive: Mr Robert Jackson, Chief Executive, Appletree Court, Beaulieu Road, Lyndhurst SO43 7PA ☎ 023 8028 5588 ✆ bob.jackson@nfdc.gov.uk

Deputy Chief Executive: Mr Colin Read, Deputy Chief Executive / Executive Head - Operations, Appletree Court, Beaulieu Road, Lyndhurst SO43 7PA ☎ 023 8028 5588 ✆ colin.read@nfdc.gov.uk

Senior Management: Mr Chris Elliott, Executive Head - Economy, Housing & Planning, Appletree Court, Beaulieu Road, Lyndhurst SO43 7PA ☎ 023 8028 5588 ✆ chris.elliott@nfdc.gov.uk

Senior Management: Ms Grainne O'Rourke, Executive Head - Governance & Regulation, Appletree Court, Beaulieu Road, Lyndhurst SO43 7PA ☎ 023 8028 5588 ✆ grainne.o'rourke@nfdc.gov.uk

Senior Management: Mr Colin Read, Deputy Chief Executive / Executive Head - Operations, Appletree Court, Beaulieu Road, Lyndhurst SO43 7PA ☎ 023 8028 5588 ☝ colin.read@nfdc.gov.uk

Senior Management: Mrs Manjit Sandhu, Executive Head - Resources, Appletree Court, Beaulieu Road, Lyndhurst SO43 7PA ☎ 023 8028 5588 ☝ manjit.sandhu@nfdc.gov.uk

Access Officer / Social Services (Disability): Mrs Heleana Aylett, Service Manager - Human Resources, Appletree Court, Beaulieu Road, Lyndhurst SO43 7PA ☎ 023 8028 5588 ☝ heleana.aylett@nfdc.gov.uk

Architect, Building / Property Services: Mrs Fiona Skeats-Sicomori, Service Manager - Property, Appletree Court, Beaulieu Road, Lyndhurst SO43 7PA ☎ 023 8028 5588 ☝ fiona.skeats-sicomori@nfdc.gov.uk

Building Control: Mr David Groom, Service Manager - Planning & Building Control, Appletree Court, Beaulieu Road, Lyndhurst SO43 7PA ☎ 023 8028 5588 ☝ david.groom@nfdc.gov.uk

PR / Communications: Mrs Sara Hamilton, Corporate Communications Manager, Appletree Court, Beaulieu Road, Lyndhurst SO43 7PA ☎ 023 8028 5588 ☝ sara.hamilton@nfdc.gov.uk

Community Safety: Mrs Rosemary Rutins, Service Manager - Democratic Services & Member Support, Appletree Court, Beaulieu Road, Lyndhurst SO43 7PA ☎ 023 8028 5588 ☝ rosemary.rutins@nfdc.gov.uk

Computer Management: Mr Rob Beere, Service Manager - ICT, Appletree Court, Beaulieu Road, Lyndhurst SO43 7PA ☎ 023 8028 5588 ☝ rob.beere@nfdc.gov.uk

Contracts: Mr Andrew Kinghorn, Service Manager - Legal, Appletree Court, Beaulieu Road, Lyndhurst SO43 7PA ☎ 023 8028 5588 ☝ andrew.kinghorn@nfdc.gov.uk

Customer Service: Mrs Rebecca Drummond, Service Manager - Business Improvement & Customer Services, Appletree Court, Beaulieu Road, Lyndhurst SO43 7PA ☎ 023 8028 5588 ☝ rebecca.drummond@nfdc.gov.uk

Economic Development: Ms Louise Evans, Service Manager - Policy & Strategy, Appletree Court, Beaulieu Road, Lyndhurst SO43 7PA ☎ 023 8028 5588 ☝ louise.evans@nfdc.gov.uk

E-Government: Mr Rob Beere, Service Manager - ICT, Appletree Court, Beaulieu Road, Lyndhurst SO43 7PA ☎ 023 8028 5588 ☝ rob.beere@nfdc.gov.uk

Electoral Registration: Mrs Rosemary Rutins, Service Manager - Democratic Services & Member Support, Appletree Court, Beaulieu Road, Lyndhurst SO43 7PA ☎ 023 8028 5588 ☝ rosemary.rutins@nfdc.gov.uk

Emergency Planning: Mr Geoff Bettle, Service Manager - Compliance & Coastal, Marsh Lane Depot, Marsh Lane, Lymington SO41 9BX ☎ 023 8028 5588 ☝ geoff.bettle@nfdc.gov.uk

Energy Management: Mrs Fiona Skeats-Sicomori, Service Manager - Property, Appletree Court, Beaulieu Road, Lyndhurst SO43 7PA ☎ 023 8028 5588 ☝ fiona.skeats-sicomori@nfdc.gov.uk

Environmental Health: Mrs Joanne McClay, Service Manager - Environment & Regulation, Appletree Court, Beaulieu Road, Lyndhurst SO43 7PA ☎ 023 8028 5588 ☝ joanne.mcclay@nfdc.gov.uk

Estates, Property & Valuation: Mr Andrew Kinghorn, Service Manager - Legal, Appletree Court, Beaulieu Road, Lyndhurst SO43 7PA ☎ 023 8028 5588 ☝ andrew.kinghorn@nfdc.gov.uk

Facilities: Mrs Fiona Skeats-Sicomori, Service Manager - Property, Appletree Court, Beaulieu Road, Lyndhurst SO43 7PA ☎ 023 8028 5588 ☝ fiona.skeats-sicomori@nfdc.gov.uk

Fleet Management: Mr Richard Bisset, Service Manager - Waste & Transport, Marsh Lane Depot, Marsh Lane, Lymington SO41 9BX ☎ 023 8028 5588 ☝ richard.bisset@nfdc.gov.uk

Grounds Maintenance: Mr Steve Jones, Service Manager - Open Spaces, Marsh Lane Depot, Marsh Lane, Lymington SO41 9BX ☎ 023 8028 5588 ☝ steve.jones@nfdc.gov.uk

Health and Safety: Mr Geoff Bettle, Service Manager - Compliance & Coastal, Marsh Lane Depot, Marsh Lane, Lymington SO41 9BX ☎ 023 8028 5588 ☝ geoff.bettle@nfdc.gov.uk

Highways: Ms Louise Evans, Service Manager - Policy & Strategy, Appletree Court, Beaulieu Road, Lyndhurst SO43 7PA ☎ 023 8028 5588 ☝ louise.evans@nfdc.gov.uk

Home Energy Conservation: Mrs Fiona Skeats-Sicomori, Service Manager - Property, Appletree Court, Beaulieu Road, Lyndhurst SO43 7PA ☎ 023 8028 5588 ☝ fiona.skeats-sicomori@nfdc.gov.uk

Housing: Mr Richard Topliss, Service Manager - Housing, Appletree Court, Beaulieu Road, Lyndhurst SO43 7PA ☎ 023 8028 5588 ☝ richard.topliss@nfdc.gov.uk

Housing Maintenance: Mr Richard Topliss, Service Manager - Housing, Appletree Court, Beaulieu Road, Lyndhurst SO43 7PA ☎ 023 8028 5588 ☝ richard.topliss@nfdc.gov.uk

Legal: Mr Andrew Kinghorn, Service Manager - Legal, Appletree Court, Beaulieu Road, Lyndhurst SO43 7PA ☎ 023 8028 5588 ☝ andrew.kinghorn@nfdc.gov.uk

Leisure and Cultural Services: Ms Joanne Bailey, Service Manager - Health & Leisure, Appletree Court, Beaulieu Road, Lyndhurst SO43 7PA ☎ 023 8028 5588 ☝ joanne.bailey@nfdc.gov.uk

Licensing: Mrs Joanne McClay, Service Manager - Environment & Regulation, Appletree Court, Beaulieu Road, Lyndhurst SO43 7PA ☎ 023 8028 5588 ☝ joanne.mcclay@nfdc.gov.uk

Lighting: Ms Louise Evans, Service Manager - Policy & Strategy, Appletree Court, Beaulieu Road, Lyndhurst SO43 7PA ☎ 023 8028 5588 ☝ louise.evans@nfdc.gov.uk

NEW FOREST

Member Services: Mrs Rosemary Rutins, Service Manager - Democratic Services & Member Support, Appletree Court, Beaulieu Road, Lyndhurst SO43 7PA ☎ 023 8028 5588
🖰 rosemary.rutins@nfdc.gov.uk

Parking: Mr Rob Lane, Service Manager - Street Scene, Marsh Lane Depot, Marsh Lane, Lymington SO41 9BX ☎ 023 8028 5588
🖰 rob.lane@nfdc.gov.uk

Personnel / HR: Mrs Heleana Aylett, Service Manager - Human Resources, Appletree Court, Beaulieu Road, Lyndhurst SO43 7PA
☎ 023 8028 5588 🖰 heleana.aylett@nfdc.gov.uk

Planning: Mr David Groom, Service Manager - Planning & Building Control, Appletree Court, Beaulieu Road, Lyndhurst SO43 7PA
☎ 023 8028 5588 🖰 david.groom@nfdc.gov.uk

Procurement: Mr Andrew Kinghorn, Service Manager - Legal, Appletree Court, Beaulieu Road, Lyndhurst SO43 7PA ☎ 023 8028 5588 🖰 andrew.kinghorn@nfdc.gov.uk

Recycling & Waste Minimisation: Mr Richard Bisset, Service Manager - Waste & Transport, Marsh Lane Depot, Marsh Lane, Lymington SO41 9BX ☎ 023 8028 5588 🖰 richard.bisset@nfdc.gov.uk

Road Safety: Ms Louise Evans, Service Manager - Policy & Strategy, Appletree Court, Beaulieu Road, Lyndhurst SO43 7PA
☎ 023 8028 5588 🖰 louise.evans@nfdc.gov.uk

Staff Training: Mrs Heleana Aylett, Service Manager - Human Resources, Appletree Court, Beaulieu Road, Lyndhurst SO43 7PA
☎ 023 8028 5588 🖰 heleana.aylett@nfdc.gov.uk

Street Scene: Mr Rob Lane, Service Manager - Street Scene, Marsh Lane Depot, Marsh Lane, Lymington SO41 9BX
☎ 023 8028 5588 🖰 rob.lane@nfdc.gov.uk

Tourism: Ms Louise Evans, Service Manager - Policy & Strategy, Appletree Court, Beaulieu Road, Lyndhurst SO43 7PA
☎ 023 8028 5588 🖰 louise.evans@nfdc.gov.uk

Traffic Management: Ms Louise Evans, Service Manager - Policy & Strategy, Appletree Court, Beaulieu Road, Lyndhurst SO43 7PA
☎ 023 8028 5588 🖰 louise.evans@nfdc.gov.uk

Waste Collection and Disposal: Mr Richard Bisset, Service Manager - Waste & Transport, Marsh Lane Depot, Marsh Lane, Lymington SO41 9BX ☎ 023 8028 5588
🖰 richard.bisset@nfdc.gov.uk

Waste Management: Mr Richard Bisset, Service Manager - Waste & Transport, Marsh Lane Depot, Marsh Lane, Lymington SO41 9BX ☎ 023 8028 5588 🖰 richard.bisset@nfdc.gov.uk

COUNCILLORS

Chair: Hoare, Alison (CON - Marchwood)
alison.hoare@newforest.gov.uk

Vice-Chair: Beck, Goff (CON - Barton)
goff.beck@newforest.gov.uk

Leader of the Council: Rickman, Barry (CON - Boldre & Sway)
barry.rickman@newforest.gov.uk

Deputy Leader of the Council: Heron, Edward (CON - Downlands & Forest)
edward.heron@newforest.gov.uk

Alvey, Alan (CON - Holbury & North Blackfield)
alan.alvey@newforest.gov.uk

Andrews, Diane (CON - Bramshaw, Copythorne North & Minstead)
diane.andrews@newforest.gov.uk

Andrews, Bill (CON - Dibden & Hythe East)
bill.andrews@newforest.gov.uk

Armstrong, Peter (CON - Butts Ash & Dibden Purlieu)
peter.armstrong@newforest.gov.uk

Beeton, Sophie (CON - Milford)
sophie.beeton@newforest.gov.uk

Bellows, Roxy (CON - Fordingbridge)
roxanne.bellows@newforest.gov.uk

Bennison, Sue (CON - Marchwood)
sue.bennison@newforest.gov.uk

Binns, James (CON - Butts Ash & Dibden Purlieu)
james.binns@newforest.gov.uk

Blunden, Geoffrey (CON - Becton)
geoffrey.blunden@newforest.gov.uk

Britton, Dean (CON - Totton North)
dean.britton@newforest.gov.uk

Brooks, Di (CON - Totton West)
di.brooks@newforest.gov.uk

Carpenter, Fran (CON - Hordle)
fran.carpenter@newforest.gov.uk

Cerasoli, Louise (CON - Totton Central)
louise.cerasoli@newforest.gov.uk

Clarke, Steve (CON - Milton)
steve.clarke@newforest.gov.uk

Cleary, Jill (CON - Fernhill)
jill.cleary@newforest.gov.uk

Coombes, Ian (CON - Totton East)
ian.coombes@newforest.gov.uk

Crisell, Kate (CON - Furzedown & Hardley)
kate.crisell@newforest.gov.uk

Davies, Steve (CON - Milton)
stevep.davies@newforest.gov.uk

Davis, Arthur (CON - Totton East)
arthur.davis@newforest.gov.uk

Dow, Bill (CON - Forest North West)
bill.dow@newforest.gov.uk

Ford, Christine (CON - Ringwood North)
christine.ford@newforest.gov.uk

Frampton, Richard (CON - Bransgore & Burley)
richard.frampton@newforest.gov.uk

Glass, Allan (CON - Holbury & North Blackfield)
allan.glass@newforest.gov.uk

Harris, Michael (CON - Brockenhurst & Forest South East)
michael.harris@newforest.gov.uk

Harris, Len (CON - Totton South)
len.harris@newforest.gov.uk

Harrison, David (LD - Totton South)
david.harrison@newforest.gov.uk

Heron, Jeremy (CON - Ringwood South)
jeremy.heron@newforest.gov.uk

Holding, Maureen (CON - Brockenhurst & Forest South East)
maureen.holding@newforest.gov.uk

Jackman, Penny (CON - Pennington)
penny.jackman@newforest.gov.uk

Kendal, Melville (CON - Milford)
melville.kendal@newforest.gov.uk

Lane, Emma (CON - Ringwood East & Sopley)
emma.lane@newforest.gov.uk

Lovelace, Penny (CON - Hordle)
penny.lovelace@newforest.gov.uk

Lucas, Brian (CON - Totton Central)
brian.lucas@newforest.gov.uk

McEvoy, Alexis (CON - Fawley, Blackfield & Langley)
alexis.mcevoy@newforest.gov.uk

Olliff-Cooper, John (CON - Buckland)
john.olliff-cooper@newforest.gov.uk

O'Sullivan, Alan (CON - Barton)
alan.osullivan@newforest.gov.uk

Penman, Neville (CON - Totton North)
neville.penman@newforest.gov.uk

Penson, Alan (CON - Lymington Town)
alan.penson@newforest.gov.uk

Poole, Dan (CON - Dibden & Hythe East)
dan.poole@newforest.gov.uk

Puttock, Leslie (CON - Ashurst, Copythorne South & Netley Marsh)
leslie.puttock@newforest.gov.uk

Rippon-Swaine, Steve (CON - Ringwood South)
steve.rippon-swain@newforest.gov.uk

Rostand, Anna (CON - Lymington Town)
anna.rostand@newforest.gov.uk

Russell, David (CON - Totton West)
david.russell@newforest.gov.uk

Sevier, Ann (CON - Fordingbridge)
ann.sevier@newforest.gov.uk

Steele, Mark (CON - Bransgore & Burley)
mark.steele@newforest.gov.uk

Thierry, Michael (CON - Ringwood North)
michael.thierry@newforest.gov.uk

Thorne, Beverley (CON - Hythe West & Langdown)
beverley.thorne@newforest.gov.uk

Tipp, Derek (CON - Ashurst, Copythorne South & Netley Marsh)
derek.tipp@newforest.gov.uk

Tungate, Neil (CON - Bashley)
neil.tungate@newforest.gov.uk

Wade, Alex (LD - Hythe West & Langdown)
alex.wade@newforest.gov.uk

Wappet, Bob (CON - Fawley, Blackfield & Langley)
bob.wappet@newforest.gov.uk

Ward, Christine (CON - Becton)
christine.ward@newforest.gov.uk

Ward, John (CON - Fernhill)
johngward@newforest.gov.uk

White, Michael (CON - Pennington)
michael.white@newforest.gov.uk

Wise, Colin (CON - Boldre & Sway)
colin.wise@newforest.gov.uk

Wyeth, Pat (CON - Lyndhurst)
pat.wyeth@newforest.gov.uk

POLITICAL COMPOSITION
CON: 58, LD: 2

COMMITTEE CHAIRS

Audit: Mr Alan O'Sullivan

Licensing: Mr Steve Clarke

Planning: Mrs Diane Andrews

Newark & Sherwood   D

Newark & Sherwood District Council, Kelham Hall, Newark NG23 5QX
☎ 01636 650000 ✆ customerservices@nsdc.info 🖳 www.newark-sherwooddc.gov.uk

FACTS AND FIGURES
Parliamentary Constituencies: Newark, Sherwood
EU Constituencies: East Midlands
Election Frequency: Elections are of whole council

PRINCIPAL OFFICERS

Chief Executive: Mr Andrew Muter, Chief Executive, Kelham Hall, Newark NG23 5QX ☎ 01636 650000 ✆ andrew.muter@nsdc.info

Deputy Chief Executive: Mrs Kirsty Cole, Deputy Chief Executive, Kelham Hall, Newark NG23 5QX ☎ 01636 650000 ✆ kirsty.cole@nsdc.info

Senior Management: Mr Matthew Finch, Director - Customers, Kelham Hall, Newark NG23 5QX

Senior Management: Mr Andy Statham, Director - Community, Kelham Hall, Newark NG23 5QX ☎ 01636 650000 ✆ andy.statham@nsdc.info

Senior Management: Mrs Karen White, Director - Safety, Kelham Hall, Newark NG23 5QX ☎ 01636 650000 ✆ karen.white@nsdc.info

Architect, Building / Property Services: Mr David Best, Deputy Business Manager - Asset Management, Kelham Hall, Newark NG23 5QX david.best@nsdc.info

PR / Communications: Ms Jill Simpson, Business Manager - Customer Services, Kelham Hall, Newark NG23 5QX ☎ 01636 650000 ✆ jill.simpson@nsdc.info

Community Safety: Mr Ben Adams, Business Manager - Community Safety, Kelham Hall, Newark NG23 5QX ☎ 01636 650000 ✆ ben.adams@nsdc.info

NEWARK & SHERWOOD

Computer Management: Mrs Sharon Parkinson, Business Manager - ICT, Kelham Hall, Newark NG23 5QX ☎ 01636 650000 ✆ sharon.parkinson@nsdc.info

Corporate Services: Mrs Kirsty Cole, Deputy Chief Executive, Kelham Hall, Newark NG23 5QX ☎ 01636 650000 ✆ kirsty.cole@nsdc.info

Customer Service: Ms Jill Simpson, Business Manager - Customer Services, Kelham Hall, Newark NG23 5QX ☎ 01636 650000 ✆ jill.simpson@nsdc.info

Economic Development: Mrs Julie Reader-Sullivan, Business Manager - Economic Development, Kelham Hall, Newark NG23 5QX julie.reader-sullivan@nsdc.info

Electoral Registration: Mr Mark Jurejko, Elections Manager, Kelham Hall, Newark NG23 5QX ☎ 01636 650000 ✆ mark.jurejko@nsdc.info

Emergency Planning: Mr Ben Adams, Business Manager - Community Safety, Kelham Hall, Newark NG23 5QX ☎ 01636 650000 ✆ ben.adams@nsdc.info

Environmental / Technical Services: Mr Andy Statham, Director - Community, Kelham Hall, Newark NG23 5QX ☎ 01636 650000 ✆ andy.statham@nsdc.info

Environmental Health: Mr Alan Batty, Business Manager - Environmental Health, Kelham Hall, Newark NG23 5QX ☎ 01636 650000 ✆ alan.batty@nsdc.info

Estates, Property & Valuation: Mr David Best, Deputy Business Manager - Asset Management, Kelham Hall, Newark NG23 5QX david.best@nsdc.info

Finance: Mr Nicky Lovely, Business Manager - Finance, Kelham Hall, Newark NG23 5QX ☎ 01636 650000 ✆ nicky.lovely@nsdc.info

Fleet Management: Mr Andrew Kirk, Business Manager - Waste, Litter & Recycling, Kelham Hall, Newark NG23 5QX ☎ 01636 650000 ✆ andrew.kirk@nsdc.info

Grounds Maintenance: Mr Philip Beard, Business Manager - Parks & Amenities, Kelham Hall, Newark NG23 5QX ☎ 01636 650000 ✆ philip.beard@nsdc.info

Health and Safety: Mr Ben Adams, Business Manager - Community Safety, Kelham Hall, Newark NG23 5QX ☎ 01636 650000 ✆ ben.adams@nsdc.info

Housing: Mr Rob Main, Strategic Housing Manager, Kelham Hall, Newark NG23 5QX ☎ 01636 650000 ✆ rob.main@nsdc.info

Legal: Mrs Karen White, Director - Safety, Kelham Hall, Newark NG23 5QX ☎ 01636 650000 ✆ karen.white@nsdc.info

Licensing: Mr Alan Batty, Business Manager - Environmental Health, Kelham Hall, Newark NG23 5QX ☎ 01636 650000 ✆ alan.batty@nsdc.info

Lifelong Learning: Mrs Tracey Mellors, Business Manager - Human Resources, Kelham Hall, Newark NG23 5QX ☎ 01636 650000 ✆ tracey.mellors@nsdc.info

Lottery Funding, Charity and Voluntary: Mr Andy Hardy, Business Manager - Community, Arts & Sports, Kelham Hall, Newark NG23 5QX ☎ 01636 650000 ✆ andy.hardy@nsdc.info

Member Services: Mr Nigel Hill, Business Manager - Democratic Services, Kelham Hall, Newark NG23 5QX ☎ 01636 650000 ✆ nigel.hill@nsdc.info

Parking: Mr Ian Harrison, Business Manager - Markets & Car Parks, Kelham Hall, Newark NG23 5QX ian.harrison@nsdc.info

Personnel / HR: Mrs Tracey Mellors, Business Manager - Human Resources, Kelham Hall, Newark NG23 5QX ☎ 01636 650000 ✆ tracey.mellors@nsdc.info

Planning: Mr Matthew Lamb, Business Manager - Development, Kelham Hall, Newark NG23 5QX ☎ 01636 650000 ✆ matt.lamb@nsdc.info

Procurement: Mr John King, Business Manager - Procurement, Kelham Hall, Newark NG23 5QX ☎ 01636 650000 ✆ john.king@nsdc.info

Recycling & Waste Minimisation: Mr Andrew Kirk, Business Manager - Waste, Litter & Recycling, Kelham Hall, Newark NG23 5QX ☎ 01636 650000 ✆ andrew.kirk@nsdc.info

Staff Training: Mrs Tracey Mellors, Business Manager - Human Resources, Kelham Hall, Newark NG23 5QX ☎ 01636 650000 ✆ tracey.mellors@nsdc.info

Transport: Mr Andrew Kirk, Business Manager - Waste, Litter & Recycling, Kelham Hall, Newark NG23 5QX ☎ 01636 650000 ✆ andrew.kirk@nsdc.info

Waste Collection and Disposal: Mr Andrew Kirk, Business Manager - Waste, Litter & Recycling, Kelham Hall, Newark NG23 5QX ☎ 01636 650000 ✆ andrew.kirk@nsdc.info

Waste Management: Mr Andrew Kirk, Business Manager - Waste, Litter & Recycling, Kelham Hall, Newark NG23 5QX ☎ 01636 650000 ✆ andrew.kirk@nsdc.info

COUNCILLORS

Chair: Roberts, Tony (CON - Beacon) tony.roberts@newark-sherwooddc.gov.uk

Vice-Chair: Tift, Linda (LAB - Rainworth North & Rufford) linda.tift@newark-sherwooddc.gov.uk

Leader of the Council: Blaney, Roger (CON - Trent) roger.blaney@newark-sherwooddc.gov.uk

Deputy Leader of the Council: Lloyd, David (CON - Beacon) david.lloyd2@newark-sherwooddc.gov.uk

Group Leader: Dawn, Gill (IND - Bridge) gill.dawn@newark-sherwooddc.gov.uk

Group Leader: Truswell, Abbie (LAB - Ollerton)
abbie.truswell@newark-sherwooddc.gov.uk

Arnold, Kathleen (LAB - Rainworth South & Blidworth)
kathleen.arnold@newark-sherwooddc.gov.uk

Batey, Derek (LAB - Ollerton)
derek.batey@newark-sherwooddc.gov.uk

Brooks, Betty (CON - Balderton South)
betty.brooks@newark-sherwooddc.gov.uk

Brooks, Celia (LAB - Edwinstowe & Clipstone)
celia.brooks@newark-sherwooddc.gov.uk

Brown, Irene (IND - Bridge)
irene.brown@newark-sherwooddc.gov.uk

Buttery, Mark (LAB - Rainworth North & Rufford)
mark.buttery@newark-sherwooddc.gov.uk

Clarke, David (CON - Collingham)
davidj.clarke@newark-sherwooddc.gov.uk

Cope, Max (CON - Devon)
max.cope@newark-sherwooddc.gov.uk

Crowe, Rita (CON - Beacon)
rita.crowe@newark-sherwooddc.gov.uk

Crowe, Bob (CON - Devon)
bob.crowe@newark-sherwooddc.gov.uk

Dobson, Maureen (IND - Collingham)
maureen.dobson@newark-sherwooddc.gov.uk

Duncan, Peter (CON - Devon)
peter.duncan@newark-sherwooddc.gov.uk

Girling, Keith (CON - Castle)
keith.girling@newark-sherwooddc.gov.uk

Handley, Paul (CON - Southwell)
paul.handley@newark-sherwooddc.gov.uk

Hurst, Lydia (CON - Balderton South)
lydia.hurst@newark-sherwooddc.gov.uk

Jackson, Roger (CON - Dover Beck)
roger.jackson@newark-sherwooddc.gov.uk

Laughton, Bruce (CON - Southwell)
bruce.laughton@newark-sherwooddc.gov.uk

Lee, Johno (CON - Balderton North & Coddington)
johno.lee@newark-sherwooddc.gov.uk

Michael, Sylvia (CON - Sutton-on-Trent)
sylvia.michael@newark-sherwooddc.gov.uk

Mison, Neill (CON - Farndon & Fernwood)
neill.mison@newark-sherwooddc.gov.uk

Payne, David (CON - Balderton North & Coddington)
david.payne@newark-sherwooddc.gov.uk

Peacock, Paul (LAB - Edwinstowe & Clipstone)
paul.peacock@newark-sherwooddc.gov.uk

Rainbow, Penny (CON - Southwell)
penny.rainbow@newark-sherwooddc.gov.uk

Saddington, Susan (CON - Muskham)
susan.saddington@newark-sherwooddc.gov.uk

Soar, Sheila (LAB - Bilsthorpe)
sheila.soar@newark-sherwooddc.gov.uk

Staples, David (LAB - Boughton)
david.staples@newark-sherwooddc.gov.uk

Taylor, Frank (CON - Farnsfield)
frank.taylor@newark-sherwooddc.gov.uk

Thompson, Dave (LAB - Edwinstowe & Clipstone)
david.thompson@newark-sherwooddc.gov.uk

Walker, Ivor (CON - Farndon & Fernwood)
ivor.walker@surfree.co.uk

Walker, Keith (CON - Farndon & Fernwood)
keith.walker@newark-sherwooddc.gov.uk

Wells, Benjamin (LAB - Ollerton)
benjamin.wells@newark-sherwooddc.gov.uk

Wendels, Tim (CON - Lowdham)
tim.wendels@newark-sherwooddc.gov.uk

Woodhead, Yvonne (LAB - Rainworth South & Blidworth)
yvonne.woodhead@newark-sherwooddc.gov.uk

POLITICAL COMPOSITION
CON: 24, LAB: 12, IND: 3

COMMITTEE CHAIRS

Economic Development: Mr David Lloyd

Homes & Communities: Mr Bruce Laughton

Leisure & Environment: Mr Peter Duncan

Licensing: Mrs Rita Crowe

Planning: Mr David Payne

Newcastle upon Tyne City   M

Newcastle upon Tyne City Council, Civic Centre, Newcastle upon Tyne NE1 8QH
☎ 0191 232 8520 ▤ 0191 211 4942 ▧ www.newcastle.gov.uk

FACTS AND FIGURES
Parliamentary Constituencies: Newcastle Central, Newcastle East, Newcastle North
EU Constituencies: North East
Election Frequency: Elections are by thirds

PRINCIPAL OFFICERS

Chief Executive: Ms Pat Ritchie, Chief Executive, Civic Centre, Newcastle upon Tyne NE1 8QH ☎ 0191 278 7878
⌨ pat.ritchie@newcastle.gov.uk

Senior Management: Mr Tony Kirkham, Director - Resources, Civic Centre, Newcastle upon Tyne NE1 8QH ☎ 0191 211 5226
⌨ tony.kirkham@newcastle.gov.uk

Senior Management: Mr Michael Murphy, Director - Communities, Civic Centre, Newcastle upon Tyne NE1 8QH
☎ 0191 211 5950 ⌨ michael.murphy@newcastle.gov.uk

Senior Management: Mr Tom Warburton, Director - Investment & Development, Civic Centre, Newcastle upon Tyne NE1 8QH
☎ 0191 211 5660 ⌨ tom.warburton@newcastle.gov.uk

Senior Management: Mr Ewen Weir, Director - Wellbeing, Care & Learning, Civic Centre, Newcastle upon Tyne NE1 8QH
☎ 0191 211 5478 ⌨ ewen.weir@newcastle.gov.uk

NEWCASTLE UPON TYNE CITY

Access Officer / Social Services (Disability): Mr Neil Swinney, Access Officer, Civic Centre, Newcastle upon Tyne NE1 8QH
☎ 0191 211 6804 ⏚ neil.swinney@newcastle.gov.uk

Architect, Building / Property Services: Mr Stuart Turnbull, Service Manager - Architecture & Building Design Services, Civic Centre, Newcastle upon Tyne NE1 8QH ☎ 0191 278 3277
⏚ stuart.turnbull@newcastle.gov.uk

Building Control: Mr David Ewles, Head of Building Control, Civic Centre, Newcastle upon Tyne NE1 8QH ☎ 0191 211 6180
⏚ david.n.ewles@newcastle.gov.uk

Catering Services: Ms Tracey Cuthbert, Service Manager - Civic Facilities, Civic Centre, Newcastle upon Tyne NE1 8QH
☎ 0191 211 6940 ⏚ tracey.cuthbert@newcastle.gov.uk

Children / Youth Services: Mr Mick McCracken, Assistant Director - Family Insights, Civic Centre, Newcastle upon Tyne NE1 8QH ☎ 0191 211 6307 ⏚ mick.mccracken@newcastle.gov.uk

Civil Registration: Ms Julie Cable, Customer Contact Specialist, Civic Centre, Newcastle upon Tyne NE1 8QH ☎ 0191 211 5006
⏚ julie.cable@newcastle.gov.uk

PR / Communications: Mr Steve Park, Assistant Director - Policy, Communication & Performance, Civic Centre, Newcastle upon Tyne NE1 8QH ☎ 0191 211 5071
⏚ steve.park@newcastle.gov.uk

Community Planning: Ms Carol Edgell, Communities Team Manager, Civic Centre, Newcastle upon Tyne NE1 8QH
☎ 0191 277 3560 ⏚ carol.edgell@newcastle.gov.uk

Community Safety: Ms Robyn Thomas, Service Manager - Community Safety, Civic Centre, Newcastle upon Tyne NE1 8QH
☎ 0191 277 7835 ⏚ robyn.thomas@newcastle.gov.uk

Computer Management: Mr James Lowden, ICT Services Manager, Civic Centre, Newcastle upon Tyne NE1 8QH
☎ 0191 277 7282 ⏚ james.lowden@newcastle.gov.uk

Consumer Protection and Trading Standards: Mr Stephen Savage, Assistant Director - Public Safety & Regulation, Civic Centre, Newcastle upon Tyne NE1 8QH ☎ 0191 211 6101
⏚ stephen.savage@newcastle.gov.uk

Contracts: Ms Rachel Baillie, Assistant Director - Commissioning & Procurement, Civic Centre, Newcastle upon Tyne NE1 8QH
☎ 0191 211 6458 ⏚ rachel.baillie@newcastle.gov.uk

Corporate Services: Mr Tony Kirkham, Director - Resources, Civic Centre, Newcastle upon Tyne NE1 8QH ☎ 0191 211 5226
⏚ tony.kirkham@newcastle.gov.uk

Customer Service: Ms Mandy Rudd, Area Manager - Customer Services, Civic Centre, Newcastle upon Tyne NE1 8QH
☎ 0191 211 5438 ⏚ mandy.rudd@newcastle.gov.uk

Direct Labour: Mr Michael Murphy, Director - Communities, Civic Centre, Newcastle upon Tyne NE1 8QH ☎ 0191 211 5950
⏚ michael.murphy@newcastle.gov.uk

Economic Development: Mr Rob Hamilton, Economic Development Principal Advisor, Civic Centre, Newcastle upon Tyne NE1 8QH ☎ 0191 277 8947 ⏚ rob.hamilton@newcastle.gov.uk

Economic Development: Ms Michelle Perry, Assistant Director - Commercial Development, Civic Centre, Newcastle upon Tyne NE1 8QH michelle.perry@newcastle.gov.uk

Education: Mr Ewen Weir, Director - Wellbeing, Care & Learning, Civic Centre, Newcastle upon Tyne NE1 8QH ☎ 0191 211 5478
⏚ ewen.weir@newcastle.gov.uk

E-Government: Mr James Lowden, ICT Services Manager, Civic Centre, Newcastle upon Tyne NE99 2BN ☎ 0191 277 7282
⏚ james.lowden@newcastle.gov.uk

Electoral Registration: Mr Ian Humphries, Principal Electoral & Members Service Officer, Civic Centre, Newcastle upon Tyne NE1 8QH ☎ 0191 277 7175 ⏚ ian.humphries@newcastle.gov.uk

Emergency Planning: Mr Stephen Savage, Assistant Director - Public Safety & Regulation, Civic Centre, Newcastle upon Tyne NE1 8PB ☎ 0191 211 6101 ⏚ stephen.savage@newcastle.gov.uk

Energy Management: Mr Simon Johnson, Senior Neighbourhood Manager - Energy Services, Allendale House, Newcastle upon Tyne NE6 2SZ ☎ 0191 278 3449 ⏚ simon.johnson@newcastle.gov.uk

Environmental / Technical Services: Mr Michael Murphy, Director - Communities, Civic Centre, Newcastle upon Tyne NE1 8QH ☎ 0191 211 5950 ⏚ michael.murphy@newcastle.gov.uk

Environmental Health: Mr Stephen Savage, Assistant Director - Public Safety & Regulation, Civic Centre, Newcastle upon Tyne NE1 8QH ☎ 0191 211 6101 ⏚ stephen.savage@newcastle.gov.uk

Estates, Property & Valuation: Mr Paul Scaplehorn, Head of Strategic Property, Civic Centre, Newcastle upon Tyne NE1 8QH
☎ 0191 211 5505 ⏚ paul.scaplehorn@newcastle.gov.uk

European Liaison: Mr Steve Park, Assistant Director - Policy, Communication & Performance, Civic Centre, Newcastle upon Tyne NE1 8QH ☎ 0191 211 5071 ⏚ steve.park@newcastle.gov.uk

Events Manager: Mr Stephen Savage, Assistant Director - Public Safety & Regulation, Civic Centre, Newcastle upon Tyne NE1 8QH
☎ 0191 211 6101 ⏚ stephen.savage@newcastle.gov.uk

Facilities: Ms Christine Herriot, Head of Facilities Services Civic Management, Civic Centre, Newcastle upon Tyne NE99 2BN
☎ 0191 277 7665 ⏚ christine.herriot@newcastle.gov.uk

Finance: Mr Tony Kirkham, Director - Resources, Civic Centre, Newcastle upon Tyne NE1 8QH ☎ 0191 211 5226
⏚ tony.kirkham@newcastle.gov.uk

Fleet Management: Mr Peter Morton, City Transport Manager, Newington Road West, Newcastle upon Tyne NE5 6BD
☎ 0191 278 3901 ⏚ peter.morton@newcastle.gov.uk

Grounds Maintenance: Mr Michael Murphy, Director - Communities, Civic Centre, Newcastle upon Tyne NE1 8QH ☎ 0191 211 5950 ✆ michael.murphy@newcastle.gov.uk

Health and Safety: Ms Katherine Chapman, Team Manager - Health & Safety, Civic Centre, Newcastle upon Tyne NE1 8QH ☎ 0191 211 5211 ✆ katherine.chapman@newcastle.gov.uk

Highways: Mr Michael Murphy, Director - Communities, Civic Centre, Newcastle upon Tyne NE1 8QH ☎ 0191 211 5950 ✆ michael.murphy@newcastle.gov.uk

Home Energy Conservation: Mr Simon Johnson, Senior Neighbourhood Manager - Energy Services, Room FF17, Allendale Road, Newcastle upon Tyne NE64 2SZ ☎ 0191 278 3449 ✆ simon.johnson@newcastle.gov.uk

Housing: Mr Mick Firth, Senior Specialist - Advisor, Civic Centre, Newcastle upon Tyne NE1 8QH ☎ 0191 211 5627 ✆ mick.firth@newcastle.gov.uk

Housing Maintenance: Mr Mick Firth, Senior Specialist - Advisor, Civic Centre, Newcastle upon Tyne NE1 8QH ☎ 0191 211 5627 ✆ mick.firth@newcastle.gov.uk

Local Area Agreement: Mr Phil Hunter, Senior Specialist, Civic Centre, Newcastle upon Tyne NE1 8QH ☎ 0191 277 7802 ✆ philip.hunter@newcastle.gov.uk

Legal: Mr John Softly, Assistant Director - Legal Services, Civic Centre, Newcastle upon Tyne NE1 8QH ☎ 0191 277 7047 ✆ john.softly@newcastle.gov.uk

Leisure and Cultural Services: Mr Tony Durcan, Assistant Director - Customers, Culture & Skills, Civic Centre, Newcastle upon Tyne NE1 8QH ☎ 0191 211 5383 ✆ tony.durcan@newcastle.gov.uk

Licensing: Mr Stephen Savage, Assistant Director - Public Safety & Regulation, Civic Centre, Newcastle upon Tyne NE1 8QH ☎ 0191 211 6101 ✆ stephen.savage@newcastle.gov.uk

Lifelong Learning: Mr Tony Durcan, Assistant Director - Customers, Culture & Skills, Civic Centre, Newcastle upon Tyne NE1 8QH ☎ 0191 211 5383 ✆ tony.durcan@newcastle.gov.uk

Lighting: Mr Michael Murphy, Director - Communities, Civic Centre, Newcastle upon Tyne NE1 8QH ☎ 0191 211 5950 ✆ michael.murphy@newcastle.gov.uk

Member Services: Ms Linda Scott, Service Manager - Democratic Services, Civic Centre, Newcastle upon Tyne NE1 8QH ☎ 0191 211 5101 ✆ linda.scott@newcastle.gov.uk

Parking: Mr Stephen Savage, Assistant Director - Public Safety & Regulation, Civic Centre, Newcastle upon Tyne NE1 8QH ☎ 0191 211 6101 ✆ stephen.savage@newcastle.gov.uk

Personnel / HR: Ms Pam Perry, Assistant Director - Human Resources, Civic Centre, Newcastle upon Tyne NE1 8QH ☎ 0191 211 5246 ✆ pam.perry@newcastle.gov.uk

Planning: Ms Kath Lawless, Assistant Director - Planning, Civic Centre, Newcastle upon Tyne NE1 8QH ☎ 0191 211 5629 ✆ kath.lawless@newcastle.gov.uk

Procurement: Ms Rachel Baillie, Assistant Director - Commissioning & Procurement, Civic Centre, Newcastle upon Tyne NE1 8QH ☎ 0191 211 6458 ✆ rachel.baillie@newcastle.gov.uk

Public Libraries: Mr Tony Durcan, Assistant Director - Customers, Culture & Skills, Civic Centre, Newcastle upon Tyne NE1 8QH ☎ 0191 211 5383 ✆ tony.durcan@newcastle.gov.uk

Recycling & Waste Minimisation: Mr Michael Murphy, Director - Communities, Civic Centre, Newcastle upon Tyne NE1 8QH ☎ 0191 211 5950 ✆ michael.murphy@newcastle.gov.uk

Regeneration: Mr Tom Warburton, Director - Investment & Development, Civic Centre, Newcastle upon Tyne NE1 8QH ☎ 0191 211 5660 ✆ tom.warburton@newcastle.gov.uk

Road Safety: Mr Michael Murphy, Director - Communities, Civic Centre, Newcastle upon Tyne NE1 8QH ☎ 0191 211 5950 ✆ michael.murphy@newcastle.gov.uk

Social Services: Mr Ewen Weir, Director - Wellbeing, Care & Learning, Civic Centre, Newcastle upon Tyne NE99 1RD ☎ 0191 211 5478 ✆ ewen.weir@newcastle.gov.uk

Social Services (Adult): Ms Cathy Bull, Assistant Director - Social Care, Civic Centre, Newcastle upon Tyne NE1 8QH ☎ 0191 211 6318 ✆ cathy.bull@newcastle.gov.uk

Social Services (Children): Mr Mick McCracken, Assistant Director - Family Insights, Civic Centre, Newcastle upon Tyne NE1 8QH ☎ 0191 211 6307 ✆ mick.mccracken@newcastle.gov.uk

Staff Training: Ms Pam Perry, Assistant Director - Human Resources, Civic Centre, Newcastle upon Tyne NE1 8QH ☎ 0191 211 5246 ✆ pam.perry@newcastle.gov.uk

Street Scene: Mr Tom Warburton, Director - Investment & Development, Civic Centre, Newcastle upon Tyne NE1 8QH ☎ 0191 211 5660 ✆ tom.warburton@newcastle.gov.uk

Sustainable Communities: Ms Carol Edgell, Communities Team Manager, Civic Centre, Newcastle upon Tyne NE1 8QH ☎ 0191 277 3560 ✆ carol.edgell@newcastle.gov.uk

Sustainable Development: Mr Tom Warburton, Director - Investment & Development, Civic Centre, Newcastle upon Tyne NE1 8QH ☎ 0191 211 5660 ✆ tom.warburton@newcastle.gov.uk

Tourism: Mr Andrew Rothwell, Culture & Tourism Manager, Civic Centre, Newcastle upon Tyne NE1 8QH ☎ 0191 211 5610 ✆ andrew.rothwell@newcastle.gov.uk

Traffic Management: Mr Michael Murphy, Director - Communities, Civic Centre, Newcastle upon Tyne NE1 8QH ☎ 0191 211 5950 ✆ michael.murphy@newcastle.gov.uk

NEWCASTLE UPON TYNE CITY

Transport: Mr Peter Morton, City Transport Manager, Newington Road West, Newcastle upon Tyne NE5 6BD ☎ 0191 278 3901 ✆ peter.morton@newcastle.gov.uk

Transport Planner: Mr Mark Wilson, Regional Transport Principal Advisor, Civic Centre, Newcastle upon Tyne NE1 8QH
☎ 0191 211 5679 ✆ mark.wilson@newcastle.gov.uk

Waste Collection and Disposal: Mr Michael Murphy, Director - Communities, Civic Centre, Newcastle upon Tyne NE1 8QH
☎ 0191 211 5950 ✆ michael.murphy@newcastle.gov.uk

Waste Management: Mr Michael Murphy, Director - Communities, Civic Centre, Newcastle upon Tyne NE1 8QH
☎ 0191 211 5950 ✆ michael.murphy@newcastle.gov.uk

Children's Play Areas: Mr Mick McCracken, Assistant Director - Family Insights, Civic Centre, Newcastle upon Tyne NE1 8QH
☎ 0191 211 6307 ✆ mick.mccracken@newcastle.gov.uk

COUNCILLORS

The Lord Mayor: Stephenson, Hazel (LAB - Benwell & Scotswood)
hazel.stephenson@newcastle.gov.uk

Leader of the Council: Forbes, Nick (LAB - Westgate)
nick.forbes@newcastle.gov.uk

Deputy Leader of the Council: McCarty, Joyce (LAB - Wingrove)
joyce.mccarty@newcastle.gov.uk

Group Leader: Lower, Anita (LD - Castle)
anita.lower@newcastle.gov.uk

Ahad, Dipu (LAB - Elswick)
dipu.ahad@newcastle.gov.uk

Ainsley, Arlene (LAB - South Jesmond)
arlene.ainsley@newcastle.gov.uk

Ali, Irim (LAB - Wingrove)
irim.ali@newcastle.gov.uk

Allen, Pauline (LD - Parklands)
pauline.allen@newcastle.gov.uk

Allibhai, Kerry (LAB - South Jesmond)
kerry.allibhai@newcastle.gov.uk

Allison, George (LAB - Byker)
george.allison@newcastle.gov.uk

Ashby, Robin (LD - Parklands)
robin.asby@newcastle.gov.uk

Beecham, Jeremy (LAB - Benwell & Scotswood)
jeremybeecham@blueyonder.co.uk

Bell, Ged (LAB - Kenton)
ged.bell@newcastle.gov.uk

Bird, Simon (LAB - Denton)
simon.bird@newcastle.gov.uk

Bowman, Mick (LAB - North Heaton)
mick.bowman@newcastle.gov.uk

Cook, David (LAB - Lemington)
david.cook@newcastle.gov.uk

Corbett, Bill (IND - Westerhope)
bill.corbett@newcastle.gov.uk

Cott, Nick (LD - West Gosforth)
nick.cott@newcastle.gov.uk

Davis, Melissa (LAB - Denton)
melissa.davis@newcastle.gov.uk

Denholm, David (LAB - Walkergate)
david.denholm@newcastle.gov.uk

Donnelly, Marc (IND - Westerhope)
marc.donnelly@newcastle.gov.uk

Down, David (LD - Parklands)
david.down@newcastle.gov.uk

Dunn, Veronica (LAB - Byker)
veronica.dunn@newcastle.gov.uk

Fairlie, Stephen (LAB - Newburn)
steve.fairlie@newcastle.gov.uk

Faulkner, David (LD - Fawdon)
david.faulkner@newcastle.gov.uk

Franks, Hilary (LAB - Newburn)
hilary.franks@newcastle.gov.uk

Gallagher, Henry (LD - East Gosforth)
henry.gallagher@newcastle.gov.uk

Graham, Ian (LD - Castle)
ian.graham@newcastle.gov.uk

Greenhough, Daniel (LAB - Denton)
daniel.greenhough@newcastle.gov.uk

Higgins, Robert (LAB - Benwell & Scotswood)
rob.higgins@newcastle.gov.uk

Hillicks, Pat (IND - Westerhope)
pat.hillicks@newcastle.gov.uk

Hindmarsh, Brenda (LD - Fawdon)
brenda.hindmarsh@newcastle.gov.uk

Holland, Paula (LAB - Ouseburn)
paula.holland@newcastle.gov.uk

Huddart, Doreen (LD - North Heaton)
doreen.huddart@newcastle.gov.uk

Hunter, Brian (LAB - Castle)
brian.hunter@newcastle.gov.uk

Jones, Denise (LAB - South Heaton)
denise.jones@newcastle.gov.uk

Kane, Gareth (LD - Ouseburn)
gareth.kane@newcastle.gov.uk

Kemp, Nick (LAB - Byker)
nick.kemp@newcastle.gov.uk

Kilgour, Karen (LAB - Fenham)
karen.kilgour@newcastle.gov.uk

Kingsland, Joanne (LAB - Westgate)
joanne.kingsland@newcastle.gov.uk

Lambert, Stephen (LAB - Kenton)
stephen.lambert@newcastle.gov.uk

Lowson, Maureen (LAB - Walkergate)
maureen.lowson@newcastle.gov.uk

McGuinness, Kim (LAB - Lemington)
kim.mcguinness@newcastle.gov.uk

Mendelson, Felicity (LAB - South Jesmond)
felicity.mendelson@newcastle.gov.uk

O'Brien, Geoff (LAB - Westgate)
geoff.obrien@newcastle.gov.uk

Pattison, George (LAB - Woolsington)
george.pattison@newcastle.gov.uk

Pattison, Sharon (LAB - Woolsington)
sharon.pattison@newcastle.gov.uk

Pearson, Sue (LAB - Blakelaw)
sue.pearson@newcastle.gov.uk

Perry, Dan (LAB - North Jesmond)
dan.perry@newcastle.gov.uk

Phillipson, Barry (LAB - Lemington)
barry.phillipson@newcastle.gov.uk

Postlethwaite, Stella (LAB - North Jesmond)
stella.postlethwaite@newcastle.gov.uk

Powers, Stephen (LAB - Ouseburn)
stephen.powers@newcastle.gov.uk

Rahman, Habib (LAB - Elswick)
habib.rahman@newcastle.gov.uk

Raymont, Dominic (LD - East Gosforth)
dominic.raymont@newcastle.gov.uk

Renton, Bob (LD - Dene)
bob.renton@newcastle.gov.uk

Riley, Ben (LAB - Blakelaw)
ben.riley@newcastle.gov.uk

Robinson, Jacqui (LAB - Woolsington)
jacqui.robinson@newcastle.gov.uk

Robinson, Karen (LD - Dene)
karen.robinson@newcastle.gov.uk

Schofield, Ann (LAB - Elswick)
ann.schofield@newcastle.gov.uk

Shepherd, Bill (LD - West Gosforth)
william.shepherd@newcastle.gov.uk

Slesenger, David (LD - East Gosforth)
david.slesenger@newcastle.gov.uk

Slesenger, Jaqueline (LD - West Gosforth)
jacqueline.slesenger@newcastle.gov.uk

Stephenson, John-Paul (LAB - South Heaton)
john-paul.stephenson@newcastle.gov.uk

Stokel-Walker, John (LAB - Walker)
john.stokel-walker@newcastle.gov.uk

Stone, Greg (LD - North Heaton)
greg.stone@newcastle.gov.uk

Streather, Jane (LAB - Kenton)
jane.streather@newcastle.gov.uk

Talbot, Marion (LAB - Fenham)
marion.talbot@newcastle.gov.uk

Taylor, Wendy (LD - Dene)
wendy.taylor@newcastle.gov.uk

Tinnion, Antoine (LAB - Fawdon)
antoine.tinnion@newcastle.gov.uk

Todd, Nigel (LAB - Wingrove)
nigel.todd@newcastle.gov.uk

Tokell, Ian (LAB - Fenham)
ian.tokell@newcastle.gov.uk

Walker, Catherine (LD - North Jesmond)
catherine.walker@newcastle.gov.uk

White, Sophie (LAB - South Heaton)
sophie.white@newcastle.gov.uk

Wood, Margaret (LAB - Walker)
margaret.wood@newcastle.gov.uk

Wood, Dave (LAB - Walker)
dave.wood@newcastle.gov.uk

Wood, Stevie (LAB - Walkergate)
stephen.wood@newcastle.gov.uk

Wright, Linda (LAB - Newburn)
linda.wright@newcastle.gov.uk

POLITICAL COMPOSITION
LAB: 54, LD: 20, IND: 3

COMMITTEE CHAIRS

Licensing: Mr George Pattison

Planning: Mr George Allison

Newcastle-under-Lyme   D

Newcastle-under-Lyme Borough Council, Civic Offices,
Merrial Street, Newcastle-under-Lyme ST5 2AG
☎ 01782 717717 🖷 01782 711032
🖑 customerservices@newcastle-staffs.gov.uk
🖳 www.newcastle-staffs.gov.uk

FACTS AND FIGURES
Parliamentary Constituencies: Newcastle-under-Lyme, Stoke-on-Trent North, Stone
EU Constituencies: West Midlands
Election Frequency: Elections are by thirds

PRINCIPAL OFFICERS

Chief Executive: Mr John Sellgren, Chief Executive, Civic Offices, Merrial Street, Newcastle-under-Lyme ST5 2AG

Senior Management: Mr Dave Adams, Executive Director - Operational Services, Civic Offices, Merrial Street, Newcastle-under-Lyme ST5 2AG ☎ 01782 742504
🖑 dave.adams@newcastle-staffs.gov.uk

Senior Management: Mr Neale Clifton, Executive Director - Regeneration & Development, Civic Offices, Merrial Street, Newcastle-under-Lyme ST5 2AG ☎ 01782 742401
🖑 neale.clifton@newcastle-staffs.gov.uk

Senior Management: Mr Kelvin Turner, Executive Director - Resources, Support Services & S151 Officer, Civic Offices, Merrial Street, Newcastle-under-Lyme ST5 2AG ☎ 01782 742106
🖑 kelvin.turner@newcastle-staffs.gov.uk

Architect, Building / Property Services: Mr Graham Williams, Head - Assets & Regeneration, Civic Offices, Merrial Street, Newcastle-under-Lyme ST5 2AG ☎ 01782 742370
🖑 graham.williams@newcastle-staffs.gov.uk

NEWCASTLE-UNDER-LYME

Building Control: Mr Guy Benson, Head - Planning & Development, Civic Offices, Merrial Street, Newcastle-under-Lyme ST5 2AG ☎ 01782 744440 ◌ guy.benson@newcastle-staffs.gov.uk

PR / Communications: Mr Phil Jones, Head - Communications, Civic Offices, Merrial Street, Newcastle-under-Lyme ST5 2AG ☎ 01782 742271 ◌ phil.jones@newcastle-staffs.gov.uk

Community Safety: Mrs Sarah Moore, Partnerships Manager, Civic Offices, Merrial Street, Newcastle-under-Lyme ST5 2AG ☎ 01782 742496 ◌ sarah.moore@newcastle-staffs.gov.uk

Computer Management: Mr David Elkington, ICT Operations & Development Manager, Civic Offices, Merrial Street, Newcastle-under-Lyme ST5 2AG ☎ 01782 742472 ◌ david.elkington@newcastle-staffs.gov.uk

Computer Management: Mrs Jeannette Hilton, Head - Customer Services & ICT Services, Civic Offices, Merrial Street, Newcastle-under-Lyme ST5 2AG ☎ 01782 742470 ◌ jeannette.hilton@newcastle-staffs.gov.uk

Contracts: Mr Roger Tait, Head - Operations, Civic Offices, Merrial Street, Newcastle-under-Lyme ST5 2AG ☎ 01782 742632 ◌ roger.tait@newcastle-staffs.gov.uk

Corporate Services: Mr Kelvin Turner, Executive Director - Resources, Support Services & S151 Officer, Civic Offices, Merrial Street, Newcastle-under-Lyme ST5 2AG ☎ 01782 742106 ◌ kelvin.turner@newcastle-staffs.gov.uk

Customer Service: Mrs Jeannette Hilton, Head - Customer Services & ICT Services, Civic Offices, Merrial Street, Newcastle-under-Lyme ST5 2AG ☎ 01782 742470 ◌ jeannette.hilton@newcastle-staffs.gov.uk

Direct Labour: Mr Paul Pickerill, Streetscene Manager, Civic Offices, Merrial Street, Newcastle-under-Lyme ST5 2AG ☎ 01782 744760

Economic Development: Mr Simon Smith, Regeneration & Economic Development Manager, Civic Offices, Merrial Street, Newcastle-under-Lyme ST5 2AG ☎ 01782 742460 ◌ simon.smith@newcastle-staffs.gov.uk

Electoral Registration: Miss Julia Cleary, Democratic Services Manager, Civic Offices, Merrial Street, Newcastle-under-Lyme ST5 2AG ☎ 01782 742227 ◌ julia.cleary@newcastle-staffs.gov.uk

Emergency Planning: Mr Graham Williams, Head - Assets & Regeneration, Civic Offices, Merrial Street, Newcastle-under-Lyme ST5 2AG ☎ 01782 742370 ◌ graham.williams@newcastle-staffs.gov.uk

Energy Management: Mr Graham Williams, Head - Assets & Regeneration, Civic Offices, Merrial Street, Newcastle-under-Lyme ST5 2AG ☎ 01782 742370 ◌ graham.williams@newcastle-staffs.gov.uk

Environmental Health: Miss Nesta Barker, Head - Environmental Health Services, Civic Offices, Merrial Street, Newcastle-under-Lyme ST5 2AG ☎ 01782 742732 ◌ nesta.barker@newcastle-staffs.gov.uk

European Liaison: Mr Simon Smith, Regeneration & Economic Development Manager, Civic Offices, Merrial Street, Newcastle-under-Lyme ST5 2AG ☎ 01782 742460 ◌ simon.smith@newcastle-staffs.gov.uk

Events Manager: Mrs Janet Baddeley, Communications Manager, Civic Offices, Merrial Street, Newcastle-under-Lyme ST5 2AG ☎ 01782 742605 ◌ janet.baddeley@newcastle-staffs.gov.uk

Facilities: Mrs Joanne Halliday, Head - Housing, Regeneration & Assets Services, Civic Offices, Merrial Street, Newcastle-under-Lyme ST5 2AG ☎ 01782 742451 ◌ joanne.halliday@newcastle-staffs.gov.uk

Finance: Mr Dave Roberts, Head - Finance, Civic Offices, Merrial Street, Newcastle-under-Lyme ST5 2AG ☎ 01782 742111 ◌ dave.roberts@newcastle-staffs.gov.uk

Finance: Mr Kelvin Turner, Executive Director - Resources, Support Services & S151 Officer, Civic Offices, Merrial Street, Newcastle-under-Lyme ST5 2AG ☎ 01782 742106 ◌ kelvin.turner@newcastle-staffs.gov.uk

Treasury: Mr Kelvin Turner, Executive Director - Resources, Support Services & S151 Officer, Civic Offices, Merrial Street, Newcastle-under-Lyme ST5 2AG ☎ 01782 742106 ◌ kelvin.turner@newcastle-staffs.gov.uk

Fleet Management: Mr Trevor Nicoll, Head - Recycling & Fleet Services, Civic Offices, Merrial Street, Newcastle-under-Lyme ST5 2AG ☎ 01782 742155 ◌ trevor.nicoll@newcastle-staffs.gov.uk

Grounds Maintenance: Mr Roger Tait, Head - Operations, Civic Offices, Merrial Street, Newcastle-under-Lyme ST5 2AG ☎ 01782 742632 ◌ roger.tait@newcastle-staffs.gov.uk

Health and Safety: Ms Claire Dodd, Corporate Health & Safety Officer, Civic Offices, Merrial Street, Newcastle-under-Lyme ST5 2AG ☎ 01782 742262 ◌ claire.dodd@newcastle-staffs.gov.uk

Home Energy Conservation: Mr Michael O'Connor, Principal Environmental Health Officer, Civic Offices, Merrial Street, Newcastle-under-Lyme ST5 2AG ☎ 01782 742564 ◌ mike.o'connor@newcastle-staffs.gov.uk

Housing: Mr Neale Clifton, Executive Director - Regeneration & Development, Civic Offices, Merrial Street, Newcastle-under-Lyme ST5 2AG ☎ 01782 742401 ◌ neale.clifton@newcastle-staffs.gov.uk

Housing: Mrs Joanne Halliday, Head - Housing, Regeneration & Assets Services, Civic Offices, Merrial Street, Newcastle-under-Lyme ST5 2AG ☎ 01782 742451 ◌ joanne.halliday@newcastle-staffs.gov.uk

Leisure and Cultural Services: Mr Robert Foster, Head - Leisure & Cultural Services, Civic Offices, Merrial Street, Newcastle-under-Lyme ST5 2AG ☎ 01782 742636 ◌ robert.foster@newcastle-staffs.gov.uk

Licensing: Miss Julia Cleary, Democratic Services Manager, Civic Offices, Merrial Street, Newcastle-under-Lyme ST5 2AG ☎ 01782 742227 ◌ julia.cleary@newcastle-staffs.gov.uk

Lottery Funding, Charity and Voluntary: Mr Robert Foster, Head - Leisure & Cultural Services, Civic Offices, Merrial Street, Newcastle-under-Lyme ST5 2AG ☎ 01782 742636 ⌨ robert.foster@newcastle-staffs.gov.uk

Member Services: Miss Julia Cleary, Democratic Services Manager, Civic Offices, Merrial Street, Newcastle-under-Lyme ST5 2AG ☎ 01782 742227 ⌨ julia.cleary@newcastle-staffs.gov.uk

Parking: Mr Graham Williams, Head - Assets & Regeneration, Civic Offices, Merrial Street, Newcastle-under-Lyme ST5 2AG ☎ 01782 742370 ⌨ graham.williams@newcastle-staffs.gov.uk

Partnerships: Mrs Sarah Moore, Partnerships Manager, Civic Offices, Merrial Street, Newcastle-under-Lyme ST5 2AG ☎ 01782 742496 ⌨ sarah.moore@newcastle-staffs.gov.uk

Personnel / HR: Mrs Sarah Taylor, Acting Head - Human Resources, Civic Offices, Merrial Street, Newcastle-under-Lyme ST5 2AG ☎ 01782 742261 ⌨ sarah.taylor@newcastle-staffs.gov.uk

Planning: Mr Guy Benson, Head - Planning & Development, Civic Offices, Merrial Street, Newcastle-under-Lyme ST5 2AG ☎ 01782 744440 ⌨ guy.benson@newcastle-staffs.gov.uk

Procurement: Mr Simon Sowerby, Procurement Officer, Civic Offices, Merrial Street, Newcastle-under-Lyme ST5 2AG ☎ 01782 742756

Recycling & Waste Minimisation: Mr Trevor Nicoll, Head - Recycling & Fleet Services, Civic Offices, Merrial Street, Newcastle-under-Lyme ST5 2AG ☎ 01782 742155 ⌨ trevor.nicoll@newcastle-staffs.gov.uk

Regeneration: Mr Neale Clifton, Executive Director - Regeneration & Development, Civic Offices, Merrial Street, Newcastle-under-Lyme ST5 2AG ☎ 01782 742401 ⌨ neale.clifton@newcastle-staffs.gov.uk

Staff Training: Mrs Sarah Taylor, Acting Head - Human Resources, Civic Offices, Merrial Street, Newcastle-under-Lyme ST5 2AG ☎ 01782 742261 ⌨ sarah.taylor@newcastle-staffs.gov.uk

Street Scene: Mr Paul Pickerill, Streetscene Manager, Civic Offices, Merrial Street, Newcastle-under-Lyme ST5 2AG ☎ 01782 744760

Sustainable Communities: Mr Neale Clifton, Executive Director - Regeneration & Development, Civic Offices, Merrial Street, Newcastle-under-Lyme ST5 2AG ☎ 01782 742401 ⌨ neale.clifton@newcastle-staffs.gov.uk

Sustainable Development: Mr Neale Clifton, Executive Director - Regeneration & Development, Civic Offices, Merrial Street, Newcastle-under-Lyme ST5 2AG ☎ 01782 742401 ⌨ neale.clifton@newcastle-staffs.gov.uk

Tourism: Mr Phil Jones, Head - Communications, Civic Offices, Merrial Street, Newcastle-under-Lyme ST5 2AG ☎ 01782 742271 ⌨ phil.jones@newcastle-staffs.gov.uk

Transport: Mr Stephen Gee, Transport Manager, Central Depot, Knutton Lane, Newcastle-under-Lyme ST5 2SL ☎ 01782 742712 ⌨ stephen.gee@newcastle-staffs.gov.uk

Transport Planner: Mr Stephen Gee, Transport Manager, Central Depot, Knutton Lane, Newcastle-under-Lyme ST5 2SL ☎ 01782 742712 ⌨ stephen.gee@newcastle-staffs.gov.uk

Waste Collection and Disposal: Mr Trevor Nicoll, Head - Recycling & Fleet Services, Civic Offices, Merrial Street, Newcastle-under-Lyme ST5 2AG ☎ 01782 742155 ⌨ trevor.nicoll@newcastle-staffs.gov.uk

Waste Management: Mr Trevor Nicoll, Head - Recycling & Fleet Services, Civic Offices, Merrial Street, Newcastle-under-Lyme ST5 2AG ☎ 01782 742155 ⌨ trevor.nicoll@newcastle-staffs.gov.uk

Waste Management: Mr Paul Pickerill, Streetscene Manager, Civic Offices, Merrial Street, Newcastle-under-Lyme ST5 2AG ☎ 01782 744760

COUNCILLORS

Mayor: Wilkes, Ian (LD - Audley & Bignall End) ian.wilkes@newcastle-staffs.gov.uk

Deputy Mayor: White, Simon (IND - Madeley) simon.white@newcastle-staffs.gov.uk

Leader of the Council: Shenton, Elizabeth (LAB - Town) elizabeth.shenton@newcastle-staffs.gov.uk

Deputy Leader of the Council: Turner, Terry (LAB - Kidsgrove) terry.turner@newcastle-staffs.gov.uk

Group Leader: Huckfield, Derrick (IND - Knutton & Silverdale) derrick.huckfield@newcastle-staffs.gov.uk

Group Leader: Owen, Kenneth (UKIP - Holditch) kenneth.owen@newcastle-staffs.gov.uk

Group Leader: Proctor, Bert (IND - Audley & Bignall End) bert.proctor@newcastle-staffs.gov.uk

Group Leader: Sweeney, Stephen (CON - Clayton) stephen.sweeney@newcastle-staffs.gov.uk

Allport, David (LAB - Talke) david.allport@newcastle-staffs.gov.uk

Astle, Margaret (LAB - Kidsgrove) margaret.astle@kidsgrove.info

Bailey, Reginald (LAB - Kidsgrove) reginald.bailey@newcastle-staffs.gov.uk

Beech, Ann (LAB - Audley & Bignall End) ann.beech@newcastle-staffs.gov.uk

Bloor, Laura (CON - Halmer End) laura.bloor@newcastle-staffs.gov.uk

Burch, Lionel (LAB - Newchapel) lionel.burch@newcastle-staffs.gov.uk

Burgess, Silvia (LAB - Butt Lane) silvia.burgess@newcastle-staffs.gov.uk

Cooper, Julie (CON - Porthill) julie.cooper@newcastle-staffs.gov.uk

Cooper, John (CON - Porthill) john.cooper@newcastle-staffs.gov.uk

NEWCASTLE-UNDER-LYME

Dillon, Laura (LAB - Ravenscliffe)
laura.dillon@newcastle-staffs.gov.uk

Dymond, Sylvia (LAB - Butt Lane)
sylviadymond@talktalk.net

Eagles, Tony (LAB - Knutton & Silverdale)
tony.eagles@newcastle-staffs.gov.uk

Fear, Andrew (CON - Seabridge)
andrew.fear@newcastle-staffs.gov.uk

Frankish, Avril (CON - Halmer End)
avril@frankish.org

Gardner, Allison (LAB - Chesterton)
allison.gardner@newcastle-staffs.gov.uk

Hailstones, Linda (CON - Westlands)
linda.hailstones@newcastle-staffs.gov.uk

Hailstones, Peter (CON - Seabridge)
peter.hailstones@newcastle-staffs.gov.uk

Hambleton, Trevor (LAB - Bradwell)
trevor.hambleton@newcastle-staffs.gov.uk

Hambleton, Sandra (LAB - Bradwell)
sandra.hambleton@newcastle-staffs.gov.uk

Harper, David (UKIP - Chesterton)
david.harper@newcastle-staff.gov.uk

Heesom, Gillian (CON - Westlands)
gillian.heesom@newcastle-staffs.gov.uk

Holland, Mark (CON - Westlands)
mark.holland@newcastle-staffs.gov.uk

Johnson, Trevor (CON - Wolstanton)
trevorgjohnson@aol.com

Jones, Dave (LAB - Bradwell)
dave.jones@newcastle-staff.gov.uk

Kearon, Tony (LAB - Keele)
tony.kearon@newcastle-staffs.gov.uk

Loades, David (CON - Loggerheads & Whitmore)
david.loades@newcastle-staffs.gov.uk

Mancey, Chloe (CON - Seabridge)
chloe.mancey@newcastle-staffs.gov.uk

Matthews, Ian (CON - May Bank)
ian.matthews@newcastle-staffs.gov.uk

Naylon, Wenslie (IND - Keele)
wenslie.naylon@newcastle-staffs.gov.uk

Northcott, Paul (CON - Loggerheads & Whitmore)
paul.northcott@newcastle-staffs.gov.uk

Olszewski, Mark (LAB - Wolstanton)
mark.olszewski@newcastle-staffs.gov.uk

Panter, Barry (CON - Loggerheads & Whitmore)
barry.panter@newcastle-staffs.gov.uk

Parker, Andrew (CON - Clayton)
mradp76@yahoo.com

Pickup, Sarah (LAB - Ravenscliffe)
s44ahg@gmail.com

Reddish, Marion (LD - Thistleberry)
marion.reddish@newcastle-staffs.gov.uk

Robinson, Kyle (LAB - Butt Lane)
kyle.robinson@newcastle-staffs.gov.uk

Rout, Amelia (LAB - Silverdale & Parksite)
amelia.rout@newcastle-staffs.gov.uk

Simpson, Sandra (LAB - Chesterton)
sandra.simpson@newcastle-staffs.gov.uk

Snell, Gareth (LAB - Silverdale & Parksite)
gareth.snell@newcastle-staffs.gov.uk

Spence, Chris (LAB - Holditch)
chris.spence@newcastle-staffs.gov.uk

Stubbs, Mike (LAB - Talke)
mike.stubbs@newcastle-staffs.gov.uk

Tagg, Simon (CON - May Bank)
simon.tagg@newcastle-staffs.gov.uk

Tagg, John (CON - May Bank)
john.tagg@newcastle-staffs.gov.uk

Walklate, June (LD - Thistleberry)
june.walklate@newcastle-staffs.gov.uk

Waring, Paul (LAB - Newchapel)
paul.waring@newcastle-staffs.gov.uk

Welsh, Billy (IND - Madeley)
billy.welsh@newcastle-staffs.gov.uk

Williams, John (LAB - Cross Heath)
john.williams@newcastle-staffs.gov.uk

Williams, Gillian (LAB - Cross Heath)
gillian.williams@newcastle-staffs.gov.uk

Winfield, Joan (LAB - Cross Heath)
joan.winfield@newcastle-staffs.gov.uk

Wing, Lucinda (CON - Thistleberry)
lucinda.wing@newcastle-staffs.gov.uk

Woolley, David (IND - Wolstanton)
david.woolley@newcastle-staffs.gov.uk

Wright, Ruth (LAB - Town)
ruth.wright@newcastle-staffs.gov.uk

POLITICAL COMPOSITION
LAB: 29, CON: 20, IND: 6, LD: 3, UKIP: 2

COMMITTEE CHAIRS

Audit: Ms Sarah Pickup

Health & Wellbeing: Mr Dave Jones

Licensing: Mr Trevor Hambleton

Planning: Mr Bert Proctor

Newham   L

Newham London Borough Council, Newham Dockside, 1000
Dockside Road, Royal Albert Dock, London E16 2QU
☎ 020 8430 2000
✆ firstname.lastname@newham.gov.uk
🖥 www.newham.gov.uk

FACTS AND FIGURES
Parliamentary Constituencies: East Ham, West Ham
EU Constituencies: London
Election Frequency: Elections are of whole council

PRINCIPAL OFFICERS

Chief Executive: Mr Kim Bromley-Derry, Chief Executive, Newham Dockside, 1000 Dockside Road, Royal Albert Dock, London E16 2QU ☎ 020 8430 2000
✆ kim.bromley-derry@newham.gov.uk

Deputy Chief Executive: Mr Nick Bracken, Chief Operating Officer, Newham Dockside, 1000 Dockside Road, Royal Albert Dock, London E16 2QU ☎ 020 8430 2000
✆ nick.bracken@newham.gov.uk

Assistant Chief Executive: Mr Tony Clements, Assistant Chief Executive & Director - Business & Growth, Newham Dockside, 1000 Dockside Road, Royal Albert Dock, London E16 2QU
☎ 020 8430 2000 ✆ tony.clements@newham.gov.uk

Assistant Chief Executive: Mr Douglas Trainer, Assistant Chief Executive - Strategic Services, Newham Dockside, 1000 Dockside Road, Royal Albert Dock, London E16 2QU ☎ 020 8430 2000
✆ douglas.trainer@newham.gov.uk

Senior Management: Mrs Deborah Hindson, Director - Financial Sustainability, Newham Dockside, 1000 Dockside Road, Royal Albert Dock, London E16 2QU ☎ 020 8430 2000
✆ deborah.hindson@newham.gov.uk

Access Officer / Social Services (Disability): Miss Grainne Siggins, Director - Commissioning (Adults), Newham Dockside, 1000 Dockside Road, Royal Albert Dock, London E16 2QU
✆ grainne.siggins@newham.gov.uk

Architect, Building / Property Services: Ms Zoe Power, Head of Programmes & Projects, Newham Dockside, 1000 Dockside Road, Royal Albert Dock, London E16 2QU ☎ 020 8430 2000
✆ zoe.power@newham.gov.uk

Building Control: Mr Terry Harvey, Building Control Surveyor, Newham Dockside, 1000 Dockside Road, Royal Albert Dock, London E16 2QU ☎ 020 8430 2000 ✆ terry.harvey@newham.gov.uk

Catering Services: Mr Michael Hales, Head of Newham Catering & Cleaning Services, Newham Catering, 242 Fernhill Street, London E16 2HZ ☎ 020 8430 2000 ✆ michael.hales@newham.gov.uk

Children / Youth Services: Mr James Thomas, Director - Commisiong (Children's Services), Newham Dockside, 1000 Dockside Road, Royal Albert Dock, London E16 2QU ☎ 020 8430 2000
✆ james.thomas@newham.gov.uk

Civil Registration: Ms Lynne Cummings, Registrars & Cemetary Manager, Newham Register Office, 207 Plashet Grove, London E6 1BT ☎ 020 8430 3616 ✆ lynne.cummings@newham.gov.uk

PR / Communications: Mr Gary Bird, Interim Head of Communications, Newham Dockside, 1000 Dockside Road, Royal Albert Dock, London E16 2QU ☎ 020 8430 2000
✆ gary.bird@newham.gov.uk

Community Planning: Mr Damian Atkinson, Head of Commissioning (Community Neighbourhoods), Newham Dockside, 1000 Dockside Road, Royal Albert Dock, London E16 2QU
☎ 020 8430 2000 ✆ damian.atkinson@newham.gov.uk

Community Safety: Mr Matthew Hooper, Director - Enforcement & Safety, Newham Dockside, 1000 Dockside Road, Royal Albert Dock, London E16 2QU ☎ 020 8430 2000
✆ matthew.hooper@newham.gov.uk

Computer Management: Mr Geoff Connell, Director - ICT Services, Newham Dockside, 1000 Dockside Road, Royal Albert Dock, London E16 2QU ☎ 020 8430 2000; 020 8430 2000
✆ geoff.connell@havering.gov.uk

Consumer Protection and Trading Standards: Ms Sheila Roberts, Enforcement Manager, Newham Dockside, 1000 Dockside Road, Royal Albert Dock, London E16 2QU ☎ 020 3373 7914
✆ sheila.roberts@newham.gov.uk

Contracts: Mr David Pridmore, Head of Procurement, Newham Dockside, 1000 Dockside Road, Royal Albert Dock, London E16 2QU ☎ 020 8430 2000 ✆ david.pridmore@newham.gov.uk

Customer Service: Mr Chris Boylett, Head of Customer Transactions, Newham Dockside, 1000 Dockside Road, Royal Albert Dock, London E16 2QU ☎ 020 8430 2000
✆ chris.boylett@newham.gov.uk

Economic Development: Mrs Jane Sherwood, Head of Commissioning (Economic Regeneration), Newham Dockside, 1000 Dockside Road, Royal Albert Dock, London E16 2QU
☎ 020 8430 2000 ✆ jane.sherwood@newham.gov.uk

Education: Mr James Thomas, Director - Commisiong (Children's Services), Newham Dockside, 1000 Dockside Road, Royal Albert Dock, London E16 2QU ☎ 020 8430 2000
✆ james.thomas@newham.gov.uk

Electoral Registration: Mr Paul Libreri, Head of Registration & Electoral Services, East Ham Town Hall, 324 Barking Road, London E6 2RP ☎ 020 8430 2000 ✆ paul.libreri@newham.gov.uk

Emergency Planning: Ms Dawn Paish, Resilience Officer, Newham Dockside, 1000 Dockside Road, Royal Albert Dock, London E16 2QU ☎ 020 8430 2000 ✆ dawn.paish@newham.gov.uk

Environmental / Technical Services: Mr Gary Alderson, Interim Director - Commissioning (Community, Environment & CI), Newham Dockside, 1000 Dockside Road, Royal Albert Dock, London E16 2QU ☎ 020 8430 2000 ✆ gary.alderson@newham.gov.uk

Environmental Health: Ms Sheila Roberts, Enforcement Manager, Newham Dockside, 1000 Dockside Road, Royal Albert Dock, London E16 2QU ☎ 020 3373 7914
✆ sheila.roberts@newham.gov.uk

Estates, Property & Valuation: Mr Gary Green, Head of Property, Newham Dockside, 1000 Dockside Road, Royal Albert Dock, London E16 2QU ☎ 020 8430 2000
✆ gary.green@newham.gov.uk

Events Manager: Mrs Sue Meiners, Deputy Head of Communications, Newham Dockside, 1000 Dockside Road, Royal Albert Dock, London E16 2QU ☎ 020 8430 2000
✆ sue.meiners@newham.gov.uk

NEWHAM

Facilities: Mr Gary Westfallen, Interim Head of Facilities Management, Newham Dockside, 1000 Dockside Road, Royal Albert Dock, London E16 2QU ☎ 020 8430 2000 ⁂ gary.westfallen@newham.gov.uk

Finance: Ms Julie Alderson, Director - Finance, Newham Dockside, 1000 Dockside Road, Royal Albert Dock, London E16 2QU ☎ 020 8430 2000 ⁂ julie.alderson@newham.gov.uk

Finance: Mrs Deborah Hindson, Director - Financial Sustainability, Newham Dockside, 1000 Dockside Road, Royal Albert Dock, London E16 2QU ☎ 020 8430 2000 ⁂ deborah.hindson@newham.gov.uk

Pensions: Mr Ian Weavers, Pensions Manager, Newham Dockside, 1000 Dockside Road, Royal Albert Dock, London E16 2QU ☎ 020 3373 8408 ⁂ ian.weavers@newham.gov.uk

Fleet Management: Mr Chapman Bradley, Fleet Management Officer, Newham Dockside, 1000 Dockside Road, Royal Albert Dock, London E16 2QU ☎ 020 8430 2000 ⁂ chapman.bradley@newham.gov.uk

Grounds Maintenance: Mr Peter Gay, Head of Commisioning (Public Space & Landscape Design), Newham Dockside, 1000 Dockside Road, Royal Albert Dock, London E16 2QU ☎ 020 3373 1996 ⁂ peter.gay@newham.gov.uk

Health and Safety: Mrs Sue Wilkes, Human Resources - Health & Safety, Newham Dockside, 1000 Dockside Road, Royal Albert Dock, London E16 2QU ☎ 020 8430 2000 ⁂ sue.wilkes@onesource.gov.uk

Highways: Mr John Biden, Head of Commissioning (Highways & Traffic), Newham Dockside, 1000 Dockside Road, Royal Albert Dock, London E16 2QU ☎ 020 8430 2000 ⁂ john.biden@newham.gov.uk

Home Energy Conservation: Mr Gary Green, Head of Property, Newham Dockside, 1000 Dockside Road, Royal Albert Dock, London E16 2QU ☎ 020 8430 2000 ⁂ gary.green@newham.gov.uk

Housing: Mr Roberto Bruni, Head of Housing Property & Initiatives Commissioning, Newham Dockside, 1000 Dockside Road, Royal Albert Dock, London E16 2QU ☎ 020 8430 2000 ⁂ roberto.bruni@newham.gov.uk

Housing Maintenance: Mr Roberto Bruni, Head of Housing Property & Initiatives Commissioning, Newham Dockside, 1000 Dockside Road, Royal Albert Dock, London E16 2QU ☎ 020 8430 2000 ⁂ roberto.bruni@newham.gov.uk

Legal: Mr Daniel Fenwick, Director - Legal & Governance / Monitoring Officer, Newham Dockside, 1000 Dockside Road, Royal Albert Dock, London E16 2QU ☎ 020 8430 2000 ⁂ daniel.fenwick@newham.gov.uk

Leisure and Cultural Services: Mr Mark Perkins, Head of Commissioning (Sports & Leisure), Newham Dockside, 1000 Dockside Road, Royal Albert Dock, London E16 2QU ☎ 020 8430 2000 ⁂ mark.perkins@newham.gov.uk

Licensing: Ms Sheila Roberts, Enforcement Manager, Newham Dockside, 1000 Dockside Road, Royal Albert Dock, London E16 2QU ☎ 020 3373 7914 ⁂ sheila.roberts@newham.gov.uk

Lifelong Learning: Mr Steve Cameron, Head of Commissioning (Skills), Connexions, 51 Broadway, London E15 4BQ ☎ 020 8430 2000 ⁂ steve.cameron@newham.gov.uk

Lighting: Mr Jaspal Sehmi, Structural Services Manager, Newham Dockside, 1000 Dockside Road, Royal Albert Dock, London E16 2QU ☎ 020 8430 2000 ⁂ jaspal.sehmi@newham.gov.uk

Parking: Mr Laurence Courtney, Parking Enforcement Manager, Newham Dockside, 1000 Dockside Road, Royal Albert Dock, London E16 2QU ☎ 020 8430 2000 ⁂ laurence.courtney@newham.gov.uk

Personnel / HR: Mrs Jan Douglas, Deputy Director - Human Resources, Newham Dockside, 1000 Dockside Road, Royal Albert Dock, London E16 2QU ☎ 020 8430 2000 ⁂ jan.douglas@onesource.co.uk

Planning: Ms Deirdra Armsby, Director - Regeneration & Planning, Newham Dockside, 1000 Dockside Road, Royal Albert Dock, London E16 2QU ☎ 020 8430 2000 ⁂ deirdra.armsby@newham.gov.uk

Procurement: Mr David Pridmore, Head of Procurement, Newham Dockside, 1000 Dockside Road, Royal Albert Dock, London E16 2QU ☎ 020 8430 2000 ⁂ david.pridmore@newham.gov.uk

Public Libraries: Mr Damian Atkinson, Head of Commissioning (Community Neighbourhoods), Newham Dockside, 1000 Dockside Road, Royal Albert Dock, London E16 2QU ☎ 020 8430 2000 ⁂ damian.atkinson@newham.gov.uk

Recycling & Waste Minimisation: Mr Gary Alderson, Interim Director - Commissioning (Community, Environment & CI), Newham Dockside, 1000 Dockside Road, Royal Albert Dock, London E16 2QU ☎ 020 8430 2000 ⁂ gary.alderson@newham.gov.uk

Regeneration: Ms Deirdra Armsby, Director - Regeneration & Planning, Newham Dockside, 1000 Dockside Road, Royal Albert Dock, London E16 2QU ☎ 020 8430 2000 ⁂ deirdra.armsby@newham.gov.uk

Road Safety: Mr John Biden, Head of Commissioning (Highways & Traffic), Newham Dockside, 1000 Dockside Road, Royal Albert Dock, London E16 2QU ☎ 020 8430 2000 ⁂ john.biden@newham.gov.uk

Social Services (Adult): Miss Grainne Siggins, Director - Commissioning (Adults), Newham Dockside, 1000 Dockside Road, Royal Albert Dock, London E16 2QU ⁂ grainne.siggins@newham.gov.uk

Social Services (Children): Mr James Thomas, Director - Commisiong (Children's Services), Newham Dockside, 1000 Dockside Road, Royal Albert Dock, London E16 2QU ☎ 020 8430 2000 ⁂ james.thomas@newham.gov.uk

Public Health: Ms Meradin Peachey, Director - Public Health, Newham Dockside, 1000 Dockside Road, Royal Albert Dock, London E16 2QU ☎ 020 8430 2000 ⌁ meradin.peachey@newham.gov.uk

Staff Training: Mrs Jan Douglas, Deputy Director - Human Resources, Newham Dockside, 1000 Dockside Road, Royal Albert Dock, London E16 2QU ☎ 020 8430 2000 ⌁ jan.douglas@onesource.co.uk

Town Centre: Ms Deirdra Armsby, Director - Regeneration & Planning, Newham Dockside, 1000 Dockside Road, Royal Albert Dock, London E16 2QU ☎ 020 8430 2000 ⌁ deirdra.armsby@newham.gov.uk

Traffic Management: Mr John Biden, Head of Commissioning (Highways & Traffic), Newham Dockside, 1000 Dockside Road, Royal Albert Dock, London E16 2QU ☎ 020 8430 2000 ⌁ john.biden@newham.gov.uk

Transport: Mr John Biden, Head of Commissioning (Highways & Traffic), Newham Dockside, 1000 Dockside Road, Royal Albert Dock, London E16 2QU ☎ 020 8430 2000 ⌁ john.biden@newham.gov.uk

Transport Planner: Mr John Biden, Head of Commissioning (Highways & Traffic), Newham Dockside, 1000 Dockside Road, Royal Albert Dock, London E16 2QU ☎ 020 8430 2000 ⌁ john.biden@newham.gov.uk

Waste Collection and Disposal: Mr Jarlath Griffin, Head of Delivery & Public Space, Newham Dockside, 1000 Dockside Road, Royal Albert Dock, London E16 2QU ☎ 020 8430 2000 ⌁ jarlath.griffin@newham.gov.uk

Waste Management: Mr Gary Alderson, Interim Director - Commissioning (Community, Environment & CI), Newham Dockside, 1000 Dockside Road, Royal Albert Dock, London E16 2QU ☎ 020 8430 2000 ⌁ gary.alderson@newham.gov.uk

COUNCILLORS

Mayor: Wales, Robin (LAB - No Ward)
mayor@newham.gov.uk

Deputy Mayor: Hudson, Lester (LAB - Wall End)
lester.hudson@newham.gov.uk

Abdulmuhit, Hanif (LAB - Green Street West)
hanif.abdulmuhit@newham.gov.uk

Akiwowo, Seyi (LAB - Forest Gate North)
seyi.akiwowo@newham.gov.uk

Alarice, Aleen (LAB - Plaistow South)
aleen.alarice@newham.gov.uk

Alexander, Jose (LAB - Green Street East)
jose.alexander@newham.gov.uk

Baikie, Andrew (LAB - Little Ilford)
andrew.baikie@newham.gov.uk

Beckles, James (LAB - Plaistow North)
james.beckles@newham.gov.uk

Bourne, Freda (LAB - West Ham)
freda.bourne@newham.gov.uk

Brayshaw, Steve (LAB - Royal Docks)
steve.brayshaw@newham.gov.uk

Chowdhury, Ayesha (LAB - Beckton)
ayesha.chowdhury@newham.gov.uk

Christie, David (LAB - Beckton)
david.christie@newham.gov.uk

Clark, Ken (LAB - Little Ilford)
ken.clark@newham.gov.uk

Clarke, Frances (LAB - Wall End)
frances.clarke@newham.gov.uk

Collier, Bryan (LAB - Canning Town South)
bryan.collier@newham.gov.uk

Corbett, Ian (LAB - East Ham Central)
ian.corbett@newham.gov.uk

Corbett, Jo (LAB - Manor Park)
jo.corbett@newham.gov.uk

Crawford, Richard (LAB - Stratford & New Town)
richard.crawford@newham.gov.uk

Desai, Unmesh (LAB - East Ham Central)
unmesh.desai@newham.gov.uk

Easter, Ann (LAB - Canning Town North)
ann.easter@newham.gov.uk

Fiaz, Rokhsana (LAB - Custom House)
rokhsana.fiaz@newham.gov.uk

Furness, Clive (LAB - Canning Town North)
clive.furness@newham.gov.uk

Gray, John (LAB - West Ham)
john.gray@newham.gov.uk

Griffiths, Alan (LAB - Canning Town South)
alan.griffiths@newham.gov.uk

Gulamussen, Zuber (LAB - East Ham North)
zuber.gulamussen@newham.gov.uk

Holland, Patricia (LAB - Custom House)
patricia.holland@newham.gov.uk

Hussain, Forhad (LAB - Plaistow North)
forhad.hussain@newham.gov.uk

Ibrahim, Idris (LAB - Green Street West)
idris.ibrahim@newham.gov.uk

Islam, Anamul (LAB - Forest Gate North)

Khan, Obaid (LAB - Boleyn)
obaid.khan@newham.gov.uk

Laguda, Joy (LAB - Plaistow North)
joy.laguda@newham.gov.uk

Marriott, Julianne (LAB - East Ham Central)
julianne.marriott@newham.gov.uk

Masters, Susan (LAB - East Ham South)
susan.masters@newham.gov.uk

McAlmont, Anthony (LAB - Royal Docks)
anthony.mcalmont@newham.gov.uk

McAuley, Conor (LAB - Custom House)
conor.mcauley@newham.gov.uk

McLean, Charlene (LAB - Stratford & New Town)
charlene.mclean@newham.gov.uk

Murphy, Patrick (LAB - Royal Docks)
patrick.murphy@newham.gov.uk

Nazeer, Farah (LAB - Little Ilford)
farah.nazeer@newham.gov.uk

NEWHAM

Nekiwala, Firoza (LAB - East Ham North)
firoza.nekiwala@newham.gov.uk

Noor, Ahmed (LAB - Plaistow South)
ahmed.noor@newham.gov.uk

Oakeshott, Veronica (LAB - Boleyn)
veronica.oakeshott@newham.gov.uk

Patel, Mukesh (LAB - Green Street East)
mukesh.patel@newham.gov.uk

Patel, Salim (LAB - Manor Park)
salim.patel@newham.gov.uk

Patel, Mas (LAB - Forest Gate South)
mas.patel@newham.gov.uk

Paul, Terence (LAB - Stratford & New Town)
terence.paul@newham.gov.uk

Peppiatt, Quintin (LAB - East Ham South)
quintin.peppiatt@newham.gov.uk

Rahman, Tahmina (LAB - Green Street West)
tahmina.rahman@newham.gov.uk

Rahman, Rohima (LAB - Green Street East)
rohima.rahman@newham.gov.uk

Sathianesan, Paul (LAB - East Ham North)
paul.sathianesan@newham.gov.uk

Scoresby, Kay (LAB - Canning Town North)
kay.scoresby@newham.gov.uk

Shah, Lakmini (LAB - East Ham South)
lakmini.shah@newham.gov.uk

Singh, Amarjit (LAB - Manor Park)
amarjit.singh@newham.gov.uk

Sparrowhawk, Ted (LAB - Wall End)
ted.sparrowhawk@newham.gov.uk

Thomas, Sheila (LAB - Canning Town South)
sheila.thomas@newham.gov.uk

Tripp, Rachel (LAB - Forest Gate North)
rachel.tripp@newham.gov.uk

Vaughan, Winston (LAB - Forest Gate South)
winston.vaughan@newham.gov.uk

Virdee, Harvinder (LAB - Boleyn)
harvinder.virdee@newham.gov.uk

Walls, Dianne (LAB - Forest Gate South)
dianne.walls@newham.gov.uk

Whitworth, John (LAB - West Ham)
john.whitworth@newham.gov.uk

Wilson, Neil (LAB - Plaistow South)
neil.wilson@newham.gov.uk

Wilson, Tonii (LAB - Beckton)
tonii.wilson@newham.gov.uk

POLITICAL COMPOSITION
LAB: 61

COMMITTEE CHAIRS

Audit: Mr Lester Hudson

Children & Young People: Ms Kay Scoresby

Health & Social Care: Ms Dianne Walls

Health & Wellbeing: Mr Clive Furness

Licensing: Mr Ian Corbett

Newport City   W

Newport City Council, Civic Centre, Newport NP20 4UR
☎ 01633 656656 🖷 01633 656611 ◌ info@newport.gov.uk
🖳 www.newport.gov.uk

FACTS AND FIGURES
Parliamentary Constituencies: Newport East, Newport West
EU Constituencies: Wales
Election Frequency: Elections are of whole council

PRINCIPAL OFFICERS

Chief Executive: Mr Will Godfrey, Chief Executive, Civic Centre, Newport NP20 4UR ☎ 01633 232002
◌ will.godfrey@newport.gov.uk

Assistant Chief Executive: Ms Sheila Davies, Strategic Director - Place, Civic Centre, Newport NP20 4UR ☎ 01633 232501
◌ sheila.davies@newport.gov.uk

Assistant Chief Executive: Mr Mike Nicholson, Strategic Director - People (Statutory Director - Social Services), Civic Centre, Newport NP20 4UR ☎ 01633 210133 ◌ mike.nicholson@newport.gov.uk

Architect, Building / Property Services: Mr Lyndon Watkins, Managing Director - Newport Homes, Telford Depot, Telford Street, Newport NP19 0ES ☎ 01633 240440
◌ lyndon.watkins@newportnorse.co.uk

Building Control: Ms Tracey Brooks, Development Service Manager, Civic Centre, Newport NP20 4UR ☎ 01633 210066
◌ tracey.brooks@newport.gov.uk

Children / Youth Services: Mr Keir Duffin, Community Regeneration Manager, Civic Centre, Newport NP20 4UR
☎ 01633 210394 ◌ keir.duffin@newport.gov.uk

Civil Registration: Ms Shan Jenkins, Registration Services Manager, Register Office, The Mansion House, 4 Stow Park Circle, Newport NP20 4HE ☎ 01633 414774

PR / Communications: Mr Jonathan Hollins, Communications & Marketing Manager, Civic Centre, Newport NP20 4UR
☎ 01633 210454 ◌ jonathan.hollins@newport.gov.uk

Community Safety: Ms Helen Wilkie, Public Protection Manager, Civic Centre, Newport NP20 4UR ☎ 01633 851695
◌ helen.wilkie@newport.gov.uk

Computer Management: Mr Rhys Cornwall, Interim Head of People & Business Change, Civic Centre, Newport NP20 4UR
☎ 01633 210649 ◌ rhys.cornwall@newport.gov.uk

Consumer Protection and Trading Standards: Ms Helen Wilkie, Public Protection Manager, Civic Centre, Newport NP20 4UR ☎ 01633 851695 ◌ helen.wilkie@newport.gov.uk

Customer Service: Ms Leanne Rowlands, Customer Services Manager, Information Station, Old Station Building, Queensway, Newport NP20 4AX ☎ 01633 851560 ⚓ leanne.rowlands@newport.gov.uk

Economic Development: Ms Beverly Owen, Head of Regeneration, Investment & Housing, Civic Centre, Newport NP20 4UR ☎ 01633 210843 ⚓ beverly.owen@newport.gov.uk

Education: Mr James Harris, Chief Education Officer, Civic Centre, Newport NP20 4UR ☎ 01495 355419; 01633 232258 ⚓ james.harris@newport.gov.uk

Electoral Registration: Mr Phillip Johnson, Electoral Registration Manager, Civic Centre, Newport NP20 4UR ☎ 01633 210742 ⚓ phillip.johnson@newport.gov.uk

Emergency Planning: Mr Alan Young, Civil Contingencies Manager, Civic Centre, Newport NP20 4UR ☎ 01633 210591 ⚓ alan.young@newport.gov.uk

Environmental Health: Ms Helen Wilkie, Public Protection Manager, Civic Centre, Newport NP20 4UR ☎ 01633 851695 ⚓ helen.wilkie@newport.gov.uk

Estates, Property & Valuation: Mr Lyndon Watkins, Managing Director - Newport Homes, Telford Depot, Telford Street, Newport NP19 0ES ☎ 01633 240440 ⚓ lyndon.watkins@newportnorse.co.uk

European Liaison: Ms Sarah Armstrong, European Officer, Civic Centre, Newport NP20 4UR ☎ 01633 210062 ⚓ sarah.armstrong@newport.gov.uk

Events Manager: Mr Jonathan Hollins, Communications & Marketing Manager, Civic Centre, Newport NP20 4UR ☎ 01633 210454 ⚓ jonathan.hollins@newport.gov.uk

Finance: Mr Meirion Rushworth, Head of Finance, Civic Centre, Newport NP20 4UR ☎ 01633 210644 ⚓ meirion.rushworth@newport.gov.uk

Fleet Management: Mr Richard Cope, Integrated Transport Unit Manager, Civic Centre, Newport NP20 4UR ☎ 01633 210475 ⚓ richard.cope@newport.gov.uk

Grounds Maintenance: Mr Paul Symonds, Head of Streetscene & City Services, Civic Centre, Newport NP20 4UR ☎ 01633 656656 ⚓ paul.symonds@newport.gov.uk

Health and Safety: Mr Mike Francis, Health & Safety Manager, Civic Centre, Newport NP20 4UR ☎ 01633 656656 ⚓ mike.francis@newport.gov.uk

Highways: Mr Paul Symonds, Head of Streetscene & City Services, Civic Centre, Newport NP20 4UR ☎ 01633 656656 ⚓ paul.symonds@newport.gov.uk

Housing: Mr Mike Jones, Housing & Property Manager, Civic Centre, Newport NP20 4UR ☎ 01633 210603 ⚓ mike.jones@newport.gov.uk

Legal: Mr Gareth Price, Head of Law & Regulations, Civic Centre, Newport NP20 4UR ☎ 01633 210726 ⚓ gareth.price@newport.gov.uk

Licensing: Ms Helen Wilkie, Public Protection Manager, Civic Centre, Newport NP20 4UR ☎ 01633 851695 ⚓ helen.wilkie@newport.gov.uk

Member Services: Mr Richard Jefferies, Chief Democratic Services Officer, Civic Centre, Newport NP20 4UR ☎ 01633 210729 ⚓ richard.jefferies@newport.gov.uk

Partnerships: Mr Rhys Cornwall, Interim Head of People & Business Change, Civic Centre, Newport NP20 4UR ☎ 01633 210649 ⚓ rhys.cornwall@newport.gov.uk

Personnel / HR: Mr Rhys Cornwall, Interim Head of People & Business Change, Civic Centre, Newport NP20 4UR ☎ 01633 210649 ⚓ rhys.cornwall@newport.gov.uk

Planning: Ms Tracey Brooks, Development Service Manager, Civic Centre, Newport NP20 4UR ☎ 01633 210066 ⚓ tracey.brooks@newport.gov.uk

Procurement: Ms Sarah Kelly, Strategic Procurement Officer, Civic Centre, Newport NP20 4UR ☎ 01633 210686 ⚓ sarah.kelly@newport.gov.uk

Public Libraries: Mr Mike Lewis, Culture & Continuing Learning Manager, Civic Centre, Newport NP20 4UR ☎ 01633 656656 ⚓ mike.lewis@newport.gov.uk

Recycling & Waste Minimisation: Ms Silvia Gonzalez-Lopez, Recycling & Sustainability Manager, Civic Centre, Newport NP20 4UR ☎ 01633 656656 ⚓ silvia.gonzalez-lopez@newport.gov.uk

Regeneration: Ms Beverly Owen, Head of Regeneration, Investment & Housing, Civic Centre, Newport NP20 4UR ☎ 01633 210843 ⚓ beverly.owen@newport.gov.uk

Social Services: Mr Mike Nicholson, Strategic Director - People (Statutory Director - Social Services), Civic Centre, Newport NP20 4UR ☎ 01633 210133 ⚓ mike.nicholson@newport.gov.uk

Social Services (Adult): Mr Chris Humphrey, Head of Adult & Community Services, Civic Centre, Newport NP20 4UR ☎ 01633 656656 ⚓ chris.humphrey@newport.gov.uk

Social Services (Children): Ms Sally Jenkins, Integrated Head of Children & Family Services, Civic Centre, Newport NP20 4UR ☎ 01633 210725 ⚓ sally.jenkins@newport.gov.uk

Staff Training: Mr Rhys Cornwall, Interim Head of People & Business Change, Civic Centre, Newport NP20 4UR ☎ 01633 210649 ⚓ rhys.cornwall@newport.gov.uk

Street Scene: Mr Paul Symonds, Head of Streetscene & City Services, Civic Centre, Newport NP20 4UR ☎ 01633 656656 ⚓ paul.symonds@newport.gov.uk

NEWPORT CITY

Tourism: Ms Lynne Richards, Tourism Officer, Civic Centre, Newport NP20 4UR ☎ 01633 233327 ◌ lynne.richards@newport.gov.uk

Traffic Management: Mr Paul Symonds, Head of Streetscene & City Services, Civic Centre, Newport NP20 4UR ☎ 01633 656656 ◌ paul.symonds@newport.gov.uk

Transport: Mr Richard Cope, Integrated Transport Unit Manager, Civic Centre, Newport NP20 4UR ☎ 01633 210475 ◌ richard.cope@newport.gov.uk

Waste Collection and Disposal: Mr Gwyn Jones, Waste Operations Manager, Civic Centre, Newport NP20 4UR ☎ 01633 235274 ◌ gwyn.jones@newport.gov.uk

Waste Management: Ms Silvia Gonzalez-Lopez, Recycling & Sustainability Manager, Civic Centre, Newport NP20 4UR ☎ 01633 656656 ◌ silvia.gonzalez-lopez@newport.gov.uk

Children's Play Areas: Mr Mike McGow, Parks & Outdoor Recreation Manager, Civic Centre, Newport NP20 4UR ☎ 01633 232830 ◌ mike.mcgow@newport.gov.uk

COUNCILLORS

Chair: Atwell, David (CON - Langstone)
david.atwell@newport.gov.uk

Leader of the Council: Wilcox, Deborah (LAB - Gaer)
debbie.wilcox@newport.gov.uk

Deputy Leader of the Council: Truman, Ray (LAB - Alway)
ray.truman@newport.gov.uk

Ali, Omar (LAB - Pillgwenlly)
omar.ali@newport.gov.uk

Al-Nuaimi, Miqdad (LAB - Stow Hill)
miqdad.al-nuaimi@newport.gov.uk

Bond, Tom (LAB - Rogerstone)
tom.bond@newport.gov.uk

Bright, Bob (LAB - Ringland)
bob.bright@newport.gov.uk

Cleverly, Janet (IND - Bettws)

Cockeram, Paul (LAB - Shaftesbury)
paul.cokeram@newport.gov.uk

Cornelious, Margaret (CON - Graig)
margaret.cornelious@newport.gov.uk

Corten, Emma (LAB - Ringland)
emma.corten@newport.gov.uk

Critchley, Ken (LAB - Lliswerry)
ken.critchley@newport.gov.uk

Davies, Deb (LAB - Beechwood)
deborah.davies@newport.gov.uk

Delahaye, Val (LAB - Bettws)
valerie.delahaye@newport.gov.uk

Evans, Matthew (CON - Allt-yr-yn)
matthew.evans@newport.gov.uk

Evans, Chris (LAB - Rogerstone)
chris.evans@newport.gov.uk

Ferris, Charles (CON - Allt-yr-yn)
charles.ferris@newport.gov.uk

Fouweather, David (CON - Allt-yr-yn)
david.fouweather@newport.gov.uk

Garland, Emma (LAB - St. Julians)
emma.garland@newport.gov.uk

Giles, Gail (LAB - Caerleon)
gail.giles@newport.gov.uk

Guy, John (LAB - Alway)
john.guy@newport.gov.uk

Hannon, Paul (LAB - Beechwood)
paul.hannon@newport.gov.uk

Harvey, Debbie (LAB - Alway)
debbie.harvey@newport.gov.uk

Hayat, Ibrahim (LAB - Pillgwenlly)
ibrahim.hayat@newport.gov.uk

Huntley, Paul (LAB - Caerleon)
paul.huntley@newport.gov.uk

Hutchings, Rhys (LAB - St. Julians)
rhys.hutchings@newport.gov.uk

Jeavons, Roger (LAB - Lliswerry)
roger.jeavons@newport.gov.uk

Jenkins, Christine (LAB - Victoria)
christine.jenkins@newport.gov.uk

Kellaway, Martyn (CON - Llanwern)
martyn.kellaway@newport.gov.uk

Linton, Malcolm (LAB - Ringland)
malcolm.linton@newport.gov.uk

Maxfield, Christine (LAB - Malpas)
christine.maxfield@newport.gov.uk

Mayer, David (LAB - Malpas)
david.mayer@newport.gov.uk

Mlewa, Sally (LAB - Rogerstone)
sally.mlewa@newport.gov.uk

Mogford, Ray (CON - Langstone)
ray.mogford@newport.gov.uk

Morris, Allan (LAB - Lliswerry)
allan.morris@newport.gov.uk

Mudd, Jane (LAB - Malpas)
jane.mudd@newport.gov.uk

Poole, Bob (LAB - Shaftesbury)
bob.poole@newport.gov.uk

Rahman, Majid (LAB - Victoria)
majid.rahman@newport.gov.uk

Richards, John (LAB - Lliswerry)
john.richards@newport.gov.uk

Spencer, Mark (LAB - Beechwood)
mark.spencer@newport.gov.uk

Suller, Tom (CON - Marshfield)
tom.suller@newport.gov.uk

Suller, Cliff (LAB - Caerleon)
cliff.suller@newport.gov.uk

Thomas, Herbert (LAB - Gaer)
herbert.thomas@newport.gov.uk

Thomas, Kate (LAB - Stow Hill)
kate.thomas@newport.gov.uk

Townsend, Carmel (LD - St. Julians)
carmel.townsend@newport.gov.uk

Watkins, Trevor (LAB - Tredegar Park)
trevor.watkins@newport.gov.uk

Whitcutt, Mark (LAB - Gaer)
mark.whitcutt@newport.gov.uk

White, Richard (CON - Marshfield)
richard.white@newport.gov.uk

Whitehead, Kevin (IND - Bettws)
kevin.whitehead@newport.gov.uk

Williams, David (CON - Graig)
david.williams@newport.gov.uk

POLITICAL COMPOSITION
LAB: 37, CON: 10, IND: 2, LD: 1

COMMITTEE CHAIRS

Licensing: Mr Cliff Suller

Planning: Mr Paul Huntley

Newry, Mourne & Down District Council　　N

Newry, Mourne & Down District Council, Newry, Mourne & Down District Council, Monaghan Row, Newry BT35 8DL
☎ 03000 132233 ⌂ info@nmandd.org 🖥 www.newrymournedown.org

PRINCIPAL OFFICERS

Chief Executive: Mr Liam Hannaway, Chief Executive, Newry, Mourne & Down District Council, Monaghan Row, Newry BT35 8DL
☎ 03000 132233

Senior Management: Mr Eddy Curtis, Director - Strategic Planning & Performance, Newry, Mourne & Down District Council, Monaghan Row, Newry BT35 8DL

Senior Management: Mr Michael Lipsett, Director - Active & Healthy Communities, Newry, Mourne & Down District Council, Monaghan Row, Newry BT35 8DL

Senior Management: Mr Canice O'Rourke, Director - Regulatory & Technical Services, Newry, Mourne & Down District Council, Monaghan Row, Newry BT35 8DL

Senior Management: Mrs Marie Ward, Director - Enterprise, Regeneration & Tourism, Newry, Mourne & Down District Council, Monaghan Row, Newry BT35 8DL

Building Control: Mrs Marie Ward, Director - Enterprise, Regeneration & Tourism, Newry, Mourne & Down District Council, Monaghan Row, Newry BT35 8DL

Computer Management: Mr Gavin Ringland, IT Manager, Newry, Mourne & Down District Council, Monaghan Row, Newry BT35 8DL

Corporate Services: Mr J McBride, Change Manager, Newry, Mourne & Down District Council, Monaghan Row, Newry BT35 8DL

Environmental / Technical Services: Mr Canice O'Rourke, Director - Regulatory & Technical Services, Newry, Mourne & Down District Council, Monaghan Row, Newry BT35 8DL

Leisure and Cultural Services: Mr Michael Lipsett, Director - Active & Healthy Communities, Newry, Mourne & Down District Council, Monaghan Row, Newry BT35 8DL

Planning: Mr Eddy Curtis, Director - Strategic Planning & Performance, Newry, Mourne & Down District Council, Monaghan Row, Newry BT35 8DL

Regeneration: Mrs Marie Ward, Director - Enterprise, Regeneration & Tourism, Newry, Mourne & Down District Council, Monaghan Row, Newry BT35 8DL

Tourism: Mrs Marie Ward, Director - Enterprise, Regeneration & Tourism, Newry, Mourne & Down District Council, Monaghan Row, Newry BT35 8DL

COUNCILLORS

Mayor: Hughes, Daire (SF - Fews)
daire.hughes@sinnfein.ie

Deputy Mayor: Quinn, Brian (SDLP - The Mournes)
brian.quinn@newryandmourne.gov.uk

Burns, William (DUP - The Mournes)
william.burns@newryandmourne.gov.uk

Carr, Michael (SDLP - Crotlieve)
michael.carr@newryandmourne.gov.uk

Casey, Charlie (SF - Newry Town)
charlie.casey@newryandmourne.gov.uk

Curran, Brendan (IND - Newry Town)
brendan.curran@newryandmourne.gov.uk

Donnelly, Geraldine (SDLP - Slieve Gullion)
geraldine.donnelly@newryandmourne.gov.uk

Doran, Sean (SF - The Mournes)
sean.doran@newryandmourne.gov.uk

Ennis, Sinead (SF - Crotlieve)
sinead.ennis@sinnfein.ie

Feehan, John (SDLP - Fews)
john.feehan@newryandmourne.gov.uk

Feely, Frank (SDLP - Newry Town)
frank.feely@newryandmourne.gov.uk

Fitzpatrick, Gillian (SDLP - Crotlieve)
gillian.fitzpatrick@newryandmourne.gov.uk

Flynn, A (SF - Slieve Gullion)

Harte, Valerie (SF - Newry Town)
valerie.harte@newryandmourne.gov.uk

Hearty, Terry (SF - Slieve Gullion)
terry.hearty@newryandmourne.gov.uk

Hyland, David (IND - Newry Town)
david.hyland@newryandmourne.gov.uk

Kimmins, Liz (SF - Slieve Gullion)
liz.kimmins@sinnfien.ie

Larkin, Mickey (SF - Slieve Gullion)
micky.larkin@sinnfien.ie

NEWRY, MOURNE & DOWN DISTRICT COUNCIL

McArdle, John (SDLP - Newry Town)
john.mcardle@newryandmourne.gov.uk

McAteer, Declan (SDLP - Crotlieve)
declan.mcateer@newryandmourne.gov.uk

McGreevy, Connaire (SDLP - Crotlieve)
connaire.mcgreevy@newryandmourne.gov.uk

McKee, Harold (UUP - The Mournes)
harold.mckee@newryandmourne.gov.uk

Moffett, A (UUP - Fews)

Mulgrew, Roisin (SF - Fews)
roisin.mulgrew@sinnfein.ie

Murphy, Mick (SF - Crotlieve)
mick.murphy@newryandmourne.gov.uk

Ó Muirí, Barry (SF - Fews)
barra.omuiri@sinnfein.ie

Patterson, Jackie (IND - Newry Town)
jackie.patterson@newryandmourne.gov.uk

Reilly, Henry (UKIP - The Mournes)
henry.reilly@newryandmourne.gov.uk

Ruane, Michael (SF - Crotlieve)
michael.ruane@newryandmourne.gov.uk

Taylor, David (UUP - Fews)
david.taylor@newryandmourne.gov.uk

POLITICAL COMPOSITION
SF: 13, SDLP: 9, IND: 3, UUP: 3, DUP: 1, UKIP: 1

Norfolk   C

Norfolk County Council, County Hall, Martineau Lane,
Norwich NR1 2DH
☎ 0344 800 8020 ≞ 0844 800 8012 ◌ information@norfolk.gov.uk
🖥 www.norfolk.gov.uk

FACTS AND FIGURES
Parliamentary Constituencies: Broadland, Great Yarmouth,
Norfolk Mid, Norfolk North, Norfolk North West, Norfolk South, Norfolk
South West, Norwich North, Norwich South
EU Constituencies: Eastern
Election Frequency: Elections are of whole council

PRINCIPAL OFFICERS

Chief Executive: Dr Wendy Thomson, Managing Director, County
Hall, Martineau Lane, Norwich NR1 2DH ☎ 01603 222000
◌ wendy.thomson@norfolk.gov.uk

Senior Management: Mr Simon George, Executive Director -
Finance, County Hall, Martineau Lane, Norwich NR1 2DH
◌ simon.george@norfolk.gov.uk

Senior Management: Ms Anne Gibson, Executive Director -
Resources, County Hall, Martineau Lane, Norwich NR1 2DH
☎ 01603 222609 ◌ anne.gibson@norfolk.gov.uk

Senior Management: Mr Tom McCabe, Executive Director -
Community & Environmental Services, County Hall, Martineau Lane,
Norwich NR1 2DH ☎ 01603 222500 ◌ tom.mccabe@norfolk.gov.uk

Senior Management: Mr Michael Rosen, Executive Director -
Children's Services, County Hall, Martineau Lane, Norwich NR1 2DH
☎ 01603 222600 ◌ michael.rosen@norfolk.gov.uk

Senior Management: Dr Louise Smith, Director - Public Health,
County Hall, Martineau Lane, Norwich NR1 2DH ☎ 01603 638074
◌ lousie.smith@norfolk.gov.uk

Senior Management: Ms Catherine Underwood, Acting
Executive Director - Adult Social Services, County Hall, Martineau
Lane, Norwich NR1 2DH ☎ 01603 224378
◌ catherine.underwood@norfolk.gov.uk

Access Officer / Social Services (Disability): Ms Catherine
Underwood, Acting Executive Director - Adult Social Services,
County Hall, Martineau Lane, Norwich NR1 2DH ☎ 01603 224378
◌ catherine.underwood@norfolk.gov.uk

Architect, Building / Property Services: Mr Michael Britch,
Managing Director - NPS & Norse Group, Lancaster House, 16
Central Avenue, St Andrews Business Park, Norwich NR7 0HR
☎ 01603 706100 ◌ mike.britch@nps.co.uk

Catering Services: Mr Peter Hawes, Managing Director - NORSE
Commercial Services, Fifers Lane, 280 Fifers Lane, Norwich NR6
6EQ ☎ 01603 894271 ◌ peter.hawes@ncsgrp.co.uk

Children / Youth Services: Mr Gordon Boyd, Assistant Director -
Education, County Hall, Martineau Lane, Norwich NR1 2DH
☎ 01603 223492 ◌ gordon.boyd@norfolk.gov.uk

Children / Youth Services: Mr Don Evans, Assistant Director -
Performance & Challenge, County Hall, Martineau Lane, Norwich
NR1 2DH ☎ 01603 223909 ◌ don.evans@norfolk.gov.uk

Children / Youth Services: Ms Cathy Mouser, Assistant Director
- Social Work, County Hall, Martineau Lane, Norwich NR1 2DH
☎ 01603 217653 ◌ cathy.mouse@norfolk.gov.uk

Children / Youth Services: Mr Michael Rosen, Executive
Director - Children's Services, County Hall, Martineau Lane, Norwich
NR1 2DH ☎ 01603 222600 ◌ michael.rosen@norfolk.gov.uk

Children / Youth Services: Ms Elly Starling, Lead HR & OD
Business Partner, County Hall, Martineau Lane, Norwich NR1 2DH
☎ 01603 223476 ◌ elly.starling@norfolk.gov.uk

Children / Youth Services: Mr Sal Thirlway, Assistant Director -
Early Help, County Hall, Martineau Lane, Norwich NR1 2DH
☎ 01603 223747 ◌ sal.thirlway@norfolk.gov.uk

Civil Registration: Mrs Caroline Clarke, Regulatory Manager,
County Hall, Martineau Lane, Norwich NR1 2DH ☎ 01603 222949
◌ caroline.clarke@norfolk.gov.uk

Civil Registration: Ms Jacqueline Lake, Senior Coroner, 69-75
Thorpe Road, Norwich NR1 1UA ☎ 01603 663302
◌ norfolk@coroner.norfolk.gov.uk

PR / Communications: Ms Christine Birchall, Manager - Corporate Communications & Marketing, County Hall, Martineau Lane, Norwich NR1 2DH ☎ 01603 222843
✆ christine.birchall@norfolk.gov.uk

PR / Communications: Mr Mark Langlands, Media & Public Affairs Manager, County Hall, Martineau Lane, Norwich NR1 2DH ☎ 01603 228888 ✆ mark.langlands@norfolk.gov.uk

Community Planning: Ms Jo Richardson, Manager - Corporate Planning & Partnerships Manager, County Hall, Martineau Lane, Norwich NR1 2DH ☎ 01603 223816 ✆ jo.richardson@norfolk.gov.uk

Community Safety: Mr Roy Harold, Chief Fire Officer, County Hall, Martineau Lane, Norwich NR1 2DH ☎ 0300 123 1383 ✆ roy.harold@fire.norfolk.gov.uk

Computer Management: Mr John Gladman, Head of ICT, County Hall, Martineau Lane, Norwich NR1 2DH ☎ 01603 222700 ✆ john.gladman@norfolk.gov.uk

Consumer Protection and Trading Standards: Mrs Sophie Leney, Trading Standards Manager, County Hall, Martineau Lane, Norwich NR1 2DH ☎ 01603 224275 ✆ sophie.leney@norfolk.gov.uk

Contracts: Mr Al Collier, Head - Procurement, County Hall, Martineau Lane, Norwich NR1 2DH ☎ 01603 223372 ✆ al.collier@norfolk.gov.uk

Corporate Services: Mrs Debbie Bartlett, Head - Business Intelligence & Performance, County Hall, Martineau Lane, Norwich NR1 2DH ☎ 01603 222475 ✆ debbie.bartlett@norfolk.gov.uk

Customer Service: Ms Ceri Summer, Customer Access & Development Manager, County Hall, Martineau Lane, Norwich NR1 2DH ☎ 01603 223398 ✆ ceri.summer@norfolk.gov.uk

Direct Labour: Mr Peter Hawes, Managing Director - NORSE Commercial Services, The Annex, County Hall, Norwich NR1 2UQ ☎ 01603 894271 ✆ peter.hawes@ncsgrp.co.uk

Economic Development: Ms Fiona McDiarmid, Assistant Director - Economic Development & Strategy, County Hall, Martineau Lane, Norwich NR1 2DH ☎ 01603 223810 ✆ fiona.mcdiarmid@norfolk.gov.uk

Education: Mr Richard Snowden, Head - Schools Admissions Service, County Hall, Martineau Lane, Norwich NR1 2DH ☎ 01603 223489 ✆ richard.snowden@norfolk.gov.uk

Emergency Planning: Mr Roy Harold, Chief Fire Officer, County Hall, Martineau Lane, Norwich NR1 2DH ☎ 0300 123 1383 ✆ roy.harold@fire.norfolk.gov.uk

Energy Management: Mr David Collinson, Assistant Director - Community & Environmental Services, County Hall, Martineau Lane, Norwich NR1 2DH ☎ 01603 222253 ✆ david.collinson@norfolk.gov.uk

Estates, Property & Valuation: Mr Michael Britch, Managing Director - NPS & Norse Group, Lancaster House, 16 Central Avenue, St Andrews Business Park, Norwich NR7 0HR ☎ 01603 706100 ✆ mike.britch@nps.co.uk

European Liaison: Ms Karen Gibson, Partnership & Delivery Manager, County Hall, Martineau Lane, Norwich NR1 2DH ☎ 01603 222598 ✆ karen.gibson@norfolk.gov.uk

Facilities: Mr Graham Wray, Facilities Manager, NPS Property Consultants Ltd, Building Surveying Group, Martineau Lane, Norwich NR1 1DH ☎ 01603 670670 ✆ graham.wray@ncsgrp.gov.uk

Finance: Mr Simon George, Executive Director - Finance, County Hall, Martineau Lane, Norwich NR1 2DH ✆ simon.george@norfolk.gov.uk

Pensions: Ms Nicola Mark, Head - Norfolk Pension Fund, Laurence House, 5 St Andrews Hill, Norwich NR2 1AD ☎ 01603 222171 ✆ nicola.mark@norfolk.gov.uk

Health and Safety: Mr Ian Wheeler, Health & Safety Manager, County Hall, Martineau Lane, Norwich NR1 2DH ☎ 01603 223432 ✆ ian.wheeler@norfolk.gov.uk

Highways: Ms Tracy Jessop, Assistant Director - Highways & Transport, County Hall, Martineau Lane, Norwich NR1 2DH ☎ 01603 223831 ✆ tracy.jessop@norfolk.gov.uk

Legal: Ms Victoria McNeill, Practice Director, County Hall, Martineau Lane, Norwich NR1 2DH ☎ 01603 223415 ✆ victoria.mcneill@norfolk.gov.uk

Leisure and Cultural Services: Mrs Jennifer Holland, Assistant Director - Community & Environmental Services & Head of Libraries, County Hall, Martineau Lane, Norwich NR1 2UA ☎ 01603 222272 ✆ jennifer.holland@norfolk.gov.uk

Leisure and Cultural Services: Mr Steve Miller, Head of Norfolk Museums Service, Shirehall, Norwich NR1 3JQ ☎ 01603 493620 ✆ steve.miller@norfolk.gov.uk

Lifelong Learning: Ms Kerry Furness, Organisational Development Manager, County Hall, Martineau Lane, Norwich NR1 2DH ☎ 01603 222909 ✆ kerry.furness@norfolk.gov.uk

Lifelong Learning: Mrs Jennifer Holland, Assistant Director - Community & Environmental Services & Head of Libraries, County Hall, Martineau Lane, Norwich NR1 2UA ☎ 01603 222272 ✆ jennifer.holland@norfolk.gov.uk

Lighting: Mr Nick Tupper, Head of Highways, County Hall, Martineau Lane, Norwich NR1 2DH ☎ 01603 224290 ✆ nick.tupper@norfolk.gov.uk

Member Services: Mr Chris Walton, Head - Democratic Services, County Hall, Martineau Lane, Norwich NR1 2DH ☎ 01603 222620 ✆ chris.walton@norfolk.gov.uk

Partnerships: Mrs Debbie Bartlett, Head - Business Intelligence & Performance, County Hall, Martineau Lane, Norwich NR1 2DH ☎ 01603 222475 ✆ debbie.bartlett@norfolk.gov.uk

NORFOLK

Personnel / HR: Ms Audrey Sharp, Acting Head - Human Resources, County Hall, Martineau Lane, Norwich NR1 2DH
☎ 01603 222796 ⌨ audrey.sharp@norfolk.gov.uk

Planning: Mr Tom McCabe, Executive Director - Community & Environmental Services, County Hall, Martineau Lane, Norwich NR1 2DH ☎ 01603 222500 ⌨ tom.mccabe@norfolk.gov.uk

Procurement: Mr Al Collier, Head - Procurement, County Hall, Martineau Lane, Norwich NR1 2DH ☎ 01603 223372 ⌨ al.collier@norfolk.gov.uk

Public Libraries: Mrs Jennifer Holland, Assistant Director - Community & Environmental Services & Head of Libraries, County Hall, Martineau Lane, Norwich NR1 2UA ☎ 01603 222272 ⌨ jennifer.holland@norfolk.gov.uk

Public Libraries: Mr Gary Tuson, County Archivist, County Hall, Martineau Lane, Norwich NR1 2DH ☎ 01603 222003 ⌨ gary.tuson@norfolk.gov.uk

Recycling & Waste Minimisation: Mr David Collinson, Assistant Director - Community & Environmental Services, County Hall, Martineau Lane, Norwich NR1 2DH ☎ 01603 222253 ⌨ david.collinson@norfolk.gov.uk

Regeneration: Ms Fiona McDiarmid, Assistant Director - Economic Development & Strategy, County Hall, Martineau Lane, Norwich NR1 2DH ☎ 01603 223810 ⌨ fiona.mcdiarmid@norfolk.gov.uk

Road Safety: Mr Iain Temperton, Team Manager - Casualty Reduction, Education & Development, County Hall, Martineau Lane, Norwich NR1 2SG ☎ 01603 223348 ⌨ iain.temperton@norfolk.gov.uk

Social Services (Adult): Ms Lorrayne Barrett, Director - Integrated Care, County Hall, Martineau Lane, Norwich NR1 2DH ☎ 01603 692415 ⌨ lorrayne.barrett@norfolk.gov.uk

Social Services (Adult): Ms Lorna Bright, Assistant Director - Social Work & Occupational Therapy, County Hall, Martineau Lane, Norwich NR1 2DH ☎ 01603 223960 ⌨ lorna.bright@norfolk.gov.uk

Social Services (Adult): Ms Janice Dane, Assistant Director - Early Help & Prevention, County Hall, Martineau Lane, Norwich NR1 2DH ☎ 01603 223438 ⌨ janice.dane@norfolk.gov.uk

Social Services (Adult): Ms Catherine Underwood, Acting Executive Director - Adult Social Services, County Hall, Martineau Lane, Norwich NR1 2DH ☎ 01603 224378 ⌨ catherine.underwood@norfolk.gov.uk

Public Health: Dr Louise Smith, Director - Public Health, County Hall, Martineau Lane, Norwich NR1 2DH ☎ 01603 638074 ⌨ lousie.smith@norfolk.gov.uk

Transport Planner: Ms Tracy Jessop, Assistant Director - Highways & Transport, County Hall, Martineau Lane, Norwich NR1 2DH ☎ 01603 223831 ⌨ tracy.jessop@norfolk.gov.uk

Waste Collection and Disposal: Mr Paul Borrett, Waste & Energy Manager, County Hall, Martineau Lane, Norwich NR1 2SG ☎ 01603 222197 ⌨ paul.borrett@norfolk.gov.uk

Waste Management: Mr David Collinson, Assistant Director - Community & Environmental Services, County Hall, Martineau Lane, Norwich NR1 2DH ☎ 01603 222253 ⌨ david.collinson@norfolk.gov.uk

COUNCILLORS

Chair: Parkinson-Hare, Rex (UKIP - Yarmouth Nelson & Southtown) rex.parkinson-hare@norfolk.gov.uk

Leader of the Council: Jordan, Cliff (CON - Yare & All Saints) cliff.jordan@norfolk.gov.uk

Deputy Leader of the Council: Thomas, Alison (CON - Long Stratton) alison.thomas@norfolk.gov.uk

Adams, Anthony (CON - Drayton & Horsford) anthony.adams@norfolk.gov.uk

Agnew, Stephen (UKIP - Marshland North) stephen.agnew@norfolk.gov.uk

Aldred, Colin (UKIP - Lothingland) colin.aldred@norfolk.gov.uk

Askew, Stephen (CON - Guiltcross) stephen.askew@norfolk.gov.uk

Baker, Michael (UKIP - Holt) michael.baker@norfolk.gov.uk

Bearman, Richard (GRN - Mancroft) richard.bearman@norfolk.gov.uk

Bird, Richard (UKIP - North Coast) richard.bird@norfolk.gov.uk

Borrett, Bill (CON - Elmham & Mattishall) bill.borrett@norfolk.gov.uk

Boswell, Andrew (GRN - Nelson) andrew.boswell@norfolk.gov.uk

Bowes, Claire (CON - Watton) claire.bowes@norfolk.gov.uk

Bradnock, Allison (LD - South Smallburgh) allison.bradnock@norfolk.gov.uk

Bremner, Bert (LAB - University) bert.bremner@norfolk.gov.uk

Brociek-Coulton, Julie (LAB - Sewell) julie.brociek-coulton@norfolk.gov.uk

Byrne, Alexander (CON - Attleborough) alexander.byrne@norfolk.gov.uk

Carttiss, Michael (CON - West Flegg)

Castle, Mick (LAB - Yarmouth North & Central) mick.castle@norfolk.gov.uk

Chamberlin, Jennifer (CON - Diss & Roydon) jennifer.chamberlin@norfolk.gov.uk

Chenery of Horsbrugh, Michael (CON - Docking) michael.chenery@norfolk.gov.uk

Childs, Jonathon (UKIP - East Flegg) jonathon.childs@norfolk.gov.uk

Clancy, Stuart (CON - Taverham)
stuart.clancy@norfolk.gov.uk

Coke, Richard (UKIP - Gayton & Nar Valley)
richard.coke@norfolk.gov.uk

Collis, David (LAB - King's Lynn North & Central)
david.collis@norfolk.gov.uk

Corlett, Emma (LAB - Town Close)
emma.corlett@norfolk.gov.uk

Cox, Hilary (CON - Cromer)
hilary.cox@norfolk.gov.uk

Crawford, Denis (UKIP - Thetford East)
denis.crawford@norfolk.gov.uk

Dearnley, Adrian (GRN - Thorpe Hamlet)
adrian.dearnley@norfolk.gov.uk

Dewsbury, Margaret (CON - Hingham)
margaret.dewsbury@norfolk.gov.uk

Dixon, Nigel (CON - Hoveton & Stalham)
nigel.dixon@norfolk.gov.uk

Dobson, John (INDNA - Dersingham)
john.dobson@norfolk.gov.uk

East, Tim (LD - Costessey)
tim.east@norfolk.gov.uk

FitzPatrick, Tom (CON - Fakenham)
tom.fitzpatrick@norfolk.gov.uk

Foulger, Colin (CON - Forehoe)
colin.foulger@norfolk.gov.uk

Garrod, Tom (CON - Wroxham)
thomas.garrod@norfolk.gov.uk

Gilmour, Paul (UKIP - Dereham South)
paul.gilmour@norfolk.gov.uk

Grey, Alan (UKIP - Breydon)
alan.grey@norfolk.gov.uk

Gurney, Shelagh (CON - Hellesdon)
shelagh.gurney@norfolk.gov.uk

Hacon, Pat (LAB - Caister-on-Sea)
pat.hacon@norfolk.gov.uk

Hannah, Brian (LD - Sheringham)
brian.hannah@norfolk.gov.uk

Harrison, David (LD - Aylsham)
david.harrison@norfolk.gov.uk

Humphrey, Harry (CON - Marshland South)
harry.humphrey@norfolk.gov.uk

Iles, Brian (CON - Acle)
brian.iles@norfolk.gov.uk

Jermy, Terry (LAB - Thetford West)
terry.jermy@norfolk.gov.uk

Joyce, James (LD - Reepham)
james.joyce@norfolk.gov.uk

Kemp, Alexanrda (INDNA - Clenchwarton & King's Lynn South)
alexandra.kemp@norfolk.gov.uk

Kiddle-Morris, Mark (CON - Necton & Launditch)
mark.kiddle-morris@norfolk.gov.uk

Law, Jason (CON - Freebridge Lynn)
jason.law@norfolk.gov.uk

Leggett, Judy (CON - Old Catton)
judy.leggett@norfolk.gov.uk

Long, Brian (CON - Fincham)
brian.long@norfolk.gov.uk

Mackie, Ian (CON - Thorpe St Andrew)
ian.mackie@norfolk.gov.uk

Monson, Ian (CON - The Brecks)
ian.monson@norfolk.gov.uk

Mooney, Joe (CON - Wymondham)
joe.mooney@norfolk.gov.uk

Morgan, Elizabeth (GRN - Wensum)
elizabeth.morgan@norfolk.gov.uk

Morphew, Steve (LAB - Catton Grove)
steve.morphew@norfolk.gov.uk

Nobbs, George (LAB - Crome)
george.nobbs@norfolk.gov.uk

Northam, Wyndham (CON - Mundesley)
wyndham.northam@norfolk.gov.uk

Perkins, Jim (UKIP - Gaywood North & Central)
jim.perkins@norfolk.gov.uk

Plant, Graham (CON - Gorleston St Andrews)

Proctor, Andrew (CON - Blofield & Brundall)
andrew.proctor@norfolk.gov.uk

Ramsbotham, David (UKIP - Melton Constable)
david.ramsbotham@norfolk.gov.uk

Richmond, William (CON - Dereham North)
william.richmond@norfolk.gov.uk

Roper, Daniel (LD - Hevingham & Spixworth)
daniel.roper@norfolk.gov.uk

Rumsby, Christine (LAB - Mile Cross)

Sands, Mike (LAB - Bowthorpe)
mike.sands@norfolk.gov.uk

Seward, Eric (LD - North Walsham East)
eric.seward@norfolk.gov.uk

Shaw, Nigel (CON - Woodside)
nigel.shaw@norfolk.gov.uk

Smith, Roger (CON - Henstead)
roger.smith@norfolk.gov.uk

Smyth, Paul (UKIP - Swaffham)
paul.smyth@norfolk.gov.uk

Somerville, Margaret (CON - Clavering)
margaret.somerville@norfolk.gov.uk

Spratt, Beverley (CON - West Depwade)
beverley.spratt@norfolk.gov.uk

Stone, Barry (CON - Loddon)
barry.stone@norfolk.gov.uk

Storey, Martin (CON - Feltwell)
martin.storey@norfolk.gov.uk

Strong, Marie (LD - Wells)
marie.strong@norfolk.gov.uk

Timewell, John (LD - North Walsham West & Erpingham)
john.timewell@norfolk.gov.uk

Virgo, Judith (CON - Humbleyard)
judith.virgo@norfolk.gov.uk

Walker, Colleen (LAB - Magdalen)
colleen.walker@norfolk.gov.uk

Ward, John (CON - Sprowston)
john.ward@norfolk.gov.uk

Watkins, Brian (LD - Eaton)
brian.watkins@norfolk.gov.uk

Whitaker, Sue (LAB - Lakenham)
sue.whitaker@norfolk.gov.uk

White, Anthony (CON - Downham Market)
anthony.white@norfolk.gov.uk

Wilby, Martin (CON - East Depwade)
martin.wilby@norfolk.gov.uk

Wilkinson, Margaret (LAB - Gaywood South)
margaret.wilkinson@norfolk.gov.uk

POLITICAL COMPOSITION
CON: 41, LAB: 14, UKIP: 13, LD: 10, GRN: 4, INDNA: 2

COMMITTEE CHAIRS

Adult Social Care: Mr Bill Borrett

Audit: Mr Ian Mackie

Children's Services: Mr Roger Smith

Environment, Development & Transport: Mr Martin Wilby

Health & Wellbeing: Mr Brian Watkins

Pensions: Mr Jason Law

Planning: Mr Mike Sands

North Ayrshire S

North Ayrshire Council, Cunninghame House, Irvine KA12 8EE
☎ 0845 603 0590 🖷 01294 324144 ✆ contactus@north-ayrshire.gov.uk
🖳 www.north-ayrshire.gov.uk

FACTS AND FIGURES
Parliamentary Constituencies: Ayrshire North and Arran
EU Constituencies: Scotland
Election Frequency: Elections are of whole council

PRINCIPAL OFFICERS

Chief Executive: Ms Elma Murray, Chief Executive, Cunninghame House, Irvine KA12 8EE ☎ 01294 324124
✆ asproul@north-ayrshire.gov.uk

Senior Management: Mr John Butcher, Executive Director - Education & Youth Employment, Cunninghame House, Irvine KA12 8EE johnbutcher@north-ayrcshire.gov.uk

Senior Management: Ms Iona Colvin, Executive Director - Health & Social Care Partnership, Cunninghame House, Irvine KA12 8EE ☎ 01294 317725 ✆ icolvin@north-ayrshire.gov.uk

Senior Management: Mr Andrew Fraser, Head of Service - Democratic Services, Cunninghame House, Irvine KA12 8EE ☎ 01294 324125 ✆ afraser@north-ayrshire.gov.uk

Senior Management: Ms Laura Friel, Executive Director - Finance & Corporate Support, Cunninghame House, Irvine KA12 8EE ☎ 01294 324152 ✆ lfriel@north-ayrshire.gov.uk

Senior Management: Mr Craig Hatton, Executive Director - Place, Cunninghame House, Irvine KA12 8EE ☎ 01294 541514 ✆ chatton@north-ayrshire.gov.uk

Senior Management: Ms Karen Yeomans, Executive Director - Economy & Communities, Cunninghame House, Irvine KA12 8EE ☎ 01294 324308 ✆ karenyeomans@north-ayrshire.gov.uk

Access Officer / Social Services (Disability): Ms Louise Kirk, Access Officer, Cunninghame House, Irvine KA12 8EE ☎ 01294 324766 ✆ lkirk@north-ayrshire.gov.uk

Architect, Building / Property Services: Ms Yvonne Baulk, Head of Physical Environment, Cunninghame House, Irvine KA12 8EE ☎ 01294 324514 ✆ jdickie@north-ayrshire.gov.uk

Best Value: Mr Andrew Fraser, Head of Service - Democratic Services, Cunninghame House, Irvine KA12 8EE ☎ 01294 324125 ✆ afraser@north-ayrshire.gov.uk

Building Control: Mr Scott McKenzie, Senior Manager - Protective Services, Cunninghame House, Irvine KA12 8EE ☎ 01294 324347 ✆ smckenzie@north-ayrshire.gov.uk

Catering Services: Mr Ken Campbell, Facilities Manager, Montgomerie House, 2A Byrehill Drive, West Byrehill Industrial Estate, Kilwinning KA13 6HN ☎ 01294 541523 ✆ kcampbell@north-ayrshire.gov.uk

Children / Youth Services: Mr John McKnight, Senior Manager - Community & Development, Cunninghame House, Irvine KA12 8EE ☎ 01294 468035 ✆ jmcknight@north-ayrshire.gov.uk

Children / Youth Services: Dr Audrey Sutton, Head of Community & Culture, Cunninghame House, Irvine KA12 8EE ☎ 01294 324414 ✆ asutton@north-ayrshire.gov.uk

PR / Communications: Ms Lynne McEwan, Corporate Communications Manager, Cunninghame House, Irvine KA12 8EE ☎ 01294 324117 ✆ lmcewan@north-ayrshire.gov.uk

Community Planning: Ms Morna Rae, Community Planning Team Leader, Cunninghame House, Irvine KA12 8EE ☎ 01294 324117 ✆ mrae@north-ayrshire.gov.uk

Community Safety: Mr Pat Kelly, Temporary Principal Officer ASB / Community Safety Services, Cunninghame House, Irvine KA12 8EE ☎ 01294 314672 ✆ pkelly@northayrshire.gov.uk

Computer Management: Mr Alan Blakely, IT Manager, Cunninghame House, Irvine KA12 8EE ☎ 01294 324272 ✆ ablakely@north-ayrshire.gov.uk

Consumer Protection and Trading Standards: Mr Andy Moynihan, Team Manager (Trading Standards), Bridgegate House, Bridgegate, Irvine KA12 8BD ☎ 01294 310117 ✆ amoynihan@north-ayrshire.gov.uk

Contracts: Mr Andrew Fraser, Head of Service - Democratic Services, Cunninghame House, Irvine KA12 8EE ☎ 01294 324125 ⚲ afraser@north-ayrshire.gov.uk

Corporate Services: Mr Andrew Fraser, Head of Service - Democratic Services, Cunninghame House, Irvine KA12 8EE ☎ 01294 324125 ⚲ afraser@north-ayrshire.gov.uk

Customer Service: Ms Esther Gunn, Customer Services Manager, Bridgegate House, Irvine KA12 8DB ☎ 01294 323690 ⚲ egunn@north-ayrshire.gov.uk

Economic Development: Ms Karen Yeomans, Executive Director - Economy & Communities, Cunninghame House, Irvine KA12 8EE ☎ 01294 324308 ⚲ karenyeomans@north-ayrshire.gov.uk

Electoral Registration: Ms Elma Murray, Chief Executive, Cunninghame House, Irvine KA12 8EE ☎ 01294 324124 ⚲ asproul@north-ayrshire.gov.uk

Emergency Planning: Ms Jane McGeorge, Civil Contingencies Co-ordinator, Ayrshire Civil Contingencies Team, Building 372, Alpha Freight Area, Robertson Road, Glasgow Prestwick Airport, Prestwick KA9 2PL ☎ 01292 692182 ⚲ jmcgeorge@north-ayrshire.gov.uk

Energy Management: Ms Jennifer Wraith, Senior Energy Officer, Perceton House, Irvine KA11 2AL jwraith@north-ayrshire.gov.uk

Environmental / Technical Services: Ms Karen Yeomans, Executive Director - Economy & Communities, Cunninghame House, Irvine KA12 8EE ☎ 01294 324308 ⚲ karenyeomans@north-ayrshire.gov.uk

Environmental Health: Mr Hugh McGhee, Team Manager - Public Health & Pollution, Cunninghame House, Irvine KA12 8EE ☎ 01294 324392 ⚲ hmcghee@north-ayrshire.gov.uk

Estates, Property & Valuation: Mr Alastair Ross, Asset Manager, Cunninghame House, Irvine KA12 8EE ⚲ aross@north-ayrshire.gov.uk

European Liaison: Ms Linda Aird, European Officer, Perceton House, Irvine KA11 2AL ☎ 01294 225195 ⚲ lindaaird@north-ayrshire.gov.uk

Events Manager: Ms Pauline Palmer, Senior Communications Officer - Marketing & Events, Cunninghame House, Irvine KA12 8EE ☎ 01294 324158 ⚲ ppalmer@north-ayrshire.gov.uk

Finance: Ms Laura Friel, Executive Director - Finance & Corporate Support, Cunninghame House, Irvine KA12 8EE ☎ 01294 324152 ⚲ lfriel@north-ayrshire.gov.uk

Fleet Management: Mr Gordon Mitchell, Transport Manager, Montgomerie House, 2A Byrehill Drive, West Byrehill Industrial Estate, Kilwinning KA13 6HN ☎ 01294 541601 ⚲ gmitchell@north-ayrshire.gov.uk

Grounds Maintenance: Mr Wallace Turpie, Senior Manager - Sreetscene, Perceton House, Irvine KA11 2AL ☎ 01294 324653 ⚲ chatton@north-ayrshire.gov.uk

Health and Safety: Ms Catherine Reilly, Team Manager - Food, Health & Safety, Cunninghame House, Irvine KA12 8EE ☎ 01294 324355 ⚲ creilly@north-ayrshire.gov.uk

Home Energy Conservation: Ms Jennifer Wraith, Senior Energy Officer, Perceton House, Irvine KA11 2AL ⚲ jwraith@north-ayrshire.gov.uk

Housing: Ms Yvonne Baulk, Head of Physical Environment, Cunninghame House, Irvine KA12 8EE ☎ 01294 324514 ⚲ jdickie@north-ayrshire.gov.uk

Housing Maintenance: Mr Michael McIntosh, Senior Mantainence Officer, Perceton House, Irvine KA11 2AL ☎ 01294 225078 ⚲ mmcintosh@north-ayrshire.gov.uk

Legal: Mr Andrew Fraser, Head of Service - Democratic Services, Cunninghame House, Irvine KA12 8EE ☎ 01294 324125 ⚲ afraser@north-ayrshire.gov.uk

Licensing: Mr William O'Brien, Senior Solicitor - Licensing, District Court & Licensing Office, Townshouse, Irvine KA12 0AZ ☎ 01294 311998 ⚲ nalexander@north-ayrshire.gov.uk

Lighting: Ms Karen Yeomans, Executive Director - Economy & Communities, Cunninghame House, Irvine KA12 8EE ☎ 01294 324308 ⚲ karenyeomans@north-ayrshire.gov.uk

Member Services: Mr Andrew Fraser, Head of Service - Democratic Services, Cunninghame House, Irvine KA12 8EE ☎ 01294 324125 ⚲ afraser@north-ayrshire.gov.uk

Parking: Mr David Lodge, Supervisory Engineer, Cunninghame House, Irvine KA12 8EE ☎ 01294 324744 ⚲ dlodge@north-ayrshire.gov.uk

Personnel / HR: Mr Gavin Macgregor, Head of Human Resources & Organisational Development, Cunninghame House, Irvine KA12 8EE ☎ 01294 324651 ⚲ gmacgregor@north-ayrshire.gov.uk

Planning: Mr James Miller, Senior Manager - Planning, Cunninghame House, Irvine KA12 8EE ☎ 01294 324315 ⚲ jmiller@north-ayrshire.gov.uk

Procurement: Ms Laura Friel, Executive Director - Finance & Corporate Support, Cunninghame House, Irvine KA12 8EE ☎ 01294 324152 ⚲ lfriel@north-ayrshire.gov.uk

Recycling & Waste Minimisation: Mr David Mackay, Waste Services Manager, Cunninghame House, Irvine KA12 8EE ☎ 01294 541525 ⚲ dmackay@north-ayrshire.gov.uk

Regeneration: Ms Karen Yeomans, Executive Director - Economy & Communities, Cunninghame House, Irvine KA12 8EE ☎ 01294 324308 ⚲ karenyeomans@north-ayrshire.gov.uk

Road Safety: Ms Karen Yeomans, Executive Director - Economy & Communities, Cunninghame House, Irvine KA12 8EE ☎ 01294 324308 ⚲ karenyeomans@north-ayrshire.gov.uk

NORTH AYRSHIRE

Social Services: Ms Iona Colvin, Executive Director - Health & Social Care Partnership, Cunninghame House, Irvine KA12 8EE
☎ 01294 317725 ◌ icolvin@north-ayrshire.gov.uk

Social Services (Adult): Mr David Rowland, Head of Service - Health & Community Care, Cunninghame House, Irvine KA12 8EE
◌ drowland@north-ayrshire.gov.uk

Social Services (Children): Mr Stephen Brown, Head of Service - Children, Families & Criminal Justice Services, Cunninghame House, Irvine KA12 8EE ☎ 01294 317727
◌ sbrown@north-ayrshire.gov.uk

Staff Training: Mr Gavin Macgregor, Head of Human Resources & Organisational Development, Cunninghame House, Irvine KA12 8EE ☎ 01294 324651 ◌ gmacgregor@north-ayrshire.gov.uk

Street Scene: Mr Russell McCutcheon, Head of Environment & Related Services, Montgomerie House, 2A Byrehill Drive, West Byrehill Industrial Estate, Kilwinning KA13 6HN ☎ 01294 541570
◌ russellmccutcheon@north-ayrshire.gov.uk

Sustainable Communities: Ms Karen Yeomans, Executive Director - Economy & Communities, Cunninghame House, Irvine KA12 8EE ☎ 01294 324308 ◌ karenyeomans@north-ayrshire.gov.uk

Sustainable Development: Ms Karen Yeomans, Executive Director - Economy & Communities, Cunninghame House, Irvine KA12 8EE ☎ 01294 324308 ◌ karenyeomans@north-ayrshire.gov.uk

Tourism: Ms Karen Yeomans, Executive Director - Economy & Communities, Cunninghame House, Irvine KA12 8EE
☎ 01294 324308 ◌ karenyeomans@north-ayrshire.gov.uk

Town Centre: Mr George Hunter, Town Centre Manager, Perceton House, Irvine KA11 2AL ☎ 01294 225177
◌ ghunter@north-ayrshire.gov.uk

Traffic Management: Mr Crawford Forsyth, Assistant Transportation Manager, Perceton House, Irvine KA11 2AL
☎ 01294 225100 ◌ cforsyth@north-ayrshire.gov.uk

Waste Collection and Disposal: Mr Russell McCutcheon, Head of Environment & Related Services, Montgomerie House, 2A Byrehill Drive, West Byrehill Industrial Estate, Kilwinning KA13 6HN ☎ 01294 541570 ◌ russellmccutcheon@north-ayrshire.gov.uk

Waste Management: Mr Russell McCutcheon, Head of Environment & Related Services, Montgomerie House, 2A Byrehill Drive, West Byrehill Industrial Estate, Kilwinning KA13 6HN ☎ 01294 541570 ◌ russellmccutcheon@north-ayrshire.gov.uk

Children's Play Areas: Mr Wallace Turpie, Senior Manager - Sreetscene, Perceton House, Irvine KA11 2AL ☎ 01294 324653 ◌ chatton@north-ayrshire.gov.uk

COUNCILLORS

ProvostSturgeon, Joan (SNP - Irvine East)
jsturgeon@north-ayrshire.gov.uk

Deputy ProvostBarr, Robert (IND - Dalry & West Kilbride)
rbarr@north-ayrshire.gov.uk

Leader of the Council: Cullinane, Joe (LAB - Kilwinning)
joecullinane@north-ayrshire.gov.uk

Deputy Leader of the Council: Bell, John (LAB - Kilbirnie & Beith)
jbell@north-ayrshire.gov.uk

Brown, Matthew (SNP - Irvine West)
mbrown@north-ayrshire.gov.uk

Bruce, John (SNP - Ardrossan & Arran)
johnbruce@north-ayrshire.gov.uk

Burns, Marie (SNP - Irvine East)
marieburns@north-ayrshire.gov.uk

Clarkson, Ian (LAB - Irvine West)
iclarkson@north-ayrshire.gov.uk

Dickson, Anthea (SNP - Kilbirnie & Beith)
antheadickson@north-ayrshire.gov.uk

Easdale, John (LAB - Irvine East)
johneasdale@north-ayrshire.gov.uk

Ferguson, John (SNP - Kilwinning)
fergusonjohn@north-ayrshire.gov.uk

Gallagher, Alex (LAB - North Coast & Cumbraes)
agallagher@north-ayrshire.gov.uk

Gibson, Willie (SNP - Saltcoats & Stevenston)
wjrgibson@north-ayrshire.gov.uk

Gurney, Anthony (SNP - Ardrossan & Arran)
agurney@north-ayrshire.gov.uk

Highgate, Jean (IND - Kilbirnie & Beith)
jhighgate@north-ayrshire.gov.uk

Hill, Alan (SNP - North Coast & Cumbraes)
alanhill@north-ayrshire.gov.uk

Hunter, John (IND - Ardrossan & Arran)
jhunter@north-ayrshire.gov.uk

Marshall, Tom (CON - North Coast & Cumbraes)
tommarshall@north-ayrshire.gov.uk

McLardy, Elizabeth (IND - Dalry & West Kilbride)
emclardy@north-ayrshire.gov.uk

McLean, Grace (SNP - North Coast & Cumbraes)
gracemclean@north-ayrshire.gov.uk

McMillan, Catherine (SNP - Dalry & West Kilbride)
catherinemcmillan@north-ayrshire.gov.uk

McNamara, Peter (LAB - Ardrossan & Arran)
pmcnamara@north-ayrshire.gov.uk

McNichol, Ronnie (IND - Saltcoats & Stevenston)
rmcnicol@north-ayrshire.gov.uk

McPhater, Louise (LAB - Irvine West)
louisemcphater@north-ayrshire.gov.uk

Montgomerie, Jim (LAB - Saltcoats & Stevenston)
jimmontgomerie@north-ayrshire.gov.uk

Munro, Alan (LAB - Saltcoats & Stevenston)
amunro@north-ayrshire.gov.uk

Oldfather, Irene (LAB - Irvine East)
ireneoldfather@north-ayrshire.gov.uk

O'Neill, David (LAB - Irvine West)
doneill@north-ayrshire.gov.uk

Reid, Donald (LAB - Kilwinning)
donaldreid@north-ayrshire.gov.uk

Steel, Robert (IND - Kilwinning)
robertsteel@north-ayrshire.gov.uk

POLITICAL COMPOSITION
LAB: 12, SNP: 11, IND: 6, CON: 1

COMMITTEE CHAIRS

Audit: Mr John Hunter

Licensing: Mr Ronnie McNichol

Planning: Mr Matthew Brown

North Devon   D

North Devon District Council, Lynton House, Commercial Road, Barnstaple EX31 1DG
☎ 01271 327711 🖨 01271 388451 ⌁ info@northdevon.gov.uk
💻 www.northdevon.gov.uk

FACTS AND FIGURES
EU Constituencies: South West
Election Frequency: Elections are of whole council

PRINCIPAL OFFICERS

Chief Executive: Mr Mike Mansell, Chief Executive, Lynton House, Commercial Road, Barnstaple EX31 1DG ☎ 01271 388252 ⌁ mike.mansell@northdevon.gov.uk

Senior Management: Mr Jeremy Mann, Head of Environmental Health & Housing, Lynton House, Commercial Road, Barnstaple EX31 1DG ☎ 01271 388341 ⌁ jeremy.mann@northdevon.gov.uk

Senior Management: Mr Ricky McCormack, Head of Operational Services, Lynton House, Commercial Road, Barnstaple EX31 1DG ☎ 01271 388503 ⌁ ricky.mccormack@northdevon.gov.uk

Senior Management: Mr Ken Miles, Head of Corporate & Community, Lynton House, Commercial Road, Barnstaple EX31 1DG ☎ 01271 388266 ⌁ ken.miles@northdevon.gov.uk

Senior Management: Mr John Triggs, Head of Resources, Lynton House, Commercial Road, Barnstaple EX31 1DG ☎ 01271 388221 ⌁ jon.triggs@northdevon.gov.uk

Architect, Building / Property Services: Ms Diana Hill, Head of Property & Technical Services, Lynton House, Commercial Road, Barnstaple EX31 1DG ☎ 01271 388377 ⌁ diana.hill@northdevon.gov.uk

Building Control: Mr Mike Tucker, Building Control Team Leader, Lynton House, Commercial Road, Barnstaple EX31 1DG ☎ 01271 388400 ⌁ mike.tucker@northdevon.gov.uk

PR / Communications: Mrs Claire Holm, Customer & Corporate Communications Manager, Lynton House, Commercial Road, Barnstaple EX31 1DG ☎ 01271 388239 ⌁ claire.holm@northdevon.gov.uk

Community Safety: Ms Amanda Palmer, Community Safety Officer, Lynton House, Commercial Road, Barnstaple EX31 1DG ☎ 01271 335241 ⌁ amanda.palmer@northdevon.gov.uk

Computer Management: Mrs Christina Cross, Head of Business Information Services, Lynton House, Commercial Road, Barnstaple EX31 1DG ☎ 01271 388226 ⌁ christina.cross@northdevon.gov.uk

Contracts: Mr Mike Mansell, Chief Executive, Lynton House, Commercial Road, Barnstaple EX31 1DG ☎ 01271 388252 ⌁ mike.mansell@northdevon.gov.uk

Customer Service: Mrs Claire Holm, Customer & Corporate Communications Manager, Lynton House, Commercial Road, Barnstaple EX31 1DG ☎ 01271 388239 ⌁ claire.holm@northdevon.gov.uk

Direct Labour: Mr Ricky McCormack, Head of Operational Services, Lynton House, Commercial Road, Barnstaple EX31 1DG ☎ 01271 388503 ⌁ ricky.mccormack@northdevon.gov.uk

Economic Development: Ms Ellen Vernon, Economic Regeneration Officer, Lynton House, Commercial Road, Barnstaple EX31 1DG ☎ 01271 388368 ⌁ ellen.vernon@northdevon.gov.uk

E-Government: Mrs Christina Cross, Head of Business Information Services, Lynton House, Commercial Road, Barnstaple EX31 1DG ☎ 01271 388226 ⌁ christina.cross@northdevon.gov.uk

Electoral Registration: Mrs Judith Dark, Electoral Services Officer, Lynton House, Commercial Road, Barnstaple EX31 1DG ☎ 01271 388277 ⌁ judith.dark@northdevon.gov.uk

Emergency Planning: Mr Andrew Millie, Environmental Protection & Emergency Planning Manager, Lynton House, Commercial Road, Barnstaple EX31 1DG ☎ 01271 388334 ⌁ andrew.millie@northdevon.gov.uk

Energy Management: Ms Diana Hill, Head of Property & Technical Services, Lynton House, Commercial Road, Barnstaple EX31 1DG ☎ 01271 388377 ⌁ diana.hill@northdevon.gov.uk

Environmental Health: Mr Jeremy Mann, Head of Environmental Health & Housing, Lynton House, Commercial Road, Barnstaple EX31 1DG ☎ 01271 388341 ⌁ jeremy.mann@northdevon.gov.uk

Estates, Property & Valuation: Ms Diana Hill, Head of Property & Technical Services, Lynton House, Commercial Road, Barnstaple EX31 1DG ☎ 01271 388377 ⌁ diana.hill@northdevon.gov.uk

Facilities: Ms Diana Hill, Head of Property & Technical Services, Lynton House, Commercial Road, Barnstaple EX31 1DG ☎ 01271 388377 ⌁ diana.hill@northdevon.gov.uk

Finance: Mr John Triggs, Head of Resources, Lynton House, Commercial Road, Barnstaple EX31 1DG ☎ 01271 388221 ⌁ jon.triggs@northdevon.gov.uk

Grounds Maintenance: Mr Mark Kentell, Contracts Delivery Manager, Lynton House, Commercial Road, Barnstaple EX31 1DG ☎ 01271 327711 ⌁ mark.kentell@northdevon.gov.uk

Health and Safety: Mr Mike Ballard, Health & Safety Advisor, Lynton House, Commercial Road, Barnstaple EX31 1DG ☎ 01271 327711 ⌁ mike.ballard@northdevon.gov.uk

NORTH DEVON

Home Energy Conservation: Mr Jeremy Mann, Head of Environmental Health & Housing, Lynton House, Commercial Road, Barnstaple EX31 1DG ☎ 01271 388341 ⌨ jeremy.mann@northdevon.gov.uk

Housing: Mr Jeremy Mann, Head of Environmental Health & Housing, Lynton House, Commercial Road, Barnstaple EX31 1DG ☎ 01271 388341 ⌨ jeremy.mann@northdevon.gov.uk

Legal: Mr Ken Miles, Head of Corporate & Community, Lynton House, Commercial Road, Barnstaple EX31 1DG ☎ 01271 388266 ⌨ ken.miles@northdevon.gov.uk

Leisure and Cultural Services: Mr Mark Kentell, Contracts Delivery Manager, Lynton House, Commercial Road, Barnstaple EX31 1DG ☎ 01271 327711 ⌨ mark.kentell@northdevon.gov.uk

Licensing: Miss Katy Nicholls, Licensing Manager, Lynton House, Commercial Road, Barnstaple EX31 1DG ☎ 01271 388312 ⌨ katy.nicholls@northdevon.gov.uk

Lifelong Learning: Mrs Nikki Gordon, Human Resources Manager, Lynton House, Commercial Road, Barnstaple EX31 1DG ☎ 01271 388548 ⌨ nikki.gordon@northdevon.gov.uk

Lottery Funding, Charity and Voluntary: Mrs Lorna Jones, Community Grants & Funding Officer, Lynton House, Commercial Road, Barnstaple EX31 1DG ☎ 01271 388327 ⌨ lorna.jones@northdevon.gov.uk

Member Services: Mrs Bev Triggs, Senior Member Services Officer, Lynton House, Commercial Road, Barnstaple EX31 1DG ☎ 01271 388254 ⌨ bev.triggs@northdevon.gov.uk

Parking: Mr Martin Williams, Procurement & Service Delivery Manager, Lynton House, Commercial Road, Barnstaple EX31 1DG ☎ 01271 388273 ⌨ martin.williams@northdevon.gov.uk

Personnel / HR: Mrs Nikki Gordon, Human Resources Manager, Lynton House, Commercial Road, Barnstaple EX31 1DG ☎ 01271 388548 ⌨ nikki.gordon@northdevon.gov.uk

Planning: Mr Mike Kelly, Planning Manager, Lynton House, Commercial Road, Barnstaple EX31 1DG ☎ 01271 388439 ⌨ mike.kelly@northdevon.gov.uk

Procurement: Mr Martin Williams, Procurement & Service Delivery Manager, Lynton House, Commercial Road, Barnstaple EX31 1DG ☎ 01271 388273 ⌨ martin.williams@northdevon.gov.uk

Recycling & Waste Minimisation: Mr Ricky McCormack, Head of Operational Services, Lynton House, Commercial Road, Barnstaple EX31 1DG ☎ 01271 388503 ⌨ ricky.mccormack@northdevon.gov.uk

Staff Training: Mrs Nikki Gordon, Human Resources Manager, Lynton House, Commercial Road, Barnstaple EX31 1DG ☎ 01271 388548 ⌨ nikki.gordon@northdevon.gov.uk

Waste Collection and Disposal: Mr Ricky McCormack, Head of Operational Services, Lynton House, Commercial Road, Barnstaple EX31 1DG ☎ 01271 388503 ⌨ ricky.mccormack@northdevon.gov.uk

Waste Management: Mr Ricky McCormack, Head of Operational Services, Lynton House, Commercial Road, Barnstaple EX31 1DG ☎ 01271 388503 ⌨ ricky.mccormack@northdevon.gov.uk

Children's Play Areas: Mr Mark Kentell, Contracts Delivery Manager, Lynton House, Commercial Road, Barnstaple EX31 1DG ☎ 01271 327711 ⌨ mark.kentell@northdevon.gov.uk

COUNCILLORS

Chair: Flynn, Jaqueline (CON - Barnstaple (Longbridge)) jacqueline.flynn@northdevon.gov.uk

Vice-Chair: Croft, Sue (CON - Chulmleigh) sue.croft@northdevon.gov.uk

Leader of the Council: Brailey, David (CON - Barnstaple (Longbridge)) david.brailey@northdevon.gov.uk

Deputy Leader of the Council: Barker, Pat (CON - Georgeham & Mortehoe) pat.barker@northdevon.gov.uk

Biederman, Frank (IND - Fremington) frank.biederman@northdevon.gov.uk

Bonds, Robin (CON - Braunton (East)) robin.bonds@northdevon.gov.uk

Bradford, Adam (LD - Barnstaple (Central Town)) adam.bradford@northdevon.gov.uk

Campbell, Jim (IND - Ilfracombe (Central)) jim.campbell@northdevon.gov.uk

Cann, Joy (LD - Barnstaple (Yeo Valley)) joy.cann@northdevon.gov.uk

Cann, Rodney (CON - Bickington & Roundswell) rodney.cann@northdevon.gov.uk

Chesters, Jasmine (CON - Braunton (West)) jasmine.chesters@northdevon.gov.uk

Chugg, Caroline (CON - Braunton (West)) caroline.chugg@northdevon.gov.uk

Crabb, Paul (CON - Ilfracombe (Central)) paul.crabb@northdevon.gov.uk

Davis, Andrea (CON - Heanton Punchardon) andrea.davis@northdevon.gov.uk

Edgell, Richard (CON - North Molton) richard.edgell@northdevon.gov.uk

Edmunds, Mike (IND - Ilfracombe (East)) mike.edmunds@northdevon.gov.uk

Fowler, Geoffery (LD - Ilfracombe (West)) geoffrey.fowler@northdevon.gov.uk

Greenslade, Brian (LD - Barnstaple (Pilton)) brian.greenslade@northdevon.gov.uk

Gubb, Yvette (IND - Combe Martin) yvette.gubb@northdevon.gov.uk

Harrison, Michael (CON - Barnstaple (Newport)) henry.harrison@northdevon.gov.uk

Haywood, Sue (LD - Barnstaple (Forches & Whiddon Valley)) suzanne.haywood@northdevon.gov.uk

Hunt, Julie (LD - Barnstaple (Forches & Whiddon Valley)) julie.hunt@northdevon.gov.uk

Jones, Dick (CON - Barnstaple (Longbridge))
dick.jones@northdevon.gov.uk

Lane, Glyn (CON - Landkey, Swimbridge & Taw)
glyn.lane@northdevon.gov.uk

Ley, Eric (IND - Bishops Nympton)
eric.ley@northdevon.gov.uk

Lovering, John (CON - Combe Martin)
john.lovering@northdevon.gov.uk

Lucas, Douglas (CON - Brauton (East))
douglas.lucas@northdevon.gov.uk

Luggar, David (CON - Landkey, Swimbridge & Taw)
david.luggar@northdevon.gov.uk

Manuel, Mair (LD - Barnstaple (Pilton))
mair.manuel@northdevon.gov.uk

Mathews, John (CON - Barnstaple (Newport))
john.mathews@northdevon.gov.uk

Meadlarkin, Ian (CON - Ilfracombe (West))
ian.meadlarkin@northdevon.gov.uk

Moore, John (INDNA - South Molton)
john.moore@northdevon.gov.uk

Moores, Brian (CON - Instow)
brian.moores@northdevon.gov.uk

Patrinos, John (IND - Lynton & Lynmouth)
john.patrinos@northdevon.gov.uk

Prowse, Malcolm (INDNA - Bratton Fleming)
malcolm.prowse@northdevon.gov.uk

Roome, Ian (LD - Barnstaple (Yeo Valley))
ian.roome@northdevon.gov.uk

Tucker, Frederick (LD - Marwood)
frederick.tucker@northdevon.gov.uk

Webber, Faye (LD - Barnstaple (Central Town))
faye.webber@northdevon.gov.uk

White, Walter (IND - Chittlehampton)
walter.white@northdevon.gov.uk

Wilkinson, Malcolm (LD - Georgeham & Mortehoe)
malcolm.wilkinson@northdevon.gov.uk

Wood, Tony (IND - Fremington)
tony.wood@northdevon.gov.uk

Worden, David (LD - South Molton)
david.worden@northdevon.gov.uk

Yabsley, Jeremy (CON - Witheridge Ward)
jeremy.yabsley@northdevon.gov.uk

POLITICAL COMPOSITION
CON: 21, LD: 12, IND: 8, INDNA: 2

COMMITTEE CHAIRS
Audit: Mrs Sue Croft

Licensing: Ms Jasmine Chesters

Planning: Mr Eric Ley

North Dorset   **D**

North Dorset District Council, Nordon, Salisbury Road,
Blandford Forum DT11 7LL

☎ 01258 454111 🖷 01258 480179 🖳 www.north-dorset.gov.uk

FACTS AND FIGURES
Parliamentary Constituencies: Dorset North
EU Constituencies: South West
Election Frequency: Elections are of whole council

PRINCIPAL OFFICERS

Chief Executive: Mr Matt Prosser, Chief Executive, Tri-Council Partnership, South Walks House, South Walks Road, Dorchester DT1 1UZ ☎ 01305 251010

Assistant Chief Executive: Mr Stuart Caundle, Assistant Chief Executive, South Walks House, South Walks Road, Dorchester DT1 1UZ ☎ 01258 484010 ⌁ scaundle@north-dorset.co.uk

Senior Management: Mr Martin Hamilton, Strategic Director, South Walks House, South Walks Road, Dorchester DT1 1UZ ☎ 01305 838086 ⌁ m.hamilton@westdorset-weymouth.gov.uk

Senior Management: Mr Stephen Hill, Strategic Director, South Walks House, South Walks Road, Dorchester DT1 1UZ ☎ 01258 484034 ⌁ shill@north-dorset.gov.uk

Senior Management: Mr Jason Vaughan, Strategic Director, South Walks House, South Walks Road, Dorchester DT1 1UZ ☎ 01305 838233; 01305 251010 ⌁ j.vaughan@westdorset-weymouth.gov.uk

Best Value: Mr Drystan Gatrell, Business Information Analyst, Nordon, Salisbury Road, Blandford Forum DT11 7LL ☎ 01258 484056 ⌁ dgatrell@north-dorset.gov.uk

Building Control: Mr Kerry Pitt-Kerby, Environment & Private Sector Housing Team Leader, Nordon, Salisbury Road, Blandford Forum DT11 7LL ☎ 01258 484311 ⌁ kpittkerby@north-dorset.gov.uk

Community Planning: Mr Hugh de Longh, Community Planning Officer, Nordon, Salisbury Road, Blandford Forum DT11 7LL ☎ 01258 484025

Community Safety: Mr John Bartlett, Community Safety Policy Officer, Nordon, Salisbury Road, Blandford Forum DT11 7LL ☎ 01258 484368 ⌁ jbartlett@north-dorset.gov.uk

Computer Management: Mr Bryan Alford, Business Technology Solutions Advisor, Nordon, Salisbury Road, Blandford Forum DT11 7LL ☎ 01258 484073 ⌁ balford@north-dorset.gov.uk

Customer Service: Ms Emma Edgeley-Long, Business Change Co-ordinator, Nordon, Salisbury Road, Blandford Forum DT11 7LL ☎ 01258 484053 ⌁ eedgeley-long@north-dorset.gov.uk

E-Government: Mr Bryan Alford, Business Technology Solutions Advisor, Nordon, Salisbury Road, Blandford Forum DT11 7LL ☎ 01258 484073 ⌁ balford@north-dorset.gov.uk

Electoral Registration: Ms Jacqui Andrews, Democratic Services Manager, Nordon, Salisbury Road, Blandford Forum DT11 7LL ☎ 01258 484325 ⌁ jandrews@north-dorset.gov.uk

Emergency Planning: Mr Roger Frost, Food Safety & Licensing Manager, Nordon, Salisbury Road, Blandford Forum DT11 7LL ☎ 01258 484316 ⌨ rfrost@north-dorset.gov.uk

Energy Management: Mr Kevin Morris, Environment, Land, Property & Commissioning Manager, Nordon, Salisbury Road, Blandford Forum DT11 7LL ☎ 01258 484276 ⌨ kmorris@north-dorset.gov.uk

Environmental / Technical Services: Mr Mike Coker, Principal Technical Officer, Nordon, Salisbury Road, Blandford Forum DT11 7LL ☎ 01258 484275 ⌨ mcoker@north-dorset.gov.uk

Environmental Health: Mr Roger Frost, Food Safety & Licensing Manager, Nordon, Salisbury Road, Blandford Forum DT11 7LL ☎ 01258 484316 ⌨ rfrost@north-dorset.gov.uk

Environmental Health: Mr Kerry Pitt-Kerby, Environment & Private Sector Housing Team Leader, Nordon, Salisbury Road, Blandford Forum DT11 7LL ☎ 01258 484311 ⌨ kpittkerby@north-dorset.gov.uk

Estates, Property & Valuation: Mr Kevin Morris, Environment, Land, Property & Commissioning Manager, Nordon, Salisbury Road, Blandford Forum DT11 7LL ☎ 01258 484276 ⌨ kmorris@north-dorset.gov.uk

Facilities: Mr Kevin Morris, Environment, Land, Property & Commissioning Manager, Nordon, Salisbury Road, Blandford Forum DT11 7LL ☎ 01258 484276 ⌨ kmorris@north-dorset.gov.uk

Finance: Mr Ian Milne, Finance Manager, Nordon, Salisbury Road, Blandford Forum DT11 7LL ☎ 01258 484115 ⌨ imilne@north-dorset.gov.uk

Finance: Mr Jason Vaughan, Strategic Director, South Walks House, South Walks Road, Dorchester DT1 1UZ ☎ 01305 838233; 01305 251010 ⌨ j.vaughan@westdorset-weymouth.gov.uk

Health and Safety: Mr Roger Frost, Food Safety & Licensing Manager, Nordon, Salisbury Road, Blandford Forum DT11 7LL ☎ 01258 484316 ⌨ rfrost@north-dorset.gov.uk

Home Energy Conservation: Mr Kerry Pitt-Kerby, Environment & Private Sector Housing Team Leader, Nordon, Salisbury Road, Blandford Forum DT11 7LL ☎ 01258 484311 ⌨ kpittkerby@north-dorset.gov.uk

Housing: Ms Sarah How, Senior Housing Needs Officer, Nordon, Salisbury Road, Blandford Forum DT11 7LL ☎ 01258 484386 ⌨ show@north-dorset.gov.uk

Legal: Mr Robert Firth, Legal Services Manager & Commissioning Manager, Nordon, Salisbury Road, Blandford Forum DT11 7LL ☎ 01258 484364 ⌨ rfirth@north-dorset.gov.uk

Leisure and Cultural Services: Mr Kevin Morris, Environment, Land, Property & Commissioning Manager, Nordon, Salisbury Road, Blandford Forum DT11 7LL ☎ 01258 484276 ⌨ kmorris@north-dorset.gov.uk

Licensing: Mr Peter Davies, Senior Licensing Officer, Nordon, Salisbury Road, Blandford Forum DT11 7LL ☎ 01258 484014 ⌨ pdavies@north-dorset.gov.uk

Member Services: Ms Jacqui Andrews, Democratic Services Manager, Nordon, Salisbury Road, Blandford Forum DT11 7LL ☎ 01258 484325 ⌨ jandrews@north-dorset.gov.uk

Parking: Mr Kevin Morris, Environment, Land, Property & Commissioning Manager, Nordon, Salisbury Road, Blandford Forum DT11 7LL ☎ 01258 484276 ⌨ kmorris@north-dorset.gov.uk

Personnel / HR: Ms Bobbie Bragg, Senior Personnel Advisor, Nordon, Salisbury Road, Blandford Forum DT11 7LL ☎ 01258 454032 ⌨ bbragg@north-dorset.gov.uk

Planning: Mr John Hammond, Development Services Manager, Nordon, Salisbury Road, Blandford Forum DT11 7LL ☎ 01258 484202 ⌨ jhammond@north-dorset.gov.uk

Recycling & Waste Minimisation: Mr Robert Firth, Legal Services Manager & Commissioning Manager, Nordon, Salisbury Road, Blandford Forum DT11 7LL ☎ 01258 484364 ⌨ rfirth@north-dorset.gov.uk

Regeneration: Mr Hugh de Longh, Community Planning Officer, Nordon, Salisbury Road, Blandford Forum DT11 7LL ☎ 01258 484025

Staff Training: Ms Bobbie Bragg, Senior Personnel Advisor, Nordon, Salisbury Road, Blandford Forum DT11 7LL ☎ 01258 454032 ⌨ bbragg@north-dorset.gov.uk

Sustainable Communities: Mr Kevin Morris, Environment, Land, Property & Commissioning Manager, Nordon, Salisbury Road, Blandford Forum DT11 7LL ☎ 01258 484276 ⌨ kmorris@north-dorset.gov.uk

Sustainable Development: Mr Paul McIntosh, Sustainability Officer, Nordon, Salisbury Road, Blandford Forum DT11 7LL ☎ 01258 484019 ⌨ pmcintosh@north-dorset.gov.uk

Waste Collection and Disposal: Mr Robert Firth, Legal Services Manager & Commissioning Manager, Nordon, Salisbury Road, Blandford Forum DT11 7LL ☎ 01258 484364 ⌨ rfirth@north-dorset.gov.uk

Waste Management: Mr Robert Firth, Legal Services Manager & Commissioning Manager, Nordon, Salisbury Road, Blandford Forum DT11 7LL ☎ 01258 484364 ⌨ rfirth@north-dorset.gov.uk

COUNCILLORS

Chair: Fox, Victor (CON - Sturminster Newton) victorfox187@btinternet.com

Leader of the Council: Croney, Deborah (CON - Hill Forts) hillfortsward@hotmail.co.uk

Deputy Leader of the Council: Walsh, David (CON - Gillingham Rural) cllr.davidwalsh@talktalk.net

Batstone, Pauline (CON - Lydden Vale)
cllr.p.batstone@btinternet.com

Batty-Smith, Bill (CON - Blackmore)
w.battysmith@readingfans.co.uk

Beer, Derek (LD - Shaftesbury Central)

Brown, Piers (CON - Hill Forts)
padbrown@icloud.com

Burch, Audrey (CON - Bulbarrow)
audreyburch01@googlemail.com

Butler, Esme (IND - Blandford Damory Down)
esbutler@sky.com

Carr-Jones, Graham (CON - Blackmore)
grahamcarrjones@aol.com

Cattaway, Andrew (CON - Motcombe & Bourton)
cattaways@tinyworld.co.uk

Cooper, Barrie (LD - Blandford Langton St. Leonard's)

Dowden, Charles (CON - Stours & Marnhull)
charles.dowden010@btinternet.com

Francis, Jo (CON - Shaftesbury East)
francisja@icloud.com

Gould, Mike (CON - Gillingham Town)
mgould@emf-ltd.co.uk

Handford, Traci (CON - Blandford Hilltop)
tracihandford@hotmail.co.uk

Jefferson, Gary (CON - Shaftesbury West)
gpjefferson@gmail.com

Jespersen, Sherry (CON - Hill Forts)
cllr.s.jespersen@btinternet.com

Kerby, Andrew (CON - Riversdale & Portman)
cllr.akerby@north-dorset.gov.uk

Langham, Catherine (CON - The Beacon)
cel@langhamfarm.co.uk

Milstead, David (LD - Gillingham Town)
david.milsted@virgin.net

Parker, Emma (CON - Abbey)
emmaparker77@hotmail.co.uk

Pothecary, Val (CON - Gillingham Town)
vpothecary@tiscali.co.uk

Pritchard, Simon (IND - Shaftesbury East)
cllrpritchard@hotmail.co.uk

Ridout, Belinda (CON - Gillingham Rural)
cllr.belindaridout@talktalk.net

Roake, Michael (CON - Sturminster Newton)
mroake5179@aol.com

Skipwith, Deirdre (CON - Lower Tarrants)
deirdreskipwith@hotmail.co.uk

Somper, Jane (CON - Abbey)
janesomper@hotmail.co.uk

Stayt, John (CON - Riversdale & Portman)
john.stayt@btinternet.com

Stayt, Jackie (CON - Blanford Old Town)
jackiestayt@uwclub.net

Tanner, John (LD - Blandford Central)
jjtanners@hotmail.com

Westbrook, Jane (CON - Stours & Marnhull)
westbrookjane@yahoo.co.uk

Williams, Peter (CON - Motcombe & Bourton)
peterwilliams53@gmail.com

POLITICAL COMPOSITION
CON: 27, LD: 4, IND: 2

COMMITTEE CHAIRS

Accounts & Audit: Mrs Audrey Burch

Licensing: Ms Sherry Jespersen

North East Derbyshire   D

North East Derbyshire District Council, 2013 Mill Lane,
Wingerworth, Chesterfield S42 6NG
☎ 01246 231111 🖷 01246 550213; 01246 550213
⌁ enquiries@ne-derbyshire.gov.uk 🖳 www.ne-derbyshire.gov.uk

FACTS AND FIGURES
Parliamentary Constituencies: Derbyshire North East
EU Constituencies: East Midlands
Election Frequency: Elections are of whole council

PRINCIPAL OFFICERS

Chief Executive: Mr Dan Swaine, Chief Executive, 2013 Mill Lane,
Wingerworth, Chesterfield S42 6NG ☎ 01246 242401
⌁ dan.swaine@ne-derbyshire.gov.uk

Senior Management: Mr Paul Hackett, Joint Executive Director -
Transformation, 2013 Mill Lane, Wingerworth, Chesterfield S42 6NG
☎ 01246 242566 ⌁ paul.hackett@ne-derbyshire.gov.uk

Senior Management: Mr Bryan Mason, Joint Executive Director -
Operations, 2013 Mill Lane, Wingerworth, Chesterfield S42 6NG
☎ 01246 242431 ⌁ bryan.mason@ne-derbyshire.gov.uk

Architect, Building / Property Services: Mr Grant Galloway,
Assistant Director - Property & Estates, 2013 Mill Lane,
Wingerworth, Chesterfield S42 6NG ☎ 01246 242284
⌁ grant.galloway@bolsover.gov.uk

Best Value: Mrs Jane Foley, Joint Assistant Director - Customer
Service & Improvement, 2013 Mill Lane, Wingerworth, Chesterfield
S42 6NG ☎ 01246 242343 ⌁ jane.foley@bolsover.gov.uk

Building Control: Mr Malcolm Clinton, Business Manager, Town
Hall, Rose Hill, Chesterfield S40 1LP ☎ 01246 345817; 01246
354900 ⌁ malcolm.clinton@ne-derbyshire.gov.uk; malcolm.clinton@
bcnconsultancy.co.uk

Children / Youth Services: Mr Karl Apps, Housing Strategy &
Enabling Manager, 2013 Mill Lane, Wingerworth, Chesterfield S42
6NG ☎ 01246 217289 ⌁ karl.apps@ne-derbyshire.gov.uk

PR / Communications: Mr Scott Chambers, Communications
Officer, 2013 Mill Lane, Wingerworth, Chesterfield S42 6NG
☎ 01246 217692 ⌁ scott.chambers@bolsover.gov.uk

NORTH EAST DERBYSHIRE

Community Planning: Mr Adrian Kirkham, Planning Services Manager, 2013 Mill Lane, Wingerworth, Chesterfield S42 6NG ☎ 01246 217591 ⏚ adrian.kirkham@ne-derbyshire.gov.uk

Community Safety: Ms Faye Green, Community Safety Manager, 2013 Mill Lane, Wingerworth, Chesterfield S42 6NG ☎ 01246 217015 ⏚ faye.green@ne-derbyshire.gov.uk

Computer Management: Mr Nick Blaney, Joint IT Services Manager, 2013 Mill Lane, Wingerworth, Chesterfield S42 6NG ☎ 01246 217103; 01246 217103; 01246 717097 ⏚ nick.blaney@ne-derbyshire.gov.uk

Contracts: Mr Bryan Mason, Joint Executive Director - Operations, 2013 Mill Lane, Wingerworth, Chesterfield S42 6NG ☎ 01246 242431 ⏚ bryan.mason@ne-derbyshire.gov.uk

Corporate Services: Mrs Sarah Sternberg, Joint Assistant Director - Governance & Monitoring Officer, 2013 Mill Lane, Wingerworth, Chesterfield S42 6NG ☎ 01246 217057 ⏚ sarah.sternberg@bolsover.gov.uk

Customer Service: Mrs Jane Foley, Joint Assistant Director - Customer Services & Improvement, 2013 Mill Lane, Wingerworth, Chesterfield S42 6NG ☎ 01246 217029 ⏚ jane.foley@bolsover.gov.uk

Customer Service: Ms Rachael Pope, Customer Services Operational Manager, 2013 Mill Lane, Wingerworth, Chesterfield S42 6NG ☎ 01246 217658 ⏚ rachael.pope@ne-derbyshire.gov.uk

Economic Development: Mrs Allison Westray-Chapman, Joint Assistant Director - Economic Growth, 2013 Mill Lane, Wingerworth, Chesterfield S42 6NG ☎ 01246 217199 ⏚ allison.westray-chapman@ne-derbyshire.gov.uk

E-Government: Mrs Sarah Sternberg, Joint Assistant Director - Governance & Monitoring Officer, 2013 Mill Lane, Wingerworth, Chesterfield S42 6NG ☎ 01246 217057 ⏚ sarah.sternberg@bolsover.gov.uk

Electoral Registration: Mrs Sarah Sternberg, Joint Assistant Director - Governance & Monitoring Officer, 2013 Mill Lane, Wingerworth, Chesterfield S42 6NG ☎ 01246 217057 ⏚ sarah.sternberg@bolsover.gov.uk

Emergency Planning: Mr Paul Hackett, Joint Executive Director - Transformation, 2013 Mill Lane, Wingerworth, Chesterfield S42 6NG ☎ 01246 242566 ⏚ paul.hackett@ne-derbyshire.gov.uk

Emergency Planning: Mr Lee Hickin, Joint Assistant Director - Leisure, 2013 Mill Lane, Wingerworth, Chesterfield S42 6NG ☎ 01246 217218 ⏚ lee.hickin@bolsover.gov.uk

Energy Management: Mr Paul Hackett, Joint Executive Director - Transformation, 2013 Mill Lane, Wingerworth, Chesterfield S42 6NG ☎ 01246 217543 ⏚ paul.hackett@ne-derbyshire.gov.uk

Environmental / Technical Services: Mr James Arnold, Joint Assistant Director - Planning & Environmental Health, 2013 Mill Lane, Wingerworth, Chesterfield S42 6NG ☎ 01246 217436 ⏚ james.arnold@bolsover.gov.uk

Environmental Health: Mr James Arnold, Joint Assistant Director - Planning & Environmental Health, 2013 Mill Lane, Wingerworth, Chesterfield S42 6NG ☎ 01246 217436 ⏚ james.arnold@bolsover.gov.uk

Estates, Property & Valuation: Mr Dave Broom, Architect, 2013 Mill Lane, Wingerworth, Chesterfield S42 6NG ☎ 01246 217374 ⏚ david.broom@ne-derbyshire.gov.uk

Estates, Property & Valuation: Mr Grant Galloway, Assistant Director - Property & Estates, 2013 Mill Lane, Wingerworth, Chesterfield S42 6NG ☎ 01246 242284 ⏚ grant.galloway@bolsover.gov.uk

Facilities: Mr Dave Broom, Architect, 2013 Mill Lane, Wingerworth, Chesterfield S42 6NG ☎ 01246 217374 ⏚ david.broom@ne-derbyshire.gov.uk

Facilities: Mr Robert Walker, Property Services Officer, 2013 Mill Lane, Wingerworth, Chesterfield S42 6NG ☎ 01246 217588 ⏚ robert.walker@ne-derbyshire.gov.uk

Finance: Ms Dawn Clarke, Joint Assistant Director - Finance, Revenues & Benefits, 2013 Mill Lane, Wingerworth, Chesterfield S42 6NG ☎ 01246 217658 ⏚ dawn.clarke@ne-derbyshire.gov.uk

Finance: Mr Bryan Mason, Joint Executive Director - Operations, 2013 Mill Lane, Wingerworth, Chesterfield S42 6NG ☎ 01246 242431 ⏚ bryan.mason@ne-derbyshire.gov.uk

Fleet Management: Mr Steve Brunt, Joint Assistant Director - Street Scene, 2013 Mill Lane, Wingerworth, Chesterfield S42 6NG ☎ 01246 217264 ⏚ steve.brunt@ne-derbyshire.gov.uk

Grounds Maintenance: Mr Steve Brunt, Joint Assistant Director - Street Scene, 2013 Mill Lane, Wingerworth, Chesterfield S42 6NG ☎ 01246 217264 ⏚ steve.brunt@ne-derbyshire.gov.uk

Grounds Maintenance: Mr Darren Mitchell, Grounds Maintenance Manager, 2013 Mill Lane, Wingerworth, Chesterfield S42 6NG ☎ 01246 217285 ⏚ darren.mitchell@ne-derbyshire.gov.uk

Health and Safety: Ms Stephanie Barker, Assistant Director - Human Resources & Payroll, 2013 Mill Lane, Wingerworth, Chesterfield S42 6NG ☎ 01246 242237 ⏚ stephanie.barker@ne-derbyshire.gov.uk

Health and Safety: Mr Paul Hackett, Joint Executive Director - Transformation, 2013 Mill Lane, Wingerworth, Chesterfield S42 6NG ☎ 01246 217543 ⏚ paul.hackett@ne-derbyshire.gov.uk

Health and Safety: Mr Mark Spotswood, Health & Safety Officer, 2013 Mill Lane, Wingerworth, Chesterfield S42 6NG ⏚ mark.spotswood@bolsover.gov.uk

Housing: Ms Lorraine Shaw, Managing Director - Rykneld Homes, 2013 Mill Lane, Wingerworth, Chesterfield S42 6NG ☎ 01246 217621 ⏚ lorraine.shaw@rykneldhomes.org.uk

Leisure and Cultural Services: Mr Paul Hackett, Joint Executive Director - Transformation, 2013 Mill Lane, Wingerworth, Chesterfield S42 6NG ☎ 01246 242566 ⌨ paul.hackett@ne-derbyshire.gov.uk

Leisure and Cultural Services: Mr Lee Hickin, Joint Assistant Director - Leisure, 2013 Mill Lane, Wingerworth, Chesterfield S42 6NG ☎ 01246 217218 ⌨ lee.hickin@bolsover.gov.uk

Licensing: Mr John Chambers, Licensing Co-ordinator, 2013 Mill Lane, Wingerworth, Chesterfield S42 6NG ☎ 01246 217216 ⌨ john.chambers@ne-derbyshire.gov.uk

Lottery Funding, Charity and Voluntary: Ms Dawn Clarke, Joint Assistant Director - Finance, Revenues & Benefits, 2013 Mill Lane, Wingerworth, Chesterfield S42 6NG ☎ 01246 217658 ⌨ dawn.clarke@ne-derbyshire.gov.uk

Member Services: Mrs Sarah Sternberg, Joint Assistant Director - Governance & Monitoring Officer, 2013 Mill Lane, Wingerworth, Chesterfield S42 6NG ☎ 01246 217057 ⌨ sarah.sternberg@bolsover.gov.uk

Partnerships: Ms Marie Romano, Policy Officer, 2013 Mill Lane, Wingerworth, Chesterfield S42 6NG ☎ 01246 217688 ⌨ marie.romano@ne-derbyshire.gov.uk

Personnel / HR: Ms Stephanie Barker, Assistant Director - Human Resources & Payroll, 2013 Mill Lane, Wingerworth, Chesterfield S42 6NG ☎ 01246 242237 ⌨ stephanie.barker@ne-derbyshire.gov.uk

Planning: Mr James Arnold, Joint Assistant Director - Planning & Environmental Health, 2013 Mill Lane, Wingerworth, Chesterfield S42 6NG ☎ 01246 217436 ⌨ james.arnold@bolsover.gov.uk

Planning: Mr Adrian Kirkham, Planning Services Manager, 2013 Mill Lane, Wingerworth, Chesterfield S42 6NG ☎ 01246 217591 ⌨ adrian.kirkham@ne-derbyshire.gov.uk

Procurement: Mr Bryan Mason, Joint Executive Director - Operations, 2013 Mill Lane, Wingerworth, Chesterfield S42 6NG ☎ 01246 242431 ⌨ bryan.mason@ne-derbyshire.gov.uk

Recycling & Waste Minimisation: Mr Steve Jowett, Joint Waste & Recycling Manager, 2013 Mill Lane, Wingerworth, Chesterfield S42 6NG ☎ 01246 217266 ⌨ steve.jowett@ne-derbyshire.gov.uk

Regeneration: Mr Dan Swaine, Chief Executive, 2013 Mill Lane, Wingerworth, Chesterfield S42 6NG ☎ 01246 242401 ⌨ dan.swaine@ne-derbyshire.gov.uk

Regeneration: Mrs Allison Westray-Chapman, Joint Assistant Director - Economic Growth, 2013 Mill Lane, Wingerworth, Chesterfield S42 6NG ☎ 01246 217199 ⌨ allison.westray-chapman@ne-derbyshire.gov.uk

Staff Training: Ms Stephanie Barker, Assistant Director - Human Resources & Payroll, 2013 Mill Lane, Wingerworth, Chesterfield S42 6NG ☎ 01246 242237 ⌨ stephanie.barker@ne-derbyshire.gov.uk

Street Scene: Mr Steve Brunt, Joint Assistant Director - Streetscene, 2013 Mill Lane, Wingerworth, Chesterfield S42 6NG ☎ 01246 217264 ⌨ steve.brunt@ne-derbyshire.gov.uk

Sustainable Communities: Mrs Debbie Whitehead, Consultation & Community Involvement Officer, 2013 Mill Lane, Wingerworth, Chesterfield S42 6NG ☎ 01246 217018 ⌨ debbie.whitehead@ne-derbyshire.gov.uk

Sustainable Development: Mrs Jane Foley, Joint Assistant Director - Customer Service & Improvement, 2013 Mill Lane, Wingerworth, Chesterfield S42 6NG ☎ 01246 242343 ⌨ jane.foley@bolsover.gov.uk

Transport: Mr Steve Brunt, Joint Assistant Director - Street Scene, 2013 Mill Lane, Wingerworth, Chesterfield S42 6NG ☎ 01246 217264 ⌨ steve.brunt@ne-derbyshire.gov.uk

Waste Collection and Disposal: Mr Steve Brunt, Joint Assistant Director - Streetscene, 2013 Mill Lane, Wingerworth, Chesterfield S42 6NG ☎ 01246 217264 ⌨ steve.brunt@ne-derbyshire.gov.uk

Waste Management: Mr Steve Brunt, Streetscene Manager, 2013 Mill Lane, Wingerworth, Chesterfield S42 6NG ☎ 01246 217624 ⌨ steve.brunt@ne-derbyshire.gov.uk

COUNCILLORS

Chair: Peters, Stephen (LAB - Tupton)

Vice-Chair: Smith, Rosie (LAB - Unstone)

Leader of the Council: Baxter, Graham (LAB - Dronfield North) cllr.baxter@ne-derbyshire.gov.uk

Deputy Leader of the Council: Hill, Elizabeth (LAB - Grassmoor) cllr.hill@ne-derbyshire.gov.uk

Antcliff, Pat (CON - Wingerworth)

Armitage, William (CON - Ashover)

Austen, Jane (LAB - Eckington North)

Barker, Nigel (LAB - North Wingfield Central) nigel.barker@ne-derbyshire.gov.uk

Barnes, Barry (LAB - Shirland)

Barry, Jayne (LAB - North Wingfield Central)

Blanshard, Liz (CON - Dronfield South)

Boyle, Shay (LAB - Sutton)

Butler, Geoff (LAB - Pilsley & Morton)

Cooper, Andrew (IND - Pilsley & Morton) andrew.cooper@ne-derbyshire.gov.uk

Cornwell, Suzy (LAB - Holmewood & Heath)

Cupit, Charlotte (CON - Shirland)

Dale, Alex (CON - Coal Aston)

Elliott, Peter (CON - Brampton & Walton) peter.elliot@ne-derbyshire.gov.uk

Ellis, Stuart (CON - Wingerworth) stuart.ellis@ne-derbyshire.gov.uk

Emmens, Michelle (CON - Gosforth Valley)

NORTH EAST DERBYSHIRE

Foster, Mark (CON - Dronfield Woodhouse)

Foster, Angelique (CON - Dronfield South)

Garrett, Alan (LAB - Killamarsh West)
alan.garrett@ne-derbyshire.gov.uk

Gordon, Michael (LAB - Ridgeway & Marsh Lane)
cllr.gordon@ne-derbyshire.gov.uk

Hall, Roger (CON - Dronfield Woodhouse)

Hill, Julie (LAB - Grassmoor)

Holmes, Patricia (LAB - Pilsley & Morton)
patricia.holmes@ne-derbyshire.gov.uk

Hopkinson, Gareth (CON - Coal Aston)

Huckerby, Carol (CON - Barlow & Holmesfield)
carol.huckerby@ne-derbyshire.gov.uk

Hunt, Clive (LAB - Eckington South)
clive.hunt@ne-derbyshire.gov.uk

Kerry, Patrick (LAB - Sutton)
patrick.kerry@ne-derbyshire.gov.uk

Laws, Harold (LAB - Killamarsh East)

Lewis, Barry (CON - Wingerworth)

Lilley, Jeff (LAB - North Wingfield Central)

Mansbridge, Ted (LAB - Clay Cross South)

Morley, Geoff (LAB - Clay Cross North)
cllr.morley@ne-derbyshire.gov.uk

Powell, Alan (CON - Gosforth Valley)

Reader, Tracy (LAB - Clay Cross North)

Rice, William (LAB - Killamarsh West)
billy.rice@ne-derbyshire.gov.uk

Ridgway, Jacqueline (LAB - Eckington South)

Ridgway, Brian (LAB - Renishaw)
brian.ridgway@ne-derbyshire.gov.uk

Robinson, Lilian (LAB - Killamarsh West)

Rouse, Kathy (LAB - Clay Cross North)

Skinner, Derrick (LAB - Shirland)

Smith, Christine (LAB - Dronfield North)
christine.smith@ne-derbyshire.gov.uk

Stone, Lee (LAB - Holmewood & Heath)
lee.stone@ne-derbyshire.gov.uk

Tait, Kevin (CON - Dronfield South)

Thacker, Martin (CON - Brampton & Walton)
martin.thacker@ne-derbyshire.gov.uk

Tite, Catherine (LAB - Eckington North)

Welton, Richard (CON - Gosforth Valley)

Windle, John (LAB - Killamarsh East)
john.windle@ne-derbyshire.gov.uk

Wright, Brian (LAB - Clay Cross South)
brian.wright@ne-derbyshire.gov.uk

POLITICAL COMPOSITION
LAB: 33, CON: 18, IND: 1, Vacant: 1

COMMITTEE CHAIRS

Audit: Mr Derrick Skinner

Licensing: Mr Michael Gordon

Planning: Mr Harold Laws

North East Lincolnshire   U

North East Lincolnshire Council, Municipal Offices, Town Hall Square, Grimsby DN31 1HU
☎ 01472 313131 🖥 www.nelincs.gov.uk

FACTS AND FIGURES
Parliamentary Constituencies: Cleethorpes, Great Grimsby
EU Constituencies: Yorkshire and the Humber
Election Frequency: Elections are by thirds

PRINCIPAL OFFICERS

Chief Executive: Mr Rob Walsh, Chief Executive, Municipal Offices, Town Hall Square, Grimsby DN31 1HU ☎ 01472 323870 ✆ rob.walsh@nelincs.gov.uk

Deputy Chief Executive: Ms Joanne Hewson, Deputy Chief Executive - Communities, Municipal Offices, Town Hall Square, Grimsby DN31 1HU ☎ 01472 323021 ✆ joanne.hewson@nelincs.gov.uk

Senior Management: Ms Angela Blake, Director - Economy & Growth, Municipal Offices, Town Hall Square, Grimsby DN31 1HU ☎ 01472 324741 ✆ angela.blake@nelincs.gov.uk

Senior Management: Ms Bev Compton, Director - Adult Services, Municipal Offices, Town Hall Square, Grimsby DN31 1HU ☎ 01472 326126 ✆ beverley.compton@nelincs.gov.uk

Senior Management: Mr Paul Cordy, Director - Children's Social Care, Municipal Offices, Town Hall Square, Grimsby DN31 1HU ☎ 01472 323255 ✆ paul.cordy@nelincs.gov.uk

Senior Management: Ms Helen Isaacs, Director - Governance, Democracy & Community, Municipal Offices, Town Hall Square, Grimsby DN31 1HU ☎ 01472 326127 ✆ helen.isaacs@nelincs.gov.uk

Senior Management: Mr Steve Kay, Director - Prevention & Early Help, Municipal Offices, Town Hall Square, Grimsby DN31 1HU ☎ 01472 323266 ✆ steve.kay@nelincs.gov.uk

Senior Management: Mr Tony Maione, Chief Legal Officer, Municipal Offices, Town Hall Square, Grimsby DN31 1HU ☎ 01472 324016 ✆ tony.maione@nelincs.gov.uk

Senior Management: Mr David Paice, Interim Director - Education, Skills & Lifelong Learning, Municipal Offices, Town Hall Square, Grimsby DN31 1HU david.paice@nelincs.gov.uk

Senior Management: Mr Stephen Pintus, Director - Health & Wellbeing, Municipal Offices, Town Hall Square, Grimsby DN31 1HU ☎ 01472 324012 ✆ stephen.pintus@nelincs.gov.uk

Senior Management: Ms Sharon Wroot, Director - Finance, Operations & Resources, Municipal Offices, Town Hall Square, Grimsby DN31 1HU ☎ 01472 324423 ⏀ sharon.wroot@nelincs.gov.uk

Architect, Building / Property Services: Mr Dave Gelder, Deputy Head of Architecture, Origin 2, Origin Way, Europarc, Grimsby DN37 9TZ ☎ 01472 324450 ⏀ david.gelder@nelincs.gov.uk

Building Control: Mr Mark Cawood, Planning & Building Control Manager, Origin 1, Origin Way, Europarc, Grimsby DN37 9TZ ☎ 01472 323280 ⏀ mark.cawood@nelincs.gov.uk

Children / Youth Services: Mr Steve Kay, Director - Prevention & Early Help, Municipal Offices, Town Hall Square, Grimsby DN31 1HU ☎ 01472 323266 ⏀ steve.kay@nelincs.gov.uk

Civil Registration: Mrs Tracy Frisby, Registrars & Civic Services Team Manager, Cleethorpes Town Hall, Knoll Street, Grimsby DN35 8LN ☎ 01472 324860 ⏀ tracy.riley@nelincs.gov.uk

PR / Communications: Mr Iain Lovell, Head of Communications, Print & Marketing, Municipal Offices, Town Hall Square, Grimsby DN31 1HU ☎ 01472 325960 ⏀ iain.lovell@nelincs.gov.uk

Community Safety: Mr Spencer Hunt, Service Manager Safer Communities, The Elms, 22 Abbey Road, Grimsby DN32 0HW ☎ 01472 325939 ⏀ spencer.hunt@neclincs.gov.uk

Computer Management: Mr Paul Hudson, ICT Group Manager, Civic Offices, Knoll Street, Cleethorpes DN35 8LN ☎ 01472 323977 ⏀ paul.hudson@nelincs.gov.uk

Consumer Protection and Trading Standards: Mr Neil Clark, Trading Standards Manager, Municipal Offices, Town Hall Square, Grimsby DN31 1HU ☎ 01472 324805 ⏀ neil.clark@nelincs.gov.uk

Contracts: Ms Debbie Dales, Contract & Commercial Service Manager, St. James House, Grimsby DN31 1EP ☎ 01472 324153 ⏀ debbie.dales@nelincs.gov.uk

Corporate Services: Ms Sharon Wroot, Director - Finance, Operations & Resources, Municipal Offices, Town Hall Square, Grimsby DN31 1HU ☎ 01472 324423 ⏀ sharon.wroot@nelincs.gov.uk

Customer Service: Ms Susan Simpson, Communities, Customer & Business Suppoer Services Manager, Municipal Offices, Town Hall Square, Grimsby DN31 1HU ☎ 01472 323757 ⏀ susan.simpson@nelincs.gov.uk

Economic Development: Mr Damien Jaines-White, Service Manager - Economic Development, Municipal Offices, Town Hall Square, Grimsby DN31 1HU ☎ 01472 324674 ⏀ damien.jaines-white@nelincs.gov.uk

Education: Ms Joanne Hewson, Deputy Chief Executive - Communities, Municipal Offices, Town Hall Square, Grimsby DN31 1HU ☎ 01472 323021 ⏀ joanne.hewson@nelincs.gov.uk

Electoral Registration: Mr Stephen McGrath, Elections & Complaints Team Manager, Municipal Offices, Town Hall Square, Grimsby DN31 1HU ☎ 01472 324160 ⏀ stephen.mcgrath@nelincs.gov.uk

Emergency Planning: Mr James Mason, Assistant Emergency Planning Manager, Fishing Hetetage Centre, Alexandra Dock, Grimsby DN31 1UZ ☎ 01472 324829 ⏀ james.mason@nelincs.gov.uk

Energy Management: Mr Tony Neul, Assistant Director - Environment, Municipal Offices, Town Hall Square, Grimsby DN31 1HU ☎ 01472 323989 ⏀ tony.neul@nelincs.gov.uk

Environmental / Technical Services: Mr Neil Beeken, Food Health Manager, Thrunscoe Centre, Highgate, Cleethorpes DN35 8NX ☎ 01472 324773 ⏀ neil.beeken@nelincs.gov.uk

Environmental Health: Mr Neil Beeken, Food Health Manager, Municipal Offices, Town Hall Square, Grimsby DN31 1HU ☎ 01472 324773 ⏀ neil.beeken@nelincs.gov.uk

Estates, Property & Valuation: Ms Wendy Fisher, Assets Service Manager, Municipal Offices, Town Hall Square, Grimsby DN31 1HU ☎ 01472 323132 ⏀ wendy.fisher@nelincs.gov.uk

Events Manager: Ms Sue Marshall, Operations Manager - Cultural Services, Fishing Heritage Centre, Grimsby DN31 1UZ ☎ 01472 323640 ⏀ sue.marshall@nelincs.gov.uk

Facilities: Mr Paul Thorpe, Building & Facilities Operations Manager, Origin 2, Origin Way, Europarc, Grimsby DN37 9TZ ☎ 01472 324782 ⏀ paul.thorpe@nelincs.gov.uk

Finance: Ms Sharon Wroot, Director - Finance, Operations & Resources, Municipal Offices, Town Hall Square, Grimsby DN31 1HU ☎ 01472 324423 ⏀ sharon.wroot@nelincs.gov.uk

Fleet Management: Mr Glenn Greetham, Head of Neighbourhood Operations, Doughty Road Depot, Grimsby DN32 0LL ☎ 01472 325709 ⏀ glenn.greetham@nelincs.gov.uk

Grounds Maintenance: Mr Glenn Greetham, Head of Neighbourhood Operations, Doughty Road Depot, Grimsby DN32 0LL ☎ 01472 325709 ⏀ glenn.greetham@nelincs.gov.uk

Health and Safety: Mr Mark Smith, Occupational Health & Safety Manager, Civic Offices, Knoll Street, Grimsby DN35 8LN ☎ 01472 324071 ⏀ mark.smith@nelincs.gov.uk

Highways: Mr Marcus Asquith, Head of Highways & Transport, Origin 2, Origin Way, Europarc, Grimsby DN37 9TZ ☎ 01472 336676 ⏀ marcus.asquith@nelincs.gov.uk

Home Energy Conservation: Ms Debra Fox, Home Energy Promotions Officer, Origin 1, 1 Origin Way, Europarc, Grimsby DN37 9TZ ☎ 01472 324782 ⏀ debra.fox@nelincs.gov.uk

Housing: Ms Debbie Fagan, Service Manager - Strategic Housing, Acorn Business Park, Unit 5, Moss Road, Grimsby DN32 0LT ☎ 01472 324977 ⏀ debbie.fagan@nelincs.gov.uk

Legal: Mr Tony Maione, Chief Legal Officer, Municipal Offices, Town Hall Square, Grimsby DN31 1HU ☎ 01472 324016 ⏀ tony.maione@nelincs.gov.uk

NORTH EAST LINCOLNSHIRE

Leisure and Cultural Services: Ms Sue Marshall, Operations Manager - Cultural Services, Fishing Heritage Centre, Grimsby DN31 1UZ ☎ 01472 323640 ✆ sue.marshall@nelincs.gov.uk

Licensing: Mr Adrian Moody, Licensing Manager, Municipal Offices, Town Hall Square, Grimsby DN31 1HU ☎ 01472 324759 ✆ adrian.moody@nelincs.gov.uk

Lighting: Mr Marcus Asquith, Head of Highways & Transport, Municipal Offices, Town Hall Square, Grimsby DN31 1HU ☎ 01472 336676 ✆ marcus.asquith@nelincs.gov.uk

Member Services: Mr Paul Windley, Democratic & Scrutiny Team Manager, Municipal Offices, Town Hall Square, Grimsby DN31 1HU ☎ 01472 324121 ✆ paul.windley@nelincs.gov.uk

Parking: Mr Christopher Mayall, CEO Supervisor, Municipal Offices, Town Hall Square, Grimsby DN31 1HU ☎ 01472 324379 ✆ christopher.mayall@nelincs.gov.uk

Personnel / HR: Ms Sue Walton, HR Group Manager, Civic Offices, Knoll Street, Cleethorpes DN35 8LN ☎ 01472 323259 ✆ sue.walton@nelincs.gov.uk

Planning: Mr Jake Newby, Lead Officer - Planning, Acorn Business, Unit 5, Moss Road, Grimsby DN32 0LT ☎ 01472 324227 ✆ jake.newby@nelincs.gov.uk

Procurement: Ms Rachel Devaney, Partnerships, Contract Management & Compliance Specialist, Central Library, Town Hall Square, Grimsby DN31 1HG ☎ 01472 324153 ✆ rachel.devaney@nelincs.gov.uk

Public Libraries: Mr Steve Hipkins, Head of Cultural Services, Central Library, Town Hall Square, Grimsby DN31 1HG ☎ 01472 323611 ✆ steve.hipkins@nelincs.gov.uk

Recycling & Waste Minimisation: Mr Tony Neul, Assistant Director - Environment, Origin 1, Europarc, Grimsby DN37 9TZ ☎ 01472 323989 ✆ tony.neul@nelincs.gov.uk

Road Safety: Mr Marcus Asquith, Head of Highways & Transport, Municipal Offices, Town Hall Square, Grimsby DN31 1HU ☎ 01472 336676 ✆ marcus.asquith@nelincs.gov.uk

Social Services: Ms Joanne Hewson, Deputy Chief Executive - Communities, Municipal Offices, Town Hall Square, Grimsby DN31 1HU ☎ 01472 323021 ✆ joanne.hewson@nelincs.gov.uk

Social Services (Adult): Ms Joanne Hewson, Deputy Chief Executive - Communities, Municipal Offices, Town Hall Square, Grimsby DN31 1HU ☎ 01472 323021 ✆ joanne.hewson@nelincs.gov.uk

Social Services (Children): Mr Paul Cordy, Director - Children's Social Care, Municipal Offices, Town Hall Square, Grimsby DN31 1HU ☎ 01472 323255 ✆ paul.cordy@nelincs.gov.uk

Public Health: Mr Stephen Pintus, Director - Health & Wellbeing, Municipal Offices, Town Hall Square, Grimsby DN31 1HU ☎ 01472 324012 ✆ stephen.pintus@nelincs.gov.uk

Staff Training: Ms Debbie Walden, Learning & Development Team Manager, Civic Offices, Knoll Street, Cleethorpes DN34 5TD ☎ 01472 324059 ✆ deborah.walden@nelincs.gov.uk

Street Scene: Mr Tony Neul, Assistant Director - Environment, Origin 1, Europarc, Grimsby DN37 9TZ ☎ 01472 323989 ✆ tony.neul@nelincs.gov.uk

Sustainable Communities: Ms Joanne Hewson, Deputy Chief Executive - Communities, Municipal Offices, Town Hall Square, Grimsby DN31 1HU ☎ 01472 323021 ✆ joanne.hewson@nelincs.gov.uk

Tourism: Ms Sue Marshall, Operations Manager - Cultural Services, Fishing Heritage Centre, Grimsby DN31 1UZ ☎ 01472 323640 ✆ sue.marshall@nelincs.gov.uk

Traffic Management: Mr Marcus Asquith, Head of Highways & Transport, Municipal Offices, Town Hall Square, Grimsby DN31 1HU ☎ 01472 336676 ✆ marcus.asquith@nelincs.gov.uk

Transport: Mr Marcus Asquith, Head of Highways & Transport, Municipal Offices, Town Hall Square, Grimsby DN31 1HU ☎ 01472 336676 ✆ marcus.asquith@nelincs.gov.uk

Transport Planner: Mr Marcus Asquith, Head of Highways & Transport, Municipal Offices, Town Hall Square, Grimsby DN31 1HU ☎ 01472 336676 ✆ marcus.asquith@nelincs.gov.uk

Waste Collection and Disposal: Mr Tony Neul, Assistant Director - Environment, Origin 1, Europarc, Grimsby DN37 9TZ ☎ 01472 323989 ✆ tony.neul@nelincs.gov.uk

Waste Management: Mr Tony Neul, Assistant Director - Environment, Origin 1, Europarc, Grimsby DN37 9TZ ☎ 01472 323989 ✆ tony.neul@nelincs.gov.uk

COUNCILLORS

Mayor: McGilligan-Fell, Christina (LD - Park) christina.mcgilliganfell@nelincs.gov.uk

Deputy Mayor: Shepherd, Ron (CON - Scartho) ron.shepherd@nelincs.gov.uk

Leader of the Council: Oxby, Ray (LAB - South) ray.oxby@nelincs.gov.uk

Deputy Leader of the Council: Watson, David (LAB - Immingham) dave.watson@nelincs.gov.uk

Barber, Clifford (LD - Freshney) cliff.barber@nelincs.gov.uk

Barfield, Ian (LD - Park) ian.barfield@nelincs.gov.uk

Beasant, Stephen (LD - East Marsh) steve.beasant@nelincs.gov.uk

Bolton, David (LAB - Immingham) david.bolton@nelincs.gov.uk

Bramley, Jane (UKIP - South) jane.bramley@nelincs.gov.uk

Brookes, Keith (CON - Haverstoe) keith.brookes@nelincs.gov.uk

Brown, Matthew (LAB - Croft Baker)
matthew.brown@nelincs.gov.uk

Burton, Mike (LAB - Immingham)
mike.burton@nelincs.gov.uk

Cairns, James (UKIP - Yarborough)
james.cairns@nelincs.gov.uk

Chase, Hazel (LAB - Sidney Sussex)
hazel.chase@nelincs.gov.uk

Colquhoun, Iain (CON - Waltham)
iain.colquhoun@nelincs.gov.uk

Cracknell, Margaret (CON - Haverstoe)
margaret.cracknell@nelincs.gov.uk

Darby, Annie (LAB - Croft Baker)
annie.darby@nelincs.gov.uk

De Freitas, Andrew (LD - Park)
andrew.defreitas@nelincs.gov.uk

Dickerson, Melanie (CON - Wolds)
melaine.dickerson@nelincs.gov.uk

Fenty, John (CON - Humberston & New Waltham)
john.fenty@ntlworld.com

Goodwin, Janet (LAB - South)
janet.goodwin@nelincs.gov.uk

Harness, Stephen (IND - Humberston & New Waltham)
stephen.harness@nelincs.gov.uk

Hasthorpe, David (CON - Wolds)
david.hasthorpe@nelincs.gov.uk

Hudson, Henry (UKIP - Scartho)
henry.hudson@nelincs.gov.uk

Hyldon-King, Jane (LAB - Yarborough)
jane.hyldon-king@nelincs.gov.uk

Jackson, Philip (CON - Waltham)
philip.jackson@nelincs.gov.uk

James, Rosalind (LAB - Heneage)
ros.james@nelincs.gov.uk

Lindley, Ian (CON - Scartho)
ian.lindley@nelincs.gov.uk

Mickleburgh, Tim (LAB - West Marsh)
tim.mickleburgh@nelincs.gov.uk

Parkinson, Bill (CON - Haverstoe)
bill.parkinson@nelincs.gov.uk

Patrick, Matthew (LAB - Heneage)
matthew.patrick@nelincs.gov.uk

Pettigrew, Nick (UKIP - Freshney)
nick.pettigrew@nelincs.gov.uk

Rogers, Gaynor (LAB - Sidney Sussex)
gaynor.rogers@nelincs.gov.uk

Rudd, Kay (LD - East Marsh)
kay.rudd@nelincs.gov.uk

Shreeve, Stan (CON - Humberston & New Waltham)
stanley.shreeve@nelincs.gov.uk

Stinson, Matt (IND - Sidney Sussex)
matt.stinson@nelincs.gov.uk

Stockton, John (UKIP - Heneage)
john.stockton@nelincs.gov.uk

Sutton, Ray (LAB - Freshney)
ray.sutton@nelincs.gov.uk

Walker, Terry (LAB - East Marsh)
terry.walker@nelincs.gov.uk

Wheatley, Kathryn (LAB - Croft Baker)
kathryn.wheatley@nelincs.gov.uk

Wheatley, Peter (LAB - Yarborough)
peter.wheatley@nelincs.gov.uk

Wilson, Karl (LAB - West Marsh)
karl.wilson@nelincs.gov.uk

POLITICAL COMPOSITION
LAB: 18, CON: 11, LD: 6, UKIP: 5, IND: 2

COMMITTEE CHAIRS

Children & Young People: Mr Ian Lindley

Licensing: Mr Matthew Brown

Regeneration, Environment & Housing: Mr Philip Jackson

North Hertfordshire   D

North Hertfordshire District Council, Council Offices, Gernon Road, Letchworth SG6 3JF
☎ 01462 474000 ✆ service@north-herts.gov.uk
🖥 www.north-herts.gov.uk

FACTS AND FIGURES
Parliamentary Constituencies: Hertfordshire North East, Hitchin and Harpenden
EU Constituencies: Eastern
Election Frequency: Elections are by thirds

PRINCIPAL OFFICERS

Chief Executive: Mr David Scholes, Chief Executive & Strategic Director - Planning, Housing & Enterprise, Council Offices, Gernon Road, Letchworth SG6 3JF ☎ 01462 474836
✆ david.scholes@north-herts.gov.uk

Senior Management: Mrs Norma Atlay, Strategic Director - Finance, Policy & Governance, Council Offices, Gernon Road, Letchworth SG6 3JF ☎ 01462 474297
✆ norma.atlay@north-herts.gov.uk

Senior Management: Mr John Robinson, Strategic Director - Customer Services, Council Offices, Gernon Road, Letchworth SG6 3JF ☎ 01462 474655 ✆ john.robinson@north-herts.gov.uk

Building Control: Mr Ian Fullstone, Head of Development & Building Control, Council Offices, Gernon Road, Letchworth SG6 3HU ☎ 01462 474480 ✆ ian.fullstone@north-herts.gov.uk

Children / Youth Services: Mrs Helen Rae, Children's & Young People's Development Manager, Council Offices, Gernon Road, Letchworth SG6 3JF ☎ 01462 474333
✆ helen.rae@north-herts.gov.uk

PR / Communications: Ms Joanna Softly, Communications Manager, Council Offices, Gernon Road, Letchworth SG6 3JF
☎ 01462 474552 ✆ joanna.softly@north-herts.gov.uk

NORTH HERTFORDSHIRE

Community Safety: Ms Rebecca Coates, Community Safety Manager, Council Offices, Gernon Road, Letchworth SG6 3JF ☎ 01462 474504 ✆ rebecca.coates@north-herts.gov.uk

Computer Management: Mr Vic Godfrey, Information Technology Manager, Town Lodge, Gernon Road, Letchworth SG6 3HN ☎ 01462 474455 ✆ vic.godfrey@north-herts.gov.uk

Corporate Services: Ms Liz Green, Head of Policy & Community Services, Council Offices, Gernon Road, Letchworth SG6 3JF ☎ 01462 474230 ✆ liz.green@north-herts.gov.uk

Corporate Services: Mr John Robinson, Strategic Director - Customer Services, Council Offices, Gernon Road, Letchworth SG6 3JF ☎ 01462 474655 ✆ john.robinson@north-herts.gov.uk

Customer Service: Ms Johanne Dufficy, Customer Services Manager, Council Offices, Gernon Road, Letchworth SG6 3JF ☎ 01462 474555 ✆ johanne.dufficy@north-herts.gov.uk

E-Government: Mr Gavin Midgley, Website Manager, Council Offices, Gernon Road, Letchworth SG6 3JF ☎ 01462 474397 ✆ gavin.midgley@north-herts.gov.uk

Electoral Registration: Mr David Miley, Democratic Services Manager, Council Offices, Gernon Road, Letchworth SG6 3JF ☎ 01462 474208 ✆ david.miley@north-herts.gov.uk

Emergency Planning: Mr Derek Wootton, Emergency Planning Officer, Council Offices, Gernon Road, Letchworth SG6 3JF ☎ 01462 474246 ✆ derek.wootton@north-herts.gov.uk

Environmental / Technical Services: Mr Vaughan Watson, Head of Leisure & Environmental Services, Council Offices, Gernon Road, Letchworth SG6 3JF ☎ 01462 474641 ✆ vaughan.watson@north-herts.gov.uk

Environmental Health: Mr Peter Carey, Head of Housing & Public Protection, Council Offices, Gernon Road, Letchworth SG6 3JF ☎ 01462 474293 ✆ peter.carey@north-herts.gov.uk

Facilities: Mr Ian Davis, Senior Building Suveyor, Council Offices, Gernon Road, Letchworth SG6 3JF ☎ 01462 474340 ✆ ian.davis@north-herts.gov.uk

Finance: Mrs Norma Atlay, Strategic Director - Finance, Policy & Governance, Council Offices, Gernon Road, Letchworth SG6 3JF ☎ 01462 474297 ✆ norma.atlay@north-herts.gov.uk

Finance: Mr Ian Couper, Head of Financial Services, Council Offices, Gernon Road, Letchworth SG6 3JF ☎ 01642 474273 ✆ ian.couper@north-herts.gov.uk

Treasury: Mr Tim Neil, Accounting & Treasury Manager, Council Offices, Gernon Road, Letchworth SG6 3JF ☎ 01462 474461 ✆ tim.neil@north-herts.gov.uk

Fleet Management: Mrs Chloe Hipwood, Service Manager - Waste Management, Council Offices, Gernon Road, Letchworth SG6 3JF ☎ 01462 474304 ✆ chloe.hipwood@north-herts.gov.uk

Grounds Maintenance: Mr Andrew Mills, Service Manager - Grounds Maintenance, Council Offices, Gernon Road, Letchworth SG6 3TR ☎ 01462 474272 ✆ andrew.mills@north-herts.gov.uk

Health and Safety: Mr Les Davidson, Health & Safety Officer, Council Offices, Gernon Road, Letchworth SG6 3TR ☎ 01462 474600 ✆ les.davidson@north-herts.gov.uk

Housing: Mr Andrew Godman, Head of Housing & Public Protection, Council Offices, Gernon Road, Letchworth SG6 3JF ☎ 01462 474293 ✆ andy.goodman@north-herts.gov.uk

Legal: Mr Anthony Roche, Corporate Legal Manager & Monitoring Officer, Council Offices, Gernon Road, Letchworth SG6 3JF ☎ 01462 474588 ✆ anthony.roche@north-herts.gov.uk

Leisure and Cultural Services: Mrs Ros Allwood, Cultural Services Manager, Council Offices, Gernon Road, Letchworth SG6 3JF ☎ 01462 435197 ✆ ros.allwood@north-herts.gov.uk

Leisure and Cultural Services: Mr Vaughan Watson, Head of Leisure & Environmental Services, Council Offices, Gernon Road, Letchworth SG6 3JF ☎ 01462 474641 ✆ vaughan.watson@north-herts.gov.uk

Licensing: Mr Steven Cobb, Licensing & Enforcement Manager, Council Offices, Gernon Road, Letchworth SG6 3JF ☎ 01462 474370 ✆ steven.cobb@north-herts.gov.uk

Member Services: Mr Ian Gourlay, Senior Committee & Member Services Officer, Council Offices, Gernon Road, Letchworth SG6 3JF ☎ 01462 474641 ✆ ian.gourlay@north-herts.gov.uk

Member Services: Mr David Miley, Democratic Services Manager, Council Offices, Gernon Road, Letchworth SG6 3JF ☎ 01462 474208 ✆ david.miley@north-herts.gov.uk

Parking: Mr Steve Crowley, Contracts & Projects Manager, Council Offices, Gernon Road, Letchworth SG6 3JF ☎ 01462 474211 ✆ steve.crowley@north-herts.gov.uk

Partnerships: Ms Liz Green, Head of Policy & Community Services, Council Offices, Gernon Road, Letchworth SG6 3JF ☎ 01462 474230 ✆ liz.green@north-herts.gov.uk

Personnel / HR: Mrs Kerry Shorrocks, Corporate Human Resources Manager, Council Offices, Gernon Road, Letchworth SG6 3JF ☎ 01462 474224 ✆ kerry.shorrocks@north-herts.gov.uk

Planning: Ms Louise Symes, Strategy Planning & Enterprise Manager, Council Offices, Gernon Road, Letchworth SG6 3JF ☎ 01462 474836 ✆ louise.symes@north-herts.gov.uk

Recycling & Waste Minimisation: Mrs Chloe Hipwood, Service Manager - Waste Management, Council Offices, Gernon Road, Letchworth SG6 3JF ☎ 01462 474304 ✆ chloe.hipwood@north-herts.gov.uk

Staff Training: Mrs Vicky Jobling, Learning & Development Manager, Council Offices, Gernon Road, Letchworth SG6 3JF ☎ 01462 474435 ✆ victoria.jobling@north-herts.gov.uk

Sustainable Communities: Mr Stuart Izzard, Community Development Manager, Council Offices, Gernon Road, Letchworth SG6 3JF ☎ 01462 474439 ✆ stuart.izzard@north-herts.gov.uk

Waste Collection and Disposal: Mrs Chloe Hipwood, Service Manager - Waste Management, Council Offices, Gernon Road, Letchworth SG6 3JF ☎ 01462 474304 ✆ chloe.hipwood@north-herts.gov.uk

Children's Play Areas: Mr Steve Geach, Parks & Countryside Development Manager, Council Offices, Gernon Road, Letchworth SG6 3JF ☎ 01462 474641 ✆ steve.geach@north-herts.gov.uk

COUNCILLORS

Chair: Booth, John (CON - Letchworth South East)
john.booth@north-herts.gov.uk

Vice-Chair: Millard, Alan (CON - Hitchin Walsworth)
alanjmillard@yahoo.com

Leader of the Council: Needham, Lynda (CON - Letchworth South West)
lynda.needham@north-herts.gov.uk

Group Leader: Jarvis, Steve (LD - Weston & Sandon)
steve.jarvis@north-herts.gov.uk

Group Leader: Radcliffe, Frank (LAB - Hitchin Oughton)
frank.radcliffe@north-herts.gov.uk

Albert, Ian (LAB - Hitchin Bearton)
ian.albert@north-herts.gov.uk

Ashley, Allison (CON - Hitchin Priory)
allison_priory@yahoo.co.uk

Barnard, David (CON - Hitchwood, Offa & Hoo)
david.barnard@north-herts.gov.uk

Billing, Clare (LAB - Letchworth Grange)
clare.billing@north-herts.gov.uk

Billing, Judi (LAB - Hitchin Bearton)
judi.billing@north-herts.gov.uk

Bishop, John (CON - Kimpton)
john.bishop@north-herts.gov.uk

Burt, Peter (CON - Royston Heath)
peter.burt@north-herts.gov.uk

Clark, Paul (LD - Hitchin Highbury)
paul.clark@north-herts.gov.uk

Cunningham, Julian (CON - Letchworth South East)
julian.cunningham@ntlworld.com

Davidson, Bill (CON - Royston Meridian)
bill.davidson@north-herts.gov.uk

Deakin-Davies, Steve (CON - Knebworth)
stephen.deakin-davies@north-herts.gov.uk

Dennis, Elizabeth (LAB - Hitchin Walsworth)
elizabeth.dennis@north-herts.gov.uk

Frost, Faye (CON - Hitchwood, Offa & Hoo)
faye.frost@north-herts.gov.uk

Gray, Jane (CON - Codicote)
jg@abboptshay.com

Green, Jean (CON - Royston Palace)
jean.green@north-herts.gov.uk

Grindal, Gary (LAB - Letchworth Wilbury)
gary.grindal@north-herts.gov.uk

Harris, Nicola (CON - Hitchin Highbury)
nicola.harris@north-herts.gov.uk

Harwood, Simon (CON - Hitchin Highbury)
simon.harwood@north-herts.gov.uk

Hemingway, Steve (CON - Knebworth)
steve.hemingway@north-herts.gov.uk

Henry, Cathryn (CON - Chesfield)
cathryn.henry@north-herts.gov.uk

Hill, Fiona (CON - Royston Heath)
fiona.hill@north-herts.gov.uk

Hone, Terry (CON - Letchworth South West)
terry.hone@north-herts.gov.uk

Hunter, Tony (CON - Royston Meridian)
tony.hunter@hertscc.gov.uk

Kercher, Lorna (LAB - Letchworth East)
lorna.kercher@north-herts.gov.uk

Levett, David (CON - Letchworth South East)
david@dlevett.co.uk

Lewis, Ben (CON - Royston Palace)
ben.lewis@north-herts.gov.uk

Lovewell, Bernard (CON - Hitchin Walsworth)
bernard.lovewell@north-herts.gov.uk

Lunn, Sandra (LAB - Letchworth Grange)
sandra.lunn@north-herts.gov.uk

Mantle, Ian (LAB - Letchworth East)
ian.mantle@north-herts.gov.uk

Marment, Paul (CON - Letchworth Grange)
paul.marment@north-herts.gov.uk

McNally, Jim (CON - Baldock Town)
jim.mcnally@north-herts.gov.uk

Morris, Gerald (CON - Ermine)
gerald.morris@north-herts.gov.uk

Muir, Michael (CON - Baldock Town)
michael.muir@hertscc.gov.uk

Paterson, Janine (CON - Arbury)
janine.paterson@north-herts.gov.uk

Rice, Mike (CON - Letchworth South West)
mike.rice@ntlworld.com

Sangha, Deepak (LAB - Letchworth Wilbury)
deepak.sangha@north-herts.gov.uk

Shanley, Valentine (CON - Baldock East)
valentine.shanley@north-herts.gov.uk

Smith, Adrian (LAB - Hitchin Bearton)
adrian.smith@north-herts.gov.uk

Spencer-Smith, Harry (CON - Cadwell)
harry.spencer-smith@north-herts.gov.uk

Strong, Claire (CON - Hitchwood, Offa & Hoo)

Thake, Richard (CON - Hitchin Priory)
richard.thake@north-herts.gov.uk

Tyler, Terry (LD - Chesfield)
terry.tyler@north-herts.gov.uk

Watson, Simon (LAB - Hitchin Oughton)

NORTH HERTFORDSHIRE

Weeks, Michael (CON - Baldock Town)
michael.weeks@north-herts.gov.uk

POLITICAL COMPOSITION
CON: 34, LAB: 12, LD: 3

COMMITTEE CHAIRS

Audit: Mr Michael Weeks

Licensing: Mr Michael Muir

Planning: Mr David Barnard

North Kesteven   D

North Kesteven District Council, District Council Offices,
Kesteven Street, Sleaford NG34 7EF
☎ 01529 414155 🖶 01529 413956
🖑 customer_services@n-kesteven.gov.uk 🖳 www.n-kesteven.gov.uk

FACTS AND FIGURES
Parliamentary Constituencies: Sleaford and North Hykeham
EU Constituencies: East Midlands
Election Frequency: Elections are of whole council

PRINCIPAL OFFICERS

Chief Executive: Mr Ian Fytche, Chief Executive, District Council
Offices, Kesteven Street, Sleaford NG34 7EF ☎ 01529 414155
🖑 ian_fytche@n-kesteven.gov.uk

Deputy Chief Executive: Miss Karen Bradford, Deputy Chief
Executive, District Council Offices, Kesteven Street, Sleaford NG34
7EF ☎ 01529 414155 🖑 karen_bradford@n-kesteven.gov.uk

Senior Management: Mr Michael Kelleher, Head of Housing
& Property Services, District Council Offices, Kesteven Street,
Sleaford NG34 7EF ☎ 01529 414155
🖑 michael_kelleher@n-kesteven.gov.uk

Senior Management: Mr Andrew McDonough, Head of
Development, Economic & Cultural Services, District Council
Offices, Kesteven Street, Sleaford NG34 7EF ☎ 01529 414155
🖑 andrew_mcdonough@n-kesteven.gov.uk

Senior Management: Mr Philip Roberts, Corporate Director,
District Council Offices, Kesteven Street, Sleaford NG34 7EF
☎ 01529 414155 🖑 philip_roberts@n-kesteven.gov.uk

Senior Management: Ms Evonne Rogers, Head of Corporate
& Customer Services, District Council Offices, Kesteven Street,
Sleaford NG34 7EF ☎ 01529 414155
🖑 evonne_rogers@n-kesteven.gov.uk

Senior Management: Mr Russell Stone, Head of Finance &
Resources, District Council Offices, Kesteven Street, Sleaford
NG34 7EF ☎ 01529 414155 🖑 russell_stone@n-kesteven.gov.uk

Senior Management: Mr Mark Taylor, Head of Environment &
Public Protection, District Council Offices, Kesteven Street, Sleaford
NG34 7EF ☎ 01529 414155; 01476 406080
🖑 mark_taylor@n-kesteven.gov.uk

Architect, Building / Property Services: Mr Michael Gadd,
Property Services Manager, District Council Offices, Kesteven
Street, Sleaford NG34 7EF ☎ 01529 414155
🖑 michael_gadd@n-kesteven.gov.uk

Building Control: Mr Paul Weldon, Building Control Manager &
Access Officer, District Council Offices, Kesteven Street, Sleaford
NG34 7EF ☎ 01529 414155 🖑 paul_weldon@n-kesteven.gov.uk

PR / Communications: Mr Jason Hippisley, Communications &
Media Manager, District Council Offices, Kesteven Street, Sleaford
NG34 7EF ☎ 01529 414155 🖑 jason_hippisley@n-kesteven.gov.uk

Community Planning: Ms Luisa McIntosh, Partnerships Manager,
District Council Offices, Kesteven Street, Sleaford NG34 7EF
☎ 01529 414155 🖑 luisa_mcintosh@n-kesteven.gov.uk

Community Safety: Mrs Heidi Ryder, Community Safety Officer,
District Council Offices, Kesteven Street, Sleaford NG34 7EF
☎ 01529 414155 🖑 heidi_ryder@n-kesteven.gov.uk

Computer Management: Ms Evonne Rogers, Head of Corporate
& Customer Services, District Council Offices, Kesteven Street,
Sleaford NG34 7EF ☎ 01529 414155
🖑 evonne_rogers@n-kesteven.gov.uk

Contracts: Mr Michael Gadd, Property Services Manager, District
Council Offices, Kesteven Street, Sleaford NG34 7EF
☎ 01529 414155 🖑 michael_gadd@n-kesteven.gov.uk

Corporate Services: Ms Evonne Rogers, Head of Corporate
& Customer Services, District Council Offices, Kesteven Street,
Sleaford NG34 7EF ☎ 01529 414155
🖑 evonne_rogers@n-kesteven.gov.uk

Customer Service: Ms Evonne Rogers, Head of Corporate &
Customer Services, District Council Offices, Kesteven Street,
Sleaford NG34 7EF ☎ 01529 414155
🖑 evonne_rogers@n-kesteven.gov.uk

Economic Development: Mr Alan Gray, Economic Development
Manager, District Council Offices, Kesteven Street, Sleaford NG34
7EF ☎ 01529 414155 🖑 alan.gray@n-kesteven.gov.uk

Electoral Registration: Mrs Marcella Heath, Democratic Services
Manager, District Council Offices, Kesteven Street, Sleaford NG34
7EF ☎ 01529 414155 🖑 marcella_heath@n-kesteven.gov.uk

Emergency Planning: Ms Sarah Golembiewski, Corporate Health,
Safety & Emergency Planning Officer, District Council Offices,
Kesteven Street, Sleaford NG34 7EF ☎ 01529 414155
🖑 sarah_golembiewski@n-kesteven.gov.uk

Energy Management: Mr Michael Gadd, Property Services
Manager, District Council Offices, Kesteven Street, Sleaford NG34
7EF ☎ 01529 414155 🖑 michael_gadd@n-kesteven.gov.uk

Environmental Health: Mr Mark Taylor, Head of Environment &
Public Protection, District Council Offices, Kesteven Street, Sleaford
NG34 7EF ☎ 01529 414155; 01476 406080
🖑 mark_taylor@n-kesteven.gov.uk

Estates, Property & Valuation: Mr Michael Gadd, Property Services Manager, District Council Offices, Kesteven Street, Sleaford NG34 7EF ☎ 01529 414155 ⏚ michael_gadd@n-kesteven.gov.uk

Finance: Mr Russell Stone, Head of Finance & Resources, District Council Offices, Kesteven Street, Sleaford NG34 7EF ☎ 01529 414155 ⏚ russell_stone@n-kesteven.gov.uk

Grounds Maintenance: Miss Nina Camm, Environmental Manager, District Council Offices, Kesteven Street, Sleaford NG34 7EF ☎ 01529 414155 ⏚ nina_camm@n-kesteven.gov.uk

Health and Safety: Ms Sarah Golembiewski, Corporate Health, Safety & Emergency Planning Officer, District Council Offices, Kesteven Street, Sleaford NG34 7EF ☎ 01529 414155 ⏚ sarah_golembiewski@n-kesteven.gov.uk

Housing: Mr Michael Kelleher, Head of Housing & Property Services, District Council Offices, Kesteven Street, Sleaford NG34 7EF ☎ 01529 414155 ⏚ michael_kelleher@n-kesteven.gov.uk

Housing Maintenance: Mr Michael Gadd, Property Services Manager, District Council Offices, Kesteven Street, Sleaford NG34 7EF ☎ 01529 414155 ⏚ michael_gadd@n-kesteven.gov.uk

Leisure and Cultural Services: Mr Mike Lock, Leisure & Cultural Services Manager, District Council Offices, Kesteven Street, Sleaford NG34 7EF ☎ 01529 414155 ⏚ mike_lock@n-kesteven.gov.uk

Licensing: Mr David Harper, Licensing Manager, District Council Offices, Kesteven Street, Sleaford NG34 7EF ☎ 01529 414155 ⏚ david_harper@n-kesteven.gov.uk

Lighting: Mr Russell Shortland, Design & Maintenance Manager, District Council Offices, Kesteven Street, Sleaford NG34 7EF ☎ 01529 414155 ⏚ russell_shortland@n-kesteven.gov.uk

Lottery Funding, Charity and Voluntary: Miss Karen Bradford, Deputy Chief Executive, District Council Offices, Kesteven Street, Sleaford NG34 7EF ☎ 01529 414155 ⏚ karen_bradford@n-kesteven.gov.uk

Member Services: Miss Pauline Collett, Civic Officer, District Council Offices, Kesteven Street, Sleaford NG34 7EF ☎ 01529 414155 ⏚ pauline_collett@n-kesteven.gov.uk

Member Services: Mrs Marcella Heath, Democratic Services Manager, District Council Offices, Kesteven Street, Sleaford NG34 7EF ☎ 01529 414155 ⏚ marcella_heath@n-kesteven.gov.uk

Personnel / HR: Ms Christine Cooper, Human Resources Manager, District Council Offices, Kesteven Street, Sleaford NG34 7EF ☎ 01529 414155 ⏚ christine_cooper@n-kesteven.gov.uk

Planning: Mr Andrew McDonough, Head of Development, Economic & Cultural Services, District Council Offices, Kesteven Street, Sleaford NG34 7EF ☎ 01529 414155 ⏚ andrew_mcdonough@n-kesteven.gov.uk

Recycling & Waste Minimisation: Miss Nina Camm, Environmental Manager, District Council Offices, Kesteven Street, Sleaford NG34 7EF ☎ 01529 414155 ⏚ nina_camm@n-kesteven.gov.uk

Staff Training: Ms Christine Cooper, Human Resources Manager, District Council Offices, Kesteven Street, Sleaford NG34 7EF ☎ 01529 414155 ⏚ christine_cooper@n-kesteven.gov.uk

Street Scene: Miss Nina Camm, Environmental Manager, District Council Offices, Kesteven Street, Sleaford NG34 7EF ☎ 01529 414155 ⏚ nina_camm@n-kesteven.gov.uk

Sustainable Communities: Mr Andrew McDonough, Head of Development, Economic & Cultural Services, District Council Offices, Kesteven Street, Sleaford NG34 7EF ☎ 01529 414155 ⏚ andrew_mcdonough@n-kesteven.gov.uk

Sustainable Development: Mrs Bonnie Bond, Sustainability Co-ordination Officer, District Council Offices, Kesteven Street, Sleaford NG34 7EF ☎ 01529 414155 ⏚ bonnie_bond@n-kesteven.gov.uk

Tourism: Mr Andrew McDonough, Head of Development, Economic & Cultural Services, District Council Offices, Kesteven Street, Sleaford NG34 7EF ☎ 01529 414155 ⏚ andrew_mcdonough@n-kesteven.gov.uk

Waste Collection and Disposal: Miss Nina Camm, Environmental Manager, District Council Offices, Kesteven Street, Sleaford NG34 7EF ☎ 01529 414155 ⏚ nina_camm@n-kesteven.gov.uk

Waste Management: Miss Nina Camm, Environmental Manager, District Council Offices, Kesteven Street, Sleaford NG34 7EF ☎ 01529 414155 ⏚ nina_camm@n-kesteven.gov.uk

COUNCILLORS

Chair: Money, John (CON - Metheringham)
cllr_john_money@n-kesteven.gov.uk

Vice-Chair: Tarry, Sally (CON - Heckington Rural)
cllr_sally_tarry@n-kesteven.gov.uk

Leader of the Council: Brighton, Marion (CON - Heighington & Washingborough)
cllr_marion_brighton@n-kesteven.gov.uk

Deputy Leader of the Council: Gallagher, Mike (CON - Bracebridge Heath & Waddington East)
cllr_mike_gallagher@n-kesteven.gov.uk

Appleby, Sally (CON - Eagle, Swinderby & Witham St Hughs)
cllr_sally_appleby@n-kesteven.gov.uk

Barrett, Kay (IND - North Hykeham Forum)
cllr_kay_barrett@n-kesteven.gov.uk

Boston, Terry (CON - Ruskington)
cllr_terry_boston@n-kesteven.gov.uk

Burley, Peter (CON - Bracebridge Heath & Waddington East)
cllr_peter_burley@n-kesteven.gov.uk

Carrington, Ian (CON - Heighington & Washingborough)
cllr_ian_carrington@n-kesteven.gov.uk

Cawrey, Lindsey (CON - Bracebridge Heath & Waddington East)
cllr_lindsey_cawrey@n-kesteven.gov.uk

NORTH KESTEVEN

Clarke, Andrea (CON - North Hykeham Mill)
cllr_andrea_clarke@n-kesteven.gov.uk

Clarke, Mike (CON - North Hykeham Mill)
cllr_mike_clarke@n-kesteven.gov.uk

Clegg, Steve (IND - Ashby De La Launde & Cranwell)
cllr_steve_clegg@n-kesteven.gov.uk

Conning, Tim (CON - Sleaford Quarrington & Mareham)
cllr_tim_conning@n-kesteven.gov.uk

Cook, Kate (CON - Osbournby)
cllr_kate_cook@n-kesteven.gov.uk

Cucksey, Ray (CON - Branston)
cllr_ray_cucksey@n-kesteven.gov.uk

Dolby, Keith (IND - Sleaford Castle)
cllr_keith_dolby@n-kesteven.gov.uk

Fields, Steve (IND - Sleaford Westholme)
cllr_steve_fields@n-kesteven.gov.uk

Goldson, Chris (IND - Skellingthorpe)
cllr_chris_goldson@n-kesteven.gov.uk

Harrison, Julia (CON - Kirkby La Thorpe & South Kyme)
cllr_julia_harrison@n-kesteven.gov.uk

Hazelwood, Geoff (CON - Sleaford Quarrington & Mareham)
cllr_geoffrey_hazelwood@n-kesteven.gov.uk

Howe, Sue (CON - Bassingham & Brant Broughton)
cllr_sue_howe@n-kesteven.gov.uk

Jackson, Glenville (IND - Sleaford Holdingham)

Kendrick, Rob (CON - Metheringham)
cllr_rob_kendrick@n-kesteven.gov.uk

Lee, Wallace (IND - North Hykeham Memorial)
cllr_wallace_lee@n-kesteven.gov.uk

Little, Ross (CON - North Hykeham Witham)
cllr_ross_little@n-kesteven.gov.uk

Lundgren, Peter (IND - Branston)
cllr_peter_lungren@n-kesteven.gov.uk

Matthan, Susanna (IND - Billinghay, Martin & North Kyme)
cllr_susanna_matthan@n-kesteven.gov.uk

Ogden, Stewart (CON - Heckington Rural)
cllr_stewart_ogden@n-kesteven.gov.uk

Ogden, Gill (CON - Billinghay, Martin & North Kyme)
cllr_gill_ogden@n-kesteven.gov.uk

Overton, Marianne (IND - Cliff Villages)
cllr_marianne_overton@n-kesteven.gov.uk

Oxby, Ron (CON - Heighington & Washingborough)
cllr_ron_oxby@n-kesteven.gov.uk

Pannell, Shirley (IND - Skellingthorpe)
cllr_shirley_pannell@n-kesteven.gov.uk

Pearce, Sarah (CON - Ashby De La Launde & Cranwell)
cllr_sarah_pearse@n-kesteven.gov.uk

Pennell, Lance (CON - Waddington West)
cllr_lance_pennell@n-kesteven.gov.uk

Suffield, Mark (IND - Sleaford Quarrington & Mareham)
cllr_mark_suffield@n-kesteven.gov.uk

Suiter, David (IND - Sleaford Navigation)
cllr_david_suiter@n-kesteven.gov.uk

Waring, Susan (CON - Leasingham & Rauceby)
cllr_susan_waring@n-kesteven.gov.uk

Wells, Barbara (IND - Eagle, Swinderby & Witham St Hughs)
cllr_barbara_wells@n-kesteven.gov.uk

Whittaker, Pam (CON - North Hykeham Moor)
cllr_pam_whittaker@n-kesteven.gov.uk

Woodman, Pat (CON - Bassingham & Brant Broughton)
cllr_pat_woodman@n-kesteven.gov.uk

Wright, Richard (CON - Ruskington)
cllr_richard_wright@n-kesteven.gov.uk

POLITICAL COMPOSITION
CON: 28, IND: 14, Vacant: 1

COMMITTEE CHAIRS

Audit: Mrs Susan Waring

Communities & Economy: Mr Peter Burley

Licensing: Mr Lance Pennell

Planning: Mrs Pat Woodman

North Lanarkshire   S

North Lanarkshire Council, Civic Centre, Motherwell ML1 1AB
☎ 01698 403200 🖳 www.northlanarkshire.gov.uk

FACTS AND FIGURES
Parliamentary Constituencies: Airdrie and Shotts, Coatbridge,
Chryston & Bellshill, Cumbernauld, Kilsyth and Kirkintilloch East,
Motherwell & Wishaw
Election Frequency: Elections are of whole council

PRINCIPAL OFFICERS

Chief Executive: Mr Paul Jukes, Chief Executive, Civic Centre,
Motherwell ML1 1AB ☎ 01698 302452 ✆ jukesp@northlan.gov.uk

Senior Management: Mr Andrew Sutherland, Executive Director
- Learning & Leisure Services, Civic Centre, Motherwell ML1 1AB
☎ 01698 302222

Senior Management: Mr Kenneth Wilson, Interim Executive
Director - Environmental Services (Head of Land Services),
Buchanan Business Park, Stepps, Glasgow G33 6HR
☎ 01698 302222 ✆ wilsonk@northlan.gov.uk

Access Officer / Social Services (Disability): Mrs Dilini
Wilkinson, Community Care Senior (Older Adults), 122 Bank Street,
Coatbridge ML5 1ET ☎ 01236 622202
✆ wilkinsondi@northlan.gov.uk

Building Control: Mr David Provan, Business Building Standards
Manager, Fleming House, 2 Tryst Road, Cumbernauld G67 1JW
☎ 01698 403200 ✆ provand@northlan.gov.uk

Catering Services: Ms Lynda Donnelly, First Stop Shop Manager,
Civic Centre, Motherwell ML1 1AB ☎ 01236 856466
✆ donnellyly@northlan.gov.uk

Children / Youth Services: Ms Alison Gordon, Head of Children,
Families & Justice Social Work Services, Scott House, 73 - 77
Merry Street, Motherwell ML1 1JE ☎ 01698 332001
✆ gordonal@northlan.gov.uk

PR / Communications: Mr Stephen Penman, Head of Corporate Communications & Marketing, Civic Centre, Motherwell ML1 1AB ☎ 01698 302591 ⌨ penmanste@northlan.gov.uk

Computer Management: Mrs Irene McKelvey, Head of E-Government & Service Development, Civic Centre, Motherwell ML1 1AB ☎ 01698 403200 ⌨ mckelveyi@northlan.gov.uk

Consumer Protection and Trading Standards: Mr Paul Bannister, Trading Standards Manager, Fleming House, 2 Tryst Road, Cumbernauld G67 1JW ☎ 01236 856460 ⌨ bannisterp@northlan.gov.uk

Corporate Services: Mr Brian Cook, Head of Revenue Services & E-Government Solutions, Dalziel Building, 7 Scott Street, Motherwell ML1 1PN ☎ 01698 403929 ⌨ cookb@northlan.gov.uk

Economic Development: Ms Shirley Linton, Head of Planning & Regeneration, Civic Centre, Motherwell ML1 1AB ☎ 01236 632650 ⌨ lintons@northlan.gov.uk

Education: Ms Isabelle Boyd, Assistant Chief Executive - Education, Skills & Employment, Municipal Buildings, Kildonan Street, Coatbridge ML5 3BT ☎ 01236 812279 ⌨ boydisab@northlan.gov.uk

Education: Mr James McKinstry, Head of Education Provision, Civic Centre, Motherwell ML1 1AB ☎ 01698 302222 ⌨ mckinstryj@northlan.gov.uk

Education: Mr Andrew Sutherland, Executive Director - Learning & Leisure Services, Civic Centre, Motherwell ML1 1AB ☎ 01698 302222

E-Government: Mrs Irene McKelvey, Head of E-Government & Service Development, Civic Centre, Motherwell ML1 1AB ☎ 01698 403200 ⌨ mckelveyi@northlan.gov.uk

Emergency Planning: Ms Aileen McMann, Contingency Planning Officer, Civic Centre, Motherwell ML1 1AB ☎ 07939 280125 ⌨ mcmanna@northlan.gov.uk

Environmental / Technical Services: Mr Paul Jukes, Chief Executive, Civic Centre, Motherwell ML1 1AB ☎ 01698 302452 ⌨ jukesp@northlan.gov.uk

Environmental Health: Mr Paul Jukes, Chief Executive, Civic Centre, Motherwell ML1 1AB ☎ 01698 302452 ⌨ jukesp@northlan.gov.uk

Estates, Property & Valuation: Mr Eric Hislop, Asset & Support Manager, Civic Centre, Motherwell ML1 1AB ☎ 01698 302372 ⌨ hislope@snorthlan.gov.uk

Facilities: Mr Graham Patrick, Head of Facility Support Services, Buchanan Tower, Stepps, Glasgow G33 6HR ☎ 01698 302222 ⌨ patrickg@northlan.gov.uk

Finance: Mr Paul Hughes, Head of Business for Financial Solutions, Civic Centre, Motherwell ML1 1AB ☎ 01698 302275 ⌨ hughesp@northlan.gov.uk

Grounds Maintenance: Mr Ken Forbes, Business Manager (Environment & Cemeteries), Old Edinburgh Road, Belshill ML4 3JS ☎ 01698 506310 ⌨ forbesk@northlan.gov.uk

Housing: Ms Elaine McHugh, Head of Housing Solutions, Civic Centre, Motherwell ML1 1AB ☎ 01698 302222 ⌨ elaine.mchugh@northlan.gov.uk

Housing Maintenance: Mr Des Murray, Assistant Chief Executive - Enterprise & Housing Resources, Civic Centre, Motherwell ML1 1AB ☎ 01698 524758 ⌨ murraydes@northlan.gov.uk

Leisure and Cultural Services: Mr Andrew Sutherland, Executive Director - Learning & Leisure Services, Civic Centre, Motherwell ML1 1AB ☎ 01698 302222

Licensing: Mr Paul Guidi, Acting Managing Solicitor, Civic Centre, Motherwell ML1 1AB ☎ 01698 302294 ⌨ guidip@northlan.gov.uk

Lifelong Learning: Ms L McMurrich, Head of Education (Skills, Lifelong Learning & Youth Employment), Municipal Buildings, Kildonan Street, Coatbridge ML5 3BT ☎ 01236 812338 ⌨ mcmurrichl@northlan.gov.uk

Lifelong Learning: Mr Andrew Sutherland, Executive Director - Learning & Leisure Services, Civic Centre, Motherwell ML1 1AB ☎ 01698 302222

Lighting: Mr Colin Nimmo, Lighting Design Manager, Civic Centre, Motherwell ML1 1AB ☎ 01236 616217 ⌨ nimmoc@northlan.gov.uk

Personnel / HR: Ms Iris Wylie, Head of Human Resources, Civic Centre, Motherwell ML1 1AB ☎ 01698 302215 ⌨ wyliei@northlan.gov.uk

Planning: Mr Paul Jukes, Chief Executive, Civic Centre, Motherwell ML1 1AB ☎ 01698 302452 ⌨ jukesp@northlan.gov.uk

Planning: Ms Shirley Linton, Head of Planning & Regeneration, Civic Centre, Motherwell ML1 1AB ☎ 01236 632650 ⌨ lintons@northlan.gov.uk

Procurement: Ms Audrey Telfer, Procurement Development & Systems Manager, Dalziel House, 7 Scott Street, Motherwell ML1 1PN ☎ 01698 403954 ⌨ telfera@northlan.gov.uk

Public Libraries: Ms Gemma Alexander, Libraries & Information Manager, Civic Centre, Motherwell ML1 1AB ☎ 01698 403200 ⌨ alexanderg@northlan.gov.uk

Regeneration: Mr Paul Jukes, Chief Executive, Civic Centre, Motherwell ML1 1AB ☎ 01698 302452 ⌨ jukesp@northlan.gov.uk

Regeneration: Ms Shirley Linton, Head of Planning & Regeneration, Civic Centre, Motherwell ML1 1AB ☎ 01236 632650 ⌨ lintons@northlan.gov.uk

Staff Training: Ms Heather Liddle, Principal Training Officer, Civic Centre, Motherwell ML1 1AB ☎ 01698 302097 ⌨ liddleh@northlan.gov.uk

NORTH LANARKSHIRE

Street Scene: Mr Harry Morgan, Business Manager - Waste Management, Bellshill Complex, Old Edinburgh Road, Bellshill ML4 3JF ☎ 01698 506271 ⏚ morganh@northlan.gov.uk

Sustainable Development: Mr David Baxter, Assistant Business Manager, Fleming House, 2 Tryst Road, Cumbernauld G67 1JW ☎ 01236 616243 ⏚ baxterd@northlan.gov.uk

Town Centre: Mr Jack Duffy, Town Centre Manager (Cumbernauld), Town Centre Initiatives Ltd, Coatbridge ML5 3EL ☎ 01263 638444 ⏚ duffyja@northlan.gov.uk

Town Centre: Ms Anne Flood, Town Centre Manager, Town Centre Initiatives Ltd, Coatbridge ML5 3EL ☎ 01263 638443 ⏚ flooda@northlan.gov.uk

Traffic Management: Mr John Marran, Business Manager (Road Strategy & Assets), Fleming House, 2 Tryst Road, Cumbernauld G67 1JW ☎ 01236 616253 ⏚ marranj@northlan.gov.uk

Transport: Mr Graham Mackay, Head of Roads & Transportation, Fleming House, 2 Tryst Road, Cumbernauld G67 1JW ☎ 01236 616202 ⏚ mackaygd@northlan.gov.uk

Transport Planner: Mr Graham Mackay, Head of Roads & Transportation, Buchanan Tower, Stepps, Glasgow G33 6HR ☎ 01236 616202 ⏚ mackaygd@northlan.gov.uk

Waste Collection and Disposal: Mr Kenneth Wilson, Interim Executive Director - Environmental Services (Head of Land Services), Buchanan Business Park, Stepps, Glasgow G33 6HR ☎ 01698 302222 ⏚ wilsonk@northlan.gov.uk

Waste Management: Mr Kenneth Wilson, Interim Executive Director - Environmental Services (Head of Land Services), Buchanan Business Park, Stepps, Glasgow G33 6HR ☎ 01698 302222 ⏚ wilsonk@northlan.gov.uk

COUNCILLORS

ProvostRobertson, James (LAB - Fortissat)
robertsonj@northlan.gov.uk

Deputy ProvostJones, Jean (LAB - Kilsyth)
jonesj@northlan.gov.uk

Baird, David (SNP - Mossend & Holytown)
bairddavid@northlan.gov.uk

Beveridge, Alan (SNP - Airdrie North)
beveridgeal@northlan.gov.uk

Bonnar, Steven (SNP - Thorniewood)
bonnars@northlan.gov.uk

Brooks, James (LAB - Coatbridge South)
brooksj@northlan.gov.uk

Burrows, Robert (LAB - Thorniewood)
BurrowsR@northlan.gov.uk

Cefferty, Charles (IND - Fortissat)
ceffertyc@northlan.gov.uk

Chadha, Balwant Singh (LAB - Cumbernauld North)
chadhab@northlan.gov.uk

Clinch, Alan (LAB - Murdostoun)
clincha@northlan.gov.uk

Cochrane, Thomas (SNP - Fortissat)
cochraneth@northlan.gov.uk

Coyle, Michael (SNP - Airdrie South)
coylem@northlan.gov.uk

Coyle, Agnes (SNP - Airdrie South)
coylea@northlan.gov.uk

Coyle, James (LAB - Mossend & Holytown)
coylej@northlan.gov.uk

Coyle, Sophia (SNP - Airdrie North)
CoyleS@northlan.gov.uk

Curley, Thomas (LAB - Airdrie South)
curleyt@northlan.gov.uk

Curran, Harry (LAB - Belshill)
curranh@northlan.gov.uk

Docherty, Kevin (LAB - Coatbridge West)
Dochertyke@northlan.gov.uk

Fagan, David (LAB - Airdrie South)
cllr.david.fagan@googlemail.com

Farooq, Shahid (SNP - Motherwell North)
farooqs@northlan.gov.uk

Goldie, William (SNP - Cumbernauld South)
GoldieW@northlan.gov.uk

Graham, Alan (LAB - Cumbernauld South)
grahamallan@northlan.gov.uk

Grant, Stephen (LAB - Abronhill, Kildrum & the Village)
grantst@northlan.gov.uk

Griffin, Stephanie (LAB - Cumbernauld South)
muirsteph@northlan.gov.uk

Harmon, Kaye (LAB - Motherwell South East & Ravenscraig)
harmonk@northlan.gov.uk

Higgins, John (LAB - Coatbridge South)
higginsjoh@northlan.gov.uk

Hogg, William (LAB - Strathkelvin)
hoggw@northlan.gov.uk

Hogg, Paddy (SNP - Cumbernauld South)
hoggp@northlan.gov.uk

Hume, Jim (SNP - Wishaw)
humej@northlan.gov.uk

Irvine, Elizabeth (SNP - Abronhill, Kildrum & the Village)
irvinee@northlan.gov.uk

Johnston, Tom (SNP - Abronhill, Kildrum & the Village)
johnstont@northlan.gov.uk

Kelly, Paul (LAB - Motherwell West)
kellyp2@northlan.gov.uk

Logue, James (LAB - Airdrie Central)
loguej@northlan.gov.uk

Love, Samuel (LAB - Wishaw)
lovesam@northlan.gov.uk

Lunny, Thomas (LAB - Motherwell South East & Ravenscraig)
lunnyt@northlan.gov.uk

Lyle, Marina (SNP - Belshill)
lylem@northlan.gov.uk

Majid, Imtiaz (SNP - Coatbridge South)
majidi@northlan.gov.uk

Masterton, Alan (SNP - Cumbernauld North)
mastertona@northlan.gov.uk

McAnulty, Julie (SNP - Coatbridge North & Glenboig)
macnultyj@northlan.oov.uk

McCabe, James (LAB - Thorniewood)
mccabej@northlan.gov.uk

McCulloch, Barry (LAB - Cumbernauld North)
mccullochb@northlan.gov.uk

McGlinchey, Frances (IND - Strathkelvin)
mcglincheyf@northlan.gov.uk

McGuigan, Harry (LAB - Belshill)
mcguiganh@northlan.gov.uk

McKay, Frank (LAB - Wishaw)
mckayf@northlan.gov.uk

McKendrick, Robert (IND - Murdostoun)
mckendrickr@northlan.gov.uk

McKenna, Helen (IND - Motherwell North)
McKennaH@northlan.gov.uk

McLaren, John (LAB - Strathkelvin)
mclarenjohn@northlan.gov.uk

McNally, Frank (LAB - Mossend & Holytown)
mcnallyf@northlan.gov.uk

McPake, Michael (LAB - Coatbridge North & Glenboig)
mcpakemi@northlan.gov.uk

McVey, Heather (LAB - Kilsyth)
mcveyh@northlan.gov.uk

Morgan, Thomas (LAB - Airdrie North)
morgant@northlan.gov.uk

Nolan, Peter (LAB - Motherwell North)
nolanp@northlan.gov.uk

O'Brien, Alan (IND - Cumbernauld North)
obrienal@northlan.gov.uk

O'Rorke, Gary (LAB - Motherwell South East & Ravenscraig)
ororkeg@northlan.gov.uk

O'Rourke, Pat (LAB - Motherwell North)
orourkep@northlan.gov.uk

Ross, Michael (LAB - Motherwell West)
rossm@northlan.gov.uk

Shevlin, Nicky (LAB - Murdostoun)
shevlinn@northlan.gov.uk

Shields, William (LAB - Coatbridge North & Glenboig)
shieldsb@northlan.gov.uk

Smith, James (LAB - Coatbridge West)
smithjam@northlan.gov.uk

Spowart, Andrew (LAB - Airdrie North)
spowarta@northlan.gov.uk

Stevenson, Alan (SNP - Kilsyth)
stevensonal@northlan.gov.uk

Stocks, David (SNP - Airdrie Central)
stocksd@northlan.gov.uk

Sullivan, Peter (LAB - Airdrie Central)
sullivanp@northlan.gov.uk

Taggart, John (SNP - Murdostoun)
taggartjo@northlan.gov.uk

Valentine, Alan (SNP - Motherwell South East & Ravenscraig)
valentinea@northlan.gov.uk

Valentine, Annette (SNP - Motherwell West)
valentinean@northlan.gov.uk

Wallace, Brian (LAB - Strathkelvin)
wallaceb@northlan.gov.uk

Welsh, Paul (SNP - Coatbridge West)
welshp@northlan.gov.uk

Zambonini, Rosa (SNP - Wishaw)
zamboninir@northlan.gov.uk

POLITICAL COMPOSITION
LAB: 40, SNP: 24, IND: 5

COMMITTEE CHAIRS

Audit: Mr David Stocks

Education: Mr Frank McNally

Housing & Social Work Services: Mr Barry McCulloch

Licensing: Mr William Hogg

Planning: Mr James Coyle

North Lincolnshire   U

North Lincolnshire Council, Pittwood House, Ashby Road, Scunthorpe DN16 1AB
☎ 01724 297000 ⌁ customerservices@northlincs.gov.uk
🖥 www.northlincs.gov.uk

FACTS AND FIGURES
Parliamentary Constituencies: Brigg and Goole, Scunthorpe
EU Constituencies: East Midlands
Election Frequency: Elections are of whole council

PRINCIPAL OFFICERS

Chief Executive: Ms Denise Hyde, Executive Director - People & Transformation, Civic Centre, Ashby Road, Scunthorpe DN16 1AB
☎ 01724 296406 ⌁ denise.hyde@northlincs.gov.uk

Senior Management: Mr Stephen Pintus, Interim Director - Public Health, Civic Centre, Ashby Road, Scunthorpe DN16 1AB
☎ 01724 298239 ⌁ stephen.pintus@northlincs.gov.uk

Access Officer / Social Services (Disability): Ms Denise Hyde, Executive Director - People & Transformation, Civic Centre, Ashby Road, Scunthorpe DN16 1AB ☎ 01724 296406 ⌁ denise.hyde@northlincs.gov.uk

Architect, Building / Property Services: Mr Peter Williams, Director - Places, Civic Centre, Ashby Road, Scunthorpe DN16 1AB ☎ 01724 296710 ⌁ peter.williams@northlincs.gov.uk

Best Value: Mr Jason Whaler, Assistant Director - Business Support, Civic Centre, Ashby Road, Scunthorpe DN16 1AB
☎ 01724 296018 ⌁ jason.whaler@northlincs.gov.uk

Building Control: Mr Marcus Walker, Assistant Director - Planning & Regeneration, Civic Centre, Ashby Road, Scunthorpe DN16 1AB ☎ 01724 297305 ⌁ marcus.walker@northlincs.gov.uk

NORTH LINCOLNSHIRE

Catering Services: Mrs Sharon Seddon, Head - Catering & Cleaning, Church Square House, Scunthorpe DN15 6NL
☎ 01724 297922 ⊷ sharon.seddon@northlincs.gov.uk

Children / Youth Services: Mr Mick Gibbs, Assistant Director - Children's Services, Hewson House, Station Road, Brigg DN20 8XJ
☎ 01724 296410 ⊷ mick.gibbs@northlincs.gov.uk

Children / Youth Services: Ms Denise Hyde, Executive Director - People & Transformation, Civic Centre, Ashby Road, Scunthorpe DN16 1AB ☎ 01724 296406 ⊷ denise.hyde@northlincs.gov.uk

Civil Registration: Mrs Alison Prestwood, Head - Registration Service, Civic Centre, Ashby Road, Scunthorpe DN16 1AB
☎ 01724 298555 ⊷ alison.prestwood@northlincs.gov.uk

PR / Communications: Mrs Sarah Howe, Acting Head - Communications, Pittwood House, Ashby Road, Scunthorpe DN16 1AB ☎ 01724 296353 ⊷ sarah.howe@northlincs.gov.uk

Community Planning: Mr David Hey, Head - Stronger Communities, Civic Centre, Ashby Road, Scunthorpe DN16 1AB
☎ 01724 296646 ⊷ dave.hey@northlincs.gov.uk

Community Safety: Mr Stuart Minto, Head - Safer Neighbourhoods, Shelford House, Scunthorpe DN15 6NU
☎ 01724 244654 ⊷ stuart.minto@northlincs.gov.uk

Computer Management: Mr Martin Oglesby, Head - IT Services, Cary Lane, Brigg DN15 6XQ ☎ 01724 296266
⊷ martin.oglesby@northlincs.gov.uk

Consumer Protection and Trading Standards: Mr Richard Copley, Trading Standards & Licensing Manager, Church Square House, Scunthorpe DL15 6QX ☎ 01724 297649
⊷ richard.copley@northlincs.gov.ui

Contracts: Mr Jason Whaler, Assistant Director - Business Support, Civic Centre, Ashby Road, Scunthorpe DN16 1AB
☎ 01724 296018 ⊷ jason.whaler@northlincs.gov.uk

Corporate Services: Mr Chris Fairbrother, Estate Services Manager, Hewson House, Station Road, Brigg DN20 8XJ
☎ 01724 927477 ⊷ chris.fairbrother@northlincs.com

Customer Service: Miss Helen Rowe, Assistant Director - Customer Services, Civic Centre, Ashby Road, Scunthorpe DN16 1AB ☎ 01724 297667 ⊷ helen.rowe@northlincs.gov.uk

Economic Development: Mr Marcus Walker, Assistant Director - Planning & Regeneration, Civic Centre, Ashby Road, Scunthorpe DN16 1AB ☎ 01724 297305 ⊷ marcus.walker@northlincs.gov.uk

Education: Mr Peter Thorpe, Assistant Director - Education, Civic Centre, Ashby Road, Scunthorpe DN16 1AB ☎ 01724 297188
⊷ peter.thorpe@northlincs.gov.uk

E-Government: Mr Jason Whaler, Assistant Director - Business Support, Civic Centre, Ashby Road, Scunthorpe DN16 1AB
☎ 01724 296018 ⊷ jason.whaler@northlincs.gov.uk

Electoral Registration: Mrs Anthia Taylor, Electoral Registrations Officer, Civic Centre, Ashby Road, Scunthorpe DN16 1AB
☎ 01724 296248 ⊷ anthia.taylor@northlincs.gov.uk

Emergency Planning: Mr Chris Wilson, Emergency Planning Officer, Humber Emergency Planning Service, Church Square House, Scunthorpe DN15 6NL ☎ 01724 297406
⊷ chris.wilson@northlincs.gov.uk

Energy Management: Mr Craig Stapleton, Energy Manager, Church Square House, Scunthorpe DN15 6NL ☎ 01724 296514
⊷ craig.stapleton@northlincs.gov.uk

Environmental / Technical Services: Mr Trevor Laming, Assistant Director - Technical & Environmental Services, Civic Centre, Ashby Road, Scunthorpe DN16 1AB ☎ 01724 297603
⊷ trevor.laming@northlincs.gov.uk

Environmental Health: Mr Trevor Laming, Assistant Director - Technical & Environmental Services, Civic Centre, Ashby Road, Scunthorpe DN16 1AB ☎ 01724 297603
⊷ trevor.laming@northlincs.gov.uk

Estates, Property & Valuation: Mr Paul Nicholson, Principal Estates & Valuation Officer, Hewson House, Station Road, Brigg DN20 8XY ☎ 01724 296789 ⊷ paul.nicholson@northlincs.gov.uk

European Liaison: Mr Marcus Walker, Assistant Director - Planning & Regeneration, Civic Centre, Ashby Road, Scunthorpe DN16 1AB ☎ 01724 297305 ⊷ marcus.walker@northlincs.gov.uk

Events Manager: Ms Margaret Price, Senior Tourism & Event Management Officer, Civic Centre, Ashby Road, Scunthorpe DN16 1AB ☎ 01724 297356 ⊷ margaret.price@northlincs.gov.uk

Facilities: Miss Helen Rowe, Assistant Director - Customer Services, Civic Centre, Ashby Road, Scunthorpe DN16 1AB
☎ 01724 297667 ⊷ helen.rowe@northlincs.gov.uk

Finance: Mr Mike Wedgewood, Director - Policy & Resources, Civic Centre, Ashby Road, Scunthorpe DN16 1AB ☎ 01724 296012
⊷ mike.wedgewood@northlincs.gov.uk

Fleet Management: Mr Chris Matthews, Assistant Director - Community Services, Civic Centre, Ashby Road, Scunthorpe DN16 1AB ☎ 01724 297366 ⊷ chris.matthews@northlincs.gov.uk

Grounds Maintenance: Mr Chris Matthews, Assistant Director - Community Services, Civic Centre, Ashby Road, Scunthorpe DN16 1AB ☎ 01724 297366 ⊷ chris.matthews@northlincs.gov.uk

Highways: Mr Chris Matthews, Assistant Director - Community Services, Civic Centre, Ashby Road, Scunthorpe DN16 1AB
☎ 01724 297366 ⊷ chris.matthews@northlincs.gov.uk

Home Energy Conservation: Mr Trevor Laming, Assistant Director - Technical & Environmental Services, Civic Centre, Ashby Road, Scunthorpe DN16 1AB ☎ 01724 297603
⊷ trevor.laming@northlincs.gov.uk

Housing: Mr Trevor Laming, Assistant Director - Technical & Environmental Services, Civic Centre, Ashby Road, Scunthorpe DN16 1AB ☎ 01724 297603 ✆ trevor.laming@northlincs.gov.uk

Legal: Mr Will Bell, Assistant Director - Legal & Democratic, Civic Centre, Ashby Road, Scunthorpe DN16 1AB ☎ 01724 296204 ✆ will.bell@northlincs.gov.uk

Leisure and Cultural Services: Miss Helen Rowe, Assistant Director - Customer Services, Civic Centre, Ashby Road, Scunthorpe DN16 1AB ☎ 01724 297667 ✆ helen.rowe@northlincs.gov.uk

Licensing: Mr Trevor Laming, Assistant Director - Technical & Environmental Services, Civic Centre, Ashby Road, Scunthorpe DN16 1AB ☎ 01724 297603 ✆ trevor.laming@northlincs.gov.uk

Lifelong Learning: Miss Helen Rowe, Assistant Director - Customer Services, Civic Centre, Ashby Road, Scunthorpe DN16 1AB ☎ 01724 297667 ✆ helen.rowe@northlincs.gov.uk

Lighting: Mr Chris Matthews, Assistant Director - Community Services, Civic Centre, Ashby Road, Scunthorpe DN16 1AB ☎ 01724 297366 ✆ chris.matthews@northlincs.gov.uk

Member Services: Mr Mel Holmes, Head - Democratic Services, Civic Centre, Ashby Road, Scunthorpe DN16 1AB ☎ 01724 296230 ✆ mel.holmes@northlincs.gov.uk

Parking: Mr Marcus Walker, Assistant Director - Planning & Regeneration, Civic Centre, Ashby Road, Scunthorpe DN16 1AB ☎ 01724 297305 ✆ marcus.walker@northlincs.gov.uk

Partnerships: Miss Rachel Johnson, Business Strategy & Transformation Manager, Civic Centre, Ashby Road, Scunthorpe DN16 1AB ☎ 01724 296391 ✆ rachel.johnson@northlincs.gov.uk

Personnel / HR: Mrs Helen Manderson, Assistant Director - Human Resources, Civic Centre, Ashby Road, Scunthorpe DN16 1AB ☎ 01724 296310 ✆ helen.manderson@northlincs.gov.uk

Planning: Mr Phil Wallis, Head - Development Management, Civic Centre, Ashby Road, Scunthorpe DN16 1AB ☎ 01724 297492 ✆ philip.wallis@northlincs.gov.uk

Procurement: Mr Jason Whaler, Assistant Director - Business Support, Civic Centre, Ashby Road, Scunthorpe DN16 1AB ☎ 01724 296018 ✆ jason.whaler@northlincs.gov.uk

Public Libraries: Miss Helen Rowe, Assistant Director - Customer Services, Civic Centre, Ashby Road, Scunthorpe DN16 1AB ☎ 01724 297667 ✆ helen.rowe@northlincs.gov.uk

Recycling & Waste Minimisation: Mr Chris Matthews, Assistant Director - Community Services, Civic Centre, Ashby Road, Scunthorpe DN16 1AB ☎ 01724 297366 ✆ chris.matthews@northlincs.gov.uk

Regeneration: Mr Marcus Walker, Assistant Director - Planning & Regeneration, Civic Centre, Ashby Road, Scunthorpe DN16 1AB ☎ 01724 297305 ✆ marcus.walker@northlincs.gov.uk

Road Safety: Mr Chris Matthews, Assistant Director - Community Services, Civic Centre, Ashby Road, Scunthorpe DN16 1AB ☎ 01724 297366 ✆ chris.matthews@northlincs.gov.uk

Social Services (Adult): Ms Karen Pavey, Assistant Director - Adult Services, Civic Centre, Ashby Road, Scunthorpe DN16 1AB ☎ 01724 296420 ✆ karen.pavey@northlincs.gov.uk

Social Services (Children): Ms Denise Hyde, Executive Director - People & Transformation, Civic Centre, Ashby Road, Scunthorpe DN16 1AB ☎ 01724 296406 ✆ denise.hyde@northlincs.gov.uk

Public Health: Mr Stephen Pintus, Interim Director - Public Health, Civic Centre, Ashby Road, Scunthorpe DN16 1AB ☎ 01724 298239 ✆ stephen.pintus@northlincs.gov.uk

Staff Training: Mrs Christine Wilkinson, Strategic Workforce Lead (Organisational & Commercial Development), Civic Centre, Ashby Road, Scunthorpe DN16 1AB ☎ 01724 296322 ✆ christine.wilkinson@northlincs.gov.uk

Street Scene: Mr Chris Matthews, Assistant Director - Community Services, Civic Centre, Ashby Road, Scunthorpe DN16 1AB ☎ 01724 297366 ✆ chris.matthews@northlincs.gov.uk

Sustainable Communities: Mr David Hey, Head - Stronger Communities, Civic Centre, Ashby Road, Scunthorpe DN16 1AB ☎ 01724 296646 ✆ dave.hey@northlincs.gov.uk

Sustainable Development: Mr Tim Allen, Environment Team Manager, Church Square House, PO Box 42, Scunthorpe DN15 6XQ ☎ 01724 297387 ✆ tim.allen@northlincs.gov.uk

Tourism: Ms Margaret Price, Senior Tourism & Event Management Officer, Civic Centre, Ashby Road, Scunthorpe DN16 1AB ☎ 01724 297356 ✆ margaret.price@northlincs.gov.uk

Town Centre: Mr Peter Williams, Director - Places, Civic Centre, Ashby Road, Scunthorpe DN16 1AB ☎ 01724 296710 ✆ peter.williams@northlincs.gov.uk

Traffic Management: Mr Chris Matthews, Assistant Director - Community Services, Civic Centre, Ashby Road, Scunthorpe DN16 1AB ☎ 01724 297366 ✆ chris.matthews@northlincs.gov.uk

Transport: Miss Jodie Booth, Team Manager - Transport Planning, Hewson House, Station Road, Scunthorpe DN20 8XJ ☎ 01724 297373 ✆ jodie.booth@northlincs.gov.uk

Transport Planner: Miss Jodie Booth, Team Manager - Transport Planning, Hewson House, Station Road, Scunthorpe DN20 8XJ ☎ 01724 297373 ✆ jodie.booth@northlincs.gov.uk

Waste Collection and Disposal: Mr John Coates, Head - Waste Services, North Linc Council, Cottage Beck Road, Scunthorpe DN16 1TS ☎ 01724 297901 ✆ john.coates@northlincs.gov.uk

Waste Management: Mr John Coates, Head - Waste Services, North Linc Council, Cottage Beck Road, Scunthorpe DN16 1TS ☎ 01724 297901 ✆ john.coates@northlincs.gov.uk

NORTH LINCOLNSHIRE

Children's Play Areas: Mr Tom Coburn, Head - Sport, Leisure & Culture, Hewson House, Station Road, Brigg DN20 8XJ
☎ 01724 297260 ⊗ tom.coburn@northlincs.gov.uk

COUNCILLORS

Mayor: Foster, Trevor (CON - Ridge)
cllr.trevorfoster@northlincs.gov.uk

Leader of the Council: Redfern, Liz (CON - Axholme Central)
cllr.lizredfern@northlincs.gov.uk

Deputy Leader of the Council: Waltham, Rob (CON - Brigg & Wolds)
rob.waltham@northlincs.gov.uk

Ali, Mashook (LAB - Town)
cllr.mashookali@northlincs.gov.uk

Allcock, Ron (CON - Axholme South)
cllr.ronallcock@northlincs.gov.uk

Armiger, Margaret (CON - Bottesford)
cllr.margaretarmiger@northlincs.gov.uk

Armitage, Susan (LAB - Brumby)
cllr.suearmitage@northlincs.gov.uk

Bainbridge, Sandra (LAB - Frodingham)
cllr.sandrabainbridge@northlincs.gov.uk

Briggs, John (CON - Axholme North)
cllr.johnbriggs@northlincs.gov.uk

Carlile, Pauline (LAB - Brumby)
paulinecarlile@aol.com

Clark, Peter (CON - Ferry)
cllr.peterclark@northlincs.gov.uk

Collinson, John (LAB - Ashby)
cllr.johncollinson@northlincs.gov.uk

Davison, Andrea (LAB - Ashby)
cllrandreadavison@aol.com

Davison, John (CON - Bottesford)
cllr.johndavison@northlincs.gov.uk

Ellerby, Anthony (LAB - Frodingham)
cllr.tonyellerby@northlincs.gov.uk

England, John (CON - Ridge)

Evison, Jonathan (CON - Barton)
cllr.jonathanevison@northlincs.gov.uk

Foster, Len (LAB - Brumby)
len.k.foster@northlincs.gov.uk

Glover, Ivan (CON - Broughton & Appleby)
cllr.ivanglover@northlincs.gov.uk

Godfrey, Susan (LAB - Kingsway with Lincoln Gardens)
cllr.susangodfrey@northlincs.gov.uk

Gosling, Antony (LAB - Kingsway with Lincoln Gardens)
cllr.tonygosling@northlincs.gov.uk

Grant, Michael (LAB - Ashby)
cllr.mickgrant@northlincs.gov.uk

Hannigan, Richard (CON - Ferry)
cllr.richardhannigan@northlincs.gov.uk

Kataria, Haque Nawaz (LAB - Town)
cllr.haquekataria@northlincs.gov.uk

Kirk, Mark (LAB - Crosby & Park)
mark.kirk@northlincs.gov.uk

Longcake, Derek (CON - Bottesford)
cllr.dereklongcake@northlincs.gov.uk

Marper, Elaine (CON - Burton Upon Stather & Winterton)
cllr.elainemarper@northlincs.gov.uk

Mumby-Croft, Holly (CON - Broughton & Appleby)
cllr.hollymumby-croft@northlincs.gov.uk

Ogg, Ralph (CON - Burton Upon Stather & Winterton)
cllr.ralphogg@northlincs.gov.uk

Oldfield, David (LAB - Burringham & Gunness)
cllr.daveoldfield@northlincs.gov.uk

O'Sullivan, Christine (LAB - Crosby & Park)
cllr.christineo'sullivan@northlincs.gov.uk

Perry, Barbara (LAB - Crosby & Park)
cllr.barbaraperry@northlincs.gov.uk

Poole, Neil (CON - Ridge)
cllr.neilpoole@northlinks.gov.uk

Reed, Julie (CON - Axholme North)
cllr.juliereed@northlincs.gov.uk

Robinson, David (CON - Axholme Central)
cllr.davidrobinson@northlincs.gov.uk

Rose, David (CON - Axholme South)
cllr.davidrose@northlincs.gov.uk

Rowson, Helen (CON - Burton Upon Stather & Winterton)
cllr.helenrowson@northlincs.gov.uk

Sherwood, Carl (CON - Brigg & Wolds)
cllr.carlsherwood@northlincs.gov.uk

Sherwood, Nigel (CON - Brigg & Wolds)
cllr.nigelsherwood@northlincs.gov.uk

Vickers, Keith (CON - Barton)
cllr.keithvickers@northlincs.gov.uk

Vickers, Paul (CON - Barton)
cllr.paulvickers@northlinks.gov.uk

Wells, David (CON - Ferry)
cllr.davidwells@northlincs.gov.uk

Wilson, Stuart (LAB - Kingsway with Lincoln Gardens)
cllr.stuartwilson@northlincs.gov.uk

POLITICAL COMPOSITION
CON: 26, LAB: 17

COMMITTEE CHAIRS

Audit: Mr Ivan Glover

Licensing: Mr Keith Vickers

Planning: Mr Nigel Sherwood

North Norfolk   D

North Norfolk District Council, Council Offices, Holt Road, Cromer NR27 9EN
☎ 01263 513811 🖷 01263 515042
⊗ districtcouncil@north-norfolk.gov.uk ▯ www.northnorfolk.org

FACTS AND FIGURES
Parliamentary Constituencies: Norfolk North
EU Constituencies: Eastern
Election Frequency: Elections are of whole council

PRINCIPAL OFFICERS

Chief Executive: Mrs Sheila Oxtoby, Chief Executive, Council Offices, Holt Road, Cromer NR27 9EN ☎ 01263 516000 ⏚ sheila.oxtoby@north-norfolk.gov.uk

Senior Management: Mr Nick Baker, Corporate Director, Council Offices, Holt Road, Cromer NR27 9EN ☎ 01263 516221 ⏚ nick.baker@north-norfolk.gov.uk

Senior Management: Mr Steve Blatch, Corporate Director, Council Offices, Holt Road, Cromer NR27 9EN ☎ 01263 516232 ⏚ steve.blatch@north-norfolk.gov.uk

Architect, Building / Property Services: Mr Russell Tanner, Assets & Property Programme Manager, Council Offices, Holt Road, Cromer NR27 9EN ☎ 01263 516196 ⏚ russell.tanner@north-norfolk.gov.uk

Building Control: Mr Stuart Tate, Building Control Manager, Council Offices, Holt Road, Cromer NR27 9EN ☎ 01263 516132 ⏚ stuart.tate@north-norfolk.gov.uk

Catering Services: Ms Tina McManus, Assets Team Leader, Council Offices, Holt Road, Cromer NR27 9EN ☎ 01263 516054 ⏚ tina.mcmanus@north-norfolk.gov.uk

PR / Communications: Mrs Sue Lawson, Communications & PR Manager, Council Offices, Holt Road, Cromer NR27 9EN ☎ 01263 516344 ⏚ sue.lawson@north-norfolk.gov.uk

Community Safety: Mr Stephen Hems, Head of Environmental Health, Council Offices, Holt Road, Cromer NR27 9EN ☎ 01263 516182 ⏚ steve.hems@north-norfolk.gov.uk

Computer Management: Mr Sean Kelly, Head of Business Transformation & IT, Council Offices, Holt Road, Cromer NR27 9EN ☎ 01263 516276 ⏚ sean.kelly@north-norfolk.gov.uk

Customer Service: Mr David Williams, Customer Services Manager, Council Offices, Holt Road, Cromer NR27 9EN ☎ 01263 516415 ⏚ david.williams@north-norfolk.gov.uk

Economic Development: Mr Robert Young, Head of Economic & Community Development, Council Offices, Holt Road, Cromer NR27 9EN ☎ 01263 516162 ⏚ robert.young@north-norfolk.gov.uk

E-Government: Mr Sean Kelly, Head of Business Transformation & IT, Council Offices, Holt Road, Cromer NR27 9EN ☎ 01263 516276 ⏚ sean.kelly@north-norfolk.gov.uk

Emergency Planning: Mr Stephen Hems, Head of Environmental Health, Council Offices, Holt Road, Cromer NR27 9EN ☎ 01263 516182 ⏚ steve.hems@north-norfolk.gov.uk

Environmental / Technical Services: Mr Stephen Hems, Head of Environmental Health, Council Offices, Holt Road, Cromer NR27 9EN ☎ 01263 516182 ⏚ steve.hems@north-norfolk.gov.uk

Environmental Health: Mr Stephen Hems, Head of Environmental Health, Council Offices, Holt Road, Cromer NR27 9EN ☎ 01263 516182 ⏚ steve.hems@north-norfolk.gov.uk

European Liaison: Mr Robert Young, Head of Economic & Community Development, Council Offices, Holt Road, Cromer NR27 9EN ☎ 01263 516162 ⏚ robert.young@north-norfolk.gov.uk

Facilities: Mr Russell Tanner, Assets & Property Programme Manager, Council Offices, Holt Road, Cromer NR27 9EN ☎ 01263 516196 ⏚ russell.tanner@north-norfolk.gov.uk

Finance: Miss Karen Sly, Director - Finance & S151 Officer, Council Offices, Holt Road, Cromer NR27 9EN ☎ 01263 516243 ⏚ karen.sly@north-norfolk.gov.uk

Treasury: Ms Caz Williams, Team Leader - the Exchequer, Council Offices, Holt Road, Cromer NR27 9EN ☎ 01263 516063 ⏚ caz.williams@north-norfolk.gov.uk

Fleet Management: Mrs Julie Cooke, Head of Organisational Development, Council Offices, Holt Road, Cromer NR27 9EN ☎ 01263 516040 ⏚ julie.cooke@north-norfolk.gov.uk

Grounds Maintenance: Mr Karl Read, Leisure & Locality Services Manager, Council Offices, Holt Road, Cromer NR27 9EN ☎ 01263 516002 ⏚ karl.read@north-norfolk.gov.uk

Health and Safety: Mrs Gemma Fairclough, Public Protection Manager, Council Offices, Holt Road, Cromer NR27 9EN ☎ 01263 516139 ⏚ gemma.fairclough@north-norfolk.gov.uk

Housing: Mrs Lisa Grice, Team Leader - Customer Services, Council Offices, Holt Road, Cromer NR27 9EN ☎ 01263 546164 ⏚ lisa.grice@north-norfolk.gov.uk

Legal: Mrs Emma Duncan, Head of Legal, Council Offices, Holt Road, Cromer NR27 9EN ☎ 01263 516045 ⏚ emma.duncan@north-norfolk.gov.uk

Leisure and Cultural Services: Mr Karl Read, Leisure & Locality Services Manager, Council Offices, Holt Road, Cromer NR27 9EN ☎ 01263 516002 ⏚ karl.read@north-norfolk.gov.uk

Licensing: Mr Stephen Hems, Head of Environmental Health, Council Offices, Holt Road, Cromer NR27 9EN ☎ 01263 516182 ⏚ steve.hems@north-norfolk.gov.uk

Lifelong Learning: Mr Robert Young, Head of Economic & Community Development, Council Offices, Holt Road, Cromer NR27 9EN ☎ 01263 516162 ⏚ robert.young@north-norfolk.gov.uk

Lottery Funding, Charity and Voluntary: Ms Sonia Shuter, Team Leader - Health & Communities, Council Offices, Holt Road, Cromer NR27 9EN ☎ 01263 516173 ⏚ sonia.shuter@north-norfolk.gov.uk

Member Services: Mrs Emma Denny, Team Leader - Democratic Services, Council Offices, Holt Road, Cromer NR27 9EN ☎ 01263 516010 ⏚ emma.denny@north-norfolk.gov.uk

NORTH NORFOLK

Parking: Mr Karl Read, Leisure & Locality Services Manager, Council Offices, Holt Road, Cromer NR27 9EN ☎ 01263 516002 ✆ karl.read@north-norfolk.gov.uk

Partnerships: Mr Robert Young, Head of Economic & Community Development, Council Offices, Holt Road, Cromer NR27 9EN ☎ 01263 516162 ✆ robert.young@north-norfolk.gov.uk

Personnel / HR: Mrs Julie Cooke, Head of Organisational Development, Council Offices, Holt Road, Cromer NR27 9EN ☎ 01263 516040 ✆ julie.cooke@north-norfolk.gov.uk

Planning: Mrs Nicola Baker, Head of Planning, Council Offices, Holt Road, Cromer NR27 9EN ☎ 01263 516135 ✆ nicola.baker@north-norfolk.gov.uk

Recycling & Waste Minimisation: Mr Stephen Hems, Head of Environmental Health, Council Offices, Holt Road, Cromer NR27 9EN ☎ 01263 516182 ✆ steve.hems@north-norfolk.gov.uk

Staff Training: Mrs Julie Cooke, Head of Organisational Development, Council Offices, Holt Road, Cromer NR27 9EN ☎ 01263 516040 ✆ julie.cooke@north-norfolk.gov.uk

Sustainable Communities: Mr Robert Young, Head of Economic & Community Development, Council Offices, Holt Road, Cromer NR27 9EN ☎ 01263 516162 ✆ robert.young@north-norfolk.gov.uk

Tourism: Mr Robert Young, Head of Economic & Community Development, Council Offices, Holt Road, Cromer NR27 9EN ☎ 01263 516162 ✆ robert.young@north-norfolk.gov.uk

Waste Collection and Disposal: Mr Scott Martin, Environmental Services Manager, Council Offices, Holt Road, Cromer NR27 9EN ☎ 01263 516341 ✆ scott.martin@north-norfolk.gov.uk

Waste Management: Mr Scott Martin, Environmental Services Manager, Council Offices, Holt Road, Cromer NR27 9EN ☎ 01263 516341 ✆ scott.martin@north-norfolk.gov.uk

Children's Play Areas: Mr Paul Ingham, Parks & Countryside Manager, Council Offices, Holt Road, Cromer NR27 9EN ☎ 01263 516001 ✆ paul.ingham@north-norfolk.gov.uk

COUNCILLORS

Chair: Lee, John (CON - Suffield Park)
john.lee@north-norfolk.gov.uk

Vice-Chair: Shepherd, Richard (CON - Sheringham South)
richard.shepherd@north-norfolk.gov.uk

Leader of the Council: FitzPatrick, Tom (CON - Walsingham)
tom.fitzpatrick@north-norfolk.gov.uk

Deputy Leader of the Council: Oliver, Judy (CON - Sheringham South)
judy.oliver@north-norfolk.gov.uk

Group Leader: Butikofer, Sarah (LD - The Runtons)
sarah.butikofer@north-norfolk.gov.uk

Arnold, Sue (CON - Roughton)
sue.arnold@north-norfolk.gov.uk

Butikofer, Pierre (LD - Astley)
pierre.butikofer@north-norfolk.gov.uk

Claussen-Reynolds, Annie (CON - Lancaster North)
annie.claussen-reynolds@north-norfolk.gov.uk

Coppack, Nicholas (CON - Gaunt)
nicolas.coppack@north-norfolk.gov.uk

Cox, Hilary (CON - Cromer)
Hilary.cox@north-norfolk.gov.uk

Dixon, Nigel (CON - Hoveton)
nigel.dixon@north-norfolk.gov.uk

English, Jenny (CON - Briston)
jenny.english@north-norfolk.gov.uk

Fitch-Tillett, Angie (CON - Poppyland)
angie.fitch-tillett@north-norfolk.gov.uk

Fitzpatrick, Vincent (CON - Priory)
vincent.fitzpatrick@north-norfolk.gov.uk

Gay, Virginia (LD - North Walsham West)
v.gay@virgin.net

Green, Ann (CON - Wensum)
ann.green@north-norfolk.gov.uk

Grove-Jones, Pauline (LD - Stalham & Sutton)
pauline.grove-jones@north-norfolk.gov.uk

Hannah, Brian (LD - Sheringham North)
brian.hannah@north-norfolk.gov.uk

Hester, Simon (CON - Priory)
simon.hester@north-norfolk.gov.uk

High, Philip (LD - Holt)
philip.high@north-norfolk.gov.uk

Jarvis, Ben (CON - Waterside)
benjamin.jarvis@north-norfolk.gov.uk

Knowles, Michael (CON - Chaucer)
mike.knowles@north-norfolk.gov.uk

Lloyd, Nigel (LD - North Walsham)
nigel.lloyd@north-norfolk.gov.uk

McGoun, Barbara (LD - St Benet)
barbara.mcgoun@north-norfolk.gov.uk

Moore, Ann (LD - North Walsham North)
ann.moore@north-norfolk.gov.uk

Moore, Peter (LD - North Walsham East)
cllrpetermoore@aol.com

Northam, Wyndham (CON - Mundesley)
wyndham.northam@north-norfolk.gov.uk

Palmer, Becky (CON - The Raynhams)
becky.palmer@north-norfolk.gov.uk

Pearce, Nigel (CON - Suffield Park)

Perry-Warnes, Georgie (CON - Corpusty)
georgie.perry-warnes@north-norfolk.gov.uk

Price, Richard (CON - Waxham)
richard.price@north-norfolk.gov.uk

Prior, Maggie (CON - Holt)
maggie.prior@north-norfolk.gov.uk

Punchard, Jeremy (CON - Lancaster South)
jeremy.punchard@north-norfolk.gov.uk

Rest, John (CON - Lancaster South)
john.arest@north-norfolk.gov.uk

Reynolds, Roy (CON - Lancaster North)
roy.reynolds@north-norfolk.gov.uk

Rice, Paul (CON - Waterside)
paul.rice@north-norfolk.gov.uk

Seward, Eric (LD - North Walsham North)
eric.seward@north-norfolk.gov.uk

Shaw, Simon (CON - Scottow)
simon.shaw@north-norfolk.gov.uk

Smith, Douglas (CON - Sheringham North)
doug.smith@norton-norfolk@gov.uk

Smith, Barry (CON - Mundesley)
barry.smith@north-norfolk.gov.uk

Smith, Norman (CON - Erpingham)
norman.smith@north-norfolk.gov.uk

Stevens, Robert (CON - Stalham & Sutton)

Uprichard, Vivienne (LD - North Walsham East)
vivienne.uprichard@north-norfolk.gov.uk

Walker, Lee (LD - Happisburgh)
gbeachkidz@btinternet.com

Williams, Glyn (CON - Worstead)
glyn.williams@north-norfolk.gov.uk

Yiasimi, Andreas (LD - Cromer Town)
andreas.yiasimi@north-norfolk.gov.uk

Young, David (LD - High Heath)
david.young@north-norfolk.gov.uk

POLITICAL COMPOSITION
CON: 32, LD: 15

COMMITTEE CHAIRS

Audit: Mr Vincent Fitzpatrick

Licensing: Mr Richard Price

North Somerset   **U**

North Somerset Council, Town Hall, Walliscote Grove Road,
Weston-super-Mare BS23 1UJ
☎ 01934 888888 🖷 01934 888822
🖰 firstname.surname@n-somerset.gov.uk 🖳 www.n-somerset.gov.uk

FACTS AND FIGURES
Parliamentary Constituencies: Weston-super-Mare
EU Constituencies: South West
Election Frequency: Elections are of whole council

PRINCIPAL OFFICERS

Chief Executive: Mr Mike Jackson, Chief Executive Officer, Town
Hall, Walliscote Grove Road, Weston-super-Mare BS23 1UJ
☎ 01934 634972 🖰 mike.jackson@n-somerset.gov.uk

Senior Management: Mr David Carter, Director - Development &
Environment, Town Hall, Walliscote Grove Road, Weston-super-Mare
BS23 1UJ ☎ 01934 888885 🖰 david.carter@n-somerset.gov.uk

Senior Management: Ms Sheila Smith, Director - People &
Communities, Town Hall, Walliscote Grove Road, Weston-super-Mare
BS23 1UJ ☎ 01934 888830 🖰 sheila.smith@n-somerset.gov.uk

Access Officer / Social Services (Disability): Mr Anthony
Rylands, Disability Equality Access Officer, Town Hall, Walliscote
Grove Road, Weston-super-Mare BS23 1UJ ☎ 01934 634989
🖰 anthony.rylands@n-somerset.gov.uk

Architect, Building / Property Services: Mr Mark McSweeney,
Property Services Manager, Town Hall, Walliscote Grove Road,
Weston-super-Mare BS23 1UJ ☎ 01275 882920
🖰 mark.mcsweeney@n-somerset.gov.uk

Best Value: Mr Paul Morris, Head - Performance Improvement &
Human Resources, Town Hall, Walliscote Grove Road, Weston-
super-Mare BS23 1UJ ☎ 01934 888843
🖰 paul.morris@n-somerset.gov.uk

Building Control: Mr John Robbins, Area Building Control Officer,
Town Hall, Walliscote Grove Road, Weston-super-Mare BS23 1UJ
☎ 01275 884548 🖰 john.robbins@n-somerset.gov.uk

Catering Services: Mrs Lynda Mitchell, Commissioning &
Contracts Manager, Town Hall, Walliscote Grove Road, Weston-
super-Mare BS23 1UJ ☎ 01275 888319
🖰 lynda.mitchell@n-somerset.gov.uk

Children / Youth Services: Ms Sheila Smith, Director - People &
Communities, Town Hall, Walliscote Grove Road, Weston-super-Mare
BS23 1UJ ☎ 01934 888830 🖰 sheila.smith@n-somerset.gov.uk

Civil Registration: Mr Nick Brain, Head - Legal & Democratic
Services, Town Hall, Walliscote Grove Road, Weston-super-Mare
BS23 1UJ ☎ 01934 634929 🖰 nicholas.brain@n-somerset.gov.uk

PR / Communications: Mrs Vanessa Andrews, Marketing &
Communications Manager, Town Hall, Walliscote Grove Road,
Weston-super-Mare BS23 1UJ ☎ 01275 888728
🖰 vanessa.andrews@n-somerset.gov.uk

Community Planning: Mr Michael Reep, Planning Policy
Manager, Town Hall, Walliscote Grove Road, Weston-super-Mare
BS23 1UJ ☎ 01934 426775 🖰 michael.reep@n-somerset.gov.uk

Community Safety: Ms Jo Mercer, Community Safety & Drug
Action Team Manager, Town Hall, Walliscote Grove Road, Weston-
super-Mare BS23 1UJ ☎ 01934 426880
🖰 jo.mercer@n-somerset.gov.uk

Computer Management: Mr Mike Riggall, Strategic ICT Client
Manager, Town Hall, Walliscote Grove Road, Weston-super-Mare
BS23 1UJ ☎ 01934 426385 🖰 mike.riggall@n-somerset.gov.uk

Consumer Protection and Trading Standards: Ms Mandy
Bishop, Assistant Director - Operations, Town Hall, Walliscote
Grove Road, Weston-super-Mare BS23 1UJ ☎ 01275 882806
🖰 mandy.bishop@n-somerset.gov.uk

Contracts: Mr Mark Roddan, Head - Procurement & Contracts,
Town Hall, Walliscote Grove Road, Weston-super-Mare BS23 1UJ
☎ 01275 884464 🖰 mark.roddan@n-somerset.gov.uk

Customer Service: Ms Simone Woolley, Customer Services
Manager, Town Hall, Walliscote Grove Road, Weston-super-Mare
BS23 1UJ ☎ 01934 427370 🖰 simon.woolley@n-somerset.gov.uk

NORTH SOMERSET

Economic Development: Mr Stephen Bashford, Head - Economic Development, Town Hall, Walliscote Grove Road, Weston-super-Mare BS23 1UJ ☎ 01275 888689 ✆ stephen.bashford@n-somerset.gov.uk

Education: Ms Jane Routledge, Interim Head - Learning & Achievement, Town Hall, Walliscote Grove Road, Weston-super-Mare BS23 1UJ ☎ 01275 884427 ✆ jane.routledge@n-somerset.gov.uk

Electoral Registration: Mr Mike Jones, Electoral Services Manager, Town Hall, Walliscote Grove Road, Weston-super-Mare BS23 1UJ ☎ 01934 634903 ✆ mike.jones@n-somerset.gov.uk

Emergency Planning: Mr Ian Wilson, Emergency Management Officer, Town Hall, Walliscote Grove Road, Weston-super-Mare BS23 1UJ ☎ 01934 426706 ✆ ian.wilson2@n-somerset.gov.uk

Environmental Health: Ms Mandy Bishop, Assistant Director - Operations, Town Hall, Walliscote Grove Road, Weston-super-Mare BS23 1UJ ☎ 01275 882806 ✆ mandy.bishop@n-somerset.gov.uk

Estates, Property & Valuation: Mr Malcolm Coe, Head - Finance & Property, Town Hall, Walliscote Grove Road, Weston-super-Mare BS23 1UJ ☎ 01934 634619 ✆ malcolm.coe@n-somerset.gov.uk

Events Manager: Mr Darren Fairchild, Seafront & Events Service Manager, Town Hall, Walliscote Grove Road, Weston-super-Mare BS23 1UJ ☎ 01934 427274 ✆ darren.fairchild@n-somerset.gov.uk

Finance: Mr Malcolm Coe, Head - Finance & Property, Town Hall, Walliscote Grove Road, Weston-super-Mare BS23 1UJ ☎ 01934 634619 ✆ malcolm.coe@n-somerset.gov.uk

Fleet Management: Mr Carl Nicholson, Fleet Supervisor, Town Hall, Walliscote Grove Road, Weston-super-Mare BS23 1UJ ☎ 01275 882935 ✆ carl.nicholson@n-somerset.gov.uk

Grounds Maintenance: Mr Ed McKay, Parks & Streetscene Contracts Officer, Town Hall, Walliscote Grove Road, Weston-super-Mare BS23 1UJ ☎ 01934 427681 ✆ edward.mckay@n-somerset.gov.uk

Health and Safety: Ms Cate Sampson, Health & Safety Manager, Town Hall, Walliscote Grove Road, Weston-super-Mare BS23 1UJ ☎ 01934 888632 ✆ cate.sampson@n-somerset.gov.uk

Highways: Mr Frank Cox, Highway Service Manager, Town Hall, Walliscote Grove Road, Weston-super-Mare BS23 1UJ ☎ 01934 426784 ✆ frank.cox@n-somerset.gov.uk

Highways: Mr Colin Medus, Head - Highways & Transport, Town Hall, Walliscote Grove Road, Weston-super-Mare BS23 1UJ ☎ 01934 426498 ✆ colin.medus@n-somerset.gov.uk

Home Energy Conservation: Ms Kim Herivel, Energy & Health Officer, Town Hall, Walliscote Grove Road, Weston-super-Mare BS23 1UJ ☎ 01934 426686 ✆ kim.herivel@n-somerset.gov.uk

Housing: Mr Mark Hughes, Head - Housing, Town Hall, Walliscote Grove Road, Weston-super-Mare BS23 1UJ ☎ 01934 426320 ✆ mark.hughes@n-somerset.gov.uk

Local Area Agreement: Ms Rhiannon Jones, Policy Development Officer, Town Hall, Walliscote Grove Road, Weston-super-Mare BS23 1UJ ☎ 01275 884204 ✆ rhiannon.jones@n-somerset.gov.uk

Legal: Mr Nick Brain, Head - Legal & Democratic Services, Town Hall, Walliscote Grove Road, Weston-super-Mare BS23 1UJ ☎ 01934 634929 ✆ nick.brain@n-somerset.gov.uk

Leisure and Cultural Services: Ms Mandy Bishop, Assistant Director - Operations, Town Hall, Walliscote Grove Road, Weston-super-Mare BS23 1UJ ☎ 01275 882806 ✆ mandy.bishop@n-somerset.gov.uk

Licensing: Ms Mandy Bishop, Assistant Director - Operations, Town Hall, Walliscote Grove Road, Weston-super-Mare BS23 1UJ ☎ 01275 882806 ✆ mandy.bishop@n-somerset.gov.uk

Lifelong Learning: Ms Jill Croskell, Community Learning Team Manager, Town Hall, Walliscote Grove Road, Weston-super-Mare BS23 1UJ ☎ 01934 426105 ✆ jill.croskell@n-somerset.gov.uk

Lighting: Mr Darren Coffin-Smith, Highways & Transport Asset Manager, Town Hall, Walliscote Grove Road, Weston-super-Mare BS23 1UJ ☎ 01275 888548 ✆ darren.coffin-smith@n-somerset.gov.uk

Lottery Funding, Charity and Voluntary: Ms Lorraine Bush, Policy & Partnerships Development Officer, Town Hall, Walliscote Grove Road, Weston-super-Mare BS23 1UJ ☎ 01934 634888 ✆ lorraine.bush@n-somerset.gov.uk

Member Services: Mr Nick Brain, Head - Legal & Democratic Services, Town Hall, Walliscote Grove Road, Weston-super-Mare BS23 1UJ ☎ 01934 634929 ✆ nicholas.brain@n-somerset.gov.uk

Parking: Mr Allan Taylor, Car Parking Services Manager, Town Hall, Walliscote Grove Road, Weston-super-Mare BS23 1UJ ☎ 01934 427293 ✆ allan.taylor@n-somerset.gov.uk

Partnerships: Mr Richard Penska, Head - Support Services Partnership, Town Hall, Walliscote Grove Road, Weston-super-Mare BS23 1UJ ☎ 01275 884256 ✆ richard.penska@n-somerset.gov.uk

Personnel / HR: Mr Paul Morris, Head - Performance Improvement & Human Resources, Town Hall, Walliscote Grove Road, Weston-super-Mare BS23 1UJ ☎ 01934 888843 ✆ paul.morris@n-somerset.gov.uk

Planning: Mr Richard Kent, Head - Development Management, Town Hall, Walliscote Grove Road, Weston-super-Mare BS23 1UJ ☎ 01275 888811 ✆ richard.kent@n-somerset.gov.uk

Public Libraries: Mr Andy Brisley, Libraries & Information Service Manager, Town Hall, Walliscote Grove Road, Weston-super-Mare BS23 1UJ ☎ 01934 426658 ✆ andy.brisley@n-somerset.gov.uk

Recycling & Waste Minimisation: Mr Colin Russell, Recycling & Waste Service Manager, Town Hall, Walliscote Grove Road, Weston-super-Mare BS23 1UJ ☎ 01934 888802 ✆ colin.russell@n-somerset.gov.uk

Regeneration: Mr Karuna Tharmananthar, Deputy Director - Development & Environment, Town Hall, Walliscote Grove Road, Weston-super-Mare BS23 1UJ ☎ 01275 888886
⌁ karuna.tharmananthar@n-somerset.gov.uk

Road Safety: Mr Frank Cox, Highway Service Manager, Town Hall, Walliscote Grove Road, Weston-super-Mare BS23 1UJ ☎ 01934 426784 ⌁ frank.cox@n-somerset.gov.uk

Social Services (Children): Mr Eifion Price, Assistant Director - Support & Safeguarding, Town Hall, Walliscote Grove Road, Weston-super-Mare BS23 1UJ ☎ 01275 884392
⌁ eifion.price@n-somerset.gov.uk

Safeguarding: Mr Eifion Price, Assistant Director - Support & Safeguarding, Town Hall, Walliscote Grove Road, Weston-super-Mare BS23 1UJ ☎ 01275 884392 ⌁ eifion.price@n-somerset.gov.uk

Public Health: Ms Natalie Field, Interim Director - Public Health, Town Hall, Walliscote Grove Road, Weston-super-Mare BS23 1UJ ☎ 01275 885132 ⌁ natalie.field@n-somerset.gov.uk

Staff Training: Mr Paul Morris, Head - Performance Improvement & Human Resources, Town Hall, Weston-super-Mare BS23 1AE ☎ 01934 888843 ⌁ paul.morris@n-somerset.gov.uk

Street Scene: Mr John Flannigan, Community & Enforcement Service Manager, Town Hall, Walliscote Grove Road, Weston-super-Mare BS23 1UJ ☎ 01934 427346
⌁ john.flannigan@n-somerset.gov.uk

Sustainable Communities: Mr David Carter, Director - Development & Environment, Town Hall, Walliscote Grove Road, Weston-super-Mare BS23 1UJ ☎ 01934 888885
⌁ david.carter@n-somerset.gov.uk

Sustainable Development: Mr Michael Reep, Planning Policy Manager, Town Hall, Walliscote Grove Road, Weston-super-Mare BS23 1UJ ☎ 01934 426775 ⌁ michael.reep@n-somerset.gov.uk

Tourism: Mr Simon Gregory, Economic Development Service Manager, Town Hall, Walliscote Grove Road, Weston-super-Mare BS23 1UJ ☎ 01934 426327 ⌁ simon.gregory@n-somerset.gov.uk

Town Centre: Mr Mark MacGregor, Head - Streets & Open Spaces, Town Hall, Walliscote Grove Road, Weston-super-Mare BS23 1UJ ☎ 01934 888802 ⌁ mark.macgregor@n-somerset.gov.uk

Traffic Management: Mr Frank Cox, Highway Service Manager, Town Hall, Walliscote Grove Road, Weston-super-Mare BS23 1UJ ☎ 01934 426784 ⌁ frank.cox@n-somerset.gov.uk

Transport: Ms Bella Fortune, Transportation Service Manager, Town Hall, Walliscote Grove Road, Weston-super-Mare BS23 1UJ ☎ 01934 427540 ⌁ bella.fortune@n-somerset.gov.uk

Transport Planner: Ms Bella Fortune, Transportation Service Manager, Town Hall, Walliscote Grove Road, Weston-super-Mare BS23 1UJ ☎ 01934 427540 ⌁ bella.fortune@n-somerset.gov.uk

Waste Collection and Disposal: Mr John Carson, Recycling & Waste Contracts Manager, Town Hall, Walliscote Grove Road, Weston-super-Mare BS23 1UJ ☎ 01934 427401
⌁ john.carson@n-somerset.gov.uk

Waste Management: Mr Colin Russell, Recycling & Waste Service Manager, Town Hall, Walliscote Grove Road, Weston-super-Mare BS23 1UJ ☎ 01934 888802 ⌁ colin.russell@n-somerset.gov.uk

Children's Play Areas: Mr Ed McKay, Parks & Streetscene Contracts Officer, Town Hall, Walliscote Grove Road, Weston-super-Mare BS23 1UJ ☎ 01934 427681
⌁ edward.mckay@n-somerset.gov.uk

COUNCILLORS

Chair: Crockford-Hawley, John (LD - Weston-super-Mare Hillside)
john.crockford-hawley@n-somerset.gov.uk

Vice-Chair: Blades, Chris (CON - Clevedon West)
christopher.blades@n-somerset.gov.uk

Leader of the Council: Ashton, Nigel (CON - Gordano Valley)
nigel.ashton@n-somerset.gov.uk

Deputy Leader of the Council: ap Rees, Elfan (CON - Hutton & Locking)
elfan.ap.rees@n-somerset.gov.uk

Group Leader: Bell, Mike (LD - Weston-super-Mare Central)
mike.bell@n-somerset.gov.uk

Group Leader: Davies, Donald (IND - Pill)
donald.davies@n-somerset.gov.uk

Group Leader: Tucker, Richard (LAB - Weston-super-Mare Milton)
richard.tucker@n-somerset.gov.uk

Baker, Felicity (CON - Portishead West)
felicity.baker@n-somerset.gov.uk

Barber, Jan (CON - Nailsea Youngwood)
jan.barber@n-somerset.gov.uk

Barclay, Karen (IND - Backwell)
karen.barclay@n-somerset.gov.uk

Blades, Ericka (CON - Clevedon Yeo)
ericka.blades@n-somerset.gov.uk

Blatchford, Mary (CON - Nailsea Yeo)
mary.blatchford@n-somerset.gov.uk

Bryant, Peter (CON - Weston-super-Mare Uphill)
peter.bryantcouncillor@n-somerset.gov.uk

Burden, Peter (CON - Portishead South)
peter.burden@n-somerset.gov.uk

Canniford, Mark (LD - Weston-super-Mare Hillside)
mark.canniford@n-somerset.gov.uk

Cave, Charles (CON - Long Ashton)
charles.cave@n-somerset.gov.uk

Clayton, James (LAB - Weston-super-Mare Bournville)
james.clayton@n-somerset.gov.uk

Cleland, Robert (CON - Weston-super-Mare Mid Worle)
robert.cleland@n-somerset.gov.uk

Codling, Sarah (CON - Weston-super-Mare Winterstoke)
sarah.codling@n-somerset.gov.uk

Cole, Andy (IND - Nailsea Golden Valley)
andy.cole@n-somerset.gov.uk

NORTH SOMERSET

Crew, Peter (CON - Weston-super-Mare South Worle)
peter.crew@n-somerset.gov.uk

Garner, Bob (CON - Clevedon South)
bob.garner@n-somerset.gov.uk

Hadley, Judith (CON - Yatton)
judith.hadley@n-somerset.gov.uk

Hall, Colin (CON - Clevedon Walton)
colin.hall@n-somerset.gov.uk

Harley, Ann (CON - Banwell & Winscombe)
ann.harley@n-somerset.gov.uk

Hitchins, David (CON - Weston-super-Mare South Worle)
david.hitchins@n-somerset.gov.uk

Iles, Jill (CON - Yatton)
jill.iles@n-somerset.gov.uk

Jacobs, Ruth (CON - Wick St Lawrence & St George's)
ruth.jacobs@n-somerset.gov.uk

Jolley, David (CON - Portishead West)
david.jolley@n-somerset.gov.uk

Knight, Reyna (CON - Portishead North)
reyna.knight@n-somerset.gov.uk

Leimdorfer, Tom (GRN - Congresbury & Puxton)
tom.leimdorfer@n-somerset.gov.uk

Ley-Morgan, John (IND - Weston-super-Mare Uphill)
john.ley-morgan@n-somerset.gov.uk

Mead, Derek (IND - Weston-super-Mare North Worle)
derek.mead@n-somerset.gov.uk

Nightingale, Richard (CON - Weston-super-Mare Central)
richard.nightingale@n-somerset.gov.uk

O'Brien, Jerry (CON - Banwell & Winscombe)

Oyns, David (CON - Portishead East)
david.oyns@n-somerset.gov.uk

Parker, Ian (LAB - Weston-super-Mare Bournville)
ian.parker@n-somerset.gov.uk

Pasley, David (CON - Portishead East)
david.pasley@n-somerset.gov.uk

Payne, Dawn (CON - Weston-super-Mare Winterstoke)
dawn.payne@n-somerset.gov.uk

Pepperall, Marcia (CON - Weston-super-Mare North Worle)
marcia.pepperall@n-somerset.gov.uk

Pilgrim, Lisa (CON - Weston-super-Mare Kewstoke)
lisa.pilgrim@n-somerset.gov.uk

Porter, Terry (CON - Hutton & Locking)
terry.porter@n-somerset.gov.uk

Shopland, David (IND - Clevedon East)

Stowey, Kate (CON - Long Ashton)
kate.stowey@n-somerset.gov.uk

Tonkin, James (IND - Nailsea West End)
james.tonkin@n-somerset.gov.uk

Wells, Elizabeth (CON - Blagdon and Churchill)

Williams, Martin (CON - Weston-super-Mare Milton)
martin.williams@n-somerset.gov.uk

Willis, Roz (CON - Weston-super-Mare Kewstoke)
roz.willis@n-somerset.gov.uk

Wilton, Nick (CON - Winford)
nick.wilton@n-somerset.gov.uk

Yamanaka, Deborah (LD - Wrington)
deborah.yamanaka@n-somerset.gov.uk

POLITICAL COMPOSITION
CON: 35, IND: 7, LD: 4, LAB: 3, GRN: 1

North Tyneside   M

North Tyneside Metropolitan Borough Council, Quadrant, The Silverlink North, Cobalt Business Park, North Tyneside, NE27 0BY

☎ 0845 200 0101 ⌨ www.northtyneside.gov.uk

FACTS AND FIGURES
Parliamentary Constituencies: Tynemouth, Tyneside North
EU Constituencies: North East
Election Frequency: Elections are by thirds

PRINCIPAL OFFICERS

Chief Executive: Mr Patrick Melia, Chief Executive & S151 Officer, Quadrant, The Silverlink North, Cobalt Business Park, North Tyneside, NE27 0BY ☎ 0191 643 2001
✆ patrick.melia@northtyneside.gov.uk

Deputy Chief Executive: Mr Paul Hanson, Deputy Chief Executive, Quadrant, The Silverlink North, Cobalt Business Park, NE27 0BY ☎ 0191 643 7001 ✆ paul.hanson@northtyneside.gov.uk

Senior Management: Mr Paul Buie, Head of Business & Economic Development, Quadrant, The Silverlink North, Cobalt Business Park, North Tyneside, NE27 0BY ☎ 0191 643 6402
✆ paul.buie@northtyneside.gov.uk

Senior Management: Ms Wendy Burke, Director - Public Health, Quadrant, The Silverlink North, Cobalt Business Park, North Tyneside, NE27 0BY ☎ 0191 643 2104
✆ wendy.burke@northtyneside.gov.uk

Senior Management: Ms Lisa Clark, Head of Commercial Services & Business Re-design, Quadrant, The Silverlink North, Cobalt Business Park, North Tyneside, NE27 0BY ☎ 0191 643 7760
✆ lisa.clark@northtyneside.gov.uk

Senior Management: Ms Vivienne Geary, Head of Law & Governance, Quadrant, The Silverlink North, Cobalt Business Park, North Tyneside, NE27 0BY ☎ 0191 643 5339
✆ vivienne.geary@northtyneside.gov.uk

Senior Management: Mrs Janice Gillespie, Head of Finance, Quadrant, The Silverlink North, Cobalt Business Park, North Tyneside, NE27 0BY ☎ 0191 6435701
✆ janice.gillespie@northtyneside.gov.uk

Senior Management: Mr Ben Kaner, Head of Digital Strategy, Quadrant, The Silverlink North, Cobalt Business Park, North Tyneside, NE27 0BY ☎ 0191 643 7760
✆ ben.kaner@northtyneside.gov.uk

Senior Management: Mrs Jackie Laughton, Head of Corporate Strategy, Quadrant, The Silverlink North, Cobalt Business Park, North Tyneside, NE27 0BY ☎ 0191 643 7070 ⌗ jacqueline.laughton@northtyneside.gov.uk

Senior Management: Ms Alison Lazazzera, Head of Human Resources & Organisation Development, Quadrant, The Silverlink North, Cobalt Business Park, North Tyneside, NE27 0BY ☎ 0191 643 5012 ⌗ alison.lazazzera@northtyneside.gov.uk

Senior Management: Mr Mark Longstaff, Head of Commissioning & Investment, Quadrant West, The Silverlink North, Cobalt Business Park, North Tyneside, NE27 0BY ☎ 0191 643 8091 ⌗ mark.longstaff@northtyneside.gov.uk

Senior Management: Mrs Jacqui Old, Head of Health, Education Care & Safeguarding, Quadrant, The Silverlink North, Cobalt Business Park, North Tyneside, NE27 0BY ☎ 0191 643 8091 ⌗ jacqui.old@northtyneside.gov.uk

Senior Management: Mr Phil Scott, Head of Environment, Housing & Leisure, Quadrant, The Silverlink North, 2nd Floor, Quadrant West, Cobalt Business Park, NE27 0BY ☎ 0191 643 7295 ⌗ phil.scott@northtyneside.gov.uk

Building Control: Mr Colin MacDonald, Senior Manager - Technical & Regulatory Services, Quadrant, The Silverlink North, Cobalt Business Park, North Tyneside, NE27 0BY ☎ 0191 643 6620 ⌗ colin.macdonald@northtyneside.gov.uk

Catering Services: Ms Barbara Patterson, Catering Manager, Quadrant, The Silverlink North, Cobalt Business Park, North Tyneside, NE27 0BY ☎ 0191 643 8340 ⌗ barbara.patterson@northtyneside.gov.uk

Children / Youth Services: Ms Jill Baker, Senior Manager - Early Help & Vulnerable Families, Quadrant, The Silverlink North, Cobalt Business Park, North Tyneside, NE27 0BY ☎ 0191 643 6462 ⌗ jill.baker2@northtyneside.gov.uk

Civil Registration: Ms Elaine Fairley, Registration Office Manager, Maritime Chambers, The Silverlink North, Cobalt Business Park, Newcastle upon Tyne NE27 0BY ☎ 0191 643 6794 ⌗ elaine.fairley@northtyneside.gov.uk

PR / Communications: Ms Dawn Tindle, Marketing Manager, Quadrant, The Silverlink North, Cobalt Business Park, North Tyneside, NE27 0BY ☎ 0191 643 7070 ⌗ dawn.tindle@northtyneside.gov.uk

Community Safety: Ms Lindsey Ojomo, Resilience, Security & Community Safety Manager, Quadrant, The Silverlink North, Cobalt Business Park, North Tyneside, NE27 0BY ☎ 0191 643 9483 ⌗ lindsey.ojomo@northtyneside.gov.uk

Computer Management: Mr Ben Kaner, Head of Digital Strategy, Quadrant, The Silverlink North, Cobalt Business Park, North Tyneside, NE27 0BY ☎ 0191 643 7760 ⌗ ben.kaner@northtyneside.gov.uk

Consumer Protection and Trading Standards: Mr Colin MacDonald, Senior Manager - Technical & Regulatory Services, Quadrant, The Silverlink North, Cobalt Business Park, North Tyneside, NE27 0BY ☎ 0191 643 6620 ⌗ colin.macdonald@northtyneside.gov.uk

Customer Service: Mrs Janice Gillespie, Head of Finance, Quadrant, The Silverlink North, Cobalt Business Park, North Tyneside, NE27 0BY ☎ 0191 6435701 ⌗ janice.gillespie@northtyneside.gov.uk

Economic Development: Mr Paul Buie, Head of Business & Economic Development, Quadrant, The Silverlink North, Cobalt Business Park, North Tyneside, NE27 0BY ☎ 0191 643 6402 ⌗ paul.buie@northtyneside.gov.uk

Education: Mrs Jacqui Old, Head of Health, Education Care & Safeguarding, Quadrant, The Silverlink North, Cobalt Business Park, North Tyneside, NE27 0BY ☎ 0191 643 8091 ⌗ jacqui.old@northtyneside.gov.uk

E-Government: Mr Ben Kaner, Head of Digital Strategy, Quadrant, The Silverlink North, Cobalt Business Park, North Tyneside, NE27 0BY ☎ 0191 643 7760 ⌗ ben.kaner@northtyneside.gov.uk

Electoral Registration: Ms Joanne McGregor, Manager - Law & Governance, Quadrant, The Silverlink North, Cobalt Business Park, North Tyneside, NE27 0BY ☎ 0191 643 5350 ⌗ joanne.mcgregor@northtyneside.gov.uk

Emergency Planning: Mr Phil Scott, Head of Environment, Housing & Leisure, Quadrant, The Silverlink North, 2nd Floor, Quadrant West, Cobalt Business Park, NE27 0BY ☎ 0191 643 7295 ⌗ phil.scott@northtyneside.gov.uk

Energy Management: Mr Phil Scott, Head of Environment, Housing & Leisure, Quadrant, The Silverlink North, 2nd Floor, Quadrant West, Cobalt Business Park, NE27 0BY ☎ 0191 643 7295 ⌗ phil.scott@northtyneside.gov.uk

Environmental / Technical Services: Mr Phil Scott, Head of Environment, Housing & Leisure, Quadrant, The Silverlink North, 2nd Floor, Quadrant West, Cobalt Business Park, NE27 0BY ☎ 0191 643 7295 ⌗ phil.scott@northtyneside.gov.uk

Environmental Health: Mr Colin MacDonald, Senior Manager - Technical & Regulatory Services, Quadrant, The Silverlink North, Cobalt Business Park, North Tyneside, NE27 0BY ☎ 0191 643 6620 ⌗ colin.macdonald@northtyneside.gov.uk

Estates, Property & Valuation: Mr Niall Cathie, Strategic Asset Manager, Quadrant, The Silverlink North, Cobalt Business Park, North Tyneside, NE27 0BY ☎ 0191 643 6517 ⌗ niall.cathie@northtyneside.gov.uk

European Liaison: Ms Melissa Wells, Policy & Intelligence Advisor, Quadrant, The Silverlink North, Cobalt Business Park, North Tyneside, NE27 0BY ☎ 0191 643 6412 ⌗ melissa.wells@northtyneside.gov.uk

Events Manager: Mr Peter Warne, Tourism & Events Development Manager, Town Hall, High Street East, Wallsend NE28 7RR ☎ 0191 643 7411 ⌗ pete.warne@northtyneside.gov.uk

NORTH TYNESIDE

Facilities: Mr Niall Cathie, Strategic Asset Manager, Quadrant, The Silverlink North, Cobalt Business Park, North Tyneside, NE27 0BY ☎ 0191 643 6517 ⌂ niall.cathie@northtyneside.gov.uk

Finance: Mrs Janice Gillespie, Head of Finance, Quadrant, The Silverlink North, Cobalt Business Park, North Tyneside, NE27 0BY ☎ 0191 6435701 ⌂ janice.gillespie@northtyneside.gov.uk

Fleet Management: Mr Steve Whitworth, Operations & Logistics Manager, Quadrant, The Silverlink North, Cobalt Business Park, North Tyneside, NE27 0BY ☎ 0191 643 7297 ⌂ steve.whitworth@northtyneside.gov.uk

Grounds Maintenance: Mr Phil Scott, Head of Environment, Housing & Leisure, Quadrant, The Silverlink North, 2nd Floor, Quadrant West, Cobalt Business Park, NE27 0BY ☎ 0191 643 7295 ⌂ phil.scott@northtyneside.gov.uk

Health and Safety: Ms Alison Lazazzera, Head of Human Resources & Organisation Development, Quadrant, The Silverlink North, Cobalt Business Park, North Tyneside, NE27 0BY ☎ 0191 643 5012 ⌂ alison.lazazzera@northtyneside.gov.uk

Highways: Mr Colin MacDonald, Senior Manager - Technical & Regulatory Services, Quadrant, The Silverlink North, Cobalt Business Park, North Tyneside, NE27 0BY ☎ 0191 643 6620 ⌂ colin.macdonald@northtyneside.gov.uk

Housing: Mr Phil Scott, Head of Environment, Housing & Leisure, Quadrant, The Silverlink North, 2nd Floor, Quadrant West, Cobalt Business Park, NE27 0BY ☎ 0191 643 7295 ⌂ phil.scott@northtyneside.gov.uk

Housing Maintenance: Mr Paul Worth, Operations Manager - Housing Services, Quadrant, The Silverlink North, Cobalt Business Park, North Tyneside, NE27 0BY ☎ 0191 643 7554 ⌂ paul.worth@northtyneside.gov.uk

Local Area Agreement: Mr Craig Anderson, Manager - Policy & Performance, Quadrant, The Silverlink North, Cobalt Business Park, North Tyneside, NE27 0BY ☎ 0191 643 5621 ⌂ craig.anderson@northtyneside.gov.uk

Legal: Ms Vivienne Geary, Head of Law & Governance, Quadrant, The Silverlink North, Cobalt Business Park, North Tyneside, NE27 0BY ☎ 0191 643 5339 ⌂ vivienne.geary@northtyneside.gov.uk

Leisure and Cultural Services: Mr Phil Scott, Head of Environment, Housing & Leisure, Quadrant, The Silverlink North, 2nd Floor, Quadrant West, Cobalt Business Park, NE27 0BY ☎ 0191 643 7295 ⌂ phil.scott@northtyneside.gov.uk

Leisure and Cultural Services: Mr Paul Youlden, Senior Manager - Sport & Leisure, Quadrant, The Silverlink North, Cobalt Business Park, North Tyneside, NE27 0BY ☎ 0191 643 7430 ⌂ paul.youlden@northtyneside.gov.uk

Licensing: Mr Colin MacDonald, Senior Manager - Technical & Regulatory Services, Quadrant, The Silverlink North, Cobalt Business Park, North Tyneside, NE27 0BY ☎ 0191 643 6620 ⌂ colin.macdonald@northtyneside.gov.uk

Lifelong Learning: Mrs Jacqui Old, Head of Health, Education Care & Safeguarding, Quadrant, The Silverlink North, Cobalt Business Park, North Tyneside, NE27 0BY ☎ 0191 643 8091 ⌂ jacqui.old@northtyneside.gov.uk

Lottery Funding, Charity and Voluntary: Mrs Jackie Laughton, Head of Corporate Strategy, Quadrant, The Silverlink North, Cobalt Business Park, North Tyneside, NE27 0BY ☎ 0191 643 7070 ⌂ jacqueline.laughton@northtyneside.gov.uk

Member Services: Ms Yvette Monaghan, Customer, Member & Governor Services Manager, Quadrant, The Silverlink North, Cobalt Business Park, North Tyneside, NE27 0BY ☎ 0191 643 5361 ⌂ yvette.monaghan@northtyneside.gov.uk

Parking: Mr Colin MacDonald, Senior Manager - Technical & Regulatory Services, Quadrant, The Silverlink North, Cobalt Business Park, North Tyneside, NE27 0BY ☎ 0191 643 6620 ⌂ colin.macdonald@northtyneside.gov.uk

Partnerships: Mrs Jackie Laughton, Head of Corporate Strategy, Quadrant, The Silverlink North, Cobalt Business Park, North Tyneside, NE27 0BY ☎ 0191 643 7070 ⌂ jacqueline.laughton@northtyneside.gov.uk

Personnel / HR: Ms Alison Lazazzera, Head of Human Resources & Organisational Development, Quadrant, The Silverlink North, Cobalt Business Park, NE27 0BY ☎ 0191 643 5012 ⌂ alison.lazazzera@northtyneside.gov.uk

Planning: Mr Colin MacDonald, Senior Manager - Technical & Regulatory Services, Quadrant, The Silverlink North, Cobalt Business Park, North Tyneside, NE27 0BY ☎ 0191 643 6620 ⌂ colin.macdonald@northtyneside.gov.uk

Procurement: Ms Allison Mitchell, Senior Manager - Internal Assurance & Risk Assessment, Quadrant, The Silverlink North, Cobalt Business Park, North Tyneside, NE27 0BY ☎ 0191 643 5720 ⌂ allison.mitchell@northtyneside.gov.uk

Public Libraries: Mr Steve Bishop, Senior Manager - Cultural Services, Quadrant, The Silverlink North, Cobalt Business Park, North Tyneside, NE27 0BY ☎ 0191 643 7410 ⌂ steve.bishop@nothtyneside.gov.uk

Recycling & Waste Minimisation: Ms Samantha Dand, Senior Manager - Local Environment Services, Quadrant, The Silverlink North, Cobalt Business Park, North Tyneside, NE27 0BY ☎ 0191 643 7294 ⌂ samantha.dand@northtyneside.gov.uk

Regeneration: Mr Graham Sword, Senior Manager - Regeneration, Quadrant, The Silverlink North, Cobalt Business Park, North Tyneside, NE27 0BY ☎ 0191 643 6421 ⌂ graham.sword@northtyneside.gov.uk

Road Safety: Mr Colin MacDonald, Senior Manager - Technical & Regulatory Services, Quadrant, The Silverlink North, Cobalt Business Park, North Tyneside, NE27 0BY ☎ 0191 643 6620 ⌂ colin.macdonald@northtyneside.gov.uk

Social Services (Adult): Mrs Jacqui Old, Head of Health, Education Care & Safeguarding, Quadrant, The Silverlink North, Cobalt Business Park, North Tyneside, NE27 0BY ☎ 0191 643 8091 ⌂ jacqui.old@northtyneside.gov.uk

Social Services (Children): Mrs Jacqui Old, Head of Health, Education Care & Safeguarding, Quadrant, The Silverlink North, Cobalt Business Park, North Tyneside, NE27 0BY ☎ 0191 643 8091 ⌂ jacqui.old@northtyneside.gov.uk

Public Health: Ms Wendy Burke, Director - Public Health, Quadrant, The Silverlink North, Cobalt Business Park, North Tyneside, NE27 0BY ☎ 0191 643 2104 ⌂ wendy.burke@northtyneside.gov.uk

Staff Training: Ms Alison Lazazzera, Head of Human Resources & Organisational Development, Quadrant, The Silverlink North, Cobalt Business Park, NE27 0BY ☎ 0191 643 5012 ⌂ alison.lazazzera@northtyneside.gov.uk

Sustainable Communities: Mr Phil Scott, Head of Environment, Housing & Leisure, Quadrant, The Silverlink North, 2nd Floor, Quadrant West, Cobalt Business Park, NE27 0BY ☎ 0191 643 7295 ⌂ phil.scott@northtyneside.gov.uk

Sustainable Development: Mr Paul Nelson, Environmental Sustainability Manager, Quadrant, The Silverlink North, Cobalt Business Park, North Tyneside, NE27 0BY ☎ 0191 643 6467 ⌂ paul.nelson@northtyneside.gov.uk

Tourism: Mr Peter Warne, Tourism & Events Development Manager, Town Hall, High Street East, Wallsend NE28 7RR ☎ 0191 643 7411 ⌂ pete.warne@northtyneside.gov.uk

Town Centre: Mr Peter Warne, Tourism & Events Development Manager, Town Hall, High Street East, Wallsend NE28 7RR ☎ 0191 643 7411 ⌂ pete.warne@northtyneside.gov.uk

Traffic Management: Mr Colin MacDonald, Senior Manager - Technical & Regulatory Services, Quadrant, The Silverlink North, Cobalt Business Park, North Tyneside, NE27 0BY ☎ 0191 643 6620 ⌂ colin.macdonald@northtyneside.gov.uk

Total Place: Mrs Jackie Laughton, Head of Corporate Strategy, Quadrant, The Silverlink North, Cobalt Business Park, North Tyneside, NE27 0BY ☎ 0191 643 7070 ⌂ jacqueline.laughton@northtyneside.gov.uk

Waste Collection and Disposal: Mr Phil Scott, Head of Environment, Housing & Leisure, Quadrant, The Silverlink North, Cobalt Business Park, North Tyneside, NE27 0BY ☎ 0191 643 7295 ⌂ phil.scott@northtyneside.gov.uk

Waste Management: Mr Phil Scott, Head of Environment, Housing & Leisure, Quadrant, The Silverlink North, Cobalt Business Park, North Tyneside, NE27 0BY ☎ 0191 643 7295 ⌂ phil.scott@northtyneside.gov.uk

Children's Play Areas: Ms Samantha Dand, Senior Manager - Local Environment Services, Quadrant, The Silverlink North, Cobalt Business Park, North Tyneside, NE27 0BY ☎ 0191 643 7294 ⌂ samantha.dand@northtyneside.gov.uk

COUNCILLORS

Directly Elected Mayor: Redfearn, Norma (LAB - No Ward)
norma.redfearn@northtyneside.gov.uk

Deputy Mayor: Pickard, Bruce (LAB - Riverside)
bruce.pickard@northtyneside.gov.uk

Allan, Jim (LAB - Camperdown)
jim.allan@ea-direct.com

Arkle, Anne (LAB - Camperdown)
anne.arkle@northtyneside.gov.uk

Austin, Alison (CON - Monkseaton North)
alison.austin@northtyneside.gov.uk

Barrie, Ken (CON - Cullercoats)
ken.barrie@northtyneside.gov.uk

Bell, Linda (LAB - Wallsend)
linda.bell@northtyneside.gov.uk

Bell, Gary (LAB - Killingworth)
gary.bell@northtyneside.gov.uk

Bolger, Karen (LAB - Tynemouth)
karen.bolgercllr@northtyneside.gov.uk

Brooks, Pamela (LAB - Preston)
p.brooks@live.co.uk

Burdis, Carole (LAB - Valley)
carole.burdis@northtyneside.gov.uk

Burdis, Brian (LAB - Valley)
valleycllrs@hotmail.com

Cassidy, Joanne (LAB - Weetslade)
joanne.cassidy@northtyneside.gov.uk

Clark, Karen (LAB - Longbenton)
karen.clark@northtyneside.gov.uk

Cox, Debbie (LAB - Collingwood)

Cox, Steve (LAB - Collingwood)
cllrstevecox@gmail.com

Craven, Naomi (LAB - Monkseaton South)
naomi.craven@northtyneside.gov.uk

Darke, Linda (LAB - Killingworth)
linda.darke@northtyneside.gov.uk

Darke, Eddie (LAB - Longbenton)
eddie.darke@northtyneside.gov.uk

Davis, Cath (LAB - Preston)
cath.davis@northtyneside.gov.uk

Day, Sarah (LAB - Tynemouth)
sarah.day@northtyneside.gov.uk

Drummond, Davey (LAB - Monkseaton South)
davey.drummond@northtyneside.gov.uk

Earley, Peter (LAB - Benton)
peter.earley@northtyneside.gov.uk

Glindon, Ray (LAB - Camperdown)
ray.glindon@northtyneside.gov.uk

Graham, Sandra (LAB - Whitley Bay)
sandra.graham@northtyneside.gov.uk

Grayson, Ian (CON - Monkseaton South)
igrayson@hotmail.com

Green, Muriel (LAB - Weetslade)
muriel.green@northtyneside.gov.uk

NORTH TYNESIDE

Hall, Margaret (LAB - Whitley Bay)
margaret.hall@northtyneside.gov.uk

Harrison, John (LAB - Howdon)
john.harrison@northtyneside.gov.uk

Hodson, Edwin (CON - St Mary's)
edwin.hodson@northtyneside.gov.uk

Hunter, Janet (LAB - Benton)
janet.hunter@northtyneside.gov.uk

Hunter, John (LAB - Howdon)
john.hunter@northtyneside.gov.uk

Huscroft, Marian (LD - Northumberland)

Huscroft, Nigel (LD - Northumberland)

Johnson, Carl (LAB - Battle Hill)
carl.johnson@northtyneside.gov.uk

Lee, Karen (LAB - Cullercoats)
karen.lee@northtyneside.gov.uk

Lott, Frank (LAB - Riverside)
frank.lott@northtyneside.gov.uk

Lott, Wendy (LAB - Riverside)
wendy.lott@northtyneside.gov.uk

Madden, Gary (LAB - Wallsend)
gary.madden@northtyneside.gov.uk

Madden, Maureen (LAB - Howdon)
maureen.madden@northtyneside.gov.uk

Mason, Paul (CON - Monkseaton North)
paul.mason@northtyneside.gov.uk

McGarr, David (LAB - Battle Hill)
david.mcgarr@northtyneside.gov.uk

McIntyre, Pam (CON - St Mary's)
pam.mcintyre@northtyneside.gov.uk

McMeekan, David (LAB - Cullercoats)
david.mcmeekan@northtyneside.gov.uk

McMullen, Anthony (LAB - Weetslade)
anthony.mcmullen@northtyneside.gov.uk

Miller, Leslie (CON - Monkseaton North)
les.miller@northtyneside.gov.uk

Mulvenna, Tommy (LAB - Valley)
tommy.mulvenna@northtyneside.gov.uk

Newman, Andy (LAB - Northumberland)
andy.newman@northtyneside.gov.uk

Oliver, Pat (LAB - Benton)
pat.oliver@northtyneside.gov.uk

Osborne, Kate (LAB - Preston)
kate.osborne@northtyneside.gov.uk

O'Shea, John (LAB - Whitley Bay)
john.o'shea@northtyneside.gov.uk

Percy, Alan (LAB - Chirton)
alan.percy@northtyneside.gov.uk

Rankin, Martin (LAB - Collingwood)
martin.rankin@northtyneside.gov.uk

Reynolds, Margaret (LAB - Chirton)
margaret.reynolds@northtyneside.gov.uk

Spillard, Lesley (LAB - Battle Hill)
lesley.spillard@northtyneside.gov.uk

Stirling, John (LAB - Chirton)
john.stirling@northtyneside.gov.uk

Thirlaway, Matthew (LAB - Wallsend)
matthew.thirlaway@northtyneside.gov.uk

Waggott-Fairley, Alison (LAB - Killingworth)
alison.waggott-fairley@northtyneside.gov.uk

Walker, Joan (LAB - Longbenton)
joan.walker@northtyneside.gov.uk

Wallace, Judith (CON - St Mary's)
judith.wallace@northtyneside.gov.uk

Weetman, Fraces (LAB - Tynemouth)
frances.weetman@northtyneside.gov.uk

POLITICAL COMPOSITION
LAB: 51, CON: 8, LD: 2

North Warwickshire   D

North Warwickshire Borough Council, The Council House,
South Street, Atherstone CV9 1DE
☎ 01827 715341 🖷 01827 719225
📧 customerservices@northwarks.gov.uk 🖳 www.northwarks.gov.uk

FACTS AND FIGURES
Parliamentary Constituencies: Warwickshire North
EU Constituencies: West Midlands
Election Frequency: Elections are of whole council

PRINCIPAL OFFICERS

Chief Executive: Mr Jerry Hutchinson, Chief Executive, Old Bank
House, 129 Long Street, Atherstone CV9 1DE ☎ 01827 715341
📧 jerryhutchinson@northwarks.gov.uk

Deputy Chief Executive: Mr Chris Brewer, Deputy Chief
Executive, The Council House, South Street, Atherstone CV9 1DE
☎ 01827 715341 📧 chrisbrewer@northwarks.gov.uk

Assistant Chief Executive: Mr Steve Maxey, Assistant Chief
Executive & Solicitor to the Council, The Council House, South
Street, Atherstone CV9 1DE ☎ 01827 719438; 01827 715341
📧 stevemaxey@northwarks.gov.uk

Assistant Chief Executive: Mr Bob Trahern, Assistant Chief
Executive - Community Services, The Council House, South Street,
Atherstone CV9 1DE ☎ 01827 715341
📧 bobtrahern@northwarks.gov.uk

Building Control: Mr Kevin Bunsell, Head of Building Control,
Town Hall, Nuneaton CV11 5AA ☎ 024 7637 6521
📧 kevin.bunsell@nuneatonandbedworth.gov.uk

PR / Communications: Miss Karen Barrow, Communications &
PR Officer, The Council House, South Street, Atherstone CV9 1DE
☎ 01827 719309 📧 karenbarrow@northwarks.gov.uk

Community Planning: Mr Jerry Hutchinson, Chief Executive, Old
Bank House, 129 Long Street, Atherstone CV9 1DE ☎ 01827 715341
📧 jerryhutchinson@northwarks.gov.uk

Community Safety: Mr Robert Beggs, Policy Support Manager, The Council House, South Street, Atherstone CV9 1DE ☎ 01827 719238 ✆ robertbeggs@northwarks.gov.uk

Computer Management: Ms Linda Bird, Assistant Director - Corporate Services, The Council House, South Street, Atherstone CV9 1DE ☎ 01827 719327 ✆ lindabird@northwarks.gov.uk

Corporate Services: Ms Linda Bird, Assistant Director - Corporate Services, The Council House, South Street, Atherstone CV9 1DE ☎ 01827 719327 ✆ lindabird@northwarks.gov.uk

Customer Service: Mr Bob Trahern, Assistant Chief Executive - Community Services, The Council House, South Street, Atherstone CV9 1DE ☎ 01827 715341 ✆ bobtrahern@northwarks.gov.uk

E-Government: Ms Linda Bird, Assistant Director - Corporate Services, The Council House, South Street, Atherstone CV9 1DE ☎ 01827 719327 ✆ lindabird@northwarks.gov.uk

Electoral Registration: Mr David Harris, Democratic Services Manager, Old Bank House, 129 Long Street, Atherstone CV9 1DE ☎ 01827 719222 ✆ davidharris@northwarks.gov.uk

Emergency Planning: Mr Robert Beggs, Policy Support Manager, The Council House, South Street, Atherstone CV9 1DE ☎ 01827 719238 ✆ robertbeggs@northwarks.gov.uk

Energy Management: Mr David Baxendale, Environmental Health Manager, The Council House, South Street, Atherstone CV9 1DE ☎ 01827 719322 ✆ davidbaxendale@northwarks.gov.uk

Environmental / Technical Services: Mr Richard Dobbs, Assistant Director - Streetscape, The Council House, South Street, Atherstone CV9 1DE ☎ 01827 719440 ✆ richarddobbs@northwarks.gov.uk

Environmental Health: Mr Steve Whiles, Environmental Health Manager, Old Bank House, South Street, Atherstone CV9 1DE ☎ 01827 715341 ✆ stephenwhiles@northwarks.gov.uk

Facilities: Mr Chris Jones, Facilities Management Manager, The Council House, South Street, Atherstone CV9 1DE ☎ 01827 719265 ✆ chrisjones@northwarks.gov.uk

Finance: Mr Chris Brewer, Deputy Chief Executive, The Council House, South Street, Atherstone CV9 1DE ☎ 01827 715341 ✆ chrisbrewer@northwarks.gov.uk

Fleet Management: Mr Richard Dobbs, Assistant Director - Streetscape, The Council House, South Street, Atherstone CV9 1DE ☎ 01827 719440 ✆ richarddobbs@northwarks.gov.uk

Grounds Maintenance: Mr Richard Dobbs, Assistant Director - Streetscape, The Council House, South Street, Atherstone CV9 1DE ☎ 01827 719440 ✆ richarddobbs@northwarks.gov.uk

Health and Safety: Miss Kerry Drakeley, HR Officer, Old Bank House, Long Street, Atherstone CV9 1DE ☎ 01827 719300 ✆ kerrydrakeley@northwarks.gov.uk

Home Energy Conservation: Mr David Baxendale, Environmental Health Manager, The Council House, South Street, Atherstone CV9 1DE ☎ 01827 719322 ✆ davidbaxendale@northwarks.gov.uk

Housing: Ms Angela Coates, Assistant Director - Housing, The Council House, South Street, Atherstone CV9 1DE ☎ 01827 715341 ✆ angelacoates@northwarks.gov.uk

Housing Maintenance: Mr Martin Juggins, Responsive Repairs Manager - Operations, Sheepy Road Depot, Atherstone CV9 1HH ☎ 01827 719308 ✆ martinjuggins@northwarks.gov.uk

Legal: Mr Steve Maxey, Assistant Chief Executive & Solicitor to the Council, The Council House, South Street, Atherstone CV9 1DE ☎ 01827 719438; 01827 715341 ✆ stevemaxey@northwarks.gov.uk

Leisure and Cultural Services: Mr Simon Powell, Assistant Director - Leisure & Community Development, The Council House, South Street, Atherstone CV9 1DE ☎ 01827 715341 ✆ simonpowell@northwarks.gov.uk

Licensing: Mr Phil Wortley, Licensing Enforcement Officer, Old Bank House, 129 Long Street, Atherstone CV9 1DE ☎ 01827 719482 ✆ philwortley@northwarks.gov.uk

Lottery Funding, Charity and Voluntary: Ms Jaki Douglas, Partnership & Development Manager, The Council House, South Street, Atherstone CV9 1DE ☎ 01827 719492 ✆ jakidouglas@northwarks.gov.uk

Member Services: Mr David Harris, Democratic Services Manager, Old Bank House, 129 Long Street, Atherstone CV9 1DE ☎ 01827 719222 ✆ davidharris@northwarks.gov.uk

Parking: Mr Richard Dobbs, Assistant Director - Streetscape, The Council House, South Street, Atherstone CV9 1DE ☎ 01827 719440 ✆ richarddobbs@northwarks.gov.uk

Partnerships: Ms Jaki Douglas, Partnership & Development Manager, The Council House, South Street, Atherstone CV9 1DE ☎ 01827 719492 ✆ jakidouglas@northwarks.gov.uk

Personnel / HR: Ms Sue Garner, Assistant Director - Finance & HR, The Council House, South Street, Atherstone CV9 1DE ☎ 01827 719374 ✆ suegarner@northwarks.gov.uk

Personnel / HR: Ms Janis McCulloch, HR Manager, Old Bank House, Long Street, Atherstone CV9 1DE ☎ 01827 719236 ✆ janismcculloch@northwarks.gov.uk

Planning: Mr Jeff Brown, Head - Development Control, The Council House, South Street, Atherstone CV9 1DE ☎ 01827 719310 ✆ jeffbrown@northwarks.gov.uk

Procurement: Mrs Elayne Cooper, Procurement Manager, The Council House, South Street, Atherstone CV9 1DE ☎ 01827 719203 ✆ elaynecooper@northwarks.gov.uk

Recycling & Waste Minimisation: Mr Richard Dobbs, Assistant Director - Streetscape, The Council House, South Street, Atherstone CV9 1DE ☎ 01827 719440 ✆ richarddobbs@northwarks.gov.uk

NORTH WARWICKSHIRE

Regeneration: Mrs Rachel Stephens, Community Development Officer - Rural Regeneration, The Council House, South Street, Atherstone CV9 1DE ☎ 01827 719301 ⏚ rachelstephens@northwarks.gov.uk

Staff Training: Ms Sue Garner, Assistant Director - Finance & HR, The Council House, South Street, Atherstone CV9 1DE ☎ 01827 719374 ⏚ suegarner@northwarks.gov.uk

Street Scene: Mr Richard Dobbs, Assistant Director - Streetscape, The Council House, South Street, Atherstone CV9 1DE ☎ 01827 719440 ⏚ richarddobbs@northwarks.gov.uk

Sustainable Communities: Mrs Julie Taylor, Senior Policy Support Officer, The Council House, South Street, Atherstone CV9 1DE ☎ 01827 719437 ⏚ julietaylor@northwarks.gov.uk

Sustainable Development: Mrs Julie Taylor, Senior Policy Support Officer, Old Bank House, 129 Long Street, Atherstone CV9 1DE ☎ 01827 719437 ⏚ julietaylor@northwarks.gov.uk

Waste Collection and Disposal: Mr Richard Dobbs, Assistant Director - Streetscape, The Council House, South Street, Atherstone CV9 1DE ☎ 01827 719440 ⏚ richarddobbs@northwarks.gov.uk

Waste Management: Mr Richard Dobbs, Assistant Director - Streetscape, The Council House, South Street, Atherstone CV9 1DE ☎ 01827 719440 ⏚ richarddobbs@northwarks.gov.uk

Children's Play Areas: Mr Simon Powell, Assistant Director - Leisure & Community Development, The Council House, South Street, Atherstone CV9 1DE ☎ 01827 715341 ⏚ simonpowell@northwarks.gov.uk

COUNCILLORS

Leader of the Council: Humphreys, David (CON - Newton Regis & Warton)
davidhumphreys@northwarks.gov.uk

Deputy Leader of the Council: Wright, David (CON - Fillongley)
davidwright@northwarks.gov.uk

Group Leader: Farrell, Adam (LAB - Coleshill North)
adamfarrell@northwarks.gov.uk

Bell, Margaret (CON - Hartshill)
margaretbell@northwarks.gov.uk

Chambers, Jacky (LAB - Dordon)
jackychambers@northwarks.gov.uk

Clews, Denise (CON - Atherstone South & Mancetter)
deniseclews@northwarks.gov.uk

Davey, Patrick (CON - Newton Regis & Warton)
patrickdavey@northwarks.gov.uk

Davis, Martin (CON - Atherstone South & Mancetter)
martindavis@northwarks.gov.uk

Dirveiks, Neil (LAB - Atherstone Central)
neildirveiks@northwarks.gov.uk

Dirveiks, Lorna (LAB - Atherstone Central)
lornadirveiks@northwarks.gov.uk

Ferro, Dominic (LAB - Coleshill North)
dominicferro@northwarks.gov.uk

Hanratty, Sue (CON - Polesworth West)
suehanratty@northwarks.gov.uk

Hayfield, Colin (CON - Arley & Whitacre)
colinhayfield@northwarks.gov.uk

Henney, Brian (LAB - Hartshill)
brianhenney@northwarks.gov.uk

Ingram, Stacey (CON - Coleshill South)
staceyingram@northwarks.gov.uk

Jarvis, Ray (CON - Atherstone North)
rayjarvis@northwarks.gov.uk

Jenns, Andy (CON - Kingsbury)
andyjenns@northwarks.gov.uk

Jones, Mark (CON - Coleshill South)
markjones@northwarks.gov.uk

Lea, Joan (CON - Curdworth)
joanlea@northwarks.gov.uk

Lewis, Ann (LAB - Hurley & Wood End)
annlewis@northwarks.gov.uk

Morson, Peter (LAB - Dordon)
petermorson@northwarks.gov.uk

Moss, Brian (LAB - Kingsbury)
brianmoss@northwarks.gov.uk

Payne, Raymond (CON - Water Orton)
raymondpayne@northwarks.gov.uk

Phillips, Hayden (LAB - Hurley & Wood End)
haydenphillips@northwarks.gov.uk

Reilly, David (CON - Water Orton)
davidreilly@northwarks.gov.uk

Simpson, Mark (CON - Arley & Whitacre)
marksimpson@northwarks.gov.uk

Singh, Mejar (CON - Atherstone North)
mejarsingh@northwarks.gov.uk

Smith, Leslie (CON - Fillongley)
lessmith@northwarks.gov.uk

Smitten, John (CON - Polesworth West)
johnsmitten@northwarks.gov.uk

Stanley, Emma (LAB - Polesworth East)
emmastanley@northwarks.gov.uk

Stanley, Michael (LAB - Polesworth East)
mickstanley@northwarks.gov.uk

Sweet, Ray (LAB - Baddesley Ensor & Grendon)
raysweet@northwarks.gov.uk

Waters, Terry (CON - Curdworth)
terrywaters@northwarks.gov.uk

Wright, Andy (CON - Baddesley Ensor & Grendon)
andywright@northwarks.gov.uk

POLITICAL COMPOSITION
CON: 21, LAB: 13

COMMITTEE CHAIRS

Planning: Mr Mark Simpson

North West Leicestershire District Council, Council Offices, Coalville LE67 3FJ
☎ 01530 454545 🖷 01530 454506
✆ customer.services@nwleicestershire.gov.uk 🖳 www.nwleics.gov.uk

FACTS AND FIGURES
Parliamentary Constituencies: Leicestershire North West
EU Constituencies: East Midlands
Election Frequency: Elections are of whole council

PRINCIPAL OFFICERS

Chief Executive: Miss Christine Fisher, Chief Executive, Council Offices, Coalville LE67 3FJ ☎ 01530 454502
✆ christine.fisher@nwleicestershire.gov.uk

Deputy Chief Executive: Mr Steve Bambrick, Director - Services & Deputy Chief Executive, Council Offices, Coalville LE67 3FJ
☎ 01530 454555 ✆ steve.bambrick@nwleicestershire.gov.uk

Senior Management: Mr Steve Bambrick, Director - Services & Deputy Chief Executive, Council Offices, Coalville LE67 3FJ
☎ 01530 454555 ✆ steve.bambrick@nwleicestershire.gov.uk

Senior Management: Mr Ray Bowmer, Head of Finance, Council Offices, Coalville LE67 3FJ ☎ 01530 454520
✆ ray.bowmer@nwleicestershire.gov.uk

Senior Management: Ms Kay Greenbank, Head of Economic Development, Council Offices, Coalville LE67 3FJ
✆ kay.greenbank@nwleicestershire.gov.uk

Senior Management: Mr Glyn Jones, Director - Housing, Council Offices, Coalville LE67 3FJ ☎ 01530 454819
✆ glyn.jones@nwleicestershire.gov.uk

Senior Management: Mr Christopher Lambert, Head of Housing, Council Offices, Coalville LE67 3FJ ☎ 01530 454780
✆ chris.lambert@nwleicestershire.gov.uk

Senior Management: Mr Jim Newton, Head of Regeneration & Planning, Council Offices, Coalville LE67 3FJ ☎ 01530 454782
✆ jim.newton@nwleicestershire.gov.uk

Senior Management: Mr John Richardson, Head of Community Services, Council Offices, Coalville LE67 3FJ ☎ 01530 454832
✆ john.richardson@nwleicestershire.gov.uk

Senior Management: Miss Elizabeth Warhurst, Head of Legal & Support Services / Monitoring Officer, Council Offices, Coalville LE67 3FJ ☎ 01530 454762 ✆ elizabeth.warhurst@nwleicestershire.gov.uk

Building Control: Mr Steve Bambrick, Director - Services & Deputy Chief Executive, Council Offices, Coalville LE67 3FJ
☎ 01530 454555 ✆ steve.bambrick@nwleicestershire.gov.uk

Building Control: Mr David Darlington, Building Control Manager, Council Offices, Coalville LE67 3FJ ☎ 01530 454691
✆ david.darlington@nwleicestershire.gov.uk

Children / Youth Services: Mr John Richardson, Head of Community Services, Council Offices, Coalville LE67 3FJ
☎ 01530 454832 ✆ john.richardson@nwleicestershire.gov.uk

PR / Communications: Ms Caroline Ashman, Communications Team Leader, Council Offices, Coalville LE67 3FJ ☎ 01530 454546
✆ caroline.ashman@nwleicestershire.gov.uk

Community Planning: Mr John Richardson, Head of Community Services, Council Offices, Coalville LE67 3FJ ☎ 01530 454832
✆ john.richardson@nwleicestershire.gov.uk

Computer Management: Mr Mike Harding, ICT Team Manager, Council Offices, Coalville LE67 3FJ ☎ 01530 454716
✆ mike.harding@nwleicestershire.gov.uk

Corporate Services: Mrs Lisa Cotton, Senior Auditor, Council Offices, Coalville LE67 3FJ ☎ 01530 454728
✆ lisa.cotton@nwleicestershire.gov.uk

Customer Service: Mr Steve McCue, Customer Team Manager, Council Offices, Coalville LE67 3FJ ☎ 01530 454557
✆ steve.mccue@nwleicestershire.gov.uk

Customer Service: Miss Elizabeth Warhurst, Head of Legal & Support Services / Monitoring Officer, Council Offices, Coalville LE67 3FJ ☎ 01530 454762
✆ elizabeth.warhurst@nwleicestershire.gov.uk

Electoral Registration: Mrs Louise Beeston, Electoral Services Officer, Council Offices, Coalville LE67 3FJ ☎ 01530 454512
✆ louise.beeston@nwleicestershire.gov.uk

Electoral Registration: Miss Christine Fisher, Chief Executive, Council Offices, Coalville LE67 3FJ ☎ 01530 454502
✆ christine.fisher@nwleicestershire.gov.uk

Electoral Registration: Mrs Melanie Phillips, Democratic & Support Services Team Manager, Whitwick Road, Coalville LE67 3FJ ☎ 01530 454511 ✆ melaine.phillips@nwleicestershire.gov.uk

Emergency Planning: Mr Mike Murphy, Human Resources Team Manager, Council Offices, Coalville LE67 3FJ ☎ 01530 454518
✆ mike.murphy@nwleicestershire.gov.uk

Environmental Health: Miss Christine Fisher, Chief Executive, Council Offices, Coalville LE67 3FJ ☎ 01530 454502
✆ christine.fisher@nwleicestershire.gov.uk

Environmental Health: Mr Lee Mansfield, Environmental Health Team Manager, Council Offices, Coalville LE67 3FJ
☎ 01530 454610 ✆ lee.mansfield@nwleicestershire.gov.uk

Environmental Health: Miss Elizabeth Warhurst, Head of Legal & Support Services / Monitoring Officer, Council Offices, Coalville LE67 3FJ ☎ 01530 454762
✆ elizabeth.warhurst@nwleicestershire.gov.uk

Estates, Property & Valuation: Mr Simon Harvey, Property Asset Manager, Council Offices, Coalville LE67 3FJ
☎ 01530 454550 ✆ simon.harvey@nwleicestershire.gov.uk

NORTH WEST LEICESTERSHIRE

Events Manager: Mr Goff Lewis, Cultural Services Team Manager, Council Offices, Coalville LE67 3FJ ☎ 01530 454601 🖰 goff.lewis@nwleicestershire.gov.uk

Finance: Mr Ray Bowmer, Head of Finance, Council Offices, Coalville LE67 3FJ ☎ 01530 454520 🖰 ray.bowmer@nwleicestershire.gov.uk

Fleet Management: Mr Charlie Clarke, Transport Manager, Council Offices, Coalville LE67 3FJ ☎ 01530 454629 🖰 charlie.clarke@nwleicestershire.gov.uk

Grounds Maintenance: Mr Jason Knight, Leisure Services Team Manager, Council Offices, Coalville LE67 3FJ ☎ 01530 454602

Health and Safety: Mr Ian Bennett, Health & Safety Officer, Council Offices, Coalville LE67 3FJ ☎ 01530 454522 🖰 ian.bennett@nwleicestershire.gov.uk

Housing: Mrs Sue Hallam, Strategic Housing Team Manager, Council Offices, Coalville LE67 3FJ ☎ 01530 454612 🖰 sue.hallam@nwleicestershire.gov.uk

Housing: Mrs Amanda Harper, Housing Management Team Manager, Council Offices, Coalville LE67 3FJ ☎ 01530 454808 🖰 amanda.harper@nwleicestershire.gov.uk

Housing: Mr Glyn Jones, Director - Housing, Council Offices, Coalville LE67 3FJ ☎ 01530 454819 🖰 glyn.jones@nwleicestershire.gov.uk

Housing: Mr Christopher Lambert, Head of Housing, Council Offices, Coalville LE67 3FJ ☎ 01530 454780 🖰 chris.lambert@nwleicestershire.gov.uk

Housing Maintenance: Mr Neil Barks, Interim Housing Maintenance Team Manager, Council Offices, Coalville LE67 3FJ ☎ 01530 454849 🖰 neil.barks@nwleicestershire.gov.uk

Legal: Miss Elizabeth Warhurst, Head of Legal & Support Services / Monitoring Officer, Council Offices, Coalville LE67 3FJ ☎ 01530 454762 🖰 elizabeth.warhurst@nwleicestershire.gov.uk

Leisure and Cultural Services: Mr Steve Bambrick, Director - Services & Deputy Chief Executive, Council Offices, Coalville LE67 3FJ ☎ 01530 454555 🖰 steve.bambrick@nwleicestershire.gov.uk

Leisure and Cultural Services: Mr Jason Knight, Leisure Services Team Manager, Council Offices, Coalville LE67 3FJ ☎ 01530 454602

Leisure and Cultural Services: Mr Goff Lewis, Cultural Services Team Manager, Council Offices, Coalville LE67 3FJ ☎ 01530 454601 🖰 goff.lewis@nwleicestershire.gov.uk

Leisure and Cultural Services: Mr John Richardson, Head of Community Services, Council Offices, Coalville LE67 3FJ ☎ 01530 454832 🖰 john.richardson@nwleicestershire.gov.uk

Licensing: Mr Lee Mansfield, Environmental Health Team Manager, Council Offices, Coalville LE67 3FJ ☎ 01530 454610 🖰 lee.mansfield@nwleicestershire.gov.uk

Member Services: Mrs Melanie Phillips, Democratic & Support Services Team Manager, Council Offices, Coalville LE67 3FJ ☎ 01530 454511 🖰 melanie.phillips@nwleicestershire.gov.uk

Member Services: Miss Elizabeth Warhurst, Head of Legal & Support Services / Monitoring Officer, Council Offices, Coalville LE67 3FJ ☎ 01530 454762 🖰 elizabeth.warhurst@nwleicestershire.gov.uk

Personnel / HR: Mr Mike Murphy, Human Resources Team Manager, Council Offices, Coalville LE67 3FJ ☎ 01530 454518 🖰 mike.murphy@nwleicestershire.gov.uk

Planning: Mr Steve Bambrick, Director - Services & Deputy Chief Executive, Council Offices, Coalville LE67 3FJ ☎ 01530 454555 🖰 steve.bambrick@nwleicestershire.gov.uk

Planning: Mr Chris Elston, Planning & Development Team Manager, Council Offices, Coalville LE67 3FJ ☎ 01530 454668 🖰 chris.elston@nwleicestershire.gov.uk

Planning: Mr Jim Newton, Head of Regeneration & Planning, Council Offices, Coalville LE67 3FJ ☎ 01530 454782 🖰 jim.newton@nwleicestershire.gov.uk

Procurement: Miss Anna Wright, Financial Services Team Manager, Council Offices, Coalville LE67 3FJ ☎ 01530 454492 🖰 anna.wright@nwleicestershire.gov.uk

Recycling & Waste Minimisation: Mr Paul Coates, Waste Services Team Manager, Council Offices, Coalville LE67 3FJ ☎ 01530 454663 🖰 paul.coates@nwleicestershire.gov.uk

Regeneration: Mr Ian Nelson, Head of Planning Policy, Council Offices, Coalville LE67 3FJ ☎ 01530 454676 🖰 ian.nelson@nwleicestershire.gov.uk

Regeneration: Mr Jim Newton, Head of Regeneration & Planning, Council Offices, Coalville LE67 3FJ ☎ 01530 454782 🖰 jim.newton@nwleicestershire.gov.uk

Street Scene: Ms Clare Proudfoot, Street Action Team Manager, Council Offices, Coalville LE67 3FJ ☎ 01530 454564 🖰 clare.proudfoot@nwleicestershire.gov.uk

Waste Collection and Disposal: Mr Paul Coates, Waste Services Team Manager, Council Offices, Coalville LE67 3FJ ☎ 01530 454545

Waste Management: Mr Paul Coates, Waste Services Team Manager, Council Offices, Coalville LE67 3FJ ☎ 01530 454663 🖰 paul.coates@nwleicestershire.gov.uk

Waste Management: Mr John Richardson, Head of Community Services, Council Offices, Coalville LE67 3FJ ☎ 01530 454832 🖰 john.richardson@nwleicestershire.gov.uk

Children's Play Areas: Mr Jason Knight, Leisure Services Team Manager, Council Offices, Coalville LE67 3FJ ☎ 01530 454602

COUNCILLORS

Chair: Cotterill, John (CON - Coalville East)
john.cotterill@nwleicestershire.gov.uk

Vice-Chair: Richichi, Virge (CON - Sence Valley)
virge.richichi@icloud.co.uk

Leader of the Council: Blunt, Richard (CON - Appleby)
richard.blunt@nwleicestershire.gov.uk

Deputy Leader of the Council: Smith, Alison (CON - Daleacre Hill)
alison.smith@nwleicestershire.gov.uk

Group Leader: McKendrick, Susuan (LAB - Blackfordby)
susan.mckendrick@nwleicestershire.gov.uk

Adams, Ron (LAB - Broom Leys)
ronnie.adams@nwleicestershire.gov.uk

Allman, Graham (CON - Ashby Money Hill)
graham.allman@mwleicestershire.gov.uk

Ashman, Robert (CON - Oakthorpe & Donisthorpe)
robert.ashman@nwleicestershire.gov.uk

Bayliss, Roger (CON - Ashby Holywell)
roger.bayliss@nwleicestershire.gov.uk

Boam, Russell (CON - Valley)
russell.boam@nwleicestershire.gov.uk

Bridges, John (CON - Ashby Woulds)
john.bridges@nwleicestershire.gov.uk

Canny, Rachel (IND - Castle Donington Central)
rachelmcanny@gmail.com

Clarke, Nick (LAB - Greenhill)
nick.clarke@nwleicestershire.gov.uk

Clarke, John (CON - Ibstock West)
john.clarke@nwleicestershire.gov.uk

Coxon, John (CON - Ashby Castle)
john.coxon@nwleicestershire.gov.uk

Everitt, David (LAB - Thringstone)
david.everitt@nwleicestershire.gov.uk

Eynon, Terri (LAB - Hugglescote St Mary's)
terri.eynon@nwleicestershire.gov.uk

Fenning, Felix (LAB - Ibstock East)
felix.fenning@nwleicestershire.gov.uk

Geary, John (LAB - Snibston South)
john.geary@nwleicestershire.gov.uk

Gillard, Stuart (CON - Hermitage)
stuart.gillard@nwleicestershire.gov.uk

Gillard, Tony (CON - Holly Hayes)
tony.gillard@nwleicestershire.gov.uk

Goacher, Louise (CON - Thornborough)
louise.goacher@nwleicestershire.gov.uk

Harrison, Dan (CON - Castle Donington Park)
daniel.harrison@nwleicestershire.gov.uk

Hoult, Gill (CON - Measham North)
gill.hoult@nwleicestershire.gov.uk

Hoult, Jim (CON - Ashby Ivanhoe)
jim.hoult@nwleicestershire.gov.uk

Johnson, Russell (LAB - Hugglescote St John's)
russell.johnson@nwleicestershire.gov.uk

Jones, Geraint (CON - Ashby Willesley)
geraint.jones@nwleicestershire.gov.uk

Legrys, John (LAB - Coalville West)
john.legrys@nwleicestershire.gov.uk

Merrie, Keith (CON - Ellistown & Battlefleet)
keith.merrie@nwleicestershire.gov.uk

Pendleton, Trevor (CON - Kegworth)
trevor.pendleton@nwleicestershire.gov.uk

Purver, Paula (CON - Snibston North)
paula.purver@nwleicestershire.gov.uk

Rushton, Nicholas (CON - Long Whatton & Diseworth)
nicholas.rushton@leics.gov.uk

Saffell, Tony (IND - Castle Donington Castle)
tony.saffell@donington.me.uk

Sheahan, Sean (LAB - Measham South)
sean.sheahan@nwleicestershire.gov.uk

Smith, Nigel (CON - Ravenstone & Packington)
nigel.smith@nwleicestershire.gov.uk

Specht, Michael (CON - Bardon)
michael.specht@nwleicestershire.gov.uk

Stevenson, David (CON - Worthington & Breedon)
david.stevenson@nwleicestershire.gov.uk

Wyatt, Michael (LD - Castle Rock)
michael.wyatt@nwleicestershire.gov.uk

POLITICAL COMPOSITION
CON: 25, LAB: 10, IND: 2, LD: 1

COMMITTEE CHAIRS

Audit: Mr John Clarke

Licensing: Mr Nigel Smith

Planning: Mr David Stevenson

North Yorkshire   C

North Yorkshire County Council, County Hall, Northallerton DL7 8AD
☎ 0845 872 7374 📠 01609 778199 🖥 www.northyorks.gov.uk

FACTS AND FIGURES
Parliamentary Constituencies: Harrogate and Knaresborough, Richmond (Yorks), Scarborough and Whitby, Skipton and Ripon
EU Constituencies: Yorkshire and the Humber
Election Frequency: Elections are of whole council

PRINCIPAL OFFICERS

Chief Executive: Mr Richard Flinton, Chief Executive, County Hall, Northallerton DL7 8AD ☎ 01609 532444
📧 richard.flinton@northyorks.gov.uk

Senior Management: Mr David Bowe, Corporate Director - Business & Environmental Services, County Hall, Northallerton DL7 8AD ☎ 01609 532128 📧 david.bowe@northyorks.gov.uk

Senior Management: Mrs Justine Brooksbank, Assistant Chief Executive - Business Support, County Hall, Northallerton DL7 8AD
☎ 01609 532103 📧 justine.brooksbank@northyorks.gov.uk

NORTH YORKSHIRE

Senior Management: Mr Peter Dwyer, Corporate Director - Children & Young People's Services, County Hall, Northallerton DL7 8AD ☎ 01609 532146 ⏱ pete.dwyer@northyorks.gov.uk

Senior Management: Mr Gary Fielding, Corporate Director - Strategic Resources, County Hall, Northallerton DL7 8AD ☎ 01609 533304 ⏱ gary.fielding@northyorks.gov.uk

Senior Management: Mr Barry Khan, Assistant Chief Executive - Legal & Democratic Services, County Hall, Northallerton DL7 8AD ☎ 01609 532173 ⏱ barry.khan@northyorks.gov.uk

Senior Management: Mr Richard Webb, Corporate Director - Local Government, County Hall, Northallerton DL7 8AD ☎ 01609 532139 ⏱ richard.webb@northyorks.gov.uk

Senior Management: Ms Helen Taylor, Corporate Director - Health & Adult Services, County Hall, Northallerton DL7 8AD ⏱ helen.taylor@northyorks.gov.uk

Architect, Building / Property Services: Mr Jon Holden, Assistant Director - Strategic Resources, County Hall, Northallerton DL7 8AD ☎ 01609 534076 ⏱ jon.holden@northyorks.gov.uk

Catering Services: Mr Keith Tillbrook, General Manager, County Hall, Northallerton DL7 8AD ☎ 01609 536871 ⏱ keith.tillbrook@northyorks.gov.uk

Civil Registration: Mr Robin Mair, General Manager - Registration, Archives & Coroners, Library Headquarters, 21 Grammar School Lane, Northallerton DL7 8AD ☎ 01609 533806 ⏱ robin.mair@northyorks.gov.uk

PR / Communications: Ms Helen Edwards, Head - Communications, County Hall, Northallerton DL7 8AD ☎ 01609 532104 ⏱ helen.edwards@northyorks.gov.uk

Community Planning: Mr Neil Irving, Assistant Director - Policy & Partnerships, County Hall, Northallerton DL7 8AD ☎ 01609 533489 ⏱ neil.irving@northyorks.gov.uk

Community Safety: Mr Neil Irving, Assistant Director - Policy & Partnerships, County Hall, Northallerton DL7 8AD ☎ 01609 533489 ⏱ neil.irving@northyorks.gov.uk

Computer Management: Mr Robert Ling, Assistant Director - Technology & Change, County Hall, Northallerton DL7 8AD ☎ 01609 533476 ⏱ robert.ling@northyorks.gov.uk

Consumer Protection and Trading Standards: Mr Graham Venn, Assistant Director - Trading Standards & Planning Services, Thornfield Business Park, Standard Way, Northallerton DL6 2XQ ☎ 01609 766408 ⏱ graham.venn@northyorks.gov.uk

Contracts: Mr Kevin Draisey, Head of Procurement & Contract Manager, County Hall, Northallerton DL7 8AD ☎ 01609 532581 ⏱ kevin.draisey@northyorks.gov.uk

Customer Service: Ms Sarah Foley, Head of Customer Services, County Hall, Northallerton DL7 8AD ☎ 01609 533872 ⏱ sarah.foley@northyorks.gov.uk

Economic Development: Mr James Farrar, Assistant Director - Economic & Partnerships Unit, County Hall, Northallerton DL7 8AD ☎ 01609 533598 ⏱ james.farrar@northyorks.gov.uk

Economic Development: Mr Matt O'Neill, Assistant Director - Growth, Planning & Trading Standards, County Hall, Northallerton DL7 8AD matt.o'neill@northyorks.gov.uk

Education: Mr Peter Dwyer, Corporate Director - Children & Young People's Services, County Hall, Northallerton DL7 8AD ☎ 01609 532146 ⏱ pete.dwyer@northyorks.gov.uk

Electoral Registration: Ms Josie O'Dowd, Democratic Services Manager, County Hall, Northallerton DL7 8AD ☎ 01609 532591 ⏱ josie.o'dowd@northyorks.gov.uk

Emergency Planning: Mr Tom Knox, Head - Emergency Planning, County Hall, Northallerton DL7 8AD ☎ 01609 532110 ⏱ tom.knox@northyorks.gov.uk

Energy Management: Ms Karen Atkinson, Energy Officer, County Hall, Northallerton DL7 8AD ☎ 01609 535775 ⏱ karen.p.atkinson@northyorks.gov.uk

Environmental Health: Mr Matt O'Neill, Assistant Director - Growth, Planning & Trading Standards, County Hall, Northallerton DL7 8AD matt.o'neill@northyorks.gov.uk

European Liaison: Mr James Farrar, Assistant Director - Economic & Partnerships Unit, County Hall, Northallerton DL7 8AD ☎ 01609 533598 ⏱ james.farrar@northyorks.gov.uk

Facilities: Mrs Karen Adamson, Corporate Property Operations Manager, County Hall, Northallerton DL7 8AD ☎ 01609 535288 ⏱ karen.adamson@northyorks.gov.uk

Finance: Mr Gary Fielding, Corporate Director - Strategic Resources, County Hall, Northallerton DL7 8AD ☎ 01609 533304 ⏱ gary.fielding@northyorks.gov.uk

Treasury: Mr Gary Fielding, Corporate Director - Strategic Resources, County Hall, Northallerton DL7 8AD ☎ 01609 533304 ⏱ gary.fielding@northyorks.gov.uk

Pensions: Mr Tom Morrison, Principal Accountant - Pension Investment Officer, County Hall, Northallerton DL7 8AD ☎ 0845 872 7374 ⏱ tom.morrison@northyorks.gov.uk

Fleet Management: Mr Ian Fielding, Assistant Director - Transport, Waste & Countryside Services, County Hall, Northallerton DL7 8AD ☎ 01609 532162 ⏱ ian.fielding@northyorks.gov.uk

Grounds Maintenance: Mrs Karen Adamson, Corporate Property Operations Manager, County Hall, Northallerton DL7 8AD ☎ 01609 535288 ⏱ karen.adamson@northyorks.gov.uk

Health and Safety: Mr Stuart Langston, Shared Head of Health & Safety, County Hall, Northallerton DL7 8AD ☎ 01609 535019 ⏱ stuart.langston@northyorks.gov.uk

Highways: Mr Barrie Mason, Assistant Director - Highways & Transportation, County Hall, Northallerton DL7 8AD ☎ 01609 532137 ⏲ barrie.mason@northyorks.gov.uk

Legal: Mr Barry Khan, Assistant Chief Executive - Legal & Democratic Services, County Hall, Northallerton DL7 8AD ☎ 01609 532173 ⏲ barry.khan@northyorks.gov.uk

Lighting: Mr Paul Gilmore, Road Lighting Team Leader, County Hall, Northallerton DL7 8AD ☎ 01609 532946 ⏲ paul.gilmore@northyorks.gov.uk

Lottery Funding, Charity and Voluntary: Ms Marie-Ann Jackson, Head of Stronger Communities, County Hall, Northallerton DL7 8AD ☎ 01609 532925 ⏲ marie-ann.jackson@northyorks.gov.uk

Member Services: Mrs Amanda Fry, Staff Officer to Chief Executive, County Hall, Northallerton DL7 8AD ☎ 01609 532705 ⏲ amanda.fry@northyorks.gov.uk

Partnerships: Mr Neil Irving, Assistant Director - Policy & Partnerships, County Hall, Northallerton DL7 8AD ☎ 01609 533489 ⏲ neil.irving@northyorks.gov.uk

Personnel / HR: Mrs Justine Brooksbank, Assistant Chief Executive - Business Support, County Hall, Northallerton DL7 8AD ☎ 01609 532103 ⏲ justine.brooksbank@northyorks.gov.uk

Planning: Mr Matt O'Neill, Assistant Director - Growth, Planning & Trading Standards, County Hall, Northallerton DL7 8AD matt.o'neill@northyorks.gov.uk

Planning: Ms Vicky Perkin, Head of Planning Services, County Hall, Northallerton DL7 8AD ☎ 01609 533323 ⏲ vicky.perkin@northyorks.gov.uk

Procurement: Mr Kevin Draisey, Head of Procurement & Contract Manager, County Hall, Northallerton DL7 8AD ☎ 01609 532581 ⏲ kevin.draisey@northyorks.gov.uk

Public Libraries: Ms Julie Blaisdale, Assistant Director - Information Services, County Hall, Northallerton DL7 8AD ☎ 01609 533494 ⏲ julie.blaisdale@northyorks.gov.uk

Recycling & Waste Minimisation: Mr Ian Fielding, Assistant Director - Transport, Waste & Countryside Services, County Hall, Northallerton DL7 8AD ☎ 01609 532162 ⏲ ian.fielding@northyorks.gov.uk

Road Safety: Mr Allan McVeigh, Traffic Management & Road Safety Group Manager, County Hall, Northallerton DL7 8AD ☎ 01609 532847 ⏲ allan.mcveigh@northyorks.gov.uk

Social Services (Children): Ms Judith Hay, Assistant Director - Children's Social Care, County Hall, Northallerton DL7 8AD ☎ 01609 533569 ⏲ judith.hay@northyorks.gov.uk

Public Health: Dr Lincoln Sargeant, Director - Public Health, County Hall, Northallerton DL7 8AD

Staff Training: Ms Tracy Harrison, Head of Training & Learning, County Hall, Northallerton DL7 8AD ☎ 01609 533125 ⏲ tracy.harrison@northyorks.gov.uk

Tourism: Mr James Farrar, Assistant Director - Economic & Partnerships Unit, County Hall, Northallerton DL7 8AD ☎ 01609 533598 ⏲ james.farrar@northyorks.gov.uk

Traffic Management: Mr Barrie Mason, Assistant Director - Highways & Transportation, County Hall, Northallerton DL7 8AD ☎ 01609 532137 ⏲ barrie.mason@northyorks.gov.uk

Transport Planner: Mr Ian Fielding, Assistant Director - Transport, Waste & Countryside Services, County Hall, Northallerton DL7 8AD ☎ 01609 532162 ⏲ ian.fielding@northyorks.gov.uk

Waste Management: Mr Ian Fielding, Assistant Director - Transport, Waste & Countryside Services, County Hall, Northallerton DL7 8AD ☎ 01609 532162 ⏲ ian.fielding@northyorks.gov.uk

COUNCILLORS

Leader of the Council: Les, Carl (CON - Catterick Bridge) cllr.carl.les@northyorks.gov.uk

Deputy Leader of the Council: Dadd, Gareth (CON - Thirsk) cllr.gareth.dadd@northyorks.gov.uk

Arnold, Val (CON - Kirkbymoorside) cllr.val.arnold@northyorks.gov.uk

Atkinson, Margaret (CON - Masham & Fountains) cllr.margaret.atkinson@northyorks.gov.uk

Backhouse, Andrew (CON - Newby) cllr.andrew.backhouse@northyorks.gov.uk

Baker, Robert (CON - Sowerby) cllr.robert.baker@northyorks.gov.uk

Barker, Arthur (CON - Swale) cllr.arthur.barker@northyorks.gov.uk

Barrett, Philip (IND - South Craven) cllr.philip.barrett@northyorks.gov.uk

Bastiman, Derek (CON - Scalby & the Coast) cllr.derek.bastiman@northyorks.gov.uk

Bateman, Bernard (CON - Ripon North) cllr.bernard.bateman@northyorks.gov.uk

Billing, David (LAB - Woodlands) cllr.david.billing@northyorks.gov.uk

Blackburn, John (CON - Hertford & Cayton) cllr.john.blackburn@scarborough.gov.uk

Blackie, John (IND - Upper Dales) cllr.john.blackie@northyorks.gov.uk

Blades, David (CON - Romanby & Broomfield) cllr.david.blades@northyorks.gov.uk

Broadbent, Eric (LAB - Northstead) cllr.eric.broadbent@northyorks.gov.uk

Burr, Lindsay (LD - Malton) cllr.lindsay.burr@northyorks.gov.uk

Butterfield, Jean (CON - Harrogate Central) cllr.jean.butterfield@northyorks.gov.uk

NORTH YORKSHIRE

Casling, Elizabeth (CON - Escrick)
cllr.elizabeth.casling@northyorks.gov.uk

Chance, David (CON - Whitby Mayfield cum Mulgrave)
cllr.david.chance@northyorks.gov.uk

Clark, Jim (CON - Harrogate Harlow)
cllr.jim.clark@northyorks.gov.uk

Clark, John (LIB - Pickering)
cllr.john.clark@northyorks.gov.uk

Cooper, Richard (CON - Harrogate Central)
cllr.richard.cooper@northyorks.gov.uk

Cross, Sam (UKIP - Filey)
cllr.sam.cross@northyorks.gov.uk

de Courcey-Bayley, Margaret-Ann (LD - Harrogate Starbeck)
cllr.margaret-ann.decourcey-bayley@northyorks.gov.uk

Dickinson, Caroline (CON - Northallerton)
cllr.caroline.dickinson@northyorks.gov.uk

Ennis, John (CON - Harrogate Oatlands)
cllr.john.ennis@northyorks.gov.uk

Fort, John (CON - Pateley Bridge)
cllr.john.fort@northyorks.gov.uk

Goss, Andrew (LD - Harrogate Bilton & Nidd Gorge)
cllr.andrew.goss@northyorks.gov.uk

Grant, Helen (IND - Central Richmondshire)
cllr.helen.grant@northyorks.gov.uk

Griffiths, Bryn (LD - Stokesley)
cllr.bryn.griffiths@northyorks.gov.uk

Harrison, Michael (CON - Lower Nidderdale & Bishop Monkton)
cllr.michael.harrison@northyorks.gov.uk

Harrison-Topham, Roger (CON - Middle Dales)
cllr.roger.harrison-topham@northyorks.gov.uk

Heseltine, Robert (IND - Skipton East)
cllr.robert.heseltine@northyorks.gov.uk

Heseltine, Michael (CON - Richmondshire North)
cllr.michael.heseltine@northyorks.gov.uk

Horton, Peter (IND - Ripon South)
cllr.peter.horton@northyorks.gov.uk

Hoult, Bill (LD - Knaresborough)
cllr.bill.hoult@northyorks.gov.uk

Ireton, David (CON - North Craven)
cllr.david.ireton@northyorks.gov.uk

Jeffels, David (CON - Seamer & Derwent Valley)
cllr.david.jeffles@scarborough.gov.uk

Jefferson, Janet (IND - Castle)
cllr.janet.jefferson@northyorks.gov.uk

Jones, Anne (LD - Knaresborough)
cllr.anne.jones@northyorks.gov.uk

Jordan, Mike (CON - South Selby)
cllr.mike.jordan@northyorks.gov.uk

Lee, Andrew (CON - Cawood & Saxton)
cllr.andrew.lee@northyorks.gov.uk

Lunn, Clifford (CON - Selby Brayton)
cllr.cliff.lunn@northyorks.gov.uk

Mackenzie, Don (CON - Harrogate Saltergate)
cllr.don.mackenzie@northyorks.gov.uk

Marsden, Penny (IND - Weaponness & Ramshill)
cllr.penny.marsden@northyorks.gov.uk

Marshall, Shelagh (CON - Mid Craven)
cllr.shelagh.marshall@northyorks.gov.uk

Marshall, Brian (LAB - Selby Barlby)
cllr.brian.marshall@northyorks.gov.uk

McCartney, John (IND - Osgoldcross)
cllr.john.mccartney@northyorks.gov.uk

Metcalfe, Chris (CON - Tadcaster)
cllr.chris.metcalfe@northyorks.gov.uk

Moorehouse, Heather (CON - Great Ayton)
cllr.heather.moorehouse@northyorks.gov.uk

Mulligan, Patrick (CON - Airedale)
cllr.patrick.mulligan@northyorks.gov.uk

Packham, Robert (LAB - Sherburn in Elmet)
cllr.robert.packham@northyorks.gov.uk

Parsons, Stuart (LD - Richmond)
cllr.stuart.parsons@northyorks.gov.uk

Patmore, Caroline (CON - Stillington)
cllr.caroline.patmore@northyorks.gov.uk

Pearson, Christopher (CON - Mid Selby)
cllr.chris.pearson@northyorks.gov.uk

Plant, Joe (CON - Whitby Streonshalh)
cllr.joe.plant@northyorks.gov.uk

Randerson, Anthony (LAB - Eastfield & Osgodby)
cllr.tony.randerson@northyorks.gov.uk

Ritchie, John (LAB - Falsgrave & Stepney)
cllr.john.ritchie@northyorks.gov.uk

Sanderson, Janet (CON - Thornton Dale & The Wolds)
cllr.janet.sanderson@northyorks.gov.uk

Savage, John (LIB - Ainsty)
cllr.john.savage@northyorks.gov.uk

Shaw-Wright, Steven (LAB - Selby Barlby)
cllr.steven.shaw-wright@northyorks.gov.uk

Shields, Elizabeth (LD - Norton)
cllr.elizabeth.shields@northyorks.gov.uk

Simister, David (UKIP - Harrogate Bilton & Nidd Gorge)
cllr.david.simister@northyorks.gov.uk

Solloway, Andy (IND - Skipton West)
Cllr.Andy.Solloway@northyorks.gov.uk

Sowray, Peter (CON - Easingwold)
cllr.peter.sowray@northyorks.gov.uk

Swales, Timothy (CON - North Hambleton)
cllr.tim.swales@northyorks.gov.uk

Swiers, Helen (CON - Esk Valley)
cllr.helen.swiers@northyorks.gov.uk

Trotter, Cliff (CON - Pannal & Lower Wharfedale)
cllr.cliff.trotter@northyorks.gov.uk

Weighell, John (CON - Bedale)
cllr.john.weighell@northyorks.gov.uk

Welch, Richard (CON - Ribblesdale)
cllr.richard.welch@northyorks.gov.uk

Windass, Robert (CON - Boroughbridge)
cllr.robert.windass@northyorks.gov.uk

Wood, Clare (CON - Hovingham & Sheriff Hutton)
cllr.clare.wood@northyorks.gov.uk

POLITICAL COMPOSITION
CON: 44, IND: 9, LD: 8, LAB: 7, LIB: 2, UKIP: 2

COMMITTEE CHAIRS

Audit: Mr Mike Jordan

Pensions: Mr John Weighell

Planning: Mr Peter Sowray

Transport, Economy & Environment: Mr Andrew Backhouse

Young People: Ms Janet Jefferson

Northampton   D

Northampton Borough Council, The Guildhall, St Giles Square, Northampton NN1 1DE
☎ 0300 330 7000 🖷 01604 837395 ✆ enquiries@northampton.gov.uk
🖳 www.northampton.gov.uk

FACTS AND FIGURES
Parliamentary Constituencies: Northampton North, Northampton South
EU Constituencies: East Midlands
Election Frequency: Elections are of whole council

PRINCIPAL OFFICERS

Chief Executive: Mr David Kennedy, Chief Executive, The Guildhall, St Giles Square, Northampton NN1 1DE ☎ 01604 837726 ✆ dkennedy@northampton.gov.uk

Senior Management: Mr Steven Boyes, Director - Regeneration, Enterprise & Planning, The Guildhall, St Giles Square, Northampton NN1 1DE ☎ 01604 838531 ✆ sboyes@northampton.gov.uk

Senior Management: Mr Francis Fernandes, Borough Secretary & Monitoring Officer, The Guildhall, Northampton NN1 1DE ☎ 01604 837334 ✆ ffernandes@northampton.gov.uk

Senior Management: Ms Julie Seddon, Director - Customers & Communities, The Guildhall, St Giles Square, Northampton NN1 1DE ☎ 01604 837379 ✆ julieseddon@northampton.gov.uk

Building Control: Mr Lee Hunter, Building Control Manager, The Guildhall, St Giles Square, Northampton NN1 1DE ☎ 01604 838920 ✆ lhunter@northampton.gov.uk

PR / Communications: Ms Deborah Denton, Communications Manager, The Guildhall, St Giles Square, Northampton NN1 1DE ☎ 01604 837393 ✆ ddenton@northampton.gov.uk

Community Safety: Ms Debbie Ferguson, Community Safety Partnership Manager, The Guildhall, St Giles Square, Northampton NN1 1DE ☎ 01604 838731 ✆ dferguson@northampton.gov.uk

Corporate Services: Mr Francis Fernandes, Borough Secretary & Monitoring Officer, The Guildhall, Northampton NN1 1DE ☎ 01604 837334 ✆ ffernandes@northampton.gov.uk

Customer Service: Ms Marion Goodman, Head of Customer & Cultural Services, The Guildhall, St Giles Square, Northampton NN1 1DE ☎ 01604 838273 ✆ mgoodman@northampton.gov.uk

Economic Development: Mr Steven Boyes, Director - Regeneration, Enterprise & Planning, The Guildhall, St Giles Square, Northampton NN1 1DE ☎ 01604 838531 ✆ sboyes@northampton.gov.uk

E-Government: Ms Marion Goodman, Head of Customer & Cultural Services, The Guildhall, St Giles Square, Northampton NN1 1DE ☎ 01604 838273 ✆ mgoodman@northampton.gov.uk

Electoral Registration: Ms Jackie Thoy, Electoral Services Administrator, The Guildhall, St Giles Square, Northampton NN1 1DE ☎ 01604 837111 ✆ jthoy@northampton.gov.uk

Emergency Planning: Ms Julia Partridge, Emergency Planning Officer, The Guildhall, St Giles Square, Northampton NN1 1DE ☎ 01604 361350 ✆ jpartridge@northampton.gov.uk

Environmental / Technical Services: Ms Ruth Austen, Environment Health Manager, The Guildhall, St Giles Square, Northampton NN1 1DE ☎ 01604 837794 ✆ rausten@northampton.gov.uk

Environmental Health: Ms Ruth Austen, Environment Health Manager, The Guildhall, St Giles Square, Northampton NN1 1DE ☎ 01604 837794 ✆ rausten@northampton.gov.uk

Estates, Property & Valuation: Mr Glenn Miller, Asset Management Team Leader, The Guildhall, St Giles Square, Northampton NN1 1DE ☎ 01604 838761 ✆ gmiller@northampton.gov.uk

Facilities: Ms Shelley Parker, Facilities Manager, The Guildhall, St Giles Square, Northampton NN1 1DE ☎ 01604 837362 ✆ sparker@northampton.gov.uk

Finance: Mr Glenn Hammons, Chief Finance Officer & S151 Officer, The Guildhall, St Giles Square, Northampton NN1 1DE ☎ 01604 366521 ✆ ghammons@northampton.gov.uk

Housing: Mr Phil Harris, Head of Housing & Wellbeing, The Guildhall, St Giles Square, Northampton NN1 1DE ☎ 01604 837666 ✆ pharris@northampton.gov.uk

Legal: Mr Francis Fernandes, Borough Secretary & Monitoring Officer, The Guildhall, Northampton NN1 1DE ☎ 01604 837334 ✆ ffernandes@northampton.gov.uk

Leisure and Cultural Services: Ms Julie Seddon, Director - Customers & Communities, The Guildhall, St Giles Square, Northampton NN1 1DE ☎ 01604 837379 ✆ julieseddon@northampton.gov.uk

Licensing: Ms Julie Seddon, Director - Customers & Communities, The Guildhall, St Giles Square, Northampton NN1 1DE ☎ 01604 837379 ✆ julieseddon@northampton.gov.uk

Lottery Funding, Charity and Voluntary: Mrs Victoria Rockall, Partnerships & Communities Manager, The Guildhall, St Giles Square, Northampton NN1 1DE ☎ 01604 837074 ✆ vrockall@northampton.gov.uk

NORTHAMPTON

Member Services: Mr Francis Fernandes, Borough Secretary & Monitoring Officer, The Guildhall, Northampton NN1 1DE
☎ 01604 837334 ◌ ffernandes@northampton.gov.uk

Parking: Mr Derrick Simpson, Town Centre Manager, The Guildhall, St Giles Square, Northampton NN1 1DE ☎ 01604 838953 ◌ dsimpson@northampton.gov.uk

Partnerships: Mrs Victoria Rockall, Partnerships & Communities Manager, The Guildhall, St Giles Square, Northampton NN1 1DE
☎ 01604 837074 ◌ vrockall@northampton.gov.uk

Planning: Mr Peter Baguley, Head of Planning, The Guildhall, St Giles Square, Northampton NN1 1DE ☎ 01604 838921
◌ pbaguley@northampton.gov.uk

Regeneration: Mr Paul Walker, Head of Economic Development & Regeneration, The Guildhall, St Giles Square, Northampton NN1 1DE ◌ pwalker@northampton.gov.uk

Town Centre: Mr Derrick Simpson, Town Centre Manager, The Guildhall, St Giles Square, Northampton NN1 1DE ☎ 01604 838953 ◌ dsimpson@northampton.gov.uk

Waste Collection and Disposal: Ms Julie Seddon, Director - Customers & Communities, The Guildhall, St Giles Square, Northampton NN1 1DE ☎ 01604 837379
◌ julieseddon@northampton.gov.uk

Waste Management: Ms Julie Seddon, Director - Customers & Communities, The Guildhall, St Giles Square, Northampton NN1 1DE
☎ 01604 837379 ◌ julieseddon@northampton.gov.uk

Children's Play Areas: Ms Julie Seddon, Director - Customers & Communities, The Guildhall, St Giles Square, Northampton NN1 1DE
☎ 01604 837379 ◌ julieseddon@northampton.gov.uk

COUNCILLORS

Mayor: Malpas, Christopher (CON - Billing)
cllr.cmalpas@northampton.gov.uk

Deputy Mayor: Eales, Gareth (LAB - Spencer)
cllr.geales@northampton.gov.uk

Leader of the Council: Markham, Mary (CON - Park)
cllr.mmarkham@northampton.gov.uk

Deputy Leader of the Council: Nunn, Jonathan (CON - Nene Valley)
cllr.jnunn@northampton.gov.uk

Group Leader: Stone, Danielle (LAB - Castle)
cllr.dstone@northampton.gov.uk

Ansell, Tony (CON - Abington)
cllr.tansell@northampton.gov.uk

Ashraf, Rufia (LAB - St James)

Azizur Rahman, Mohammed (CON - Spring Park)
cllr.maziz@northampton.gov.uk

Beardsworth, Sally (LD - Kingsthorpe)
cllr.sbeardsworth@northampton.gov.uk

Birch, Jane (LAB - Trinity)
cllr.jbirch@northampton.gov.uk

Bottwood, Alan (CON - Upton)
cllr.abottwood@northampton.gov.uk

Cali, Muna (LAB - Castle)
cllr.mcali@northampton.gov.uk

Caswell, John (CON - New Duston)
cllr.jcaswell@northampton.gov.uk

Choudary, Nazim (LAB - St Davids)
cllr.nchoudary@northampton.gov.uk

Chunga, Clemennt (LAB - Brookside)
cllr.cchunga@northampton.gov.uk

Clubard, Vicky (LAB - Delapre & Briar Hill)
cllr.vclubard@northampton.gov.uk

Davenport, Julie (LAB - Delapre & Briar Hill)
cllr.jdavenport@northampton.gov.uk

Duffy, Janice (LAB - Talavera)
cllr.jduffy@northampton.gov.uk

Eales, Terrie (LAB - Kings Heath)
cllr.teales@northampton.gov.uk

Eldred, Brandon (CON - East Hunsbury)
cllr.beldred@northampton.gov.uk

Flavell, Penelope (CON - Rushmills)
cllr.pflavell@northampton.gov.uk

Golby, Matthew (CON - New Duston)
cllr.mgolby@northampton.gov.uk

Gowen, Elizabeth (LAB - Eastfield)
cllr.egowen@northampton.gov.uk

Hadland, Tim (CON - Old Duston)
cllr.thadland@northampton.gov.uk

Hallam, Mike (CON - Parklands)
cllr.mhallam@northampton.gov.uk

Haque (Enam), Anamul (LAB - Castle)
cllr.ahaque@northampton.gov.uk

Hibbert, Stephen (CON - Riverside)
cllr.shibbert@northampton.gov.uk

Hill, James (CON - Rectory Farm)
cllr.jhill@northampton.gov.uk

Hill, Michael (CON - Nene Valley)
northamptonhill@yahoo.com

Kilbride, Andrew (CON - Billing)
cllr.akilbridge@northampton.gov.uk

King, Anna (CON - Phippsville)
cllr.aking@northampton.gov.uk

Lane, Jamie (CON - Boothville)
cllr.jlane@northampton.gov.uk

Larratt, Phil (CON - East Hunsbury)
cllr.plarratt@northampton.gov.uk

Markham, Brian (LD - Westone)
cllr.bmarkham@northampton.gov.uk

Marriott, Les (LAB - Semilong)
cllr.lmarriott@northampton.gov.uk

McCutcheon, Arthur (LAB - Headlands)
amccutcheon@northampton.gov.uk

Meredith, Dennis (LD - Talavera)
cllr.dmeredith@northampton.gov.uk

Oldham, Brian (CON - West Hunsbury)
cllr.boldham@northampton.gov.uk

Parekh, Nilesh (CON - Sunnyside)
cllr.nparekh@northampton.gov.uk

Patel, Suresh (CON - Old Duston)
cllr.spatel@northampton.gov.uk

Russell, Catherine (LAB - Kingsley)
cllr.crussell@northampton.gov.uk

Sargeant, Brian (CON - Upton)
cllr.bsargeant@northampton.gov.uk

Shaw, Samual (CON - Obelisk)
cllr.sshaw@northampton.gov.uk

Smith, Zoe (LAB - Abington)
cllr.zsmith@northampton.gov.uk

Walker, Graham (CON - Delapre & Briar Hill)
cllr.gwalker@northampton.gov.uk

POLITICAL COMPOSITION
CON: 25, LAB: 17, LD: 3

COMMITTEE CHAIRS

Audit: Ms Penelope Flavell

Licensing: Mr Phil Larratt

Planning: Mr Brian Oldham

Northamptonshire   C

Northamptonshire County Council, County Hall, Northampton
NN1 1AN
☎ 0300 126 1000 🖷 01604 236223 🖳 www.northamptonshire.gov.uk

FACTS AND FIGURES
EU Constituencies: East Midlands
Election Frequency: Elections are of whole council

PRINCIPAL OFFICERS

Chief Executive: Mr Paul Blantern, Chief Executive, County Hall,
Northampton NN1 1AN ☎ 01604 367100
🖑 pblantern@northamptonshire.gov.uk

Senior Management: Akeem Ali, Director - Public Health, County
Hall, Northampton NN1 1AN aali@northamptonshire.gov.uk

Senior Management: Mr Tony Ciaburro, Corporate Director -
Place Commissioning, County Hall, Northampton NN1 1AN
☎ 01604 366740 🖑 tciaburro@northamptonshire.gov.uk

Senior Management: Mrs Carolyn Kus, Director - Adult Social
Care Services, Room 72, County Hall, Northampton NN1 1AN
☎ 01604 367670 🖑 ckus@northamptonshire.gov.uk

Access Officer / Social Services (Disability): Ms Palvinder
Kudhail, Assistant Director - Early Help & Prevention, County Hall,
Northampton NN1 1AN ☎ 01604 367561
🖑 pkudhail@northamptonshire.gov.uk

Architect, Building / Property Services: Mr James Wheeler,
Head of Property Services (Strategic Asset Manager), County Hall,
Northampton NN1 1AN ☎ 01604 366447
🖑 jwheeler@northamptonshire.gov.uk

Building Control: Mr James Wheeler, Head of Property Services
(Strategic Asset Manager), County Hall, Northampton NN1 1AN
☎ 01604 366447 🖑 jwheeler@northamptonshire.gov.uk

Children / Youth Services: Ms Palvinder Kudhail, Assistant
Director - Early Help & Prevention, County Hall, Northampton
NN1 1AN ☎ 01604 367561 🖑 pkudhail@northamptonshire.gov.uk

Civil Registration: Mr Jeremy Rawlings, Registration Service
Manager, County Hall, Northampton NN1 1AN ☎ 0300 126 1010
🖑 jrawlings@northamptonshire.gov.uk

PR / Communications: Mr Simon Deacon, Head of
Communications & Marketing, Room 90, County Hall, Northampton
NN1 1AN ☎ 01604 367323 🖑 sdeacon@northamptonshire.gov.uk

Community Planning: Mr Roy Boulton, Assistant Director -
Environmental & Planning, County Hall, Northampton NN1 1AN
☎ 01604 366056 🖑 rboulton@northamptonshire.gov.uk

Community Safety: Ms Deborah Mahon, Safe & Sustainable
Communities Manager, County Hall, Northampton NN1 1AN
☎ 01604 367596 🖑 dmahon@northamptonshire.gov.uk

Computer Management: Mr Ian Farrar, Head of IT, County Hall,
Northampton NN1 1AN ☎ 0300 126 1000
🖑 ifarrar@cambridge.gov.uk

Consumer Protection and Trading Standards: Mr David
Hedger, Trading Standards Manager, Trading Standards, Wootton
Hall Park, Northampton NN4 0GB ☎ 01604 362498
🖑 dhedger@northamptonshire.gov.uk

Contracts: Mr Matt Bowmer, Director - Finance, County Hall,
Northampton NN1 1AN ☎ 01604 366550
🖑 m.bowmer@northamptonshire.gov.uk

Corporate Services: Ms Alison Parry, Head of Commercial
Management, County Hall, Northampton NN1 1AN ☎ 01604 366838
🖑 aparry@northamptonshire.gov.uk

Customer Service: Ms Leanne Hanwell, Head of CSC, County
Hall, Northampton NN1 1AN ☎ 01604 367952
🖑 lhanwell@northamptonshire.gov.uk

Economic Development: Mr Tony Ciaburro, Corporate Director -
Place Commissioning, County Hall, Northampton NN1 1AN
☎ 01604 366740 🖑 tciaburro@northamptonshire.gov.uk

Education: Ms Lesley Hagger, Director - Children, Families &
Education, County Hall, Northampton NN1 1AN ☎ 01604 366359
🖑 lhagger@northamptonshire.gov.uk

E-Government: Mr Matt Bowmer, Director - Finance, County Hall,
Northampton NN1 1AN ☎ 01604 366550
🖑 m.bowmer@northamptonshire.gov.uk

NORTHAMPTONSHIRE

Emergency Planning: Mr Matthew Hoy, Emergency Planning Manager, County Hall, Northampton NN1 1AN ☎ 01604 361348 ✆ mhoy@northamptonshire.gov.uk

Energy Management: Dr Darren Perry, Strategic Leader - Energy & Carbon Management, County Hall, Northampton NN1 1AN ☎ 01604 366948 ✆ daperry@northamptonshire.gov.uk

Estates, Property & Valuation: Mr Jeffrey Snell, Estates Operations Manager, County Hall, Northampton NN1 1AN ☎ 01604 236447 ✆ jsnell@northamptonshire.gov.uk

European Liaison: Mr Tony Ciaburro, Corporate Director - Place Commissioning, PO Box 93, County Hall, Northampton NN1 1AN ☎ 01604 366740 ✆ tciaburro@northamptonshire.gov.uk

Facilities: Ms Catherine Kimmett, Facilities Manager, County Hall, Northampton NN1 1AN ✆ ckimmet@northamptonshire.gov.uk

Finance: Mr Matt Bowmer, Director - Finance, County Hall, Northampton NN1 1AN ☎ 01604 366550 ✆ m.bowmer@northamptonshire.gov.uk

Pensions: Mr Paul Tysoe, Group Accountant for the Pension Fund, John Dryden House, 8-10 The Lakes, Northampton NN4 7DD ☎ 01604 368671 ✆ p.tysoe@northamptonshire.gov.uk

Pensions: Mr Mark Whitby, Head of Pensions Operations, John Dryden House ✆ - 10 The Lakes, Northampton NN4 7DD ☎ 01604 366636 ✆ mwhitby@northamptonshire.gov.uk

Grounds Maintenance: Mr James Wheeler, Head of Property Services (Strategic Asset Manager), County Hall, Northampton NN1 1AN ☎ 01604 366447 ✆ jwheeler@northamptonshire.gov.uk

Health and Safety: Ms Sue Stagg, Health & Safety Manager, County Hall, Northampton NN1 1AN ☎ 01604 366447 ✆ sstagg@northamptonshire.gov.uk

Highways: Ms Debbie Taylor-Bond, Head of Highways, Transport & Infrastructure, County Hall, Northampton NN1 1AN dtaylorbond@northamptonshire.gov.uk

Local Area Agreement: Mr Peter McLaren, Head of Partnership Support Unit, County Hall, Northampton NN1 1AN ☎ 01604 237106 ✆ pmclaren@northamptonshire.gov.uk

Leisure and Cultural Services: Ms Janet Doran, Assistant Director - Place, Transformation & Wellbeing, County Hall, Northampton NN1 1AN ☎ 01604 366023 ✆ jdoran@northamptonshire.gov.uk

Licensing: Mr David Hedger, Trading Standards Manager, Trading Standards, Wootton Hall Park, Northampton NN4 0GB ☎ 01604 362498 ✆ dhedger@northamptonshire.gov.uk

Lighting: Mr Geoff Emmins, Highways Maintenance Manager, Riverside House, Riverside Way, Bedford Road, Northampton NN1 5NX ☎ 01604 654481 ✆ gemmins@northamptonshire.gov.uk

Lottery Funding, Charity and Voluntary: Mr Thomas Tansey, Third Sector Liaison, County Hall, Northampton NN1 1AN ☎ 01604 366025 ✆ ttansey@northamptonshire.gov.uk

Member Services: Mr Quentin Baker, Director - Law, Property & Governance, County Hall, Northampton NN1 1AN ☎ 0300 126 1000 ✆ qbaker@cambridgeshire.gov.uk

Parking: Ms Debbie Taylor-Bond, Head of Highways, Transport & Infrastructure, County Hall, Northampton NN1 1AN ✆ dtaylorbond@northamptonshire.gov.uk

Personnel / HR: Mrs Christine Reed, Director - People, Transformation & Transactional Services, PO Box 93, County Hall, Northampton NN1 1AN ☎ 01604 367291 ✆ creed@northamptonshire.gov.uk

Planning: Mr Roy Boulton, Assistant Director - Environmental & Planning, PO Box 93, County Hall, Northampton NN1 1AN ☎ 01604 366056 ✆ rboulton@northamptonshire.gov.uk

Procurement: Mr Paul White, Head of LGSS Procurement, PO Box 93, County Hall, Northampton NN1 1DN ☎ 01604 236465 ✆ pwhite@northamptonshire.gov.uk

Public Libraries: Ms Jane Battye, Customer & Library Service Manager, County Hall, Northampton NN1 1AN ✆ jbattye@northamptonshire.gov.uk

Recycling & Waste Minimisation: Ms Fiona Urqhart, Manager - Waste Management, County Hall, Northampton NN1 1AN

Regeneration: Mr Tony Ciaburro, Corporate Director - Place Commissioning, PO Box 93, County Hall, Northampton NN1 1AN ☎ 01604 366740 ✆ tciaburro@northamptonshire.gov.uk

Road Safety: Mr John Spencer, Team Leader - Road Safety & Sustainability, Riverside Way, Bedford Road, Northampton NN1 5NX ☎ 01604 654430 ✆ jspencer@mqwsp.co.uk

Social Services: Mrs Carolyn Kus, Director - Adult Social Care Services, Room 72, County Hall, Northampton NN1 1AN ☎ 01604 367670 ✆ ckus@northamptonshire.gov.uk

Social Services (Adult): Mrs Carolyn Kus, Director - Adult Social Care Services, Room 72, County Hall, Northampton NN1 1AN ☎ 01604 367670 ✆ ckus@northamptonshire.gov.uk

Social Services (Children): Ms Lesley Hagger, Director - Children, Families & Education, County Hall, Northampton NN1 1AN ☎ 01604 366359 ✆ lhagger@northamptonshire.gov.uk

Public Health: Akeem Ali, Director - Public Health, County Hall, Northampton NN1 1AN aali@northamptonshire.gov.uk

Staff Training: Mrs Kay Maybin, Head of Organisational & Workplace Development, John Dryen House, Northampton NN4 7YD kmaybin@northamptonshire.gov.uk

Sustainable Communities: Mr Tony Ciaburro, Corporate Director - Place Commissioning, PO Box 93, County Hall, Northampton NN1 1AN ☎ 01604 366740
⌨ tciaburro@northamptonshire.gov.uk

Sustainable Development: Mr Tony Ciaburro, Corporate Director - Place Commissioning, PO Box 93, County Hall, Northampton NN1 1AN ☎ 01604 366740
⌨ tciaburro@northamptonshire.gov.uk

Traffic Management: Ms Debbie Taylor-Bond, Head of Highways, Transport & Infrastructure, County Hall, Northampton NN1 1AN ⌨ dtaylorbond@northamptonshire.gov.uk

Transport: Ms Debbie Taylor-Bond, Head of Highways, Transport & Infrastructure, County Hall, Northampton NN1 1AN
⌨ dtaylorbond@northamptonshire.gov.uk

Transport Planner: Ms Debbie Taylor-Bond, Head of Highways, Transport & Infrastructure, County Hall, Northampton NN1 1AN dtaylorbond@northamptonshire.gov.uk

Waste Collection and Disposal: Mr Wade Siddiqui, Manager of Waste Management, County Hall, Northampton NN1 1AN
☎ 01604 367147 ⌨ wsiddiqui@northamptonshire.gov.uk

Waste Management: Mr Wade Siddiqui, Manager of Waste Management, County Hall, Northampton NN1 1AN ☎ 01604 367147
⌨ wsiddiqui@northamptonshire.gov.uk

COUNCILLORS

Leader of the Council: Smith, Heather (CON - Oundle)
hsmith@northamptonshire.gov.uk

Deputy Leader of the Council: Gonzalez De Savage, Andrew (CON - East Hunsbury & Shelfleys)
adesavage@northamptonshire.gov.uk

Beardsworth, Sally (LD - Kingsthorpe South)
sbeardsworth@northamptonshire.gov.uk

Bell, Paul (CON - Earls Barton)
pbell@northamptonshire.gov.uk

Brackenbury, Wendy (CON - Thrapston)
wbrackenbury@northamptonshire.gov.uk

Brookfield, Julie (LAB - Corby West)
jbrookfield@northamptonshire.gov.uk

Broomfield, Jim (UKIP - Brackley)
jbroomfield@northamptonshire.gov.uk

Brown, Michael (UKIP - Kingsthorpe North)
mibrown@northamptonshire.gov.uk

Brown, Robin (CON - Woodford & Weedon)
rwbrown@northamptonshire.gov.uk

Butcher, Mary (LAB - Oakley)
mbutcher@northamptonshire.gov.uk

Clarke, Michael (CON - Hackleton & Grange Park)
mclarke@northamptonshire.gov.uk

Collyer, Adam (UKIP - Daventry West)
acollyer@northamptonshire.gov.uk

Coombe, Elizabeth (LAB - Brickhill & Queensway)
ecoombe@northamptonshire.gov.uk

Eales, Gareth (LAB - Dallington Spencer)
gaeales@northamptonshire.gov.uk

Glynane, Brendan (LD - Delapre & Rushmere)
bglynane@northamptonshire.gov.uk

Golby, Matthew (CON - Duston West & St Crispin)
mgolby@northamptonshire.gov.uk

Groome, Christopher (IND - Burton & Broughton)
cgroome@northamptonshire.gov.uk

Hakewill, James (CON - Rothwell & Mawsley)
jhakewill@northamptonshire.gov.uk

Hales, Eileen (LAB - Windmill)
eihales@northamptonshire.gov.uk

Hallam, Mike (CON - Boothville & Parklands)
mhallam@northamptonshire.gov.uk

Harker, Jim (CON - Ise)
jharker@northamptonshire.gov.uk

Heggs, Stan (CON - Corby Rural)
sheggs@northamptonshire.gov.uk

Hills, Alan (CON - Daventry East)
ahills@northamptonshire.gov.uk

Homer, Sue (CON - Irchester)
shomer@northamptonshire.gov.uk

Hope, Jill (LD - Sixfields)
jhope@northamptonshire.gov.uk

Hughes, Dudley (CON - Raunds)
dhughes@northanptonshire.gov.uk

Hughes, Sylvia (CON - Irthlingborough)
shughes@northamptonshire.gov.uk

Irving-Swift, Cecile (CON - Brixworth)
cirving-swift@northamptonshire.gov.uk

Kirkbride, Joan (CON - Bugbrooke)
jkirkbride@northamptonshire.gov.uk

Larratt, Phill (CON - Nene Valley)
cllr.plarratt@northampton.gov.uk

Lawman, Graham (CON - Croyland & Swanspool)
gmlawman@northamptonshire.gov.uk

Lawson, Derek (CON - Higham Ferrers)
dlawson@northamptonshire.gov.uk

Legg, Stephen (CON - Riverside Park)
slegg@northamtonshire.gov.uk

Lofts, Chris (LD - Towcester & Roade)

Longley, Malcolm (CON - Braunston & Crick)

Mackintosh, David (CON - Billing & Rectory Farm)
dmackintosh@northamptonshire.gov.uk

Matthews, Allan (CON - Desborough)
amatthews@northamptonshire.gov.uk

McCutcheon, Arthur (LAB - Headlands)
amccutcheon@northamptonshire.gov.uk

McGhee, John (LAB - Kingswood)
jmcghee@northamptonshire.gov.uk

Mercer, Andy (CON - Rushden South)
amercer@northamptonshire.gov.uk

Meredith, Dennis (LD - Talavera)
dmeredith@northamptonshire.gov.uk

NORTHAMPTONSHIRE

Morris, Ian (CON - Silverstone)
imorris@northamptonshire.gov.uk

Osborne, Steve (CON - Long Buckby)
sjosborne@northamptonshire.gov.uk

Parker, Bill (CON - Clover Hill)
bparker@northamptonshire.gov.uk

Patel, Suresh (CON - Duston East)
supatel@northamptonshire.gov.uk

Patel, Bhupendra (CON - Finedon)
bpatel@northamptonshire.gov.uk

Roberts, Russell (CON - Wicksteed)
rroberts@northamptonshire.gov.uk

Sawbridge, Ron (CON - Middleton Cheney)

Scott, Bob (LAB - Lloyds)
bascott@northamptonshire.gov.uk

Scrimshaw, Mick (LAB - Northall)
mscrimshaw@northamptonshire.gov.uk

Shephard, Judith (CON - Moulton)
jshephard@northamptonshire.gov.uk

Stone, Danielle (LAB - Abington & Phippsville)
dstone@northamptonshire.gov.uk

Strachan, Winston (LAB - Castle)
wstrachan@northamptonshire.gov.uk

Tye, Michael (CON - Rushden Pemberton West)
mtye@northamptonshire.gov.uk

Uldall, Sarah (LD - St George)
suldall@northamptonshire.gov.uk

Walker, Allen (CON - Deanshanger)
awalker@northamptonshire.gov.uk

Waters, Malcolm (CON - Hatton Park)
mwaters@northamptonshire.gov.uk

POLITICAL COMPOSITION
CON: 36, LAB: 11, LD: 6, UKIP: 3, IND: 1

COMMITTEE CHAIRS

Children, Learning & Communities: Mr Dudley Hughes

Environment, Development & Transport: Ms Elizabeth Coombe

Finance: Mr James Hakewill

Health & Wellbeing: Mr Robin Brown

Health, Adult Care & Wellbeing: Mr Phill Larratt

Pensions: Mr Graham Lawman

Northumberland   U

Northumberland Council, County Hall, Morpeth NE61 2EF
☎ 0845 600 6400 🖷 01670 534117 🖑 ask@northumberland.gov.uk
🖵 www.northumberland.gov.uk

FACTS AND FIGURES
Parliamentary Constituencies: Berwick-upon-Tweed, Blyth Valley, Hexham, Wansbeck
EU Constituencies: North East
Election Frequency: Elections are of whole council

PRINCIPAL OFFICERS

Chief Executive: Mr Steven Mason, Chief Executive, County Hall, Morpeth NE61 2EF ☎ 01670 622929
🖑 steven.mason@northumberland.gov.uk

Deputy Chief Executive: Mrs Daljit Lally, Deputy Chief Executive, County Hall, Morpeth NE61 2EF ☎ 01670 622682
🖑 daljit.lally@northumberland.gcsx.gov.uk

Senior Management: Mr Geoff Paul, Director - Planning & Economy, County Hall, Morpeth NE61 2EF ☎ 01670 622388
🖑 geoff.paul@northumberland.gov.uk

Architect, Building / Property Services: Mr Mike Turner, Head of Property & Capital Programme, County Hall, Morpeth NE61 2EF
☎ 01670 622905 🖑 mike.turner@northumberland.gov.uk

Building Control: Mr Alex Bennett, Chief Fire Officer, Fire & Rescue Service Headquarters, West Hartford Business Park, Cramlington NE23 3JP ☎ 01670 621112
🖑 alex.bennett@northumberland.gov.uk

Children / Youth Services: Mr Andy Johnson, Director - Education & Skills, County Hall, Morpeth NE61 2EF
☎ 01670 622767 🖑 andy.johnson@northumberland.gov.uk

Civil Registration: Mrs Lorraine Dewison, Registration & Coronial Manager, County Hall, Morpeth NE61 2EF ☎ 01670 622544
🖑 lorraine.dewison@northumberland.gov.uk

PR / Communications: Mrs Michelle Atkinson, Head of Communications, County Hall, Morpeth NE61 2EF ☎ 01670 622416
🖑 michelle.atkinson@northumberland.gov.uk

Community Safety: Mr Alex Bennett, Chief Fire Officer, Fire & Rescue Service Headquarters, West Hartford Business Park, Cramlington NE23 3JP ☎ 01670 621112
🖑 alex.bennett@northumberland.gov.uk

Computer Management: Mr Neil Arnold, Chief Information Officer, County Hall, Morpeth NE61 2EF ☎ 01670 623238
🖑 neil.arnold@northumberland.gov.uk

Consumer Protection and Trading Standards: Mr Alex Bennett, Chief Fire Officer, Fire & Rescue Service Headquarters, West Hartford Business Park, Cramlington NE23 3JP
☎ 01670 621112 🖑 alex.bennett@northumberland.gov.uk

Contracts: Ms Teresa Palmer, Shared Head of Procurement, County Hall, Morpeth NE61 2EF ☎ 01670 622357
🖑 teresa.palmer@northumberland.gov.uk

Corporate Services: Mrs Alison Elsdon, Director - Corporate Resources, County Hall, Morpeth NE61 2EF ☎ 01670 622168
🖑 alison.elsdon@nothumberland.gov.uk

Customer Service: Mrs Alison Elsdon, Director - Corporate Resources, County Hall, Morpeth NE61 2EF ☎ 01670 622168
🖑 alison.elsdon@nothumberland.gov.uk

Education: Mr Andy Johnson, Director - Education & Skills, County Hall, Morpeth NE61 2EF ☎ 01670 622767
🖰 andy.johnson@northumberland.gov.uk

E-Government: Mr Neil Arnold, Chief Information Officer, County Hall, Morpeth NE61 2EF ☎ 01670 623238
🖰 neil.arnold@northumberland.gov.uk

Electoral Registration: Mr Geoff Paul, Director - Planning & Economy, County Hall, Morpeth NE61 2EF ☎ 01670 622388
🖰 geoff.paul@northumberland.gov.uk

Emergency Planning: Mr Alex Bennett, Chief Fire Officer, Fire & Rescue Service Headquarters, West Hartford Business Park, Cramlington NE23 3JP ☎ 01670 621112
🖰 alex.bennett@northumberland.gov.uk

Energy Management: Ms Teresa Palmer, Shared Head of Procurement, County Hall, Morpeth NE61 2EF ☎ 01670 622357
🖰 teresa.palmer@northumberland.gov.uk

Environmental Health: Mr Peter Simpson, Public Health Protection Manager, County Hall, Morpeth NE61 2EF
☎ 01670 623696 🖰 peter.simpson@northumberland.gov.uk

Estates, Property & Valuation: Mr Mike Turner, Head of Property & Capital Programme, County Hall, Morpeth NE61 2EF
☎ 01670 622905 🖰 mike.turner@northumberland.gov.uk

Events Manager: Mr James Fell, Heritage & Events Development Manager, County Hall, Morpeth NE61 2EF ☎ 01670 624722
🖰 jfell@activenorthumberland.org.uk

Finance: Mrs Alison Elsdon, Director - Corporate Resources, County Hall, Morpeth NE61 2EF ☎ 01670 622168
🖰 alison.elsdon@nothumberland.gov.uk

Pensions: Ms Clare Gorman, Principal Accountant (Pensions), County Hall, Morpeth NE61 2EF ☎ 01670 623579
🖰 clare.gorman@northumberland.gov.uk

Pensions: Mr Alan Whittle, Pensions Administration Manager, County Hall, Morpeth NE61 2EF ☎ 01670 623569
🖰 alan.whittle@northumberland.gov.uk

Fleet Management: Mr Paul Jones, Head of Neighbourhood Services, County Hall, Morpeth NE61 2EF ☎ 01670 623432
🖰 paul.jones01@northumberland.gov.uk

Grounds Maintenance: Mr Paul Jones, Head of Neighbourhood Services, County Hall, Morpeth NE61 2EF ☎ 01670 623432
🖰 paul.jones01@northumberland.gov.uk

Health and Safety: Mr John Froud, Corporate Health & Safety Manager, County Hall, Morpeth NE61 2EF ☎ 01670 623806
🖰 john.froud@northumberland.gov.uk

Highways: Mr David Laux, Head of Technical Services, County Hall, Morpeth NE61 2EF ☎ 01670 623139
🖰 david.laux@northumberland.gcsx.gov.uk

Housing: Mr Philip Soderquest, Head of Housing, County Hall, Morpeth NE61 2EF ☎ 01670 623696
🖰 philip.soderquest@northumberland.gcsx.gov.uk

Housing Maintenance: Mr Mike Turner, Head of Property & Capital Programme, County Hall, Morpeth NE61 2EF
☎ 01670 622905 🖰 mike.turner@northumberland.gov.uk

Legal: Mr Liam Henry, Legal Services Manager, County Hall, Morpeth NE61 2EF ☎ 01670 623324
🖰 liam.henry@northumberland.gov.uk

Leisure and Cultural Services: Mr Stuart Crichton, Interim Chief Executive - Active Northumberland, County Hall, Morpeth NE61 2EF
☎ 01670 622237 🖰 scrichton@activenorthumberland.org.uk

Licensing: Mr David Sayer, Business Compliance & Public Safety Manager, County Hall, Morpeth NE61 2EF ☎ 01670 623702
🖰 david.sayer@northumberland.gov.uk

Lifelong Learning: Mr Andy Johnson, Director - Education & Skills, County Hall, Morpeth NE61 2EF ☎ 01670 622767
🖰 andy.johnson@northumberland.gov.uk

Lighting: Mr David Laux, Head of Technical Services, County Hall, Morpeth NE61 2EF ☎ 01670 623139
🖰 david.laux@northumberland.gcsx.gov.uk

Member Services: Mrs Jackie Roll, Service Manager - Democracy, County Hall, Morpeth NE61 2EF ☎ 01670 622603
🖰 jackie.roll@northumberland.gov.uk

Parking: Mr David Laux, Head of Technical Services, County Hall, Morpeth NE61 2EF ☎ 01670 623139
🖰 david.laux@northumberland.gcsx.gov.uk

Personnel / HR: Ms Kelly Angus, Director - Human Resources, County Hall, Morpeth NE61 2EF ☎ 01670 623134
🖰 kelly.angus@northumberland.gov.uk

Planning: Mr Mark Ketley, Senior Planning Manager, County Hall, Morpeth NE61 2EF ☎ 01670 625542 🖰 mark.ketley@northumberland.gov.uk

Procurement: Ms Teresa Palmer, Shared Head of Procurement, County Hall, Morpeth NE61 2EF ☎ 01670 622357
🖰 teresa.palmer@northumberland.gov.uk

Public Libraries: Mr Nigel Walsh, Service Manager - Culture, Heritage & Libraries, County Hall, Morpeth NE61 2EF
☎ 01670 624753 🖰 nwalsh@activenorthumberland.gov.uk

Recycling & Waste Minimisation: Mr Paul Jones, Head of Neighbourhood Services, County Hall, Morpeth NE61 2EF
☎ 01670 623432 🖰 paul.jones01@northumberland.gov.uk

Road Safety: Mr David Laux, Head of Technical Services, County Hall, Morpeth NE61 2EF ☎ 01670 623139
🖰 david.laux@northumberland.gcsx.gov.uk

NORTHUMBERLAND

Social Services (Adult): Mrs Vanessa Bainbridge, Director - Adult & Community Care Services, County Hall, Morpeth NE61 2EF
☎ 01670 622680
✆ vanessa.bainbridge@northumbria-healthcare.nhs.uk

Social Services (Children): Mrs Daljit Lally, Deputy Chief Executive, County Hall, Morpeth NE61 2EF ☎ 01670 622682
✆ daljit.lally@northumberland.gcsx.gov.uk

Public Health: Ms Penny Spring, Director - Public Health, County Hall, Morpeth NE61 2EF ☎ 01670 623963
✆ penny.spring@northumberland.gov.uk

Staff Training: Mr Paul Brooks, Learning & OD Manager, County Hall, Morpeth NE61 2EF ☎ 01670 623142
✆ paul.brooks@northumberland.gov.uk

Street Scene: Mr Paul Jones, Head of Neighbourhood Services, County Hall, Morpeth NE61 2EF ☎ 01670 623432
✆ paul.jones01@northumberland.gov.uk

Sustainable Development: Mr Geoff Paul, Director - Planning & Economy, County Hall, Morpeth NE61 2EF ☎ 01670 622388
✆ geoff.paul@northumberland.gov.uk

Tourism: Mr Nigel Walsh, Service Manager - Culture, Heritage & Libraries, County Hall, Morpeth NE61 2EF ☎ 01670 624753
✆ nwalsh@activenorthumberland.gov.uk

Traffic Management: Mr David Laux, Head of Technical Services, County Hall, Morpeth NE61 2EF ☎ 01670 623139
✆ david.laux@northumberland.gcsx.gov.uk

Transport: Mr David Laux, Head of Technical Services, County Hall, Morpeth NE61 2EF ☎ 01670 623139
✆ david.laux@northumberland.gcsx.gov.uk

Transport Planner: Mr David Laux, Head of Technical Services, County Hall, Morpeth NE61 2EF ☎ 01670 623139
✆ david.laux@northumberland.gcsx.gov.uk

Waste Collection and Disposal: Mr Paul Jones, Head of Neighbourhood Services, County Hall, Morpeth NE61 2EF
☎ 01670 623432 ✆ paul.jones01@northumberland.gov.uk

Waste Management: Mr Paul Jones, Head of Neighbourhood Services, County Hall, Morpeth NE61 2EF ☎ 01670 623432
✆ paul.jones01@northumberland.gov.uk

COUNCILLORS

Civic HeadNisbet, Kath (LAB - Croft)
kath.nisbet@northumberland.gov.uk

Leader of the Council: Davey, Grant (LAB - Kitty Brewster)
grant.davey@northumberland.gov.uk

Deputy Leader of the Council: Ledger, David (LAB - Choppington)
david.ledger@northumberland.gov.uk

Group Leader: Jackson, Peter (CON - Ponteland South with Heddon)
peter.jackson@northumberland.gov.uk

Arckless, George (LAB - Amble)
robert.arckless99@northumberland.gov.uk

Armstrong, Eileen (CON - Ponteland East & Stannington)
eileen.armstrong@northumberland.gov.uk

Bawn, David (CON - Morpeth North)
david.bawn@northumberland.gov.uk

Bridgett, Steven (INDNA - Rothbury)
steven.bridgett@northumberland.gov.uk

Burt, Eileen (LAB - Prudhoe North)
eileen.burt@northumberland.gov.uk

Cairns, Heather (LD - Alnwick)
heather.cairns@northumberland.gov.uk

Cairns, Kate (LD - Longhoughton)
kate.cairns@northumberland.gov.uk

Campbell, Deirdre (LAB - Newsham)

Cartie, Eileen (LAB - Wensleydale)
eileen.carter@northumberland.gov.uk

Castle, Gordon (IND - Alnwick)
gordon.castle@northumberland.gov.uk

Dale, Anne (IND - Stocksfield & Broomhaugh)
anne.dale@northumberland.gov.uk

Daley, Wayne (CON - Cramlington North)
wayne.daley@northumberland.gov.uk

Davey, Susan (LAB - Cowpen)
susan.davey@northumberland.gov.uk

Dickinson, Scott (LAB - Druridge Bay)
scott.dickinson@northumberland.gov.uk

Dodd, Richard (CON - Ponteland North)
richard.dodd@northumberland.gov.uk

Douglas, Milburn (IND - Lynemouth)
milburn.douglas@northumberland.gov.uk

Dungworth, Susan (LAB - Hartley)
susan.dungworth@northumberland.gov.uk

Fearon, Jean (CON - Corbridge)
jean.fearon@northumberland.gov.uk

Flux, Barry (CON - Cramlington West)
barry.flux@northumberland.gov.uk

Foster, Julie (LAB - Stakeford)
julied.foster@northumberland.gov.uk

Gallacher, Brian (LAB - Haydon)
brian.gallacher@northumberland.gov.uk

Gibson, Rupert (CON - Humshaugh)
rupert.gibson@northumberland.gov.uk

Gobin, Jeff (LAB - Sleekburn)

Graham, Kathy (LAB - Cramlington Village)
kathy.graham@northumberland.gov.uk

Grimshaw, Lynne (LAB - Bothal)
lynne.grimshaw@northumberland.gov.uk

Hepple, Allan (LAB - Cramlington South East)
allan.hepple@northumberland.gov.uk

Homer, Cath (CON - Hexham East)
cath.homer@northumberland.gov.uk

Horncastle, Colin (CON - South Tynedale)
colin.horncastle@northumberland.gov.uk

Hunter, Elizabeth (LD - Berwick West with Ord)
isabel.hunter@northumberland.gov.uk

Hutchinson, Ian (CON - Haltwhistle)
ian.hutchinson@northumberland.gov.uk

Johnstone, Terry (LAB - Bedlington West)
terry.johnstone@northumberland.gov.uk

Jones, Gavin (LD - Berwick North)
gavin.jones@northumberland.gov.uk

Jones, Veronica (CON - Ponteland West)
veronica.jones@northumberland.gov.uk

Kelly, Paul (IND - Bywell)
paul.kelly@northumberland.gov.uk

Kennedy, Derek (INDNA - Hexham West)
derek.kennedy@northumberland.gov.uk

Lang, Jim (LAB - Seaton with Newbiggin West)
jim.lang@northumberland.gov.uk

Lindley, Ian (INDNA - Morpeth Stobhill)
ian.lindley@northumberland.gov.uk

Murray, Anthony (CON - Wooler)
anthony.murray99@northumberland.gov.uk

Parry, Ken (LAB - Hirst)
ken.parry@northumberland.gov.uk

Pidcock, Laura (LAB - Cramlington Eastfield)
laura.pidcock@northumberland.gov.uk

Pidcock, Bernard (LAB - Holywell)
bernard.pidcock@northumberland.gov.uk

Purvis, Mark (LAB - College)
mark.purvis@northumberland.gov.uk

Reid, Tony (LAB - Prudhoe South)
tony.reid@northumberland.gov.uk

Reid, Jeff (LD - Plessey)
jeff.reid@northumberland.gov.uk

Richards, Margaret (LAB - Seghill with Seaton Delaval)
margaret.richards01@northumberland.gov.uk

Rickerby, Lesley (LD - South Blyth)
lesley.rickerby@northumberland.gov.uk

Riddle, John (CON - Bellingham)
john.riddle@northumberland.gov.uk

Robson, Terry (CON - Hexham Central with Acomb)
terry.robson@northumberland.gov.uk

Sambrook, Alan (LAB - Pegswood)
alan.sambrook@northumberland.gov.uk

Sanderson, Glen (CON - Longhorsley)
glen.sanderson@northumberland.gov.uk

Sharp, Alan (LD - Haydon & Hadrian)
alan.sharp@northumberland.gov.uk

Simpson, Elizabeth (LAB - Newbiggin Central & East)
elizabeth.simpson@northumberland.gov.uk

Smith, James (LD - Berwick East)
james.smith@northumberland.gov.uk

Swithenbank, Ian (LAB - Cramlington East)
ian.switchenbank@northumberland.gov.uk

Tebbutt, Andrew (LD - Morpeth Kirkhill)
andrew.tebbutt@northumberland.gov.uk

Thorne, Trevor (CON - Shilbottle)
embletonhall@btinternet.com

Tyler, Valerie (LAB - Bedlington East)
valerie.tyler@northumberland.gov.uk

Wallace, Alyson (LAB - Bedlington Central)
alyson.wallace@northumberland.gov.uk

Watkin, Richard (LD - Norham & Islandshires)
douwatkin@aol.com

Watson, Jeffrey (CON - Amble West & Warkworth)
jeffrey.watson@northumberland.gov.uk

Webb, Gordon (LAB - Isabella)
gordon.webb@northumberland.gov.uk

Wilson, Thomas (LAB - Ashington Central)
thomas.wilson@northumberland.gov.uk

Woodman, John (CON - Bamburgh)
john.woodman@northumberland.gov.uk

POLITICAL COMPOSITION
LAB: 31, CON: 19, LD: 10, IND: 4, INDNA: 3

COMMITTEE CHAIRS

Audit: Mrs Anne Dale

Economic Growth & Strategic Transport: Mr Alan Sambrook

Family & Children's Services: Mr Brian Gallacher

Health & Wellbeing: Ms Susan Dungworth

Licensing: Mr Ken Parry

Pensions: Mr Tony Reid

Planning: Mr Milburn Douglas

Norwich City   D

Norwich City Council, City Hall, St. Peter's Street, Norwich
NR2 1NH
☎ 0344 980 3333 ⬧ info@norwich.gov.uk ▣ www.norwich.gov.uk

FACTS AND FIGURES
Parliamentary Constituencies: Norwich North, Norwich South
EU Constituencies: Eastern
Election Frequency: Elections are by thirds

PRINCIPAL OFFICERS

Chief Executive: Ms Laura McGillivray, Chief Executive, City Hall,
St. Peter's Street, Norwich NR2 1NH ☎ 01603 212001; 01603 213001
⬧ lauramcgillivray@norwich.gov.uk

Senior Management: Mr Anthony Bull, Executive Head -
Business Relationship Management & Democracy, City Hall, St.
Peter's Street, Norwich NR2 1NH ☎ 01603 212326
⬧ anthonybull@norwich.gov.uk

Senior Management: Mr Bob Cronk, Executive Head -
Neighbourhoods, City Hall, St Peter's Street, Norwich NR2 1NH
☎ 01603 212373 ⬧ bobcronk@norwich.gov.uk

Senior Management: Ms Justine Hartley, Chief Finance Officer
(S151 Officer), City Hall, St. Peter's Street, Norwich NR2 1NH
☎ 01603 212440 ⬧ justinehartley@norwich.gov.uk

NORWICH CITY

Senior Management: Mr David Moorcroft, Executive Head - Regeneration & Development, City Hall, St. Peter's Street, Norwich NR2 1NH ☎ 01603 212225 🖑 davidmoorcroft@norwich.gov.uk

Senior Management: Ms Nikki Rotsos, Executive Head - Customers, Communications & Culture, City Hall, St. Peter's Street, Norwich NR2 1NH ☎ 01603 212211 🖑 nikkirotsos@norwich.gov.uk

Access Officer / Social Services (Disability): Mr David Moorcroft, Executive Head - Regeneration & Development, City Hall, St. Peter's Street, Norwich NR2 1NH ☎ 01603 212225 🖑 davidmoorcroft@norwich.gov.uk

Architect, Building / Property Services: Mr David Moorcroft, Executive Head - Regeneration & Development, City Hall, St. Peter's Street, Norwich NR2 1NH ☎ 01603 212225 🖑 davidmoorcroft@norwich.gov.uk

Best Value: Mr Phil Shreeve, Transformation Manager, City Hall, St. Peter's Street, Norwich NR2 1NH ☎ 01603 212356 🖑 philshreeve@norwich.gov.uk

Building Control: Mr David Moorcroft, Executive Head - Regeneration & Development, City Hall, St. Peter's Street, Norwich NR2 1NH ☎ 01603 212225 🖑 davidmoorcroft@norwich.gov.uk

Building Control: Mr Graham Nelson, Head of Planning Services, City Hall, St. Peter's Street, Norwich NR2 1NH ☎ 01603 212530 🖑 grahamnelson@norwich.gov.uk

PR / Communications: Mr Richard Balls, Communications Manager, City Hall, St. Peter's Street, Norwich NR2 1NH ☎ 01603 212991 🖑 richardballs@norwich.gov.uk

Community Planning: Mr Bob Cronk, Executive Head - Neighbourhoods, City Hall, St Peter's Street, Norwich NR2 1NH ☎ 01603 212373 🖑 bobcronk@norwich.gov.uk

Community Planning: Mr David Moorcroft, Executive Head - Regeneration & Development, City Hall, St. Peter's Street, Norwich NR2 1NH ☎ 01603 212225 🖑 davidmoorcroft@norwich.gov.uk

Community Safety: Mr Bob Cronk, Executive Head - Neighbourhoods, City Hall, St Peter's Street, Norwich NR2 1NH ☎ 01603 212373 🖑 bobcronk@norwich.gov.uk

Community Safety: Mr David Moorcroft, Executive Head - Regeneration & Development, City Hall, St. Peter's Street, Norwich NR2 1NH ☎ 01603 212225 🖑 davidmoorcroft@norwich.gov.uk

Computer Management: Mr Anthony Bull, Executive Head - Business Relationship Management & Democracy, City Hall, St. Peter's Street, Norwich NR2 1NH ☎ 01603 212326 🖑 anthonybull@norwich.gov.uk

Contracts: Mr Anthony Bull, Executive Head - Business Relationship Management & Democracy, City Hall, St. Peter's Street, Norwich NR2 1NH ☎ 01603 212326 🖑 anthonybull@norwich.gov.uk

Corporate Services: Mr Russell O'Keefe, Executive Head - Strategy, People & Neighbourhoods, Norwich City Council, City Hall, St Peter's Street, Norwich NR2 1NH ☎ 01603 212908 🖑 russello'keefe@norwich.gov.uk

Customer Service: Mrs Tina Pocklington, Head of Customer Services, City Hall, St. Peter's Street, Norwich NR2 1NH ☎ 01603 212759 🖑 tinapocklington@norwich.gov.uk

Economic Development: Ms Ellen Tilney, Economic Development Manager, City Hall, St. Peter's Street, Norwich NR2 1NH ☎ 01603 212225 🖑 ellentilney@norwich.gov.uk

E-Government: Mrs Anne Sibley, Systems Support Team Leader, City Hall, St. Peter's Street, Norwich NR2 1NH ☎ 0344 980 3333

Electoral Registration: Mr Stuart Guthrie, Electoral Services Manager, City Hall, St. Peter's Street, Norwich NR2 1NH ☎ 01603 212055 🖑 stuartguthrie@norwich.gov.uk

Emergency Planning: Ms Teresa Cannon, Emergency Planning Manager, City Hall, St. Peter's Street, Norwich NR2 1NH ☎ 01603 212474 🖑 teresacanon@norwich.gov.uk

Environmental / Technical Services: Mr Adrian Akester, Head of Citywide Services, City Hall, St. Peter's Street, Norwich NR2 1NH ☎ 01603 213521 🖑 adrianakester@norwich.gov.uk

Environmental Health: Mr Michael Stephenson, Public Protection Manager, City Hall, St. Peter's Street, Norwich NR2 1NH ☎ 01603 212283 🖑 michaelstephenson@norwich.gov.uk

Estates, Property & Valuation: Mr Andy Watt, Head of City Development Services, City Hall, St. Peter's Street, Norwich NR2 1NH ☎ 01603 212691 🖑 andywatt@norwich.gov.uk

Events Manager: Ms Helen Selleck, Culture & Events Manager, City Hall, St. Peter's Street, Norwich NR2 1NH ☎ 01603 212317 🖑 helenselleck@norwich.gov.uk

Facilities: Mr Eamonn Pellican, Facilities Manager - NPS Norwich, City Hall, St. Peter's Street, Norwich NR2 1NH ☎ 0344 980 3333 🖑 eamonn.pellican@nps.co.uk

Finance: Ms Justine Hartley, Chief Finance Officer (S151 Officer), City Hall, St. Peter's Street, Norwich NR2 1NH ☎ 01603 212440 🖑 justinehartley@norwich.gov.uk

Grounds Maintenance: Mr Adrian Akester, Head of Citywide Services, City Hall, St. Peter's Street, Norwich NR2 1NH ☎ 01603 213521 🖑 adrianakester@norwich.gov.uk

Health and Safety: Mr Adrian Akester, Head of Citywide Services, City Hall, St. Peter's Street, Norwich NR2 1NH ☎ 01603 213521 🖑 adrianakester@norwich.gov.uk

Highways: Mr Andy Watt, Head of City Development Services, City Hall, St. Peter's Street, Norwich NR2 1NH ☎ 01603 212691 🖑 andywatt@norwich.gov.uk

Home Energy Conservation: Mr Richard Wilson, Environmental Strategy Manager, City Hall, St. Peter's Street, Norwich NR2 1NH ☎ 01603 212312 ⌁ richardwilson@norwich.gov.uk

Housing: Mr Lee Robson, Head of Neighbourhood & Strategic Housing, City Hall, St. Peter's Street, Norwich NR2 1NH ☎ 01603 212939 ⌁ leerobson@norwich.gov.uk

Leisure and Cultural Services: Ms Nikki Rotsos, Executive Head of Customers, Communications & Culture, City Hall, St. Peter's Street, Norwich NR2 1NH ☎ 01603 212211; 01603 212010 ⌁ nikkirotsos@norwich.gov.uk

Licensing: Mr Adrian Akester, Head of Citywide Services, City Hall, St. Peter's Street, Norwich NR2 1NH ☎ 01603 213521 ⌁ adrianakester@norwich.gov.uk

Lottery Funding, Charity and Voluntary: Mr Bob Cronk, Executive Head - Neighbourhoods, City Hall, St Peter's Street, Norwich NR2 1NH ☎ 01603 212373 ⌁ bobcronk@norwich.gov.uk

Member Services: Mr Andy Emms, Democratic Services Manager, City Hall, St. Peter's Street, Norwich NR2 1NH ☎ 01603 212459 ⌁ andyemms@norwich.gov.uk

Parking: Mr Andy Watt, Head of City Development Services, City Hall, St. Peter's Street, Norwich NR2 1NH ☎ 01603 212691 ⌁ andywatt@norwich.gov.uk

Personnel / HR: Mrs Dawn Bradshaw, Head of HR & Learning, City Hall, Norwich, NR2 1NH, Norwich NR2 1NH ☎ 01603 212434 ⌁ dawnbradshaw@norwich.gov.uk

Planning: Mr Graham Nelson, Head of Planning, City Hall, St. Peter's Street, Norwich NR2 1NH ☎ 01603 212530 ⌁ grahamnelson@norwich.gov.uk

Procurement: Mr Anthony Bull, Executive Head - Business Relationship Management & Democracy, City Hall, St. Peter's Street, Norwich NR2 1NH ☎ 01603 212326 ⌁ anthonybull@norwich.gov.uk

Recycling & Waste Minimisation: Mr Adrian Akester, Head of Citywide Services, City Hall, St. Peter's Street, Norwich NR2 1NH ☎ 01603 213521 ⌁ adrianakester@norwich.gov.uk

Regeneration: Mr Andy Watt, Head of City Development Services, City Hall, St. Peter's Street, Norwich NR2 1NH ☎ 01603 212691 ⌁ andywatt@norwich.gov.uk

Road Safety: Mr Andy Watt, Head of City Development Services, City Hall, St. Peter's Street, Norwich NR2 1NH ☎ 01603 212691 ⌁ andywatt@norwich.gov.uk

Street Scene: Mr Adrian Akester, Head of Citywide Services, City Hall, St. Peter's Street, Norwich NR2 1NH ☎ 01603 213521 ⌁ adrianakester@norwich.gov.uk

Street Scene: Mr Andy Watt, Head of City Development Services, City Hall, St. Peter's Street, Norwich NR2 1NH ☎ 01603 212691 ⌁ andywatt@norwich.gov.uk

Sustainable Communities: Mr David Moorcroft, Executive Head - Regeneration & Development, City Hall, St. Peter's Street, Norwich NR2 1NH ☎ 01603 212225 ⌁ davidmoorcroft@norwich.gov.uk

Tourism: Ms Michelle Hurren, Tourist Development Manager, City Hall, St. Peter's Street, Norwich NR2 1NH ☎ 01603 212211; 01603 212010 ⌁ michellehurren@norwich.gov.uk

Traffic Management: Mr Andy Watt, Head of City Development Services, City Hall, St. Peter's Street, Norwich NR2 1NH ☎ 01603 212396 ⌁ andywatt@norwich.gov.uk

Transport: Mr David Moorcroft, Executive Head - Regeneration & Development, City Hall, St. Peter's Street, Norwich NR2 1NH ☎ 01603 212225 ⌁ davidmoorcroft@norwich.gov.uk

Transport: Mr Andy Watt, Head of City Development Services, City Hall, St. Peter's Street, Norwich NR2 1NH ☎ 01603 212396 ⌁ andywatt@norwich.gov.uk

Transport Planner: Mr David Moorcroft, Executive Head - Regeneration & Development, City Hall, St. Peter's Street, Norwich NR2 1NH ☎ 01603 212225 ⌁ davidmoorcroft@norwich.gov.uk

Transport Planner: Mr Andy Watt, City Development Services, City Hall, St. Peter's Street, Norwich NR2 1NH ☎ 01603 212396 ⌁ andywatt@norwich.gov.uk

Waste Collection and Disposal: Mr Adrian Akester, Head of Citywide Services, City Hall, St. Peter's Street, Norwich NR2 1NH ☎ 01603 213521 ⌁ adrianakester@norwich.gov.uk

Waste Management: Mr Adrian Akester, Head of Citywide Services, City Hall, St. Peter's Street, Norwich NR2 1NH ☎ 01603 213521 ⌁ adrianakester@norwich.gov.uk

Children's Play Areas: Mr Simon Meek, Parks & Open Spaces Manager, City Hall, St. Peter's Street, Norwich NR2 1NH ☎ 01603 212403 ⌁ simonmeek@norwich.gov.uk

COUNCILLORS

The Lord Mayor: Maxwell, Marion (LAB - Crome)
m.maxwell@cllr.norwich.gov.uk

Leader of the Council: Waters, Alan (LAB - Crome)
a.waters@cllr.norwich.gov.uk

Deputy Leader of the Council: Harris, Gail (LAB - Catton Grove)
g.harris@cllr.norwich.gov.uk

Ackroyd, Carolyne (LD - Eaton)
c.ackroyd@cllr.norwich.gov.uk

Bogelein, Sandra (GRN - Wensum)
s.bogelein@cllr.norwich.gov.uk

Bradford, David (LAB - Crome)
d.bradford@cllr.norwich.gov.uk

Bremner, Bert (LAB - University)
b.bremner@cllr.norwich.gov.uk

Brociek-Coulton, Julie (LAB - Sewell)
j.brociekcoulton@cllr.norwich.gov.uk

Button, Sally (LAB - Bowthorpe)
s.button@cllr.norwich.gov.uk

NORWICH CITY

Carlo, Denise (GRN - Nelson)
d.carlo@cllr.norwich.gov.uk

Coleshill, Ed (LAB - Sewell)
e.coleshill@cllr.norwich.gov.uk

Davis, Karen (LAB - Town Close)
k.davis@cllr.norwich.gov.uk

Driver, Keith (LAB - Lakenham)
k.driver@cllr.norwich.gov.uk

Fullman, David (LAB - Mancroft)
d.fullman@cllr.norwich.gov.uk

Grahame, Lesley (GRN - Thorpe Hamlet)
l.grahame@cllr.norwich.gov.uk

Haynes, Ash (GRN - Town Close)
a.haynes@cllr.norwich.gov.uk

Henderson, Jo (GRN - Thorpe Hamlet)
j.henderson@cllr.norwich.gov.uk

Herries, Chris (LAB - Lakenham)
c.herries@cllr.norwich.gov.uk

Jackson, Simeon (GRN - Mancroft)
s.jackson@cllr.norwich.gov.uk

Jones, Beth (LAB - University)
b.jones@cllr.norwich.gov.uk

Jones, Tim (GRN - Nelson)
t.jones@cllr.norwich.gov.uk

Kendrick, Paul (LAB - Catton Grove)
p.kendrick@cllr.norwich.gov.uk

Lubbock, Judith (LD - Eaton)
j.lubbock@cllr.norwich.gov.uk

Maguire, Kevin (LAB - Wensum)
k.maguire@cllr.norwich.gov.uk

Malik, Hugo (LAB - Nelson)
h.malik@cllr.norwich.gov.uk

Manning, Patrick (LAB - Lakenham)
p.manning@cllr.norwich.gov.uk

Packer, Matthew (LAB - Sewell)
m.packer@cllr.norwich.gov.uk

Peek, Martin (LAB - Wensum)
m.peek@cllr.norwich.gov.uk

Price, Ben (GRN - Thorpe Hamlet)
b.price@cllr.norwich.gov.uk

Raby, David (GRN - Town Close)
d.raby@cllr.norwich.gov.uk

Ryan, Roger (LAB - University)
r.ryan@cllr.norwich.gov.uk

Sands, Mike (LAB - Bowthorpe)
m.sands@cllr.norwich.gov.uk

Sands, Susan (LAB - Bowthorpe)
s.sands@cllr.norwich.gov.uk

Schmierer, Martin (GRN - Mancroft)
m.schmierer@cllr.norwich.gov.uk

Stonard, Mike (LAB - Catton Grove)
m.stonard@cllr.norwich.gov.uk

Thomas, Vivien (LAB - Mile Cross)
vivien.thomas@cllr.norwich.gov.uk

Thomas, Vaughan (LAB - Mile Cross)
vaughan.thomas@cllr.norwich.gov.uk

Woollard, Charmain (LAB - Mile Cross)
c.woollard@cllr.norwich.gov.uk

Wright, James (LD - Eaton)
j.wright@cllr.norwich.gov.uk

POLITICAL COMPOSITION
LAB: 26, GRN: 10, LD: 3

COMMITTEE CHAIRS

Audit: Mr Ben Price

Licensing: Ms Sally Button

Planning: Ms Chris Herries

Nottingham City   U

Nottingham City Council, Loxley House, Station Street,
Nottingham NG2 3NG
☎ 0115 915 5555 🖷 0115 915 4636 🖳 www.nottinghamcity.gov.uk

FACTS AND FIGURES
Parliamentary Constituencies: Nottingham East, Nottingham
North, Nottingham South
EU Constituencies: East Midlands
Election Frequency: Elections are of whole council

PRINCIPAL OFFICERS

Chief Executive: Mr Ian Curryer, Chief Executive, Loxley House,
Station Street, Nottingham NG2 3NG ☎ 0115 876 3600
🖰 ian.curryer@nottinghamcity.gov.uk

Senior Management: Ms Alison Michalska, Loxley House,
Station Street, Nottingham NG2 3NG ☎ 0115 876 3332
🖰 alison.michalska@nottinghamcity.gov.uk

Senior Management: Mr David Bishop, Corporate Director -
Development, Loxley House, Station Street, Nottingham NG2 3NG
☎ 0115 876 3758 🖰 david.bishop@nottinghamcity.gov.uk

Senior Management: Mr Andy Vaughan, Corporate Director -
Commerical & Operational Services, Loxley House, Station Street,
Nottingham NG2 3NG ☎ 0115 876 5627
🖰 andy.vaughan@nottinghamcity.gov.uk

Senior Management: Ms Candida Brudenell, Corporate Director
- Resilience, Loxley House, Station Street, Nottingham NG2 3NG
☎ 0115 876 3609 🖰 candida.brudenell@nottinghamcity.gov.uk

Building Control: Mr Robert De Rosa, Head - Building Control,
Loxley House, Station Street, Nottingham NG2 3NG
☎ 0115 876 4026 🖰 robert.derosa@nottinghamcity.gov.uk

Catering Services: Ms Liz Dobson, Head - Catering & Cleaning
Services, Medway Building, Eastcroft Depot, London Road,
Nottingham NG2 3AH ☎ 0115 915 5555
🖰 liz.dobson@nottinghamcity.gov.uk

Children / Youth Services: Mrs Candida Brudenell, Strategic Director - Early Intervention, Loxley House, Station Street, Nottingham NG2 3NG ☎ 0115 876 3609
⌂ candida.brudenell@nottinghamcity.gov.uk

Civil Registration: Ms Lucy Lee, Head - Civic Coronial & Celebratory Services, The Council House, Old Market Square, Nottingham NG1 2DT ☎ 0115 876 5480
⌂ lucy.lee@nottinghamcity.gov.uk

Community Safety: Ms Emma Orrock, Business Development Manager, Central Police Station, North Church Street, Nottingham NG1 4BH ☎ 0115 915 5555 ⌂ emma.orrock@nottinghamcity.gov.uk

Computer Management: Mr Ivor Nicholson, Service Director - IT, Loxley House, Station Street, Nottingham NG2 3NG
☎ 0115 915 5555 ⌂ ivor.nicholson@nottinghamcity.gov.uk

Consumer Protection and Trading Standards: Mr Richard Antcliff, Chief Licensing, Trading Standards & ASB Officer, Loxley House, Station Street, Nottingham NG2 3NG ☎ 0115 967 0999
⌂ richard.antcliff@nottinghamshire.pnn.police.uk

Customer Service: Ms Lynne North, Business Engagement Officer, Loxley House, Station Street, Nottingham NG2 3NG
☎ 0115 876 4950 ⌂ lynne.north@nottinghamcity.gov.uk

Economic Development: Mr Matt Lockley, Programme Director - Economic Development & Devolution, Loxley House, Station Street, Nottingham NG2 3NG ☎ 0115 915 5555
⌂ matt.lockley@nottinghamcity.gov.uk

Education: Mr Colin Pettigrew, Corporate Director - Children, Families & Cultural Services, Loxley House, Station Street, Nottingham NG2 3NG ☎ 0115 915 5555
⌂ colin.pettigrew@nottinghamcity.gov.uk

Electoral Registration: Ms Sarah Wilson, Electoral Services Manager, Loxley House, Station Street, Nottingham NG2 3NG
☎ 0115 876 4308 ⌂ sarah.wilson@nottinghamcity.gov.uk

Emergency Planning: Mr Paul Millward, Head - Resilience, Island Block, The Guildhall, Nottingham NG1 4BT ☎ 0115 876 2980
⌂ paul.millward@nottinghamcity.gov.uk

Energy Management: Ms Gail Scholes, Director - Energy Services, Loxley House, Station Street, Nottingham NG2 3NG
☎ 0115 876 5652 ⌂ gail.scholes@nottinghamcity.gov.uk

Environmental Health: Mr Andy Vaughan, Corporate Director - Commerical & Operational Services, Loxley House, Station Street, Nottingham NG2 3NG ☎ 0115 876 5627
⌂ andy.vaughan@nottinghamcity.gov.uk

European Liaison: Mr John Connelly, Digital Manager, Loxley House, Station Street, Nottingham NG2 3NG ☎ 0115 876 4490
⌂ john.connelly@nottinghamcity.gov.uk

Events Manager: Ms Kate Collins, Conference & Events Manager, Royal Centre, Theatre Square, Nottingham NG1 5ND
☎ 0115 989 5530 ⌂ kate.collins@nottinghamcity.gov.uk

Facilities: Mr Gary Shaw, Workplace Partner, Loxley House, Station Street, Nottingham NG2 3NG ☎ 0115 876 3098
⌂ gary.shaw@nottinghamcity.gov.uk

Fleet Management: Mr Tony Hall, Fleet Operations Manager, Humber Building, Eastcroft Depot, London Road, Nottingham NG2 3AH ☎ 0115 915 5555 ⌂ tony.hall@nottinghamcity.gov.uk

Highways: Mr Chris Keane, Head - Highways & Energy Infrastructure, Humber Building, Eastcroft Depot, London Road, Nottingham NG2 3AH ☎ 0115 876 1363
⌂ chris.keane@nottinghamcity.gov.uk

Housing: Ms Gill Moy, Director - Housing, Loxley House, Station Street, Nottingham NG2 3NG ☎ 0115 915 5555
⌂ gill.moy@nottinghamcityhomes.org.uk

Legal: Mr Glen O'Connell, Corporate Director - Resilience, Loxley House, Station Street, Nottingham NG2 3NG ☎ 0115 876 4330
⌂ glen.oconnell@nottinghamcity.gov.uk

Leisure and Cultural Services: Mr Nigel Hawkins, Head - Culture & Libraries, Loxley House, Station Street, Nottingham NG2 3NG ☎ 0115 876 4969 ⌂ nigel.hawkins@nottinghamcity.gov.uk

Licensing: Ms Angela Rawson, Manager - Licensing, Tamar Building, Eastcroft Depot, London Road, Nottingham NG2 3AH ☎ 0115 876 1749 ⌂ angela.rawson@nottinghamcity.gov.uk

Member Services: Ms Debra La Mola, Head - Democratic Services, Loxley House, Station Street, Nottingham NG2 3NG
☎ 0115 915 5555 ⌂ debra.lamola@nottinghamcity.gov.uk

Parking: Mr Pete Mitchell, Head - Licensing, Permits & Regulations, Central Police Station, North Church Street, Nottingham NG1 4BH ☎ 0115 915 5555
⌂ pete.mitchell@nottinghamshire.pnn.police.uk

Planning: Mr Jas Hundal, Service Director - Environment, Transport & Property, Loxley House, Station Street, Nottingham NG2 3NG ☎ 0115 915 5555 ⌂ jas.hundal@nottinghamcity.gov.uk

Procurement: Ms Jo Pettifor, Strategic Procurement Manager, Loxley House, Station Street, Nottingham NG2 3NG
☎ 0115 876 5026 ⌂ jo.pettifor@nottinghamcity.gov.uk

Recycling & Waste Minimisation: Mr Daniel Ayrton, Commercial Operations Manager, Tyne Building, Eastcroft Depot, London Road, Nottingham NG2 3AH ☎ 0115 876 1830
⌂ daniel.ayrton@nottinghamcity.gov.uk

Regeneration: Ms Gill Callingham, Regeneration Specialist, Loxley House, Station Street, Nottingham NG2 3NG
☎ 0115 876 3469 ⌂ gill.callingham@nottinghamcity.gov.uk

Road Safety: Mr Francis Ashton, Broadhurst Project Manager, Loxley House, Station Street, Nottingham NG2 3NG
☎ 0115 876 5224 ⌂ francis.ashton@nottinghamcity.gov.uk

NOTTINGHAM CITY

Social Services: Mr David Pearson, Deputy Chief Executive & Corporate Director - Adult Social Care, Health & Public Protection, Loxley House, Station Street, Nottingham NG2 3NG
☎ 0115 915 5555 ✆ david.pearson@nottinghamcity.gov.uk

Social Services (Adult): Mr David Pearson, Deputy Chief Executive & Corporate Director - Adult Social Care, Health & Public Protection, Loxley House, Station Street, Nottingham NG2 3NG
☎ 0115 915 5555 ✆ david.pearson@nottinghamcity.gov.uk

Social Services (Children): Mr Steve Edwards, Service Director - Children's Social Care, Loxley House, Station Street, Nottingham NG2 3NG ☎ 0115 915 5555 ✆ steve.edwards@nottinghamcity.gov.uk

Public Health: Ms Barbara Brady, Acting Director - Public Health, Loxley House, Station Street, Nottingham NG2 3NG
☎ 0115 915 5555 ✆ barbara.brady@nottinghamcity.gov.uk

Staff Training: Ms Denise Willis, Development Manager, Loxley House, Station Street, Nottingham NG2 3NG ☎ 0115 876 3463
✆ denise.willis@nottinghamcity.gov.uk

Street Scene: Mr Dave Halstead, Director - Neighbourhood Services, Loxley House, Station Street, Nottingham NG2 3NG
☎ 0115 876 5634 ✆ dave.halstead@nottinghamcity.gov.uk

Tourism: Mr Simon Redgate, Tourism Centre Manager, Nottingham Tourist Centre, 1-4 Smithy Row, Nottingham NG1 2BY
☎ 0115 876 2969 ✆ simon.redgate@nottinghamcity.gov.uk

Traffic Management: Ms Caroline Nash, Service Manager - Traffic & Safety, Loxley House, Station Street, Nottingham NG2 3NG ☎ 0115 876 5243 ✆ caroline.nash@nottinghamcity.gov.uk

Transport: Mr Adrian Hill, Head - Commercial Development, Loxley House, Station Street, Nottingham NG2 3NG
☎ 0115 876 5632 ✆ adrian.hill@nottinghamcity.gov.uk

Transport Planner: Ms Kerry Perruzza, Senior Transport Planner, Loxley House, Station Street, Nottingham NG2 3NG
☎ 0115 876 3947 ✆ kerry.perruzza@nottinghamcity.gov.uk

Transport Planner: Mr Robert Smith, Senior Transport Planner, Loxley House, Station Street, Nottingham NG2 3NG
☎ 0115 876 3604 ✆ robert.smith@nottinghamcity.gov.uk

Waste Collection and Disposal: Mr Paul Marshall, Manager - Waste Operations, Tyne House, Eastcroft Depot, London Road, Nottingham NG2 3AH ☎ 0115 876 1834
✆ paul.marshall@nottinghamcity.gov.uk

Waste Management: Mr Paul Marshall, Manager - Waste Operations, Tyne House, Eastcroft Depot, London Road, Nottingham NG2 3AH ☎ 0115 876 1834
✆ paul.marshall@nottinghamcity.gov.uk

COUNCILLORS

The Lord Mayor: Saghir, Mohammed (LAB - Leen Valley)
cllrmohammed.saghir@nottinghamcity.gov.uk

Sheriff: Morris, Jackie (LAB - Bulwell)
jackie.morris@nottinghamcity.gov.uk

Leader of the Council: Collins, Jon (LAB - St Ann's)
jon.collins@nottinghamcity.gov.uk

Deputy Leader of the Council: Chapman, Graham (LAB - Aspley)
graham.chapman@nottinghamcity.gov.uk

Ali, Liaqat (LAB - Radford & Park)
liaqat.ali@nottinghamcity.gov.uk

Armstrong, Jim (CON - Wollaton West)
jim.armstrong@nottinghamcity.gov.uk

Arnold, Cat (LAB - Basford)
cat.arnold@nottinghamcity.gov.uk

Ayoola, Leslie (LAB - Mapperley)
leslie.ayoola@nottinghamcity.gov.uk

Aziz, Ilyas (LAB - Radford & Park)
ilyas.aziz@nottinghamcity.gov.uk

Ball, Alex (LAB - Sherwood)
alex.ball@nottinghamcity.gov.uk

Battlemuch, Steve (LAB - Wollaton West)
steve.battlemuch@nottinghamcity.gov.uk

Bryan, Merlita (LAB - Arboretum)
merlita.bryan@nottinghamcity.gov.uk

Campbell, Eunice (LAB - Bulwell Forest)
eunice.campbell@nottinghamcity.gov.uk

Choudhry, Azad (LAB - Arboretum)
azad.choudhry@nottinghamcity.gov.uk

Clark, Alan (LAB - Bulwell Forest)
alan.clark@nottinghamcity.gov.uk

Cook, Josh (LAB - Clifton North)
josh.cook@nottinghamcity.gov.uk

Culley, Georgina (CON - Wollaton West)
georgina.culley@nottinghamcity.gov.uk

Edwards, Michael (LAB - Bridge)
michael.edwards@nottinghamcity.gov.uk

Ferguson, Pat (LAB - Clifton North)
pat.ferguson@nottinghamcity.gov.uk

Gibson, Chris (LAB - Clifton South)
chris.gibson@nottinghamcity.gov.uk

Grocock, Brian (LAB - Bestwood)
brian.grocock@nottinghamcity.gov.uk

Hartshorne, John (LAB - Bulwell)
john.hartshorne@nottinghamcity.gov.uk

Healy, Rosemary (LAB - Mapperley)
rosemary.healy@nottinghamcity.gov.uk

Heaton, Nicola (LAB - Bridge)
nicola.heaton@nottinghamcity.gov.uk

Ibrahim, Mohammed (LAB - Berridge)
mohammed.ibrahim@nottinghamcity.gov.uk

Ifediora, Patience (LAB - Aspley)
patience.ifediora@nottinghamcity.gov.uk

Jenkins, Corall (LAB - Clifton South)
corall.jenkins@nottinghamcity.gov.uk

Jenkins, Glyn (LAB - Leen Valley)
glyn.jenkins@nottinghamcity.gov.uk

Johnson, Sue (LAB - St Ann's)
sue.johnson@nottinghamcity.gov.uk

Jones, Carole-Ann (LAB - Berridge)
carole-ann.jones@nottinghamcity.gov.uk

Khan, Neghat Nawaz (LAB - Dales)
neghat.khan@nottinghamcity.gov.uk

Khan, Gul (LAB - Dales)
gul.khan@nottinghamcity.gov.uk

Klein, Ginny (LAB - Bulwell)
ginny.klein@nottinghamcity.gov.uk

Liversidge, David (LAB - St Ann's)
dave.liversidge@nottinghamcity.gov.uk

Longford, Sally (LAB - Wollaton East & Lenton Abbey)
sally.longford@nottinghamcity.gov.uk

McCulloch, Carole (LAB - Aspley)
carole.mcculloch@nottinghamcity.gov.uk

McDonald, Nick (LAB - Bulwell Forest)
nick.mcdonald@nottinghamcity.gov.uk

Mellen, David (LAB - Dales)
david.mellen@nottinghamcity.gov.uk

Neal, Toby (LAB - Berridge)
toby.neal@nottinghamcity.gov.uk

Norris, Alex (LAB - Basford)
alex.norris@nottinghamcity.gov.uk

Parbutt, Brian (LAB - Sherwood)
brian.parbutt@nottinghamcity.gov.uk

Peach, Anne (LAB - Radford & Park)
anne.peach@nottinghamcity.gov.uk

Piper, Sarah (LAB - Dunkirk & Lenton)
sarah.piper@nottinghamcity.gov.uk

Rule, Andrew (CON - Clifton North)
andrew.rule@nottinghamcity.gov.uk

Smith, Wendy (LAB - Bilborough)
wendy.smith@nottinghamcity.gov.uk

Smith, David (LAB - Bestwood)
cllr-david smith@nottinghamcity.gov.uk

Tansley, Chris (LAB - Mapperley)
chris.tansley@nottinghamcity.gov.uk

Trimble, David (LAB - Dunkirk & Lenton)
dave.trimble@nottinghamcity.gov.uk

Urquhart, Jane (LAB - Sherwood)
jane.arquhart@nottinghamcity.gov.uk

Watson, Marcia (LAB - Bilborough)
marcia.watson@nottinghamcity.gov.uk

Webster, Sam (LAB - Wollaton East & Lenton Abbey)
sam.webster@nottinghamcity.gov.uk

Wildgust, Mick (LAB - Bestwood)
mick.wildgust@nottinghamcity.gov.uk

Wood, Malcolm (LAB - Bilborough)
malcolm.wood@nottinghamcity.gov.uk

Woodings, Linda (LAB - Basford)
linda.wooding@nottinghamcity.gov.uk

Young, Steve (LAB - Clifton South)
steve.young@nottinghamcity.gov.uk

POLITICAL COMPOSITION
LAB: 52, CON: 3

COMMITTEE CHAIRS

Audit: Ms Sarah Piper

Health & Wellbeing: Mr Alex Norris

Licensing: Mr Brian Grocock

Planning: Mr Chris Gibson

Nottinghamshire   C

Nottinghamshire County Council, County Hall, West Bridgford NG2 7QP
☎ 0300 500 8080 ⏚ enquiries@nottscc.gov.uk
🖥 www.nottinghamshire.gov.uk

FACTS AND FIGURES
EU Constituencies: East Midlands
Election Frequency: Elections are of whole council

PRINCIPAL OFFICERS

Chief Executive: Mr Anthony May, Chief Executive, County Hall, West Bridgford NG2 7QP ☎ 0115 977 3582 ⏚ anthony.may@nottscc.gov.uk

Deputy Chief Executive: Mr David Pearson, Corporate Director - Adult Social Care, Health & Public Protection, County Hall, West Bridgford NG2 7QP ☎ 0115 977 4636 ⏚ david.pearson@nottscc.gov.uk

Senior Management: Ms Jayne Francis-Ward, Corporate Director - Resources, County Hall, West Bridgford NG2 7QP ☎ 0115 977 3478 ⏚ jayne.francis-ward@nottscc.gov.uk

Senior Management: Mr Tim Gregory, Corporate Director - Environment & Resources, County Hall, West Bridgford NG2 7QP ☎ 0115 977 3404 ⏚ tim.gregory@nottscc.gov.uk

Senior Management: Mr Colin Pettigrew, Corporate Director - Children, Families & Cultural Services, County Hall, West Bridgford NG2 7QP colin.pettigrew@nottinghamshire.gov.uk

Access Officer / Social Services (Disability): Ms Caroline Baria, Service Director - Strategic Commissioning, Access & Safeguarding, County Hall, West Bridgford NG2 7QP ☎ 0115 977 4671 ⏚ caroline.baria@nottscc.gov.uk

Architect, Building / Property Services: Mr Tim Gregory, Corporate Director - Environment & Resources, County Hall, West Bridgford NG2 7QP ☎ 0115 977 3404 ⏚ tim.gregory@nottscc.gov.uk

Architect, Building / Property Services: Mr Jas Hundal, Service Director - Transport, Property & Environment, Trent Bridge House, Fox Road, West Bridgford NG2 6BJ ☎ 0115 977 4257 ⏚ jas.hundal@nottscc.gov.uk

Best Value: Mr Matthew Garrard, Performance, Intelligence & Policy Team Manager, County Hall, West Bridgford NG2 7QP ☎ 0115 977 2892 ⏚ matthew.garrard@nottscc.gov.uk

Catering Services: Mr Shane Grayson, Acting Group Manager - Catering & Facilities Management, County Hall, West Bridgford NG2 7QP ☎ 0115 977 4369 ⏚ shane.grayson@nottscc.gov.uk

NOTTINGHAMSHIRE

Catering Services: Mr Jas Hundal, Service Director - Transport, Property & Environment, Trent Bridge House, Fox Road, West Bridgford NG2 6BJ ☎ 0115 977 4257 ⌨ jas.hundal@nottscc.gov.uk

Children / Youth Services: Mr Steve Edwards, Service Director - Children's Social Care, County Hall, West Bridgford NG2 7QP ☎ 0115 977 4782; 0115 977 2420 ⌨ steve.edwards@nottscc.gov.uk

Children / Youth Services: Mr Colin Pettigrew, Corporate Director - Children, Families & Cultural Services, County Hall, West Bridgford NG2 7QP colin.pettigrew@nottinghamshire.gov.uk

Children / Youth Services: Mr Chris Warren, Group Manager - Adolescence & Early Help Locality Services, County Hall, West Bridgford NG2 7QP ☎ 0115 977 4430 ⌨ christopher.warren@nottscc.gov.uk

Civil Registration: Mr Rob Fisher, Group Manager - Emergency Management & Registration, County Hall, West Bridgford NG2 7QP ☎ 0115 977 3681 ⌨ rob.fisher@nottscc.gov.uk

Civil Registration: Mr Paul McKay, Service Director - Access & Public Protection, County Hall, West Bridgford NG2 7QP ☎ 0115 977 3909 ⌨ paul.mckay@nottscc.gov.uk

PR / Communications: Mr Martin Done, Service Director - Communications & Marketing, County Hall, West Bridgford NG2 7QP ☎ 0115 977 2026 ⌨ martin.done@nottscc.gov.uk

Community Planning: Ms Sally Gill, Group Manager - Planning, Voluntary & Community Services, County Hall, West Bridgford NG2 7QP ☎ 0115 993 2608 ⌨ sally.gill@nottscc.gov.uk

Computer Management: Mr Ivor Nicholson, Service Director - ICT, County Hall, West Bridgford NG2 7QP ☎ 0115 977 3300 ⌨ ivor.nicholson@nottscc.gov.uk

Consumer Protection and Trading Standards: Mr Paul McKay, Service Director - Access & Public Protection, County Hall, West Bridgford NG2 7QP ☎ 0115 977 3909 ⌨ paul.mckay@nottscc.gov.uk

Contracts: Ms Clare Winter, Group Manager - Procurement, County Hall, West Bridgford NG2 7QP ☎ 0115 977 2619 ⌨ clare.winter@nottscc.gov.uk

Corporate Services: Ms Jayne Francis-Ward, Corporate Director - Resources, County Hall, West Bridgford NG2 7QP ☎ 0115 977 3478 ⌨ jayne.francis-ward@nottscc.gov.uk

Corporate Services: Ms Celia Morris, Group Manager - Performance & Improvement, Trent Bridge House, Fox Road, West Bridgford NG2 6BJ ☎ 0115 977 2043 ⌨ celia.morris@nottscc.gov.uk

Customer Service: Ms Marie Rowney, Group Manager - Customer Services, Customer Service Centre, Mercury House, Little Oak Drive, Sherwood Business Park, Nottingham NG15 0DR ☎ 01623 434901 ⌨ marie.rowney@nottscc.gov.uk

Customer Service: Ms Marjorie Toward, Service Director - HR & Customer Services, County Hall, West Bridgford NG2 7QP ☎ 0115 977 4404 ⌨ marje.toward@nottscc.gov.uk

Economic Development: Mr Matthew Lockley, Team Manager - Economic Development & Devolution, County Hall, West Bridgford NG2 7QP ☎ 0115 977 2446 ⌨ matthew.lockley@nottscc.gov.uk

Education: Ms Marion Clay, Acting Service Director - Education, Standards & Inclusion, County Hall, West Bridgford NG2 7QP ☎ 0115 977 2073 ⌨ marion.clay@nottscc.gov.uk

Education: Mr Colin Pettigrew, Corporate Director - Children, Families & Cultural Services, County Hall, West Bridgford NG2 7QP colin.pettigrew@nottinghamshire.gov.uk

E-Government: Mr Ivor Nicholson, Service Director - ICT, County Hall, West Bridgford NG2 7QP ☎ 0115 977 3300 ⌨ ivor.nicholson@nottscc.gov.uk

Emergency Planning: Mr Rob Fisher, Group Manager - Emergency Management & Registration, County Hall, West Bridgford NG2 7QP ☎ 0115 977 3681 ⌨ rob.fisher@nottscc.gov.uk

Emergency Planning: Mr Paul McKay, Service Director - Access & Public Protection, County Hall, West Bridgford NG2 7QP ☎ 0115 977 3909 ⌨ paul.mckay@nottscc.gov.uk

Energy Management: Mr Mick Allen, Group Manager - Waste & Energy Management, Trent Bridge House, Fox Road, West Bridgford NG2 6BJ ☎ 0115 977 4684 ⌨ mick.allen@nottscc.gov.uk

Estates, Property & Valuation: Mr Jas Hundal, Service Director - Transport, Property & Environment, Trent Bridge House, Fox Road, West Bridgford NG2 6BJ ☎ 0115 977 4257 ⌨ jas.hundal@nottscc.gov.uk

Facilities: Mr Shane Grayson, Acting Group Manager - Catering & Facilities Management, County Hall, West Bridgford NG2 7QP ☎ 0115 977 4369 ⌨ shane.grayson@nottscc.gov.uk

Pensions: Mr Simon Cunnington, Senior Accountant, Pensions Office, Business Support Centre, County Hall, West Bridgford NG2 7QP ☎ 0115 977 2581 ⌨ simon.cunnington@nottsc.gov.uk

Pensions: Mr John Fairbanks, Pensions Manager, BSC, Oak House, Ruddington Fields Business Park, Ruddington, Nottingham NG11 6JW ☎ 0115 846 3347 ⌨ john.fairbanks@nottsc.gov.uk

Fleet Management: Mr Neil Hodgson, Acting Service Director - Highways, Trent Bridge House, Fox Road, West Bridgford NG2 6BJ ☎ 0115 977 2720 ⌨ neil.hodgson@nottscc.gov.uk

Grounds Maintenance: Mr Neil Hodgson, Acting Service Director - Highways, Trent Bridge House, Fox Road, West Bridgford NG2 6BJ ☎ 0115 977 2720 ⌨ neil.hodgson@nottscc.gov.uk

Health and Safety: Mr John Nilan, Team Manager - Health & Safety, Lawn View House, Station Road, Sutton-in-Ashfield NG17 5GA ☎ 01623 434560 ⌨ john.nilan@nottscc.gov.uk

Highways: Mr Neil Hodgson, Acting Service Director - Highways, Trent Bridge House, Fox Road, West Bridgford NG2 6BJ ☎ 0115 977 2720 ⌨ neil.hodgson@nottscc.gov.uk

Legal: Ms Heather Dickinson, Group Manager - Legal Services, County Hall, West Bridgford NG2 7QP ☎ 0115 977 4835 ✆ heather.dickinson@nottscc.gov.uk

Legal: Ms Jayne Francis-Ward, Corporate Director - Resources, County Hall, West Bridgford NG2 7QP ☎ 0115 977 3478 ✆ jayne.francis-ward@nottscc.gov.uk

Leisure and Cultural Services: Mr Colin Pettigrew, Corporate Director - Children, Families & Cultural Services, County Hall, West Bridgford NG2 7QP colin.pettigrew@nottinghamshire.gov.uk

Lighting: Mr Neil Hodgson, Acting Service Director - Highways, Trent Bridge House, Fox Road, West Bridgford NG2 6BJ ☎ 0115 977 2720 ✆ neil.hodgson@nottscc.gov.uk

Lighting: Mr Gary Wood, Group Manager - Transport Policy & Programmes, Trent Bridge House, Fox Road, West Bridgford NG2 6BJ ☎ 0115 977 4270 ✆ gary.wood@nottscc.gov.uk

Member Services: Mr Keith Ford, Team Manager - Democratic Services, County Hall, West Bridgford NG2 7QP ☎ 0115 977 2590 ✆ keith.ford@nottscc.gov.uk

Parking: Mr Peter Goode, Traffic Manager, County Hall, West Bridgford NG2 7QP ☎ 0115 977 4269 ✆ peter.goode@nottscc.gov.uk

Personnel / HR: Ms Marjorie Toward, Service Director - HR & Customer Services, County Hall, West Bridgford NG2 7QP ☎ 0115 977 4404 ✆ marje.toward@nottscc.gov.uk

Planning: Ms Sally Gill, Group Manager - Planning, Voluntary & Community Services, County Hall, West Bridgford NG2 7QP ☎ 0115 993 2608 ✆ sally.gill@nottscc.gov.uk

Procurement: Ms Clare Winter, Group Manager - Procurement, County Hall, West Bridgford NG2 7QP ☎ 0115 977 2619 ✆ clare.winter@nottscc.gov.uk

Public Libraries: Mr Peter Gaw, Group Manager - Libraries, Archives, Information & Learning, County Hall, West Bridgford NG2 7QP ☎ 0115 977 4201 ✆ peter.gaw@nottscc.gov.uk

Recycling & Waste Minimisation: Mr Mick Allen, Group Manager - Waste & Energy Management, Trent Bridge House, Fox Road, West Bridgford NG2 6BJ ☎ 0115 977 4684 ✆ mick.allen@nottscc.gov.uk

Regeneration: Mr Matthew Lockley, Team Manager - Economic Development & Devolution, County Hall, West Bridgford NG2 7QP ☎ 0115 977 2446 ✆ matthew.lockley@nottscc.gov.uk

Road Safety: Ms Suzanne Heydon, Group Manager - Highway Safety, Trent Bridge House, Fox Road, West Bridgford NG2 6BJ ☎ 0115 977 4487 ✆ suzanne.heydon@nottscc.gov.uk

Social Services: Ms Ainsley Macdonnell, Service Director - North Nottinghamshire, County Hall, West Bridgford NG2 7QP ☎ 0115 977 3804 ✆ ainsley.macdonnell@nottscc.gov.uk

Social Services (Adult): Ms Sue Batty, Service Director - Mid Nottinghamshire, County Hall, West Bridgford NG2 7QP ☎ 0115 977 4876 ✆ sue.batty@nottscc.gov.uk

Social Services (Adult): Mr Paul McKay, Service Director - Access & Public Protection, County Hall, West Bridgford NG2 7QP ☎ 0115 977 3909 ✆ paul.mckay@nottscc.gov.uk

Social Services (Children): Mr Steve Edwards, Service Director - Children's Social Care, County Hall, West Bridgford NG2 7QP ☎ 0115 977 4782; 0115 977 2420 ✆ steve.edwards@nottscc.gov.uk

Social Services (Children): Ms Pam Rosseter, Group Manager - Safeguarding & Independent Review, County Hall, West Bridgford NG2 7QP ☎ 0115 977 3921 ✆ pam.rosseter@nottscc.gov.uk

Public Health: Ms Barbara Brady, Interim Director - Public Health, County Hall, West Bridgford NG2 7QP ☎ 0115 977 2851 ✆ barbara.brady@nottscc.gov.uk

Staff Training: Ms Marjorie Toward, Service Director - HR & Customer Services, County Hall, West Bridgford NG2 7QP ☎ 0115 977 4404 ✆ marje.toward@nottscc.gov.uk

Traffic Management: Mr Chris Charnley, Group Manager - Highways Management, County Hall, West Bridgford NG2 7QP ☎ 0115 977 2065 ✆ chris.charnley@nottscc.gov.uk

Traffic Management: Mr Peter Goode, Traffic Manager, County Hall, West Bridgford NG2 7QP ☎ 0115 977 4269 ✆ peter.goode@nottscc.gov.uk

Transport: Mr Neil Hodgson, Acting Service Director - Highways, Trent Bridge House, Fox Road, West Bridgford NG2 6BJ ☎ 0115 977 2720 ✆ neil.hodgson@nottscc.gov.uk

Transport Planner: Mr Chris Ward, Manager - Transport & Travel Services, Trent Bridge House, Fox Road, West Bridgford NG2 6BJ ☎ 0115 977 3520 ✆ chris.ward@nottscc.gov.uk

Waste Management: Mr Mick Allen, Group Manager - Waste & Energy Management, Trent Bridge House, Fox Road, West Bridgford NG2 6BJ ☎ 0115 977 4684 ✆ mick.allen@nottscc.gov.uk

COUNCILLORS

Chair: Woodhead, Yvonne (LAB - Blidworth)
cllr.yvonne.woodhead@nottscc.gov.uk

Leader of the Council: Rhodes, Alan (LAB - Worksop North East & Carlton)
cllr.alan.rhodes@nottscc.gov.uk

Deputy Leader of the Council: Bosnjak, Joyce (LAB - Mansfield North)
cllr.joyce.bosnjak@nottscc.gov.uk

Adair, Reg (CON - Ruddington)
cllr.reg.adair@nottscc.gov.uk

Allan, Pauline (LAB - Arnold North)
cllr.pauline.allan@nottscc.gov.uk

Allan, Roy (LAB - Arnold South)
cllr.roy.allan@nottscc.gov.uk

NOTTINGHAMSHIRE

Allin, John (LAB - Warsop)
cllr.john.allin@nottscc.gov.uk

Barnfather, Chris (CON - Newstead)
cllr.chris.barnfather@nottscc.gov.uk

Bell, Alan (LAB - Mansfield East)
cllr.alan.bell@nottscc.gov.uk

Brooks, Nikki (LAB - Carlton East)
cllr.nicki.brooks@nottscc.gov.uk

Brown, Andrew (CON - Soar Valley)
cllr.andrew1.brown@nottscc.gov.uk

Butler, Richard (CON - Cotgrave)
cllr.richard.butler@nottscc.gov.uk

Calvert, Steve (LAB - West Bridgford Central & South)
cllr.steve.calvert@nottscc.gov.uk

Campbell, Ian (IND - Retford West)
cllr.ian.campbell@nottscc.gov.uk

Carr, Steve (LD - Beeston North)
cllr.steve.carr@nottscc.gov.uk

Carroll, Steve (LAB - Sutton in Ashfield East)
cllr.steven.carroll@nottscc.gov.uk

Clarke, John (LAB - Carlton East)
cllr.john.clarke@nottscc.gov.uk

Cottee, John (CON - Keyworth)
cllr.john.cottee@nottscc.gov.uk

Creamer, Jim (LAB - Carlton West)
cllr.jim.creamer@nottscc.gov.uk

Cutts, Kay (CON - Radcliffe-on-Trent)
cllr.katherine.cutts@nottscc.gov.uk

Dobson, Maureen (IND - Collingham)
cllr.maureen.dobson@nottscc.gov.uk

Doddy, John (CON - Chilwell & Toton)
cllr.john.doddy@nottscc.gov.uk

Elliot, Boyd (CON - Calverton)
cllr.boyd.elliot@nottscc.gov.uk

Fielding, Sybil (LAB - Worksop North)
cllr.sybil.fielding@nottscc.gov.uk

Foale, Kate (LAB - Beeston South & Attenborough)
cllr.kate.foale@nottscc.gov.uk

Garner, Stephen (IND - Mansfield South)
cllr.stephen.garner@nottscc.gov.uk

Gilfoyle, Glynn (LAB - Worksop East)
cllr.glyn.gilfoyle@nottscc.gov.uk

Greaves, Kevin (LAB - Worksop West)
cllr.kevin.greaves@nottscc.gov.uk

Grice, Alice (LAB - Hucknall)
cllr.alice.grice@nottscc.gov.uk

Handley, John (CON - Beauvale)
cllr.john.handley@nottscc.gov.uk

Harwood, Colleen (LAB - Mansfield East)
cllr.collen.harwood@nottscc.gov.uk

Heptinstall, Stan (LD - Bramcote & Stapleford)
cllr.stan.heptinstall@nottscc.gov.uk

Hollis, Tom (LD - Sutton in Ashfield West)
tom@aldmail.co.uk

Jackson, Roger (CON - Farnsfield & Lowdham)
cllr.roger.jackson@nottscc.gov.uk

Jackson, Richard (CON - Chilwell & Toton)
cllr.richard.jackson@nottscc.gov.uk

Kirkham, David (LAB - Sutton in Ashfield Central)
cllr.david.kirkham@nottscc.gov.uk

Knight, John (LAB - Kirkby in Ashfield North)
cllr.john.knight@nottscc.gov.uk

Langton, Darren (LAB - Mansfield West)
cllr.darren.langton@nottscc.gov.uk

Laughton, Bruce (CON - Southwell & Caunton)
cllr.bruce.laughton@nottscc.gov.uk

Longdon, Keith (LD - Eastwood)
cllr.keith.longdon@nottscc.gov.uk

Madden, Rachel (LD - Kirkby in Ashfield South)
cllr.rachel.madden@nottscc.gov.uk

Martin, David (IND - Selston)
cllr.david.martin@nottscc.gov.uk

Meale, Diana (LAB - Mansfield West)
cllr.diana.meale@nottscc.gov.uk

Ogle, John (CON - Tuxford)
cllr.john.ogle@nottscc.gov.uk

Owen, Philip (CON - Nuthall)
cllr.philip.owen@nottscc.gov.uk

Payne, Michael (LAB - Arnold North)
cllr.michael.payne@nottscc.gov.uk

Peck, John (LAB - Rufford)
cllr.john.peck@nottscc.gov.uk

Place, Sheila (LAB - Blyth & Harworth)
cllr.sheila.place@nottscc.gov.uk

Plant, Liz (LAB - West Bridgford Central & South)
cllr.liz.plant@nottscc.gov.uk

Pringle, Mike (LAB - Ollerton)
cllr.mike.pringle@nottscc.gov.uk

Pulk, Darrell (LAB - Carlton West)
cllr.darrell.pulk@nottscc.gov.uk

Purdue-Horan, Francis (CON - Bingham)
cllr.francis.purdue-horan@nottscc.gov.uk

Rigby, Ken (LD - Kimberley & Trowell)
cllr.ken.rigby@nottscc.gov.uk

Roberts, Tony (CON - Newark West)
cllr.tony.roberts@nottscc.gov.uk

Saddington, Sue (CON - Farndon & Muskham)
cllr.susan.saddington@nottscc.gov.uk

Sissons, Andy (IND - Mansfield South)
cllr.andy.sissons@nottscc.gov.uk

Skelding, Pamela (LAB - Retford East)
cllr.pamela.skelding@nottscc.gov.uk

Tsimbiridis, Parry (LAB - Mansfield North)
cllr.parry.tsimbiridis@nottscc.gov.uk

Walker, Keith (CON - Balderton)
cllr.keith.walker@nottscc.gov.uk

Wallace, Stuart (CON - Newark East)
cllr.stuart.wallace@nottscc.gov.uk

Weisz, Muriel (LAB - Arnold South)
cllr.muriel.weisz@nottscc.gov.uk

Wheeler, Gordon (CON - West Bridgford West)
cllr.gordon.wheeler@nottscc.gov.uk

Wilkinson, John (LAB - Hucknall)
cllr.john.hucknall@nottscc.gov.uk

Williams, Jacky (LD - Bramcote & Stapleford)
cllr.jacky.williams@nottscc.gov.uk

Wilmott, John (LAB - Hucknall)
cllr.john.wilmott@nottscc.gov.uk

Yates, Liz (CON - Misterton)
cllr.liz.yates@nottscc.gov.uk

Zadrozny, Jason (LD - Sutton in Ashfield North)
cllr.jason.zadrozny@nottscc.gov.uk

POLITICAL COMPOSITION
LAB: 33, CON: 21, LD: 8, IND: 5

COMMITTEE CHAIRS

Adult Social Care & Health: Ms Muriel Weisz

Audit: Mr Keith Walker

Children & Young People: Mr John Peck

Economic Development: Mr Darren Langton

Health & Wellbeing: Ms Joyce Bosnjak

Pensions: Mr Reg Adair

Planning & Licensing: Mr John Wilkinson

Transport & Highways: Mr Kevin Greaves

Nuneaton & Bedworth   D

Nuneaton & Bedworth Borough Council, Town Hall, Nuneaton CV11 5AA
☎ 024 7637 6376 🖷 024 7637 6583
🖳 www.nuneatonandbedworth.gov.uk

FACTS AND FIGURES
Parliamentary Constituencies: Nuneaton
EU Constituencies: West Midlands
Election Frequency: Elections are biennial

PRINCIPAL OFFICERS

Chief Executive: Mr Alan Franks, Managing Director, Town Hall, Nuneaton CV11 5AA ☎ 024 7637 6438
🖑 alan.franks@nuneatonandbedworth.gov.uk

Senior Management: Mr Brent Davis, Director - Assets & Street Services, Council House, Nuneaton CV11 5AA ☎ 024 7637 6347; 024 7637 6465 🖑 brent.davis@nuneatonandbedworth.gov.uk

Senior Management: Mrs Dawn Dawson, Director - Housing & Communities, Town Hall, Nuneaton CV11 5AA ☎ 024 7637 6408
🖑 dawn.dawson@nuneatonandbedworth.gov.uk

Senior Management: Mrs Simone Hines, Director - Corporate Finance & Procurement, Town Hall, Nuneaton CV11 5AA
☎ 024 7637 6264 🖑 simone.hines@nuneatonandbedworth.gov.uk

Senior Management: Mr Ian Powell, Director - Regeneration & Public Protection, Town Hall, Nuneaton CV11 5AA ☎ 024 7637 6396; 0870 608 9492 🖑 ian.powell@nuneatonandbedworth.gov.uk

Senior Management: Mr Philip Richardson, Director - Governance & Recreation, Town Hall, Nuneaton CV11 5AA ☎ 024 7637 6233; 0870 608 9457
🖑 philip.richardson@nuneatonandbedworth.gov.uk

Senior Management: Ms Chris Tydeman, Director - Business Improvement, Town Hall, Nuneaton CV11 5AA

Architect, Building / Property Services: Mr Brent Davis, Director - Assets & Street Services, Council House, Nuneaton CV11 5AA ☎ 024 7637 6347; 024 7637 6465
🖑 brent.davis@nuneatonandbedworth.gov.uk

Building Control: Mr Kevin Bunsell, Head of Building Control, Town Hall, Nuneaton CV11 5AA ☎ 024 7637 6521
🖑 kevin.bunsell@nuneatonandbedworth.gov.uk

Corporate Services: Mrs Linda Downes, Head of Internal Audit, Town Hall, Nuneaton CV11 5AA ☎ 024 7637 6260
🖑 linda.downes@nuneatonandbedworth.gov.uk

Economic Development: Mr Les Snowdon, Head of Estates & Town Centres, Town Hall, Nuneaton CV11 5AA ☎ 024 7637 6376
🖑 les.snowdon@nuneatonandbedworth.gov.uk

Electoral Registration: Mrs Debbie Davies, Principal Democratic Services Offices, Town Hall, Nuneaton CV11 5AA ☎ 024 7637 6221
🖑 debbie.davies@nuneatonandbedworth.gov.uk

Environmental Health: Mr Ian Powell, Director - Regeneration & Public Protection, Town Hall, Nuneaton CV11 5AA ☎ 024 7637 6396; 0870 608 9492 🖑 ian.powell@nuneatonandbedworth.gov.uk

Estates, Property & Valuation: Mr Les Snowdon, Head of Estates & Town Centres, Town Hall, Nuneaton CV11 5AA ☎ 024 7637 6376 🖑 les.snowdon@nuneatonandbedworth.gov.uk

Treasury: Mr Craig Pugh, Treasury & Technical Manager, Council House, Nuneaton CV11 5AA ☎ 024 7637 6376
🖑 craig.pugh@nuneatonandbedworth.gov.uk

Health and Safety: Mr John Ashton, Health & Safety Manager, Town Hall, Nuneaton CV11 5AA ☎ 024 7637 6213
🖑 john.ashton@nuneatonandbedworth.gov.uk

Housing Maintenance: Mr Brent Davis, Director - Assets & Street Services, Council House, Nuneaton CV11 5AA ☎ 024 7637 6347; 024 7637 6465 🖑 brent.davis@nuneatonandbedworth.gov.uk

Legal: Mr Philip Richardson, Director - Governance & Recreation, Town Hall, Nuneaton CV11 5AA ☎ 024 7637 6233; 0870 608 9457
🖑 philip.richardson@nuneatonandbedworth.gov.uk

Licensing: Mr Ian Powell, Director - Regeneration & Public Protection, Town Hall, Nuneaton CV11 5AA ☎ 024 7637 6396; 0870 608 9492 🖑 ian.powell@nuneatonandbedworth.gov.uk

NUNEATON & BEDWORTH

Member Services: Mrs Shirley Round, Principal Democratic Services Officer, Town Hall, Nuneaton CV11 5AA ☎ 024 7637 6563 ⌨ shirley.round@nuneatonandbedworth.gov.uk

Recycling & Waste Minimisation: Ms Sue Cummine, Waste Reduction & Compliance Officer, St. Mary's Road Depot, Nuneaton CV11 5AR ☎ 024 7637 6025 ⌨ sue.cummine@nuneatonandbedworth.gov.uk

Waste Collection and Disposal: Mr Glen McGrandle, Head of Waste & Transport, St Mary's Road Depot, Nuneaton CV11 5AA ☎ 024 7637 6049 ⌨ glen.mcgrandle@nuneatonandbedworth.gov.uk

Waste Management: Mr Glen McGrandle, Head of Waste & Transport, St Mary's Road Depot, Nuneaton CV11 5AA ☎ 024 7637 6049 ⌨ glen.mcgrandle@nuneatonandbedworth.gov.uk

COUNCILLORS

Mayor: Sheppard, Jill (LAB - Abbey)
jill.sheppard@nuneatonandbedworth.gov.uk

Deputy Mayor: Hancox, William (LAB - Bede)
bill.hancox@nuneatonandbedworth.gov.uk

Leader of the Council: Harvey, Dennis (LAB - Camp Hill)
dennis.harvey@nuneatonandbedworth.gov.uk

Deputy Leader of the Council: Jackson, Julie (LAB - Wem Brook)
julie.jackson@nuneatonandbedworth.gov.uk

Aldington, Danny (LAB - Heath)
danny.aldington@nuneatonandbedworth.gov.uk

Beaumont, John (LAB - Bulkington)
john.beaumont@nuneatonandbedworth.gov.uk

Bennett, Christine (LAB - Galley Common)
christine.bennett@nuneatonbedworth.gov.uk

Bonner, Ian (GRN - Weddington)
ian.bonner@nuneatonbedworth.gov.uk

Brindley, Kathryn (CON - St Nicholas)
kathryn.brindley@nuneatonandbedworth.gov.uk

Copland, Robert (LAB - Poplar)
bob.copland@nuneatonandbedworth.gov.uk

Daffern, Georgina (LAB - Heath)
georgina.daffern@nuneatonandbedworth.gov.uk

Doherty, Terry (LAB - Bulkington)
terry.doherty@nuneatonandbedworth.gov.uk

Doughty, Sara (LAB - Exhall)
sara.doughty@nuneatonandbedworth.gov.uk

Elliott, Tricia (LAB - Bar Pool)
patricia.elliott@nuneatonandbedworth.gov.uk

Gissane, Daniel (CON - Galley Common)
daniel.gissane@nuneatonandbedworth.gov.uk

Glass, John (LAB - Poplar)
john.glass@nuneatonandbedworth.gov.uk

Golby, Clare (CON - Arbury)

Gran, Sebastian (CON - Slough)
sebastian.gran@nuneatonandbedworth.gov.uk

Gutteridge, Julian (CON - Whitestone)
julian.gutteridge@nuneatonandbedworth.gov.uk

Haynes, John (LAB - Bede)
john.haynes@nuneatonandbedworth.gov.uk

Kondakor, Keith (GRN - Weddington)
keith.kondakor@nuneatonandbedworth.gov.uk

Lloyd, Anthony (LAB - Slough)
anthony.lloyd@nuneatonandbedworth.gov.uk

Lloyd, Ian (LAB - Camp Hill)
ian.lloyd@nuneatonandbedworth.gov.uk

Longden, Barry (LAB - Kingswood)
barry.longden@nuneatonandbedworth.gov.uk

Margrave, Sam (LAB - Attleborough)
sam.margrave@nuneatonandbedworth.gov.uk

Phillips, Neil (LAB - Abbey)
neil.phillips@nuneatonandbedworth.gov.uk

Phillips, Caroline (LAB - Arbury)
caroline.phillips@nuneatonandbedworth.gov.uk

Pomfrett, Gwynne (LAB - Bar Pool)
gwynne.pomfrett@nuneatonandbedworth.gov.uk

Pomfrett, Margaret (LAB - Exhall)
margaret.pomfrett@nuneatonandbedworth.gov.uk

Sheppard, Tracy (LAB - Wem Brook)
tracy.sheppard@nuneatonandbedworth.gov.uk

Tandy, June (LAB - Attleborough)
june.tandy@nuneatonandbedworth.gov.uk

Tromans, Rob (CON - St Nicholas)
robert.tromans@nuneatonandbedworth.gov.uk

Watkins, Christopher (LAB - Kingswood)
christopher.watkins@nuneatonandbedworth.gov.uk

Wilson, Kristofer (CON - Whitestone)
kristofer.wilson@nuneatonandbedworth.gov.uk

POLITICAL COMPOSITION
LAB: 25, CON: 7, GRN: 2

COMMITTEE CHAIRS

Audit: Mr John Haynes

Licensing: Mr Robert Copland

Planning: Mr William Hancox

Oadby & Wigston — D

Oadby & Wigston Borough Council, Council Offices, Station Road, Wigston LE18 2DR
☎ 0116 288 8961 🖷 0116 288 7828 🖳 www.oadby-wigston.gov.uk

FACTS AND FIGURES
Parliamentary Constituencies: Harborough
EU Constituencies: East Midlands
Election Frequency: Elections are of whole council

PRINCIPAL OFFICERS

Chief Executive: Mr Mark Hall, Chief Executive, Council Offices, Station Road, Wigston LE18 2DR ☎ 0116 257 2600 ⌨ mark.hall@oadby-wigston.gov.uk

Senior Management: Mrs Anne Court, Director - Service Delivery, Council Offices, Station Road, Wigston LE18 2DR ☎ 0116 257 2602 📧 anne.court1@oadby-wigston.gov.uk

Community Planning: Mrs Anita Pathak-Mould, Head of Community, Council Offices, Station Road, Wigston LE18 2DR ☎ 0116 257 2674 📧 anita.pathak-mould@oadby-wigston.gov.uk

Community Safety: Mrs Anita Pathak-Mould, Head of Community, Council Offices, Station Road, Wigston LE18 2DR ☎ 0116 257 2674 📧 anita.pathak-mould@oadby-wigston.gov.uk

Computer Management: Mr Paul Langham, ICT Manager, Council Offices, Station Road, Wigston LE18 2DR ☎ 01455 255995 📧 paul.langham@oadby-wigston.gov.uk

Corporate Services: Mrs Kalv Garcha, Head of Corporate Resources, Council Offices, Station Road, Wigston LE18 2DR ☎ 0116 257 2626 📧 kalv.garcha@oadby-wigston.gov.uk

Economic Development: Adrian Thorpe, Planning Policy & Regeneration Manager, Council Offices, Station Road, Wigston LE18 2DR ☎ 0116 257 2645 📧 adrian.thorpe@oadby-wigston.gov.uk

Emergency Planning: Ms Avril Lennox, Leisure Development Officer, Brocks Hill Country Park, Oadby LE2 5JJ ☎ 0116 257 2735 📧 avril.lennox@oadby-wigston.gov.uk

Environmental Health: Mrs Anita Pathak-Mould, Head of Community, Council Offices, Station Road, Wigston LE18 2DR ☎ 0116 257 2674 📧 anita.pathak-mould@oadby-wigston.gov.uk

Fleet Management: Brian Kew, Depot Manager, The Depot, Wigston Road, Oadby LE2 5JE ☎ 0116 257 2830 📧 brian.kew@oadby-wigston.gov.uk

Grounds Maintenance: Brian Kew, Depot Manager, The Depot, Wigston Road, Oadby LE2 5JE ☎ 0116 257 2830 📧 brian.kew@oadby-wigston.gov.uk

Health and Safety: Mrs Kalv Garcha, Head of Corporate Resources, Council Offices, Station Road, Wigston LE18 2DR ☎ 0116 257 2626 📧 kalv.garcha@oadby-wigston.gov.uk

Housing: Mrs Anita Pathak-Mould, Head of Community, Council Offices, Station Road, Wigston LE18 2DR ☎ 0116 257 2674 📧 anita.pathak-mould@oadby-wigston.gov.uk

Housing Maintenance: Mrs Anita Pathak-Mould, Head of Community, Council Offices, Station Road, Wigston LE18 2DR ☎ 0116 257 2674 📧 anita.pathak-mould@oadby-wigston.gov.uk

Legal: Mrs Kalv Garcha, Head of Corporate Resources, Council Offices, Station Road, Wigston LE18 2DR ☎ 0116 257 2626 📧 kalv.garcha@oadby-wigston.gov.uk

Leisure and Cultural Services: Ms Avril Lennox, Leisure Development Officer, Brocks Hill Country Park, Washbrook Lane, Oadby LE2 5JJ ☎ 0116 257 2735 📧 avril.lennox@oadby-wigston.gov.uk

Licensing: Mrs Kalv Garcha, Head of Corporate Resources, Council Offices, Station Road, Wigston LE18 2DR ☎ 0116 257 2626 📧 kalv.garcha@oadby-wigston.gov.uk

Member Services: Mrs Anne Court, Director - Service Delivery, Council Offices, Station Road, Wigston LE18 2DR ☎ 0116 257 2602 📧 anne.court1@oadby-wigston.gov.uk

Parking: Ms Margaret Smith, Administration & Facilities Manager, The Depot, Wigston Road, Oadby LE2 5JE ☎ 0116 257 2832 📧 margaret.smith@oadby-wigston.gov.uk

Personnel / HR: Mrs Kalv Garcha, Head of Corporate Resources, Council Offices, Station Road, Wigston LE18 2DR ☎ 0116 257 2626 📧 kalv.garcha@oadby-wigston.gov.uk

Planning: Chris Forrett, Planning Control Manager, Council Offices, Station Road, Wigston LE18 2DR ☎ 0116 257 2710 📧 chris.forrett@oadby-wigston.gov.uk

Procurement: Mr Paul Loveday, Head of Finance, Council Offices, Station Road, Wigston LE18 2DR ☎ 0116 257 2750 📧 paul.loveday@oadby-wigston.gov.uk

Recycling & Waste Minimisation: Ms Karen Parkes, Recycling Co-ordinator, The Depot, Wigston Road, Oadby LE2 5JE ☎ 0116 257 2841 📧 karen.parkes@oadby-wigston.gov.uk

Regeneration: Adrian Thorpe, Planning Policy & Regeneration Manager, Council Offices, Station Road, Wigston LE18 2DR ☎ 0116 257 2645 📧 adrian.thorpe@oadby-wigston.gov.uk

Staff Training: Mrs Kalv Garcha, Head of Corporate Resources, Council Offices, Station Road, Wigston LE18 2DR ☎ 0116 257 2626 📧 kalv.garcha@oadby-wigston.gov.uk

Sustainable Communities: Mrs Anita Pathak-Mould, Head of Community, Council Offices, Station Road, Wigston LE18 2DR ☎ 0116 257 2674 📧 anita.pathak-mould@oadby-wigston.gov.uk

Town Centre: Adrian Thorpe, Planning Policy & Economic Development Manager, Council Offices, Station Road, Wigston LE18 2DR ☎ 0116 257 2645 📧 adrian.thorpe@oadby-wigston.gov.uk

Waste Collection and Disposal: Brian Kew, Depot Manager, The Depot, Wigston Road, Oadby LE2 5JE ☎ 0116 257 2830 📧 brian.kew@oadby-wigston.gov.uk

Waste Management: Brian Kew, Depot Manager, The Depot, Wigston Road, Oadby LE2 5JE ☎ 0116 257 2830 📧 brian.kew@oadby-wigston.gov.uk

Children's Play Areas: Ms Margaret Smith, Administration & Facilities Manager, The Depot, Wigston Road, Oadby LE2 5JE ☎ 0116 257 2832 📧 margaret.smith@oadby-wigston.gov.uk

COUNCILLORS

Mayor: Eaton, Robert (LD - Wigston Meadowcourt) robert.eaton@oadby-wigston.gov.uk

Deputy Mayor: Haq, Samia (LD - Oadby Uplands) samia.haq@oadby-wigston.gov.uk

OADBY & WIGSTON

Leader of the Council: Boyce, John (LD - South Wigston)
john.boyce@oadby-wigston.gov.uk

Deputy Leader of the Council: Charlesworth, Michael (LD - Wigston All Saints)
michael.charlesworth@oadby-wigston.gov.uk

Group Leader: Dave, Bhupendra (CON - Oadby Woodlands)
bhupendra.dave@oadby-wigston.gov.uk

Atwal, Gurpal (LAB - Oadby Uplands)
gurpal.atwal@oadby-wigston.gov.uk

Barr, Ted (CON - Wigston Meadowcourt)
ted.barr@oadby-wigston.gov.uk

Bentley, Lee (LD - Wigston All Saints)
lee.bentley@oadby-wigston.gov.uk

Bond, Anne (CON - Oadby St Peters)
anne.bond@oadby-wigston.gov.uk

Boulter, Bill (LD - Wigston Fields)
bill.boulter@oadby-wigston.gov.uk

Broadley, Linda (LD - Wigston St Wolstans)
linda.broadley@oadby-wigston.gov.uk

Broadley, Frank (LD - Wigston St Wolstans)
frank.broadley@oadby-wigston.gov.uk

Carter, David (LD - Oadby St Peters)
david.carter@oadby-wigston.gov.uk

Chalk, Kerree (LD - Wigston St Wolstans)
kerree.chalk@oadby-wigston.gov.uk

Chamberlain, Marie (LD - Wigston Meadowcourt)
marie.chamberlain@oadby-wigston.gov.uk

Darr, Latif (LD - Oadby Brocks Hill)
latif.darr@oadby-wigston.gov.uk

Eaton, Lynda (LD - Wigston All Saints)
lynda.eaton@oadby-wigston.gov.uk

Fahey, Bob (CON - Oadby Grange)
bob.fahey@oadby-wigston.gov.uk

Gamble, Dean (LD - Oadby Woodlands)
dean.gamble@oadby-wigston.gov.uk

Kaufman, Jeffrey (LD - Oadby Brocks Hill)
jeffrey.kaufman@oadby-wigston.gov.uk

Khong, Teck (CON - Oadby Grange)
teck.khong@oadby-wigston.gov.uk

Loydall, Helen (LD - Wigston Fields)
helen.loydall@oadby-wigston.gov.uk

Loydall, Kevin (LD - Wigston Fields)
kevin.loydall@oadby-wigston.gov.uk

Morris, Richard (LD - South Wigston)
richard.morris@oadby-wigston.gov.uk

Morris, Sharon (LD - South Wigston)
sharon.morris@oadby-wigston.gov.uk

Thakor, Ravendra (CON - Oadby Grange)
ravendra.thakor@oadby-wigston.gov.uk

POLITICAL COMPOSITION
LD: 19, CON: 6, LAB: 1

COMMITTEE CHAIRS

Children & Young People: Mr Richard Morris

Development Control: Mr Lee Bentley

Health & Wellbeing: Mr Jeffrey Kaufman

Licensing: Mrs Linda Broadley

Oldham   M

Oldham Metropolitan Borough Council, Civic Centre, West Street, Oldham OL1 1UG
☎ 0161 770 3000 🖷 0161 770 5185 🖳 www.oldham.gov.uk

FACTS AND FIGURES
Parliamentary Constituencies: Ashton under Lyne, Oldham East and Saddleworth, Oldham West and Royton
EU Constituencies: North West
Election Frequency: Elections are by thirds

PRINCIPAL OFFICERS

Chief Executive: Dr Carolyn Wilkins, Chief Executive, Civic Centre, West Street, Oldham OL1 1UG ☎ 0161 770 4190
🖑 carolyn.wilkins@oldham.gov.uk

Senior Management: Ms Maggie Kufeldt, Executive Director - Health & Wellbeing, Civic Centre, West Street, Oldham OL1 1UG
☎ 0161 770 4208 🖑 maggie.kufeldt@oldham.gov.uk

Senior Management: Ms Helen Lockwood, Executive Director - Economy, Skills & Neighbourhoods, Civic Centre, West Street, Oldham OL1 1UG ☎ 0161 770 1848
🖑 helen.lockwood@oldham.gov.uk

Building Control: Mr John Rooney, Interim Head of Planning & Infrastructure, Civic Centre, West Street, Oldham OL1 1UG
☎ 0161 770 4558 🖑 john.rooney@oldham.gov.uk

Catering Services: Ms Anne Burns, Catering Manager, Civic Centre, West Street, Oldham OL1 1UG ☎ 0161 770 4262
🖑 anne.burns@oldham.gov.uk

Children / Youth Services: Mr Neil Consterdine, Head of Integrated Youth, Civic Centre, West Street, Oldham OL1 1UG
☎ 0161 770 8734 🖑 neil.consterdine@oldham.gov.uk

Children / Youth Services: Ms Kim Scragg, Director - Safeguarding, Civic Centre, West Street, Oldham OL1 1UG
☎ 0161 770 4751 🖑 kim.scragg@oldham.gov.uk

Civil Registration: Ms Marina Brown, Registration Services Manager, Chadderton Town Hall, Oldham OL9 6PP
☎ 0161 770 8963 🖑 marina.brown@oldham.gov.uk

PR / Communications: Mr Carl Marsden, Head of Communications, Room 437, Civic Centre, West Street, Oldham OL1 1UG ☎ 0161 770 4323 🖑 carl.marsden@oldham.gov.uk

Community Safety: Ms Jill Beaumont, Director - Community Services, Civic Centre, West Street, Oldham OL1 1UG
☎ 0161 770 4778 🖑 jill.beaumont@oldham.gov.uk

Computer Management: Ms Helen Gerling, Interim Director - Commercial & Transformational Services, Civic Centre, West Street, Oldham OL1 1UG ☎ 0161 770 3468 🖑 helen.gerling@oldham.gov.uk

Consumer Protection and Trading Standards: Ms Carol Brown, Director - Environmental Services, Civic Centre, West Street, Oldham OL1 1UG ☎ 0161 770 4452 ⏱ carol.brown@oldham.gov.uk

Contracts: Mrs Nicola Wadley, Interim Head of Strategic Planning, Civic Centre, West Street, Oldham OL1 1UG ☎ 0161 770 8105 ⏱ nicola.wadley@oldham.gov.uk

Corporate Services: Ms Jackie Wilson, Head of Strategy, Partnerships & Policy, Civic Centre, West Street, Oldham OL1 1UG ☎ 0161 770 5755 ⏱ jackie.wilson@oldham.gov.uk

Customer Service: Mr Bola Odunsi, Interim Head of Revenues, Benefits & Business Support, PO Box 160, Civic Centre, West Street, Oldham OL1 1UG ☎ 0161 770 4905 ⏱ bola.odunsi@oldham.gov.uk

Economic Development: Mr Darren Jones, Director - Economic Development, Civic Centre, West Street, Oldham OL1 1UG ☎ 0161 770 1659 ⏱ darren.jones@oldham.gov.uk

Education: Ms Carrie Sutton, Director - Education & Early Years, Civic Centre, West Street, Oldham OL1 1UG ☎ 0161 770 1675 ⏱ carrie.sutton@oldham.gov.uk

Electoral Registration: Ms Julie Bruce, Head of Elections & Land Charges, Civic Centre, West Street, Oldham OL1 1UG ☎ 0161 770 4712 ⏱ julie.bruce@oldham.gov.uk

Energy Management: Mr Barney Harle, Capital Works & Energy Manager, Henshaw House, Oldham OL1 3AB ☎ 0161 770 1985 ⏱ barney.harle@oldham.gov.uk

Environmental Health: Mr Neil Crabtree, Head of Service - Public Protection, Sir Robert Peacock House, Vulcan Street, Oldham OL4 1LA ☎ 0161 770 4141 ⏱ neil.crabtree@oldham.gov.uk

European Liaison: Mr Dave Catherall, Principal Officer - External Funding, Civic Centre, West Street, Oldham OL1 1UG ☎ 0161 770 5165 ⏱ dave.catherall@oldham.gov.uk

Facilities: Mr Peter Wood, Head of Facilities Management, Civic Centre, West Street, Oldham OL1 1UG ☎ 0161 770 4028 ⏱ peter.wood@oldham.gov.uk

Finance: Ms Anne Ryans, Director - Finance, PO Box 196, Civic Centre, West Street, Oldham OL1 1UG ☎ 0161 770 4902 ⏱ anne.ryans@oldham.gov.uk

Fleet Management: Mr Craig Dale, Head of Service - Highways, Operations, Waste & Fleet Management, Moorhey Street Depot, Oldham OL4 1JF ☎ 0161 770 4441 ⏱ craig.dale@oldham.gov.uk

Grounds Maintenance: Mr Glenn Dale, Group Manager - Environmental Services, Alexandra Park, Oldham OL8 2BN ☎ 0161 770 4065 ⏱ glenn.dale@oldham.gov.uk

Housing: Ms Jill Beaumont, Director - Community Services, Civic Centre, West Street, Oldham OL1 1UG ☎ 0161 770 4778 ⏱ jill.beaumont@oldham.gov.uk

Legal: Mr Paul Entwistle, Director - Legal Services, PO Box 33, Civic Centre, West Street, Oldham OL1 1UL ☎ 0161 770 4822 ⏱ paul.entwistle@oldham.gov.uk

Leisure and Cultural Services: Ms Sheena MacFarlane, Head of Heritage Libraries & Art, PO Box 335, Civic Centre, West Street, Oldham OL1 1XJ ☎ 0161 770 4664 ⏱ sheena.macfarlane@oldham.gov.uk

Licensing: Mr John Garforth, Licensing Manager & Trading Standards, Sir Robert Peacock House, Vulcan Street, Oldham OL1 4LA ☎ 0161 770 5026 ⏱ john.garforth@oldham.gov.uk

Lifelong Learning: Ms Lynda Fairhurst, Head of Lifelong Learning Services, Civic Centre, West Street, Oldham OL1 1UG ☎ 0161 770 8055 ⏱ lynda.fairhurst@oldham.gov.uk

Lighting: Mr John McAuley, PFI Lighting Manager, Lees Road Depot, Lees Road, Oldham OL4 1HD ☎ 0161 770 1669 ⏱ john.mcauley@oldhamrochdalestreetlights.gov.uk

Member Services: Mr Paul Entwistle, Director - Legal Services, PO Box 33, Civic Centre, West Street, Oldham OL1 1UL ☎ 0161 770 4822 ⏱ paul.entwistle@oldham.gov.uk

Parking: Ms Angela Lees, Parking Client Manager, Henshaw House, Oldham OL1 3AB ☎ 0161 770 3638 ⏱ angela.lees@oldham.gov.uk

Personnel / HR: Ms Dianne Frost, Director - People Services, Civic Centre, West Street, Oldham OL1 1UG ☎ 0161 770 4965 ⏱ dianne.frost@oldham.gov.uk

Planning: Mr John Rooney, Interim Head of Planning & Infrastructure, Civic Centre, West Street, Oldham OL1 1UG ☎ 0161 770 4558 ⏱ john.rooney@oldham.gov.uk

Procurement: Mrs Nicola Wadley, Interim Head of Strategic Planning, Civic Centre, West Street, Oldham OL1 1UG ☎ 0161 770 8105 ⏱ nicola.wadley@oldham.gov.uk

Public Libraries: Ms Sheena MacFarlane, Head of Heritage Libraries & Art, PO Box 335, Civic Centre, West Street, Oldham OL1 1XJ ☎ 0161 770 4664 ⏱ sheena.macfarlane@oldham.gov.uk

Recycling & Waste Minimisation: Mr Craig Dale, Head of Service - Highways, Operations, Waste & Fleet Management, Civic Centre, West Street, Oldham OL1 1UG ☎ 0161 770 4441 ⏱ craig.dale@oldham.gov.uk

Regeneration: Ms Imogen Fuller, Principal Regeneration Officer, Civic Centre, West Street, Oldham OL1 1UG ☎ 0161 770 5164 ⏱ imogen.fuller@oldham.gov.uk

Regeneration: Mr Tom Stannard, Director - Enterprise & Skills, Civic Centre, West Street, Oldham OL1 1UG ⏱ tom.stannard@oldham.gov.uk

Road Safety: Mr Gary Sutcliffe, Principal Engineer, Henshaw House, Cheapside, Oldham OL1 1NY ☎ 0161 770 3046 ⏱ gary.sutcliffe@oldham.gov.uk

OLDHAM

Social Services (Adult): Mr Mark Warren, Director - Adults' Services, Civic Centre, West Street, Oldham OL1 1UG
☎ 0161 770 4317 ◌ mark.warren@oldham.gov.uk

Social Services (Children): Ms Kim Scragg, Director - Safeguarding, Civic Centre, West Street, Oldham OL1 1UG
☎ 0161 770 4751 ◌ kim.scragg@oldham.gov.uk

Public Health: Mr Alan Higgins, Director - Public Health, Civic Centre, West Street, Oldham OL1 1UG ☎ 0161 770 4750
◌ alan.higgins@oldham.gov.uk

Street Scene: Mr Glenn Dale, Group Manager - Environmental Services, Alexandra Park, Oldham OL8 2BN ☎ 0161 770 4065
◌ glenn.dale@oldham.gov.uk

Town Centre: Ms Sara Hewitt, Town Centre Manager, Level 3, Business Centre, Cromwell Street, Oldham OL1 1BB
☎ 0161 770 5282 ◌ sara.hewitt@oldham.gov.uk

Waste Collection and Disposal: Mr Craig Dale, Head of Service - Highways, Operations, Waste & Fleet Management, Moorhey Street Depot, Oldham OL4 1JF ☎ 0161 770 4441
◌ craig.dale@oldham.gov.uk

Waste Management: Mr Craig Dale, Head of Service - Highways, Operations, Waste & Fleet Management, Moorhey Street Depot, Moorhey Street, Oldham OL4 1JF ☎ 0161 770 4441
◌ craig.dale@oldham.gov.uk

COUNCILLORS

Leader of the Council: Stretton, Jean (LAB - Hollinwood)
jean.stretton@oldham.gov.uk

Deputy Leader of the Council: Jabbar, Abdul (LAB - Coldhurst)
abdul.jabbar@oldham.gov.uk

Ahmed, Riaz (LAB - Waterhead)
riaz.ahmad@oldham.gov.uk

Akhtar, Shoab (LAB - Werneth)
shoab.akhtar@oldham.gov.uk

Alexander, Adrian (LAB - Saddleworth West & Lees)
cllr.a.alexander@oldham.gov.uk

Alexander, Ginny (LAB - St. James)
ginny.alexander@oldham.gov.uk

Ali, Mohon (LAB - Chadderton North)
mohon.ali@oldham.gov.uk

Ames, Brian (LAB - Hollinwood)
brian.ames@oldham.gov.uk

Azad, Montaz Ali (LAB - Coldhurst)
cllr.m.azad@oldham.gov.uk

Ball, Cath (LAB - St. James)
cath.ball@oldham.gov.uk

Bashforth, Steven (LAB - Royton South)
steven.bashforth@oldham.gov.uk

Bashforth, Marie (LAB - Royton South)
marie.bashforth@oldham.gov.uk

Bates, Warren (UKIP - Failsworth West)
warren.bates@oldham.gov.uk

Blyth, Rod (LD - Shaw)
rod.blyth@oldham.gov.uk

Briggs, Norman (LAB - Failsworth East)
norman.briggs@oldham.gov.uk

Brock, Cherryl (LAB - Failsworth East)
cherryl.brock@oldham.gov.uk

Brownridge, Barbara (LAB - Chadderton North)
barbara.brownridge@oldham.gov.uk

Chadderton, Amanda (LAB - Royton South)
amanda.chadderton@oldham.gov.uk

Chauhan, Zahid (LAB - Alexandra)
zahid.chauhan@oldham.gov.uk

Cosgrove, Angela (LAB - St. James)
angela.cosgrove@oldham.gov.uk

Dean, Peter (LAB - Waterhead)
cllr.p.dean@oldham.gov.uk

Dearden, Susan (LAB - Chadderton Central)
susan.dearden@oldham.gov.uk

Fielding, Sean (LAB - Failsworth West)
sean.fielding@oldham.gov.uk

Garry, Elaine (LAB - Failsworth West)
elaine.garry@oldham.gov.uk

Gloster, Chris (LD - Shaw)
chris.gloster@oldham.gov.uk

Goodwin, Chris (LAB - Chadderton South)
chris.goodwin@oldham.gov.uk

Haque, Fazlul (LAB - Chadderton North)
fazlul.haque@oldham.gov.uk

Harkness, Garth (LD - Saddleworth North)
garth.harkness@oldham.gov.uk

Harrison, Jenny (LAB - Alexandra)
cllr.j.harrison@oldham.gov.uk

Heffernan, Derek (LD - Saddleworth North)
derek.heffenan@oldham.gov.uk

Hewitt, Stephen (LAB - Saddleworth West & Lees)
stephen.hewitt@oldham.gov.uk

Hudson, John (CON - Saddleworth South)
john.hudson@oldham.gov.uk

Hussain, Fida (LAB - Werneth)
fida.hussain@oldham.gov.uk

Hussain, Aftab (IND - St. Mary's)
aftab.hussain@oldham.gov.uk

Iqbal, Javid (LAB - Werneth)
javid.iqbal@oldham.gov.uk

Kirkham, Nikki (IND - Saddleworth North)
nikki.kirkham@oldham.gov.uk

Klonowski, Peter (UKIP - Saddleworth West & Lees)
peter.klonowski@oldham.gov.uk

Larkin, James (LAB - Royton North)
james.larkin@oldham.gov.uk

Larkin, Tony (LAB - Royton North)
tony.larkin@oldham.gov.uk

Malik, Abdul (LAB - Coldhurst) abdul.malik@oldham.gov.uk

McCann, John (LD - Saddleworth South)
john.mccann@oldham.gov.uk

McLaren, Colin (LAB - Chadderton Central)
colin.mclaren@oldham.gov.uk

McMahon, Jim (LAB - Failsworth East)
cllr.j.mcmahon@oldham.gov.uk

Moores, Eddie (LAB - Chadderton Central)
cllr.e.moores@oldham.gov.uk

Murphy, Dave (LD - Crompton)
dave.murphy@oldham.gov.uk

Mushtaq, Shaid (LAB - Alexandra)
shaid.mushtaq@oldham.gov.uk

Price, Vita (LAB - Waterhead)
vita.price@oldham.gov.uk

Qumer, Shadab (LAB - St. Mary's)
shadab.qumer@oldham.gov.uk

Rehman, Kaiser (LAB - Medlock Vale)
cllr.k.rehman@oldham.gov.uk

Roberts, Hannah (LAB - Royton North)
hannah.roberts@oldham.gov.uk

Salamat, Ali Aqueel (LAB - St. Mary's)
a.a.salamat@oldham.gov.uk

Sheldon, Graham (CON - Saddleworth South)
cllr.g.sheldon@oldham.gov.uk

Shuttleworth, Graham (LAB - Chadderton South)
cllr.g.shuttleworth@oldham.gov.uk

Sykes, Howard (LD - Shaw)
howard.sykes@oldham.gov.uk

Toor, Yasmin (LAB - Medlock Vale)
yasmin.toor@oldham.gov.uk

Turner, Julia (LD - Crompton)
Julia.Turner@oldham.gov.uk

Ur-Rehman, Ateeque (LAB - Medlock Vale)
ateeque.urrehman@oldham.gov.uk

Williams, Steve (LAB - Hollinwood)
cllr.s.williams@oldham.gov.uk

Williamson, Diane (LD - Crompton)
diane.williamson@oldham.gov.uk

Wrigglesworth, Joy (LAB - Chadderton South)
joy.wrigglesworth@oldham.gov.uk

POLITICAL COMPOSITION
LAB: 45, LD: 9, UKIP: 2, CON: 2, IND: 2

COMMITTEE CHAIRS

Health & Wellbeing: Ms Susan Dearden

Licensing: Mr Abdul Malik

Planning: Mr Steven Bashforth

Orkney   S

Orkney Islands Council, Council Offices, School Place,
Kirkwall KW15 1NY
☎ 01856 873535 🖶 01856 874615 ⁰ customerservice@orkney.gov.uk
🖳 www.orkney.gov.uk

FACTS AND FIGURES
Parliamentary Constituencies: Orkney and Shetland
EU Constituencies: Scotland
Election Frequency: Elections are of whole council

PRINCIPAL OFFICERS

Chief Executive: Mr Alistair Buchan, Chief Executive, Council
Offices, School Place, Kirkwall KW15 1NY ☎ 01856 873535; 01865
876158 ⁰ chief.executive@orkney.gov.uk

Senior Management: Mr Gavin Barr, Executive Director -
Development & Infrastructure, Council Offices, School Place,
Kirkwall KW15 1NY ☎ 01856 873535; 01856 876094
⁰ gavin.barr@orkney.gov.uk

Senior Management: Mrs Gillian Morrison, Executive Director -
Corporate Services, Council Offices, School Place, Kirkwall KW15
1NY ☎ 01856 873535; 01856 876158
⁰ gillian.morrison@orkney.gov.uk

Senior Management: Ms Caroline Sinclair, Chief Officer -
Integrated Health & Social Care, Council Offices, School Place,
Kirkwall KW15 1NY ☎ 01856 873535; 01856 876453
⁰ caroline.sinclair@orkney.gov.uk

Senior Management: Mr Wilfred Weir, Executive Director -
Education, Leisure & Housing, Council Offices, School Place,
Kirkwall KW15 1NY ☎ 01856 873535 ⁰ wilf.weir@orkney.gov.uk

Access Officer / Social Services (Disability): Mr Tom McGuire,
Service Manager, Council Offices, School Place, Kirkwall KW15 1NY
☎ 01856 873535; 01856 886453 ⁰ tom.mcguire@nhs.net

Architect, Building / Property Services: Mrs Jan Falconer,
Head of Strategic Development & Regeneration, Council Offices,
School Place, Kirkwall KW15 1NY ☎ 01856 873535 ext 2714; 01856
876094 ⁰ jan.falconer@orkney.gov.uk

Best Value: Mr Jim Love, Corporate Services Officer, Council
Offices, School Place, Kirkwall KW15 1NY ☎ 01856 873535
⁰ jim.love@orkney.gov.uk

Building Control: Mr Jack Leslie, Principal Building Standards
Officer, Council Offices, School Place, Kirkwall KW15 1NY
☎ 01856 873535; 01856 886451 ⁰ jack.leslie@orkney.gov.uk

Catering Services: Ms Anne Harrison, Catering Manager, St
Rognvald Street, Kirkwall KW15 1PR ☎ 01856 879238; 01856
879239 ⁰ anne.harrison@orkney.gov.uk

Children / Youth Services: Mr Jon Humphreys, Head of
Children & Families, Criminal Justice & Chief Social Work Officer,
Council Offices, School Place, Kirkwall KW15 1NY ☎ 01856 873535
⁰ jon.humphreys@orkney.gov.uk

Civil Registration: Ms Patricia Breck, Senior Registrar, Council
Offices, School Place, Kirkwall KW15 1NY ☎ 01856 873535
⁰ patricia.breck@orkney.gov.uk

PR / Communications: Mr David Hartley, Communications
Officer, Council Offices, School Place, Kirkwall KW15 1NY
☎ 01856 873535; 01856 874615 ⁰ david.hartley@orkney.gov.uk

ORKNEY

Community Planning: Mrs Marie Love, Community Planning Officer, Council Offices, School Place, Kirkwall KW15 1NY ☎ 01856 873535 ◌ marie.love@orkney.gov.uk

Computer Management: Mr Kenny MacPherson, IT Service Manager, 9 King Street, Kirkwall KW15 1JF ☎ 01856 873535 ◌ kenny.macpherson@orkney.gov.uk

Consumer Protection and Trading Standards: Mr Gary Foubister, Trading Standards Manager, Council Offices, School Place, Kirkwall KW15 1NY ☎ 01856 873535; 01856 886450 ◌ gary.foubister@orkney.gov.uk

Contracts: Mr Gavin Barr, Executive Director - Development & Infrastructure, Council Offices, School Place, Kirkwall KW15 1NY ☎ 01856 873535; 01856 876094 ◌ gavin.barr@orkney.gov.uk

Corporate Services: Ms Karen Greaves, Interim Head of Executive Support Services, Council Offices, School Place, Kirkwall KW15 1NY ☎ 01856 873535; 01856 870302 ◌ karen.greaves@orkney.gov.uk

Corporate Services: Mrs Gillian Morrison, Executive Director - Corporate Services, Council Offices, School Place, Kirkwall KW15 1NY ☎ 01856 873535; 01856 876158 ◌ gillian.morrison@orkney.gov.uk

Customer Service: Mrs Catherine Foubister, Customer Services Manager, Council Offices, School Place, Kirkwall KW15 1NY ☎ 01856 873535 ◌ catherine.foubister@orkney.gov.uk

Direct Labour: Mr Gavin Barr, Executive Director - Development & Infrastructure, Council Offices, School Place, Kirkwall KW15 1NY ☎ 01856 873535; 01856 876094 ◌ gavin.barr@orkney.gov.uk

Economic Development: Mrs Jan Falconer, Head of Strategic Development & Regeneration, Council Offices, School Place, Kirkwall KW15 1NY ☎ 01856 873535 ext 2714: 01856 876094 ◌ jan.falconer@orkney.gov.uk

Education: Mr Wilfred Weir, Executive Director - Education, Leisure & Housing, Council Offices, School Place, Kirkwall KW15 1NY ☎ 01856 873535 ◌ wilf.weir@orkney.gov.uk

E-Government: Mr Kenny MacPherson, IT Service Manager, 9 King Street, Kirkwall KW15 1JF ☎ 01856 873535 ◌ kenny.macpherson@orkney.gov.uk

Electoral Registration: Mr Dennis Stevenson, Electoral Registration Officer 8 Broad Street, Kirkwall KW15 1NX ☎ 01856 876222 ◌ ero@orkney.gov.uk

Emergency Planning: Mr Malcolm Russell, Safety & Contingencies Manager, Council Offices, School Place, Kirkwall KW15 1NY ☎ 01856 873535; 01856 874615 ◌ malcolm.russell@orkney.gov.uk

Energy Management: Mr Alistair Morton, Energy & Utilities Officer, Council Offices, School Place, Kirkwall KW15 1NY ☎ 01856 873535; 01856 876094 ◌ alistair.morton@orkney.gov.uk

Environmental / Technical Services: Mr Gavin Barr, Executive Director - Development & Infrastructure, Council Offices, School Place, Kirkwall KW15 1NY ☎ 01856 873535; 01856 876094 ◌ gavin.barr@orkney.gov.uk

Environmental Health: Mr David Brown, Environmental Health Manager, Council Offices, School Place, Kirkwall KW15 1NY ☎ 01856 873535; 01856 876450 ◌ david.brown@orkney.gov.uk

Estates, Property & Valuation: Mr Graeme Christie, Estates Manager, Council Offices, School Place, Kirkwall KW15 1NY ☎ 01856 873535; 01856 876094 ◌ graeme.christie@orkney.gov.uk

European Liaison: Miss Phyllis Harvey, European Liaison Officer, Council Offices, School Place, Kirkwall KW15 1NY ☎ 01856 873535; 01856 875846 ◌ phyllis.harvey@orkney.gov.uk

Events Manager: Mrs Maureen Spence, Democratic Services Manager, Council Offices, School Place, Kirkwall KW15 1NY ☎ 01856 873535; 01856 871604 ◌ maureen.spence@orkney.gov.uk

Facilities: Mr Gwyn Evans, Facilities Manager, Council Offices, School Place, Kirkwall KW15 1NY ☎ 01856 873535; 01856 876094 ◌ gwyn.evans@orkney.gov.uk

Finance: Mr Gareth Waterson, Head of Finance, Council Offices, School Place, Kirkwall KW15 1NY ☎ 01856 873535; 01856 876158 ◌ finance@orkney.gov.uk

Pensions: Mr Bryan Hay, Pensions Manager, Council Offices, School Place, Kirkwall KW15 1NY ☎ 01856 873535; 01856 876158 ◌ bryan.hay@orkney.gov.uk

Fleet Management: Mr Kenny Copland, Fleet Manager, Council Offices, School Place, Kirkwall KW15 1NY ☎ 01856 872311; 01856 874311 ◌ kenny.copland@orkney.gov.uk

Grounds Maintenance: Mr Peter Bevan, Engineering Services Manager, Council Offices, School Place, Kirkwall KW15 1NY ☎ 01856 873535; 01856 876094 ◌ peter.bevan@orkney.gov.uk

Health and Safety: Mr Malcolm Russell, Safety & Contingencies Manager, Council Offices, School Place, Kirkwall KW15 1NY ☎ 01856 873535; 01856 874615 ◌ malcolm.russell@orkney.gov.uk

Highways: Mr Darren Richardson, Head of Roads & Environmental Services, Council Offices, School Place, Kirkwall KW15 1NY ☎ 01856 873535; 01856 876094 ◌ darren.richardson@orkney.gov.uk

Home Energy Conservation: Mr Alistair Morton, Energy & Utilities Officer, Council Offices, School Place, Kirkwall KW15 1NY ☎ 01856 873535; 01856 876094 ◌ alistair.morton@orkney.gov.uk

Housing: Ms Frances Troup, Head of Housing & Homelessness, Council Offices, School Place, Kirkwall KW15 1NY ☎ 01856 873535 ◌ frances.troup@orkney.gov.uk

Housing Maintenance: Ms Frances Troup, Head of Housing & Homelessness, Council Offices, School Place, Kirkwall KW15 1NY ☎ 01856 873535 ◌ frances.troup@orkney.gov.uk

Legal: Mr Gavin Mitchell, Head of Legal Services, Council Offices, School Place, Kirkwall KW15 1NY ☎ 01856 873535
✆ gavin.mitchell@orkney.gov.uk

Leisure and Cultural Services: Ms Karen Greaves, Interim Head of Executive Support Services, Council Offices, School Place, Kirkwall KW15 1NY ☎ 01856 873535; 01856 870302
✆ karen.greaves@orkney.gov.uk

Licensing: Mr Gavin Mitchell, Head of Legal Services, Council Offices, School Place, Kirkwall KW15 1NY ☎ 01856 873535
✆ gavin.mitchell@orkney.gov.uk

Lifelong Learning: Ms Karen Greaves, Interim Head of Executive Support Services, Council Offices, School Place, Kirkwall KW15 1NY ☎ 01856 873535; 01856 870302 ✆ karen.greaves@orkney.gov.uk

Lighting: Mr Darren Richardson, Head of Roads & Environmental Services, Council Offices, School Place, Kirkwall KW15 1NY ☎ 01856 873535; 01856 876094 ✆ darren.richardson@orkney.gov.uk

Member Services: Mrs Maureen Spence, Democratic Services Manager, Council Offices, School Place, Kirkwall KW15 1NY ☎ 01856 873535; 01856 871604 ✆ maureen.spence@orkney.gov.uk

Parking: Mr Darren Richardson, Head of Roads & Environmental Services, Council Offices, School Place, Kirkwall KW15 1NY ☎ 01856 873535; 01856 876094 ✆ darren.richardson@orkney.gov.uk

Personnel / HR: Mr Andrew Groundwater, Head of HR & Performance, Council Offices, School Place, Kirkwall KW15 1NY ☎ 01856 873535; 01856 888779
✆ andrew.groundwater@orkney.gov.uk

Planning: Mr Roddy Mackay, Head of Planning & Regulatory Services, Council Offices, School Place, Kirkwall KW15 1NX ☎ 01856 873535; 01856 886451 ✆ roddy.mackay@orkney.gov.uk

Procurement: Mr Gary Butler, Procurement Manager, Council Offices, School Place, Kirkwall KW15 1NY ☎ 01856 873535; 01856 876158 ✆ gary.butler@orkney.gov.uk

Public Libraries: Mr Gary Amos, Library & Archive Manager, The Orkney Library & Archive, Junction Road, Kirkwall KW15 1AG ☎ 01856 873166; 01856 875260 ✆ gary.amos@orkneylibrary.org.uk

Recycling & Waste Minimisation: Ms Maria Cuthbertson, Waste Services Manager, Council Offices, School Place, Kirkwall KW15 1NY ☎ 01856 873535 ext 2702; 01856 876094 ✆ maria.cuthbertson@orkney.gov.uk

Regeneration: Mrs Jan Falconer, Head of Strategic Development & Regeneration, Council Offices, School Place, Kirkwall KW15 1NY ☎ 01856 873535 ext 2714; 01856 876094 ✆ jan.falconer@orkney.gov.uk

Road Safety: Mrs Yvonne Scott, Community Safety Officer, Council Offices, School Place, Kirkwall KW15 1NY ☎ 01856 873535 ✆ yvonne.scott@orkney.gov.uk

Social Services (Adult): Ms Caroline Sinclair, Chief Officer - Integrated Health & Social Care, Council Offices, School Place, Kirkwall KW15 1NY ☎ 01856 873535; 01856 876453 ✆ caroline.sinclair@orkney.gov.uk

Social Services (Children): Mr Jon Humphreys, Head of Children & Families, Criminal Justice & Chief Social Work Officer, Council Offices, School Place, Kirkwall KW15 1NY ☎ 01856 873535 ✆ jon.humphreys@orkney.gov.uk

Staff Training: Mrs Alison Skea, Learning & Development Manager, Council Offices, School Place, Kirkwall KW15 1NY ☎ 01856 873535 ✆ alison.skea@orkney.gov.uk

Sustainable Development: Mrs Jan Falconer, Head of Strategic Development & Regeneration, Council Offices, School Place, Kirkwall KW15 1NY ☎ 01856 873535 ext 2714; 01856 876094 ✆ jan.falconer@orkney.gov.uk

Sustainable Development: Mr Roddy Mackay, Head of Planning & Regulatory Services, Council Offices, School Place, Kirkwall KW15 1NX ☎ 01856 873535; 01856 886451 ✆ roddy.mackay@orkney.gov.uk

Tourism: Mrs Jan Falconer, Head of Strategic Development & Regeneration, Council Offices, School Place, Kirkwall KW15 1NY ☎ 01856 873535 ext 2714; 01856 876094 ✆ jan.falconer@orkney.gov.uk

Traffic Management: Mr Darren Richardson, Head of Roads & Environmental Services, Council Offices, School Place, Kirkwall KW15 1NY ☎ 01856 873535; 01856 876094 ✆ darren.richardson@orkney.gov.uk

Transport: Ms Laura Cromarty, Transport Manager, Council Offices, School Place, Kirkwall KW15 1NY ☎ 01856 873535 ✆ laura.cromarty@orkney.gov.uk

Transport Planner: Ms Phyllis Towrie, Transport Planner, Council Offices, School Place, Kirkwall KW15 1NY ☎ 01856 873535; 01856 886466 ✆ phyllis.towrie@orkney.gov.uk

Waste Collection and Disposal: Ms Maria Cuthbertson, Waste Services Manager, Council Offices, School Place, Kirkwall KW15 1NY ☎ 01856 873535 ext 2702; 01856 876094 ✆ maria.cuthbertson@orkney.gov.uk

Children's Play Areas: Mr Gary Burton, Sports & Leisure Manager, Council Offices, School Place, Kirkwall KW15 1NY ☎ 01856 883535 ext 2440 ✆ gary.burton@orkney.gov.uk

COUNCILLORS

Convener: Heddle, Steven (IND - Kirkwall East)
steven.heddle@orkney.gov.uk

Annal, Janice (IND - Kirkwall East)
janice.annal@orkney.gov.uk

Clackson, Stephen (IND - North Isles)
stephen.clackson@orkney.gov.uk

Clouston, Alan (IND - Kirkwall West & Orphir)
alan.clouston@orkney.gov.uk

ORKNEY

Crichton, Rob (IND - Stromness & South Isles)
rob.crichton@orkney.gov.uk

Davidson, Maurice (IND - Stromness & South Isles)
maurice.davidson@orkney.gov.uk

Drever, Andrew (IND - East Mainland, South Ronaldsay & Burray)
andrew.drever@orkney.gov.uk

Foubister, Jim (IND - East Midland, South Ronaldsay & Burray)
james.foubister@orkney.gov.uk

Hagan, Stephen (IND - North Isles)
stephen.hagan@orkney.com

Johnston, Harvey (IND - West Mainland)
harvey.johnston@orkney.gov.uk

King, Rachael (IND - West Mainland)
rachael.king@orkney.gov.uk

Madge, Russ (IND - East Mainland, South Ronaldsay & Burray)
russ.madge@orkney.gov.uk

Manson, Leslie (IND - Kirkwall West & Orphir)
cllr.leslie.manson@orkney.gov.uk

Moar, Jimmy (IND - West Mainland)
james.moar@orkney.gov.uk

Richards, John (IND - Kirkwall West & Orphir)
john.richards@orkney.gov.uk

Shearer, Gwenda (IND - Kirkwall East)
gwenda.shearer@orkney.gov.uk

Sinclair, Graham (IND - North Isles)
graham.sinclair@orkney.gov.uk

Stockan, James (IND - Stromness & South Isles)
james.stockan@orkney.gov.uk

Stout, Bill (IND - Kirkwall East)
bill.stout@orkney.gov.uk

Tierney, Owen (IND - West Mainland)
owen.tierney@orkney.gov.uk

Tullock, David (IND - Kirkwall West & Orphir)
david.tullock@orkney.gov.uk

POLITICAL COMPOSITION
IND: 21

Oxford City   D

Oxford City Council, Town Hall, St. Aldate's, Oxford OX1 1BX
☎ 01865 249811 ⌨ www.oxford.gov.uk

FACTS AND FIGURES
Parliamentary Constituencies: Oxford East, Oxford West and Abingdon
EU Constituencies: South East
Election Frequency: Elections are biennial

PRINCIPAL OFFICERS

Chief Executive: Mr Peter Sloman, Chief Executive, St. Aldate's Chambers, 109 St. Aldate's, Oxford OX1 1BX ☎ 01865 252354
⌁ psloman@oxford.gov.uk

Assistant Chief Executive: Ms Caroline Green, Assistant Chief Executive, St. Aldate's Chambers, 109 St. Aldate's, Oxford OX1 1BX ☎ 01865 252562 ⌁ cgreen@oxford.gov.uk

Senior Management: Mr David Edwards, Executive Director - City Regeneration & Housing, St. Aldate's Chambers, 109 St. Aldate's, Oxford OX1 1BX ☎ 01865 252463
⌁ dedwards@oxford.gov.uk

Senior Management: Mr Tim Sadler, Executive Director - Community Services, St. Aldate's Chambers, 109 St. Aldate's, Oxford OX1 1BX ☎ 01865 252313 ⌁ tsadler@oxford.gov.uk

Senior Management: Ms Jacqueline Yates, Executive Director - Organisational Development & Corporate Services, St. Aldate's Chambers, 109 St. Aldate's, Oxford OX1 1BX ☎ 01865 252339
⌁ jyates@oxford.gov.uk

Community Safety: Mr Richard Adams, Community Safety Manager, St. Aldate's Chambers, 109 St. Aldate's, Oxford OX1 1BX ☎ 01865 252283 ⌁ rjadams@oxford.gov.uk

Customer Service: Ms Helen Bishop, Head - Customer Services, St. Aldate's Chambers, 109 St. Aldate's, Oxford OX1 1BX ☎ 01865 252233 ⌁ hbishop@oxford.gov.uk

Direct Labour: Mr Graham Bourton, Head - Direct Services, Cowley Marsh Depot, Marsh Road, Oxford OX4 2HH ☎ 01865 252974 ⌁ gbourton@oxford.gov.uk

E-Government: Mr Christopher Lee, Web Contact Manager, St. Aldate's Chambers, 109 St. Aldate's, Oxford OX1 1BX ☎ 01865 249811 ⌁ clee@oxford.gov.uk

Electoral Registration: Mr Martin John, Electoral Services Manager, Town Hall, St. Aldate's, Oxford OX1 1BX ☎ 01865 252518 ⌁ mjohn@oxford.gov.uk

Finance: Mr Nigel Kennedy, Head - Finance, St. Aldate's Chambers, 109 St. Aldate's, Oxford OX1 1BX ☎ 01865 252708
⌁ nkennedy@oxford.gov.uk

Treasury: Ms Anna Winship, Treasury & VAT Manager, St Aldgate's Chambers, 109 - 113 St Aldgate's, Oxford OX1 1DS ☎ 01865 252517 ⌁ awinship@oxford.gov.uk

Fleet Management: Mr Ian Bourton, Motor Transport & Fleet Manager, Cowley Marsh Depot, Marsh Road, Oxford OX4 2HH ☎ 01865 252978 ⌁ ibourton@oxford.gov.uk

Grounds Maintenance: Mr Stuart Fitzsimmons, Parks & Open Spaces Manager, Cutteslowe Park, Oxford OX2 8ES ☎ 01865 467270 ⌁ sfitzsimmons@oxford.gov.uk

Highways: Mr Shaun Hatton, Highways Manager, Cowley Marsh Depot, Marsh Road, Oxford OX4 2HH ☎ 01865 249811
⌁ shatton@oxford.gov.uk

Home Energy Conservation: Mr Paul Robinson, Team Leader - Energy & Climate Change, St Aldate's Chambers, St Aldate's, Oxford OX1 1DS ☎ 01865 252541; 01865 252344
⌁ probinson@oxford.gov.uk

Housing Maintenance: Mr Graham Bourton, Head - Direct Services, Cowley Marsh Depot, Marsh Road, Oxford OX4 2HH ☎ 01865 252974 ⌁ gbourton@oxford.gov.uk

Legal: Mr Jeremy Thomas, Head - Law & Governance, St. Aldate's Chambers, 109 St. Aldate's, Oxford OX1 1BX ☎ 01865 252224 ✆ jthomas@oxford.gov.uk

Leisure and Cultural Services: Mr Ian Brooke, Head - Leisure & Parks, St. Aldate's Chambers, 109 St. Aldate's, Oxford OX1 1BX ☎ 01865 467232 ✆ ibrooke@oxford.gov.uk

Parking: Mr Jason Munro, Car Parks Manager, St. Aldate's Chambers, 109 St. Aldate's, Oxford OX1 1BX ☎ 01865 252125 ✆ jmunro@oxford.gov.uk

Partnerships: Mrs Val Johnson, Partnership Development Manager, Town Hall, St. Aldate's, Oxford OX1 1BX ☎ 01865 252209 ✆ vjohnson@oxford.gov.uk

Planning: Ms Patsy Dell, Head of Planning & Regulatory, St. Aldate's Chambers, 109 St. Aldate's, Oxford OX1 1BX ☎ 01865 252356 ✆ pdell@oxford.gov.uk

Regeneration: Mr David Edwards, Executive Director - City Regeneration & Housing, St. Aldate's Chambers, 109 St. Aldate's Street, Oxford OX1 1BX ☎ 01865 252463 ✆ dedwards@oxford.gov.uk

Street Scene: Mr Andrew Wright, Street Scene Area Manager, Cowley Marsh Depot, Marsh Road, Oxford OX4 2HH ☎ 01865 282967 ✆ awright@oxford.gov.uk

Town Centre: Ms Laurie-Jane Taylor, City Centre Manager, St. Aldate's Chambers, 109 St. Aldate's, Oxford OX1 1BX ☎ 01865 252080 ✆ ltaylor@oxford.gov.uk

Transport: Mr Ian Bourton, Motor Transport & Fleet Manager, Cowley Marsh Depot, Marsh Road, Oxford OX4 2HH ☎ 01865 252978 ✆ ibourton@oxford.gov.uk

Waste Collection and Disposal: Mr David Huddle, Street Scene Area Manager, Cowley Marsh Depot, Marsh Road, Oxford OX4 2HH ☎ 01865 252955 ✆ dhuddle@oxford.gov.uk

COUNCILLORS

The Lord Mayor: Altaf-Khan, Mohammed (LD - Headington)
cllrmaltaf-khan@oxford.gov.uk

Deputy Lord Mayor: Humberstone, Rae (LAB - Blackbird Leys)
cllrrhumberstone@oxford.gov.uk

SheriffBrown, Susan (LAB - Churchill)
cllrsbrown@oxford.gov.uk

Leader of the Council: Price, Bob (LAB - Hinksey Park)
cllrbprice@oxford.gov.uk

Deputy Leader of the Council: Turner, Ed (LAB - Rose Hill & Iffley)
cllreturner@oxford.gov.uk

Group Leader: Grant, Andrew (LD - Summertown)
cllragrant@oxford.gov.uk

Group Leader: Simmons, Craig (GRN - St. Mary's)
cllrcsimmons@oxford.gov.uk

Abbasi, Mohammed (LAB - Cowley Marsh)
cllrmabbasi@oxford.gov.uk

Anwar, Farida (LAB - Headington Hill & Northway)
cllrfanwar@oxford.gov.uk

Begum Azad, Jamila (LAB - St. Clement's)
cllrjazad@oxford.gov.uk

Brandt, Ruthi (GRN - Car)
cllrrbrandt@oxford.gov.uk

Chapman, Nigel (LAB - Headington Hill & Northway)
cllrnchapman@oxford.gov.uk

Clarkson, Mary (LAB - Marston)
cllrmclarkson@oxford.gov.uk

Cook, Colin (LAB - Jericho & Osney)
cllrccook@oxford.gov.uk

Coulter, Van (LAB - Barton & Sandhills)
cllrvcoulter@oxford.gov.uk

Curran, Steve (LAB - Iffley Fields)
cllrscurran@oxford.gov.uk

Fooks, Jean (LD - Summertown)
cllrjfooks@oxford.gov.uk

Fry, James (LAB - North)
cllrjfry@oxford.gov.uk

Goddard, Stephen (LD - Wolvercote)
cllrsgoddard@oxford.gov.uk

Goff, Angie (LD - Wolvercote)
cllragoff@oxford.gov.uk

Haines, Mick (IND - Marston)
cllrmhaines@oxford.gov.uk

Hayes, Tom (LAB - St. Clement's)
cllrthayes@oxford.gov.uk

Henwood, David (LAB - Cowley)
cllrdhenwood@oxford.gov.uk

Hollingsworth, Alex (LAB - Car)
cllrahollingsworth@oxford.gov.uk

Iley-Williamson, Dan (LAB - Holywell)
cllrdiley-williamson@oxford.gov.uk

Kennedy, Pat (LAB - Lye Valley)
cllrpkennedy@oxford.gov.uk

Landell Mills, Tom (LD - St. Margaret's)
cllrtlandellmills@oxford.gov.uk

Lloyd-Shogbesan, Ben (LAB - Lye Valley)
cllrblloyd-shogbesan@oxford.gov.uk

Lygo, Mark (LAB - Churchill)
cllrmlygo@oxford.gov.uk

Malik, Sajjad (LAB - Cowley Marsh)
cllrsmalik@oxford.gov.uk

Munkonge, Chewe (LAB - Quarry & Risinghurst)
cllrcmunkonge@oxford.gov.uk

Paule, Michelle (LAB - Rose Hill & Iffley)
cllrmpaule@oxford.gov.uk

Pegg, Jennifer (LAB - Northfield Brook)
cllrjpegg@oxford.gov.uk

Pressel, Susanna (LAB - Jericho & Osney)
cllrspressel@oxford.gov.uk

Rowley, Mike (LAB - Barton & Sandhills)
cllrmrowley@oxford.gov.uk

Sanders, Gillian (LAB - Littlemore)
cllrgsanders@oxford.gov.uk

Simm, Christine (LAB - Cowley)
cllrcsimm@oxford.gov.uk

Sinclair, Dee (LAB - Quarry & Risinghurst)
cllrdsinclair@oxford.gov.uk

Smith, Linda (LAB - Blackbird Leys)
cllrlsmith@oxford.gov.uk

Tanner, John (LAB - Littlemore)
cllrjtanner@oxford.gov.uk

Tarver, Richard (LAB - Iffley Fields)
cllrrtarver@oxford.gov.uk

Taylor, Sian (LAB - Northfield Brook)
cllrstaylor@oxford.gov.uk

Thomas, David (GRN - Holywell)
cllrdthomas@oxford.gov.uk

Tidball, Marie (LAB - Hinksey Park)
cllrmtidball@oxford.gov.uk

Upton, Louise (LAB - North)
cllrlupton@oxford.gov.uk

Wade, Elizabeth (LD - St. Margaret's)
cllrlwade@oxford.gov.uk

Wilkinson, Ruth (LD - Headington)
cllrrwilkinson@oxford.gov.uk

Wolff, Dick (GRN - St. Mary's)
cllrdwolff@oxford.gov.uk

POLITICAL COMPOSITION
LAB: 35, LD: 8, GRN: 4, IND: 1

COMMITTEE CHAIRS

Audit: Mr James Fry

Licensing: Mr Colin Cook

Planning: Mr James Fry

Oxfordshire   C

Oxfordshire County Council, County Hall, New Road, Oxford
OX1 1ND
☎ 01865 792422 ◌ online@oxfordshire.gov.uk
🖳 www.oxfordshire.gov.uk

FACTS AND FIGURES
Parliamentary Constituencies: Banbury, Henley, Oxford East,
Oxford West and Abingdon, Wantage, Witney
EU Constituencies: South East
Election Frequency: Elections are of whole council

PRINCIPAL OFFICERS

Chief Executive: Mr Peter Clark, Head of Paid Service, County
Hall, New Road, Oxford OX1 1ND ☎ 01865 323907
◌ peter.clark@oxfordshire.gov.uk

Senior Management: Mr Jim Leivers, Director - Children,
Families & Education, County Hall, New Road, Oxford OX1 1ND
☎ 01865 815122 ◌ jim.lievers@oxfordshire.gov.uk

Senior Management: Mr Jonathan McWilliam, Director - Public
Health, County Hall, New Road, Oxford OX1 1ND ☎ 01865 325004
◌ jonathan.mcwilliam@oxfordshire.gov.uk

Senior Management: Ms Bev Hindle, Acting Director -
Environment & Economy, County Hall, New Road, Oxford OX1 1ND
☎ 01865 815113 ◌ bev.hindle@oxfordshire.gov.uk

Senior Management: Ms Kate Terroni, Director - Adult Social
Services, County Hall, New Road, Oxford OX1 1ND ☎ 01865 815792
◌ kate.terroni@oxfordshire.gov.uk

Access Officer / Social Services (Disability): Ms Kate Terroni,
Director - Adult Social Services, County Hall, New Road, Oxford
OX1 1ND ☎ 01865 815792 ◌ kate.terroni@oxfordshire.gov.uk

Architect, Building / Property Services: Mr Mark Kemp,
Deputy Director - Commercial, County Hall, New Road, Oxford OX1
1ND ☎ 01865 815845 ◌ mark.kemp@oxfordshire.gov.uk

Children / Youth Services: Mr Jim Leivers, Director - Children,
Families & Education, County Hall, New Road, Oxford OX1 1ND
☎ 01865 815122 ◌ jim.lievers@oxfordshire.gov.uk

Civil Registration: Mrs Jacquie Bugeja, Head of Registration &
Coroner Services, 1 Tidmarsh Lane, Oxford OX1 1NS
☎ 01865 816288 ◌ jacquie.bugeja@oxfordshire.gov.uk

PR / Communications: Mr Eddie Gibb, Head of Communications,
County Hall, New Road, Oxford OX1 1ND ☎ 01865 896198
◌ eddie.gibb@oxfordshire.gov.uk

Community Safety: Mr David Etheridge, Chief Fire Officer &
Head of Community Safety, County Hall, New Road, Oxford OX1
1ND ☎ 01865 855205 ◌ david.etheridge@oxfordshire.gov.uk

Computer Management: Mr Martyn Ward, Service Manager -
ICT Business Delivery, Unipart House, Garsington Road, Oxford
OX4 2GQ ☎ 07786 691134 ◌ martyn.ward@oxfordshire.gov.uk

Consumer Protection and Trading Standards: Mr Richard
Webb, Trading Standards & Community Safety Manager, Graham
Hill House, Electric Avenue, Ferry Hinksey Road, Oxford OX2 0BY
☎ 01865 815791 ◌ richard.webb@oxfordshire.gov.uk

Contracts: Ms Kate Terroni, Director - Adult Social Services,
County Hall, New Road, Oxford OX1 1ND ☎ 01865 815792
◌ kate.terroni@oxfordshire.gov.uk

Customer Service: Mr Graham Shaw, Deputy Director - Oxfordshire
Customer Services, Unipart House, Garsington Road, Oxford
OX4 2GQ ☎ 07939 069084 ◌ graham.shaw@oxfordshire.gov.uk

Economic Development: Ms Bev Hindle, Acting Director -
Environment & Economy, County Hall, New Road, Oxford OX1 1ND
☎ 01865 815113 ◌ bev.hindle@oxfordshire.gov.uk

Education: Mr Jim Leivers, Director - Children's Services, County
Hall, New Road, Oxford OX1 1ND ☎ 01865 815122
◌ jim.lievers@oxfordshire.gov.uk

E-Government: Mr Graham Shaw, Deputy Director - Oxfordshire Customer Services, Unipart House, Garsington Road, Oxford OX4 2GQ ☎ 07939 069084 🖰 graham.shaw@oxfordshire.gov.uk

Emergency Planning: Ms Carol MacKay, Principal Emergency Planning Officer, Woodeaton Manor Lodge, Oxford OX3 9GU ☎ 01865 323763 🖰 carol.mackay@oxfordshire.gov.uk

Energy Management: Ms Bev Hindle, Deputy Director - Strategy & Infrastructure Planning, County Hall, New Road, Oxford OX1 1ND ☎ 01865 815113 🖰 bev.hindle@oxfordshire.gov.uk

Environmental / Technical Services: Ms Bev Hindle, Deputy Director - Strategy & Infrastructure Planning, County Hall, New Road, Oxford OX1 1ND ☎ 01865 815113 🖰 bev.hindle@oxfordshire.gov.uk

Estates, Property & Valuation: Mr Mark Kemp, Deputy Director - Commercial, County Hall, New Road, Oxford OX1 1ND ☎ 01865 815845 🖰 mark.kemp@oxfordshire.gov.uk

Facilities: Mr Mark Kemp, Deputy Director - Commercial, County Hall, New Road, Oxford OX1 1ND ☎ 01865 815845 🖰 mark.kemp@oxfordshire.gov.uk

Finance: Ms Lorna Baxter, Chief Finance Officer, County Hall, New Road, Oxford OX1 1ND ☎ 01865 323971 🖰 lorna.baxter@oxfordshire.gov.uk

Treasury: Ms Lorna Baxter, Chief Finance Officer, County Hall, New Road, Oxford OX1 1ND ☎ 01865 323971 🖰 lorna.baxter@oxfordshire.gov.uk

Pensions: Ms Sally Fox, Pensions Services Manager, Pension Services, Oxfordshire County Council, Unipart House, Garsington Road, Oxford 0X4 2GQ ☎ 01865 323854 🖰 sally.fox@oxfordshire. gov.uk

Pensions: Ms Donna Ross, Principal Financial Manager, Treasury & Pension Fund Investment Team, Oxfordshire County Council, 3rd Floor, County Hall, New Road, Oxford OX1 1ND ☎ 01865 323976 🖰 donna.ross@oxfordshire.gov.uk

Health and Safety: Ms Sue Corrigan, County HR Manager, County Hall, New Road, Oxford OX1 1ND ☎ 01865 810280

Highways: Mr Mark Kemp, Deputy Director - Commercial, County Hall, New Road, Oxford OX1 1ND ☎ 01865 815845 🖰 mark.kemp@oxfordshire.gov.uk

Legal: Mr Nick Graham, Chief Legal Officer, County Hall, New Road, Oxford OX1 1ND nick.graham@oxfordshire.gov.uk

Leisure and Cultural Services: Ms Vicky Field, Cultural Services Manager, County Hall, New Road, Oxford OX1 1ND ☎ 01865 797196 🖰 vicky.field@oxfordshire.gov.uk

Member Services: Mr Nick Graham, Chief Legal Officer, County Hall, New Road, Oxford OX1 1ND nick.graham@oxfordshire.gov.uk

Partnerships: Mr Eddie Gibb, Head of Communications, County Hall, New Road, Oxford OX1 1ND ☎ 01865 896198 🖰 eddie.gibb@oxfordshire.gov.uk

Personnel / HR: Mr Steve Munn, Chief Human Resources Officer, County Hall, New Road, Oxford OX1 1ND ☎ 01865 815191 🖰 steve.munn@oxfordshire.gov.uk

Planning: Ms Bev Hindle, Deputy Director - Strategy & Infrastructure Planning, County Hall, New Road, Oxford OX1 1ND ☎ 01865 815113 🖰 bev.hindle@oxfordshire.gov.uk

Procurement: Mr Graham Collins, Interim County Procurement officer, County Hall, New Road, Oxford OX1 1ND ☎ 01865 323111 🖰 graham.collins@oxfordshire.gov.uk

Public Libraries: Ms Jillian Southwell, Library Services Manager, Oxford Central Library, Oxford OX1 1DJ ☎ 01865 810203 🖰 jillian.southwell@oxfordshire.gov.uk

Recycling & Waste Minimisation: Ms Bev Hindle, Deputy Director - Strategy & Infrastructure Planning, County Hall, New Road, Oxford OX1 1ND ☎ 01865 815113 🖰 bev.hindle@oxfordshire.gov.uk

Road Safety: Mr Mark Kemp, Deputy Director - Commercial, County Hall, New Road, Oxford OX1 1ND ☎ 01865 815845 🖰 mark.kemp@oxfordshire.gov.uk

Social Services: Ms Kate Terroni, Director - Adult Social Services, County Hall, New Road, Oxford OX1 1ND ☎ 01865 815792 🖰 kate.terroni@oxfordshire.gov.uk

Social Services (Adult): Ms Seona Douglas, Deputy Director - Adult Social Care, County Hall, New Road, Oxford OX1 1ND ☎ 01865 323570

Social Services (Children): Ms Lucy Butler, Director - Children's Social Care, County Hall, New Road, Oxford OX1 1ND ☎ 01865 815165 🖰 lucy.butler@oxfordshire.gov.uk

Public Health: Mr Jonathan McWilliam, Director - Public Health, County Hall, New Road, Oxford OX1 1ND ☎ 01865 325004 🖰 jonathan.mcwilliam@oxfordshire.gov.uk

Staff Training: Ms Karen Hopwood, Learning & Development Manager, County Hall, New Road, Oxford OX1 1ND ☎ 07557 082597 🖰 karen.hopwood@oxfordshire.gov.uk

Sustainable Communities: Ms Bev Hindle, Deputy Director - Strategy & Infrastructure Planning, County Hall, New Road, Oxford OX1 1ND ☎ 01865 815113 🖰 bev.hindle@oxfordshire.gov.uk

Sustainable Development: Ms Bev Hindle, Deputy Director - Strategy & Infrastructure Planning, County Hall, New Road, Oxford OX1 1ND ☎ 01865 815113 🖰 bev.hindle@oxfordshire.gov.uk

Sustainable Development: Ms Sue Scane, Director - Environment & Economy, County Hall, New Road, Oxford OX1 1ND ☎ 01865 816399 🖰 sue.scane@oxfordshire.gov.uk

OXFORDSHIRE

Traffic Management: Mr Mark Kemp, Deputy Director - Commercial, County Hall, New Road, Oxford OX1 1ND
☎ 01865 815845 ✆ mark.kemp@oxfordshire.gov.uk

Transport: Mr Mark Kemp, Deputy Director - Commercial, County Hall, New Road, Oxford OX1 1ND ☎ 01865 815845 ✆ mark.kemp@oxfordshire.gov.uk

Transport Planner: Ms Bev Hindle, Deputy Director - Strategy & Infrastructure Planning, County Hall, New Road, Oxford OX1 1ND
☎ 01865 815113 ✆ bev.hindle@oxfordshire.gov.uk

Waste Management: Mr Mark Kemp, Deputy Director - Commercial, County Hall, New Road, Oxford OX1 1ND
☎ 01865 815845 ✆ mark.kemp@oxfordshire.gov.uk

COUNCILLORS

Chair: Waine, Michael (CON - Bicester Town)
michael.waine@oxfordshire.gov.uk

Leader of the Council: Hudspeth, Ian (CON - Woodstock)
ian.hudspeth@oxfordshire.gov.uk

Deputy Leader of the Council: Rose, Rodney (CON - Charlbury & Wychwood)
rodney.rose@oxfordshire.gov.uk

Atkins, Lynda (IND - Wallingford)
lynda.atkins@oxfordshire.gov.uk

Azad, Jamila (LAB - St Clement's & Cowley Marsh)
jamila.azad@oxfordshire.gov.uk

Bartholomew, David (CON - Sonning Common)
david.bartholomew@oxfordshire.gov.uk

Beal, Mike (LAB - Banbury Grimsbury & Castle)
mike.beal@oxfordshire.gov.uk

Billington, Maurice (CON - Kidlington South)
maurice.billington@oxfordshire.gov.uk

Brighouse, Liz (LAB - Churchill & Lye Valley)
liz.brighouse@oxfordshire.gov.uk

Bulmer, Kevin (CON - Goring)
kevin.bulmer@oxfordshire.gov.uk

Carter, Nick (CON - Thame & Chinnor)
nick.carter@oxfordshire.gov.uk

Chapman, Louise (CON - Hanborough & Minster Lovell)
louise.chapman@oxfordshire.gov.uk

Cherry, Mark (LAB - Banbury Calthorpe)
mark.cherry@oxfordshire.gov.uk

Christie, John (LAB - Banbury Ruscote)
john.christie@oxfordshire.gov.uk

Coates, Sam (GRN - University Park)
sam.coates@oxfordshire.gov.uk

Constance, Yvonne (CON - Shrivenham)
yvonne.constance@oxfordshire.gov.uk

Curran, Steve (LAB - Leys)
stephen.curran@oxfordshire.gov.uk

Dhesi, Surinder (LAB - Banbury Hardwick)
surinder.dhesi@oxfordshire.gov.uk

Fatemian, Arash (CON - Deddington)
arash.fatemian@oxfordshire.gov.uk

Fawcett, Neil (LD - Abingdon South)
neil.fawcett@oxfordshire.gov.uk

Fooks, Jean (LD - Wolvercote & Summertown)
jean.fooks@oxfordshire.gov.uk

Fulljames, Catherine (CON - Ploughley)
catherine.fulljames@oxfordshire.gov.uk

Gearing, Anthony (CON - Kirtlington & Kidlington North)
anthony.gearing@oxfordshire.gov.uk

Godden, Janet (LD - North Hinksey)
janet.godden@oxfordshire.gov.uk

Gray, Mark (CON - Benson & Cholsey)
mark.gray2@oxfordshire.gov.uk

Greene, Patrick (CON - Didcot East & Hagbourne)
patrick.greene@oxfordshire.gov.uk

Hallchurch, Tim (CON - Otmoor)
timothy.hallchurch@oxfordshire.gov.uk

Handley, Pete (CON - Carterton South & West)
peter.handley@oxfordshire.gov.uk

Hannaby, Jenny (LD - Grove & Wantage)
jenny.hannaby@oxfordshire.gov.uk

Hards, Nick (LAB - Didcot West)
nick.hards@oxfordshire.gov.uk

Harris, Neville (INDNA - Didcot Ladygrove)
nevhar@aol.com

Harrod, Steve (CON - Chalgrove & Watlington)
steve.harrod@oxfordshire.gov.uk

Heathcoat, Judith (CON - Faringdon)
judith.heathcoat@oxfordshire.gov.uk

Hibbert-Biles, Hilary (CON - Chipping Norton)
hilary.biles@oxfordshire.gov.uk

Howson, John (LD - St Margaret's)
john.howson@oxfordshire.gov.uk

Johnston, Bob (LD - Kennington & Radley)
bob.johnston@oxfordshire.gov.uk

Langridge, Richard (CON - Witney North & East)
richard.langridge@oxfordshire.gov.uk

Lilly, Stewart (CON - Hendreds & Harwell)
stewart.lilly@oxfordshire.gov.uk

Lindsay-Gale, Lorraine (CON - Berinsfield & Garsington)
lorraine.lindsay-gale@oxfordshire.gov.uk

Lovatt, Sandy (CON - Abingdon North)
sandy.lovatt@oxfordshire.gov.uk

Lygo, Mark (LAB - Marston & Northway)
mark.lygo@oxfordshire.gov.uk

Mallon, Kieron (CON - Bloxham & Easington)
kieron.mallon@oxfordshire.gov.uk

Matthew, Charles (CON - Eynsham)
charles.matthew@oxfordshire.gov.uk

Mills, James (CON - Witney West & Bampton)
james.mills@oxfordshire.gov.uk

Nimmo Smith, David (CON - Henley-on-Thames)
david.nimmo-smith@oxfordshire.gov.uk

Owen, Neil (CON - Burford & Carterton North)
neil.owen@oxfordshire.gov.uk

Patrick, Zoé (LD - Grove & Wantage)
zoe.patrick@oxfordshire.gov.uk

Phillips, Glynis (LAB - Barton, Sandhills & Risinghurst)
glynis.phillips@oxfordshire.gov.uk

Pressel, Susanna (LAB - Jericho & Osney)
susanna.pressel@oxfordshire.gov.uk

Price, Laura (LAB - Witney South & Central)
laura.price@oxfordshire.gov.uk

Purse, Anne (LD - Wheatley)
anne.purse@oxfordshire.gov.uk

Reynolds, George (CON - Wroxton & Hook Norton)
george.reynolds@oxfordshire.gov.uk

Rooke, Alison (LD - Abingdon East)
alison.rooke@oxfordshire.gov.uk

Sanders, John (LAB - Cowley)
john.sanders@oxfordshire.gov.uk

Sanders, Gill (LAB - Rose Hill & Littlemore)
gill.sanders@oxfordshire.gov.uk

Sibley, Les (IND - Bicester West)
les.sibley@oxfordshire.gov.uk

Smith, Roz (LD - Headington & Quarry)
roz.smith@oxfordshire.gov.uk

Stratford, Lawrie (CON - Bicester North)
lawrie.stratford@oxfordshire.gov.uk

Tanner, John (LAB - Isis)
john.tanner@oxfordshire.gov.uk

Tilley, Melinda (CON - Kingston & Cumnor)
melinda.tilley@oxfordshire.gov.uk

Webber, Richard (LD - Sutton Courtenay & Marcham)
richard.webber@oxfordshire.gov.uk

Williams, David (GRN - Iffley Fields & St Mary's)
david.williams@oxfordshire.gov.uk

Wilmshurst, David (CON - Thame & Chinnor)
david.wilmshurst@oxfordshire.gov.uk

POLITICAL COMPOSITION
CON: 32, LAB: 15, LD: 11, GRN: 2, IND: 2, INDNA: 1

COMMITTEE CHAIRS

Audit: Mr Sandy Lovatt

Health & Wellbeing: Mr Ian Hudspeth

Pensions: Mr Stewart Lilly

Planning: Mrs Catherine Fulljames

Pembrokeshire   W

Pembrokeshire County Council, County Hall, Haverfordwest
SA61 1TP
☎ 01437 764551 🖨 01437 775303 ✆ enquiries@pembrokeshire.gov.uk
🖳 www.pembrokeshire.gov.uk

FACTS AND FIGURES
Parliamentary Constituencies: Carmarthen West and South
Pembrokeshire, Preseli Pembrokeshire
EU Constituencies: Wales
Election Frequency: Elections are of whole council

PRINCIPAL OFFICERS

Chief Executive: Mr Ian Westley, Chief Executive, County Hall,
Haverfordwest SA61 1TP ☎ 01437 764551
✆ ian.westley@pembrokeshire.gov.uk

Senior Management: Ms Kate Evan-Hughes, Director - Children
& Schools, County Hall, Haverfordwest SA61 1TP
☎ 01437 764551 ✆ kate.evanhughes@pembrokeshire.gov.uk

Senior Management: Dr Steven Jones, Director - Development,
County Hall, Haverfordwest SA61 1TP ☎ 01437 764551
✆ steven_jones@pembrokeshire.gov.uk

Senior Management: Mrs Pam Marsden, Director - Social
Services & Leisure, County Hall, Haverfordwest SA61 1TP
☎ 01437 764551 ✆ pam.marsden@pembrokeshire.gov.uk

Senior Management: Mr Jonathan Haswell, Chief Finance
Officer, County Hall, Haverfordwest SA61 1TP ☎ 01437 764551
✆ jonathan.haswell@pembrokeshire.gov.uk

Access Officer / Social Services (Disability): Mr Alan Hunt,
Access Officer, County Hall, Haverfordwest SA61 1TP
☎ 01437 764551 ✆ alan.hunt@pembrokeshire.gov.uk

Architect, Building / Property Services: Mr Barry Cooke, Head
of Property, County Hall, Haverfordwest SA61 1TP ☎ 01437 764551
✆ barry.cooke@pembrokeshire.gov.uk

Best Value: Dr Steven Jones, Director - Development, County
Hall, Haverfordwest SA61 1TP ☎ 01437 764551
✆ steven_jones@pembrokeshire.gov.uk

Building Control: Mr David Fitzsimon, Head of Planning, County
Hall, Haverfordwest SA61 1TP ☎ 01437 764551
✆ david.fitzsimon@pembrokeshire.gov.uk

Catering Services: Mr Ian Eynon, Head of Business Services,
County Hall, Haverfordwest SA61 1TP ☎ 01437 764451
✆ ian.eynon@pembrokeshire.gov.uk

Children / Youth Services: Ms Kate Evan-Hughes, Director -
Children & Schools, County Hall, Haverfordwest SA61 1TP
☎ 01437 764551 ✆ kate.evanhughes@pembrokeshire.gov.uk

Children / Youth Services: Ms Allison Parkinson, Head of
Children's Services, County Hall, Haverfordwest SA61 1TP
☎ 01437 764551 ✆ allison.parkinson@pembrokeshire.gov.uk

Civil Registration: Mr John Roberts, Head of Information
Technology & Central Support Services, County Hall, Haverfordwest
SA61 1TP ☎ 01437 764551 ✆ john.roberts@pembrokeshire.gov.uk

PR / Communications: Mr Len Mullins, Press & Public Relations
Manager, County Hall, Haverfordwest SA61 1TP ☎ 01437 764551
✆ len.mullins@pembrokeshire.gov.uk

Community Planning: Dr Steven Jones, Director - Development,
County Hall, Haverfordwest SA61 1TP ☎ 01437 764551
✆ steven_jones@pembrokeshire.gov.uk

PEMBROKESHIRE

Community Safety: Mr Mark Elliott, Head of Public Protection, County Hall, Haverfordwest SA61 1TP ☎ 01437 764551 🖰 mark.elliott@pembrokeshire.gov.uk

Computer Management: Mr John Roberts, Head of Information Technology & Central Support Services, County Hall, Haverfordwest SA61 1TP ☎ 01437 764551 🖰 john.roberts@pembrokeshire.gov.uk

Consumer Protection and Trading Standards: Mr Mark Elliott, Head of Public Protection, County Hall, Haverfordwest SA61 1TP ☎ 01437 764551 🖰 mark.elliott@pembrokeshire.gov.uk

Contracts: Mr Paul Ashley-Jones, Head of Procurement, County Hall, Haverfordwest SA61 1TP ☎ 01437 764551; 01437 776510 🖰 paul.ashley-jones@pembrokeshire.gov.uk

Corporate Services: Mr John Roberts, Head of Information Technology & Central Support Services, County Hall, Haverfordwest SA61 1TP ☎ 01437 764551 🖰 john.roberts@pembrokeshire.gov.uk

Customer Service: Mr John Roberts, Head of Information Technology & Central Support Services, County Hall, Haverfordwest SA61 1TP ☎ 01437 764551 🖰 john.roberts@pembrokeshire.gov.uk

Economic Development: Mr Martin White, Head of Regeneration, County Hall, Haverfordwest SA61 1TP ☎ 01437 764551 🖰 martin.white@pembrokeshire.gov.uk

Education: Ms Kate Evan-Hughes, Director - Children & Schools, County Hall, Haverfordwest SA61 1TP ☎ 01437 764551 🖰 kate.evanhughes@pembrokeshire.gov.uk

Education: Mr Ian Eynon, Head of Business Services, County Hall, Haverfordwest SA61 1TP ☎ 01437 764451 🖰 ian.eynon@pembrokeshire.gov.uk

Education: Mr James White, Head of Performance & Community, County Hall, Haverfordwest SA61 1TP 🖰 james.white@pembrokeshire.gov.uk

E-Government: Mr John Roberts, Head of Information Technology & Central Support Services, County Hall, Haverfordwest SA61 1TP ☎ 01437 764551 🖰 john.roberts@pembrokeshire.gov.uk

Electoral Registration: Mr Glynne Morgan, Electoral Services Manager, County Hall, Haverfordwest SA61 1TP ☎ 01437 764551 🖰 glynne.morgan@pembrokeshire.gov.uk

Emergency Planning: Mr Richard Brown, Head of Environment & Civil Contingencies, County Hall, Haverfordwest SA61 1TP ☎ 01437 764551 🖰 richard.brown@pembrokeshire.gov.uk

Energy Management: Mr Darren Thomas, Head of Highways & Construction, County Hall, Haverfordwest SA61 1TP ☎ 01437 764551; 01437 775008 🖰 darren.thomas@pembrokeshire.gov.uk

Environmental / Technical Services: Mr Richard Brown, Head of Environment & Civil Contingencies, County Hall, Haverfordwest SA61 1TP ☎ 01437 764551 🖰 richard.brown@pembrokeshire.gov.uk

Environmental Health: Mr Mark Elliott, Head of Public Protection, County Hall, Haverfordwest SA61 1TP ☎ 01437 764551 🖰 mark.elliott@pembrokeshire.gov.uk

Estates, Property & Valuation: Mr Barry Cooke, Head of Property, County Hall, Haverfordwest SA61 1TP ☎ 01437 764551 🖰 barry.cooke@pembrokeshire.gov.uk

European Liaison: Mr Gwyn Evans, European Manager, County Hall, Haverfordwest SA61 1TP ☎ 01437 764551; 01437 776184 🖰 gwyn.evans@pembrokeshire.gov.uk

Facilities: Mr Gareth Howells, Facilities Manager, County Hall, Haverfordwest SA61 1TP ☎ 01437 764551; 01437 775303 🖰 gareth.howells@pembrokeshire.gov.uk

Finance: Mr Jonathan Haswell, Chief Finance Officer, County Hall, Haverfordwest SA61 1TP ☎ 01437 764551 🖰 jonathan.haswell@pembrokeshire.gov.uk

Finance: Mr Kerry Macdermott, Head of Revenue & Assurance, County Hall, Haverfordwest SA61 1TP ☎ 01437 775755 🖰 kerry.macdermott@pembrokeshire.gov.uk

Fleet Management: Mr Hubert Mathias, Transport & Fleet Manager, County Hall, Haverfordwest SA61 1TP ☎ 01437 764551 🖰 hubert.mathias@pembrokeshire.gov.uk

Grounds Maintenance: Mr Richard Brown, Head of Environment & Civil Contingencies, County Hall, Haverfordwest SA61 1TP ☎ 01437 764551 🖰 richard.brown@pembrokeshire.gov.uk

Grounds Maintenance: Mr Glenville Codd, Area Maintenance Manager for the South, County Hall, Haverfordwest SA61 1TP ☎ 01437 764551 🖰 glenville.codd@pembrokeshire.gov.uk

Health and Safety: Mr Paul Eades, Risk Manager & Business Continuity, County Hall, Haverfordwest SA61 1TP ☎ 01437 764551 🖰 paul.eades@pembrokeshire.gov.uk

Highways: Mr Darren Thomas, Head of Highways & Construction, County Hall, Haverfordwest SA61 1TP ☎ 01437 764551; 01437 775008 🖰 darren.thomas@pembrokeshire.gov.uk

Home Energy Conservation: Mr Steven Keating, Energy Manager, County Hall, Haverfordwest SA61 1TP ☎ 01437 764551 🖰 steve.keating@pembrokeshire.gov.uk

Housing: Mrs Lyn Hambidge, Head of Housing, County Hall, Haverfordwest SA61 1TP ☎ 01437 764551 🖰 lyn.hambidge@pembrokeshire.gov.uk

Housing Maintenance: Mrs Lyn Hambidge, Head of Housing, County Hall, Haverfordwest SA61 1TP ☎ 01437 764551 🖰 lyn.hambidge@pembrokeshire.gov.uk

Local Area Agreement: Dr Steven Jones, Director - Development, County Hall, Haverfordwest SA61 1TP ☎ 01437 764551 🖰 steven_jones@pembrokeshire.gov.uk

Legal: Ms Claire Incledon, Head of Legal & Committee Services, County Hall, Haverfordwest SA61 1TP ☎ 01437 764551
⬧ claire.incledon@pembrokeshire.gov.uk

Leisure and Cultural Services: Mr Mike Cavanagh, Head of Cultural Services, County Hall, Haverfordwest SA61 1TP
☎ 01437 764551 ⬧ mike.cavanagh@pembrokeshire.gov.uk

Leisure and Cultural Services: Mr Chris Payne, Leisure Services Manager, County Hall, Haverfordwest SA61 1TP ☎ 01437 764551; 01437 775303 ⬧ chris.payne@pembrokeshire.gov.uk

Licensing: Mr Mark Elliott, Head of Public Protection, County Hall, Haverfordwest SA61 1TP ☎ 01437 764551
⬧ mark.elliott@pembrokeshire.gov.uk

Lifelong Learning: Mr James White, Head of Performance & Community, County Hall, Haverfordwest SA61 1TP
⬧ james.white@pembrokeshire.gov.uk

Lighting: Mr Darren Thomas, Head of Highways & Construction, County Hall, Haverfordwest SA61 1TP ☎ 01437 764551; 01437 775008 ⬧ darren.thomas@pembrokeshire.gov.uk

Member Services: Ms Claire Incledon, Head of Legal & Committee Services, County Hall, Haverfordwest SA61 1TP
☎ 01437 764551 ⬧ claire.incledon@pembrokeshire.gov.uk

Parking: Mr Marc Owen, Streetcare Manager, County Hall, Haverfordwest SA61 1TP ☎ 01437 764551
⬧ marc.owen@pembrokeshire.gov.uk

Partnerships: Dr Steven Jones, Director - Development, County Hall, Haverfordwest SA61 1TP ☎ 01437 764551
⬧ steven_jones@pembrokeshire.gov.uk

Personnel / HR: Mr Ceri Davies, Head of Human Resources, County Hall, Haverfordwest SA61 1TP ☎ 01437 764551
⬧ ceri.davies@pembrokeshire.gov.uk

Planning: Mr David Fitzsimon, Head of Planning, County Hall, Haverfordwest SA61 1TP ☎ 01437 764551
⬧ david.fitzsimon@pembrokeshire.gov.uk

Planning: Dr Steven Jones, Director - Development, County Hall, Haverfordwest SA61 1TP ☎ 01437 764551
⬧ steven_jones@pembrokeshire.gov.uk

Procurement: Mr Paul Ashley-Jones, Head of Procurement, County Hall, Haverfordwest SA61 1TP ☎ 01437 764551; 01437 776510 ⬧ paul.ashley-jones@pembrokeshire.gov.uk

Public Libraries: Mr Mike Cavanagh, Head of Cultural Services, County Hall, Haverfordwest SA61 1TP ☎ 01437 764551
⬧ mike.cavanagh@pembrokeshire.gov.uk

Recycling & Waste Minimisation: Mr Richard Brown, Head of Environment & Civil Contingencies, County Hall, Haverfordwest SA61 1TP ☎ 01437 764551 ⬧ richard.brown@pembrokeshire.gov.uk

Regeneration: Mr Martin White, Head of Regeneration, County Hall, Haverfordwest SA61 1TP ☎ 01437 764551
⬧ martin.white@pembrokeshire.gov.uk

Road Safety: Ms Kirstie-Anne Donoghue, Road Safety Officer, County Hall, Haverfordwest SA61 1TP ☎ 01437 764551; 01437 775008 ⬧ kirstie-anne.donoghue@pembrokeshire.gov.uk

Social Services: Mrs Pam Marsden, Director - Social Services & Leisure, County Hall, Haverfordwest SA61 1TP ☎ 01437 764551 ⬧ pam.marsden@pembrokeshire.gov.uk

Social Services (Adult): Mr Jonathan Griffiths, Head of Adult Care, County Hall, Haverfordwest SA61 1TP ☎ 01437 754551
⬧ jonathan.griffiths@pembrokeshire.gov.uk

Social Services (Children): Ms Allison Parkinson, Head of Children's Services, County Hall, Haverfordwest SA61 1TP
☎ 01437 764551 ⬧ allison.parkinson@pembrokeshire.gov.uk

Staff Training: Mrs Sue Swan, Learning & Development Manager, County Hall, Haverfordwest SA61 1TP ☎ 01437 764551
⬧ sue.swan@pembrokeshire.gov.uk

Street Scene: Mr Darren Thomas, Head of Highways & Construction, County Hall, Haverfordwest SA61 1TP ☎ 01437 764551; 01437 775008 ⬧ darren.thomas@pembrokeshire.gov.uk

Sustainable Communities: Dr Steven Jones, Director - Development, County Hall, Haverfordwest SA61 1TP
☎ 01437 764551 ⬧ steven_jones@pembrokeshire.gov.uk

Sustainable Development: Dr Steven Jones, Director - Development, County Hall, Haverfordwest SA61 1TP
☎ 01437 764551 ⬧ steven_jones@pembrokeshire.gov.uk

Tourism: Mr Martin White, Head of Regeneration, County Hall, Haverfordwest SA61 1TP ☎ 01437 764551
⬧ martin.white@pembrokeshire.gov.uk

Town Centre: Dr Steven Jones, Director of Development, County Hall, Haverfordwest SA61 1TP ☎ 01437 764551
⬧ steven_jones@pembrokeshire.gov.uk

Traffic Management: Mr Darren Thomas, Head of Highways & Construction, County Hall, Haverfordwest SA61 1TP
☎ 01437 764551; 01437 775008
⬧ darren.thomas@pembrokeshire.gov.uk

Transport: Mr Hubert Mathias, Transport & Fleet Manager, County Hall, Haverfordwest SA61 1TP ☎ 01437 764551
⬧ hubert.mathias@pembrokeshire.gov.uk

Transport Planner: Mr Darren Thomas, Head of Highways & Construction, County Hall, Haverfordwest SA61 1TP
☎ 01437 764551; 01437 775008
⬧ darren.thomas@pembrokeshire.gov.uk

Total Place: Mr John Roberts, Head of Information Technology & Central Support Services, County Hall, Haverfordwest SA61 1TP
☎ 01437 764551 ⬧ john.roberts@pembrokeshire.gov.uk

PEMBROKESHIRE

Waste Collection and Disposal: Mr Richard Brown, Head of Environment & Civil Contingencies, County Hall, Haverfordwest SA61 1TP ☎ 01437 764551 ✆ richard.brown@pembrokeshire.gov.uk

Waste Management: Mr Richard Brown, Head of Environment & Civil Contingencies, County Hall, Haverfordwest SA61 1TP ☎ 01437 764551 ✆ richard.brown@pembrokeshire.gov.uk

Children's Play Areas: Mr Richard Brown, Head of Environment & Civil Contingencies, County Hall, Haverfordwest SA61 1TP ☎ 01437 764551 ✆ richard.brown@pembrokeshire.gov.uk

COUNCILLORS

Chair: Brinsden, John (INDNA - Amroth)
brinsden-2@supanet.com

Vice-Chair: Harries, Paul (IND - Newport)
cllr.paul.harries@pembrokeshire.gov.uk

Leader of the Council: Adams, James (IND - Camrose)
cllr.jamie.adams@pembrokeshire.gov.uk

Deputy Leader of the Council: Lewis, Keith (IND - Crymych)
cllr.keith.lewis@pembrokeshire.gov.uk

Group Leader: Howlett, David (CON - Wiston)
cllr.david.howlett@pembrokeshire.gov.uk

Group Leader: Kilmister, Bob (IND - Dinas Cross)
cllr.bob.kilmister@pembrokeshire.gov.uk

Group Leader: Miller, Paul (LAB - Neyland West)
cllr.paul.miller@pembrokeshire.gov.uk

Group Leader: Williams, Michael (PC - Tenby North)
cllr.michael.williams@pembrokeshire.gov.uk

Allen-Mirehouse, John (IND - Hundleton)
cllr.john.allen-mirehouse@pembrokeshire.gov.uk

Baker, Philip (INDNA - Saundersfoot)
cllr.phil.baker@pembrokeshire.gov.uk

Bowen, Roderick (PC - Clydau)
cllr.rod.bowen@pembrokeshire.gov.uk

Bryan, David (CON - Haverfordwest Priory)
cllr.david.bryan@pembrokeshire.gov.uk

Bush, Daphne (IND - Pembroke St. Mary South)
cllr.daphne.bush@pembrokeshire.gov.uk

Davies, John (IND - Cilgerran)
john.cwmbetws@virgin.net

Davies, Pat (LAB - Fishguard North West)
cllr.pat.davies@pembrokeshire.gov.uk

Edwards, David (IND - Haverfordwest Prendergast)
cllr.mark.edwards@pembrokeshire.gov.uk

Evans, Mike (INDNA - Tenby South)
sumo.evans@hotmail.co.uk

Evans, Wynne (IND - Narberth)
cllr.wynne.evans@pembrokeshire.gov.uk

Frayling, Lyndon (IND - Haverfordwest Garth)
cllr.lyndon.frayling@pembrokeshire.gov.uk

George, Huw (IND - Maenclochog)
cllr.huw.george@pembrokeshire.gov.uk

Hall, Brian (IND - Pembroke Dock Market)
cllr.brian.hall@pembrokeshire.gov.uk

Hancock, Simon (IND - Neyland East)
simon615@btinternet.com

Havard, Umelda (IND - Merlins Bridge)
cllr.umelda.havard@pembrokeshire.gov.uk

Hodgson, Tessa (INDNA - Lamphey)
cllr.tessa.hodgson@pembrokeshire.gov.uk

Hudson, Stanley (CON - Milford North)
cllr.stanley.hudson@pembrokeshire.gov.uk

James, Owen (IND - Scleddau)
cllr.owen.james@pembrokeshire.gov.uk

James, Mike (IND - St. Dogmaels)
cllr.mike.james@pembrokeshire.gov.uk

Jenkins, Lyn (IND - Solva)
cllr.lyn.jenkins@pembrokeshire.gov.uk

John, Michael (IND - Llangwm)
cllr.michael.john@pembrokeshire.gov.uk

Joseph, Stephen (INDNA - Milford Central)
cllr.stephen.joseph@pembrokeshire.gov.uk

Kidney, Phillip (INDNA - Manorbier)
cllr.phillip.kidney@pembrokeshire.gov.uk

Lee, Alison (NP - Pembroke Dock Central)
cllr.alison.lee@pembrokeshire.gov.uk

Lewis, Robert (IND - Martletwy)
cllr.rob.lewis@pembrokeshire.gov.uk

Llewellyn, Pearl (INDNA - Pembroke Monkton)
cllr.pearl.llewellyn@pembrokeshire.gov.uk

Lloyd, David (INDNA - St. Davids)
cllr.david.lloyd@pembrokeshire.gov.uk

Morgan, Peter (IND - The Havens)
cllr.peter.morgan@pembrokeshire.gov.uk

Morse, Elwyn (IND - Narberth Rural)
cllr.elwyn.morse@pembrokeshire.gov.uk

Neale, David (IND - Carew)
cllr.david.neale@pembrokeshire.gov.uk

Nutting, Jonathan (IND - Pembroke St. Michael)
cllr.jonathan.nutting@pembrokeshire.gov.uk

Owens, Reg (IND - St. Ishmaels)
cllr.reg.owens@pembrokeshire.gov.uk

Pepper, Myles (IND - Fishguard North East)
cllr.myles.pepper@pembrokeshire.gov.uk

Perkins, Susan (IND - Pembroke Dock Llanion)
cllr.susan.perkins@pembrokeshire.gov.uk

Preston, Jonathan (PC - Penally)
cllr.jonathan.preston@pembrokeshire.gov.uk

Price, Gwilym (LAB - Goodwick)
cllr.gwilym.price@pembrokeshire.gov.uk

Pugh, David (IND - Kilgetty / Begelly)
cllr.david.pugh@pembrokeshire.gov.uk

Rees, David (IND - Llanrhian)
cllr.david.rees@pembrokeshire.gov.uk

Richards, Thomas (IND - Letterston)
cllr.tom.richards@pembrokeshire.gov.uk

Rowlands, Ken (IND - Johnston)
cllr.ken.rowlands@pembrokeshire.gov.uk

Simpson, David (INDNA - Lampeter Velfrey)
cllr.david.simpson@pembrokeshire.gov.uk

Sinnett, Rhys (PC - Milford West)
cllr.rhys.sinnett@pembrokeshire.gov.uk

Stock, Peter (INDNA - Haverfordwest Portfield)
cllr.peter.stock@pembrokeshire.gov.uk

Stoddart, Robert (INDNA - Milford Hakin)
cllr.mike.stoddart@pembrokeshire.gov.uk

Stoddart, Vivien (INDNA - Milford Hubberston)
vivien.stoddart@virgin.net

Summons, Robert (IND - Burton)
cllr.rob.summons@pembrokeshire.gov.uk

Tudor, Thomas (LAB - Haverfordwest Castle)
cllr.thomas.tudor@pembrokeshire.gov.uk

Wilcox, Anthony (LAB - Pembroke Dock Pennar)
cllr.tony.wilcox@pembrokeshire.gov.uk

Williams, William (IND - Pembroke St. Mary North)
cllr.arwyn.williams@pembrokeshire.gov.uk

Williams, Jacob (INDNA - East Williamston)
jw@jacobwilliams.com

Woodham, Guy (LAB - Milford East)
cllr.guy.woodham@pembrokeshire.gov.uk

Yelland, Steve (IND - Rudbaxton)
cllr.steve.yelland@pembrokeshire.gov.uk

POLITICAL COMPOSITION
IND: 33, INDNA: 13, LAB: 6, PC: 4, CON: 3, NP: 1

COMMITTEE CHAIRS

Children & Families: Ms Pat Davies

Licensing: Ms Daphne Bush

Planning: Mr Peter Stock

Pendle D

Pendle Borough Council, Town Hall, Market Street, Nelson BB9 7LG
☎ 01282 661661 🖶 01282 661630 🖳 www.pendle.gov.uk

FACTS AND FIGURES
Parliamentary Constituencies: Pendle
EU Constituencies: North West
Election Frequency: Elections are by thirds

PRINCIPAL OFFICERS

Senior Management: Mr Dean Langton, Strategic Director, Town Hall, Market Street, Nelson BB9 7LG ☎ 01282 661602
🖰 dean.langton@pendle.gov.uk

Senior Management: Mr Philip Mousdale, Corporate Director, Town Hall, Market Street, Nelson BB9 7LG ☎ 01282 661634
🖰 philip.mousdale@pendle.gov.uk

Architect, Building / Property Services: Ms Sharon Livesey, Head of Property Services, Number One Market Street, Nelson BB9 7LJ ☎ 01282 878937 🖰 sharon.livesey@liberata.com

Building Control: Mr Neil Watson, Planning, Building Control & Licensing Services Manager, Town Hall, Market Street, Nelson BB9 7LG ☎ 01282 661706 🖰 neil.watson@pendle.gov.uk

PR / Communications: Ms Alice Barnett, Principal Communications Officer, Town Hall, Market Street, Nelson BB9 7LG ☎ 01282 661780

Community Planning: Mr Peter Atkinson, Neighbourhood Services Manager, Elliott House, 9 Market Square, Nelson BB9 0LX ☎ 01282 661063 🖰 peter.atkinson@pendle.gov.uk

Community Safety: Mr Geoff Whitehead, Localities, Communities & Policy Supervisor, Elliott House, 9 Market Square, Nelson BB9 0LX ☎ 01282 661660 🖰 geoff.whitehead@pendle.gov.uk

Computer Management: Mrs Sharon Hargraves, ICT Service Delivery Manager, Number One Market Street, Nelson BB9 7LJ ☎ 07976 969835 🖰 shargraves@burnley.gov.uk

Customer Service: Ms Vicky McGurk, Pendle Service Delivery Manager, Liberata UK Ltd, Manor Lane, Sheffield S2 1TR ☎ 01282 878501 🖰 vicky.mcgurk@liberata.com

Economic Development: Ms Julie Whittaker, Housing, Health & Economic Development Services Manager, Elliott House, 9 Market Square, Nelson BB9 0LX ☎ 01282 661038
🖰 julie.whittaker@pendle.gov.uk

E-Government: Mrs Sharon Hargraves, ICT Service Delivery Manager, Number One Market Street, Nelson BB9 7LJ ☎ 07976 969835 🖰 shargraves@burnley.gov.uk

Electoral Registration: Ms Gillian Turpin, Elections & Registration Manager, Town Hall, Market Street, Nelson BB9 7LG ☎ 01282 661919 🖰 gillian.turpin@pendle.gov.uk

Emergency Planning: Mr David Walker, Environmental Services Manager, Fleet Street Depot, Nelson BB9 7YQ ☎ 01282 661746 🖰 david.walker@pendle.gov.uk

Energy Management: Ms Sharon Livesey, Head of Property Services, Number One Market Street, Nelson BB9 7LJ ☎ 01282 878937 🖰 sharon.livesey@liberata.com

Environmental Health: Ms Julie Whittaker, Housing, Health & Economic Development Services Manager, Elliott House, 9 Market Square, Nelson BB9 0LX ☎ 01282 661038
🖰 julie.whittaker@pendle.gov.uk

Environmental Health: Ms Julie Whittaker, Housing, Health & Economic Development Services Manager, Elliott House, 9 Market Square, Nelson BB9 0LX ☎ 01282 661038
🖰 julie.whittaker@pendle.gov.uk

Estates, Property & Valuation: Ms Sharon Livesey, Head of Property Services, Number One Market Street, Nelson BB9 7LJ ☎ 01282 878937 🖰 sharon.livesey@liberata.com

Events Manager: Mr Michael Williams, Tourism Officer, Elliott House, 9 Market Square, Nelson BB9 0LX ☎ 01282 661963 🖰 michael.williams@pendle.gov.uk

PENDLE

Finance: Mr Vince Green, Financial Services Manager, Elliott House, 9 Market Square, Nelson BB9 0LX ☎ 01282 661867 ⌂ vince.green@pendle.gov.uk

Fleet Management: Mr David Walker, Environmental Services Manager, Fleet Street Depot, Nelson BB9 7YQ ☎ 01282 661746 ⌂ david.walker@pendle.gov.uk

Grounds Maintenance: Mr Keith Higson, Parks Technical Officer, Fleet Street Depot, Nelson BB9 7YQ ☎ 01282 661597 ⌂ keith.higson@pendle.gov.uk

Health and Safety: Mr David Walker, Environmental Services Manager, Fleet Street Depot, Nelson BB9 7YQ ☎ 01282 661746 ⌂ david.walker@pendle.gov.uk

Home Energy Conservation: Ms Julie Whittaker, Housing, Health & Economic Development Services Manager, Elliott House, 9 Market Square, Nelson BB9 0LX ☎ 01282 661038 ⌂ julie.whittaker@pendle.gov.uk

Housing: Ms Julie Whittaker, Housing, Health & Economic Development Services Manager, Elliott House, 9 Market Square, Nelson BB9 0LX ☎ 01282 661038 ⌂ julie.whittaker@pendle.gov.uk

Legal: Mr Richard Townson, Democratic & Legal Manager, Town Hall, Market Street, Nelson BB9 7LG ☎ 01282 661650 ⌂ richard.townson@pendle.gov.uk

Leisure and Cultural Services: Mrs Alison Goode, Chief Executive of Pendle Leisure Trust, Colne Town Hall, Albert Road, Colne BB8 0AQ ☎ 01282 661224 ⌂ alison.goode@pendleleisuretrust.co.uk

Licensing: Mr Neil Watson, Planning, Building Control & Licensing Services Manager, Town Hall, Market Street, Nelson BB9 7LG ☎ 01282 661706 ⌂ neil.watson@pendle.gov.uk

Lifelong Learning: Mr Simon Tisdale, Learning & Organisational Development Officer, Number One, Market Street, Nelson BB9 7LJ ☎ 01282 878805 ⌂ simon.tisdale@liberata.com

Member Services: Mrs Jane Watson, Senior Committee Administrator, Town Hall, Market Street, Nelson BB9 7LG ☎ 01282 661648 ⌂ jane.watson@pendle.gov.uk

Parking: Mrs Sandra Farnell, Transport & Co-ordination Manager, Elliott House, 9 Market Square, Nelson BB9 0LX ☎ 01282 661053 ⌂ sandra.farnell@pendle.gov.uk

Personnel / HR: Ms Lesley Ritchie, Human Resources Manager, Number One Market Square, Nelson BB9 7LJ ☎ 01282 878800 ⌂ lesley.ritchie@liberata.gov.uk

Planning: Mr Neil Watson, Planning, Building Control & Licensing Services Manager, Town Hall, Market Street, Nelson BB9 7LG ☎ 01282 661706 ⌂ neil.watson@pendle.gov.uk

Procurement: Mr Vince Green, Financial Services Manager, Elliott House, 9 Market Square, Nelson BB9 0LX ☎ 01282 661867 ⌂ vince.green@pendle.gov.uk

Recycling & Waste Minimisation: Mr David Walker, Environmental Services Manager, Fleet Street Depot, Nelson BB9 7YQ ☎ 01282 661746 ⌂ david.walker@pendle.gov.uk

Regeneration: Ms Julie Whittaker, Housing, Health & Economic Development Services Manager, Elliott House, 9 Market Square, Nelson BB9 0LX ☎ 01282 661038 ⌂ julie.whittaker@pendle.gov.uk

Staff Training: Ms Lesley Ritchie, Human Resources Manager, Number One Market Square, Nelson BB9 7LJ ☎ 01282 878800 ⌂ lesley.ritchie@liberata.gov.uk

Tourism: Mr Michael Williams, Tourism Officer, Elliott House, 9 Market Square, Nelson BB9 0LX ☎ 01282 661963 ⌂ michael.williams@pendle.gov.uk

Town Centre: Ms Hannah Latty, Town Centres Officer, Elliott House, 9 Market Square, Nelson BB9 0LX ☎ 01282 661677 ⌂ hannah.latty@pendle.gov.uk

Waste Collection and Disposal: Mr David Walker, Environmental Services Manager, Fleet Street Depot, Nelson BB9 7YQ ☎ 01282 661746 ⌂ david.walker@pendle.gov.uk

Waste Management: Mr David Walker, Environmental Services Manager, Fleet Street Depot, Nelson BB9 7YQ ☎ 01282 661746 ⌂ david.walker@pendle.gov.uk

Children's Play Areas: Mr Keith Higson, Parks Technical Officer, Fleet Street Depot, Nelson BB9 7YQ ☎ 01282 661597 ⌂ keith.higson@pendle.gov.uk

COUNCILLORS

Leader of the Council: Iqbal, Mohammed (LAB - Bradley) mohammed.iqbal@pendle.gov.uk

Deputy Leader of the Council: Greaves, Tony (LD - Waterside) tonygreaves@cix.co.uk

Adam, George (LAB - Walverden) georgeadam876@gmail.com

Adams, Marjorie (LD - Coates) adamsmarjorie7@gmail.com

Ahmed, Nadeem (LD - Whitefield) nadeem.ahmed@pendle.gov.uk

Ahmed, Nawaz (LAB - Brierfield) mna2010@hotmail.co.uk

Allen, Robert (LAB - Reedley) robert.allen@pendle.gov.uk

Ammer, Mohammed (LAB - Southfield) mammer786@aol.com

Ansar, Eileen (LAB - Clover Hill)

Arshad, Mohammed (LAB - Brierfield) mohammed.arshad@pendle.gov.uk

Arshad, Musawar (CON - Reedley) musraza@live.co.uk

Ashraf, Naeem (LAB - Brierfield) naeem.ashraf@pendle.gov.uk

Blackburn, Wayne (LAB - Clover Hill)
wblackburn@outlook.com

Butterworth, Neil (CON - Horsfield)
neil14@live.co.uk

Carroll, Rosemary (CON - Earby)
rosemary@carro-step.co.uk

Clegg, David (LD - Vivary Bridge)
david.clegg@pendle.gov.uk

Cockburn-Price, Sarah (CON - Boulsworth)
sarah@cockburn-price.com

Cooney, Tommy (CON - Marsden)
tommy.cooney@pendle.gov.uk

Cooney, Joe (CON - Vivary Bridge)
joe.cooney@pendle.gov.uk

Crossley, Linda (CON - Barrowford)
linda.crossley@pendle.gov.uk

Davy, Lyle (CON - Coates)
lyledavy@hotmail.com

Foxley, Margaret (CON - Boulsworth)
margaret@foxley5.orangehome.co.uk

Goulthrop, Mike (CON - Earby)
msgoulthrop@hotmail.co.uk

Hartley, Ken (LD - Craven)
kenknhrt@gmai.com

Henderson, Julie (LAB - Walverden)
julie.henderson@pendle.gov.uk

Horsfield, Morris (CON - Earby)

Iqbal, Yasser (LAB - Reedley)
yasser.iqbal@hotmail.co.uk

Lord, Dorothy (LD - Waterside)
dorothy.lord@lancashire.gov.uk

Mahmood, Asjad (LAB - Whitefield)
asjad.mahmood@pendle.gov.uk

McCollum, Nathan (CON - Vivary Bridge)
mccollum6767@hotmail.co.uk

McEvoy, Noel (CON - Blacko & Higherford)
noel.mcevoy@pendle.gov.uk

Newman, Brian (LD - Old Laund Booth)
brian.newman@pendle.gov.uk

Nixon, Jonathan (CON - Horsfield)
jonathan.nixon@pendle.gov.uk

Parker, Brian (BNP - Marsden)
brian.parker@pendle.gov.uk

Petty, Steve (CON - Horsfield)
steven.petty@btinternet.com

Purcell, Jenny (CON - Craven)
cllrjenniferpurcell@tiscali.co.uk

Roach, Graham (LD - Waterside)
graham.roach@pendle.gov.uk

Sakib, Mohammad (LAB - Bradley)
mohammadsakib@hotmail.co.uk

Shore, Kathleen (LAB - Clover Hill)

Starkie, James (CON - Higham & Pendleside)
james.starkie@pendle.gov.uk

Teal, Claire (LD - Coates)
cteall05@aol.com

Turner, Ken (CON - Barrowford)
ken.turner@live.co.uk

Wakeford, Christian (CON - Barrowford)
christian.wakeford@lancashire.gov.uk

Waugh, Graham (CON - Foulridge)
grwaugh@yahoo.co.uk

Whalley, David (LAB - Southfield)
david.whalley@pendle.gov.uk

Whipp, David (LD - Craven)
david.whipp@pendle.gov.uk

White, Paul (CON - Boulsworth)
cllrwhite@icloud.com

Wicks, Sheila (LAB - Southfield)
sheila.wicks@pendle.gov.uk

Younis, Nadeem (LAB - Bradley)
nadeem.younis@pendle.gov.uk

POLITICAL COMPOSITION
CON: 21, LAB: 17, LD: 10, BNP: 1

COMMITTEE CHAIRS

Accounts & Audit: Mr Lyle Davy

Development Management: Mr Ken Hartley

Perth & Kinross   S

Perth & Kinross Council, Perth & Kinross Council, 2 High Street, Perth PH1 5PH
☎ 01738 475000 📠 01738 475710 ✎ enquiries@pkc.gov.uk
🖥 www.pkc.gov.uk

FACTS AND FIGURES
Parliamentary Constituencies: Ochil and Perthshire South, Perth and Perthshire North
EU Constituencies: Scotland
Election Frequency: Elections are of whole council

PRINCIPAL OFFICERS

Chief Executive: Ms Bernadette Malone, Chief Executive, The Atrium, 137 Glover Street, Perth PH2 0LQ ☎ 01738 475009; 01738 475008 ✎ chiefexec@pkc.gov.uk

Deputy Chief Executive: Mr John Fyffe, Senior Depute Chief Executive, The Atrium, 137 Glover Street, Perth PH2 0LQ ☎ 01738 475445; 01738 475510 ✎ jfyffe@pkc.gov.uk

Deputy Chief Executive: Mr Jim Valentine, Depute Chief Executive, The Atrium, 137 Glover Street, Perth PH2 0LQ ☎ 01738 476502; 01738 475310 ✎ jvalentine@pkc.gov.uk

Deputy Chief Executive: Mr John Walker, Depute Chief Executive, The Atrium, 137 Glover Street, Perth PH2 0LQ ☎ 01738 476001 ✎ jwalker@pkc.gov.uk

PERTH & KINROSS

Senior Management: Mr Bill Atkinson, Director - Social Work & Chief Social Work Officer, Pullar House, 35 Kinnoull Street, Perth PH1 5GD ☎ 01738 476009 ⏁ batkinson@pkc.gov.uk

Senior Management: Ms Sheena Devlin, Director - Education & Children's Services, Pullar House, 35 Kinnoull Street, Perth PH1 5GD ☎ 01738 476312 ⏁ sdevlin@pkc.gov.uk

Senior Management: Mrs Barbara Renton, Director - Environment, Pullar House, 35 Kinnoull Street, Perth PH1 5GD ☎ 01738 476505; 01738 476510 ⏁ brenton@pkc.gov.uk

Access Officer / Social Services (Disability): Mr Bill Atkinson, Director - Social Work & Chief Social Work Officer, Pullar House, 35 Kinnoull Street, Perth PH1 5GD ☎ 01738 476009 ⏁ batkinson@pkc.gov.uk

Architect, Building / Property Services: Mr Stephen Crawford, Head of Property Services, Pullar House, 35 Kinnoull Street, Perth PH1 5GD ☎ 01738 476503 ⏁ scrawford@pkc.gov.uk

Building Control: Mr David Littlejohn, Head of Planning & Regeneration, Pullar House, 35 Pullar House, Perth PH1 5GD ☎ 01738 477942; 01738 475955 ⏁ dlittlejohn@pkc.gov.uk

Children / Youth Services: Ms Jacquie Pepper, Head of Children & Families Services, Pullar House, 35 Kinnoull Street, Perth PH1 5GD ☎ 01738 476205 ⏁ jpepper@pkc.gov.uk

Civil Registration: Mrs Gillian Taylor, Head of Democratic Services, The Atrium, 137 Glover Street, Perth PH2 0LQ ☎ 01738 475135; 01738 475008 ⏁ gataylor@pkc.gov.uk

PR / Communications: Mrs Gillian Taylor, Head of Democratic Services, The Atrium, 137 Glover Street, Perth PH2 0LQ ☎ 01738 475135; 01738 475008 ⏁ gataylor@pkc.gov.uk

Community Planning: Ms Fiona Robertson, Head of Public Service Reform, Culture & Community Development, Pullar House, 35 Pullar House, Perth PH1 5GD ☎ 01738 476270 ⏁ fionarobertson@pkc.gov.uk

Community Safety: Mr John Walker, Depute Chief Executive, The Atrium, 137 Glover Street, Perth PH2 0LQ ☎ 01738 476001 ⏁ jwalker@pkc.gov.uk

Computer Management: Mr Alan Taylor, Head of Corporate IT & Revenues, Pullar House, 35 Pullar Street, Perth PH1 5GD ☎ 01738 476702 ⏁ amtaylor@pkc.gov.uk

Consumer Protection and Trading Standards: Mr Willie Young, Head of Environmental & Consumer Services, Pullar House, 35 Kinnoull Street, Perth PH1 5GD ☎ 01738 476518 ⏁ wayoung@pkc.gov.uk

Contracts: Ms Lisa Simpson, Head of Legal Services, Blackfriars Development Centre, North Port, Perth PH1 5LU ☎ 01738 475503 ⏁ lisimpson@pkc.gov.uk

Customer Service: Mr Ian Caldow, Service Centre Manager, Pullar House, 35 Kinnoull Street, Perth PH1 5GD ☎ 01738 477911 ⏁ imcaldow@pkc.gov.uk

Economic Development: Mr David Littlejohn, Head of Planning & Regeneration, Pullar House, 35 Pullar House, Perth PH1 5GD ☎ 01738 477942; 01738 475955 ⏁ dlittlejohn@pkc.gov.uk

Education: Ms Sharon Johnston, Head of Education Services (Early Years & Primary), Pullar House, 35 Kinnoull Street, Perth PH1 5GD ☎ 01738 477447 ⏁ sjohnston@pkc.gov.uk

Education: Mr P McAvoy, Head of Education Services (Secondary), Pullar House, 35 Kinnoull Street, Perth PH1 5GD ☎ 01738 476387 ⏁ pmcavoy@pkc.gov.uk

Electoral Registration: Ms Bernadette Malone, Chief Executive, The Atrium, 137 Glover Street, Perth PH2 0LQ ☎ 01738 475009; 01738 475008 ⏁ chiefexec@pkc.gov.uk

Emergency Planning: Mrs Barbara Renton, Director - Environment, Pullar House, 35 Kinnoull Street, Perth PH1 5GD ☎ 01738 476505; 01738 476510 ⏁ brenton@pkc.gov.uk

Energy Management: Mr David Littlejohn, Head of Planning & Regeneration, Pullar House, 35 Pullar House, Perth PH1 5GD ☎ 01738 477942; 01738 475955 ⏁ dlittlejohn@pkc.gov.uk

Environmental / Technical Services: Mrs Barbara Renton, Director - Environment, Pullar House, 35 Kinnoull Street, Perth PH1 5GD ☎ 01738 476505; 01738 476510 ⏁ brenton@pkc.gov.uk

Environmental Health: Mr Willie Young, Head of Environmental & Consumer Services, Pullar House, 35 Kinnoull Street, Perth PH1 5GD ☎ 01738 476518 ⏁ wayoung@pkc.gov.uk

Estates, Property & Valuation: Mr Stephen Crawford, Head of Property Services, Pullar House, 35 Kinnoull Street, Perth PH1 5GD ☎ 01738 476503 ⏁ scrawford@pkc.gov.uk

European Liaison: Mr David Littlejohn, Head of Planning & Regeneration, Pullar House, 35 Pullar House, Perth PH1 5GD ☎ 01738 477942; 01738 475955 ⏁ dlittlejohn@pkc.gov.uk

Events Manager: Mr David Littlejohn, Head of Planning & Regeneration, Pullar House, 35 Pullar House, Perth PH1 5GD ☎ 01738 477942; 01738 475955 ⏁ dlittlejohn@pkc.gov.uk

Facilities: Mr Stephen Crawford, Head of Property Services, Pullar House, 35 Kinnoull Street, Perth PH1 5GD ☎ 01738 476503 ⏁ scrawford@pkc.gov.uk

Finance: Mr John Symon, Head of Finance, Blackfriars Development Centre, North Port, Perth PH1 5LU ☎ 01738 475504; 01738 475110 ⏁ jsymon@pkc.gov.uk

Fleet Management: Mrs Barbara Renton, Director - Environment, Pullar House, 35 Kinnoull Street, Perth PH1 5GD ☎ 01738 476505; 01738 476510 ⏁ brenton@pkc.gov.uk

Grounds Maintenance: Mrs Barbara Renton, Director - Environment, Pullar House, 35 Kinnoull Street, Perth PH1 5GD ☎ 01738 476505; 01738 476510 ⏁ brenton@pkc.gov.uk

Health and Safety: Mr Stuart Mackenzie, Head of Performance & Resources, Pullar House, 35 Pullar House, Perth PH1 5GD ☎ 01738 475531; 01738 476510 ⌁ smackenzie@pkc.gov.uk

Highways: Mrs Barbara Renton, Director - Environment, Pullar House, 35 Kinnoull Street, Perth PH1 5GD ☎ 01738 476505; 01738 476510 ⌁ brenton@pkc.gov.uk

Home Energy Conservation: Mrs Barbara Renton, Director - Environment, Pullar House, 35 Kinnoull Street, Perth PH1 5GD ☎ 01738 476505; 01738 476510 ⌁ brenton@pkc.gov.uk

Housing: Mr Bill Atkinson, Director - Social Work & Chief Social Work Officer, Pullar House, 35 Kinnoull Street, Perth PH1 5GD ☎ 01738 476009 ⌁ batkinson@pkc.gov.uk

Housing: Ms Lorna Cameron, Head of Housing & Strategic Commissioning, Pullar House, 35 Kinnoull Street, Perth PH1 5GD ☎ 01738 476705 ⌁ lecameron@pkc.gov.uk

Housing Maintenance: Ms Lorna Cameron, Head of Housing & Strategic Commissioning, Pullar House, 35 Kinnoull Street, Perth PH1 5GD ☎ 01738 476705 ⌁ lecameron@pkc.gov.uk

Local Area Agreement: Mrs Barbara Renton, Director - Environment, Pullar House, 35 Kinnoull Street, Perth PH1 5GD ☎ 01738 476505; 01738 476510 ⌁ brenton@pkc.gov.uk

Legal: Ms Lisa Simpson, Head of Legal Services, Blackfriars Development Centre, North Port, Perth PH1 5LU ☎ 01738 475503 ⌁ lisimpson@pkc.gov.uk

Leisure and Cultural Services: Ms Fiona Robertson, Head of Public Service Reform, Culture & Community Development, Pullar House, 35 Pullar House, Perth PH1 5GD ☎ 01738 476270 ⌁ fionarobertson@pkc.gov.uk

Licensing: Ms Lisa Simpson, Head of Legal Services, Blackfriars Development Centre, North Port, Perth PH1 5LU ☎ 01738 475503 ⌁ lisimpson@pkc.gov.uk

Lifelong Learning: Ms Sheena Devlin, Director - Education & Children's Services, Pullar House, 35 Kinnoull Street, Perth PH1 5GD ☎ 01738 476312 ⌁ sdevlin@pkc.gov.uk

Lottery Funding, Charity and Voluntary: Mr David Littlejohn, Head of Planning & Regeneration, Pullar House, 35 Pullar House, Perth PH1 5GD ☎ 01738 477942; 01738 475955 ⌁ dlittlejohn@pkc.gov.uk

Member Services: Mrs Gillian Taylor, Head of Democratic Services, The Atrium, 137 Glover Street, Perth PH2 0LQ ☎ 01738 475135; 01738 475008 ⌁ gataylor@pkc.gov.uk

Parking: Mrs Barbara Renton, Director - Environment, Pullar House, 35 Kinnoull Street, Perth PH1 5GD ☎ 01738 476505; 01738 476510 ⌁ brenton@pkc.gov.uk

Personnel / HR: Mrs Karen Donaldson, Corporate Human Resources Manager, Blackfriars Development Centre, North Port, Perth PH1 5LU ☎ 01738 475430 ⌁ kadonaldson@pkc.gov.uk

Planning: Mr David Littlejohn, Head of Planning & Regeneration, Pullar House, 35 Pullar House, Perth PH1 5GD ☎ 01738 477942; 01738 475955 ⌁ dlittlejohn@pkc.gov.uk

Procurement: Ms Lorna Cameron, Head of Housing & Strategic Commissioning, Pullar House, 35 Kinnoull Street, Perth PH1 5GD ☎ 01738 476705 ⌁ lecameron@pkc.gov.uk

Public Libraries: Ms Fiona Robertson, Head of Public Service Reform, Culture & Community Development, Pullar House, 35 Pullar House, Perth PH1 5GD ☎ 01738 476270 ⌁ fionarobertson@pkc.gov.uk

Recycling & Waste Minimisation: Mr Willie Young, Head of Environmental & Consumer Services, Pullar House, 35 Kinnoull Street, Perth PH1 5GD ☎ 01738 476518 ⌁ wayoung@pkc.gov.uk

Regeneration: Mr David Littlejohn, Head of Planning & Regeneration, Pullar House, 35 Pullar House, Perth PH1 5GD ☎ 01738 477942; 01738 475955 ⌁ dlittlejohn@pkc.gov.uk

Road Safety: Mrs Barbara Renton, Director - Environment, Pullar House, 35 Kinnoull Street, Perth PH1 5GD ☎ 01738 476505; 01738 476510 ⌁ brenton@pkc.gov.uk

Social Services: Mr Bill Atkinson, Director - Social Work & Chief Social Work Officer, Pullar House, 35 Kinnoull Street, Perth PH1 5GD ☎ 01738 476009 ⌁ batkinson@pkc.gov.uk

Social Services (Adult): Mr Bill Atkinson, Director - Social Work & Chief Social Work Officer, Pullar House, 35 Kinnoull Street, Perth PH1 5GD ☎ 01738 476009 ⌁ batkinson@pkc.gov.uk

Staff Training: Mrs Karen Donaldson, Corporate Human Resources Manager, Blackfriars Development Centre, North Port, Perth PH1 5LU ☎ 01738 475430 ⌁ kadonaldson@pkc.gov.uk

Tourism: Mr David Littlejohn, Head of Planning & Regeneration, Pullar House, 35 Pullar House, Perth PH1 5GD ☎ 01738 477942; 01738 475955 ⌁ dlittlejohn@pkc.gov.uk

Town Centre: Mr David Littlejohn, Head of Planning & Regeneration, Pullar House, 35 Pullar House, Perth PH1 5GD ☎ 01738 477942; 01738 475955 ⌁ dlittlejohn@pkc.gov.uk

Traffic Management: Mrs Barbara Renton, Director - Environment, Pullar House, 35 Kinnoull Street, Perth PH1 5LU ☎ 01738 476505; 01738 476510 ⌁ brenton@pkc.gov.uk

Transport: Mrs Barbara Renton, Director - Environment, Pullar House, 35 Kinnoull Street, Perth PH1 5LU ☎ 01738 476505; 01738 476510 ⌁ brenton@pkc.gov.uk

Waste Collection and Disposal: Mr Willie Young, Head of Environmental & Consumer Services, Pullar House, 35 Kinnoull Street, Perth PH1 5GD ☎ 01738 476518 ⌁ wayoung@pkc.gov.uk

Waste Management: Mr Willie Young, Head of Environmental & Consumer Services, Pullar House, 35 Kinnoull Street, Perth PH1 5GD ☎ 01738 476518 ⌁ wayoung@pkc.gov.uk

PERTH & KINROSS

COUNCILLORS

Provost: Grant, Liz (SNP - Blairgowrie & Glens)
egrant@pkc.gov.uk

Deputy Provost: Band, Bob (SNP - Perth City South)
bband@pkc.gov.uk

Leader of the Council: Miller, Ian (SNP - Strathmore)
imiller@pkc.gov.uk

Deputy Leader of the Council: Grant, Alan (SNP - Strathmore)
adgrant@pkc.gov.uk

Group Leader: Barrett, Peter (LD - Perth City Centre)
pabarrett@pkc.gov.uk

Group Leader: Cuthbert, Dave (IND - Kinross shire)
dcuthbert@pkc.gov.uk

Group Leader: MacLellan, Archie (LAB - Perth City Centre)
aamaclellan@pkc.gov.uk

Group Leader: Roberts, Mac (CON - Carse of Gowrie)
mroberts@pkc.gov.uk

Anderson, Henry (SNP - Almond & Earn)
handerson@pkc.gov.uk

Barnacle, Michael (IND - Kinross shire)
mbarnacle@pkc.gov.uk

Brock, Rhona (IND - Strathearn)
rbrock@pkc.gov.uk

Campbell, Ian (CON - Highland)
icampbell@pkc.gov.uk

Cowan, Ann (CON - Strathearn)
acowan@pkc.gov.uk

Doogan, Dave (SNP - Perth City North)
ddoogan@pkc.gov.uk

Ellis, Bob (SNP - Blairgowrie & Glens)
rellis@pkc.gov.uk

Flynn, John (LAB - Perth City North)
jmflynn@pkc.gov.uk

Gaunt, Ann (LD - Strathallan)
agaunt@pkc.gov.uk

Giacopazzi, Joe (SNP - Kinross shire)
jgiacopazzi@pkc.gov.uk

Gillies, Callum (LAB - Perth City North)
cgillies@pkc.gov.uk

Gray, Tom (SNP - Strathallan)
tomgray@pkc.gov.uk

Howie, Kate (SNP - Highland)
khowie@pkc.gov.uk

Jack, Alan (IND - Almond & Earn)
hajack@pkc.gov.uk

Kellas, John (SNP - Strathtay)
jkellas@pkc.gov.uk

Laing, Grant (SNP - Strathtay)
glaing@pkc.gov.uk

Livingstone, Alan (CON - Almond & Earn)
alivingstone@pkc.gov.uk

Lyle, Murray (CON - Strathallan)
mlyle@pkc.gov.uk

Maclachlan, Elspeth (SNP - Perth City North)
emaclachlan@pkc.gov.uk

Melloy, Dennis (CON - Strathmore)
dmelloy@pkc.gov.uk

Munro, Alistair (LAB - Perth City South)
alistairmunro@pkc.gov.uk

Parrott, Andrew (SNP - Perth City Centre)
aparrott@pkc.gov.uk

Pover, Douglas (SNP - Carse of Gowrie)
dpover@pkc.gov.uk

Robertson, Willie (LD - Kinross shire)
wrobertson@pkc.gov.uk

Shiers, Caroline (CON - Blairgowrie & Glens)
cshiers@pkc.gov.uk

Simpson, Lewis (LD - Strathmore)
lddsimpson@pkc.gov.uk

Stewart, Alexander (CON - Perth City South)
astewart@pkc.gov.uk

Stewart, Heather (CON - Perth City Centre)
heatherstewart@pkc.gov.uk

Vaughan, Barbara (CON - Strathtay)
bvaughan@pkc.gov.uk

Walker, Gordon (SNP - Carse of Gowrie)
gordonwalker@pkc.gov.uk

Williamson, Mike (SNP - Highland)
mwilliamson@pkc.gov.uk

Wilson, Willie (LD - Perth City South)
wowilson@pkc.gov.uk

Younger, Anne (SNP - Strathearn)
ayounger@pkc.gov.uk

POLITICAL COMPOSITION
SNP: 18, CON: 10, LD: 5, IND: 4, LAB: 4

COMMITTEE CHAIRS

Audit: Ms Barbara Vaughan

Development Management: Mr Tom Gray

Licensing: Mr Bob Ellis

Peterborough City   U

Peterborough City Council, Town Hall, Bridge Street,
Peterborough PE1 1HG
☎ 01733 747474 🖷 01733 452537 ✍ ask@peterborough.gov.uk
🖥 www.peterborough.gov.uk

FACTS AND FIGURES
Parliamentary Constituencies: Cambridgeshire North West,
Peterborough
EU Constituencies: Eastern
Election Frequency: Elections are by thirds

PRINCIPAL OFFICERS

Chief Executive: Mrs Gillian Beasley, Chief Executive, Town Hall,
Bridge Street, Peterborough PE1 1HL ☎ 01733 452390
✍ gillian.beasley@peterborough.gov.uk

Senior Management: Ms Amanda Best, Operations Director, Manor Drive, Paston Parkway, Peterborough PE4 7AP
☎ 01733 863749 ⌀ amanda.best@peterborough.gov.uk

Senior Management: Mr John Harrison, Corporate Director - Resources, Town Hall, Bridge Street, Peterborough PE1 1HG
☎ 01733 452520 ⌀ john.harrison@peterborough.gov.uk

Senior Management: Mr Simon Machen, Corporate Director - Growth & Regeneration, Town Hall, Bridge Street, Peterborough PE1 1HG ☎ 01733 453475 ⌀ simon.machen@peterborough.gov.uk

Senior Management: Ms Wendi Ogle-Welbourn, Corporate Director - People & Communities, Bayard Place, Broadway, Peterborough PE1 1FB ☎ 01733 863749
⌀ wendi.ogle-welbourn@peterborough.gov.uk

Senior Management: Dr Liz Robin, Director - Public Health, Town Hall, Bridge Street, Peterborough PE1 1HG ☎ 01733 207175
⌀ liz.robin@peterborough.gov.u

Senior Management: Ms Kim Sawyer, Director - Governance, Town Hall, Bridge Street, Peterborough PE1 1HG ☎ 01733 452361
⌀ kim.sawyer@peterborough.gov.uk

Architect, Building / Property Services: Mr Richard Porter, Head of Strategic Property, Manor Drive, Paston Parkway, Peterborough PE4 7AP ☎ 01733 384544
⌀ richard.porter@peterborough.gov.uk

Architect, Building / Property Services: Mr Martin Raper, Account Director, Amey, Nursery Lane, Fengate, Peterborough PE1 5BG ☎ 01733 425325 ⌀ martin.raper@amey.gov.uk

Building Control: Mr Kevin Dawson, Head of Resilience, Town Hall, Bridge Street, Peterborough PE1 1HG ☎ 01733 453464
⌀ kevin.dawson@peterborough.gov.uk

Building Control: Mr Nick Harding, Head of Planning, Transport & Engineering Services, Town Hall, Bridge Street, Peterborough PE1 1HG ☎ 01733 454441 ⌀ nicholas.harding@peterborough.gov.uk

Building Control: Ms Melissa Shaw, Head of Service Management, Enterprise Peterborough, Nursery Lane, Fengate, Peterborough PE1 5BG ☎ 01733 425325
⌀ melissa.shaw@enterprisepeterborough.co.uk

Catering Services: Ms Melissa Shaw, Head of Service Management, Enterprise Peterborough, Nursery Lane, Fengate, Peterborough PE1 5BG ☎ 01733 425325
⌀ melissa.shaw@enterprisepeterborough.co.uk

Children / Youth Services: Mrs Alison Bennett, Head of Service, Quality Assurance & Safeguarding, Bayard Place, Broadway, Peterborough PE1 1FB ☎ 01733 863627
⌀ alison.bennett@peterborough.gov.uk

Children / Youth Services: Mr Iain Easton, Head of Youth Offending Service, Youth Offending Service, 13/15 Cavell Court, Lincoln Road, Peterborough PE1 ZRJ ☎ 01733 864237
⌀ iain.easton@peterborough.gov.uk

Civil Registration: Ms Ruth Hodson, Registration Manager, Register Office, 33 Thorpe Road, Peterborough PE3 6AB
☎ 01733 864640 ⌀ ruth.hodson@peterborough.gov.uk

PR / Communications: Ms Rachael Thornton, Head of Communications, Town Hall, Bridge Street, Peterborough PE1 1HQ
☎ 01733 452477 ⌀ rachael.thornton@peterborough.gov.uk

Community Planning: Mr Adrian Chapman, Service Director - Adult Services & Communities, Bayard Place, Broadway, Peterborough PE1 1HZ ☎ 01733 863887
⌀ adrian.chapman@peterborough.gov.uk

Community Safety: Mr Adrian Chapman, Service Director - Adult Services & Communities, Bayard Place, Broadway, Peterborough PE1 1HZ ☎ 01733 863887 ⌀ adrian.chapman@peterborough.gov.uk

Computer Management: Mr Richard Godfrey, Assistant Director - Digital Peterborough, Town Hall, Bridge Street, Peterborough PE1 1HG ☎ 01733 317989 ⌀ richard.godfrey@peterborough.gov.uk

Contracts: Mr Andy Cox, Senior Contracts & Partnership Manager, Town Hall, Bridge Street, Peterborough PE1 1HG ☎ 01733 452465
⌀ andy.cox@peterborough.gov.uk

Corporate Services: Mr Steve Crabtree, Head of Internal Audit, The Guildhall, Cambridge CB2 3QJ ☎ 01223 458181
⌀ steve.crabtree@cambridge.gov.uk

Corporate Services: Mr John Harrison, Corporate Director - Resources, Town Hall, Bridge Street, Peterborough PE1 1HG
☎ 01733 452520 ⌀ john.harrison@peterborough.gov.uk

Corporate Services: Mr Richard Hodgson, Head of Strategic Projects, Town Hall, Bridge Street, Peterborough PE1 1HG
☎ 01733 384535 ⌀ richard.hodgson@peterborough.gov.uk

Corporate Services: Mr Steven Pilsworth, Head of Strategic Finance, Town Hall, Bridge Street, Peterborough PE1 1HG
☎ 01733 384564 ⌀ steven.pilsworth@peterborough.gov.uk

Customer Service: Mr Mark Sandhu, Head of Customer Services, Customer Service Centre, Bayard Place, Broadway, Peterborough PE1 1FZ ☎ 01733 296321 ⌀ mark.sandhu@serco.com

Economic Development: Mr Steve Bowyer, Acting Chief Executive, Peters Court, City Road, Peterborough PE1 1SA
☎ 01733 317489 ⌀ steve.bowyer@peterborough.gov.uk

Education: Mr Jonathan Lewis, Assistant Director - Education & Resources, Children's Services Dept, Bayard Place, Broadway, Peterborough PE1 1FB ☎ 01733 863912
⌀ jonathan.lewis@peterborough.gov.uk

E-Government: Mr Richard Godfrey, Assistant Director - Digital Peterborough, Town Hall, Bridge Street, Peterborough PE1 1HG
☎ 01733 317989 ⌀ richard.godfrey@peterborough.gov.uk

Electoral Registration: Mr Mark Emson, Electoral Services Officer, Town Hall, Bridge Street, Peterborough PE1 1HG
☎ 01733 452282 ⌀ mark.emson@peterborough.gov.uk

PETERBOROUGH CITY

Electoral Registration: Ms Rachel Parnell, Compliance Manager (Elections), Town Hall, Bridge Street, Peterborough PE1 1HG ☎ 01733 452277 ⁖ rachel.parnell@peterborough.gov.uk

Emergency Planning: Mr Kevin Dawson, Head of Resilience, Town Hall, Bridge Street, Peterborough PE1 1HG ☎ 01733 453464 ⁖ kevin.dawson@peterborough.gov.uk

Environmental / Technical Services: Mr Simon Machen, Director - Growth & Regeneration, Town Hall, Bridge Street, Peterborough PE1 1HG ☎ 01733 453475 ⁖ simon.machen@peterborough.gov.uk

Environmental Health: Mr Peter Gell, Strategic Regulatory Services Manager, Bayard Place, Broadway, Peterborough PE1 1HZ ☎ 01733 453419 ⁖ peter.gell@peterborough.gov.uk

Estates, Property & Valuation: Mr Richard Porter, Head of Strategic Property, Manor Drive, Paston Parkway, Peterborough PE4 7AP ☎ 01733 384544 ⁖ richard.porter@peterborough.gov.uk

European Liaison: Ms Annette Joyce, Head of Commercial Operations, Town Hall, Bridge Street, Peterborough PE1 1HG ☎ 01733 452280 ⁖ annette.joyce@peterborough.gov.uk

Events Manager: Ms Annette Joyce, Head of Commercial Operations, Town Hall, Bridge Street, Peterborough PE1 1HG ☎ 01733 452280 ⁖ annette.joyce@peterborough.gov.uk

Facilities: Ms Sue Scott, Premises Manager, Manor Drive, Paston Parkway, Peterborough PE4 7AP ☎ 01733 384542 ⁖ sue.scott@peterborough.gov.uk

Finance: Mr John Harrison, Corporate Director - Resources, Town Hall, Bridge Street, Peterborough PE1 1HG ☎ 01733 452520 ⁖ john.harrison@peterborough.gov.uk

Grounds Maintenance: Mr Martin Raper, Account Director, Amey, Nursery Lane, Fengate, Peterborough PE1 5BG ☎ 01733 425325 ⁖ martin.raper@amey.gov.uk

Health and Safety: Mr Andy Baker, Health & Safety Adviser, Town Hall, Bridge Street, Peterborough PE1 1HG ☎ 01733 453526 ⁖ andy.baker@peterborough.gov.uk

Highways: Mr Andy Tatt, Head of Highway Services, Town Hall, Bridge Street, Peterborough PE1 1HG ☎ 01733 453469 ⁖ andy.tatt@peterborough.gov.uk

Housing: Ms Belinda Child, Head of Housing & Health Improvement, Bayard Place, Broadway, Peterborough PE1 1HZ ☎ 01733 863769 ⁖ belinda.child@peterborough.gov.uk

Local Area Agreement: Mr Richard Astle, Director - GPP, 25 Priestgate, Peterborough PE1 1JL ☎ 01733 207340 ⁖ richard@gpp-peterborough.org.uk

Legal: Ms Kim Sawyer, Director - Governance, Town Hall, Bridge Street, Peterborough PE1 1HG ☎ 01733 452361 ⁖ kim.sawyer@peterborough.gov.uk

Leisure and Cultural Services: Mr Kevin Tighe, Head of Cultural Services, Vivacity, Central Library, Broadway, Peterborough PE1 1HZ ☎ 01733 863784 ⁖ kevin.tighe@vivacity-peterborough.com

Licensing: Mr Adrian Day, Licensing Manager, Bayard Place, Broadway, Peterborough PE1 1HZ ☎ 01733 454437 ⁖ adrian.day@peterborough.gov.uk

Lifelong Learning: Mrs Lou Williams, Service Director - Children's Services & Safeguarding, Bayard Place, Broadway, Peterborough PE1 1FB ☎ 01733 863606 ⁖ lou.williams@peterborough.gov.uk

Lighting: Mr Mark Speed, Transport & Infrastructure Planning Manager, Town Hall, Bridge Street, Peterborough PE1 1HG ☎ 01733 317471 ⁖ mark.speed@peterborough.gov.uk

Member Services: Ms Kim Sawyer, Director - Governance, Town Hall, Bridge Street, Peterborough PE1 1HG ☎ 01733 452361 ⁖ kim.sawyer@peterborough.gov.uk

Parking: Mr Darren Bell, Parking Operations Manager, Town Hall, Bridge Street, Peterborough PE1 1HG ☎ 01733 452375 ⁖ darren.bell@peterborough.gov.uk

Partnerships: Mr Dominic Hudson, Strategic Partnerships Manager, Town Hall, Bridge Street, Peterborough PE1 1HG ☎ 01733 452384 ⁖ dominic.hudson@peterborough.gov.uk

Personnel / HR: Mrs Mandy Pullen, Acting Head of Human Resources, Town Hall, Bridge Street, Peterborough PE1 1HG ☎ 01733 863628 ⁖ mandy.pullen@peterborough.gov.uk

Planning: Mr Simon Machen, Director - Growth & Regeneration, Town Hall, Bridge Street, Peterborough PE1 1HG ☎ 01733 453475 ⁖ simon.machen@peterborough.gov.uk

Procurement: Mr Andy Cox, Senior Contracts & Partnership Manager, Town Hall, Bridge Street, Peterborough PE1 1HG ☎ 01733 452465 ⁖ andy.cox@peterborough.gov.uk

Public Libraries: Ms Heather Walton, Library & Customer Services Manager, Vivacity, Central Library, Broadway, Peterborough PE1 1HZ ☎ 01733 864271 ⁖ heather.walton@vivacity-peterborough.com

Recycling & Waste Minimisation: Mr Richard Pearn, Waste Partnership Manager, Town Hall, Bridge Street, Peterborough PE1 1HG ☎ 01733 864739 ⁖ richard.pearn@peterborough.gov.uk

Regeneration: Mr Simon Machen, Director - Growth & Regeneration, Town Hall, Bridge Street, Peterborough PE1 1HG ☎ 01733 453475 ⁖ simon.machen@peterborough.gov.uk

Road Safety: Ms Clair George, Road Safety Officer, Bayard Place, Broadway, Peterborough PE1 1ZX ☎ 01733 453576 ⁖ clair.george@peterborough.gov.uk

Road Safety: Mr Peter Tebb, Network & Traffic Manager, Town Hall, Bridge Street, Peterborough PE1 1HG ☎ 01733 453519 ⁖ peter.tebb@peterborough.gov.uk

Social Services (Adult): Mr Adrian Chapman, Service Director - Adult Services & Communities, Bayard Place, Broadway, Peterborough PE1 1HZ ☎ 01733 863887 ✆ adrian.chapman@peterborough.gov.uk

Social Services (Children): Mrs Lou Williams, Service Director - Children's Services & Safeguarding, Bayard Place, Broadway, Peterborough PE1 1FB ☎ 01733 863606 ✆ lou.williams@peterborough.gov.uk

Public Health: Dr Liz Robin, Director - Public Health, Town Hall, Bridge Street, Peterborough PE1 1HG ☎ 01733 207175 ✆ liz.robin@peterborough.gov.u

Staff Training: Mr Colin Wilson, Training & Development Manager, Town Hall, Bridge Street, Peterborough PE1 1HG ☎ 01733 864626 ✆ colin.wilson@peterborough.gov.uk

Street Scene: Mr Martin Raper, Account Director, Amey, Nursery Lane, Fengate, Peterborough PE1 5BG ☎ 01733 425325 ✆ martin.raper@amey.gov.uk

Sustainable Communities: Ms Wendi Ogle-Welbourn, Corporate Director - People & Communities, Bayard Place, Broadway, Peterborough PE1 1FB ☎ 01733 863749 ✆ wendi.ogle-welbourn@peterborough.gov.uk

Sustainable Development: Mr Simon Machen, Director - Growth & Regeneration, Town Hall, Bridge Street, Peterborough PE1 1HG ☎ 01733 453475 ✆ simon.machen@peterborough.gov.uk

Tourism: Ms Annette Joyce, Head of Commercial Operations, City Centre Services, Town Hall, Bridge Street, Peterborough PE1 1HG ☎ 01733 452280 ✆ annette.joyce@peterborough.gov.uk

Town Centre: Ms Annette Joyce, Head of Commercial Operations, Town Hall, Bridge Street, Peterborough PE1 1HG ☎ 01733 452280 ✆ annette.joyce@peterborough.gov.uk

Traffic Management: Mr Simon Machen, Director - Growth & Regeneration, Town Hall, Bridge Street, Peterborough PE1 1HG ☎ 01733 453475 ✆ simon.machen@peterborough.gov.uk

Transport: Mr Mark Speed, Transport & Infrastructure Planning Manager, Town Hall, Bridge Street, Peterborough PE1 1HG ☎ 01733 317471 ✆ mark.speed@peterborough.gov.uk

Transport Planner: Mr Mark Speed, Transport & Infrastructure Planning Manager, Town Hall, Bridge Street, Peterborough PE1 1HG ☎ 01733 317471 ✆ mark.speed@peterborough.gov.uk

Total Place: Ms Annette Joyce, Head of Commercial Operations, Town Hall, Bridge Street, Peterborough PE1 1HG ☎ 01733 452280 ✆ annette.joyce@peterborough.gov.uk

Waste Collection and Disposal: Mr Martin Raper, Account Director, Amey, Nursery Lane, Fengate, Peterborough PE1 5BG ☎ 01733 425325 ✆ martin.raper@amey.gov.uk

Waste Management: Mr Richard Pearn, Waste Partnership Manager, Town Hall, Bridge Street, Peterborough PE1 1HG ☎ 01733 864739 ✆ richard.pearn@peterborough.gov.uk

Children's Play Areas: Mrs Denise Noble, Voyager Area Manager, Bayard Place, Broadway, Peterborough PE1 1FB ☎ 01733 742581 ✆ denise.noble@peterborough.gov.uk

COUNCILLORS

Mayor: Sanders, David (CON - Eye, Thorney & Newborough) david.sanders@peterborough.gov.uk

Deputy Mayor: Sharp, Keith (LIB - Dogsthorpe) keith.sharp@peterborough.gov.uk

Leader of the Council: Holdich, John (CON - Glinton & Castor) john.holdich@peterborough.gov.uk

Deputy Leader of the Council: Fitzgerald, Wayne (CON - West) wayne.fitzgerald@peterborough.gov.uk

Group Leader: Fox, John (IND - Werrington) john.fox@peterborough.gov.uk

Group Leader: Sandford, Nick (LD - Paston & Walton) nick.sandford@peterborough.gov.uk

Aitken, Kim (CON - Orton Waterville) kim.aitken@peterborough.gov.uk

Ali, Ansar (LAB - North) ansar.ali@peterborough.gov.uk

Allen, Steve (CON - Eye, Thorney & Newborough)

Ash, Chris (LIB - Dogsthorpe) chris.ash@peterborough.gov.uk

Ayres, Lynne (CON - West) lynne.ayres@peterborough.gov.uk

Barkham, Simon (LD - Paston & Walton) simon.barkham@peterborough.gov.uk

Bisby, Ray (CON - Stanground South) ray.bisby@peterborough.gov.uk

Bond, Andrew (LD - Gunthorpe)

Brown, Richard (CON - Eye, Thorney & Newborough) richard.brown@peterborough.gov.uk

Bull, June (CON - Orton Longueville) june.bull@peterborough.gov.uk

Casey, Graham (CON - Orton Longueville) graham.casey@peterborough.gov.uk

Cereste, Marco (CON - Hampton Vale) marco.cereste@peterborough.gov.uk

Clark, Alan (LAB - Fletton & Stanground)

Coles, Andy (CON - Fletton & Woodston) andy.coles@peterborough.gov.uk

Davidson, Julia (LD - Gunthorpe) julia.davidson@peterborough.gov.uk

Dowson, Alan (LAB - Fletton & Woodston) alan.dowson@peterborough.gov.uk

Ellis, Angus (LAB - Bretton North)

Elsey, Gavin (CON - Orton Waterville) gavin.elsey@peterborough.gov.uk

Ferris, Richard (LAB - Park) richard.ferris@peterborough.gov.uk

Fower, Darren (LD - Gunthorpe) darren.fower@peterborough.gov.uk

PETERBOROUGH CITY

Fox, Judy (IND - Werrington)
judy.fox@peterborough.gov.uk

Fuller, Howard (CON - Hargate & Hempsted)
howard.fuller@peterborough.gov.uk

Goodwin, Janet (CON - Hargate & Hempsted)
janet.goodwin@peterborough.gov.uk

Harper, Chris (CON - Stanground South)
chris.harper@peterborough.gov.uk

Hiller, Peter (CON - Glinton & Castor)
peter.hiller@peterborough.gov.uk

Hussain, Mahboob (LAB - Central)
mahboob.hussain@peterborough.gov.uk

Iqbal, Amjad (LAB - Central)
amjad.iqbal@peterborough.gov.uk

Iqbal, Azher (CON - East)
azher.iqbal@peterborough.gov.uk

Jamil, Mohammed (LAB - Central)
mohammed.jamil@peterborough.gov.uk

Johnson, Jo (LAB - East)
jo.johnson@peterborough.gov.uk

Khan, Nazim (LAB - North)
nazim.khan@peterborough.gov.uk

King, Dave (CON - Hampton Vale)

Lamb, Diane (CON - Wittering)
diane.lamb@peterborough.gov.uk

Lane, Stephen (IND - Werrington)
stephen.lane@peterborough.gov.uk

Lillis, James (LD - Fletton & Stanground)
james.lillis@peterborough.gov.uk

Martin, Stuart (LAB - Bretton North)
stuart.martin@peterborough.gov.uk

Murphy, Ed (LAB - Ravensthorpe)
ed.murphy@peterborough.gov.uk

Nadeem, Mohammed (CON - North)
mohammed.nadeem@peterborough.gov.uk

Nawaz, Gul (CON - Ravensthorpe)
gul.nawaz@peterborough.gov.uk

Okonkowski, John (UKIP - Orton Longueville)
john.okonkowski@peterborough.gov.uk

Over, David (CON - Barnack)
david.over@peterborough.gov.uk

Peach, John (CON - Park)
john.peach@peterborough.gov.uk

Rush, Brian (CON - Stanground South)
brian.rush@peterborough.gov.uk

Saltmarsh, Bella (LIB - Dogsthorpe)
bella.saltmarsh@peterborough.gov.uk

Seaton, David (CON - Hampton Vale)
david.seaton@peterborough.gov.uk

Serluca, Lucia (CON - Fletton & Woodston)
lucia.serluca@peterborough.gov.uk

Shaheed, Asif (LD - Paston & Walton)
asif.shaheed@peterborough.gov.uk

Shearman, John (LAB - Park)
john.shearman@peterborough.gov.uk

Sims, Marcus (CON - East)
marcus.sims@peterborough.gov.uk

Smith, Sam (CON - Ravensthorpe)
sam.smith@peterborough.gov.uk

Stokes, June (CON - Orton Waterville)
june.stokes@peterborough.gov.uk

Sylvester, Ann (LAB - Bretton North)
ann.sylvester@peterborough.gov.uk

Walsh, Irene (CON - Hargate & Hempsted)
irene.walsh@peterborough.gov.uk

Whitby, John (UKIP - Fletton & Stanground)
john.whitby@peterborough.gov.uk

POLITICAL COMPOSITION
CON: 31, LAB: 14, LD: 7, LIB: 3, IND: 3, UKIP: 2

COMMITTEE CHAIRS

Audit: Mr Howard Fuller

Health & Wellbeing: Mr John Holdich

Licensing: Ms Lynne Ayres

Planning & Environmental Protection: Mr Chris Harper

Plymouth City   U

Plymouth City Council, Civic Centre, Royal Parade, Plymouth PL1 2AA
☎ 01752 668000 ⌨ enquiries@plymouth.gov.uk
🖥 www.plymouth.gov.uk

FACTS AND FIGURES
EU Constituencies: South West
Election Frequency: Elections are by thirds

PRINCIPAL OFFICERS

Chief Executive: Ms Tracey Lee, Chief Executive, Ballard House, West Hoe Road, Plymouth PL1 3BJ ☎ 01752 668000 ⌨ tracey.lee@plymouth.gov.uk

Assistant Chief Executive: Mr Giles Perritt, Assistant Chief Executive, Plymouth City Council, Plymouth PL1 2AA ☎ 01752 668000 ⌨ giles.peritt@plymouth.gov.uk

Senior Management: Ms Lesa Annear, Director - Transformation, Civic Centre, Royal Parade, Plymouth PL1 2AA ☎ 01752 668000 ⌨ lesa.annear@plymouth.gov.uk

Senior Management: Mrs Carole Burgoyne, Director - People, Plymouth City Council, Plymouth PL1 2AA ☎ 01752 668000 ⌨ carole.burgoyne@plymouth.gov.uk

Senior Management: Mr Kelechi Nnoaham, Director - Public Health, Plymouth City Council, Plymouth PL1 2AA ☎ 01752 668000 ⌨ kelechi.nnoaham@plymouth.gov.uk

Senior Management: Mr Anthony Payne, Director - Place, Plymouth City Council, Plymouth PL1 2AA ☎ 01752 668000 ⌨ anthony.payne@plymouth.gov.uk

Architect, Building / Property Services: Mr Anthony Payne, Director - Place, Plymouth City Council, Plymouth PL1 2AA
☎ 01752 668000 ⁂ anthony.payne@plymouth.gov.uk

Building Control: Mr Paul Barnard, Assistant Director - Strategic Planning & Infrastructure, Plymouth City Counil, Plymouth PL1 2AA
☎ 01752 668000 ⁂ paul.barnard@plymouth.gov.uk

Catering Services: Mr Brad Pearce, Managing Director - CaterEd, Plymouth City Council, Plymouth PL1 2AA ☎ 01752 668000 ⁂ brad.pearce@plymouth.gov.uk

Children / Youth Services: Ms Judith Harwood, Assistant Director - Education, Learning & Families, Plymouth City Council, Plymouth PL1 2AA ☎ 01752 668000 ⁂ judith.harwood@plymouth.gov.uk

PR / Communications: Mr Richard Longford, Head of Communications, Plymouth City Council, Plymouth PL1 2AA
☎ 01752 305405 ⁂ richard.longford@plymouth.gov.uk

Community Safety: Mr Peter Aley, Head of Community Services, Plymouth City Council, Plymouth PL1 2AA ☎ 01752 668000 ⁂ pete.aley@plymouth.gov.uk

Consumer Protection and Trading Standards: Mr Alexander Fry, Service Manager - Trading Standards, Building 4, Derriford Business Park, Plymouth PL6 5QZ ☎ 01752 668000 ⁂ alexander.fry@plymouth.gov.uk

Contracts: Mr Howard Goffin, Procurement Services Manager, Floor 2, Ballard House, West Hoe Road, Plymouth PL1 3BJ
☎ 01752 668000 ⁂ howard.goffin@plymouth.gov.uk

Customer Service: Ms Faye Batchelor-Hambleton, Assistant Director - Customer Services, Plymouth City Council, Plymouth PL1 2AA ☎ 01752 668000

Economic Development: Mr David Draffan, Assistant Director - Economic Development, Plymouth City Council, Plymouth PL1 2AA
☎ 01752 668000 ⁂ david.draffan@plymouth.gov.uk

Education: Ms Judith Harwood, Assistant Director - Education, Learning & Families, Plymouth City Council, Plymouth PL1 2AA
☎ 01752 668000 ⁂ judith.harwood@plymouth.gov.uk

Electoral Registration: Mr Amerjit Kang, Interim Electoral Services Manager, Ballard House, West Hoe Road, Plymouth PL1 3BJ ☎ 01752 668000 ⁂ amerjit.kang@plymouth.gov.uk

Emergency Planning: Mr Scott Senior, Civil Protection Manager, Plymouth City Council, Plymouth PL1 2AA ☎ 01752 668000 ⁂ scott.senior@plymouth.gov.uk

Energy Management: Mr Alistair Macpherson, Low Carbon City Manager, Ballard House, West Hoe Road, Plymouth PL1 3BJ
☎ 01752 668000 ⁂ alistair.macpherson@plymouth.gov.uk

Environmental Health: Ms Katherin O'Connor, Public Protection Service Manager, Ballard House, West Hoe Road, Plymouth PL1 3BJ ☎ 01752 668000 ⁂ katherin.o'connor@plymouth.gov.uk

Events Manager: Mr Jamie Yabsley, Visitor, Marketing & Events Manager, Floor 2, Ballard House, West Hoe Road, Plymouth PL1 3BJ ☎ 01752 668000 ⁂ jamie.yabsley@plymouth.gov.uk

Facilities: Mr Anthony Dangar, Facilities Manager, Floor 2, Ballard House, West Hoe Road, Plymouth PL1 3BJ ☎ 01752 668000 ⁂ anthony.dangar@plymouth.gov.uk

Fleet Management: Mr John Simpson, Fleet & Garage Manager, Prince Rock Depot, Macadam Road, Plymouth PL4 0RZ
☎ 01752 668000 ⁂ john.simpson@plymouth.gov.uk

Grounds Maintenance: Mr Gareth Harrison-Poole, Street Cleansing & Grounds Manager, Prince Rock Depot, Macadam Road, Plymouth PL4 0RZ ☎ 01752 668000 ⁂ gareth.harrison-poole@plymouth.gov.uk

Health and Safety: Ms Emma Rose, Head of Health, Safety & Wellbeing, Plymouth City Council, Plymouth PL1 2AA
☎ 01752 668000 ⁂ emma.rose@plymouth.gov.uk

Highways: Mr Adrian Trim, Head of Highways, Parks & Maritime Services, Plymouth City Council, Plymouth PL1 2AA
☎ 01752 668000 ⁂ adrian.trim@plymouth.gov.uk

Housing: Mr Matt Garrett, Head of Housing Services, Ballard House, West Hoe Road, Plymouth PL1 3BJ ☎ 01752 668000 ⁂ matt.garrett@plymouth.gov.uk

Legal: Mr David Shepperd, Head of Legal Services, Plymouth City Council, Plymouth PL1 2AA ☎ 01752 668000 ⁂ david.shepperd@plymouth.gov.uk

Leisure and Cultural Services: Ms Nicola Moyle, Head of Arts & Heritage, Plymouth City Council, Plymouth PL1 2AA
☎ 01752 668000 ⁂ nicola.moyle@plymouth.gov.uk

Licensing: Mr Andrew Netherton, Licensing Service Manager, Ballard House, West Hoe Road, Plymouth PL1 3BJ
☎ 01752 668000 ⁂ andrew.netherton@plymouth.gov.uk

Member Services: Ms Judith Shore, Democratic & Member Services Manager, Plymouth City Council, Plymouth PL1 2AA
☎ 01752 668000 ⁂ judith.shore@plymouth.gov.uk

Parking: Mr Mike Artherton, Parking & Marine Service Manager, Plymouth City Council, Plymouth PL1 2AA ☎ 01752 668000 ⁂ mike.artherton@plymouth.gov.uk

Personnel / HR: Mr Giles Perritt, Assistant Chief Executive, Plymouth City Council, Plymouth PL1 2AA ☎ 01752 668000 ⁂ giles.peritt@plymouth.gov.uk

Planning: Mr Paul Barnard, Assistant Director - Strategic Planning & Infrastructure, Plymouth City Council, Plymouth PL1 2AA
☎ 01752 668000 ⁂ paul.barnard@plymouth.gov.uk

Procurement: Mr Howard Goffin, Procurement Services Manager, Floor 2, Ballard House, West Hoe Road, Plymouth PL1 3BJ
☎ 01752 668000 ⁂ howard.goffin@plymouth.gov.uk

PLYMOUTH CITY

Recycling & Waste Minimisation: Mr Gareth Harrison-Poole, Street Cleansing & Grounds Manager, Prince Rock Depot, Macadam Road, Plymouth PL4 0RZ ☎ 01752 668000 ⌨ gareth.harrison-poole@plymouth.gov.uk

Regeneration: Mr Anthony Payne, Director - Place, Plymouth City Council, Plymouth PL1 2AA ☎ 01752 668000 ⌨ anthony.payne@plymouth.gov.uk

Road Safety: Ms Susan Keith, Road Safety Officer, Plymouth City Council, Plymouth PL1 2AA ☎ 01752 668000 ⌨ susan.keith@plymouth.gov.uk

Social Services (Adult): Mrs Carole Burgoyne, Director - People, Plymouth City Council, Plymouth PL1 2AA ☎ 01752 668000 ⌨ carole.burgoyne@plymouth.gov.uk

Social Services (Children): Ms Alison Botham, Assistant Director - Children's Social Care, Plymouth City Council, Plymouth PL1 2AA ☎ 01752 668000 ⌨ alison.botham@plymouth.gov.uk

Public Health: Mr Kelechi Nnoaham, Director - Public Health, Plymouth City Council, Plymouth PL1 2AA ☎ 01752 668000 ⌨ kelechi.nnoaham@plymouth.gov.uk

Street Scene: Mr Gareth Harrison-Poole, Street Cleansing & Grounds Manager, Prince Rock Depot, Macadam Road, Plymouth PL4 0RZ ☎ 01752 668000 ⌨ gareth.harrison-poole@plymouth.gov.uk

Tourism: Mr David Draffan, Assistant Director - Economic Development, Plymouth City Council, Plymouth PL1 2AA ☎ 01752 668000 ⌨ david.draffan@plymouth.gov.uk

Town Centre: Mr Jon Walton, City Centre Manager - Plymouth City Centre Company, Ballard House, West Hoe Road, Plymouth PL1 3BJ ☎ 01752 668000 ⌨ jon.watson@plymouth.gov.uk

Traffic Management: Mr Adrian Trim, Head of Highways, Parks & Maritime Services, Plymouth City Council, Plymouth PL1 2AA ☎ 01752 668000 ⌨ adrian.trim@plymouth.gov.uk

Transport Planner: Mr Adrian Trim, Head of Highways, Parks & Maritime Services, Plymouth City Council, Plymouth PL1 2AA ☎ 01752 668000 ⌨ adrian.trim@plymouth.gov.uk

Waste Collection and Disposal: Mr Simon Dale, Assistant Director - Street Scene Services (Interim), Plymouth City Council, Plymouth PL1 2AA ☎ 01752 668000 ⌨ simon.dale@plymouth.gov.uk

Waste Management: Mr Gareth Harrison-Poole, Street Cleansing & Grounds Manager, Prince Rock Depot, Macadam Road, Plymouth PL4 0RZ ☎ 01752 668000 ⌨ gareth.harrison-poole@plymouth.gov.uk

Children's Play Areas: Mr Gareth Harrison-Poole, Street Cleansing & Grounds Manager, Prince Rock Depot, Macadam Road, Plymouth PL4 0RZ ☎ 01752 668000 ⌨ gareth.harrison-poole@plymouth.gov.uk

COUNCILLORS

The Lord Mayor: Murphy, Pauline (LAB - Efford & Lipson) pauline.murphy@plymouth.gov.uk

Deputy Lord Mayor: Davey, Sam (LAB - Stoke) sam.davey@plymouth.gov.uk

Leader of the Council: Bowyer, Ian (CON - Eggbuckland) ian.bowyer@plymouth.gov.uk

Deputy Leader of the Council: Nicholson, Patrick (CON - Plympton St Mary) patrick.nicholson@plymouth.gov.uk

Group Leader: Evans, Tudor (LAB - Ham) tudor.evans@plymouth.gov.uk

Aspinall, Mary (LAB - Sutton & Mount Gould) mary.aspinall@plymouth.gov.uk

Ball, Richard (CON - Compton) richard.ball@plymouth.gov.uk

Beer, Terri (CON - Plympton Erle) terri.beer@plymouth.gov.uk

Bowie, Sally (LAB - St Budeaux) sally.bowie@plymouth.gov.uk

Bowyer, Lynda (CON - Eggbuckland) lynda.bowyer@plymouth.gov.uk

Bridgeman, Maddi (UKIP - Moor View) maddi.bridgeman@plymouth.gov.uk

Carson, Tony (CON - Peverell) tony.carson@plymouth.gov.uk

Churchill, Nigel (CON - Plymstock Dunstone) nigel.churchill@plymouth.gov.uk

Coker, Mark (LAB - Devonport) mark.coker@plymouth.gov.uk

Cook, Heath (CON - Eggbuckland) heath.cook@plymouth.gov.uk

Dann, Sue (LAB - Sutton & Mount Gould) sue.dann@plymouth.gov.uk

Darcy, Ian (CON - Plympton Erle) ian.darcy@plymouth.gov.uk

Davey, Philippa (LAB - Stoke) philippa.davey@plymouth.gov.uk

Deacon, Mark (CON - Southway) mark.deacon@plymouth.gov.uk

Downie, David (CON - Budshead) dave.downie@plymouth.gov.uk

Drean, Jonathan (CON - Budshead) jonathan.drean@plymouth.gov.uk

Fletcher, David (CON - Compton) david.fletcher@plymouth.gov.uk

Foster, Wendy (CON - Plymstock Radford) wendy.foster@plymouth.gov.uk

Foster, Ken (CON - Plymstock Radford) kenneth.foster@plymouth.gov.uk

Fry, Ted (CON - Compton) ted.fry@plymouth.gov.uk

Hendy, Neil (LAB - Efford & Lipson) neil.hendy@plymouth.gov.uk

James, David (CON - Plympton St Mary)
david.i.james@plymouth.gov.uk

Jordan, Glenn (CON - Plympton Chaddlewood)
glenn.jordan@plymouth.gov.uk

Kelly, Nick (CON - Moor View)
nick.kelly@plymouth.gov.uk

Leaves, Sam (CON - Plympton Chaddlewood)
samantha.leaves@plymouth.gov.uk

Leaves, Martin (CON - Peverell)
martin.leaves@plymouth.gov.uk

Leaves, Michael (CON - Plymstock Radford)
michael.leaves@plymouth.gov.uk

Loveridge, Andrea (CON - Plympton St Mary)
andrea.loveridge@plymouth.gov.uk

Lowry, Mark (LAB - Honicknowle)
mark.lowry@plymouth.gov.uk

Mahony, John (CON - Peverell)
john.mahony@plymouth.gov.uk

Mavin, Christopher (LAB - Moor View)
chris.mavin@plymouth.gov.uk

McDonald, Susan (LAB - St Peter & the Waterfront)
susan.mcdonald@plymouth.gov.uk

Morris, Jonny (LAB - Southway)
jonny.morris@plymouth.gov.uk

Parker, Lorraine (LAB - Southway)
lorraine.parker@plymouth.gov.uk

Penberthy, Chris (LAB - St Peter & the Waterfront)
chris.penberthy@plymouth.gov.uk

Pengelly, Vivien (CON - Plymstock Dunstone)
vivien.pengelly@plymouth.gov.uk

Rennie, Eddie (LAB - Sutton & Mount Gould)
eddie.rennie@plymouth.gov.uk

Ricketts, Steven (CON - Drake)
steven.ricketts@plymouth.gov.uk

Riley, John (UKIP - Honicknowle)
john.riley@plymouth.gov.uk

Singh, Chaz (LAB - Drake)
chaz.singh@plymouth.gov.uk

Smith, Peter (LAB - Honicknowle)
peter.smith@plymouth.gov.uk

Sparling, Michael (LAB - Stoke)
mike.sparling@plymouth.gov.uk

Stevens, William (LAB - Devonport)
william.stevens@plymouth.gov.uk

Storer, Christopher (UKIP - Ham)
chris.storer@plymouth.gov.uk

Taylor, Kate (LAB - Devonport)
kate.taylor@plymouth.gov.uk

Taylor, John (LAB - Budshead)
jon.taylor@plymouth.gov.uk

Tuffin, Ian (LAB - St Peter & the Waterfront)
ian.tuffin@plymouth.gov.uk

Tuohy, Tina (LAB - Ham)
tina.tuohy@plymouth.gov.uk

Vincent, Brian (LAB - Efford & Lipson)
brian.vincent@plymouth.gov.uk

Wheeler, George (LAB - St Budeaux)
george.wheeler@plymouth.gov.uk

Wigens, Kevin (CON - Plymstock Dunstone)
kevin.wigens@plymouth.gov.uk

Winter, Darren (LAB - St Budeaux)
darren.winter@plymouth.gov.uk

POLITICAL COMPOSITION
CON: 27, LAB: 27, UKIP: 3

COMMITTEE CHAIRS

Audit: Ms Sam Leaves

Health & Wellbeing: Ms Lynda Bowyer

Licensing: Dr John Mahony

Planning: Mr Kevin Wigens

Poole   U

Borough of Poole, Civic Centre, Poole BH15 2RU
☎ 01202 633633 📠 01202 633706 ✆ enquiries@poole.gov.uk
💻 www.boroughofpoole.com

FACTS AND FIGURES
Parliamentary Constituencies: Dorset Mid and Poole North, Poole
EU Constituencies: South West
Election Frequency: Elections are of whole council

PRINCIPAL OFFICERS

Chief Executive: Mr Andrew Flockhart, Interim Chief Executive,
Civic Centre, Poole BH15 2RU ☎ 01202 633201
✆ a.flockhart@poole.gov.uk

Senior Management: Mrs Kate Ryan, Strategic Director - Place,
Civic Centre, Poole BH15 2RU ☎ 01202 633202
✆ k.ryan@poole.gov.uk

Senior Management: Ms Jan Thurgood, Strategic Director -
People, Civic Centre, Poole BH15 2RU ☎ 01202 633207
✆ j.thurgood@poole.gov.uk

Access Officer / Social Services (Disability): Mr David Vitty,
Head of Adult Social Care Services, Civic Centre Annexe, Poole
BH15 2RU ☎ 01202 261132 ✆ d.vitty@poole.gov.uk

Architect, Building / Property Services: Mr Adam Richens,
Head of Financial Services, Civic Centre, Poole BH15 2RU
☎ 01202 633183; 01202 633811 ✆ a.richens@poole.gov.uk

Best Value: Ms Bridget West, Corporate Communications &
Information Manager, Civic Centre, Poole BH15 2RU
☎ 01202 633085; 01202 633899 ✆ bridget.west@poole.gov.uk

Building Control: Mr Stephen Thorne, Head of Planning &
Regeneration Services, Civic Centre, Poole BH15 2RU
☎ 01202 633327; 01202 633345 ✆ s.thorne@poole.gov.uk

POOLE

Catering Services: Ms Tina Hayter, Executive Catering Manager, Crown Buildings 4th Floor, Civic Centre, Poole BH15 2RU ☎ 01202 261178; 01202 261001 ✆ t.hayter@poole.gov.uk

Children / Youth Services: Mrs Vicky Wales, Head of Children, Young People & Learning, The Dolphin Centre, Poole BH15 1SZ ☎ 01202 262251 ✆ v.wales@poole.gov.uk

Civil Registration: Mr Tim Martin, Head of Legal, Democratic & Strategy Services, Civic Centre, Poole BH15 2RU ☎ 01202 633021; 01202 633040 ✆ t.martin@poole.gov.uk

PR / Communications: Mr Ian Turner, Communications Manager, Civic Centre, Poole BH15 2RU ☎ 01202 633269 ✆ l.turner@poole.gov.uk

Community Planning: Mr Tim Martin, Head of Legal, Democratic & Strategy Services, Civic Centre, Poole BH15 2RU ☎ 01202 633021; 01202 633040 ✆ t.martin@poole.gov.uk

Community Safety: Mrs Anthi Minhinnick, Community Safety Partnership Manager, Civic Centre, Poole BH15 2RU ☎ 01202 223320 ✆ a.minhinnick@poole.gov.uk

Computer Management: Mrs Katie Lacey, Head of ICT & Customer Support, Civic Centre, Poole BH15 2RU ☎ 01202 633156 ✆ k.lacey@poole.gov.uk

Consumer Protection and Trading Standards: Mr Shaun Robson, Head of Environmental & Consumer Protection, Unit 1, Newfields Business Park, 2 Stinsford Road, Poole BH17 0NF ☎ 01202 261701; 01202 262240 ✆ s.robson@poole.gov.uk

Contracts: Mr Adam Richens, Head of Financial Services, Civic Centre, Poole BH15 2RU ☎ 01202 633183; 01202 633811 ✆ a.richens@poole.gov.uk

Customer Service: Mrs Katie Lacey, Head of ICT & Customer Support, Civic Centre, Poole BH15 2RU ☎ 01202 633156 ✆ k.lacey@poole.gov.uk

Economic Development: Mr Stephen Thorne, Head of Planning & Regeneration Services, Civic Centre, Poole BH15 2RU ☎ 01202 633327; 01202 633345 ✆ s.thorne@poole.gov.uk

Education: Mrs Vicky Wales, Head of Children, Young People & Learning, The Dolphin Centre, Poole BH15 1SZ ☎ 01202 262251 ✆ v.wales@poole.gov.uk

Electoral Registration: Mr Paul Morris, Registration Services Manager, Room 157, Civic Centre, Poole BH15 2RH ☎ 01202 633028; 01202 633094 ✆ p.morris@poole.gov.uk

Emergency Planning: Mr Adam Richens, Head of Financial Services, Civic Centre, Poole BH15 2RU ☎ 01202 633183; 01202 633811 ✆ a.richens@poole.gov.uk

Environmental / Technical Services: Mr Shaun Robson, Head of Environmental & Consumer Protection, Unit 1, Newfields Business Park, 2 Stinsford Road, Poole BH17 0NF ☎ 01202 261701; 01202 262240 ✆ s.robson@poole.gov.uk

Environmental Health: Mr Shaun Robson, Head of Environmental & Consumer Protection, Unit 1, Newfields Business Park, 2 Stinsford Road, Poole BH17 0NF ☎ 01202 261701; 01202 262240 ✆ s.robson@poole.gov.uk

Estates, Property & Valuation: Mr Adam Richens, Head of Financial Services, Civic Centre, Poole BH15 2RU ☎ 01202 633183; 01202 633811 ✆ a.richens@poole.gov.uk

European Liaison: Mr Stephen Thorne, Head of Planning & Regeneration Services, Civic Centre, Poole BH15 2RU ☎ 01202 633327; 01202 633345 ✆ s.thorne@poole.gov.uk

Facilities: Mr Julian McLaughlin, Head of Transportation Services, Civic Centre, Poole BH15 2RU ☎ 01202 262143 ✆ julian.mclaughlin@poole.gov.uk

Finance: Mr Adam Richens, Head of Financial Services, Civic Centre, Poole BH15 2RU ☎ 01202 633183; 01202 633811 ✆ a.richens@poole.gov.uk

Fleet Management: Mr Shaun Robson, Head of Environmental & Consumer Protection, Unit 1, Newfields Business Park, 2 Stinsford Road, Poole BH17 0NF ☎ 01202 261701; 01202 262240 ✆ s.robson@poole.gov.uk

Grounds Maintenance: Mr Kevin McErlane, Head of Culture & Community Learning, Poole Central Library, The Dolphin Centre, Poole BH15 1QE ☎ 01202 262400; 01202 262431 ✆ k.mcerlane@poole.gov.uk

Health and Safety: Mr Vincent Axford, Health & Safety Officer, Unit 1, Newfields Business Park, 2 Stinsford Road, Poole BH17 0NF ☎ 01202 633463; 01202 633477 ✆ v.axford@poole.gov.uk

Highways: Mr Julian McLaughlin, Head of Transportation Services, Civic Centre, Poole BH15 2RU ☎ 01202 262143 ✆ julian.mclaughlin@poole.gov.uk

Home Energy Conservation: Mr Paul Cooling, Carbon Reduction Manager, Civic Centre, Poole BH15 2RU ☎ 01202 633719 ✆ p.cooling@poole.gov.uk

Housing: Ms Cally Antill, Head of Housing & Community Services, Civic Centre, Poole BH15 2RU ☎ 01202 633440 ✆ c.antill@poole.gov.uk

Housing Maintenance: Mr Joe Logan, Head of Poole Housing Partnership (PHP) Ltd, Poole Housing Partnership (PHP) Ltd, Beech House, 28 - 30 Wimbourne Road, Poole BH15 2BU ☎ 01202 264444

Local Area Agreement: Mr Tim Martin, Head of Legal, Democratic & Strategy Services, Civic Centre, Poole BH15 2RU ☎ 01202 633021; 01202 633040 ✆ t.martin@poole.gov.uk

Legal: Mr Tim Martin, Head of Legal, Democratic & Strategy Services, Civic Centre, Poole BH15 2RU ☎ 01202 633021; 01202 633040 ✆ t.martin@poole.gov.uk

Leisure and Cultural Services: Mr Kevin McErlane, Head of Culture & Community Learning, Poole Central Library, The Dolphin Centre, Poole BH15 1QE ☎ 01202 262400; 01202 262431 ✆ k.mcerlane@poole.gov.uk

Licensing: Mr Shaun Robson, Head of Environmental & Consumer Protection, Unit 1, Newfields Business Park, 2 Stinsford Road, Poole BH17 0NF ☎ 01202 261701; 01202 262240 ✆ s.robson@poole.gov.uk

Lifelong Learning: Mr Kevin McErlane, Head of Culture & Community Learning, Poole Central Library, The Dolphin Centre, Poole BH15 1QE ☎ 01202 262400; 01202 262431 ✆ k.mcerlane@poole.gov.uk

Lighting: Mr Julian McLaughlin, Head of Transportation Services, Civic Centre, Poole BH15 2RU ☎ 01202 262143 ✆ julian.mclaughlin@poole.gov.uk

Lottery Funding, Charity and Voluntary: Mr Kevin McErlane, Head of Culture & Community Learning, Poole Central Library, The Dolphin Centre, Poole BH15 1QE ☎ 01202 262400; 01202 262431 ✆ k.mcerlane@poole.gov.uk

Lottery Funding, Charity and Voluntary: Ms Karen Naylor, Principal Officer - Planning & Quality Assurance, Crown Buildings 3rd Floor, Poole BH15 2RU ☎ 01202 261130; 01202 261161 ✆ k.naylor@poole.gov.uk

Member Services: Miss Pauline Gill, Democratic Services Manager, Civic Centre, Poole BH15 2RU ☎ 01202 633043; 01202 633040 ✆ p.gill@poole.gov.uk

Parking: Mr Julian McLaughlin, Head of Transportation Services, Civic Centre, Poole BH15 2RU ☎ 01202 262143 ✆ julian.mclaughlin@poole.gov.uk

Partnerships: Mr Tim Martin, Head of Legal, Democratic & Strategy Services, Civic Centre, Poole BH15 2RU ☎ 01202 633021; 01202 633040 ✆ t.martin@poole.gov.uk

Personnel / HR: Mr Carl Wilcox, Head of Human Resources, Civic Centre, Poole BH15 2RU ☎ 01202 633452; 01202 633477 ✆ c.wilcox@poole.gov.uk

Planning: Mr Stephen Thorne, Head of Planning & Regeneration Services, Civic Centre, Poole BH15 2RU ☎ 01202 633327; 01202 633345 ✆ s.thorne@poole.gov.uk

Procurement: Mr Adam Richens, Head of Financial Services, Civic Centre, Poole BH15 2RU ☎ 01202 633183; 01202 633811 ✆ a.richens@poole.gov.uk

Public Libraries: Mr Kevin McErlane, Head of Culture & Community Learning, Poole Central Library, The Dolphin Centre, Poole BH15 1QE ☎ 01202 262400; 01202 262431 ✆ k.mcerlane@poole.gov.uk

Recycling & Waste Minimisation: Ms Ruzina Begum, Waste Management Officer, Unit 1, New Field Business Park, Stinsford Road, Poole BH17 0NF ☎ 01202 261742; 01202 261717 ✆ r.begum@poole.gov.uk

Regeneration: Mr Stephen Thorne, Head of Planning & Regeneration Services, Civic Centre, Poole BH15 2RU ☎ 01202 633327; 01202 633345 ✆ s.thorne@poole.gov.uk

Road Safety: Mr Julian McLaughlin, Head of Transportation Services, Civic Centre, Poole BH15 2RU ☎ 01202 262143 ✆ julian.mclaughlin@poole.gov.uk

Social Services: Ms Jan Thurgood, Strategic Director - People, Civic Centre, Poole BH15 2RU ☎ 01202 633207 ✆ j.thurgood@poole.gov.uk

Social Services (Adult): Mr Phil Hornsby, Head of Commissioning & Improvement (People Services), Crown Buildings, 4th Floor, Civic Centre, Poole BH15 2RU ☎ 01202 261030 ✆ p.hornsby@poole.gov.uk

Social Services (Adult): Mr David Vitty, Head of Adult Social Care Services, Civic Centre Annexe, Poole BH15 2RU ☎ 01202 261132 ✆ d.vitty@poole.gov.uk

Social Services (Children): Ms Gerry Moore, Head of Children & Young People's Social Care, 14a Commercial Road, Poole BH15 0JW ☎ 01202 714715; 01202 715589 ✆ gerry.moore@poole.gov.uk

Public Health: Ms Sophia Callaghan, Assistant Director - Public Health, Civic Centre Annexe, Poole BH15 2RU ☎ 01202 611107 ✆ s.callaghan@poole.gov.uk

Staff Training: Mr Carl Wilcox, Head of Human Resources, Civic Centre, Poole BH15 2RU ☎ 01202 633452; 01202 633477 ✆ c.wilcox@poole.gov.uk

Street Scene: Mr Shaun Robson, Head of Environmental & Consumer Protection, Unit 1, Newfields Business Park, 2 Stinsford Road, Poole BH17 0NF ☎ 01202 261701; 01202 262240 ✆ s.robson@poole.gov.uk

Sustainable Communities: Ms Jan Thurgood, Strategic Director - People, Civic Centre, Poole BH15 2RU ☎ 01202 633207 ✆ j.thurgood@poole.gov.uk

Sustainable Development: Mrs Kate Ryan, Strategic Director - Place, Civic Centre, Poole BH15 2RU ☎ 01202 633202 ✆ k.ryan@poole.gov.uk

Tourism: Mr Graham Richardson, Tourism Manager, Enefco House, Visitor Welcome Centre, 19 Strand Street, The Quay, Poole BH15 1HE ☎ 01202 262539; 01202 262684 ✆ g.richardson@pooletourism.com

Town Centre: Mr Graham Richardson, Tourism Manager, Enefco House, Visitor Welcome Centre, 19 Strand Street, The Quay, Poole BH15 1HE ☎ 01202 262539; 01202 262684 ✆ g.richardson@pooletourism.com

Traffic Management: Mr Julian McLaughlin, Head of Transportation Services, Civic Centre, Poole BH15 2RU ☎ 01202 262143 ✆ julian.mclaughlin@poole.gov.uk

POOLE

Transport: Mr Julian McLaughlin, Head of Transportation Services, Civic Centre, Poole BH15 2RU ☎ 01202 262143
✆ julian.mclaughlin@poole.gov.uk

Transport Planner: Mr Julian McLaughlin, Head of Transportation Services, Civic Centre, Poole BH15 2RU ☎ 01202 262143
✆ julian.mclaughlin@poole.gov.uk

Waste Collection and Disposal: Mr Shaun Robson, Head of Environmental & Consumer Protection, Unit 1, Newfields Business Park, 2 Stinsford Road, Poole BH17 0NF ☎ 01202 261701; 01202 262240 ✆ s.robson@poole.gov.uk

Waste Management: Mr Shaun Robson, Head of Environmental & Consumer Protection, Unit 1, Newfields Business Park, 2 Stinsford Road, Poole BH17 0NF ☎ 01202 261701; 01202 262240 ✆ s.robson@poole.gov.uk

Children's Play Areas: Mr Kevin McErlane, Head of Culture & Community Learning, Poole Central Library, The Dolphin Centre, Poole BH15 1QE ☎ 01202 262400; 01202 262431 ✆ k.mcerlane@poole.gov.uk

COUNCILLORS

Mayor: Dion, Xena (CON - Penn Hill)
x.dion@poole.gov.uk

Deputy Mayor: Stribley, Ann (CON - Parkstone)
a.stribley@poole.gov.uk

SheriffWilson, Lindsay (CON - Newtown)
lindsay.wilson@poole.giv.uk

Leader of the Council: Walton, Janet (CON - Oakdale)
j.walton@poole.gov.uk

Deputy Leader of the Council: Haines, May (CON - Canford Cliffs)
m.haines@poole.gov.uk

Adams, Peter (CON - Oakdale)
p.adams@poole.gov.uk

Atkinson, Elaine (CON - Penn Hill)
elaine.atkinson@poole.gov.uk

Bagwell, Julie (IND - Hamworthy West)
j.bagwell@poole.gov.uk

Brooke, Michael (LD - Broadstone)
m.brooke@poole.gov.uk

Brown, David (LD - Merley & Bearwood)
d.brown@poole.gov.uk

Burden, Les (CON - Creekmoor)
l.burden@poole.gov.uk

Butt, Judy (CON - Creekmoor)
j.butt@poole.gov.uk

Challinor, John (CON - Parkstone)
j.challinor@poole.gov.uk

Eades, Phillip (LD - Branksome West)
p.eades@poole.gov.uk

Farrell, Malcolm (CON - Newtown)
m.farrell@poole.gov.uk

Fisher, Mike (UKIP - Alderney)
m.fisher@poole.gov.uk

Gabriel, Sean (CON - Canford Heath West)
s.gabriel@poole.gov.uk

Garner-White, Andy (CON - Pooel Town)
a.garner-white@poole.gov.uk

Gupta, Vishal (CON - Hamworthy East)
v.gupta@poole.gov.uk

Hadley, Andy (IND - Poole Town)
a.hadley@poole.gov.uk

Hodges, Jennie (LD - Canford Heath East)
j.hodges@poole.gov.uk

Howell, Mark (IND - Poole Town)
m.howel@poole.gov.uk

Iyengar, Mohan (CON - Canford Cliffs)
m.iyengar@poole.gov.uk

Le Poidevin, Marion (LD - Branksome West)
m.lepoidevin@gov.uk

Mellor, Drew (CON - Branksome East)
d.mellor@poole.gov.uk

Moore, Sandra (LD - Canford Heath East)
s.moore@poole.gov.uk

Newell, David (CON - Broadstone)
d.newell@poole.gov.uk

Newell, Jane (CON - Merley & Bearwood)
j.newell@poole.gov.uk

Parker, Ron (CON - Penn Hill)
r.parker@poole.gov.uk

Pawlowski, Peter (CON - Canford Cliffs)
p.pawlowski@poole.gov.uk

Pope, Marion (CON - Merley & Bearwood)
m.pope@poole.gov.uk

Potter, Ian (CON - Oakdale)
i.potter@poole.gov.uk

Rampton, Karen (CON - Branksome East)
k.rampton@poole.gov.uk

Rampton, John (CON - Creekmoor)
j.rampton@poole.gov.uk

Russell, Louise (CON - Alderney)
l.russell@poole.gov.uk

Tindle, Ray (CON - Canford Heath West)
r.tindle@poole.gov.uk

Trent, Russell (CON - Alderney)
r.trent@poole.gov.uk

White, Michael (CON - Hamworthy East)
mike.white@poole.gov.uk

Wilkins, Michael (CON - Hamworthy West)
m.wilkins@poole.gov.uk

Williams, Emma (CON - Parkstone)
e.williams@poole.gov.uk

Wilson, Graham (LD - Newtown)
g.wilson@poole.gov.uk

POLITICAL COMPOSITION
CON: 30, LD: 7, IND: 3, UKIP: 1, Vacant: 1

Portsmouth City   U

Portsmouth City Council, Civic Offices, Guildhall Square, Portsmouth PO1 2AL

☎ 023 9282 2251 🖶 023 9282 8441 🖥 www.portsmouth.gov.uk

FACTS AND FIGURES

Parliamentary Constituencies: Portsmouth North, Portsmouth South

EU Constituencies: South East

Election Frequency: Elections are by thirds

PRINCIPAL OFFICERS

Chief Executive: Mr David Williams, Chief Executive, Civic Offices, Guildhall Square, Portsmouth PO1 2AL ☎ 023 9283 4009 ⌁ david.williams@portsmouthcc.gov.uk

Deputy Chief Executive: Mr Michael Lawther, Deputy Chief Executive & City Solicitor, Civic Offices, Guildhall Square, Portsmouth PO1 2AL ☎ 023 9284 1116 ⌁ michael.lawther@portsmouthcc.gov.uk

Senior Management: Ms Alison Jeffery, Director - Children's Services, Civic Offices, Guildhall Square, Portsmouth PO1 2AL ☎ 023 9282 2251 ⌁ alison.jeffery@portsmouthcc.gov.uk

Senior Management: Dr Janet Maxwell, Director - Public Health, Civic Offices, Guildhall Square, Portsmouth PO1 2AL ⌁ janet.maxwell@portsmouthcc.gov.uk

Senior Management: Ms Kathy Wadsworth, Strategic Director & Director - Regeneration, Civic Offices, Guildhall Square, Portsmouth PO1 2AL ☎ 023 9282 2251 ⌁ kathy.wadsworth@portsmouthcc.gov.uk

Access Officer / Social Services (Disability): Ms Gina Perryman, Equality Advisor, Civic Offices, Guildhall Square, Portsmouth PO1 2AL ☎ 023 9283 4789 ⌁ gina.perryman@portsmouthcc.gov.uk

Architect, Building / Property Services: Mr Peter Chilton, Team Leader - Quantity Surveyors, Civic Offices, Guildhall Square, Portsmouth PO1 2AL ☎ 023 9282 2251 ⌁ peter.chilton@portsmouthcc.gov.uk

Civil Registration: Ms Lorraine Porter, Superintendent Registrar, Births, Deaths & Marriages, Milldam House, Burnaby Road, Portsmouth PO1 3AF ☎ 023 9282 9041 ⌁ lorraine.porter@portsmouthcc.gov.uk

PR / Communications: Mr Lee Todd, Communications Manager, Civic Offices, Guildhall Square, Portsmouth PO1 2AL ⌁ lee.todd@portsmouthcc.gov.uk

Community Planning: Mr Paddy May, Corporate Strategy Manager, Civic Offices, Guildhall Square, Portsmouth PO1 2AL ☎ 023 9283 4020 ⌁ paddy.may@portsmouthcc.gov.uk

Community Safety: Ms Rachael Dalby, Director - Regulatory Services & Community Services, Civic Offices, Guildhall Square, Portsmouth PO1 2AL ☎ 023 9283 4040 ⌁ rachael.dalby@portsmouthcc.gov.uk

Computer Management: Mr Chris Ward, Chief Finance Officer, Civic Offices, Guildhall Square, Portsmouth PO1 2AL ☎ 023 9283 4423 ⌁ chris.ward@portsmouthcc.gov.uk

Consumer Protection and Trading Standards: Mr Peter Emmett, Trading Standards Manager, Civic Offices, Guildhall Square, Portsmouth PO1 2AL ☎ 023 9284 1291 ⌁ peter.emmett@portsmouthcc.gov.uk

Corporate Services: Mr Jon Bell, Director - HR, Legal & Performance, Civic Offices, Guildhall Square, Portsmouth PO1 2AL ☎ 023 8782 ⌁ jon.bell@portsmouthcc.gov.uk

Customer Service: Ms Louise Wilders, Director - Community & Communications, Civic Offices, Guildhall Square, Portsmouth PO1 2AL ☎ 023 9268 8545 ⌁ louise.wilders@portsmouthcc.gov.uk

Economic Development: Mr Stephen Baily, Head of City Development & Cultural Services, Civic Offices, Guildhall Square, Portsmouth PO1 2AL ☎ 023 9283 4399 ⌁ stephen.baily@portsmouthcc.gov.uk

Economic Development: Mr Mark Pembleton, Economic Growth Manager, Civic Offices, Guildhall Square, Portsmouth PO1 2AL ⌁ mark.pembleton@portsmouthcc.gov.uk

Emergency Planning: Ms Cindy Jones, Civil Contingencies Manager, Civic Offices, Guildhall Square, Portsmouth PO1 2AL ☎ 023 9268 8050 ⌁ cindy.jones@portsmouthcc.gov.uk

Environmental Health: Mr Richard Lee, Environmental Health Manager, Civic Offices, Guildhall Square, Portsmouth PO1 2AL ☎ 023 9283 4857 ⌁ richard.lee@portsmouthcc.gov.uk

Events Manager: Ms Claire Looney, Partnership & Commissioning Manager, Civic Offices, Guildhall Square, Portsmouth PO1 2AL ☎ 023 9283 4185 ⌁ claire.looney@portsmouthcc.gov.uk

Facilities: Ms Michelle Miller, Landlord Services, Civic Offices, Guildhall Square, Portsmouth PO1 2AL ☎ 023 9283 4992 ⌁ michelle.miller@portsmouthcc.gov.uk

Finance: Mr Chris Ward, Chief Finance Officer, Civic Offices, Guildhall Square, Portsmouth PO1 2AL ☎ 023 9283 4423 ⌁ chris.ward@portsmouthcc.gov.uk

Grounds Maintenance: Mr Seamus Meyer, Strategic Project Manager, Civic Offices, Guildhall Square, Portsmouth PO1 2AL ☎ 023 9283 4163 ⌁ seamus.meyer@portsmouthcc.gov.uk

Housing: Mr Owen Buckwell, Director - Property & Housing, Civic Offices, Guildhall Square, Portsmouth PO1 2AL ☎ 023 9283 4503 ⌁ owen.buckwell@portsmouthcc.gov.uk

Local Area Agreement: Mr Paddy May, Corporate Strategy Manager, Civic Offices, Guildhall Square, Portsmouth PO1 2AL ☎ 023 9283 4020 ⌁ paddy.may@portsmouthcc.gov.uk

Legal: Mr Michael Lawther, Deputy Chief Executive & City Solicitor, Civic Offices, Guildhall Square, Portsmouth PO1 2AL ☎ 023 9284 1116 ⌁ michael.lawther@portsmouthcc.gov.uk

PORTSMOUTH CITY

Leisure and Cultural Services: Mr Stephen Baily, Head of City Development & Cultural Services, Civic Offices, Guildhall Square, Portsmouth PO1 2AL ☎ 023 9283 4399 ⌂ stephen.baily@portsmouthcc.gov.uk

Licensing: Mrs Nicki Humphreys, Licensing Manager, Civic Offices, Guildhall Square, Portsmouth PO1 2AL ☎ 023 9283 4604 ⌂ licensing@portsmouthcc.gov.uk

Lifelong Learning: Ms Jan Paterson, Head of Learning & Development, Civic Offices, Guildhall Square, Portsmouth PO1 2AL ☎ 023 9283 4458 ⌂ jan.paterson@portsmouthcc.gov.uk

Lighting: Ms Jane Tume, PFI Contract Manager, Civic Offices, Guildhall Square, Portsmouth PO1 2AL ☎ 023 9282 2251 ⌂ jane.tume@portsmouthcc.gov.uk

Parking: Mr Michael Robinson, Parking Manager, Civic Offices, Guildhall Square, Portsmouth PO1 2AL ☎ 023 9268 8497 ⌂ michael.robinson@portsmouthcc.gov.uk

Personnel / HR: Mr Jon Bell, Director - HR, Legal & Performance, Civic Offices, Guildhall Square, Portsmouth PO1 2AL ☎ 023 8782 ⌂ jon.bell@portsmouthcc.gov.uk

Planning: Ms Claire Upton-Brown, City Development Manager, Civic Offices, Guildhall Square, Portsmouth PO1 2AL ⌂ claire.upton-brown@portsmouthcc.gov.uk

Procurement: Mr Greg Povey, Assistant Director - Contract, Procurement & Commercial, Civic Offices, Guildhall Square, Portsmouth PO1 2AL ☎ 023 9283 4406 ⌂ grey.povey@portsmouthcc.gov.uk

Public Libraries: Ms Lindy Elliott, Library Services Manager, Civic Offices, Guildhall Square, Portsmouth PO1 2AL ☎ 023 9268 8058 ⌂ lindy.elliott@portsmouthcc.gov.uk

Recycling & Waste Minimisation: Mr Paul Fielding, Assistant Head of Service - Environment & Recreation, Civic Offices, Guildhall Square, Portsmouth PO1 2AL ☎ 023 9283 4625 ⌂ paul.fielding@portsmouthcc.gov.uk

Social Services (Adult): Mr Innes Richens, Adult Services Lead, Civic Offices, Guildhall Square, Portsmouth PO1 2AL ⌂ innes.richens@portsmouthcc.gov.uk

Social Services (Children): Ms Sarah Newman, Deputy Director - Children's Social Care, Civic Offices, Guildhall Square, Portsmouth PO1 2AL ☎ 023 9282 2251 ⌂ sarah.newman@portsmouthcc.gov.uk

Public Health: Dr Janet Maxwell, Director - Public Health, Civic Offices, Guildhall Square, Portsmouth PO1 2AL ⌂ janet.maxwell@portsmouthcc.gov.uk

Staff Training: Ms Liz Aplin, Operational Training Manager, Civic Offices, Guildhall Square, Portsmouth PO1 2AL ☎ 023 9268 8551 ⌂ liz.aplin@portsmouthcc.gov.uk

Street Scene: Mr Paul Fielding, Assistant Head of Service - Environment & Recreation, Civic Offices, Guildhall Square, Portsmouth PO1 2AL ☎ 023 9283 4625 ⌂ paul.fielding@portsmouthcc.gov.uk

Tourism: Ms Jane Singh, Visitor Services & Development Manager, Civic Offices, Guildhall Square, Portsmouth PO1 2AL ☎ 023 9283 4636 ⌂ jane.singh@portsmouthcc.gov.uk

Town Centre: Mr Barry Walker, City Centre Manager, Civic Offices, Guildhall Square, Portsmouth PO1 2AL ☎ 023 9282 2251 ⌂ barry.walker@portsmouthcc.gov.uk

Waste Collection and Disposal: Mr Paul Fielding, Assistant Head of Service - Environment & Recreation, Civic Offices, Guildhall Square, Portsmouth PO1 2AL ☎ 023 9283 4625 ⌂ paul.fielding@portsmouthcc.gov.uk

COUNCILLORS

The Lord Mayor: Fuller, David (LD - Fratton)
cllr.david.fuller@portsmouthcc.gov.uk

Deputy Lord Mayor: Ellcome, Ken (CON - Drayton & Farlington)
cllr.ken.ellcome@portsmouthcc.gov.uk

Leader of the Council: Jones, Donna (CON - Hilsea)
cllr.donna.jones@portsmouthcc.gov.uk

Deputy Leader of the Council: Stubbs, Luke (CON - Eastney & Craneswater)
cllr.luke.stubbs@portsmouthcc.gov.uk

Group Leader: Ferrett, John (LAB - Paulsgrove)
cllr.john.ferrett@portsmouthcc.gov.uk

Group Leader: Galloway, Colin (UKIP - Nelson)
cllr_galloway@outlook.com

Group Leader: Vernon-Jackson, Gerald (LD - Milton)
geraldvj@gmail.com

Ashmore, Dave (LD - Fratton)
cllr.dave.ashmore@portsmouthcc.gov.uk

Bosher, Simon (CON - Drayton & Farlington)
cllr.simon.bosher@portsmouthcc.gov.uk

Brent, Ryan (CON - St Thomas)
cllr.ryan.brent@portsmouthcc.gov.uk

Brent, Jennie (CON - Eastney & Craneswater)
cllr.jennie.brent@portsmouthcc.gov.uk

Chowdhury, Yahiya (LAB - Charles Dickens)
cllr.yahiya.chowdhury@portmsouthcc.gov.uk

Denny, Alicia (UKIP - Copnor)
a.denny.ukipcopnor@gmail.com

Dowling, Ben (LD - Milton)
btldowling@yahoo.co.uk

Fleming, Jim (CON - Cosham)
cllr.jim.fleming@portsmouthcc.gov.uk

Godier, Paul (INDNA - Charles Dickens)
cllr.paul.godier@portsmouthcc.gov.uk

Harris, Scott (CON - Hilsea)
cllr.scott.harris@portsmouthcc.gov.uk

Hastins, Steve (CON - Baffins)
cllr_hastings@outlook.com

Hockaday, Hannah (CON - Cosham)
hannah.hockaday@me.com

Horton, Suzy (LD - Central Southsea)
cllr.suzy.horton@portsmouthcc.gov.uk

Hunt, Lee (LD - Central Southsea)
cllr.lee.hunt@portsmouthcc.gov.uk

Jonas, Frank (CON - Hilsea)
cllr.frank.jonas@portsmouthcc.gov.uk

Lyon, Ian (CON - Nelson)
cllr.ian.lyon@portsmouthcc.gov.uk

Madden, Leo (LD - Nelson)
cllr.leo.madden@portsmouthcc.gov.uk

Mason, Lee (CON - Cosham)
cllr.lee.mason@portsmouthcc.gov.ukl

Mason, Hugh (LD - St Jude)
cllr.hugh.mason@portsmouthcc.gov.uk

Morgan, Stephen (LAB - Charles Dickens)
cllr.stephen.morgan@portsmouthcc.gov.uk

New, Robert (CON - Copnor)
cllr.robert.new@portsmouthcc.gov.uk

New, Gemma (CON - Paulsgrove)
cllr.gemma.new@portsmouthcc.gov.uk

Potter, Stuart (UKIP - Paulsgrove)
cllr_potter@ukipportsmouth.org

Purvis, Will (LD - Milton)
cllr.will.purvis@portsmouthcc.gov.uk

Sanders, Darren (LD - Baffins)
cllr.darren.sanders@portsmouthcc.gov.uk

Smith, Phil (LD - Central Southsea)
cllr.phil.smith@portsmouthcc.gov.uk

Stagg, Lynne (LD - Baffins)
cllr.lynne.stagg@portsmouthcc.gov.uk

Swan, Julie (UKIP - Fratton)
cllrswan@outlook.com

Symes, Linda (CON - St Jude)
cllr.linda.symes@portsmouthcc.gov.uk

Tompkins, David (CON - St Jude)
cllr.david.tomkins@portsmouthcc.gov.uk

Wemyss, Steve (CON - Drayton & Farlington)
cllr.steve.wemyss@portsmouthcc.gov.uk

Winnington, Matthew (LD - Eastney & Craneswater)
cllr.matthew.winnington@portsmouthcc.gov.uk

Wood, Tom (LD - St Thomas)
cllr.tom.wood@portsmouthcc.gov.uk

Wood, Rob (LD - St Thomas)
cllr.rob.wood@portsmouthcc.gov.uk

Young, Neil (CON - Copnor)
cllr.neill.young@portsmouthcc.gov.uk

POLITICAL COMPOSITION
CON: 19, LD: 15, UKIP: 4, LAB: 3, INDNA: 1

COMMITTEE CHAIRS
Audit: Mr Ian Lyon

Economic Development, Culture & Leisure: Ms Hannah Hockaday

Education, Children & Young People: Mr Will Purvis

Housing & Social Care: Mr Darren Sanders

Licensing: Ms Julie Swan

Planning: Mr Frank Jonas

Powys   W

Powys County Council, County Hall, Llandrindod Wells LD1 5LG
☎ 01597 826000 🖨 01597 826230 ⌕ customer@powys.gov.uk
💻 www.powys.gov.uk

FACTS AND FIGURES
Parliamentary Constituencies: Brecon and Radnorshire, Montgomeryshire
EU Constituencies: Wales
Election Frequency: Elections are of whole council

PRINCIPAL OFFICERS

Chief Executive: Mr Jeremy Patterson, Chief Executive, County Hall, Llandrindod Wells LD1 5LG ☎ 01597 826082; 01597 826220 ⌕ jeremy.patterson@powys.gov.uk

Senior Management: Mr Paul Griffiths, Strategic Director - Place, County Hall, Llandrindod Wells LD1 5LG ☎ 01597 826464 ⌕ paul.griffiths@powys.gov.uk

Senior Management: Ms Amanda Lewis, Strategic Director - People, County Hall, Llandrindod Wells LD1 5LG ☎ 01597 826906 ⌕ amanda.lewis@powys.gov.uk

Senior Management: Mr Nick Philpott, Director - Change & Governance, County Hall, Llandrindod Wells LD1 5LG ☎ 01597 826093 ⌕ nick.philpott@powys.gov.uk

Senior Management: Mr Clive Pinney, Solicitor to the Council, County Hall, Llandrindod Wells LD1 5LG ☎ 01597 826746 ⌕ clive.pinney@powys.gov.uk

Senior Management: Mr David Powell, Strategic Director - Resources, County Hall, Llandrindod Wells LD1 5LG ☎ 01597 826729 ⌕ david.powell@powys.gov.uk

Architect, Building / Property Services: Ms Sarah Jowett, Senior Manager - Regeneration & Property, County Hall, Llandrindod Wells LD1 5LG ☎ 01597 826553 ⌕ sarah.jowett@powys.gov.uk

Best Value: Mr Nick Philpott, Director - Change & Governance, County Hall, Llandrindod Wells Ld1 5LG ☎ 01597 826093 ⌕ nick.philpott@powys.gov.uk

Catering Services: Mr Jason Rawbone, Principal Catering Officer, The Gwalia, Llandrindod Wells LD1 6AA ☎ 01597 827291 ⌕ jason.rawbone@powys.gov.uk

Civil Registration: Mrs Suzanne Morgan, Registration Services Manager, Neuadd Brycheiniog, Brecon LD3 7HR ☎ 01874 624334 ⌕ suzanne.morgan@powys.gov.uk

POWYS

PR / Communications: Ms Anya Richards, Senior Communications Manager, County Hall, Llandrindod Wells LD1 5LG ☎ 01597 826089 ⏚ anya.richards@powys.gov.uk

Computer Management: Mr Andrew Durant, Head of ICT & Programme Office, County Hall, Llandrindod Wells LD1 5LG ☎ 01597 826207 ⏚ andrew.duran@powys.gov.uk

Consumer Protection and Trading Standards: Mr Ken Yorston, Senior Manager - Regulatory Services, County Hall, Llandrindod Wells LD1 5LG ☎ 01597 826570 ⏚ ken.yorston@powys.gov.uk

Customer Service: Ms Kelly Watts, Customer Services Manager, The Gwalia, Llandrindod Wells LD1 6AA ☎ 01597 827540 ⏚ kelly.watts@powys.gov.uk

Economic Development: Ms Susan Bolter, Head of Regeneration Property & Commissioning, County Hall, Llandrindod Wells LD1 5LG ☎ 01597 826195 ⏚ susan.bolter@powys.gov.uk

Education: Mr Ian Roberts, Head of Schools, County Hall, Llandrindod Wells LD1 5LG ☎ 01597 826422 ⏚ ian.roberts@powys.gov.uk

Electoral Registration: Ms Sandra Matthews, Principal Elections Officer, County Hall, Llandrindod Wells LD1 5LG ☎ 01597 826747; 01597 826220 ⏚ sandra.matthews@powys.gov.uk

Emergency Planning: Mr Wayne Jones, Prinicpal Emergency Planning Officer, County Hall, Llandrindod Wells LD1 5LG ☎ 01597 826000

Energy Management: Mr Gareth Richards, Energy Management Officer, County Hall, Llandrindod Wells LD1 5LG ☎ 01597 826629 ⏚ garethr@powys.gov.uk

Environmental Health: Ms Nia Hughes, Professional Lead Environmental Health, Neuadd Maldwyn, Welshpool SY21 7AS ☎ 01938 551299 ⏚ nia.hughes@powys.gov.uk

Estates, Property & Valuation: Ms Susan Bolter, Head of Regeneration Property & Commissioning, County Hall, Llandrindod Wells LD1 5LG ☎ 01597 826195 ⏚ susan.bolter@powys.gov.uk

European Liaison: Ms Kay Francis, European & External Funding Officer, The Gwalia, Llandrindod Wells LD1 6AA ☎ 01597 826180 ⏚ kay.francis@powys.gov.uk

Facilities: Mr Neil Clutton, Property Manager, County Hall, Llandrindod Wells LD1 5LG ☎ 01597 826595 ⏚ neil.clutton@powys.gov.uk

Finance: Mr David Powell, Strategic Director - Resources, County Hall, Llandrindod Wells LD1 5LG ☎ 01597 826729 ⏚ david.powell@powys.gov.uk

Pensions: Mr Joe Rollin, Pensions Manager, County Hall, Llandrindod Wells LD1 5LG ☎ 01597 826306 ⏚ joe.rollin@powys.gov.uk

Fleet Management: Mr Tim Washington, Interim Fleet Manager, County Hall, Llandrindod Wells LD1 5LG ☎ 01597 829846 ⏚ tim.washington@powys.gov.uk

Housing: Mr Simon Inkson, Head of Housing, County Hall, Llandrindod Wells LD1 5LG ☎ 01597 826639 ⏚ simon.inkson@powys.gov.uk

Housing Maintenance: Mr Dafydd Evans, Senior Manager - Housing Solutions, Neuadd Maldwyn, Severn Road, Welshpool SY21 7AS ☎ 01938 551214 ⏚ dafydd.evans@powys.gov.uk

Legal: Mr Clive Pinney, Solicitor to the Council, County Hall, Llandrindod Wells LD1 5LG ☎ 01597 826746 ⏚ clive.pinney@powys.gov.uk

Leisure and Cultural Services: Mr Paul Griffiths, Strategic Director - Place, County Hall, Llandrindod Wells LD1 5LG ☎ 01597 826464 ⏚ paul.griffiths@powys.gov.uk

Member Services: Mr Wyn Richards, Head of Democratic Services, County Hall, Llandrindod Wells LD1 5LG ☎ 01597 826375 ⏚ wyn.richards@powys.gov.uk

Personnel / HR: Ms Julie Rowles, Joint Director - Workforce & Organisation Development, County Hall, Llandrindod Wells LD1 5LG ☎ 01597 826319 ⏚ julie.rowles@powys.gov.uk

Planning: Mr Gwilym Davies, Lead Professional Development Management, County Hall, Llandrindod Wells LD1 5LG ☎ 01597 827344 ⏚ gwilym.davies@powys.gov.uk

Recycling & Waste Minimisation: Mr Ashley Collins, Waste Services Manager, County Hall, Llandrindod Wells LD1 5LG ☎ 01597 826974 ⏚ ashley.collins@powys.gov.uk

Regeneration: Ms Susan Bolter, Head of Regeneration Property & Commissioning, County Hall, Llandrindod Wells LD1 5LG ☎ 01597 826195 ⏚ susan.bolter@powys.gov.uk

Road Safety: Mr Tony Caine, Road Safety & Traffic Systems Manager, County Hall, Llandrindod Wells LD1 5LG ☎ 0845 607 6652 ⏚ tony.caine@powys.gov.uk

Social Services: Ms Amanda Lewis, Strategic Director - People, County Hall, Llandrindod Wells LD1 5LG ☎ 01597 826906 ⏚ amanda.lewis@powys.gov.uk

Social Services (Adult): Ms Louise Barry, Head of Operations for Adult Services, County Hall, Llandrindod Wells LD1 5LG ☎ 01597 821000 ⏚ louise.barry@powys.gov.uk

Social Services (Children): Ms Pauline Higham, Head of Children's Services, 1 High Street, Llandrindod Wells LD1 6AG ☎ 01597 827084 ⏚ pauline.higham@powys.gov.uk

Staff Training: Ms Sarah Powell, Professional Lead - Culture & Leadership Development, Neuadd Brycheiniog, Brecon LD3 7HR ☎ 01874 612351 ⏚ sarah.powell@powys.gov.uk

Sustainable Development: Ms Heather Delonnette, Sustainable Development Co-ordinator, County Hall, Llandrindod Wells LD1 5LG
☎ 01597 826165 ⤏ heather.delonnette@powys.gov.uk

Tourism: Ms Julie Lewis, Tourism Officer, Brecon Tourist Information Centre, Cattle Market Car Park, Brecon LD3 9DA
☎ 01874 612275 ⤏ julie.lewis@powys.gov.uk

Traffic Management: Mr Tony Caine, Road Safety & Traffic Systems Manager, County Hall, Llandrindod Wells LD1 5LG
☎ 0845 607 6652 ⤏ tony.caine@powys.gov.uk

Transport: Mr John Forsey, Transport Passenger Manager, County Hall, Llandrindod Wells LD1 5LG ☎ 01597 826642
⤏ john.forsey@powys.gov.uk

Transport Planner: Mr John Forsey, Transport Passenger Manager, County Hall, Llandrindod Wells LD1 5LG ☎ 01597 826642
⤏ john.forsey@powys.gov.uk

Waste Collection and Disposal: Mr Ashley Collins, Waste Services Manager, County Hall, Llandrindod Wells LD1 5LG
☎ 01597 826974 ⤏ ashley.collins@powys.gov.uk

Waste Management: Mr Ashley Collins, Waste Services Manager, County Hall, Llandrindod Wells LD1 5LG ☎ 01597 826974
⤏ ashley.collins@powys.gov.uk

COUNCILLORS

Chair: Ashton, Paul (LD - St Mary)
cllr.paul.ashton@powys.gov.uk

Vice-Chair: Tampin, Keith (NP - Llandrindod East / Llandrindod West)
cllr.keith.tampin@powys.gov.uk

Leader of the Council: Thomas, Barry (NP - Llanfihangel)
cllr.barry.thomas@powys.gov.uk

Deputy Leader of the Council: Brown, Graham (IND - Llandrinio)
cllr.graham.brown@powys.gov.uk

Group Leader: Davies, Sandra (LAB - Cwm-Twrch)
cllr.sandra.davies@powys.gov.uk

Group Leader: Davies, Aled (CON - Llanrhaeadr-ym-Mochnant / Llansilin)
cllr.aled.davies@powys.gov.uk

Group Leader: Davies, Chris (CON - Glasbury)
cllr.chris.davies@powys.gov.uk

Alexander, Myfanwy (IND - Banwy)
cllr.myfanwy.alexander@powys.gov.uk

Bailey, Dawn (IND - Trewern)
cllr.dawn.bailey@powys.gov.uk

Banks, Garry (NP - Presteigne)
cllr.garry.banks@powys.gov.uk

Bowker, Gemma-Jane (LD - Newtown Llanwchaiarn North)
cllr.gemma.jane.bowker@powys.gov.uk

Brunt, John (IND - Beguildy)
cllr.john.brunt@powys.gov.uk

Corfield, Linda (IND - Forden)
cllr.linda.corfield@powys.gov.uk

Curry, Kelvyn (LD - Rhayader)
cllr.kelvyn.curry@powys.gov.uk

Davies, Dai (NP - Berriew)
cllr.dai.davies@powys.gov.uk

Davies, Stephen (IND - Bronllys)
cllr.stephen.davies@powys.gov.uk

Davies, Rachel (IND - Caersws)
cllr.rachel.davies@powys.gov.uk

Davies, Roche (NP - Llandinam)
cllr.roche.davies@powys.gov.uk

Davies, Melanie (INDNA - Llangors)
cllr.melanie.davies@powys.gov.uk

Dorrance, Matthew (LAB - St John)
cllr.matthew.dorrance@powys.gov.uk

Evans, David (IND - Nantmel)
cllr.david.evans@powys.gov.uk

Evans, Viola (IND - Llanfair Caereinion)
cllr.viola.evans@powys.gov.uk

Evans, John (IND - Llanyre)
cllr.john.evans@powys.gov.uk

Fitzpatrick, Liam (IND - Talybont-on-Usk)
cllr.liam.fitzpatrick@powys.gov.uk

George, Russell (CON - Newtown Central)
cllr.russell.george@powys.gov.uk

Harris, Rosemarie (NP - Llangynidr)
cllr.rosemarie.harris@powys.gov.uk

Harris, Peter (INDNA - Newtown Llanllwchaiarn West)
cllr.peter.harris@powys.gov.uk

Hayes, Stephen (IND - Montgomery)
cllr.stephen.hayes@powys.gov.uk

Holloway, Ann (IND - Welshpool Llanerchyddol)
cllr.ann.holloway@powys.gov.uk

Holmes, Jeff (NP - Llangattock)
cllr.jeff.holmes@powys.gov.uk

Hopkins, Geraint (IND - Gwernyfed)
cllr.geraint.hopkins@powys.gov.uk

Jones, Dai (IND - Llanbrynmair)
cllr.dai.jones@powys.gov.uk

Jones, Graham (CON - Blaen Hafren)
cllr.graham.jones@powys.gov.uk

Jones, Joy (LD - Newtown East)
cllr.joy.jones@powys.gov.uk

Jones, Michael (IND - Churchstoke)
cllr.michael.john.jones@powys.gov.uk

Jones, Arwel (IND - Llandysilio)
cllr.arwel.jones@powys.gov.uk

Jones, Wynne (IND - Dolforwyn)
cllr.wynne.jones@powys.gov.uk

Jones, Michael (IND - Old Radnor)
cllr.michael.jones@powys.gov.uk

Jones, Eldrydd (NP - Meifod)
cllr.eldrydd.jones@powys.gov.uk

Jones, David (IND - Guilsfield)
cllr.david.jones@powys.gov.uk

Jump, Francesca (LD - Welshpool Gungrog)
cllr.francesca.jump@powys.gov.uk

Lewis, Peter (CON - Llanfyllin)
cllr.peter.lewis@powys.gov.uk

Lewis, Hywel (IND - Llangunllo)
cllr.hywel.lewis@powys.gov.uk

Mackenzie, Maureen (LD - Llanelwedd)
cllr.maureen.mackenzie@powys.gov.uk

Mayor:, Darren (NP - Llanwddyn)
cllr.darren.mayor@powys.gov.uk

McNicholas, Susan (LAB - Ynescedwyn)
cllr.susan.mcnicholas@powys.gov.uk

Medlicott, Peter (IND - Knighton)
cllr.peter.medlicott@powys.gov.uk

Meredith, David (LAB - St David Within)
cllr.david.meredith@powys.gov.uk

Mills, Bob (IND - Newtown South)
cllr.bob.mills@powys.gov.uk

Morgan, Gareth (IND - Llanidloes)
cllr.gareth.morgan@powys.gov.uk

Morgan, Evan (IND - Maescar / Llywel)
cllr.evan.morgan@powys.gov.uk

Morris, John (LD - Crickhowell)
cllr.john.morris@powys.gov.uk

Powell, William (LD - Talgarth)
cllr.william.powell@powys.gov.uk

Powell, John (IND - Llanbadarn Fawr)
cllr.john.powell@powys.gov.uk

Price, David (IND - Llanafanfawr)
cllr.david.price@powys.gov.uk

Price, Gary (CON - Llandrindod North)
cllr.gary.price@powys.gov.uk

Pritchard, Philip (IND - Welshpool Castle)
cllr.phil.pritchard@powys.gov.uk

Ratcliffe, Gareth (IND - Hay)
cllr.gareth.ratcliffe@powys.gov.uk

Roberts-Jones, Kath (IND - Kerry)
cllr.kath.roberts-jones@powys.gov.uk

Shearer, Joy (IND - Rhiwcynon)
cllr.joy.shearer@powys.gov.uk

Silk, Kathryn (LD - Bwlch)
cllr.kathryn.silk@powys.gov.uk

Thomas, Gillian (IND - Yscir)
cllr.gillian.thomas@powys.gov.uk

Thomas, David (LAB - Tawe Uchaf)
cllr.david.thomas@powys.gov.uk

Thomas, Gwynfor (CON - Llansanffraid)
cllr.gwynfor.thomas@powys.gov.uk

Thomas, Tony (IND - Felin-fach)
cllr.tony.thomas@powys.gov.uk

Turner, Tom (CON - Llandrindod South)
cllr.tom.turner@powys.gov.uk

Van-Rees, Tim (IND - Llanwrtyd Wells)
cllr.tim.van-rees@powys.gov.uk

Vaughan, Gwilym (IND - Glantwymyn)
cllr.gwilym.vaughan@powys.gov.uk

Williams, Michael (IND - Machynlleth)
cllr.michael.williams@powys.gov.uk

Williams, Huw (NP - Ystradgynlais)
cllr.huw.williams@powys.gov.uk

Williams, Sarah (LAB - Aber-craf)
cllr.sarah.williams@powys.gov.uk

Williams, Gwilym (CON - Disserth & Trecoed)
cllr.gwilym.williams@powys.gov.uk

York, Avril (IND - Builth)
cllr.avril.york@powys.gov.uk

POLITICAL COMPOSITION
IND: 37, NP: 10, LD: 9, CON: 9, LAB: 6, INDNA: 2

COMMITTEE CHAIRS

Adult Social Care & Children: Mr David Jones

Audit: Mr John Morris

Licensing: Mr Michael Williams

Pensions: Mr Tony Thomas

Planning: Mr David Price

Preston   D

Preston City Council, Town Hall, Lancaster Road, Preston
PR1 2RL
☎ 01772 906900 🖷 01772 906901 ✆ info@preston.gov.uk
🖳 www.preston.gov.uk

FACTS AND FIGURES
Parliamentary Constituencies: Preston
EU Constituencies: North West
Election Frequency: Elections are by thirds

PRINCIPAL OFFICERS

Chief Executive: Ms Lorraine Norris, Chief Executive, Town Hall,
Lancaster Road, Preston PR1 2RL ☎ 01772 906101; 01772 906366
✆ l.norris@preston.gov.uk

Assistant Chief Executive: Mr Derek Whyte, Assistant Chief
Executive, Town Hall, Lancaster Road, Preston PR1 2RL
☎ 01772 903430 ✆ d.whyte@preston.gov.uk

Senior Management: Mrs Alison Brown, Director - Corporate
Services, Town Hall, Lancaster Road, Preston PR1 2RL
☎ 01772 906197 ✆ a.brown@preston.gov.uk

Senior Management: Mr Neil Fairhurst, Director - Customer
Services, PO Box 10, Town Hall, Lancaster Road, Preston PR1 2RL
☎ 01772 906197 ✆ n.fairhurst@preston.gov.uk

Senior Management: Mr Chris Hayward, Director - Development,
Lancastria House, Preston PR1 2RH ☎ 01772 906171
✆ c.hayward@preston.gov.uk

Senior Management: Mr Adrian Phillips, Director - Environment, Lancastria House, Lancaster Road, Preston PR1 2RH
☎ 01772 906171 ◌ a.phillips@preston.gov.uk

Building Control: Mr D Tomlinson, Head of Building Services, Town Hall, Lancaster Road, Preston PR1 2RL ☎ 01772 906536
◌ d.tomlinson@preston.gov.uk

PR / Communications: Mr Stephen Parkinson, Head of Communications, Town Hall, Lancaster Road, Preston PR1 2RL
☎ 01772 906464; 01771 906822 ◌ s.parkinson@preston.gov.uk

Community Safety: Mrs Michelle Pilling, Community Safety Manager, MAPS Team, Preston Police Preston, Lancaster Road North, Preston PR1 2SA ☎ 01772 209796 ◌ m.pilling@preston.gov.uk

Computer Management: Mr Neil Fairhurst, Director - Customer Services, Town Hall, Lancaster Road, Preston PR1 2RL
☎ 01772 906197 ◌ n.fairhurst@preston.gov.uk

Contracts: Ms Caron Parmenter, Head of Legal Services, Town Hall, Lancaster Road, Preston PR1 2RL ☎ 01772 906373
◌ c.parmenter@preston.gov.uk

Corporate Services: Mrs Alison Brown, Director - Corporate Services, Town Hall, Lancaster Road, Preston PR1 2RL
☎ 01772 906197 ◌ a.brown@preston.gov.uk

Customer Service: Mr Peter Kerry, Call Centre Manager, Town Hall, Lancaster Road, Preston PR1 2RL ☎ 01772 906939; 01772 906336 ◌ p.kerry@preston.gov.uk

Direct Labour: Mr Adrian Phillips, Director - Environment, Lancastria House, Lancaster Road, Preston PR1 2RH
☎ 01772 906171 ◌ a.phillips@preston.gov.uk

Economic Development: Mr Derek Whyte, Assistant Chief Executive, Town Hall, Lancaster Road, Preston PR1 2RL
☎ 01772 903430 ◌ d.whyte@preston.gov.uk

E-Government: Mr Neil Fairhurst, Director - Customer Services, Town Hall, Lancaster Road, Preston PR1 2RL ☎ 01772 906197
◌ n.fairhurst@preston.gov.uk

Electoral Registration: Mr Peter Welsh, Head of Electoral Services, Town Hall, Lancaster Road, Preston PR1 2RL
☎ 01772 906115 ◌ p.welsh@preston.gov.uk

Emergency Planning: Mr Alan Murray, Emergency Planning Officer, Town Hall, Lancaster Road, Preston PR1 2RL
☎ 01772 906162; 01772 906822 ◌ a.murray@preston.gov.uk

Energy Management: Mr Adrian Phillips, Director - Environment, Town Hall, Lancaster Road, Preston PR1 2RL ☎ 01772 906171
◌ a.phillips@preston.gov.uk

Environmental Health: Mr Craig Sharp, Chief Environmental Health Officer, Town Hall, Lancaster Road, Preston PR1 2RL
☎ 01772 906301 ◌ c.sharp@preston.gov.uk

Estates, Property & Valuation: Mr Derek Woods, Head of Property Management, Town Hall, Lancaster Road, Preston PR1 2RL ☎ 01772 906519 ◌ d.woods@preston.gov.uk

European Liaison: Mr Derek Whyte, Assistant Chief Executive, Town Hall, Lancaster Road, Preston PR1 2RL ☎ 01772 903430
◌ d.whyte@preston.gov.uk

Events Manager: Mr Tim Joel, Events Manager, Town Hall, Lancaster Road, Preston PR1 2RL ☎ 01772 903660
◌ t.joel@preston.gov.uk

Facilities: Mr Adrian Phillips, Director - Environment, Town Hall, Lancaster Road, Preston PR1 2RL ☎ 01772 906171
◌ a.phillips@preston.gov.uk

Finance: Mr A Robinson, Head of Shared Services, Town Hall, Lancaster Road, Preston PR1 2RL ☎ 01772 906023
◌ a.robinson@preston.gov.uk

Finance: Ms Jackie Wilding, City Treasurer, Town Hall, Lancaster Road, Preston PR1 2RL ☎ 01772 906808
◌ j.wilding@prestong.gov.uk

Fleet Management: Mr Adrian Phillips, Director - Environment, Town Hall, Lancaster Road, Preston PR1 2RL ☎ 01772 906171
◌ a.phillips@preston.gov.uk

Grounds Maintenance: Mr Matt Kelly, Head of Parks & Horticultural Services, Argyll Road, Preston PR1 6JY
☎ 01772 906141; 01772 558488 ◌ m.kelly@preston.gov.uk

Health and Safety: Ms Lesley Routh, Health & Safety Manager, Town Hall, Lancaster Road, Preston PR1 2RL ☎ 01772 906385; 01772 906822 ◌ l.routh@preston.gov.uk

Home Energy Conservation: Mr Craig Sharp, Chief Environmental Health Officer, Town Hall, Lancaster Road, Preston PR1 2RL ☎ 01772 906301 ◌ c.sharp@preston.gov.uk

Housing: Mr Craig Sharp, Chief Environmental Health Officer, Town Hall, Lancaster Road, Preston PR1 2RL ☎ 01772 906301
◌ c.sharp@preston.gov.uk

Legal: Ms Caron Parmenter, Head of Legal Services, Town Hall, Lancaster Road, Preston PR1 2RL ☎ 01772 906373
◌ c.parmenter@preston.gov.uk

Leisure and Cultural Services: Mr Jon Finch, Project Leader - Re-Imagining the Harris, Harris Museum, Market Square, Preston PR1 2PP ☎ 01772 905407 ◌ j.r.finch@preston.gov.uk

Leisure and Cultural Services: Mr Jimmy Khan, Head of Sport & Leisure, Town Hall, Lancaster Road, Preston PR1 2RL
☎ 01772 903126 ◌ j.khan@preston.gov.uk

Licensing: Mr Mike Thorpe, Head of Licensing Services, Town Hall, Lancaster Road, Preston PR1 2RL ☎ 01772 906114
◌ m.thorpe@preston.gov.uk

PRESTON

Lottery Funding, Charity and Voluntary: Ms Liz Mossop, Head of Community Services, Town Hall, Lancaster Road, Preston PR1 2RL ☎ 01772 906419 ✆ l.mossop@preston.gov.uk

Member Services: Ms Julie Grundy, Head of Member Services, Town Hall, Lancaster Road, Preston PR1 2RL ☎ 01772 906112 ✆ j.grundy@preston.gov.uk

Parking: Mr Steve Lawson, Parking & Cleaning Manager, Town Hall, Lancaster Road, Preston PR1 2RL ☎ 01772 906253 ✆ s.lawson@preston.gov.uk

Personnel / HR: Mrs Alison Brown, Director - Corporate Services, Town Hall, Lancaster Road, Preston PR1 2RL ☎ 01772 906197 ✆ a.brown@preston.gov.uk

Planning: Mr Chris Hayward, Director - Development, Lancastria House, Preston PR1 2RH ☎ 01772 906171 ✆ c.hayward@preston.gov.uk

Procurement: Mr Mervyn Sheppard, Corporate Projects Legal Advisor, Town Hall, Lancaster Road, Preston PR1 2RL ☎ 01772 906104 ✆ m.sheppard@preston.gov.uk

Recycling & Waste Minimisation: Ms Debbie Slater, Senior Recycling & Waste Management Officer, Argyll Road, Preston PR1 6JY ☎ 01772 906786 ✆ d.slater@preston.gov.uk

Regeneration: Mr Derek Whyte, Assistant Chief Executive, Town Hall, Lancaster Road, Preston PR1 2RL ☎ 01772 903430 ✆ d.whyte@preston.gov.uk

Staff Training: Mrs Steph Hayes, Training & Development Manager, Town Hall, Lancaster Road, Preston PR1 2RL ☎ 01772 906399; 01772 906822 ✆ s.hayes@preston.gov.uk

Street Scene: Mr Mark Taylor, Deputy Head of Parks, Street Scene & Transport, Argyll Road, Preston PR1 6JY ☎ 01772 906219 ✆ m.a.taylor@preston.gov.uk

Tourism: Mr Tim Joel, Events & Cultural Services Manager, Town Hall, Lancaster Road, Preston PR1 2RL ☎ 01772 903660 ✆ t.joel@preston.gov.uk

Transport: Mr Adrian Phillips, Director - Environment, Town Hall, Lancaster Road, Preston PR1 2RL ☎ 01772 906171 ✆ a.phillips@preston.gov.uk

Waste Collection and Disposal: Mr Adrian Phillips, Director - Environment, Town Hall, Lancaster Road, Preston PR1 2RL ☎ 01772 906171 ✆ a.phillips@preston.gov.uk

Waste Management: Mr Adrian Phillips, Director - Environment, Town Hall, Lancaster Road, Preston PR1 2RL ☎ 01772 906171 ✆ a.phillips@preston.gov.uk

COUNCILLORS

Mayor: Collins, John (LAB - Moor Park)
cllr.j.collins@preston.gov.uk

Deputy Mayor: Rollo, Brian (LAB - Ribbleton)
cllr.b.rollo@preston.gov.uk

Leader of the Council: Rankin, Peter John (LAB - Tulketh)

Deputy Leader of the Council: Swindells, John (LAB - University)

Group Leader: Cartwright, Neil (CON - Preston Rural East)
cllr.n.cartwright@preston.gov.uk

Abram, Christine (CON - Lea)
cllr.c.abram@preston.gov.uk

Bax, Ismail (LAB - Deepdale)
cllr.i.bax@preston.gov.uk

Borrow, David (LAB - Moor Park)
cllr.d.borrow@preston.gov.uk

Boswell, Robert (LAB - Tulketh)
cllr.r.boswell@preston.gov.uk

Brown, Matthew (LAB - Tulketh)
cllr.m.brown@preston.gov.uk

Brown, Pauline (LD - Ingol)
cllr.p.brown@preston.gov.uk

Browne, John (LAB - Brookfield)
cllr.j.browne@preston.gov.uk

Cartwright, Kathleen (CON - College)
cllr.b.cartwright@preston.gov.uk

Corker, Philip (LAB - Brookfield)
cllr.p.corker@preston.gov.uk

Coupland, Zafar (LAB - Fishwick)
cllr.z.coupland@preston.gov.uk

Crompton, Carl (LAB - University)
cllr.c.crompton@preston.gov.uk

Crompton, Linda (LAB - Riversway)
cllr.l.crompton@preston.gov.uk

Crowe, Phil (LAB - Larches)
cllr.p.crowe@preston.gov.uk

Darby, Neil (LD - Ingol)
cllr.n.darby@preston.gov.uk

Davies, Thomas (CON - Preston Rural East)
cllr.t.davies@preston.gov.uk

Desai, Salim (LAB - Town Centre)
cllr.s.desai@preston.gov.uk

Dewhurst, Daniel (CON - Lea)
cllr.d.dewhurst@preston.gov.uk

Eaves, Nerys (LAB - Brookfield)
cllr.n.eaves@preston.gov.uk

Edmondson, Rowena (CON - Greyfriars)
cllr.r.edmondson@preston.gov.uk

Faruki, Anis (LAB - St George's)
cllr.a.faruki@preston.gov.uk

Gale, Drew (LAB - Town Centre)
cllr.d.gale@preston.gov.uk

Gildert, Sonia (CON - Sharoe Green)
cllr.s.gildert@preston.gov.uk

Greenhalgh, Stuart (CON - Garrison)
cllr.s.greenhalgh@preston.gov.uk

Hammond, David (CON - Greyfriars)
cllr.d.hammond@preston.gov.uk

Hart, Trevor (CON - Lea)
cllr.t.hart@preston.gov.uk

Hull, James (LAB - St George's)
cllr.j.hull@preston.gov.uk

Iqbal, Javed (LAB - St. Matthew's)
cllr.j.iqbal@preston.gov.uk

Jeffrey, Jason (LD - Ingol)
cllr.j.jeffrey@preston.gov.uk

Kelly, Peter (LAB - Riversway)
cllr.p.kelly@preston.gov.uk

Leach, Charlotte (CON - Garrison)
cllr.c.leach@preston.gov.uk

Leeming, Roy (LAB - St. Matthew's)
cllr.r.leeming@preston.gov.uk

McManus, Margaret (CON - Sharoe Green)
cllr.m.mcmanus@preston.gov.uk

Moore, Damien (CON - Greyfriars)
cllr.d.moore@preston.gov.uk

Morgan, Jade (LAB - St. Matthew's)
cllr.j.morgan@preston.gov.uk

Moss, Peter (LAB - Riversway)
cllr.p.moss@preston.gov.uk

Mullen, Stephen (LD - Cadley)
cllr.s.mullen@preston.gov.uk

Patel, Yakub (LAB - Town Centre)
cllr.y.patel@preston.gov.uk

Pomfret, Nicholas (LAB - Ribbleton)
cllr.n.pomfret@preston.gov.uk

Potter, John (LD - Cadley)
cllr.j.potter@preston.gov.uk

Rawlinson, Martyn (LAB - Fishwick)
cllr.m.rawlinson@preston.gov.uk

Routeledge, Mark (LAB - Ashton)
cllr.m.routledge@preston.gov.uk

Saksena, Jonathan (LAB - Ribbleton)
cllr.j.saksena@preston.gov.uk

Seddon, Harry (CON - College)
cllr.h.seddon@preston.gov.uk

Smith, Lona (CON - Preston Rural North)
cllr.l.smith@preston.gov.uk

Thomas, Christine (CON - Garrison)
cllr.c.thomas@preston.gov.uk

Thompson, Stephen (CON - Preston Rural North)
cllr.s.thompson@preston.gov.uk

Vodden, Angela (LAB - Ashton)
cllr.a.vodden@preston.gov.uk

Walker, David (CON - Sharoe Green)
cllr.d.walker@preston.gov.uk

Wallace, Lynne (LAB - Deepdale)
cllr.l.wallace@preston.gov.uk

Whittam, Susan (CON - Preston Rural North)
cllr.s.whittam@preston.gov.uk

Yates, Rebecca (LAB - Larches)
cllr.r.yates@preston.gov.uk

Yates, Mark (LAB - Larches)
cllr.m.yates@preston.gov.uk

POLITICAL COMPOSITION
LAB: 33, CON: 19, LD: 5

COMMITTEE CHAIRS

Audit: Mr Damien Moore

Planning: Mr Brian Rollo

Purbeck   D

Purbeck District Council, Westport House, Worgret Road, Wareham BH20 4PP
☎ 01929 556561 🖷 01929 552688 ✒ enquiries@purbeck-dc.gov.uk
🖳 www.purbeck.gov.uk

FACTS AND FIGURES
Parliamentary Constituencies: Dorset Mid and Poole North, Dorset South
EU Constituencies: South West
Election Frequency: Elections are by thirds

PRINCIPAL OFFICERS

Chief Executive: Mr Steve Mackenzie, Chief Executive, Westport House, Worgret Road, Wareham BH20 4PP ☎ 01929 557235 ✒ stevemackenzie@purbeck-dc.gov.uk

Senior Management: Ms Bridget Downton, General Manager - Planning & Community Services Section, Westport House, Worgret Road, Wareham BH20 4PP ☎ 01929 557268 ✒ bridgetdownton@purbeck-dc.gov.uk

Senior Management: Mrs Sue Joyce, General Manager - Resources, Westport House, Worgret Road, Wareham BH20 4PP ☎ 01929 557321 ✒ suejoyce@purbeck-dc.gov.uk

Senior Management: Ms Rebecca Kirk, General Manager - Public Health & Housing Services, Westport House, Worgret Road, Wareham BH20 4PP ☎ 01929 557208 ✒ rebeccakirk@purbeck-dc.gov.uk

Best Value: Ms Jane Hay, Performance & Information Officer, Westport House, Worgret Road, Wareham BH20 4PP ☎ 01929 557325 ✒ janehay@purbeck-dc.gov.uk

Building Control: Mr David Kitcatt, Building Control Manager, Westport House, Worgret Road, Wareham BH20 4PP ☎ 01929 557272 ✒ davidkitcatt@purbeck-dc.gov.uk

PR / Communications: Miss Claire Lodge, Communications Officer, Westport House, Worgret Road, Wareham BH20 4PP ☎ 01929 557201 ✒ clairelodge@purbeck-dc.gov.uk

Community Planning: Ms Anna Lee, Planning Policy Manager, Westport House, Worgret Road, Wareham BH20 4PP ☎ 01929 557339 ✒ annalee@purbeck-dc.gov.uk

Community Safety: Ms Laura Brewer, Public Health Manager, Westport House, Worgret Road, Wareham BH20 4PP ☎ 01929 557275 ✒ laurabrewer@purbeck-dc.gov.uk

Computer Management: Mr Paul Gammon, IT Manager, Westport House, Worgret Road, Wareham BH20 4PP ☎ 01929 557316 ✒ paulgammon@purbeck-dc.gov.uk

PURBECK

Contracts: Mrs Jacquie Hall, Property & Procurement Team Leader, Westport House, Worgret Road, Wareham BH20 4PP ☎ 01929 557299 ⊕ jacquiehall@purbeck-dc.gov.uk

Corporate Services: Ms Jane Hay, Performance & Information Officer, Westport House, Worgret Road, Wareham BH20 4PP ☎ 01929 557325 ⊕ janehay@purbeck-dc.gov.uk

Customer Service: Ms Sharon Attwater, Customer Services Team Leader, Westport House, Worgret Road, Wareham BH20 4PP ☎ 01929 557250 ⊕ sharonattwater@purbeck-dc.gov.uk

Economic Development: Mr Richard Wilson, Environmental Design Manager, Westport House, Worgret Road, Wareham BH20 4PP ☎ 01929 557320 ⊕ richardwilson@purbeck-dc.gov.uk

E-Government: Mr Paul Gammon, IT Manager, Westport House, Worgret Road, Wareham BH20 4PP ☎ 01929 557316 ⊕ paulgammon@purbeck-dc.gov.uk

Electoral Registration: Ms Kirsty Riglar, Democratic & Electoral Services Manager, Westport House, Worgret Road, Wareham BH20 4PP ☎ 01929 557221 ⊕ kirstyriglar@purbeck-dc.gov.uk

Emergency Planning: Ms Kirsty Riglar, Democratic & Electoral Services Manager, Westport House, Worgret Road, Wareham BH20 4PP ☎ 01929 557221 ⊕ kirstyriglar@purbeck-dc.gov.uk

Environmental / Technical Services: Mr Richard Conway, Environment Manager, Westport House, Worgret Road, Wareham BH20 4PP ☎ 01929 557267 ⊕ richardconway@purbeck-dc.gov.uk

Estates, Property & Valuation: Mrs Jacquie Hall, Property & Procurement Team Leader, Westport House, Worgret Road, Wareham BH20 4PP ☎ 01929 557299 ⊕ jacquiehall@purbeck-dc.gov.uk

Facilities: Mrs Jacquie Hall, Property & Procurement Team Leader, Westport House, Worgret Road, Wareham BH20 4PP ☎ 01929 557299 ⊕ jacquiehall@purbeck-dc.gov.uk

Finance: Mrs Sue Joyce, General Manager - Resources, Westport House, Worgret Road, Wareham BH20 4PP ☎ 01929 557321 ⊕ suejoyce@purbeck-dc.gov.uk

Health and Safety: Mrs Christine Dewey, Human Resources Manager, Westport House, Worgret Road, Wareham BH20 4PP ☎ 01929 557204 ⊕ christinedewey@purbeck-dc.gov.uk

Housing: Ms Fiona Brown, Housing Manager, Westport House, Worgret Road, Wareham BH20 4PP ☎ 01929 557310 ⊕ fionabrown@purbeck-dc.gov.uk

Legal: Mr David Fairbairn, Solicitor to the Council / Monitoring Officer, Westport House, Worgret Road, Wareham BH20 4PP ☎ 01929 557223 ⊕ davidfairbairn@purbeck-dc.gov.uk

Leisure and Cultural Services: Ms Michelle Goodman, Purbeck Sports Centre Manager, Westport House, Worgret Road, Wareham BH20 4PP ☎ 01929 500000 ⊕ michellegoodman@purbeck-dc.gov.uk

Licensing: Mr Richard Conway, Environment Manager, Westport House, Worgret Road, Wareham BH20 4PP ☎ 01929 557267 ⊕ richardconway@purbeck-dc.gov.uk

Member Services: Ms Kirsty Riglar, Democratic & Electoral Services Manager, Westport House, Worgret Road, Wareham BH20 4PP ☎ 01929 557221 ⊕ kirstyriglar@purbeck-dc.gov.uk

Parking: Mrs Jacquie Hall, Property & Procurement Team Leader, Westport House, Worgret Road, Wareham BH20 4PP ☎ 01929 557299 ⊕ jacquiehall@purbeck-dc.gov.uk

Partnerships: Mr Steve Mackenzie, Chief Executive, Westport House, Worgret Road, Wareham BH20 4PP ☎ 01929 557235 ⊕ stevemackenzie@purbeck-dc.gov.uk

Personnel / HR: Mrs Christine Dewey, Human Resources Manager, Westport House, Worgret Road, Wareham BH20 4PP ☎ 01929 557204 ⊕ christinedewey@purbeck-dc.gov.uk

Planning: Ms Bridget Downton, General Manager - Planning & Community Services Section, Westport House, Worgret Road, Wareham BH20 4PP ☎ 01929 557268 ⊕ bridgetdownton@purbeck-dc.gov.uk

Procurement: Mrs Jacquie Hall, Property & Procurement Team Leader, Westport House, Worgret Road, Wareham BH20 4PP ☎ 01929 557299 ⊕ jacquiehall@purbeck-dc.gov.uk

Regeneration: Mr Richard Wilson, Environmental Design Manager, Westport House, Worgret Road, Wareham BH20 4PP ☎ 01929 557320 ⊕ richardwilson@purbeck-dc.gov.uk

Staff Training: Mrs Christine Dewey, Human Resources Manager, Westport House, Worgret Road, Wareham BH20 4PP ☎ 01929 557204 ⊕ christinedewey@purbeck-dc.gov.uk

Sustainable Communities: Ms Anna Lee, Planning Policy Manager, Westport House, Worgret Road, Wareham BH20 4PP ☎ 01929 557339 ⊕ annalee@purbeck-dc.gov.uk

Sustainable Development: Ms Anna Lee, Planning Policy Manager, Westport House, Worgret Road, Wareham BH20 4PP ☎ 01929 557339 ⊕ annalee@purbeck-dc.gov.uk

Tourism: Ms Alison Turnock, Natural Heritage & Tourism Manager, Westport House, Worgret Road, Wareham BH20 4PP ☎ 01929 557337 ⊕ alisonturnock@purbeck-dc.gov.uk

COUNCILLORS

Chair: Trite, Bill (CON - Swanage North)
swanbase.w@virgin.net

Vice-Chair: Morris, Tim (CON - Swanage South)
cllr.morris@purbeck-dc.gov.uk

Leader of the Council: Suttle, Gary (CON - Swanage South)
gary.suttle@gmsuttle.co.uk

Deputy Leader of the Council: Quinn, Barry (CON - Lulworth & Winfrith)
cllr.quinn@purbeck-dc.gov.uk

Barnes, Malcolm (CON - Creech Barrow)
mb@malcolmbarnes.co.uk

Brooks, Cherry (CON - Wool)
cllr.brooks@purbeck-dc.gov.uk

Brown, Graham (CON - Wool)
cllr.brown@purbeck-dc.gov.uk

Budd, David (LD - Wareham)
cllr.budd@purbeck-dc.gov.uk

Dragon, Nigel (IND - Castle)
cllr.Dragon@purbeck-dc.gov.uk

Drane, Fred (LD - Lytchett Minster and Upton East)
cllr.freddrane@ntlworld.com

Ezzard, Beryl (LD - St. Martin)
cllr.ezzard@purbeck-dc.gov.uk

Finch, Caroline (CON - Swanage South)
cllr.finch@purbeck.gov.uk

Goodinge, Hilary (CON - Wareham)
hilarygoodinge@btinternet.com

Lovell, Mike (CON - Langton)
mwjlovell@gmail.com

Marsh, Gloria (CON - Swanage North)
cllr.Marsh@purbeck-dc.gov.uk

Meaden, Wendy (CON - Lytchett Matravers)
cllr.eaden@purbeck-dc.gov.uk

Miller, Laura (CON - Wool)
cllr.miller@purbeck-dc.gov.uk

Pipe, Claire (CON - Lytchett Minster and Upton West)
clairepipe2011@gmail.com

Pipe, Bill (CON - Lytchett Minster and Upton West)
magpiebillpipe@freeuk.com

Tilling, Carol (LD - Lytchett Minster and Upton East)
cllrcaroltilling@gmail.com

Unsworth, Mark (CON - St. Martin)
cllr.unsworth@purbeck-dc.gov.uk

Webb, Peter (CON - Lytchett Matravers)
cllr.webb@purbeck-dc.gov.uk

Wharf, Peter (CON - Bere Regis)
peter.wharf@btopenworld.com

Whitwam, Mike (CON - Swanage North)
cllr.whitwam@purbeck-dc.gov.uk

Wiggins, Mike (CON - Wareham)
mike.wiggins@btconnect.gov.uk

POLITICAL COMPOSITION
CON: 20, LD: 4, IND: 1

Reading U

Reading Borough Council, Civic Offices, Bridge Street,
Reading RG1 2LU
☎ 0118 937 3737 🖨 0118 958 9770
⌖ forename.surname@reading.gov.uk
🖳 www.reading.gov.uk

FACTS AND FIGURES
Parliamentary Constituencies: Reading East, Reading West
EU Constituencies: South East
Election Frequency: Elections are by thirds

PRINCIPAL OFFICERS

Chief Executive: Mr Simon Warren, Interim Managing Director,
Civic Offices, Bridge Street, Reading RG1 2LU
⌖ simon.warren@reading.gov.uk

Senior Management: Ms Alison Bell, Director - Environment &
Neighbourhood Services, Civic Offices, Bridge Street, Reading
RG1 2LU ☎ 0118 937 2457 ⌖ alison.bell@reading.gov.uk

Senior Management: Mr Christopher Brooks, Head of Legal
& Democratic Services (Monitoring Officer), Civic Offices, Bridge
Street, Reading RG1 2LU ☎ 0118 937 2602; 0118 937 2767
⌖ chris.brooks@reading.gov.uk

Senior Management: Ms Wendy Fabbro, Director - Adult Care &
Health Services, Civic Offices, Bridge Street, Reading RG1 2LU
☎ 0118 937 2072 ⌖ wendy.fabbro@reading.gov.uk

Senior Management: Ms Helen McMullen, Director - Children,
Education & Early Help, Civic Offices, Bridge Street, Reading RG1
2LU ☎ 0118 937 4771 ⌖ helen.mcmullen@reading.gov.uk

Best Value: Mrs Zoe Hanim, Head of Customer Services, Civic
Offices, Bridge Street, Reading RG1 2LU ☎ 0118 937 2173; 0118 937
2155 ⌖ zoe.hanim@reading.gov.uk

Civil Registration: Mr Matthew Golledge, Trading Standards
Manager, Civic Offices, Bridge Street, Reading RG1 2LU
☎ 0118 937 2497; 0118 937 2557 ⌖ matthew.golledge@reading.gov.uk

Community Planning: Mr Grant Thornton, Head of Economic &
Cultural Development, Civic Offices, Bridge Street, Reading RG1
2LU ☎ 0118 937 2416; 0118 937 2155
⌖ grant.thornton@reading.gov.uk

Computer Management: Mr John Barnfield, ICT Manager, Civic
Offices, Bridge Street, Reading RG1 2LU ☎ 0118 937 7286
⌖ john.barnfield@reading.gov.uk

Customer Service: Mrs Zoe Hanim, Head of Customer Services,
Civic Offices, Bridge Street, Reading RG1 2LU ☎ 0118 937 2173;
0118 937 2155 ⌖ zoe.hanim@reading.gov.uk

Education: Mr Richard Blackmore, Head of Education &
Commissioning Services, Civic Offices, Bridge Street, Reading RG1
2LU ☎ 0118 937 4240 ⌖ richard.blackmore@reading.gov.uk

E-Government: Mrs Zoe Hanim, Head of Customer Services, Civic
Offices, Bridge Street, Reading RG1 2LU ☎ 0118 937 2173; 0118 937
2155 ⌖ zoe.hanim@reading.gov.uk

Electoral Registration: Mrs Julie Kempen, Electoral Services
Manager, Civic Offices, Bridge Street, Reading RG1 2LU
☎ 0118 937 2731; 0118 937 2591 ⌖ julie.kempen@reading.gov.uk

Emergency Planning: Mr Brett Dyson, Emergency Planning &
Risk Officer, Civic Offices, Bridge Street, Reading RG1 2LU
☎ 0118 937 2235; 0118 397 2559 ⌖ brett.dyson@reading.gov.uk

Energy Management: Mr Ben Burfoot, Sustainability Manager,
Civic Offices, Bridge Street, Reading RG1 2LU ☎ 0118 937 2232;
0118 937 2155 ⌖ ben.burfoot@reading.ac.uk

READING

Estates, Property & Valuation: Mr Bruce Tindall, Head of Development, Civic Offices, Bridge Street, Reading RG1 2LU ☎ 0118 937 2594; 0118 937 2767 ✆ bruce.tindall@reading.gov.uk

European Liaison: Mr Grant Thornton, Head of Economic & Cultural Development, Civic Offices, Bridge Street, Reading RG1 2LU ☎ 0118 937 2416; 0118 937 2155 ✆ grant.thornton@reading.gov.uk

Facilities: Ms Jan Sagoo, Head of Civic Services / New Civic Project, Civic Offices, Bridge Street, Reading RG1 2LU ☎ 0118 937 2304; 0118 937 2591 ✆ jan.sagoo@reading.gov.uk

Finance: Mr Alan Cross, Head of Finance, Civic Offices, Bridge Street, Reading RG1 2LU ☎ 0118 937 2058; 0118 937 2278 ✆ alan.cross@reading.gov.uk

Finance: Mr Dave Fisher, Chief Accountant, Civic Offices, Bridge Street, Reading RG1 2LU ☎ 0118 937 2747; 0118 937 2278 ✆ dave.fisher@reading.gov.uk

Fleet Management: Ms Michelle Crick, Neighbourhood Services Support Manager, 19 Bennet Road, Reading RG2 0QX ☎ 0118 937 3993 ✆ peter.butler@reading.gov.uk

Health and Safety: Mr Robin Pringle, Corporate Safety & Workforce Development, Civic Offices, Bridge Street, Reading RG1 2LU ☎ 0118 937 2519 ✆ robin.pringle@reading.gov.uk

Highways: Mr Vaughan Norris, Highways Manager, Civic Offices, Bridge Street, Reading RG1 2LU ☎ 0118 937 2669; 0119 937 2609 ✆ vaughan.norris@reading.gov.uk

Home Energy Conservation: Mr Paul Taylor, Housing Stock Regeneration Manager, ⌨ Darwin Close, Reading RG2 0RB ☎ 0118 939 0224; 0118 975 3334 ✆ paul.taylor@reading.gov.uk

Housing: Mr Phil Eldridge, Property Services Manager, Civic Offices, Bridge Street, Reading RG1 2LU ☎ 0118 937 2266; 0118 937 2052 ✆ phil.eldridge@reading.gov.uk

Housing Maintenance: Mr Phil Eldridge, Property Services Manager, Civic Offices, Bridge Street, Reading RG1 2LU ☎ 0118 937 2266; 0118 937 2052 ✆ phil.eldridge@reading.gov.uk

Local Area Agreement: Mrs Zoe Hanim, Head of Customer Services, Civic Offices, Bridge Street, Reading RG1 2LU ☎ 0118 937 2173; 0118 937 2155 ✆ zoe.hanim@reading.gov.uk

Legal: Mr Christopher Brooks, Head of Legal & Democratic Services (Monitoring Officer), Civic Offices, Bridge Street, Reading RG1 2LU ☎ 0118 937 2602; 0118 937 2767 ✆ chris.brooks@reading.gov.uk

Leisure and Cultural Services: Mr Rhodri Thomas, Museum & Town Hall General Manager, Reading Central Library, Abbey Square, Reading RG1 3BQ ☎ 0118 937 3943; 0118 956 6719 ✆ rhodri.thomas@reading.gov.uk

Licensing: Ms Clare Bradley, Environmental Health Manager (Licensing & Environmental Protection), Civic Offices, Bridge Street, Reading RG1 2LU ☎ 0118 937 2322; 0118 937 2557 ✆ clare.bradley@reading.gov.uk

Lighting: Mr Vaughan Norris, Highways Manager, Civic Offices, Bridge Street, Reading RG1 2LU ☎ 0118 937 2669; 0119 937 2609 ✆ vaughan.norris@reading.gov.uk

Lottery Funding, Charity and Voluntary: Ms Irene Cameron, Team Leader - Funding Services, Civic Offices, Bridge Street, Reading RG1 2LU ☎ 0118 937 2387; 0118 939 0155 ✆ irene.cameron@reading.gov.uk

Member Services: Ms Jan Sagoo, Head of Civic Services / New Civic Project, Civic Offices, Bridge Street, Reading RG1 2LU ☎ 0118 937 2304; 0118 937 2591 ✆ jan.sagoo@reading.gov.uk

Parking: Mr Mark Smith, Head of Transportation & Streetcare, Civic Offices, Bridge Street, Reading RG1 2LU ☎ 0118 937 2813 ✆ mark.smith@reading.gov.uk

Partnerships: Ms Sarah Gee, Head of Housing, Neighbourhoods & Communities, Civic Offices, Bridge Street, Reading RG1 2LU ☎ 0118 937 2973; 0118 937 2786 ✆ sarah.gee@reading.gov.uk

Planning: Ms Alison Bell, Director - Environment & Neighbourhood Services, Civic Offices, Bridge Street, Reading RG1 2LU ☎ 0118 937 2457 ✆ alison.bell@reading.gov.uk

Procurement: Mr John Littlefair, Procurement & Partnership Manager, Civic Offices, Bridge Street, Reading RG1 2LU ☎ 0118 937 2748; 0118 958 0278 ✆ andy.allen@reading.gov.uk

Recycling & Waste Minimisation: Mr Oliver Burt, Project Manager, 2-4 Darwin Close, Reading RG2 0RB ☎ 0118 937 3990 ✆ oliver.burt@reading.gov.uk

Regeneration: Mr Chris Bloomfield, Neighbourhood Regeneration Manager, Civic Offices, Bridge Street, Reading RG1 2LU ☎ 0118 937 2176; 0118 937 2155 ✆ chris.bloomfield@reading.gov.uk

Road Safety: Mr Simon Beasley, Network & Parking Services Manager, Civic Offices, Bridge Street, Reading RG1 2LU ☎ 0118 937 2228; 0118 937 2633 ✆ simon.beasley@reading.gov.uk

Social Services: Ms Sue Gosling, CRT Business Support Team Leader, Civic Offices, Bridge Street, Reading RG1 2LU ☎ 0118 937 3676; 0118 955 3744 ✆ sue.gosling@reading.gov.uk

Social Services (Adult): Ms Wendy Fabbro, Director - Adult Care & Health Services, Civic Offices, Bridge Street, Reading RG1 2LU ☎ 0118 937 2072 ✆ wendy.fabbro@reading.gov.uk

Public Health: Ms Jo Hawthorne, Consultant in Public Health, Civic Offices, Bridge Street, Reading RG1 2LU ☎ 0118 937 2115 ✆ jo.hawthorne@reading.gov.uk

Staff Training: Mr Russell Gabini, Organisational & Workforce Development Manager, Civic Offices, Bridge Street, Reading RG1 2LU ☎ 0118 937 2115 ✆ russell.gabini@reading.gov.uk

Street Scene: Mr Chris Camfield, Street Environment Manager, 19 Bennetts Road, Reading RG2 0QX ☎ 0118 937 2040 ✆ chris.camfield@reading.gov.uk

Sustainable Communities: Mr Ben Burfoot, Sustainability Manager, Civic Offices, Bridge Street, Reading RG1 2LU
☎ 0118 937 2232; 0118 937 2155 ✆ ben.burfoot@reading.ac.uk

Sustainable Development: Mr Ben Burfoot, Sustainability Manager, Civic Offices, Bridge Street, Reading RG1 2LU
☎ 0118 937 2232; 0118 937 2155 ✆ ben.burfoot@reading.ac.uk

Tourism: Ms Sue Brackley, Economic Development Manager, Reading Central Library, Abbey Square, Reading RG1 3BQ
☎ 0118 900 1624; 0118 939 9885 ✆ sue.brackley@reading.gov.uk

Traffic Management: Mr Simon Beasley, Network & Parking Services Manager, Civic Offices, Bridge Street, Reading RG1 2LU
☎ 0118 937 2228; 0118 937 2633 ✆ simon.beasley@reading.gov.uk

Waste Collection and Disposal: Mr Oliver Burt, Project Manager, 2-4 Darwin Close, Reading RG2 0RB ☎ 0118 937 3990 ✆ oliver.burt@reading.gov.uk

Waste Collection and Disposal: Mr Chris Green, Waste Operations Manager, 2-4 Darwin Close, Reading RG2 0RB
☎ 0118 937 3950 ✆ chris.green@reading.gov.uk

COUNCILLORS

Mayor: Ayub, Mohammed (LAB - Abbey)
mohammed.ayub@reading.gov.uk

Leader of the Council: Lovelock, Jo (LAB - Norcot)
jo.lovelock@reading.gov.uk

Deputy Leader of the Council: Page, Tony (LAB - Abbey)
tony.page@reading gov;uk

Group Leader: Duveen, Ricky (LD - Tilehurst)
ricky.duveen@reading.gov.uk

Group Leader: Skeats, Jeanette (CON - Thames)
jeanette.skeats@reading.gov.uk

Group Leader: White, Rob (GRN - Park)
rob.white@reading.gov.uk

Absolom, David (LAB - Redlands)
david.absolom@reading.gov.uk

Absolom, Debs (LAB - Norcot)
debs.absolom@reading.gov.uk

Ballsdon, Isobel (CON - Mapledurham)
isobel.ballsden@reading.gov.uk

Brock, Jason (LAB - Southcote)
jason.brock@reading.gov.uk

Chrisp, Rachael (LAB - Caversham)
rachael.crisp@reading.gov.uk

Davies, Richard (LAB - Caversham)
richard.davies@reading.gov.uk

Dennis, Glenn (LAB - Kentwood)
glenn.dennis@reading.gov.uk

Eden, Rachel (LAB - Whitley)
rachel.eden@reading.gov.uk

Edwards, Kelly (LAB - Whitley)
kelly.edwards@reading.gov.uk

Edwards, Deborah (LAB - Southcote)
deborah.edwards@reading.gov.uk

Ennis, John (LAB - Southcote)
john.ennis@reading.gov.uk

Gavin, Jan (LAB - Redlands)
jan.gavin@reading.gov.uk

Gittings, Paul (LAB - Minster)
paul.gittings@reading.gov.uk

Grashoff, Clare (CON - Peppard)
clare.grashoff@reading.gov.uk

Hacker, Sarah (LAB - Battle)
sarah-jane.hacker@reading.gov.uk

Hopper, Ed (CON - Thames)
ed.hopper@reading.gov.uk

Hoskin, Graeme (LAB - Norcot)
graeme.hoskin@reading.gov.uk

James, Sophia (LAB - Katesgrove)
sophia.james@reading.gov.uk

Jones, Tony (LAB - Redlands)
tony.jones@reading.gov.uk

Khan, Gul (LAB - Battle)
gul.khan@reading.gov.uk

Livingston, Marian (LAB - Minster)
marian.livingston@reading.gov.uk

Maskell, Chris (LAB - Battle)
chris.maskell@reading.gov.uk

McDonald, Claire (CON - Caversham)
claire.mcdonald@reading.gov.uk

McElligott, Eileen (LAB - Church)
eileen.mcelligott@reading.gov.uk

McGonigle, Brenda (GRN - Park)

McKenna, Emmett (LAB - Whitley)
emmett.mckenna@reading.gov.uk

O'Connell, Meri (LD - Tilehurst)
meri.o'connell@reading.vo.uk

Pearce, Ashley (LAB - Church)
ashley.pearce@reaind.gov.uk

Robinson, Simon (CON - Peppard)
simon.robinson@reading.gov.uk

Rodda, Matt (LAB - Katesgrove)
matt.rodda@reading.gov.uk

Singh, Daya Pal (LAB - Kentwood)
daya.pal.singh@reading.gov.uk

Stanford-Beale, Jane (CON - Peppard)
jane.stanford-beale@reading.gov.uk

Steele, Tom (CON - Kentwood)
tom.steele@reading.gov.uk

Stevens, David (CON - Thames)
david.stevens@reading.gov.uk

Terry, Liz (LAB - Minster)
liz.terry@reading.gov.uk

Tickner, Bet (LAB - Abbey)
bet.tickner@reading.gov.uk

READING

Vickers, Sandra (CON - Tilehurst)
sandra.vickers@reading.gov.uk

Williams, Rose (LAB - Katesgrove)
rose.williams@reading.gov.uk

Williams, Josh (GRN - Park)
josh.williams@reading.gov.uk

Woodward, Paul (LAB - Church)
paul.woodward@reading.gov.uk

POLITICAL COMPOSITION
LAB: 31, CON: 10, GRN: 3, LD: 2

COMMITTEE CHAIRS

Adult Social Care, Children's Services & Education: Ms Eileen McElligott

Health & Wellbeing: Mr Graeme Hoskin

Housing, Neighbourhoods & Leisure: Ms Sophia James

Licensing: Mr Paul Woodward

Planning: Ms Marian Livingston

Strategic Environment, Planning & Transport: Mr David Absolom

Redbridge   L

Redbridge London Borough Council, Town Hall, High Road, Ilford IG1 1DD
☎ 020 8554 5000 ᐰ customer.cc@redbridge.gov.uk
🖳 www.redbridge.gov.uk

FACTS AND FIGURES
Parliamentary Constituencies: Chingford and Woodford, Ilford North, Ilford South, Leyton and Wanstead
EU Constituencies: London
Election Frequency: Elections are of whole council

PRINCIPAL OFFICERS

Chief Executive: Mr Andy Donald, Chief Executive & Head of Paid Service, Lynton House, High Road, Ilford IG1 1NY
☎ 020 8708 2100 ᐰ andy.donald@redbridge.gov.uk

Senior Management: Ms Fiona Alderman, Head of Legal & Constitutional Services, Lynton House, High Road, Ilford IG1 1NY
☎ 020 8708 2201 ᐰ fiona.alderman@redbridge.gov.uk

Senior Management: Mr Mirsad Bakalovic, Operational Director - Civic Pride, Lynton House, High Road, Ilford IG1 1NY
☎ 020 8708 7849 ᐰ mirsad.bakalovic@redbridge.gov.uk

Senior Management: Ms Caroline Bruce, Corporate Director - Place, Lynton House, High Road, Ilford IG1 1NY ☎ 020 8708 3567 ᐰ caroline.bruce@redbridge.gov.uk

Senior Management: Ms Maria Christofi, Corporate Director - Resources, Lynton House, High Road, Ilford IG1 1NY
☎ 020 8708 3588 ᐰ maria.christofi@redbridge.gov.uk

Senior Management: Mrs Caroline Cutts, Operational Director - Children & Families, Lynton House, 255 - 259 High Road, Ilford IG1 1NY ☎ 020 8708 5304 ᐰ caroline.cutts@redbridge.gov.uk

Senior Management: Mr Matthew Essex, Operational Director - Regeneration & Planning, Lynton House, High Road, Ilford IG1 1NY
☎ 020 8708 2809 ᐰ matthew.essex@redbridge.gov.uk

Senior Management: Ms Vicky Hobart, Director - Public Health, Lynton House, High Road, Ilford IG1 1NY ☎ 020 8708 5731
ᐰ vicky.hobart@redbridge.gov.uk

Senior Management: Mr Adrian Loades, Corporate Director - People, Lynton House, High Road, Ilford IG1 1NY ☎ 020 8708 5742
ᐰ adrian.loades@redbridge.gov.uk

Senior Management: Ms Caroline Maclean, Operational Director - Adult Social Services, Lynton House, High Road, Ilford IG1 1NY
☎ 020 8708 5595 ᐰ caroline.maclean@redbridge.gov.uk

Senior Management: Ms Jackie Odunoye, Operational Director - Housing, Lynton House, High Road, Ilford IG1 1NY
☎ 020 8708 4149 ᐰ jackie.odunoye@redbridge.gov.uk

Senior Management: Mr Simon Parker, Corporate Director - Strategy, Lynton House, High Road, Ilford IG1 1NY
☎ 020 8708 2228 ᐰ simon.parker@redbridge.gov.uk

Senior Management: Ms Julie Sharp, Head of Audit, Lynton House, High Road, Ilford IG1 1NY ☎ 020 8708 3130
ᐰ julie.sharp@redbridge.gov.uk

Access Officer / Social Services (Disability): Ms Leila Hussain, Head of Service - Health & Adult Social Services, Lynton House, 255 - 259 High Road, Ilford IG1 1NY ☎ 020 8708 5169
ᐰ leila.hussain@redbridge.gov.uk

Building Control: Mr Amrik Notta, Building Control Manager, Town Hall, High Road, Ilford IG1 1DD ☎ 020 8708 2521
ᐰ amrik.notta@redbridge.gov.uk

Catering Services: Ms Therese Hamshaw, Catering Manager, PO Box 2, Town Hall, High Road, Ilford IG1 1DD ☎ 020 8708 2003
ᐰ therese.hamshaw@redbridge.gov.uk

Children / Youth Services: Mr Adrian Loades, Corporate Director - People, Lynton House, High Road, Ilford IG1 1NY
☎ 020 8708 5742 ᐰ adrian.loades@redbridge.gov.uk

Civil Registration: Ms Christine Casson, Registrar of Births & Deaths / Deputy Superintendent, Queen Victoria House, 794 Cranbrook Road, Barkingside, Ilford IG6 1JS ☎ 020 8708 7165
ᐰ christine.casson@redbridge.gov.uk

PR / Communications: Ms Kirsty Tobin, Head of Marketing & Communications, Town Hall, High Road, Ilford IG1 1DD
☎ 020 8708 3766 ᐰ kirsty.tobin@redbridge.gov.uk

Community Safety: Mr Mirsad Bakalovic, Operational Director - Civic Pride, Lynton House, High Road, Ilford IG1 1NY
☎ 020 8708 7849 ᐰ mirsad.bakalovic@redbridge.gov.uk

Computer Management: Mr Lee Edwards, Head of IT, 17/23 Clements Road, Ilford IG1 1AG ☎ 020 8708 4100
ᐰ lee.edwards@redbridge.gov.uk

Consumer Protection and Trading Standards: Mr Alan Drake, Head of Community Protection & Enforcement, Lynton House, High Road, Ilford IG1 1NY ☎ 020 8708 5490 ✉ alan.drake@redbridge.gov.uk

Contracts: Mr Taraq Bashir, Interim Head of Procurement, Lynton House, High Road, Ilford IG1 1NY ☎ 020 8708 3268 ✉ taraq.bashir@redbridge.gov.uk

Corporate Services: Mr Kevin Wackett, Head of Parks & Open Spaces, 210 Wash Lodge, Cranbrook Road, Ilford IG1 4TG ☎ 020 8708 3223 ✉ kevin.wackett@visionrcl.org.uk

Customer Service: Mr Peter Ratnarajah, Head of Revenues, Benefits & Customer Services, 22 - 26 Clements Road, Ilford IG1 1BD ☎ 020 8708 4519 ✉ peter.ratnarajah@redbridge.gov.uk

Direct Labour: Mr Mirsad Bakalovic, Operational Director - Civic Pride, Lynton House, High Road, Ilford IG1 1NY ☎ 020 8708 7849 ✉ mirsad.bakalovic@redbridge.gov.uk

Economic Development: Mr Matthew Essex, Operational Director - Regeneration & Planning, Lynton House, High Road, Ilford IG1 1NY ☎ 020 8708 2809 ✉ matthew.essex@redbridge.gov.uk

Education: Mrs Caroline Cutts, Operational Director - Children & Families, Lynton House, 255 - 259 High Road, Ilford IG1 1NY ☎ 020 8708 5304 ✉ caroline.cutts@redbridge.gov.uk

Education: Mr Chris Hilliard, Interim Operational Director - Education & Inclusion, Lynton House, High Road, Ilford IG1 1NY ☎ 020 8708 3378 ✉ chris.hilliard@redbridge.gov.uk

Education: Ms Caroline Maclean, Operational Director - Adult Social Services, Lynton House, High Road, Ilford IG1 1NY ☎ 020 8708 5595 ✉ caroline.maclean@redbridge.gov.uk

E-Government: Mr Lee Edwards, Head of IT, 17/23 Clements Road, Ilford IG1 1AG ☎ 020 8708 4100 ✉ lee.edwards@redbridge.gov.uk

Electoral Registration: Mr George Sullivan, Electoral Services Manager, Queen Victoria House, 794 Cranbrook Road, Barkingside, Ilford IG6 1JS ☎ 020 8708 7170 ✉ george.sullivan@redbridge.gov.uk

Emergency Planning: Mr Jeremy Reynolds, Emergency Planning & Business Continuity Manager, Redbridge Control Centre, Ley Street Depot, Ley Street, Ilford IG2 7QX ☎ 020 8708 5520 ✉ jeremy.reynolds@redbridge.gov.uk

Energy Management: Mr Garry Proctor, Electrical & Mechanical Services Manager, Lynton House, 255 - 259 High Road, Ilford IG1 1NY ☎ 020 8708 3324 ✉ garry.proctor@redbridge.gov.uk

Environmental Health: Mr Themis Skouros, Environmental Protection Manager, Lynton House, 255 - 258 High Road, Ilford IG1 1NY ☎ 020 8708 5687 ✉ themis.skouros@redbridge.gov.uk

Estates, Property & Valuation: Mr David Pethen, Head of Estates & Asset Management, Lynton House, 255-259 High Road, Ilford IG1 1NY ☎ 020 8708 3215 ✉ david.pethen@redbridge.gov.uk

Events Manager: Ms Fiona O'Connor, Event Manager, 210 Wash Lodge, Cranbrook Road, Ilford IG1 4TG ☎ 020 8708 3747 ✉ fiona.o'connor@visionrcl.org.uk

Facilities: Mr Dyfrig Walters, Head of Facilities Management & Accommodation Strategy, Town Hall, High Road, Ilford IG1 1DD ☎ 020 8708 3960 ✉ dyfrig.walters@redbridge.gov.uk

Finance: Ms Maria Christofi, Corporate Director - Resources, Lynton House, High Road, Ilford IG1 1NY ☎ 020 8708 3588 ✉ maria.christofi@redbridge.gov.uk

Pensions: Mr Doug Falconer, Pensions Manager, HR - Pensions, Lynton House, 255-259 High Road, Ilford IG1 1NY ☎ 020 8708 3549 ✉ doug.falconer@redbridge.gov.uk

Fleet Management: Mr Eddie Cross, Head of Transport Engineering Service, Ley Street Depot, Ley Street, Ilford IG2 7QX ☎ 020 8708 5212 ✉ eddie.cross@redbridge.gov.uk

Grounds Maintenance: Mr Gary Simpson, Grounds Service Manager, Security Compound, Valentines Park, Ilford IG2 6EA ☎ 020 8708 5326 ✉ gary.simpson@redbridge.gov.uk

Health and Safety: Mr Ian Wringe, Health & Safety Manager, Lynton House, 255 - 259 High Road, Ilford IG1 1NY ☎ 020 8708 3152 ✉ ian.wringe@redbridge.gov.uk

Highways: Mr Cliff Woolnoth, Head of Engineering, Lynton House, 255-259 High Road, Ilford IG1 1NY ☎ 020 8708 3570 ✉ cliff.woolnoth@redbridge.gov.uk

Housing: Ms Elaine Gosling, Head of Housing Management, West Housing Office, 152 Broadmead Road, Woodford Green, Ilford IG8 0AG ☎ 020 8708 7657 ✉ elaine.gosling@redbridge.gov.uk

Housing Maintenance: Ms Ola Akinfe, Interim Head of Asset Management (Housing), West Housing Office, 152 Broadmead Road, Woodford Green, Ilford IG8 0AG ☎ 020 8708 8305 ✉ ola.akinfe@redbridge.gov.uk

Legal: Ms Fiona Alderman, Head of Legal & Constitutional Services, Lynton House, High Road, Ilford IG1 1NY ☎ 020 8708 2201 ✉ fiona.alderman@redbridge.gov.uk

Leisure and Cultural Services: Mr Iain Varah, Chief Executive - Vision-Redbridge Culture & Leisure, Central Library, Clements Road, Ilford IG1 1EA ☎ 020 8708 2012 ✉ iain.varah@visionrcl.org.uk

Licensing: Mr Alan Drake, Head of Community Protection & Enforcement ✉ Perth Terrace, Perth Road, Ilford IG2 6AT ☎ 020 8708 5490 ✉ alan.drake@redbridge.gov.uk

Lifelong Learning: Mr Iain Varah, Chief Executive - Vision-Redbridge Culture & Leisure, Central Library, Clements Road, Ilford IG1 1EA ☎ 020 8708 2012 ✉ iain.varah@visionrcl.org.uk

Lighting: Mr Cliff Woolnoth, Head of Engineering, Lynton House, 255-259 High Road, Ilford IG1 1NY ☎ 020 8708 3570 ✉ cliff.woolnoth@redbridge.gov.uk

REDBRIDGE

Member Services: Ms Antoinette Davis, Head of Constitutional Services, Town Hall, High Road, Ilford IG1 1DD ☎ 020 8708 2352
✆ antoinette.davis@redbridge.gov.uk

Member Services: Mr Tony Prescod, Head of Constitutional Services, Town Hall, High Road, Ilford IG1 1DD ☎ 020 8708 2204
✆ tony.prescod@redbridge.gov.uk

Parking: Mr Michael Jackson, Parking Manager, Lynton House, High Road, Ilford IG1 1NY ☎ 020 8708 3646
✆ michael.jackson@redbridge.gov.uk

Partnerships: Mr John Turkson, Principal Officer - Community Partnerships, Lynton House, High Road, Ilford IG1 1NY
☎ 020 8708 2381 ✆ john.turkson@redbridge.gov.uk

Personnel / HR: Ms Marj Keddy, Chief Human Resources Officer, Lynton House, 255-259 High Road, Ilford IG1 1NY
☎ 020 8708 3974 ✆ marj.keddy@redbridge.gov.uk

Planning: Ms Sharon Strutt, Strategic Head of Delivery, Town Hall, High Road, Ilford IG1 1DD ☎ 020 8708 2143
✆ sharon.strutt@redbridge.gov.uk

Planning: Ms Joanne Woodward, Strategic Head of Planning & Building Control, Town Hall, High Road, Ilford IG1 1DD
☎ 020 8708 2052 ✆ joanne.woodward@redbridge.gov.uk

Procurement: Mr Taraq Bashir, Interim Head of Procurement, Lynton House, High Road, Ilford IG1 1NY ☎ 020 8708 3268
✆ taraq.bashir@redbridge.gov.uk

Public Libraries: Mr Gareth Morley, Head of Culture & Libraries, Central Library, Clements Road, Ilford IG1 1EA ☎ 020 8708 3426
✆ gareth.morley@visionrcl.org.uk

Recycling & Waste Minimisation: Mr Lawrence McGlynn, Waste Services Manager, Ley Street Depot, Ley Street, Ilford IG2 7QX ☎ 020 8708 5024 ✆ lawrence.mcglynn@redbridge.gov.uk

Regeneration: Mr Matthew Essex, Operational Director - Regeneration & Planning, Lynton House, High Road, Ilford IG1 1NY
☎ 020 8708 2809 ✆ matthew.essex@redbridge.gov.uk

Road Safety: Ms Jane Arthur, Road Safety Group Manager, Lynton House, 255-259 High Road, Ilford IG1 1NY ☎ 020 8708 3971
✆ jane.arthur@redbridge.gov.uk

Social Services (Adult): Ms Caroline Maclean, Operational Director - Adult Social Services, Lynton House, High Road, Ilford IG1 1NY ☎ 020 8708 5595 ✆ caroline.maclean@redbridge.gov.uk

Social Services (Children): Mrs Caroline Cutts, Operational Director - Children & Families, Lynton House, 255 - 259 High Road, Ilford IG1 1NY ☎ 020 8708 5304 ✆ caroline.cutts@redbridge.gov.uk

Social Services (Children): Mr Adrian Loades, Corporate Director - People, Lynton House, High Road, Ilford IG1 1NY
☎ 020 8708 5742 ✆ adrian.loades@redbridge.gov.uk

Public Health: Ms Vicky Hobart, Director - Public Health, Town Hall, Forest Road, London E17 4JF ☎ 020 8708 5731
✆ vicky.hobart@redbridge.gov.uk

Staff Training: Ms Ann Butler, HR Workforce Development Manager, Lynton House, 255-259 High Road, Ilford IG1 1NY
☎ 020 8708 3446 ✆ ann.butler@redbridge.gov.uk

Street Scene: Mr Russell Ward, Head of Environmental Services, Ley Street Depot, Ley Street, Ilford IG2 7QX ☎ 020 8708 5511
✆ russell.ward@redbridge.gov.uk

Town Centre: Ms Rubie Charalambous, Exchange Manager, The Management Suite, The Exchange Mall, High Road, Ilford IG1 1RS
☎ 020 8553 3000 ✆ rubie.charalambous@theexchangeilford.gov.uk

Town Centre: Mr Daniel Moore, Interim Business Liason Officer, Town Hall, High Road, Ilford IG1 1DD ☎ 020 8708 2563
✆ daniel.moore@redbridge.gov.uk

Traffic Management: Mr Syed Hussain, Traffic Group Manager, Lynton House, 255-259 High Road, Ilford IG1 1NY ☎ 020 8708 3651
✆ syed.hussain@redbridge.gov.uk

Transport: Mr Cliff Woolnoth, Head of Engineering, Lynton House, 255-259 High Road, Ilford IG1 1NY ☎ 020 8708 3570
✆ cliff.woolnoth@redbridge.gov.uk

Transport Planner: Mr Cliff Woolnoth, Head of Engineering, Lynton House, 255-259 High Road, Ilford IG1 1NY
☎ 020 8708 3570 ✆ cliff.woolnoth@redbridge.gov.uk

Total Place: Ms Caroline Bruce, Corporate Director - Place, Lynton House, High Road, Ilford IG1 1NY ☎ 020 8708 3567
✆ caroline.bruce@redbridge.gov.uk

Waste Collection and Disposal: Mr Lawrence McGlynn, Waste Services Manager, Ley Street Depot, Ley Street, Ilford IG2 7QX
☎ 020 8708 5024 ✆ lawrence.mcglynn@redbridge.gov.uk

Waste Management: Mr Russell Ward, Head of Environmental Services, Ley Street Depot, Ley Street, Ilford IG2 7QX
☎ 020 8708 5511 ✆ russell.ward@redbridge.gov.uk

COUNCILLORS

Mayor: Bhamra, Gurdial (LAB - Clayhall)
gurdial.bhamra@redbridge.gov.uk

Leader of the Council: Athwal, Jas (LAB - Mayfield)
jas.athwal@redbridge.gov.uk

Deputy Leader of the Council: Norman, Elaine (LAB - Newbury)
elaine.norman@redbridge.gov.uk

Group Leader: Bond, Ian (LD - Roding)
ian.bond@redbridge.gov.uk

Group Leader: Canal, Paul (CON - Bridge)
paul.canal@redbridge.gov.uk

Ahmad, Shakil (LAB - Loxford)
shakil.ahmad@redbridge.gov.uk

Ahmed, Mohammed (LAB - Loxford)
mohammed.ahmed@redbridge.gov.uk

Ahmed, Mushtaq (LAB - Cranbrook)
mushtaq.ahmed@redbridge.gov.uk

Bain, Sheila (LAB - Wanstead)
sheila.bain@redbridge.gov.uk

Bellwood, Stuart (LAB - Seven Kings)
stuart.bellwood@redbridge.gov.uk

Best, Emma (CON - Church End)
emma.best@redbridge.gov.uk

Bola, Varinder (LAB - Cranbrook)
varinder.singhbola@redbridge.gov.uk

Bromiley, David (CON - Fullwell)
david.bromiley@redbridge.gov.uk

Chaudhary, Mahboob (CON - Cranbrook)
mahboob.chaudhary@redbridge.gov.uk

Choudhary, Aziz (LAB - Chadwell)
aziz.choudhary@redbridge.gov.uk

Chowdhury, Khayer (LAB - Valentines)
khayer.chowdhury@redbridge.gov.uk

Cleaver, Hugh (LD - Church End)
hugh.cleaver@redbridge.gov.uk

Cole, Robert (CON - Clayhall)
robert.cole@redbridge.gov.uk

Coomb, Helen (LAB - Clementswood)
helen.coomb@redbridge.gov.uk

Cronin, Colin (CON - Snaresbrook)
colin.cronin@redbridge.gov.uk

Cummins, Christopher (CON - Snaresbrook)
christopher.cummins@redbridge.gov.uk

Deakins, Gwyneth (LD - Roding)
gwyneth.deakins@redbridge.gov.uk

Duddridge, Lloyd (LAB - Roding)
lloyd.duddridge@redbridge.gov.uk

Dunn, Michelle (CON - Wanstead)
michelle.dunn@redbridge.gov.uk

Emmett, Roy (LAB - Hainault)
roy.emmett@redbridge.gov.uk

Fairley-Churchill, John (CON - Bridge)
john.fairley-churchill@redbridge.gov.uk

Flint, Kay (LAB - Mayfield)
kay.flint@redbridge.gov.uk

Haran, Jeevah (CON - Fullwell)
jeevah.haran@redbridge.gov.uk

Hatfull, Ross (LAB - Valentines)
ross.hatfull@redbridge.gov.uk

Hayes, Nicholas (CON - Fullwell)
nicholas.hayes@redbridge.gov.uk

Hehir, Joe (LAB - Hainault)
joe.hehir@redbridge.gov.uk

Howard, John (LAB - Aldborough)
john.howard@redbridge.gov.uk

Huggett, Linda (CON - Monkhams)
linda.huggett@redbridge.gov.uk

Hussain, Zulfiqar (LAB - Clementswood)
cllr.hussain@redbridge.gov.uk

Hussain, Farah (LAB - Valentines)
farah.hussain@redbridge.gov.uk

Javed, Muhammed (LAB - Clementswood)
muhammed.javed@redbridge.gov.uk

Jeyaranjan, Thavathuray (LAB - Newbury)
thavathuray.jeyaranjan@redbridge.gov.uk

Jones, Bert (LAB - Goodmayes)
bert.jones@redbridge.gov.uk

Kaur-Thiara, Debbie (LAB - Aldborough)
debbie.kaur-thiara@redbridge.gov.uk

Kissin, Ashley (CON - Barkingside)
ashley.kissin@redbridge.gov.uk

Lambert, Brian (CON - Fairlop)
brian.lambert@redbridge.gov.uk

Littlewood, Robert (LAB - Seven Kings)
bob.littlewood@redbridge.gov.uk

McLaren, Tom (CON - Church End)
tom.mclaren@redbridge.gov.uk

Merry, Paul (LAB - Wanstead)
paul.merry@redbridge.gov.uk

Nijjar, Baldesh (LAB - Seven Kings)
baldesh.nijjar@redbridge.gov.uk

Nolan, Suzanne (CON - Snaresbrook)
suzanne.nolan@redbridge.gov.uk

O'Shea, James (CON - Monkhams)
cllr.o'shea@redbridge.gov.uk

Packer, Karen (CON - Barkingside)
karen.packer@redbridge.gov.uk

Parkash, Ayodhiya (LAB - Mayfield)
ayodhiya.parkash@redbridge.gov.uk

Prince, Keith (CON - Barkingside)
keith.prince@redbridge.gov.uk

Rai, Kam (LAB - Goodmayes)
kam.rai@redbridge.gov.uk

Rashid, Taifur (LAB - Loxford)
taifur.rashid@redbridge.gov.uk

Ryan, Joyce (CON - Fairlop)

Sachs, Anne (LAB - Chadwell)
anne.sachs@redbridge.gov.uk

Santos, Mark (LAB - Hainault)
mark.santos@redbridge.gov.uk

Sharma, Dev (LAB - Newbury)
dev.sharma@redbridge.gov.uk

Sharpe, Tom (CON - Fairlop)
tom.sharpe@redbridge.gov.uk

Stark, Michael (CON - Monkhams)
michael.stark@redbridge.gov.uk

Streeting, Wes (LAB - Aldborough)
wes.streeting@redbridge.gov.uk

Turbefield, Robin (CON - Bridge)
robin.turbefield@redbridge.gov.uk

Weinberg, Alan (CON - Clayhall)
alan.weinberg@redbridge.gov.uk

REDBRIDGE

White, Barbara (LAB - Goodmayes)
barbara.white@redbridge.gov.uk

Zammett, Neil (LAB - Chadwell)
neil.zammett@redbridge.gov.uk

POLITICAL COMPOSITION
LAB: 36, CON: 24, LD: 3

COMMITTEE CHAIRS

Children & Young People Service: Mr Muhammed Javed

Health & Wellbeing: Mr Aziz Choudhary

Pensions: Ms Elaine Norman

Remuneration & Staffing: Mr Jas Athwal

Redcar & Cleveland   U

Redcar & Cleveland Borough Council, Town Hall, Fabian
Road, South Bank, Redcar TS6 9AR
☎ 01642 774774 ⁰ contactus@redcar-cleveland.gov.uk
🖥 www.redcar-cleveland.gov.uk

FACTS AND FIGURES
Parliamentary Constituencies: Middlesbrough South and
Cleveland East, Redcar
EU Constituencies: North East
Election Frequency: Elections are of whole council

PRINCIPAL OFFICERS

Chief Executive: Ms Amanda Skelton, Chief Executive, Redcar
and Cleveland House, Kirkleatham Street, Redcar TS10 1RT
☎ 01642 444003 ⁰ amanda.skelton@redcar-cleveland.gov.uk

Senior Management: Mr Mike Greene, Assistant Director -
Neighbourhoods & Customer Services, Redcar and Cleveland
House, Kirkleatham Street, Redcar TS10 1RT ☎ 01642 444346
⁰ mike.greene@redcar-cleveland.gov.uk

Senior Management: Mrs Pauline Kavanagh, Assistant Director
- Organisational Change, Redcar and Cleveland House, Kirkleatham
Street, Redcar TS10 1RT ☎ 01642 444021
⁰ pauline.kavanagh@redcar-cleveland.gov.uk

Senior Management: Mr John Sampson, Corporate Director -
Corporate Resources, Redcar and Cleveland House, Kirkleatham
Street, Redcar TS10 1RT ☎ 01642 771144
⁰ john.sampson@redcar-cleveland.gov.uk

Senior Management: Ms Barbara Shaw, Corporate Director -
People's Services, Seafield House, Kirkleatham Street, Redcar TS10
1SP ☎ 01642 771674 ⁰ barbara.shaw@redcar-cleveland.gov.uk

Architect, Building / Property Services: Mrs Sarah Lamont,
Asset Manager, Fairway House, Limerick Road, Dormanstown,
Redcar TS10 5JU ☎ 01642 776951
⁰ sarah.lamont@redcar-cleveland.gov.uk

Building Control: Mr Mike Pengilley, Principal Building Control
Surveyor, Redcar & Cleveland House, Kirkleatham Street, Redcar
TS10 1RT ☎ 01287 612358
⁰ mike.pengilley@redcar-cleveland.gov.uk

Children / Youth Services: Mrs Linda Bulmer, Service Manager
- Children & Families, Town Hall, Fabian Road, South Bank, Redcar
TS6 9AR ☎ 01642 771751 ⁰ linda.bulmer@redcar-cleveland.gov.uk

Children / Youth Services: Miss Agnes Scott, Team Manager -
Youth & Community, 25k Centre, Ayton Drive, Redcar TS10 4EW
☎ 01642 777544 ⁰ aggie.scott@redcar-cleveland.gov.uk

Civil Registration: Ms Jennifer Brodie, Deputy Registrar / Office
Manager, Town Hall, Fabian Road, South Bank, Redcar TS6 9AR
☎ 01642 444648 ⁰ jennifer.brodie@redcar-cleveland.gov.uk

PR / Communications: Mrs Miranda Sykes, Communications &
Media Manager, Redcar and Cleveland House, Kirkleatham Street,
Redcar TS10 1RT ☎ 01642 444458
⁰ miranda.sykes@redcar-cleveland.gov.uk

Computer Management: Mrs Sarah Lamont, Corporate
Resources, Fairway House, Limerick Road, Dormanstown, Redcar
TS10 5JU ☎ 01642 776951 ⁰ sarah.lamont@redcar-cleveland.gov.uk

Consumer Protection and Trading Standards: Mr Julian
Sorrell, Principal Trading Standards Officer, Belmont House,
Rectory Lane, Guisborough TS14 7FD ☎ 01287 612322
⁰ julian.sorrell@redcar-cleveland.gov.uk

Contracts: Mrs Deborah Thorne, Commissioning & Procurement
Manager, Belmont House, Rectory Lane, Guisborough TS14 7FD
☎ 01642 771256 ⁰ deborah.thorne@redcar-cleveland.gov.uk

Corporate Services: Mr John Sampson, Corporate Director -
Corporate Resources, Redcar and Cleveland House, Kirkleatham
Street, Redcar TS10 1RT ☎ 01642 771144
⁰ john.sampson@redcar-cleveland.gov.uk

Customer Service: Mr Mike Oyston, Service Lead - Customer
Services & Libraries, Redcar & Cleveland House, Kirkleatham
Street, Redcar TS10 1RT ☎ 01642 444309
⁰ mike.oyston@redcar-cleveland.gov.uk

Education: Mr David Major, Head of Learning & Achivement
(Senior School Improvement Advisor), Seafield House, Kirkleatham
Street, Redcar TS10 1SP ☎ 01642 837743
⁰ david.major@redcar-cleveland.gov.uk

Electoral Registration: Mrs Sue Bridges, Principal Governance
Officer, Redcar Heart, Ridley Street, Redcar TS10 1RT
☎ 01642 444092 ⁰ sue.bridges@redcar-cleveland.gov.uk

Emergency Planning: Mr Stuart Marshall, Emergency Planning
Officer, Redcar & Cleveland House, Kirkleatham Street, Redcar
TS10 1RT ☎ 01642 444202
⁰ stuart.marshall@redcar-cleveland.gov.uk

Energy Management: Mr Stewart Kerr, Energy Management
Specialist, Fairway House, Limerick Road, Dormanstown, Redcar
TS10 5JU ☎ 01642 771288 ⁰ stewart.kerr@redcar-cleveland.gov.uk

Environmental / Technical Services: Ms Tracy Hilton, Principal
Officer - Environmental Protection, Belmont House, Rectory Lane,
Guisborough TS14 7FD ☎ 01287 612420
⁰ tracy.hilton@redcar-cleveland.gov.uk

Environmental Health: Mrs Vikki Bell, Principal Environmental Health Officer, Belmont House, Rectory Lane, Guisborough TS14 7FD ☎ 01287 612404 ✆ vikki.bell@redcar-cleveland.gov.uk

Estates, Property & Valuation: Mrs Sarah Lamont, Asset Manager, Fairway House, Limerick Road, Dormanstown, Redcar TS10 5JU ☎ 01642 776951 ✆ sarah.lamont@redcar-cleveland.gov.uk

Events Manager: Mr Malcolm Armstrong, Cultural Services Manager, Bellamy Pavilion, Kirkleatham, Redcar TS10 5NW ☎ 01642 496422 ✆ malcolm.armstrong@redcar-cleveland.gov.uk

Facilities: Mr Brian Stephenson, Building Manager, Fairway House, Limerick Road, Dormanstown, Redcar TS10 5JU ☎ 01642 776905 ✆ brian.stephenson@redcar-cleveland.gov.uk

Finance: Mr John Sampson, Corporate Director - Corporate Resources, Redcar and Cleveland House, Kirkleatham Street, Redcar TS10 1RT ☎ 01642 771144 ✆ john.sampson@redcar-cleveland.gov.uk

Fleet Management: Mr Anthony Smith, Waste, Recyling & Fleet Operations Manager, Fairway House, Limerick Road, Dormanstown, Redcar TS10 5JU ☎ 01642 776971 ✆ anthony.smith@redcar-cleveland.gov.uk

Grounds Maintenance: Mr Gary Cummins, Streetscene Operations Manager, Fairway House, Limerick Road, Dormanstown, Redcar TS10 5JU ☎ 01642 776960 ✆ gary.cummins@redcar-cleveland.gov.uk

Health and Safety: Mr John Summers, Health & Safety Manager, Redcar & Cleveland House, Kirkleatham Street, Redcar TS10 1RT ☎ 01642 444064 ✆ john.summers@redcar-cleveland.gov.uk

Highways: Mr Andrew Mollon, Service Lead - Engineering, Highways, Licensing & Parking, Redcar & Cleveland House, Kirkleatham Street, Redcar TS10 1RT ☎ 01287 612581 ✆ andrew.mollon@redcar-cleveland.gov.uk

Home Energy Conservation: Mr Stewart Kerr, Energy Management Specialist, Fairway House, Limerick Road, Dormanstown, Redcar TS10 5JU ☎ 01642 771288 ✆ stewart.kerr@redcar-cleveland.gov.uk

Housing: Mr Roger Kay, Housing Strategy Lead, Redcar and Cleveland House, Kirkleatham Street, Redcar TS10 1RT ☎ 01287 612450 ✆ roger.kay@redcar-cleveland.gov.uk

Local Area Agreement: Mr Rob Mitchell, Head of Policy & Performance, Redcar and Cleveland House, Kirkleatham Street, Redcar TS10 1RT ☎ 01642 444507 ✆ rob.mitchell@redcar-cleveland.gov.uk

Legal: Mr Andrew Nixon, Commercial & Legal Manager, Redcar Heart, Ridley Street, Redcar TS10 1RT ☎ 01642 444536 ✆ andrew.nixon@redcar-cleveland.gov.uk

Leisure and Cultural Services: Mr Malcolm Armstrong, Cultural Services Manager, Bellamy Pavilion, Kirkleatham, Redcar TS10 5NW ☎ 01642 496422 ✆ malcolm.armstrong@redcar-cleveland.gov.uk

Licensing: Mr Stephen Brown, Principal Licensing Officer, Redcar & Cleveland House, Kirkleatham Street, Redcar TS10 1RT ☎ 01287 612402 ✆ stephen.brown@redcar-cleveland.gov.uk

Lighting: Mr Andrew Mollon, Service Lead - Engineering, Highways, Licensing & Parking, Redcar & Cleveland House, Kirkleatham Street, Redcar TS10 1RT ☎ 01287 612581 ✆ andrew.mollon@redcar-cleveland.gov.uk

Member Services: Mrs Alison Pearson, Governance Manager, Redcar Heart, Ridley Street, Redcar TS10 1RT ☎ 01642 444063 ✆ alison.pearson@redcar-cleveland.gov.uk

Parking: Mr Stephen Brown, Principal Licensing Officer, Redcar & Cleveland House, Kirkleatham Street, Redcar TS10 1RT ☎ 01287 612402 ✆ stephen.brown@redcar-cleveland.gov.uk

Partnerships: Ms Val Mitchell, Stronger Communities Manager, Redcar & Cleveland House, Kirkleatham Street, Redcar TS10 1RT ☎ 01642 776948 ✆ val.mitchell@redcar-cleveland.gov.uk

Personnel / HR: Mrs Pauline Kavanagh, Assistant Director - Organisational Change, Redcar and Cleveland House, Kirkleatham Street, Redcar TS10 1RT ☎ 01642 444021 ✆ pauline.kavanagh@redcar-cleveland.gov.uk

Planning: Mr Alex Conti, Planning Strategy Team Leader, Redcar & Cleveland House, Kirkleatham Street, Redcar TS10 1RT ☎ 01287 612353 ✆ alex.conti@redcar-cleveland.gov.uk

Procurement: Mrs Deborah Thorne, Commissioning & Procurement Manager, Redcar & Cleveland House, Kirkleatham Street, Redcar TS10 1RT ☎ 01642 771256 ✆ deborah.thorne@redcar-cleveland.gov.uk

Public Libraries: Mr Mike Oyston, Service Lead - Customer Services & Libraries, Redcar & Cleveland House, Kirkleatham Street, Redcar TS10 1RT ☎ 01642 444309 ✆ mike.oyston@redcar-cleveland.gov.uk

Recycling & Waste Minimisation: Mr Anthony Smith, Waste, Recyling & Fleet Operations Manager, Fairway House, Limerick Road, Dormanstown, Redcar TS10 5JU ☎ 01642 776971 ✆ anthony.smith@redcar-cleveland.gov.uk

Social Services: Ms Barbara Shaw, Corporate Director - People's Services, Seafield House, Kirkleatham Street, Redcar TS10 1SP ☎ 01642 771674 ✆ barbara.shaw@redcar-cleveland.gov.uk

Social Services (Adult): Mr Patrick Rice, Assistant Director - Commissioning Adults, Seafield House, Kirkleatham Street, Redcar TS10 1SP ☎ 01642 771676 ✆ patrick.rice@redcar-cleveland.gov.uk

Social Services (Children): Mrs Linda Bulmer, Service Manager - Children & Families, Town Hall, Fabian Road, South Bank, Redcar TS6 9AR ☎ 01642 771751 ✆ linda.bulmer@redcar-cleveland.gov.uk

Public Health: Dr Toks Sangowawa, Clinical Director - Public Health, Seafield House, Kirkleatham Street, Redcar TS10 1SP toks.sangowawa@redcar-cleveland.gov.uk

REDCAR & CLEVELAND

Staff Training: Mrs Angela Wright, Workforce Development Manager, Belmont House, Rectory Lane, Guisborough TS14 7FD
☎ 01642 444523 〜 angela.wright@redcar-cleveland.gov.uk

Street Scene: Mr Gary Cummins, Streetscene Operations Manager, Fairway House, Limerick Road, Dormanstown, Redcar TS10 5JU ☎ 01642 776960
〜 gary.cummins@redcar-cleveland.gov.uk

Tourism: Mr Malcolm Armstrong, Cultural Services Manager, Bellamy Pavilion, Kirkleatham, Redcar TS10 5NW ☎ 01642 496422
〜 malcolm.armstrong@redcar-cleveland.gov.uk

Town Centre: Ms Jane Hierons, Visitor & Town Centre Team Leader, Redcar and Cleveland House, Kirkleatham Street, Redcar TS10 1RT ☎ 01642 771180 〜 jane.hierons@redcar-cleveland.gov.uk

Traffic Management: Mr Colin Bowley, Waste & Fleet Manager, Fleet Depot, Limerick Road, Dormanstown, Redcar TS10 5JU
☎ 01642 776909 〜 colin.bowley@redcar-cleveland.gov.uk

Transport: Mr Colin Bowley, Waste & Fleet Manager, Fleet Depot, Limerick Road, Dormanstown, Redcar TS10 5JU ☎ 01642 776909
〜 colin.bowley@redcar-cleveland.gov.uk

Transport Planner: Mr Colin Bowley, Waste & Fleet Manager, Fleet Depot, Limerick Road, Dormanstown, Redcar TS10 5JU
☎ 01642 776909 〜 colin.bowley@redcar-cleveland.gov.uk

Total Place: Mr Rob Mitchell, Head of Policy & Performance, Redcar and Cleveland House, Kirkleatham Street, Redcar TS10 1RT
☎ 01642 444507 〜 rob.mitchell@redcar-cleveland.gov.uk

Waste Collection and Disposal: Mr Anthony Smith, Waste, Recyling & Fleet Operations Manager, Fleet Depot, Limerick Road, Dormanstown, Redcar TS10 5JU ☎ 01642 776971
〜 anthony.smith@redcar-cleveland.gov.uk

Waste Management: Mr Anthony Smith, Waste, Recyling & Fleet Operations Manager, Fairway House, Limerick Road, Dormanstown, Redcar TS10 5JU ☎ 01642 776971
〜 anthony.smith@redcar-cleveland.gov.uk

COUNCILLORS

Mayor: Hunt, Barry (IND - Brotton)
barry.hunt@redcar-cleveland.gov.uk

Leader of the Council: Jeffrey, Sue (LAB - South Bank)
sue.jeffrey@redcar-cleveland.gov.uk

Deputy Leader of the Council: Walsh, David (LAB - Skelton)
dave.walsh@redcar-cleveland.gov.uk

Abbott, Christopher (LD - Newcomen)
chris.abbott@redcar-cleveland.gov.uk

Ayre, Billy (LAB - Normanby)
billy.ayre@redcar-cleveland.gov.uk

Baldwin, Neil (LAB - Coatham)
neil.baldwin@redcar-cleveland.gov.uk

Benbdelow, Neil (LAB - South Bank)
neil.bendelow@redcar-cleveland.gov.uk

Brown, Alec (LAB - Dormanstown)
alec.brown@redcar-cleveland.gov.uk

Cawley, Ceri (LAB - Dormanstown)
cari.cawley@redcar-cleveland.gov.uk

Clarke, Bill (IND - Guisborough)
bill.clarke@redcar-cleveland.gov.uk

Cooney, Norah (CON - Longbeck)
norah.cooney@redcar-cleveland.gov.uk

Davies, Wayne (IND - Loftus)
wayne.davies@redcar-cleveland.gov.uk

Dennis, Brian (LAB - Normanby)
brian.dennis@redcar-cleveland.gov.uk

Dick, Michael (LAB - Brotton)
michael.dick@redcar-cleveland.gov.uk

Findley, Mike (IND - Longbeck)
mike.findley@redcar-cleveland.gov.uk

Firman, Kevin (LAB - Kirkleatham)
kevin.firman@redcar-cleveland.gov.uk

Foggo, Chris (CON - Skelton)
cliff.fogg@redcar-cleveland.gov.uk

Foley-McCormack, Chris (LAB - Normanby)
chris.foley-mccormack@redcar-cleveland.gov.uk

Forster, Brenda (LAB - Kirkleatham)
brenda.forster@redcar-cleveland.gov.uk

Goddard, Ray (LAB - Dormanstown)
ray.goddard@redcar-cleveland.gov.uk

Griffiths, Malcolm (CON - Brotton)
malcolm.griffiths@redcar-cleveland.gov.uk

Halton, Valerie (CON - Hutton)
valerie.halton@redcar-cleveland.gov.uk

Hannaway, Craig (LAB - Saltburn)
craig.hannaway@redcar-cleveland.gov.uk

Harding, Lisa (LD - West Dyke)
lisa.harding@redcar-cleveland.gov.uk

Higgins, Ann (IND - Eston)

Hodgson, Robert (LAB - Teesville)
robert.hodgson@redcar-cleveland.gov.uk

Holyoake, Shelagh (LAB - Guisborough)
shelagh.holyoake@redcar-cleveland.gov.uk

Jackson, Eric (LAB - Loftus)
eric.jackson@redcar-cleveland.gov.uk

Jackson, Caroline (CON - Hutton)
caroline.jackson@redcar-cleveland.gov.uk

Jeffery, Graham (CON - Hutton)
graham.jeffery@redcar-cleveland.gov.uk

Jeffery, Carole (CON - Westworth)
carole.jeffery@redcar-cleveland.gov.uk

Jeffrey, Ian (LAB - South Bank)
ian.jeffrey@redcar-cleveland.gov.uk

Jones, Chris (LD - West Dyke)
chris.jones@redcar-cleveland.gov.uk

Kay, Steve (O - Lockwood)
steve.kay@redcar-cleveland.gov.uk

King, Karen (LD - St Germains)
karen.king@redcar-cleveland.gov.uk

Lanigan, Mary (IND - Loftus)
mary.lanigan@redcar-cleveland.gov.uk

Mason, Josh (LD - Zetland)
josh.mason@redcar-cleveland.gov.uk

Massey, Christopher (LAB - Eston)
christopher.massey@redcar-cleveland.gov.uk

McLuckie, Helen (LAB - Skelton)
helen.mccluckie@redcar-cleveland.gov.uk

Morgan, Carole (LD - Ormesby)
carole.morgan@redcar-cleveland.gov.uk

Moses, Marjorie (LD - St Germains)
marjorie.moses@redcar-cleveland.gov.uk

Nightingale, Glyn (LD - Ormesby)
glyn.nightingale@redcar-cleveland.gov.uk

Nightingale, Irene (LD - Ormesby)
irene.nightingale@redcar-cleveland.gov.uk

Norton, Bob (LAB - Teesville)
bob.norton@redcar-cleveland.gov.uk

O'Brien, Neil (LAB - Zetland)
neil.obrien@redcar-cleveland.gov.uk

Ovens, Mary (LD - West Dyke)
mary.ovens@redcar-cleveland.gov.uk

Pallister, Lynn (LAB - Grangetown)
lynn.pallister@redcar-cleveland.gov.uk

Quartermain, Carl (LAB - Coatham)
carl.quartermain@redcar-cleveland.co.uk

Quigley, Dale (LAB - Kirkleatham)
dale.quigley@redcar-cleveland.gov.uk

Reed, Leanne (LAB - Teesville)
leanne.reed@redcar-cleveland.gov.uk

Smith, Stuart (IND - Saltburn)
stuart.smith@redcar-cleveland.gov.uk

Stainthorpe, Jade (LAB - Grangetown)
jade.stainthorpe@redcar-cleveland.gov.uk

Teasdale, Dennis (CON - Guisborough)
dennis.teasdale@redcar-cleveland.gov.uk

Thomson, Philip (CON - Saltburn)
philip.thomson@redcar-cleveland.gov.uk

Turner, Steve (UKIP - Longbeck)
steve.turner@redcar-cleveland.gov.uk

Watts, Anne (IND - Westworth)
anne.watts@redcar-cleveland.gov.uk

Wells, Billy (LAB - Newcomen)
billy.wells@redcar-cleveland.gov.uk

Williams, Geraldine (LAB - Eston)
geraldine.williams@redcar-cleveland.gov.uk

Wilson, Margaret (LD - St Germains)
margaret.wilson@redcar-cleveland.gov.uk

POLITICAL COMPOSITION
LAB: 29, LD: 11, CON: 9, IND: 8, O: 1, UKIP: 1

COMMITTEE CHAIRS

Health & Wellbeing: Mrs Sue Jeffrey

Personnel & General Purposes: Mrs Mary Ovens

Redditch   D

Redditch, Town Hall, Walter Stranz Square, Redditch B98 8AH
☎ 01527 64252 ⊕ contact.centre@bromsgroveandredditch.gov.uk
🖥 www.redditchbc.gov.uk

FACTS AND FIGURES
Parliamentary Constituencies: Redditch
EU Constituencies: West Midlands
Election Frequency: Elections are by thirds

PRINCIPAL OFFICERS

Chief Executive: Mr Kevin Dicks, Chief Executive, Town Hall, Walter Stranz Square, Redditch B98 8AH ☎ 01527 881484
⊕ k.dicks@bromsgroveandredditch.gov.uk

Deputy Chief Executive: Mrs Susan Hanley, Deputy Chief Executive, Town Hall, Walter Stranz Square, Redditch B98 8AH ☎ 01527 534118 ⊕ s.hanley@bromsgroveandredditch.gov.uk

Senior Management: Ms Jayne Pickering, Executive Director & S151 Officer, Town Hall, Walter Stranz Square, Redditch B98 8AH ☎ 01527 881400 ⊕ j.pickering@bromsgroveandredditch.gov.uk

Building Control: Mr Adrian Wyre, Principal Building Control Surveyor, The Council House, Burcot Lane, Bromsgrove B60 1AA ☎ 01527 881350 ⊕ a.wyre@bromsgroveandredditch.gov.uk

Children / Youth Services: Mr John Godwin, Head of Leisure, Town Hall, Walter Stranz Square, Redditch B98 8AH ☎ 01527 881742 ⊕ j.godwin@bromsgroveandredditch.gov.uk

PR / Communications: Mrs Anne-Marie Harley, Communications & Publicity Manager, Town Hall, Walter Stranz Square, Redditch B98 8AH ☎ 01527 881296 ⊕ a.harley@bromsgroveandredditch.gov.uk

Community Planning: Ms Ruth Bamford, Head of Planning & Regeneration Services, Town Hall, Walter Stranz Square, Redditch B98 8AH ☎ 01527 64252 Ext 3201
⊕ r.bamford@bromsgroveandredditch.gov.uk

Community Safety: Mrs Judith Willis, Acting Head of Community Services, Town Hall, Walter Stranz Square, Redditch B98 8AH ☎ 01527 64252; 01527 65216
⊕ judith.willis@bromsgroveandredditch.gov.uk

Contracts: Ms Jayne Pickering, Executive Director & S151 Officer, Town Hall, Walter Stranz Square, Redditch B98 8AH ☎ 01527 881400 ⊕ j.pickering@bromsgroveandredditch.gov.uk

Corporate Services: Ms Jayne Pickering, Executive Director & S151 Officer, Town Hall, Walter Stranz Square, Redditch B98 8AH ☎ 01527 881400 ⊕ j.pickering@bromsgroveandredditch.gov.uk

Customer Service: Ms Amanda Singleton, Head of Customer Services & Financial Support, Town Hall, Walter Stranz Square, Redditch B98 8AH ☎ 01527 64252
⊕ a.singleton@bromsgroveandredditch.gov.uk

REDDITCH

Economic Development: Ms Ruth Bamford, Head of Planning & Regeneration Services, Town Hall, Walter Stranz Square, Redditch B98 8AH ☎ 01527 64252 Ext 3201
✆ r.bamford@bromsgroveandredditch.gov.uk

Economic Development: Mr Steve Singleton, Economic Development Manager - North Worcestershire, Wyre Forest House, Finepoint Way, Kidderminster DY11 7WF ☎ 01562 732168
✆ steve.singleton@nwedr.org.uk

E-Government: Mrs Deb Poole, Head of Business Transformation & Organisational, Town Hall, Walter Stranz Square, Redditch B98 8AH ☎ 01527 881256 ✆ d.poole@bromsgroveandredditch.gov.uk

Emergency Planning: Ms Rebecca Pritchard, North Worcestershire Civil Contingencies & Resilience Manager, Civic Centre, New Street, Stourport DY13 8UJ
✆ r.pritchard@bromsgroveandredditch.gov.uk

Energy Management: Ms Jayne Pickering, Executive Director & S151 Officer, Town Hall, Walter Stranz Square, Redditch B98 8AH ☎ 01527 881400 ✆ j.pickering@bromsgroveandredditch.gov.uk

Environmental / Technical Services: Mr Guy Revans, Head of Environmental Services, Town Hall, Walter Stranz Square, Redditch B98 8AH ☎ 01527 64252 Ext 3292
✆ g.revans@bromsgroveandredditch.gov.uk

Environmental Health: Mr Guy Revans, Head of Environmental Services, Town Hall, Walter Stranz Square, Redditch B98 8AH ☎ 01527 64252 Ext 3292
✆ g.revans@bromsgroveandredditch.gov.uk

Events Manager: Mr Ray Cooke, Leisure Services Manager, Town Hall, Walter Stranz Square, Redditch B98 8AH ☎ 01527 64252 Extn 3248; 01527 65216 ✆ r.cooke@redditchbc.gov.uk

Events Manager: Mr Huw Moseley, Arts Development & Special Events Officer, The Council House, Burcot Lane, Bromsgrove B60 1AA ☎ 01527 881381 ✆ h.mosley@bromsgroveandredditch.gov.uk

Finance: Ms Sam Morgan, Finance Manager, Town Hall, Walter Stranz Square, Redditch B98 8AH ☎ 01527 64252
✆ sam.morgan@bromsgroveandredditch.gov.uk

Finance: Ms Jayne Pickering, Executive Director & S151 Officer, Town Hall, Walter Stranz Square, Redditch B98 8AH ☎ 01527 881400 ✆ j.pickering@bromsgroveandredditch.gov.uk

Fleet Management: Mr Kevin Hirons, Environmental Services Manager, Town Hall, Walter Stranz Square, Redditch B98 8AH ☎ 01527 64252 ✆ k.hirons@bromsgroveandredditch.gov.uk

Grounds Maintenance: Mr Guy Revans, Head of Environmental Services, Town Hall, Walter Stranz Square, Redditch B98 8AH ☎ 01527 64252 Ext 3292 ✆ g.revans@bromsgroveandredditch.gov.uk

Health and Safety: Ms Becky Talbot, Human Resources Manager, Town Hall, Walter Stranz Square, Redditch B98 8AH ☎ 01527 64252; 01527 65216 ✆ b.talbot@redditchbc.gov.uk

Home Energy Conservation: Mr Guy Revans, Head of Environmental Services, Town Hall, Walter Stranz Square, Redditch B98 8AH ☎ 01527 64252 Ext 3292
✆ g.revans@bromsgroveandredditch.gov.uk

Housing: Mrs Liz Tompkin, Head of Housing, Town Hall, Walter Stranz Square, Redditch B98 8AH ☎ 01527 64252 ext. 3304; 01527 65216 ✆ l.tompkin@bromsgrove.gov.uk

Housing Maintenance: Mrs Liz Tompkin, Head of Housing, Town Hall, Walter Stranz Square, Redditch B98 8AH ☎ 01527 64252 ext. 3304; 01527 65216 ✆ l.tompkin@bromsgrove.gov.uk

Legal: Mrs Claire Felton, Head of Legal, Equalities & Democratic Services, Town Hall, Walter Stranz Square, Redditch B98 8AH ☎ 01527 881429 ✆ c.felton@bromsgroveandredditch.gov.uk

Leisure and Cultural Services: Mr John Godwin, Head of Leisure, Town Hall, Walter Stranz Square, Redditch B98 8AH ☎ 01527 881742 ✆ j.godwin@bromsgroveandredditch.gov.uk

Lottery Funding, Charity and Voluntary: Mrs Judith Willis, Acting Head of Community Services, Town Hall, Walter Stranz Square, Redditch B98 8AH ☎ 01527 64252; 01527 65216 ✆ judith.willis@bromsgroveandredditch.gov.uk

Member Services: Mrs Sheena Jones, Democratic Services Manager, The Council House, Burcot Lane, Bromsgrove B60 1AA ☎ 01527 548240 ✆ s.jones@bromsgroveandredditch.gov.uk

Parking: Mr Peter Liddington, Civil Enforcement Parking Officer, Town Hall, Walter Stranz Square, Redditch B98 8AH ☎ 01527 64252; 01527 65216 ✆ p.liddington@redditchbc.gov.uk

Partnerships: Mrs Rebecca Dunn, Policy Manager, Bromsgrove District Council, The Council House, Burcot Lane, Bromsgrove B66 1AA ☎ 01527 881616 ✆ r.dunn@bromsgroveandredditch.gov.uk

Personnel / HR: Ms Becky Barr, Human Resources Manager, Town Hall, Walter Stranz Square, Redditch B98 8AH ☎ 01527 64252; 01527 65216 ✆ b.talbot@redditchbc.gov.uk

Planning: Ms Ruth Bamford, Head of Planning & Regeneration Services, Town Hall, Walter Stranz Square, Redditch B98 8AH ☎ 01527 64252 Ext 3201 ✆ r.bamford@bromsgroveandredditch.gov.uk

Procurement: Ms Carmen Young, Procurement Officer, Town Hall, Walter Stranz Square, Redditch B98 8AH ☎ 01527 64252 ✆ c.young@bromsgroveandredditch.gov.uk

Recycling & Waste Minimisation: Mr Guy Revans, Head of Environmental Services, Town Hall, Walter Stranz Square, Redditch B98 8AH ☎ 01527 64252 Ext 3292
✆ g.revans@bromsgroveandredditch.gov.uk

Regeneration: Ms Ruth Bamford, Head of Planning & Regeneration Services, Town Hall, Walter Stranz Square, Redditch B98 8AH ☎ 01527 64252 Ext 3201
✆ r.bamford@bromsgroveandredditch.gov.uk

Staff Training: Ms Becky Barr, Human Resources Manager, Town Hall, Walter Stranz Square, Redditch B98 8AH ☎ 01527 64252; 01527 65216 🖳 b.talbot@redditchbc.gov.uk

Street Scene: Mr Guy Revans, Head of Environmental Services, Town Hall, Walter Stranz Square, Redditch B98 8AH ☎ 01527 64252 Ext 3292 🖳 g.revans@bromsgroveandredditch.gov.uk

Town Centre: Ms Ruth Bamford, Head of Planning & Regeneration Services, Town Hall, Walter Stranz Square, Redditch B98 8AH ☎ 01527 64252 Ext 3201 🖳 r.bamford@bromsgroveandredditch.gov.uk

Transport: Mr Kevin Hirons, Environmental Services Manager, Town Hall, Walter Stranz Square, Redditch B98 8AH ☎ 01527 64252 🖳 k.hirons@bromsgroveandredditch.gov.uk

Transport Planner: Mr Kevin Hirons, Environmental Services Manager, Town Hall, Walter Stranz Square, Redditch B98 8AH ☎ 01527 64252 🖳 k.hirons@bromsgroveandredditch.gov.uk

Waste Collection and Disposal: Mr Guy Revans, Head of Environmental Services, Town Hall, Walter Stranz Square, Redditch B98 8AH ☎ 01527 64252 Ext 3292 🖳 g.revans@bromsgroveandredditch.gov.uk

Waste Management: Mr Guy Revans, Head of Environmental Services, Town Hall, Walter Stranz Square, Redditch B98 8AH ☎ 01527 64252 Ext 3292 🖳 g.revans@bromsgroveandredditch.gov.uk

Children's Play Areas: Mr John Godwin, Head of Leisure, Town Hall, Walter Stranz Square, Redditch B98 8AH ☎ 01527 881742 🖳 j.godwin@bromsgroveandredditch.gov.uk

COUNCILLORS

Mayor: Baker, Joe (LAB - Greenlands)
joe.baker@redditchbc.gov.uk

Leader of the Council: Hartnett, Bill (LAB - Church Hill)
bill.hartnett@redditchbc.gov.uk

Deputy Leader of the Council: Chance, Greg (LAB - Central)
greg.chance@redditchbc.gov.uk

Baker-Price, Tom (CON - Headless Corss & Oakenshaw)

Bennett, Roger (CON - Headless Cross & Oakenshaw)
roger.bennett@redditchbc.gov.uk

Brookes, Natalie (LAB - Batchley & Brockhill)
natalie.brookes@redditchbc.gov.uk

Brunner, Juliet (CON - Matchborough)
juliet.brunner@redditchbc.gov.uk

Bush, David (CON - West)
david.bush@redditchbc.gov.uk

Chalk, Michael (CON - Abbey)
michael.chalk@redditch.gov.uk

Clayton, Anita (CON - Batchley & Brockhill)

Clayton, Brandon (CON - Astwood Bank & Feckenham)
brandon.clayton@redditchbc.gov.uk

Dormer, Mathew (CON - West)
matthew.dormer@redditchbc.gov.uk

Fisher, John (LAB - Matchborough)
john.fisher@redditchbc.gov.uk

Fry, Andy (LAB - Lodge Park)
andy.fry@redditchbc.gov.uk

Hill, Pattie (LAB - Batchley & Brockhill)
pattie.hill@redditchbc.gov.uk

Hopkins, Gay (CON - Headless Cross & Oakenshaw)
gay.hopkins@redditchbc.gov.uk

King, Wanda (LAB - Greenlands)
wanda.king@redditchbc.gov.uk

Potter, Jane (CON - Astwood Bank & Feckenham)
jane.potter@redditchbc.gov.uk

Prosser, Gareth (CON - Crabbs Cross)
gareth.prosser@redditchbc.gov.uk

Pulsford, Antonia (CON - Winyates)
antonia.pulsford@redditchbc.gov.uk

Shurmer, Mark (LAB - Lodge Park)
mark.shurmer@redditchbc.gov.uk

Smith, Yvonne (LAB - Winyates)
yvonne.smith@redditchbc.gov.uk

Smith, Rachael (LAB - Abbey)
rachael.smith@redditchbc.gov.uk

Swansborough, Paul (UKIP - Winyates)
paul.swansborough@redditchbc.gov.uk

Taylor, Debbie (LAB - Central)
debbie.taylor@redditchbc.gov.uk

Thain, David (CON - Crabbs Cross)
david.thain@redditchbc.gov.uk

Wheeler, Jennifer (LAB - Greenlands)

Witherspoon, Pat (LAB - Church Hill)
pat.witherspoon@redditchbc.gov.uk

Wood-Ford, Nina (LAB - Church Hill)
nina.wood-ford@redditchbc.gov.uk

POLITICAL COMPOSITION
LAB: 15, CON: 13, UKIP: 1

COMMITTEE CHAIRS

Licensing: Mr Pat Witherspoon

Planning: Cllr Andy Fry

Reigate & Banstead   D

Reigate & Banstead Borough Council, Town Hall, Castlefield Road, Reigate RH2 0SH
☎ 01737 276000 📠 01737 276718
🖳 customer.services@reigate-banstead.gov.uk
🖳 www.reigate-banstead.gov.uk

FACTS AND FIGURES
Parliamentary Constituencies: Reigate
EU Constituencies: South East
Election Frequency: Elections are by thirds

REIGATE & BANSTEAD

PRINCIPAL OFFICERS

Chief Executive: Mr John Jory, Chief Executive, Town Hall, Castlefield Road, Reigate RH2 0SH ☎ 01737 276151 ⏚ mary.nicholls@reigate-banstead.gov.uk

Senior Management: Mr Frank Etheridge, Recycling & Cleansing Manager, Town Hall, Castlefield Road, Reigate RH2 0SH ☎ 01737 276219 ⏚ frank.etheridge@reigate-banstead.gov.uk

Senior Management: Mr Michael Graham, Legal Services Manager, Town Hall, Castlefield Road, Reigate RH2 0SH ☎ 01737 276106 ⏚ michael.graham@reigate-banstead.gov.uk

Senior Management: Mr Gavin Handford, Head of Corporate Policy, Performance & Parking, Town Hall, Castlefield Road, Reigate RH2 0SH ☎ 01737 276027 ⏚ gavin.handford@reigate-banstead.gov.uk

Senior Management: Mr Tom Kealey, Leisure Services Manager, Town Hall, Castlefield Road, Reigate RH2 0SH ☎ 01737 276840 ⏚ tom.kealey@reigate-banstead.gov.uk

Senior Management: Mr Bill Pallett, Finance Manager, Town Hall, Castlefield Road, Reigate RH2 0SH ☎ 01737 276560; 01737 276513 ⏚ bill.pallett@reigate-banstead.gov.uk

Senior Management: Mr John Reed, Property Manager, Town Hall, Castlefield Road, Reigate RH2 0SH ☎ 01737 276571; 01737 276070 ⏚ john.reed@reigate-banstead.gov.uk

Senior Management: Ms Mari Roberts-Wood, Head of People & Welfare, Town Hall, Castlefield Road, Reigate RH2 0SH ☎ 01737 276030 ⏚ mari.roberts-wood@reigate-banstead.gov.uk

Customer Service: Ms Fiona Cullen, Head of Customers, Communication & Change, Town Hall, Castlefield Road, Reigate RH2 0SH ☎ 01737 276296 ⏚ communications@reigate-banstead.gov.uk

Architect, Building / Property Services: Mr John Reed, Property Manager, Town Hall, Castlefield Road, Reigate RH2 0SH ☎ 01737 276571; 01737 276070 ⏚ john.reed@reigate-banstead.gov.uk

Building Control: Mr Tom Kealey, Leisure Services Manager, Town Hall, Castlefield Road, Reigate RH2 0SH ☎ 01737 276840 ⏚ tom.kealey@reigate-banstead.gov.uk

PR / Communications: Ms Fiona Cullen, Head of Customers, Communication & Change, Town Hall, Castlefield Road, Reigate RH2 0SH ☎ 01737 276296 ⏚ communications@reigate-banstead.gov.uk

Community Planning: Mr Simon Bland, Business & Community Engagement Manager, Town Hall, Castlefield Road, Reigate RH2 0SH ☎ 01737 276303; 01737 276404 ⏚ simon.bland@reigate-banstead.gov.uk

Computer Management: Ms Fiona Cullen, Head of Customers, Communication & Change, Town Hall, Castlefield Road, Reigate RH2 0SH ☎ 01737 276296 ⏚ communications@reigate-banstead.gov.uk

Contracts: Mr Michael Graham, Legal Services Manager, Town Hall, Castlefield Road, Reigate RH2 0SH ☎ 01737 276106 ⏚ michael.graham@reigate-banstead.gov.uk

Corporate Services: Mr Gavin Handford, Head of Corporate Policy, Performance & Parking, Town Hall, Castlefield Road, Reigate RH2 0SH ☎ 01737 276027 ⏚ gavin.handford@reigate-banstead.gov.uk

Customer Service: Ms Fiona Cullen, Head of Customers, Communication & Change, Town Hall, Castlefield Road, Reigate RH2 0SH ☎ 01737 276296 ⏚ communications@reigate-banstead.gov.uk

Economic Development: Mr Simon Bland, Business & Community Engagement Manager, Town Hall, Castlefield Road, Reigate RH2 0SH ☎ 01737 276303; 01737 276404 ⏚ simon.bland@reigate-banstead.gov.uk

E-Government: Ms Fiona Cullen, Head of Customers, Communication & Change, Town Hall, Castlefield Road, Reigate RH2 0SH ☎ 01737 276296 ⏚ communications@reigate-banstead.gov.uk

Electoral Registration: Ms Sally Crawford, Electoral Services Manager, Town Hall, Castlefield Road, Reigate RH2 0SH ☎ 01737 276440 ⏚ sally.crawford@reigate-banstead.gov.uk

Emergency Planning: Mr Gavin Handford, Head of Corporate Policy, Performance & Parking, Town Hall, Castlefield Road, Reigate RH2 0SH ☎ 01737 276027 ⏚ gavin.handford@reigate-banstead.gov.uk

Energy Management: Mr John Reed, Property Manager, Town Hall, Castlefield Road, Reigate RH2 0SH ☎ 01737 276571; 01737 276070 ⏚ john.reed@reigate-banstead.gov.uk

Environmental Health: Mr Tom Kealey, Leisure Services Manager, Town Hall, Castlefield Road, Reigate RH2 0SH ☎ 01737 276840 ⏚ tom.kealey@reigate-banstead.gov.uk

Estates, Property & Valuation: Mr John Reed, Property Manager, Town Hall, Castlefield Road, Reigate RH2 0SH ☎ 01737 276571; 01737 276070 ⏚ john.reed@reigate-banstead.gov.uk

Facilities: Mr John Reed, Property Manager, Town Hall, Castlefield Road, Reigate RH2 0SH ☎ 01737 276571; 01737 276070 ⏚ john.reed@reigate-banstead.gov.uk

Finance: Mr Bill Pallett, Finance Manager, Town Hall, Castlefield Road, Reigate RH2 0SH ☎ 01737 276560; 01737 276513 ⏚ bill.pallett@reigate-banstead.gov.uk

Fleet Management: Mr Bill Sedgman, Transport Fleet Manager, Town Hall, Castlefield Road, Reigate RH2 0SH ☎ 01737 276000 ⏚ bill.sedgman@reigate-banstead.gov.uk

Grounds Maintenance: Mr Emanuel Flecken, Clean Spaces Services Manager, Town Hall, Castlefield Road, Reigate RH2 0SH ☎ 01737 276226 ⏚ emanuel.flecken@reigate-banstead.gov.uk

Health and Safety: Ms Mari Roberts-Wood, Head of People & Welfare, Town Hall, Castlefield Road, Reigate RH2 0SH
☎ 01737 276030 ᛏ mari.roberts-wood@reigate-banstead.gov.uk

Housing: Ms Mari Roberts-Wood, Head of People & Welfare, Town Hall, Castlefield Road, Reigate RH2 0SH ☎ 01737 276030
ᛏ mari.roberts-wood@reigate-banstead.gov.uk

Legal: Mr Michael Graham, Legal Services Manager, Town Hall, Castlefield Road, Reigate RH2 0SH ☎ 01737 276106
ᛏ michael.graham@reigate-banstead.gov.uk

Leisure and Cultural Services: Mr Tom Kealey, Leisure Services Manager, Town Hall, Castlefield Road, Reigate RH2 0SH
☎ 01737 276840 ᛏ tom.kealey@reigate-banstead.gov.uk

Licensing: Mr Ben Murray, Manager - Licensing, Community Safety, JET Team & Environmental Health, Town Hall, Castlefield Road, Reigate RH2 0SH ☎ 01737 276069
ᛏ ben.murray@reigate-banstead.gov.uk

Lottery Funding, Charity and Voluntary: Mr Simon Bland, Business & Community Engagement Manager, Town Hall, Castlefield Road, Reigate RH2 0SH ☎ 01737 276303; 01737 276404 ᛏ simon.bland@reigate-banstead.gov.uk

Member Services: Mr Gavin Handford, Head of Corporate Policy, Performance & Parking, Town Hall, Castlefield Road, Reigate RH2 0SH ☎ 01737 276027
ᛏ gavin.handford@reigate-banstead.gov.uk

Parking: Mr Gavin Handford, Head of Corporate Policy, Performance & Parking, Town Hall, Castlefield Road, Reigate RH2 0SH ☎ 01737 276027 ᛏ gavin.handford@reigate-banstead.gov.uk

Personnel / HR: Ms Mari Roberts-Wood, Head of People & Welfare, Town Hall, Castlefield Road, Reigate RH2 0SH
☎ 01737 276030 ᛏ mari.roberts-wood@reigate-banstead.gov.uk

Planning: Ms Luci Mould, Head of Places & Planning, Town Hall, Castlefield Road, Reigate RH2 0SH ☎ 01737 276214
ᛏ luci.mould@reigate-banstead.gov.uk

Procurement: Mr Bill Pallett, Finance Manager, Town Hall, Castlefield Road, Reigate RH2 0SH ☎ 01737 276560; 01737 276513
ᛏ bill.pallett@reigate-banstead.gov.uk

Recycling & Waste Minimisation: Mr Frank Etheridge, Recycling & Cleansing Manager, Town Hall, Castlefield Road, Reigate RH2 0SH ☎ 01737 276219
ᛏ frank.etheridge@reigate-banstead.gov.uk

Regeneration: Ms Luci Mould, Head of Places & Planning, Town Hall, Castlefield Road, Reigate RH2 0SH ☎ 01737 276214
ᛏ luci.mould@reigate-banstead.gov.uk

Staff Training: Ms Mari Roberts-Wood, Head of People & Welfare, Town Hall, Castlefield Road, Reigate RH2 0SH
☎ 01737 276030 ᛏ mari.roberts-wood@reigate-banstead.gov.uk

Street Scene: Mr Frank Etheridge, Recycling & Cleansing Manager, Town Hall, Castlefield Road, Reigate RH2 0SH
☎ 01737 276219 ᛏ frank.etheridge@reigate-banstead.gov.uk

Sustainable Communities: Ms Luci Mould, Head of Places & Planning, Town Hall, Castlefield Road, Reigate RH2 0SH
☎ 01737 276214 ᛏ luci.mould@reigate-banstead.gov.uk

Sustainable Development: Ms Luci Mould, Head of Places & Planning, Town Hall, Castlefield Road, Reigate RH2 0SH
☎ 01737 276214 ᛏ luci.mould@reigate-banstead.gov.uk

Waste Collection and Disposal: Mr Frank Etheridge, Recycling & Cleansing Manager, Town Hall, Castlefield Road, Reigate RH2 0SH ☎ 01737 276219 ᛏ frank.etheridge@reigate-banstead.gov.uk

Children's Play Areas: Mr Emanuel Flecken, Clean Spaces Services Manager, Town Hall, Castlefield Road, Reigate RH2 0SH
☎ 01737 276226 ᛏ emanuel.flecken@reigate-banstead.gov.uk

COUNCILLORS

Mayor: Powell, David (CON - Horley Central)

Deputy Mayor: Foreman, Keith (CON - Chipstead, Hooley & Woodmansterne)
cllr.foreman@reigate-banstead.gov.uk

Leader of the Council: Broad, Victor (CON - Tadworth and Walton)
cllr.broad@reigate-banstead.gov.uk

Absalom, Rosemary (CON - Reigate Central)
cllr.absalom@reigate-banstead.gov.uk

Allcard, Derek (CON - South Park & Woodhatch)
cllr.allcard@reigate-banstead.gov.uk

Ascough, Liam (CON - Horley West)

Blacker, Michael (CON - Reigate Central)

Bramhall, Natalie (CON - Redhill West)
cllr.mrsbramhall@reigate-banstead.gov.uk

Bray, Jill (R - Tattenhams)
cllr.bray@reigate-banstead.gov.uk

Brunt, Mark (CON - Merstham)
cllr.brunt@reigate-banstead.gov.uk

Clarke, James (CON - Tadworth & Walton)
cllr.clarke@reigate-banstead.gov.uk

Coad, Richard (CON - Redhill East)
cllr.coad@reigate-banstead.gov.uk

Crome, Graeme (CON - Merstham)
cllr.crome@reigate-banstead.gov.uk

Durrant, James (CON - Earlswood & Whitbushes)
cllr.durrant@reigate-banstead.gov.uk

Ellacott, Julian (CON - Redhill West)

Essex, Jonathan (GRN - Redhill East)
cllr.essex@reigate-banstead.gov.uk

Godden, John (CON - Meadvale & St John's)
cllr.godden@reigate-banstead.gov.uk

Grant-Duff, Zully (CON - Reigate Hill)
cllr.grant-duff@reigate-banstead.gov.uk

REIGATE & BANSTEAD

Hack, Lynne (CON - Banstead Village)
cllr.hack@reigate-banstead.gov.uk

Harper, Robert (R - Tattenhams)
cllr.harper@reigate-banstead.gov.uk

Harrison, Nicholas (R - Tattenhams)
cllr.harrison@reigate-banstead.gov.uk

Horwood, Alexander (CON - Horley West)
cllr.horwood@reigate-banstead.gov.uk

Humphreys, Eddy (CON - Banstead Village)
cllr.humphreys@reigate-banstead.gov.uk

Jackson, David (CON - Horley West)
cllr.jackson@reigate-banstead.gov.uk

Kelly, Frank (CON - Merstham)
cllr.kelly@reigate-banstead.gov.uk

King, James (CON - South Park & Woodhatch)
cllr.king@reigate-banstead.gov.uk

Knight, Graham (CON - Horley East)
cllr.knight@reigate-banstead.gov.uk

Kulka, Stephen (LD - Meadvale & St John's)
cllr.kulka@reigate-banstead.gov.uk

Lynch, Andrew (CON - Horley Central)
cllr.lynch@reigate-banstead.gov.uk

Mantle, Richard (CON - Chipstead, Hooley & Woodmansterne)
cllr.mantle@reigate-banstead.gov.uk

McKenna, Steve (GRN - Redhill East)

Mill, Rosalind (CON - Kingswood with Burgh Heath)
cllr.mill@reigate-banstead.gov.uk

Newstead, Roger (CON - Reigate Hill)
cllr.newstead@reigate-banstead.gov.uk

Parnall, Simon (CON - Kingswood with Burgh Heath)
cllr.parnall@reigate-banstead.gov.uk

Paul, Jamie (CON - Preston)
cllr.paul@reigate-banstead.gov.uk

Pay, David (CON - Redhill West)
cllr.pay@reigate-banstead.gov.uk

Renton, Rita (CON - Earlswood & Whitebushes)
cllr.renton@reigate-banstead.gov.uk

Rickman, Simon (CON - South Park & Woodhatch)

Ross-Tomlin, Dorothy (CON - Salfords & Sidlow)
cllr.ross-tomlin@reigate-banstead.gov.uk

Schofield, Tony (CON - Horley East)

Selby, Michael (R - Nork)
cllr.selby@reigate-banstead.gov.uk

Stead, Brian (R - Nork)
cllr.stead@reigate-banstead.gov.uk

Stephenson, John (CON - Chipstead, Hooley & Woodmansterne)
cllr.stephenson@reigate-banstead.gov.uk

Stevens, Christian (UKIP - Horley Central)
cllr.stevens@reigate-banstead.gov.uk

Tarrant, Annna (LD - Meadvale & St John's)

Thompson, Barbara (CON - Earlswood & Whitebushes)
cllr.thomson@reigate-banstead.gov.uk

Turner, Rachel (CON - Tadworth & Walton)
cllr.turner@reigate-banstead.gov.uk

Walsh, Samuel (CON - Banstead Village)
cllr.walsh@reigate-banstead.gov.uk

Whinney, Christopher (R - Reigate Central)
cllr.whinney@reigate-banstead.gov.uk

White, Jonathan (R - Nork)

POLITICAL COMPOSITION
CON: 38, R: 7, GRN: 2, LD: 2, UKIP: 1, Vacant: 1

Renfrewshire   S

Renfrewshire Council, Renfrewshire House, Cotton Street, Paisley PA1 1UJ
☎ 0300 300 0300 ◌ chiefexec@renfrewshire.gov.uk
▭ www.renfrewshire.gov.uk

FACTS AND FIGURES
Parliamentary Constituencies: Paisley and Renfrewshire North, Paisley and Renfrewshire South
EU Constituencies: Scotland
Election Frequency: Elections are of whole council

PRINCIPAL OFFICERS

Chief Executive: Ms Sandra Black, Chief Executive, Renfrewshire House, Cotton Street, Paisley PA1 1TR ☎ 0141 618 7355; 0141 842 5055 ◌ sandra.black@renfrewshire.gov.uk

Senior Management: Ms Mary Crearie, Director - Development & Housing Services, Renfrewshire House, Cotton Street, Paisley PA1 1JD ☎ 0141 618 6256; 0141 842 5552 ◌ mary.crearie@renfrewshire.gov.uk

Senior Management: Mrs Shona MacDougall, Director - Community Resources, Renfrewshire House, Cotton Street, Paisley PA1 1BU ☎ 0141 618 7626; 0141 840 3233 ◌ shona.i.macdougall@renfrewshire.gov.uk

Senior Management: Mr Peter Macleod, Director - Children's Services, Renfrewshire House, Cotton Street, Paisley PA1 1TZ ☎ 0141 842 5167; 0141 842 5144 ◌ peter.macleod@renfrewshire.gov.uk

Senior Management: Mr Alan Russell, Director - Finance & Resources, Renfrewshire House, Cotton Street, Paisley PA1 1UJ ☎ 0141 618 7363 ◌ alan.russell@renfrewshire.gov.uk

Access Officer / Social Services (Disability): Mr Peter Macleod, Director - Children's Services, Renfrewshire House, Cotton Street, Paisley PA1 1TZ ☎ 0141 842 5167; 0141 842 5144 ◌ peter.macleod@renfrewshire.gov.uk

Architect, Building / Property Services: Mr Joe Lynch, Head of Property, Renfrewshire House, Cotton Street, Paisley PA1 1UJ ☎ 0141 618 6159 ◌ joe.lynch@renfrewshire.gov.uk

Building Control: Ms Mary Crearie, Director - Development & Housing Services, Renfrewshire House, Cotton Street, Paisley PA1 1JD ☎ 0141 618 6256; 0141 842 5552 ◌ mary.crearie@renfrewshire.gov.uk

Catering Services: Mrs Shona MacDougall, Director - Community Resources, Renfrewshire House, Cotton Street, Paisley PA1 1BU ☎ 0141 618 7626; 0141 840 3233 ⌂ shona.i.macdougall@renfrewshire.gov.uk

Children / Youth Services: Ms Dorothy Hawthorn, Head of Child Care & Criminal Justice, Renfrewshire House, Cotton Street, Paisley PA1 1UJ ☎ 0141 618 6827 ⌂ dorothy.hawthorn@renfrewshire.gsx.gov.uk

Civil Registration: Mr Ken Graham, Head of Corporate Governance, Renfrewshire House, Cotton Street, Paisley PA1 1TR ☎ 0141 618 7360; 0141 840 3635 ⌂ ken.graham@renfrewshire.gov.uk

PR / Communications: Ms Lucy Adamson, Corporate Communications & Public Affairs Manager, Renfrewshire House, Cotton Street, Paisley PA1 1UJ ☎ 0300 300 0300 ⌂ lucy.adamson@renfrewshire.gov.uk

Community Safety: Mrs Shona MacDougall, Director - Community Resources, Renfrewshire House, Cotton Street, Paisley PA1 1BU ☎ 0141 618 7626; 0141 840 3233 ⌂ shona.i.macdougall@renfrewshire.gov.uk

Community Safety: Mr Oliver Reid, Head of Public Protection, Renfrewshire House, Cotton Street, Paisley PA1 1WU ☎ 0141 618 7352; 0141 840 3349 ⌂ oliver.reid@renfrewshire.gov.uk

Computer Management: Mr Patrick Murray, Head of ICT, Renfrewshire House, Cotton Street, Paisley PA1 1UJ ⌂ patrick.murray@renfrewshire.gcsx.gov.uk

Consumer Protection and Trading Standards: Mrs Shona MacDougall, Director - Community Resources, Renfrewshire House, Cotton Street, Paisley PA1 1BU ☎ 0141 618 7626; 0141 840 3233 ⌂ shona.i.macdougall@renfrewshire.gov.uk

Contracts: Mr Ken Graham, Head of Corporate Governance, Renfrewshire House, Cotton Street, Paisley PA1 1TR ☎ 0141 618 7360; 0141 840 3635 ⌂ ken.graham@renfrewshire.gov.uk

Corporate Services: Mr Alan Russell, Director - Finance & Resources, Renfrewshire House, Cotton Street, Paisley PA1 1UJ ☎ 0141 618 7363 ⌂ alan.russell@renfrewshire.gov.uk

Customer Service: Ms Rhona McGrath, Head of Customer & Business Services, Renfrewshire House, Cotton Street, Paisley PA1 1UJ ☎ 0141 618 6879 ⌂ rhona.mcgrath@renfrewshire.gcsx.gov.uk

Economic Development: Ms Mary Crearie, Director - Development & Housing Services, Renfrewshire House, Cotton Street, Paisley PA1 1JD ☎ 0141 618 6256; 0141 842 5552 ⌂ mary.crearie@renfrewshire.gov.uk

Education: Mr Peter Macleod, Director - Children's Services, Renfrewshire House, Cotton Street, Paisley PA1 1TZ ☎ 0141 842 5167; 0141 842 5144 ⌂ peter.macleod@renfrewshire.gov.uk

Electoral Registration: Mr Alasdair MacTaggart, Assessor & Electoral Registration Officer, 16 Glasgow Road, Paisley PA1 3QF ☎ 0141 618 5903 ⌂ alasdair.mactaggar@renfrewshire-vjb.gov.uk

Emergency Planning: Mr David Mair, Senior Civil Contingencies Officer, Renfrewshire House, Cotton Street, Paisley PA1 1WB ☎ 0300 300 0300 ⌂ david.mair@renfrewshire.gsx.gov.uk

Energy Management: Ms Mary Crearie, Director - Development & Housing Services, Renfrewshire House, Cotton Street, Paisley PA1 1JD ☎ 0141 618 6256; 0141 842 5552 ⌂ mary.crearie@renfrewshire.gov.uk

Environmental / Technical Services: Ms Mary Crearie, Director - Development & Housing Services, Renfrewshire House, Cotton Street, Paisley PA1 1JD ☎ 0141 618 6256; 0141 842 5552 ⌂ mary.crearie@renfrewshire.gov.uk

Environmental Health: Mrs Shona MacDougall, Director - Community Resources, Renfrewshire House, Cotton Street, Paisley PA1 1BU ☎ 0141 618 7626; 0141 840 3233 ⌂ shona.i.macdougall@renfrewshire.gov.uk

Estates, Property & Valuation: Mr Frank Hughes, Asset Manager, Renfrewshire House, Cotton Street, Paisley PA1 1UJ ☎ 0141 618 6175 ⌂ frank.hughes@renfrewshire.gov.uk

European Liaison: Ms Ruth Cooper, Economic Development Manager, Renfrewshire House, Cotton Street, Paisley PA1 1LL ☎ 0300 300 0300 ⌂ ruth.cooper@renfrewshire.gov.uk

Events Manager: Ms Amanda Moulson, Town Centre & Events Manager, Renfrewshire House, Cotton Street, Paisley PA1 1LL ☎ 0141 618 7857; 0141 842 5833 ⌂ amanda.moulson@renfrewshire.gov.uk

Facilities: Mrs Diane Gillies, Head of Facilities Management, Renfrewshire House, Cotton Street, Paisley PA1 1UJ ☎ 0141 648 4672 ⌂ diane.gillies@renfrewshire.gov.uk

Finance: Mr Alan Russell, Director - Finance & Resources, Renfrewshire House, Cotton Street, Paisley PA1 1UJ ☎ 0141 618 7363 ⌂ alan.russell@renfrewshire.gov.uk

Fleet Management: Mr Scott Allan, Head of Amenity Services, Renfrewshire House, Cotton Street, Paisley PA1 1UJ ☎ 0141 618 7932 ⌂ scott.allan@renfrewshire.gov.uk

Grounds Maintenance: Mrs Shona MacDougall, Director - Community Resources, Renfrewshire House, Cotton Street, Paisley PA1 1BU ☎ 0141 618 7626; 0141 840 3233 ⌂ shona.i.macdougall@renfrewshire.gov.uk

Health and Safety: Ms Carole Donnelly, Head of HR, OD & Workforce Strategy, Renfrewshire House, Cotton Street, Paisley PA1 1UJ ☎ 0300 300 0300 ⌂ carole.donnelly@renfrewshire.gov.uk

Highways: Mr Scott Allan, Head of Amenity Services, Renfrewshire House, Cotton Street, Paisley PA1 1UJ ☎ 0141 618 7932 ⌂ scott.allan@renfrewshire.gov.uk

Home Energy Conservation: Ms Mary Crearie, Director - Development & Housing Services, Renfrewshire House, Cotton Street, Paisley PA1 1JD ☎ 0141 618 6256; 0141 842 5552 ⌂ mary.crearie@renfrewshire.gov.uk

RENFREWSHIRE

Housing: Ms Mary Crearie, Director - Development & Housing Services, Renfrewshire House, Cotton Street, Paisley PA1 1JD
☎ 0141 618 6256; 0141 842 5552 ✆ mary.crearie@renfrewshire.gov.uk

Housing Maintenance: Mr Frank Hughes, Asset Manager, Renfrewshire House, Cotton Street, Paisley PA1 1UJ
☎ 0141 618 6175 ✆ frank.hughes@renfrewshire.gov.uk

Legal: Mr Ken Graham, Head of Corporate Governance, Renfrewshire House, Cotton Street, Paisley PA1 1TR ☎ 0141 618 7360; 0141 840 3635 ✆ ken.graham@renfrewshire.gov.uk

Leisure and Cultural Services: Mrs Joyce McKellar, Chief Executive, Renfrewshire House, Cotton Street, Paisley PA1 1TR
☎ 0141 618 7191 ✆ joyce.mckellar@renfrewshire.gsx.gov.uk

Licensing: Mr Ken Graham, Head of Corporate Governance, Renfrewshire House, Cotton Street, Paisley PA1 1TR ☎ 0141 618 7360; 0141 840 3635 ✆ ken.graham@renfrewshire.gov.uk

Lifelong Learning: Mr Peter Macleod, Director - Children's Services, Renfrewshire House, Cotton Street, Paisley PA1 1TZ
☎ 0141 842 5167; 0141 842 5144 ✆ peter.macleod@renfrewshire.gov.uk

Lighting: Mr Scott Allan, Head of Amenity Services, Renfrewshire House, Cotton Street, Paisley PA1 1UJ ☎ 0141 618 7932
✆ scott.allan@renfrewshire.gov.uk

Member Services: Mr Ken Graham, Head of Corporate Governance, Renfrewshire House, Cotton Street, Paisley PA1 1TR
☎ 0141 618 7360; 0141 840 3635 ✆ ken.graham@renfrewshire.gov.uk

Parking: Mr Scott Allan, Head of Amenity Services, Renfrewshire House, Cotton Street, Paisley PA1 1UJ ☎ 0141 618 7932
✆ scott.allan@renfrewshire.gov.uk

Personnel / HR: Ms Carole Donnelly, Head of HR, OD & Workforce Strategy, Renfrewshire House, Cotton Street, Paisley PA1 1UJ ☎ 0300 300 0300 ✆ carole.donnelly@renfrewshire.gov.uk

Planning: Ms Mary Crearie, Director - Development & Housing Services, Renfrewshire House, Cotton Street, Paisley PA1 1JD
☎ 0141 618 6256; 0141 842 5552 ✆ mary.crearie@renfrewshire.gov.uk

Procurement: Mr David Amos, Head of Policy & Commissioning, Renfrewshire House, Cotton Street, Paisley PA1 1UJ
☎ 0141 618 4702 ✆ david.amos@renfrewshire.gov.uk

Public Libraries: Mrs Joyce McKellar, Chief Executive, Renfrewshire House, Cotton Street, Paisley PA1 1TR
☎ 0141 618 7191 ✆ joyce.mckellar@renfrewshire.gsx.gov.uk

Recycling & Waste Minimisation: Mrs Shona MacDougall, Director - Community Resources, Renfrewshire House, Cotton Street, Paisley PA1 1BU ☎ 0141 618 7626; 0141 840 3233 ✆ shona.i.macdougall@renfrewshire.gov.uk

Regeneration: Mr Alasdair Morrison, Head of Regeneration, Renfrewshire House, Cotton Street, Paisley PA1 1UJ

Road Safety: Mr Scott Allan, Head of Amenity Services, Renfrewshire House, Cotton Street, Paisley PA1 1UJ
☎ 0141 618 7932 ✆ scott.allan@renfrewshire.gov.uk

Social Services: Mr Peter Macleod, Director - Children's Services, Renfrewshire House, Cotton Street, Paisley PA1 1TZ
☎ 0141 842 5167; 0141 842 5144
✆ peter.macleod@renfrewshire.gov.uk

Social Services (Adult): Mr David Leese, Chief Officer Designate, Renfrewshire House, Cotton Street, Paisley PA1 1UJ
☎ 0141 618 7648 ✆ david.leese@ggc.scot.nhs.uk

Social Services (Children): Mr Peter Macleod, Director - Children's Services, Renfrewshire House, Cotton Street, Paisley PA1 1TZ ☎ 0141 842 5167; 0141 842 5144
✆ peter.macleod@renfrewshire.gov.uk

Staff Training: Ms Carole Donnelly, Head of HR, OD & Workforce Strategy, Renfrewshire House, Cotton Street, Paisley PA1 1UJ
☎ 0300 300 0300 ✆ carole.donnelly@renfrewshire.gov.uk

Street Scene: Mr Scott Allan, Head of Amenity Services, Renfrewshire House, Cotton Street, Paisley PA1 1UJ
☎ 0141 618 7932 ✆ scott.allan@renfrewshire.gov.uk

Town Centre: Ms Amanda Moulson, Town Centre & Events Manager, Renfrewshire House, Cotton Street, Paisley PA1 1LL
☎ 0141 618 7857; 0141 842 5833
✆ amanda.moulson@renfrewshire.gov.uk

Traffic Management: Mr Scott Allan, Head of Amenity Services, Renfrewshire House, Cotton Street, Paisley PA1 1UJ
☎ 0141 618 7932 ✆ scott.allan@renfrewshire.gov.uk

Transport: Mr Scott Allan, Head of Amenity Services, Renfrewshire House, Cotton Street, Paisley PA1 1UJ
☎ 0141 618 7932 ✆ scott.allan@renfrewshire.gov.uk

Transport: Mrs Shona MacDougall, Director - Community Resources, Renfrewshire House, Cotton Street, Paisley PA1 1BU
☎ 0141 618 7626; 0141 840 3233
✆ shona.i.macdougall@renfrewshire.gov.uk

Transport Planner: Mr Scott Allan, Head of Amenity Services, Renfrewshire House, Cotton Street, Paisley PA1 1UJ
☎ 0141 618 7932 ✆ scott.allan@renfrewshire.gov.uk

Waste Collection and Disposal: Mrs Shona MacDougall, Director - Community Resources, Renfrewshire House, Cotton Street, Paisley PA1 1BU ☎ 0141 618 7626; 0141 840 3233
✆ shona.i.macdougall@renfrewshire.gov.uk

Waste Management: Mrs Shona MacDougall, Director - Community Resources, Renfrewshire House, Cotton Street, Paisley PA1 1BU ☎ 0141 618 7626; 0141 840 3233
✆ shona.i.macdougall@renfrewshire.gov.uk

COUNCILLORS

Provost: Hall, Anne (LAB - Houston, Crosslee and Linwood)
cllr.anne.hall@renfrewshire.gov.uk

Bibby, Derek (LAB - Johnstone North, Kilbarchan & Lochwinnoch)
cllr.derek.bibby@renfrewshire.gov.uk

Brown, Maria (SNP - Bishopton, Bridge of Weir and Langbank)
cllr.maria.brown@renfrewshire.gov.uk

Brown, Bill (LAB - Renfrew North)
cllr.bill.brown@renfrewshire.gov.uk

Caldwell, John (LAB - Johnstone South, Elderslie and Howwood)
cllr.john.caldwell@renfrewshire.gov.uk

Cameron, Lorraine (SNP - Paisley South West)
cllr.lorraine.cameron@renfrewshire.gov.uk

Clark, Stuart (LAB - Houston, Crosslee and Linwood)
cllr.stuart.clark@renfrewshire.gov.uk

Devine, Eddie (LAB - Paisley South)
cllr.eddie.devine@renfrewshire.gov.uk

Devine, Margaret (LAB - Renfrew South and Gallowhill)
cllr.margaret.devine@renfrewshire.gov.uk

Doig, Audrey (SNP - Houston, Crosslee and Linwood)
cllr.audrey.doig@renfrewshire.gov.uk

Doig, Andy (SNP - Johnstone North, Kilbarchan and Lochwinnoch)
cllr.andy.doig@renfrewshire.gov.uk

Gilmour, Christopher (LAB - Johnstone North, Kilbarchan and Lochwinnoch)
cllr.christopher.gilmour@renfrewshire.gov.uk

Glen, Roy (LAB - Paisley South)
cllr.roy.glen@renfrewshire.gov.uk

Harte, Jim (LAB - Erskine and Inchinnan)
cllr.james.harte@renfrewshire.gov.uk

Henry, Jacqueline (LAB - Paisley South West)
cllr.jacqueline.henry@renfrewshire.gov.uk

Holmes, Michael (LAB - Bishopton, Bridge of Weir and Langbank)
cllr.michael.holmes@renfrewshire.gov.uk

Hood, John (LAB - Johnstone South, Elderslie and Howwood)
cllr.john.hood@renfrewshire.gov.uk

Kelly, Terry (LAB - Paisley North West)
cllr.terry.kelly@renfrewshire.gov.uk

Lawson, Brian (SNP - Paisley East and Ralston)
cllr.brian.lawson@renfrewshire.gov.uk

Mack, Paul (IND - Paisley South)
cllr.paul.mack@renfrewshire.gov.uk

MacLaren, Kenny (SNP - Paisley North West)
cllr.kenny.maclaren@renfrewshire.gov.uk

Maclaren, James (CON - Bishopton, Bridge of Weir and Langbank)
cllr.james.maclaren@renfrewshire.gov.uk

MacLaren, Mags (SNP - Paisley North West)
cllr.mags.maclaren@renfrewshire.gov.uk

Macmillan, Mark (LAB - Paisley South West)
cllr.mark.macmillan@renfrewshire.gov.uk

McCartin, Eileen (LD - Paisley South West)
cllr.eileen.mccartin@renfrewshire.gov.uk

McEwan, Cathy (SNP - Renfrew South and Gallowhill)
cllr.cathy.mcewan@renfrewshire.gov.uk

McGee, Stephen (SNP - Johnstone South, Elderslie and Howwood)
cllr.stephen.mcgee@renfrewshire.gov.uk

McGurk, Marie (SNP - Paisley South)
cllr.marie.mcgurk@renfrewshire.gov.uk

McMillan, Iain (LAB - Johnstone South, Elderslie and Howwood)
cllr.iain.mcmillan@renfrewshire.gov.uk

McQuade, James (SNP - Erskine and Inchinnan)
cllr.james.mcquade@renfrewshire.gov.uk

Mullin, Sam (LAB - Erskine and Inchinnan)
cllr.sam.mullin@renfrewshire.gov.uk

Murrin, Alexander (LAB - Renfrew North)
cllr.alex.murrin@renfrewshire.gov.uk

Mylet, Will (SNP - Paisley East and Ralston)
cllr.will.mylet@renfrewshire.gov.uk

Nicolson, Iain (SNP - Erskine and Inchinnan)
cllr.iain.nicholson@renfrewshire.gov.uk

Noon, Allan (SNP - Houston, Crosslee and Linwood)
cllr.allan.noon@renfrewshire.gov.uk

Paterson, Jim (SNP - Renfrew South and Gallowhill)

Perrie, Bill (SNP - Renfrew North)
cllr.bill.perrie@renfrewshire.gov.uk

Sharkey, Jim (LAB - Paisley East and Ralston)
cllr.jim.sharkey@renfrewshire.gov.uk

Sharkey, Maureen (LAB - Paisley East and Ralston)
cllr.maureen.sharkey@renfrewshire.gov.uk

Williams, Thomas (LAB - Paisley North West)
cllr.tommy.williams@renfrewshire.gov.uk

POLITICAL COMPOSITION
LAB: 21, SNP: 16, LD: 1, CON: 1, IND: 1

COMMITTEE CHAIRS

Education & Children Policy: Mrs Jacqueline Henry

Planning: Mr Bill Brown

Rhondda Cynon Taff W

Rhondda Cynon Taff County Borough Council, The Pavilions, Cambrian Park, Clydach Vale, Tonypandy CF40 2XX
☎ 01443 425005 🖳 www.rctcbc.gov.uk

FACTS AND FIGURES
Parliamentary Constituencies: Cynon Valley, Pontypridd, Rhondda
EU Constituencies: Wales
Election Frequency: Elections are of whole council

PRINCIPAL OFFICERS

Chief Executive: Mr Chris Bradshaw, Chief Executive, The Pavilions, Cambrian Park, Clydach Vale, Tonypandy CF40 2XX
☎ 01443 424026; 01443 424027 ✆ christopher.d.bradshaw@rctcbc.gov.uk

Senior Management: Mr Gio Isingrini, Group Director - Community & Children's Services, The Pavilions, Cambrian Park, Clydach Vale, Tonypandy CF40 2XX ☎ 01443 424140; 01443 424027 ✆ gio.isingrini@rctcbc.gov.uk

RHONDDA CYNON TAFF

Senior Management: Mr Christopher Lee, Group Director - Corporate & Frontline Services, The Pavilions, Cambrian Park, Clydach Vale, Tonypandy CF40 2XX ☎ 01443 424026; 01443 424027 ⌂ christopher.d.lee@rctcbc.gov.uk

Senior Management: Mr Paul Lucas, Director - Legal & Democratic Services, The Pavilions, Cambrian Park, Clydach Vale, Tonypandy CF40 2XX ☎ 01443 424105; 01443 424027 ⌂ paul.j.lucas@rctcbc.gov.uk

Senior Management: Mr Tony Wilkins, Director - Human Resources, The Pavilions, Cambrian Park, Clydach Vale, CF40 2XX ☎ 01443 424166; 01443 424025 ⌂ tony.wilkins@rctcbc.gov.uk

Architect, Building / Property Services: Mr Colin Atyeo, Director - Corporate Estates & Procurement, Valleys Innovation Centre, Navigation Park, Abercynon, Mountain Ash CF44 4SN ☎ 01443 744555; 01443 744557 ⌂ colin.m.atyeo@rctcbc.gov.uk

Best Value: Mr Paul Griffiths, Service Director - Performance & Improvement, Bronwydd, Porth CF39 9DL ☎ 01443 680609 ⌂ d.paul.griffiths@rctcbc.gov.uk

Building Control: Mr Neil Parfitt, Building Control - Business Manager, Sardis House, Sardis Road, Pontypridd CF37 1DU ☎ 01443 494845; 01443 494774 ⌂ neil.parfitt@rctcbc.gov.uk

Catering Services: Mrs Anne Bull, Head of Catering Services & Schools Facilities Services, Ty Trevithick, Abercynon, Mountain Ash CF45 4UQ ☎ 01443 744155; 01443 744290 ⌂ anne.bull@rctcbc.gov.uk

Children / Youth Services: Mrs Ann Batley, Service Director - Children's Services, Unit 3, Ty Pennant, Catherine Street, Pontypridd CF45 4UQ ☎ 01443 495118 ⌂ ann.batley@rctcbc.gov.uk

Children / Youth Services: Mr Geraint Evans, Youth Support Services Manager, Ty Trevithick, Abercynon, Mountain Ash CF45 4UQ ☎ 01443 744039 ⌂ geraint.t.evans@rctcbc.gov.uk

Civil Registration: Ms Sue Cunnick, Superintendent Registrar, Municipal Buildings, Gelliwastad Road, Pontypridd CF37 2DP ☎ 01443 494024 ⌂ susan.cunnick@rctcbc.gov.uk

PR / Communications: Mr Christian Hanagan, Service Director - Cabinet Office & PR, The Pavilions, Cambrian Park, Clydach Vale, Tonypandy CF40 2XX ☎ 01443 424005; 01443 424004 ⌂ christian.sj.hanagan@rctcbc.gov.uk

Community Safety: Ms Louise Davies, Head of Environmental Health, Trading Standards & Community Safety, Ty Elai, Dinas Isaf Industrial Estate, Williamstown, Tonypandy CF40 1NY ☎ 01443 425640 ⌂ louise.m.davies@rctcbc.gov.uk

Computer Management: Mr Tim Jones, Head of ICT, Council Offices, Porth CF39 9DL ☎ 01443 562271 ⌂ tim.d.jones@rctcbc.gov.uk

Consumer Protection and Trading Standards: Ms Louise Davies, Head of Environmental Health, Trading Standards & Community Safety, Ty Elai, Dinas Isaf Industrial Estate, Williamstown, Tonypandy CF40 1NY ☎ 01443 425640 ⌂ louise.m.davies@rctcbc.gov.uk

Corporate Services: Mr Christopher Lee, Group Director - Corporate & Frontline Services, The Pavilions, Cambrian Park, Clydach Vale, Tonypandy CF40 2XX ☎ 01443 424026; 01443 424027 ⌂ christopher.d.lee@rctcbc.gov.uk

Customer Service: Mrs Roseann Edwards, Head of Customer Care, Ty Elai, Dinas Isaf Industrial Estate, Williamstown, Tonypandy CF40 1NY ☎ 01443 444402 ⌂ roseann.edwards@rctcbc.gov.uk

Economic Development: Ms Jane Cook, Director - Regeneration & Planning, Sardis House, Sardis Road, Pontypridd CF37 1DU ☎ 01443 495161; 01443 407725 ⌂ jane.cook@rctcbc.gov.uk

Education: Mrs Esther Thomas, Temporary Director - Education & Lifelong Learning, Ty Trevithick, Abercynon, Tonypandy CF45 4UQ ☎ 01443 744009; 01443 744023 ⌂ esther.k.thomas@rctcbc.gov.uk

E-Government: Mr Tim Jones, Head of ICT, Council Offices, Porth CF39 9DL ☎ 01443 562271 ⌂ tim.d.jones@rctcbc.gov.uk

Electoral Registration: Mr Mark Green, Head of Business Support & Elections, Maritime Business Park, Maritime Industrial Estate, Pontypridd CF37 1NY ☎ 01443 490100; 01443 485776 ⌂ william.m.green@rctcbc.gov.uk

Emergency Planning: Mr Ian Woodland, Resilience & Sustainability Lead Advisor, Sardis House, Sardis Road, Pontypridd CF37 1DU ☎ 01443 490415 ⌂ ian.m.woodland@rctcbc.gov.uk

Energy Management: Mr Joseph Pearson, Energy Compliance Officer, Valleys Innovation Centre, Navigation Park, Abercynon, Mountain Ash CF45 4SN ☎ 01443 744416; 01443 744466 ⌂ joseph.s.pearson@rctcbc.gov.uk

Environmental Health: Mr Clive Osmond, Senior Environmental Health Officer, Ty Elai, Dina Isaf Industrial Estate, Williamstown, Tonypandy CF40 1NY ☎ 01443 425380 ⌂ clive.g.osmond@rctcbc.gov.uk

Estates, Property & Valuation: Mr Colin Atyeo, Director - Corporate Estates & Procurement, Valleys Innovation Centre, Navigation Park, Abercynon, Mountain Ash CF45 4SN ☎ 01443 744555; 01443 744557 ⌂ colin.m.atyeo@rctcbc.gov.uk

Events Manager: Mr Ian Christopher, Strategic Manager, The Pavilions, Cambrian Park, Clydach Vale, Tonypandy CF40 2XX ☎ 0143 424017 ⌂ ian.christopher@rctcbc.gov.uk

Facilities: Ms Jackie Jones, Facilities Cleaning Manager, Ty Glantaf, Unit B23, Taff Falls Road, Treforest Industrial Estate, Pontypridd CF37 5TT ☎ 01443 827705; 01443 844310 ⌂ jackie.m.jones@rctcbc.gov.uk

Finance: Mr Barrie Davies, Director - Financial Services, Bronwydd House, Porth CF39 9DL ☎ 01443 680559; 01443 680504 ⌂ barrie.j.davies@rctcbc.gov.uk

Pensions: Mr Ian Traylor, Head of Service - Payroll, Pensions & Payments, Bronwydd House, Porth CF39 9DL ☎ 01443 680591; 01443 680717 ⌂ ian.f.taylor@rctcbc.gov.uk

Fleet Management: Mrs Julie Waites, Fleet Manager, Ty Glantaf, Unit B23, Taff Falls Road, Treforest Industrial Estate, Pontypridd CF37 5TT ☎ 01443 827750 ⌁ julie.y.waites@rctcbc.gov.uk

Health and Safety: Mr Mike Murphy, Health & Safety Advisor, Ty Elai, Dinas Isaf Industrial Estate, Williamstown, Tonypandy CF40 1NY ☎ 01443 425536; 01443 444534 ⌁ mike.murphy@rctcbc.gov.uk

Highways: Mr Roger Waters, Service Director - Highways & Streetcare, Sardis House, Sardis Road, Pontypridd CF37 1DU ☎ 01443 494702; 01443 491414 ⌁ roger.j.waters@rctcbc.gov.uk

Housing: Mr Phillip Howells, Head of Community Housing Services, Ty Elai, Dinas Isaf Industrial Estate, Williamstown, Tonypandy CF40 1NY ☎ 01443 425746 ⌁ phillip.howells@rctcbc.gov.uk

Local Area Agreement: Mr Simon Gale, Service Director - Planning, Sardis House, Sardis Road, Pontypridd CF37 1DU ☎ 01443 494716; 01443 494799 ⌁ simon.gale@rctcbc.gov.uk

Legal: Mr Paul Lucas, Director - Legal & Democratic Services, The Pavilions, Cambrian Park, Clydach Vale, Tonypandy CF40 2XX ☎ 01443 424105; 01443 424027 ⌁ paul.j.lucas@rctcbc.gov.uk

Leisure and Cultural Services: Mr Dave Batten, Head of Leisure, Parks & Countryside, Ty Elai, Dinas Isaf Industrial Estate, Williamstown, Tonypandy CF40 1NY ☎ 01443 425592; 01443 425080 ⌁ david.c.batten@rctcbc.gov.uk

Leisure and Cultural Services: Mrs Strinda Davies, Head of Arts Service, Rhondda Heritage Park, Lewis Merthyr Colliery, Coed Cae Road, Trehafod, Mountain Ash CF37 7NP ☎ 01443 682036 ⌁ strinda.p.davies@rctcbc.gov.uk

Licensing: Mrs Meryl Williams, Licensing Manager, Ty Elai, Dinas Isaf Industrial Estate, Williamstown, Tonypandy CF40 1NY ☎ 01443 425361; 01443 425301 ⌁ meryl.d.williams@rctcbc.gov.uk

Lifelong Learning: Mrs Esther Thomas, Temporary Director - Education & Lifelong Learning, Ty Trevithick, Abercynon, Tonypandy CF45 4UQ ☎ 01443 744009; 01443 744023 ⌁ esther.k.thomas@rctcbc.gov.uk

Lighting: Mr Mark Anderson, Senior Engineer - Street Lighting, Sardis House, Sardis Road, Pontypridd CF37 1DU ☎ 01443 494792 ⌁ mark.anderson@rctcbc.gov.uk

Lottery Funding, Charity and Voluntary: Mr Peter Mortimer, Regeneration & Resources Manager, Level 5, Unit 3, Ty Pennant, Catherine Street, Pontypridd CF37 2TB ☎ 01443 490407; 01443 407725 ⌁ peter.j.mortimer@rctcbc.gov.uk

Member Services: Mrs Karyl May, Democratic Services Manager, The Pavilions, Cambrian Park, Clydach Vale, Tonypandy CF40 2XX ☎ 01443 424045; 01443 424115 ⌁ karyl.may@rctcbc.gov.uk

Parking: Mr Alistair Critchlow, Parking Services & Streetworks Manager, Sardis House, Sardis Road, Pontypridd CF37 1DU ☎ 01443 494751; 01443 494778 ⌁ alistair.critchlow@rctcbc.gov.uk

Personnel / HR: Mr Tony Wilkins, Director - Human Resources, The Pavilions, Cambrian Park, Clydach Vale, CF40 2XX ☎ 01443 424166; 01443 424025 ⌁ tony.wilkins@rctcbc.gov.uk

Planning: Mr Simon Gale, Service Director - Planning, Sardis House, Sardis Road, Pontypridd CF37 1DU ☎ 01443 494716; 01443 494799 ⌁ simon.gale@rctcbc.gov.uk

Procurement: Mr Vince Hanly, Service Director - Procurement, Bronwydd, Porth CF39 9DL ☎ 01443 680538; 01443 680787 ⌁ vince.hanly@rctcbc.gov.uk

Public Libraries: Mrs Wendy Edwards, Head of Community Learning, Ty Trevithick, Abercynon, Mountain Ash CF45 4UQ ☎ 01443 744111 ⌁ wendy.edwards@rctcbc.gov.uk

Recycling & Waste Minimisation: Mr Nigel Wheeler, Service Director - Street Care, Ty Glantaf, Unit B23, Taff Falls Road, Treforest Industrial Estate, Pontypridd CF37 5TT ☎ 01443 827707; 01443 827730 ⌁ nigel.wheeler@rctcbc.gov.uk

Regeneration: Ms Jane Cook, Director - Regeneration & Planning, Floor 5, Unit 3, Ty Pennant, Catherine Street, Pontypridd CF37 2TB ☎ 01443 495161; 01443 407725 ⌁ jane.cook@rctcbc.gov.uk

Road Safety: Ms Jessica White, Road Safety Manager, Sardis House, Sardis Road, Pontypridd CF37 1DU ☎ 01443 494785 ⌁ jessica.j.white@rctcbc.gov.uk

Social Services: Mr Gio Isingrini, Group Director - Community & Children's Services, The Pavilions, Cambrian Park, Clydach Vale, Tonypandy CF40 2XX ☎ 01443 424140; 01443 424027 ⌁ gio.isingrini@rctcbc.gov.uk

Social Services (Adult): Mr Bob Gatis, Service Director - Adult Locality & Short Term Intervention, Ty Elai, Dinas Isaf Industrial Estate, Williamstown, Tonypandy CF40 1NY ☎ 01443 425401; 01443 425440 ⌁ robert.e.gatis@rctcbc.gov.uk

Social Services (Children): Mr Andrew Gwynn, Service Director - Children's Services, Unit 3, Ty Pennant, Catherine Street, Pontypridd CF45 4UQ ☎ 01443 495118; 01443 406290 ⌁ andrew.v.gwynn@rctcbc.gov.uk

Staff Training: Ms Deborah Hughes, Head of Organisational Development, The Pavilions, Cambrian Park, Clydach Vale, Tonypandy CF40 2XX ☎ 01443 424103; 01443 424025 ⌁ deborah.hughes@rctcbc.gov.uk

Street Scene: Mr Steve Owen, Head of Street Care, Ty Glantaf, Unit B23, Taff Falls Road, Treforest Industrial Estate, Pontypridd CF37 5TT ☎ 01443 827702; 01143 827730 ⌁ steve.owen@rctcbc.gov.uk

Sustainable Development: Mr Ian Woodland, Resilience & Sustainability Lead Advisor, Sardis House, Sardis Road, Pontypridd CF37 1DU ☎ 01443 490415 ⌁ ian.m.woodland@rctcbc.gov.uk

Tourism: Ms Luan Oestrich, Tourism Manager, The Pavilions, Cambrian Park, Clydach Vale, Tonypandy CF40 2XX ☎ 01443 424009; 01443 425553 ⌁ luan.oestrich@rctcbc.gov.uk

RHONDDA CYNON TAFF

Town Centre: Mr Peter Mortimer, Regeneration & Resources Manager, Sardis House, Sardis Road, Pontypridd CF37 1DU
☎ 01443 490407; 01443 407725 ⌨ peter.j.mortimer@rctcbc.gov.uk

Transport: Mr Charlie Nelson, Transportation Manager, Sardis House, Sardis Road, Pontypridd CF37 1DU ☎ 01443 494818; 01443 494875 ⌨ charlie.e.nelson@rctcbc.gov.uk

Transport Planner: Mr Adrian Morgan, Strategic Transport Planner, Sardis House, Sardis Road, Pontypridd CF37 1DU
☎ 01443 494714 ⌨ adrian.c.morgan@rctcbc.gov.uk

Waste Collection and Disposal: Ms Lynette Beddow, Trade Waste & Recycling Officer, Ty Glantaf, Unti B23, Taff Falls Road, Treforest Industrial Estate, Pontypridd CF37 5TT ☎ 01443 827721; 01443 827730 ⌨ lynette.beddow@rctcbc.gov.uk

Waste Management: Ms Nicola Jones, Waste Services Strategic Operations Officer, Ty Glantaf, Unit B23, Taff Falls Road, Treforest Industrial Estate, Pontypridd CF37 5TT ☎ 01443 827720; 01443 827730 ⌨ nicola.jones@rctcbc.gov.uk

Children's Play Areas: Ms Lisa Austin, Play & Recreation Facilities Manager, Hepworth Business Park, Coed Cae Lane Industrial Estate, Pontyclun CF72 9DX ☎ 01443 562293 ⌨ lisa.austin@rctcbc.gov.uk

COUNCILLORS

Leader of the Council: Morgan, Andrew (LAB - Mountain Ash West)
andrew.morgan2@rhondda-cynon-taff.gov.uk

Deputy Leader of the Council: Montague, Keiron (LAB - Maerdy)

Adams, Mark (LAB - Tylorstown)
lewis.m.adams@rhondda-cynon-taff.gov.uk

Baccara, Paul (IND - Talbot Green)
paul.baccara@rhondda-cynon-taff.gov.uk

Bates, Teressa (LAB - Hawthorn)
teressa.a.bates@rhondda-cynon-taff.gov.uk

Bevan, Robert (LAB - Tylorstown)
robert.bevan@rhondda-cynon-taff.gov.uk

Boggis, Helen (LAB - Penywaun)
helen.boggis@rhondda-cynon-taff.gov.uk

Bonetto, Jill (LAB - Taffs Well)
jill.bonetto@rhondda-cynon-taff.gov.uk

Bradwick, Steven (LAB - Aberdare East)
steven.a.bradwick@rhondda-cynon-taff.gov.uk

Bunnage, Jacqui (LAB - Llantwit Fardre)
jacqui.bunnage@rhondda-cynon-taff.gov.uk

Calvert, Anita (LAB - Aberaman South)
anita.calvert@rhondda-cynon-taff.gov.uk

Cannon, Paul (LAB - Ystrad)
paul.cannon@rhondda-cynon-taff.gov.uk

Carter, Steve Laurence (LAB - Pontypridd Town)

Cass, Joyce (LAB - Graig)
joyce.cass@rhondda-cynon-taff.gov.uk

Crimmings, Ann (LAB - Aberdare West with Llwydcoed)
ann.crimmings@rhondda-cynon-taff.gov.uk

David, John (LAB - Tonteg)
john.david@rhondda-cynon-taff.gov.uk

Davies, Annette (LAB - Ferndale)
annette.davies@rhondda-cynon-taff.gov.uk

Davies, Albert (LAB - Abercynon)
alby.davies@rhondda-cynon-taff.gov.uk

Davies, Cennard (PC - Treorchy)

Davies, Geraint (PC - Treherbert)
geraint.r.davies@btconnect.com

Davies, Margaret (LAB - Porth)
margaret.davies2@rhondda-cynon-taff.gov.uk

Davies, John (LAB - Aberdare West with Llwydcoed)
john.davies2@rhondda-cynon-taff.gov.uk

De Vet, Linda (LAB - Aberaman North)
linda.devet@rhondda-cynon-taff.gov.uk

Elliott, Jeffrey (LAB - Cwmbach)
jeffrey.elliott@rhondda-cynon-taff.gov.uk

Evans, Sheryl (LAB - Aberaman North)
sheryl.m.evans@rctcbc.gov.uk

Evans-Fear, Sera (PC - Treorchy)
treorci@yahoo.com

Forey, Michael (LAB - Aberdare East)
mike.forey@rhondda-cynon-taff.gov.uk

Fox, Adam (LAB - Penrhiwceiber)
adam.s.fox@rhondda-cynon-taff.gov.uk

Griffiths, Margaret (LAB - Pontyclun)
margaret.griffiths@rhondda-cynon-taff.gov.uk

Griffiths, Paul (LAB - Pontyclun)
paul.griffiths@rhondda-cynon-taff.gov.uk

Hanagan, Eudine (LAB - Tonyrefail West)

Holmes, Glynne (LAB - Llantrisant Town)
glynne.holmes@rhondda-cynon-taff.gov.uk

Hopkins, Geraint (LAB - Llanharan)
geraint.e.hopkins@rhondda-cynon-taff.gov.uk

Howe, Philip (IND - Ferndale)
philip.howe@rhondda-cynon-taff.gov.uk

James, Joel (CON - Llantwit Fardre)
joel.s.james@rhondda-cynon-taff.gov.uk

Jarman, Pauline (PC - Mountain Ash East)

Jones, Sylvia (LAB - Llwynpia)
sylvia.j.jones@rhondda-cynon-taff.gov.uk

Langford, Lionel (LAB - Ynyshir)
lionel.langford@rhondda-cynon-taff.gov.uk

Lewis, Rhys (LAB - Abercynon)
rhys.lewis@rhondda-cynon-taff.gov.uk

Leyshon, Christina (LAB - Rhondda)
christina.leyshon@rhondda-cynon-taff.gov.uk

Lloyd, Simon (LAB - Mountain Ash West)
simon.lloyd@rhondda-cynon-taff.gov.uk

McDonald, Robert (LAB - Tonyrefail East)
robert.mcdonald@rhondda-cynon-taff.gov.uk

Middle, Craig (LAB - Tonypandy)
craig.j.middle@rhondda-cynon-taff.gov.uk

Morgan, Karen (PC - Hirwaun)
karen.morgan2@rhondda-cynon-taff.gov.uk

Morgan, Barrie (LAB - Cilfynydd)
barrie.j.morgan@rhondda-cynon-taff.gov.uk

Norris, Mark (LAB - Cwm Clydach)
mark.a.norris@rhondda-cynon-taff.gov.uk

Pearce, Irene Elizabeth (PC - Treherbert)
irene.e.pearce@rhondda-cynon-taff.gov.uk

Pickering, Sue (LAB - Ynysybwl)
sue.pickering@rhondda-cynon-taff.gov.uk

Powderhill, Steve (LAB - Treforest)
steve.powderhill@rhondda-cynon-taff.gov.uk

Powell, Michael (LD - Trallwng)
michael.j.powell@rhondda-cynon-taff.gov.uk

Privett, Kenneth (LAB - Penygraig)

Rees, Sharon (LAB - Aberdare West with Llwydcoed)
sharon.rees2@rhondda-cynon-taff.gov.uk

Rees-Owen, Shelley (PC - Pentre)
shelley.rees-owen@rhondda-cynon-taff.gov.uk

Roberts, Aurfron (LAB - Gilfach Goch)
aurfron.roberts@rhondda-cynon-taff.gov.uk

Rosser, Joy (LAB - Trealaw)

Smith, Graham (LAB - Porth)
graham.smith@rhondda-cynon-taff.gov.uk

Smith, Robert (LAB - Rhondda)
robert.w.smith@rhondda-cynon-taff.gov.uk

Stacey, Graham (LAB - Church Village)
graham.stacey@rhondda-cynon-taff.gov.uk

Stephens, Barry (LAB - Llanharry)
barry.stephens2@rhondda-cynon-taff.gov.uk

Tegg, Margaret (LAB - Cymmer)
margaret.tegg@rhondda-cynon-taff.gov.uk

Thomas, Graham (LAB - Rhigos)
graham.p.thomas@rhondda-cynon-taff.gov.uk

Turner, Roger (LAB - Brynna)
roger.k.turner@rhondda-cynon-taff.gov.uk

Walker, Lyndon (IND - Tonteg)
lyndon.walker@rhondda-cynon-taff.gov.uk

Ward, Jane (LAB - Penrhiwceiber)
jane.ward@rhondda-cynon-taff.gov.uk

Wasley, Paul (IND - Tonyrefail East)
paul.wasley@rhondda-cynon-taff.gov.uk

Watts, John (LAB - Ystrad)
malcolm.j.watts@rhondda-cynon-taff.gov.uk

Weaver, Maureen (PC - Pentre)
maureenowen54@gmail.com

Webber, Maureen (LAB - Rhydfelin Central)
maureen.webber@rhondda-cynon-taff.gov.uk

Webster, Emyr John (PC - Treorchy)
emry.j.webster@rhondda-cynon-taff.gov.uk

Weeks, Dennis (LAB - Penygraig)
william.d.weeks@rhondda-cynon-taff.gov.uk

Williams, Doug (LAB - Glyncoch)
doug.williams@rhondda-cynon-taff.gov.uk

Williams, Christopher (LAB - Cymmer)
christopher.j.williams3@rhondda-cynon-taff.gov.uk

Williams, Tina (LAB - Aberaman South)
tina.williams@rhondda-cynon-taff.gov.uk

Willis, Clayton (LAB - Tyn-y-Nant)
clayton.j.willis@rhondda-cynon-taff.gov.uk

Yeo, Richard (LAB - Beddau)
richard.yeo@rhondda-cynon-taff.gov.uk

POLITICAL COMPOSITION
LAB: 60, PC: 9, IND: 4, CON: 1, LD: 1

COMMITTEE CHAIRS

Children & Young People: Ms Christina Leyshon

Development Control: Mr Graham Stacey

Education & Lifelong Learning: Ms Christina Leyshon

Health & Wellbeing: Mr Robert Smith

Licensing: Mr Adam Fox

Ribble Valley   D

Ribble Valley Borough Council, Council Offices, Church Walk, Clitheroe BB7 2RA
☎ 01200 425111 🖷 01200 414488 ✆ contact@ribblevalley.gov.uk
🖳 www.ribblevalley.gov.uk

FACTS AND FIGURES
Parliamentary Constituencies: Ribble Valley
EU Constituencies: North West
Election Frequency: Elections are of whole council

PRINCIPAL OFFICERS

Chief Executive: Mr Marshal Scott, Chief Executive, Council Offices, Church Walk, Clitheroe BB7 2RA ☎ 01200 425111; 01200 414488 ✆ marshal.scott@ribblevalley.gov.uk

Senior Management: Mr John Heap, Director - Community Services, Council Offices, Church Walk, Clitheroe BB7 2RA ☎ 01200 425111; 01200 414488 ✆ john.heap@ribblevalley.gov.uk

Senior Management: Mrs Jane Pearson, Director - Resources, Council Offices, Church Walk, Clitheroe BB7 2RA ☎ 01200 425111 ✆ jane.pearson@ribblevalley.gov.uk

Architect, Building / Property Services: Mr Adrian Harper, Head of Engineering, Council Offices, Church Walk, Clitheroe BB7 2RA ☎ 01200 425111 ✆ adrian.harper@ribblevalley.gov.uk

Best Value: Mrs Jane Pearson, Director - Resources, Council Offices, Church Walk, Clitheroe BB7 2RA ☎ 01200 425111 ✆ jane.pearson@ribblevalley.gov.uk

Building Control: Mrs Heather Coar, Head of Environmental Health, Council Offices, Church Walk, Clitheroe BB7 2RA ☎ 01200 425111 ✆ heather.coar@ribblevalley.gov.uk

RIBBLE VALLEY

PR / Communications: Mrs Theresa Sanderson, Corporate Communications Officer, Council Offices, Church Walk, Clitheroe BB7 2RA ☎ 01200 425111 ✆ theresa.sanderson@ribblevalley.gov.uk

PR / Communications: Mrs Michelle Smith, Head of HR, Council Offices, Church Walk, Clitheroe BB7 2RA ☎ 01200 425111; 01200 414488 ✆ michelle.smith@ribblevalley.gov.uk

Community Planning: Mr Colin Hirst, Head of Regeneration & Housing, Council Offices, Church Walk, Clitheroe BB7 2RA ☎ 01200 425111; 01200 414487 ✆ colin.hirst@ribblevalley.gov.uk

Computer Management: Mr Stuart Haworth, ICT Manager, Council Offices, Church Walk, Clitheroe BB7 2RA ☎ 01200 425111

Consumer Protection and Trading Standards: Mrs Heather Coar, Head of Environmental Health, Council Offices, Church Walk, Clitheroe BB7 2RA ☎ 01200 425111 ✆ heather.coar@ribblevalley.gov.uk

Contracts: Mr Adrian Harper, Head of Engineering, Council Offices, Church Walk, Clitheroe BB7 2RA ☎ 01200 425111 ✆ adrian.harper@ribblevalley.gov.uk

Contracts: Mr John Heap, Director - Community Services, Council Offices, Church Walk, Clitheroe BB7 2RA ☎ 01200 425111; 01200 414488 ✆ john.heap@ribblevalley.gov.uk

Customer Service: Mrs Toni Bates, Customer Services Supporter, Council Offices, Church Walk, Clitheroe BB7 2RA ☎ 01200 425111 ✆ toni.bates@ribblevalley.gov.uk

Direct Labour: Mr Adrian Harper, Head of Engineering, Council Offices, Church Walk, Clitheroe BB7 2RA ☎ 01200 425111 ✆ adrian.harper@ribblevalley.gov.uk

Electoral Registration: Mrs Diane Rice, Head of Legal & Democratic Services, Council Offices, Church Walk, Clitheroe BB7 2RA ☎ 01200 425111; 01200 414488 ✆ diane.rice@ribblevalley.gov.uk

Emergency Planning: Mr Chris Shuttleworth, Building Control Surveyor, Council Offices, Church Walk, Clitheroe BB7 2RA ☎ 01200 425111; 01200 414488 ✆ chris.shuttleworth@ribblevalley.gov.uk

Energy Management: Mr Alan Coar, Principal Surveyor, Council Offices, Church Walk, Clitheroe BB7 2RA ☎ 01200 425111 ✆ alan.coar@ribblevalley.gov.uk

Environmental Health: Mrs Heather Coar, Head of Environmental Health, Council Offices, Church Walk, Clitheroe BB7 2RA ☎ 01200 425111 ✆ heather.coar@ribblevalley.gov.uk

Events Manager: Mr Tom Pridmore, Tourism & Events Officer, Council Offices, Church Walk, Clitheroe BB7 2RA ☎ 01200 425111 ✆ tom.pridmore@ribblevalley.gov.uk

Finance: Mr Lawson Oddie, Head of Financial Services, Council Offices, Church Walk, Clitheroe BB7 2RA ☎ 01200 425111 ✆ lawson.oddie.ribblevalley.gov.uk

Finance: Mrs Jane Pearson, Director - Resources, Council Offices, Church Walk, Clitheroe BB7 2RA ☎ 01200 425111 ✆ jane.pearson@ribblevalley.gov.uk

Grounds Maintenance: Mr Alan Boyer, Amenity Cleansing Manager, Council Offices, Church Walk, Clitheroe BB7 2RA ☎ 01200 425111; 01200 414488 ✆ alan.boyer@ribblevalley.gov.uk

Health and Safety: Mr Phil Dodd, Health & Safety Officer, Council Offices, Church Walk, Clitheroe BB7 2RA ☎ 01200 425111; 01200 414488 ✆ phil.dodd@ribblevalley.gov.uk

Health and Safety: Mrs Michelle Smith, Head of HR, Council Offices, Church Walk, Clitheroe BB7 2RA ☎ 01200 425111; 01200 414488 ✆ michelle.smith@ribblevalley.gov.uk

Housing: Mr Colin Hirst, Head of Regeneration & Housing, Council Offices, Church Walk, Clitheroe BB7 2RA ☎ 01200 425111; 01200 414487 ✆ colin.hirst@ribblevalley.gov.uk

Housing Maintenance: Mrs Rachael Stott, Housing Strategy Officer, Council Offices, Church Walk, Clitheroe BB7 2RA ☎ 01200 425111 ✆ rachael.stott@ribblevalley.gov.uk

Local Area Agreement: Mr Colin Hirst, Head of Regeneration & Housing, Council Offices, Church Walk, Clitheroe BB7 2RA ☎ 01200 425111; 01200 414487 ✆ colin.hirst@ribblevalley.gov.uk

Legal: Mrs Diane Rice, Head of Legal & Democratic Services, Council Offices, Church Walk, Clitheroe BB7 2RA ☎ 01200 425111; 01200 414488 ✆ diane.rice@ribblevalley.gov.uk

Leisure and Cultural Services: Mr Mark Beveridge, Head of Cultural & Leisure Services, Council Offices, Church Walk, Clitheroe BB7 2RA ☎ 01200 425111; 01200 414488 ✆ mark.beveridge@ribblevalley.gov.uk

Licensing: Mrs Diane Rice, Head of Legal & Democratic Services, Council Offices, Church Walk, Clitheroe BB7 2RA ☎ 01200 425111; 01200 414488 ✆ diane.rice@ribblevalley.gov.uk

Lifelong Learning: Mrs Michelle Smith, Head of HR, Council Offices, Church Walk, Clitheroe BB7 2RA ☎ 01200 425111; 01200 414488 ✆ michelle.smith@ribblevalley.gov.uk

Lottery Funding, Charity and Voluntary: Mr Mark Beveridge, Head of Cultural & Leisure Services, Council Offices, Church Walk, Clitheroe BB7 2RA ☎ 01200 425111; 01200 414488 ✆ mark.beveridge@ribblevalley.gov.uk

Member Services: Mrs Diane Rice, Head of Legal & Democratic Services, Council Offices, Church Walk, Clitheroe BB7 2RA ☎ 01200 425111; 01200 414488 ✆ diane.rice@ribblevalley.gov.uk

Personnel / HR: Mrs Michelle Smith, Head of HR, Council Offices, Church Walk, Clitheroe BB7 2RA ☎ 01200 425111; 01200 414488 ✆ michelle.smith@ribblevalley.gov.uk

Planning: Mr John Macholc, Head of Planning Services, Ribble Valley Borough Council, Church Walk, Clitheroe BB7 2RA ☎ 01200 425111; 01200 414488 ✆ john.macholc@ribblevalley.gov.uk

Procurement: Mrs Jane Pearson, Director - Resources, Council Offices, Church Walk, Clitheroe BB7 2RA ☎ 01200 425111 ✆ jane.pearson@ribblevalley.gov.uk

Recycling & Waste Minimisation: Mr Adrian Harper, Head of Engineering, Council Offices, Church Walk, Clitheroe BB7 2RA ☎ 01200 425111 ✆ adrian.harper@ribblevalley.gov.uk

Recycling & Waste Minimisation: Mr John Heap, Director - Community Services, Council Offices, Church Walk, Clitheroe BB7 2RA ☎ 01200 425111; 01200 414488 ✆ john.heap@ribblevalley.gov.uk

Recycling & Waste Minimisation: Mr Peter McGeorge, Waste Management Officer, Council Offices, Church Walk, Clitheroe BB7 2RA ☎ 01200 425111; 01200 414488 ✆ peter.mcgeorge@ribblevalley.gov.uk

Regeneration: Mr Colin Hirst, Head of Regeneration & Housing, Council Offices, Church Walk, Clitheroe BB7 2RA ☎ 01200 425111; 01200 414487 ✆ colin.hirst@ribblevalley.gov.uk

Staff Training: Mrs Michelle Smith, Head of HR, Council Offices, Church Walk, Clitheroe BB7 2RA ☎ 01200 425111; 01200 414488 ✆ michelle.smith@ribblevalley.gov.uk

Street Scene: Mr Adrian Harper, Head of Engineering, Council Offices, Church Walk, Clitheroe BB7 2RA ☎ 01200 425111 ✆ adrian.harper@ribblevalley.gov.uk

Sustainable Communities: Mr Colin Hirst, Head of Regeneration & Housing, Council Offices, Church Walk, Clitheroe BB7 2RA ☎ 01200 425111; 01200 414487 ✆ colin.hirst@ribblevalley.gov.uk

Tourism: Mr Mark Beveridge, Head of Cultural & Leisure Services, Council Offices, Church Walk, Clitheroe BB7 2RA ☎ 01200 425111; 01200 414488 ✆ mark.beveridge@ribblevalley.gov.uk

Tourism: Mr Tom Pridmore, Tourism & Events Officer, Council Offices, Church Walk, Clitheroe BB7 2RA ☎ 01200 425111 ✆ tom.pridmore@ribblevalley.gov.uk

Waste Collection and Disposal: Mr Adrian Harper, Head of Engineering, Council Offices, Church Walk, Clitheroe BB7 2RA ☎ 01200 425111 ✆ adrian.harper@ribblevalley.gov.uk

Waste Collection and Disposal: Mr John Heap, Director - Community Services, Council Offices, Church Walk, Clitheroe BB7 2RA ☎ 01200 425111; 01200 414488 ✆ john.heap@ribblevalley.gov.uk

Waste Management: Mr Adrian Harper, Head of Engineering, Council Offices, Church Walk, Clitheroe BB7 2RA ☎ 01200 425111 ✆ adrian.harper@ribblevalley.gov.uk

Waste Management: Mr John Heap, Director - Community Services, Council Offices, Church Walk, Clitheroe BB7 2RA ☎ 01200 425111; 01200 414488 ✆ john.heap@ribblevalley.gov.uk

Waste Management: Mr Peter McGeorge, Waste Management Officer, Council Offices, Church Walk, Clitheroe BB7 2RA ☎ 01200 425111; 01200 414488 ✆ peter.mcgeorge@ribblevalley.gov.uk

Children's Play Areas: Mr Adrian Harper, Head of Engineering, Council Offices, Church Walk, Clitheroe BB7 2RA ☎ 01200 425111 ✆ adrian.harper@ribblevalley.gov.uk

COUNCILLORS

Mayor: Holgate, Joyce (CON - Whalley)
cllr.holgate@ribblevalley.gov.uk

Leader of the Council: Hirst, Stuart (CON - Wilpshire)
cllr.hirst@ribblevalley.gov.uk

Ainsworth, Peter (CON - Clayton-le-Dale with Ramsgreave)
cllr.ainsworth@ribblevalley.gov.uk

Alcock, Janet (CON - Aighton, Bailey & Chaigley)
cllr.alcock@ribblevalley.gov.uk

Atkinson, Stephen (CON - Billington & Old Langho)
cllr.atkinson@ribblevalley.gov.uk

Bennett, Richard (CON - Read & Simonstone)
cllr.bennett@ribblevalley.gov.uk

Bibby, Susan (CON - Wilpshire)
cllr.bibby@ribblevalley.gov.uk

Brown, Alison (CON - Langho)
cllr.abrown@ribblevalley.gov.uk

Brown, Ian (CON - Salthill)
cllr.brown@ribblevalley.gov.uk

Brunskill, Stella (CON - Mellor)
cllr.brunskill@ribblevalley.gov.uk

Carefoot, Stuart (CON - Derby & Thornley)
cllr.carefoot@ribblevalley.gov.uk

Dobson, Paula (CON - Langho)
cllr.dobson@ribblevalley.gov.uk

Dowson, Pamela (CON - Salthill)
cllr.dowson@ribblevalley.gov.uk

Elms, Rosemary (CON - Bowland, Newton & Slaidburn)
cllr.elms@ribblevalley.gov.uk

Elms, Paul (CON - Waddington & West Bradford)
cllr.pelms@ribblevalley.gov.uk

Fenton, Maureen (LAB - Edisford & Low Moor)
cllr.fenton@ribblevalley.gov.uk

French, Mark (LD - Littlemoor)
cllr.french@ribblevalley.gov.uk

Geldard, Graham (CON - St Marys)
cllr.geldard@ribblevalley.gov.uk

Graves, Lesley (CON - Read & Simonstone)
cllr.graves@ribblevalley.gov.uk

Hargreaves, Ruth (LD - St Marys)
cllr.hargreaves@ribblevalley.gov.uk

Hill, Terry (CON - Whalley)
cllr.thill@ribblevalley.gov.uk

Hilton, Bridget (CON - Waddington & West Bradford)
cllr.hilton@ribblevalley.gov.uk

Hind, Sue (CON - Edisford & Low Moor)
cllr.shind@ribblevalley.gov.uk

Hind, Ken (CON - Dilworth)
cllr.hind@ribblevalley.gov.uk

RIBBLE VALLEY

Hore, Simon (CON - Chipping)
cllr.hore@ribblevalley.gov.uk

Knox, Susan (LD - Littlemoor)
cllr.sknox@ribblevalley.gov.uk

Knox, Allan (LD - Primrose)
cllr.knox@ribblevalley.gov.uk

Mirfin, Ged (CON - Billington & Old Langho)
cllr.mirfin@ribblevalley.gov.uk

Newmark, Richard (CON - Sabden)
cllr.newmark@ribblevalley.gov.uk

Robinson, Mary (LD - Primrose)
cllr.robinson@ribblevalley.gov.uk

Rogerson, James (IND - Alston & Hothersall)
cllr.rogerson@ribblevalley.gov.uk

Sayers, Ian (CON - Ribchester)
cllr.sayers@ribblevalley.gov.uk

Scott, Gary (CON - Chatburn)
cllr.scott@ribblevalley.gov.uk

Sherras, Richard (CON - Gisburn & Rimington)
cllr.sherras@ribblevalley.gov.uk

Smith, David (CON - Alston & Hothersall)
cllr.smith@ribblevalley.gov.uk

Swarbrick, Rupert (CON - Dilworth)
cllr.swarbrick@ribblevalley.gov.uk

Taylor, Doreen (CON - Clayton-le-Dale with Ramsgreave)
cllr.dtaylor@ribblevalley.gov.uk

Thompson, Robert (CON - Wiswell & Pendleton)
cllr.thompson@ribblevalley.gov.uk

Walsh, Noel (CON - Mellor)
cllr.walsh@ribblevalley.gov.uk

White, Jim (CON - Derby & Thornley)
cllr.white@ribblevalley.gov.uk

POLITICAL COMPOSITION
CON: 33, LD: 5, IND: 1, LAB: 1

Richmond upon Thames   L

Richmond upon Thames London Borough Council, Civic
Centre, 44 York Street, Twickenham TW1 3BZ
☎ 020 8891 1411 🖥 www.richmond.gov.uk

FACTS AND FIGURES
Parliamentary Constituencies: Richmond Park, Twickenham
EU Constituencies: London
Election Frequency: Elections are of whole council

PRINCIPAL OFFICERS

Chief Executive: Mr Paul Martin, Chief Executive & Director -
Administration, Town Hall, Wandsworth High Street, London SW18
2PU ☎ 020 8871 6001 ◌ pmartin@wandsworth.gov.uk

Deputy Chief Executive: Mr Mark Maidment, Deputy Chief
Executive & Director - Resources, Civic Centre, 44 York Street,
Twickenham TW1 3BZ ☎ 020 8891 7171; 020 8891 7333
◌ m.maidment@richmond.gov.uk

Senior Management: Ms Anna Bryden, Public Health Consultant,
Civic Centre, 44 York Street, Twickenham TW1 3BZ
☎ 020 8734 3027 ◌ anna.bryden@richmond.gov.uk

Senior Management: Mr Paul Chadwick, Director - Environment
& Community Services, Civic Centre, 44 York Street, Twickenham
TW1 3BZ ☎ 020 8891 7870; 020 8891 7361
◌ p.chadwick@richmond.gov.uk

Senior Management: Ms Cathy Kerr, Director - Adult Social
Services, Civic Centre, 44 York Street, Twickenham TW1 3BZ
☎ 020 8891 7360 ◌ ckerr@wandsworth.gov.uk

Senior Management: Mr Mark Maidment, Deputy Chief
Executive, Civic Centre, 44 York Street, Twickenham TW1 3BZ
☎ 020 8891 7171; 020 8891 7333 ◌ m.maidment@richmond.gov.uk

Senior Management: Ms Anna Raleigh, Public Health
Consultant, Civic Centre, 44 York Street, Twickenham TW1 3BZ
☎ 020 8734 3014 ◌ anna.raleigh@richmond.gov.uk

Senior Management: Mr Nick Whitfield, Chief Executive Officer
- Achieving for Children, Civic Centre, 44 York Street, Twickenham
TW1 3BZ ☎ 020 8891 7906; 020 8831 6216
◌ nick.whitfield@achievingforchildren.org.uk

Senior Management: Mr Brian Reilly, Director - Housing &
Regeneration, Civic Centre, 44 York Street, Twickenham TW1 3BZ
☎ 020 8871 6591 ◌ brian.reilly@achievingforchildren.org.uk

Architect, Building / Property Services: Mr Paul Chadwick,
Director - Environment, Civic Centre, 44 York Street, Twickenham
TW1 3BZ ☎ 020 8891 7870; 020 8891 7361
◌ p.chadwick@richmond.gov.uk

Best Value: Ms Gill Ford, Head of Performance & Quality
Assurance, Civic Centre, 44 York Street, Twickenham TW1 3BZ
☎ 020 8487 5016; 020 8487 5026 ◌ g.ford@richmond.gov.uk

Building Control: Mr David Batsford, Head of Building Control,
2nd Floor, Civic Centre, 44 York Street, Twickenham TW1 3BZ
☎ 020 8891 7346; 020 8891 7347 ◌ d.batsford@richmond.gov.uk

Children / Youth Services: Mr Nick Whitfield, Chief Executive
Officer - Achieving for Children, Civic Centre, 44 York Street,
Twickenham TW1 3BZ ☎ 020 8891 7906; 020 8831 6216
◌ nick.whitfield@achievingforchildren.org.uk

Civil Registration: Miss Alison Parr, Superintendent Registrar,
Register Office, 1 Spring Terrace, Richmond TW9 1LW
☎ 020 8891 7188 ◌ alison.parr@richmond.gov.uk

PR / Communications: Mrs Elinor Firth, Head of
Communications, Civic Centre, 44 York Street, Twickenham TW1
3BZ ☎ 020 8487 5159 ◌ e.firth@richmond.gov.uk

PR / Communications: Ms Katrina Waite, Community
Engagement Manager, Civic Centre, 44 York Street, Twickenham
TW1 3BZ ☎ 020 8831 6289 ◌ katrina.waite@richmond.gov.uk

Community Planning: Ms Mandy Skinner, Assistant Director - Commissioning, Corporate Policy & Strategy, Civic Centre, 44 York Street, Twickenham TW1 3BZ ☎ 020 8891 7929; 020 8891 7703 ⌁ mandy.skinner@richmond.gov.uk

Community Planning: Ms Katrina Waite, Community Engagement Manager, Civic Centre, 44 York Street, Twickenham TW1 3BZ ☎ 020 8831 6289 ⌁ katrina.waite@richmond.gov.uk

Community Safety: Mr Michael Allen, Acting Community Safety Manager, Civic Centre, 44 York Street, Twickenham TW1 3BZ ☎ 020 8831 6198 ⌁ michael.allen@richmond.gov.uk

Computer Management: Mr Adrian Boylan, Head of ICT, Civic Centre, 44 York Street, Twickenham TW1 3BZ ☎ 020 8891 7177 ⌁ a.boylan@richmond.gov.uk

Computer Management: Mr Mike Gravatt, Assistant Director - Finance & Corporate Services, Civic Centre, 44 York Street, Twickenham TW1 3BZ ☎ 020 8891 7238; 020 8891 7233 ⌁ m.gravatt@richmond.gov.uk

Consumer Protection and Trading Standards: Mr Paul Foster, Head of Regulatory Services Partnership, Civic Centre, 44 York Street, Twickenham TW1 3BZ ☎ 020 8979 7258 ⌁ paul.foster@ merton.gov.uk

Corporate Services: Ms Gill Ford, Head of Performance & Quality Assurance, Civic Centre, 44 York Street, Twickenham TW1 3BZ ☎ 020 8487 5016; 020 8487 5026 ⌁ g.ford@richmond.gov.uk

Corporate Services: Mrs Carol McBean, Head of Corporate Partnership & Policy, Civic Centre, 44 York Street, Twickenham TW1 3BZ ☎ 020 8831 6231 ⌁ c.macbean@richmond.gov.uk

Corporate Services: Mr Graham Russell, Assistant Director - Finance & Corporate Services, Civic Centre, 44 York Street, Twickenham TW1 3BZ ☎ 020 8891 7226 ⌁ g.russell@richmond.gov.uk

Customer Service: Mr Simon Batchelor, Head of Customer Services, Civic Centre, 44 York Street, Twickenham TW1 3BZ ☎ 020 8487 5219 ⌁ simon.batchelor@richmond.gov.uk

Direct Labour: Mr Graham Beattie, Assistant Director - Highways & Transport, Civic Centre, 44 York Street, Twickenham TW1 3BZ ☎ 020 8891 7309 ⌁ graham.beattie@richmond.gov.uk

Economic Development: Mr Sean Gillen, Economic Development Manager, Civic Centre, 44 York Street, Twickenham TW1 3BZ ☎ 020 8831 6219; 020 8891 7347 ⌁ sean.gillen@richmond.gov.uk

Education: Mr Nick Whitfield, Chief Executive Officer - Achieving for Children, Civic Centre, 44 York Street, Twickenham TW1 3BZ ☎ 020 8891 7906; 020 8831 6216 ⌁ nick.whitfield@achievingforchildren.org.uk

E-Government: Mr Mike Gravatt, Assistant Director - Finance & Corporate Services, Civic Centre, 44 York Street, Twickenham TW1 3BZ ☎ 020 8891 7238; 020 8891 7233 ⌁ m.gravatt@richmond.gov.uk

Electoral Registration: Ms Cathy Potter, Head of Electoral Services, York House, Richmond Road, Twickenham TW1 3AA ☎ 020 8891 7784 ⌁ cathy.potter@richmond.gov.uk

Emergency Planning: Mr Paul Cook, Corporate Facilities Manager, Civic Centre, 44 York Street, Twickenham TW1 3BZ ☎ 020 8891 7463 ⌁ p.cook@richmond.gov.uk

Energy Management: Miss Ishbel Murray, Assistant Director - Environment, Property, Parks & Sustainability, Civic Centre, 44 York Street, Twickenham TW1 3BZ ☎ 020 8891 7310 ⌁ ishbel.murray@richmond.gov.uk

Environmental / Technical Services: Mr Jon Freer, Assistant Director - Environment, Civic Centre, 44 York Street, Twickenham TW1 3BZ ☎ 020 8891 7319 ⌁ j.freer@richmond.gov.uk

Environmental Health: Mr Paul Foster, Head of Regulatory Services Partnership, Civic Centre, 44 York Street, Twickenham TW1 3BZ ☎ 020 8979 7258 ⌁ paul.foster@merton.gov.uk

Environmental Health: Mr Paul Foster, Head of Regulatory Services Partnership, Civic Centre, 44 York Street, Twickenham TW1 3BZ ☎ 020 8979 7258 ⌁ paul.foster@merton.gov.uk

Estates, Property & Valuation: Mr Paul Chadwick, Director - Environment, Civic Centre, 44 York Street, Twickenham TW1 3BZ ☎ 020 8891 7870; 020 8891 7361 ⌁ p.chadwick@richmond.gov.uk

Estates, Property & Valuation: Mr Peter Southcombe, Head of Estates & Valuation, Civic Centre, 44 York Street, Twickenham TW1 3BZ ☎ 020 8487 5118; 020 8487 5125 ⌁ peter.southcombe@babcockinternational.com

Events Manager: Ms Laura Steele, Community Events Manager, Civic Centre, 44 York Street, Twickenham TW1 3BZ ☎ 020 8891 7074 ⌁ laura.steele@richmond.gov.uk

Facilities: Mr Paul Cook, Corporate Facilities Manager, Civic Centre, 44 York Street, Twickenham TW1 3BZ ☎ 020 8891 7463 ⌁ p.cook@richmond.gov.uk

Finance: Mr Mike Gravatt, Assistant Director - Finance & Corporate Services, Civic Centre, 44 York Street, Twickenham TW1 3BZ ☎ 020 8891 7238; 020 8891 7233 ⌁ m.gravatt@richmond.gov.uk

Finance: Mr Mark Maidment, Deputy Chief Executive, York House Annexe, York House, Twickenham TW1 3AA ☎ 020 8891 7171; 020 8891 7333 ⌁ m.maidment@richmond.gov.uk

Treasury: Ms Sue Cornwell, Treasury Manager, Ground Floor, Civic Centre, 44 York Street, Twickenham TW1 3BZ ☎ 020 8891 7252 ⌁ s.cornwell@richmond.gov.uk

Pensions: Ms Colette Hollands, Pensions Manager, Town Hall, Wandsworth High Street, London SW18 2PU ☎ 020 8871 6522 ⌁ chollands@wandsworth.gov.uk

Fleet Management: Mr Jon Freer, Assistant Director - Environment, Civic Centre, 44 York Street, Twickenham TW1 3BZ ☎ 020 8891 7319 ⌁ j.freer@richmond.gov.uk

RICHMOND UPON THAMES

Grounds Maintenance: Miss Ishbel Murray, Assistant Director - Environment, Property, Parks & Sustainability, Civic Centre, 44 York Street, Twickenham TW1 3BZ ☎ 020 8891 7310 ⌨ ishbel.murray@richmond.gov.uk

Health and Safety: Mr Paul Cook, Corporate Facilities Manager, Civic Centre, 44 York Street, Twickenham TW1 3BZ ☎ 020 8891 7463 ⌨ p.cook@richmond.gov.uk

Highways: Mr Graham Beattie, Assistant Director - Highways & Transport, Civic Centre, 44 York Street, Twickenham TW1 3BZ ☎ 020 8891 7309 ⌨ graham.beattie@richmond.gov.uk

Home Energy Conservation: Mr Colin Coomber, Energy Efficiency Co-ordinator, Civic Centre, 44 York Street, Twickenham TW1 3BZ ☎ 020 8891 7663; 020 8831 6404 ⌨ c.coomber@richmond.gov.uk

Housing: Mr Brian Castle, Assistant Director - Community Service Operations, Civic Centre, 44 York Street, Twickenham TW1 3BZ ☎ 020 8891 7482; 020 8891 7792 ⌨ b.castle@richmond.gov.uk

Local Area Agreement: Ms Carol MacBean, Head of Strategy & Policy, Civic Centre, 44 York Street, Twickenham TW1 3BZ ☎ 020 8831 6231 ⌨ c.macbean@richmond.gov.uk

Legal: Mr Paul Evans, Assistant Director - Corporate Governance & Head of Shared Legal Services, 1st Floor, Gifford House Legal Services, 67c St Helier Avenue, Morden SM4 6HY ☎ 020 8545 3338 ⌨ paul.evans@merton.gov.uk

Leisure and Cultural Services: Mr Colin Sinclair, Head of Sport & Fitness, Regal House, London Road, Twickenham TW1 3QB ☎ 020 8831 6140; 020 8891 7904 ⌨ c.sinclair@richmond.gov.uk

Leisure and Cultural Services: Ms Rachel Tranter, Head of Arts, Orleans House Gallery, Riverside, Twickenham TW1 3DJ ☎ 020 8831 6462 ⌨ r.tranter@richmond.gov.uk

Licensing: Mr Paul Foster, Head of Regulatory Services Partnership, Civic Centre, 44 York Street, Twickenham TW1 3BZ ☎ 020 8979 7258 ⌨ paul.foster@merton.gov.uk

Lifelong Learning: Mr Ian Dodds, Director - Standards & Improvements, Achieving for Children, Civic Centre, 44 York Street, Twickenham TW1 3BZ ☎ 020 8831 6116 ⌨ ian.dodds@achievingforchildren.org.uk

Lighting: Mr Andrew Porter, Principal Engineer - Street Lighting, Civic Centre, 44 York Street, Twickenham TW1 3BZ ☎ 020 8891 7086 ⌨ andrew.porter@richmond.gov.uk

Member Services: Ms Kathryn Thomas, Head of Democratic Services, York House, Richmond Road, Twickenham TW1 3AA ☎ 020 8891 7860; 020 8891 7701 ⌨ kathryn.thomas@richmond.gov.uk

Parking: Mr James Marshall, Head of Parking Services, Civic Centre, 44 York Street, Twickenham TW1 3BZ ☎ 020 8831 6439 ⌨ james.marshall@richmond.gov.uk

Personnel / HR: Mr Mike Gravatt, Assistant Director - Finance & Corporate Services, Civic Centre, 44 York Street, Twickenham TW1 3BZ ☎ 020 8891 7238; 020 8891 7233 ⌨ m.gravatt@richmond.gov.uk

Planning: Mr Robert Angus, Head of Development & Enforcement, Civic Centre, 44 York Street, Twickenham TW1 3BZ ☎ 020 8891 7271; 020 8891 7789 ⌨ r.angus@richmond.gov.uk

Procurement: Mr Jo Warren, Head of Procurement, Civic Centre, 44 York Street, Twickenham TW1 3BZ ☎ 020 8891 7282 ⌨ jo.warren@richmond.gov.uk

Public Libraries: Ms Amanda Stirrup, Library Operations Manager, Civic Centre, 44 York Street, Twickenham TW1 3BZ ☎ 020 8734 3322 ⌨ amanda.stirrup@richmond.gov.uk

Recycling & Waste Minimisation: Mr Jon Freer, Assistant Director - Development & Street Scene, Civic Centre, 44 York Street, Twickenham TW1 3BZ ☎ 020 8891 7319 ⌨ j.freer@richmond.gov.uk

Regeneration: Ms Andrea Kitzberger-Smith, Planning Policy Manager, Civic Centre, 44 York Street, Twickenham TW1 3BZ ☎ 020 8891 7364 ⌨ andrea.kitzberger@richmond.gov.uk

Road Safety: Mr Sam Merison, Principal Safety Education Officer, Civic Centre, 44 York Street, Twickenham TW1 3BZ ☎ 020 8487 5356 ⌨ sam.merison@richmond.gov.uk

Social Services: Ms Cathy Kerr, Director - Adult Social Services, Civic Centre, 44 York Street, Twickenham TW1 3BZ ☎ 020 8891 7360 ⌨ ckerr@wandsworth.gov.uk

Social Services (Adult): Mr Derek Oliver, Assistant Director - Community Care Services, Civic Centre, 44 York Street, Twickenham TW1 3BZ ☎ 020 8891 7608 ⌨ derek.oliver@richmond.gov.uk

Social Services (Children): Mr Nick Whitfield, Chief Executive Officer - Achieving for Children, Civic Centre, 44 York Street, Twickenham TW1 3BZ ☎ 020 8891 7906; 020 8831 6216 ⌨ nick.whitfield@achievingforchildren.org.uk

Public Health: Ms Anna Bryden, Public Health Consultant, Civic Centre, 44 York Street, Twickenham TW1 3BZ ☎ 020 8734 3027 ⌨ anna.bryden@richmond.gov.uk

Public Health: Ms Anna Raleigh, Public Health Consultant, Civic Centre, 44 York Street, Twickenham TW1 3BZ ☎ 020 8734 3014 ⌨ anna.raleigh@richmond.gov.uk

Street Scene: Mr Jon Freer, Assistant Director - Development & Street Scene, Civic Centre, 44 York Street, Twickenham TW1 3BZ ☎ 020 8891 7319 ⌨ j.freer@richmond.gov.uk

Sustainable Communities: Mr Robert Angus, Head of Development & Enforcement, Civic Centre, 44 York Street, Twickenham TW1 3BZ ☎ 020 8891 7271; 020 8891 7789 ⌨ r.angus@richmond.gov.uk

Sustainable Development: Miss Ishbel Murray, Assistant Director - Environment, Property, Parks & Sustainability, Civic Centre, 44 York Street, Twickenham TW1 3BZ ☎ 020 8891 7310 ⌨ ishbel.murray@richmond.gov.uk

Tourism: Ms Angela Ivey, Principal Tourism & Marketing Manager, Civic Centre, 44 York Street, Twickenham TW1 3BZ
☎ 020 8487 5047; 020 8891 7347 ◌ a.ivey@richmond.gov.uk

Traffic Management: Mr Graham Beattie, Assistant Director - Highways & Transport, Civic Centre, 44 York Street, Twickenham TW1 3BZ ☎ 020 8891 7309 ◌ graham.beattie@richmond.gov.uk

Transport: Mr Graham Beattie, Assistant Director - Highways & Transport, Civic Centre, 44 York Street, Twickenham TW1 3BZ
☎ 020 8891 7309 ◌ graham.beattie@richmond.gov.uk

Transport Planner: Mr Graham Beattie, Assistant Director - Highways & Transport, Civic Centre, 44 York Street, Twickenham TW1 3BZ ☎ 020 8891 7309 ◌ graham.beattie@richmond.gov.uk

Waste Collection and Disposal: Mr Jon Freer, Assistant Director - Environment, Civic Centre, 44 York Street, Twickenham TW1 3BZ ☎ 020 8891 7319 ◌ j.freer@richmond.gov.uk

Waste Management: Mr Jon Freer, Assistant Director - Environment, Civic Centre, 44 York Street, Twickenham TW1 3BZ
☎ 020 8891 7319 ◌ j.freer@richmond.gov.uk

Children's Play Areas: Mr David Allister, Head of Parks & Open Spaces, Civic Centre, 44 York Street, Twickenham TW1 3BZ
☎ 020 8831 6135 ◌ d.allister@richmond.gov.uk

COUNCILLORS

Mayor: Linnette, David (CON - Kew)
cllr.dlinnette@richmond.gov.uk

Deputy Mayor: Howard, Kate (CON - Hampton North)
cllr.khoward@richmond.gov.uk

Leader of the Council: True, Nicholas (CON - East Sheen)
cllr.lordtrue@richmond.gov.uk

Deputy Leader of the Council: Samuel, Geoffrey (CON - Hampton North)
cllr.gsamuel@richmond.gov.uk

Group Leader: Roberts, Gareth (LD - Hampton)
cllr.groberts@richmond.gov.uk

Acton, Geoff (LD - St Margaret's & North Twickenham)
cllr.gacton@richmond.gov.uk

Allen, Piers (LD - West Twickenham)
cllr.pallen@richmond.gov.uk

Arbour, Tony (CON - Hampton Wick)
cllr.tarbour@richmond.gov.uk

Avon, Paul (CON - Mortlake & Barnes Common)
cllr.pavon@richmond.gov.uk

Blakemore, Lisa (CON - North Richmond)
cllr.lblakemore@richmond.gov.uk

Bond, Meena (CON - Kew)
cllr.mbond@richmond.gov.uk

Boulton, Jane (CON - West Twickenham)
cllr.jboulton@richmond.gov.uk

Boyle, Mark (CON - Fulwell & Hampton Hill)
cllr.mboyle@richmond.gov.uk

Buckwell, Peter (CON - South Richmond)
cllr.pbuckwell@richmond.gov.uk

Butler, Margaret (CON - North Richmond)
cllr.mbutler@richmond.gov.uk

Butler, Alan (CON - Heathfield)
cllr.abutler@richmond.gov.uk

Cardy, Jonathan (LD - Fulwell & Hampton Hill)
cllr.jcardy@richmond.gov.uk

Chappell, Susan (CON - Twickenham Riverside)
cllr.schappell@richmond.gov.uk

Churchill, Jennifer (LD - Teddington)
cllr.jchurchill@richmond.gov.uk

Coombs, John (LD - Heathfield)
cllr.jcoombs@richmond.gov.uk

Curran, Gemma (CON - Mortlake & Barnes Common)
cllr.gcurran@richmond.gov.uk

Dias, Benedict (CON - Twickenham Riverside)
cllr.bdias@richmond.gov.uk

Ehmann, Alexander (LD - St Margaret's & North Twickenham)
cllr.aehmann@richmond.gov.uk

Elengorn, Martin (LD - Teddington)
cllr.melengorn@richmond.gov.uk

Elliot, Gareth (CON - Whitton)
cllr.gelliot@richmond.gov.uk

Elloy, Jerry (LD - Fulwell & Hampton Hill)
cllr.jelloy@richmond.gov.uk

Evans, Gareth (CON - Hampton Wick)
cllr.gevans@richmond.gov.uk

Fleming, Pamela (CON - South Richmond)
cllr.pfleming@richmond.gov.uk

Frost, Penelope (LD - Ham, Petersham & Richmond Riverside)
cllr.pfrost@richmond.gov.uk

Hambidge, Annie (CON - Heathfield)
cllr.ahambidge@richmond.gov.uk

Head, Clare (CON - South Twickenham)
cllr.chead@richmond.gov.uk

Healy, Grant (CON - Whitton)
cllr.ghealy@richmond.gov.uk

Hill, Helen (CON - Twickenham Riverside)
cllr.hhill@richmond.gov.uk

Hodgins, Paul (CON - Barnes)
cllr.phodgins@richmond.gov.uk

Horner, Monica (CON - Kew)
cllr.mhorner@richmond.gov.uk

Jaeger, Liz (LD - Whitton)
cllr.ljaeger@richmond.gov.uk

Khosa, Ben (LD - St Margaret's & North Twickenham)
cllr.bkhosa@richmond.gov.uk

Knight, Stephen (LD - Teddington)
cllr.sknight@richmond.gov.uk

Lee-Parsons, Helen (LD - West Twickenham)
cllr.hlee-parsons@richmond.gov.uk

Locke, Geraldine (LD - Hampton Wick)

Loveland, Jean (CON - Ham, Petersham & Richmond Riverside)
cllr.jloveland@richmond.gov.uk

Marcel, Brian (CON - East Sheen)
cllr.bmarcel@richmond.gov.uk

RICHMOND UPON THAMES

Marlow, David (CON - South Twickenham)
cllr.dmarlow@richmond.gov.uk

Martin, Richard (CON - Mortlake & Barnes Common)
cllr.rmartin@richmond.gov.uk

Nicholson, Suzette (LD - Hampton)
cllr.snicholson@richmond.gov.uk

O'Malley, Thomas (CON - South Richmond)
cllr.tomalley@richmond.gov.uk

Palmer, Rita (CON - Barnes)
cllr.rpalmer@richmond.gov.uk

Percival, Christine (CON - Barnes)
cllr.cpercival@richmond.gov.uk

Porter, David (CON - South Twickenham)
cllr.dporter@richmond.gov.uk

Sale, Petra (CON - Hampton)
cllr.psale@richmond.gov.uk

Seymour, Martin (CON - Hampton North)
cllr.mseymour@richmond.gov.uk

Speak, Stephen (CON - North Richmond)
democratic.services@richmond.gov.uk

Thompson, Robert (CON - East Sheen)
cllr.rthompson@richmond.gov.uk

Tippett, Sarah (CON - Ham, Petersham & Richmond Riverside)
cllr.stippett@richmond.gov.uk

POLITICAL COMPOSITION
CON: 38, LD: 16

COMMITTEE CHAIRS

Audit: Mr Jonathan Cardy

Health & Wellbeing: Ms Christine Percival

Planning: Ms Gemma Curran

Richmondshire   D

Richmondshire District Council, Mercury House, Station Road, Richmond DL10 4JX
☎ 01748 829100 🖷 01748 825071 ✆ enquiries@richmondshire.gov.uk
🖵 www.richmondshire.gov.uk

FACTS AND FIGURES
Parliamentary Constituencies: Richmond (Yorks)
EU Constituencies: Yorkshire and the Humber
Election Frequency: Elections are of whole council

PRINCIPAL OFFICERS

Chief Executive: Mr Tony Clark, Chief Executive, Mercury House, Station Road, Richmond DL10 4JX ☎ 01748 829100; 01748 826186 ✆ julia.chapman@richmondshire.gov.uk

Senior Management: Mr Colin Dales, Corporate Director - Operational Services, Mercury House, Station Road, Richmond DL10 4JX ☎ 01748 829100; 01748 826186 ✆ colin.dales@richmondshire.gov.uk

Senior Management: Mr Callum McKeon, Corporate Director - Strategy & Regulatory / Monitoring Officer, Mercury House, Station Road, Richmond DL10 4JX ☎ 01748 829100; 01748 826186 ✆ callum.mckeon@richmondshire.gov.uk

Senior Management: Ms Sian Moore, Corporate Director - Resources & S151 Officer, Mercury House, Station Road, Richmond DL10 4JX ☎ 01748 829100; 01748 826186 ✆ sian.moore@richmondshire.gov.uk

Community Safety: Ms Pat Wilson, Business & Community Safety Manager, Mercury House, Station Road, Richmond DL10 4JX ☎ 01748 829100; 01748 826186 ✆ pat.wilson@richmondshire.gov.uk

Computer Management: Mr Graeme Thistlethwaite, ICT & Business Change Manager, Mercury House, Station Road, Richmond DL10 4JX ☎ 01748 829100 ✆ graeme.thistlethwaite@richmondshire.gov.uk

Customer Service: Ms Carole Dew, Customer Services Manager, Mercury House, Station Road, Richmond DL10 4JX ☎ 01748 829100; 01748 826186 ✆ carole.dew@richmondshire.gov.uk

Electoral Registration: Ms Sandra Hullah, Electoral Services Officer, Mercury House, Station Road, Richmond DL10 4JX ☎ 01748 829100; 01748 826186 ✆ sandra.hullah@richmondshire.gov.uk

Emergency Planning: Mr Callum McKeon, Corporate Director - Strategy & Regulatory / Monitoring Officer, Mercury House, Station Road, Richmond DL10 4JX ☎ 01748 829100; 01748 826186 ✆ callum.mckeon@richmondshire.gov.uk

Environmental Health: Mr Stuart Wears, Environmental Health Manager, Mercury House, Station Road, Richmond DL10 4JX ☎ 01748 829100 ✆ stuart.wears@richmondshire.gov.uk

Finance: Ms Sian Moore, Corporate Director - Resources & S151 Officer, Mercury House, Station Road, Richmond DL10 4JX ☎ 01748 829100; 01748 826186 ✆ sian.moore@richmondshire.gov.uk

Grounds Maintenance: Mr Gary Hudson, Open Spaces & Amenities Manager, Mercury House, Station Road, Richmond DL10 4JX ☎ 01748 829100; 01748 826186 ✆ gary.hudson@richmondshire.gov.uk

Health and Safety: Mr Tim Burrows, Health & Safety Advisor, Mercury House, Station Road, Richmond DL10 4JX ☎ 01748 829100; 01748 826186 ✆ tim.burrows@richmondshire.gov.uk

Housing: Mr Colin Dales, Corporate Director - Operational Services, Mercury House, Station Road, Richmond DL10 4JX ☎ 01748 829100; 01748 826186 ✆ colin.dales@richmondshire.gov.uk

Housing Maintenance: Ms Sara Smith, Landlord Services Manager, Mercury House, Station Road, Richmond DL10 4JX ☎ 01748 829100; 01748 826186 ✆ sara.smith@richmondshire.gov.uk

Leisure and Cultural Services: Mr Colin Dales, Corporate Director - Operational Services, Mercury House, Station Road, Richmond DL10 4JX ☎ 01748 829100; 01748 826186 ✆ colin.dales@richmondshire.gov.uk

Licensing: Mr Stuart Wears, Environmental Health Manager, Mercury House, Station Road, Richmond DL10 4JX ☎ 01748 829100 🖰 stuart.wears@richmondshire.gov.uk

Member Services: Mr Michael Dowson, Democratic Services Manager, Mercury House, Station Road, Richmond DL10 4JX ☎ 01748 829100; 01748 826186 🖰 michael.dowson@richmondshire.gov.uk

Parking: Mr Gary Hudson, Open Spaces & Amenities Manager, Mercury House, Station Road, Richmond DL10 4JX ☎ 01748 829100; 01748 826186 🖰 gary.hudson@richmondshire.gov.uk

Personnel / HR: Ms Laura Sellers, HR & Payroll Manager, Mercury House, Station Road, Richmond DL10 4JX ☎ 01718 829100 🖰 laura.sellers@richmondshire.gov.uk

Planning: Mr Peter Featherstone, Planning & Development Manager, Mercury House, Station Road, Richmond DL10 4JX ☎ 01748 829100; 01748 826186 🖰 peter.featherstone@richmondshire.gov.uk

Recycling & Waste Minimisation: Ms Amanda Dyson, Waste & Street Scene Manager, Mercury House, Station Road, Richmond DL10 4JX ☎ 01748 829100 🖰 amanda.dyson@richmondshire.gov.uk

Street Scene: Ms Amanda Dyson, Waste & Street Scene Manager, Mercury House, Station Road, Richmond DL10 4JX ☎ 01748 829100 🖰 amanda.dyson@richmondshire.gov.uk

Transport: Ms Amanda Dyson, Waste & Street Scene Manager, Mercury House, Station Road, Richmond DL10 4JX ☎ 01748 829100 🖰 amanda.dyson@richmondshire.gov.uk

Waste Collection and Disposal: Ms Amanda Dyson, Waste & Street Scene Manager, Mercury House, Station Road, Richmond DL10 4JX ☎ 01748 829100 🖰 amanda.dyson@richmondshire.gov.uk

COUNCILLORS

Chair: Thornton-Berry, Caroline (CON - Penhill)
cllr.c.thornton-berry@richmondshire.gov.uk

Leader of the Council: Peacock, Yvonne (CON - Addlebrough)
cllr.y.peacock@richmondshire.gov.uk

Deputy Leader of the Council: Threlfall, Ian (CON - Brompton on Swale & Scorton)
cllr.i.threlfall@richmondshire.gov.uk

Amsden, John (IND - Bolton Castle)
cllr.j.amsden@richmondshire.gov.uk

Beal, Richard (IND - Reeth & Arkengarthdale)
cllr.r.beal@richmondshire.gov.uk

Blackie, John (IND - Hawes & High Abbotside)
cllr.j.blackie@richmondshire.gov.uk

Blows, Richard (CON - Swaledale)
cllr.r.blows@richmondshire.gov.uk

Cameron, Jamie (CON - Newsham with Eppleby)
cllr.j.cameron@richmondshire.gov.uk

Cullen, Paul (IND - Hipswell)
cllr.p.cullen@richmondshire.gov.uk

Curran DL, Linda (IND - Richmond West)
cllr.l.curran@richmondshire.gov.uk

Dale, Angie (IND - Colburn)
cllr.a.dale@richmondshire.gov.uk

Dawson, Campbell (CON - Barton)
cllr.c.dawson@richmondshire.gov.uk

Dickens, Louise (CON - Richmond East)
cllr.l.dickens@richmondshire.gov.uk

Duff, Tony (CON - Leyburn)
cllr.t.duff@richmondshire.gov.uk

Fairhurst, Susan (CON - Middleham)
cllr.s.fairhurst@richmondshire.gov.uk

Gibbs, Sam (CON - Croft)
cllr.s.gibbs@richmondshire.gov.uk

Gill, Danny (CON - Brompton on Swale & Scorton)
cllr.d.gill@richmondshire.gov.uk

Glover, William (CON - Colburn)
cllr.w.glover@richmondshire.gov.uk

Grant, Helen (IND - Scotton)
cllr.h.grant@richmondshire.gov.uk

Grose, Lawrence (CON - Hipswell)
cllr.l.grose@richmondshire.gov.uk

Heslop, William (IND - Gilling)
cllr.w.heslop@richmondshire.gov.uk

Hodgson, Lorraine (IND - Richmond Central)
cllr.l.hodgson@richmondshire.gov.uk

Linehan, Geoffrey (CON - Hornby Castle)
cllr.g.linehan@richmondshire.gov.uk

Lord, Russel (IND - Richmond East)
cllr.r.lord@richmondshire.gov.uk

Middlemiss, Patricia (CON - Scotton)
cllr.p.middlemiss@richmondshire.gov.uk

Ormston, Richard (CON - Lower Wensleydale)
cllr.r.ormston@richmondshire.gov.uk

Parsons, Stuart (IND - Richmond West)
cllr.s.parsons@richmondshire.gov.uk

Partridge, Bev (CON - Colburn)
cllr.b.partridge@richmondshire.gov.uk

Sedgwick, Karin (CON - Leyburn)
cllr.k.sedgwick@richmondshire.gov.uk

Thompson, Angus (CON - Middleton Tyas)
cllr.a.thompson@richmondshire.gov.uk

Wilson-Petch, Jimmy (CON - Melsonby)
cllr.j.wilson-petch@richmondshire.gov.uk

World, Clive (LD - Richmond Central)
cllr.c.world@richmondshire.gov.uk

Wyrill, Stephen (CON - Catterick)
cllr.s.wyrill@richmondshire.gov.uk

Young, Simon (CON - Catterick)
cllr.s.young@richmondshire.gov.uk

POLITICAL COMPOSITION
CON: 22, IND: 11, LD: 1

RICHMONDSHIRE

COMMITTEE CHAIRS

Audit: Mr Geoffrey Linehan

Licensing: Mr Jimmy Wilson-Petch

Planning: Mr Campbell Dawson

Rochdale   M

Rochdale Metropolitan Borough Council, Municipal Offices, Smith Street, Rochdale OL16 1LQ
☎ 01706 647474 ⌨ council@rochdale.gov.uk 🖥 www.rochdale.gov.uk

FACTS AND FIGURES
Parliamentary Constituencies: Heywood and Middleton, Rochdale
EU Constituencies: North West
Election Frequency: Elections are by thirds

PRINCIPAL OFFICERS

Chief Executive: Mr Steve Rumbelow, Chief Executive, Municipal Offices, Smith Street, Rochdale OL16 1LQ ☎ 01706 924703 ⌨ steve.rumbelow@rochdale.gov.uk

Senior Management: Ms Sheila Downey, Director - Adult Care, Floor 3, Number One Riverside, Smith Street, Rochdale OL16 1XU ☎ 01706 922975 ⌨ sheila.downey@rochdale.gov.uk

Senior Management: Ms Andrea Fallon, Director - Public Health & Wellbeing, Number One Riverside, Smith Street, Rochdale OL16 1XU ⌨ andrea.fallon@rochdale.gov.uk

Senior Management: Ms Gail Hopper, Director - Children's Services, Floor 2, Number One Riverside, Smith Street, Rochdale OL16 1XU ☎ 01706 825000 ⌨ gail.hopper@rochdale.gov.uk

Senior Management: Mrs Pauline Kane, Director - Resources, Floor 2, Number One Riverside, Smith Street, Rochdale OL16 1XU ☎ 01706 925002 ⌨ pauline.kane@rochdale.gov.uk

Senior Management: Mr John Searle, Director - Economy, Number One Riverside, Smith Street, Rochdale OL16 1XU ⌨ john.searle@rochdale.gov.uk

Senior Management: Mr Mark Widdup, Director - Neighbourhoods, Number One Riverside, Smith Street, Rochdale OL16 1XU ☎ 01706 925284 ⌨ mark.widdup@rochdale.gov.uk

Access Officer / Social Services (Disability): Ms Sheila Downey, Director - Adult Care, Floor 3, Number One Riverside, Smith Street, Rochdale OL16 1XU ☎ 01706 922975 ⌨ sheila.downey@rochdale.gov.uk

Architect, Building / Property Services: Mr Len Windle, Head of Facilities Management, Building Surveying & Technical, Floor 2, Number One Riverside, Smith Street, Rochdale OL16 1XU ☎ 01706 923346 ⌨ len.windle@rochdale.gov.uk

Building Control: Mr David Oakes, Building Control Manager, Floor 3, Number One Riverside, Smith Street, Rochdale OL16 1XU ☎ 01706 924324 ⌨ david.oakes@rochdale.gov.uk

Catering Services: Mr Peter Gurney, Facilities Manager - Catering, Municipal Offices, Smith Street, Rochdale OL16 1LQ ☎ 01706 925775 ⌨ peter.gurney@rochdale.gov.uk

Children / Youth Services: Ms Sandra Bowness, Assistant Director - Early Help & Schools, Floor 2, Number One Riverside, Smith Street, Rochdale OL16 1XU ☎ 01706 925159 ⌨ sandra.bowness@rochdale.gov.uk

Civil Registration: Mrs Aileen Bollard, Superintendent Registrar, PO Box 15, Ground Floor, Town Hall, Rochdale OL16 1AB ☎ 01706 924779 ⌨ aileen.bollard@rochdale.gov.uk

PR / Communications: Mr Danny Brierley, Head of Communications, Floor 2, Number One Riverside, Smith Street, Rochdale OL16 1XU ☎ 01706 925724 ⌨ danny.brierley@rochdale.gov.uk

Community Safety: Mr Mark Dalzell, Head of Neighbourhood Services, Floor 3, Number One Riverside, Smith Street, Rochdale OL16 1XU ☎ 01706 924987 ⌨ mark.dalzell@rochdale.gov.uk

Consumer Protection and Trading Standards: Ms Nicola Rogers, Service Manager - Communities, Floor 3, Number One Riverside, Smith Street, Rochdale OL16 1XU ☎ 01706 924124 ⌨ nicola.rogers@rochdale.gov.uk

Customer Service: Mr Julian Massel, Assistant Director - Information, Customers & Communities, Floor 2, Number One Riverside, Smith Street, Rochdale OL16 1XU ☎ 01706 925015 ⌨ julian.massel@rochdale.gov.uk

Economic Development: Ms Susan Ayres, Economic Affairs Manager, Floor 3, Number One Riverside, Smith Street, Rochdale OL16 1XU ☎ 01706 925636 ⌨ susan.ayres@rochdale.gov.uk

Education: Ms Gail Hopper, Director - Children's Services, Floor 2, Number One Riverside, Smith Street, Rochdale OL16 1XU ☎ 01706 825000 ⌨ gail.hopper@rochdale.gov.uk

Electoral Registration: Mrs Clare Poole, Electoral Services Manager, Town Hall, Rochdale OL16 1AB ☎ 01706 924759; 0844 963 2311 ⌨ clare.poole@rochdale.gov.uk

Emergency Planning: Mr Mark Dalzell, Head of Neighbourhood Services, Floor 3, Number One Riverside, Smith Street, Rochdale OL16 1XU ☎ 01706 924987 ⌨ mark.dalzell@rochdale.gov.uk

Energy Management: Ms Donna Bowler, Assistant Director - Place, Floor 2, Number One Riverside, Smith Street, Rochdale OL16 1XU ☎ 01706 924849 ⌨ donna.bowler@rochdale.gov.uk

Environmental / Technical Services: Mr Mark Widdup, Director - Neighbourhoods, Number One Riverside, Smith Street, Rochdale OL16 1XU ☎ 01706 925284 ⌨ mark.widdup@rochdale.gov.uk

Environmental Health: Ms Nicola Rogers, Service Manager - Communities, Floor 3, Number One Riverside, Smith Street, Rochdale OL16 1XU ☎ 01706 924124 ⌨ nicola.rogers@rochdale.gov.uk

Estates, Property & Valuation: Mr Peter Gregory, Senior Property Manager - Estates, Floor 2, Number One Riverside, Smith Street, Rochdale OL16 1XU ☎ 01706 923271 ⌨ peter.gregory@rochdale.gov.uk

Facilities: Ms Donna Bowler, Assistant Director - Place, Floor 2, Number One Riverside, Smith Street, Rochdale OL16 1XU ☎ 01706 924849 ⏚ donna.bowler@rochdale.gov.uk

Finance: Mrs Pauline Kane, Director - Resources, Floor 2, Number One Riverside, Smith Street, Rochdale OL16 1XU ☎ 01706 925002 ⏚ pauline.kane@rochdale.gov.uk

Fleet Management: Mr Martin Taylor, Service Manager - Environmental Management, Green Lane, Heywood, Rochdale OL10 2DY ☎ 01706 922004 ⏚ martin.taylor@rochdale.gov.uk

Grounds Maintenance: Mr Martin Taylor, Service Manager - Environmental Management, Green Lane, Heywood, Rochdale OL10 2DY ☎ 01706 922004 ⏚ martin.taylor@rochdale.gov.uk

Health and Safety: Ms Nancy Wilson, Corporate Safety Adviser, Floor 2, Number One Riverside, Smith Street, Rochdale OL16 1XU ☎ 01706 925057 ⏚ nancy.wilson@rochdale.gov.uk

Highways: Mr Steve Reay, Highways Manager, Floor 2, Number One Riverside, Smith Street, Rochdale OL16 1XU ☎ 01706 924461 ⏚ steve.reay@rochdale.gov.uk

Home Energy Conservation: Ms Donna Bowler, Assistant Director - Place, Floor 2, Number One Riverside, Smith Street, Rochdale OL16 1XU ☎ 01706 924849 ⏚ donna.bowler@rochdale.gov.uk

Housing: Ms Donna Bowler, Assistant Director - Place, Floor 2, Number One Riverside, Smith Street, Rochdale OL16 1XU ☎ 01706 924849 ⏚ donna.bowler@rochdale.gov.uk

Legal: Mr David Wilcocks, Assistant Director - Legal, Governance & Workforce, Brook House, Oldham Road, Middleton, Manchester M24 1AY ☎ 01706 924703 ⏚ david.wilcocks@rochdale.gov.uk

Leisure and Cultural Services: Ms Andrea Fallon, Director - Public Health & Wellbeing, Number One Riverside, Smith Street, Rochdale OL16 1XU andrea.fallon@rochdale.gov.uk

Licensing: Mrs Beverley Wilkinson, Service Manager - Licensing, Floor 3, Number One Riverside, Smith Street, Rochdale OL16 1XU ☎ 01706 924178 ⏚ beverley.wilkinson@rochdale.gov.uk

Lifelong Learning: Ms Sandra Bowness, Assistant Director - Early Help & Schools, Floor 2, Number One Riverside, Smith Street, Rochdale OL16 1XU ☎ 01706 925159 ⏚ sandra.bowness@rochdale.gov.uk

Lighting: Mr Jonathan Hartley, Street Lighting Client Team Manager, Floor 2, Number One Riverside, Smith Street, Rochdale OL16 1XU ☎ 0161 770 1681 ⏚ jonathan.hartley@rochdale.gov.uk

Member Services: Mr Mark Hardman, Governance & Committee Manager, Floor 2, Number One Riverside, Smith Street, Rochdale OL16 1XU ☎ 01706 824704 ⏚ mark.hardman@rochdale.gov.uk

Parking: Mr Steve Reay, Highways Manager, Floor 2, Number One Riverside, Smith Street, Rochdale OL16 1XU ☎ 01706 924461 ⏚ steve.reay@rochdale.gov.uk

Personnel / HR: Ms Margo Kane, Head of Workforce & Organisational Development, Floor 2, Number One Riverside, Smith Street, Rochdale OL16 1XU ☎ 01706 925776 ⏚ margo.kane@rochdale.gov.uk

Planning: Mr Mark Robinson, Assistant Director - Planning & Development, Floor 3, Number One Riverside, Smith Street, Rochdale OL16 1XU ☎ 01706 924308; 01706 924185 ⏚ mark.robinson@rochdale.gov.uk

Procurement: Mrs Pauline Kane, Director - Resources, Floor 2, Number One Riverside, Smith Street, Rochdale OL16 1XU ☎ 01706 925002 ⏚ pauline.kane@rochdale.gov.uk

Public Libraries: Mr Julian Massel, Assistant Director - Information, Customers & Communities, Floor 2, Number One Riverside, Smith Street, Rochdale OL16 1XU ☎ 01706 925015 ⏚ julian.massel@rochdale.gov.uk

Recycling & Waste Minimisation: Mr Martin Taylor, Service Manager - Environmental Management, Green Lane, Heywood, Rochdale OL10 2DY ☎ 01706 922004 ⏚ martin.taylor@rochdale.gov.uk

Regeneration: Mr John Searle, Director - Economy, Floor 3, Number One Riverside, Smith Street, Rochdale OL16 1XU ⏚ john.searle@rochdale.gov.uk

Road Safety: Mr Steve Reay, Highways Manager, Floor 2, Number One Riverside, Smith Street, Rochdale OL16 1XU ☎ 01706 924461 ⏚ steve.reay@rochdale.gov.uk

Social Services (Adult): Ms Sheila Downey, Director - Adult Care, Floor 3, Number One Riverside, Smith Street, Rochdale OL16 1XU ☎ 01706 922975 ⏚ sheila.downey@rochdale.gov.uk

Public Health: Ms Andrea Fallon, Director - Public Health & Wellbeing, Number One Riverside, Smith Street, Rochdale OL16 1XU andrea.fallon@rochdale.gov.uk

Staff Training: Ms Margo Kane, Head of Workforce & Organisational Development, Floor 2, Number One Riverside, Smith Street, Rochdale OL16 1XU ☎ 01706 925776 ⏚ margo.kane@rochdale.gov.uk

Street Scene: Mr Martin Taylor, Service Manager - Environmental Management, Green Lane, Heywood, Rochdale OL10 2DY ☎ 01706 922004 ⏚ martin.taylor@rochdale.gov.uk

Sustainable Development: Mr Mark Robinson, Assistant Director - Planning & Development, Floor 3, Number One Riverside, Smith Street, Rochdale OL16 1XU ☎ 01706 924308; 01706 924185 ⏚ mark.robinson@rochdale.gov.uk

Tourism: Ms Susan Ayres, Economic Affairs Manager, Floor 3, Number One Riverside, Smith Street, Rochdale OL16 1XU ☎ 01706 925636 ⏚ susan.ayres@rochdale.gov.uk

Traffic Management: Mr Steve Reay, Highways Manager, Floor 2, Number One Riverside, Smith Street, Rochdale OL16 1XU ☎ 01706 924461 ⏚ steve.reay@rochdale.gov.uk

ROCHDALE

Transport: Mr Martin Taylor, Service Manager - Environmental Management, Green Lane, Heywood, Rochdale OL10 2DY
☎ 01706 922004 ⬦ martin.taylor@rochdale.gov.uk

Waste Collection and Disposal: Mr Martin Taylor, Service Manager - Environmental Management, Green Lane, Heywood, Rochdale OL10 2DY ☎ 01706 922004 ⬦ martin.taylor@rochdale.gov.uk

Waste Management: Mr Martin Taylor, Service Manager - Environmental Management, Green Lane, Heywood, Rochdale OL10 2DY ☎ 01706 922004 ⬦ martin.taylor@rochdale.gov.uk

Children's Play Areas: Mr Martin Taylor, Service Manager - Environmental Management, Green Lane, Heywood, Rochdale OL10 2DY ☎ 01706 922004 ⬦ martin.taylor@rochdale.gov.uk

COUNCILLORS

Mayor: Biant, Surinder (LAB - Spotland & Falinge)
surinder.biant@rochdale.gov.uk

Mayor: Dutton, Raymond (LAB - North Heywood)
raymond.dutton@rochdale.gov.uk

Deputy Mayor: Duckworth, Ian (CON - Bamford)
ian.duckworth@rochdale.gov.uk

Leader of the Council: Farnell, Richard (LAB - Balderstone & Kirkholt)
richard.farnell@rochdale.gov.uk

Deputy Leader of the Council: Beswick, Jacqueline (LAB - West Heywood)
jacqui.beswick@rochdale.gov.uk

Deputy Leader of the Council: Brett, Allen (LAB - Milkstone & Deeplish)
allen.brett@rochdale.gov.uk

Group Leader: Dearnley, Ashley (CON - Wardle & West Littleborough)
ashley.dearnley@rochdale.gov.uk

Ahmed, Iftikhar (LAB - Central Rochdale)
iftikhar.ahmed@rochdale.gov.uk

Ahmed, Shakil (LAB - Kingsway)
shakil.ahmed@rochdale.gov.uk

Ahmed, Ali (LAB - Central Rochdale)
ali.ahmed@rochdale.gov.uk

Ali, Daalat (LAB - Kingsway)
daalat.ali@rochdale.gov.uk

Ali, Sultan (LAB - Central Rochdale)
sultan.ali@rochdale.gov.uk

Bell, Andy (LAB - South Middleton)
andrew.bell@rochdale.gov.uk

Biant, Cecile (LAB - Spotland & Falinge)
cecile.biant@rochdale.gov.uk

Blundell, John (LAB - Smallbridge & Firgrove)
john.blundell@rochdale.gov.uk

Boriss, Malcolm (LAB - East Middleton)
malcolm.boriss@rochdale.gov.uk

Brosnan, Lynne (LAB - Kingsway)
lynne.brosnan@rochdale.gov.uk

Burke, Philip (LAB - West Middleton)
philip.burke@rochdale.gov.uk

Butterworth, Neil (LAB - Milnrow & Newhey)
neil.butterworth@rochdale.gov.uk

Clegg, Robert (CON - Wardle & West Littleborough)
robert.clegg@rochdale.gov.uk

Cocks, Wendy (LAB - Spotland & Falinge)
wendy.cocks@rochdale.gov.uk

Davidson, Irene (LD - Milnrow & Newhey)
irene.davidson@rochdale.gov.uk

Emmott, Susan (LAB - Hopwood Hall)
susan.emmott@rochdale.gov.uk

Emmott, Neil (LAB - West Middleton)
neil.emmott@rochdale.gov.uk

Emsley, Janet (LAB - Littleborough Lakeside)
janet.emsley@rochdale.gov.uk

Furlong, Christopher (LAB - North Middleton)
christopher.furlong@rochdale.gov.uk

Gartside, James (CON - Norden)
james.gartside@rochdale.gov.uk

Hartley, John (LAB - Littleborough Lakeside)
john.hartley@rochdale.gov.uk

Heakin, Kieran (LAB - Healey)
kieran.heakin@rochdale.gov.uk

Holly, Michael (CON - Norden)
michael.holly@rochdale.gov.uk

Hornby, Jean (LAB - Castleton)
jean.hornby@rochdale.gov.uk

Howard, Jane (CON - Bamford)
jane.howard@rochdale.gov.uk

Hussain, Aftab (LAB - Smallbridge & Firgrove)
aftab.hussain2@rochdale.gov.uk

Joinson, Peter (LAB - South Middleton)
peter.joinson@rochdale.gov.uk

Kelly, Andy (LD - Milnrow & Newhey)
andy.kelly@rochdale.gov.uk

Malcolm, Peter (LAB - West Heywood)
peter.malcolm@rochdale.gov.uk

Martin, Donna (LAB - East Middleton)
donna.martin@rochdale.gov.uk

McCarthy, Alan (LAB - West Heywood)
alanmmccarthy@btinternet.com

Meredith, Daniel (LAB - Balderstone & Kirkholt)
daniel.meredith@rochdale.gov.uk

Mir, Amna (LAB - Smallbridge & Firgrove)
amna.mir@rochdale.gov.uk

Nickson, Kathleen (LAB - Balderstone & Kirkholt)
kathleen.nickson@rochdale.gov.uk

O'Neill, Shaun (LAB - Healey)
shaun.o'neill@rochdale.gov.uk

O'Rourke, Liam (LAB - North Heywood)
liam.o'rourke@rochdale.gov.uk

Paolucci-Escobar, Rina (CON - Wardle & West Littleborough)
rina.paolucci@rochdale.gov.uk

Rashid, Aasim (LAB - Castleton)
aasim.rashid@rochdale.gov.uk

Robinson, Linda (LAB - Hopwood Hall)
linda.robinson@rochdale.gov.uk

Rowbotham, Sara (LAB - North Middleton)
sara.rowbotham@rochdale.gov.uk

Rush, Peter (LD - North Heywood)
peter.rush@rochdale.gov.uk

Sheerin, Billy (LAB - Castleton)
billy.sheerin@rochdale.gov.uk

Smith, Susan (LAB - West Middleton)
susan.smith@rochdale.gov.uk

Stott, Ann (CON - Littleborough Lakeside)
ann.stott2@rochdale.gov.uk

Sullivan, Patricia (CON - Bamford)
patricia.sullivan@rochdale.gov.uk

Wardle, Carol (LAB - Hopwood Hall)
carolwardle1@gmail.com

Wazir, Shah (LAB - Healey)
shah.wazir@rochdale.gov.uk

West, June (LAB - East Middleton)
june.west@rochdale.gov.uk

Williams, Peter (LAB - South Middleton)
peter.williams@rochdale.gov.uk

Williams, Donna (LAB - North Middleton)
donna.williams@rochdale.gov.uk

Winkler, Peter (CON - Norden)
peter.winkler@rochdale.gov.uk

Zaheer, Sameena (LAB - Milkstone & Deeplish)
sameena.zaheer@rochdale.gov.uk

Zaman, Mohammed (LAB - Milkstone & Deeplish)
mohammed.zaman@rochdale.gov.uk

POLITICAL COMPOSITION
LAB: 47, CON: 10, LD: 3

COMMITTEE CHAIRS

Audit: Mr Liam O'Rourke

Communities, Regeneration & Environment: Mr Neil Butterworth

Health & Wellbeing: Ms Janet Emsley

Health, Schools & Care: Ms Sara Rowbotham

Planning & Licensing: Ms Carol Wardle

Rochford   D

Rochford District Council, Council Offices, South Street, Rochford SS4 1BW
☎ 01702 546366 🖷 01702 545737 ✆ information@rochford.gov.uk
🖳 www.rochford.gov.uk

FACTS AND FIGURES
Parliamentary Constituencies: Rayleigh and Wickford, Rochford and Southend East
EU Constituencies: Eastern
Election Frequency: Elections are by thirds

PRINCIPAL OFFICERS

Chief Executive: Mr Shaun Scrutton, Managing Director & Head of Paid Service, Council Offices, South Street, Rochford SS4 1BW
☎ 01702 318100 ✆ shaun.scrutton@rochford.gov.uk

Senior Management: Mr John Bostock, Assistant Director - Democratic Services, Council Offices, South Street, Rochford SS4 1BW ☎ 01702 318140 ✆ john.bostock@rochford.gov.uk

Senior Management: Mr Matt Harwood-White, Assistant Director - Commercial Services, Council Offices, South Street, Rochford SS4 1BW ☎ 01702 318164 ✆ matt.harwoodwhite@rochford.gov.uk

Senior Management: Mr Marcus Hotten, Assistant Director - Environmental Services, Council Offices, South Street, Rochford SS4 1BW ☎ 01702 318117 ✆ marcus.hotten@rochford.gov.uk

Senior Management: Mr Nicholas Khan, Executive Director, Council Offices, South Street, Rochford SS4 1BW ☎ 01702 318169 ✆ nicholas.khan@rochford.gov.uk

Senior Management: Ms Angela Law, Assistant Director - Legal Services, Council Offices, South Street, Rochford SS4 1BW
☎ 01702 318131 ✆ angela.law@rochford.gov.uk

Senior Management: Mr Robert Manning, Section 151 Officer, Council Offices, South Street, Rochford SS4 1BW ☎ 01702 546366 ✆ robert.manning@rochford.gov.uk

Senior Management: Ms Louisa Moss, Assistant Director - Housing & Community Services, Council Offices, South Street, Rochford SS4 1BW ✆ louisa.moss@rochford.gov.uk

Senior Management: Mrs Dawn Tribe, Assistant Director - Customer, Revenues & Benefits Services, Council Offices, South Street, Rochford SS4 1BW ☎ 01702 318098 ✆ dawn.tribe@rochford.gov.uk

Building Control: Mr Steve Tonge, Senior Building Control Officer, Council Offices, South Street, Rochford SS4 1BW
☎ 01702 546366 ✆ steve.tonge@rochford.gov.uk

PR / Communications: Ms Laura Bliss, Senior Corporate Communications Officer, Council Offices, South Street, Rochford SS4 1BW ☎ 01702 318139 ✆ laura.bliss@rochford.gov.uk

Community Safety: Mr Graham Browne, Community Safety Officer, Council Offices, South Street, Rochford SS4 1BW
☎ 01702 546366 ✆ graham.browne@rochford.gov.uk

Computer Management: Mr Andrew Mowbray, Assistant Director - Transformational Services, Council Offices, South Street, Rochford SS4 1BW ☎ 01702 318402 ✆ andrew.mowbray@rochford.gov.uk

Contracts: Ms Vanessa Yuen-Roberts, Procurement Co-ordinator, Council Offices, South Street, Rochford SS4 1BW ☎ 01702 318080 ✆ vanessa.yuen-roberts@rochford.gov.uk

Customer Service: Mrs Sarah Orchard, Customer Service Supervisor, Council Offices, South Street, Rochford SS4 1BW
☎ 01702 318133 ✆ sarah.orchard@rochford.gov.uk

ROCHFORD

Economic Development: Mrs Paula Chapman, Economic Development Officer, Council Offices, South Street, Rochford SS4 1BW ☎ 01702 318060 ◌ paula.chapman@rochford.gov.uk

Electoral Registration: Ms Karen Bridge, Electoral Services Manager, Council Offices, South Street, Rochford SS4 1BW ☎ 01702 318136; 01702 545737 ◌ karen.bridge@rochford.gov.uk

Emergency Planning: Mr Jeff Stacey, Emergency Planning & Business Continuity Officer, Council Offices, South Street, Rochford SS4 1BW ☎ 01702 318132 ◌ jeff.stacey@rochford.gov.uk

Environmental / Technical Services: Mr Martin Howlett, Principal Environmental Officer, Council Offices, South Street, Rochford SS4 1BW ☎ 01702 318049 ◌ martin.howlett@rochford.gov.uk

Environmental Health: Mr Andrew Paddon, Senior Environmental Officer, Council Offices, South Street, Rochford SS4 1BW ☎ 01702 318056 ◌ andrew.paddon@rochford.gov.uk

Estates, Property & Valuation: Mr Alan Thomas, Asset Manager, Council Offices, South Street, Rochford SS4 1BW ☎ 01702 546366 ◌ alan.thomas@rochford.gov.uk

Grounds Maintenance: Mr Marcus Hotten, Assistant Director - Environmental Services, Council Offices, South Street, Rochford SS4 1BW ☎ 01702 318117 ◌ marcus.hotten@rochford.gov.uk

Health and Safety: Mr Robert French, Health & Safety Officer, Council Offices, South Street, Rochford SS4 1BW ☎ 01702 546366 ◌ robert.french@rochford.gov.uk

Housing: Ms Jeanette Hurrell, Senior Housing & Homeless Officer, Council Offices, South Street, Rochford SS4 1BW ☎ 01702 318069 ◌ jeanette.hurrell@rochford.gov.uk

Legal: Ms Angela Law, Assistant Director - Legal Services, Council Offices, South Street, Rochford SS4 1BW ☎ 01702 318131 ◌ angela.law@rochford.gov.uk

Leisure and Cultural Services: Mr Mark Aldous, Sports Development Officer, Council Offices, South Street, Rochford SS4 1BW ☎ 01702 318121 ◌ mark.aldous@rochford.gov.uk

Licensing: Ms Jan Fowler, Senior Licensing Officer, Civic Suite, 2 Hockley Road, Rayleigh SS6 8EB ☎ 01702 318058 ◌ jan.fowler@rochford.gov.uk

Member Services: Mr John Bostock, Assistant Director - Democratic Services, Council Offices, South Street, Rochford SS4 1BW ☎ 01702 318140 ◌ john.bostock@rochford.gov.uk

Parking: Mr Jonathan Desmond, Assistant Transportation Manager, Civic Suite, 2 Hockley Road, Rayleigh SS6 8EB ☎ 01268 798605 ◌ jonathan.desmond@rochford.gov.uk

Partnerships: Mr Andrew Lowing, Strategic Partnership Officer, Council Offices, South Street, Rochford SS4 1BW ☎ 01702 318061 ◌ andrew.lowing@rochford.gov.uk

Personnel / HR: Ms Nicky Amor, HR Business Partner, Council Offices, South Street, Rochford SS4 1BW ☎ 01702 546366 ◌ nicky.amor@rochford.gov.uk

Planning: Mr Mike Stranks, Team Leader - Development Control, Council Offices, South Street, Rochford SS4 1BW ☎ 01702 546366 ◌ mike.stranks@rochford.gov.uk

Recycling & Waste Minimisation: Ms Lesley Athey, Principal Street Scene Officer, Council Offices, South Street, Rochford SS4 1BW ☎ 01702 546366 ◌ lesley.athey@rochford.gov.uk

Staff Training: Ms Nicky Amor, HR Business Partner, Council Offices, South Street, Rochford SS4 1BW ☎ 01702 546366 ◌ nicky.amor@rochford.gov.uk

Street Scene: Ms Lesley Athey, Principal Street Scene Officer, Council Offices, South Street, Rochford SS4 1BW ☎ 01702 546366 ◌ lesley.athey@rochford.gov.uk

Transport: Mr Jonathan Desmond, Assistant Transportation Manager, Civic Suite, 2 Hockley Road, Rayleigh SS6 8EB ☎ 01268 798605 ◌ jonathan.desmond@rochford.gov.uk

Waste Collection and Disposal: Ms Lesley Athey, Principal Street Scene Officer, Council Offices, South Street, Rochford SS4 1BW ☎ 01702 546366 ◌ lesley.athey@rochford.gov.uk

Waste Management: Ms Lesley Athey, Principal Street Scene Officer, Council Offices, South Street, Rochford SS4 1BW ☎ 01702 546366 ◌ lesley.athey@rochford.gov.uk

COUNCILLORS

Chair: Weston, Carole (CON - Hockley & Ashingdon)
cllrcarole.weston@rochford.gov.uk

Leader of the Council: Cutmore, Terry (CON - Hockley & Ashingdon)
cllrterry.cutmore@rochford.gov.uk

Deputy Leader of the Council: Steptoe, Mike (CON - Roche South)
cllrmike.steptoe@rochford.gov.uk

Group Leader: Hookway, Neil (UKIP - Foulness & The Wakerings)
cllrneil.hookway@rochford.gov.uk

Black, Chris (LD - Downhall & Rawreth)
cllrchris.black@rochford.gov.uk

Burton, Jamie (IND - Wheatley)
cllrjamie.burton@rochford.gov.uk

Butcher, Lesley (CON - Hawkwell East)
cllrlesley.butcher@rochford.gov.uk

Carter, Michael (CON - Hockley & Ashingdon)
cllrmichael.carter@rochford.gov.uk

Cassar, Irena (R - Hockley)
cllrirena.cassar@rochford.gov.uk

Cooper, Nicholas (UKIP - Roche North & Rural)
cllrnicholas.cooper@rochford.gov.uk

Dray, Robin (CON - Wheatley)
cllrrobin.dray@rochford.gov.uk

Efde, Daniel (UKIP - Foulness & The Wakerings)
cllrdaniel.efde@rochford.gov.uk

Eves, Adrian (R - Hockley)
cllradrian.eves@rochford.gov.uk

Gooding, Julie (CON - Hawkwell West)
cllrjulie.gooding@rochford.gov.uk

Griffin, John (CON - Wheatley)
cllrjohn.griffin@rochford.gov.uk

Hazlewood, Brian (CON - Hockley)
cllrbrian.hazlewood@rochford.gov.uk

Hoy, Diane (GRN - Hullbridge)
cllrdiane.hoy@rochford.gov.uk

Hoy, Michael (GRN - Hullbridge)
cllrmichael.hoy@rochford.gov.uk

Hughes, Tina (UKIP - Foulness & The Wakerings)
cllrtina.hughes@rochford.gov.uk

Ioannou, George (CON - Roche North & Rural)
cllrgeorge.ioannou@rochford.gov.uk

Lucas-Gill, Mike (CON - Roche South)
cllrmike.lucas-gill@rochford.gov.uk

Lumley, June (CON - Sweyne Park & Grange)
cllrjune.lumley@rochford.gov.uk

Mason, Christine (R - Hawkwell West)
cllrchristine.mason@rochford.gov.uk

Mason, John (R - Hawkwell West)
cllrjohn.mason@rochford.gov.uk

Mason, Elliot (R - Hawkwell East)
cllrelliot.mason@rochford.gov.uk

Merrick, David (CON - Trinity)
cllrdavid.merrick@rochford.gov.uk

Milne, Robert (CON - Lodge)
cllrbob.milne@rochford.gov.uk

Mountain, Toby (R - Sweyne Park & Grange)
cllrtoby.mountain@rochford.gov.uk

Newport, James (LD - Sweyne Park & Grange)
cllrjames.newport@rochford.gov.uk

Oatham, Ron (LD - Downhall & Rawreth)
cllrron.oatham@rochford.gov.uk

Roe, Cheryl (CON - Trinity)
cllrcheryl.roe@rochford.gov.uk

Shaw, Laureen (CON - Roche North & Rural)
cllrlaureen.shaw@rochford.gov.uk

Smith, Simon (CON - Lodge)
cllrsimon.smith@rochford.gov.uk

Sperring, Dave (CON - Trinity)
cllrdave.sperring@rochford.gov.uk

Stanley, Chris (LD - Downhall & Rawreth)
cllrchris.stanley@rochford.gov.uk

Ward, Ian (CON - Lodge)
cllrian.ward@rochford.gov.uk

Webb, Mike (CON - Hawkwell East)
cllrmike.webb@rochford.gov.uk

Williams, Arthur (CON - Roche South)
cllrarthur.williams@rochford.gov.uk

Wilson, Stuart (GRN - Hullbridge)
cllrstuart.wilson@rochford.gov.uk

POLITICAL COMPOSITION
CON: 21, R: 6, LD: 4, UKIP: 4, GRN: 3, IND: 1

COMMITTEE CHAIRS

Audit: Mrs Lesley Butcher

Development: Mr Michael Carter

Licensing: Mr Mike Webb

Rossendale   D

Rossendale Borough Council, The Business Centre, Futures Park, Newchurch Road, Bacup OL13 0BB
☎ 01706 217777 ⌨ generalenquiries@rossendalebc.gov.uk
🖥 www.rossendale.gov.uk

FACTS AND FIGURES
Parliamentary Constituencies: Hyndburn, Rossendale and Darwen
EU Constituencies: North West
Election Frequency: Elections are by thirds

PRINCIPAL OFFICERS

Chief Executive: Mr Stuart Sugarman, Chief Executive, The Business Centre, Futures Park, Newchurch Road, Bacup OL13 0BB
☎ 01706 252440; 01706 873577
⌨ stuartsugarman@rossendalebc.gov.uk

Senior Management: Mrs Clare Birtwistle, Monitoring Officer, The Business Centre, Futures Park, Newchurch Road, Bacup OL13 0BB ☎ 01706 252438 ⌨ clarebirtwistle@rossendalebc.gov.uk

Senior Management: Ms Sarah Davies, Director - Business, The Business Centre, Futures Park, Newchurch Road, Bacup OL13 0BB ☎ 01706 252440 ⌨ sarahdavies@rossendalebc.gov.uk

Senior Management: Mr Phil Seddon, Head of Finance & Property, The Business Centre, Futures Park, Newchurch Road, Bacup OL13 0BB ☎ 01706 252465; 01706 873577
⌨ philseddon@rossendalebc.gov.uk

Architect, Building / Property Services: Mr Lee Childs, Property & Facilities Services Officer, The Business Centre, Futures Park, Bacup OL13 0BB ☎ 01706 252527; 01706 873577
⌨ leechilds@rossendalebc.gov.uk

Building Control: Mr Alan Dixon, District Building Control Officer, The Business Centre, Futures Park, Newchurch Road, Bacup OL13 0BB ☎ 01706 252525 ⌨ alandixon@rossendalebc.gov.uk

Building Control: Mr Andrew Pearson, District Building Control Officer, The Business Centre, Futures Park, Newchurch Road, Bacup OL13 0BB ☎ 01706 252524
⌨ andrewpearson@rossendalebc.gov.uk

PR / Communications: Ms Katie Gee, Corporate Officer, The Business Centre, Futures Park, Newchurch Road, Bacup OL13 0BB ☎ 01706 252554; 01706 873577 ⌨ katiegee@rossendalebc.gov.uk

Computer Management: Mr Andrew Buckle, Head of Customer Services & ICT, The Business Centre, Futures Park, Newchurch Road, Bacup OL13 0BB ☎ 01706 238606; 01706 873577
⌨ andrewbuckle@rossendalebc.gov.uk

ROSSENDALE

Consumer Protection and Trading Standards: Ms Tracy Brzozowski, Licensing & Enforcement Manager, The Business Centre, Futures Park, Newchurch Road, Bacup OL13 0BB
☎ 01706 238602 ⏎ tracybrzozowski@rossendalebc.gov.uk

Contracts: Mrs Clare Birtwistle, Monitoring Officer, The Business Centre, Futures Park, Newchurch Road, Bacup OL13 0BB
☎ 01706 252438 ⏎ clarebirtwistle@rossendalebc.gov.uk

Customer Service: Mr Andrew Buckle, Head of Customer Services & ICT, The Business Centre, Futures Park, Newchurch Road, Bacup OL13 0BB ☎ 01706 238606; 01706 873577
⏎ andrewbuckle@rossendalebc.gov.uk

Economic Development: Mr David Presto, Economic Development & External Funding Manager, The Business Centre, Futures Park, Newchurch Road, Bacup OL13 0BB
☎ 01706 252477; 01706 873577 ⏎ davidpresto@rossendalebc.gov.uk

E-Government: Mr Andrew Buckle, Head of Customer Services & ICT, The Business Centre, Futures Park, Newchurch Road, Bacup OL13 0BB ☎ 01706 238606; 01706 873577
⏎ andrewbuckle@rossendalebc.gov.uk

Electoral Registration: Ms Joanne Smith, Elections Manager, The Business Centre, Futures Park, Newchurch Road, Bacup OL13 0BB ☎ 01706 252461 ⏎ joannesmith@rossendalebc.gov.uk

Emergency Planning: Mrs Clare Law, HR Manager, The Business Centre, Futures Park, Newchurch Road, Bacup OL13 0BB
☎ 01706 252457 ⏎ clarelaw@rossendalebc.gov.uk

Energy Management: Mr Lee Childs, Property & Facilities Services Officer, The Business Centre, Futures Park, Bacup OL13 0BB
☎ 01706 252527; 01706 873577 ⏎ leechilds@rossendalebc.gov.uk

Environmental / Technical Services: Mr Paul McHenry, Head of Operations, Henrietta Street Depot, Bacup OL13 0AR
☎ 01706 252519 ⏎ paulmchenry@rossendalebc.gov.uk

Environmental Health: Mr Dave Pierce, Principal EHO, The Business Centre, Futures Park, Newchurch Road, Bacup OL13 0BB
☎ 01706 252560 ⏎ davidpierce@rossendalebc.gov.uk

Estates, Property & Valuation: Mr Lee Childs, Property & Facilities Services Officer, The Business Centre, Futures Park, Bacup OL13 0BB ☎ 01706 252527; 01706 873577
⏎ leechilds@rossendalebc.gov.uk

Events Manager: Ms Katie Gee, Corporate Officer, The Business Centre, Futures Park, Newchurch Road, Bacup OL13 0BB
☎ 01706 252554; 01706 873577 ⏎ katiegee@rossendalebc.gov.uk

Facilities: Mr Lee Childs, Property & Facilities Services Officer, The Business Centre, Futures Park, Bacup OL13 0BB
☎ 01706 252527; 01706 873577 ⏎ leechilds@rossendalebc.gov.uk

Finance: Mr Phil Seddon, Head of Finance & Property, The Business Centre, Futures Park, Newchurch Road, Bacup OL13 0BB
☎ 01706 252465; 01706 873577 ⏎ philseddon@rossendalebc.gov.uk

Fleet Management: Ms Christine Chadderton, Transport Co-ordinator, Henrietta Street Depot, Bacup OL13 0AR
☎ 01706 878660 ⏎ christinechadderton@rossendalebc.gov.uk

Fleet Management: Mr Paul McHenry, Head of Operations, Henrietta Street Depot, Bacup OL13 0AR ☎ 01706 252519
⏎ paulmchenry@rossendalebc.gov.uk

Grounds Maintenance: Mr Paul McHenry, Head of Operations, Henrietta Street Depot, Bacup OL13 0AR ☎ 01706 252519
⏎ paulmchenry@rossendalebc.gov.uk

Health and Safety: Mr Steve Tomlinson, Health & Safety Officer, The Business Centre, Futures Park, Newchurch Road, Bacup OL13 0BB ☎ 01706 873577 ⏎ stevetomlinson@rossendalebc.gov.uk

Legal: Mrs Clare Birtwistle, Monitoring Officer, The Business Centre, Futures Park, Newchurch Road, Bacup OL13 0BB
☎ 01706 252438 ⏎ clarebirtwistle@rossendalebc.gov.uk

Leisure and Cultural Services: Mr Ken Masser, General Manager, The Business Centre, Futures Park, Newchurch Road, Bacup OL13 0BB ☎ 01706 242319 ⏎ ken.masser@rossendalebc.gov.uk

Licensing: Ms Tracy Brzozowski, Licensing & Enforcement Manager, The Business Centre, Futures Park, Newchurch Road, Bacup OL13 0BB ☎ 01706 238602
⏎ tracybrzozowski@rossendalebc.gov.uk

Lifelong Learning: Mrs Clare Law, HR Manager, The Business Centre, Futures Park, Newchurch Road, Bacup OL13 0BB
☎ 01706 252457; 01706 873577 ⏎ clarelaw@rossendalebc.gov.uk

Member Services: Mrs Carolyn Sharples, Committee & Member Services Manager, The Business Centre, Futures Park, Newchurch Road, Bacup OL13 0BB ☎ 01706 252422; 01706 873577
⏎ carolynsharples@rossendalebc.gov.uk

Personnel / HR: Mrs Clare Law, HR Manager, The Business Centre, Futures Park, Newchurch Road, Bacup OL13 0BB
☎ 01706 252457; 01706 873577 ⏎ clarelaw@rossendalebc.gov.uk

Planning: Ms Nicola Hopkins, Planning Manager, The Business Centre, Futures Park, Newchurch Road, Bacup OL13 0BB
☎ 01706 252420 ⏎ nicolahopkins@rossendalebc.gov.uk

Procurement: Mr Phil Seddon, Head of Finance & Property, The Business Centre, Futures Park, Newchurch Road, Bacup OL13 0BB
☎ 01706 252465; 01706 873577 ⏎ philseddon@rossendalebc.gov.uk

Recycling & Waste Minimisation: Mr Paul McHenry, Head of Operations, Henrietta Street Depot, Bacup OL13 0AR
☎ 01706 252519 ⏎ paulmchenry@rossendalebc.gov.uk

Regeneration: Mr David Presto, Economic Development & External Funding Manager, The Business Centre, Futures Park, Newchurch Road, Bacup OL13 0BB ☎ 01706 252477; 01706 873577 ⏎ davidpresto@rossendalebc.gov.uk

Staff Training: Mrs Clare Law, HR Manager, The Business Centre, Futures Park, Newchurch Road, Bacup OL13 0BB ☎ 01706 252457; 01706 873577 ⏎ clarelaw@rossendalebc.gov.uk

Street Scene: Mr Paul McHenry, Head of Operations, Henrietta Street Depot, Bacup OL13 0AR ☎ 01706 252519
✆ paulmchenry@rossendalebc.gov.uk

Sustainable Development: Ms Nicola Hopkins, Planning Manager, The Business Centre, Futures Park, Newchurch Road, Bacup OL13 0BB ☎ 01706 252420
✆ nicolahopkins@rossendalebc.gov.uk

Sustainable Development: Mr David Presto, Economic Development & External Funding Manager, The Business Centre, Futures Park, Newchurch Road, Bacup OL13 0BB ☎ 01706 252477; 01706 873577 ✆ davidpresto@rossendalebc.gov.uk

Tourism: Mr David Presto, Economic Development & External Funding Manager, The Business Centre, Futures Park, Newchurch Road, Bacup OL13 0BB ☎ 01706 252477; 01706 873577 ✆ davidpresto@rossendalebc.gov.uk

Town Centre: Mr David Presto, Economic Development & External Funding Manager, The Business Centre, Futures Park, Newchurch Road, Bacup OL13 0BB ☎ 01706 252477; 01706 873577 ✆ davidpresto@rossendalebc.gov.uk

Transport: Ms Christine Chadderton, Transport Co-ordinator, Henrietta Street Depot, Bacup OL13 0AR ☎ 01706 878660
✆ christinechadderton@rossendalebc.gov.uk

Waste Collection and Disposal: Mr Paul McHenry, Head of Operations, Henrietta Street Depot, Bacup OL13 0AR
☎ 01706 252519 ✆ paulmchenry@rossendalebc.gov.uk

COUNCILLORS

Mayor: Morris, Granville (CON - Greenfield)
granvillemorris@rossendalebc.gov.uk

Deputy Mayor: Crawforth, Colin (LAB - Hareholme)
colincrawforth@rossendalebc.gov.uk

Leader of the Council: Barnes, Alyson (LAB - Goodshaw)
alysonbarnes@rossendalebc.gov.uk

Deputy Leader of the Council: Lamb, Christine (LAB - Stacksteads)
christinelamb@rossendalebc.gov.uk

Group Leader: Cheetham, Anne (CON - Eden)
annecheetham@rossendalebc.gov.uk

Aldred, Tom (LAB - Facit & Shawforth)
tomaldred@rossendalebc.gov.uk

Ashworth, Barbara (LAB - Greensclough)
barbaraashworth@rossendalebc.gov.uk

Barnes, Lynda (CON - Facit & Shawforth)
lyndabarnes@rossendalebc.gov.uk

Bromley, Pam (LAB - Whitewell)
pambromley@rossendalebc.gov.uk

Eaton, Janet (CON - Irwell)
janeteaton@rossendalebc.gov.uk

Eaton, James (CON - Greensclough)
jameseaton@rossendalebc.gov.uk

Essex, Brian (CON - Helmshore)
brianessex@rossendalebc.gov.uk

Farrington, Dorothy (LAB - Goodshaw)
dorothyfarrington@rossendalebc.gov.uk

Fletcher, Andrea (LAB - Cribden)
andreafletcher@rossendalebc.gov.uk

Graham, Janet (CON - Cribden)
janetgraham@rossendalebc.gov.uk

Haworth, Tony (CON - Helmshore)
tonyhaworth@rossendalebc.gov.uk

Hughes, Steve (LAB - Longholme)
stevehughes@rossendalebc.gov.uk

Johnson, Janice (LAB - Eden)
janicejohnson@rossendalebc.gov.uk

Kempson, Karl (CON - Whitewell)
karlkempson@rossendalebc.gov.uk

Kenyon, Ann (LAB - Worsley)
annkenyon@rossendalebc.gov.uk

Lythgoe, Adrian (LAB - Worsley)
adrianlythgoe@rossendalebc.gov.uk

MacNae, Andy (LAB - Hareholme)
andrewmacnae@rossendalebc.gov.uk

Marriott, Patrick (LAB - Hareholme)
patrickmarriott@rossendalebc.gov.uk

McMahon, Annie (LAB - Longholme)
anniemcmahon@rossendalebc.gov.uk

Neal, Alan (IND - Healey & Whitworth)
alanneal@rossendalebc.gov.uk

Oakes, Jackie (LAB - Stacksteads)
jackieoakes@rossendalebc.gov.uk

Procter, Marilyn (LAB - Worsley)
marilynprocter@rossendalebc.gov.uk

Roberts, Val (CON - Greenfield)
valroberts@rossendalebc.gov.uk

Robertson, Amanda (LAB - Whitewell)
amandarobertson@rossendalebc.gov.uk

Serridge, Sean (LAB - Healey & Whitworth)
seanserridge@rossendalebc.gov.uk

Shipley, Annabel (CON - Greenfield)
annabelshipley@rossendalebc.gov.uk

Smallridge, Sam (LAB - Longholme)
samsmallridge@rossendalebc.gov.uk

Smith, Michelle (LAB - Irwell)
michellesmith@rossendalebc.gov.uk

Stansfield, David (CON - Helmshore)
davidstansfield@rossendalebc.gov.uk

Steen, Peter (CON - Greensclough)
petersteen@rossendalebc.gov.uk

Walmsley, Andrew (LAB - Irwell)
andrewwalmsley@rossendalebc.gov.uk

POLITICAL COMPOSITION
LAB: 22, CON: 13, IND: 1

COMMITTEE CHAIRS

Audit: Mr Tom Aldred

Development Control: Mrs Marilyn Procter

ROSSENDALE

Licensing: Mr Steve Hughes

Rother   D

Rother District Council, Town Hall, Bexhill-on-Sea TN39 3JX
☎ 01424 787878 🖷 01424 787879 ⏚ chiefexec@rother.gov.uk
🖥 www.rother.gov.uk

FACTS AND FIGURES
Parliamentary Constituencies: Bexhill and Battle
EU Constituencies: South East
Election Frequency: Elections are of whole council

PRINCIPAL OFFICERS

Senior Management: Mr Malcolm Johnston, Executive Director
- Resources & Head of Paid Service, Town Hall, Bexhill-on-Sea
TN39 3JX ☎ 01424 787000; 01424 787879
⏚ malcolm.johnston@rother.gov.uk

Senior Management: Dr Anthony Leonard, Executive Director
- Business Operations & Head of Paid Service, Town Hall, Bexhill-
on-Sea TN39 3JX ☎ 01424 787500; 01424 787520

Best Value: Ms Joanne Wright, Policy Officer, Town Hall, Bexhill-
on-Sea TN39 3JX ☎ 01424 787816; 01424 787879
⏚ joanne.wright@rother.gov.uk.

Building Control: Mr Jonathan Cornell, Building Control Manager,
Town Hall, Bexhill-on-Sea TN39 3JX ☎ 01424 787680; 01424
787657 ⏚ jonathan.cornell@rother.gov.uk

Building Control: Mr Jonathan Cornell, Chief Building Control
Officer, Town Hall, Bexhill-on-Sea TN39 3JX ☎ 01424 787670
⏚ jonathan.cornell@rother.gov.uk

Community Planning: Mrs Brenda Mason, Service Manager -
Community & Economy, Town Hall, Bexhill-on-Sea TN39 3JX
☎ 01424 787000; 01424 787520 ⏚ brenda.mason@rother.gov.uk

Computer Management: Mr John Collins, Manager for
Corporate HR, Town Hall, Bexhill-on-Sea TN39 3JX
☎ 01424 787000; 01424 787000 ⏚ john.collins@rother.gov.uk

Corporate Services: Ms Suzanne Collins, Head of Corporate
Services, Town Hall, Bexhill-on-Sea TN39 3JX ☎ 01424 787835;
01424 787879 ⏚ suzanne.collins@rother.gov.uk

Customer Service: Mr Mark Adams, Customer Services Officer,
Town Hall, Bexhill-on-Sea TN39 3JX ☎ 01424 787000
⏚ mark.adams@rother.gov.uk

Economic Development: Mr Graham Burgess, Head of
Regeneration, Town Hall, Bexhill-on-Sea TN39 3JX
☎ 01424 787000 ⏚ graham.burgess@rother.gov.uk

Electoral Registration: Ms Suzanne Collins, Head of Corporate
Services, Town Hall, Bexhill-on-Sea TN39 3JX ☎ 01424 787835;
01424 787879 ⏚ suzanne.collins@rother.gov.uk

Environmental Health: Mr Richard Parker-Harding, Head of
Environmental Health, 14 Beeching Road, Bexhill-on-Sea TN39 3LG
richard.parker-harding@rother.gov.uk

Estates, Property & Valuation: Ms Suzanne Collins, Head of
Corporate Services, Town Hall, Bexhill-on-Sea TN39 3JX
☎ 01424 787835; 01424 787879 ⏚ suzanne.collins@rother.gov.uk

Facilities: Ms Kim Ross, Head of Amenities, Town Hall, Bexhill-on-
Sea TN39 3JX ☎ 01424 787000 ⏚ kim.ross@rother.gov.uk

Finance: Mr Malcolm Johnston, Executive Director - Resources &
Head of Paid Service, Town Hall, Bexhill-on-Sea TN39 3JX
☎ 01424 787000; 01424 787879 ⏚ malcolm.johnston@rother.gov.uk

Finance: Mr Robin Vennard, Head of Finance, Town Hall, Bexhill-
on-Sea TN39 3JX ☎ 01424 787000 ⏚ robin.vennard@rother.gov.uk

Treasury: Mr Clive Jefferson, Treasurer, Town Hall, Bexhill-on-Sea
TN39 3JX ☎ 01424 787000 ⏚ clive.jefferson@rother.gov.uk

Health and Safety: Mr John Collins, Manager for Corporate
HR, Town Hall, Bexhill-on-Sea TN39 3JX ☎ 01424 787000; 01424
787000 ⏚ john.collins@rother.gov.uk

Housing: Mr Martin Bolton, Housing Needs Manager, Town Hall,
Bexhill-on-Sea TN39 3JX ☎ 01424 787000
⏚ martin.bolton@rother.gov.uk

Legal: Ms Suzanne Collins, Head of Corporate Services, Town Hall,
Bexhill-on-Sea TN39 3JX ☎ 01424 787835; 01424 787879
⏚ suzanne.collins@rother.gov.uk

Leisure and Cultural Services: Ms Kim Ross, Head of
Amenities, Town Hall, Bexhill-on-Sea TN39 3JX ☎ 01424 787000
⏚ kim.ross@rother.gov.uk

Licensing: Mr Richard Parker-Harding, Head of Environmental
Health, 14 Beeching Road, Bexhill-on-Sea TN39 3LG
⏚ richard.parker-harding@rother.gov.uk

Member Services: Ms Suzanne Collins, Head of Corporate
Services, Town Hall, Bexhill-on-Sea TN39 3JX ☎ 01424 787835;
01424 787879 ⏚ suzanne.collins@rother.gov.uk

Parking: Ms Kim Ross, Head of Amenities, Town Hall, Bexhill-on-
Sea TN39 3JX ☎ 01424 787000 ⏚ kim.ross@rother.gov.uk

Personnel / HR: Mr John Collins, Manager for Corporate HR,
Town Hall, Bexhill-on-Sea TN39 3JX ☎ 01424 787000; 01424
787000 ⏚ john.collins@rother.gov.uk

Planning: Mr Tim Hickling, Manager for Strategy & Planning,
Town Hall, Bexhill-on-Sea TN39 3JX ☎ 01424 787000
⏚ tim.hickling@rother.gov.uk

Recycling & Waste Minimisation: Ms Kim Ross, Head of
Amenities, 14 Beeching Road, Bexhill-on-Sea TN39 3LG
☎ 01424 787000 ⏚ kim.ross@rother.gov.uk

Regeneration: Mr Graham Burgess, Head of Regeneration, Town
Hall, Bexhill-on-Sea TN39 3JX ☎ 01424 787000
⏚ graham.burgess@rother.gov.uk

Staff Training: Mr John Collins, Manager for Corporate HR, Town Hall, Bexhill-on-Sea TN39 3JX ☎ 01424 787000; 01424 787000 ⊕ john.collins@rother.gov.uk

Sustainable Communities: Mrs Brenda Mason, Service Manager - Community & Economy, Town Hall, Bexhill-on-Sea TN39 3JX ☎ 01424 787000; 01424 787520 ⊕ brenda.mason@rother.gov.uk

Sustainable Development: Mrs Brenda Mason, Service Manager - Community & Economy, Town Hall, Bexhill-on-Sea TN39 3JX ☎ 01424 787000; 01424 787520 ⊕ brenda.mason@rother.gov.uk

Tourism: Mr Graham Burgess, Head of Regeneration, Town Hall, Bexhill-on-Sea TN39 3JX ☎ 01424 787000 ⊕ graham.burgess@rother.gov.uk

COUNCILLORS

Chair: Osborne, Paul (CON - Eastern Rother)
cllr.paul.osborne@rother.gov.uk

Leader of the Council: Maynard, Carl (CON - Brede Valley)
cllr.carl.maynard@rother.gov.uk

Deputy Leader of the Council: Kenward, Martin (CON - Bexhill Kewhurst)
cllr.martin.kenward@rother.gov.uk

Ampthill, (CON - Rye)
cllr.lord.ampthill@rother.gov.uk

Azad, Abul (CON - Bexhill Central)
cllr.abul.azad@rother.gov.uk

Barnes, Mary (CON - Ticehurst & Etchingham)
cllr.mary.barnes@rother.gov.uk

Bird, Roger (CON - Marsham)
cllr.roger.bird@rother.gov.uk

Browne, Graham (CON - Salehurst)
cllr.graham.browne@rother.gov.uk

Carroll, James (CON - Bexhill Sidley)
cllr.jim.carroll@rother.gov.uk

Carroll, Richard (CON - Bexhill Central)
cllr.richard.carroll@rother.gov.uk

Clark, Charles (IND - Bexhill St Michaels)
cllr.charles.clark@rother.gov.uk

Curtis, Gary (CON - Crowhurst)
cllr.gary.curtis@rother.gov.uk

Dixon, Kevin (LD - Battle)
cllr.kevin.dixon@rother.gov.uk

Douart, Patrick (CON - Bexhill Sackville)
cllr.patrick.douart@rother.gov.uk

Earl, Stuart (IND - Bexhill St Marks)
cllr.stuart.earl@rother.gov.uk

Elford, Simon (CON - Bexhill St Michaels)
cllr.simon.elford@rother.gov.uk

Elliston, Robert (CON - Ticehurst & Etchingham)
cllr.robert.elliston@rother.gov.uk

Field, Kathryn (LD - Battle)
cllr.kathryn.field@rother.ac.uk

Ganly, Anthony (CON - Ewhurst & Sedlescombe)
cllr.tony.ganly@rother.gov.uk

George, Bridget (CON - Bexhill St Stephens)
cllr.bridget.george@rother.gov.uk

Graham, Tom (CON - Bexhill St Marks)
cllr.tom.graham@rother.gov.uk

Hart, Sally-Ann (CON - Eastern Rother)
cllr.sally-ann.hart@rother.gov.uk

Hollidge, Ian (CON - Bexhill Sackville)
cllr.ian.hollidge@rother.gov.uk

Hughes, Joyce (CON - Bexhill Central)
cllr.joy.hughes@rother.gov.uk

Jenkins, Ian (CON - Rother Levels)
cllr.ian.jenkins@rother.gov.uk

Johnson, Gillian (CON - Bexhill Old Town)
cllr.gillian.johnson@rother.gov.uk

Johnson, Jonathan (CON - Brede Valley)
cllr.jonathon.johnson@rother.gov.uk

Kentfield, Brian (CON - Bexhill Kewhurst)
cllr.brian.kentfield@rother.gov.uk

Kirby-Green, Eleanor (CON - Darwell)
cllr.eleanor.kirby-green@rother.gov.uk

Mooney, Martin (CON - Rother Levels)
cllr.martin.mooney@rother.gov.uk

Oliver, Douglas (IND - Bexhill Collington)
cllr.doug.oliver@rother.gov.uk

Potts, Jacqueline (CON - Bexhill Old Town)
cllr.jacqueline.potts@rother.gov.uk

Prochak, Susan (LD - Salehurst)
cllr.susan.prochak@rother.gov.uk

Saint, Chris (CON - Marsham)
cllr.chris.saint@rother.gov.uk

Stevens, Gennette (CON - Rye)
cllr.gennette.stevens@rother.gov.uk

Watson, Maurice (LAB - Bexhill Sidley)
cllr.maurice.watson@rother.gov.uk

POLITICAL COMPOSITION
CON: 29, IND: 3, LD: 3, LAB: 1

COMMITTEE CHAIRS

Audit: Mr Martin Mooney

Planning: Mr Brian Kentfield

Rotherham M

Rotherham Metropolitan Borough Council, Riverside House, Main Street, Rotherham S60 1AE
☎ 01709 382121 ⊕ customerservices@rotherham.gov.uk
🖥 www.rotherham.gov.uk

FACTS AND FIGURES
Parliamentary Constituencies: Rother Valley, Rotherham, Wentworth and Dearne
EU Constituencies: Yorkshire and the Humber
Election Frequency: Elections are by thirds

PRINCIPAL OFFICERS

ROTHERHAM

Chief Executive: Ms Sharon Kemp, Chief Executive, Riverside House, Main Street, Rotherham S60 1AE ☎ 01709 822770 ✆ sharon.kemp@rotherham.gov.uk

Assistant Chief Executive: Mr Shokat Lal, Assistant Chief Executive, Riverside House, Main Street, Rotherham S60 1AE ✆ shokat.lal@rotherham.gov.uk

Senior Management: Ms Teresa Roche, Director - Public Health, Riverside House, Main Street, Rotherham S60 1AE ☎ 01709 255845 ✆ teresa.roche@rotherham.gov.uk

Senior Management: Mr Ian Thomas, Strategic Director - Children's Services, Riverside House, Main Street, Rotherham S60 1AE ☎ 01709 822506 ✆ ian.thomas@rotherham.gov.uk

Senior Management: Ms Judith Badger, Strategic Director - Finance & Customer Services, Riverside House, Main Street, Rotherham S60 1AE ✆ judith.badger@rotherham.gov.uk

Senior Management: Mr Damien Wilson, Strategic Director - Regeneration & Environment, Riverside House, Main Street, Rotherham S60 1AE ☎ 01709 822971 ✆ damien.wilson@rotherham.gov.uk

Senior Management: Ms Anne-Marie Lubanski, Strategic Director - Adult Social Care & Housing, Riverside House, Main Street, Rotherham S60 1AE ✆ anne-marie.lubanski@rotherham.gov.uk

Access Officer / Social Services (Disability): Mr Stuart Carr, Disability Co-ordinator, Riverside House, Main Street, Rotherham S60 1AE ☎ 01709 254022 ✆ stuart.carr@rotherham.gov.uk

Building Control: Mr Bruce Carter, Building Control Manager, Riverside House, Main Street, Rotherham S60 1AE ☎ 01709 829841 ✆ bruce.carter@rotherham.gov.uk

Catering Services: Mr Kim Phillips, Principal Catering Officer, Riverside House, Main Street, Rotherham S60 1AE ☎ 01709 254025 ✆ kim.phillips@rotherham.gov.uk

Children / Youth Services: Ms Karen Borthwick, Head of Schools Effectiveness Service, Riverside House, Main Street, Rotherham S60 1AE ☎ 01709 334075 ✆ karen.borthwick@rotherham.gov.uk

Children / Youth Services: Mr Ian Thomas, Strategic Director - Children's Services, Riverside House, Main Street, Rotherham S60 1AE ☎ 01709 822506 ✆ ian.thomas@rotherham.gov.uk

Civil Registration: Ms Louise Sennitt, Superintendant Registrar, Riverside House, Main Street, Rotherham S60 1AE ☎ 01709 822896

PR / Communications: Mrs Tracy Holmes, Head - Communications, Riverside House, Main Street, Rotherham S60 1AE ☎ 01709 822735 ✆ tracy.holmes@rotherham.gov.uk

Community Safety: Mr Steve Parry, Neighbourhood Crime & Justice Manager, Riverside House, Main Street, Rotherham S60 1AE ☎ 01709 334565 ✆ steve.parry@rotherham.gov.uk

Consumer Protection and Trading Standards: Mrs Janice Manning, Principal Officer - Environmental Health, Riverside House, Main Street, Rotherham S60 1AE ☎ 01709 823126 ✆ janice.manning@rotherham.gov.uk

Corporate Services: Mr Justin Homer, Head of Policy Improvement & Partnerships, Riverside House, Main Street, Rotherham S60 1AE ☎ 01709 823618 ✆ justin.homer@rotherham.gov.uk

Customer Service: Ms Zoe Oxley, Customer & Cultural Services Officer, Riverside House, Main Street, Rotherham S60 1AE ☎ 01709 334283 ✆ zoe.oxley@rotherham.gov.uk

Economic Development: Mr Paul Woodcock, Director - Planning & Regeneration, Riverside House, Main Street, Rotherham S60 1AE ☎ 01709 822971 ✆ paul.woodcock@rotherham.gov.uk

Education: Ms Karen Borthwick, Head of Schools Effectiveness Service, Riverside House, Main Street, Rotherham S60 1AE ☎ 01709 334075 ✆ karen.borthwick@rotherham.gov.uk

Emergency Planning: Ms Claire Hanson, Interim Emergency & Safety Manager, Riverside House, Main Street, Rotherham S60 1AE ☎ 01709 823787 ✆ claire.hanson@rotherham.gov.uk

Energy Management: Mr David Rhodes, Environmental Officer, Riverside House, Main Street, Rotherham S60 1AE ☎ 01709 822166 ✆ david.rhodes@rotherham.gov.uk

Estates, Property & Valuation: Mr Paul Smith, Corporate Property Manager, Riverside House, Main Street, Rotherham S60 1AE ☎ 01709 254061 ✆ paul.smith@rotherham.gov.uk

European Liaison: Mr Michael Holmes, Policy & Partnerships Officer, Riverside House, Main Street, Rotherham S60 1AE ☎ 01709 254417 ✆ michael.holmes@rotherham.gov.uk

Facilities: Mr Stuart Carr, Facilities Manager, Riverside House, Main Street, Rotherham S60 1AE ☎ 01709 254021 ✆ stuart.carr@rotherham.gov.uk

Finance: Ms Judith Badger, Strategic Director - Finance & Customer Services, Riverside House, Main Street, Rotherham S60 1AE ☎ 01709 822034 ✆ judith.badger@rotherham.gov.uk

Highways: Mr Colin Knight, Network Manager, Riverside House, Main Street, Rotherham S60 1AE ☎ 01709 822828 ✆ colin.knight@rotherham.gov.uk

Home Energy Conservation: Mr Paul Maplethorpe, Manager - Affordable Warmth & Sustainable Energy Co-ordinator, Riverside House, Main Street, Rotherham S60 1AE ☎ 01709 334964 ✆ paul.maplethorpe@rotherham.gov.uk

Legal: Mr Dermot Pearson, Director - Legal Services, Riverside House, Main Street, Rotherham S60 1AE ☎ 01709 255768 ✆ dermot.pearson@rotherham.gov.uk

Leisure and Cultural Services: Ms Elenore Fisher, Head - Cultural Services, Riverside House, Main Street, Rotherham S60 1AE ☎ 01709 823623 ✆ elenore.fisher@rotherham.gov.uk

Leisure and Cultural Services: Mr Steve Hallsworth, Leisure Services Manager, Riverside House, Main Street, Rotherham S60 1AE ☎ 01709 822483 ⁁ steve.hallsworth@rotherham.gov.uk

Licensing: Ms Janette Hicks, Licensing Manager, Riverside House, Main Street, Rotherham S60 1AE ☎ 01709 822524 ⁁ jenette.hicks@rotherham.gov.uk

Lifelong Learning: Ms Karen Borthwick, Head of Schools Effectiveness Service, Riverside House, Main Street, Rotherham S60 1AE ☎ 01709 334075 ⁁ karen.borthwick@rotherham.gov.uk

Lottery Funding, Charity and Voluntary: Ms Carole Haywood, Manager - Policy & Partnerships, Riverside House, Main Street, Rotherham S60 1AE ☎ 01709 254435 ⁁ carole.haywood@rotherham.gov.uk

Member Services: Mr James McLaughlin, Democratic Services Manager, Riverside House, Main Street, Rotherham S60 1AE ☎ 01709 822054 ⁁ james.mclaughlin@rotherham.gov.uk

Parking: Mr Martin Beard, Parking Services Manager, Riverside House, Main Street, Rotherham S60 1AN ☎ 01709 822929 ⁁ martin.beard@rotherham.gov.uk

Partnerships: Ms Carole Haywood, Manager - Policy & Partnerships, Riverside House, Main Street, Rotherham S60 1AE ☎ 01709 254435 ⁁ carole.haywood@rotherham.gov.uk

Public Libraries: Ms Elenore Fisher, Head - Cultural Services, Riverside House, Main Street, Rotherham S60 1AE ☎ 01709 823623 ⁁ elenore.fisher@rotherham.gov.uk

Regeneration: Mr Damien Wilson, Strategic Director - Regeneration & Environment, Riverside House, Main Street, Rotherham S60 1AE ☎ 01709 822971 ⁁ damien.wilson@rotherham.gov.uk

Social Services (Adult): Mr Graeme Betts, Director - Health & Wellbeing, Riverside House, Main Street, Rotherham S60 1AE ☎ 01709 823928 ⁁ graeme.betts@rotherham.gov.uk

Social Services (Adult): Ms Sam Newton, Director - Asset & Care Management, Riverside House, Main Street, Rotherham S60 1AE ☎ 01709 824062 ⁁ sam.newton@rotherham.gov.uk

Social Services (Children): Ms Mel Meggs, Deputy Strategic Director - Children & Young People's Services, Riverside House, Main Street, Rotherham S60 1AE ☎ 01709 823905 ⁁ mel.meggs@rotherham.gov.uk

Public Health: Ms Teresa Roche, Director - Public Health, Riverside House, Main Street, Rotherham S60 1AE ☎ 01709 255845 ⁁ teresa.roche@rotherham.gov.uk

Staff Training: Mrs Tracey Parkin, Human Resources Manager, Riverside House, Main Street, Rotherham S60 1AE ☎ 01709 823742 ⁁ tracey.parkin@rotherham.gov.uk

Town Centre: Ms Bernadette Rushton, Town Centre Manager, Riverside House, Main Street, Rotherham S60 1AE ☎ 01709 254888 ⁁ bernadette.rushton@rotherham.gov.uk

Traffic Management: Mr Ian Ashmore, Principal Traffic Officer, Riverside House, Main Street, Rotherham S60 1AN ☎ 01709 822825 ⁁ ian.ashmore@rotherham.gov.uk

Transport: Mr Colin Knight, Network Manager, Riverside House, Main Street, Rotherham S60 1AE ☎ 01709 822828 ⁁ colin.knight@rotherham.gov.uk

COUNCILLORS

Leader of the Council: Read, Chris (LAB - Wickersley) chris.read@rotherham.gov.uk

Deputy Leader of the Council: Watson, Gordon (LAB - Wales) gordon.watson@rotherham.gov.uk

Alam, Saghir (LAB - Boston Castle) saghir.alam@rotherham.gov.uk

Albiston, Kerry (LAB - Valley) kerry.albiston@rotherham.gov.uk

Allcock, Leon (LAB - Rother Vale) leon.allcock@rotherham.gov.uk

Allen, Sarah (LAB - Wingfield) sarah.allen@rotherham.gov.uk

Andrews, Jenny (LAB - Hellaby) jenny.andrews@rotherham.gov.uk

Atkin, Alan (LAB - Wath) alan.aitken@rotherham.gov.uk

Beaumont, Christine (LAB - Maltby) christine.beaumont@rotherham.gov.uk

Beck, Dominic (LAB - Wales) dominic.beck@rotherham.gov.uk

Bird, Bob (LAB - Rawmarsh) robert.bird@rotherham.gov.uk

Brookes, Amy (LAB - Rother Vale) amy.brookes@rotherham.gov.uk

Buckley, Alan (LAB - Brinsworth & Catcliffe) alan.buckley@rotherham.gov.uk

Clark, Maggi (LAB - Keppel) maggi.clark@rotherham.gov.uk

Cooksey, Wendy (LAB - Rotherham East) wendy.cooksey@rotherham.gov.uk

Cowles, Allen (UKIP - Sitwell) allen.cowles@rotherham.gov.uk

Cusworth, Victoria (LAB - Swinton) victoria.cusworth@rotherham.gov.uk

Cutts, Brian (UKIP - Hellaby) brian.cutts@rotherham.gov.uk

Cutts, David (UKIP - Keppel) dave.cutts@rotherham.gov.uk

Elliot, Jayne (LAB - Wath) jayne.elliot@rotherham.gov.uk

Elliott, Mick (UKIP - Holderness) michael.elliott@rotherham.gov.uk

Elliott, Robert (UKIP - Wingfield) robert.elliott@rotherham.gov.uk

ROTHERHAM

Ellis, Sue (LAB - Wickersley)
sue.ellis@rotherham.gov.uk

Evans, Simon (LAB - Wath)
simon.evans@rotherham.gov.uk

Fenwick-Green, Deborah (LAB - Rotherham East)
deborah.fenwick-green@rotherham.gov.uk

Finnie, Ian (UKIP - Dinnington)
ian.finnie@rotherham.gov.uk

Hague, Paul (UKIP - Keppel)
paul.hague@rotherham.gov.uk

Hoddinott, Emma (LAB - Wickersley)
emma.hoddinott@rotherham.gov.uk

Ireland, Jonathan (LAB - Anston & Woodsetts)
jonathan.ireland@rotherham.gov.uk

Jarvis, Pat (LAB - Rotherham West)
pat.jarvis@rotherham.gov.uk

Jepson, Clive (IND - Anston & Woodsetts)
clive.jepson@rotherham.gov.uk

Jones, Ian (LAB - Rotherham West)
ian.jones@rotherham.gov.uk

Khan, Tajamal (LAB - Rotherham East)
tajamal.khan@rotherham.gov.uk

Lelliott, Denise (LAB - Hoober)
denise.lelliott@rotherham.gov.uk

Mallinder, Jeanette (LAB - Dinnington)
jeanette.mallinder@rotherham.gov.uk

Marles, Steve (LAB - Silverwood)
steven.marles@rotherham.gov.uk

Marriott, Sandra (UKIP - Rawmarsh)
sandra.marriott@rotherham.gov.uk

McNeely, Rose (LAB - Boston Castle)
rose.mcneely@rotherham.gov.uk

Napper, Alan (UKIP - Silverwood)
alan.napper@rotherham.gov.uk

Pitchley, Lyndsay (LAB - Holderness)
lyndsay.pitchley@rotherham.gov.uk

Price, Richard (LAB - Maltby)
richard.price@rotherham.gov.uk

Reeder, Kathleen (UKIP - Valley)
kath.reeder@rotherham.gov.uk

Roche, David (LAB - Hoober)
david.roche@rotherham.gov.uk

Roddison, Andrew (LAB - Brinsworth & Catcliffe)
andrew.roddison@rotherham.gov.uk

Rose Keenen, Eve (LAB - Rotherham West)
eve.rose@rotherham.gov.uk

Rushforth, Amy (LAB - Maltby)
amy.rushworth@rotherham.gov.uk

Russell, Gwendoline (LAB - Silverwood)
ann.russell@rotherham.gov.uk

Sansom, Stuart (LAB - Swinton)
stuart.sansome@rotherham.gov.uk

Senior, Jayne (LAB - Valley)
jayne.senior@rotherham.gov.uk

Sheppard, David (LAB - Rawmarsh)
david.sheppard@rotherham.gov.uk

Short, Peter (UKIP - Sitwell)
peter.short@rotherham.gov.uk

Simpson, Nigel (UKIP - Brinsworth & Catcliffe)
nigel.simpson@rotherham.gov.uk

Steele, Brian (LAB - Hoober)
brian.steele@rotherham.gov.uk

Taylor, Robert (LAB - Holderness)
robert.taylor@rotherham.gov.uk

Turner, John (UKIP - Hellaby)
john.turner@rotherham.gov.uk

Turner, Julie (UKIP - Sitwell)
julie.turner@rotherham.gov.uk

Tweed, Simon (LAB - Dinnington)
simon.tweed@rotherham.gov.uk

Walsh, Bob (LAB - Rother Vale)
bob.walsh@rotherham.gov.uk

Whysall, Jennifer (LAB - Wales)
jennifer.whysall@rotherham.gov.uk

Williams, John (LAB - Wingfield)
john.williams@rotherham.gov.uk

Wilson, Katherine (LAB - Anston & Woodsetts)
katherine.wilson@rotherham.gov.uk

Wyatt, Ken (LAB - Swinton)
ken.wyatt@rotherham.gov.uk

Yasseen, Taiba (LAB - Boston Castle)
taiba.yasseen@rotherham.gov.uk

POLITICAL COMPOSITION
LAB: 48, UKIP: 14, IND: 1

COMMITTEE CHAIRS

Audit: Mr Ken Wyatt

Children, Young People & Families: Ms Christine Beaumont

Licensing: Ms Sue Ellis

Planning: Mr Alan Atkin

Rugby   D

Rugby Borough Council, Town Hall, Evreux Way, Rugby
CV21 2RR

☎ 01788 533533 ◌ contact.centre@rugby.gov.uk 🖳 www.rugby.gov.uk

FACTS AND FIGURES
Parliamentary Constituencies: Nuneaton, Rugby
EU Constituencies: West Midlands
Election Frequency: Elections are by thirds

PRINCIPAL OFFICERS

Chief Executive: Mr Ian Davis, Executive Director, Town Hall,
Evreux Way, Rugby CV21 2RR ☎ 01788 533700
◌ ian.davis@rugby.gov.uk

Chief Executive: Mr Adam Norburn, Executive Director, Town Hall, Evreux Way, Rugby CV21 2RR ☎ 01788 533550; 01788 533409 ✆ adam.norburn@rugby.gov.uk

Senior Management: Mr Rob Back, Head of Planning & Recreation, Town Hall, Evreux Way, Rugby CV21 2RR ☎ 01788 533533 ✆ rob.back@rugby.gov.uk

Senior Management: Mrs Raj Chand, Head of Housing & Customer Information Services, Town Hall, Evreux Way, Rugby CV21 2RR ☎ 01788 533870 ✆ raj.chand@rugby.gov.uk

Senior Management: Mrs Mannie Grewal Ketley, Head of Resources, Town Hall, Evreux Way, Rugby CV21 2RR ☎ 01788 533533 ✆ manniegrewalketley@rugby.gov.uk

Senior Management: Mr Sean Lawson, Head of Environmental Services, Town Hall, Evreux Way, Rugby CV21 2RR ☎ 01788 533737 ✆ sean.lawson@rugby.gov.uk

PR / Communications: Mr Matthew Deaves, Communication, Consultation & Information Manager, Town Hall, Evreux Way, Rugby CV21 2RR ☎ 01788 533562 ✆ matthew.deaves@rugby.gov.uk

Community Safety: Mr David Burrows, Regulatory Services Manager, Town Hall, Evreux Way, Rugby CV21 2RR ☎ 01788 533806 ✆ david.burrows@rugby.gov.uk

Computer Management: Mr Andrew Singleton, Corporate ICT Manager, Town Hall, Evreux Way, Rugby CV21 2RR ☎ 01788 533533 ✆ andy.singleton@rugby.gov.uk

Contracts: Mrs Catrina Rimen, Procurement Officer, Town Hall, Evreux Way, Rugby CV21 2RR ☎ 01788 533732 ✆ catrina.rimen@rugby.gov.uk

Customer Service: Ms Debbie McCarthy, Customer Services Manager, Town Hall, Evreux Way, Rugby CV21 2RR ☎ 01788 533290 ✆ debbie.mccarthy@rugby.gov.uk

Direct Labour: Mr Sean Lawson, Head of Environmental Services, Town Hall, Evreux Way, Rugby CV21 2RR ☎ 01788 533737 ✆ sean.lawson@rugby.gov.uk

Economic Development: Mr Michael Beirne, Economic Development Officer, Town Hall, Evreux Way, Rugby CV21 2RR ☎ 01788 533752 ✆ michael.beirne@rugby.gov.uk

Electoral Registration: Mrs Sandy Veal, Electoral Services Officer, Town Hall, Evreux Way, Rugby CV21 2RR ☎ 01788 533595 ✆ sandy.veal@rugby.gov.uk

Emergency Planning: Mr Sean Lawson, Head of Environmental Services, Town Hall, Evreux Way, Rugby CV21 2RR ☎ 01788 533737 ✆ sean.lawson@rugby.gov.uk

Energy Management: Mr Rob Kindon, Property Manager, Town Hall, Evreux Way, Rugby CV21 2RR ☎ 01788 533533 ✆ rob.kindon@rugby.gov.uk

Environmental / Technical Services: Mr Sean Lawson, Head of Environmental Services, Town Hall, Evreux Way, Rugby CV21 2RR ☎ 01788 533737 ✆ sean.lawson@rugby.gov.uk

Environmental Health: Mr Sean Lawson, Head of Environmental Services, Town Hall, Evreux Way, Rugby CV21 2RR ☎ 01788 533737 ✆ sean.lawson@rugby.gov.uk

Finance: Mrs Mannie Grewal Ketley, Head of Resources, Town Hall, Evreux Way, Rugby CV21 2RR ☎ 01788 533533 ✆ manniegrewalketley@rugby.gov.uk

Grounds Maintenance: Mr Chris Worman, Parks & Grounds Manager, Town Hall, Evreux Way, Rugby CV21 2RR ☎ 01788 533706 ✆ chris.worman@rugby.gov.uk

Health and Safety: Mr David Burrows, Regulatory Services Manager, Town Hall, Evreux Way, Rugby CV21 2RR ☎ 01788 533806 ✆ david.burrows@rugby.gov.uk

Housing: Mrs Raj Chand, Head of Housing & Customer Information Services, Town Hall, Evreux Way, Rugby CV21 2RR ☎ 01788 533870 ✆ raj.chand@rugby.gov.uk

Housing Maintenance: Mrs Mannie Grewal Ketley, Head of Resources, Town Hall, Evreux Way, Rugby CV21 2RR ☎ 01788 533533 ✆ manniegrewalketley@rugby.gov.uk

Legal: Mrs Deborah Tyrrell, Legal Manager, Town Hall, Evreux Way, Rugby CV21 2RR ☎ 01788 533510 ✆ deborah.tyrrell@rugby.gov.uk

Leisure and Cultural Services: Mr Rob Back, Head of Planning & Recreation, Town Hall, Evreux Way, Rugby CV21 2RR ☎ 01788 533533 ✆ rob.back@rugby.gov.uk

Licensing: Mr David Burrows, Regulatory Services Manager, Town Hall, Evreux Way, Rugby CV21 2RR ☎ 01788 533806 ✆ david.burrows@rugby.gov.uk

Member Services: Mr Steve Garrison, Democratic Services Manager, Town Hall, Evreux Way, Rugby CV21 2RR ☎ 01788 533521 ✆ steve.garrison@rugby.gov.uk

Parking: Mr David Burrows, Regulatory Services Manager, Town Hall, Evreux Way, Rugby CV21 2RR ☎ 01788 533806 ✆ david.burrows@rugby.gov.uk

Personnel / HR: Ms Suzanne Turner, Human Resources Manager, Town Hall, Evreux Way, Rugby CV21 2RR ☎ 01788 533570 ✆ suzanne.turner@rugby.gov.uk

Planning: Mr Nick Freer, Planning Services Manager, Town Hall, Evreux Way, Rugby CV21 2RR ☎ 01788 533737 ✆ nick.freer@rugby.gov.uk

Procurement: Mrs Catrina Rimen, Procurement Officer, Town Hall, Evreux Way, Rugby CV21 2RR ☎ 01788 533732 ✆ catrina.rimen@rugby.gov.uk

Recycling & Waste Minimisation: Mrs Gill Russell, Refuse & Recycling Manager, Works Services Unit, Newbold Road, Rugby CV21 1DH ☎ 01788 533315; ✆ gill.russell@rugby.gov.uk

RUGBY

Staff Training: Ms Elaine McGladdery, Learning & Organisational Development Officer, Town Hall, Evreux Way, Rugby CV21 2RR
☎ 01788 533574 ✆ elaine.mcgladdery@rugby.gov.uk

Street Scene: Mr Paul Mernagh, Street Scene Team Leader, Works Services Unit, Newbold Road, Rugby CV21 1DH
☎ 01788 533782 ✆ paul.mernagh@rugby.gov.uk

Sustainable Development: Ms Sarah Alexander, Forward Planning Manager, Town Hall, Evreux Way, Rugby CV21 2RR
☎ 01788 533668 ✆ sarah.alexander@rugby.gov.uk

Tourism: Mrs Nikki Grange, Arts Heritage & Tourism Manager, Rugby Art Gallery & Museum, Little Elborow Street, Rugby CV21 3BZ ☎ 01788 533203 ✆ nikki.grange@rugby.gov.uk

Waste Collection and Disposal: Mrs Gill Russell, Refuse & Recycling Manager, Works Services Unit, Newbold Road, Rugby CV21 1DH ☎ 01788 533315; ✆ gill.russell@rugby.gov.uk

COUNCILLORS

Mayor: Bragg, Sally (CON - Wolston & the Lawfords)
sally.bragg@rugby.gov.uk

Deputy Mayor: Taylor, Helen (CON - Coton & Boughton)
helen.taylor@rugby.gov.uk

Leader of the Council: Stokes, Michael (CON - Admirals & Cawston)
michael.stokes@rugby.gov.uk

Group Leader: Edwards, Claire (LAB - Newbold & Brownsover)
claire.edwards@rugby.gov.uk

Group Leader: Roodhouse, Jerry (LD - Paddox)
jerry.roodhouse@rugby.gov.uk

A'Barrow, Julie (CON - Bilton)
julie.abarrow@rugby.gov.uk

Allen, Nigel (CON - Hillmorton)
nigel.allen@rugby.gov.uk

Avis, Tina (LAB - New Bilton)
tina.avis@rugby.gov.uk

Birkett, Steven (LAB - New Bilton)
stevenwbirkett@hotmail.com

Brown, Kieren (LAB - Newbold & Brownsover)
kierenbrown@yahoo.com

Butlin, Peter (CON - Admirals & Cawston)
peter.butlin@rugby.gov.uk

Cade, Chris (CON - Bilton)
chris.cade@rugby.gov.uk

Crane, Emma (CON - Leam Valley)
emma.crane@rugby.gov.uk

Cranham, David (CON - Hillmorton)
david.cranham@rugby.gov.uk

Douglas, Tim (LD - Paddox)
tim.douglas@rugby.gov.uk

Dumbleton, Carrie-Anne (LD - Rokeby & Overslade)
carrie-anne.dumbleton@rugby.gov.uk

Ellis, David (CON - Wolston & the Lawfords)
david.ellis@rugby.gov.uk

Garcia, Belinda (CON - Revel & Binley Woods)
belindagb@aol.com

Gillias, Anthony (CON - Revel & Binley Woods)
anthony.gillias@rugby.gov.uk

Hunt, Leigh (CON - Clifton, Newton & Churchover)
leigh.hunt@rugby.gov.uk

Keeling, Dale (LD - Eastlands)
dale.keeling@rugby.gov.uk

Lawrence, Kathryn (CON - Hillmorton)
kathryn.lawrence@rugby.gov.uk

Lewis, Bill (LD - Rokeby & Overslade)
bill.lewis@rugby.gov.uk

Mahoney, Tom (LAB - Benn)
tom.mahoney@rugby.gov.uk

Mistry, Ish (LAB - New Bilton)
ishmistry@hotmail.co.uk

Nash, Marion (LD - Rokeby & Overslade)
marion.nash@rugbylibdems.org.uk

New, Noreen (LD - Paddox)
noreen.new@rugby.gov.uk

O'Rourke, Maggie (LAB - Benn)
maggie.o'rourke@rugby.gov.uk

Pacey-Day, Chris (CON - Wolvey & Shilton)
chris@hi-tekdial.co.uk

Parker, Lisa (CON - Bilton)
lisa.parker@rugby.gov.uk

Poole, Derek (CON - Wolston & the Lawfords)
derek.poole@rugby.gov.uk

Robbins, Carolyn (CON - Coton & Boughton)
carolyn.robbins@rugby.gov.uk

Roberts, Deepah (IND - Dunsmore)
deepah.roberts@rugby.gov.uk

Roberts, Howard (IND - Dunsmore)
howard.roberts@rugby.gov.uk

Roodhouse, Sue (LD - Eastlands)
sue.roodhouse@rugby.gov.uk

Sandison, Neil (LD - Eastlands)
neil.sandison@rugby.gov.uk

Shera, Jim (LAB - Benn)
jim.shera@rugby.gov.uk

Simpson-Vince, Jill (CON - Coton & Boughton)
jill.simpson-vince@rugby.gov.uk

Srivastava, Ramesh (LAB - Newbold & Brownsover)
ramesh.srivastava@rugby.gov.uk

Timms, Heather (CON - Revel & Binley Woods)
heather.timms@rugby.gov.uk

Watson-Merret, Carolyn (CON - Dunsmore)
cagsie@rugby.gov.uk

Williams, Mark (CON - Admirals & Cawston)
mark.williams@rugby.gov.uk

POLITICAL COMPOSITION
CON: 22, LAB: 9, LD: 9, IND: 2

COMMITTEE CHAIRS

Licensing: Ms Kathryn Lawrence

Planning: Ms Jill Simpson-Vince

Runnymede — D

Runnymede Borough Council, Civic Centre, Station Road, Addlestone KT15 2AH
☎ 01932 838383 🖷 01932 838384
📧 general.enquiries@runnymede.gov.uk 🖳 www.runnymede.gov.uk

FACTS AND FIGURES
Parliamentary Constituencies: Runnymede and Weybridge
EU Constituencies: South East
Election Frequency: Elections are by thirds

PRINCIPAL OFFICERS

Chief Executive: Mr Paul Turrell, Chief Executive, Civic Centre, Station Road, Addlestone KT15 2AH ☎ 01932 425500; 01932 838384 📧 paul.turrell@runnymede.gov.uk

Senior Management: Mr Mario Leo, Corporate Head - Law & Governance, Civic Centre, Station Road, Addlestone KT15 2AH ☎ 01932 425640; 01932 838384 📧 mario.leo@runnymede.gov.uk

Senior Management: Mr Ian Maguire, Corporate Head - Planning & Environmental Services, Civic Centre, Station Road, Addlestone KT15 2AH ☎ 01932 415240; 01932 838384 📧 ian.maguire@runnymede.gov.uk

Senior Management: Mrs Jane Margetts, Corporate Head - Housing & Community Development, Civic Centre, Station Road, Addlestone KT15 2AH ☎ 01932 425824; 01932 838384 📧 jane.margetts@runnymede.gov.uk

Senior Management: Mr Peter McKenzie, Corporate Head - Resources, Civic Centre, Station Road, Addlestone KT15 2AH ☎ 01932 425320; 01932 838384 📧 peter.mckenzie@runnymede.gov.uk

Senior Management: Ms Sarah Walsh, Head of Strategy, Civic Centre, Station Road, Addlestone KT15 2AH ☎ 01932 425693 📧 sarah.walsh@runnymede.gov.uk

Architect, Building / Property Services: Mr Richard Webb, Principal Building Services Manager, Civic Centre, Station Road, Addlestone KT15 2AH ☎ 01932 425171; 01932 838384 📧 richard.webb@runnymede.gov.uk

Building Control: Mr David Jones, Building Control Manager, Civic Centre, Station Road, Addlestone KT15 2AH ☎ 01932 425160; 01932 838384 📧 david.jones@runnymede.gov.uk

PR / Communications: Mr Mike Russell, Communications & Marketing Officer, Civic Centre, Station Road, Addlestone KT15 2AH ☎ 01932 425503 📧 mike.russell@runnymede.gov.uk

Community Safety: Ms Shazia Sarwar, Community Safety Officer, Civic Centre, Station Road, Addlestone KT15 2AH ☎ 01932 425065 📧 shazia.sarwar@runnymede.gov.uk

Computer Management: Mrs Helen Dunn, Head of ICT, Civic Centre, Station Road, Addlestone KT15 2AH ☎ 01932 425550; 01748 451499 📧 helen.dunn@runnymede.gov.uk

Contracts: Mr Mario Leo, Corporate Head - Law & Governance, Civic Centre, Station Road, Addlestone KT15 2AH ☎ 01932 425640; 01932 838384 📧 mario.leo@runnymede.gov.uk

Customer Service: Mrs Julie Kitchenside, Customer Services Manager, Civic Centre, Station Road, Addlestone KT15 2AH ☎ 01932 425130 📧 julie.kitchenside@runnymede.gov.uk

Economic Development: Mr Paul Turrell, Chief Executive, Civic Centre, Station Road, Addlestone KT15 2AH ☎ 01932 425500; 01932 838384 📧 paul.turrell@runnymede.gov.uk

E-Government: Mrs Helen Dunn, Head of ICT, Civic Centre, Station Road, Addlestone KT15 2AH ☎ 01932 425550; 01748 451499 📧 helen.dunn@runnymede.gov.uk

Electoral Registration: Mrs Samantha Clifton, Election Services Manager, Civic Centre, Station Road, Addlestone KT15 2AH ☎ 01932 425650; 01932 838384 📧 sam.clifton@runnymede.gov.uk

Emergency Planning: Mr Nick Moon, Managing Director - Applied Resilience, Civic Centre, Station Road, Addlestone KT15 2AH ☎ 01932 425178; 01784 451499; 01932 838384 📧 nick@appliedresilience.org

Energy Management: Mr Richard Webb, Principal Building Services Manager, Civic Centre, Station Road, Addlestone KT15 2AH ☎ 01932 425171; 01932 838384 📧 richard.webb@runnymede.gov.uk

Environmental / Technical Services: Mr Ian Maguire, Corporate Head - Planning & Environmental Services, Civic Centre, Station Road, Addlestone KT15 2AH ☎ 01932 415240; 01932 838384 📧 ian.maguire@runnymede.gov.uk

Environmental Health: Mr Ian Maguire, Corporate Head - Planning & Environmental Services, Civic Centre, Station Road, Addlestone KT15 2AH ☎ 01932 415240; 01932 838384 📧 ian.maguire@runnymede.gov.uk

Estates, Property & Valuation: Mr David Yetton, Assistant Valuer, Civic Centre, Station Road, Addlestone KT15 2AH ☎ 01932 425696 📧 david.yetton@runnymede.gov.uk

Facilities: Mr Richard Webb, Principal Building Services Manager, Civic Centre, Station Road, Addlestone KT15 2AH ☎ 01932 425171; 01932 838384 📧 richard.webb@runnymede.gov.uk

Finance: Mr Peter McKenzie, Corporate Head - Resources, Civic Centre, Station Road, Addlestone KT15 2AH ☎ 01932 425320; 01932 838384 📧 peter.mckenzie@runnymede.gov.uk

Fleet Management: Mr Alan Potter, Transport Officer, Chertsey Depot, Ford Road, Chertsey KT16 8HG ☎ 01932 425770; 01932 425771 📧 alan.potter@runnymede.gov.uk

RUNNYMEDE

Grounds Maintenance: Mr Peter Winfield, Community Development Manager - Green Space, Civic Offices, Station Road, Addlestone KT15 2AH ☎ 01932 425673; 01932 838384 ⏃ peter.winfield@runnymede.gov.uk

Highways: Mr Ian Maguire, Corporate Head - Planning & Environmental Services, Civic Centre, Station Road, Addlestone KT15 2AH ☎ 01932 415240; 01932 838384 ⏃ ian.maguire@runnymede.gov.uk

Home Energy Conservation: Mrs Verena Boxall, Energy Project Manager, Civic Centre, Station Road, Addlestone KT15 2AH ☎ 01932 425172; 01932 838384 ⏃ verena.boxall@runnymede.gov.uk

Housing: Mrs Jane Margetts, Corporate Head - Housing & Community Development, Civic Centre, Station Road, Addlestone KT15 2AH ☎ 01932 425824; 01932 838384 ⏃ jane.margetts@runnymede.gov.uk

Housing Maintenance: Mr Andrew Davidson, Housing Maintenance Manager, Civic Centre, Station Road, Addlestone KT15 2AH ☎ 01932 425840; 01932 838384 ⏃ andrew.davidson@runnymede.gov.uk

Legal: Mr Mario Leo, Corporate Head - Law & Governance, Civic Centre, Station Road, Addlestone KT15 2AH ☎ 01932 425640; 01932 838384 ⏃ mario.leo@runnymede.gov.uk

Leisure and Cultural Services: Mr Chris Hunt, Head of Community Development, Civic Centre, Station Road, Addlestone KT15 2AH ☎ 01932 425670; 01938 838384 ⏃ chris.hunt@runnymede.gov.uk

Licensing: Mr Robert Smith, Licensing Officer, Civic Centre, Station Road, Addlestone KT15 2AH ☎ 01932 425722; 01932 838384 ⏃ robert.smith@runnymede.gov.uk

Member Services: Mr Bernard Fleckney, Democratic Services Manager, Civic Centre, Station Road, Addlestone KT15 2AH ☎ 01932 425620; 01932 838384 ⏃ bernard.fleckney@runnymede.gov.uk

Parking: Mr Ian Maguire, Corporate Head - Planning & Environmental Services, Civic Centre, Station Road, Addlestone KT15 2AH ☎ 01932 415240; 01932 838384 ⏃ ian.maguire@runnymede.gov.uk

Partnerships: Mrs Suzanne Stronge, Community Partnership Officer, Civic Centre, Station Road, Addlestone KT15 2AH ☎ 01932 425869; 01932 838384 ⏃ suzanne.stronge@runnymede.gov.uk

Personnel / HR: Mrs Fiona Skene, Head of HR, Civic Centre, Station Road, Addlestone KT15 2AH ☎ 01932 425510 ⏃ fiona.skene@runnymede.gov.uk

Planning: Mr Ian Maguire, Corporate Head - Planning & Environmental Services, Civic Centre, Station Road, Addlestone KT15 2AH ☎ 01932 415240; 01932 838384 ⏃ ian.maguire@runnymede.gov.uk

Procurement: Mr Mario Leo, Corporate Head - Law & Governance, Civic Centre, Station Road, Addlestone KT15 2AH ☎ 01932 425640; 01932 838384 ⏃ mario.leo@runnymede.gov.uk

Recycling & Waste Minimisation: Mr Ian Maguire, Corporate Head - Planning & Environmental Services, Civic Centre, Station Road, Addlestone KT15 2AH ☎ 01932 415240; 01932 838384 ⏃ ian.maguire@runnymede.gov.uk

Regeneration: Mr Paul Turrell, Chief Executive, Civic Centre, Station Road, Addlestone KT15 2AH ☎ 01932 425500; 01932 838384 ⏃ paul.turrell@runnymede.gov.uk

Staff Training: Mrs Nadja Rupnik-Swindell, Human Resources Officer, Civic Centre, Station Road, Addlestone KT15 2AH ☎ 01932 425512 ⏃ nadja.rupnkik-swindell@runnymede.gov.uk

Street Scene: Mr Ian Maguire, Corporate Head - Planning & Environmental Services, Civic Centre, Station Road, Addlestone KT15 2AH ☎ 01932 415240; 01932 838384 ⏃ ian.maguire@runnymede.gov.uk

Tourism: Mr Chris Hunt, Head of Community Development, Civic Centre, Station Road, Addlestone KT15 2AH ☎ 01932 425670; 01938 838384 ⏃ chris.hunt@runnymede.gov.uk

Town Centre: Mr Ian Maguire, Corporate Head - Planning & Environmental Services, Civic Centre, Station Road, Addlestone KT15 2AH ☎ 01932 415240; 01932 838384 ⏃ ian.maguire@runnymede.gov.uk

Transport: Mr Alan Potter, Transport Officer, Chertsey Depot, Ford Road, Chertsey KT16 8HG ☎ 01932 425770; 01932 425771 ⏃ alan.potter@runnymede.gov.uk

Waste Collection and Disposal: Mr Dave Stedman, Direct Services Organisation Manager, Chertsey Depot, Ford Road, Chertsey KT16 8HG ☎ 01932 425760; 01932 425771 ⏃ dave.stedman@runnymede.gov.uk

COUNCILLORS

Mayor: Alderson, Alan (R - Egham Town) cllr.alan.alderson@runnymede.gov.uk

Deputy Mayor: Chaudhri, Iftikhar (CON - Foxhills) cllr.iftikhar.chaudhri@runnymede.gov.uk

Leader of the Council: Waddell, Peter (CON - Addlestone Bourneside) cllr.peter.waddell@runnymede.gov.uk

Anderson-Bassey, David (CON - Woodham) cllr.david.anderson-bassey@runnymede.gov.uk

Ashmore, John (R - Egham Town) cllr.john.ashmore@runnymede.gov.uk

Broadhead, Jim (CON - Addlestone North) cllr.jim.broadhead@runnymede.gov.uk

Butterfield, Howard (CON - Foxhills) cllr.howard.butterfield@runnymede.gov.uk

Clarke, Dolsie (CON - Chertsey St. Ann's) cllr.dolsie.clarke@runnymede.gov.uk

Cotty, Derek (CON - Chertsey Meads)
cllr.derek.cotty@runnymede.gov.uk

Dicks, Terry (CON - Chertsey South & Row Town)
cllr.terry.dicks@runnymede.gov.uk

Edis, Richard (CON - Chertsey St. Ann's)
cllr.richard.edis@runnymede.gov.uk

Furey, John (CON - Addlestone Bourneside)
cllr.john.furey@runnymede.gov.uk

Gill, Elaine (R - Thorpe)
cllr.elaine.gill@runnymede.gov.uk

Gillham, Linda (R - Thorpe)
cllr.linda.gillham@runnymede.gov.uk

Gracey, Jacqui (CON - New Haw)
cllr.jacqui.gracey@runnymede.gov.uk

Gracey, Tom (CON - Woodham)
cllr.tom.gracey@runnymede.gov.uk

Harnden, Margaret (R - Thorpe)
cllr.margaret.harnden@runnymede.gov.uk

Heath, Marisa (CON - Englefield Green East)
cllr.marisa.heath@runnymede.gov.uk

Khalique, Dannielle (CON - Foxhills)
cllr.danniellekhalique@runnymede.gov.uk

King, Nigel (CON - Englefield Green West)
cllr.nigel.king@runnymede.gov.uk

Kingerley, Gail (CON - Woodham)
cllr.gail.kingerley@runnymede.gov.uk

Knight, David (R - Egham Town)
cllr.david.knight@runnymede.gov.uk

Kusneraitis, Michael (CON - Englefield Green West)
cllr.michael.kusneraitis@runnymede.gov.uk

Lay, Yvonna (CON - Egham Hythe)
cllr.yvonna.lay@runnymede.gov.uk

Lewis, Scott (CON - Chertsey South & Rowtown)
cllr.scott.lewis@runnymede.gov.uk

Mackay, Stewart (CON - Addlestone North)
cllr.stewart.mackay@runnymede.gov.uk

Maddox, Mark (CON - New Haw)
cllr.mark.maddox@runnymeade.gov.uk

Manduca, Carol (CON - Virginia Water)
cllr.carol.manduca@runnymede.gov.uk

Nuti, Mark (CON - Chertsey Meads)
cllr.mark.nuti@runnymede.gov.uk

Parr, David (CON - Addlestone North)
cllr.david.parr@runnymede.gov.uk

Pitt, Barry (CON - Chertsey South & Row Town)
cllr.barry.pitt@runnymede.gov.uk

Prescot, Nick (CON - Englefield Green West)
cllr.nick.prescot@runnymede.gov.uk

Roberts, Patrick (CON - Englefield Green East)
cllr.patrick.roberts@runnymede.gov.uk

Simmons, Cherith (CON - Addlestone Bourneside)
cllr.cherith.simmons@runnymede.gov.uk

Sohi, Japneet (CON - Englefield Green East)
cllr.japneet.sohi@runnymede.gov.uk

Sohi, Parshotam (CON - Virginia Water)
cllr.parshotam.sohi@runnymede.gov.uk

Tollett, Adrian (CON - New Haw)
cllr.adrian.tollett@runnymede.gov.uk

Tuley, Paul (CON - Chertsey Meads)
cllr.paul.tuley@runnymede.gov.uk

Warner, Gill (CON - Egham Hythe)
cllr.gill.warner@runnymede.gov.uk

Wase-Rogers, Nick (CON - Virginia Waters)
cllr.nick.wase-rogers@runnymede.gov.uk

Willingale, Myles (CON - Chertsey St. Ann's)
cllr.myles.willingale@runnymede.gov.uk

Wilson, Jonathan (CON - Egham Hythe)
cllr.jonathan.wilson@runnymede.gov.uk

POLITICAL COMPOSITION
CON: 36, R: 6

COMMITTEE CHAIRS

Audit: Mr Nick Prescot

Housing: Mrs Cherith Simmons

Licensing: Ms Jacqui Gracey

Planning: Ms Gail Kingerley

Rushcliffe   D

Rushcliffe Borough Council, Civic Centre, Pavilion Road, West Bridgford NG2 5FE
☎ 0115 981 9911 🖨 0115 945 5882 ✆ customerservices@rushcliffe.gov.uk
🖥 www.rushcliffe.gov.uk

FACTS AND FIGURES
Parliamentary Constituencies: Rushcliffe
EU Constituencies: East Midlands
Election Frequency: Elections are of whole council

PRINCIPAL OFFICERS

Chief Executive: Mr Allen Graham, Chief Executive, Civic Centre, Pavilion Road, West Bridgford NG2 5FE ☎ 0115 914 8349 ✆ agraham@rushcliffe.gov.uk

Deputy Chief Executive: Ms Kath Marriott, Executive Manager - Transformation, Civic Centre, Pavilion Road, West Bridgford NG2 5FE ☎ 0115 914 8291 ✆ kmarriott@rushcliffe.gov.uk

Senior Management: Mr David Banks, Executive Manager - Neighbourhoods, Civic Centre, Pavilion Road, West Bridgford NG2 5FE ☎ 0115 914 8438 ✆ dbanks@rushcliffe.gov.uk

Senior Management: Mr Peter Linfield, Executive Manager - Finance & Corporate Services, Civic Centre, Pavilion Road, West Bridgford NG2 5FE ☎ 0115 914 8439 ✆ plinfield@rushcliffe.gov.uk

Senior Management: Mr David Mitchell, Executive Manager - Communities, Civic Centre, Pavilion Road, West Bridgford NG2 5FE ☎ 0115 914 8267 ✆ dmitchell@rushcliffe.gov.uk

RUSHCLIFFE

Architect, Building / Property Services: Mr Adrian Hutson, Construction & Energy Manager, Civic Centre, Pavilion Road, West Bridgford NG2 5FE ☎ 0115 914 8442 ✆ ahutson@rushcliffe.gov.uk

PR / Communications: Ms Caroline Newson, Performance & Reputation Team Leader, Civic Centre, Pavilion Road, West Bridgford NG2 5FE ☎ 0115 914 8570 ✆ cnewson@rushcliffe.gov.uk

Community Safety: Mr Ben Adams, Neighbourhood Manager, Civic Centre, Pavilion Road, West Bridgford NG2 5FE ☎ 0115 914 8487 ✆ badams@rushcliffe.gov.uk

Computer Management: Mr Greg Dwyer, ICT Service Delivery Manager, Civic Centre, Pavilion Road, West Bridgford NG2 5FE ☎ 0115 914 8411 ✆ gdwyer@rushcliffe.gov.uk

Customer Service: Ms Shirley Woltman, Customer Services Manager, Civic Centre, Pavilion Road, West Bridgford NG2 5FE ☎ 0115 981 9911 ✆ swoltman@rushcliffe.gov.uk

Electoral Registration: Mr Jeff Saxby, Elections & Corporate Information Manager, Civic Centre, Pavilion Road, West Bridgford NG2 5FE ☎ 0115 981 9216 ✆ jsaxby@rushcliffe.gov.uk

Emergency Planning: Ms Karen Emery, Emergency Planning Officer, Civic Centre, Pavilion Road, West Bridgford NG2 5FE ☎ 0115 977 3678 ✆ kemery@rushcliffe.gov.uk

Environmental Health: Mr David Banks, Executive Manager - Neighbourhoods, Civic Centre, Pavilion Road, West Bridgford NG2 5FE ☎ 0115 914 8438 ✆ dbanks@rushcliffe.gov.uk

Estates, Property & Valuation: Mr Adrian Hutson, Construction & Energy Manager, Civic Centre, Pavilion Road, West Bridgford NG2 5FE ☎ 0115 914 8442 ✆ ahutson@rushcliffe.gov.uk

Events Manager: Mrs Nicola Wells, Arts & Events Officer, Civic Centre, Pavilion Road, West Bridgford NG2 5FE ☎ 0115 914 8517 ✆ nwells@rushcliffe.gov.uk

Fleet Management: Mr Darryl Burch, Waste & Fleet Operations Manager, Civic Centre, Pavilion Road, West Bridgford NG2 5FE ☎ 0115 914 8405 ✆ dburch@rushcliffe.gov.uk

Grounds Maintenance: Ms Donna Dwyer, Strategic Housing Manager, Civic Centre, Pavilion Road, West Bridgford NG2 5FE ☎ 0115 914 8275 ✆ ddwyer@rushcliffe.gov.uk

Health and Safety: Ms Joanne Wilkinson, Health & Safety Advisor, Civic Centre, Pavilion Road, West Bridgford NG2 5FE ☎ 0115 914 8561 ✆ jwilkinson@rushcliffe.gov.uk

Housing: Ms Donna Dwyer, Strategic Housing Manager, Civic Centre, Pavilion Road, West Bridgford NG2 5FE ☎ 0115 914 8275 ✆ ddwyer@rushcliffe.gov.uk

Legal: Mr Paul Cox, Borough Solicitor, Civic Centre, Pavilion Road, West Bridgford NG2 5FE ☎ 0115 914 8215 ✆ pcox@rushcliffe.gov.uk

Leisure and Cultural Services: Mr Craig Taylor, Cultural Services Manager, Civic Centre, Pavilion Road, West Bridgford NG2 5FE ☎ 0115 914 8345 ✆ ctaylor@rushcliffe.gov.uk

Licensing: Mr Ben Adams, Neighbourhood Manager, Civic Centre, Pavilion Road, West Bridgford NG2 5FE ☎ 0115 914 8487 ✆ badams@rushcliffe.gov.uk

Member Services: Ms Vivien Nightingale, Member Services Manager, Civic Centre, Pavilion Road, West Bridgford NG2 5FE ☎ 0115 914 8481 ✆ vnightingale@rushcliffe.gov.uk

Partnerships: Mr David Mitchell, Executive Manager - Communities, Civic Centre, Pavilion Road, West Bridgford NG2 5FE ☎ 0115 914 8267 ✆ dmitchell@rushcliffe.gov.uk

Personnel / HR: Mrs Juli Hicks, Strategic Human Resources Manager, Civic Centre, Pavilion Road, West Bridgford NG2 5FE ☎ 0115 914 8316 ✆ jhicks@rushcliffe.gov.uk

Planning: Mr Andrew Pegram, Development Control Manager, Civic Centre, Pavilion Road, West Bridgford NG2 5FE ☎ 0115 914 8598 ✆ apegram@rushcliffe.gov.uk

Procurement: Ms Emma Galloway, Procurement Officer, Civic Centre, Pavilion Road, West Bridgford NG2 5FE ✆ egalloway@rushcliffe.gov.uk

Recycling & Waste Minimisation: Mr Darryl Burch, Waste & Fleet Operations Manager, Civic Centre, Pavilion Road, West Bridgford NG2 5FE ☎ 0115 914 8405 ✆ dburch@rushcliffe.gov.uk

Staff Training: Mrs Juli Hicks, Strategic Human Resources Manager, Civic Centre, Pavilion Road, West Bridgford NG2 5FE ☎ 0115 914 8316 ✆ jhicks@rushcliffe.gov.uk

Waste Collection and Disposal: Mr Darryl Burch, Waste & Fleet Operations Manager, Civic Centre, Pavilion Road, West Bridgford NG2 5FE ☎ 0115 914 8405 ✆ dburch@rushcliffe.gov.uk

Children's Play Areas: Mr Craig Taylor, Cultural Services Manager, Civic Centre, Pavilion Road, West Bridgford NG2 5FE ☎ 0115 914 8345 ✆ ctaylor@rushcliffe.gov.uk

COUNCILLORS

Mayor: Davidson, George (IND - Bingham East) cllr.davidison@rushcliffe.gov.uk

Deputy Mayor: Cooper, Leslie (CON - Gamston South) cllr.lcooper@rushcliffe.gov.uk

Leader of the Council: Clarke, Neil (CON - Radcliffe on Trent) cllr.nclarke@rushcliffe.gov.uk

Deputy Leader of the Council: Robinson, Simon (CON - Edwalton) cllr.srobinson@rushcliffe.gov.uk

Adair, Reginald (CON - Bunny) cllr.radair@rushcliffe.gov.uk

Beardsall, Kevin (CON - Edwalton) cllr.kbeardsall@rushcliffe.gov.uk

Brown, Andrew (CON - Sutton Bonington)
cllr.abrown@rushcliffe.gov.uk

Buckle, Martin (CON - Ruddington)
cllr.mbuckle@rushcliffe.gov.uk

Buschman, Brian (CON - Abbey)
cllr.bbuschman@rushcliffe.gov.uk

Butler, Richard (CON - Cotgrave)
cllr.rlbutler@rushcliffe.gov.uk

Chewings, Hayley (LAB - Cotgrave)
cllr.hchewings@rushcliffe.gov.uk

Combellack, Tina (CON - Nevile & Langar)
cllr.tcombellack@rushcliffe.gov.uk

Cottee, John (CON - Keyworth & Wolds)
cllr.jcottee@rushcliffe.gov.uk

Dickinson, Angela (CON - Abbey)
cllr.adickinson@rushcliffe.gov.uk

Donoghue, Julie (CON - Lutterell)
cllr.jdonoghue@rushcliffe.gov.uk

Edwards, Martin (LAB - Lutterell)
cllr.medwards@rushcliffe.gov.uk

Edyvean, Andrew (CON - Keyworth & Wolds)
cllr.aedyvean@rushcliffe.gov.uk

Greenwood, Jean (CON - Ruddington)
cllr.jgreenwood@rushcliffe.gov.uk

Hetherington, Ronald (CON - Leake)
cllr.rhetherington.gov.uk

Hull, Susan (IND - Bingham East)
cllr.shull@rushcliffe.gov.uk

Inglis, Robert (CON - Keyworth & Wolds)
cllr.ringlis@rushcliffe.gov.uk

Jeffreys, Christine (CON - Cotgrave)
cllr.cjeffreys:rushcliffe.gov.uk

Jones, Rod (LD - Musters)
cllr.rjones@rushcliffe.gov.uk

Khan, Karrar (LD - Musters)
cllr.kkhan@rushcliffe.gov.uk

Lawrence, Nigel (CON - East Bridgford)
cllr.nlawrence@rushcliffe.gov.uk

Lungley, John (CON - Ruddington)
cllr.jlungley@rushcliffe.gov.uk

MacInnes, Alistair (LAB - Trent Bridge)
cllr.amacinnes@rushcliffe.gov.uk

Males, Marie (CON - Leake)
cllr.mmales@rushcliffe.gov.uk

Mallender, Richard (GRN - Lady Bay)
cllr.rmallender@rushcliffe.gov.uk

Mallender, Susan (GRN - Lady Bay)
cllrsmallender@rushcliffe.gov.uk

Mason, Debbie (CON - Tollerton)
cllr.dmason@rushcliffe.gov.uk

Matthews, Stuart (CON - Gotham)
cllr.smatthews@rushcliffe.gov.uk

Moore, Gordon (CON - Cropwell)
cllr.gmoore@rushcliffe.gov.uk

Pell, Adeline (CON - Thoroton)
cllr.apell@rushcliffe.gov.uk

Phillips, Alan (CON - Compton Acres)
cllr.aphillips@rushcliffe.gov.uk

Plant, Liz (LAB - Trent Bridge)
cllr.eplant@rushcliffe.gov.uk

Purdue-Horan, Francis (CON - Bingham West)
cllr.fpurdue-horan@rushcliffe.gov.uk

Smith, Jean (CON - Radcliffe on Trent)
cllr.jsmith@rushcliffe.gov.uk

Stockwood, John (CON - Bingham West)
cllr.jstockwood@rushcliffe.gov.uk

Suthers, Martin (CON - Cranmer)
cllr.msuthers@rushcliffe.gov.uk

Thurman, John (CON - Leake)
cllr.jthurman@rushcliffe.gov.uk

Upton, Roger (CON - Radcliffe on Trent)
cllr.rupton@rushcliffe.gov.uk

Wheeler, Douglas (CON - Compton Acres)
cllr.dwheeler@rushcliffe.gov.uk

Wheeler, Jonathan (CON - Gamston North)
cllr.jwheeler@rushcliffe.gov.uk

POLITICAL COMPOSITION
CON: 34, LAB: 4, LD: 2, GRN: 2, IND: 2

Rushmoor   D

Rushmoor Borough Council, Council Offices, Farnborough
Road, Farnborough GU14 7JU
☎ 01252 398399 ✆ customerservices@rushmoor.gov.uk
🖥 www.rushmoor.gov.uk

FACTS AND FIGURES
Parliamentary Constituencies: Aldershot
EU Constituencies: South East
Election Frequency: Elections are by thirds

PRINCIPAL OFFICERS

Chief Executive: Mr Andrew Lloyd, Chief Executive, Council
Offices, Farnborough Road, Farnborough GU14 7JU
☎ 01252 398396; 01252 524017 ✆ andrew.lloyd@rushmoor.gov.uk

Deputy Chief Executive: Mr Ian Harrison, Corporate Director,
Council Offices, Farnborough Road, Farnborough GU14 7JU
☎ 01252 398401; 01252 524017 ✆ ian.harrison@rushmoor.gov.uk

Senior Management: Mrs Karen Edwards, Corporate Director,
Council Offices, Farnborough Road, Farnborough GU14 7JU
☎ 01252 398800 ✆ karen.edwards@rushmoor.gov.uk

Architect, Building / Property Services: Mr John Curtis,
Building Surveyor, Council Offices, Farnborough Road, Farnborough
GU14 7JU ☎ 01252 398414 ✆ john.curtis@rushmoor.gov.uk

Architect, Building / Property Services: Mr Alan Kingswell,
Building Surveyor, Council Offices, Farnborough Road, Farnborough
GU14 7JU ☎ 01252 398414 ✆ alan.kingswell@rushmoor.gov.uk

RUSHMOOR

Building Control: Mr Martin Hobley, Building Control Partnership Manager, Council Offices, Farnborough Road, Farnborough GU14 7JU ☎ 01252 398720 ⊕ martin.hobley@rushmoor.gov.uk

PR / Communications: Miss Gill Chisnall, Corporate Communications Manager, Council Offices, Farnborough Road, Farnborough GU14 7JU ☎ 01252 398744; 01252 398806 ⊕ gill.chisnall@rushmoor.gov.uk

Community Planning: Mrs Karen Edwards, Corporate Director, Council Offices, Farnborough Road, Farnborough GU14 7JU ☎ 01252 398800 ⊕ karen.edwards@rushmoor.gov.uk

Community Safety: Mr Peter Amies, Head of Community & Environmental Services, Council Offices, Farnborough Road, Farnborough GU14 7JU ☎ 01252 398750; 01252 398765 ⊕ peter.amies@rushmoor.gov.uk

Computer Management: Mr Nick Harding, Head of Information Technology & Facilities Services, Council Offices, Farnborough Road, Farnborough GU14 7JU ☎ 01252 398650 ⊕ nick.harding@rushmoor.gov.uk

Contracts: Mr Peter Amies, Head of Community & Environmental Services, Council Offices, Farnborough Road, Farnborough GU14 7JU ☎ 01252 398750; 01252 398765 ⊕ peter.amies@rushmoor.gov.uk

Corporate Services: Ms Amanda Fahey, Head of Financial Services & Chief Finance Officer, Council Offices, Farnborough Road, Farnborough GU14 7JU ☎ 01252 398440 ⊕ amanda.fahey@rushmoor.gov.uk

Customer Service: Mr Andrew Colver, Head of Democratic & Customer Services, Council Offices, Farnborough Road, Farnborough GU14 7JU ☎ 01252 398820; 01252 524017 ⊕ andrew.colver@rushmoor.gov.uk

Economic Development: Mr Phil Stoneman, Economic Development Officer, Council Offices, Farnborough Road, Farnborough GU14 7JU ☎ 01252 398760 ⊕ phil.stoneman@rushmoor.gov.uk

Electoral Registration: Mr Andrew Colver, Head of Democratic & Customer Services, Council Offices, Farnborough Road, Farnborough GU14 7JU ☎ 01252 398820; 01252 524017 ⊕ andrew.colver@rushmoor.gov.uk

Emergency Planning: Mr Jon Rundle, Head of Strategy, Performance & Partnership Management, Council Offices, Farnborough Road, Farnborough GU14 7JU ☎ 01252 398801; 01252 398806 ⊕ jon.rundle@rushmoor.gov.uk

Energy Management: Mr Les Murrell, Energy & Environment Manager, Council Offices, Farnborough Road, Farnborough GU14 7JU ☎ 01252 398538 ⊕ les.murrell@rushmoor.gov.uk

Environmental / Technical Services: Miss Qamer Yasin, Head of Environmental Health & Housing Services, Council Offices, Farnborough Road, Farnborough GU14 7JU ☎ 01252 398640; 01252 398552 ⊕ qamer.yasin@rushmoor.gov.uk

Environmental Health: Miss Qamer Yasin, Head of Environmental Health & Housing Services, Council Offices, Farnborough Road, Farnborough GU14 7JU ☎ 01252 398640; 01252 398552 ⊕ qamer.yasin@rushmoor.gov.uk

Estates, Property & Valuation: Mrs Ann Greaves, Solicitor to the Council, Council Offices, Farnborough Road, Farnborough GU14 7JU ☎ 01252 398600 ⊕ ann.greaves@rushmoor.gov.uk

Events Manager: Mr David Phillips, Town Centre & Cultural Manager, Princes Hall, Princes Way, Aldershot GU11 1NX ☎ 01252 398570 ⊕ david.phillips@rushmoor.gov.uk

Facilities: Mr Nick Harding, Head of Information Technology & Facilities Services, Council Offices, Farnborough Road, Farnborough GU14 7JU ☎ 01252 398650 ⊕ nick.harding@rushmoor.gov.uk

Finance: Ms Amanda Fahey, Head of Financial Services & Chief Finance Officer, Council Offices, Farnborough Road, Farnborough GU14 7JU ☎ 01252 398440 ⊕ amanda.fahey@rushmoor.gov.uk

Grounds Maintenance: Mr Andy Ford, Parks Development Officer, Council Offices, Farnborough Road, Farnborough GU14 7JU ☎ 01252 398771 ⊕ andy.ford@rushmoor.gov.uk

Health and Safety: Mr Roger Sanders, Health & Safety Officer, Council Offices, Farnborough Road, Farnborough GU14 7JU ☎ 01252 398160 ⊕ roger.sanders@rushmoor.gov.uk

Highways: Mr John Trusler, Principal Engineer, Council Offices, Farnborough Road, Farnborough GU14 7JU ☎ 01252 398377 ⊕ john.trusler@rushmoor.gov.uk

Home Energy Conservation: Mr Les Murrell, Energy & Environment Manager, Council Offices, Farnborough Road, Farnborough GU14 7JU ☎ 01252 398538 ⊕ les.murrell@rushmoor.gov.uk

Housing: Miss Qamer Yasin, Head of Environmental Health & Housing Services, Council Offices, Farnborough Road, Farnborough GU14 7JU ☎ 01252 398640; 01252 398552 ⊕ qamer.yasin@rushmoor.gov.uk

Legal: Mrs Ann Greaves, Solicitor to the Council, Council Offices, Farnborough Road, Farnborough GU14 7JU ☎ 01252 398600 ⊕ ann.greaves@rushmoor.gov.uk

Leisure and Cultural Services: Mr Peter Amies, Head of Community & Environmental Services, Council Offices, Farnborough Road, Farnborough GU14 7JU ☎ 01252 398750; 01252 398765 ⊕ peter.amies@rushmoor.gov.uk

Licensing: Mr John McNab, Environmental Health Manager of Licensing, Council Offices, Farnborough Road, Farnborough GU14 7JU ☎ 01252 398886 ⊕ john.mcnab@rushmoor.gov.uk

Lifelong Learning: Mrs Karen Edwards, Corporate Director, Council Offices, Farnborough Road, Farnborough GU14 7JU ☎ 01252 398800 ⊕ karen.edwards@rushmoor.gov.uk

Lottery Funding, Charity and Voluntary: Mr Peter Amies, Head of Community & Environmental Services, Council Offices, Farnborough Road, Farnborough GU14 7JU ☎ 01252 398750; 01252 398765 ⌨ peter.amies@rushmoor.gov.uk

Member Services: Mr Andrew Colver, Head of Democratic & Customer Services, Council Offices, Farnborough Road, Farnborough GU14 7JU ☎ 01252 398820; 01252 524017 ⌨ andrew.colver@rushmoor.gov.uk

Parking: Mrs Kirsty Hosey, Parking Manager, Council Offices, Farnborough Road, Farnborough GU14 7JU ☎ 01252 398510 ⌨ kirsty.hosey@rushmoor.gov.uk

Partnerships: Miss Annie Denton, Strategic Partnership Officer, Council Offices, Farnborough Road, Farnborough GU14 7JU ☎ 01252 398221 ⌨ annie.denton@rushmoor.gov.uk

Personnel / HR: Mrs Rachel Gray, Interim Human Resources Manager, Council Offices, Farnborough Road, Farnborough GU14 7JU ☎ 01252 398463 ⌨ rachel.gray@rushmoor.gov.uk

Planning: Mr Keith Holland, Head of Planning Services, Council Offices, Farnborough Road, Farnborough GU14 7JU ☎ 01252 398790; 01252 398668 ⌨ keith.holland@rushmoor.gov.uk

Procurement: Mrs Katherine Brooker, Principal Procurement Officer, Council Offices, Farnborough Road, Farnborough GU14 7JU ☎ 01252 398466 ⌨ katherine.brooker@rushmoor.gov.uk

Recycling & Waste Minimisation: Mr James Duggin, Contracts Manager, Council Offices, Farnborough Road, Farnborough GU14 7JU ☎ 01252 398167 ⌨ james.duggin@rushmoor.gov.uk

Regeneration: Mrs Debbie Whitcombe, Regeneration Officer, Council Offices, Farnborough Road, Farnborough GU14 7JU ☎ 01252 398793 ⌨ debbie.whitcombe@rushmoor.gov.uk

Staff Training: Mrs Rachel Gray, Interim Human Resources Manager, Council Offices, Farnborough Road, Farnborough GU14 7JU ☎ 01252 398463 ⌨ rachel.gray@rushmoor.gov.uk

Sustainable Communities: Mr Les Murrell, Energy & Environment Manager, Council Offices, Farnborough Road, Farnborough GU14 7JU ☎ 01252 398538 ⌨ les.murrell@rushmoor.gov.uk

Sustainable Development: Mr Les Murrell, Energy & Environment Manager, Council Offices, Farnborough Road, Farnborough GU14 7JU ☎ 01252 398538 ⌨ les.murrell@rushmoor.gov.uk

Tourism: Mr Peter Amies, Head of Community & Environmental Services, Council Offices, Farnborough Road, Farnborough GU14 7JU ☎ 01252 398750; 01252 398765 ⌨ peter.amies@rushmoor.gov.uk

Town Centre: Mr David Phillips, Town Centre & Cultural Manager, Princes Hall, Princes Way, Aldershot GU11 1NX ☎ 01252 398570 ⌨ david.phillips@rushmoor.gov.uk

Traffic Management: Mr John Trusler, Principal Engineer, Council Offices, Farnborough Road, Farnborough GU14 7JU ☎ 01252 398377 ⌨ john.trusler@rushmoor.gov.uk

Transport Planner: Mr Jim Pettitt, Transportation Strategy Officer, Council Offices, Farnborough Road, Farnborough GU14 7JU ☎ 01252 398200 ⌨ jim.pettitt@rushmoor.gov.uk

Waste Collection and Disposal: Mr James Duggin, Contracts Manager, Council Offices, Farnborough Road, Farnborough GU14 7JU ☎ 01252 398167 ⌨ james.duggin@rushmoor.gov.uk

Children's Play Areas: Mr Andy Ford, Parks Development Officer, Council Offices, Farnborough Road, Farnborough GU14 7JU ☎ 01252 398771 ⌨ andy.ford@rushmoor.gov.uk

COUNCILLORS

Mayor: Vosper, Jacqui (CON - St. John's) jacqui.vosper@rushmoor.gov.uk

Deputy Mayor: Choudhary, Sophia (CON - Rowhill) sophia.choudhary@rushmoor.gov.uk

Leader of the Council: Clifford, David (CON - Empress) david.clifford@rushmoor.gov.uk

Deputy Leader of the Council: Muschamp, Ken (CON - Fernhill) ken@laulind.co.uk

Group Leader: Staplehurst, Mark (UKIP - West Heath) ukip.westheath@virginmedia.com

Bedford, Diane (CON - St. Mark's) diane.bedford@tiscali.co.uk

Bell, David (UKIP - West Heath) dave.bell100@ntworld.com

Bridgeman, Terry (LAB - Aldershot Park) bridgemanterry@yahoo.co.uk

Carter, Sue (CON - Cove & Southwood) sue.carter@rushmoor.gov.uk

Choudhary, Charles (CON - Rowhill) charles.choudhary@btinternet.com

Cooper, Rod (CON - West Heath) rod.cooper@rushmoor.gov.uk

Corps, Liz (CON - St. Mark's) liz.corps@ntlworld.com

Crawford, Alex (LAB - Wellington) alex.crawford06@btinternet.com

Crerar, Peter (CON - Manor Park) peter_crerar@btinternet.com

Dibble, Sue (LAB - North Town) sue.dibble@rushmoor.gov.uk

Dibble, Keith (LAB - North Town) keith.dibble@rushmoor.gov.uk

Dibbs, Roland (CON - Knellwood) rlgdibbs@aol.com

Evans, Jennifer (LAB - Wellington) evans.jenniferevans@gmail.com

Gladstone, David (CON - St. Mark's) gladstone.conservative@gmail.com

Grattan, Clive (LAB - Cherrywood) clive.grattan@rushmoor.gov.uk

Hurst, Barbara (CON - St. John's) barbara@pbhurst.com

RUSHMOOR

Jackman, Adam (CON - Knellwood)
adam@jackman.org.uk

Jones, Barry (LAB - Cherrywood)
barry.jones@rushmoor.gov.uk

Lyon, Gareth (CON - Empress)
gareth.lyon@rushmoor.gov.uk

Marsh, John (CON - Fernhill)
johnmarsh@ntlworld.com

Masterson, Stephen (CON - Cove & Southwood)
steve@stationroad1958.fsnet.co.uk

Moyle, Peter (CON - St. John's)
peter.moyle@rushmoor.gov.uk

Munro, Marina (CON - Empress)
mmunrorushmoor@gmail.com

Newell, Adrian (CON - Aldershot Park)
adriannewell@msn.com

Preece, Jeremy (LAB - Wellington)
jeremy.preece@rushmoor.gov.uk

Roberts, Mike (LAB - Aldershot Park)
mike.roberts@rushmoor.gov.uk

Rust, Frank (LAB - North Town)
frank.rust@rushmoor.gov.uk

Sheehan, Maurice (CON - Rowhill)
maurice.sheehan@btinternet.com

Smith, Mike (CON - Empress)
mdsmithrushmoor@gmail.com

Taylor, Paul (CON - Knellwood)
paul.taylor@rsuhmoor.gov.uk

Taylor, Les (LAB - Cherrywood)
les.taylor@rushmoor.gov.uk

Tennant, Martin (CON - Cove & Southwood)
martin.tennant@rushmoor.gov.uk

Thomas, Bruce (CON - Manor Park)
bruce.thomas@ntlworld.com

Woolley, John (CON - Fernhill)
john.woolley@rushmoor.gov.uk

POLITICAL COMPOSITION
CON: 26, LAB: 11, UKIP: 2

COMMITTEE CHAIRS

Development Management: Mr Bruce Thomas

Licensing: Mr Martin Tennant

Rutland   U

Rutland County Council, Council Offices, Catmose, Oakham LE15 6HP
☎ 01572 722577 🖨 01572 758307 ✆ enquiries@rutland.gov.uk
🖳 www.rutland.gov.uk

FACTS AND FIGURES
Parliamentary Constituencies: Rutland and Melton
EU Constituencies: East Midlands
Election Frequency: Elections are of whole council

PRINCIPAL OFFICERS

Chief Executive: Mrs Helen Briggs, Chief Executive, Council Offices, Catmose, Oakham LE15 6HP ☎ 01572 758203
✆ hbriggs@rutland.gov.uk

Deputy Chief Executive: Dr Tim O'Neill, Deputy Chief Executive & Director - People, Council Offices, Catmose, Oakham LE15 6HP
☎ 01572 758402 ✆ toneill@rutland.gov.uk

Senior Management: Mr Dave Brown, Director - Places, Environment, Planning & Transport, Council Offices, Catmose, Oakham LE15 6HP ☎ 01572 758461 ✆ dbrown@rutland.gov.uk

Senior Management: Ms Debbie Mogg, Director - Resources, Council Offices, Catmose, Oakham LE15 6HP ☎ 01572 758358
✆ dmogg@rutland.gov.uk

Senior Management: Dr Tim O'Neill, Deputy Chief Executive & Director - People, Council Offices, Catmose, Oakham LE15 6HP
☎ 01572 758402 ✆ toneill@rutland.gov.uk

Senior Management: Mr Paul Phillipson, Director - Places, Development & Economy, Council Offices, Catmose, Oakham LE15 6HP ☎ 01572 758321 ✆ pphillipson@rutland.gov.uk

Architect, Building / Property Services: Mr Paul Phillipson, Director - Places, Development & Economy, Council Offices, Catmose, Oakham LE15 6HP ☎ 01572 758321
✆ pphillipson@rutland.gov.uk

Building Control: Mr Paul Phillipson, Director - Places, Development & Economy, Council Offices, Catmose, Oakham LE15 6HP ☎ 01572 758321 ✆ pphillipson@rutland.gov.uk

Children / Youth Services: Dr Tim O'Neill, Deputy Chief Executive & Director - People, Council Offices, Catmose, Oakham LE15 6HP ☎ 01572 758402 ✆ toneill@rutland.gov.uk

Civil Registration: Ms Samantha Corbett, Superintendent Registrar, Council Offices, Catmose, Oakham LE15 6HP
☎ 01572 758380 ✆ scorbett@rutland.gov.uk

PR / Communications: Mr Mat Waik, Strategic Communications Advisor, Council Offices, Catmose, Oakham LE15 6HP
☎ 01572 758328 ✆ mwaik@rutland.gov.uk

Community Safety: Mr Hugh Crouch, Senior Community Safety Officer, Council Offices, Catmose, Oakham LE15 6HP
☎ 01572 756655 ✆ hcrouch@rutland.gov.uk

Computer Management: Mr Andy Nix, Head of IT, Council Offices, Catmose, Oakham LE15 6HP ☎ 01572 758360
✆ anix@rutland.gov.uk

Consumer Protection and Trading Standards: Mr Paul Phillipson, Director - Places, Development & Economy, Council Offices, Catmose, Oakham LE15 6HP ☎ 01572 758321
✆ pphillipson@rutland.gov.uk

Contracts: Ms Louise Gallagher, Team Manager - Contracts, Council Offices, Catmose, Oakham LE15 6HP ☎ 01572 758292
✆ lgallagher@rutland.gov.uk

Corporate Services: Ms Debbie Mogg, Director - Resources, Council Offices, Catmose, Oakham LE15 6HP ☎ 01572 758358 ✆ dmogg@rutland.gov.uk

Customer Service: Mr Jay Khetani, Customer Services Manager, Council Offices, Catmose, Oakham LE15 6HP ☎ 01572 758326 ✆ jkhetani@rutland.gov.uk

Economic Development: Ms Libby Kingsley, Senior Economic Development Manager, Council Offices, Catmose, Oakham LE15 6HP ☎ 01572 722577 ✆ lkingsley@rutland.gov.uk

Education: Dr Tim O'Neill, Deputy Chief Executive & Director - People, Council Offices, Catmose, Oakham LE15 6HP ☎ 01572 758402 ✆ toneill@rutland.gov.uk

Electoral Registration: Ms Samantha Ramsay, Electoral Services Officer, Council Offices, Catmose, Oakham LE15 6HP ☎ 01572 720907 ✆ sramsay@rutland.gov.uk

Emergency Planning: Mr Dave Brown, Director - Places, Environment, Planning & Transport, Council Offices, Catmose, Oakham LE15 6HP ☎ 01572 758461 ✆ dbrown@rutland.gov.uk

Environmental Health: Mr Mark Loran, Senior Environmental Health Officer, Council Offices, Catmose, Oakham LE15 6HP ☎ 01572 758430 ✆ mloran@rutland.gov.uk

Estates, Property & Valuation: Mr Paul Phillipson, Director - Places, Development & Economy, Council Offices, Catmose, Oakham LE15 6HP ☎ 01572 758321 ✆ pphillipson@rutland.gov.uk

Finance: Mr Sav Della Rocca, Assistant Director - Finance, Council Offices, Catmose, Oakham LE15 6HP ☎ 01572 758159 ✆ sdellarocca@rutland.gov.uk

Finance: Ms Debbie Mogg, Director - Resources, Council Offices, Catmose, Oakham LE15 6HP ☎ 01572 758358 ✆ dmogg@rutland.gov.uk

Grounds Maintenance: Mr Mark Loran, Senior Environmental Health Officer, Council Offices, Catmose, Oakham LE15 6HP ☎ 01572 758430 ✆ mloran@rutland.gov.uk

Health and Safety: Mr Iain Watt, Corporate Health & Safety Officer, Council Offices, Catmose, Oakham LE15 6HP ☎ 01572 722577 ✆ iwatt@rutland.gov.uk

Highways: Mr Neil Tomlinson, Senior Highways Officer, Council Offices, Catmose, Oakham LE15 6HP ☎ 01572 758342 ✆ ntomlinson@rutland.gov.uk

Legal: Mrs Diane Baker, Head of Corporate Governance, Council Offices, Catmose, Oakham LE15 6HP ☎ 01572 758202 ✆ dbaker@rutland.gov.uk

Leisure and Cultural Services: Mr Robert Clayton, Head of Culture & Leisure, Council Offices, Catmose, Oakham LE15 6HP ☎ 01572 758435 ✆ rclayton@rutland.gov.uk

Licensing: Mr John Dwyer, Licensing Officer, Council Offices, Catmose, Oakham LE15 6HP ✆ jdwyer@rutland.gov.uk

Lifelong Learning: Mr Mark Fowler, Interim Head of Service - Lifelong Learning, Council Offices, Catmose, Oakham LE15 6HP ☎ 01572 722577 ✆ mfowler@rutland.gov.uk

Lighting: Mr Neil Tomlinson, Senior Highways Officer, Council Offices, Catmose, Oakham LE15 6HP ☎ 01572 758342 ✆ ntomlinson@rutland.gov.uk

Member Services: Mrs Diane Baker, Head of Corporate Governance, Council Offices, Catmose, Oakham LE15 6HP ☎ 01572 758202 ✆ dbaker@rutland.gov.uk

Parking: Mr James Von der Voelsungen, Parking Services Manager, Council Offices, Catmose, Oakham LE15 6HP ☎ 01572 720989 ✆ jvondervolesungen@rutland.gov.uk

Personnel / HR: Ms Carol Snell, Senior HR Adviser, Council Offices, Catmose, Oakham LE15 6HP ☎ 01572 722577 ✆ csnell@rutland.gov.uk

Planning: Mr Dave Brown, Director - Places, Environment, Planning & Transport, Council Offices, Catmose, Oakham LE15 6HP ☎ 01572 758461 ✆ dbrown@rutland.gov.uk

Public Libraries: Mr Robert Clayton, Head of Culture & Leisure, Council Offices, Catmose, Oakham LE15 6HP ☎ 01572 758435 ✆ rclayton@rutland.gov.uk

Recycling & Waste Minimisation: Mr Mark Loran, Senior Environmental Health Officer, Council Offices, Catmose, Oakham LE15 6HP ☎ 01572 758430 ✆ mloran@rutland.gov.uk

Road Safety: Mr Dave Brown, Director - Places, Environment, Planning & Transport, Council Offices, Catmose, Oakham LE15 6HP ☎ 01572 758461 ✆ dbrown@rutland.gov.uk

Social Services: Dr Tim O'Neill, Deputy Chief Executive & Director - People, Council Offices, Catmose, Oakham LE15 6HP ☎ 01572 758402 ✆ toneill@rutland.gov.uk

Social Services (Adult): Dr Tim O'Neill, Deputy Chief Executive & Director - People, Council Offices, Catmose, Oakham LE15 6HP ☎ 01572 758402 ✆ toneill@rutland.gov.uk

Social Services (Children): Dr Tim O'Neill, Deputy Chief Executive & Director - People, Council Offices, Catmose, Oakham LE15 6HP ☎ 01572 758402 ✆ toneill@rutland.gov.uk

Staff Training: Ms Carol Snell, Senior HR Adviser, Council Offices, Catmose, Oakham LE15 6HP ☎ 01572 722577 ✆ csnell@rutland.gov.uk

Tourism: Mrs Mary Copley, Tourism Advisor, Council Offices, Catmose, Oakham LE15 6HP mcopley@rutland.gov.uk

Traffic Management: Mr Neil Tomlinson, Senior Highways Officer, Council Offices, Catmose, Oakham LE15 6HP ☎ 01572 758342 ✆ ntomlinson@rutland.gov.uk

Transport: Mrs Emma Odabas, Group Manager - Transport & Accessibility, Council Offices, Catmose, Oakham LE15 6HP ☎ 01572 720923 ✆ eodabas@rutland.gov.uk

RUTLAND

Waste Collection and Disposal: Mr Mark Loran, Senior Environmental Health Officer, Council Offices, Catmose, Oakham LE15 6HP ☎ 01572 758430 ⌘ mloran@rutland.gov.uk

COUNCILLORS

Chair: Bool, Kenneth (CON - Normanton)
kbool@rutland.gov.uk

Vice-Chair: Baines, Edward (CON - Martinsthorpe)
ebaines@rutland.gov.uk

Leader of the Council: King, Terry (CON - Exton)
tking@rutland.gov.uk

Deputy Leader of the Council: Mathias, Tony (CON - Oakham South East)
tmathias@rutland.gov.uk

Begy, Nick (CON - Greetham)
nbegy@rutland.gov.uk

Bird, Oliver (IND - Oakham South West)
obird@rutland.gov.uk

Burkitt, Rachel (CON - Uppingham)
rburkitt@rutland.gov.uk

Callaghan, Ben (IND - Oakham South East)
bcallaghan@rutland.gov.uk

Clifton, Richard (CON - Oakham South West)
rclifton@rutland.gov.uk

Conde, Gary (CON - Ketton)
gconde@rutland.gov.uk

Cross, William (CON - Braunston & Belton)
wcross@rutland.gov.uk

Dale, Jeffrey (IND - Oakham North East)
jdale@rutland.gov.uk

Foster, Richard (CON - Cottesmore)
rfoster@rutland.gov.uk

Gale, Richard (IND - Oakham North West)
rgale@rutland.gov.uk

Hemsley, Oliver (CON - Langham)
ohemsley@rutland.gov.uk

Lammie, James (CON - Lyddington)
jlammie@rutland.gov.uk

MacDuff, Diane (CON - Ketton)
dmacduff@rutland.gov.uk

Mann, Alistair (CON - Oakham North West)
amann@rutland.gov.uk

Oxley, Marc (IND - Uppingham)
moxley@rutland.gov.uk

Parsons, Chris (IND - Ryhall & Casterton)
cparsons@rutland.gov.uk

Stephenson, Lucy (CON - Uppingham)
lstephenson@rutland.gov.uk

Stewart, Andrew (CON - Cottesmore)
astewart@rutland.gov.uk

Thomas, Kevin (LD - Whissendine)
kthomas@rutland.gov.uk

Waller, Gale (LD - Normanton)
gwaller@rutland.gov.uk

Walters, Alan (IND - Oakham North East)
awalters@rutland.gov.uk

Wilby, David (CON - Ryhall & Casterton)
dwilby@rutland.gov.uk

POLITICAL COMPOSITION
CON: 17, IND: 7, LD: 2

COMMITTEE CHAIRS

Adults & Health: Mr Gary Conde

Audit: Mrs Diane MacDuff

Children: Mr Jeffrey Dale

Development Control & Licensing: Mr Edward Baines

Health & Wellbeing: Mr Terry King

Licensing: Mrs Lucy Stephenson

Ryedale   D

Ryedale District Council, Ryedale House, Malton YO17 7HH
☎ 01653 600666 🖷 01653 696801 ⌘ enquiries@ryedale.gov.uk
🖳 www.ryedale.gov.uk

FACTS AND FIGURES
Parliamentary Constituencies: Thirsk & Malton
EU Constituencies: Yorkshire and the Humber
Election Frequency: Elections are of whole council

PRINCIPAL OFFICERS

Chief Executive: Ms Janet Waggott, Chief Executive, Ryedale House, Malton YO17 7HH ☎ 01653 600666 Ext 200 ⌘ janet.waggott@ryedale.gov.uk

Senior Management: Mrs Beckie Bennett, Head of Environment, Streetscene & Facilities, Ryedale House, Malton YO17 7HH ☎ 01653 600666 Ext 483 ⌘ beckie.bennett@ryedale.gov.uk

Senior Management: Mr Gary Housden, Head of Planning & Housing, Ryedale House, Malton YO17 7HH ☎ 01653 600666 Ext 307; 01653 696801 ⌘ gary.housden@ryedale.gov.uk

Senior Management: Mr Peter Johnson, Finance Manager, Ryedale House, Malton YO17 7HH ☎ 01653 600666 Ext 385; 01653 696801 ⌘ peter.johnson@ryedale.gov.uk

Senior Management: Mr Phil Long, Corporate Director, Ryedale House, Malton YO17 7HH ☎ 01653 600666 Ext 461 ⌘ phil.long@ryedale.gov.uk

Senior Management: Mr Julian Rudd, Head of Economy & Infrastructure, Ryedale House, Malton YO17 7HH ☎ 01653 600666 Ext 218; 01653 696801 ⌘ julian.rudd@ryedale.gov.uk

Senior Management: Mrs Clare Slater, Head of Corporate Services, Ryedale House, Malton YO17 7HH ☎ 01653 600666 Ext 347; 01653 696801 ⌘ clare.slater@ryedale.gov.uk

Senior Management: Mr Anthony Winship, Council Solicitor, Ryedale House, Malton YO17 7HH ☎ 01653 600666 Ext 267; 01653 696801 ⌘ anthony.winship@ryedale.gov.uk

Architect, Building / Property Services: Mrs Beckie Bennett, Head of Environment, Streetscene & Facilities, Ryedale House, Malton YO17 7HH ☎ 01653 600666 Ext 483 ⏍ beckie.bennett@ryedale.gov.uk

Best Value: Mrs Clare Slater, Head of Corporate Services, Ryedale House, Malton YO17 7HH ☎ 01653 600666 Ext 347; 01653 696801 ⏍ clare.slater@ryedale.gov.uk

Building Control: Mr Les Chapman, Building Control Manager, The Suite 2, Coxwold House, Easingwold Business Park, Easingwold, York YO61 3FB ☎ 01904 720281; 01904 720282 ⏍ les.chapman@ryedale.gov.uk

PR / Communications: Mrs Clare Slater, Head of Corporate Services, Ryedale House, Malton YO17 7HH ☎ 01653 600666 Ext 347; 01653 696801 ⏍ clare.slater@ryedale.gov.uk

Community Planning: Mrs Jos Holmes, Economy Manager, Ryedale House, Malton YO17 7HH ☎ 01653 600666 Ext 240; 01653 696801 ⏍ jos.holmes@ryedale.gov.uk

Community Planning: Mrs Clare Slater, Head of Corporate Services, Ryedale House, Malton YO17 7HH ☎ 01653 600666 Ext 347; 01653 696801 ⏍ clare.slater@ryedale.gov.uk

Community Safety: Ms Gail Cook, Technical Support Officer, Ryedale House, Malton YO17 7HH ☎ 01653 600666 Ext 314 ⏍ gail.cook@ryedale.gov.uk

Computer Management: Mr Tim Sedman, IT Manager, Ryedale House, Malton YO17 7HH ☎ 01653 600666 Ext 378 ⏍ tim.sedman@ryedale.gov.uk

Corporate Services: Mrs Clare Slater, Head of Corporate Services, Ryedale House, Malton YO17 7HH ☎ 01653 600666 Ext 347; 01653 696801 ⏍ clare.slater@ryedale.gov.uk

Customer Service: Angela Jones, Business Support Manager, Ryedale House, Malton YO17 7HH ☎ 01653 600666 Ext 220; 01653 696801 ⏍ angela.jones@ryedale.gov.uk

Customer Service: Mrs Clare Slater, Head of Corporate Services, Ryedale House, Malton YO17 7HH ☎ 01653 600666 Ext 347; 01653 696801 ⏍ clare.slater@ryedale.gov.uk

Economic Development: Mr Julian Rudd, Head of Economy & Infrastructure, Ryedale House, Malton YO17 7HH ☎ 01653 600666 Ext 218; 01653 696801 ⏍ julian.rudd@ryedale.gov.uk

E-Government: Mr Phil Long, Corporate Director, Ryedale House, Malton YO17 7HH ☎ 01653 600666 Ext 461 ⏍ phil.long@ryedale.gov.uk

Electoral Registration: Mr Simon Copley, Democratic Services Manager, Ryedale House, Malton YO17 7HH ☎ 01653 600666 Ext 277; 01653 696801 ⏍ simon.copley@ryedale.gov.uk

Emergency Planning: Mr Phil Long, Corporate Director, Ryedale House, Malton YO17 7HH ☎ 01653 600666 Ext 461 ⏍ phil.long@ryedale.gov.uk

Environmental / Technical Services: Mrs Beckie Bennett, Head of Environment, Streetscene & Facilities, Ryedale House, Malton YO17 7HH ☎ 01653 600666 Ext 483 ⏍ beckie.bennett@ryedale.gov.uk

Environmental Health: Mr Steven Richmond, Environmental Health Manager, Ryedale House, Malton YO17 7HH ☎ 01653 600666 Ext 247; 01653 600764 ⏍ steve.richmond@ryedale.gov.uk

European Liaison: Mr Julian Rudd, Head of Economy & Infrastructure, Ryedale House, Malton YO17 7HH ☎ 01653 600666 Ext 218; 01653 696801 ⏍ julian.rudd@ryedale.gov.uk

Events Manager: Mrs Jos Holmes, Economy Manager, Ryedale House, Malton YO17 7HH ☎ 01653 600666 Ext 240; 01653 696801 ⏍ jos.holmes@ryedale.gov.uk

Facilities: Mrs Beckie Bennett, Head of Environment, Streetscene & Facilities, Ryedale House, Malton YO17 7HH ☎ 01653 600666 Ext 483 ⏍ beckie.bennett@ryedale.gov.uk

• **Fleet Management:** Mrs Beckie Bennett, Head of Environment, Streetscene & Facilities, Ryedale House, Malton YO17 7HH ☎ 01653 600666 Ext 483 ⏍ beckie.bennett@ryedale.gov.uk

Grounds Maintenance: Mrs Beckie Bennett, Head of Environment, Streetscene & Facilities, Ryedale House, Malton YO17 7HH ☎ 01653 600666 Ext 483 ⏍ beckie.bennett@ryedale.gov.uk

Grounds Maintenance: Mrs Beckie Bennett, Head of Environment, Streetscene & Facilities, Ryedale House, Malton YO17 7HH ☎ 01653 600666 Ext 483 ⏍ beckie.bennett@ryedale.gov.uk

Health and Safety: Mr Steven Richmond, Environmental Health Manager, Ryedale House, Malton YO17 7HH ☎ 01653 600666 Ext 247; 01653 600764 ⏍ steve.richmond@ryedale.gov.uk

Home Energy Conservation: Ms Serena Williams, Environmental Health Officer, Ryedale House, Malton YO17 7HH ☎ 01653 600666 Ext 320 ⏍ serena.williams@ryedale.gov.uk

Housing: Mr Gary Housden, Head of Planning & Housing, Ryedale House, Malton YO17 7HH ☎ 01653 600666 Ext 307; 01653 696801 ⏍ gary.housden@ryedale.gov.uk

Housing: Ms Kim Robertshaw, Housing Services Manager, Ryedale House, Malton YO17 7HH ☎ 01653 600666 Ext 383 ⏍ kim.robertshaw@ryedale.gov.uk

Legal: Mr Anthony Winship, Council Solicitor, Ryedale House, Malton YO17 7HH ☎ 01653 600666 Ext 267; 01653 696801 ⏍ anthony.winship@ryedale.gov.uk

Leisure and Cultural Services: Mr Steven Richmond, Environmental Health Manager, Ryedale House, Malton YO17 7HH ☎ 01653 600666 Ext 247; 01653 600764 ⏍ steve.richmond@ryedale.gov.uk

Licensing: Mr Steven Richmond, Environmental Health Manager, Ryedale House, Malton YO17 7HH ☎ 01653 600666 Ext 247; 01653 600764 ⏍ steve.richmond@ryedale.gov.uk

RYEDALE

Lottery Funding, Charity and Voluntary: Mrs Jos Holmes, Economy Manager, Ryedale House, Malton YO17 7HH
☎ 01653 600666 Ext 240; 01653 696801 ◌ jos.holmes@ryedale.gov.uk

Member Services: Mr Simon Copley, Democratic Services Manager, Ryedale House, Malton YO17 7HH ☎ 01653 600666 Ext 277; 01653 696801 ◌ simon.copley@ryedale.gov.uk

Member Services: Mrs Clare Slater, Head of Corporate Services, Ryedale House, Malton YO17 7HH ☎ 01653 600666 Ext 347; 01653 696801 ◌ clare.slater@ryedale.gov.uk

Parking: Mrs Beckie Bennett, Head of Environment, Streetscene & Facilities, Ryedale House, Malton YO17 7HH ☎ 01653 600666 Ext 483 ◌ beckie.bennett@ryedale.gov.uk

Partnerships: Mrs Clare Slater, Head of Corporate Services, Ryedale House, Malton YO17 7HH ☎ 01653 600666 Ext 347; 01653 696801 ◌ clare.slater@ryedale.gov.uk

Personnel / HR: Mrs Denise Hewitt, Human Resources Manager, Ryedale House, Malton YO17 7HH ☎ 01653 600666 Ext 394 ◌ denise.hewitt@ryedale.gov.uk

Planning: Mr Gary Housden, Head of Planning & Housing, Ryedale House, Malton YO17 7HH ☎ 01653 600666 Ext 307; 01653 696801 ◌ gary.housden@ryedale.gov.uk

Procurement: Mrs Clare Slater, Head of Corporate Services, Ryedale House, Malton YO17 7HH ☎ 01653 600666 Ext 347; 01653 696801 ◌ clare.slater@ryedale.gov.uk

Recycling & Waste Minimisation: Mrs Beckie Bennett, Head of Environment, Streetscene & Facilities, Ryedale House, Malton YO17 7HH ☎ 01653 600666 Ext 483 ◌ beckie.bennett@ryedale.gov.uk

Regeneration: Mr Julian Rudd, Head of Economy & Infrastructure, Ryedale House, Malton YO17 7HH ☎ 01653 600666 Ext 218; 01653 696801 ◌ julian.rudd@ryedale.gov.uk

Staff Training: Mrs Denise Hewitt, Human Resources Manager, Ryedale House, Malton YO17 7HH ☎ 01653 600666 Ext 394 ◌ denise.hewitt@ryedale.gov.uk

Street Scene: Mrs Beckie Bennett, Head of Environment, Streetscene & Facilities, Ryedale House, Malton YO17 7HH ☎ 01653 600666 Ext 483 ◌ beckie.bennett@ryedale.gov.uk

Sustainable Communities: Mr Julian Rudd, Head of Economy & Infrastructure, Ryedale House, Malton YO17 7HH ☎ 01653 600666 Ext 218; 01653 696801 ◌ julian.rudd@ryedale.gov.uk

Tourism: Mrs Jos Holmes, Economy Manager, Ryedale House, Malton YO17 7HH ☎ 01653 600666 Ext 240; 01653 696801 ◌ jos.holmes@ryedale.gov.uk

Waste Collection and Disposal: Mrs Beckie Bennett, Head of Environment, Streetscene & Facilities, Ryedale House, Malton YO17 7HH ☎ 01653 600666 Ext 483 ◌ beckie.bennett@ryedale.gov.uk

COUNCILLORS

Chair: Gardiner, Bob (CON - Kirkbymoorside)

Vice-Chair: Oxley, William (CON - Pickering East)

Leader of the Council: Cowling, Linda (CON - Pickering West)
cllr.linda.cowling@ryedale.gov.uk

Group Leader: Burr, Lindsay (IND - Malton)
cllr.lindsay.burr@ryedale.gov.uk

Group Leader: Clark, John (LIB - Cropton)
cllr.john.clark@ryedale.gov.uk

Group Leader: Shields, Elizabeth (LD - Norton East)
cllr.elizabeth.shields@ryedale.gov.uk

Group Leader: Wainwright, Robert (IND - Hovingham)
cllr.robert.wainwright@ryedale.gov.uk

Acomb, Geoffrey (CON - Thornton Dale)
cllr.geoffrey.acomb@ryedale.gov.uk

Andrews, Paul (IND - Malton)

Andrews, Joy (LD - Pickering East)

Arnold, Steve (CON - Helmsley)
cllr.stephen.arnold@ryedale.gov.uk

Arnold, Val (CON - Sinnington)

Bailey, James (CON - Ampleforth)
cllr.james.bailey@ryedale.gov.uk

Cleary, Michael (CON - Derwent)

Cussons, David (CON - Kirkbymoorside)
cllr.david.cussons@ryedale.gov.uk

Duncan, Keane (CON - Norton East)

Farnell, Fiona (CON - Amotherby)

Frank, Janet (CON - Dales)
cllr.janet.frank@ryedale.gov.uk

Goodrick, Caroline (CON - Ryedale South West)
cllr.caroline.goodrick@ryedale.gov.uk

Hope, Eric (CON - Sheriff Hutton)
cllr.eric.hope@ryedale.gov.uk

Ives, Luke (CON - Norton West)
cllr.luke.ives@ryedale.gov.uk

Jainu-Dean, Tharik (CON - Wolds)

Jowitt, Ed (IND - Malton)

Keal, Dinah (LD - Norton West)
cllr.dinah.keal@ryedale.gov.uk

Maud, Brian (IND - Rillington)
cllr.brian.maud@ryedale.gov.uk

Potter, Mike (LIB - Derwent)

Raper, John (CON - Sherburn)
cllr.john.raper@ryedale.gov.uk

Sanderson, Janet (CON - Thornton Dale)
cllr.janet.sanderson@ryedale.gov.uk

Thornton, Tim (LIB - Pickering West)

Wildress, John (CON - Helmsley)
cllr.john.wildress@ryedale.gov.uk

POLITICAL COMPOSITION
CON: 19, IND: 5, LIB: 3, LD: 3

Salford City	M

Salford City Council, Civic Centre, Chorley Road, Swinton, Salford M27 5FJ

☎ 0161 794 4711 ⊟ 0161 793 3043 ▣ www.salford.gov.uk

FACTS AND FIGURES
Parliamentary Constituencies: Blackley and Broughton, Salford and Eccles, Worsley and Eccles South
EU Constituencies: North West
Election Frequency: Elections are by thirds

PRINCIPAL OFFICERS

Chief Executive: Mr Jim Taylor, City Director, Civic Centre, Chorley Road, Swinton, Salford M27 5FJ ☎ 0161 793 3400 ☖ jim.taylor@salford.gov.uk

Senior Management: Mr Ben Dolan, Strategic Director - Environment & Community Safety, Civic Centre, Chorley Road, Swinton, Salford M27 5FJ ☎ 0161 925 1112 ☖ ben.dolan@salford.gov.uk

Senior Management: Mr David Herne, Director - Public Health, Unity House, Chorley Road, Swinton M27 5AW ☎ 0161 793 3518 ☖ david.herne@salford.gov.uk

Senior Management: Ms Charlotte Ramsden, Strategic Director - Children & Adult Services, Civic Centre, Chorley Road, Swinton, Salford M27 5FJ ☎ 0161 778 0130 ☖ charlotte.ramsden@salford.gov.uk

Architect, Building / Property Services: Mr Les Woolhouse, Building Surveying Manager, Urban Vision Partnership Ltd, Emerson House, Albert Street, Eccles M30 0TE ☎ 0161 779 4961 ☖ les.woolhouse@urbanvision.org.uk

Building Control: Mr Dave Jolley, Director - Planning & Building Control, Urban Vision Partnership Ltd, Emerson House, Albert Street, Eccles M30 0TE ☎ 0161 604 7784 ☖ dave.jolley@urbanvision.org.uk

Catering Services: Mr Dominic Clarke, Head of Service - Citywide & Community Services, Turnpike House, 631 Eccles New Road, Salford M50 1SW ☎ 0161 925 1109 ☖ dominic.clarke@salford.gov.uk

Children / Youth Services: Mr Tim Rumley, Senior Youth Services Manager, The Beacon Centre, London Street, Salford M6 6QT ☎ 0161 603 6834 ☖ tim.rumley@salford.gov.uk

Civil Registration: Ms Rebecca Roberts, Superintendent Registrar, Civic Centre, Chorley Road, Swinton, Salford M27 5FJ ☎ 0161 603 6880 ☖ rebecca.roberts@salford.gov.uk

PR / Communications: Ms Debbie Brown, Director - Service Reform & Development, Unity House, Chorley Road, Swinton M27 5DA ☎ 0161 607 8600 ☖ debbie.brown@salford.gov.uk

PR / Communications: Ms Sue Hill, Head of Communications, Civic Centre, Chorley Road, Swinton, Salford M27 5FJ ☎ 0161 793 2600 ☖ sue.hill@salford.gov.uk

Community Safety: Mr Mark Reeves, Deputy Director - Environment & Community Safety, Civic Centre, Chorley Road, Swinton, Salford M27 5FJ ☎ 0161 925 1113 ☖ mark.reeves@salford.gov.uk

Computer Management: Mr David Hunter, Assistant Director - Corporate ICT, Civic Centre, Chorley Road, Swinton, Salford M27 5FJ ☎ 0161 793 3911 ☖ david.hunter@salford.gov.uk

Consumer Protection and Trading Standards: Mr John Wooderson, Head of Service - Regulatory Services, Unity House, Chorley Road, Swinton, Salford M27 5AW ☎ 0161 793 2623 ☖ john.wooderson@salford.gov.uk

Contracts: Mr Andrew White, Procurement Manager, Unity House, Chorley Road, Swinton M27 5AW ☎ 0161 607 6295 ☖ andrew.white@salford.gov.uk

Customer Service: Mr John Tanner, Assistant Director - Customer Services, Unity House, Chorley Road, Swinton M27 5DA ☎ 0161 793 3364 ☖ john.tanner@salford.gov.uk

Economic Development: Ms Bernie Vaudrey, Head of Business & Funding, Civic Centre, Chorley Road, Swinton, Salford M27 5FJ ☎ 0161 793 2283 ☖ bernie.vaudrey@salford.gov.uk

Education: Mrs Cathy Starbuck, Assistant Director - Education & Helping Families, Unity House, Chorley Road, Swinton M27 5AW ☎ 0161 778 0183 ☖ cathy.starbuck@salford.gov.uk

E-Government: Mr David Hunter, Assistant Director - Corporate ICT, Civic Centre, Chorley Road, Swinton, Salford M27 5FJ ☎ 0161 793 3911 ☖ david.hunter@salford.gov.uk

Electoral Registration: Mr Neil Watts, Principal Democratic Services Advisor of Elections, Civic Centre, Chorley Road, Swinton, Salford M27 5FJ ☎ 0161 793 3446 ☖ neil.watts@salford.gov.uk

Emergency Planning: Mr David Hunter, Assistant Director - Corporate ICT, Civic Centre, Chorley Road, Swinton, Salford M27 5FJ ☎ 0161 793 3911 ☖ david.hunter@salford.gov.uk

Energy Management: Mr Majid Maqbool, Energy Manager, 4th Floor, Emmerson House, Eccles M30 0TE ☎ 0161 607 6987 ☖ majid.maqbool@salford.gov.uk

Environmental Health: Mr John Wooderson, Head of Service - Regulatory Services, Unity House, Chorley Road, Swinton, Salford M27 5AW ☎ 0161 793 2623 ☖ john.wooderson@salford.gov.uk

Estates, Property & Valuation: Mr Richard Wynne, Director - Property & Development, Urban Vision Partnership Ltd, Emerson House, Albert Street, Eccles M30 0TE ☎ 0161 779 6127 ☖ richard.wynne@urbanvision.org.uk

European Liaison: Mr Ian Thompson, Funding & Development Officer, Civic Centre, Chorley Road, Swinton, Salford M27 5FJ ☎ 0161 793 2415 ☖ ian.thompson@salford.gov.uk

Events Manager: Mrs Lindsey Hebden, Tourism Marketing Manager, Civic Centre, Chorley Road, Swinton, Salford M27 5FJ ☎ 0161 793 2375 ☖ lindsey.hebden@salford.gov.uk

SALFORD CITY

Facilities: Mr David Horsler, Head of Facilities Management, Civic Centre, Chorley Road, Swinton, Salford M27 5FJ ☎ 0161 607 6994 ⌂ david.horsler@salford.gov.uk

Finance: Mr Neil Thornton, Director - Finance & Corporate Business, Unity House, Chorley Road, Swinton M27 5AW ☎ 0161 686 6200 ⌂ neil.thornton@salford.gov.uk

Fleet Management: Mr Terry Dixie, Head of Service - Transportation, Turnpike House, 631 Eccles New Road, Salford M50 1SW ☎ 0161 925 1046 ⌂ terry.dixie@salford.gov.uk

Grounds Maintenance: Mr David Seager, Assistant Director - Operational & Commercial Services, Civic Centre, Chorley Road, Swinton, Salford M27 5FJ ☎ 0161 925 1115 ⌂ david.seager@salford.gov.uk

Health and Safety: Mr John Wooderson, Head of Service - Regulatory Services, Unity House, Chorley Road, Swinton, Salford M27 5AW ☎ 0161 793 2623 ⌂ john.wooderson@salford.gov.uk

Highways: Mr Shoaib Mohammaed, Director - Engineering, Urban Vision Partnership Ltd, Emerson House, Albert Street, Eccles M30 0TE ☎ 0161 779 4800 ⌂ shoaib.mohammaed@capita.co.uk

Home Energy Conservation: Mr Leslie Laws, Principal Officer - Affordable Warmth, Civic Centre, Chorley Road, Swinton, Salford M27 5FJ ☎ 0161 793 2264 ⌂ leslie.laws@salford.gov.uk

Housing: Mrs Sarah Clayton, Head of Service - Strategy & Enabling, Unity House, Chorley Road, Swinton, Salford M27 5AW ☎ 0161 793 2366 ⌂ sarah.clayton@salford.gov.uk

Housing Maintenance: Mr Steve Haywood, Project Consultant - Salix Homes, Diamond House, 2 Peel Cross Road, Salford M5 4BT ☎ 0161 779 8899 ⌂ steve.haywood@salixhomes.org

Legal: Ms Miranda Carruthers-Watt, Assistant Director - Legal & Governance, Civic Centre, Chorley Road, Swinton, Salford M27 5FJ ☎ 0161 793 3620 ⌂ miranda.carruthers-watt@salford.gov.uk

Leisure and Cultural Services: Mr David Seager, Assistant Director - Operational & Commercial Services, Civic Centre, Chorley Road, Swinton, Salford M27 5FJ ☎ 0161 925 1115 ⌂ david.seager@salford.gov.uk

Licensing: Mr John Wooderson, Head of Service - Regulatory Services, Unity House, Chorley Road, Swinton, Salford M27 5AW ☎ 0161 793 2623 ⌂ john.wooderson@salford.gov.uk

Lighting: Mrs Sinead Hayes, Highways Operations Manager, Urban Vision Partnership Ltd, Emerson House, Albert Street, Eccles M30 0TE ☎ 07734 884519 ⌂ sinead.hayes@urbanvision.org.uk

Lottery Funding, Charity and Voluntary: Ms Sue Ford, Funding & Development Manager, Civic Centre, Chorley Road, Swinton, Salford M27 5FJ ☎ 0161 793 3443 ⌂ sue.ford@salford.gov.uk

Member Services: Mrs Karen Lucas, Principal Democratic Services Advisor, Civic Centre, Chorley Road, Swinton, Salford M27 5FJ ☎ 0161 793 3318 ⌂ karen.lucas@aslford.gov.uk

Parking: Mr William Earnshaw, Group Engineer - Parking Services, Urban Vision Partnership Ltd, Emerson House, Albert Street, Eccles M30 0TE ☎ 0161 779 4924 ⌂ william.earnshaw@urbanvision.org.uk

Personnel / HR: Ms Sam Betts, Assistant Director - Human Resources, Civic Centre, Chorley Road, Swinton, Salford M27 5FJ ☎ 0161 607 8600 ⌂ samantha.betts@salford.gov.uk

Planning: Mr Christopher Findley, Assistant Director - Planning & Housing, Civic Centre, Chorley Road, Swinton, Salford M27 5FJ ☎ 0161 793 3654 ⌂ chris.findley@salford.gov.uk

Procurement: Mr Andrew White, Procurement Manager, Unity House, Chorley Road, Swinton M27 5AW ☎ 0161 607 6295 ⌂ andrew.white@salford.gov.uk

Public Libraries: Ms Sarah Spence, Head of Libraries & Heritage, Civic Centre, Chorley Road, Swinton, Salford M27 5FJ ☎ 0161 778 0840 ⌂ sarah.spence@scll.co.uk

Recycling & Waste Minimisation: Mr David Seager, Assistant Director - Operational & Commercial Services, Civic Centre, Chorley Road, Swinton, Salford M27 5FJ ☎ 0161 925 1115 ⌂ david.seager@salford.gov.uk

Road Safety: Mr Andy Devine, Group Engineer, Urban Vision Partnership Ltd, Emerson House, Albert Street, Eccles M30 0TE ☎ 0161 779 4859 ⌂ andy.devine@urbanvision.org.uk

Social Services: Ms Sharon Hubber, Assistant Director - Specialist Services, Unity House, Chorley Road, Swinton M27 5AW ☎ 0161 603 4311 ⌂ sharon.hubber@salford.gov.uk

Social Services: Ms Sue Woodgate, Assistant Director - SEN, Access & Inclusion, Children's Services, 2nd Floor, Unity House, Chorley Road, Swinton M27 5AW ☎ 0161 778 0229 ⌂ sue.woodgate@salford.gov.uk

Social Services (Adult): Mr Keith Darragh, Assistant Director - Resources, Civic Centre, Chorley Road, Swinton, Salford M27 5FJ ☎ 0161 793 3225 ⌂ keith.darragh@salford.gov.uk

Social Services (Adult): Ms Bernadette Enright, Assistant Director - Assessment & Care Management, Civic Centre, Chorley Road, Swinton, Salford M27 5FJ ☎ 0161 793 2489 ⌂ bernadette.enright@salford.gov.uk

Social Services (Adult): Mrs Janice Lowndes, Assistant Director - Health Improvement Service, Civic Centre, 2nd Floor, Phase 2, Chorley Road, Swinton M27 5BY ☎ 0161 793 3603 ⌂ janice.lowndes@salford.gov.uk

Social Services (Adult): Ms Jennifer McGovern, Assistant Director - Joint Commissioning, Civic Centre, 2nd Floor, Phase 2, Chorley Road, Swinton M27 5BY ☎ 0161 793 2234 ⌂ jennifer.mcgovern@salford.gov.uk

Social Services (Children): Ms Lana Shannon, Interim Head of Service, Unity House, Chorley Road, Swinton M27 5AW ☎ 0161 603 4546 ⌂ lana.shannon@salford.gov.uk

Public Health: Mr Ian Ashworth, Consultant in Public Health, Unity House, Chorley Road, Swinton, Salford M27 5AW ☎ 0161 793 3552 ᐧᵈ ian.ashworth@salford.gov.uk

Public Health: Mrs Deborah Blackburn, Assistant Director - Public Health Nursing, Unity House, Chorley Road, Swinton, Salford M27 5AW ☎ 0161 607 6678 ᐧᵈ deborah.blackburn@salford.gov.uk

Public Health: Ms Siobhan Farmer, Consultant in Public Health, Unity House, Chorley Road, Swinton, Salford M27 5AW ☎ 0161 607 6938 ᐧᵈ siobhan.farmer@salford.gov.uk

Public Health: Mr David Herne, Director - Public Health, Unity House, Chorley Road, Swinton M27 5AW ☎ 0161 793 3518 ᐧᵈ david.herne@salford.gov.uk

Public Health: Ms Jacquie Russell, Assistant Director - Strategy & Change, Unity House, Chorley Road, Swinton M27 5AW ☎ 0161 793 3577 ᐧᵈ jacquie.russell@salford.gov.uk

Staff Training: Ms Sam Betts, Assistant Director - Human Resources, Civic Centre, Chorley Road, Swinton, Salford M27 5FJ ☎ 0161 607 8600 ᐧᵈ samantha.betts@salford.gov.uk

Street Scene: Mrs Sinead Hayes, Highways Operations Manager, Urban Vision Partnership Ltd, Emerson House, Albert Street, Eccles M30 0TE ☎ 07734 884519 ᐧᵈ sinead.hayes@urbanvision.org.uk

Sustainable Communities: Mr Ben Dolan, Strategic Director - Environment & Community Safety, Civic Centre, Chorley Road, Swinton, Salford M27 5FJ ☎ 0161 920 8400 ᐧᵈ ben.dolan@salford.gov.uk

Sustainable Development: Mr Christopher Findley, Assistant Director - Planning & Housing, Civic Centre, Chorley Road, Swinton, Salford M27 5FJ ☎ 0161 793 3654 ᐧᵈ chris.findley@salford.gov.uk

Tourism: Mrs Lindsey Hebden, Tourism Marketing Manager, Civic Centre, Chorley Road, Swinton, Salford M27 5FJ ☎ 0161 793 2375 ᐧᵈ lindsey.hebden@salford.gov.uk

Town Centre: Ms Elaine Davis, Senior Development Manager, Civic Centre, Chorley Road, Swinton, Salford M27 5FJ ☎ 0161 686 7420 ᐧᵈ elaine.davis@salford.gov.uk

Traffic Management: Mr Andy Devine, Group Engineer, Urban Vision Partnership Ltd, Emerson House, Albert Street, Eccles M30 0TE ☎ 0161 779 4859 ᐧᵈ andy.devine@urbanvision.org.uk

Transport: Mr Terry Dixie, Head of Service - Transportation, Turnpike House, 631 Eccles New Road, Salford M50 1SW ☎ 0161 925 1046 ᐧᵈ terry.dixie@salford.gov.uk

Transport Planner: Mr Lee Evans, Transportation Engineer, Civic Centre, Chorley Road, Swinton, Salford M27 5FJ ☎ 0161 793 3081 ᐧᵈ lee.evans@salford.gov.uk

Waste Collection and Disposal: Mr David Seager, Assistant Director - Operational & Commercial Services, Civic Centre, Chorley Road, Swinton, Salford M27 5FJ ☎ 0161 925 1115 ᐧᵈ david.seager@salford.gov.uk

Waste Management: Mr David Seager, Assistant Director - Operational & Commercial Services, Civic Centre, Chorley Road, Swinton, Salford M27 5FJ ☎ 0161 925 1115 ᐧᵈ david.seager@salford.gov.uk

COUNCILLORS

Directly Elected Mayor: Dennett, Paul (LAB - No Ward)

Ceremonial Mayor: Garrido, Karen (CON - Worsley)
councillor.garrido@salford.gov.uk

Ceremonial Deputy Mayor: Connor, Peter (LAB - Kersal)
councillor.connor@salford.gov.uk

Deputy Mayor: Boshell, Paula (LAB - Winton)
councillor.boshell@salford.gov.uk

Deputy Mayor: Merry, John (LAB - Broughton)
councillor.merry@salford.gov.uk

Group Leader: Turner, Les (CON - Walkden South)
councillor.turner@salford.gov.uk

Antrobus, Derek (LAB - Swinton North)
councillor.antrobus@salford.gov.uk

Balkind, Howard (LAB - Swinton South)
councillor.balkind@salford.gov.uk

Barnes, Michele (LAB - Barton)
councillor.barnes@salford.gov.uk

Bellamy, Sammie (LAB - Walkden North)
councillor.bellamy@salford.gov.uk

Bentham, Barbara (LAB - Claremont)
councillor.bentham@salford.gov.uk

Brocklehurst, Adrian (LAB - Walkden North)
councillor.brocklehurst@salford.gov.uk

Burch, Tanya (LAB - Ordsall)
councillor.burch@salford.gov.uk

Clarke, Bob (CON - Boothstown & Ellenbrook)
councillor.clarke@salford.gov.uk

Clarkson, Christopher (CON - Worsley)
councillor.clarkson@salford.gov.uk

Coen, Stephen (LAB - Irwell Riverside)
councillor.coen@salford.gov.uk

Collinson, Jillian (CON - Boothstown & Ellenbrook)
councillor.collinson@salford.gov.uk

Compton, Graham (CON - Worsley)
councillor.compton@salford.gov.uk

Critchley, Richard (LAB - Walkden South)
councillor.critchley@salford.gov.uk

Davies, Harry (LAB - Kersal)
councillor.davies@salford.gov.uk

Dawson, Jim (LAB - Swinton North)
councillor.dawson@salford.gov.uk

Dirir, Sareda (LAB - Claremont)
councillor.dirir@salford.gov.uk

Dobbs, Peter (LAB - Ordsall)
councillor.dobbs@salford.gov.uk

Ferguson, John (LAB - Pendlebury)
councillor.ferguson@salford.gov.uk

Fletcher, Heather (LAB - Swinton South)
councillor.fletcher@salford.gov.uk

SALFORD CITY

Garrido, Robin (CON - Boothstown & Ellenbrook)
councillor.rgarrido@salford.gov.uk

Hamilton, Jane (LAB - Irwell Riverside)
councillor.hamilton@salford.gov.uk

Hesling, Stephen (LAB - Weaste and Seedley)
councillor.hesling@salford.gov.uk

Hinds, Bill (LAB - Swinton North)
councillor.hinds@salford.gov.uk

Hudson, Christine (LAB - Cadishead)
councillor.hudson@salford.gov.uk

Humphreys, Ann-Marie (LAB - Kersal)
councillor.humphreys@salford.gov.uk

Hunt, Jimmy (LAB - Cadishead)
councillor.hunt@salford.gov.uk

Jolley, David (LAB - Barton)
councillor.jolley@salford.gov.uk

Jones, Roger (LAB - Irlam)
councillor.jones@salford.gov.uk

Kelly, Tracy (LAB - Irlam)
councillor.kelly@salford.gov.uk

King, Jim (LAB - Broughton)
councillor.king@salford.gov.uk

Lancaster, David (LAB - Winton)
councillor.lancaster@salford.gov.uk

Lea, Bernard (LAB - Pendlebury)
councillor.blea@salford.gov.uk

Lewis, Kate (LAB - Little Hutton)
councillor.lewis@salford.gov.uk

Lindley, Iain (CON - Walkden South)
councillor.lindley@salford.gov.uk

Longshaw, Paul (LAB - Langworthy)
councillor.longshaw@salford.gov.uk

Mashiter, Ray (LAB - Ordsall)
councillor.mashiter@salford.gov.uk

McIntyre, Charles (LAB - Broughton)
councillor.mcintyre@salford.gov.uk

Morris, Margaret (LAB - Winton)
councillor.morris@salford.gov.uk

Mullen, John (LAB - Barton)
councillor.mullen@salford.gov.uk

Murphy, Joe (LAB - Claremont)
councillor.jmurphy@salford.gov.uk

Ord, Stephen (LAB - Irwell Riverside)
councillor.ord@salford.gov.uk

Reynolds, Gina (LAB - Langworthy)
councillor.reynolds@salford.gov.uk

Ryan, Brendan (LAB - Walkden North)
councillor.bryan@salford.gov.uk

Sharpe, Rob (LAB - Little Hulton)
councillor.sharpe@salford.gov.uk

Stone, Lisa (LAB - Eccles)
councillor.stone@salford.gov.uk

Taylor, Peter (LAB - Irlam)
councillor.taylor@salford.gov.uk

Walsh, John (LAB - Cadishead)
councillor.walsh@salford.gov.uk

Warmisham, John (LAB - Langworthy)
councillor.warmisham@salford.gov.uk

Warner, Barry (LAB - Pendlebury)
councillor.warner@salford.gov.uk

Watkin, Neil (IND - Swinton South)
councillor.watkin@salford.gov.uk

Weir, Colette (LAB - Little Hulton)
councillor.weir@salford.gov.uk

Wheeler, Michael (LAB - Eccles)
councillor.wheeler@salford.gov.uk

Wheeler, Peter (LAB - Eccles)
councillor.pwheeler@salford.gov.uk

Wilson, Ronnie (LAB - Weaste and Seedley)
councillor.rwilson@salford.gov.uk

Wilson, Paul (LAB - Weaste and Seedley)
councillor.p.wilson@salford.gov.uk

POLITICAL COMPOSITION
LAB: 52, CON: 8, IND: 1

COMMITTEE CHAIRS

Children: Mr Adrian Brocklehurst

Community & Neighbourhoods: Ms Tanya Burch

Health & Adults: Ms Margaret Morris

Licensing: Mr John Warmisham

Planning & Transportation: Mr Ray Mashiter

Sandwell   M

Sandwell Metropolitan Borough Council, Sandwell Council
House, Oldbury B69 3DE
☎ 0121 569 2200 🖷 0121 569 3100 ✆ smbc@sandwell.gov.uk
🖳 www.sandwell.gov.uk

FACTS AND FIGURES
Parliamentary Constituencies: Halesowen and Rowley Regis,
Warley, West Bromwich East, West Bromwich West
EU Constituencies: West Midlands
Election Frequency: Elections are by thirds

PRINCIPAL OFFICERS

Chief Executive: Mr Jan Britton, Chief Executive, Sandwell
Council House, Oldbury B69 3DE ☎ 0121 569 3500
✆ jan_britton@sandwell.gov.uk

Assistant Chief Executive: Ms Melanie Dudley, Assistant Chief
Executive, Sandwell Council House, Oldbury B69 3DE
☎ 0121 569 3548 ✆ melanie_dudley@sandwell.gov.uk

Senior Management: Ms Jyoti Atri, Director - Public Health,
Sandwell Council House, Oldbury B69 3DE ☎ 0845 352 7645
✆ jyoti_atri@sandwell.gov.uk

Senior Management: Mr Nick Bubalo, Director - Regeneration & Economy, Sandwell Council House, Oldbury B69 3DE
☎ 0121 569 4253 ✆ nick_bubalo@sandwell.gov.uk

Senior Management: Mr Stuart Lackenby, Chief Operating Officer - Adults, Sandwell Council House, Oldbury B69 3DE
☎ 0121 569 5060 ✆ stuart_lackenby@sandwell.gov.uk

Senior Management: Mrs Sharon Moore, Director - Children & Families, Sandwell Council House, Oldbury B69 3DE
☎ 0121 569 8378 ✆ sharon_moore@sandwell.gov.uk

Senior Management: Mr Matthew Sampson, Director - Children's Services, Sandwell Council House, Oldbury B69 3DE
☎ 0121 569 8204 ✆ matthew_sampson@sandwell.gov.uk

Senior Management: Mr Adrian Scarrott, Director - Neighbourhoods, Sandwell Council House, Oldbury B69 3DE
☎ 0121 569 5034 ✆ adrian_scarrott@sandwell.gov.uk

Senior Management: Mrs Neeraj Sharma, Director - Governance & Risk, Sandwell Council House, Oldbury B69 3DE
☎ 0121 569 3172 ✆ neeraj_sharma@sandwell.gov.uk

Senior Management: Mr David Stevens, Director - Adult Social Care, Health & Wellbeing, Sandwell Council House, Oldbury B69 3DE ☎ 0121 569 5887 ✆ david_stevens@sandwell.gov.uk

Senior Management: Mr Chris Ward, Director - Learning, Sandwell Council House, Oldbury B69 3DE ☎ 0121 569 8194 ✆ chris_ward@sandwell.gov.uk

Access Officer / Social Services (Disability): Mr David Dwyer, Assistant Access Officer, Sandwell Council House, Oldbury B69 3DE ☎ 0121 569 3413 ✆ david_dwyer@sandwell.gov.uk

Building Control: Mr John Baker, Development & Regulatory Services Manager, Sandwell Council House, Oldbury B69 3DE
☎ 0121 569 4037 ✆ john_baker@sandwell.gov.uk

Catering Services: Ms Tracey Pace, Sandwell Inspired Partnership Service, Sandwell Council House, Oldbury B69 3DE
☎ 0121 296 3000 ✆ tracey_pace@sandwell.gov.uk

Children / Youth Services: Mr Charlie Spencer, Divisional Manager - Targeted Youth Support, Sandwell Council House, Oldbury B69 3DE ☎ 0845 352 7701
✆ charlie_spencer@sandwell.gov.uk

Civil Registration: Mr Paul Sheldon, Registration Services Manager, Sandwell Register Office, Highfields, High Street, West Bromwich B70 8RJ ☎ 0121 569 2471
✆ paul_sheldon@sandwell.gov.uk

PR / Communications: Mr Richard Wyatt, Communications Manager, Sandwell Council House, Oldbury B69 3DE
☎ 0121 569 3439 ✆ richard_wyatt@sandwell.gov.uk

Community Planning: Ms Philippa Smith, Spatial Policy & Development Manager, Sandwell Council House, Oldbury B69 3DE
☎ 0121 569 4195 ✆ philippa_smith@sandwell.gov.uk

Community Safety: Mr Mark Peniket, General Manager - Neighbourhood Services, Sandwell Council House, Oldbury B69 3DE ☎ 0121 569 6040 ✆ mark_peniket@sandwell.gov.uk

Computer Management: Mr Andy Nicholls, ICT Strategy & Client Manager, Sandwell Council House, Oldbury B69 3DE
☎ 0121 569 3371 ✆ andy_nicholls@sandwell.gov.uk

Consumer Protection and Trading Standards: Ms Jyoti Atri, Director - Public Health, Sandwell Council House, Oldbury B69 3DE
☎ 0845 352 7645 ✆ jyoti_atri@sandwell.gov.uk

Customer Service: Mr Paul Haden, Strategic Lead - Customer Focus, Sandwell Council House, Oldbury B69 3DE ☎ 0121 569 3471
✆ paul_haden@sandwell.gov.uk

Education: Mr Chris Ward, Director - Learning, Sandwell Council House, Oldbury B69 3DE ☎ 0121 569 8194
✆ chris_ward@sandwell.gov.uk

Electoral Registration: Mr Philip Hardy, Electoral Services Manager, PO Box 2374, Sandwell Council House, Oldbury B69 3DE
☎ 0121 569 3244 ✆ philip_hardy@sandwell.gov.uk

Emergency Planning: Mr Alan Boyd, Resilience Manager, Sandwell Council House, Oldbury B69 3DE ☎ 0121 569 3060; 0121 569 3983 ✆ alan_boyd@sandwell.gov.uk

Environmental / Technical Services: Mr Max Cookson, Environment Services Manager, Shidas Lane, Oldbury B69 2BP
☎ 0121 569 4117 ✆ max_cookson@sandwell.gov.uk

Environmental Health: Mr Max Cookson, Environment Services Manager, Shidas Lane, Oldbury B69 2BP ☎ 0121 569 4117
✆ max_cookson@sandwell.gov.uk

Estates, Property & Valuation: Mr Mark Peniket, General Manager - Neighbourhood Services, Sandwell Council House, Oldbury B69 3DE ☎ 0121 569 6040 ✆ mark_peniket@sandwell.gov.uk

Events Manager: Mr Tony Potter, Events & Projects Manager, Sandwell Valley Park Farm, Slaters Lane, West Bromwich B71 4BG
☎ 0121 553 0220 ✆ tony_potter@sandwell.gov.uk

Facilities: Ms Christine Bailey, Facilities Services Manager, Sandwell Council House, Oldbury B69 3DE ☎ 0121 569 3941
✆ christine_bailey@sandwell.gov.uk

Fleet Management: Ms Carole Bishop, Fleet Manager, Transport Depot, Waterfall Lane, Cradley Heath B64 6RL ☎ 0121 569 6846
✆ carole_bishop@sandwell.gov.uk

Health and Safety: Mr Chris Wiliams, Health, Safety & Welfare Manager, PO Box 2374, Sandwell Council House, Oldbury B69 3DE
☎ 0121 569 8328 ✆ chris_williams@sandwell.gov.uk

Highways: Mr Robin Weare, Highways Service Manager, Sandwell Council House, Oldbury B69 3DE ☎ 0121 569 4171
✆ robin_weare@sandwell.gov.uk

SANDWELL

Housing: Mr Norman Fletcher, Service Manager - Housing Strategy & Partnerships, Sandwell Council House, Oldbury B69 3DE ☎ 0121 569 5108 ⏿ norman_fletcher@sandwell.gov.uk

Housing Maintenance: Mr Steve Greenhouse, Housing Repairs Service Manager, Operations & Development Centre, Roway Lane, Oldbury B69 3ES ☎ 0121 569 6441 ⏿ steve_greenhouse@sandwell.gov.uk

Legal: Mrs Neeraj Sharma, Director - Governance & Risk, Sandwell Council House, PO Box 2374, Oldbury B69 3DE ☎ 0121 569 3172 ⏿ neeraj_sharma@sandwell.gov.uk

Leisure and Cultural Services: Mr John Satchwell, Parks & Countryside Manager, Sandwell Council House, Oldbury B69 3DE ☎ 0121 569 6812 ⏿ john_satchwell@sandwell.gov.uk

Licensing: Ms Jyoti Atri, Director - Public Health, Sandwell Council House, Oldbury B69 3DE ☎ 0845 352 7645 ⏿ jyoti_atri@sandwell.gov.uk

Lifelong Learning: Mr Chris Ward, Director - Learning, Sandwell Council House, Oldbury B69 3DE ☎ 0121 569 8194 ⏿ chris_ward@sandwell.gov.uk

Lighting: Mr Nigel Wilkins, Group Manager - Development, Sandwell Council House, Oldbury B69 3DE ☎ 0121 569 4027 ⏿ nigel_wilkins@sandwell.gov.uk

Lottery Funding, Charity and Voluntary: Ms Heather Chinner, Voluntary Sector Liason & Development Manager, Sandwell Council House, Oldbury B69 3DE ☎ 0121 569 3020 ⏿ heather_chinner@sandwell.gov.uk

Member Services: Mr Rob Hevican, Member Services Manager, Sandwell Council House, Oldbury B69 3DE ☎ 0121 569 3043 ⏿ robert_hevican@sandwell.gov.uk

Parking: Mr Robin Weare, Highways Service Manager, Sandwell Council House, Oldbury B69 3DE ☎ 0121 569 4171 ⏿ robin_weare@sandwell.gov.uk

Personnel / HR: Ms Cathi Dodd, Service Manager - Improvement & Efficiency / Strategic HR, Sandwell Council House, Oldbury B69 3DE ☎ 0121 569 3289 ⏿ cathi_dodd@sandwell.gov.uk

Planning: Mr Nick Bubalo, Director - Regeneration & Economy, Sandwell Council House, Oldbury B69 3DE ☎ 0121 569 4253 ⏿ nick_bubalo@sandwell.gov.uk

Procurement: Mr Neil Whitehouse, Senior Category Manager, Sandwell Council House, Oldbury B69 3DE ☎ 0121 569 3625 ⏿ neil_whitehouse@sandwell.gov.uk

Public Libraries: Mr Jim Wells, Service Lead - Leisure, Culture & Lifelong Learning, Sandwell Council House, Oldbury B69 3DE ☎ 0121 569 8242 ⏿ jim_wells@sandwell.gov.uk

Recycling & Waste Minimisation: Mr Max Cookson, Environment Services Manager, Shidas Lane, Oldbury B69 2BP ☎ 0121 569 4117 ⏿ max_cookson@sandwell.gov.uk

Regeneration: Mr Nick Bubalo, Director - Regeneration & Economy, Sandwell Council House, Oldbury B69 3DE ☎ 0121 569 4253 ⏿ nick_bubalo@sandwell.gov.uk

Road Safety: Mr Irfan Choudry, Highways Service Manager, Sandwell Council House, Oldbury B69 3DE ☎ 0121 569 1857 ⏿ irfan_choudry@sandwell.gov.uk

Social Services: Mr Simon White, Director - Children's Services, Sandwell Council House, Oldbury B69 3DE ☎ 0121 569 8204 ⏿ simon_white@sandwell.gov.uk

Social Services (Adult): Mr David Stevens, Director - Adult Social Care, Health & Wellbeing, Sandwell Council House, Oldbury B69 3DE ☎ 0121 569 5887 ⏿ david_stevens@sandwell.gov.uk

Social Services (Children): Mrs Sharon Moore, Director - Children & Families, Sandwell Council House, Oldbury B69 3DE ☎ 0121 569 8378 ⏿ sharon_moore@sandwell.gov.uk

Public Health: Ms Jyoti Atri, Director - Public Health, Sandwell Council House, Oldbury B69 3DE ☎ 0845 352 7645 ⏿ jyoti_atri@sandwell.gov.uk

Staff Training: Ms Melanie Dudley, Assistant Chief Executive, Sandwell Council House, Oldbury B69 3DE ☎ 0121 569 3548 ⏿ melanie_dudley@sandwell.gov.uk

Street Scene: Mr Nick Bubalo, Director - Regeneration & Economy, Sandwell Council House, Oldbury B69 3DE ☎ 0121 569 4253 ⏿ nick_bubalo@sandwell.gov.uk

Sustainable Communities: Mr Gary Bowman, Service Manager - Area Working, Sandwell Council House, Oldbury B69 3DE ☎ 0121 569 3447 ⏿ gary_bowman@sandwell.gov.uk

Sustainable Development: Mr John Baker, Development & Regulatory Services Manager, Sandwell Council House, Oldbury B69 3DE ☎ 0121 569 4037 ⏿ john_baker@sandwell.gov.uk

Tourism: Mr Jim Wells, Service Lead - Leisure, Culture & Lifelong Learning, Sandwell Council House, Oldbury B69 3DE ☎ 0121 569 8242 ⏿ jim_wells@sandwell.gov.uk

Town Centre: Mr John Baker, Development & Regulatory Services Manager, Sandwell Council House, Oldbury B69 3DE ☎ 0121 569 4037 ⏿ john_baker@sandwell.gov.uk

Traffic Management: Mr Robin Weare, Highways Service Manager, Sandwell Council House, Oldbury B69 3DE ☎ 0121 569 4171 ⏿ robin_weare@sandwell.gov.uk

Waste Collection and Disposal: Mr Max Cookson, Environment Services Manager, Shidas Lane, Oldbury B69 2BP ☎ 0121 569 4117 ⏿ max_cookson@sandwell.gov.uk

Waste Management: Mr Max Cookson, Environment Services Manager, Shidas Lane, Oldbury B69 2BP ☎ 0121 569 4117 ⏿ max_cookson@sandwell.gov.uk

Children's Play Areas: Mr John Satchwell, Parks & Countryside Manager, Sandwell Council House, Oldbury B69 3DE
☎ 0121 569 6812 ✏ john_satchwell@sandwell.gov.uk

COUNCILLORS

Leader of the Council: Eling, Steve (LAB - Abbey)
steve_eling@sandwell.gov.uk

Deputy Leader of the Council: Khatun, Syeda (LAB - Tipton Green)
syeda_khatun@cllr.sandwell.gov.uk

Ahmed, Zahoor (LAB - St. Paul's)
zahoor_ahmed@sandwell.gov.uk

Allcock, Keith (LAB - Newton)
keith_allcock@cllr.sandwell.org.uk

Allen, Peter (LAB - Great Bridge)
peter_allen@sandwell.gov.uk

Ashman, Lorraine (LAB - Tividale)
lorraine_ashman@sandwell.gov.uk

Bawa, Babu (LAB - St. Paul's)
babu_singhbawa@cllr.sandwell.org.uk

Carmichael, Kerrie (LAB - Blackheath)
blackheathlabour@hotmail.co.uk

Cherrington, Bill (LAB - Princes End)
bill_cherrington@sandwell.gov.uk

Costigan, Elaine (LAB - Wednesbury North)
elainecostigan@hotmail.co.uk

Crompton, Maria (LAB - Tividale)
maria_crompton@sandwell.gov.uk

Crumpton, Trevor (LAB - Old Warley)
t.crumpton@talktalk.net

Crumpton, Susan (LAB - Old Warley)
sue_crumpton@cllr.sandwell.org.uk

Davies, Yvonne (LAB - Langley)
ydavies16@btinternet.com

Davies, Patricia (LAB - Hateley Heath)
patdavies2006@yahoo.co.uk

Davies, Sharon (LAB - Langley)
cllrsharon_davies@sandwell.gov.uk

Davies, Keith (LAB - Smethwick)
keith_davies@cllr.sandwell.org.uk

Dhallu, Bawa (LAB - West Bromwich Central)
bawa_singhdhallu@cllr.sandwell.org.uk

Downing, Susan (LAB - Oldbury)
susan_downing@cllr.sandwell.org.uk

Eaves, Susan (LAB - Rowley)
susan_eaves@sandwell.gov.uk

Edis, Joy (LAB - Friar Park)
joy_edis@cllr.sandwell.org.uk

Edwards, John (LAB - Greets Green & Lyng)
john_edwards@cllr.sandwell.org.uk

Frear, Steven (LAB - Bristnall)
steven.frear@btinternet.com

Garrett, Philip (UKIP - Princes End)
philip_garrett@sandwell.gov.uk

Gavan, Bill (LAB - Langley)
bill_gavan@sandwell.gov.uk

Giles, Elizabeth (LAB - Charlemont with Grove Vale)
elizabeth_giles@cllr.sandwell.gov.uk

Giles, Elaine (LAB - Bristnall)
elaine_giles@cllr.sandwell.org.uk

Gill, Preet (LAB - St. Paul's)
preet_kaurgill@sandwell.gov.uk

Goult, Carol (LAB - Bristnall)
carol_goult@cllr.sandwell.org.uk

Hackett, Simon (LAB - Friar Park)
simon_hackett@sandwell.gov.uk

Hadley, Joanne (LAB - Great Bridge)
joanne_hadley@cllr.sandwell.org.uk

Haque, Ahmadul (LAB - Tipton Green)
ahmadul_haque@cllr.sandwell.org.uk

Hartwell, Suzanne (LAB - Oldbury)
suzanne_hartwell@cllr.sandwell.gov.uk

Hevican, Sandra (LAB - Tividale)
sandra_hevican@sandwell.gov.uk

Hickey, Laura (LAB - West Bromwich Central)
laura_hickey@cllr.sandwell.org.uk

Horton, Linda (LAB - Smethwick)
linda_horton@sandwell.gov.uk

Horton, Roger (LAB - Soho & Victoria)
roger_horton@cllr.sandwell.org.uk

Hosell, Shirley (LAB - Great Barr with Yew Tree)
shirley_hosell@sandwell.gov.uk

Hosell, David (LAB - Newton)
hoselld@blueyonder.co.uk

Hughes, Pam (LAB - Wednesbury South)
pam_hughes@sandwell.gov.uk

Hughes, Peter (LAB - Wednesbury North)
cllrpeter_hughes@sandwell.gov.uk

Hussain, Mahboob (LAB - Oldbury)
mahoob_hussain@sandwell.gov.uk

Jaron, Ann (LAB - Abbey)
ann_jaron@sandwell.gov.uk

Jarvis, Ann (LAB - Great Bridge)
ann_jarvis@cllr.sandwell.org.uk

Jones, Olwen (LAB - Wednesbury South)
olwen.jones53@gmail.com

Jones, Ian (LAB - Tipton Green)
ian_jones@sandwell.gov.uk

Jones, Stephen (LAB - Princes End)
cllrstephen_jones@sandwell.gov.uk

Lewis, Geoffrey (LAB - Friar Park)
geoffreyjlewis@fsmail.net

Lloyd, Bob (LAB - Wednesbury South)
bob_lloyd@sandwell.gov.uk

Marshall, Richard (LAB - Smethwick)
richard_marshall@sandwell.gov.uk

Meehan, Tony (LAB - Wednesbury North)
tony_meehan@sandwell.gov.uk

Melia, Steve (LAB - Great Barr with Yew Tree)
smelia5751@aol.com

SANDWELL

Millard, Danny (LAB - Blackheath)
danny_millard@cllr.sandwell.org.uk

Moore, Paul (LAB - Hateley Heath)
paul_moore@sandwell.gov.uk

Phillips, Sue (LAB - Charlemont with Grove Vale)
sue_phillips@sandwell.gov.uk

Piper, Bob (LAB - Abbey)
bob.piper@gmail.com

Preece, Liam (LAB - Charlemont with Grove Vale)
liam_preece@sandwell.gov.uk

Price, Barbara (LAB - Rowley)
councillor-mrs@bprice31.freeserve.co.uk

Price, Robert (LAB - Blackheath)
councillor@bprice31.freeserve.co.uk

Rouf, Mohammed (LAB - Soho & Victoria)
mohammad_rouf@cllr.sandwell.org.uk

Sandars, Paul (LAB - Hateley Heath)
sandarspaul@hotmail.com

Shackleton, Ann (LAB - Cradley Heath & Old Hill)
ann_shackleton@sandwell.gov.uk

Shaeen, Farut (LAB - Soho & Victoria)
farut_shaeen@cllr.sandwell.org.uk

Sidhu, Gurcharan (LAB - Greets Green & Lyng)
gucharen_singhsidhu@cllr.sandwell.org.uk

Tagger, Mohinder (LAB - West Bromwich Central)
mohinder_singhtagger@cllr.sandwell.gov.uk

Taylor, Jackie (LAB - Greets Green & Lyng)
jackie_taylor@sandwell.gov.uk

Tranter, Chris (LAB - Rowley)
chris_tranter@sandwell.gov.uk

Trow, Steve (LAB - Old Warley)
stevetrow@blueyonder.co.uk

Underhill, Joyce (LAB - Newton)
joyceunderhill@btinternet.com

Webb, Julie (LAB - Cradley Heath & Old Hill)
juliewebb55@hotmail.com

White, Caroline (LAB - Cradley Heath & Old Hill)
caroline_white@cllr.sandwell.org.uk

Worsey, Christopher (LAB - Great Barr with Yew Tree)
chirs_worsey@sandwell.gov.uk

POLITICAL COMPOSITION
LAB: 71, UKIP: 1

COMMITTEE CHAIRS

Audit: Mr Gurcharan Sidhu

Children's Services & Education: Mrs Joyce Underhill

Community Safety, Highways & Environment: Ms Maria Crompton

Health & Adult Social Care: Ms Yvonne Davies

Licensing: Mr Peter Allen

Planning: Mr Steven Frear

Scarborough Borough Council, Town Hall, St. Nicholas Street, Scarborough YO11 2HG
☎ 01723 232323 ◌ ce@scarborough.gov.uk
🖥 www.scarborough.gov.uk

FACTS AND FIGURES
Parliamentary Constituencies: Scarborough and Whitby
EU Constituencies: Yorkshire and the Humber
Election Frequency: Elections are of whole council

PRINCIPAL OFFICERS

Chief Executive: Mr Jim Dillon, Chief Executive, Town Hall, St. Nicholas Street, Scarborough YO11 2HG ☎ 01723 232300 ◌ jim.dillon@scarborough.gov.uk

Senior Management: Mrs Lisa Dixon, Director, Town Hall, St. Nicholas Street, Scarborough YO11 2HG ☎ 01723 232350 ◌ lisa.dixon@scarborough.gov.uk

Senior Management: Mr Nick Edwards, Director, Town Hall, St. Nicholas Street, Scarborough YO11 2HG ☎ 01723 232410 ◌ nick.edwards@scarborough.gov.uk

Senior Management: Mr Trevor Watson, Director, Town Hall, St. Nicholas Street, Scarborough YO11 2HG ☎ 01723 232493 ◌ trevor.watson@scarborough.gov.uk

Architect, Building / Property Services: Mr Martin Pedley, Asset & Risk Manager, Town Hall, St. Nicholas Street, Scarborough YO11 2HG ☎ 01723 232359 ◌ martin.pedley@scarborough.gov.uk

PR / Communications: Ms Gabrielle Jandzio, Communications Officer, Town Hall, St. Nicholas Street, Scarborough YO11 2HG ☎ 01723 232306 ◌ gabrielle.jandzio@scarborough.gov.uk

Community Safety: Ms Jo Ireland, Customers, Communities & Partnerships Manager, Town Hall, St. Nicholas Street, Scarborough YO11 2HG ☎ 01723 234315 ◌ jo.ireland@scarborough.gov.uk

Computer Management: Mr Greg Harper, ICT Delivery Manager, Town Hall, St. Nicholas Street, Scarborough YO11 2HG ☎ 01723 384333 ◌ greg.harper@scarborough.gov.uk

Contracts: Miss Rebecca Jackson, Legal Services Manager, Town Hall, St. Nicholas Street, Scarborough YO11 2HG ☎ 01723 232352 ◌ rebecca.jackson@scarborough.gov.uk

Customer Service: Ms Jo Ireland, Customers, Communities & Partnerships Manager, Town Hall, St. Nicholas Street, Scarborough YO11 2HG ☎ 01723 234315 ◌ jo.ireland@scarborough.gov.uk

Economic Development: Mr David Kelly, Economic Development Manager, Town Hall, St. Nicholas Street, Scarborough YO11 2HG ☎ 01723 232321 ◌ david.kelly@scarborough.gov.uk

E-Government: Mr Greg Harper, ICT Delivery Manager, Town Hall, St. Nicholas Street, Scarborough YO11 2HG ☎ 01723 384333 ◌ greg.harper@scarborough.gov.uk

Electoral Registration: Miss Kerry Russett, Transformation, Elections & Civic Manager, Town Hall, St. Nicholas Street, Scarborough YO11 2HG ☎ 01723 383506 ⏚ kerry.russett@scarborough.gov.uk

Emergency Planning: Mr Paul Thompson, Operations, Transport & Countryside Manager, Dean Road Depot, Scarborough YO12 7QS ☎ 01723 383112 ⏚ paul.thompson@scarborough.gov.uk

Energy Management: Mr Jeremy Carter, Energy Manager, Town Hall, St. Nicholas Street, Scarborough YO11 2HG ☎ 01723 223243 ⏚ jeremy.carter@scarborough.gov.uk

Environmental / Technical Services: Mr Trevor Watson, Director, Town Hall, St. Nicholas Street, Scarborough YO11 2HG ☎ 01723 232493 ⏚ trevor.watson@scarborough.gov.uk

Environmental Health: Mr Jonathan Bramley, Environment & Regulation Manager, Town Hall, St. Nicholas Street, Scarborough YO11 2HG ☎ 01723 232506 ⏚ jonathan.bramley@scarborough.gov.uk

Estates, Property & Valuation: Mr Martin Pedley, Asset & Risk Manager, Town Hall, St. Nicholas Street, Scarborough YO11 2HG ☎ 01723 232359 ⏚ martin.pedley@scarborough.gov.uk

Events Manager: Ms Rowena Marsden, Culture, Events & Filming Officer, Town Hall, St. Nicholas Street, Scarborough YO11 2HG ☎ 01723 383615 ⏚ rowena.marsden@scarborough.gov.uk

Facilities: Mr Martin Pedley, Asset & Risk Manager, Town Hall, St. Nicholas Street, Scarborough YO11 2HG ☎ 01723 232359 ⏚ martin.pedley@scarborough.gov.uk

Finance: Mr Nick Edwards, Director, Town Hall, St. Nicholas Street, Scarborough YO11 2HG ☎ 01723 232410 ⏚ nick.edwards@scarborough.gov.uk

Fleet Management: Mr Paul Thompson, Operations, Transport & Countryside Manager, Dean Road Depot, Scarborough YO12 7QS ☎ 01723 383112 ⏚ paul.thompson@scarborough.gov.uk

Grounds Maintenance: Mr Paul Thompson, Operations, Transport & Countryside Manager, Dean Road Depot, Scarborough YO12 7QS ☎ 01723 383112 ⏚ paul.thompson@scarborough.gov.uk

Health and Safety: Mr Robert Webster, Health & Safety Officer, Town Hall, St. Nicholas Street, Scarborough YO11 2HG ☎ 01723 232101 ⏚ robert.webster@scarborough.gov.uk

Housing: Mr Andrew Rowe, Housing Manager, Town Hall, St. Nicholas Street, Scarborough YO11 2HG ☎ 01723 383598 ⏚ andrew.rowe@scarborough.gov.uk

Legal: Miss Rebecca Jackson, Legal Services Manager, Town Hall, St. Nicholas Street, Scarborough YO11 2HG ☎ 01723 232352 ⏚ rebecca.jackson@scarborough.gov.uk

Leisure and Cultural Services: Mr Stuart Clark, Parking CCTV & Venues Manager, Town Hall, St. Nicholas Street, Scarborough YO11 2HG ☎ 01723 383582 ⏚ stuart.clark@scarborough.gov.uk

Licensing: Ms Una Faithfull, Licensing Manager, Town Hall, St. Nicholas Street, Scarborough YO11 2HG ☎ 01723 232522 ⏚ una.faithfull@scarborough.gov.uk

Lottery Funding, Charity and Voluntary: Ms Rowena Marsden, Culture, Events & Filming Officer, Town Hall, St. Nicholas Street, Scarborough YO11 2HG ☎ 01723 383615 ⏚ rowena.marsden@scarborough.gov.uk

Member Services: Mr David Kitson, Regulatory & Governance Manager, Town Hall, St. Nicholas Street, Scarborough YO11 2HG ☎ 01723 234319 ⏚ david.kitson@scarborough.gov.uk

Parking: Mr Stuart Clark, Parking CCTV & Venues Manager, Town Hall, St. Nicholas Street, Scarborough YO11 2HG ☎ 01723 383582 ⏚ stuart.clark@scarborough.gov.uk

Partnerships: Ms Jo Ireland, Customers, Communities & Partnerships Manager, Town Hall, St. Nicholas Street, Scarborough YO11 2HG ☎ 01723 234315 ⏚ jo.ireland@scarborough.gov.uk

Personnel / HR: Mrs Elaine Blades, Human Resources Manager, Town Hall, St. Nicholas Street, Scarborough YO11 2HG ☎ 01723 383560 ⏚ elaine.blades@scarborough.gov.uk

Planning: Mr David Walker, Planning Manager, Town Hall, St. Nicholas Street, Scarborough YO11 2HG ☎ 01723 232438 ⏚ david.walker@scarborough.gov.uk

Procurement: Mr David Gomersall, Procurement Officer, Town Hall, St. Nicholas Street, Scarborough YO11 2HG ☎ 01723 232344 ⏚ david.gomersall@scarborough.gov.uk

Recycling & Waste Minimisation: Mr Harry Briggs, Environment, Enforcement & Contract Manager, Dean Road Depot, Scarborough YO12 7QS ☎ 01723 383189 ⏚ harry.briggs@scarborough.gov.uk

Regeneration: Mr David Kelly, Economic Development Manager, Town Hall, St. Nicholas Street, Scarborough YO11 2HG ☎ 01723 232321 ⏚ david.kelly@scarborough.gov.uk

Staff Training: Mr Roger Paterson, Principal HR Officer, Town Hall, St. Nicholas Street, Scarborough YO11 2HG ☎ 01723 232314 ⏚ roger.paterson@scarborough.gov.uk

Street Scene: Mr Paul Thompson, Operations, Transport & Countryside Manager, Dean Road Depot, Scarborough YO12 7QS ☎ 01723 383112 ⏚ paul.thompson@scarborough.gov.uk

Sustainable Communities: Ms Jo Ireland, Customers, Communities & Partnerships Manager, Town Hall, St. Nicholas Street, Scarborough YO11 2HG ☎ 01723 234315 ⏚ jo.ireland@scarborough.gov.uk

Tourism: Mrs Janet Deacon, Tourism Manager, Town Hall, St. Nicholas Street, Scarborough YO11 2HG ☎ 01723 232570 ⏚ janet.deacon@scarborough.gov.uk

Town Centre: Mr Nick Taylor, Investment Manager, Town Hall, St. Nicholas Street, Scarborough YO11 2HG ☎ 01723 232440 ⏚ nick.taylor@scarborough.gov.uk

SCARBOROUGH

Traffic Management: Mr Stuart Clark, Parking CCTV & Venues Manager, Town Hall, St. Nicholas Street, Scarborough YO11 2HG
☎ 01723 383582 ✆ stuart.clark@scarborough.gov.uk

Transport: Mr Paul Thompson, Operations, Transport & Countryside Manager, Dean Road Depot, Scarborough YO12 7QS
☎ 01723 383112 ✆ paul.thompson@scarborough.gov.uk

Transport Planner: Mr Paul Thompson, Operations, Transport & Countryside Manager, Dean Road Depot, Scarborough YO12 7QS
☎ 01723 383112 ✆ paul.thompson@scarborough.gov.uk

Waste Collection and Disposal: Mr Paul Thompson, Operations, Transport & Countryside Manager, Dean Road Depot, Scarborough YO12 7QS ☎ 01723 383112 ✆ paul.thompson@scarborough.gov.uk

Waste Management: Mr Paul Thompson, Operations, Transport & Countryside Manager, Dean Road Depot, Scarborough YO12 7QS
☎ 01723 383112 ✆ paul.thompson@scarborough.gov.uk

COUNCILLORS

Mayor: Green, Simon (CON - Cayton)
cllr.simon.green@scarborough.gov.uk

Deputy Mayor: Smith, Martin (CON - North Bay)
cllr.martin.smith@scarborough.gov.uk

Leader of the Council: Bastiman, Derek (CON - Scalby)
cllr.derek.bastiman@scarborough.gov.uk

Deputy Leader of the Council: Mallory, Helen (CON - Seamer)
cllr.helen.mallory@scarborough.gov.uk

Group Leader: Cross, Sam (UKIP - Filey)
cllr.sam.cross@scarborough.gov.uk

Group Leader: Plant, Joseph (CON - Whitby West Cliff)
cllr.joseph.plant@scarborough.gov.uk

Group Leader: Siddons, Steve (LAB - Ramshill)
cllr.steve.siddens@scarborough.gov.uk

Abbot, Alf (CON - Whitby West Cliff)
cllr.alf.abbott@scarborough.gov.uk

Allanson, Godfrey (CON - Hertford)
cllr.godgrey.allanson@scarborough.gov.uk

Backhouse, Luke (CON - Newby)
cllr.luke.backhouse@scarborough.gov.uk

Backhouse, Andrew (CON - Lindhead)
cllr.andrew.backhouse@scarborough.gov.uk

Barnett, Rob (LAB - Streonshalh)
cllr.rob.barnett@scarborough.gov.uk

Bastiman, Lynn (CON - Stepney)
cllr.lynn.bastiman@scarborough.gov.uk

Billing, David (LAB - Central)
cllr.david.billing@scarborough.gov.uk

Broadbent, Eric (LAB - Central)
cllr.eric.broadbent@scarborough.gov.uk

Chance, David (CON - Mayfield)
clld.david.chance@scarborough.gov.uk

Chatt, William (IND - Woodlands)
cllr.bill.chatt@scarborough.gov.uk

Cluer, Dilys (GRN - Stepney)
cllr.dilys.cluer@scarborough.gov.uk

Cockerill, Mike (IND - Filey)
cllr.mike.cockerill@scarborough.gov.uk

Colling, Liz (LAB - Falsgrave Park)
cllr.liz.colling@scarborough.gov.uk

Coulson, Guy (CON - Esk Valley)
cllr.guy.coulson@scarborough.gov.uk

Cross, Paul (LAB - Castle)
cllr.paul.cross@scarborough.gov.uk

Dennett, Gerald (LAB - Mayfield)
cllr.gerald.dennett@scarborough.gov.uk

Dodds, Jonathan (UKIP - Eastfield)
cllr.jonathan.dodds@scarborough.gov.uk

Donohue-Moncrieff, Michelle (CON - Hertford)
cllr.michelle.donohue-moncrieff@scarborough.gov.uk

Fox, Thomas (CON - Weaponness)
cllr.tom.fox@scarborough.gov.uk

Haddington, Colin (UKIP - Filey)
cllr.colin.haddington@scarborough.gov.uk

Harland, Marie (CON - Mulgrave)
cllr.marie.harland@scarborough.gov.uk

Inman, Vanda (LAB - Newby)
cllr.vanda.inman@scarborough.gov.uk

Jeffels, David (CON - Derwent Valley)
cllr.david.jeffels@scarborough.gov.uk

Jefferson, Janet (IND - Castle)
cllr.janet.jefferson@scarborough.gov.uk

Jenkinson, Andrew (CON - Newby)
cllr.andrew.jenkinson@scarborough.gov.uk

Lynskey, Hazel (CON - Scalby)
cllr.hazel.lynskey@scarborough.gov.uk

Maw, Carl (LAB - Northstead)
cllr.carl.maw@scarborough.gov.uk

Moody, Richard (LAB - Woodlands)
cllr.richard.moody@scarborough.gov.uk

Mortimer, Jane (CON - Flyingdales)
cllr.jane.mortimer@scarborough.gov.uk

Murphy, Norman (UKIP - Northstead)
cllr.norman.murphy@scarborough.gov.uk

Murphy, Roxanne (UKIP - Seamer)
cllr.roxanne.murphy@scarborough.gov.uk

Nock, John (CON - Mulgrave)
cllr.john.nock@scarborough.gov.uk

Pearson, Clive (CON - Danby)
cllr.clive.pearson@scarborough.gov.uk

Phillips, Heather (CON - Derwent Valley)
cllr.heather.phillips@scarborough.gov.uk

Price, Neil (LAB - North Bay)
cllr.neil.price@scarborough.gov.uk

Randerson, Tony (LAB - Eastfield)
cllr.tony.randerson@scarborough.gov.uk

Ritchie, John (LAB - Falsgrave Park)
cllr.john.ritchie@scarborough.gov.uk

Swiers, Roberta (CON - Cayton)
cllr.roberta.swiers@scarborough.gov.uk

Trumper, Phillip (CON - Esk Valley)
cllr.phil.trumper@scarborough.gov.uk

Turner, Sandra (CON - Streonshalh)
cllr.sandra.turner@scarborough.gov.uk

Vesey, Mark (GRN - Ramshill)
cllr.mark.vesey@scarborough.gov.uk

Walsh, Callam (CON - Weaponness)
cllr.callam.walsh@scarborough.gov.uk

Warburton, John (LAB - Eastfield)
cllr.john.warburton@scarborough.gov.uk

POLITICAL COMPOSITION
CON: 26, LAB: 14, UKIP: 5, IND: 3, GRN: 2

COMMITTEE CHAIRS

Audit: Mr David Chance

Licensing: Mr Martin Smith

Planning & Development: Mr Phillip Trumper

Scottish Borders   S

Scottish Borders Council, Council Headquarters, Newtown St. Boswells, Melrose TD6 0SA
☎ 0300 100 1800 ◌ enquiries@scotborders.gov.uk
🖥 www.scotborders.gov.uk

FACTS AND FIGURES
Parliamentary Constituencies: Berwickshire, Roxburgh and Selkirk, Dumfriesshire, Clydesdale and Tweedale
EU Constituencies: Scotland
Election Frequency: Elections are of whole council

PRINCIPAL OFFICERS

Chief Executive: Ms Tracey Logan, Chief Executive, Council Headquarters, Newtown St. Boswells, Melrose TD6 0SA
☎ 01835 825055 ◌ tracey.logan@scotborders.gov.uk

Deputy Chief Executive: Mr Philip Barr, Depute Chief Executive - Place, Council Headquarters, Newtown St. Boswells, Melrose TD6 0SA ☎ 01835 825132 ◌ philip.barr@scotborders.gov.uk

Deputy Chief Executive: Ms Jeanette McDiarmid, Depute Chief Executive - People, Council Headquarters, Newtown St. Boswells, Melrose TD6 0SA ☎ 01835 825217 ◌ jeanette.mcdiarmid@scotborders.gov.uk

Assistant Chief Executive: Ms Jenny Wilkinson, Clerk to the Council, Council Headquarters, Newtown St. Boswells, Melrose TD6 0SA ☎ 01835 825004 ◌ jjwilkinson@scotborder.gov.uk

Senior Management: Mrs Jenni Craig, Service Director - Neighbourhood Services, Council Headquarters, Newtown St. Boswells, Melrose TD6 0SA ☎ 01835 825013 ◌ jcraig@scotborders.gov.uk

Senior Management: Mr Rob Dickson, Corporate Transformation & Service Director, Council Headquarters, Newtown St. Boswells, Melrose TD6 0SA ☎ 01835 825075 ◌ rob.dickson@scotborders.gov.uk

Senior Management: Mr Brian Frater, Service Director - Regulatory Services, Council Headquarters, Newtown St. Boswells, Melrose TD6 0SA ☎ 01835 825067 ◌ bfrater@scotborders.gov.uk

Senior Management: Ms Clair Hepburn, Chief Officer - Human Resources, Council Headquarters, Newtown St. Boswells, Melrose TD6 0SA ☎ 01835 826667 ◌ chepburn@scotborders.gov.uk

Senior Management: Mr Martin Joyce, Service Director - Asset & Infrastructure, Council Headquarters, Newtown St. Boswells, Melrose TD6 0SA ☎ 01835 825082 ◌ martin.joyce@scotborders.gov.uk

Senior Management: Mr Tim Patterson, Director - Public Health, Council Headquarters, Newtown St. Boswells, Melrose TD6 0SA ☎ 01835 825086 ◌ tim.patterson@scotborders.gcsx.gov.uk

Senior Management: Mr David Robertson, Chief Financial Officer, Council Headquarters, Newtown St. Boswells, Melrose TD6 0SA ☎ 01835 825012 ◌ david.robertson@scotborders.gov.uk

Senior Management: Mrs Elaine Torrance, Chief Social Work Officer, Council Headquarters, Newtown St. Boswells, Melrose TD6 0SA ☎ 01835 825084 ◌ etorrance@scotborders.gov.uk

Senior Management: Mr Martin Wanless, Powered Planning Manager, Council Headquarters, Newtown St. Boswells, Melrose TD6 0SA ☎ 01835 825063 ◌ mwanless@scotborders.gov.uk

Architect, Building / Property Services: Mr Paul Frankland, Design Manager, Council Headquarters, Newtown St. Boswells, Melrose TD6 0SA ☎ 01835 825179 ◌ pfrankland@scotborders.gov.uk

Architect, Building / Property Services: Mr Stuart Mawson, Property Manager, Council Headquarters, Newtown St. Boswells, Melrose TD6 0SA ☎ 01835 826550 ◌ stuart.mawson@scotborders.gov.uk

Building Control: Mr John Hayward, Development Standards Manager, Council Headquarters, Newtown St. Boswells, Melrose TD6 0SA ☎ 01835 825068 ◌ jhayward@scotborders.gov.uk

Catering Services: Mr Alastair McIntyre, Catering & Services Manager, Council Headquarters, Newtown St. Boswells, Melrose TD6 0SA ☎ 01835 826564 ◌ amcintyre@scotborders.gov.uk

Children / Youth Services: Mrs Elaine Torrance, Chief Social Work Officer, Council Headquarters, Newtown St. Boswells, Melrose TD6 0SA ☎ 01835 825084 ◌ etorrance@scotborders.gov.uk

Civil Registration: Ms Lisa Davenport, Chief Registrar, Council Headquarters, Newtown St. Boswells, Melrose TD6 0SA ☎ 01450 364710 ◌ lisa.davenport@scotborder.gcsx.gov.uk

SCOTTISH BORDERS

PR / Communications: Ms Tracey Graham, Communications & Partnerships Manager, Council Headquarters, Newtown St. Boswells, Melrose TD6 0SA ☎ 01835 826592 ◌ tgraham@scotborders.gov.uk

Community Planning: Ms Shona Smith, Communities & Partnerships Manager, Council Headquarters, Newtown St. Boswells, Melrose TD6 0SA ☎ 01835 825054 ◌ smsmith@scotborders.gov.uk

Community Safety: Mr Tony Hodges, Chief Inspector Police Scotland / Safer Communities Manager, Council Headquarters, Newtown St. Boswells, Melrose TD6 0SA ☎ 01835 825857 ◌ tony.hodges@scotborders.gov.uk

Consumer Protection and Trading Standards: Mr Anthony Carson, Regulatory Services Manager, Council Headquarters, Newtown St. Boswells, Melrose TD6 0SA ☎ 00835 825142 ◌ acarson@scotborders.gov.uk

Customer Service: Mr Les Grant, Customer Services Manager, Council Headquarters, Newtown St. Boswells, Melrose TD6 0SA ☎ 01835 825547 ◌ lgrant@scotborders.gov.uk

Direct Labour: Mr Brian Park, Chief Officer - Roads, Council Headquarters, Newtown St. Boswells, Melrose TD6 0SA ☎ 01835 825054 ◌ brian.park@scotborders.gov.uk

Economic Development: Mr Bryan McGrath, Chief Officer - Economic Development, Council Headquarters, Newtown St. Boswells, Melrose TD6 0SA ☎ 01835 826525 ◌ bmcgrath@scotborders.gov.uk

Education: Ms Michelle Strong, Chief Officer - Education, Council Headquarters, Newtown St. Boswells, Melrose TD6 0SA ☎ 01835 825798 ◌ mstrong@scotborders.gov.uk

Electoral Registration: Mr Mark Dickson, Assessor & Electoral Registration Officer, Council Headquarters, Newtown St. Boswells, Melrose TD6 0SA ☎ 01835 825100 ◌ mdickson@scotborders.gov.uk

Emergency Planning: Mr Jim Fraser, Emergency Planning Officer, Council Headquarters, Newtown St. Boswells, Melrose TD6 0SA ☎ 01835 825056 ◌ jfraser@scotborders.gov.uk

Energy Management: Mr Stuart Mawson, Property Manager, Council Headquarters, Newtown St. Boswells, Melrose TD6 0SA ☎ 01835 826550 ◌ stuart.mawson@scotborders.gov.uk

Environmental Health: Mr Anthony Carson, Regulatory Services Manager, Council Headquarters, Newtown St. Boswells, Melrose TD6 0SA ☎ 00835 825142 ◌ acarson@scotborders.gov.uk

Estates, Property & Valuation: Mr Neil Hastie, Estates Manager, Council Headquarters, Newtown St. Boswells, Melrose TD6 0SA ☎ 01835 825167 ◌ nhastie@scotborders.gov.uk

European Liaison: Mr Douglas Scott, Senior Policy Advisor, Council Headquarters, Newtown St. Boswells, Melrose TD6 0SA ☎ 01835 824000 ◌ dscott@scotborders.gov.uk

Events Manager: Ms Jane Warcup, Events Officer - Strategy Development, Council Headquarters, Newtown St. Boswells, Melrose TD6 0SA ☎ 01835 825060 ◌ jwarcup@scotborders.gov.uk

Facilities: Mr John Gray, Cleaning & Facilities Manager, Council Headquarters, Newtown St. Boswells, Melrose TD6 0SA ☎ 01835 826670 ◌ john.gray@scotborders.gov.uk

Finance: Mr David Robertson, Chief Financial Officer, Council Headquarters, Newtown St. Boswells, Melrose TD6 0SA ☎ 01835 825012 ◌ david.robertson@scotborders.gov.uk

Pensions: Mr Ian Angus, HR Shared Services Manager, Council Headquarters, Newtown St. Boswells, Melrose TD6 0SA ☎ 01835 824000 ◌ iangus@scotborders.gov.uk

Fleet Management: Mr John Martin, Fleet Manager, Council Headquarters, Newtown St. Boswells, Melrose TD6 0SA ☎ 01835 825119 ◌ jmartin@scotborders.gov.uk

Grounds Maintenance: Mr Jason Hedley, Neighbourhood Operating & Services Manager, Council Headquarters, Newtown St. Boswells, Melrose TD6 0SA ☎ 01835 828037 ◌ jhedley@scotborders.gov.uk

Health and Safety: Mr Rob Dickson, Corporate Transformation & Service Director, Council Headquarters, Newtown St. Boswells, Melrose TD6 0SA ☎ 01835 825075 ◌ rob.dickson@scotborders.gov.uk

Highways: Mr Colin Ovens, Infrastructure Manager, Council Headquarters, Newtown St. Boswells, Melrose TD6 0SA ☎ 01835 826635 ◌ covens@scotborders.gov.uk

Home Energy Conservation: Ms Cathie Fancy, Group Manager of Housing Strategy & Services, Council Headquarters, Newtown St. Boswells, Melrose TD6 0SA ☎ 01835 825080 ◌ cfancy@scotborders.gov.uk

Legal: Ms Nuala McKinley, Chief Legal Officer, Council Headquarters, Newtown St. Boswells, Melrose TD6 0SA ☎ 01835 825220 ◌ nmckinley@scotborders.gov.uk

Leisure and Cultural Services: Mr Rob Dickson, Corporate Transformation & Service Director, Council Headquarters, Newtown St. Boswells, Melrose TD6 0SA ☎ 01835 825075 ◌ rob.dickson@scotborders.gov.uk

Licensing: Ms Nuala McKinley, Chief Legal Officer, Council Headquarters, Newtown St. Boswells, Melrose TD6 0SA ☎ 01835 825220 ◌ nmckinley@scotborders.gov.uk

Lighting: Mr Brian Young, Network Manager, Council Headquarters, Newtown St. Boswells, Melrose TD6 0SA ☎ 01835 825178 ◌ byoung@scotborders.gov.uk

Lottery Funding, Charity and Voluntary: Ms Jean Robertson, Funding & Project Officer, Council Headquarters, Newtown St. Boswells, Melrose TD6 0SA ☎ 01835 824000 ◌ jarobertson@scotborders.gov.uk

Member Services: Ms Pauline Bolson, Democratic Services Officer, Council Headquarters, Newtown St. Boswells, Melrose TD6 0SA ☎ 01835 826053 ✆ pbolson@scotborders.gov.uk

Parking: Mr Brian Young, Network Manager, Council Headquarters, Newtown St. Boswells, Melrose TD6 0SA ☎ 01835 825178 ✆ byoung@scotborders.gov.uk

Partnerships: Ms Shona Smith, Communities & Partnerships Manager, Council Headquarters, Newtown St. Boswells, Melrose TD6 0SA ☎ 01835 825054 ✆ smsmith@scotborders.gov.uk

Personnel / HR: Ms Clair Hepburn, Chief Officer - Human Resources, Council Headquarters, Newtown St. Boswells, Melrose TD6 0SA ☎ 01835 826667 ✆ chepburn@scotborders.gov.uk

Planning: Mr John Hayward, Development Standards Manager, Council Headquarters, Newtown St. Boswells, Melrose TD6 0SA ☎ 01835 825068 ✆ jhayward@scotborders.gov.uk

Procurement: Ms Kathryn Dickson, Procurement Manager, Council Headquarters, Newtown St. Boswells, Melrose TD6 0SA ☎ 01835 826646 ✆ kathryn.dickson@scotborders.gov.uk

Public Libraries: Mr Ian Brown, Community Services Business Manager, Council Headquarters, Newtown St. Boswells, Melrose TD6 0SA ☎ 01835 826606 ✆ iabrown@scotborders.gov.uk

Recycling & Waste Minimisation: Mr Ross Sharp-Dent, Waste Manager, Council Headquarters, Newtown St. Boswells, Melrose TD6 0SA ☎ 01835 825111 ✆ rsharp-dent@scotborders.gov.uk

Regeneration: Mr Bryan McGrath, Chief Officer - Economic Development, Council Headquarters, Newtown St. Boswells, Melrose TD6 0SA ☎ 01835 826525 ✆ bmcgrath@scotborders.gov.uk

Road Safety: Mr Colin Ovens, Infrastructure Manager, Council Headquarters, Newtown St. Boswells, Melrose TD6 0SA ☎ 01835 826635 ✆ covens@scotborders.gov.uk

Social Services: Mrs Elaine Torrance, Chief Social Work Officer, Council Headquarters, Newtown St. Boswells, Melrose TD6 0SA ☎ 01835 825084 ✆ etorrance@scotborders.gov.uk

Social Services (Adult): Mrs Elaine Torrance, Chief Social Work Officer, Council Headquarters, Newtown St. Boswells, Melrose TD6 0SA ☎ 01835 825084 ✆ etorrance@scotborders.gov.uk

Sustainable Communities: Mr Douglas Scott, Senior Policy Advisor, Council Headquarters, Newtown St. Boswells, Melrose TD6 0SA ☎ 01835 824000 ✆ dscott@scotborders.gov.uk

Sustainable Development: Mr Bryan McGrath, Chief Officer - Economic Development, Council Headquarters, Newtown St. Boswells, Melrose TD6 0SA ☎ 01835 826525 ✆ bmcgrath@scotborders.gov.uk

Tourism: Mr Bryan McGrath, Chief Officer - Economic Development, Council Headquarters, Newtown St. Boswells, Melrose TD6 0SA ☎ 01835 826525 ✆ bmcgrath@scotborders.gov.uk

Town Centre: Mr Bryan McGrath, Chief Officer - Economic Development, Council Headquarters, Newtown St. Boswells, Melrose TD6 0SA ☎ 01835 826525 ✆ bmcgrath@scotborders.gov.uk

Traffic Management: Mr Brian Young, Network Manager, Council Headquarters, Newtown St. Boswells, Melrose TD6 0SA ☎ 01835 825178 ✆ byoung@scotborders.gov.uk

Transport Planner: Mr Graeme Johnstone, Principal Officer - Strategic Transport, Council Headquarters, Newtown St. Boswells, Melrose TD6 0SA ☎ 01835 825138 ✆ gjohnstone@scotborders.gov.uk

Waste Collection and Disposal: Mr Ross Sharp-Dent, Waste Manager, Council Headquarters, Newtown St. Boswells, Melrose TD6 0SA ☎ 01835 825111 ✆ rsharp-dent@scotborders.gov.uk

Waste Management: Mrs Jenni Craig, Service Director - Neighbourhood Services, Council Headquarters, Newtown St. Boswells, Melrose TD6 0SA ☎ 01835 825013 ✆ jcraig@scotborders.gov.uk

Children's Play Areas: Mrs Jenni Craig, Service Director - Neighbourhood Services, Council Headquarters, Newtown St. Boswells, Melrose TD6 0SA ☎ 01835 825013 ✆ jcraig@scotborders.gov.uk

COUNCILLORS

Convener: Garvie, Graham (LD - Tweedale East) ggarvie@scotborders.gov.uk

Vice Convener: Brown, Jim (SNP - Jedburgh and District) jbrown@scotborders.gov.uk

Leader of the Council: Parker, David (IND - Leaderdale and Melrose) dparker@scotborders.gov.uk

Deputy Leader of the Council: Mitchell, John (SNP - Galashiels and District) jmitchell@scotborders.gov.uk

Group Leader: Aitchison, Sandy (IND - Galashiels and District) saitchison@scotborders.gov.uk

Group Leader: Ballantyne, Michelle (CON - Selkirkshire) michelle.ballantyne@scotborders.gov.uk

Archibald, Willie (SNP - Tweedale West) warchibald@scotborders.gov.uk

Bell, Stuart (SNP - Tweedale East) stuart.bell@scotborders.gov.uk

Bhatia, Catriona (LD - Tweedale West) cbhatia@scotborders.gov.uk

Campbell, Joan (SNP - East Berwickshire) joan.campbell@scotborders.gov.uk

Cockburn, Keith (CON - Tweedale West) keith.cockburn@scotborders.gov.uk

Cook, Michael (IND - East Berwickshire) mcook@scotborders.gov.uk

Cranston, Alastair (SNP - Hawick and Denholm) alastair.cranston@scotborders.gov.uk

Davidson, Vicky (LD - Selkirkshire) vdavidson@scotborders.gov.uk

SCOTTISH BORDERS

Edgar, Gordon (IND - Selkirkshire)
gordon.edgar@scotborders.gov.uk

Fullarton, Jim (CON - East Berwickshire)
jfullarton@scotborders.gov.uk

Gillespie, Iain (IND - Leaderdale and Melrose)
iain.gillespie@scotborders.gov.uk

Greenwell, John (CON - Mid Berwickshire)
john.greenwell@scotborders.gov.uk

Herd, Bill (SNP - Galashiels and District)
bherd@scotborders.gov.uk

Logan, Gavin (CON - Tweedale East)
glogan@scotborders.gov.uk

Marshall, Stuart (IND - Hawick and Denholm)
smarshall@scotborders.gov.uk

McAteer, Watson (IND - Hawick and Denholm)
watson.mcateer@scotborders.gov.uk

Moffat, Donald (SNP - Mid Berwickshire)
dmoffat@scotborders.gov.uk

Mountford, Simon (CON - Kelso and District)
simon.mountford@scotborders.gov.uk

Nicol, Alec (LD - Kelso and District)
anicol@scotborders.gov.uk

Paterson, David (IND - Hawick and Hermitage)
dpaterson@scotborders.gov.uk

Renton, Frances (LD - Mid Berwickshire)
frenton@scotborders.gov.uk

Scott, Sandy (CON - Jedburgh and District)
sandyscott@scotborders.gov.uk

Smith, Ron (LD - Hawick and Hermitage)
rsmith@scotborders.gov.uk

Stewart, Rory (IND - Jedburgh and District)
rory.stewart@scotborders.gov.uk

Torrance, Jim (SNP - Leaderdale and Melrose)
jim.torrance@scotborders.gov.uk

Turnbull, George (CON - Hawick and Hermitage)
gturnbull@scotborders.gov.uk

Weatherston, Tom (CON - Kelso and District)
tweatherston@scotborders.gov.uk

White, Bill (IND - Galashiels and District)
bill.white@scotborders.gov.uk

POLITICAL COMPOSITION
IND: 10, CON: 9, SNP: 9, LD: 6

COMMITTEE CHAIRS

Audit: Ms Michelle Ballantyne

Licensing: Mr Willie Archibald

Pensions: Mr Bill White

Planning & Building Standards: Mr Ron Smith

Standards: Mr Alec Nicol

Sedgemoor District Council, Bridgwater House, King Square, Bridgwater TA6 3AR
☎ 0300 303 7800 ☙ customer.services@sedgemoor.gov.uk
💻 www.sedgemoor.gov.uk

FACTS AND FIGURES
Parliamentary Constituencies: Bridgwater and Somerset West, Wells
EU Constituencies: South West
Election Frequency: Elections are of whole council

PRINCIPAL OFFICERS

Chief Executive: Mr Kerry Rickards, Chief Executive, Bridgwater House, King Square, Bridgwater TA6 3AR ☎ 01278 435423
☙ kerry.rickards@sedgemoor.gov.uk

Senior Management: Mr Doug Bamsey, Corporate Director, Bridgwater House, King Square, Bridgwater TA6 3AR
☎ 01278 435435 ☙ doug.bamsey@sedgemoor.gov.uk

Senior Management: Mr Bob Brown, Corporate Director, Bridgwater House, King Square, Bridgwater TA6 3AR
☎ 01278 435327 ☙ bob.brown@sedgemoor.gov.uk

Senior Management: Mrs Allison Griffin, Corporate Director, Bridgwater House, King Square, Bridgwater TA6 3AR
☎ 01278 435741 ☙ allison.griffin@sedgemoor.gov.uk

Architect, Building / Property Services: Mr Tim Mander, Estates, Property & Valuation Officer, Bridgwater House, King Square, Bridgwater TA6 3AR ☎ 01278 435435
☙ tim.mander@sedgemoor.gov.uk

Best Value: Mr Robin Starr, Information Officer, Bridgwater House, King Square, Bridgwater TA6 3AR ☎ 01278 435435
☙ robin.starr@sedgemoor.gov.uk

Building Control: Mr Nigel Hunt, Somerset Building Control Partnership Manager, Bridgwater House, Kings Square, Bridgwater TA6 9ZY ☎ 01823 356473 ☙ nigel.hunt@mendip.gov.uk

PR / Communications: Ms Claire Faun, Corporate Relations Manager, Bridgwater House, King Square, Bridgwater TA6 3AR
☎ 01278 435320 ☙ pressoffice@sedgemoor.gov.uk

PR / Communications: Mrs Samantha Taylor, Community Relations Officer, Sedgemoor District Council, King Square, Bridgwater TA6 3AR ☎ 01278 435517 ☙ sam.taylor@sedgemoor.gov.uk

Community Planning: Ms Julie Cooper, Team Leader - Environment & Climate Change, SDC, Bridgwater House, King Square, Bridgwater TA6 3AR ☎ 01278 435425
☙ julie.cooper@sedgemoor.gov.uk

Community Planning: Mr Nick Tait, Service Manager - Policy, Bridgwater House, King Square, Bridgwater TA6 3AR
☎ 01278 435435 ☙ nick.tait@sedgemoor.gov.uk

Community Safety: Mrs Kristy Blackwell, Community Safety & Environmental Services Officer, Bridgwater House, King Square, Bridgwater TA6 3AR ☎ 01278 435435 ✆ kristy.blackwell@sedgemoor.gov.uk

Computer Management: Mr Paul Davidson, Head - E-Government, Bridgwater House, King Square, Bridgwater TA6 3AR ☎ 01278 435435 ✆ paul.davidson@sedgemoor.gov.uk

Computer Management: Mr Craig Wilkins, Head of Information Systems, Sedgemoor District Council, King Square, Bridgwater TA6 3AR ☎ 01278 435435 ✆ craig.wilkins@sedgemoor.gov.uk

Contracts: Mrs Joanna Hutchins, Procurement Officer, Sedgemoor District Council, King Square, Bridgwater TA6 3AR ☎ 01278 435435 ✆ joanna.hutchins@sedgemoor.gov.uk

Contracts: Ms Melanie Wellman, Group Manager - Legal & Procurement, Bridgwater House, King Square, Bridgwater TA6 3AR ☎ 01278 435435 ✆ melanie.wellman@sedgemoor.gov.uk

Corporate Services: Mr Julian Street, Group Manager, Bridgwater House, King Square, Bridgwater TA6 3AR ☎ 01278 435435 ✆ julian.street@sedgemoor.gov.uk

Customer Service: Mrs Viv Reading, Customer Contact Manager, Sedgemoor District Council, King Square, Bridgwater TA6 3AR ☎ 01278 435435 ✆ viv.reading@sedgemoor.gov.uk

Economic Development: Mrs Claire Pearce, Group Manager - Strategy & Business Services, Bridgwater House, King Square, Bridgwater TA6 3AR ☎ 01278 435435 ✆ claire.pearce@sedgemoor.gov.uk

E-Government: Mr Paul Davidson, Head - E-Government, Bridgwater House, King Square, Bridgwater TA6 3AR ☎ 01278 435435 ✆ paul.davidson@sedgemoor.gov.uk

Electoral Registration: Mrs Louise Potter, Electoral Services Officer, Bridgwater House, King Square, Bridgwater TA6 3AR ☎ 01278 435435 ✆ louise.potter@sedgemoor.gov.uk

Emergency Planning: Mrs Sarah Dowden, Team Leader - Food & Safety, Bridgwater House, King Square, Bridgwater TA6 3AR ☎ 01278 435748 ✆ sarah.dowden@sedgemoor.gov.uk

Energy Management: Mr David Baxter, Street Housing Manager, Bridgwater House, King Square, Bridgwater TA6 3AR ☎ 01278 435435 ✆ david.baxter@sedgemoor.gov.uk

Energy Management: Ms Julie Cooper, Team Leader- Environment & Climate change, SDC, Bridgwater House, King Square, Bridgwater TA6 3AR ☎ 01278 435435 ✆ julie.cooper@sedgemoor.gov.uk

Environmental / Technical Services: Mr Adrian Gardner, Group Manager - Environmental Health, Bridgwater House, King Square, Bridgwater TA6 3AR ☎ 01278 435435 ✆ adrian.gardner@sedgemoor.gov.uk

Estates, Property & Valuation: Mr Tim Mander, Estates, Property & Valuation Officer, Bridgwater House, King Square, Bridgwater TA6 3AR ☎ 01278 435435 ✆ tim.mander@sedgemoor.gov.uk

Estates, Property & Valuation: Mr Julian Street, Group Manager, Bridgwater House, King Square, Bridgwater TA6 3AR ☎ 01278 435435 ✆ julian.street@sedgemoor.gov.uk

Facilities: Mr Bill Smith, Facilities Manager, Bridgwater House, King Square, Bridgwater TA6 3AR ☎ 01278 435435 ✆ bill.smith@sedgemoor.gov.uk

Finance: Mrs Alison Turner, Group Finance & Section 151 Manager, Bridgwater House, King Square, Bridgwater TA6 3AR ☎ 01278 435426 ✆ alison.turner@sedgemoor.gov.uk

Fleet Management: Mr Bob Kondys, Transport Supervisor, Bridgwater House, King Square, Bridgwater TA6 3AR ☎ 01278 435435 ✆ bob.kondys@sedgemoor.gov.uk

Grounds Maintenance: Mr Richard Stokes, Interim Operations Manager - Clear Surroundings, Bridgwater House, King Square, Bridgwater TA6 3AR ☎ 01278 435435 ✆ richard.stokes@sedgemoor.gov.uk

Health and Safety: Mr Derrick Cox, Corporate Health & Safety Officer, Bridgwater House, King Square, Bridgwater TA6 3AR ☎ 01278 435435 ✆ derrick.cox@sedgemoor.gov.uk

Home Energy Conservation: Mr David Baxter, Street Housing Manager, Bridgwater House, King Square, Bridgwater TA6 3AR ☎ 01278 435435 ✆ david.baxter@sedgemoor.gov.uk

Home Energy Conservation: Ms Julie Cooper, Team Leader - Stronger Communities & Environment, Sedgemoor District Council, King Square, Bridgwater TA6 3AR ☎ 01278 435435 ✆ julie.cooper@sedgemoor.gov.uk

Housing: Mr David Baxter, Street Housing Manager, Bridgwater House, King Square, Bridgwater TA6 3AR ☎ 01278 435435 ✆ david.baxter@sedgemoor.gov.uk

Housing: Mrs Teresa Harvey, Group Manager, Bridgwater House, King Square, Bridgwater TA6 3AR ☎ 01278 435435 ✆ teresa.harvey@sedgemoor.gov.uk

Housing Maintenance: Mr Paul Barry, Partnering Manager - Homes in Sedgemoor, Bridgwater House, King Square, Bridgwater TA6 3AR ☎ 01278 435380 ✆ paul.barry@sedgemoor.gov.uk

Legal: Ms Melanie Wellman, Group Manager - Legal & Procurement, Bridgwater House, King Square, Bridgwater TA6 3AR ☎ 01278 435435 ✆ melanie.wellman@sedgemoor.gov.uk

Licensing: Mr Alan Weldon, Licensing & Fraud Manager, Bridgwater House, King Square, Bridgwater TA6 3AR ☎ 01278 435435 ✆ alan.weldon@sedgemoor.gov.uk

Member Services: Mr Andrew Melhuish, Democratic Services Team Leader, Sedgemoor District Council, King Square, Bridgwater TA6 3AR ☎ 01278 435435 ✆ andrew.melhuish@sedgemoor.gov.uk

SEDGEMOOR

Parking: Mr Tom Dougall, Transportation Officer, Bridgwater House, King Square, Bridgwater TA6 3AR ☎ 01278 435435 📠 tom.dougal@sedgemoor.gov.uk

Personnel / HR: Mrs Clare Johnson, Training & Development Manager, Bridgwater House, King Square, Bridgwater TA6 3AR ☎ 01278 435435 📠 clare.johnson@sedgemoor.gov.uk

Planning: Mr Stuart Houlet, Service Manager, Bridgwater House, King Square, Bridgwater TA6 3AR ☎ 01278 435435 📠 stuart.houlet@sedgemoor.gov.uk

Planning: Mrs Claire Pearce, Group Manager - Strategy & Business Services, Bridgwater House, King Square, Bridgwater TA6 3AR ☎ 01278 435435 📠 claire.pearce@sedgemoor.gov.uk

Procurement: Ms Melanie Wellman, Group Manager - Legal & Procurement, Bridgwater House, King Square, Bridgwater TA6 3AR ☎ 01278 435435 📠 melanie.wellman@sedgemoor.gov.uk

Recycling & Waste Minimisation: Mr Adrian Gardner, Group Manager - Environmental Health, Bridgwater House, King Square, Bridgwater TA6 3AR ☎ 01278 435435 📠 adrian.gardner@sedgemoor.gov.uk

Regeneration: Mr Doug Bamsey, Corporate Director, Bridgwater House, King Square, Bridgwater TA6 3AR ☎ 01278 435435 📠 doug.bamsey@sedgemoor.gov.uk

Staff Training: Mrs Caroline Derrick, Training & Development Manager, Bridgwater House, King Square, Bridgwater TA6 3AR ☎ 01278 435435 📠 caroline.derrick@sedgemoor.gov.uk

Sustainable Communities: Ms Julie Cooper, Team Leader - Stronger Communities & Environment, Bridgwater House, King Square, Bridgwater TA6 3AR ☎ 01278 435435 📠 julie.cooper@sedgemoor.gov.uk

Sustainable Development: Mrs Claire Pearce, Group Manager - Strategy & Business Services, Bridgwater House, King Square, Bridgwater TA6 3AR ☎ 01278 435435 📠 claire.pearce@sedgemoor.gov.uk

Tourism: Mrs Victoria Banham, Tourism Officer, Bridgwater House, King Square, Bridgwater TA6 3AR ☎ 01278 435435 📠 victoria.banham@sedgemoor.gov.uk

Town Centre: Mrs Allison Griffin, Corporate Director, Sedgemoor District Council, King Square, Bridgwater TA6 3AR ☎ 01278 435435 📠 allison.griffin@sedgemoor.gov.uk

Transport: Mr Bob Kondys, Transport Supervisor, Bridgwater House, King Square, Bridgwater TA6 3AR ☎ 01278 435435 📠 bob.kondys@sedgemoor.gov.uk

Transport Planner: Mr Tom Dougall, Transportation Officer, Bridgwater House, King Square, Bridgwater TA6 3AR ☎ 01278 435435 📠 tom.dougal@sedgemoor.gov.uk

Waste Collection and Disposal: Mr Adrian Gardner, Group Manager - Environmental Health, Bridgwater House, King Square, Bridgwater TA6 3AR ☎ 01278 435435 📠 adrian.gardner@sedgemoor.gov.uk

Waste Management: Mr Adrian Gardner, Group Manager - Environmental Health, Bridgwater House, King Square, Bridgwater TA6 3AR ☎ 01278 435435 📠 adrian.gardner@sedgemoor.gov.uk

Children's Play Areas: Mr Scott Mason, Parks Project Officer, Bridgwater House, King Square, Bridgwater TA6 3AR ☎ 01278 435435 📠 scott.mason@sedgemoor.gov.uk

Children's Play Areas: Mrs Marina Turner, Parks Officer, Bridgwater House, King Square, Bridgwater TA6 3AR ☎ 01278 435435 📠 marina.turner@sedgemoor.gov.uk

COUNCILLORS

Chair: Dyer, Ian (CON - Cannington & Wembdon) ian.dyer@sedgemoor.gov.uk

Vice-Chair: Cresswell, Mike (CON - Bridgwater Fair) mike.cresswell@sedgemoor.gov.uk

Leader of the Council: McGinty, Duncan (CON - East Polden) duncan.mcginty@sedgemoor.gov.uk

Deputy Leader of the Council: Hill, Dawn (CON - Cheddar & Shipham) dawn.hill@sedgemoor.gov.uk

Alder, Derek (CON - King's Isle) derek.alder@sedgemoor.gov.uk

Bown, Ann (CON - Cannington & Wembdon) ann.bown@sedgemoor.gov.uk

Bradford, Alan (CON - North Petherton) alan.bradford@sedgemoor.gov.uk

Brown, Moira (LAB - Bridgwater Eastover) moira.brown@sedgemoor.gov.uk

Burnett, Cheryl (CON - Burnham North) cheryl.burnett@sedgemoor.gov.uk

Burridge-Clayton, Peter (CON - Burnham North) peter.clayton@sedgemoor.gov.uk

Caswell, Michael (CON - Quantocks) michael.caswell@sedgemoor.gov.uk

Caswell, Rachael (CON - Bridgwater Wyndham) rachael.caswell@sedgemoor.gov.uk

Clarke, Michael (CON - Burnham Central) michael.clarke@sedgemoor.gov.uk

Clarke, Maria (CON - Burnham Central) maria.clarke@sedgemoor.gov.uk

Corke, Lorna (UKIP - Highbridge & Burnham Marine) lorna.corke@sedgemoor.gov.uk

Costello, Polly (CON - Wedmore & Mark) polly.costello@sedgemoor.gov.uk

Denbee, John (CON - Axevale) john.denbee@sedgemoor.gov.uk

Downing, Peter (CON - Cheddar & Shipham) peter.downing@sedgemoor.gov.uk

Duddridge, Lance (CON - Bridgwater Victoria) lance.duddridge@sedgemoor.gov.uk

Facey, Mike (CON - Burnham Central) mike.facey@sedgemoor.gov.uk

Filmer, Bob (CON - Knoll) bob.filmer@sedgemoor.gov.uk

Fraser, Anne (CON - North Petherton)
anne.fraser@sedgemoor.gov.uk

Gilling, Andrew (CON - Knoll)
andrew.gilling@sedgemoor.gov.uk

Glassford, Alex (LAB - Bridgwater Fair)
alex.glassford@sedgemoor.gov.uk

Granter, Graham (LAB - Bridgwater Fair)
graham.granter@sedgemoor.gov.uk

Grimes, Tony (CON - Berrow)
tony.grimes@sedgemoor.gov.uk

Hamlin, Alison (CON - Puriton & Woolavington)
alison.hamlin@sedgemoor.gov.uk

Healey, Mark (CON - Puriton & Woolavington)
mark.healey@sedgemoor.gov.uk

Herbert, Paul (CON - Burnham North)
paul.herbert@sedgemoor.gov.uk

Hinckes, Wes (LAB - Bridgwater Hamp)
wes.hinckes@sedgemoor.gov.uk

Human, Will (CON - Wedmore & Mark)
will.human@sedgemoor.gov.uk

Keen, Janet (CON - Highbridge & Burnham Marine)
janet.keen@sedgemoor.gov.uk

Keen, Roger (CON - Highbridge & Burnham Marine)
roger.keen@sedgemoor.gov.uk

Kingham, Stuart (CON - West Polden)
stuart.kingham@sedgemoor.gov.uk

Lerry, Mick (LAB - Bridgwater Victoria)
michael.lerry@sedgemoor.gov.uk

Loveridge, Dave (LAB - Bridgwater Eastover)
david.loveridge@sedgemoor.gov.uk

Moore, Adrian (LAB - Bridgwater Hamp)
adrian.moore@sedgemoor.gov.uk

Pay, Julie (CON - Quantocks)
julie.pay@sedgemoor.gov.uk

Pearce, Kathy (LAB - Bridgwater Westover)
kathy.pearce@sedgemoor.gov.uk

Perry, Liz (CON - King's Isle)
liz.perry@sedgemoor.gov.uk

Redman, Leigh (LAB - Bridgwater Dunwear)
leigh.redman@sedgemoor.gov.uk

Revans, Bill (LD - North Petherton)
bill.revans@sedgemoor.gov.uk

Savage, Jeff (CON - Cheddar & Shipham)
jeff.savage@sedgemoor.gov.uk

Scammell, Richard (UKIP - Bridgwater Dunwear)
richard.scammell@sedgmoor.gov.uk

Scott, Liz (CON - Axevale)
liz.scott@sedgemoor.gov.uk

Slocombe, Gill (CON - Bridgwater Wyndham)
gill.slocombe@sedgemoor.gov.uk

Smedley, Brian (LAB - Bridgwater Westover)
brian.smedley@sedgemoor.gov.uk

Woodman, John (CON - Huntspill & Pawlett)
john.woodman@sedgemoor.gov.uk

POLITICAL COMPOSITION
CON: 35, LAB: 10, UKIP: 2, LD: 1

Sefton   M

Sefton Metropolitan Borough Council, Town Hall, Southport
PR8 1DA

☎ 01704 533133 📠 0151 934 2293 💻 www.sefton.gov.uk

FACTS AND FIGURES
Parliamentary Constituencies: Bootle, Sefton Central, Southport
EU Constituencies: North West
Election Frequency: Elections are by thirds

PRINCIPAL OFFICERS

Chief Executive: Mrs Margaret Carney, Chief Executive, Town
Hall, Southport PR8 1DA ☎ 0151 934 2057
📧 margaret.carney@sefton.gov.uk

Senior Management: Ms Charlotte Bailey, Executive Director,
Bootle Town Hall, Oriel Road, Bootle L20 7AE ☎ 0151 934 4269
📧 charlotte.bailey@sefton.gov.uk

Senior Management: Mr Dwayne Johnson, Director - Social
Care & Health, Merton House, Stanley Road, Bootle L20 3DL
☎ 0151 934 4900 📧 dwayne.johnson@sefton.gov.uk

Senior Management: Ms Sarah Kemp, Executive Director, Bootle
Town Hall, Oriel Road, Bootle L20 7AE ☎ 0151 934 4770
📧 sarah.kemp@sefton.gov.uk

Children / Youth Services: Ms Vicky Buchanan, Head -
Children's Social Care, 9th Floor, Merton House, Stanley Road,
Bootle L20 3JA ☎ 0151 934 3128 📧 vicky.buchanan@sefton.gov.uk

Civil Registration: Ms Jill Coule, Head - Regulation &
Compliance, Ground Floor, Magdalen House, 30 Trinity Road,
Bootle L20 3NJ ☎ 0151 934 2031 📧 jill.coule@sefton.gov.uk

Community Safety: Ms Andrea Watts, Head of Service -
Communities, Town Hall, Southport PR8 1DA ☎ 0151 934 2030
📧 andrea.watts@sefton.gov.uk

Consumer Protection and Trading Standards: Ms Jill Coule,
Head - Regulation & Compliance, Ground Floor, Magdalen House,
30 Trinity Road, Bootle L20 3NJ ☎ 0151 934 2031
📧 jill.coule@sefton.gov.uk

Corporate Services: Mr Stephan Van Arendsen, Head -
Resources, Magdalen House, 30 Trinity Road, Bootle L20 3NJ
☎ 0151 934 4081 📧 stephan.vanarendsen@sefton.gov.uk

Economic Development: Mr Mark Long, Head - Inward
Investment & Employment, Magdalen House, Trinity Road, Bootle
L20 3NJ ☎ 0151 934 3471 📧 mark.long@sefton.gov.uk

Education: Mr Mike McSorley, Head - Schools & Families,
Magdalen House, Trinity Road, Bootle L20 3NJ ☎ 0151 934 3428
📧 mike.mcsorley@sefton.gov.uk

SEFTON

Electoral Registration: Ms Jill Coule, Head - Regulation & Compliance, Ground Floor, Magdalen House, 30 Trinity Road, Bootle L20 3NJ ☎ 0151 934 2031 🖱 jill.coule@sefton.gov.uk

Environmental / Technical Services: Mr Philip Cresswall, Head - Regeneration & Housing, Magdalen House, 30 Trinity Road, Bootle L20 3NJ ☎ 0151 934 2171 🖱 phil.cresswall@sefton.gov.uk

Environmental Health: Ms Jill Coule, Head - Regulation & Compliance, Ground Floor, Magdalen House, 30 Trinity Road, Bootle L20 3NJ ☎ 0151 934 2031 🖱 jill.coule@sefton.gov.uk

Finance: Mr Stephan Van Arendsen, Head - Resources, Magdalen House, 30 Trinity Road, Bootle L20 3NJ ☎ 0151 934 4081 🖱 stephan.vanarendsen@sefton.gov.uk

Fleet Management: Mr Jim Black, Head - Locality Services - Commissioned, Magdalen House, Trinity Road, Bootle L20 3NJ ☎ 0151 288 6133 🖱 jim.black@sefton.gov.uk

Health and Safety: Mr Stephan Van Arendsen, Head - Resources, Magdalen House, 30 Trinity Road, Bootle L20 3NJ ☎ 0151 934 4081 🖱 stephan.vanarendsen@sefton.gov.uk

Highways: Mr Jim Black, Head - Locality Services - Commissioned, Magdalen House, Trinity Road, Bootle L20 3NJ ☎ 0151 288 6133 🖱 jim.black@sefton.gov.uk

Housing: Mr Philip Cresswall, Head - Regeneration & Housing, Magdalen House, 30 Trinity Road, Bootle L20 3NJ ☎ 0151 934 2171 🖱 phil.cresswall@sefton.gov.uk

Legal: Ms Jill Coule, Head - Regulation & Compliance, Ground Floor, Magdalen House, 30 Trinity Road, Bootle L20 3NJ ☎ 0151 934 2031 🖱 jill.coule@sefton.gov.uk

Licensing: Ms Jill Coule, Head - Regulation & Compliance, Ground Floor, Magdalen House, 30 Trinity Road, Bootle L20 3NJ ☎ 0151 934 2031 🖱 jill.coule@sefton.gov.uk

Lifelong Learning: Mr Mike McSorley, Head - Schools & Families, Town Hall, Southport PR8 1DA ☎ 0151 934 3428 🖱 mike.mcsorley@sefton.gov.uk

Member Services: Ms Jill Coule, Head - Regulation & Compliance, Ground Floor, Magdalen House, 30 Trinity Road, Bootle L20 3NJ ☎ 0151 934 2031 🖱 jill.coule@sefton.gov.uk

Parking: Ms Jill Coule, Head - Regulation & Compliance, Ground Floor, Magdalen House, 30 Trinity Road, Bootle L20 3NJ ☎ 0151 934 2031 🖱 jill.coule@sefton.gov.uk

Personnel / HR: Mr Mark Dale, Chief Personnel Officer, 2nd Floor, Magdalen House, 30 Trinity Road, Bootle L20 3NJ ☎ 0151 934 3949 🖱 mark.dale@sefton.gov.uk

Planning: Mr Stuart Barnes, Chief Planning Officer, Magdalen House, Trinity Road, Bootle L20 3NJ ☎ 0151 934 3544 🖱 stuart.barnes@sefton.gov.uk

Public Libraries: Ms Andrea Watts, Head of Service - Communities, Bootle Town Hall, Trinity Road, Bootle L20 3NJ ☎ 0151 934 2030 🖱 andrea.watts@sefton.gov.uk

Recycling & Waste Minimisation: Mr Andrew Walker, Head - Locality Services, Hawthorne Road Depot, Hawthorne Road, Bootle L20 9PR ☎ 0151 288 6159 🖱 andrew.walker@sefton.gov.uk

Regeneration: Mr Philip Cresswall, Head - Regeneration & Housing, Magdalen House, 30 Trinity Road, Bootle L20 3NJ ☎ 0151 934 2171 🖱 phil.cresswall@sefton.gov.uk

Social Services (Adult): Mr Dwayne Johnson, Director - Social Care & Health, Merton House, Stanley Road, Bootle L20 3DL ☎ 0151 934 4900 🖱 dwayne.johnson@sefton.gov.uk

Social Services (Adult): Ms Tina Wilkins, Head of Service - Adult Social Care, Town Hall, Southport PR8 1DA ☎ 01704 533133 🖱 tina.wilkins@sefton.gov.uk

Social Services (Children): Ms Vicky Buchanan, Head - Children's Social Care, 9th Floor, Merton House, Stanley Road, Bootle L20 3JA ☎ 0151 934 3128 🖱 vicky.buchanan@sefton.gov.uk

Staff Training: Mr Mark Dale, Chief Personnel Officer, 2nd Floor, Magdalen House, 30 Trinity Road, Bootle L20 3NJ ☎ 0151 934 3949 🖱 mark.dale@sefton.gov.uk

Tourism: Mr Mark Long, Head - Inward Investment & Employment, Magdalen House, Trinity Road, Bootle L20 3NJ ☎ 0151 934 3471 🖱 mark.long@sefton.gov.uk

Waste Collection and Disposal: Mr Andrew Walker, Head - Locality Services, Hawthorne Road Depot, Hawthorne Road, Bootle L20 9PR ☎ 0151 288 6159 🖱 andrew.walker@sefton.gov.uk

Waste Management: Mr Jim Black, Head - Locality Services - Commissioned, Magdalen House, Trinity Road, Bootle L20 3NJ ☎ 0151 288 6133 🖱 jim.black@sefton.gov.uk

Children's Play Areas: Ms Andrea Watts, Head of Service - Communities, Magdalen House, Trinity Road, Bootle L20 3NJ ☎ 0151 934 2030 🖱 andrea.watts@sefton.gov.uk

COUNCILLORS

Mayor: Brodie-Browne, Iain (LD - Birkdale)
iain.brodie.brown@councillors.sefton.gov.uk

Deputy Mayor: Cluskey, Kevin (LAB - Ford)
kevin.cluskey@councillors.sefton.gov.uk

Leader of the Council: Maher, Ian (LAB - Netherton & Orrell)
ian.maher@councillors.sefton.gov.uk

Deputy Leader of the Council: Fairclough, John (LAB - Linacre)
john.fairclough@councillors.sefton.gov.uk

Group Leader: McGuire, Sue (LD - Cambridge)
sue.mcguire@councillors.sefton.gov.uk

Ashton, Nigel (LD - Meols)
nigel.ashton@councillors.sefton.gov.uk

Atkinson, Marion (LAB - Molyneux)
marion.atkinson@councillors.sefton.gov.uk

Ball, Pat (CON - Dukes)
pat.ball@councillors.sefton.gov.uk

Barton, Jo (LD - Meols)
jo.barton@councillors.sefton.gov.uk

Barton, David (CON - Dukes)
david.barton@councillors.sefton.gov.uk

Bennett, Maria (O - Ravenmeols)
maria.bennett@councillors.sefton.gov.uk

Bliss, Harry (CON - Cambridge)
harry.bliss@councillors.sefton.gov.uk

Booth, Mike (LD - Kew)
mike.booth@councillors.sefton.gov.uk

Bradshaw, Susan (LAB - Netherton & Orrell)
susan.bradshaw@councillors.sefton.gov.uk

Brennan, Robert (LAB - Netherton & Orrell)
robert.brennan@councillors.sefton.gov.uk

Burns, June (LAB - Park)
june.burns@councillors.sefton.gov.uk

Byrom, Leslie (LAB - Victoria)
les.byrom@councillors.sefton.gov.uk

Carr, Anthony (LAB - Molyneux)
anthony.carr@councillors.sefton.gov.uk

Carragher, Clare (LAB - Manor)
clare.carragher@councillors.sefton.gov.uk

Cluskey, Linda (LAB - St. Oswald)
linda.cluskey@councillors.sefton.gov.uk

Cummins, Paul (LAB - Church)
paul.cummins@councillors.sefton.gov.uk

Dams, Andy (LAB - Blundellsands)
andy.dams@councillors.sefton.gov.uk

Dawson, Tony (LD - Dukes)
tony.dawson@councillors.sefton.gov.uk

Dodd, John (LD - Meols)
john.dodd@councillors.sefton.gov.uk

Dutton, Denise (CON - Harington)
denise.dutton@councillors.sefton.gov.uk

Friel, Gordon (LAB - Linacre)
gordon.friel@councillors.sefton.gov.uk

Gannon, Matt (IND - Sudell)
matt.gannon@councillors.sefton.gov.uk

Grace, Janet (LAB - Victoria)
janet.grace@councillors.sefton.gov.uk

Hands, Richard (LD - Birkdale)
richard.hands@councillors.sefton.gov.uk

Hardy, Patricia (LAB - Litherland)
patricia.hardy@councillors.sefton.gov.uk

Jamieson, Simon (CON - Harington)
simon.jamieson@councillors.sefton.gov.uk

Jones, Terry (CON - Ainsdale)
terry.jones@councillors.sefton.gov.uk

Keith, Pat (LD - Cambridge)
pat.keith@councillors.sefton.gov.uk

Kelly, John (LAB - Litherland)
john.kelly@councillors.sefton.gov.uk

Kelly, John (LAB - Manor)
john.joseph.kelly@councillors.sefton.gov.uk

Lappin, Paulette (LAB - Ford)
paulette.lappin@councillors.sefton.gov.uk

Lewis, Daniel (LAB - Blundellsands)
Dan.T.Lewis@councillors.sefton.gov.uk

Lewis, Daniel (LD - Norwood)
daniel.lewis@councillors.sefton.gov.uk

McCann, Bob (IND - Ravenmeols)
bob.mccann@councillors.sefton.gov.uk

McGinnity, Steve (LAB - Manor)
steve.mcginnity@councillors.sefton.gov.uk

McKinley, Patrick (LAB - Sudell)
patrick.mckinley@councillors.sefton.gov.uk

Moncur, Ian (LAB - Ford)
ian.moncur@councillors.sefton.gov.uk

Murphy, Paula (LAB - Molyneux)
paula.murphy@councillors.sefton.gov.uk

O'Brien, Michael (LAB - Derby)
michael.o'brien@councillors.sefton.gov.uk

O'Brien, Brenda (LAB - Linacre)
bebebaker01@hotmail.com

O'Hanlon, Pat (IND - Park)
pat.o'hanlon@councillors.sefton.gov.uk

Owens, Robert (LAB - Sudell)
robert.owens@councillors.sefton.gov.uk

Page, Catie (LAB - Ravenmeols)
catie.page@councillors.sefton.gov.uk

Pitt, Michael (CON - Harington)
michael.pitt@councillors.sefton.gov.uk

Preece, Haydn (LD - Ainsdale)
preecehay@aol.com

Pullin, David (LD - Kew)
david.pullin@councillors.sefton.gov.uk

Robinson, Dave (LAB - Derby)
dave.robinson@councillors.sefton.gov.uk

Roche, Michael (LAB - Victoria)
michael.roche@councillors.sefton.gov.uk

Roscoe, Diane (LAB - Blundellsands)
diane.roscoe@councillors.sefton.gov.uk

Sayers, John (LAB - Park)
john.sayers@councillors.sefton.gov.uk

Shaw, Simon (LD - Birkdale)
simon.shaw@councillors.sefton.gov.uk

Spencer, Paula (LAB - St. Oswald)
paula.spencer@councillors.sefton.gov.uk

Thomas, Carla (LAB - St. Oswald)
cllrcarlathomas@gmail.com

Thompson, Anne (LAB - Derby)
anne.thompson@councillors.sefton.gov.uk

Thompson, Lynne (LD - Ainsdale)
lynne.thompson@councillors.sefton.gov.uk

Tweed, Paul (LAB - Litherland)
paul.tweed@councillors.sefton.gov.uk

SEFTON

Veidman, Daren (LAB - Church)
daren.veidman@councillors.sefton.gov.uk

Weavers, Frederick (LD - Kew)
frederick.weavers@councillors.sefton.gov.uk

Webster, Veronica (LAB - Church)
veronica.webster@councillors.sefton.gov.uk

Welsh, Marianne (LD - Norwood)
marianne.welsh@councillors.sefton.gov.uk

Welsh, Bill (LD - Norwood)
bill.welsh@councillors.sefton.gov.uk

POLITICAL COMPOSITION
LAB: 38, LD: 17, CON: 7, IND: 3, O: 1

COMMITTEE CHAIRS

Audit: Mr Robert Brennan

Health & Wellbeing: Mr Ian Moncur

Licensing: Mr John Kelly

Planning: Mr Daren Veidman

Selby   D

Selby District Council, Civic Centre, Doncaster Road, Selby
YO8 9FT
☎ 01757 705101 ✆ info@selby.gov.uk 🖥 www.selby.gov.uk

FACTS AND FIGURES
Parliamentary Constituencies: Selby and Ainsty
EU Constituencies: Yorkshire and the Humber
Election Frequency: Elections are of whole council

PRINCIPAL OFFICERS

Chief Executive: Ms Janet Waggott, Interim Chief Executive, Civic
Centre, Doncaster Road, Selby YO8 9FT ☎ 01609 537411
✆ jwaggott@selby.gov.uk

Senior Management: Mr Keith Cadman, Head of Commissioning,
Contracts & Procurement, Civic Centre, Doncaster Road, Selby
YO8 9FT ☎ 01757 705101 ✆ kcadman@selby.gov.uk

Senior Management: Mr James Cokeham, Head of Strategic
Planning Policy & Economic Development, Civic Centre, Doncaster
Road, Selby YO8 9FT ☎ 01757 705101 ✆ jcokeham@selby.gov.uk

Senior Management: Mrs Karen Iveson, Chief Finance Officer,
Civic Centre, Portholme Road, Selby YO8 4SB ☎ 01757 292056
✆ kiveson@selby.gov.uk

Senior Management: Mrs Gillian Marshall, Solicitor to the
Council, Civic Centre, Doncaster Road, Selby YO8 9FT
☎ 01757 705101 ✆ gmarshall@selby.gov.uk

Senior Management: Mrs Rose Norris, Head of Community
Partnerships & Customers, Civic Centre, Portholme Road, Selby
YO8 4SB ☎ 01757 705101 ✆ rnorris@selby.gov.uk

Senior Management: Ms June Rothwell, Head of Operational
Services (Access Selby), Civic Centre, Doncaster Road, Selby
YO8 9FT ☎ 01757 705101 ✆ jrothwell@selby.gov.uk

Architect, Building / Property Services: Mr Keith Cadman,
Head of Commissioning, Contracts & Procurement, Civic Centre,
Doncaster Road, Selby YO8 9FT ☎ 01757 705101
✆ kcadman@selby.gov.uk

Building Control: Mr Les Chapman, Building Control Manager,
Suite 2, North Yorkshire Building Control, Coxwold House,
Easingwold Business Park, Easingwold, York YO16 3FB
☎ 01347 822703 ✆ lchapman@selby.gov.uk

PR / Communications: Mr Mike James, Lead Officer - Marketing
& Communications, Civic Centre, Doncaster Road, Selby YO8 9FT
☎ 01757 705101 ✆ mjames@selby.gov.uk

Community Planning: Mrs Rose Norris, Head of Community
Partnerships & Customers, Civic Centre, Portholme Road, Selby
YO8 4SB ☎ 01757 705101 ✆ rnorris@selby.gov.uk

Computer Management: Mr Glenn Shelley, Business Manager,
Civic Centre, Doncaster Road, Selby YO8 9FT ☎ 01757 292007
✆ gshelley@selby.gov.uk

Contracts: Mr Keith Cadman, Head of Commissioning, Contracts
& Procurement, Civic Centre, Doncaster Road, Selby YO8 9FT
☎ 01757 705101 ✆ kcadman@selby.gov.uk

Customer Service: Mr Simon Parkinson, Lead Officer -
Community Support Team, Civic Centre, Doncaster Road, Selby
YO8 9FT ☎ 01757 705101 ✆ sparkinson@selby.gov.uk

Economic Development: Mr James Cokeham, Head of Strategic
Planning Policy & Economic Development, Civic Centre, Doncaster
Road, Selby YO8 9FT ☎ 01757 705101 ✆ jcokeham@selby.gov.uk

E-Government: Mr Chris Smith, Lead Officer - Data & Systems,
Civic Centre, Doncaster Road, Selby YO8 9FT ☎ 01757 705101
✆ csmith@selby.gov.uk

Electoral Registration: Mrs Janice Senior, Business Support
Supervisor, Civic Centre, Doncaster Road, Selby YO8 9FT
☎ 01757 705101 ✆ jsenior@selby.gov.uk

Emergency Planning: Mr Dean Richardson, Business Manager,
Civic Centre, Doncaster Road, Selby YO8 9FT ☎ 01757 705101
✆ drichardson@selby.gov.uk

Environmental / Technical Services: Mr Wayne Palmer, Lead
Officer - Environmental Health & Housing, Civic Centre, Doncaster
Road, Selby YO8 9FT ☎ 01757 705101 ✆ wpalmer@selby.gov.uk

Environmental Health: Mr Wayne Palmer, Lead Officer -
Environmental Health & Housing, Civic Centre, Doncaster Road,
Selby YO8 9FT ☎ 01757 705101 ✆ wpalmer@selby.gov.uk

Estates, Property & Valuation: Mr Dave Maycock, Lead Officer
- Assets, Civic Centre, Doncaster Road, Selby YO8 9FT
☎ 01757 705101 ✆ dmaycock@selby.gov.uk

Finance: Mrs Karen Iveson, Chief Finance Officer, Civic Centre,
Portholme Road, Selby YO8 4SB ☎ 01757 292056
✆ kiveson@selby.gov.uk

Health and Safety: Ms Jackie Humphries, Lead Officer - HR, Civic Centre, Doncaster Road, Selby YO8 9FT ☎ 01757 705101 ⌨ jhumphries@selby.gov.uk

Housing: Mr Wayne Palmer, Lead Officer - Environmental Health & Housing, Civic Centre, Doncaster Road, Selby YO8 9FT ☎ 01757 705101 ⌨ wpalmer@selby.gov.uk

Housing Maintenance: Mr Dave Maycock, Lead Officer - Assets, Civic Centre, Doncaster Road, Selby YO8 9FT ☎ 01757 705101 ⌨ dmaycock@selby.gov.uk

Legal: Mrs Gillian Marshall, Solicitor to the Council, Civic Centre, Doncaster Road, Selby YO8 9FT ☎ 01757 705101 ⌨ gmarshall@selby.gov.uk

Leisure and Cultural Services: Mr Keith Cadman, Head of Commissioning, Contracts & Procurement, Civic Centre, Doncaster Road, Selby YO8 9FT ☎ 01757 705101 ⌨ kcadman@selby.gov.uk

Licensing: Ms Helen McNeil, Lead Officer - Debt Control & Enforcement, Civic Centre, Doncaster Road, Selby YO8 9FT ☎ 01757 705101 ⌨ hmcneil@selby.gov.uk

Member Services: Mr Palbinder Mann, Democratic Services Manager, Civic Centre, Doncaster Road, Selby YO8 9FT ☎ 01757 705101 ⌨ pmann@selby.gov.uk

Parking: Mr Keith Cadman, Head of Commissioning, Contracts & Procurement, Civic Centre, Doncaster Road, Selby YO8 9FT ☎ 01757 705101 ⌨ kcadman@selby.gov.uk

Partnerships: Mr Keith Cadman, Head of Commissioning, Contracts & Procurement, Civic Centre, Doncaster Road, Selby YO8 9FT ☎ 01757 705101 ⌨ kcadman@selby.gov.uk

Personnel / HR: Ms Jackie Humphries, Lead Officer - HR, Civic Centre, Doncaster Road, Selby YO8 9FT ☎ 01757 705101 ⌨ jhumphries@selby.gov.uk

Planning: Mr Richard Sunter, Lead Officer - Planning, Civic Centre, Doncaster Road, Selby YO8 9FT ☎ 01757 705101 ⌨ rsunter@selby.gov.uk

Procurement: Mr Keith Cadman, Head of Commissioning, Contracts & Procurement, Civic Centre, Doncaster Road, Selby YO8 9FT ☎ 01757 705101 ⌨ kcadman@selby.gov.uk

Recycling & Waste Minimisation: Mr Keith Cadman, Head of Commissioning, Contracts & Procurement, Civic Centre, Doncaster Road, Selby YO8 9FT ☎ 01757 705101 ⌨ kcadman@selby.gov.uk

Regeneration: Mr James Cokeham, Head of Strategic Planning Policy & Economic Development, Civic Centre, Doncaster Road, Selby YO8 9FT ☎ 01757 705101 ⌨ jcokeham@selby.gov.uk

Staff Training: Ms Jackie Humphries, Lead Officer - HR, Civic Centre, Doncaster Road, Selby YO8 9FT ☎ 01757 705101 ⌨ jhumphries@selby.gov.uk

Street Scene: Mr Keith Cadman, Head of Commissioning, Contracts & Procurement, Civic Centre, Doncaster Road, Selby YO8 9FT ☎ 01757 705101 ⌨ kcadman@selby.gov.uk

Waste Collection and Disposal: Mr Keith Cadman, Head of Commissioning, Contracts & Procurement, Civic Centre, Doncaster Road, Selby YO8 9FT ☎ 01757 705101 ⌨ kcadman@selby.gov.uk

Waste Management: Mr Keith Cadman, Head of Commissioning, Contracts & Procurement, Civic Centre, Doncaster Road, Selby YO8 9FT ☎ 01757 705101 ⌨ kcadman@selby.gov.uk

COUNCILLORS

Chair: Duckett, Stephanie (LAB - Barlby Village)
sduckett@selby.gov.uk

Vice-Chair: Chilvers, Judith (CON - Selby West)
jchilvers@selby.gov.uk

Leader of the Council: Crane, Mark (CON - Brayton)
mcrane@selby.gov.uk

Deputy Leader of the Council: Mackman, John (CON - Monk Fryston)
jmackman@selby.gov.uk

Arthur, Karl (CON - Derwent)
karthur@selby.gov.uk

Buckle, David (CON - Sherburn in Elmet)
dbuckle@selby.gov.uk

Casling, Liz (CON - Escrick)
ecasling@selby.gov.uk

Cattanach, John (CON - Cawood with Wistow)
jcattanach@selby.gov.uk

Chilvers, Ian (CON - Brayton)
ichilvers@selby.gov.uk

Deans, James (CON - Derwent)
jdeans@selby.gov.uk

Ellis, Keith (CON - Appleton Roebuck & Church Fenton)
kellis@selby.gov.uk

Hobson, Mel (CON - Sherburn in Elmet)
mhobson@selby.gov.uk

Hutchinson, David (CON - South Milford)
dhutchinson@selby.gov.uk

Jordan, Mike (CON - Camblesforth & Carlton)
mjordan@selby.gov.uk

Lunn, Clifford (CON - Thorpe Willoughby)
clunn@selby.gov.uk

Mackay, Donald (CON - Tadcaster)
dbain-mackay@selby.gov.uk

Marshall, Brian (LAB - Selby East)
bmarshall@selby.gov.uk

McCartney, Mary (IND - Eggborough)
mmccartney@selby.gov.uk

Metcalfe, Christopher (CON - Tadcaster)
cmetcalfe@selby.gov.uk

Musgrave, Richard (CON - Appleton Roebuck & Church Fenton)
rmusgrave@selby.gov.uk

Packham, Robert (LAB - Sherburn in Elmet)
rpackham@selby.gov.uk

SELBY

Pearson, Christopher (CON - Hambleton)
cpearson@selby.gov.uk

Peart, Dave (CON - Camblesforth & Carlton)
dpeart@selby.gov.uk

Reynolds, Ian (CON - Riccall)
ireynolds@selby.gov.uk

Sage, Bryn (CON - Byram & Brotherton)
bsage@selby.gov.uk

Shaw-Wright, Jennifer (LAB - Selby West)
jshawwright@selby.gov.uk

Sweeting, Richard (CON - Tadcaster)
rsweeting@selby.gov.uk

Thurlow, Anthony (LAB - Selby West)

Welch, Paul (LAB - Selby East)
pwelch@selby.gov.uk

White, Debbie (CON - Whitley)
dewhite@selby.gov.uk

POLITICAL COMPOSITION
CON: 23, LAB: 6, IND: 1

COMMITTEE CHAIRS

Audit: Mr Mike Jordan

Licensing: Mr Christopher Pearson

Sevenoaks   D

Sevenoaks District Council, Council Offices, Argyle Road, Sevenoaks TN13 1HG
☎ 01732 227000 ⁺ information@sevenoaks.gov.uk
🖥 www.sevenoaks.gov.uk

FACTS AND FIGURES
Parliamentary Constituencies: Dartford, Sevenoaks, Tonbridge and Malling
EU Constituencies: South East
Election Frequency: Elections are of whole council

PRINCIPAL OFFICERS

Chief Executive: Dr Pav Ramewal, Chief Executive, Council Offices, Argyle Road, Sevenoaks TN13 1HG ☎ 01732 227000
⁺ pav.ramewal@sevenoaks.gov.uk

Senior Management: Mrs Lesley Bowles, Chief Officer - Communities & Business, Council Offices, Argyle Road, Sevenoaks TN13 1HG ☎ 01732 227000 ⁺ lesley.bowles@sevenoaks.gov.uk

Senior Management: Mr Jim Carrington-West, Chief Officer - Corporate Services, Council Offices, Argyle Road, Sevenoaks TN13 1HG ☎ 01732 227000 ⁺ jim.carrington-west@sevenoaks.gov.uk

Senior Management: Mr Richard Morris, Chief Planning Officer, Council Offices, Argyle Road, Sevenoaks TN13 1HG
☎ 01732 277000 ⁺ richard.morris@worcester.gov.uk

Senior Management: Mr Adrian Rowbotham, Chief Finance Officer, Council Offices, Argyle Road, Sevenoaks TN13 1HG
☎ 01732 227000 ⁺ adrian.rowbotham@sevenoaks.gov.uk

Senior Management: Mr Richard Wilson, Chief Officer - Environmental & Operational Services, Council Offices, Argyle Road, Sevenoaks TN13 1HG ☎ 01732 227000
⁺ richard.wilson@sevenoaks.gov.uk

Architect, Building / Property Services: Miss Emma Vincent, Property & Facilities Manager, Council Offices, Argyle Road, Sevenoaks TN13 1HG ☎ 01732 227000
⁺ emma.vincent@sevenoaks.gov.uk

Building Control: Mr Kevin Tomsett, Head of Parking & Surveying, Council Offices, Argyle Road, Sevenoaks TN13 1HG
☎ 01732 227000 ⁺ kevin.tomsett@sevenoaks.gov.uk

PR / Communications: Mr Daniel Whitmarsh, Communications & Consultation Manager, Council Offices, Argyle Road, Sevenoaks TN13 1HG ☎ 01732 227000 ⁺ daniel.whitmarsh@sevenoaks.gov.uk

Community Planning: Mr Alan Whiting, Community Planning & Projects Officer, Council Offices, Argyle Road, Sevenoaks TN13 1HG ☎ 01732 227000 ⁺ alan.whiting@sevenoaks.gov.uk

Community Safety: Ms Kelly Webb, Community Safety Co-ordinator, Council Offices, Argyle Road, Sevenoaks TN13 1HG
☎ 01732 227000 ⁺ kelly.webb@sevenoaks.gov.uk

Customer Service: Mrs Amy Wilton, Contact Centre Manager, Council Offices, Argyle Road, Sevenoaks TN13 1HG
☎ 01732 227000 ⁺ amy.wilton@sevenoaks.gov.uk

Direct Labour: Mr Ian Finch, Head of Direct Services, Sevenoaks Direct Services, Dunbrik Depot, 2 Main Road, Sundridge, Sevenoaks TN14 6EP ☎ 01732 227000 ⁺ ian.finch@sevenoaks.gov.uk

Emergency Planning: Mr Kevin Tomsett, Head of Parking & Surveying, Council Offices, Argyle Road, Sevenoaks TN13 1HG
☎ 01732 227000 ⁺ kevin.tomsett@sevenoaks.gov.uk

Environmental Health: Mrs Annie Sargent, Environmental Health Manager, Dartford Borough Council, Civic Centre, Home Gardens, Dartford DA1 1DR ☎ 01322 343434 ⁺ annie.sargent@dartford.gov.uk

Facilities: Miss Emma Vincent, Property & Facilities Manager, Council Offices, Argyle Road, Sevenoaks TN13 1HG
☎ 01732 227000 ⁺ emma.vincent@sevenoaks.gov.uk

Finance: Mr Adrian Rowbotham, Chief Finance Officer, Council Offices, Argyle Road, Sevenoaks TN13 1HG ☎ 01732 227000
⁺ adrian.rowbotham@sevenoaks.gov.uk

Fleet Management: Mr Kenneth Naylor, Transport Manager, Sevenoaks Direct Services, Dunbrik Depot, 2 Main Road, Sundridge, Sevenoaks TN14 6EP ☎ 01959 567000
⁺ kenneth.naylor@sevenoaks.gov.uk

Grounds Maintenance: Mr David Boorman, Senior Parking & Amenities Officer, Council Offices, Argyle Road, Sevenoaks TN13 1HG ☎ 01732 227000 ⁺ david.boorman@sevenoaks.gov.uk

Health and Safety: Mr Richard Wilson, Chief Officer - Environmental & Operational Services, Council Offices, Argyle Road, Sevenoaks TN13 1HG ☎ 01732 227000 ✆ richard.wilson@sevenoaks.gov.uk

Home Energy Conservation: Mr Daniel Shaw, Energy Conservation & Initiatives Officer, Council Offices, Argyle Road, Sevenoaks TN13 1HG ☎ 01732 227000 ✆ daniel.shaw@sevenoaks.gov.uk

Local Area Agreement: Mrs Lesley Bowles, Chief Officer - Communities & Business, Council Offices, Argyle Road, Sevenoaks TN13 1HG ☎ 01732 227000 ✆ lesley.bowles@sevenoaks.gov.uk

Legal: Mr Martin Goodman, Head of Legal & Democratic Services, Council Offices, Argyle Road, Sevenoaks TN13 1HG ☎ 01732 227000 ✆ martin.goodman@sevenoaks.gov.uk

Leisure and Cultural Services: Mrs Hayley Brooks, Health & Leisure Manager, Council Offices, Argyle Road, Sevenoaks TN13 1HG ☎ 01732 227000 ✆ hayley.brooks@sevenoaks.gov.uk

Licensing: Mrs Claire Perry, Licensing Partnership Manager, Council Offices, Argyle Road, Sevenoaks TN13 1HG ☎ 01732 227325; 07970 731616 ✆ claire.perry@tunbridgewells.gov.uk

Lottery Funding, Charity and Voluntary: Mrs Lesley Bowles, Chief Officer - Communities & Business, Council Offices, Argyle Road, Sevenoaks TN13 1HG ☎ 01732 227000 ✆ lesley.bowles@sevenoaks.gov.uk

Parking: Mr John Strachan, Parking Manager, Council Offices, Argyle Road, Sevenoaks TN13 1HG ☎ 01732 227000 ✆ john.strachan@sevenoaks.gov.uk

Personnel / HR: Mrs Nuala Beattie, Human Resources Manager, Council Offices, Argyle Road, Sevenoaks TN13 1HG ☎ 01732 227000 ✆ nuala.beattie@sevenoaks.gov.uk

Planning: Mr Richard Morris, Chief Planning Officer, Council Offices, Argyle Road, Sevenoaks TN13 1HG ☎ 01732 277000 ✆ richard.morris@worcester.gov.uk

Procurement: Mr Bami Cole, Audit, Risk & Anti-Fraud Manager, Dartford Borough Council, Civic Centre, Home Gardens, Dartford DA1 1DR ☎ 01322 343023 ✆ bami.cole@dartford.gov.uk

Recycling & Waste Minimisation: Mr Ian Finch, Head of Direct Services, Sevenoaks Direct Services, Dunbrik Depot, 2 Main Road, Sundridge, Sevenoaks TN14 6EP ☎ 01732 227000 ✆ ian.finch@sevenoaks.gov.uk

Staff Training: Mrs Nuala Beattie, Human Resources Manager, Council Offices, Argyle Road, Sevenoaks TN13 1HG ☎ 01732 227000 ✆ nuala.beattie@sevenoaks.gov.uk

Street Scene: Mr Ian Finch, Head of Direct Services, Sevenoaks Direct Services, Dunbrik Depot, 2 Main Road, Sundridge, Sevenoaks TN14 6EP ☎ 01732 227000 ✆ ian.finch@sevenoaks.gov.uk

Waste Collection and Disposal: Mr Ian Finch, Head of Direct Services, Sevenoaks Direct Services, Dunbrik Depot, 2 Main Road, Sundridge, Sevenoaks TN14 6EP ☎ 01732 227000 ✆ ian.finch@sevenoaks.gov.uk

Waste Management: Mr Richard Wilson, Chief Officer - Environmental & Operational Services, Council Offices, Argyle Road, Sevenoaks TN13 1HG ☎ 01732 227000 ✆ richard.wilson@sevenoaks.gov.uk

Children's Play Areas: Mr David Boorman, Senior Parking & Amenities Officer, Council Offices, Argyle Road, Sevenoaks TN13 1HG ☎ 01732 227000 ✆ david.boorman@sevenoaks.gov.uk

COUNCILLORS

Chair: Raikes, Simon (CON - Sevenoaks Town & St. John's)
cllr.raikes@sevenoaks.gov.uk

Vice-Chair: Abraham, Lawrence (CON - Hartley & Hodsoll Street)
cllr.abraham@sevenoaks.gov.uk

Leader of the Council: Fleming, Peter (CON - Sevenoaks Town & St. John's)
cllr.fleming@tory.co.uk

Deputy Leader of the Council: Lowe, Michelle (CON - Otford & Shoreham)
cllr.lowe@sevenoaks.gov.uk

Group Leader: Canet, Merilyn (LD - Sevenoaks Northern)
cllr.canet@sevenoaks.gov.uk

Group Leader: Halford, James (UKIP - Swanley White Oak)

Ball, Laurence (CON - Swanley White Oak)
cllr.ball@sevenoaks.gov.uk

Barnes, John (CON - Swanley Christchurch & Swanley Village)
cllr.barnes@sevenoaks.gov.uk

Bayley, Kim (CON - Dunton Green & Riverhead)
cllr.bayley@sevenoaks.gov.uk

Bosley, Patricia (CON - Fawkham & West Kingsdown)
cllrp.bosley@sevenoaks.gov.uk

Bosley, Ian (CON - Fawkham & West Kingsdown)
cllr.bosley@sevenoaks.gov.uk

Brown, Cameron (CON - Dunton Green & Riverhead)
cllr.brown@sevenoaks.gov.uk

Clack, Graham (CON - Sevenoaks Town & St. John's)
cllr.clack@sevenoaks.gov.uk

Clark, Cameron (CON - Ash & New Ash Green)
cllr.c.clark@sevenoaks.gov.uk

Cooke, Patrick (CON - Penshurst, Forcombe & Chiddingstone)
cllr.cooke@sevenoaks.gov.uk

Dickins, Matthew (CON - Cowden & Hever)
cllr.dickins@sevenoaks.gov.uk

Dyball, Lesley (CON - Swanley St Mary's)
cllr.dyball@sevenoaks.gov.uk

Edwards-Winser, John (CON - Otford & Shoreham)
cllr.edwards-winser@sevenoaks.gov.uk

Esler, Diana (CON - Westerham & Crockham Hill)
cllr.esler@sevenoaks.gov.uk

Eyre, Andrew (CON - Sevenoaks Kippington)
cllr.eyre@sevenoaks.gov.uk

SEVENOAKS

Firth, Anna (CON - Brasted, Chevening & Sundridge)
cllr.firth@sevenoaks.gov.uk

Gaywood, James (CON - Hartley & Hodsoll Street)
cllr.gaywood@sevenoaks.gov.uk

Grint, John (CON - Halstead, Knockholt & Badgers Mount)
cllr.grint@sevenoaks.gov.uk

Hogarth, Roderick (CON - Seal & Weald)
cllr.hogarth@sevenoaks.gov.uk

Hogg, Michael (LAB - Swanley St. Mary's)
cllr.hogg@sevenoaks.gov.uk

Horwood, Michael (CON - Eynsford)
cllr.horwood@sevenoaks.gov.uk

Hunter, Avril (CON - Sevenoaks Kippington)
cllr.hunter@sevenoaks.gov.uk

Kelly, John (CON - Hartley & Hodsoll Street)
cllr.kelly@sevenoaks.gov.uk

Kitchener, Darren (IND - Hextable)
darrenkitchener@outlook.com

Krogdahl, Jonathan (CON - Sevenoaks Northern)
jkrogdahl@hotmail.com

Lake, Peter (CON - Leigh & Chiddingstone Causeway)
cllr.lake@sevenoaks.gov.uk

Layland, Alan (CON - Edenbridge South & West)
cllr.layland@sevenoaks.gov.uk

Lindsay, Stephen (UKIP - Crockenhill & Well Hill)
cllr.lindsay@sevenoaks.gov.uk

London, James (CON - Brasted, Chevening & Sundridge)
cllr.london@sevenoaks.gov.uk

Maskell, Kevin (CON - Westerham & Crockham Hill)
cllr.maskell@sevenoaks.gov.uk

McArthur, Margot (CON - Edenbridge South & West)
cllr.mcarthur@sevenoaks.gov.uk

McGarvey, Philip (CON - Farningham, Horton Kirby & South Darenth)
cllr.mcgarvey@sevenoaks.gov.uk

McGregor, Stuart (CON - Edenbridge North & East)
cllr.mcgregor@sevenoaks.gov.uk

Morris, Dee (CON - Hextable)
cllr.morris@sevenoaks.gov.uk

Parkin, Faye (CON - Fawkham & West Kingsdown)
cllr.parkin@sevenoaks.gov.uk

Parson, Edward (CON - Sevenoaks Eastern)
cllr.parson@sevenoaks.gov.uk

Pearsall, Claire (CON - Ash & New Ash Green)
cllr.pearsall@sevenoaks.gov.uk

Pett, Alan (CON - Ash & New Ash Green)
cllr.pett@sevenoaks.gov.uk

Piper, Robert (CON - Brasted, Chevening & Sundridge)
cllr.piper@sevenoaks.gov.uk

Purves, Elizabeth (LD - Sevenoaks Eastern)
cllr.purves@sevenoaks.gov.uk

Reay, Simon (CON - Kemsing)
cllr.reay@sevenoaks.gov.uk

Scholey, John (CON - Edenbridge North & East)
cllr.scholey@sevenoaks.gov.uk

Scott, Nina (CON - Swanley White Oak)
cllr.scott@sevenoaks.gov.uk

Searles, Tony (CON - Swanley Christchurch & Swanley Villlage)
cllr.searles@sevenoaks.gov.uk

Stack, Lorraine (CON - Kemsing)
cllr.stack@sevenoaks.gov.uk

Tennessee, Ingrid (CON - Farningham, Horton Kirby & South Darenth)
cllr.tennessee@sevenoaks.gov.uk

Thornton, Julia (CON - Seal & Weald)
cllr.thornton@sevenoaks.gov.uk

Williamson, Gary (CON - Halstead, Knockholt & Badgers Mount)
cllr.williamson@sevenoaks.gov.uk

POLITICAL COMPOSITION
CON: 47, LD: 2, UKIP: 2, IND: 1, LAB: 1

COMMITTEE CHAIRS

Audit: Mr John Grint

Development Control: Mr Gary Williamson

Licensing: Mrs Dee Morris

Sheffield City   M

Sheffield City Council, Sheffield City Council, Town Hall, Sheffield S1 2HH

☎ 0114 273 4567 🖳 www.sheffield.gov.uk

FACTS AND FIGURES
Parliamentary Constituencies: Sheffield Brightside and Hillsborough, Sheffield South East, Sheffield, Central, Sheffield, Hallam, Sheffield, Heeley
EU Constituencies: Yorkshire and the Humber
Election Frequency: Elections are by thirds

PRINCIPAL OFFICERS

Chief Executive: Mr John Mothersole, Chief Executive, Room 126, Town Hall, Pinstone Street, Sheffield S1 2HH ☎ 0114 273 4002 ⊕ john.mothersole@sheffield.gov.uk

Senior Management: Mr Simon Green, Executive Director - Place, Room 212, Town Hall, Pinstone Street, Sheffield S1 2HH ☎ 0114 273 4201 ⊕ simon.green@sheffield.gov.uk

Senior Management: Mr James Henderson, Director - Policy, Performance & Communications, Town Hall, Pinstone Street, Sheffield S1 2HH ☎ 0114 205 3126 ⊕ james.henderson@sheffield.gov.uk

Senior Management: Ms Jayne Ludlam, Executive Director - Children, Young People & Families, Room 140, Town Hall, Pinstone Street, Sheffield S1 2HH ☎ 0114 273 5726 ⊕ jayne.ludlam@sheffield.gov.uk

Senior Management: Ms Laraine Manley, Executive Director - Communities, Room 208, Town Hall, Pinstone Street, Sheffield S1 2HH ☎ 0114 273 4300 ⊕ laraine.manley@sheffield.gov.uk

Senior Management: Mr Eugene Walker, Interim Executive Director - Resources, Town Hall, Pinstone Street, Sheffield S1 2DB ☎ 0114 273 5167 ✆ eugene.walker@sheffield.gov.uk

Access Officer / Social Services (Disability): Mr Brian Messider, Disability Access Officer, 4th Floor, Howden House, Union Street, Sheffield S1 2SH ☎ 0114 273 4197 ✆ brian.messider@sheffield.gov.uk

Architect, Building / Property Services: Mr Nalin Seneviratne, Director - Capital & Major Projects, 5th Floor, Howden House, 1 Union Street, Sheffield S1 2SH ☎ 0114 205 7017 ✆ nalin.seneviratne@sheffield.gov.uk

Building Control: Mr Ralph Bennett, Chief Building Control Manager, 4th Floor, Howden House, 1 Union Street, Sheffield S1 2SH ☎ 0114 2734485 ✆ ralph.bennett@sheffield.gov.uk

Catering Services: Mr Mark Cummins, Operations Manager, Town Hall, Pinstone Street, Sheffield S1 2HH ☎ 0114 273 4537 ✆ mark.cummins@kier.co.uk

Children / Youth Services: Ms Jayne Ludlam, Executive Director - Children, Young People & Families, Room 140, Town Hall, Pinstone Street, Sheffield S1 2HH ☎ 0114 273 5726 ✆ jayne.ludlam@sheffield.gov.uk

Civil Registration: Mrs Samantha Williams, Register Office Manager, Town Hall, Pinstone Street, Sheffield S1 2DB ☎ 0114 203 9434 ✆ samantha.williams@sheffield.gov.uk

PR / Communications: Mr James Henderson, Director - Policy, Performance & Communications, Town Hall, Pinstone Street, Sheffield S1 2HH ☎ 0114 205 3126 ✆ james.henderson@sheffield.gov.uk

Community Planning: Ms Dawn Shaw, Head of Libraries & Community Services, Floor 9, West Wing, Moorfield Building, 1 Moorfoot, Sheffield S1 4PL ☎ 0114 273 4486 ✆ dawn.shaw@sheffield.gov.uk

Community Safety: Ms Sarah Banks, Head of Safer Communities, New Bank House, Queen Street, Sheffield S1 2WA ☎ 0114 273 6605 ✆ sarah.banks@sheffield.gov.uk

Computer Management: Mrs Aline Hayes, Director - Business Change & Information Solutions, Town Hall, Pinstone Street, Sheffield S1 2DB ☎ 0114 273 6818 ✆ aline.hayes@sheffield.gov.uk

Consumer Protection and Trading Standards: Mr Philip Glaves, Principal Officer - Fair Trading & Policy, 5th Floor, Howden House, 1 Union Street, Sheffield S1 2SH ☎ 0114 273 6284 ✆ philip.glaves@sheffield.gov.uk

Contracts: Mrs Marianne Betts, Director - Commercial Services, Level 2, North Wing, Morfoot Building, 1 Moorfoot, Sheffield S1 4PL ☎ 0114 205 7303 ✆ marianne.betts@sheffield.gov.uk

Customer Service: Ms Julie Toner, Director - Human Resources, Room 216C, Town Hall, Pinstone Street, Sheffield S1 2HH ☎ 0114 273 4081 ✆ julie.toner@sheffield.gov.uk

Economic Development: Mr Edward Highfield, Director - Creative Sheffield, Creative Sheffield, 2nd Floor, 11 Broad Street West, Sheffield S1 2SH ☎ 0114 223 2349 ✆ edward.highfield@sheffield.gov.uk

Education: Ms Jayne Ludlam, Executive Director - Children, Young People & Families, Room 140, Town Hall, Pinstone Street, Sheffield S1 2HH ☎ 0114 273 5726 ✆ jayne.ludlam@sheffield.gov.uk

Electoral Registration: Mr John Tomlinson, Electoral Services Manager, Room LG42, Town Hall, Pinstone Street, Sheffield S1 2HH ☎ 0114 273 4091 ✆ john.tomlinson@sheffield.gov.uk

Energy Management: Mr Chris Trotter, Energy & Utility Manager, Level 3, East Wing, Morfoot Building, Sheffield S1 4PL ☎ 0114 273 4562 ✆ chris.trotter@sheffield.gov.uk

Environmental / Technical Services: Mr Simon Green, Executive Director - Place, Room 212, Town Hall, Pinstone Street, Sheffield S1 2HH ☎ 0114 273 4201 ✆ simon.green@sheffield.gov.uk

Environmental Health: Mr Mick Crofts, Director of Business Strategy & Regulation, 4th Floor, Howden House, 1 Union Street, Sheffield S1 2SH ☎ 0114 273 5776 ✆ mick.crofts@sheffield.gov.uk

Estates, Property & Valuation: Mr Nalin Seneviratne, Director - Capital & Major Projects, 5th Floor, Howden House, 1 Union Street, Sheffield S1 2SH ☎ 0114 205 7017 ✆ nalin.seneviratne@sheffield.gov.uk

Events Manager: Ms Natasha Wagstaff, Events Manager, Town Hall, Pinstone Street, Sheffield S1 2HH ☎ 0114 273 6620 ✆ natasha.wagstaff@sheffield.gov.uk

Facilities: Mr Neil Dawson, Director - Transport & Facilities Management, Staniforth Road, Sheffield S9 3GZ ☎ 0114 203 7592 ✆ neil.dawson@sheffield.gov.uk

Finance: Mr Eugene Walker, Interim Executive Director - Resources, Town Hall, Pinstone Street, Sheffield S1 2DB ☎ 0114 273 5167 ✆ eugene.walker@sheffield.gov.uk

Fleet Management: Mr Neil Dawson, Director - Transport & Facilities Management, Staniforth Road, Sheffield S9 3GZ ☎ 0114 203 7592 ✆ neil.dawson@sheffield.gov.uk

Grounds Maintenance: Mr Paul Billington, Director of Culture & Environment, 5th Floor, Howden House, Union Street, Sheffield S1 2SH ☎ 0114 273 4700 ✆ paul.billington@sheffield.gov.uk

Health and Safety: Mr Gary Lund, Health, Safety & Wellbeing Service Manager, Moorfoot, 1 Moorfoot, Sheffield S1 4PL ☎ 0114 273 4082 ✆ gary.lund@sheffield.gov.uk

Highways: Mr Steve Robinson, Head of Highway Maintenance, 4th Floor, Howden House, Union Street, Sheffield S1 2SH ☎ 0114 273 5553 ✆ steve.robinson@sheffield.gov.uk

Home Energy Conservation: Ms Renia Kotynia, Programme Manager - Energy Management, Reduction & Resilience, Moorfoot Building, 1 Moorfoot, Sheffield S1 4PL ☎ 0114 273 4193 ✆ renia.kotynia@sheffield.gov.uk

SHEFFIELD CITY

Housing: Ms Janet Sharpe, Director - Housing & Neighbourhoods Service, Floor 9, West Wing, Moorfield Building, 1 Moorfoot, Sheffield S1 4PL ☎ 0114 273 5493 ◌ janet.sharpe@sheffield.gov.uk

Housing Maintenance: Mr Neil Piper, Project Officer, 4th Floor, Howden House, 1 Union Street, Sheffield S1 2SH ☎ 0114 273 4617 ◌ neil.piper@sheffield.gov.uk

Local Area Agreement: Mr David Hewitt, Corporate Performance Officer, Level 3, West Wing, Moorfoot Building, 1 Moorfoot, Sheffield S1 4PL ☎ 0114 273 5773 ◌ david.hewitt@sheffield.gov.uk

Legal: Ms Gillian Duckworth, Director of Legal & Governance / Monitoring Officer, 5th Floor, Howden House, Union Street, Sheffield S1 2SH ☎ 0114 273 4018 ◌ gillian.duckworth@sheffield.gov.uk

Leisure and Cultural Services: Mr Paul Billington, Director of Culture & Environment, Central Library, Surrey Street, Sheffield S1 1XZ ☎ 0114 273 4700 ◌ paul.billington@sheffield.gov.uk

Licensing: Mr Steve Lonnia, Chief Licensing Officer, Block C, Staniforth Road Depot, 609 Staniforth Road, Sheffield S9 3GZ ☎ 0114 205 3798 ◌ stephen.lonnia@sheffield.gov.uk

Lifelong Learning: Mr Tony Tweedy, Director of Lifelong Learning, Skills & Employment, 145 Crookesmoor Road, Sheffield S6 3FP ☎ 0114 229 6140 ◌ tony.tweedy@sheffield.gov.uk

Lighting: Mr Steve Robinson, Head of Highway Maintenance, 5th Floor, Howden House, 1 Union Street, Sheffield S1 2SH ☎ 0114 273 5553 ◌ steve.robinson@sheffield.gov.uk

Lottery Funding, Charity and Voluntary: Ms Dawn Shaw, Head of Libraries & Community Services, Floor 9, West Wing, Moorfield Building, 1 Moorfoot, Sheffield S1 4PL ☎ 0114 273 4486 ◌ dawn.shaw@sheffield.gov.uk

Member Services: Mr Jason Dietsch, Head of Member Services, G13, Town Hall, Pinstone Street, Sheffield S1 2HH ☎ 0114 273 4117 ◌ jason.dietsch@sheffield.gov.uk

Member Services: Mr Paul Robinson, Head of Democratic Services - Council & Members, G13, Town Hall, Pinstone Street, Sheffield S1 2HH ☎ 0114 273 4029 ◌ paul.robinson@sheffield.gov.uk

Parking: Mr Tom Finnegan-Smith, Head of Strategic Transport, Traffic & Infrastructure, 5th Floor, Howden House, 1 Union Street, Sheffield S1 2SH ☎ 0114 273 6030 ◌ tom.finnegan-smith@sheffield.gov.uk

Partnerships: Mrs Marianne Betts, Director - Commercial Services, Level 2, North Wing, Morfoot Building, 1 Moorfoot, Sheffield S1 4PL ☎ 0114 205 7303 ◌ marianne.betts@sheffield.gov.uk

Personnel / HR: Ms Julie Toner, Director - Human Resources, Room 216C, Town Hall, Pinstone Street, Sheffield S1 2HH ☎ 0114 273 4081 ◌ julie.toner@sheffield.gov.uk

Planning: Mr David Caulfield, Director - Regeneration & Development Services, Floor 5 Howden House, Union Street, Sheffield S1 2SH ☎ 0114 273 5499 ◌ david.caulfield@sheffield.gov.uk

Planning: Mr Simon Green, Executive Director - Place, Room 212, Town Hall, Pinstone Street, Sheffield S1 2HH ☎ 0114 273 4201 ◌ simon.green@sheffield.gov.uk

Procurement: Mrs Marianne Betts, Director - Commercial Services, Level 2, North Wing, Morfoot Building, 1 Moorfoot, Sheffield S1 4PL ☎ 0114 205 7303 ◌ marianne.betts@sheffield.gov.uk

Public Libraries: Ms Dawn Shaw, Head of Libraries & Community Services, Floor 9, West Wing, Moorfield Building, 1 Moorfoot, Sheffield S1 4PL ☎ 0114 273 4486 ◌ dawn.shaw@sheffield.gov.uk

Recycling & Waste Minimisation: Ms Gillian Charters, Head of Waste Management, 5th Floor, Howden House, 1 Union Street, Sheffield S1 2SH ☎ 0114 203 7528 ◌ gillian.charters@sheffield.gov.uk

Regeneration: Mr Simon Ogden, Head of City Regeneration, Floor 4, Howden House, 1 Union Street, Sheffield S1 2SH ☎ 0114 273 4189 ◌ simon.ogden@sheffield.gov.uk

Road Safety: Mr Tom Finnegan-Smith, Head of Strategic Transport, Traffic & Infrastructure, 5th Floor, Howden House, 1 Union Street, Sheffield S1 2SH ☎ 0114 273 6030 ◌ tom.finnegan-smith@sheffield.gov.uk

Social Services: Ms Laraine Manley, Executive Director - Communities, Room 208, Town Hall, Pinstone Street, Sheffield S1 2HH ☎ 0114 273 4300 ◌ laraine.manley@sheffield.gov.uk

Social Services (Adult): Mr Phil Holmes, Director - Adult Services, Town Hall, Pinstone Street, Sheffield S1 2DB ☎ 0114 273 6751 ◌ phil.holmes@sheffield.gov.uk

Social Services (Children): Ms Jayne Ludlam, Executive Director - Children, Young People & Families, Room 140, Town Hall, Pinstone Street, Sheffield S1 2HH ☎ 0114 273 5726 ◌ jayne.ludlam@sheffield.gov.uk

Public Health: Mr Greg Fell, Director - Public Health, Town Hall, Pinstone Street, Sheffield S1 2DB ☎ 0114 205 7462 ◌ greg.fell@sheffield.gcsx.gov.uk

Staff Training: Ms Julie Toner, Director - Human Resources, Room 216C, Town Hall, Pinstone Street, Sheffield S1 2HH ☎ 0114 273 4081 ◌ julie.toner@sheffield.gov.uk

Street Scene: Mr Steve Robinson, Head of Highway Maintenance, 5th Floor, Howden House, 1 Union Street, Sheffield S1 2SH ☎ 0114 273 5553 ◌ steve.robinson@sheffield.gov.uk

Sustainable Communities: Ms Laraine Manley, Executive Director - Communities, Room 208, Town Hall, Pinstone Street, Sheffield S1 2HH ☎ 0114 273 4300 ◌ laraine.manley@sheffield.gov.uk

Sustainable Development: Mr Nalin Seneviratne, Director - Capital & Major Projects, 5th Floor, Howden House, 1 Union Street, Sheffield S1 2SH ☎ 0114 205 7017 ◌ nalin.seneviratne@sheffield.gov.uk

Tourism: Miss Wendy Ulyett, Tourism Manager, Creative Sheffield, 2nd Floor, 11 Broad Street West, Sheffield S1 2BQ ☎ 0114 273 4129 ⌐ wendy.ulyett@sheffield.gov.uk

Town Centre: Mr Richard Eyre, Head of City Centre Management & Major Events, Town Hall, Pinstone Street, Sheffield S1 2HH ☎ 0114 273 4704 ⌐ richard.eyre@sheffield.gov.uk

Traffic Management: Mr Tom Finnegan-Smith, Head of Strategic Transport, Traffic & Infrastructure, 5th Floor, Howden House, 1 Union Street, Sheffield S1 2SH ☎ 0114 273 6030 ⌐ tom.finnegan-smith@sheffield.gov.uk

Transport: Mr Stephen Ash, Assistant Transport Services Manager, Staniforth Road, Sheffield S9 3GZ ☎ 0114 203 7056 ⌐ stephen.ash@sheffield.gov.uk

Transport Planner: Mr Tom Finnegan-Smith, Head of Strategic Transport, Traffic & Infrastructure, 5th Floor, Howden House, 1 Union Street, Sheffield S1 2SH ☎ 0114 273 6030 ⌐ tom.finnegan-smith@sheffield.gov.uk

Waste Collection and Disposal: Ms Gillian Charters, Head of Waste Management, 5th Floor, Howden House, 1 Union Street, Sheffield S1 2SH ☎ 0114 203 7528 ⌐ gillian.charters@sheffield.gov.uk

Waste Management: Ms Gillian Charters, Head of Waste Management, 5th Floor, Howden House, 1 Union Street, Sheffield S1 2SH ☎ 0114 203 7528 ⌐ gillian.charters@sheffield.gov.uk

Children's Play Areas: Mr Paul Billington, Director of Culture & Environment, 5th Floor, Howden House, Union Street, Sheffield S1 2SH ☎ 0114 273 4700 ⌐ paul.billington@sheffield.gov.uk

COUNCILLORS

The Lord Mayor: Fox, Denise (LAB - Birley)
denise.fox@sheffield.gov.uk

Deputy Lord Mayor: Murphy, Anne (LAB - Crookes & Crosspool)
anne.murphy@sheffield.gov.uk

Leader of the Council: Dore, Julie (LAB - Park & Arbourthorne)
julie.dore@sheffield.gov.uk

Deputy Leader of the Council: Bramall, Leigh (LAB - Southey)
leigh.bramall@sheffield.gov.uk

Group Leader: Mohammed, Shaffaq (LD - Eccleshall)
shaffaq.mohammed@sheffield.gov.uk

Akther, Nasima (LAB - Nether Edge & Sharrow)
nasima.akther@sheffield.gov.uk

Alston, Sue (LD - Fulwood)
sue.alston@sheffield.gov.uk

Andrews, Pauline (UKIP - East Ecclesfield)
pauline.andrews@sheffield.gov.uk

Auckland, Ian (LD - Graves Park)
ian.auckland@sheffield.gov.uk

Auckland, Sue (LD - Graves Park)
sue.auckland@sheffield.gov.uk

Ayris, Steve (LD - Graves Park)
steve.ayris@sheffield.gov.uk

Bainbridge, Andy (LAB - East Ecclesfield)
andy.bainbridge@sheffield.gov.uk

Baker, David (LD - Stannington)
david.baker@sheffield.gov.uk

Baker, Penny (LD - Stannington)
penny.baker@sheffield.gov.uk

Banes, Lisa (LAB - Manor Castle)
lisa.banes@sheffield.gov.uk

Barker, David (LAB - Mosborough)
david.barker@sheffield.gov.uk

Blake, Olivia (LAB - Walkley)
olivia.blake@sheffield.gov.uk

Booker, John (UKIP - West Ecclesfield)
john.booker@sheffield.gov.uk

Clarkson, Jack (UKIP - Stocksbridge & Upper Don)
jack.clarkson@sheffield.gov.uk

Cook, Michelle (LAB - Broomhill & Sharrow Vale)
michelle.cook@sheffield.gov.uk

Crowther, Richard (LAB - Stocksbridge & Upper Don)
richard.crowther@sheffield.gov.uk

Curran, Ben (LAB - Walkley)
ben.curran@sheffield.gov.uk

Dagnall, Lewis (LAB - Gleadless Valley)
lewis.dagnall@sheffield.gov.uk

Dale, Dawn (LAB - Shiregreen & Brightside)
dawn.dale@sheffield.gov.uk

Damms, Tony (LAB - Southey)
anthony.damms@sheffield.gov.uk

Davis, Keith (UKIP - Stocksbridge & Upper Don)
keith.davis@sheffield.gov.uk

Davison, Roger (LD - Eccleshall)
roger.davison@sheffield.gov.uk

Downing, Tony (LAB - Mosborough)
tony.downing@sheffield.gov.uk

Drabble, Mike (LAB - Richmond)
mike.drabble@sheffield.gov.uk

Drayton, Jackie (LAB - Burngreave)
jackie.drayton@sheffield.gov.uk

Dunn, Jayne (LAB - Southey)
jayne.dunn@sheffield.gov.uk

Fox, Terry (LAB - Manor Castle)
terry.fox2@sheffield.gov.uk

Gamble Pugh, Craig (LAB - Crookes & Crosspool)
craig.gamblepugh@sheffield.gov.uk

Gibson, Neale (LAB - Walkley)
neale.gibson@sheffield.gov.uk

Hanrahan, Adam (LD - Crookes & Crosspool)
adam.hanrahan@sheffield.gov.uk

Harpham, Kieran (LAB - Broomhill & Sharrow Vale)
kieran.harpham@sheffield.gov.uk

Hurst, Dianne (LAB - Richmond)
dianne.hurst@sheffield.gov.uk

Hurst, Adam (LAB - West Ecclesfield)
adam.hurst@sheffield.gov.uk

Hussain, Talib (LAB - Burngreave)
talib.hussain@sheffield.gov.uk

SHEFFIELD CITY

Iqbal, Mazher (LAB - Darnall)
mazher.iqbal@sheffield.gov.uk

Johnson, Bob (LAB - Hillsborough)
robert.johnson2@sheffield.gov.uk

Johnson, Douglas (GRN - City)
douglas.johnson@sheffield.gov.uk

Jones, Mark (LAB - Burngreave)
mark.jonescllr@sheffield.gov.uk

Khayum, Abdul (LAB - Firth Park)
abdul.khayum@sheffield.gov.uk

Law, Alan (LAB - Firth Park)
alan.law@sheffield.gov.uk

Lea, Mary (LAB - Darnall)
mary.lea@sheffield.gov.uk

Lindars-Hammond, George (LAB - Hillsborough)
george.lindars-hammond@sheffield.gov.uk

Lodge, Bryan (LAB - Birley)
bryan.lodge@sheffield.gov.uk

Magid, Magid (GRN - Broomhill & Sharrow Vale)
magid@sheffield.gov.uk

Maroof, Mohammed (LAB - Nether Edge & Sharrow)
mohammed.maroof@sheffield.gov.uk

McDonald, Cate (LAB - Gleadless Valley)
cate.mcdonald@sheffield.gov.uk

McGowan, Karen (LAB - Birley)
karen.mcgowan@sheffield.gov.uk

Midgley, Pat (LAB - Manor Castle)
patricia.midgley@sheffield.gov.uk

Mirfin-Boukouris, Helen (LAB - Beighton)
helen.mirfin-boukouris@sheffield.gov.uk

Miskell, Ben (LAB - Park & Arbourthorne)
ben.miskell@sheffield.gov.uk

Mohamed, Abtisam (LAB - Firth Park)
abtisam.mohamed@sheffield.gov.uk

Murphy, Robert (GRN - City)
robert.murphy@sheffield.gov.uk

Nash, Andy (LD - Beauchief & Greenhill)
andy.nash@sheffield.gov.uk

Naz, Zahira (LAB - Darnall)
zahira.naz@sheffield.gov.uk

O'Rourke, Moya (LAB - City)
maya.orourke@sheffield.gov.uk

Otten, Joe (LD - Dore & Totley)
joe.otten@sheffield.gov.uk

Pace, Chris (LAB - Gleadless Valley)
chris.pace@sheffield.gov.uk

Paszek, Josie (LAB - Hillsborough)
josie.paszek@sheffield.gov.uk

Price, Peter (LAB - Shiregreen & Brightside)
peter.price@sheffield.gov.uk

Priestley, Vickie (LD - Stannington)
vickie.priestley@sheffield.gov.uk

Pullin, Bob (LD - Beauchief & Greenhill)
bob.pullin@sheffield.gov.uk

Rippon, Peter (LAB - Richmond)
peter.rippon@sheffield.gov.uk

Rooney, Mick (LAB - Woodhouse)
michael.rooney@sheffield.gov.uk

Rosling-Josephs, Chris (LAB - Beighton)
c.rosling-josephs@sheffield.gov.uk

Ross, Colin (LD - Dore & Totley)
colin.ross@sheffield.gov.uk

Sangar, Andrew (LD - Fulwood)
andrew.sangar@sheffield.gov.uk

Satur, Jackie (LAB - Woodhouse)
jackie.satur@sheffield.gov.uk

Saunders, Ian (LAB - Beighton)
ian.saunders@sheffield.gov.uk

Scott, Jack (LAB - Park & Arbourthorne)
jack.scott@sheffield.gov.uk

Scriven, Paul (LD - Ecclesall)
paul.scriven@sheffield.gov.uk

Shaw, Richard (LD - Beauchief & Greenhill)
richard.shaw@sheffield.gov.uk

Smith, Martin (LD - Dore & Totley)
martin.smith@sheffield.gov.uk

Smith, Gail (LD - Mosborough)
gail.smith@sheffield.gov.uk

Sykes, Zoe (LAB - West Ecclesfield)
zoe.sykes@sheffield.gov.uk

Teal, Alison (GRN - Nether Edge & Sharrow)
alison.teal@sheffield.gov.uk

Weatherall, Garry (LAB - Shiregreen & Brightside)
garry.weatherall@sheffield.gov.uk

Wilson, Steve (LAB - East Ecclesfield)
steven.wilson@sheffield.gov.uk

Wood, Paul (LAB - Woodhouse)
paul.wood3@sheffield.gov.uk

Woodcraft, Cliff (LD - Fulwood) cliff.woodcraft@sheffield.gov.uk

POLITICAL COMPOSITION
LAB: 56, LD: 20, GRN: 4, UKIP: 4

COMMITTEE CHAIRS

Audit: Ms Josie Paszek

Children, Young People & Families: Mr Ian Saunders

Health & Wellbeing: Ms Julie Dore

Healthier Communities & Adult Social Care: Ms Pat Midgley

Planning & Highways: Mr Chris Rosling-Josephs

Planning & Highways: Mr Peter Rippon

Safer & Stronger Communities: Mr Tony Damms

Shepway   D

Shepway District Council, Civic Centre, Castle Hill Avenue, Folkestone CT20 2QY
☎ 01303 853000 📠 01303 245978 ✆ sdc@shepway.gov.uk
🖥 www.shepway.gov.uk

FACTS AND FIGURES
Parliamentary Constituencies: Folkestone and Hythe
EU Constituencies: South East
Election Frequency: Elections are of whole council

PRINCIPAL OFFICERS

Chief Executive: Mr Alistair Stewart, Chief Executive, Civic Centre, Castle Hill Avenue, Folkestone CT20 2QY ☎ 01303 853203 ~ alistair.stewart@shepway.gov.uk

Senior Management: Mr Jeremy Chambers, Corporate Director - Strategic Operations, Civic Centre, Castle Hill Avenue, Folkestone CT20 2QY ☎ 01303 853263 ~ jeremy.chambers@shepway.gov.uk

Senior Management: Dr Susan Priest, Corporate Director - Strategic Development, Civic Centre, Castle Hill Avenue, Folkestone CT20 2QY ☎ 01303 853000 ~ susan.priest@shepway.gov.uk

Architect, Building / Property Services: Mr Paul Marshall, Estate Management Officer, Civic Centre, Castle Hill Avenue, Folkestone CT20 2QY ☎ 01303 853439 ~ paul.marshall@shepway.gov.uk

Building Control: Mr Nick Lewington, Principal Building Control Officer, Civic Centre, Castle Hill Avenue, Folkestone CT20 2QY ☎ 01303 853478 ~ nick.lewington@shepway.gov.uk

Children / Youth Services: Mrs Tamasin Jarrett, Community Development Officer, Civic Centre, Castle Hill Avenue, Folkestone CT20 2QY ☎ 01303 853277 ~ tamasin.jarrett@shepway.gov.uk

PR / Communications: Mr Mark Luetchford, Communications Manager, Civic Centre, Castle Hill Avenue, Folkestone CT20 2QY ☎ 01303 853000 ~ mark.luetchford@shepway.gov.uk

Community Planning: Mr Christopher Lewis, SDC Planning Advisor, Civic Centre, Castle Hill Avenue, Folkestone CT20 2QY ☎ 01303 853456 ~ chris.lewis@shepway.gov.uk

Community Safety: Ms Jyotsna Leney, Community Safety Manager, Civic Centre, Castle Hill Avenue, Folkestone CT20 2QY ☎ 01303 853460 ~ jyotsna.leney@shepway.gov.uk

Computer Management: Mr Steve Makin, ICT Officer, Civic Centre, Castle Hill Avenue, Folkestone CT20 2QY ☎ 01303 853541 ~ steve.makin@shepway.gov.uk

Consumer Protection and Trading Standards: Ms Jyotsna Leney, Community Safety Manager, Civic Centre, Castle Hill Avenue, Folkestone CT20 2QY ☎ 01303 853460 ~ jyotsna.leney@shepway.gov.uk

Contracts: Mr Andy Rush, Corporate Contracts Manager, Civic Centre, Castle Hill Avenue, Folkestone CT20 2QY ☎ 01303 853271 ~ andy.rush@shepway.gov.uk

Corporate Services: Mr Jeremy Chambers, Corporate Director - Strategic Operations, Civic Centre, Castle Hill Avenue, Folkestone CT20 2QY ☎ 01303 853263 ~ jeremy.chambers@shepway.gov.uk

Customer Service: Mr Jason Couch, Head of Customer Contact, Civic Centre, Castle Hill Avenue, Folkestone CT20 2QY ☎ 01303 853678 ~ jason.couch@shepway.gov.uk

Economic Development: Ms Katherine Harvey, Head of Economic Development, Civic Centre, Castle Hill Avenue, Folkestone CT20 2QY ☎ 01303 853000 ~ katherine.harvey@shepway.gov.uk

Emergency Planning: Ms Dee Chambers, Policy & Improvement Officer, Civic Centre, Castle Hill Avenue, Folkestone CT20 2QY ☎ 01303 853000 ~ dee.chambers@shepway.gov.uk

Environmental / Technical Services: Mr Roger Walton, Head of Environmental Services, Civic Centre, Castle Hill Avenue, Folkestone CT20 2QY ☎ 01303 853000 ~ roger.walton@shepway.gov.uk

Environmental Health: Mr Arthur Atkins, Principal Environmental Health Officer, Civic Centre, Castle Hill Avenue, Folkestone CT20 2QY ☎ 01303 853242 ~ arthur.atkins@shepway.gov.uk

Facilities: Mrs Sarah House, Senior Front Office Officer, Civic Centre, Castle Hill Avenue, Folkestone CT20 2QY ☎ 01303 853336 ~ sarah.house@shepway.gov.uk

Finance: Ms Pat Main, Interim Chief Finance Officer & S151 Officer, Civic Centre, Castle Hill Avenue, Folkestone CT20 2QY ☎ 01303 853000 ~ pat.main@shepway.gov.uk

Housing: Ms Sarah Robson, Head of Communities, Civic Centre, Castle Hill Avenue, Folkestone CT20 2QY ☎ 01303 853000 ~ sarah.robson@shepway.gov.uk

Legal: Mr Amandeep Khroud, Head of Democratic Services & Law, Civic Centre, Castle Hill Avenue, Folkestone CT20 2QY ☎ 01303 853000 ~ armandeep.khroud@shepway.gov.uk

Parking: Mr Fred Miller, Transportation Manager, Civic Centre, Castle Hill Avenue, Folkestone CT20 2QY ☎ 01303 853207 ~ fred.miller@shepway.gov.uk

Personnel / HR: Mrs Andrina Smith, Head of HR, Civic Centre, Castle Hill Avenue, Folkestone CT20 2QY ☎ 01303 853405 ~ andrina.smith@shepway.gov.uk

Planning: Mr Ben Geering, Head of Planning, Civic Centre, Castle Hill Avenue, Folkestone CT20 2QY ☎ 01303 853000 ~ ben.geering@shepway.gov.uk

Staff Training: Mrs Jo Gage, HR Business Partner of Organisational Development, Civic Centre, Castle Hill Avenue, Folkestone CT20 2QY ☎ 01303 853322 ~ jo.gage@shepway.gov.uk

COUNCILLORS

Chair: Holben, Janet (CON - Sandgate & West Folkestone) janet.holben@shepway.gov.uk

Vice-Chair: Owen, David (CON - Hythe) david.owen@shepway.gov.uk

Leader of the Council: Monk, David (CON - Folkestone Central) david.monk@shepway.gov.uk

Deputy Leader of the Council: Hollingsbee, Jennifer (CON - North Downs West) jennifer.hollingsbee@shepway.gov.uk

SHEPWAY

Group Leader: Laws, Len (UKIP - Walland & Denge Marsh)
len.laws@shepway.gov.uk

Berry, Anne (CON - Broadmead)
annecllr.berry@shepway.gov.uk

Carey, Susan (CON - North Downs West)
susan.carey@shepway.gov.uk

Collier, John (CON - Cheriton)
john.collier@shepway.gov.uk

Dearden, Malcolm (CON - Hythe)
malcolm.dearden@shepway.gov.uk

Ewart-James, Alan (CON - Hythe)
alan.ewart-james@shepway.gov.uk

Gane, Peter (CON - Cheriton)
peter.gane@shepway.gov.uk

Goddard, Clive (CON - Walland & Denge Marsh)
clive.goddard@shepway.gov.uk

Godfrey, David (CON - North Downs East)
david.godfrey@shepway.gov.uk

Govett, Susie (UKIP - New Romney)
susie.govett@shepway.gov.uk

Jeffrey, Claire (CON - East Folkestone)
claire.jeffrey@shepway.gov.uk

Lawes, Mary (UKIP - Folkestone Harbour)
mary.lawes@shepway.gov.uk

Love, Rory (CON - Sandgate & West Folkestone)
rory.love@shepway.gov.uk

Lyons, Michael (CON - Hythe Rural)
michael.lyons@shepway.gov.uk

Martin, Phillip (CON - North Downs East)
philip.martin@shepway.gov.uk

McKenna, Frank (UKIP - East Folkestone)
frank.mckenna@shepway.gov.uk

Meyers, Ian (UKIP - Romney Marsh)

Pascoe, Richard (CON - Folkestone Central)
richard.pascoe@shepway.gov.uk

Peacock, Paul (CON - Hythe Rural)
paul.peacock@shepway.gov.uk

Peall, Stuart (CON - North Downs East)
stuart.peall@shepway.gov.uk

Robinson, Damon (UKIP - Cheriton)
damon.robinson@shepway.gov.uk

Sacre, Carol (UKIP - East Folkestone)
carolo.sacre@shepway.gov.uk

Simmons, Peter (CON - New Romney)
peter.simmons@shepway.gov.uk

Wallace, Susan (CON - Folkestone Harbour)
susan.wallace@shepway.gov.uk

Wheeler, Rodica (CON - Folkestone Central)
rodica.wheeler@shepway.gov.uk

Wilkins, Roger (CON - Romney Marsh)
roger.wilkins@shepway.gov.uk

POLITICAL COMPOSITION
CON: 23, UKIP: 7

COMMITTEE CHAIRS

Audit: Mr David Owen

Planning & Licensing: Mr Clive Goddard

Shetland   S

Shetland Islands Council, Office Headquarters, 8 North Ness Business Park, Lerwick ZE1 0LZ
☎ 01595 693535 🖨 01595 744509 🖰 info@shetland.gov.uk
🖥 www.shetland.gov.uk

FACTS AND FIGURES
Parliamentary Constituencies: Orkney and Shetland
EU Constituencies: Scotland
Election Frequency: Elections are of whole council

PRINCIPAL OFFICERS

Chief Executive: Mr Mark Boden, Chief Executive, Office Headquarters, 8 North Ness Business Park, Lerwick ZE1 0LZ
☎ 01595 744500 🖰 chief.executive@shetland.gov.uk

Architect, Building / Property Services: Mr Robert Sinclair, Executive Manager - Capital Programmes, Office Headquarters, 8 North Ness Business Park, Lerwick ZE1 0LZ ☎ 01595 744144
🖰 robert.sinclair@shetland.gov.uk

Architect, Building / Property Services: Mr Carl Symons, Executive Manager - Estate Operations, Gremista, Lerwick ZE1 0PX
☎ 015959 744100 🖰 carl.symons@shetland.gov.uk

Best Value: Mr Crawford McIntyre, Executive Manager - Audit, Risk & Improvement, Office Headquarters, 8 North Ness Business Park, Lerwick ZE1 0LZ ☎ 01595 744546
🖰 crawford.mcintyre@shetland.gov.uk

Building Control: Mr Iain McDiarmid, Executive Manager - Planning, Office Headquarters, 8 North Ness Business Park, Lerwick ZE1 0LZ ☎ 01595 744813 🖰 planning@shetland.gov.uk

Catering Services: Mrs Lynda Duck, Catering & Cleaning Manager, Hayfield House, Hayfield Lane, Lerwick ZE1 0QD
☎ 01595 744129 🖰 lynda.duck@shetland.gov.uk

Children / Youth Services: Mrs Helen Budge, Director - Children's Services, Hayfield House, Hayfield Lane, Lerwick ZE1 0QD ☎ 01595 744064 🖰 helen.budge@shetland.gov.uk

Civil Registration: Mrs Marilyn Williamson, Chief Registrar, Town Hall, Lerwick ZE1 0BH ☎ 01595 744562
🖰 registrar@shetland.gov.uk

Community Planning: Ms Vaila Simpson, Executive Manager - Community Planning & Development, Solarhus, 3 North Ness Business Park, Lerwick ZE1 0LZ ☎ 01595 744375
🖰 vaila.simpson@shetland.gov.uk

Computer Management: Mrs Susan Msalila, Executive Manager - ICT, Garthspool, Lerwick ZE1 0NP ☎ 01595 744763
🖰 susan.msalila@shetland.gov.uk

Consumer Protection and Trading Standards: Mr David Marsh, Service Manager - Trading Standards, Charlotte House, Commercial Road, Lerwick ZE1 0LX ☎ 01595 744862 ✆ trading.standards@shetland.gov.uk

Contracts: Mr Colin Black, Procurement Manager, Office Headquarters, 8 North Ness Business Park, Lerwick ZE1 0LZ ☎ 01595 744595 ✆ colin.black@shetland.gov.uk

Corporate Services: Mrs Christine Ferguson, Director - Corporate Services, Office Headquarters, 8 North Ness Business Park, Lerwick ZE1 0LZ ☎ 01595 743819 ✆ christine.ferguson@shetland.gov.uk

Direct Labour: Mr Carl Symons, Executive Manager - Estate Operations, Gremista, Lerwick ZE1 0PX ☎ 015959 744100 ✆ carl.symons@shetland.gov.uk

Economic Development: Mr Neil Grant, Director - Development Services, Office Headquarters, North Ness Business Park, Lerwick ZE1 0LZ ☎ 01595 744968 ✆ mail.development@shetland.gov.uk

Education: Mrs Helen Budge, Director - Children's Services, Hayfield House, Hayfield Lane, Lerwick ZE1 0QD ☎ 01595 744064 ✆ helen.budge@shetland.gov.uk

Electoral Registration: Mr Michael Forbes, Electoral Registration Officer, 20 Commercial Road, Lerwick ZE1 0LX ☎ 01595 745700 ✆ ero@shetland.gov.uk

Electoral Registration: Mr Jan-Robert Riise, Executive Manager - Governance & Law, Office Headquarters, 8 North Ness Business Park, Lerwick ZE1 0LZ ☎ 01595 744551 ✆ legal@shetland.gov.uk

Emergency Planning: Ms Ingrid Gall, Emergency Planning & Resilience Officer, 20 Commercial Road, Lerwick ZE2 0LX ☎ 01595 744740 ✆ emergency.planning@shetland.gov.uk

Energy Management: Mrs Mary Lisk, Team Leader - Environment, Gremista, Lerwick ZE1 0LX ☎ 01595 744818 ✆ mary.lisk@shetland.gov.uk

Energy Management: Mr John Simpson, Energy Manager, Gremista, Lerwick ZE1 0PX ☎ 01595 744819 ✆ john.simpson@shetland.gov.uk

Environmental Health: Mrs Maggie Sandison, Director - Infrastructure Services, Gremista, Lerwick ZE1 0PX ☎ 01595 744841 ✆ margaret.sandison@shetland.gov.uk

European Liaison: Miss Sally Spence, European Project Manager, Solarhus 3, North Ness Business Park, Lerwick ZE1 0LZ ☎ 01595 744915 ✆ sally.spence@shetland.gov.uk

Events Manager: Ms Nicola Halcrow, Development Co-ordinator, Solarhus 3, North Ness Business Park, Lerwick ZE1 0LZ ☎ 01595 744944 ✆ nicola.halcrow@shetland.gov.uk

Finance: Mr Jonathan Belford, Executive Manager - Finance, Office Headquarters, 8 North Ness Business Park, Lerwick ZE1 0LZ ☎ 01595 744607 ✆ jonathan.belford@shetland.gov.uk

Treasury: Mr Jonathan Belford, Executive Manager - Finance, Office Headquarters, 8 North Ness Business Park, Lerwick ZE1 0LZ ☎ 01595 744607 ✆ jonathan.belford@shetland.gov.uk

Pensions: Ms Mary Smith, Team Leader - Expenditure, Office Headquarters, 8 North Ness Business Park, Lerwick ZE1 0LZ ☎ 01595 744669 ✆ mary.smith@shetland.gov.uk

Fleet Management: Mr Michael Craigie, Executive Manager - Transport Planning, 🖳 North Ness Business Park, Lerwick ZE1 0LZ ☎ 01595 744160 ✆ michael.craigie@shetland.gov.uk

Health and Safety: Mrs Fiona Johnson, Health & Safety Manager, Office Headquarters, 8 North Ness Business Park, Lerwick ZE1 0LZ ☎ 01595 744567 ✆ fiona.johnson@shetland.gov.uk

Highways: Mr Dave Coupe, Executive Manager - Roads Maintenance, Gremista, Lerwick ZE1 0PX ☎ 01595 744104 ✆ dave.coupe@shetland.gov.uk

Home Energy Conservation: Mr John Simpson, Energy Manager, Gremista, Lerwick ZE1 0PX ☎ 01595 744819 ✆ john.simpson@shetland.gov.uk

Housing: Mrs Anita Jamieson, Executive Manager - Housing 🖳 North Ness Business Park, Lerwick ZE1 0LZ ☎ 01595 744360 ✆ housing@shetland.gov.uk

Housing Maintenance: Mrs Anita Jamieson, Executive Manager - Housing, 🖳 North Ness Business Park, Lerwick ZE1 0LZ ☎ 01595 744360 ✆ housing@shetland.gov.uk

Legal: Ms Susan Brunton, Team Leader - Legal, Office Headquarters, 8 North Ness Business Park, Lerwick ZE1 0LZ ☎ 01595 744550 ✆ susan.brunton@shetland.gov.uk

Leisure and Cultural Services: Mr Neil Watt, Executive Manager - Sport & Leisure, Hayfield House, Hayfield Lane, Lerwick ZE1 0QD ☎ 01595 744046 ✆ neil.watt@shetland.gov.uk

Licensing: Mr Jan-Robert Riise, Executive Manager - Governance & Law, Office Headquarters, 8 North Ness Business Park, Lerwick ZE1 0LZ ☎ 01595 744551 ✆ legal@shetland.gov.uk

Lifelong Learning: Ms June Porter, Team Leader - Community Development, Solarhus 3, North Ness Business Park, Lerwick ZE1 0LZ ☎ 01595 743880 ✆ june.porter@shetland.gov.uk

Lighting: Mr Dave Coupe, Executive Manager - Roads Maintenance, Gremista, Lerwick ZE1 0PX ☎ 01595 744104 ✆ dave.coupe@shetland.gov.uk

Lighting: Mr Dave Coupe, Executive Manager - Roads Maintenance, Gremista, Lerwick ZE1 0PX ☎ 01595 744104 ✆ dave.coupe@shetland.gov.uk

Member Services: Mrs Anita Sparrow, Member Support Officer, Town Hall, Lerwick ZE1 0HB ☎ 01595 744505 ✆ anita.sparrow@shetlend.gov.uk

SHETLAND

Parking: Mr Dave Coupe, Executive Manager - Roads Maintenance, Gremista, Lerwick ZE1 0PX ☎ 01595 744104 ⁂ dave.coupe@shetland.gov.uk

Personnel / HR: Mrs Denise Bell, Executive Manager - Human Resources, Office Headquarters, 8 North Ness Business Park, Lerwick ZE1 0LZ ☎ 01595 744573 ⁂ denise.bell@shetland.gov.uk

Planning: Mr Iain McDiarmid, Executive Manager - Planning, Office Headquarters, 8 North Ness Business Park, Lerwick ZE1 0LZ ☎ 01595 744813 ⁂ planning@shetland.gov.uk

Procurement: Mr Colin Black, Procurement Manager, Office Headquarters, 8 North Ness Business Park, Lerwick ZE1 0LZ ☎ 01595 744595 ⁂ colin.black@shetland.gov.uk

Public Libraries: Ms Karen Fraser, Library & Information Services Manager, Shetland Libary, Lower Hillhead, Lerwick ZE1 0EL ☎ 01595 743868 ⁂ karen.fraser@shetland.gov.uk

Recycling & Waste Minimisation: Mrs Mary Lisk, Team Leader - Environment, Gremista, Lerwick ZE1 0PX ☎ 01595 744818 ⁂ mary.lisk@shetland.gov.uk

Regeneration: Mr Neil Grant, Director - Development Services, Office Headquarters, 8 North Ness Business Park, Lerwick ZE1 0LZ ☎ 01595 744968 ⁂ mail.development@shetland.gov.uk

Road Safety: Mr Dave Coupe, Executive Manager - Roads Maintenance, Gremista, Lerwick ZE1 0PX ☎ 01595 744104 ⁂ dave.coupe@shetland.gov.uk

Social Services (Adult): Mr Stephen Morgan, Executive Manager - Community Care, Grantfield, Lerwick ZE1 0NT ☎ 01595 744400 ⁂ stephen.morgan@shetland.gov.uk

Social Services (Children): Mrs Martha Nicolson, Executive Manager - Children & Families, Hayfield House, Hayfield Lane, Lerwick ZE1 0QD ☎ 01595 744000 ⁂ martha.nicolson@shetland.gov.uk

Staff Training: Mr Tommy Coutts, Business Development & Training Manager - Shetland College UHI, North Gremista Industrial Estate, Lerwick ZE1 0PX ☎ 01595 744744 ⁂ thomas.coutts@shetland.gov.uk

Sustainable Communities: Mr Douglas Irvine, Executive Manager - Economic Development, Solarhus 3, North Ness Business Park, Lerwick ZE1 0LZ ☎ 01595 744932 ⁂ douglas.irvine@shetland.gov.uk

Sustainable Development: Mr Austin Taylor, Development Plans & Heritage Team Leader, Office Headquarters, 8 North Ness Business Park, Lerwick ZE1 0LZ ☎ 01595 744833 ⁂ john.taylor@shetland.gov.uk

Tourism: Mrs Linda Coutts, Project Manager, Solarhus 3, North Ness Business Park, Lerwick ZE1 0LZ ☎ 01595 744943 ⁂ linda.coutts@shetland.gov.uk

Town Centre: Mr Iain McDiarmid, Executive Manager - Planning, Office Headquarters, 8 North Ness Business Park, Lerwick ZE1 0NT ☎ 01595 744813 ⁂ planning@shetland.gov.uk

Traffic Management: Mr Dave Coupe, Executive Manager - Roads Maintenance, Gremista, Lerwick ZE1 0PX ☎ 01595 744104 ⁂ dave.coupe@shetland.gov.uk

Transport: Mr Michael Craigie, Executive Manager - Transport Planning, Office Headquarters, 8 North Ness Business Park, Lerwick ZE1 0LZ ☎ 01595 744160 ⁂ michael.craigie@shetland.gov.uk

Transport Planner: Mr Michael Craigie, Executive Manager - Transport Planning, Office Headquarters, 8 North Ness Business Park, Lerwick ZE1 0LZ ☎ 01595 744160 ⁂ michael.craigie@shetland.gov.uk

COUNCILLORS

Convener: Bell, Malcolm (IND - Lerwick North) convener@shetland.gov.uk

Deputy Convener: Smith, Cecil (IND - Lerwick South) cecil.smith@shetland.gov.uk

Deputy Leader of the Council: Fox, Billy (IND - Shetland South) billy.fox@shetland.gov.uk

Group Leader: Robinson, Gary (IND - Shetland West) gary.robinson@shetland.gov.uk

Burgess, Mark (NP - Shetland Central) mark.burgess@shetland.gov.uk

Campbell, Peter (IND - Lerwick South) peter.campbell@shetland.gov.uk

Cleaver, Gary (IND - North Isles) gary.cleaver@shetland.gov.uk

Cooper, Alastair (IND - Shetland North) alastair.cooper@shetland.gov.uk

Coutts, Steven (NP - North Isles) steven.coutts@shetland.gov.uk

Duncan, Allison (IND - Shetland South) allison.duncan@shetland.gov.uk

Henderson, Robert S (IND - North Isles) robert.henderson@shetland.gov.uk

Manson, Andrea (IND - Shetland North) andrea.manson@shetland.gov.uk

Ratter, Drew (NP - Shetland North) drew.ratter@shetland.gov.uk

Robertson, Frank (IND - Shetland West) frank.robertson@shetland.gov.uk

Sandison, Davie (IND - Shetland Central) davie.sandison@shetland.gov.uk

Smith, George (IND - Shetland South) george.smith@shetland.gov.uk

Smith, Theo (IND - Shetland West) theo.smith@shetland.gov.uk

Stout, Michael (IND - Lerwick North) michael.stout@shetland.gov.uk

Westlake, Amanda (IND - Lerwick South)
amanda.westlake@shetland.gov.uk

Wills, Jonathan (IND - Lerwick South)
jonathanwills47@gmail.com

Wishart, Vaila (IND - Shetland Central)
vaila.wishart@shetland.gov.uk

Wishart, Allan (IND - Lerwick North)
allan.wishart@shetland.gov.uk

POLITICAL COMPOSITION
IND: 19, NP: 3

COMMITTEE CHAIRS

Audit: Mr Allison Duncan

Licensing: Cllr George Smith

Planning: Mr Frank Robertson

Shropshire Unitary   U

Shropshire Council, Shirehall, Abbey Foregate, Shrewsbury
SY2 6ND
☎ 0345 678 9000 ⌂ customer.service@shropshire.gov.uk
🖳 www.shropshire.gov.uk

FACTS AND FIGURES
Parliamentary Constituencies: Ludlow, Shrewsbury and Atcham,
Shropshire North, Wrekin, The

PRINCIPAL OFFICERS

Chief Executive: Mr Clive Wright, Chief Executive, Shirehall,
Abbey Foregate, Shrewsbury SY2 6ND ☎ 01743 258675
⌂ clive.wright@shropshire.gov.uk

Senior Management: Mr Andy Begley, Director - Adult Services,
Shirehall, Abbey Foregate, Shrewsbury SY2 6ND ☎ 01743 258911
⌂ andy.begley@shropshire.gov.uk

Senior Management: Ms Karen Bradshaw, Director - Children's
Services, Shirehall, Abbey Foregate, Shrewsbury SY2 6ND
☎ 01743 254201 ⌂ karen.bradshaw@shropshire.gov.uk

Senior Management: Mr George Candler, Director - Place &
Enterprise, Shirehall, Abbey Foregate, Shrewsbury SY2 6ND
☎ 01743 258671 ⌂ george.candler@shropshire.gov.uk

Senior Management: Prof Rod Thomson, Director - Public
Health, Shirehall, Abbey Foregate, Shrewsbury SY2 6ND
☎ 01432 383783 ⌂ rod.thomson@herefordshire.gov.uk

Building Control: Mr Stephen Rigney, Principal Building Control
Surveyor, Shirehall, Abbey Foregate, Shrewsbury SY2 6ND
☎ 01743 258747 ⌂ stephen.rigney@shropshire.gov.uk

Children / Youth Services: Ms Karen Bradshaw, Director -
Children's Services, Shirehall, Abbey Foregate, Shrewsbury
SY2 6ND ☎ 01743 254201 ⌂ karen.bradshaw@shropshire.gov.uk

PR / Communications: Ms Michele Leith, Head of Human
Resources & Development, Shirehall, Abbey Foregate, Shrewsbury
SY2 6ND ☎ 01743 254402 ⌂ michele.leith@shropshire.gov.uk

Community Planning: Mr Ian Kilby, Planning Services Manager,
Shirehall, Abbey Foregate, Shrewsbury SY2 6ND ☎ 01743 252622
⌂ ian.kilby@shropshire.gov.uk

Computer Management: Mr Paul Voogt, Business
Transformation Programme Manager - ICT Digital Strategy
Programme, Shirehall, Abbey Foregate, Shrewsbury SY2 6ND
☎ 01743 254776 ⌂ paul.voogt@shropshire.gov.uk

Customer Service: Ms Michele Leith, Head of Human Resources
& Development, Shirehall, Abbey Foregate, Shrewsbury SY2 6ND
☎ 01743 254402 ⌂ michele.leith@shropshire.gov.uk

Education: Ms Karen Bradshaw, Director - Children's Services,
Shirehall, Abbey Foregate, Shrewsbury SY2 6ND ☎ 01743 254201
⌂ karen.bradshaw@shropshire.gov.uk

Electoral Registration: Mrs Stacey Ijewsky, Elections Officer,
Shirehall, Abbey Foregate, Shrewsbury SY2 6ND ☎ 01743 252334
⌂ stacey.ijewsky@shropshire.gov.uk

Electoral Registration: Ms Claire Porter, Head of Legal, Strategy
& Democratic Services, Shirehall, Abbey Foregate, Shrewsbury
SY2 6ND ☎ 01743 252763 ⌂ claire.porter@shropshire.gov.uk

Emergency Planning: Ms Angie Beechey, Risk & Insurance
Manager, Shirehall, Abbey Foregate, Shrewsbury SY2 6ND
☎ 01743 252073 ⌂ angela.beechey@shropshire.gov.uk

Environmental Health: Prof Rod Thomson, Director - Public
Health, Shirehall, Abbey Foregate, Shrewsbury SY2 6ND
☎ 01432 383783 ⌂ rod.thomson@herefordshire.gov.uk

Estates, Property & Valuation: Mr Tim Smith, Head of Business
Enterprise & Commercial Services, Shirehall, Abbey Foregate,
Shrewsbury SY2 6ND ☎ 01743 258998
⌂ tim.smith@shropshire.gov.uk

Facilities: Mr Tim Smith, Head of Business Enterprise &
Commercial Services, Shirehall, Abbey Foregate, Shrewsbury SY2
6ND ☎ 01743 258998 ⌂ tim.smith@shropshire.gov.uk

Finance: Mr James Walton, Head of Finance, Governance &
Assurance (S151 Officer), Shirehall, Abbey Foregate, Shrewsbury
SY2 6ND ☎ 01743 258915 ⌂ james.walton@shropshire.gov.uk

Treasury: Mr James Walton, Head of Finance, Governance &
Assurance (S151 Officer), Shirehall, Abbey Foregate, Shrewsbury
SY2 6ND ☎ 01743 258915 ⌂ james.walton@shropshire.gov.uk

Pensions: Ms Debbie Sharp, Pensions Administration Manager,
Shirehall, Abbey Foregate, Shrewsbury SY2 6ND ☎ 01743 252192
⌂ debbie.sharp@shropshire.gov.uk

Health and Safety: Mrs Carol Fox, Occupational Health & Safety
Manager, Shirehall, Abbey Foregate, Shrewsbury SY2 6ND
☎ 01743 252814 ⌂ carol.fox@shropshire.gov.uk

SHROPSHIRE UNITARY

Highways: Mr Chris Edwards, Head of Infrastructure & Communities, Shirehall, Abbey Foregate, Shrewsbury SY2 6ND ☎ 01743 258912 ✆ chris.edwards@shropshire.gov.uk

Legal: Ms Claire Porter, Head of Legal, Strategy & Democratic Services, Shirehall, Abbey Foregate, Shrewsbury SY2 6ND ☎ 01743 252763 ✆ claire.porter@shropshire.gov.uk

Leisure and Cultural Services: Mr George Candler, Director - Place & Enterprise, Shirehall, Abbey Foregate, Shrewsbury SY2 6ND ☎ 01743 258671 ✆ george.candler@shropshire.gov.uk

Licensing: Prof Rod Thomson, Director - Public Health, Shirehall, Abbey Foregate, Shrewsbury SY2 6ND ☎ 01432 383783 ✆ rod.thomson@herefordshire.gov.uk

Member Services: Ms Jane Palmer, Senior Democratic Services Officer, Shirehall, Abbey Foregate, Shrewsbury SY2 6ND ☎ 01743 257712 ✆ jane.palmer@shropshire.gov.uk

Member Services: Ms Claire Porter, Head of Legal, Strategy & Democratic Services, Shirehall, Abbey Foregate, Shrewsbury SY2 6ND ☎ 01743 252763 ✆ claire.porter@shropshire.gov.uk

Partnerships: Mr George Candler, Director - Place & Enterprise, Shirehall, Abbey Foregate, Shrewsbury SY2 6ND ☎ 01743 258671 ✆ george.candler@shropshire.gov.uk

Personnel / HR: Ms Michele Leith, Head of Human Resources & Development, Shirehall, Abbey Foregate, Shrewsbury SY2 6ND ☎ 01743 254402 ✆ michele.leith@shropshire.gov.uk

Planning: Mr Ian Kilby, Planning Services Manager, Shirehall, Abbey Foregate, Shrewsbury SY2 6ND ☎ 01743 252622 ✆ ian.kilby@shropshire.gov.uk

Procurement: Mr Nigel Denton, Commissioning Development & Procurement Manager, Shirehall, Abbey Foregate, Shrewsbury SY2 6ND ☎ 01743 252993 ✆ nigel.denton@shropshire.gov.uk

Public Libraries: Mr Michael Lewis, Library Service Manager, Shirehall, Abbey Foregate, Shrewsbury SY2 6ND ☎ 01743 255023 ✆ michael.lewis@shropshire.gov.uk

Recycling & Waste Minimisation: Mr Chris Edwards, Head of Infrastructure & Communities, Shirehall, Abbey Foregate, Shrewsbury SY2 6ND ☎ 01743 258912 ✆ chris.edwards@shropshire.gov.uk

Regeneration: Mr Andrew Stirling, Physical Regeneration Manager, Shirehall, Abbey Foregate, Shrewsbury SY2 6ND ☎ 01743 252316 ✆ andrew.stirling@shropshire.gov.uk

Social Services: Mr Andy Begley, Director - Adult Services, Shirehall, Abbey Foregate, Shrewsbury SY2 6ND ☎ 01743 258911 ✆ andy.begley@shropshire.gov.uk

Social Services (Adult): Mr Andy Begley, Director - Adult Services, Shirehall, Abbey Foregate, Shrewsbury SY2 6ND ☎ 01743 258911 ✆ andy.begley@shropshire.gov.uk

Social Services (Children): Ms Karen Bradshaw, Director - Children's Services, Shirehall, Abbey Foregate, Shrewsbury SY2 6ND ☎ 01743 254201 ✆ karen.bradshaw@shropshire.gov.uk

Social Services (Children): Ms Tina Russell, Head of Safeguarding, Shirehall, Abbey Foregate, Shrewsbury SY2 6ND ☎ 01743 254254 ✆ tina.russell@shropshire.gov.uk

Public Health: Prof Rod Thomson, Director - Public Health, Shirehall, Abbey Foregate, Shrewsbury SY2 6ND ☎ 01432 383783 ✆ rod.thomson@herefordshire.gov.uk

Staff Training: Ms Michele Leith, Head of Human Resources & Development, Shirehall, Abbey Foregate, Shrewsbury SY2 6ND ☎ 01743 254402 ✆ michele.leith@shropshire.gov.uk

Transport: Mr Chris Edwards, Head of Infrastructure & Communities, Shirehall, Abbey Foregate, Shrewsbury SY2 6ND ☎ 01743 258912 ✆ chris.edwards@shropshire.gov.uk

Waste Management: Mr Paul Beard, Waste Contracts Manager, Shirehall, Abbey Foregate, Shrewsbury SY2 6ND ☎ 01743 255996 ✆ paul.beard@shropshire.gov.uk

COUNCILLORS

Chair: Hartley, Ann (CON - Ellesmere Urban) ann.hartley@shropshire.gov.uk

Vice-Chair: Lloyd, David (CON - Gobowen, Selattyn & Weston Rhyn) david.lloyd@shropshire.gov.uk

Leader of the Council: Pate, Malcolm (CON - Albrighton) malcolm.pate@shropshire.gov.uk

Deputy Leader of the Council: Charmley, Stephen (CON - Whittington) steve.charmley@shropshire.gov.uk

Group Leader: Dee, Pauline (IND - Wem) pauline.dee@shropshire.gov.uk

Group Leader: Evans, Roger (LD - Longden) roger.evans@shropshire.gov.uk

Group Leader: Mosley, Alan (LAB - Castlefields & Ditherington) alan.mosley@shropshire.gov.uk

Adams, Peter (CON - Bowbrook) peter.m.adams@shropshire.gov.uk

Bannerman, Andrew (LD - Coton Hill & Quarry) andrew.bannerman@shropshire.gov.uk

Bardsley, Nicholas (CON - Ruyton & Baschurch) nick.bardsley@shropshire.gov.uk

Barker, Timothy (CON - Burnell) tim.baker@shropshire.gov.uk

Barrow, Joyce (CON - St Oswald) joyce.barrow@shropshire.gov.uk

Bebb, Tudor (CON - Rea Valley) tudor.bebb@shropshire.gov.uk

Biggins, Thomas (CON - Whitchurch North) thomas.biggins@shropshire.gov.uk

Boddington, Andy (LD - Ludlow North) andy.boddington@shropshire.gov.uk

Bushell, Vernon (LAB - Harlescott)
vernon.bushell@shropshire.gov.uk

Butler, Gwilym (CON - Cleobury Mortimer)
gwilym.butler@shropshire.gov.uk

Cadwallader, John (CON - Market Drayton East)
john.cadwallader@shropshire.gov.uk

Calder, Karen (CON - Hodnet)
karen.calder@shropshire.gov.uk

Carroll, Dean (CON - Bagley)
dean.carroll@shropshire.gov.uk

Chapman, Lee (CON - Church Stretton & Craven Arms)
lee.chapman@shropshire.gov.uk

Chebsey, Anne (LD - Porthill)
anne.chebsey@shropshire.gov.uk

Cherrington, Peter (IND - Oswestry East)
peter.cherrington@shropshire.gov.uk

Clarke, Ted (LAB - Bayston Hill, Column & Sutton)
ted.clarke@shropshire.gov.uk

Dakin, Gerald (CON - Whitchurch South)
gerald.dakin@shropshire.gov.uk

Davenport, Steve (CON - St Martin's)
steve.davenport@shropshire.gov.uk

Davies, Andrew (CON - Cheswardine)
andrew.b.davies@shropshire.gov.uk

Evans, David (CON - Church Stretton & Craven Arms)
david.evans@shropshire.gov.uk

Everall, John (CON - Tern)
john.everall@shropshire.gov.uk

Fraser, Hannah (LD - Abbey)
hannah.fraser@shropshire.gov.uk

Hartin, Nigel (LD - Clun)
nigel.hartin@shropshire.gov.uk

Huffer, Tracey (LD - Ludlow East)
tracey.huffer@shropshire.gov.uk

Huffer, Richard (LD - Clee)
richard.huffer@shropshire.gov.uk

Hughes, Roger (CON - Market Drayton West)
roger.hughes@shropshire.gov.uk

Hunt, Vincent (CON - Oswestry West)
vince.hunt@shropshire.gov.uk

Hurst-Knight, John (CON - Bridgnorth West & Tasley)
john.hurst-knight@shropshire.gov.uk

Jones, Jean (LAB - Broseley)
jean.e.jones@shropshire.gov.uk

Jones, Simon (CON - Shawbury)
simon.p.jones@shropshire.gov.uk

Keeley, Jonny (LD - Bishop's Castle)

Kenny, Miles (LD - Underdale)
miles.kenny@shropshire.gov.uk

Kerr, Duncan (INDNA - Oswestry South)

Kidd, Heather (LD - Chirbury & Worthen)
heather.kidd@shropshire.gov.uk

Lea, Christian (CON - Bridgnorth East & Astley Abbots)
christian.lea@shropshire.gov.uk

Liebich, Amy (LAB - Belle Vue)
amy.liebich@shropshire.gov.uk

Macey, Robert (CON - Gobowen, Selattyn & Weston Rhyn)
robert.macey@shropshire.gov.uk

Mackenzie, Jane (LAB - Bayston Hill, Column & Sutton)
jane.mackenzie@shropshire.gov.uk

Mellings, Christopher (LD - Wem)
chris.mellings@shropshire.gov.uk

Minnery, David (CON - Market Drayton West)
david.minnery@shropshire.gov.uk

Moseley, Pamela (LAB - Monkmoor)
pam.moseley@shropshire.gov.uk

Motley, Cecilia (CON - Corvedale)
cecilia.motley@shropshire.gov.uk

Mullock, Peggy (CON - Whitchurch North)
peggy.mullock@shropshire.gov.uk

Nutting, Peter (CON - Copthorne)
peter.nutting@shropshire.gov.uk

Owen, Mike (CON - Meole)
mike.owen@shropshire.gov.uk

Pardy, Kevin (LAB - Sundorne)
kevin.pardy@shropshire.gov.uk

Parr, William (CON - Bridgnorth East & Astley Abbots)
william.parr@shropshire.gov.uk

Parry, Vivienne (LD - Ludlow South)
vivienne.parry@shropshire.gov.uk

Price, John (CON - Oswestry East)
john.price@shropshire.gov.uk

Price, Malcolm (CON - Battlefield)
malcolm.price@shropshire.gov.uk

Roberts, David (CON - Loton)
david.roberts@shropshire.gov.uk

Roberts, Keith (CON - Radbrook)
keith.roberts@shropshire.gov.uk

Shineton, Madge (IND - Cleobury Mortimer)
madge.shineton@shropshire.gov.uk

Tandy, Jon (LAB - Bayston Hill, Column & Sutton)
jon.tandy@shropshire.gov.uk

Tindall, Robert (CON - Brown Clee)
robert.tindal@shropshire.gov.uk

Tremellen, Dave (INDNA - Highley)
dave.tremellen@shropshire.gov.uk

Turley, Kevin (IND - Shifnal North)
kevin.turley@shropshire.gov.uk

Turner, David (CON - Much Wenlock)
david.turner@shropshire.gov.uk

Walpole, Arthur (CON - Llanymynech)
arthur.walpole@shropshire.gov.uk

West, Stuart (CON - Shifnal South & Cosford)
stuart.west@shropshire.gov.uk

Wild, Claire (CON - Severn Valley)
claire.wild@shropshire.gov.uk

Williams, Brian (CON - The Meres)
brian.williams@shropshire.gov.uk

SHROPSHIRE UNITARY

Winwood, Les (CON - Bridgnorth West & Tasley)
les.winwood@shropshire.gov.uk

Wood, Michael (CON - Worfield)
michael.wood@shropshire.gov.uk

Woodward, Tina (CON - Alveley & Claverley)
tina.woodward@shropshire.gov.uk

Wynn, Paul (CON - Prees)
paul.wynn@shropshire.gov.uk

POLITICAL COMPOSITION
CON: 46, LD: 13, LAB: 9, IND: 4, INDNA: 2

COMMITTEE CHAIRS
Audit: Mr Timothy Barker

Health & Wellbeing: Mrs Karen Calder

Licensing: Mr Keith Roberts

Pensions: Mr Malcolm Pate

Slough   U

Slough Borough Council, St Martin's Place, Bath Road, Slough SL1 3UQ
☎ 01753 552288 ▤ 01753 692499 ▢ www.slough.gov.uk

FACTS AND FIGURES
Parliamentary Constituencies: Slough, Windsor
EU Constituencies: South East
Election Frequency: Elections are by thirds

PRINCIPAL OFFICERS

Chief Executive: Ms Ruth Bagley, Chief Executive, St Martin's Place, Bath Road, Slough SL1 3UQ ☎ 01753 875000
⬥ ruth.bagley@slough.gov.uk

Senior Management: Mr Mike England, Interim Strategic Director - Regeneration, Housing & Resources, St Martin's Place, Bath Road, Slough SL1 3UQ ☎ 01753 875301
⬥ mike.england@slough.gov.uk

Senior Management: Mr Roger Parkin, Director - Customer & Community Services, St Martin's Place, Bath Road, Slough SL1 3UQ
☎ 01753 875207 ⬥ roger.parkin@slough.gov.uk

Senior Management: Ms Krutika Pau, Interim Strategic Director - Children's Services, St Martin's Place, Bath Road, Slough SL1 3UQ
☎ 01753 875751 ⬥ krutika.pau@slough.gov.uk

Architect, Building / Property Services: Mr Adrian Thomas, Property Manager, St Martin's Place, Bath Road, Slough SL1 3UQ
☎ 01753 875446 ⬥ adrian.thomas@slough.gov.uk

Best Value: Ms Christina Hefferon, Assistant Director - Organisational Development & HR, St Martin's Place, Bath Road, Slough SL1 3UQ ☎ 01753 875213 ⬥ christina.hefferon@slough.gov.uk

Building Control: Mr Sanjay Dhuna, Head of Building Control & Planning, St Martin's Place, Bath Road, Slough SL1 3UQ
☎ 01753 875810 ⬥ sanjay.dhuna@slough.gov.uk

Children / Youth Services: Ms Krutika Pau, Interim Strategic Director - Children's Services, St Martin's Place, Bath Road, Slough SL1 3UQ ☎ 01753 875751 ⬥ krutika.pau@slough.gov.uk

Civil Registration: Mr Roger Parkin, Director - Customer & Community Services, St Martin's Place, Bath Road, Slough SL1 3UQ
☎ 01753 875207 ⬥ roger.parkin@slough.gov.uk

PR / Communications: Mrs Kate Pratt, Communications Manager, St Martin's Place, Bath Road, Slough SL1 3UQ
☎ 01753 875088 ⬥ kate.pratt@slough.gov.uk

Community Safety: Mr Garry Tallett, Community Safety Partnership Manager, St Martin's Place, Bath Road, Slough SL1 3UQ ☎ 01753 477907 ⬥ garry.tallett@slough.gov.uk

Computer Management: Mr Simon Pallett, Head of Information Systems & Technology, St Martin's Place, Bath Road, Slough SL1 3UQ ☎ 01753 875095 ⬥ simon.pallett@slough.gov.uk

Consumer Protection and Trading Standards: Ms Ginny DeHaan, Head of Consumer Protection & Business Compliance, St Martin's Place, Bath Road, Slough SL1 3UQ ☎ 01753 477912
⬥ ginny.dehaan@slough.gov.uk

Contracts: Ms Amardip Healy, Head of Legal Services, St Martin's Place, Bath Road, Slough SL1 3UQ ☎ 01753 875035
⬥ amardip.healy@slough.gov.uk

Corporate Services: Mr Mike England, Interim Strategic Director - Regeneration, Housing & Resources, St Martin's Place, Bath Road, Slough SL1 3UQ ☎ 01753 875301
⬥ mike.england@slough.gov.uk

Economic Development: Ms Shabnam Ali, Economic Growth & Enterprise Manager, St Martin's Place, Bath Road, Slough SL1 3UQ ☎ 01753 875849 ⬥ shabnam.ali@slough.gov.uk

Education: Mr Tony Browne, Head of School Services, St Martin's Place, Bath Road, Slough SL1 3UQ ☎ 01753 875717
⬥ tony.browne@slough.gov.uk

Education: Ms Krutika Pau, Interim Strategic Director - Children's Services, St Martin's Place, Bath Road, Slough SL1 3UQ
☎ 01753 875751 ⬥ krutika.pau@slough.gov.uk

E-Government: Mr Roger Parkin, Director - Customer & Community Services, St Martin's Place, Bath Road, Slough SL1 3UQ
☎ 01753 875207 ⬥ roger.parkin@slough.gov.uk

Emergency Planning: Mr Dean Trussler, Emergency Planning Officer, St Martin's Place, Bath Road, Slough SL1 3UQ
☎ 01753 875131 ⬥ dean.trussler@slough.gov.uk

Environmental Health: Ms Ginny DeHaan, Head of Consumer Protection & Business Compliance, St Martin's Place, Bath Road, Slough SL1 3UQ ☎ 01753 477912 ⬥ ginny.dehaan@slough.gov.uk

Estates, Property & Valuation: Mr Adrian Thomas, Property Manager, St Martin's Place, Bath Road, Slough SL1 3UQ
☎ 01753 875446 ⬥ adrian.thomas@slough.gov.uk

Events Manager: Ms Lynsey Hellewell, Commercial Officer, St Martin's Place, Bath Road, Slough SL1 3UQ ☎ 01753 875194 ✆ lynsey.hellewell@slough.gov.uk

Facilities: Ms Charan Dhillon, Head of Facilities Management, St Martin's Place, Bath Road, Slough SL1 3UF ☎ 01753 845945 ✆ charan.dhillon@slough.gov.uk

Finance: Mr Stephen Fitzgerald, Assistant Director - Finance & Audit, St Martin's Place, Bath Road, Slough SL1 3UQ ☎ 01753 875358 ✆ stephen.fitzgerald@slough.gov.uk

Health and Safety: Mr Robin Pringle, Health & Safety Manager, St Martin's Place, Bath Road, Slough SL1 3UQ ☎ 01753 875763 ✆ robin.pringle@slough.gov.uk

Highways: Mr Savio DeCruz, Head of Transport & Highways, St Martin's Place, Bath Road, Slough SL1 3UQ ☎ 01753 875640 ✆ savio.decruz@slough.gov.uk

Housing: Mr Neil Aves, Assistant Director - Housing Environment, St Martin's Place, Bath Road, Slough SL1 3UQ ☎ 01753 875527 ✆ neil.aves@slough.gov.uk

Housing Maintenance: Mr Neil Aves, Assistant Director - Housing Environment, St Martin's Place, Bath Road, Slough SL1 3UQ ☎ 01753 875527 ✆ neil.aves@slough.gov.uk

Legal: Ms Amardip Healy, Head of Legal Services, St Martin's Place, Bath Road, Slough SL1 3UQ ☎ 01753 875035 ✆ amardip.healy@slough.gov.uk

Leisure and Cultural Services: Mr Ketain Gandi, Head of Wellbeing & Community Services, St Martin's Place, Bath Road, Slough SL1 3UQ ☎ 01753 696099 ✆ ketain.gandi@slough.gov.uk

Licensing: Mr Michael Sims, Licensing Manager, Landmark Place, Windsor Road, Slough SL1 1JL ☎ 01753 477387 ✆ michael.sims@slough.gov.uk

Lifelong Learning: Mr Philip Wright, Head of Learning & Community Services, St Martin's Place, Bath Road, Slough SL1 3UF ☎ 01753 875741 ✆ philip.wright@slough.gov.uk

Lighting: Mr Sing-Wai Yu, Principal Engineer - Highways, St Martin's Place, Bath Road, Slough SL1 3UQ ☎ 01753 875628 ✆ sing-wai.yu@slough.gov.uk

Lottery Funding, Charity and Voluntary: Mr Alex Bowman, Strategic Commissioning Manager, St Martin's Place, Bath Road, Slough SL1 3UQ ☎ 01753 474037 ✆ alex.bowman@slough.gov.uk

Parking: Mr Garry Sullivan, Team Leader - Traffic Development, St Martin's Place, Bath Road, Slough SL1 3UQ ☎ 01753 477337 ✆ garry.sullivan@slough.gov.uk

Partnerships: Mr Gurpreet Anand, Assistant Director - Procurement & Commercial Services, St Martin's Place, Bath Road, Slough SL1 3UQ ☎ 01753 875216 ✆ gurpreet.anand@slough.gov.uk

Personnel / HR: Ms Christina Hefferon, Assistant Director - Organisational Development & HR, St Martin's Place, Bath Road, Slough SL1 3UQ ☎ 01753 875213 ✆ christina.hefferon@slough.gov.uk

Planning: Mr Paul Stimpson, Strategic Lead - Planning Policy & Projects, St Martin's Place, Bath Road, Slough SL1 3UQ ☎ 01753 875820 ✆ paul.stimpson@slough.gov.uk

Procurement: Mr Gurpreet Anand, Assistant Director - Procurement & Commercial Services, St Martin's Place, Bath Road, Slough SL1 3UQ ☎ 01753 875216 ✆ gurpreet.anand@slough.gov.uk

Public Libraries: Ms Claire Skeates, Service Development Manager, St Martin's Place, Bath Road, Slough SL1 3UQ ☎ 01753 875578 ✆ claire.skeates@slough.gov.uk

Recycling & Waste Minimisation: Mr Nicholas Hannon, Environmental Strategy & Governance Manager, St Martin's Place, Bath Road, Slough SL1 3UQ ☎ 01753 875275 ✆ nicholas.hannon@slough.gov.uk

Road Safety: Ms Lynsey Brookfield, Engineer - Traffic Engineering, St Martin's Place, Bath Road, Slough SL1 3UQ ☎ 01753 875622 ✆ lynsey.brookfield@slough.gov.uk

Social Services: Ms Krutika Pau, Interim Strategic Director - Children's Services, St Martin's Place, Bath Road, Slough SL1 3UQ ☎ 01753 875751 ✆ krutika.pau@slough.gov.uk

Social Services (Adult): Mr Alan Sinclair, Assistant Director - Adult Social Care, St Martin's Place, Bath Road, Slough SL1 3UQ ☎ 01753 875752 ✆ alan.sinclair@slough.gov.uk

Social Services (Children): Ms Krutika Pau, Interim Strategic Director - Children's Services, St Martin's Place, Bath Road, Slough SL1 3UQ ☎ 01753 875751 ✆ krutika.pau@slough.gov.uk

Public Health: Dr Lise Llewellyn, Director - Public Health, Easthampstead House, Town Square, Bracknell RG12 1AQ ☎ 01344 352000 ✆ lise.llewellyn@bracknell-forest.gov.uk

Street Scene: Mr Mike England, Interim Strategic Director - Regeneration, Housing & Resources, St Martin's Place, Bath Road, Slough SL1 3UQ ☎ 01753 875301 ✆ mike.england@slough.gov.uk

Tourism: Mrs Kate Pratt, Communications Manager, St Martin's Place, Bath Road, Slough SL1 3UQ ☎ 01753 875088 ✆ kate.pratt@slough.gov.uk

Traffic Management: Mr Savio DeCruz, Head of Transport & Highways, St Martin's Place, Bath Road, Slough SL1 3UQ ☎ 01753 875640 ✆ savio.decruz@slough.gov.uk

Transport: Mr Savio DeCruz, Head of Transport & Highways, St Martin's Place, Bath Road, Slough SL1 3UQ ☎ 01753 875640 ✆ savio.decruz@slough.gov.uk

Transport Planner: Mr Joe Carter, Assistant Director - Assets, Infrastructure & Regeneration, St Martin's Place, Bath Road, Slough SL1 3UQ ☎ 01753 575653 ✆ joe.carter@slough.gov.uk

SLOUGH

Waste Collection and Disposal: Mr Nicholas Hannon, Environmental Strategy & Governance Manager, St Martin's Place, Bath Road, Slough SL1 3UQ ☎ 01753 875275 ⏚ nicholas.hannon@slough.gov.uk

Waste Management: Mr Nicholas Hannon, Environmental Strategy & Governance Manager, St Martin's Place, Bath Road, Slough SL1 3UQ ☎ 01753 875275 ⏚ nicholas.hannon@slough.gov.uk

Children's Play Areas: Mr Ollie Kelly, Parks & Open Spaces Manager, St Martin's Place, Bath Road, Slough SL1 3UQ ☎ 01753 875252 ⏚ ollie.kelly@slough.gov.uk

COUNCILLORS

Mayor: Dhaliwal, Arvind (LAB - Elliman)
arvind.dhaliwal@slough.gov.uk

Deputy Mayor: Shah, Ishrat (LAB - Foxborough)
ishrat08@hotmail.co.uk

Leader of the Council: Munawar, Sohail (LAB - Elliman)
sohail.munawar@slough.gov.uk

Deputy Leader of the Council: Hussain, Sabia (LAB - Chalvey)
sabiahussain786@gmail.com

Group Leader: Chahal, Wal (CON - Upton)
wal.chahal@slough.gov.uk

Ajaib, Zaffar (LAB - Central)
zaffar.ajaib@slough.gov.uk

Anderson, Robert (LAB - Britwell & Northborough)
rob.anderson@slough.gov.uk

Bains, Rayman (CON - Upton)
rayman.bains@slough.gov.uk

Bal, Joginder (LAB - Farnham)
joginder.bal@slough.gov.uk

Bedi, Madhuri (LAB - Foxborough)
madhuri.bedi@slough.gov.uk

Brooker, Preston (LAB - Langley Kederminster)
preston.brooker@slough.gov.uk

Carter, Martin (LAB - Britwell & Northborough)
martin.carter@slough.gov.uk

Chaudhry, Shafiq (LAB - Central)
shafiq.chaudhry@slough.gov.uk

Cheema, Avtar (LAB - Colnbrook with Poyle)
avtar.cheema@slough.gov.uk

Chohan, Nimrit (LAB - Cippenham Meadows)
nimrit.chohan@slough.gov.uk

Coad, Diana (UKIP - Langley St. Mary's)
dianacoad@aol.com

Dar, Haqeeq (LAB - Wexham Lea)
haqeeq.dar@slough.gov.uk

Davis, Roger (LAB - Cippenham Green)
roger_rebel40@hotmail.com

Dhaliwal, Amarpreet (CON - Langley St. Mary's)
amapreet.dhaliwal@slough.gov.uk

Holledge, Michael (LAB - Langley Kederminster)
michael.holledge@slough.gov.uk

Holledge, Nora (LAB - Cippenham Green)
nora.holledge@slough.gov.uk

Mann, Pavitar (LAB - Central)
pavy2@hotmail.com

Matloob, Fiza (LAB - Baylis & Stoke)
fizamatloob@yahoo.co.uk

Morris, Darren (CON - Haymill & Lynch Hill)
darren.morris@slough.gov.uk

Nazir, Mohammed (LAB - Baylis & Stoke)
mohammed.nazir@slough.gov.uk

Pantelic, Natasa (LAB - Cippenham Meadows)
natasa.pantelic@slough.gov.uk

Parmar, Satpal (LAB - Cippenham Meadows)
satpal.parmar@slough.gov.uk

Plenty, Ted (LAB - Upton)
ted.plenty@slough.gov.uk

Qaseem, Naveeda (LAB - Elliman)
naveeda.qaseem@slough.gov.uk

Rana, Mandeep (LAB - Langley Kederminster)
mandeep.rana@slough.gov.uk

Rasib, Mohammed (LAB - Farnham)
mohammed.rasib@slough.gov.uk

Sadiq, Shabnum (LAB - Wexham Lea)
shabnum.sadiq@slough.gov.uk

Sandhu, Atiq (LAB - Chalvey)
atiq.sandhu@slough.gov.uk

Sandhu, Rajinder (CON - Upton)
rajinder.sandhu@slough.gov.uk

Sarfraz, Sunyia (LAB - Baylis & Stoke)
sunyia.sarfraz@slough.gov.uk

Sharif, Mohamemd (LAB - Chalvey)
gbsharim@yahoo.co.uk

Smith, Dexter (CON - Colnbrook with Poyle)
dexter.j.smith@btinternet.com

Sohal, Paul (LAB - Wexham Lea)
Sohal51@aol.com

Strutton, Wayne (CON - Haymill & Lynch Hill)
w.strutton@sky.com

Swindlehurst, James (LAB - Cippenham Green)
james.swindlehurst@slough.gov.uk

Usmani, Khaula (LAB - Chalvey)
khaula.usmani@slough.gov.uk

Wright, Anna (CON - Haymill & Lynch Hill)
anna.s.wright@hotmail.com

POLITICAL COMPOSITION
LAB: 33, CON: 8, UKIP: 1

COMMITTEE CHAIRS

Audit: Ms Shabnum Sadiq

Education & Children's Services: Mr Preston Brooker

Licensing: Mr Roger Davis

Neighbourhoods & Community Services: Mr Ted Plenty

Planning: Mr Haqeeq Dar

Solihull   M

Solihull Metropolitan Borough Council, Council House, Manor Square, Solihull B91 3QB
☎ 0121 704 6000 🖷 0121 704 6114 🖃 connectcc@solihull.gov.uk
🖳 www.solihull.gov.uk

FACTS AND FIGURES
Parliamentary Constituencies: Meriden, Solihull
EU Constituencies: West Midlands
Election Frequency: Elections are by thirds

PRINCIPAL OFFICERS

Chief Executive: Mr Nick Page, Chief Executive, Solihull Metropolitan Borough Council, PO Box 18, Council House, Solihull B91 9QS

Deputy Chief Executive: Mr Paul Johnson, Director - Resources, Solihull Metropolitan Borough Council, PO Box 18, Council House, Solihull B91 9QS ☎ 0121 704 6194 🖃 pjohnson@solihull.gov.uk

Senior Management: Ms Anne Brereton, Director - Managed Growth & Communities, Solihull Metropolitan Borough Council, PO Box 18, Council House, Solihull B91 9QS ☎ 0121 704 6364 🖃 abrereton@solihull.gov.uk

Senior Management: Ms Susan Dale, Interim Director - Adult Social Care, Solihull Metropolitan Borough Council, PO Box 18, Council House, Solihull B91 9QS ☎ 0121 704 6667 🖃 susan.dale@solihull.gov.uk

Senior Management: Ms Sally Hodges, Director - Children's Services & Skills, Solihull Metropolitan Borough Council, PO Box 18, Council House, Solihull B91 9QS ☎ 0121 704 6734 🖃 sally.hodges@solihull.gov.uk

Senior Management: Mr Paul Johnson, Director - Resources, Solihull Metropolitan Borough Council, PO Box 18, Council House, Solihull B91 9QS ☎ 0121 704 6194 🖃 pjohnson@solihull.gov.uk

Senior Management: Dr Stephen Munday, Director - Public Health & Commissioning, Solihull Metropolitan Borough Council, PO Box 18, Council House, Solihull B91 9QS ☎ 0121 704 6187 🖃 stephen.munday@solihull.gov.uk

Access Officer / Social Services (Disability): Ms Clare Shannon, Head of Disability Services, Solihull Metropolitan Borough Council, PO Box 18, Council House, Solihull B91 9QS ☎ 0121 709 7043 🖃 clare.shannon@solihull.gov.uk

Children / Youth Services: Mr Tony Griffin, Interim Assistant Director - Children, Young People & Families, Solihull Metropolitan Borough Council, PO Box 18, Council House, Solihull B91 9QS ☎ 0121 704 8325 🖃 tony.griffin@solihull.gov.uk

PR / Communications: Ms Deborah Martin-Williams, Head - Communications, Solihull Metropolitan Borough Council, PO Box 18, Council House, Solihull B91 9QS ☎ 0121 704 6772 🖃 dmartinwilliams@solihull.gov.uk

Community Safety: Ms Caroline Naven, Head - Neighbourhood Services, Solihull Metropolitan Borough Council, PO Box 18, Council House, Solihull B91 9QS ☎ 0121 704 8753 🖃 cnaven@solihull.gov.uk

Computer Management: Mr Paul Langham, Head - ICT & Information Governance, Solihull Metropolitan Borough Council, PO Box 18, Council House, Solihull B91 9QS ☎ 0121 704 6196 🖃 paul.langham@solihull.gov.uk

Customer Service: Ms Emma Mayhew, Head - Customer Services, Solihull Metropolitan Borough Council, PO Box 18, Council House, Solihull B91 9QS ☎ 0121 704 8667 🖃 emayhew@solihull.gov.uk

Education: Ms Heather Loveridge, Interim Assistant Director - Learning, Skills & Progression, Solihull Metropolitan Borough Council, PO Box 18, Council House, Solihull B91 9QS ☎ 0121 704 8282 🖃 heather.loveridge@solihull.gov.uk

Environmental / Technical Services: Mr Alan Brown, Assistant Director - Highways & Environment, Solihull Metropolitan Borough Council, PO Box 18, Council House, Solihull B91 9QS ☎ 0121 704 8334 🖃 albrown@solihull.gov.uk

Facilities: Mr Paul Evans, Head - Corporate Property Services, Solihull Metropolitan Borough Council, PO Box 18, Council House, Solihull B91 9QS ☎ 0121 704 6494 🖃 pevans@solihull.gov.uk

Finance: Mr Paul Johnson, Director - Resources, Solihull Metropolitan Borough Council, PO Box 18, Council House, Solihull B91 9QS ☎ 0121 704 6194 🖃 pjohnson@solihull.gov.uk

Treasury: Ms Samantha Gilbert, Head - Financial Operations, Solihull Metropolitan Borough Council, PO Box 18, Council House, Solihull B91 9QS ☎ 0121 704 6278 🖃 sgilbert@solihull.gov.uk

Grounds Maintenance: Mr Alan Brown, Assistant Director - Highways & Environment, Solihull Metropolitan Borough Council, PO Box 18, Council House, Solihull B91 9QS ☎ 0121 704 8334 🖃 albrown@solihull.gov.uk

Highways: Mr Alan Brown, Assistant Director - Highways & Environment, Solihull Metropolitan Borough Council, PO Box 18, Council House, Solihull B91 9QS ☎ 0121 704 8334 🖃 albrown@solihull.gov.uk

Highways: Mr Ashley Prior, Head - Highway Services, Solihull Metropolitan Borough Council, PO Box 18, Council House, Solihull B91 9QS ☎ 0121 704 8558 🖃 ashley.prior@solihull.gov.uk

Housing: Mr Ken Harrison, Head - Policy & Spatial Planning, Solihull Metropolitan Borough Council, PO Box 18, Council House, Solihull B91 9QS ☎ 0121 704 8320 🖃 ken.harrison@solihull.gov.uk

Housing: Mr Jim Harte, Assistant Director - Highways, Neighbourhoods & Environment Services, Solihull Metropolitan Borough Council, PO Box 18, Council House, Solihull B91 9QS ☎ 0121 704 6453 🖃 jharte@solihull.gov.uk

Legal: Ms Deborah Merry, Head - Legal & Democratic Services, Solihull Metropolitan Borough Council, PO Box 18, Council House, Solihull B91 9QS ☎ 0121 704 6022 🖃 dmerry@solihull.gov.uk

Leisure and Cultural Services: Ms Tracey Cox, Head - Service, Libraries, Arts & Information, Solihull Metropolitan Borough Council, PO Box 18, Council House, Solihull B91 9QS ☎ 0121 704 6945 🖃 tcox@solihull.gov.uk

SOLIHULL

Lighting: Mr Ashley Prior, Head - Highway Services, Solihull Metropolitan Borough Council, PO Box 18, Council House, Solihull B91 9QS ☎ 0121 704 8558 ⁻ᐟ ashley.prior@solihull.gov.uk

Member Services: Ms Deborah Merry, Head - Legal & Democratic Services, Solihull Metropolitan Borough Council, PO Box 18, Council House, Solihull B91 9QS ☎ 0121 704 6022 ⁻ᐟ dmerry@solihull.gov.uk

Parking: Mr Ashley Prior, Head - Highway Services, Solihull Metropolitan Borough Council, PO Box 18, Council House, Solihull B91 9QS ☎ 0121 704 8558 ⁻ᐟ ashley.prior@solihull.gov.uk

Partnerships: Ms Melanie Lockey, Head - Partnership Commissioning, Solihull Metropolitan Borough Council, PO Box 18, Council House, Solihull B91 9QS ☎ 0121 704 8403 ⁻ᐟ mlockey@solihull.gov.uk

Personnel / HR: Mr Adrian Cattell, Head - Human Resources, Solihull Metropolitan Borough Council, PO Box 18, Council House, Solihull B91 9QS ☎ 0121 704 6038 ⁻ᐟ acattell@solihull.gov.uk

Personnel / HR: Ms Viv Lawrence, Head - Organisational & Workforce Development, Solihull Metropolitan Borough Council, PO Box 18, Council House, Solihull B91 9QS ☎ 0121 704 6524 ⁻ᐟ vlawrence@solihull.gov.uk

Planning: Mr Ken Harrison, Head - Policy & Spatial Planning, Solihull Metropolitan Borough Council, PO Box 18, Council House, Solihull B91 9QS ☎ 0121 704 8320 ⁻ᐟ ken.harrison@solihull.gov.uk

Planning: Mr Martin Taylor, Head - Design & Development Management Services, Solihull Metropolitan Borough Council, PO Box 18, Council House, Solihull B91 9QS ☎ 0121 704 6311 ⁻ᐟ martin.taylor@solihull.gov.uk

Procurement: Ms Liz Welton, Head - Procurement, Solihull Metropolitan Borough Council, PO Box 18, Council House, Solihull B91 9QS ☎ 0121 704 6088 ⁻ᐟ lizwelton@solihull.gov.uk

Public Libraries: Ms Tracey Cox, Head - Service, Libraries, Arts & Information, Solihull Metropolitan Borough Council, PO Box 18, Council House, Solihull B91 9QS ☎ 0121 704 6945 ⁻ᐟ tcox@solihull.gov.uk

Recycling & Waste Minimisation: Mr Alan Brown, Assistant Director - Highways & Environment, Solihull Metropolitan Borough Council, PO Box 18, Council House, Solihull B91 9QS ☎ 0121 704 8334 ⁻ᐟ albrown@solihull.gov.uk

Regeneration: Ms Anne Brereton, Director - Managed Growth & Communities, Solihull Metropolitan Borough Council, PO Box 18, Council House, Solihull B91 9QS ☎ 0121 704 6364 ⁻ᐟ abrereton@solihull.gov.uk

Road Safety: Mr Ashley Prior, Head - Highway Services, Solihull Metropolitan Borough Council, PO Box 18, Council House, Solihull B91 9QS ☎ 0121 704 8558 ⁻ᐟ ashley.prior@solihull.gov.uk

Social Services (Adult): Ms Susan Dale, Interim Director - Adult Social Care, Solihull Metropolitan Borough Council, PO Box 18, Council House, Solihull B91 9QS ☎ 0121 704 6667 ⁻ᐟ susan.dale@solihull.gov.uk

Social Services (Children): Ms Sally Hodges, Director - Children's Services & Skills, Solihull Metropolitan Borough Council, PO Box 18, Council House, Solihull B91 9QS ☎ 0121 704 6734 ⁻ᐟ sally.hodges@solihull.gov.uk

Social Services (Children): Mr Frank McSheffrey, Head of Service - Children in Need & Child Protection, Solihull Metropolitan Borough Council, PO Box 18, Council House, Solihull B91 9QS ☎ 0121 704 8709 ⁻ᐟ fmcsheff@solihull.gov.uk

Fostering & Adoption: Ms Jane Wilton, Head - Children in Care, Solihull Metropolitan Borough Council, PO Box 18, Council House, Solihull B91 9QS ☎ 0121 788 4227 ⁻ᐟ jwilton@solihull.gov.uk

Looked after Children: Ms Jane Wilton, Head - Children in Care, Solihull Metropolitan Borough Council, PO Box 18, Council House, Solihull B91 9QS ☎ 0121 788 4227 ⁻ᐟ jwilton@solihull.gov.uk

Childrens Social Care: Mr Frank McSheffrey, Head of Service - Children in Need & Child Protection, Solihull Metropolitan Borough Council, PO Box 18, Council House, Solihull B91 9QS ☎ 0121 704 8709 ⁻ᐟ fmcsheff@solihull.gov.uk

Public Health: Dr Stephen Munday, Director - Public Health & Commissioning, Solihull Metropolitan Borough Council, PO Box 18, Council House, Solihull B91 9QS ☎ 0121 704 6187 ⁻ᐟ stephen.munday@solihull.gov.uk

Staff Training: Ms Viv Lawrence, Head - Organisational & Workforce Development, Solihull Metropolitan Borough Council, PO Box 18, Council House, Solihull B91 9QS ☎ 0121 704 6524 ⁻ᐟ vlawrence@solihull.gov.uk

Town Centre: Ms Caroline Naven, Head - Neighbourhood Services, Solihull Metropolitan Borough Council, PO Box 18, Council House, Solihull B91 9QS ☎ 0121 704 8753 ⁻ᐟ cnaven@solihull.gov.uk

Traffic Management: Mr Ashley Prior, Head - Highway Services, Solihull Metropolitan Borough Council, PO Box 18, Council House, Solihull B91 9QS ☎ 0121 704 8558 ⁻ᐟ ashley.prior@solihull.gov.uk

Waste Collection and Disposal: Mr Alan Brown, Assistant Director - Highways & Environment, Solihull Metropolitan Borough Council, PO Box 18, Council House, Solihull B91 9QS ☎ 0121 704 8334 ⁻ᐟ albrown@solihull.gov.uk

Waste Management: Mr Alan Brown, Assistant Director - Highways & Environment, Solihull Metropolitan Borough Council, PO Box 18, Council House, Solihull B91 9QS ☎ 0121 704 8334 ⁻ᐟ albrown@solihull.gov.uk

COUNCILLORS

Mayor: Robinson, Michael (CON - Castle Bromwich) mrobinson@solihull.gov.uk

Deputy Mayor: Slater, Glenis (LD - Elmdon) gslater@solihihull.gov.uk

Leader of the Council: Sleigh, Robert (CON - Bickenhill) rsleigh@solihull.gov.uk

Deputy Leader of the Council: Courts, Ian (CON - Dorridge & Hockley Heath) icourts@solihull.gov.uk

Group Leader: Evans, Debbie (UKIP – Kingshurst & Fordbridge)
debra.evans@solihull.gov.uk

Group Leader: Windmill, John (LD – Olton)
jwindmill@solihull.gov.uk

Adeyemo, Ade (LD – Lyndon)
ade.adeyemo@solihull.gov.uk

Allen, Howard (GRN – Shirley West)
hallen@solihull.gov.uk

Allsopp, Ken (CON – Meriden)
kallsopp@solihull.gov.uk

Bassett, Margaret (CON – Silhill)
margaret.bassett@solihull.gov.uk

Bell, David (CON – Meriden)
dbell@solihull.gov.uk

Burn, James (GRN – Chelmsey Wood)
james.burn@solihull.gov.uk

Davis, Stuart (CON – St Alphege)
sdavis@solihull.gov.uk

Dicicco, Tony (CON – Meriden)
tony.dicicco@solihull.gov.uk

Fairburn, Jo (LD – Olton)
jo.fairburn@solihull.gov.uk

Grinsell, Karen (CON – Shirley East)
karen.grinsall@solihull.gov.uk

Grinsell, Robert (CON – Olton)
robert.grinsell@solihull.gov.uk

Hall, Robert (UKIP – Kingshurst & Fordbridge)
robert.hall@solihull.gov.uk

Hamilton, Jean (GRN – Smith's Wood)
jean.hamilton@solihull.gov.uk

Hawkins, Ken (CON – Blythe)
khawkins@solihull.gov.uk

Hewings, Martin (LD – Elmdon)
mhewings@solihull.gov.uk

Hodgson, Tim (GRN – Shirley West)
tim.hodgson@solihull.gov.uk

Hodgson, Andrew (GRN – Shirley South)
ahodgson@solihull.gov.uk

Hogarth, Peter (CON – Silhill)
phogarth@solihull.gov.uk

Holl-Allen, Diana (CON – Knowle)
dhollallen@solihull.gov.uk

Holmes, Brian (CON – Shirley West)
brian.holmes@solihull.gov.uk

Holt, Richard (CON – Blythe)
richard.holt@solihull.gov.uk

Holt, Stephen (GRN – Smith's Wood)
stephen.holt@solihull.gov.uk

Hulland, Robert (CON – Silhill)
rhulland@solihull.gov.uk

Hulland, Julie (CON – Lyndon)
julie.hulland@solihull.gov.uk

Insley, Alex (CON – Blythe)
alex.insley@solihull.gov.uk

Ludlow, Tony (LD – Lyndon)
anthony.ludlow@solihull.gov.uk

Mackenzie, Annette (CON – Shirley East)
annette.mackenzie@solihull.gov.uk

Mackiewicz, Andrew (CON – Dorridge & Hockley Heath)
amackiewicz@solihull.gov.uk

Macnaughton, Karl (GRN – Chelmsley Wood)
kmacnaughton@solihull.gov.uk

McCarthy, Martin (CON – Elmdon)
martin.mccarthy@solihull.gov.uk

McLoughlin, Max (GRN – Shirley South)
max.mcloughlin@solihull.gov.uk

Meeson, Ken (CON – Dorridge & Hockley Heath)
kmeeson@solihull.gov.uk

Nash, Florence (LAB – Kingshurst & Fordbridge)
flo.nash@solihull.gov.uk

Parker, Mark (CON – Shirley East)
mparker@solihull.gov.uk

Potts, Jeffrey (CON – Knowle)
jpotts@solihull.gov.uk

Rebeiro, Alan (CON – Knowle)
arebeiro@solihull.gov.uk

Richards, Ted (CON – Castle Bromwich)
grichards@solihull.gov.uk

Rolf, Alison (CON – Bickenhill)
alison.rolf@solihull.gov.uk

Ryan, Jim (CON – Bickenhill)
jiryan@solihull.gov.uk

Sandison, Angela (CON – Shirley South)
angela.sandison@solihull.gov.uk

Sleigh, Gail (CON – Castle Bromwich)
gsleigh@solihull.gov.uk

Tildesley, Joe (CON – St Alphege)
joetildesley@solihull.gov.uk

Wild, Kate (CON – St Alphege)
kwild@solihull.gov.uk

Williams, Chris (GRN – Chelmsley Wood)
chris.williams@solihull.gov.uk

Wilson, Mark (GRN – Smith's Wood)
mark.wilson@solihull.gov.uk

POLITICAL COMPOSITION
CON: 32, GRN: 10, LD: 6, UKIP: 2, LAB: 1

COMMITTEE CHAIRS

Health & Adult Social Care: Mrs Gail Sleigh

Health & Wellbeing: Mr Ken Meeson

Licensing: Mr Peter Hogarth

Planning: Mr David Bell

Somerset   C

Somerset County Council, County Hall, Taunton TA1 4DY
☎ 0300 123 2224 ✆ generalenquiries@somerset.gov.uk
🖳 www.somerset.gov.uk

SOMERSET

FACTS AND FIGURES
Parliamentary Constituencies: Somerset North, Somerset North East
EU Constituencies: South West
Election Frequency: Elections are of whole council

PRINCIPAL OFFICERS

Chief Executive: Mr Patrick Flaherty, Chief Executive, County Hall, Taunton TA1 4DY ☎ 01823 359001 ⁌ pflherty@somerset.gov.uk

Senior Management: Mr Stephen Chandler, Lead Commissioner - Adults & Health, County Hall, Taunton TA1 4DY ☎ 01823 359025 ⁌ stchandler@somerset.gov.uk

Senior Management: Mr Simon Clifford, Customers & Communities Director, County Hall, Taunton TA1 4DY ☎ 01823 359166 ⁌ sclifford@somerset.gov.uk

Senior Management: Ms Trudi Grant, Director - Public Health, County Hall, Taunton TA1 4DY ⁌ tgrant@somerset.gov.uk

Senior Management: Ms Paula Hewitt, Director - Commissioning & Lead Commissioner - Economic & Community Infrastructure, County Hall, Taunton TA1 4DY ☎ 01823 356020 ⁌ prhewitt@somerset.gov.uk

Senior Management: Mr Kevin Nacey, Finance & Performance Director, County Hall, Taunton TA1 4DY ☎ 01823 355213 ⁌ kbnacey@somerset.gov.uk

Senior Management: Mr Richard Williams, Commercial & Business Services Director, County Hall, Taunton TA1 4DY ☎ 01823 355036 ⁌ rowilliams@somerset.gov.uk

Senior Management: Mr Julian Wooster, Director - Children's Services, County Hall, Taunton TA1 4DY ☎ 01823 355886 ⁌ jwooster@somerset.gov.uk

Children / Youth Services: Mr Julian Wooster, Director - Children's Services, County Hall, Taunton TA1 4DY ☎ 01823 355886 ⁌ jwooster@somerset.gov.uk

PR / Communications: Mr Mark Ford, Head of Communications, County Hall, Taunton TA1 4DY ☎ 01823 357143 ⁌ mford@somerset.gov.uk

PR / Communications: Ms Deborah Porter, Deputy Head of Communications, County Hall, Taunton TA1 4DY ☎ 01823 355018 ⁌ dporter@somerset.gov.uk

Community Safety: Ms Lucy Macready, Commissioning Manager - Community Safety, County Hall, Taunton TA1 4DY ☎ 01823 357114 ⁌ lmacready@somerset.gov.uk

Computer Management: Mr Alan Webb, Strategic Manager - ICT Lead & Client, County Hall, Taunton TA1 4DY ☎ 01823 355293 ⁌ awebb@somerset.gov.uk

Contracts: Ms Donna Fitzgerald, Strategic Manager - Business Client, County Hall, Taunton TA1 4DY ☎ 01823 355243 ⁌ dmfitzgerald@somerset.gov.uk

Corporate Services: Mr Richard Williams, Commercial & Business Services Director, County Hall, Taunton TA1 4DY ☎ 01823 355036 ⁌ rowilliams@somerset.gov.uk

Economic Development: Mr Paul Hickson, Strategic Manager - Economy & Planning, County Hall, Taunton TA1 4DY ☎ 01823 355661 ⁌ phickson@somerset.gov.uk

Education: Mr Julian Wooster, Director - Children's Services, County Hall, Taunton TA1 4DY ☎ 01823 355886 ⁌ jwooster@somerset.gov.uk

E-Government: Mr Alan Webb, Strategic Manager - ICT Lead & Client, County Hall, Taunton TA1 4DY ☎ 01823 355293 ⁌ awebb@somerset.gov.uk

Electoral Registration: Mr Julian Gale, Strategic Manager - Governance & Risk, County Hall, Taunton TA1 4DY ☎ 01823 359047 ⁌ jjgale@somerset.gov.uk

Emergency Planning: Ms Nicola Dawson, Civil Contingencies Manager, County Hall, Taunton TA2 8LQ ☎ 01823 364612 ⁌ ndawson@somerset.gov.uk

Estates, Property & Valuation: Mr James Stubbs, Strategic Manager - Property, County Hall, Taunton TA1 4DY ☎ 01823 355364 ⁌ jstubbs@somerset.gov.uk

European Liaison: Mr Jamshid Ahmadi, Service Manager - Economy Commissioning, County Hall, Taunton TA1 4DY ☎ 01823 356131 ⁌ jahmadi@somerset.gov.uk

Facilities: Ms Heidi Boyle, Facilities Manager, County Hall, Taunton TA1 4DY ☎ 01823 365524 ⁌ hboyle@somerset.gov.uk

Finance: Mr Kevin Nacey, Finance & Performance Director, County Hall, Taunton TA1 4DY ☎ 01823 355213 ⁌ kbnacey@somerset.gov.uk

Pensions: Ms Catherine Drew, Service Manager - Pensions, County Hall, Taunton TA1 4DY ☎ 01823 355466 ⁌ cmdrew@somerset.gov.uk

Pensions: Ms Claire Druce, Senior Pension Investments Officer, County Hall, Taunton TA1 4DY ☎ 01823 355449 ⁌ cdruce@somerset.gov.uk

Health and Safety: Mr Brian Oldham, Operations Manager - Health & Safety, County Hall, Taunton TA1 4DY ☎ 01823 355089 ⁌ boldham@somerset.gov.uk

Highways: Mr Geoff Dight, Strategic Manager - Highways Maintenance, County Hall, Taunton TA1 4DY ☎ 01823 483064 ⁌ gdight@somerset.gov.uk

Legal: Mrs Honor Clarke, Deputy County Solicitor, County Hall, Taunton TA1 4DY ☎ 01823 355012 ⁌ hcclarke@somerset.gov.uk

Lifelong Learning: Ms Ros Pither, Strategic Manager - Learning, County Hall, Taunton TA1 4DY ☎ 01823 357867 ⁌ rpither@somerset.gov.uk

Lighting: Mr Stephen Parkinson, Service Manager - Traffic Control & Lighting, County Hall, Taunton TA1 4DY ☎ 0845 345 9166 📧 sparkinson@somerset.gov.uk

Member Services: Mr Julian Gale, Strategic Manager - Governance & Risk, County Hall, Taunton TA1 4DY ☎ 01823 359047 📧 jjgale@somerset.gov.uk

Planning: Mr Philip Higginbottom, Service Manager - Planning Control, County Hall, Taunton TA1 4DY ☎ 01823 356939 📧 phigginbottom@somerset.gov.uk

Procurement: Ms Donna Fitzgerald, Strategic Manager - Business Client, County Hall, Taunton TA1 4DY ☎ 01823 355243 📧 dmfitzgerald@somerset.gov.uk

Public Libraries: Ms Sue Crowley, Strategic Manager - Library Services, County Hall, Taunton TA1 4DY ☎ 01278 458373 📧 sacrowley@somerset.gov.uk

Recycling & Waste Minimisation: Mr Steve Read, Managing Director - Somerset Waste Partnership, Monmouth House, Blackbrook Park Avenue, Taunton TA1 2PX ☎ 01823 625708 📧 sread@somerset.gov.uk

Regeneration: Ms Paula Hewitt, Director - Commissioning & Lead Commissioner - Economic & Community Infrastructure, County Hall, Taunton TA1 4DY ☎ 01823 356020 📧 prhewitt@somerset.gov.uk

Road Safety: Mr Terrance Beale, Service Manager - Road Safety, County Hall, Taunton TA1 4DY ☎ 01823 340014 📧 tbeale@somerset.gov.uk

Social Services (Adult): Ms Clare Steel, Lead Commissioner - Adults & Health, County Hall, Taunton TA1 4DY ☎ 01823 355100 📧 csteel@somerset.gov.uk

Social Services (Children): Mr Julian Wooster, Director - Children's Services, County Hall, Taunton TA1 4DY ☎ 01823 355886 📧 jwooster@somerset.gov.uk

Public Health: Ms Trudi Grant, Director - Public Health, County Hall, Taunton TA1 4DY 📧 tgrant@somerset.gov.uk

Staff Training: Mr Hugh Griffith, Strategic Manager - HR Organisational Development, County Hall, Taunton TA1 4DY ☎ 01823 356124 📧 dhgriffith@somerset.gov.uk

Tourism: Mr Paul Hickson, Strategic Manager - Economy & Planning, County Hall, Taunton TA1 4DY ☎ 01823 355661 📧 phickson@somerset.gov.uk

Traffic Management: Ms Beverley Norman, Service Manager - Traffic Mangement, County Hall, Taunton TA1 4DY ☎ 01823 358089 📧 bjnorman@somerset.gov.uk

Transport: Mr Phil Lowndes, Strategic Manager - Traffic & Transport Development, County Hall, Taunton TA1 4DY ☎ 01823 356139 📧 aplowndes@somerset.gov.uk

Transport Planner: Mr Mike O'Dowd-Jones, Strategic Manager - Highways & Transport, County Hall, Taunton TA1 4DY ☎ 01823 356238 📧 modowdjones@somerset.gov.uk

Waste Collection and Disposal: Mr Steve Read, Managing Director - Somerset Waste Partnership, Monmouth House, Blackbrook Park Avenue, Taunton TA1 2PX ☎ 01823 625708 📧 sread@somerset.gov.uk

Waste Management: Mr Steve Read, Managing Director - Somerset Waste Partnership, Monmouth House, Blackbrook Park Avenue, Taunton TA1 2PX ☎ 01823 625708 📧 sread@somerset.gov.uk

COUNCILLORS

Chair: Lawrence, Christine (CON - Dunster)
cmlawrence@somerset.gov.uk

Leader of the Council: Osman, John (CON - Wells)
jdosman@somerset.gov.uk

Deputy Leader of the Council: Hall, David (CON - Bridgwater East & Bawdrip)
dhall@somerset.gov.uk

Adkins, Michael (CON - Taunton North)
madkins@somerset.gov.uk

Bailey, John (LD - Martock)
jabailey@somerset.gov.uk

Bown, Ann (CON - Bridgwater West)
aebown@somerset.gov.uk

Brown, Richard (CON - North Petherton)
rjbrown@somerset.gov.uk

Burridge-Clayton, Peter (CON - Burnham on Sea North)
pburridgeclayton@somerset.gov.uk

Clayton, Justine (LD - Bishops Hul & Taunton West)
jmclayton@sccmembers.org.uk

Coles, Simon (LD - Taunton East)
scoles@somerset.gov.uk

Crabb, Samuel (LD - Brympton)
sdcrabb@somerset.gov.uk

Davies, Hugh (IND - Watchet & Stogursey)
hdavies@somerset.gov.uk

Denbee, John (CON - Brent)
jdenbee@somerset.gov.uk

Dimmick, Alan (UKIP - Yeovil Central)
adimmick@somerset.gov.uk

Dyke, John (LD - Crewkerne)
jdyke@somerset.gov.uk

Edney, John (CON - Cannington)
jedney@somerset.gov.uk

Fothergill, David (CON - Monkton & North Curry)
djafothergill@somerset.gov.uk

Fysh, Marcus (CON - Coker)
mfysh@somerset.gov.uk

Gloak, Alan (LD - Glastonbury & Street)
afgloak@somerset.gov.uk

Govier, Andrew (LAB - Wellington)
ajgovier@somerset.gov.uk

SOMERSET

Greene, David (IND - Yeovil South)
dagreene@somerset.gov.uk

Groskop, Anna (CON - Wincanton & Bruton)
amgroskop@somerset.gov.uk

Ham, Philip (CON - Mendip Central & East)
pjham@somerset.gov.uk

Healey, Mark (CON - Huntspill)
mhealey@somerset.gov.uk

Henley, Ross (LD - Blackdown & Neroche)
rlhenley@somerset.gov.uk

Hill, Dawn (CON - Cheddar)
dmhill@somerset.gov.uk

Horsfall, Alvin (LD - Frome East)
ajhorsfall@somerset.gov.uk

Hunt, James (CON - Upper Tone)
jahunt@somerset.gov.uk

Huxtable, David (CON - King Alfred)
djhuxtable@somerset.gov.uk

Le Hardy, Christopher (CON - South Petherton & Islemoor)
clehardy@somerset.gov.uk

Lewis, Michael (CON - Castle Cary)
mblewis@somerset.gov.uk

Lock, Jane (LD - Yeovil West)
jlock@somerset.gov.uk

Lock, Tony (LD - Yeovil East)
tlock@somerset.gov.uk

Loveridge, David (LAB - Bridgwater North & Central)
dloveridge@somerset.gov.uk

Napper, Terry (CON - Glastonbury & Street)
twenapper@somerset.gov.uk

Nicholson, Frances (CON - Dulverton & Exmoor)
fmnicholson@somerset.gov.uk

Noel, Graham (CON - Mendip West)
gnoel@somerset.gov.uk

Oliver, Linda (CON - Frome North)
loliver@somerset.gov.uk

Parham, John (CON - Shepton Mallet)
jparham@somerset.gov.uk

Pearson, Nigel (UKIP - Chard North)
ncpearson@somerset.gov.uk

Prior-Sankey, Hazel (LD - Taunton South)
hrprior-sankey@somerset.gov.uk

Redman, Leigh (LAB - Bridgwater South)
lredman@somerset.gov.uk

Rigby, Mike (IND - Lydeard)
msrigby@somerset.gov.uk

Ruddle, Dean (CON - Somerton)
ddruddle@somerset.gov.uk

Shortland, Jill (LD - Chard South)
jcshortland@somerset.gov.uk

Siggs, Harvey (CON - Mendip North West)
hsiggs@somerset.gov.uk

Tanswell, Derek (UKIP - Frome West)
dfetanswell@somerset.gov.uk

Venner, Terry (UKIP - Minehead)
tvenner@somerset.gov.uk

Vijeh, Linda (CON - Ilminster)
lpvijeh@somerset.gov.uk

Wallace, William (CON - Blackmoor Vale)
wwallace@somerset.gov.uk

Wedderkopp, Danny (LD - Rowbarton & Staplegrove)
dwedderkopp@somerset.gov.uk

Wedderkopp, Alan (LD - Comeytrowe & Trull)
awedderkopp@somerset.gov.uk

Woodman, John (CON - Highbridge & Burnham South)
jwoodman@somerset.gov.uk

Woollcombe-Adams, Nigel (CON - Mendip South)
nwoollcombeadams@somerset.gov.uk

Yeomans, Derek (CON - Curry Rivel & Langport)
dnyeomans@somerset.gov.uk

POLITICAL COMPOSITION
CON: 31, LD: 14, UKIP: 4, IND: 3, LAB: 3

COMMITTEE CHAIRS

Audit: Mrs Dawn Hill

Children & Families: Mr Leigh Redman

Health & Wellbeing: Miss Ann Bown

South Ayrshire   S

South Ayrshire Council, County Buildings, Wellington Square, Ayr KA7 1DR

☎ 0300 123 0900 ▤ 01292 612143 ▢ www.south-ayrshire.gov.uk

FACTS AND FIGURES
Parliamentary Constituencies: Ayr, Carrick and Cumnock, Ayrshire Central
EU Constituencies: Scotland
Election Frequency: Elections are of whole council

PRINCIPAL OFFICERS

Chief Executive: Mrs Eileen Howat, Chief Executive, County Buildings, Wellington Square, Ayr KA7 1DR ☎ 01292 612612
⌁ eileen.howat@south-ayrshire.gov.uk

Senior Management: Ms Valerie Andrews, Executive Director - Resources, Governance & Organisation, County Buildings, Wellington Square, Ayr KA7 1DR ☎ 01292 612466
⌁ valerie.andrews@south-ayrshire.gov.uk

Senior Management: Mrs Lesley Bloomer, Executive Director - Economy, Neighbourhood & Environment, County Buildings, Wellington Square, Ayr KA7 1DR ☎ 01290 612185
⌁ lesley.bloomer@south-ayrshire.gov.uk

Senior Management: Mr Tim Eltringham, Director - Health & Social Care, County Buildings, Wellington Square, Ayr KA7 1DR
☎ 01292 612419 ⌁ tim.eltringham@south-ayrshire.gov.uk

Senior Management: Mr Douglas Hutchinson, Director - Educational Services, County Buildings, Wellington Square, Ayr KA7 1DR ☎ 01292 621134 ⌁ douglas.hutchinson@south-ayrshire.gov.uk

Architect, Building / Property Services: Mr Donald Gillies, Head of Property & Risk, County Buildings, Wellington Square, Ayr KA7 1DR ☎ 01292 612777 ◌ donald.gillies@south-ayrshire.gov.uk

Best Value: Mr Mark Baker, Head of Policy & Performance, County Buildings, Wellington Square, Ayr KA7 1DR ☎ 01292 612354 ◌ mark.baker@south-ayrshire.gov.uk

Building Control: Mr Mike Newall, Head of Neighbourhood Services, County Buildings, Wellington Square, Ayr KA7 1DR ☎ 01292 616231 ◌ mike.newall@south-ayrshire.gov.uk

Catering Services: Ms Jennifer Rodden, Facilities Manager, County Buildings, Wellington Square, Ayr KA7 1DR ☎ 01292 616045 ◌ jennifer.rodden@south-ayrshire.gov.uk

Children / Youth Services: Ms Paula Godfrey, Head of Children's Healthcare & Criminal Justice, County Buildings, Wellington Square, Ayr KA7 1DR ☎ 01292 642244 ◌ paula.godfrey@south-ayrshire.gov.uk

PR / Communications: Mr Mark Baker, Head of Policy & Performance, County Buildings, Wellington Square, Ayr KA7 1DR ☎ 01292 612354 ◌ mark.baker@south-ayrshire.gov.uk

Community Planning: Ms Claire Monaghan, Head of Communities, County Buildings, Wellington Square, Ayr KA7 1DR ☎ 01292 612757 ◌ claire.monaghan@south-ayrshire.gov.uk

Community Safety: Ms Linda Warwick, Community Safety Co-ordinator, County Buildings, Wellington Square, Ayr KA7 1DR ☎ 01292 559403 ◌ linda.warwick@south-ayrshire.gov.uk

Computer Management: Mr Tim Baulk, Head of Finance & IT, County Buildings, Wellington Square, Ayr KA7 1DR ☎ 01292 612620 ◌ tim.baulk@south-ayrshire.gov.uk

Consumer Protection and Trading Standards: Mr Mike Newall, Head of Neighbourhood Services, County Buildings, Wellington Square, Ayr KA7 1DR ☎ 01292 616231 ◌ mike.newall@south-ayrshire.gov.uk

Contracts: Mr Donald Gillies, Head of Property & Risk, County Buildings, Wellington Square, Ayr KA7 1DR ☎ 01292 612777 ◌ donald.gillies@south-ayrshire.gov.uk

Customer Service: Ms Kate O'Hagan, Head of Employee & Customer Services, County Buildings, Wellington Square, Ayr KA7 1DR ☎ 01292 612696 ◌ kate.ohagan@south-ayrshire.gov.uk

Economic Development: Mr Jim Johnstone, Enterprise Manager, Burns House, Burns Statue Square, Ayr KA7 1UT ☎ 01292 616347 ◌ jim.johnstone@south-ayrshire.gov.uk

Education: Mr Douglas Hutchinson, Director - Educational Services, County Buildings, Wellington Square, Ayr KA7 1DR ☎ 01292 621134 ◌ douglas.hutchinson@south-ayrshire.gov.uk

E-Government: Mrs Eileen Howat, Chief Executive, County Buildings, Wellington Square, Ayr KA7 1DR ☎ 01292 612612 ◌ eileen.howat@south-ayrshire.gov.uk

Electoral Registration: Ms Helen McPhee, Assessor & Electoral Registration Officer, County Buildings, Wellington Square, Ayr KA7 1DR ☎ 01292 612540 ◌ helen.mcphee@south-ayrshire.gov.uk

Emergency Planning: Mrs Jane McGeorge, Civil Contingencies Manager, Prestwick Airport, Building 372 Alpha Freight Area, Robertson Road, Prestwick KA9 2PL ☎ 01292 692180 ◌ jane.mcgeorge@south-ayrshire.gov.uk

Environmental / Technical Services: Mrs Lesley Bloomer, Executive Director - Economy, Neighbourhood & Environment, County Buildings, Wellington Square, Ayr KA7 1DR ☎ 01290 612185 ◌ lesley.bloomer@south-ayrshire.gov.uk

Environmental Health: Mr David Thomson, Trading Standards & Environmental Health Manager, River Terrace, Ayr KA8 0BJ ☎ 01292 616055 ◌ david.thomson@south-ayrshire.gov.uk

Estates, Property & Valuation: Mr Donald Gillies, Head of Property & Risk, County Buildings, Wellington Square, Ayr KA7 1DR ☎ 01292 612777 ◌ donald.gillies@south-ayrshire.gov.uk

European Liaison: Ms Claire Monaghan, Head of Communities, County Buildings, Wellington Square, Ayr KA7 1DR ☎ 01292 612757 ◌ claire.monaghan@south-ayrshire.gov.uk

Events Manager: Mr Jim Johnstone, Enterprise Manager, Burns House, Burns Statue Square, Ayr KA7 1UT ☎ 01292 616347 ◌ jim.johnstone@south-ayrshire.gov.uk

Facilities: Ms Jennifer Rodden, Facilities Manager, County Buildings, Wellington Square, Ayr KA7 1DR ☎ 01292 616045 ◌ jennifer.rodden@south-ayrshire.gov.uk

Finance: Mr Tim Baulk, Head of Finance & IT, County Buildings, Wellington Square, Ayr KA7 1DR ☎ 01292 612620 ◌ tim.baulk@south-ayrshire.gov.uk

Fleet Management: Mr Mike Newall, Head of Neighbourhood Services, Burns House, Burns Statue Square, Ayr KA7 1UT ☎ 01292 616231 ◌ mike.newall@south-ayrshire.gov.uk

Grounds Maintenance: Mr Kenny Dalrymple, Neighbourhood Services Manager, Burns House, Burns Statue Square, Ayr KA7 1UT ☎ 01292 612041 ◌ kenny.dalrymple@south-ayrshire.gov.uk

Health and Safety: Ms Kate O'Hagan, Head of Employee & Customer Services, County Buildings, Wellington Square, Ayr KA7 1DR ☎ 01292 612696 ◌ kate.ohagan@south-ayrshire.gov.uk

Highways: Mr Stewart Turner, Head of Roads, The Johnnie Walker Bond, 15 Strand Street, Kilmarnock KA1 1HU ☎ 01563 503164 ◌ stewart.turner@south-ayrshire.gov.uk

Housing: Mr David Burns, Head of Housing & Facilities, County Buildings, Wellington Square, Ayr KA7 1DR ☎ 01292 613079 ◌ david.burns@south-ayrshire.gov.uk

Housing Maintenance: Mr David Burns, Head of Housing & Facilities, County Buildings, Wellington Square, Ayr KA7 1DR ☎ 01292 613079 ◌ david.burns@south-ayrshire.gov.uk

SOUTH AYRSHIRE

Local Area Agreement: Ms Claire Monaghan, Head of Communities, County Buildings, Wellington Square, Ayr KA7 1DR
☎ 01292 612757 ⏚ claire.monaghan@south-ayrshire.gov.uk

Legal: Mr Ralf Riddiough, Head of Legal & Democratic Services, County Buildings, Wellington Square, Ayr KA7 1DR ☎ 01292 612245 ⏚ ralf.riddiough@south-ayrshire.gov.uk

Leisure and Cultural Services: Mrs Jill Cronin, Head of Development & Leisure, County Buildings, Wellington Square, Ayr KA7 1DR ☎ 01292 612473 ⏚ jill.cronin@south-ayrshire.gov.uk

Licensing: Mr Ralf Riddiough, Head of Legal & Democratic Services, County Buildings, Wellington Square, Ayr KA7 1DR
☎ 01292 612245 ⏚ ralf.riddiough@south-ayrshire.gov.uk

Lifelong Learning: Mr Douglas Hutchinson, Director - Educational Services, County Buildings, Wellington Square, Ayr KA7 1DR
☎ 01292 621134 ⏚ douglas.hutchinson@south-ayrshire.gov.uk

Lottery Funding, Charity and Voluntary: Ms Claire Monaghan, Head of Communities, County Buildings, Wellington Square, Ayr KA7 1DR ☎ 01292 612757 ⏚ claire.monaghan@south-ayrshire.gov.uk

Member Services: Mr Ralf Riddiough, Head of Legal & Democratic Services, County Buildings, Wellington Square, Ayr KA7 1DR ☎ 01292 612245 ⏚ ralf.riddiough@south-ayrshire.gov.uk

Parking: Mr Stewart Turner, Head of Roads, The Johnnie Walker Bond, 15 Strand Street, Kilmarnock KA1 1HU ☎ 01563 503164 ⏚ stewart.turner@south-ayrshire.gov.uk

Partnerships: Ms Claire Monaghan, Head of Communities, County Buildings, Wellington Square, Ayr KA7 1DR ☎ 01292 612757 ⏚ claire.monaghan@south-ayrshire.gov.uk

Personnel / HR: Ms Kate O'Hagan, Head of Employee & Customer Services, County Buildings, Wellington Square, Ayr KA7 1DR ☎ 01292 612696 ⏚ kate.ohagan@south-ayrshire.gov.uk

Planning: Ms Christina Cox, Planning Manager, Burns House, Burns Statue Square, Ayr KA7 1UT ☎ 01292 616234 ⏚ christina.cox@south-ayrshire.gov.uk

Procurement: Mr Ralf Riddiough, Head of Legal & Democratic Services, County Buildings, Wellington Square, Ayr KA7 1DR ☎ 01292 612245 ⏚ ralf.riddiough@south-ayrshire.gov.uk

Public Libraries: Mrs Jill Cronin, Head of Development & Leisure, County Buildings, Wellington Square, Ayr KA7 1DR ☎ 01292 612473 ⏚ jill.cronin@south-ayrshire.gov.uk

Recycling & Waste Minimisation: Mr Kenny Dalrymple, Neighbourhood Services Manager, Burns House, Burns Statue Square, Ayr KA7 1UT ☎ 01292 612041 ⏚ kenny.dalrymple@south-ayrshire.gov.uk

Regeneration: Mrs Jill Cronin, Head of Development & Leisure, County Buildings, Wellington Square, Ayr KA7 1DR ☎ 01292 612473 ⏚ jill.cronin@south-ayrshire.gov.uk

Road Safety: Mr Stewart Turner, Head of Roads, The Johnnie Walker Bond, 15 Strand Street, Kilmarnock KA1 1HU
☎ 01563 503164 ⏚ stewart.turner@south-ayrshire.gov.uk

Social Services: Mr Tim Eltringham, Director - Health & Social Care, County Buildings, Wellington Square, Ayr KA7 1DR
☎ 01292 612419 ⏚ tim.eltringham@south-ayrshire.gov.uk

Social Services (Adult): Mr Kenny Leinster, Head of Community Health & Care Services, County Buildings, Wellington Square, Ayr KA7 1DR ☎ 01292 612735 ⏚ kenny.leinster@south-ayrshire.gov.uk

Social Services (Children): Ms Paula Godfrey, Head of Children's Healthcare & Criminal Justice, County Buildings, Wellington Square, Ayr KA7 1DR ☎ 01292 642244 ⏚ paula.godfrey@south-ayrshire.gov.uk

Staff Training: Ms Kate O'Hagan, Head of Employee & Customer Services, County Buildings, Wellington Square, Ayr KA7 1DR ☎ 01292 612696 ⏚ kate.ohagan@south-ayrshire.gov.uk

Sustainable Communities: Ms Claire Monaghan, Head of Communities, County Buildings, Wellington Square, Ayr KA7 1DR ☎ 01292 612757 ⏚ claire.monaghan@south-ayrshire.gov.uk

Sustainable Development: Mr Mike Newall, Head of Neighbourhood Services, Burns House, Burns Statue Square, Ayr KA7 1UT ☎ 01292 616231 ⏚ mike.newall@south-ayrshire.gov.uk

Tourism: Mr Jim Johnstone, Enterprise Manager, Burns House, Burns Statue Square, Ayr KA7 1UT ☎ 01292 616347 ⏚ jim.johnstone@south-ayrshire.gov.uk

Town Centre: Mr David Bell, Managing Director of Ayr Renaissance, County Buildings, Wellington Square, Ayr KA7 1DR ☎ 01292 612477 ⏚ david.bell@south-ayrshire.gov.uk

Transport: Mr Mike Newall, Head of Neighbourhood Services, Burns House, Burns Statue Square, Ayr KA7 1UT ☎ 01292 616231 ⏚ mike.newall@south-ayrshire.gov.uk

Waste Collection and Disposal: Mr Kenny Dalrymple, Neighbourhood Services Manager, Burns House, Burns Statue Square, Ayr KA7 1UT ☎ 01292 612041 ⏚ kenny.dalrymple@south-ayrshire.gov.uk

Waste Management: Mr Kenny Dalrymple, Neighbourhood Services Manager, Burns House, Burns Statue Square, Ayr KA7 1UT ☎ 01292 612041 ⏚ kenny.dalrymple@south-ayrshire.gov.uk

COUNCILLORS

Provost Moonie, Helen (LAB - Prestwick)
helen.moonie@south-ayrshire.gov.uk

Deputy Provost Kilpatrick, Mary (CON - Ayr East)
mary.kilpatrick@south-ayrshire.gov.uk

Leader of the Council: McIntosh, Bill (CON - Troon)
bill.mcintosh@south-ayrshire.gov.uk

Deputy Leader of the Council: McDowall, John (LAB - Girvan & South Carrick)
john.mcdowall@south-ayrshire.gov.uk

Allan, John (SNP - Kyle)
john.allan@south-ayrshire.gov.uk

Campbell, Douglas (SNP - Ayr North)
douglas.campbell@south-ayrshire.gov.uk

Campbell, Andy (LAB - Kyle)
andy.campbell@south-ayrshire.gov.uk

Cavana, Ian (LAB - Ayr North)
ian.cavana@south-ayrshire.gov.uk

Clark, Alec (IND - Girvan & South Carrick)
alec.clark@south-ayrshire.gov.uk

Cochrane, Ian (SNP - Prestwick)
ian.cochrane@south-ayrshire.gov.uk

Connolly, Brian (IND - Maybole, North Carrick & Coylton)
brian.connolly@south-ayrshire.gov.uk

Convery, Peter (CON - Troon)
peter.convery@south-ayrshire.gov.uk

Darwent, Kirsty (LAB - Ayr West)
kirsty.darwent@south-ayrshire.gov.uk

Davies, Hywel (IND - Kyle)
hywel.davies@south-ayrshire.gov.uk

Dorans, Allan (SNP - Ayr West)
allan.dorans@south-ayrshire.gov.uk

Douglas, Ian (SNP - Ayr East)
ian.douglas@south-ayrshire.gov.uk

Galbraith, Ann (CON - Maybole, North Carrick & Coylton)
ann.galbraith@south-ayrshire.gov.uk

Goldie, Sandra (LAB - Maybole, North Carrick & Coylton)
sandra.goldie@south-ayrshire.gov.uk

Grant, Bill (CON - Ayr West)
bill.grant@south-ayrshire.gov.uk

Grant, William (SNP - Maybole, North Carrick & Coylton)
william.grant@south-ayrshire.gov.uk

Hampton, John (CON - Ayr North)
john.hampton@south-ayrshire.gov.uk

Hunter, Hugh (CON - Prestwick)
hugh.hunter@south-ayrshire.gov.uk

McFarlane, Nan (SNP - Troon)
nan.mcfarlane@south-ayrshire.gov.uk

McGinley, Brian (LAB - Ayr East)
brian.mcginley@south-ayrshire.gov.uk

Miller, Rita (LAB - Ayr North)
rita.miller@south-ayrshire.gov.uk

Oattes, Alec (SNP - Girvan & South Carrick)
alec.oattes@south-ayrshire.gov.uk

Reid, Robin (CON - Ayr West)
robin.reid@south-ayrshire.gov.uk

Saxton, Phil (LAB - Troon)
philip.saxton@south-ayrshire.gov.uk

Toner, Margaret (CON - Prestwick)
margaret.toner@south-ayrshire.gov.uk

POLITICAL COMPOSITION
CON: 9, LAB: 9, SNP: 8, IND: 3

South Bucks   D

South Bucks District Council, Council Offices, Capswood, Oxford Road, Denham UB9 4LH
☎ 01895 837200 🖷 01895 837277 🖰 sbdc@southbucks.gov.uk
🖳 www.southbucks.gov.uk

FACTS AND FIGURES
Parliamentary Constituencies: Beaconsfield
EU Constituencies: South East
Election Frequency: Elections are of whole council

PRINCIPAL OFFICERS

Chief Executive: Mr Bob Smith, Acting Chief Executive, Council Offices, Capswood, Oxford Road, Denham UB9 4LH
☎ 01494 732178 🖰 bsmith@chiltern.gov.uk

Senior Management: Mr Jim Burness, Director - Resources, Council Offices, Capswood, Oxford Road, Denham UB9 4LH
☎ 01494 732095 🖰 jburness@chiltern.gov.uk

Senior Management: Ms Anita Cacchioli, Interim Director - Services, Council Offices, Capswood, Oxford Road, Denham UB9 4LH ☎ 01494 732235 🖰 acacchioli@chiltern.gov.uk

Architect, Building / Property Services: Ms Anita Cacchioli, Interim Director - Services, Council Offices, Capswood, Oxford Road, Denham UB9 4LH ☎ 01494 732235 🖰 acacchioli@chiltern.gov.uk

Building Control: Ms Anita Cacchioli, Interim Director - Services, Council Offices, Capswood, Oxford Road, Denham UB9 4LH
☎ 01494 732235 🖰 acacchioli@chiltern.gov.uk

Children / Youth Services: Mr Martin Holt, Head of Healthy Communities, Council Offices, King George V Road, Amersham HP6 5AW ☎ 01494 732055 🖰 mholt@chiltern.gov.uk

PR / Communications: Mrs Rachel Prance, Community & Partnerships Manager, Council Offices, King George V Road, Amersham HP6 5AW ☎ 01494 732903 🖰 rprance@chiltern.gov.uk

Community Safety: Mr Martin Holt, Head of Healthy Communities, Council Offices, King George V Road, Amersham HP6 5AW ☎ 01494 732055 🖰 mholt@chiltern.gov.uk

Computer Management: Mr Jim Burness, Director - Resources, Council Offices, Capswood, Oxford Road, Denham UB9 4LH
☎ 01494 732095 🖰 jburness@chiltern.gov.uk

Computer Management: Mrs Simonette Dixon, Head of Business Support, Council Offices, King George V Road, Amersham HP6 5AW ☎ 01494 732087 🖰 sdixon@chiltern.gov.uk

Contracts: Ms Anita Cacchioli, Interim Director - Services, Council Offices, Capswood, Oxford Road, Denham UB9 4LH
☎ 01494 732235 🖰 acacchioli@chiltern.gov.uk

Corporate Services: Mr Jim Burness, Director - Resources, Council Offices, Capswood, Oxford Road, Denham UB9 4LH
☎ 01494 732095 🖰 jburness@chiltern.gov.uk

SOUTH BUCKS

Customer Service: Mrs Nicola Ellis, Head of Customer Services, Council Offices, King George V Road, Amersham HP6 5AW
☎ 01494 732231 ⌨ nellis@chiltern.gov.uk

Economic Development: Ms Anita Cacchioli, Interim Director - Services, Council Offices, Capswood, Oxford Road, Denham UB9 4LH ☎ 01494 732235 ⌨ acacchioli@chiltern.gov.uk

Electoral Registration: Mrs Joanna Swift, Head of Legal & Democratic Services, Council Offices, Capswood, Oxford Road, Denham UB9 4LH ☎ 01895 837229; 01494 732761 ⌨ jswift@chiltern.gov.uk

Electoral Registration: Mrs Kulvinder Tumber, Democratic & Electoral Services Manager, Council Offices, Capswood, Oxford Road, Denham UB9 4LH ☎ 01895 837225 ⌨ kully.tumber@southbucks.gov.uk

Emergency Planning: Mr Ben Coakley, Environmental Health Manager, Council Offices, King George V Road, Amersham HP6 5AW ☎ 01494 732060 ⌨ ben.coakley@southbucks.gov.uk

Energy Management: Ms Anita Cacchioli, Interim Director - Services, Council Offices, Capswood, Oxford Road, Denham UB9 4LH ☎ 01494 732235 ⌨ acacchioli@chiltern.gov.uk

Environmental / Technical Services: Mr Peter Beckford, Head of Sustainable Development, Council Offices, Capswood, Oxford Road, Denham UB9 4LH ☎ 01895 837208; 01494 732036 ⌨ pbeckford@chiltern.gov.uk

Environmental / Technical Services: Mr Chris Marchant, Head of Environment, Council Offices, Capswood, Oxford Road, Denham UB9 4LH ☎ 01895 837360; 01494 732250 ⌨ cmarchant@chiltern.gov.uk

Environmental Health: Ms Anita Cacchioli, Interim Director - Services, Council Offices, Capswood, Oxford Road, Denham UB9 4LH ☎ 01494 732235 ⌨ acacchioli@chiltern.gov.uk

Environmental Health: Mr Martin Holt, Head of Healthy Communities, Council Offices, King George V Road, Amersham HP6 5AW ☎ 01494 732055 ⌨ mholt@chiltern.gov.uk

Estates, Property & Valuation: Ms Anita Cacchioli, Interim Director - Services, Council Offices, Capswood, Oxford Road, Denham UB9 4LH ☎ 01494 732235 ⌨ acacchioli@chiltern.gov.uk

Facilities: Mr Kevin Kelly, Facilities Manager, Council Offices, Capswood, Oxford Road, Denham UB9 4LH ☎ 01895 837000 ⌨ kevin.kelly@southbucks.gov.uk

Finance: Mr Jim Burness, Director - Resources, Council Offices, Capswood, Oxford Road, Denham UB9 4LH ☎ 01494 732095 ⌨ jburness@chiltern.gov.uk

Finance: Mr Rodney Fincham, Head of Finance, Council Offices, Capswood, Oxford Road, Denham UB9 4LH ☎ 01895 837268 ⌨ rodney.fincham@southbucks.gov.uk

Health and Safety: Ms Anita Cacchioli, Interim Director - Services, Council Offices, Capswood, Oxford Road, Denham UB9 4LH ☎ 01494 732235 ⌨ acacchioli@chiltern.gov.uk

Housing: Ms Anita Cacchioli, Interim Director - Services, Council Offices, Capswood, Oxford Road, Denham UB9 4LH ☎ 01494 732235 ⌨ acacchioli@chiltern.gov.uk

Legal: Mrs Joanna Swift, Head of Legal & Democratic Services, Council Offices, Capswood, Oxford Road, Denham UB9 4LH ☎ 01895 837229; 01494 732761 ⌨ jswift@chiltern.gov.uk

Leisure and Cultural Services: Mr Martin Holt, Head of Healthy Communities, Council Offices, King George V Road, Amersham HP6 5AW ☎ 01494 732055 ⌨ mholt@chiltern.gov.uk

Licensing: Ms Anita Cacchioli, Interim Director - Services, Council Offices, Capswood, Oxford Road, Denham UB9 4LH ☎ 01494 732235 ⌨ acacchioli@chiltern.gov.uk

Member Services: Mrs Kulvinder Tumber, Democratic & Electoral Services Manager, Council Offices, Capswood, Oxford Road, Denham UB9 4LH ☎ 01895 837225 ⌨ kully.tumber@southbucks.gov.uk

Parking: Mr Chris Marchant, Head of Environment, Council Offices, Capswood, Oxford Road, Denham UB9 4LH ☎ 01895 837360; 01494 732250 ⌨ cmarchant@chiltern.gov.uk

Partnerships: Mrs Rachel Prance, Community & Partnerships Manager, Council Offices, King George V Road, Amersham HP6 5AW ☎ 01494 732903 ⌨ rprance@chiltern.gov.uk

Personnel / HR: Ms Judy Benson, HR Manager, Council Offices, Capswood, Oxford Road, Denham UB9 4LH ☎ 01895 837334 ⌨ judy.benson@southbucks.gov.uk

Planning: Ms Anita Cacchioli, Interim Director - Services, Council Offices, Capswood, Oxford Road, Denham UB9 4LH ☎ 01494 732235 ⌨ acacchioli@chiltern.gov.uk

Procurement: Mr Rodney Fincham, Head of Finance, Council Offices, Capswood, Oxford Road, Denham UB9 4LH ☎ 01895 837268 ⌨ rodney.fincham@southbucks.gov.uk

Recycling & Waste Minimisation: Ms Anita Cacchioli, Interim Director - Services, Council Offices, Capswood, Oxford Road, Denham UB9 4LH ☎ 01494 732235 ⌨ acacchioli@chiltern.gov.uk

Regeneration: Mr Peter Beckford, Head of Sustainable Development, Council Offices, Capswood, Oxford Road, Denham UB9 4LH ☎ 01895 837208; 01494 732036 ⌨ pbeckford@chiltern.gov.uk

Sustainable Communities: Mr Martin Holt, Head of Healthy Communities, Council Offices, King George V Road, Amersham HP6 5AW ☎ 01494 732055 ⌨ mholt@chiltern.gov.uk

Sustainable Development: Ms Anita Cacchioli, Interim Director - Services, Council Offices, Capswood, Oxford Road, Denham UB9 4LH ☎ 01494 732235 ⌨ acacchioli@chiltern.gov.uk

Waste Collection and Disposal: Ms Anita Cacchioli, Interim Director - Services, Council Offices, Capswood, Oxford Road, Denham UB9 4LH ☎ 01494 732235 ✆ acacchioli@chiltern.gov.uk

Waste Management: Ms Anita Cacchioli, Interim Director - Services, Council Offices, Capswood, Oxford Road, Denham UB9 4LH ☎ 01494 732235 ✆ acacchioli@chiltern.gov.uk

COUNCILLORS

Chair: Smith, Duncan (CON - Gerrards Cross)
cllr.duncan.smith@southbucks.gov.uk

Leader of the Council: Bagge, Ralph (CON - Stoke Poges)
cllr.ralph.bagge@southbucks.gov.uk

Deputy Leader of the Council: Naylor, Nick (CON - Burnham Church & Beeches)
cllr.nick.naylor@southbucks.gov.uk

Anthony, David (CON - Farnham & Hedgerley)
cllr.david.anthony@southbucks.gov.uk

Bastiman, Philip (CON - Beaconsfield West)
cllr.philip.bastiman@southbucks.gov.uk

Bradford, Malcolm (CON - Wexham & Fulmer)
cllr.malcolm.bradford@southbucks.gov.uk

Chhokar, Santokh (CON - Gerrards Cross)
cllr.santokh.chhokar@southbucks.gov.uk

Dhillon, Dev (CON - Farnham & Hedgerley)
cllr.dev.dhillon@southbucks.gov.uk

Egleton, Trevor (CON - Stoke Poges)
cllr.trevor.egleton@southbucks.gov.uk

Gibbs, Barbara (CON - Gerrards Cross)
cllr.barbara.gibbs@southbucks.gov.uk

Griffin, Paul (IND - Iver Village & Richings Park)
cllr.paul.griffin@southbucks.gov.uk

Harding, Barry (CON - Denham)
cllr.barry.harding@southbucks.gov.uk

Hazell, Lin (CON - Burnham Church & Beeches)
cllr.lin.hazell@southbucks.gov.uk

Hogan, Patrick (CON - Beaconsfield West)
cllr.patrick.hogan@southbucks.gov.uk

Hollis, Guy (CON - Denham)
cllr.guy.hollis@southbucks.gov.uk

Jordan, Jilly (CON - Iver Village & Richings Park)
cllr.jilly.jordan@southbucks.gov.uk

Kelly, Paul (CON - Burnham Church & Beeches)
cllr.paul.kelly@southbucks.gov.uk

Lewis, Marlene (CON - Farnham & Hedgerley)
cllr.marlene.lewis@southbucks.gov.uk

Lowen-Cooper, Jacquetta (CON - Beaconsfield South)
cllr.jacquetta.lowen-cooper@southbucks.gov.uk

Matthews, Wendy (CON - Iver Village & Richings Park)
cllr.wendy.matthews@southbucks.gov.uk

Pepler, David (CON - Burnham Lent Rise & Taplow)
cllr.david.pepler@southbucks.gov.uk

Read, John (CON - Beaconsfield South)
cllr.john.read@southbucks.gov.uk

Reed, Roger (CON - Denham)
cllr.roger.reed@southbucks.gov.uk

Samson, Alan (CON - Burnham Lent Rise & Taplow)
cllr.alan.samson@southbucks.gov.uk

Sandy, George (CON - Burnham Lent Rise & Taplow)
cllr.george.sandy@southbucks.gov.uk

Sangster, Ray (CON - Iver Heath)
cllr.ray.sangster@southbucks.gov.uk

Sullivan, Luisa (CON - Iver Heath)
cllr.luisa.sullivan@southbucks.gov.uk

Walters, Alan (CON - Beaconsfield North)
cllr.alan.walters@southbucks.gov.uk

POLITICAL COMPOSITION
CON: 27, IND: 1

COMMITTEE CHAIRS

Audit: Mr Malcolm Bradford

Licensing: Mr Alan Walters

Planning: Mrs Jacquetta Lowen-Cooper

South Cambridgeshire   D

South Cambridgeshire District Council, South Cambridgeshire Hall, Cambourne Business Park, Cambourne, Cambridge CB23 6EA
☎ 03450 450500 ▤ 01954 713149 ✆ scdc@scambs.gov.uk
⌨ www.scambs.gov.uk

FACTS AND FIGURES
Parliamentary Constituencies: Cambridgeshire South, Cambridgeshire South East
EU Constituencies: Eastern
Election Frequency: Elections are by thirds

PRINCIPAL OFFICERS

Chief Executive: Mr Alex Colyer, Acting Chief Executive & Chief Finance Officer, South Cambridgeshire Hall, Cambourne Business Park, Cambourne, Cambridge CB23 6EA ☎ 01954 713023 ✆ alex.colyer@scambs.gov.uk

Senior Management: Ms Susan Gardner Craig, Human Resources Manager, South Cambridgeshire Hall, Cambourne Business Park, Cambourne, Cambridge CB3 6EA
☎ 03450 450 500 ✆ susan.gardnercraig@scambs.gov.uk

Senior Management: Mr Mike Hill, Director - Health & Environmental Services, South Cambridgeshire Hall, Cambourne Business Park, Cambourne, Cambridge CB23 6EA
☎ 03450 450500 ✆ mike.hill@scambs.gov.uk

Senior Management: Mr Stephen Hills, Director - Housing, South Cambridgeshire Hall, Cambourne Business Park, Cambourne, Cambridge CB23 6EA ☎ 03450 450500
✆ stephen.hills@scambs.gov.uk

Senior Management: Mr Stephen Kelly, Director - Planning & Economic Development, The Guildhall, Cambridge CB2 3QJ
☎ 01223 457103 ✆ stephen.kelly@cambridge.gov.uk

Best Value: Mr John Garnham, Head of Finance, Policy & Performance, South Cambridgeshire Hall, Cambourne Business Park, Cambourne, Cambridge CB23 6EA ☎ 03450 450500 ⌨ john.garnham@scambs.gov.uk

Best Value: Mr Sean Missin, Procurement Officer, South Cambridgeshire Hall, Cambourne Business Park, Cambourne, Cambridge CB3 6EA ☎ 01954 713378 ⌨ sean.missin@scambs.gov.uk

Building Control: Mr Andrew Dearlove, Interim Building Control Manager, South Cambridgeshire Hall, Cambourne Business Park, Cambourne, Cambridge CB23 6EA ☎ 03450 450450 ⌨ andrew.dearlove@scambs.gov.uk

Building Control: Mr John Thompson, Building Control Manager, The Guildhall, Cambridge CB2 3QJ ☎ 01223 457111 ⌨ john.thompson@3csharedservices.org

Catering Services: Mrs Eileen Simmons, Catering Manager, South Cambridgeshire Hall, Cambourne Business Park, Cambourne, Cambridge CB23 6EA ☎ 03450 450 500 ⌨ eileen.simmons@scambs.gov.uk

PR / Communications: Mr Gareth Bell, Communications Manager, South Cambridgeshire Hall, Cambourne Business Park, Cambourne, Cambridge CB23 6EA ☎ 03450 450500 ⌨ gareth.bell@scambs.gov.uk

Community Safety: Mr Phil Aldis, Community Safety Officer, South Cambridgeshire District Council, South Cambridgeshire Hall, Cambourne, Cambridge CB23 6EA ☎ 03450 450 500 ⌨ phil.aldis@scambs.gov.uk

Computer Management: Mr Stephen Rayment, Head of ICT, South Cambridgeshire Hall, Cambourne Business Park, Cambourne, Cambridge CB23 6EA ☎ 03450 450 500 ⌨ steve.rayment@scambs.gov.uk

Contracts: Mr Paul Quigley, Environment Services Manager, South Cambridgeshire Hall, Cambourne Business Park, Cambourne, Cambridge CB23 6EA ☎ 03450 450 500 ⌨ paul.quigley@scambs.gov.uk

Corporate Services: Mr Steve Crabtree, Head of Internal Audit, The Guildhall, Cambridge CB2 3QJ ☎ 01223 458181 ⌨ steve.crabtree@cambridge.gov.uk

Customer Service: Miss Rachael Fox-Jackson, Customer Contact Manager, South Cambridgeshire Hall, Cambourne Business Park, Cambourne, Cambridge CB23 6EA ☎ 03450 450500 ⌨ rachael.fox-jackson@scambs.gov.uk

Economic Development: Mrs Caroline Hunt, Planning Policy Manager, South Cambridgeshire Hall, Cambourne Business Park, Cambourne, Cambridge CB23 6EA ☎ 03450 450 500 ⌨ caroline.hunt@scambs.gov.uk

E-Government: Mr Stephen Rayment, Head of ICT, South Cambridgeshire Hall, Cambourne Business Park, Cambourne, Cambridge CB23 6EA ☎ 03450 450 500 ⌨ steve.rayment@scambs.gov.uk

Electoral Registration: Mr Andrew Francis, Electoral & Support Services Manager, South Cambridgeshire Hall, Cambourne Business Park, Cambourne, Cambridge CB23 6EA ☎ 03450 450 500 ⌨ andrew.francis@scambs.gov.uk

Emergency Planning: Mr Mike Hill, Director - Health & Environmental Services, South Cambridgeshire Hall, Cambourne Business Park, Cambourne, Cambridge CB23 6EA ☎ 03450 450500 ⌨ mike.hill@scambs.gov.uk

Emergency Planning: Mr Paul Parry, Corporate H&S and Emergency Planning Manager, The Guildhall, Cambridge CB2 3QJ ☎ 01223 458033 ⌨ paul.parry@cambridge.gov.uk

Energy Management: Ms Siobhan Mellon, Partnerships Officer, South Cambridgeshire Hall, Cambourne Business Park, Cambourne, Cambridge CB23 6EA ☎ 03450 450500 ⌨ siobhan.mellon@scambs.gov.uk

Environmental / Technical Services: Mr Paul Quigley, Environment Services Manager, South Cambridgeshire Hall, Cambourne Business Park, Cambourne, Cambridge CB23 6EA ☎ 03450 450 500 ⌨ paul.quigley@scambs.gov.uk

Environmental Health: Mr Paul Quigley, Environment Services Manager, South Cambridgeshire Hall, Cambourne Business Park, Cambourne, Cambridge CB23 6EA ☎ 03450 450 500 ⌨ paul.quigley@scambs.gov.uk

Facilities: Mr Michael Turner, Facilities Manager, South Cambridgeshire Hall, Cambourne Business Park, Cambourne, Cambridge CB23 6EA ☎ 03450 450500 ⌨ michael.turner@scambs.gov.uk

Finance: Mr Alex Colyer, Acting Chief Executive & Chief Finance Officer, South Cambridgeshire Hall, Cambourne Business Park, Cambourne, Cambridge CB23 6EA ☎ 01954 713023 ⌨ alex.colyer@scambs.gov.uk

Finance: Ms Caroline Ryba, Head of Finance, The Guildhall, Cambridge CB2 3QJ ☎ 01223 458134 ⌨ caroline.ryba@cambridge.gov.uk

Home Energy Conservation: Mr Paul Quigley, Environment Services Manager, South Cambridgeshire Hall, Cambourne Business Park, Cambourne, Cambridge CB23 6EA ☎ 03450 450 500 ⌨ paul.quigley@scambs.gov.uk

Housing: Ms Anita Goddard, Housing Services Manager, South Cambridgeshire Hall, Cambourne Business Park, Cambourne, Cambridge CB23 6EA ☎ 03450 450 500 ⌨ anita.goddard@scambs.gov.uk

Housing: Mr Stephen Hills, Director - Housing, South Cambridgeshire Hall, Cambourne Business Park, Cambourne, Cambridge CB23 6EA ☎ 03450 450500 ⌨ stephen.hills@scambs.gov.uk

Housing Maintenance: Ms Anita Goddard, Housing Services Manager, South Cambridgeshire Hall, Cambourne Business Park, Cambourne, Cambridge CB23 6EA ☎ 03450 450 500 ⌨ anita.goddard@scambs.gov.uk

Housing Maintenance: Mr Stephen Hills, Director - Housing, South Cambridgeshire Hall, Cambourne Business Park, Cambourne, Cambridge CB23 6EA ☎ 03450 450500
🖰 stephen.hills@scambs.gov.uk

Legal: Mr Tom Lewis, Head of Legal Practice, The Guildhall, Cambridge CB2 3QJ ☎ 01223 457401
🖰 tom.lewis@cambridge.gov.uk

Legal: Mrs Fiona McMillan, Head of Legal & Democratic Services, South Cambridgeshire District Council, South Cambridgeshire Hall, Cambourne, Cambridge CB23 6EA ☎ 03450 450500
🖰 fiona.mcmillan@scambs.gov.uk

Licensing: Mr Myles Bebbington, Licensing Officer, South Cambridgeshire Hall, Cambourne Business Park, Cambourne, Cambridge CB23 6EA ☎ 03450 450 500
🖰 myles.bebbington@scambs.gov.uk

Lighting: Mr Paul Quigley, Environment Services Manager, South Cambridgeshire Hall, Cambourne Business Park, Cambourne, Cambridge CB23 6EA ☎ 03450 450 500
🖰 paul.quigley@scambs.gov.uk

Member Services: Mr Graham Watts, Democratic Services Manager, South Cambridgeshire Hall, Cambourne Business Park, Cambourne, Cambridge CB23 6EA ☎ 03450 450450
🖰 graham.watts@scambs.gov.uk

Partnerships: Ms Gemma Barron, Partnerships Manager, South Cambridgeshire Hall, Cambourne Business Park, Cambourne, Cambridge CB23 6EA ☎ 03450 450500
🖰 gemma.barron@scambs.gov.uk

Personnel / HR: Ms Susan Gardner Craig, Human Resources Manager, South Cambridgeshire Hall, Cambourne Business Park, Cambourne, Cambridge CB3 6EA ☎ 03450 450 500
🖰 susan.gardnercraig@scambs.gov.uk

Planning: Mrs Caroline Hunt, Planning Policy Manager, South Cambridgeshire Hall, Cambourne Business Park, Cambourne, Cambridge CB23 6EA ☎ 03450 450 500
🖰 caroline.hunt@scambs.gov.uk

Planning: Mr Stephen Kelly, Director - Planning & Economic Development, The Guildhall, Cambridge CB2 3QJ ☎ 01223 457103
🖰 stephen.kelly@cambridge.gov.uk

Procurement: Mr Sean Missin, Procurement Officer, South Cambridgeshire Hall, Cambourne Business Park, Cambourne, Cambridge CB23 6EA ☎ 01954 713378
🖰 sean.missin@scambs.gov.uk

Recycling & Waste Minimisation: Ms Kylie Laws, Waste Policy, Change & Innovations Manager, Dickerson Industrial Estate, Ely Road, Waterbeach, Cambridge CB25 9PG ☎ 01954 713192
🖰 kylie.laws@scambs.gov.uk

Recycling & Waste Minimisation: Mr Paul Quigley, Environment Services Manager, South Cambridgeshire Hall, Cambourne Business Park, Cambourne, Cambridge CB23 6EA
☎ 03450 450 500 🖰 paul.quigley@scambs.gov.uk

Staff Training: Ms Susan Gardner Craig, Human Resources Manager, South Cambridgeshire Hall, Cambourne Business Park, Cambourne, Cambridge CB3 6EA ☎ 03450 450 500
🖰 susan.gardnercraig@scambs.gov.uk

Sustainable Communities: Mr Richard Hales, Strategic Sustainability Officer, South Cambridgeshire District Council, South Cambridgeshire Hall, Cambourne, Cambridge CB23 6EA
☎ 03450 450500 🖰 richard.hales@scambs.gov.uk

Transport Planner: Mr Jonathan Dixon, Principal Planning Policy Officer of Transport, South Cambridgeshire Hall, Cambourne Business Park, Cambourne, Cambridge CB3 6EA
☎ 03450 450 500 🖰 jonathan.dixon@scambs.gov.uk

Waste Collection and Disposal: Mr Paul Vanston, Head of Waste Resources, Dickerson Industrial Estate, Ely Road, Waterbeach, Cambridge CB25 9PG ☎ 01954 713154
🖰 paul.vanston@cambridge.gov.uk

Waste Management: Mr Paul Vanston, Head of Waste Resources, Dickerson Industrial Estate, Ely Road, Waterbeach, Cambridge CB25 9PG ☎ 01954 713154
🖰 paul.vanston@cambridge.gov.uk

COUNCILLORS

Chair: Ellington, Sue (CON - Swavesey)
cllr.ellington@scambs.gov.uk

Vice-Chair: McCraith, David (CON - Bassingbourn)
cllr.mccraith@scambs.gov.uk

Leader of the Council: Topping, Peter (CON - Whittlesford)
cllr.topping@scambs.gov.uk

Group Leader: De Lacey, Douglas (IND - Girton)
cllr.delacey@scambs.gov.uk

Group Leader: Smith, Bridget (LD - Gamlingay)
cllr.smithbz@scambs.gov.uk

Bard, David (CON - Sawston)
cllr.bard@scambs.gov.uk

Barrett, Val (CON - Melbourn)
cllr.barrettvm@scambs.gov.uk

Batchelor, Henry (LD - Linton)
cllr.batchelor@scambs.gov.uk

Batchelor, John (LD - Linton)
cllr.batchelorj@scambs.gov.uk

Bradnam, Anna (LD - Milton)
cllr.bradnam@scambs.gov.uk

Burkitt, Francis (CON - Barton)
cllr.burkitt@scambs.gov.uk

Burling, Brian (CON - Willingham & Over)
cllr.burling@scambs.gov.uk

Bygott, Thomas (CON - Girton)
cllr.bygott@scambs.gov.uk

Cathcart, Nigel (LAB - Bassingbourn)
cllr.cathcart@scambs.gov.uk

Cattermole, Doug (LD - Haslingfield & the Eversdens)
cllr.cattermole@scambs.gov.uk

Chamberlain, Grenville (CON - Hardwick)
cllr.chamberlain@scambs.gov.uk

SOUTH CAMBRIDGESHIRE

Chuffley, Kevin (CON - Sawston)
cllr.chuffley@scambs.gov.uk

Cone, Graham (CON - Fulbourn)
cllr.cone@scambs.gov.uk

Corney, Pippa (CON - Willingham & Over)
cllr.corney@scambs.gov.uk

Crocker, Simon (CON - Bourn)
cllr.crocker@scambs.gov.uk

Cross, Christopher (CON - Histon & Impington)
cllr.cross@scambs.gov.uk

Davies, Neil (IND - Histon & Impington)
cllr.davies@scambs.gov.uk

Edwards, Simon (CON - Cottenham)
cllr.edwards@scambs.gov.uk

Fraser, Andrew (CON - Balsham)
cllr.fraser@scambs.gov.uk

Hales, Jose (LD - Melbourn)
cllr.hales@scambs.gov.uk

Hall, Roger (CON - Bar Hill)
cllr.hall@scambs.gov.uk

Harford, Lynda (CON - Cottenham)
cllr.harford@scambs.gov.uk

Hart, Philippa (LD - Meldreth)
cllr.hart@scambs.gov.uk

Hawkins, Tumi (LD - Caldecote)
cllr.hawkins@scambs.gov.uk

Howell, Mark (CON - Papworth & Elsworth)
cllr.howell@scambs.gov.uk

Hunt, Caroline (CON - Teversham)
cllr.hunt@scambs.gov.uk

Johnson, Peter (CON - Waterbeach)
cllr.johnson@scambs.gov.uk

Kindersley, Sebastian (LD - Gamlingay)
cllr.kindersley@scambs.gov.uk

Lockwood, Janet (LD - Harston & Hauxton)
cllr.lockwood@scambs.gov.uk

Loynes, Mervyn (CON - Bourn)
cllr.loynes@scambs.gov.uk

Manning, Ray (CON - Willingham & Over)
cllr.manning@scambs.gov.uk

Martin, Mick (CON - Duxford)
cllr.martin@scambs.gov.uk

Matthews, Raymond (CON - Sawston)
cllr.matthews@scambs.gov.uk

Murfitt, Cicely (IND - The Mordens)
cllr.murfitt@scambs.gov.uk

Nightingale, Charles (CON - The Shelfords & Stapleford)
cllr.nightingale@scambs.gov.uk

O'Brien, Des (CON - Bourn)
cllr.obrien@scambs.gov.uk

Orgee, Tony (CON - The Abingtons)
cllr.orgee@scambs.gov.uk

Riley, Alex (CON - Longstanton)
cllr.riley@scambs.gov.uk

Roberts, Deborah (IND - Fowlmere & Foxton)
cllr.roberts@scambs.gov.uk

Scott, Tim (CON - Comberton)
cllr.scott@scambs.gov.uk

Shelton, Ben (CON - The Shelfords & Stapleford)
cllr.shelton@scambs.gov.uk

Smith, Hazel (LD - Milton)
cllr.smithhm@scambs.gov.uk

Stonham, Edd (IND - Histon & Impington)
cllr.stonham@scambs.gov.uk

Tregoing, Ingrid (LD - Waterbeach)
cllr.tregoing@scambs.gov.uk

Turner, Robert (CON - The Wilbrahams)
cllr.turner@scambs.gov.uk

Turner, Richard (CON - Balsham)
cllr.turnerrm@scambs.gov.uk

Van de Weyer, Aidan (LD - Orwell & Barrington)
cllr.vandeweyer@scambs.gov.uk

Waters, Bunty (CON - Bar Hill)
cllr.waters@scambs.gov.uk

Whiteman-Downes, David (CON - The Shelfords & Stapleford)
cllr.whiteman-downes@scambs.gov.uk

Williams, John G (LD - Fulbourn)
cllr.williamsjg@scambs.gov.uk

Wotherspoon, Tim (CON - Cottenham)
cllr.wotherspoon@scambs.gov.uk

Wright, Nick (CON - Papworth & Elsworth)
cllr.wright@scambs.gov.uk

POLITICAL COMPOSITION
CON: 37, LD: 14, IND: 5, LAB: 1

COMMITTEE CHAIRS

Audit: Mr Andrew Fraser

Licensing: Mr Alex Riley

Planning: Dr David Bard

South Derbyshire   D

South Derbyshire District Council, Civic Offices, Civic Way, Swadlincote DE11 0AH
☎ 01283 595795 ⏚ customer.services@south-derbys.gov.uk
⌨ www.south-derbys.gov.uk

FACTS AND FIGURES
Parliamentary Constituencies: Derbyshire South
EU Constituencies: East Midlands
Election Frequency: Elections are of whole council

PRINCIPAL OFFICERS

Chief Executive: Mr Frank McArdle, Chief Executive, Civic Offices, Civic Way, Swadlincote DE11 0AH ☎ 01283 595702 ⏚ frank.mcardle@south-derbys.gov.uk

Senior Management: Mr Stuart Batchelor, Director - Community & Planning Services, Civic Offices, Civic Way, Swadlincote DE11 0AH ☎ 01283 595820 ⏚ stuart.batchelor@south-derbys.gov.uk

Senior Management: Mr Mike Haynes, Director - Housing & Environmental Services, Civic Offices, Civic Way, Swadlincote DE11 0AH ☎ 01283 595775 ⏏ mike.haynes@south-derbys.gov.uk

Senior Management: Mrs Ardip Kaur, Monitoring Officer & Council Solicitor, Civic Offices, Civic Way, Swadlincote DE11 0AH ☎ 01283 595715 ⏏ ardip.kaur@south-derbys.gov.uk

Senior Management: Mr Kevin Stackhouse, Director - Finance & Corporate Services, Civic Offices, Civic Way, Swadlincote DE11 0AH ☎ 01283 595811 ⏏ kevin.stackhouse@south-derbys.gov.uk

Building Control: Mr Stuart Batchelor, Director - Community & Planning Services, Civic Offices, Civic Way, Swadlincote DE11 0AH ☎ 01283 595820 ⏏ stuart.batchelor@south-derbys.gov.uk

PR / Communications: Mr Keith Bull, Head of Communications, Civic Offices, Civic Way, Swadlincote DE11 0AH ☎ 01283 818705 ⏏ keith.bull@northgate-is.com

Community Safety: Mr Stuart Batchelor, Director - Community & Planning Services, Civic Offices, Civic Way, Swadlincote DE11 0AH ☎ 01283 595820 ⏏ stuart.batchelor@south-derbys.gov.uk

Computer Management: Mr Mark Sabin, ICT Service Delivery Manager, Civic Offices, Civic Way, Swadlincote DE11 0AH ☎ 01283 595703 ⏏ mark.sabin@northgate-is.com

Corporate Services: Mr Kevin Stackhouse, Director - Finance & Corporate Services, Civic Offices, Civic Way, Swadlincote DE11 0AH ☎ 01283 595811 ⏏ kevin.stackhouse@south-derbys.gov.uk

Customer Service: Mrs Angela Leese, Customer Contact Manager, Civic Offices, Civic Way, Swadlincote DE11 0AH ☎ 01283 595989 ⏏ angela.leese@northgate-is.com

Direct Labour: Mr Mike Haynes, Director - Housing & Environmental Services, Civic Offices, Civic Way, Swadlincote DE11 0AH ☎ 01283 595775 ⏏ mike.haynes@south-derbys.gov.uk

Economic Development: Mr Mike Roylance, Economic Development Manager, Civic Offices, Civic Way, Swadlincote DE11 0AH ☎ 01283 595725 ⏏ mike.roylance@south-derbys.gov.uk

E-Government: Mr Mark Sabin, ICT Service Delivery Manager, Civic Offices, Civic Way, Swadlincote DE11 0AH ☎ 01283 595703 ⏏ mark.sabin@northgate-is.com

Electoral Registration: Mr Frank McArdle, Chief Executive, Civic Offices, Civic Way, Swadlincote DE11 0AH ☎ 01283 595702 ⏏ frank.mcardle@south-derbys.gov.uk

Emergency Planning: Mr Frank McArdle, Chief Executive, Civic Offices, Civic Way, Swadlincote DE11 0AH ☎ 01283 595702 ⏏ frank.mcardle@south-derbys.gov.uk

Environmental / Technical Services: Mr Mike Haynes, Director - Housing & Environmental Services, Civic Offices, Civic Way, Swadlincote DE11 0AH ☎ 01283 595775 ⏏ mike.haynes@south-derbys.gov.uk

Environmental Health: Mr Matthew Holford, Environmental Health Manager, Civic Offices, Civic Way, Swadlincote DE11 0AH ☎ 01283 595856 ⏏ matthew.holford@south-derbys.gov.uk

Estates, Property & Valuation: Mr Steve Baker, Corporate Asset Manager, Civic Offices, Civic Way, Swadlincote DE11 0AH ☎ 01283 595965 ⏏ steve.baker@south-derbys.gov.uk

European Liaison: Mr Frank McArdle, Chief Executive, Civic Offices, Civic Way, Swadlincote DE11 0AH ☎ 01283 595702 ⏏ frank.mcardle@south-derbys.gov.uk

Finance: Mr Kevin Stackhouse, Director - Finance & Corporate Services, Civic Offices, Civic Way, Swadlincote DE11 0AH ☎ 01283 595811 ⏏ kevin.stackhouse@south-derbys.gov.uk

Treasury: Mr Kevin Stackhouse, Director - Finance & Corporate Services, Civic Offices, Civic Way, Swadlincote DE11 0AH ☎ 01283 595811 ⏏ kevin.stackhouse@south-derbys.gov.uk

Grounds Maintenance: Mr Mike Haynes, Director - Housing & Environmental Services, Civic Offices, Civic Way, Swadlincote DE11 0AH ☎ 01283 595775 ⏏ mike.haynes@south-derbys.gov.uk

Health and Safety: Mr David Clamp, Head of Organisational Development, Civic Offices, Civic Way, Swadlincote DE11 0AH ☎ 01283 595729 ⏏ david.clamp@northgate-is.com

Home Energy Conservation: Mr Mike Haynes, Director - Housing & Environmental Services, Civic Offices, Civic Way, Swadlincote DE11 0AH ☎ 01283 595775 ⏏ mike.haynes@south-derbys.gov.uk

Housing: Mr Mike Haynes, Director - Housing & Environmental Services, Civic Offices, Civic Way, Swadlincote DE11 0AH ☎ 01283 595775 ⏏ mike.haynes@south-derbys.gov.uk

Housing Maintenance: Mr Mike Haynes, Director - Housing & Environmental Services, Civic Offices, Civic Way, Swadlincote DE11 0AH ☎ 01283 595775 ⏏ mike.haynes@south-derbys.gov.uk

Legal: Mrs Ardip Kaur, Monitoring Officer & Council Solicitor, Civic Offices, Civic Way, Swadlincote DE11 0AH ☎ 01283 595715 ⏏ ardip.kaur@south-derbys.gov.uk

Leisure and Cultural Services: Mr Stuart Batchelor, Director - Community & Planning Services, Civic Offices, Civic Way, Swadlincote DE11 0AH ☎ 01283 595820 ⏏ stuart.batchelor@south-derbys.gov.uk

Licensing: Mrs Ardip Kaur, Monitoring Officer & Council Solicitor, Civic Offices, Civic Way, Swadlincote DE11 0AH ☎ 01283 595715 ⏏ ardip.kaur@south-derbys.gov.uk

Lifelong Learning: Mrs Ardip Kaur, Monitoring Officer & Council Solicitor, Civic Offices, Civic Way, Swadlincote DE11 0AH ☎ 01283 595715 ⏏ ardip.kaur@south-derbys.gov.uk

Lottery Funding, Charity and Voluntary: Mr Stuart Batchelor, Director - Community & Planning Services, Civic Offices, Civic Way, Swadlincote DE11 0AH ☎ 01283 595820 ⏏ stuart.batchelor@south-derbys.gov.uk

SOUTH DERBYSHIRE

Member Services: Mrs Ardip Kaur, Monitoring Officer & Council Solicitor, Civic Offices, Civic Way, Swadlincote DE11 0AH
☎ 01283 595715 📧 ardip.kaur@south-derbys.gov.uk

Partnerships: Mr Kevin Stackhouse, Director - Finance & Corporate Services, Civic Offices, Civic Way, Swadlincote DE11 0AH
☎ 01283 595811 📧 kevin.stackhouse@south-derbys.gov.uk

Personnel / HR: Mr David Clamp, Head of Organisational Development, Civic Offices, Civic Way, Swadlincote DE11 0AH
☎ 01283 595729 📧 david.clamp@northgate-is.com

Planning: Mr Stuart Batchelor, Director - Community & Planning Services, Civic Offices, Civic Way, Swadlincote DE11 0AH
☎ 01283 595820 📧 stuart.batchelor@south-derbys.gov.uk

Procurement: Mr Kevin Stackhouse, Director - Finance & Corporate Services, Civic Offices, Civic Way, Swadlincote DE11 0AH
☎ 01283 595811 📧 kevin.stackhouse@south-derbys.gov.uk

Recycling & Waste Minimisation: Mr Mike Haynes, Director - Housing & Environmental Services, Civic Offices, Civic Way, Swadlincote DE11 0AH ☎ 01283 595775
📧 mike.haynes@south-derbys.gov.uk

Staff Training: Mr David Clamp, Head of Organisational Development, Civic Offices, Civic Way, Swadlincote DE11 0AH
☎ 01283 595729 📧 david.clamp@northgate-is.com

Sustainable Development: Mr Stuart Batchelor, Director - Community & Planning Services, Civic Offices, Civic Way, Swadlincote DE11 0AH ☎ 01283 595820
📧 stuart.batchelor@south-derbys.gov.uk

Tourism: Mr Mike Roylance, Economic Development Manager, Civic Offices, Civic Way, Swadlincote DE11 0AH ☎ 01283 595725
📧 mike.roylance@south-derbys.gov.uk

Waste Collection and Disposal: Mr Mike Haynes, Director - Housing & Environmental Services, Civic Offices, Civic Way, Swadlincote DE11 0AH ☎ 01283 595775
📧 mike.haynes@south-derbys.gov.uk

Waste Management: Mr Mike Haynes, Director - Housing & Environmental Services, Civic Offices, Civic Way, Swadlincote DE11 0AH ☎ 01283 595775 📧 mike.haynes@south-derbys.gov.uk

COUNCILLORS

Leader of the Council: Wheeler, Robert (CON - Linton)
bob.wheeler@south-derbys.gov.uk

Atkin, Neil (CON - Aston)
neil.atkin@south-derbys.gov.uk

Bambrick, Sean (LAB - Newhall & Stanton)
sean.bambrick@south-derbys.gov.uk

Billings, Andy (CON - Hilton)
andy.billings@south-derbys.gov.uk

Brown, Lisa (CON - Etwall)
lisa.brown@south-derbys.gov.uk

Chahal, Manjit (LAB - Stenson)
manji.chahal@south-derbys.gov.uk

Coe, Robert (CON - Swadlincote)
robert.coe@south-derbys.gov.uk

Coe, Kim (CON - Woodville)
kim.coe@south-derbys.gov.uk

Coyle, Hilary (CON - Aston)
hilary.coyle@south-derbys.gov.uk

Dunn, Paul (LAB - Midway)
paul.dunn@south-derbys.gov.uk

Farrington, Gillian (CON - Woodville)
gillian.farrington@south-derbys.gov.uk

Ford, Martyn (CON - Willington & Findern)
martyn.ford@south-derbys.gov.uk

Grant, John (CON - Linton)
john.grant@south-derbys.gov.uk

Hall, Margaret (CON - Seales)
margaret.hall@south-derbys.gov.uk

Harrison, John (CON - Melbourne)
john.harrison@south-derbys.gov.uk

Hewlett, Jim (CON - Melbourne)
jim.hewlett@south-derbys.gov.uk

MacPherson, Andrew (CON - Willington & Findern)
andrew.macpherson@southoderbys.gov.uk

Muller, David (CON - Etwall)
david.muller@south-derbys.gov.uk

Murray, Patrick (CON - Seales)
pat.murray@south-derbys.gov.uk

Patten, Julie (CON - Hilton)
julie.patten@south-derbys.gov.uk

Pearson, Robert (LAB - Midway)
rob.pearson@south-derbys.gov.uk

Plenderleith, Amy (CON - Hilton)
amy.plenderleith@south-derbys.gov.uk

Rhind, Gordon (LAB - Church Gresley)
gordon.rhind@south-derbys.gov.uk

Richards, Kevin (LAB - Newhall & Stanton)
kevin.richards@south-derbys.gov.uk

Roberts, Andy (CON - Hatton)
andy.roberts@south-derbys.gov.uk

Shepherd, David (LAB - Stenson)
david.shepherd@south-derbys.gov.uk

Smith, Peter (CON - Repton)
peter.smith@south-derbys.gov.uk

Southerd, Trevor (LAB - Church Gresley)
trevor.southerd@south-derbys.gov.uk

Stanton, Michael (CON - Repton)
michael.stanton@south-derbys.gov.uk

Stuart, Linda (LAB - Newhall & Stanton)
linda.stuart@south-derbys.gov.uk

Swann, Stuart (CON - Church Gresley)
stuart.swann@south-derbys.gov.uk

Taylor, Stephen (LAB - Woodville)
stephen.taylor@south-derbys.gov.uk

Tilley, Neil (LAB - Swadlincote)
neil.tilley@south-derbys.gov.uk

Watson, Peter (CON - Aston)
peter.watson@south-derbys.gov.uk

Wilkins, Peter (LAB - Midway)
peter.wilkins@south-derbys.gov.uk

Wyatt, Sandra (CON - Swadlincote)
sandra.wyatt@south-derbys.gov.uk

POLITICAL COMPOSITION
CON: 24, LAB: 12

COMMITTEE CHAIRS

Housing & Community Services: Mr Jim Hewlett

Planning: Mr Andy Roberts

South Gloucestershire   U

South Gloucestershire Council, The Council Offices,
Badminton Road, Yate BS37 5AF
☎ 01454 868009 ◌ mailbox@southglos.gov.uk
🖳 www.southglos.gov.uk

FACTS AND FIGURES
Parliamentary Constituencies: Bristol North West, Filton and
Bradley Stoke, Kingswood, Thornbury and Yate
EU Constituencies: South West
Election Frequency: Elections are of whole council

PRINCIPAL OFFICERS

Chief Executive: Mrs Amanda Deeks, Chief Executive, The
Council Offices, Badminton Road, Yate BS37 5AF ☎ 01454 863851
◌ amanda.deeks@southglos.gov.uk

Deputy Chief Executive: Mr David Perry, Director - Corporate
Services & Deputy Chief Executive, The Council Offices, Badminton
Road, Yate BS37 5AF ☎ 01454 865001
◌ dave.perry@southglos.gov.uk

Senior Management: Mr Steve Evans, Director - Environment &
Community Services, The Council Offices, Badminton Road, Yate
BS37 5AF ☎ 01454 865811 ◌ steve.evans@southglos.gov.uk

Senior Management: Mr Peter Murphy, Director - Children,
Adults & Health, The Council Offices, Badminton Road, Yate BS37
5AF ☎ 01454 863253 ◌ peter.murphy@southglos.gov.uk

Senior Management: Dr Mark Pietroni, Director - Public Health,
The Council Offices, Badminton Road, Yate BS37 5AF
☎ 014554 864200 ◌ directorofpublichealth@southglos.gov.uk

Access Officer / Social Services (Disability): Ms Alice Cleaveland,
Access Officer, The Council Offices, Badminton Road, Yate BS37 5AF
☎ 01454 863860 ◌ alice.cleaveland@southglos.gov.uk

Architect, Building / Property Services: Mr Stephen Lewis,
Head of ICT, The Council Offices, Badminton Road, Yate BS37 5AF
☎ 01454 865070 ◌ stephen.lewis@southglos.gov.uk

Best Value: Ms Sue Covello, Transformation & Efficiency
Manager, The Council Offices, Badminton Road, Yate BS37 5AF
☎ 01454 864703 ◌ sue.covello@southglos.gov.uk

Building Control: Mr Brian Glasson, Head of Strategic Planning
& Housing, The Council Offices, Badminton Road, Yate BS37 5AF
☎ 01454 863535 ◌ brian.glasson@southglos.gov.uk

Catering Services: Ms Suzanna Hinnell, Interim Managing Director
- Traded Services, The Council Offices, Badminton Road, Yate
BS37 5AF ☎ 01454 868445 ◌ suzanna.hinnell@southglos.gov.uk

Children / Youth Services: Ms Geri Palfreeman, Service
Manager - Preventative Services, Kingswood Locality Hub, High
Street, Kingswood BS15 9TR ☎ 01454 863152
◌ geri.palfreeman@southglos.gov.uk

Civil Registration: Ms Chris Benstock, Superintendent Registrar,
The Council Offices, Badminton Road, Yate BS37 5AF
☎ 01454 863604 ◌ chris.benson@southglos.gov.uk

PR / Communications: Mr Daniel Ward, Senior External
Communications Officer, The Council Offices, Badminton Road,
Yate BS37 5AF ☎ 01454 863291 ◌ daniel.ward@southglos.gov.uk

Community Planning: Ms Marian Jones, Community
Engagement Team Leader, The Council Offices, Badminton Road,
Yate BS37 5AF ☎ 01454 865839 ◌ marian.jones@southglos.gov.
uk

Community Safety: Mr Robert Walsh, Head of Safe Strong
Communities, The Council Offices, Badminton Road, Yate BS37
5AF ☎ 01454 865818 ◌ robert.walsh@southglos.gov.uk

Computer Management: Mr Stephen Lewis, Head of ICT, The
Council Offices, Badminton Road, Yate BS37 5AF ☎ 01454 865070
◌ stephen.lewis@southglos.gov.uk

Contracts: Ms Sue Covello, Transformation & Efficiency Manager,
The Council Offices, Badminton Road, Yate BS37 5AF
☎ 01454 864703 ◌ sue.covello@southglos.gov.uk

Corporate Services: Mr Andrew Birch, Deputy Head of Finance,
The Council Offices, Badminton Road, Yate BS37 5AF
☎ 01454 865985 ◌ andrew.birch@southglos.gov.uk

Corporate Services: Mr Martin Dear, Head of Business Support,
The Council Offices, Badminton Road, Yate BS37 5AF
☎ 01454 863197 ◌ martin.dear@southglos.gov.uk

Corporate Services: Mr Mike Hayesman, Head of Finance &
Customer Services, The Council Offices, Badminton Road, Yate
BS37 5AF ☎ 01454 865290 ◌ mike.hayesman@southglos.gov.uk

Corporate Services: Ms Clare Medland, Head of Strategy
Development, The Council Offices, Badminton Road, Yate BS37
5AF ☎ 01454 863239 ◌ clare.medland@southglos.gov.uk

Corporate Services: Mr David Perry, Director - Corporate Services
& Deputy Chief Executive, The Council Offices, Badminton Road,
Yate BS37 5AF ☎ 01454 865001 ◌ dave.perry@southglos.gov.uk

Customer Service: Ms Tracy Allison, Head of Integrated Locality
Children's Services, The Council Offices, Badminton Road, Yate
BS37 5AF ☎ 01454 863254 ◌ tracy.allison@southglos.gov.uk

SOUTH GLOUCESTERSHIRE

Customer Service: Mr Jim Anderson, Team Manager - Preventative Services, Kingswood Hub, High Street, Kingswood BS15 9TR ☎ 01454 863799 ✆ jim.anderson@southglos.gov.uk

Customer Service: Mr Mike Hayesman, Head of Finance & Customer Services, The Council Offices, Badminton Road, Yate BS37 5AF ☎ 01454 865290 ✆ mike.hayesman@southglos.gov.uk

Customer Service: Ms Denise Porter, Head of Adult Social Care & Housing, The Council Offices, Badminton Road, Yate BS37 5AF ☎ 01454 866325 ✆ denise.porter@southglos.gov.uk

Direct Labour: Mr Mark King, Head of Street Care, Broad Lane Offices, Engine Common Lane, Yate BS37 7PN ☎ 01454 863912 ✆ mark.king@southglos.gov.uk

Economic Development: Mr Steve Evans, Director - Environment & Community Services, The Council Offices, Badminton Road, Yate BS37 5AF ☎ 01454 865811 ✆ steve.evans@southglos.gov.uk

Education: Ms Susannah Hill, Interim Head of Education, Skills & Learning, The Council Offices, Badminton Road, Yate BS37 5AF ☎ 01454 863271 ✆ susannah.hill@southglos.gov.uk

Education: Mr Peter Murphy, Director - Children, Adults & Health, The Council Offices, Badminton Road, Yate BS37 5AF ☎ 01454 863253 ✆ peter.murphy@southglos.gov.uk

E-Government: Mr Stephen Lewis, Head of ICT, The Council Offices, Badminton Road, Yate BS37 5AF ☎ 01454 865070 ✆ stephen.lewis@southglos.gov.uk

Electoral Registration: Ms Natalie Carr, Democratic Services Group Manager, The Council Offices, Badminton Road, Yate BS37 5AF ☎ 01454 868198 ✆ natalie.carr@southglos.gov.uk

Emergency Planning: Mr Simon Hailwood, Senior Emergency Planning Officer, The Council Offices, Badminton Road, Yate BS37 5AF ☎ 01454 863869 ✆ simon.hailwood@southglos.gov.uk

Energy Management: Mr Sean Prior, Senior Energy Engineer, The Council Offices, Badminton Road, Yate BS37 5AF ☎ 01454 865141 ✆ sean.prior@southglos.gov.uk

Environmental / Technical Services: Mr Gerald Madden, Health Manager, The Council Offices, Badminton Road, Yate BS37 5AF ☎ 01454 863569 ✆ gerald.madden@southglos.gov.uk

Environmental Health: Mr Brian Glasson, Head of Strategic Planning & Housing, The Council Offices, Badminton Road, Yate BS37 5AF ☎ 01454 863535 ✆ brian.glasson@southglos.gov.uk

Environmental Health: Mr Chris Taylor, Environmental Protection Manager, The Council Offices, Badminton Road, Yate BS37 5AF ☎ 01454 863474 ✆ chris.taylor@southglos.gov.uk

Estates, Property & Valuation: Mr Mike Hayesman, Head of Finance & Customer Services, The Council Offices, Badminton Road, Yate BS37 5AF ☎ 01454 865290 ✆ mike.hayesman@southglos.gov.uk

European Liaison: Mr George Kousouros, Community Project Manager, The Council Offices, Badminton Road, Yate BS37 5AF ☎ 01454 868152 ✆ george.kousouros@southglos.gov.uk

Facilities: Mr Andrew Davies, Facilities Officer, The Council Offices, Badminton Road, Yate BS37 5AF ☎ 01454 865058 ✆ andrew.davies@southglos.gov.uk

Finance: Mr Andrew Birch, Deputy Head of Finance, The Council Offices, Badminton Road, Yate BS37 5AF ☎ 01454 865985 ✆ andrew.birch@southglos.gov.uk

Finance: Mr Mike Hayesman, Head of Finance & Customer Services, The Council Offices, Badminton Road, Yate BS37 5AF ☎ 01454 865290 ✆ mike.hayesman@southglos.gov.uk

Finance: Mr David Perry, Director - Corporate Services & Deputy Chief Executive, The Council Offices, Badminton Road, Yate BS37 5AF ☎ 01454 865001 ✆ dave.perry@southglos.gov.uk

Fleet Management: Mr Ron Dovey, Fleet Operations Manager - Transport, Broad Lane Offices, Engine Common Lane, Yate BS37 7PN ☎ 01454 863918 ✆ ron.dovey@southglos.gov.uk

Grounds Maintenance: Mr Simon Spedding, Group Manager - Design & Operations, Broad Lane Offices, Engine Common Lane, Yate BS37 7PN ☎ 01454 863971 ✆ simon.spedding@southglos.gov.uk

Health and Safety: Mr Tom Magnone, Health & Safety Manager, The Council Offices, Badminton Road, Yate BS37 5AF ☎ 01454 863096 ✆ tom.magnone@southglos.gov.uk

Highways: Mr Steve Evans, Director - Environment & Community Services, Broad Lane Offices, Engine Common Lane, Yate BS37 7PN ☎ 01454 865811 ✆ steve.evans@southglos.gov.uk

Highways: Mr Chris Sane, Head of Transport & Strategic Projects, The Council Offices, Badminton Road, Yate BS37 5AF ☎ 01454 863402 ✆ chris.sane@southglos.gov.uk

Home Energy Conservation: Ms Debby Paice, Home Energy Co-ordinator (Enabling), The Council Offices, High Street, Kingswood BS15 9TR ☎ 01454 865453 ✆ debby.paice@southglos.gov.uk

Housing: Mr Jon Shaw, Head of Strategy & Commissioning, The Council Offices, Badminton Road, Yate BS37 5AF ☎ 01454 865547 ✆ jon.shaw@southglos.gov.uk

Local Area Agreement: Mrs Yvonne Davis, Strategic Partnerships & Planning Manager, The Council Offices, Badminton Road, Yate BS37 5AF ☎ 01454 863865 ✆ yvonne.davis@southglos.gov.uk

Legal: Mr John McCormack, Head of Legal & Democratic Services & Monitoring, The Council Offices, Badminton Road, Yate BS37 5AF ☎ 01454 865980 ✆ john.mccormack@southglos.gov.uk

Leisure and Cultural Services: Mr Steve Evans, Director - Environment & Community Services, The Council Offices, Badminton Road, Yate BS37 5AF ☎ 01454 865811 ✆ steve.evans@southglos.gov.uk

Lifelong Learning: Ms Susannah Hill, Interim Head of Education, Skills & Learning, The Council Offices, Badminton Road, Yate BS37 5AF ☎ 01454 863271 ⏚ susannah.hill@southglos.gov.uk

Lighting: Mr Andrew Porter, Electrical & Building Maintenance Manager, The Council Offices, Badminton Road, Yate BS37 5AF ☎ 01454 863982 ⏚ andrew.porter@southglos.gov.uk

Lottery Funding, Charity and Voluntary: Ms Marian Jones, Community Engagement Team Leader, The Council Offices, Badminton Road, Yate BS37 5AF ☎ 01454 865839 ⏚ marian.jones@southglos.gov.uk

Member Services: Ms Natalie Carr, Democratic Services Group Manager, The Council Offices, Badminton Road, Yate BS37 5AF ☎ 01454 868198 ⏚ natalie.carr@southglos.gov.uk

Parking: Mr Alan Garwood, Senior ECO, Broad Lane Offices, Engine Common Lane, Yate BS37 7PN ☎ 01454 868494 ⏚ alan.garwood@southglos.gov.uk

Partnerships: Mrs Yvonne Davis, Strategic Partnerships & Planning Manager, The Council Offices, Badminton Road, Yate BS37 5AF ☎ 01454 863865 ⏚ yvonne.davis@southglos.gov.uk

Personnel / HR: Mrs Claire Kerswill, Head of HR & HRBP for Corporate Resources, The Council Offices, Badminton Road, Yate BS37 5AF ☎ 01454 866348 ⏚ claire.kerswill@southglos.gov.uk

Planning: Mr Steve Evans, Director - Environment & Community Services, The Council Offices, Badminton Road, Yate BS37 5AF ☎ 01454 865811 ⏚ steve.evans@southglos.gov.uk

Planning: Mr Brian Glasson, Head of Strategic Planning & Housing, The Council Offices, Badminton Road, Yate BS37 5AF ☎ 01454 863535 ⏚ brian.glasson@southglos.gov.uk

Procurement: Ms Sue Covello, Transformation & Efficiency Manager, The Council Offices, Badminton Road, Yate BS37 5AF ☎ 01454 864703 ⏚ sue.covello@southglos.gov.uk

Public Libraries: Mr Martin Burton, Community Cultural Services Manager, The Council Offices, Badminton Road, Yate BS37 5AF ☎ 01454 865782 ⏚ martin.burton@southglos.gov.uk

Recycling & Waste Minimisation: Mr Robert Lambourne, Waste Manager, The Council Offices, Badminton Road, Yate BS37 5AF ☎ 01454 865840 ⏚ robert.lambourne@southglos.gov.uk

Regeneration: Mr Mike Luton, Senior Principal Planning Officer - Policy, The Council Offices, Badminton Road, Yate BS37 5AF ☎ 01454 863573 ⏚ mike.luton@southglos.gov.uk

Road Safety: Mr Chris Studley, Stakeholder Manager, The Council Offices, Badminton Road, Yate BS37 5AF ☎ 01454 863751 ⏚ chris.studley@southglos.gov.uk

Social Services: Ms Tracy Allison, Head of Integrated Locality Children's Services, The Council Offices, Badminton Road, Yate BS37 5AF ☎ 01454 863254 ⏚ tracy.allison@southglos.gov.uk

Social Services: Mr Peter Murphy, Director - Children, Adults & Health, The Council Offices, Badminton Road, Yate BS37 5AF ☎ 01454 863253 ⏚ peter.murphy@southglos.gov.uk

Social Services (Adult): Ms Sheila Turner, Safeguarding Adults Manager, Civic Centre, High Street, Kingswood BS15 9TR ☎ 01454 866273 ⏚ sheila.turner@southglos.gov.uk

Social Services (Children): Mr Peter Murphy, Director - Children, Adults & Health, The Council Offices, Badminton Road, Yate BS37 5AF ☎ 01454 863253 ⏚ peter.murphy@southglos.gov.uk

Public Health: Dr Mark Pietroni, Director - Public Health, The Council Offices, Badminton Road, Yate BS37 5AF ☎ 014554 864200 ⏚ directorofpublichealth@southglos.gov.uk

Staff Training: Ms Nicola Plant, HR Business Partner, The Council Offices, Badminton Road, Yate BS37 5AF ☎ 01454 863093 ⏚ nicola.plant@southglos.gov.uk

Street Scene: Mr Simon Spedding, Group Manager - Design & Operations, Broad Lane Offices, Engine Common Lane, Yate BS37 7PN ☎ 01454 863971 ⏚ simon.spedding@southglos.gov.uk

Traffic Management: Mr Chris Studley, Stakeholder Manager, The Council Offices, Badminton Road, Yate BS37 5AF ☎ 01454 863751 ⏚ chris.studley@southglos.gov.uk

Transport: Mr Steve Evans, Director - Environment & Community Services, The Council Offices, Badminton Road, Yate BS37 5AF ☎ 01454 865811 ⏚ steve.evans@southglos.gov.uk

Transport: Mr Chris Sane, Head of Transport & Strategic Projects, The Council Offices, Badminton Road, Yate BS37 5AF ☎ 01454 863402 ⏚ chris.sane@southglos.gov.uk

Transport Planner: Ms Emma Blackham, Transport Policy & Promotions Group Manager, The Council Offices, Badminton Road, Yate BS37 5AF ☎ 01454 864115 ⏚ emma.blackham@southglos.gov.uk

Waste Collection and Disposal: Mr Robert Lambourne, Waste Manager, The Council Offices, Badminton Road, Yate BS37 5AF ☎ 01454 865840 ⏚ robert.lambourne@southglos.gov.uk

Waste Management: Mr Steve Evans, Director - Environment & Community Services, Broad Lane Offices, Engine Common Lane, Yate BS37 7PN ☎ 01454 865811 ⏚ steve.evans@southglos.gov.uk

COUNCILLORS

Chair: Williams, Erica (CON - Bitton)
erica.williams@southglos.gov.uk

Leader of the Council: Riddle, Matthew (CON - Severn)
matthew.riddle@southglos.gov.uk

Group Leader: Davis, Ruth (LD - Yate Central)
ruth.davis@southglos.gov.uk

Group Leader: Rooney, Pat (LAB - Woodstock)
pat.ronney@southglos.gov.uk

Adams, Judy (CON - Rodway)
judy.adams@southglos.gov.uk

SOUTH GLOUCESTERSHIRE

Adams, Ian (CON - Siston)
ian.adams@southglos.gov.uk

Allinson, Brian (CON - Stoke Gifford)
brian.allinson@southglos.gov.uk

Ashe, John (CON - Bradley Stoke South)
john.ashe@southglos.gov.uk

Avenin, Roger (CON - Bradley Stoke South)
roger.avenin@southglos.gov.uk

Bamford, June (CON - Hanham)
june.bamford@southglos.gov.uk

Barrett, Nick (CON - Parkwall)
nick.barrett@southglos.gov.uk

Barrett, Kaye (CON - Parkwall)
kaye.barrett@southglos.gov.uk

Begley, April (LAB - King's Chase)
april.begley@southglos.gov.uk

Bell, Michael (LAB - Rodway)
michael.bell@southglos.gov.uk

Biggin, Janet (CON - Downend)
janet.biggin@southglos.gov.uk

Blair, Ian (LD - Yate North)
ian.blair@southglos.gov.uk

Boon, Linda (LD - Chipping Sodbury)
linda.boon@southglos.gov.uk

Boulton, Ian (LAB - Staple Hill)
ian.boulton@southglos.gov.uk

Bowles, Tim (CON - Winterbourne)
tim.bowles@southglos.gov.uk

Bromiley, Samuel (CON - Oldland Common)
samuel.bromiley@southglos.gov.uk

Brown, Ernie (CON - Stoke Gifford)
ernie.brown@southglos.gov.uk

Burchell, Keith (CON - Almondsbury)
keith.burchell@southglos.gov.uk

Chubb, David (CON - Thornbury North)
david.chubb@southglos.gov.uk

Cranney, Keith (CON - Stoke Gifford)
keith.cranney@southglos.gov.uk

Creer, Rob (CON - Chipping Sodbury)
rob.creer@southglos.gov.uk

Dando, Ken (CON - Patchway)
kenneth.dando2@southglos.gov.uk

Davis, Tony (LD - Dodington)
tony.davis@southglos.gov.uk

Davis, John (LD - Yate North)
john.davis@southglos.gov.uk

Drew, Mike (LD - Yate North)
mike.drew@southglos.gov.uk

Fardell, Clare (LD - Thornbury North)
clare.fardell@southglos.gov.uk

Farmer, Martin (LAB - King's Chase)
martin.farmer@southglos.gov.uk

Goddard, Heather (CON - Hanham)
heather.goddard@southglos.gov.uk

Goddard, John (CON - Hanham)

Griffin, Robert (CON - Pilning & Severn Beach)
robert.griffin@southglos.gov.uk

Hardwick, Paul (CON - Bradley Stoke North)
paul.hardwick@southglos.gov.uk

Hockey, Dave (LD - Frampton Cotterell)
dave.hockey@southglos.gov.uk

Hockey, Pat (LD - Frampton Cotterell)
pat.hockey@southglos.gov.uk

Holloway, Shirley (LD - Thornbury South & Alveston)
shirley.holloway@southglos.gov.uk

Hope, Sue (LD - Cotswold Edge)
sue.hope@southglos.gov.uk

Hopkinson, Brian (CON - Bradley Stoke Central & Stoke Lodge)
brian.hopkinson@southglos.gov.uk

Hughes, Paul (CON - Oldland Common)
paul.hughes@southglos.gov.uk

Hunt, Jon (CON - Downend)
jon.hunt@southglos.gov.uk

Hunt, Colin (CON - Emersons Green)
colin.hunt@southglos.gov.uk

Hunt, Rachael (CON - Emersons Green)
rachael.hunt@southglos.gov.uk

Hutchinson, Roger (LAB - Filton)
roger.hutchinson@southglos.gov.uk

Jones, Trevor (CON - Frenchay & Stoke Park)
trevor.jones@southglos.gov.uk

Kearns, Dave (CON - Emersons Green)
dave.kearns@southglos.gov.uk

Lewis, Marian (CON - Ladden Brook)
marian.lewis@southglos.gov.uk

Mannig, Martin (CON - Winterbourne)
martin.manning@southglos.gov.uk

Manson, Gary (LAB - Woodstock)
gareth.manson@southglos.gov.uk

Monk, Adam (LAB - Filton)
adam.monk@southglos.gov.uk

Morris, Katherine (CON - Downend)
katherine.morris@southglos.gov.uk

O'Neil, John (LD - Charfield)
john.o'neil@southglos.gov.uk

Opren, Eve (LAB - Patchway)
eve.opren@southglos.gov.uk

Perkins, Andy (LAB - Woodstock)
andy.perkins@southglos.gov.uk

Pomfret, Sarah (CON - Bradley Stoke Central & Stoke Lodge)
sarah.pomfret@southglos.gov.uk

Potts, Shirley (LAB - Staple Hill)
shirley.potts@southglos.gov.uk

Price, Christine (CON - Longwell Green)
christine.price@southglos.gov.uk

Pullin, Bob (CON - Frenchay & Stoke Park)
bob.pullin@southglos.gov.uk

Reade, Steve (CON - Boyd Valley)
stephen.reade.southglos.gov.uk

Savage, Toby (CON - Longwell Green)
toby.savage@southglos.gov.uk

Scott, Ian (LAB - Filton)
ian.scott@southglos.gov.uk

Scudamore, Kim (LAB - King's Chase)
kim.scudamore@southglos.gov.uk

Stephen, Gloria (LD - Dodington)
gloria.stephen@southglos.gov.uk

Stokes, Benjamin (CON - Boyd Valley)
ben.stokes@southglos.gov.uk

Sullivan, John (CON - Rodway)
john.sullivan@southglos.gov.uk

Tyrrell, Maggie (LD - Thornbury South & Alveston)
maggie.tyrrell@southglos.gov.uk

Walker, Sue (LD - Yate Central)
sue.walker@southglos.gov.uk

Walker, Keith (LAB - Patchway)
keith.walker@southglos.gov.uk

Young, Claire (LD - Westerleigh)
claire.young@southglos.gov.uk

POLITICAL COMPOSITION
CON: 40, LD: 16, LAB: 14

COMMITTEE CHAIRS

Adults, Housing & Public Health: Mr Benjamin Stokes

Audit: Mr Nick Barrett

Health & Wellbeing: Mr Matthew Riddle

South Hams   D

South Hams District Council, Follaton House, Plymouth Road, Totnes TQ9 5NE
☎ 01803 861234 🖷 01803 866151
-🖑 customer.services@southhams.gov.uk 🖳 www.southhams.gov.uk

FACTS AND FIGURES
Parliamentary Constituencies: Totnes
EU Constituencies: South West
Election Frequency: Elections are of whole council

PRINCIPAL OFFICERS

Chief Executive: Mr Steve Jorden, Executive Director - Strategy & Commissioning & Head of Paid Service, Follaton House, Plymouth Road, Totnes TQ9 5NE ☎ 01803 861105
-🖑 steve.jorden@swdevon.gov.uk

Deputy Chief Executive: Ms Sophie Hosking, Executive Director - Service Delivery & Commercial Development, Follaton House, Plymouth Road, Totnes TQ9 5NE ☎ 01803 861105
-🖑 sophie.hosking@swdevon.gov.uk

Senior Management: Mr Darren Arulvasagam, Group Manager - Business Development, Follaton House, Plymouth Road, Totnes TQ9 5NE ☎ 01803 861234 -🖑 darren.arulvasagam@swdevon.gov.uk

Senior Management: Mrs Helen Dobby, Group Manager - Commercial Services, Follaton House, Plymouth Road, Totnes TQ9 5NE ☎ 01822 813600 -🖑 helen.dobby@swdevon.gov.uk

Senior Management: Mr Steve Mullineaux, Group Manager - Support Services, Follaton House, Plymouth Road, Totnes TQ9 5NE ☎ 01822 813600 -🖑 steve.mullineaux@swdevon.gov.uk

Architect, Building / Property Services: Mr Chris Brook, Community of Practice - Assets, Follaton House, Plymouth Road, Totnes TQ9 5NE ☎ 01822 813600 -🖑 chris.brook@swdevon.gov.uk

Building Control: Mr Andrew Carpenter, Head of Building Control Partnership, Forde House, Brunel Road, Newton Abbot TQ12 4XX ☎ 01626 215721 -🖑 andrew.carpenter@teignbridge.gov.uk

PR / Communications: Ms Lesley Crocker, Lead Specialist - Communications & Media, Follaton House, Plymouth Road, Totnes TQ9 5NE ☎ 01803 861321 -🖑 lesley.crocker@swdevon.gov.uk

Community Planning: Mr Ross Kennerley, Lead Specialist - Place Strategy, Follaton House, Plymouth Road, Totnes TQ9 5NE ☎ 01822 813647 -🖑 ross.kennerley@swdevon.gov.uk

Computer Management: Mr Mike Ward, ICT Community of Practice Lead, Follaton House, Plymouth Road, Totnes TQ9 5NE ☎ 01803 861234 -🖑 mike.ward@swdevon.gov.uk

Electoral Registration: Mrs Elizabeth Tucker, Electoral Administrator, Follaton House, Plymouth Road, Totnes TQ9 5NE ☎ 01803 861234 -🖑 liz.tucker@southhams.gov.uk

Emergency Planning: Mr James Kershaw, Head of Emergency Planning, Follaton House, Plymouth Road, Totnes TQ9 5NE ☎ 01822 813600 -🖑 james.kershaw@swdevon.gov.uk

Estates, Property & Valuation: Mr Chris Brook, Community of Practice - Assets, Follaton House, Plymouth Road, Totnes TQ9 5NE ☎ 01822 813600 -🖑 chris.brook@swdevon.gov.uk

Treasury: Miss Lisa Buckle, Head of Finance & Audit, Follaton House, Plymouth Road, Totnes TQ9 5NE ☎ 01822 813644 -🖑 lisa.buckle@westdevon.gov.uk

Fleet Management: Mrs Helen Dobby, Group Manager - Commercial Services, Follaton House, Plymouth Road, Totnes TQ9 5NE ☎ 01822 813600 -🖑 helen.dobby@swdevon.gov.uk

Grounds Maintenance: Mrs Helen Dobby, Group Manager - Commercial Services, Follaton House, Plymouth Road, Totnes TQ9 5NE ☎ 01822 813600 -🖑 helen.dobby@swdevon.gov.uk

Housing: Ms Isabel Blake, Head of Housing, Follaton House, Plymouth Road, Totnes TQ9 5NE ☎ 01822 813600 -🖑 isabel.blake@swdevon.gov.uk

Legal: Ms Catherine Bowen, Monitoring Officer, Follaton House, Plymouth Road, Totnes TQ9 5NE -🖑 catherine.bowen@swdevon.gov.uk

SOUTH HAMS

Leisure and Cultural Services: Mr Ross Kennerley, Lead Specialist - Place Strategy, Follaton House, Plymouth Road, Totnes TQ9 5NE ☎ 01822 813647 ⌐ ross.kennerley@swdevon.gov.uk

Member Services: Mr Darryl White, Member Services Manager, Follaton House, Plymouth Road, Totnes TQ9 5NE ☎ 01803 861234 ⌐ darryl.white@southhams.gov.uk

Parking: Mrs Catherine Aubertin, Car Parking & Contracts Performance Manager, Follaton House, Plymouth Road, Totnes TQ9 5NE ☎ 01822 813650 ⌐ caubertin@westdevon.gov.uk

Personnel / HR: Mr Andy Wilson, Head of Corporate Services, Follaton House, Plymouth Road, Totnes TQ9 5NE ☎ 01822 813600 ⌐ andy.wilson@swdevon.gov.uk

Staff Training: Mr Andy Wilson, Head of Corporate Services, Follaton House, Plymouth Road, Totnes TQ9 5NE ☎ 01822 813600 ⌐ andy.wilson@swdevon.gov.uk

Street Scene: Mrs Catherine Aubertin, Car Parking & Contracts Performance Manager, Follaton House, Plymouth Road, Totnes TQ9 5NE ☎ 01822 813650 ⌐ caubertin@westdevon.gov.uk

COUNCILLORS

Chair: Smerdon, Peter (CON - South Brent)
cllr.smerdon@southhams.gov.uk

Leader of the Council: Tucker, John (CON - West Dart)
cllr.tucker@southhams.gov.uk

Deputy Leader of the Council: Ward, Lindsay (CON - Charterlands)
cllr.lward@southhams.gov.uk

Group Leader: Baldry, Keith (LD - Newton & Yealmpton)
cllr.baldry@southhams.gov.uk

Bastone, Hilary (CON - Dartmouth & East Dart)
cllr.bastone@southhams.gov.uk

Birch, John (LD - Totnes)
cllr.birch@southhams.gov.uk

Blackler, Ian (CON - Newton & Yealmpton)
cllr.blackler@southhams.gov.uk

Bramble, Ian (CON - Loddiswell & Aveton Gifford)
cllr.bramble@southhams.gov.uk

Brazil, Julian (LD - Stokenham)
cllr.brazil@southhams.gov.uk

Brown, Daniel (CON - Wembury & Brixton)
cllr.brown@southhams.gov.uk

Cane, Basil (CON - Wembury & Brixton)
cllr.cane@southhams.gov.uk

Cuthbert, Kathy (CON - Ivybridge East)
cllr.cuthbert@southhams.gov.uk

Foss, Richard (CON - Allington & Strete)
cllr.foss@southhams.gov.uk

Gilbert, Rufus (CON - Kingsbridge)
cllr.gilbert@southhams.gov.uk

Green, John (GRN - Totnes)
cllr.green@southhams.gov.uk

Hawkins, Jonathan (CON - Dartmouth & East Dart)
cllr.hawkins@southhams.gov.uk

Hicks, Michael (CON - Blackawton & Stoke Fleming)
cllr.hicks@southhams.gov.uk

Hitchins, Bill (CON - Bickleigh & Cornwood)
cllr.hitchins@southhams.gov.uk

Hodgson, Jacqi (GRN - Dartington & Staverton)
cllr.hodgson@southhams.gov.uk

Holway, Tom (CON - Ermington & Ugborough)
cllr.holway@southhams.gov.uk

Hopwood, Nicky (CON - Woolwell)
cllr.hopwood@southhams.gov.uk

May, David (CON - Ivybridge West)
cllr.may@southhams.gov.uk

Pearce, Judy (CON - Salcombe & Thurlestone)
cllr.pearce@southhams.gov.uk

Pennington, Trevor (CON - Marldon & Littlehempston)
cllr.pennington@southhams.gov.uk

Pringle, Karen (CON - Ivybridge East)
cllr.pringle@southhams.gov.uk

Rowe, Rosemary (CON - Dartmouth & East Dart)
cllr.rowe@southhams.gov.uk

Saltern, Michael (CON - Ivybridge West)
cllr.saltern@southhams.gov.uk

Steer, Robert (CON - South Brent)
cllr.steer@southhams.gov.uk

Vint, Robert (GRN - Totnes)
cllr.vint@southhams.gov.uk

Wingate, Keith (CON - Kingsbridge)
cllr.wingate@southhams.gov.uk

Wright, Simon (CON - Westville & Alvington)
cllr.wright@southhams.gov.uk

POLITICAL COMPOSITION
CON: 25, LD: 3, GRN: 3

COMMITTEE CHAIRS

Audit: Mr Keith Wingate

Development Management: Mr Robert Steer

South Holland District Council   D

South Holland District Council, Council Offices, Priory Road, Spalding PE11 2XE
☎ 01775 761161 🖷 01775 711253 ⌐ info@sholland.gov.uk
🖵 www.sholland.gov.uk

FACTS AND FIGURES
Parliamentary Constituencies: South Holland and The Deepings
EU Constituencies: East Midlands
Election Frequency: Elections are of whole council

PRINCIPAL OFFICERS

Chief Executive: Ms Anna Graves, Chief Executive, Council Offices, Priory Road, Spalding PE11 2XE ☎ 07833 503139 ⌐ chief.executive@breckland-sholland.go.uk

Senior Management: Ms Julie Kennealy, Executive Director - Commercialisation, Council Offices, Priory Road, Spalding PE11 2XE ☎ 01775 764567 📧 julie.kennealy@breckland-sholland.gov.uk

Senior Management: Mrs Maxine O'Mahony, Executive Director - Strategy & Governance, Council Offices, Priory Road, Spalding PE11 2XE ☎ 01775 764603 📧 maxine.omahony@breckland-sholland.gov.uk

Senior Management: Mr Robert Walker, Executive Director - Place, Council Offices, Priory Road, Spalding PE11 2XE ☎ 07867 988826 📧 robert.walker@breckland-sholland.gov.uk

Architect, Building / Property Services: Mrs Emily Spicer, Environmental Services Manager, Council Offices, Priory Road, Spalding PE11 2XE ☎ 01775 764884 📧 emily.spicer@sholland.gov.uk

Best Value: Mr Greg Pearson, Corporate Improvement & Performance Manager, Council Offices, Priory Road, Spalding PE11 2XE ☎ 01775 761161 📧 greg.pearson@breckland-sholland.gov.uk

Building Control: Mr Paul Jackson, South Holland Place Manager, Council Offices, Priory Road, Spalding PE11 2XE ☎ 01775 764402 📧 paul.jackson@breckland-sholland.gov.uk

PR / Communications: Mr David Ogden, Communications Manager, Council Offices, Priory Road, Spalding PE11 2XE ☎ 01775 764682 📧 dogden@sholland.gov.uk

Community Planning: Mr Paul Jackson, South Holland Place Manager, Council Offices, Priory Road, Spalding PE11 2XE ☎ 01775 764402 📧 paul.jackson@breckland-sholland.gov.uk

Community Safety: Miss Emily Holmes, Communities Manager, Council Offices, Priory Road, Spalding PE11 2XE ☎ 01775 764469 📧 eholmes@sholland.gov.uk

Computer Management: Mr Rob Leigh, Shared Executive Manager - People & Information, Council Offices, Priory Road, Spalding PE11 2XE ☎ 01775 761161 📧 rob.leigh@breckland-sholland.gov.uk

Contracts: Mr Greg Pearson, Corporate Improvement & Performance Manager, Council Offices, Priory Road, Spalding PE11 2XE ☎ 01775 761161 📧 greg.pearson@breckland-sholland.gov.uk

Customer Service: Mr Andy Prior, Digital & Customer Access Manager, Council Offices, Priory Road, Spalding PE11 2XE ☎ 01775 761161 📧 andy.prior@breckland-sholland.gov.uk

Direct Labour: Mr Richard Scorthorne, Housing Landlord Manager, Council Offices, Priory Road, Spalding PE11 2XE ☎ 01775 764671 📧 rscorthorne@sholland.gov.uk

Economic Development: Mr Nigel Burch, Interim Inward Investment Manager, Council Offices, Priory Road, Spalding PE11 2XE ☎ 01775 764563 📧 nburch@sholland.gov.uk

E-Government: Mr Rob Leigh, Shared Executive Manager - People & Information, Council Offices, Priory Road, Spalding PE11 2XE ☎ 01775 761161 📧 rob.leigh@breckland-sholland.gov.uk

Electoral Registration: Mr Mark Stinson, Shared Executive Manager - Governance, Council Offices, Priory Road, Spalding PE11 2XE ☎ 01775 764612 📧 mark.stinson@breckland-sholland.gov.uk

Emergency Planning: Miss Emily Holmes, Communities Manager, Council Offices, Priory Road, Spalding PE11 2XE ☎ 01775 764469 📧 eholmes@sholland.gov.uk

Environmental / Technical Services: Mrs Emily Spicer, Environmental Services Manager, Council Offices, Priory Road, Spalding PE11 2XE ☎ 01775 764884 📧 emily.spicer@sholland.gov.uk

Environmental Health: Mr Phil Adams, Shared Executive Manager - Public Protection, Council Offices, Priory Road, Spalding PE11 2XE ☎ 01775 764657 📧 phillip.adams@breckland-sholland.gov.uk

Estates, Property & Valuation: Mrs Emily Spicer, Environmental Services Manager, Council Offices, Priory Road, Spalding PE11 2XE ☎ 01775 764884 📧 emily.spicer@sholland.gov.uk

European Liaison: Mr Nigel Burch, Interim Inward Investment Manager, Council Offices, Priory Road, Spalding PE11 2XE ☎ 01775 764563 📧 nburch@sholland.gov.uk

Facilities: Mrs Emily Spicer, Environmental Services Manager, Council Offices, Priory Road, Spalding PE11 2XE ☎ 01775 764884 📧 emily.spicer@sholland.gov.uk

Fleet Management: Mrs Emily Spicer, Environmental Services Manager, Council Offices, Priory Road, Spalding PE11 2XE ☎ 01775 764884 📧 emily.spicer@sholland.gov.uk

Grounds Maintenance: Mrs Emily Spicer, Environmental Services Manager, Council Offices, Priory Road, Spalding PE11 2XE ☎ 01775 764884 📧 emily.spicer@sholland.gov.uk

Health and Safety: Mr Phil Adams, Shared Executive Manager - Public Protection, Council Offices, Priory Road, Spalding PE11 2XE ☎ 01775 764657 📧 phillip.adams@breckland-sholland.gov.uk

Housing: Mr Richard Scorthorne, Housing Landlord Manager, Council Offices, Priory Road, Spalding PE11 2XE ☎ 01775 764671 📧 rscorthorne@sholland.gov.uk

Housing Maintenance: Mr Richard Scorthorne, Housing Landlord Manager, Council Offices, Priory Road, Spalding PE11 2XE ☎ 01775 764671 📧 rscorthorne@sholland.gov.uk

Legal: Ms Sarah Wolstenholme-Smy, Interim Legal Services Manager, Council Offices, Priory Road, Spalding PE11 2XE ☎ 01775 761161 📧

Leisure and Cultural Services: Miss Emily Holmes, Communities Manager, Council Offices, Priory Road, Spalding PE11 2XE ☎ 01775 764469 📧 eholmes@sholland.gov.uk

Licensing: Ms Donna Hall, Licensing & Business Support Manager, Council Offices, Priory Road, Spalding PE11 2XE ☎ 01775 761161 📧

SOUTH HOLLAND DISTRICT COUNCIL

Lottery Funding, Charity and Voluntary: Miss Emily Holmes, Communities Manager, Council Offices, Priory Road, Spalding PE11 2XE ☎ 01775 764469 ✆ eholmes@sholland.gov.uk

Member Services: Ms Rhonda Booth, Democratic Services Team Leader, Council Offices, Priory Road, Spalding PE11 2XE ☎ 01775 764705 ✆ rbooth@sholland.gov.uk

Parking: Mrs Emily Spicer, Environmental Services Manager, Council Offices, Priory Road, Spalding PE11 2XE ☎ 01775 764884 ✆ emily.spicer@sholland.gov.uk

Personnel / HR: Mr Greg Pearson, Corporate Improvement & Performance Manager, Council Offices, Priory Road, Spalding PE11 2XE ☎ 01775 761161 ✆ greg.pearson@breckland-sholland.gov.uk

Planning: Mr Paul Jackson, South Holland Place Manager, Elizabeth House, Walpole Loke, Dereham NR19 1EE ☎ 01775 764402 ✆ paul.jackson@breckland-sholland.gov.uk

Procurement: Mr Greg Pearson, Corporate Improvement & Performance Manager, Council Offices, Priory Road, Spalding PE11 2XE ☎ 01775 761161 ✆ greg.pearson@breckland-sholland.gov.uk

Recycling & Waste Minimisation: Mrs Emily Spicer, Environmental Services Manager, Council Offices, Priory Road, Spalding PE11 2XE ☎ 01775 764884 ✆ emily.spicer@sholland.gov.uk

Regeneration: Mr Nigel Burch, Interim Inward Investment Manager, Council Offices, Priory Road, Spalding PE11 2XE ☎ 01775 764563 ✆ nburch@sholland.gov.uk

Street Scene: Mrs Emily Spicer, Environmental Services Manager, Council Offices, Priory Road, Spalding PE11 2XE ☎ 01775 764884 ✆ emily.spicer@sholland.gov.uk

Tourism: Miss Emily Holmes, Communities Manager, Council Offices, Priory Road, Spalding PE11 2XE ☎ 01775 764469 ✆ eholmes@sholland.gov.uk

Town Centre: Mr Paul Jackson, South Holland Place Manager, Elizabeth House, Walpole Loke, Dereham NR19 1EE ☎ 01775 764402 ✆ paul.jackson@breckland-sholland.gov.uk

Waste Collection and Disposal: Mrs Emily Spicer, Environmental Services Manager, Council Offices, Priory Road, Spalding PE11 2XE ☎ 01775 764884 ✆ emily.spicer@sholland.gov.uk

Waste Management: Mrs Emily Spicer, Environmental Services Manager, Council Offices, Priory Road, Spalding PE11 2XE ☎ 01775 764884 ✆ emily.spicer@sholland.gov.uk

COUNCILLORS

Chair: Seymour, Michael (CON - The Saints) mseymour@sholland.gov.uk

Vice-Chair: Grocock, Rodney (CON - Moulton, Weston & Cowbit) rgrocock@sholland.gov.uk

Leader of the Council: Porter, Gary (CON - Spalding St Mary's) gporter@sholland.gov.uk

Deputy Leader of the Council: Chandler, Malcolm (CON - Whaplode & Holbeach St Johns) mchandler@sholland.gov.uk

Deputy Leader of the Council: Worth, Charles (CON - Holbeach Hurn) nworth@sholland.gov.uk

Group Leader: Newton, Angela (IND - Spalding Monkshouse) anewton@sholland.gov.uk

Alcock, Bryan (IND - Crowland & Deeping St Nicholas) balcock@sholland.gov.uk

Aley, George (CON - Spalding Monkshouse) galey@sholland.gov.uk

Ashby, David (CON - Spalding St Paul's) david.ashby@sholland.gov.uk

Astill, Jim (CON - Crowland & Deeping St Nicholas) jastill@sholland.gov.uk

Avery, James (CON - Pinchbeck & Surfleet) javery@sholland.gov.uk

Biggadike, Francis (CON - Holbeach Town) fbiggadike@sholland.gov.uk

Booth, Michael (IND - Sutton Bridge) mbooth@sholland.gov.uk

Brewis, Christopher (IND - Sutton Bridge) cbrewis@sholland.gov.uk

Carter, Tracey (CON - Holbeach Town) tcarter@sholland.gov.uk

Casson, Anthony (CON - Moulton, Weston & Cowbit) acasson@sholland.gov.uk

Clark, Robert (CON - Donington, Quadring & Gosberton) rclark@sholland.gov.uk

Coupland, Peter (CON - Fleet) pcoupland@sholland.gov.uk

Dark, Graham (IND - Spalding St John's) gdark@sholland.gov.uk

Drury, Harry (CON - Spalding St Mary's) hdrury@sholland.gov.uk

Eldridge, Laura (CON - Long Sutton) leldridge@sholland.gov.uk

Foyster, Paul (UKIP - Holbeach Town) pfoyster@sholland.gov.uk

Gambba-Jones, Roger (CON - Spalding Wygate) rgambba-jones@sholland.gov.uk

Harrison, Angela (CON - Crowland & Deeping St Nicholas) angelaharrison@sholland.gov.uk

Johnson, Colin (CON - Donington, Quadring & Gosberton) cjohnson@sholland.gov.uk

King, Jane (IND - Donington, Quadring & Gosberton) jane.king@sholland.gov.uk

Lawton, Christine (CON - Spalding Wygate) clawton@sholland.gov.uk

McLean, Jack (CON - Spalding St John's) jmclean@sholland.gov.uk

Pullen, Michael (CON - Whaplode & Holbeach St John's)
mpullen@sholland.gov.uk

Reynolds, Joanne (CON - Gedney)
jreynolds@sholland.gov.uk

Slade, Sally-Ann (CON - Pinchbeck & Surfleet)
sally-ann.slade@sholland.gov.uk

Sneath, Elizabeth (CON - Pinchbeck & Surfleet)
elizabeth.sneath@sholland.gov.uk

Taylor, Gary (CON - Spalding Castle)
gtaylor@sholland.gov.uk

Tennant, Andrew (IND - Long Sutton)
atennant@sholland.gov.uk

Tyrrell, Jack (CON - Long Sutton)
jtyrell@sholland.gov.uk

Williams, Peter (UKIP - Spalding St Paul's)
pwilliams@sholland.gov.uk

Woolf, Andrew (CON - Moulton, Weston & Cowbit)
awoolf@sholland.gov.uk

POLITICAL COMPOSITION
CON: 28, IND: 7, UKIP: 2

COMMITTEE CHAIRS

Audit: Mr George Aley

Licensing: Mrs Angela Harrison

Planning: Mr Roger Gambba-Jones

South Kesteven   D

South Kesteven District Council, Council Offices, St. Peter's Hill, Grantham NG31 6PZ
☎ 01476 406080 🖷 01476 406000 ✐ frontdesk@southkesteven.gov.uk
🖥 www.southkesteven.gov.uk

FACTS AND FIGURES
Parliamentary Constituencies: Grantham and Stamford
EU Constituencies: East Midlands
Election Frequency: Elections are of whole council

PRINCIPAL OFFICERS

Chief Executive: Ms Beverly Agass, Chief Executive, Council Offices, St. Peter's Hill, Grantham NG31 6PZ ☎ 01476 406100 ✐ b.agass@southkesteven.gov.uk

Senior Management: Ms Tracey Blackwell, Strategic Director - Environment & Property, Council Offices, St. Peter's Hill, Grantham NG31 6PZ

Senior Management: Mr Steve Ingram, Strategic Director - Development Management & Growth, Council Offices, St. Peter's Hill, Grantham NG31 6PZ ✐ s.ingram@southkesteven.gov.uk

Senior Management: Mr Daren Turner, Strategic Director - Commercial, Council Offices, St. Peter's Hill, Grantham NG31 6PZ ☎ 01476 406301 ✐ d.turner@southkesteven.gov.uk

Architect, Building / Property Services: Mr Neil Cucksey, Executive Manager - Property, Council Offices, St. Peter's Hill, Grantham NG31 6PZ ☎ 01476 406224 ✐ n.cucksey@southkesteven.gov.uk

Building Control: Mrs Heather Jones, Building Control Manager, Council Offices, St. Peter's Hill, Grantham NG31 6PZ ☎ 01476 401225 ✐ h.jones@southkesteven.gov.uk

PR / Communications: Mr Geoff O'Neil, Reputation, Public Relations, Communications, Consultation & Engagement Business Manager, Council Offices, St. Peter's Hill, Grantham NG31 6PZ ☎ 01476 406020 ✐ pr@southkesteven.gov.uk

Community Safety: Mr Mark Jones, Neighbourhoods Business Manager, Council Offices, St. Peter's Hill, Grantham NG31 6PZ ☎ 01476 406080 ✐ m.jones@southkesteven.gov.uk

Community Safety: Mr Sandy Kavanagh, Community Safety Officer, Council Offices, St. Peter's Hill, Grantham NG31 6PZ ☎ 01476 406107 ✐ s.kavanagh@southkesteven.gov.uk

Contracts: Mr Andrew Sweeney, Assets & Facilities Business Manager, Council Offices, St. Peter's Hill, Grantham NG31 6PZ ☎ 01476 406080 ✐ a.sweeney@southkesteven.gov.uk

Corporate Services: Mrs Lucy Youles, Executive Manager - Corporate, Council Offices, St. Peter's Hill, Grantham NG31 6PZ ☎ 01476 406105 ✐ l.youles@southkesteven.gov.uk

Direct Labour: Mr Keith Rowe, Street Care Services Business Manager, Council Offices, St. Peter's Hill, Grantham NG31 6PZ ☎ 01476 406080 ✐ k.rowe@southkesteven.gov.uk

Economic Development: Mr Roger Ranson, Spatial & Economic Growth Business Manager, Council Offices, St. Peter's Hill, Grantham NG31 6PZ ☎ 01476 406080 ✐ r.ranson@southkesteven.gov.uk

Electoral Registration: Ms Julie Edwards, Elections & Democratic Services Team Leader, Council Offices, St. Peter's Hill, Grantham NG31 6PZ ☎ 01476 406078 ✐ j.edwards@southkesteven.gov.uk

Emergency Planning: Mr Mark Jones, Neighbourhoods Business Manager, Council Offices, St. Peter's Hill, Grantham NG31 6PZ ☎ 01476 406080 ✐ m.jones@southkesteven.gov.uk

Energy Management: Mr K Munford, Energy Officer, Council Offices, St. Peter's Hill, Grantham NG31 6PZ ☎ 01476 406080 ✐ k.munford@southkesteven.gov.uk

Environmental / Technical Services: Ms AnnMarie Coulthard, Environmental Health Business Manager, Council Offices, St. Peter's Hill, Grantham NG31 6PZ ☎ 01476 406080 ✐ a.coulthard@southkesteven.gov.uk

Environmental Health: Ms AnnMarie Coulthard, Environmental Health Business Manager, Council Offices, St. Peter's Hill, Grantham NG31 6PZ ☎ 01476 406080 ✐ a.coulthard@southkesteven.gov.uk

SOUTH KESTEVEN

Estates, Property & Valuation: Mr Neil Cucksey, Executive Manager - Property, Council Offices, St. Peter's Hill, Grantham NG31 6PZ ☎ 01476 406224 ✆ n.cucksey@southkesteven.gov.uk

Facilities: Mr Paul Stokes, Venues & Facilities Business Manager, Council Offices, St. Peter's Hill, Grantham NG31 6PZ ☎ 01476 406410 ✆ p.stokes@southkesteven.gov.uk

Finance: Mr Richard Wyles, Corporate Finance Officer, Council Offices, St. Peter's Hill, Grantham NG31 6PZ ☎ 01476 406210 ✆ r.wyles@southkesteven.gov.uk

Grounds Maintenance: Mr Mike Smith, Facilities Team Leader - Operations, Council Offices, St. Peter's Hill, Grantham NG31 6PZ ☎ 01476 406080 ✆ m.smith@southkesteven.gov.uk

Health and Safety: Ms AnnMarie Coulthard, Environmental Health Business Manager, Council Offices, St. Peter's Hill, Grantham NG31 6PZ ☎ 01476 406080 ✆ a.coulthard@southkesteven.gov.uk

Home Energy Conservation: Mr K Munford, Energy Officer, Council Offices, St. Peter's Hill, Grantham NG31 6PZ ☎ 01476 406080 ✆ k.munford@southkesteven.gov.uk

Housing: Ms Lisa Barker, Housing Business Manager, Council Offices, St. Peter's Hill, Grantham NG31 6PZ ☎ 01476 406251 ✆ l.barker@southkesteven.gov.uk

Legal: Mr John Armstrong, Legal & Democratic Business Manager, Council Offices, St. Peter's Hill, Grantham NG31 6PZ ☎ 014476 406103 ✆ j.armstrong@southkesteven.gov.uk

Leisure and Cultural Services: Ms Susie McCahon, Leisure & Amenities Team Leader, Council Offices, St. Peter's Hill, Grantham NG31 6PZ ☎ 01476 406080 ✆ s.mccahon@southkesteven.gov.uk

Licensing: Mr Mark Jones, Neighbourhoods Business Manager, Council Offices, St. Peter's Hill, Grantham NG31 6PZ ☎ 01476 406080 ✆ m.jones@southkesteven.gov.uk

Member Services: Mrs Lucy Youles, Executive Manager - Corporate, Council Offices, St. Peter's Hill, Grantham NG31 6PZ ☎ 01476 406105 ✆ l.youles@southkesteven.gov.uk

Parking: Mr Paul Stokes, Venues & Facilities Business Manager, Council Offices, St. Peter's Hill, Grantham NG31 6PZ ☎ 01476 406410 ✆ p.stokes@southkesteven.gov.uk

Personnel / HR: Mrs Elaine Pepper, Business Manager - People & OD, Council Offices, St. Peter's Hill, Grantham NG31 6PZ ☎ 01476 406132 ✆ e.pepper@southkesteven.gov.uk

Planning: Mr Paul Thomas, Executive Manager - Development & Growth, Council Offices, St. Peter's Hill, Grantham NG31 6PZ ☎ 01476 406162 ✆ p.thomas@southkesteven.gov.uk

Procurement: Mr Richard Wyles, Corporate Finance Officer, Council Offices, St. Peter's Hill, Grantham NG31 6PZ ☎ 01476 406210 ✆ r.wyles@southkesteven.gov.uk

Recycling & Waste Minimisation: Mr Keith Rowe, Street Care Services Business Manager, Council Offices, St. Peter's Hill, Grantham NG31 6PZ ☎ 01476 406080 ✆ k.rowe@southkesteven.gov.uk

Regeneration: Mr Roger Ranson, Spatial & Economic Growth Business Manager, Council Offices, St. Peter's Hill, Grantham NG31 6PZ ☎ 01476 406080 ✆ r.ranson@southkesteven.gov.uk

Staff Training: Mrs Elaine Pepper, Business Manager - People & OD, Council Offices, St. Peter's Hill, Grantham NG31 6PZ ☎ 01476 406132 ✆ e.pepper@southkesteven.gov.uk

Street Scene: Mr Keith Rowe, Street Care Services Business Manager, Council Offices, St. Peter's Hill, Grantham NG31 6PZ ☎ 01476 406080 ✆ k.rowe@southkesteven.gov.uk

COUNCILLORS

Chair: Smith, Judy (CON - Bourne East)
judy.smith@southkesteven.gov.uk

Vice-Chair: Smith, Jacky (CON - Grantham St. Wulfram's)
jacky.smith@southkesteven.gov.uk

Leader of the Council: Adams, Bob (CON - Isaac Newton)
b.adams@southkesteven.gov.uk

Deputy Leader of the Council: Craft, Nick (CON - Belmont)
n.craft@southkesteven.gov.uk

Ashwell, Duncan (CON - Bourne Austerby)
d.ashwell@southkesteven.gov.uk

Baxter, Ashley (IND - Market & West Deeping)

Benn, Stephen (CON - Deeping St James)
s.benn@southkesteven.gov.uk

Bosworth, Pam (CON - Belvoir)
p.bosworth@southkesteven.gov.uk

Broughton, Robert (IND - Market & West Deeping)
b.broughton@southkesteven.gov.uk

Brown, Katherine (CON - Stamford St. George's)
k.brown@southkesteven.gov.uk

Bryant, Terl (CON - Stamford St. John's)
t.bryant@southkesteven.gov.uk

Cartwright, Frances (CON - Morton)
f.cartwright@southkesteven.gov.uk

Chivers, George (CON - Belmont)
g.chivers@southkesteven.gov.uk

Cook, Michael (CON - Grantham St. Vincent's)
m.cook@southkesteven.gov.uk

Cooke, Kelham (CON - Casewick)
k.cooke@southkesteven.gov.uk

Coutts, Lynda (CON - Grantham Barrowby Gate)
l.coutts@southkesteven.gov.uk

Cunningham, Felicity (UKIP - Grantham Earlesfield)
f.cunningham@southkesteven.gov.uk

Dilks, Phil (LAB - Deeping St James)
p.dilks@southkesteven.gov.uk

Dobson, Barry (CON - Dole Wood)
b.dobson@southkesteven.gov.uk

Evans, Damian (CON - Stamford St. John's)

Exton, Mike (CON - Stamford All Saints)
m.exton@southkesteven.gov.uk

Forman, Tracey (LAB - Grantham Earlesfield)
t.forman@southkesteven.gov.uk

Goral, Helen (CON - Grantham Arnoldfield)
h.goral@southkesteven.gov.uk

Griffin, Breda (CON - Stamford All Saints)
b.griffin@southkesteven.gov.uk

Jeal, Graham (CON - Grantham St. Vincent's)
g.jeal@southkesteven.gov.uk

Kaberry-Brown, Rosemary (CON - Peascliffe & Ridgeway)
r.kaberry-brown@southkesteven.gov.uk

King, Michael (CON - Toller)
m.king@southkesteven.gov.uk

Kingman, Jane (CON - Bourne Austerby)
j.kingman@southkesteven.gov.uk

Lee, Matthew (CON - Stamford St. Mary's)
m.lee@southkesteven.gov.uk

Manterfield, Nikki (CON - Grantham Springfield)
n.manterfield@southkesteven.gov.uk

Mapp, David (CON - Bourne West)
d.mapp@southkesteven.gov.uk

Morgan, Charmaine (LAB - Grantham St. Vincent's)
c.morgan@southkesteven.gov.uk

Moseley, Peter (CON - Aveland)
p.moseley@southkesteven.gov.uk

Neilson, Nick (CON - Market & West Deeping)
n.neilson@southkesteven.gov.uk

Powell, Helen (IND - Bourne West)
h.powell@southkesteven.gov.uk

Reid, Robert (CON - Bourne Austerby)
r.reid@southkesteven.gov.uk

Robins, Nick (CON - Castle)
n.robins@southkesteven.gov.uk

Russell, Bob (CON - Bourne East)
b.russell@southkesteven.gov.uk

Sampson, Bob (IND - Loveden Heath)
b.sampson@southkesteven.gov.uk

Selby, Ian (INDNA - Grantham Harrowby)
i.selby@southkesteven.gov.uk

Stephens, Peter (CON - Lincrest)
p.stephens@southkesteven.gov.uk

Stevens, Judy (IND - Deeping St James)
j.stevens@southkesteven.gov.uk

Stokes, Adam (CON - Grantham Springfield)
a.stokes@southkesteven.gov.uk

Stokes, Sarah (CON - Viking)
s.stokes@southkesteven.gov.uk

Stokes, Ian (CON - Peascliffe & Ridgeway)
i.stokes@southkesteven.gov.uk

Sumner, Brian (CON - Stamford St. Mary's)
brian.sumner@southkesteven.gov.uk

Sumner, Brenda (CON - Stamford St. George's)
brenda.sumner@southkesteven.gov.uk

Turner, Frank (CON - Grantham Barrowby Gate)
f.turner@southkesteven.gov.uk

Ward, Dean (CON - Grantham Arnoldfield)
d.ward@southkesteven.gov.uk

Webster, Andrea (CON - Isaac Newton)
a.webster@southkesteven.gov.uk

Westropp, Hannah (CON - Belvoir)
h.westropp@southkesteven.gov.uk

Wilkins, Martin (CON - Glen)
m.wilkins@southkesteven.gov.uk

Wood, Paul (IND - Viking)
p.wood@southkesteven.gov.uk

Woolley, Rosemary (CON - Casewick)
rh.woolley@southkesteven.gov.uk

Wootten, Linda (CON - Grantham Harrowby)
l.wootten@southkesteven.gov.uk

Wootten, Ray (CON - Grantham St. Wulfram's)
r.wootten@southkesteven.gov.uk

POLITICAL COMPOSITION
CON: 45, IND: 6, LAB: 3, UKIP: 1, INDNA: 1

COMMITTEE CHAIRS

Audit: Mr Nick Neilson

Development Control: Mr Martin Wilkins

Licensing: Mrs Pam Bosworth

South Lakeland   D

South Lakeland District Council, South Lakeland House,
Lowther Street, Kendal LA9 4UQ
☎ 01539 733333 ✆ info@southlakeland.gov.uk
🖥 www.southlakeland.gov.uk

FACTS AND FIGURES
Parliamentary Constituencies: Westmorland and Lonsdale
EU Constituencies: North West
Election Frequency: Elections are by thirds

PRINCIPAL OFFICERS

Chief Executive: Mr Lawrence Conway, Chief Executive, South
Lakeland House, Lowther Street, Kendal LA9 4UD
☎ 01539 733333 ✆ l.conway@southlakeland.gov.uk

Senior Management: Ms Debbie Storr, Corporate Director -
Policy & Performance, South Lakeland House, Lowther Street,
Kendal LA9 4UQ ☎ 01539 733333 ✆ d.storr@southlakeland.gov.uk

Senior Management: Mr David Sykes, Director - People &
Places, South Lakeland House, Lowther Street, Kendal LA9 4UQ
☎ 01539 733333 ✆ d.sykes@southlakeland.gov.uk

Building Control: Mr Mark Shipman, Development Management
Group Manager, South Lakeland House, Lowther Street, Kendal
LA9 4UQ ☎ 01536 733333 ✆ m.shipman@southlakeland.gov.uk

SOUTH LAKELAND

PR / Communications: Mr Simon Reynolds, Communications & Customer Services Manager, South Lakeland House, Lowther Street, Kendal LA9 4UQ ☎ 01539 733333 ⁅ s.reynolds@southlakeland.gov.uk

Community Planning: Ms Claire Gould, Policy & Partnership Manager, South Lakeland House, Lowther Street, Kendal LA9 4UQ ☎ 01539 733333 ⁅ c.gould@southlakeland.gov.uk

Community Safety: Ms Claire Gould, Policy & Partnership Manager, South Lakeland House, Lowther Street, Kendal LA9 4UQ ☎ 01539 733333 ⁅ c.gould@southlakeland.gov.uk

Computer Management: Mr Ben Wright, Shared IT Services Manager, South Lakeland House, Lowther Street, Kendal LA9 4UQ ☎ 01768 212206 ⁅ ben.wright@eden.gov.uk

Corporate Services: Ms Debbie Storr, Corporate Director - Policy & Performance, South Lakeland House, Lowther Street, Kendal LA9 4UQ ☎ 01539 733333 ⁅ d.storr@southlakeland.gov.uk

Customer Service: Mr Simon Reynolds, Communications & Customer Services Manager, South Lakeland House, Lowther Street, Kendal LA9 4UQ ☎ 01539 733333 ⁅ s.reynolds@southlakeland.gov.uk

Economic Development: Mr Ian Hassall, Assistant Director - Strategic Development, South Lakeland House, Lowther Street, Kendal LA9 4UQ ☎ 01539 733333 ⁅ ian.hassall@southlakeland.gov.uk

Economic Development: Mr David Sykes, Director - People & Places, South Lakeland House, Lowther Street, Kendal LA9 4UQ ☎ 01539 733333 ⁅ d.sykes@southlakeland.gov.uk

E-Government: Mr Simon Mcvey, Assistant Director - Policy & Performance, South Lakeland House, Lowther Street, Kendal LA9 4UQ ☎ 01539 733333 ⁅ s.mcvey@southlakeland.gov.uk

Electoral Registration: Ms Debbie Storr, Corporate Director - Policy & Performance, South Lakeland House, Lowther Street, Kendal LA9 4UQ ☎ 01539 733333 ⁅ d.storr@southlakeland.gov.uk

Emergency Planning: Mr Lawrence Conway, Chief Executive, South Lakeland House, Lowther Street, Kendal LA9 4UD ☎ 01539 733333 ⁅ l.conway@southlakeland.gov.uk

Energy Management: Ms Claire Gould, Policy & Partnership Manager, South Lakeland House, Lowther Street, Kendal LA9 4UQ ☎ 01539 733333 ⁅ c.gould@southlakeland.gov.uk

Environmental / Technical Services: Ms Fiona Inston, Public Protection Manager, South Lakeland House, Lowther Street, Kendal LA9 4UQ ☎ 01539 733333 ⁅ fiona.inston@southlakeland.gov.uk

Environmental Health: Mr Simon Rowley, Assistant Director - Neighbourhood Services, South Lakeland House, Lowther Street, Kendal LA9 4UQ ☎ 01539 733333 ⁅ s.rowley@southlakeland.gov.uk

Estates, Property & Valuation: Mr Ian Hassall, Assistant Director - Strategic Development, South Lakeland House, Lowther Street, Kendal LA9 4UQ ☎ 01539 733333 ⁅ ian.hassall@southlakeland.gov.uk

Events Manager: Ms Imelda Winters-Lewis, Arts & Events Officer, South Lakeland House, Lowther Street, Kendal LA9 4UQ ☎ 01539 733333 ⁅ l.winterslewis@southlakeland.gov.uk

Facilities: Mr Ian Hassall, Assistant Director - Strategic Development, South Lakeland House, Lowther Street, Kendal LA9 4UQ ☎ 01539 733333 ⁅ ian.hassall@southlakeland.gov.uk

Finance: Ms Shelagh McGregor, Assistant Director - Resources, South Lakeland House, Lowther Street, Kendal LA9 4UQ ☎ 01539 733333 ⁅ s.mcgregor@southlakeland.gov.uk

Fleet Management: Mr George Sierpinski, Fleet Manager, South Lakeland House, Lowther Street, Kendal LA9 4UQ ☎ 01539 733333 ⁅ g.sierpinski@southlakeland.gov.uk

Grounds Maintenance: Mrs Deborah Clarke, Principal Community Spaces Officer, South Lakeland House, Lowther Street, Kendal LA9 4UQ ☎ 01539 733333 ⁅ deborah.clarke@southlakeland.gov.uk

Health and Safety: Mr Andrew Reay, Human Resources Manager, South Lakeland House, Lowther Street, Kendal LA9 4UQ ☎ 01539 733333 ⁅ a.reay@southlakeland.gov.uk

Home Energy Conservation: Mr Ian Hassall, Assistant Director - Strategic Development, South Lakeland House, Lowther Street, Kendal LA9 4UQ ☎ 01539 733333 ⁅ ian.hassall@southlakeland.gov.uk

Home Energy Conservation: Mr David Sykes, Director - People & Places, South Lakeland House, Lowther Street, Kendal LA9 4UQ ☎ 01539 733333 ⁅ d.sykes@southlakeland.gov.uk

Housing: Mr David Sykes, Director - People & Places, South Lakeland House, Lowther Street, Kendal LA9 4UQ ☎ 01539 733333 ⁅ d.sykes@southlakeland.gov.uk

Housing Maintenance: Mrs Cath Purdy, Chief Executive - South Lakes Housing, Bridge Mills Business Centre, Stramongate, Kendal LA9 4BD ☎ 01539 717717 ⁅ c.purdy@southlakeshousing.co.uk

Local Area Agreement: Ms Claire Gould, Policy & Partnership Manager, South Lakeland House, Lowther Street, Kendal LA9 4UQ ☎ 01539 733333 ⁅ c.gould@southlakeland.gov.uk

Legal: Ms Anthea Lowe, Principal Solicitor, South Lakeland House, Lowther Street, Kendal LA9 4UQ ⁅ a.lowe@southlakeland.gov.uk

Leisure and Cultural Services: Mr Ian Hassall, Assistant Director - Strategic Development, South Lakeland House, Lowther Street, Kendal LA9 4UQ ☎ 01539 733333 ⁅ ian.hassall@southlakeland.gov.uk

Leisure and Cultural Services: Mr David Sykes, Director - People & Places, South Lakeland House, Lowther Street, Kendal LA9 4UQ ☎ 01539 733333 ⁅ d.sykes@southlakeland.gov.uk

Licensing: Mr Simon Rowley, Assistant Director - Neighbourhood Services, South Lakeland House, Lowther Street, Kendal LA9 4UQ ☎ 01539 733333 ⁅ s.rowley@southlakeland.gov.uk

Lighting: Mr Simon Rowley, Assistant Director - Neighbourhood Services, South Lakeland House, Lowther Street, Kendal LA9 4UQ ☎ 01539 733333 ⌂ s.rowley@southlakeland.gov.uk

Lottery Funding, Charity and Voluntary: Mr Lawrence Conway, Chief Executive, South Lakeland House, Lowther Street, Kendal LA9 4UD ☎ 01539 733333 ⌂ l.conway@southlakeland.gov.uk

Member Services: Ms Debbie Storr, Corporate Director - Policy & Performance, South Lakeland House, Lowther Street, Kendal LA9 4UQ ☎ 01539 733333 ⌂ d.storr@southlakeland.gov.uk

Parking: Mr Simon Rowley, Assistant Director - Neighbourhood Services, South Lakeland House, Lowther Street, Kendal LA9 4UQ ☎ 01539 733333 ⌂ s.rowley@southlakeland.gov.uk

Partnerships: Ms Claire Gould, Policy & Partnership Manager, South Lakeland House, Lowther Street, Kendal LA9 4UQ ☎ 01539 733333 ⌂ c.gould@southlakeland.gov.uk

Personnel / HR: Mr Andrew Reay, Human Resources Manager, South Lakeland House, Lowther Street, Kendal LA9 4UQ ☎ 01539 733333 ⌂ a.reay@southlakeland.gov.uk

Planning: Mr Ian Hassall, Assistant Director - Strategic Development, South Lakeland House, Lowther Street, Kendal LA9 4UQ ☎ 01539 733333 ⌂ ian.hassall@southlakeland.gov.uk

Planning: Mr David Sykes, Director - People & Places, South Lakeland House, Lowther Street, Kendal LA9 4UQ ☎ 01539 733333 ⌂ d.sykes@southlakeland.gov.uk

Procurement: Ms Karen Crump, Procurement & Contracts Manager, South Lakeland House, Lowther Street, Kendal LA9 4UQ ☎ 01539 733333 ⌂ karen.crump@southlakeland.gov.uk

Recycling & Waste Minimisation: Mr Lawrence Conway, Chief Executive, South Lakeland House, Lowther Street, Kendal LA9 4UD ☎ 01539 733333 ⌂ l.conway@southlakeland.gov.uk

Regeneration: Mr David Sykes, Director - People & Places, South Lakeland House, Lowther Street, Kendal LA9 4UQ ☎ 01539 733333 ⌂ d.sykes@southlakeland.gov.uk

Staff Training: Ms Andrea Wilson, Human Resources Services Manager, South Lakeland House, Lowther Street, Kendal LA9 4UQ ☎ 01539 733333 ⌂ a.wilson@southlakeland.gov.uk

Street Scene: Mr Nick Pearson, Street Scene Manager, South Lakeland House, Lowther Street, Kendal LA9 4UQ ☎ 01539 733333 ⌂ n.pearson@southlakeland.gov.uk

Sustainable Communities: Ms Claire Gould, Policy & Partnership Manager, South Lakeland House, Lowther Street, Kendal LA9 4UQ ☎ 01539 733333 ⌂ c.gould@southlakeland.gov.uk

Sustainable Development: Mr David Sykes, Director - People & Places, South Lakeland House, Lowther Street, Kendal LA9 4UQ ☎ 01539 733333 ⌂ d.sykes@southlakeland.gov.uk

Tourism: Mr David Sykes, Director - People & Places, South Lakeland House, Lowther Street, Kendal LA9 4UQ ☎ 01539 733333 ⌂ d.sykes@southlakeland.gov.uk

Town Centre: Mr David Sykes, Director - People & Places, South Lakeland House, Lowther Street, Kendal LA9 4UQ ☎ 01539 733333 ⌂ d.sykes@southlakeland.gov.uk

Transport: Mr Simon Rowley, Assistant Director - Neighbourhood Services, South Lakeland House, Lowther Street, Kendal LA9 4UQ ☎ 01539 733333 ⌂ s.rowley@southlakeland.gov.uk

Waste Collection and Disposal: Mr Simon Rowley, Assistant Director - Neighbourhood Services, South Lakeland House, Lowther Street, Kendal LA9 4UQ ☎ 01539 733333 ⌂ s.rowley@southlakeland.gov.uk

Waste Management: Mr Simon Rowley, Assistant Director - Neighbourhood Services, South Lakeland House, Lowther Street, Kendal LA9 4UQ ☎ 01539 733333 ⌂ s.rowley@southlakeland.gov.uk

COUNCILLORS

Chair: Emmott, Sylvia (LD - Kendal Stonecross) s.emmott@southlakeslibdems.org.uk

Vice-Chair: Morrell, Eric (LD - Grange North) emorrell5@gmail.com

Leader of the Council: Archibald, Giles (LD - Kendal Fell) g.archibald@southlakeland.gov.uk

Deputy Leader of the Council: Sanderson, Sue (LD - Staveley-in-Cartmel) s.sanderson@southlakeland.gov.uk

Group Leader: Wilson, Mark (LAB - Ulverston East) marcowils@tiscali.co.uk

Airey, James (CON - Low Furness) james.airey@cumbria.gov.uk

Airey, Caroline (CON - Mid Furness) carolineairey@me.com

Audland, Rupert (LD - Milnthorpe) mdc16@gmx.com

Berry, Ben (CON - Windermere Applethwaite & Troutbeck) me@ben-berry.co.uk

Bingham, Roger (CON - Burton & Holme) roger.bingham@cumbria.gov.uk

Bishop-Rowe, Norman (CON - Ulverston Central) normanbishoprowe@gmail.com

Brook, Jonathan (LD - Kendal Parks) j.brook@southlakeland.gov.uk

Butcher, Andrew (CON - Mid Furness) andrewbutcher@talktalk.net

Clough, John (LAB - Ulverston Town) jvcgc2925@gmail.com

Coleman, Stephen (LD - Kendal Strickland) s.coleman@southlakeslibdems.org.uk

Collins, Stan (LD - Staveley-in-Westmorland) stanstheman@cix.co.uk

Cooper, Brian (CON - Burton & Holme) b.cooper47@yahoo.co.uk

SOUTH LAKELAND

Cotton, Nick (LD - Sedbergh & Kirkby Lonsdale)
n.cotton@southlakeslibdems.org.uk

Curwen, Joss (IND - Broughton)

Dixon, Philip (LD - Kendal Highgate)
p.dixon@southlakeslibdems.org.uk

Eccles, Sheila (LD - Crooklands)
sheila.eccles@yahoo.co.uk

Evans, Shirley (LD - Kendal Far Cross)
s.evans@southlakeslibdems.org.uk

Evans, David (LD - Kendal Mintsfeet)
d.evans@southlakeslibdems.org.uk

Feeney-Johnson, Claire (LD - Kendal Nether)
c.feeney-johnson@southlakeslibdems.org.uk

Finch, Alvin (LD - Kendal Kirkland)
a.finch@southlakeslibdems.org.uk

Fletcher, David (LIB - Hawkeshead)
d.fletecher@southlakeslibdems.org.uk

Gardner, Gill (LD - Holker)
gilliangardner@icloud.com

Gray, Brenda (LD - Kendal Oxenholme & Natland)
brendacgray@yahoo.co.uk

Hall, Anne (CON - Coniston & Crake Valley)
annehall070@gmail.com

Halliday, Heidi (LD - Ambleside & Grasmere)
heidihalliday@gmail.com

Harvey, Tom (CON - Grange South)
tom@tom-harvey.co.uk

Hogg, Chris (LD - Kendal Castle)
chris.hogg@southlakeland.gov.uk

Holmes, John (CON - Lyth Valley)
cjh@coyote-software.com

Hurst-Jones, Keith (LD - Burneside)
fairhurst3@googlemail.com

Irving, Helen (CON - Ulverston North)
helen1961@talktalk.net

Jenkinson, Janette (CON - Ulverston West)
jejenky@aol.com

Jones, Dyan (LD - Windermere Town)
djjonessldc@btinternet.com

Lancaster, Kevin (CON - Sedbergh & Kirkby Lonsdale)
kevin@sarthwaite.com

Mackie, Mel (CON - Sedbergh & Kirkby Lonsdale)
mel.mac@uwclub.net

McSweeney, Pete (LD - Arnside & Beetham)
p.mcsweeney@southlakeslibdems.org.uk

Rawlinson, Annie (LD - Levens)
annierawlinson@hotmail.com

Rees, Vivienne (LD - Ambleside & Grasmere)
v.rees@southlakeslibdems.org.uk

Rigg, Amanda (CON - Ulverston South)
riggamanda76@gmail.com

Severn, Matt (LD - Kendal Underley)
m.severn@southlakeslibdems.org.uk

Stewart, Ian (LD - Arnside & Beetham)
l.stewart@southlakeslibdems.org.uk

Thornton, Peter (LD - Whinfell)
p.thornton@southlakeland.gov.uk

Vincent, Graham (LD - Kendal Romney)
g.vincent@southlakeland.gov.uk

Walker, Phil (LD - Kendal Heron Hill)
phil.walker@southlakeland.gov.uk

Williams, David (CON - Windermere Bowness South)
fellake@aol.com

Wilson, Mary (LD - Cartmel & Grange West)
rodmary.wilson@googlemail.com

POLITICAL COMPOSITION
LD: 30, CON: 16, LAB: 2, LIB: 1, IND: 1, Vacant: 1

COMMITTEE CHAIRS
Audit: Mr Stephen Coleman

Licensing: Mrs Sheila Eccles

Planning: Mrs Mary Wilson

South Lanarkshire   S

South Lanarkshire Council, Council Offices, Almada Street, Hamilton ML3 0AA
☎ 01698 454444 🖷 01698 454275 🖥 www.southlanarkshire.gov.uk

FACTS AND FIGURES
Parliamentary Constituencies: Dumfriesshire, Clydesdale and Tweedale, East Kilbride, Strathaven and Lesmahagow, Lanark & Hamilton East, Rutherglen and Hamilton West
EU Constituencies: Scotland
Election Frequency: Elections are of whole council

PRINCIPAL OFFICERS

Chief Executive: Mr Lindsay Freeland, Chief Executive, Council Offices, Almada Street, Hamilton ML3 0AL ☎ 01698 454208
⌐ lindsay.freeland@southlanarkshire.gov.uk

Senior Management: Ms Val de Souza, Director - Health & Social Care, Council Offices, Almada Street, Hamilton ML3 0AA
☎ 01698 453700 ⌐ val.desouza@southlanarkshire.gov.uk

Senior Management: Mr Jim Gilhooly, Executive Director - Education Resources, Council Offices, Almada Street, Hamilton ML3 0AA ☎ 01698 454379 ⌐ jim.gilhooly@southlanarkshire.gov.uk

Senior Management: Mr Danny Lowe, Executive Director - Housing & Technical Resources, Council Offices, Almada Street, Hamilton ML3 0AA ☎ 01698 455621
⌐ danny.lowe@southlanarkshire.gov.uk

Senior Management: Mr Paul Manning, Executive Director - Finance & Corporate Resources, Council Offices, Almada Street, Hamilton ML3 0AA ☎ 01698 454530
⌐ paul.manning@southlanarkshire.gov.uk

SOUTH LANARKSHIRE

Senior Management: Mr Michael McGlynn, Executive Director - Community & Enterprise Resources, Montrose House, 154 Montrose Crescent, Hamilton ML3 6LB ☎ 01698 454294 ✆ michael.mcglynn@southlanarkshire.gov.uk

Architect, Building / Property Services: Mr Danny Lowe, Executive Director - Housing & Technical Resources, Council Offices, Almada Street, Hamilton ML3 0AA ☎ 01698 455621 ✆ danny.lowe@southlanarkshire.gov.uk

Building Control: Mr Michael McGlynn, Executive Director - Community & Enterprise Resources, Montrose House, 154 Montrose Crescent, Hamilton ML3 6LB ☎ 01698 454294 ✆ michael.mcglynn@southlanarkshire.gov.uk

Children / Youth Services: Ms Anne Donaldson, Head of Education (Inclusion), Council Offices, Almada Street, Hamilton ML3 0AA ☎ 01698 454452 ✆ anne.donaldson@southlanarkshire.gov.uk

Civil Registration: Ms Teresa Stone, Licensing & Registration Manager, Council Offices, Almada Street, Hamilton ML3 0AA ☎ 01698 454806 ✆ teresa.stone@southlanarkshire.gov.uk

PR / Communications: Mr Tom Little, Head of Communications & Strategy, Council Offices, Almada Street, Hamilton ML3 0AA ☎ 01698 454904 ✆ tom.little@southlanarkshire.gov.uk

Community Planning: Mr Alistair McKinnon, Head of Support Services - Community & Enterprise, Council Offices, Almada Street, Hamilton ML3 0AA ☎ 01698 454700 ✆ alistair.mckinnon@southlanarkshire.gov.uk

Community Planning: Mr Neil Reid, Improvement & Community Planning Manager, Council Offices, Almada Street, Hamilton ML3 0AA ☎ 01698 454618 ✆ neil.reid@southlanarkshire.gov.uk

Computer Management: Mr Brian Teaz, Head of Information Technology Services, Council Offices, Almada Street, Hamilton ML3 0AA ☎ 01698 455648 ✆ brian.teaz@southlanarkshire.gov.uk

Corporate Services: Mr Paul Manning, Executive Director - Finance & Corporate Resources, Council Offices, Almada Street, Hamilton ML3 0AA ☎ 01698 454530 ✆ paul.manning@southlanarkshire.gov.uk

Corporate Services: Ms Geraldine McCann, Head of Administration & Legal Services, Montrose House, 154 Montrose Crescent, Hamilton ML3 6LL ☎ 01698 454516 ✆ geraldine.mccann@southlanarkshire.gov.uk

Economic Development: Ms Pauline Elliot, Head of Planning & Economic Development, Montrose House, 154 Montrose Crescent, Hamilton ML3 6LB ☎ 01698 455126 ✆ pauline.elliot@southlanarkshire.gov.uk

Education: Mr Jim Gilhooly, Executive Director - Education Resources, Council Offices, Almada Street, Hamilton ML3 0AA ☎ 01698 454379 ✆ jim.gilhooly@southlanarkshire.gov.uk

Education: Mr Tony McDaid, Head of Education (Curriculum & Quality), Council Offices, Almada Street, Hamilton ML3 0AA ☎ 01698 454475 ✆ tony.mcdaid@southlanarkshire.gov.uk

E-Government: Mr Brian Teaz, Head of Information Technology Services, Council Offices, Almada Street, Hamilton ML3 0AA ☎ 01698 455648 ✆ brian.teaz@southlanarkshire.gov.uk

Electoral Registration: Mr Paul Manning, Executive Director - Finance & Corporate Resources, Council Offices, Almada Street, Hamilton ML3 0AA ☎ 01698 454530 ✆ paul.manning@southlanarkshire.gov.uk

Emergency Planning: Mr Ken Wratten, Resilience Adviser, Council Offices, Almada Street, Hamilton ML3 0AA ☎ 01698 454648 ✆ ken.wratten@southlanarkshire.gov.uk

Environmental Health: Ms Shirley Clelland, Head of Environmental & Fleet Services, Council Offices, Almada Street, Hamilton ML3 0AA ☎ 01698 454708 ✆ shirley.clelland@southlanarkshire.gov.uk

Estates, Property & Valuation: Mr Frank McCafferty, Head of Property Services, Council Offices, Almada Street, Hamilton ML3 0AA ☎ 01698 454073 ✆ frank.mccafferty@southlanarkshire.gov.uk

Events Manager: Mrs Angie Moakler, Design & Production Manager, Council Offices, Almada Street, Hamilton ML3 0AA ☎ 01698 453853 ✆ angie.moakler@southlanarkshire.gov.uk

Facilities: Mr Stephen Kelly, Head of Facilities & Cultural Services, Community Resources, Council Offices, Almada Street, Hamilton ML3 0AA ☎ 01698 454705 ✆ stephen.kelly@southlanarkshire.gov.uk

Finance: Mr Paul Manning, Executive Director - Finance & Corporate Resources, Council Offices, Almada Street, Hamilton ML3 0AA ☎ 01698 454530 ✆ paul.manning@southlanarkshire.gov.uk

Fleet Management: Ms Shirley Clelland, Head of Environmental & Fleet Services, Blantyre, Hamilton G72 0JP ☎ 01698 454708 ✆ shirley.clelland@southlanarkshire.gov.uk

Grounds Maintenance: Mr Steven Kelly, Head of Land & Fleet Services, Blantyre, Hamilton G72 0JP ☎ 01698 454577 ✆ steven.kelly@southlanarkshire.gov.uk

Health and Safety: Mr Ken Wratten, Resilience Adviser, Council Offices, Almada Street, Hamilton ML3 0AA ☎ 01698 454648 ✆ ken.wratten@southlanarkshire.gov.uk

Highways: Mr Gordon Mackay, Head of Roads & Transportation, Montrose House, 154 Montrose Crescent, Hamilton ML3 6LL ☎ 01698 454484 ✆ gordon.mackay@southlanarkshire.gov.uk

Housing: Mr Danny Lowe, Executive Director - Housing & Technical Resources, Council Offices, Almada Street, Hamilton ML3 0AA ☎ 01698 455621 ✆ danny.lowe@southlanarkshire.gov.uk

Housing: Mr Patrick Murphy, Head of Support Services for Housing & Tech Resources, Council Offices, Almada Street, Hamilton ML3 0AA ☎ 01698 454065 ✆ patrick.j.murphy@southlanarkshire.gov.uk

Legal: Ms Geraldine McCann, Head of Administration & Legal Services, Montrose House, 154 Montrose Crescent, Hamilton ML3 6LL ☎ 01698 454516 ✆ geraldine.mccann@southlanarkshire.gov.uk

SOUTH LANARKSHIRE

Leisure and Cultural Services: Mr Gerry Campbell, General Manager, South Lanarkshire Leisure Ltd, Floor 1, North Stand, Cadzow Avenue, Hamilton ML3 0LX ☎ 01698 476095 ✒ gerry.campbell@southlanarkshire.gov.uk

Licensing: Ms Geraldine McCann, Head of Administration & Legal Services, Montrose House, 154 Montrose Crescent, Hamilton ML3 6LL ☎ 01698 454516 ✒ geraldine.mccann@southlanarkshire.gov.uk

Lifelong Learning: Ms Anne Donaldson, Head of Education (Inclusion), Council Offices, Almada Street, Hamilton ML3 0AA ☎ 01698 454452 ✒ anne.donaldson@southlanarkshire.gov.uk

Lighting: Mr David McNair, Lighting Engineer, Montrose House, 154 Montrose Crescent, Hamilton ML3 6LL ☎ 01698 452401 ✒ david.black@southlanarkshire.gov.uk

Lottery Funding, Charity and Voluntary: Mr John Batchelor, Team Leader - Funding & Development, Enterprise Resources, 154 Montrose Crescent, Hamilton ML3 6LB ☎ 01698 455129 ✒ john.batchelor@southlanarkshire.gov.uk

Member Services: Ms Linda Cunningham, Member Services Manager & PA to Leader, Council Offices, Almada Street, Hamilton ML3 0AA ☎ 01698 454027 ✒ linda.cunningham@southlanarkshire.gov.uk

Parking: Mr Donald Gibson, Parking Manager, Brandon Gate, 1 Leechlee Road, Hamilton ML3 0XB ☎ 01698 453528 ✒ donald.gibson@southlanarkshire.gov.uk

Personnel / HR: Ms Kay McVeigh, Head of Personnel Services, Council Offices, Almada Street, Hamilton ML3 0AA ☎ 01698 454330 ✒ kay.mcveigh@southlanarkshire.gov.uk

Planning: Mr Michael McGlynn, Executive Director - Community & Enterprise Resources, Montrose House, 154 Montrose Crescent, Hamilton ML3 6LB ☎ 01698 454294 ✒ michael.mcglynn@southlanarkshire.gov.uk

Procurement: Mr Peter Field, Procurement Manager, Council Offices, Almada Street, Hamilton ML3 0AA ☎ 01698 454707 ✒ peter.field@southlanarkshire.gov.uk

Public Libraries: Mr Iain Walker, Library & Community Learning Services Manager, Council Offices, Almada Street, Hamilton ML3 0AA ☎ 01698 456144 ✒ iain.walker@southlanarkshire.gov.uk

Recycling & Waste Minimisation: Mr Charlie Kelly, Land Services Manager - Environmental, Council Offices, Almada Street, Hamilton ML3 0AA ☎ 01698 717777 ✒ land.services@southlanarkshire.gov.uk

Regeneration: Ms Pauline Elliot, Head of Planning & Economic Development, Montrose House, 154 Montrose Crescent, Hamilton ML3 6LB ☎ 01698 455126 ✒ pauline.elliot@southlanarkshire.gov.uk

Road Safety: Ms Eleanor Gibson, Road Safety Officer, Montrose House, 154 Montrose Crescent, Hamilton ML3 6LL ☎ 01698 453617 ✒ eleanor.gibson@southlanarkshire.gov.uk

Social Services: Ms Val de Souza, Director - Health & Social Care, Council Offices, Almada Street, Hamilton ML3 0AA ☎ 01698 453700 ✒ val.desouza@southlanarkshire.gov.uk

Social Services: Ms Brenda Hutchinson, Head of Older People & Adult Services, Council Offices, Almada Street, Hamilton ML3 0AA ☎ 01698 453783 ✒ brenda.hutchinson@southlanarkshire.gov.uk

Staff Training: Mrs Gill Bhatti, Employee Development & Diversity Manager, Council Offices, Almada Street, Hamilton ML3 0AQ ☎ 01698 455604 ✒ gill.bhatti@southlanarkshire.gov.uk

Sustainable Communities: Mr Simon Carey, Regeneration & Inclusion Manager, Enterprise Resources, 154 Montrose Crescent, Hamilton ML3 6LB ☎ 01698 453812 ✒ simon.carey@southlanarkshire.gov.uk

Sustainable Development: Mr Charlie Kelly, Land Services Manager - Environmental, Council Offices, Almada Street, Hamilton ML3 0AA ☎ 01698 717777 ✒ land.services@southlanarkshire.gov.uk

Town Centre: Mr Jim McNally, Town Centre Manager, Enterprise Resources, 154 Montrose Crescent, Hamilton ML3 6LB ☎ 01698 455103 ✒ jim.mcnally@southlanarkshire.gov.uk

Traffic Management: Mr Gordon Mackay, Head of Roads & Transportation, Montrose House, 154 Montrose Crescent, Hamilton ML3 6LL ☎ 01698 454484 ✒ gordon.mackay@southlanarkshire. gov.uk

Transport: Mr Gordon Mackay, Head of Roads & Transportation, Montrose House, 154 Montrose Crescent, Hamilton ML3 6LL ☎ 01698 454484 ✒ gordon.mackay@southlanarkshire.gov.uk

Waste Collection and Disposal: Mr Steven Kelly, Head of Land & Fleet Services, Blantyre, Hamilton G72 0JP ☎ 01698 454577 ✒ steven.kelly@southlanarkshire.gov.uk

Waste Management: Mr Steven Kelly, Head of Land & Fleet Services, Blantyre, Hamilton G72 0JP ☎ 01698 454577 ✒ steven.kelly@southlanarkshire.gov.uk

COUNCILLORS

Leader of the Council: McAvoy, Edward (LAB - Rutherglen Central & North)
councillor.mcavoy@southlanarkshire.gov.uk

Adams, Lynn (SNP - Hamilton North & East)
lynn.adams@southlanarkshire.gov.uk

Anderson, John (SNP - East Kilbride Central South)
j.anderson@southlanarkshire.gov.uk

Archer, Ed (IND - Clydesdale North)
ed.archer@southlanarkshire.gov.uk

Barker, Ralph (LAB - Clydesdale East)
ralph.barker@southlanarkshire.gov.uk

Brogan, Walter (LAB - Cambuslang East)
walter.brogan@southlanarkshire.gov.uk

Brown, Robert (LD - Rutherglen South)
robert.brown@southlanarkshire.gov.uk

Buchanan, Archie (SNP - East Kilbride South)
archie.buchanan@southlanarkshire.gov.uk

Burns, Jackie (LAB - Larkhall)
jackie.burns@southlanarkshire.gov.uk

Cairney, John (LAB - East Kilbride East)
john.cairney@southlanarkshire.gov.uk

Campbell, Graeme (IND - Avondale & Stonehouse)
graeme.campbell@southlanarkshire.gov.uk

Carmichael, Andy (LAB - Larkhall)
andy.carmichael@southlanarkshire.gov.uk

Clark, Gordon (SNP - Rutherglen Central & North)
gordon.clark@southlanarkshire.gov.uk

Clearie, Russell (LAB - Cambuslang West)
russell.clearie@southlanarkshire.gov.uk

Clearie, Pam (LAB - Cambuslang East)
pamela.clearie@southlanarkshire.gov.uk

Convery, Gerry (LAB - East Kilbride Central South)
gerry.convery@southlanarkshire.gov.uk

Cooper, Margaret (LAB - Avondale & Stonehouse)
margaret.cooper@southlanarkshire.gov.uk

Craig, Peter (SNP - Larkhall)
peter.craig@southlanarkshire.gov.uk

Deanie, Christine (SNP - Cambuslang East)
christine.deanie@southlanarkshire.gov.uk

Devlin, Maureen (LAB - Bothwell & Uddingston)
maureen.devlin@southlanarkshire.gov.uk

Docherty, James (LAB - East Kilbride South)
james.dockerty@southlanarkshire.gov.uk

Dorman, Isobel (SNP - Avondale & Stonehouse)
isobel.dorman@southlanarkshire.gov.uk

Dunsmuir, Hugh (LAB - Blantyre)
hugh.dunsmuir@southlanarkshire.gov.uk

Edwards, Douglas (SNP - East Kilbride South)
douglas.edwards@southlanarkshire.gov.uk

Falconer, Allan (LAB - Hamilton West & Earnock)
allan.falconer@southlanarkshire.gov.uk

Gallacher, Stuart (LAB - Hamilton South)
stuart.gallacher@southlanarkshire.gov.uk

Gauld, Bev (IND - Clydesdale East)
beverly.gauld@southlanarkshire.gov.uk

Greenshields, George (LAB - Clydesdale South)
george.greenshields@southlanarkshire.gov.uk

Hamilton, Lynsey (LAB - Clydesdale West)
lynsey.hamilton@southlanarkshire.gov.uk

Handibode, Jim (LAB - Blantyre)
james.handibode@southlanarkshire.gov.uk

Holman, Bill (SNP - Avondale & Stonehouse)
bill.holman@southlanarkshire.gov.uk

Horne, Graeme (SNP - Hamilton West & Earnock)
graeme.horne@southlanarkshire.gov.uk

Kegg, Anne (CON - Bothwell & Uddingston)
anne.kegg@southlanarkshire.gov.uk

Kerr, Susan (LAB - East Kilbride Central South)
susan.kerr@southlanarkshire.gov.uk

Killen, Gerard (LAB - Rutherglen South)
gerard.killen@southlanarkshire.gov.uk

Lee, Pat (SNP - Clydesdale West)
pat.lee@southlanarkshire.gov.uk

Lennon, Monica (LAB - Hamilton North & East)
monica.lennon@southlanarkshire.gov.uk

Logan, Eileen (LAB - Clydesdale West)
eileen.logan@southlanarkshire.gov.uk

Lowe, Joe (LAB - Hamilton South)
joe.lowe@southlanarkshire.gov.uk

Maggs, Anne (SNP - East Kilbride Central North)
anne.maggs@southlanarkshire.gov.uk

McCaig, Brian (LAB - Hamilton South)
brian.mccaig@southlanarkshire.gov.uk

McClymont, Catherine (LAB - Clydesdale North)
catherine.mcclymon@southlanarkshire.gov.uk

McColl, Clare (SNP - Cambuslang West)
clare.mccoll@southlanarshire.gov.uk

McDonald, Lesley (SNP - Larkhall)
lesley.mcdonald@southlanarkshire.gov.uk

McGinaly, Janice (LAB - East Kilbride West)
janice.mcginlay@southlanarkshire.gov.uk

McGuigan, Jim (SNP - Bothwell & Uddingston)
jim.mcguigan@southlanarkshire.gov.uk

McInnes, Alex (LAB - Clydesdale South)
alex.mcinnes@southlanarkshire.gov.uk

McKenna, Brian (LAB - Rutherglen South)
brian.mckenna@southlanarkshire.gov.uk

McKenna, Denis (LAB - Rutherglen Central & North)
denis.mckenna@southlanarkshire.gov.uk

McKeown, Jean (LAB - Hamilton West & Earnock)
jean.mckeown@southlanarkshire.gov.uk

McLachlan, Davie (LAB - Hamilton North & East)
davie.mclachlan@southlanarkshire.gov.uk

McNamee, John (LAB - Blantyre)
john.mcnamee@southlanarkshire.gov.uk

Menzies, John (SNP - Hamilton West & Earnock)
john.menzies@southlanarkshire.gov.uk

Miller, Gladys (SNP - East Kilbride East)
gladys.miller@southlanarkshire.gov.uk

Mitchell, Alice-Marie (LAB - East Kilbride Central North)
alice.mitchell@southlanarkshire.gov.uk

Muir, Gordon (LAB - Clydesdale South)
gordon.muir@southlanarkshire.gov.uk

Ross, John (SNP - Hamilton South)
johnm.ross@southlanarkshire.gov.uk

Shaw, Vivienne (SNP - Clydesdale North)
vivienne.shaw@southlanarkshire.gov.uk

Shearer, David (SNP - Clydesdale West)
david.shearer@southlanarkshire.gov.uk

Simpson, Graham (CON - East Kilbride West)
graham.simpson@southlanarkshire.gov.uk

Stewart, Hamish (CON - Clydesdale East)
hamish.stewart@southlanarkshire.gov.uk

SOUTH LANARKSHIRE

Thompson, Chris (LAB - East Kilbride Central North)
councillor.thompson@southlanarkshire.gov.uk

Thomson, Bert (LAB - Blantyre)
bert.thomson@southlanarkshire.gov.uk

Tullett, Richard (LAB - Cambuslang West)
richard.tullett@southlanarkshire.gov.uk

Wardhaugh, Sheena (SNP - East Kilbride Central North)
sheena.wardhaugh@southlanarkshire.gov.uk

Wardhaugh, Jim (SNP - East Kilbride East)
james.wardhaugh@southlanarkshire.gov.uk

Watson, David (SNP - East Kilbride West)
david.watson@southlanarkshire.gov.uk

POLITICAL COMPOSITION
LAB: 37, SNP: 23, CON: 3, IND: 3, LD: 1

South Norfolk   D

South Norfolk District Council, South Norfolk House, Swan
Lane, Long Stratton NR15 2XE
☎ 01508533633 ⁰ council@s-norfolk.gov.uk
🖥 www.south-norfolk.gov.uk

FACTS AND FIGURES
Parliamentary Constituencies: Norfolk Mid, Norfolk South,
Norwich South
EU Constituencies: Eastern
Election Frequency: Elections are of whole council

PRINCIPAL OFFICERS

Chief Executive: Ms Sandra Dinneen, Chief Executive, South
Norfolk House, Swan Lane, Long Stratton NR15 2XE
☎ 01508 533603 ⁰ sdinneen@s-norfolk.gov.uk

Senior Management: Mrs Paula Boyce, Director - Community
Services, South Norfolk House, Swan Lane, Long Stratton NR15
2XE ☎ 01508 533703 ⁰ pboyce@s-norfolk.gov.uk

Senior Management: Mr Tim Horspole, Director - Growth &
Localism, South Norfolk House, Swan Lane, Long Stratton NR15
2XE ☎ 01508 533806 ⁰ thorspole@s-norfolk.gov.uk

Senior Management: Mrs Debbie Lorimer, Director - Business
Development, South Norfolk House, Swan Lane, Long Stratton
NR15 2XE ☎ 01508 533981 ⁰ dlorimer@s-norfolk.gov.uk

Architect, Building / Property Services: Ms Renata Garfoot,
Property Manager, South Norfolk House, Swan Lane, Long Stratton
NR15 2XE ☎ 01508 533749 ⁰ rgarfoot@s-norfolk.gov.uk

Best Value: Mr Andrew Mewes, Projects & Performance Manager,
South Norfolk House, Swan Lane, Long Stratton NR15 2XE
☎ 01508 533656 ⁰ amewes@s-norfolk.gov.uk

Building Control: Ms Emma Youngman, CNC Service Manager,
South Norfolk House, Swan Lane, Long Stratton NR15 2XE
☎ 01508 533983 ⁰ eyoungman@s-norfolk.gov.uk

Catering Services: Mr Neil Dyball, Facilities Manager, South
Norfolk House, Swan Lane, Long Stratton NR15 2XE
☎ 01508 533786 ⁰ ndyball@s-norfolk.gov.uk

PR / Communications: Mr Jon Pyle, Communications Manager,
South Norfolk House, Swan Lane, Long Stratton NR15 2XE
☎ 01508 533631 ⁰ jpyle@s-norfolk.gov.uk

Community Planning: Mr Adam Nicholls, Planning Policy
Manager, South Norfolk House, Swan Lane, Long Stratton NR15
2XE ☎ 01508 533809 ⁰ anicholls@s-norfolk.gov.uk

Community Safety: Mr Bob Wade, Head of Environmental
Services, South Norfolk House, Swan Lane, Long Stratton NR15
2XE ☎ 01508 533787 ⁰ bwade@s-norfolk.gov.uk

Computer Management: Mr Alan Quinton, ICT Operations
Manager, South Norfolk House, Swan Lane, Long Stratton NR15
2XE ☎ 01508 533876 ⁰ aquinton@s-norfolk.gov.uk

Corporate Services: Mrs Debbie Lorimer, Director - Business
Development, South Norfolk House, Swan Lane, Long Stratton
NR15 2XE ☎ 01508 533981 ⁰ dlorimer@s-norfolk.gov.uk

Customer Service: Ms Amanda Adams, Corporate Customer
Services Manager, South Norfolk House, Swan Lane, Long Stratton
NR15 2XE ☎ 01508 533773 ⁰ aadams@s-norfolk.gov.uk

Economic Development: Mr Julian Munson, Head of Growth &
Economic Development, South Norfolk House, Swan Lane, Long
Stratton NR15 2XE ☎ 01508 533763 ⁰ jmunson@s-norfolk.gov.uk

E-Government: Mr Michael Sage, Head of Business Improvement,
South Norfolk House, Swan Lane, Long Stratton NR15 2XE
☎ 01508 535345 ⁰ msage@s-norfolk.gov.uk

Electoral Registration: Ms Julia Tovee-Galey, Electoral Services
Manager, South Norfolk House, Swan Lane, Long Stratton NR15
2XE ☎ 01508 533795 ⁰ jtovee@s-norfolk.gov.uk

Emergency Planning: Ms Jenny Bloomfield, Emergency Planning
Officer, South Norfolk House, Swan Lane, Long Stratton NR15 2XE
☎ 01508 533607 ⁰ jbloomfield@s-norfolk.gov.uk

Energy Management: Mr Tony Cooke, Housing Access &
Standards Manager, South Norfolk Council, Swan Lane, Long
Stratton NR15 2XE ☎ 01508 533712 ⁰ tcooke@s-norfolk.gov.uk

Environmental / Technical Services: Mrs Paula Boyce, Director
- Community Services, South Norfolk House, Swan Lane, Long
Stratton NR15 2XE ☎ 01508 533703 ⁰ pboyce@s-norfolk.gov.uk

Environmental / Technical Services: Mr Bob Wade, Head of
Environmental Services, South Norfolk House, Swan Lane, Long
Stratton NR15 2XE ☎ 01508 533787 ⁰ bwade@s-norfolk.gov.uk

Environmental Health: Mr Adrian Nicholas, Environmental
Protection Manager, South Norfolk House, Swan Lane, Long
Stratton NR15 2XE ☎ 01508 533722 ⁰ anicholas@s-norfolk.gov.uk

Environmental Health: Mr Bob Wade, Head of Environmental Services, South Norfolk House, Swan Lane, Long Stratton NR15 2XE ☎ 01508 533787 ⁂ bwade@s-norfolk.gov.uk

Estates, Property & Valuation: Ms Renata Garfoot, Property Manager, South Norfolk House, Swan Lane, Long Stratton NR15 2XE ☎ 01508 533749 ⁂ rgarfoot@s-norfolk.gov.uk

Events Manager: Ms Laura Woollacott, Events Co-ordinator, South Norfolk House, Swan Lane, Long Stratton NR15 2XE ☎ 01508 533816 ⁂ lwoollacott@s-norfolk.gov.uk

Facilities: Mr Neil Dyball, Facilities Manager, South Norfolk House, Swan Lane, Long Stratton NR15 2XE ☎ 01508 533786 ⁂ ndyball@s-norfolk.gov.uk

Finance: Mrs Debbie Lorimer, Director - Business Development, South Norfolk House, Swan Lane, Long Stratton NR15 2XE ☎ 01508 533981 ⁂ dlorimer@s-norfolk.gov.uk

Grounds Maintenance: Mr James Fairclough, Waste & Cleansing Service Manager, South Norfolk House, Swan Lane, Long Stratton NR15 2XE ☎ 01603 819992 ⁂ jfairclough@s-norfolk.gov.uk

Grounds Maintenance: Mr Bob Wade, Head of Environmental Services, South Norfolk House, Swan Lane, Long Stratton NR15 2XE ☎ 01508 533787 ⁂ bwade@s-norfolk.gov.uk

Health and Safety: Mr Phil Rose, Health & Safety Advisor, South Norfolk House, Swan Lane, Long Stratton NR15 2XE ☎ 01508 533667 ⁂ prose@s-norfolk.gov.uk

Housing: Mr Martyn Swann, Housing & Public Health Manager, South Norfolk House, Swan Lane, Long Stratton NR15 2XE ☎ 01508 533694 ⁂ mswann@s-norfolk.gov.uk

Legal: Ms Leah Micklebourgh, Governance & Business Manager, South Norfolk House, Swan Lane, Long Stratton NR15 2XE ☎ 01508 533954 ⁂ lmicklebourgh@s-norfolk.gov.uk

Leisure and Cultural Services: Mr Steve Goddard, Head of Leisure Services, South Norfolk House, Swan Lane, Long Stratton NR15 2XE ☎ 01508 533962 ⁂ sgoddard@s-norfolk.gov.uk

Licensing: Ms Grizelle Britton, Licensing, Food & Safety Team Leader, South Norfolk House, Swan Lane, Long Stratton NR15 2XE ☎ 01508 533697 ⁂ gbritton@s-norfolk.gov.uk

Licensing: Mr Julian Munson, Head of Growth & Economic Development, South Norfolk House, Swan Lane, Long Stratton NR15 2XE ☎ 01508 533763 ⁂ jmunson@s-norfolk.gov.uk

Member Services: Mrs Claire White, Democratic Services Team Leader, South Norfolk House, Swan Lane, Long Stratton NR15 2XE ☎ 01508 533669 ⁂ cwhite@s-norfolk.gov.uk

Parking: Ms Grizelle Britton, Licensing, Food & Safety Team Leader, South Norfolk House, Swan Lane, Long Stratton NR15 2XE ☎ 01508 533697 ⁂ gbritton@s-norfolk.gov.uk

Partnerships: Ms Sam Cayford, Independent Living Team Leader, South Norfolk House, Swan Lane, Long Stratton NR15 2XE ☎ 01508 533694 ⁂ scayford@s-norfolk.gov.uk

Personnel / HR: Ms Serena Bremner, Head of HR, South Norfolk House, Swan Lane, Long Stratton NR15 2XE ☎ 01508 533664 ⁂ sbremner@s-norfolk.gov.uk

Planning: Ms Helen Mellors, Development Manager, South Norfolk House, Swan Lane, Long Stratton NR15 2XE ☎ 01508 533789 ⁂ hmellors@s-norfolk.gov.uk

Procurement: Mr Matthew Fernandez-Graham, Accountancy Manager & Deputy S151 Officer, South Norfolk House, Swan Lane, Long Stratton NR15 2XE ☎ 01508 533919 ⁂ mgraham@s-norfolk.gov.uk

Procurement: Mr Ian Purdom, Procurement Manager, South Norfolk House, Swan Lane, Long Stratton NR15 2XE ☎ 01508 533645 ⁂ ipurdom@s-norfolk.gov.uk

Recycling & Waste Minimisation: Mrs Paula Boyce, Director - Community Services, South Norfolk House, Swan Lane, Long Stratton NR15 2XE ☎ 01508 533703 ⁂ pboyce@s-norfolk.gov.uk

Recycling & Waste Minimisation: Mr Bob Wade, Head of Environmental Services, South Norfolk House, Swan Lane, Long Stratton NR15 2XE ☎ 01508 533787 ⁂ bwade@s-norfolk.gov.uk

Regeneration: Mr Julian Munson, Head of Growth & Economic Development, South Norfolk House, Swan Lane, Long Stratton NR15 2XE ☎ 01508 533763 ⁂ jmunson@s-norfolk.gov.uk

Staff Training: Ms Jeanette Evans, Learning & Development Advisor, South Norfolk House, Swan Lane, Long Stratton NR15 2XE ☎ 01508 533937 ⁂ jevans@s-norfolk.gov.uk

Street Scene: Mr Bob Wade, Head of Environmental Services, South Norfolk House, Swan Lane, Long Stratton NR15 2XE ☎ 01508 533787 ⁂ bwade@s-norfolk.gov.uk

Sustainable Communities: Mr Tim Horspole, Director - Growth & Localism, South Norfolk House, Swan Lane, Long Stratton NR15 2XE ☎ 01508 533806 ⁂ thorspole@s-norfolk.gov.uk

Sustainable Development: Mr Tim Horspole, Director - Growth & Localism, South Norfolk House, Swan Lane, Long Stratton NR15 2XE ☎ 01508 533806 ⁂ thorspole@s-norfolk.gov.uk

Tourism: Mr Julian Munson, Head of Growth & Economic Development, South Norfolk House, Swan Lane, Long Stratton NR15 2XE ☎ 01508 533763 ⁂ jmunson@s-norfolk.gov.uk

Town Centre: Mr David Disney, Market Towns Co-ordinator, South Norfolk House, Swan Lane, Long Stratton NR15 2XE ☎ 01508 533745 ⁂ ddisney@s-norfolk.gov.uk

Waste Collection and Disposal: Mrs Paula Boyce, Director - Community Services, South Norfolk House, Swan Lane, Long Stratton NR15 2XE ☎ 01508 533703 ⁂ pboyce@s-norfolk.gov.uk

SOUTH NORFOLK

Waste Collection and Disposal: Mr Bob Wade, Head of Environmental Services, South Norfolk House, Swan Lane, Long Stratton NR15 2XE ☎ 01508 533787 ✎ bwade@s-norfolk.gov.uk

Waste Management: Mrs Paula Boyce, Director - Community Services, South Norfolk House, Swan Lane, Long Stratton NR15 2XE ☎ 01508 533703 ✎ pboyce@s-norfolk.gov.uk

Children's Play Areas: Mr Andrew Sheppard, Community Assets Lead, South Norfolk House, Swan Lane, Long Stratton NR15 2XE ☎ 01508 533913 ✎ asheppard@s-norfolk.gov.uk

COUNCILLORS

Chair: Wheatley, Garry (CON - Cringleford)
gwheatley@s-norfolk.gov.uk

Vice-Chair: Duffin, Barry (CON - Forncett)
bduffin@s-norfolk.gov.uk

Leader of the Council: Fuller, John (CON - Brooke)
jfuller@s-norfolk.gov.uk

Deputy Leader of the Council: Edney, Michael (CON - Wicklewood)
medney@s-norfolk.gov.uk

Group Leader: Lewis, Trevor (LD - Stoke Holy Cross)
tlewis@s-norfolk.gov.uk

Amis, John (LD - New Costessey)
jamis@s-norfolk.gov.uk

Bell, Vivienne (LD - New Costessey)
vbell@s-norfolk.gov.uk

Bendle, Yvonne (CON - Hingham & Deopham)
Ybendle@s-norfolk.gov.uk

Bernard, Brendon (LD - Ditchingham & Broome)
bbernard@s-norfolk.gov.uk

Billig, Kay (CON - Gillingham)
kbillig@s-norfolk.gov.uk

Bills, David (CON - Hethersett)
dbills@s-norfolk.gov.uk

Blundell, Sharon (LD - Old Costessey)
sblundell@s-norfolk.gov.uk

Broome, Peter (CON - Rustens)
pbroome@s-norfolk.gov.uk

Dale, Leslie (CON - Hethersett)
ldale@s-norfolk.gov.uk

Dewsbury, Margaret (CON - Easton)
mdewsbury@s-norfolk.gov.uk

Easton, Charles (CON - Bunwell)
ceaston@s-norfolk.gov.uk

Ellis, Florence (CON - Tasburgh)
fellis@s-norfolk.gov.uk

Foulger, Colin (CON - Mulbarton)

Fulcher, Des (CON - Stratton)
dfulcher@s-norfolk.gov.uk

Goldson, David (CON - Roydon)
dgoldson@s-norfolk.gov.uk

Gould, Colin (CON - Loddon)
cgould@s-norfolk.gov.uk

Gray, Murray (LD - Earsham)
mgray@s-norfolk.gov.uk

Hardy, Phil (CON - Newton Flotman)
phardy@s-norfolk.gov.uk

Hornby, Jack (CON - Cromwells)
jhornby@s-norfolk.gov.uk

Hornby, Lee (CON - Town)
lhornby@s-norfolk.gov.uk

Hudson, Clayton (CON - Beck Vale)
chudson@s-norfolk.gov.uk

Kemp, William (CON - Thurlton)
wkemp@s-norfolk.gov.uk

Kemp, Christopher (CON - Cringleford)
ckemp@s-norfolk.gov.uk

Kiddie, Keith (CON - Diss)
kkiddie@s-norfolk.gov.uk

Larner, Jaan (CON - Chedgrave & Thurton)
jlarner@s-norfolk.gov.uk

Legg, Nigel (CON - Mulbarton)
nlegg@s-norfolk.gov.uk

Minshull, Graham (CON - Diss)
gminsull@s-norfolk.gov.uk

Mooney, Joseph (CON - Northfields)
jmooney@s-norfolk.gov.uk

Neal, Lisa (CON - Poringland with the Framinghams)
lneal@s-norfolk.gov.uk

Overton, John (CON - Poringland with the Framlinghams)
joverton@s-norfolk.gov.uk

Palmer, Tony (CON - Diss)
tpalmer@s-norfolk.gov.uk

Pond, Andrew (CON - Old Costessey)
apond@s-norfolk.gov.uk

Riches, Brian (CON - Harleston)
briches@s-norfolk.gov.uk

Savage, Robert (CON - Abbey)
rsavage@s-norfolk.gov.uk

Savage, Jeremy (CON - Harleston)
jsavage@s-norfolk.gov.uk

Stone, Barry (CON - Bressingham & Burston)
bstone@s-norfolk.gov.uk

Thomas, Alison (CON - Hempnall)
athomas@s-norfolk.gov.uk

Thomson, Vic (CON - Rockland)
vthomson@s-norfolk.gov.uk

Wilby, Jenny (CON - Scole)
jwilby@s-norfolk.gov.uk

Wilby, Martin (CON - Dickleburgh)
mwilby@s-norfolk.gov.uk

Worsley, Kevin (CON - Stratton)
kworsely@s-norfolk.gov.uk

POLITICAL COMPOSITION
CON: 40, LD: 6

COMMITTEE CHAIRS

Audit: Mr Phil Hardy

Development Management: Mr Vic Thomson

Licensing: Mr David Goldson

South Northamptonshire   D

South Northamptonshire Council, The Forum, Moat Lane,
Towcester NN12 6AD
☎ 01327 322322 ◌ customerservice@southnorthants.gov.uk
🖳 www.southnorthants.gov.uk

FACTS AND FIGURES
Parliamentary Constituencies: Daventry, Northamptonshire South
EU Constituencies: East Midlands
Election Frequency: Elections are of whole council

PRINCIPAL OFFICERS

Chief Executive: Mrs Sue Smith, Chief Executive, Bodicote
House, Bodicote, Banbury OX15 4AA ☎ 01295 221573
◌ sue.smith@cherwellandsouthnorthants.gov.uk

Senior Management: Mr Scott Barnes, Director - Strategy &
Commissioning, The Forum, Moat Lane, Towcester NN12 6AD
☎ 0300 003 0102 ◌ scott.barnes@cherwellandsouthnorthants.gov.uk

Senior Management: Mr Ian Davies, Director - Operational
Delivery, The Forum, Moat Lane, Towcester NN12 6AD
☎ 01327 322302; 0300 003 0101
◌ ian.davies@cherwellandsouthnorthants.gov.uk

Architect, Building / Property Services: Mr Chris Stratford,
Head of Regeneration & Housing, The Forum, Moat Lane,
Towcester NN12 6AD ☎ 01295 251871; 0300 003 0111
◌ chris.stratford@cherwellandsouthnorthants.gov.uk

Best Value: Ms Jo Pitman, Head of Transformation, The Forum,
Moat Lane, Towcester NN12 6AD ☎ 0300 003 0108
◌ jo.pitman@cherwellandsouthnorthants.gov.uk

Building Control: Mr Andy Preston, Head of Development
Management, The Forum, Moat Lane, Towcester NN12 6AD
☎ 0300 003 0109 ◌ andy.preston@cherwellandsouthnorthants.gov.uk

Catering Services: Mr Steve Wright, Facilities Management
Officer, The Forum, Moat Lane, Towcester NN12 6AD
☎ 01327 322322 ◌ stephen.wright@southnorthants.gov.uk

PR / Communications: Mrs Janet Ferris, Corporate
Communications & Marketing Manager, The Forum, Moat Lane,
Towcester NN12 6AD ☎ 0300 003 0114
◌ janet.ferris@cherwellandsouthnorthants.gov.uk

Community Planning: Mr Adrian Colwell, Head of Strategic
Planning & the Economy, The Forum, Moat Lane, Towcester NN12
6AD ☎ 0300 003 0110
◌ adrian.colwell@cherwellandsouthnorthants.gov.uk

Community Safety: Ms Jackie Fitzsimons, Public Protection &
Environmental Health Manager, The Forum, Moat Lane, Towcester
NN12 6AD ☎ 01327 322283
◌ jackie.fitzsimmons@southnorthants.gov.uk

Computer Management: Mr Tim Spiers, IT Transition & Service
Manager, The Forum, Moat Lane, Towcester NN12 6AD
☎ 01295 753715 ◌ tim.spiers@cherwellandsouthnorthants.gov.uk

Contracts: Mr Richard Stirling, Corporate Procurement Manager,
The Forum, Moat Lane, Towcester NN12 6AD ☎ 01327 322113
◌ richard.stirling@southnorthants.gov.uk

Corporate Services: Mr Kevin Lane, Head of Law & Governance,
The Forum, Moat Lane, Towcester NN12 6AD ☎ 0300 003 0107
◌ kevin.lane@cherwellandsouthnorthants.gov.uk

Customer Service: Ms Natasha Barnes, Customer Service
Manager, The Forum, Moat Lane, Towcester NN12 6AD
☎ 01295 227965 ◌ natasha.barnes@southnorthants.gov.uk

Economic Development: Mr Adrian Colwell, Head of Strategic
Planning & the Economy, The Forum, Moat Lane, Towcester
NN12 6AD ☎ 0300 003 0110
◌ adrian.colwell@cherwellandsouthnorthants.gov.uk

Electoral Registration: Mr James Doble, Democratic & Elections
Manager, The Forum, Moat Lane, Towcester NN12 6AD
☎ 01295 221587 ◌ james.doble@cherwellandsouthnorthants.gov.uk

Emergency Planning: Mr Gary Crook, Emergency Planning
Officer, The Forum, Moat Lane, Towcester NN12 6AD
☎ 01327 322293 ◌ gary.crook@southnorthants.gov.uk

Environmental / Technical Services: Ms Jackie Fitzsimons,
Public Protection & Environmental Health Manager, The Forum,
Moat Lane, Towcester NN12 6AD ☎ 01327 322283
◌ jackie.fitzsimmons@southnorthants.gov.uk

Environmental Health: Ms Jackie Fitzsimons, Public Protection
& Environmental Health Manager, The Forum, Moat Lane,
Towcester NN12 6AD ☎ 01327 322283
◌ jackie.fitzsimmons@southnorthants.gov.uk

Estates, Property & Valuation: Mr Chris Stratford, Head of
Regeneration & Housing, The Forum, Moat Lane, Towcester NN12
6AD ☎ 01295 251871; 0300 003 0111
◌ chris.stratford@cherwellandsouthnorthants.gov.uk

European Liaison: Mrs Sue Smith, Chief Executive, The Forum,
Moat Lane, Towcester NN12 6AD ☎ 01295 221573
◌ sue.smith@cherwellandsouthnorthants.gov.uk

Events Manager: Mrs Janet Ferris, Corporate Communications &
Marketing Manager, The Forum, Moat Lane, Towcester NN12 6AD
☎ 0300 003 0114 ◌ janet.ferris@cherwellandsouthnorthants.gov.uk

Facilities: Mr Steve Wright, Facilities Management Officer, The
Forum, Moat Lane, Towcester NN12 6AD ☎ 01327 322322
◌ stephen.wright@southnorthants.gov.uk

SOUTH NORTHAMPTONSHIRE

Finance: Mr Paul Sutton, Head of Finance & Procurement, The Forum, Moat Lane, Towcester NN12 6AD ☎ 0300 003 0116 ⌂ paul.sutton@cherwellandsouthnorthants.gov.uk

Health and Safety: Mr David Bennett, Corporate Health & Safety Adviser, The Forum, Moat Lane, Towcester NN12 6AD ☎ 01295 221738 ⌂ dave.bennett@cherwellandsouthnorthants.gov.uk

Housing: Ms Jo Harrison, Strategic Housing Manager, The Forum, Moat Lane, Towcester NN12 6AD ☎ 01327 322369 ⌂ jo.harrison@southnorthants.gov.uk

Legal: Mr Kevin Lane, Head of Law & Governance, The Forum, Moat Lane, Towcester NN12 6AD ☎ 0300 003 0107 ⌂ kevin.lane@cherwellandsouthnorthants.gov.uk

Leisure and Cultural Services: Mr Ashley Davey, Lead Officer - Leisure Services, The Forum, Moat Lane, Towcester NN12 6AD ☎ 01327 322338 ⌂ ashley.davey@southnorthants.gov.uk

Licensing: Ms Jackie Fitzsimons, Public Protection & Environmental Health Manager, The Forum, Moat Lane, Towcester NN12 6AD ☎ 01327 322283 ⌂ jackie.fitzsimmons@southnorthants.gov.uk

Lottery Funding, Charity and Voluntary: Ms Katie Arnold, Grants Officer, The Forum, Moat Lane, Towcester NN12 6AD ☎ 01327 322216 ⌂ katie.arnold@southnorthants.gov.uk

Member Services: Ms Natasha Clark, Democratic & Elections Team Leader, Bodicote House, Bodicote, Banbury OX15 4AA ☎ 01295 221589 ⌂ natasha.clark@cherwellandsouthnorthants.gov.uk

Parking: Ms Sharon Bolton, Leisure Facilities & Projects Manager, Council Offices, Springfields, Towcester NN12 6AE ☎ 01295 221714 ⌂ sharon.bolton@cherwellandsouthnorthants.gov.uk

Partnerships: Ms Nicola Riley, Community Partnerships & Recreation Manager, Council Offices, Springfields, Towcester NN12 6AE ☎ 01295 221724 ⌂ nicola.riley@cherwellandsouthnorthants.gov.uk

Personnel / HR: Ms Paula Goodwin, Shared HR & OD Manager, The Forum, Moat Lane, Towcester NN12 6AD ☎ 01295 221735 ⌂ paula.goodwin@cherwellandsouthnorthants.gov.uk

Planning: Mr Andy Preston, Head of Development Management, The Forum, Moat Lane, Towcester NN12 6AD ☎ 0300 003 0109 ⌂ andy.preston@cherwellandsouthnorthants.gov.uk

Procurement: Mr Richard Stirling, Corporate Procurement Manager, The Forum, Moat Lane, Towcester NN12 6AD ☎ 01327 322113 ⌂ richard.stirling@southnorthants.gov.uk

Recycling & Waste Minimisation: Mr Ed Potter, Head of Environmental Services, The Forum, Moat Lane, Towcester NN12 6AD ☎ 01295 227023; 0300 003 0105 ⌂ ed.potter@cherwellandsouthnorthants.gov.uk

Regeneration: Mr Adrian Colwell, Head of Strategic Planning & the Economy, The Forum, Moat Lane, Towcester NN12 6AD ☎ 0300 003 0110 ⌂ adrian.colwell@cherwellandsouthnorthants.gov.uk

Staff Training: Ms Paula Goodwin, Shared HR & OD Manager, The Forum, Moat Lane, Towcester NN12 6AD ☎ 01295 221735 ⌂ paula.goodwin@cherwellandsouthnorthants.gov.uk

Street Scene: Mr Ed Potter, Head of Environmental Services, The Forum, Moat Lane, Towcester NN12 6AD ☎ 01295 227023; 0300 003 0105 ⌂ ed.potter@cherwellandsouthnorthants.gov.uk

Tourism: Mr Adrian Colwell, Head of Strategic Planning & the Economy, The Forum, Moat Lane, Towcester NN12 6AD ☎ 0300 003 0110 ⌂ adrian.colwell@cherwellandsouthnorthants.gov.uk

Waste Collection and Disposal: Mr Ed Potter, Head of Environmental Services, The Forum, Moat Lane, Towcester NN12 6AD ☎ 01295 227023; 0300 003 0105 ⌂ ed.potter@cherwellandsouthnorthants.gov.uk

Waste Management: Mr Ed Potter, Head of Environmental Services, The Forum, Moat Lane, Towcester NN12 6AD ☎ 01295 227023; 0300 003 0105 ⌂ ed.potter@cherwellandsouthnorthants.gov.uk

COUNCILLORS

Chair: Billingham, Caryl (IND - Brackley South) caryl@billingham-brackley.com

Vice-Chair: Baker, Fiona (CON - Brackley West) fiona.baker@southnorthants.gov.uk

Leader of the Council: McCord, Ian (CON - Cosgrove & Grafton) ian.mccord@southnorthants.gov.uk

Deputy Leader of the Council: Bignell, Phil (CON - Heyfords & Bugbrooke) phil.bignell@southnorthants.gov.uk

Group Leader: Johns, Martin (LD - Towcester Brook) martin.johns@southnorthants.gov.uk

Addison, Ann (CON - Harpole & Grange) ann.addison@southnorthants.gov.uk

Atkinson, Robert (CON - Hackleton) bob.atkinson@southnorthants.gov.uk

Bagot-Webb, Anthony (CON - Brackley East) anthony.bagot-webb@southnorthants.gov.uk

Bambridge, Dermot (CON - Silverstone) dermot.bambridge@southnorthants.gov.uk

Barnes, Sandra (CON - Tove) sandra.barnes@southnorthants.gov.uk

Baxter, Judith (CON - Middleton Cheney) judith.baxter@southnorthants.gov.uk

Bowen, Lizzy (CON - Whittlewood) lizzy.bowen@southnorthants.gov.uk

Breese, Rebecca (CON - Steane) rebecca.breese@southnorthants.gov.uk

Budden, John (CON - Salcey) john.budden@southnorthants.gov.uk

Clarke, Roger (CON - Blakesley & Cote) roger.clarke@southnorthants.gov.uk

Clarke, Carole (CON - Brafield & Yardley) carole.clarke@southnorthants.gov.uk

Clarke, Stephen (CON - Blisworth & Roade)
stephen.clarke@southnorthants.gov.uk

Cooper, Karen (CON - Harpole & Grange)
karen.cooper@southnorthants.gov.uk

Dallyn, Richard (CON - Towcester Brook)
richard.dallyan@southnorthants.gov.uk

Davies, Hywel (CON - Blisworth & Roade)
hywel.davies@southnorthants.gov.uk

Davies, Peter (CON - Washington)
peter.davies@southnorthants.gov.uk

Furniss, Valerie (CON - Middleton Cheney)
val.furniss@southnorthants.gov.uk

Harries, David (IND - Heyfords & Bugbrooke)
david.harries@southnorthants.gov.uk

Herring, Rosie (CON - Danvers & Wardoun)
rosie.herring@southnorthants.gov.uk

Hollowell, Steven (IND - Brafield & Yardley)
steven.hollowell@southnorthants.gov.uk

Lofts, Chris (LD - Towcester Mill)
chris.lofts@southnorthants.gov.uk

Loveland, Dennis (CON - Deanshanger)
dennis.loveland@southnorthants.gov.uk

Manners, Charles (CON - Kingthorn)
charles.manners@southnorthants.gov.uk

Marinker, Simon (CON - Astwell)
simon.marinker@southnorthants.gov.uk

Morris, Ian (CON - King's Sutton)
ian.morris@southnorthants.gov.uk

Ord, Alice (CON - Brackley South)
alice.ord@southnorthants.gov.uk

Rawlinson, Peter (CON - Brackley East)
peter.rawlinson@southnorthants.gov.uk

Sadygov, Adil (CON - Grange Park)
adil.sadygov@southnorthants.gov.uk

Samiotis, Lisa (LD - Towcester Brook)
lisa.samiotis@southnorthants.gov.uk

Sergison-Brooke, Mary-Anne (CON - Danvers & Wardoun)

Smallman, Sandi (CON - Blakesley & Cote)
sandi.smallman@southnorthants.gov.uk

Tarbun, Catharine (LD - Towcester Mill)
catharine.tarbun@southnorthants.gov.uk

Townsend, John (CON - Little Brook)
john.townsend@southnorthants.gov.uk

Walker, Allen (CON - Deanshanger)
allen.walker@southnorthants.gov.uk

Wiltshire, Elaine (CON - Brackley West)
elaine.wiltshire@southnorthants.gov.uk

POLITICAL COMPOSITION
CON: 33, LD: 4, IND: 3

COMMITTEE CHAIRS

Audit: Mrs Sandra Barnes

Development Control: Mrs Sandi Smallman

Licensing: Mr Hywel Davies

Planning & Regeneration: Ms Ann Addison

South Oxfordshire — D

South Oxfordshire District Council, 135 Eastern Avenue,
Milton Park, Milton OX14 4SB
☎ 01491 823000 ⌕ info@southoxon.gov.uk 🖥 www.southoxon.gov.uk

FACTS AND FIGURES
Parliamentary Constituencies: Henley, Wantage
EU Constituencies: South East
Election Frequency: Elections are of whole council

PRINCIPAL OFFICERS

Chief Executive: Mr David Hill, Chief Executive, 135 Eastern
Avenue, Milton Park, Milton OX14 4SB ☎ 01235 547612
⌕ david.hill@southandvale.gov.uk

Deputy Chief Executive: Mr Steve Bishop, Strategic Director, 135
Eastern Avenue, Milton Park, Milton, Abingdon OX14 4SB
☎ 01235 540332 ⌕ steve.bishop@southandvale.gov.uk

Senior Management: Mr Andrew Down, Head of HR, IT &
Technical Services, 135 Eastern Avenue, Milton Park, Milton,
Abingdon OX14 4SB ☎ 01235 540372
⌕ andrew.down@southandvale.gov.uk

Senior Management: Mr Adrian Duffield, Head of Planning, 135
Eastern Avenue, Milton Park, Milton, Abingdon OX14 4SB
☎ 01235 540340 ⌕ adrian.duffield@southandvale.gov.uk

Senior Management: Mr William Jacobs, Head of Finance, 135
Eastern Avenue, Milton Park, Milton, Abingdon OX14 4SB
☎ 01235 540526 ⌕ william.jacobs@southandvale.gov.uk

Senior Management: Mrs Clare Kingston, Head of Corporate
Strategy, 135 Eastern Avenue, Milton Park, Milton, Abingdon
OX14 4SB ☎ 01235 540356 ⌕ clare.kingston@southandvale.gov.uk

Senior Management: Mrs Margaret Reed, Head of Legal &
Democratic Services, 135 Eastern Avenue, Milton Park, Milton,
Abingdon OX14 4SB ☎ 01235 540407
⌕ margaret.reed@southandvale.gov.uk

Building Control: Mr Adrian Duffield, Head of Planning, 135
Eastern Avenue, Milton Park, Milton, Abingdon OX14 4SB
☎ 01235 540340 ⌕ adrian.duffield@southandvale.gov.uk

PR / Communications: Mrs Clare Kingston, Head of Corporate
Strategy, 135 Eastern Avenue, Milton Park, Milton, Abingdon
OX14 4SB ☎ 01235 540356 ⌕ clare.kingston@southandvale.gov.uk

PR / Communications: Mrs Shona Ware, Communications &
Grants Manager, 135 Eastern Avenue, Milton Park, Milton, Abingdon
OX14 4SB ☎ 01235 540406 ⌕ shona.ware@southandvale.gov.uk

Community Safety: Mrs Liz Hayden, Legal, Licensing &
Community Safety Manager, 135 Eastern Avenue, Milton Park,
Milton, Abingdon OX14 4SB ☎ 01491 823705
⌕ liz.hayden@southandvale.gov.uk

SOUTH OXFORDSHIRE

Community Safety: Mrs Margaret Reed, Head of Legal & Democratic Services, 135 Eastern Avenue, Milton Park, Milton, Abingdon OX14 4SB ☎ 01235 540407 ✆ margaret.reed@southandvale.gov.uk

Computer Management: Mr Andrew Down, Head of HR, IT & Technical Services, 135 Eastern Avenue, Milton Park, Milton, Abingdon OX14 4SB ☎ 01235 540372 ✆ andrew.down@southandvale.gov.uk

Computer Management: Mr Simon Turner, IT Operations Manager, 135 Eastern Avenue, Milton Park, Milton, Abingdon OX14 4SB ☎ 01235 540400 ✆ simon.turner@southandvale.gov.uk

Contracts: Mrs Margaret Reed, Head of Legal & Democratic Services, 135 Eastern Avenue, Milton Park, Milton, Abingdon OX14 4SB ☎ 01235 540407 ✆ margaret.reed@southandvale.gov.uk

Economic Development: Mrs Suzanne Malcolm, Economic Development Manager, 135 Eastern Avenue, Milton Park, Milton, Abingdon OX14 4SB ☎ 01235 547619 ✆ suzanne.malcolm@southandvale.gov.uk

E-Government: Mr Andrew Down, Head of HR, IT & Technical Services, 135 Eastern Avenue, Milton Park, Milton, Abingdon OX14 4SB ☎ 01235 540372 ✆ andrew.down@southandvale.gov.uk

Electoral Registration: Mr Steven Corrigan, Democratic Services Manager, 135 Eastern Avenue, Milton Park, Milton, Abingdon OX14 4SB ☎ 01235 547675 ✆ steven.corrigan@southandvale.gov.uk

Electoral Registration: Mrs Margaret Reed, Head of Legal & Democratic Services, 135 Eastern Avenue, Milton Park, Milton, Abingdon OX14 4SB ☎ 01235 540407 ✆ margaret.reed@southandvale.gov.uk

Emergency Planning: Mr John Backley, Technical & Facilities Manager, 135 Eastern Avenue, Milton Park, Milton, Abingdon OX14 4SB ☎ 01235 540443 ✆ john.backley@southandvale.gov.uk

Emergency Planning: Mr Andrew Down, Head of HR, IT & Technical Services, 135 Eastern Avenue, Milton Park, Milton, Abingdon OX14 4SB ☎ 01235 540372 ✆ andrew.down@southandvale.gov.uk

Environmental / Technical Services: Mr John Backley, Technical & Facilities Manager, 135 Eastern Avenue, Milton Park, Milton, Abingdon OX14 4SB ☎ 01235 540443 ✆ john.backley@southandvale.gov.uk

Environmental / Technical Services: Mr Andrew Down, Head of HR, IT & Technical Services, 135 Eastern Avenue, Milton Park, Milton, Abingdon OX14 4SB ☎ 01235 540372 ✆ andrew.down@southandvale.gov.uk

Environmental Health: Mr Paul Holland, Environmental Protection Manager, 135 Eastern Avenue, Milton Park, Milton, Abingdon OX14 4SB ☎ 01235 540454 ✆ paul.hollans@southandvale.gov.uk

Environmental Health: Mrs Clare Kingston, Head of Corporate Strategy, 135 Eastern Avenue, Milton Park, Milton, Abingdon OX14 4SB ☎ 01235 540356 ✆ clare.kingston@southandvale.gov.uk

Environmental Health: Ms Diane Moore, Food & Safety Manager, 135 Eastern Avenue, Milton Park, Milton, Abingdon OX14 4SB ☎ 01235 540382 ✆ diane.moore@southandvale.gov.uk

Estates, Property & Valuation: Mr John Backley, Technical & Facilities Manager, 135 Eastern Avenue, Milton Park, Milton, Abingdon OX14 4SB ☎ 01235 540443 ✆ john.backley@southandvale.gov.uk

Facilities: Mr John Backley, Technical & Facilities Manager, 135 Eastern Avenue, Milton Park, Milton, Abingdon OX14 4SB ☎ 01235 540443 ✆ john.backley@southandvale.gov.uk

Facilities: Mr Andrew Down, Head of HR, IT & Technical Services, 135 Eastern Avenue, Milton Park, Milton, Abingdon OX14 4SB ☎ 01235 540372 ✆ andrew.down@southandvale.gov.uk

Finance: Mr Steve Bishop, Strategic Director, 135 Eastern Avenue, Milton Park, Milton, Abingdon OX14 4SB ☎ 01235 540332 ✆ steve.bishop@southandvale.gov.uk

Finance: Mr William Jacobs, Head of Finance, 135 Eastern Avenue, Milton Park, Milton, Abingdon OX14 4SB ☎ 01235 540526 ✆ william.jacobs@southandvale.gov.uk

Grounds Maintenance: Mrs Clare Kingston, Head of Corporate Strategy, 135 Eastern Avenue, Milton Park, Milton, Abingdon OX14 4SB ☎ 01235 540356 ✆ clare.kingston@southandvale.gov.uk

Grounds Maintenance: Mr Ian Matten, Waste & Parks Manager, 135 Eastern Avenue, Milton Park, Milton, Abingdon OX14 4SB ☎ 01235 540373 ✆ ian.matten@southandvale.gov.uk

Health and Safety: Mrs Clare Kingston, Head of Corporate Strategy, 135 Eastern Avenue, Milton Park, Milton, Abingdon OX14 4SB ☎ 01235 540356 ✆ clare.kingston@southandvale.gov.uk

Health and Safety: Ms Sally Truman, Policy, Partnership & Engagement Manager, 135 Eastern Avenue, Milton Park, Milton, Abingdon OX14 4SB ☎ 01235 450408 ✆ sally.truman@southandvale.gov.uk

Housing: Mr Phil Ealey, Housing Needs Manager, 135 Eastern Avenue, Milton Park, Milton, Abingdon OX14 4SB ☎ 01235 547623 ✆ phil.ealey@southandvale.gov.uk

Legal: Mrs Liz Hayden, Legal, Licensing & Community Safety Manager, 135 Eastern Avenue, Milton Park, Milton, Abingdon OX14 4SB ☎ 01491 823705 ✆ liz.hayden@southandvale.gov.uk

Legal: Mrs Margaret Reed, Head of Legal & Democratic Services, 135 Eastern Avenue, Milton Park, Milton, Abingdon OX14 4SB ☎ 01235 540407 ✆ margaret.reed@southandvale.gov.uk

Leisure and Cultural Services: Miss Kate Arnold, Leisure Manager, 135 Eastern Avenue, Milton Park, Milton, Abingdon OX14 4SB ☎ 01235 547632 ✆ kate.arnold@southandvale.gov.uk

Leisure and Cultural Services: Miss Emma Dolman, Arts Manager, Cornerstone, 25 Station Road, Didcot OX11 7NE ☎ 01235 515131 ✆ emma.dolman@southandvale.gov.uk

Licensing: Mrs Margaret Reed, Head of Legal & Democratic Services, 135 Eastern Avenue, Milton Park, Milton, Abingdon OX14 4SB ☎ 01235 540407 ✆ margaret.reed@southandvale.gov.uk

Member Services: Mr Steven Corrigan, Democratic Services Manager, 135 Eastern Avenue, Milton Park, Milton, Abingdon OX14 4SB ☎ 01235 547675 ✆ steven.corrigan@southandvale.gov.uk

Member Services: Mrs Margaret Reed, Head of Legal & Democratic Services, 135 Eastern Avenue, Milton Park, Milton, Abingdon OX14 4SB ☎ 01235 540407 ✆ margaret.reed@southandvale.gov.uk

Parking: Mr John Backley, Technical & Facilities Manager, 135 Eastern Avenue, Milton Park, Milton, Abingdon OX14 4SB ☎ 01235 540443 ✆ john.backley@southandvale.gov.uk

Parking: Mr Andrew Down, Head of HR, IT & Technical Services, 135 Eastern Avenue, Milton Park, Milton, Abingdon OX14 4SB ☎ 01235 540372 ✆ andrew.down@southandvale.gov.uk

Partnerships: Mrs Clare Kingston, Head of Corporate Strategy, 135 Eastern Avenue, Milton Park, Milton, Abingdon OX14 4SB ☎ 01235 540356 ✆ clare.kingston@southandvale.gov.uk

Partnerships: Ms Sally Truman, Policy, Partnership & Engagement Manager, 135 Eastern Avenue, Milton Park, Milton, Abingdon OX14 4SB ☎ 01235 450408 ✆ sally.truman@southandvale.gov.uk

Personnel / HR: Mr Andrew Down, Head of HR, IT & Technical Services, 135 Eastern Avenue, Milton Park, Milton, Abingdon OX14 4SB ☎ 01235 540372 ✆ andrew.down@southandvale.gov.uk

Personnel / HR: Mr Mark Gibbons, Human Resources Manager, 135 Eastern Avenue, Milton Park, Milton, Abingdon OX14 4SB ☎ 01491 823412 ✆ mark.gibbons@southandvale.gov.uk

Planning: Mr Adrian Duffield, Head of Planning, 135 Eastern Avenue, Milton Park, Milton, Abingdon OX14 4SB ☎ 01235 540340 ✆ adrian.duffield@southandvale.gov.uk

Planning: Miss Paula Fox, Development Manager (South), 135 Eastern Avenue, Milton Park, Milton, Abingdon OX14 4SB ☎ 01235 540361 ✆ paula.fox@southandvale.gov.uk

Planning: Ms Emily Hamerton, Development Manager (Vale), 135 Eastern Avenue, Milton Park, Milton OX14 4SB ✆ emily.hamerton@southandvale.gov.uk

Recycling & Waste Minimisation: Mrs Clare Kingston, Head of Corporate Strategy, 135 Eastern Avenue, Milton Park, Milton, Abingdon OX14 4SB ☎ 01235 540356 ✆ clare.kingston@southandvale.gov.uk

Recycling & Waste Minimisation: Mr Ian Matten, Waste & Parks Manager, 135 Eastern Avenue, Milton Park, Milton, Abingdon OX14 4SB ☎ 01235 540373 ✆ ian.matten@southandvale.gov.uk

Regeneration: Mr Gerry Brough, Interim Head of Development & Regeneration, 135 Eastern Avenue, Milton Park, Milton OX14 4SB ✆ gerry.brough@southandvale.gov.uk

Staff Training: Mr Andrew Down, Head of HR, IT & Technical Services, 135 Eastern Avenue, Milton Park, Milton, Abingdon OX14 4SB ☎ 01235 540372 ✆ andrew.down@southandvale.gov.uk

Staff Training: Mr Mark Gibbons, Human Resources Manager, 135 Eastern Avenue, Milton Park, Milton, Abingdon OX14 4SB ☎ 01491 823412 ✆ mark.gibbons@southandvale.gov.uk

Sustainable Communities: Mr Adrian Duffield, Head of Planning, 135 Eastern Avenue, Milton Park, Milton, Abingdon OX14 4SB ☎ 01235 540340 ✆ adrian.duffield@southandvale.gov.uk

Sustainable Development: Mrs Clare Kingston, Head of Corporate Strategy, 135 Eastern Avenue, Milton Park, Milton, Abingdon OX14 4SB ☎ 01235 540356 ✆ clare.kingston@southandvale.gov.uk

Sustainable Development: Ms Sally Truman, Policy, Partnership & Engagement Manager, 135 Eastern Avenue, Milton Park, Milton, Abingdon OX14 4SB ☎ 01235 450408 ✆ sally.truman@southandvale.gov.uk

Town Centre: Mrs Suzanne Malcolm, Economic Development Manager, 135 Eastern Avenue, Milton Park, Milton, Abingdon OX14 4SB ☎ 01235 547619 ✆ suzanne.malcolm@southandvale.gov.uk

Waste Collection and Disposal: Mrs Clare Kingston, Head of Corporate Strategy, 135 Eastern Avenue, Milton Park, Milton, Abingdon OX14 4SB ☎ 01235 540356 ✆ clare.kingston@southandvale.gov.uk

Waste Collection and Disposal: Mr Ian Matten, Waste & Parks Manager, 135 Eastern Avenue, Milton Park, Milton, Abingdon OX14 4SB ☎ 01235 540373 ✆ ian.matten@southandvale.gov.uk

Waste Management: Mrs Clare Kingston, Head of Corporate Strategy, 135 Eastern Avenue, Milton Park, Milton, Abingdon OX14 4SB ☎ 01235 540356 ✆ clare.kingston@southandvale.gov.uk

COUNCILLORS

Chair: Harrison, Paul (CON - Sonning Common)
paul.harrison@suk.sas.com

Vice-Chair: Matelot, Jeannette (CON - Thame)
jeannette.matelot@southoxon.gov.uk

Leader of the Council: Cotton, John (CON - Berinsfield)
leader@southoxon.gov.uk

Deputy Leader of the Council: Murphy, Jane (CON - Cholsey)
jane.murphy@southoxon.gov.uk

Badcock, Anna (CON - Watlington)
annabadcock1@gmail.com

Bailey, Charles (CON - Woodcote & Rotherfield)
charles.bailey@southoxon.gov.uk

Bland, Joan (CON - Henley-on-Thames)
joan@asquiths.com

Bloomfield, Felix (CON - Benson & Crowmarsh)
felixbloomfield@hotmail.com

Bulmer, Kevin (CON - Goring)
kevin.bulmer@southoxon.gov.uk

SOUTH OXFORDSHIRE

Champken-Woods, Nigel (CON - Thame)
nigel.champken-woods@southoxon.gov.uk

Connel, Steve (CON - Didcot North East)
sconnel@hotmail.com

Davies, Margaret (LAB - Didcot South)
mldaviesbb@btinternet.com

Dawe, Pat (CON - Cholsey)
pat.dawe@southoxon.gov.uk

Dearlove, Anthony (CON - Didcot South)
anthony.dearlove@aol.co.uk

Dodds, David (CON - Thame)
david.dodds@southoxon.gov.uk

Gawrysiak, Stefan (R - Henley-on-Thames)
stefan.gawrysiak@southoxon.gov.uk

Gillespie, Elizabeth (CON - Garsington & Horspath)
elizabethgillespie@uk2.net

Hall, Will (CON - Sonning Common)
wahhall@gmail.com

Harbour, Tony (CON - Didcot North East)
tony.harbour@southoxon.gov.uk

Harrod, Stephen (CON - Haseley Brook)
stephen.harrod@southoxon.gov.uk

Hillier, Lorraine (CON - Henley-on-Thames)
lorraine.hillier@southoxon.gov.uk

Hornsby, Elaine (CON - Wallingford)
elaine.hornsby@southoxon.gov.uk

Lawson, Sue (CON - Sandford & the Wittenhams)
sue.lawson@southoxon.gov.uk

Lloyd, Lynn (CON - Chinnor)
lynn.lloyd@btinternet.com

Lokhon, Imran (CON - Wallingford)
imran@yourwallingford.gov.uk

Nash, Anthony (CON - Didcot South)
anthony.nash@southandvale.gov.uk

Newman, Toby (CON - Wheatley)
toby.newman@southoxon.gov.uk

Nimmo-Smith, David (CON - Woodcote & Rotherfield)
david.nimmo-smith@southoxon.gov.uk

Pullen, Richard (CON - Benson & Crowmarsh)
richard.pullen@southoxon.gov.uk

Service, Bill (CON - Didcot North East)
bill.service@hotmail.co.uk

Simister, Robert (CON - Kidmore End & Whitchurch)
robert.simister@southoxon.gov.uk

Thompson, Alan (CON - Didcot West)
alan.thompson@southoxon.gov.uk

Turner, Margaret (CON - Didcot West)
margaret.turner@southoxon.gov.uk

Turner, David (LD - Chalgrove)
david.turner@southoxon.gov.uk

Walsh, John (CON - Forest Hill & Holton)
john.walsh@southoxon.gov.uk

White, Ian (CON - Chinnor)
ian.white@southoxon.gov.uk

POLITICAL COMPOSITION
CON: 33, LAB: 1, LD: 1, R: 1

COMMITTEE CHAIRS
Licensing: Mr David Dodds

Planning: Mr Felix Bloomfield

South Ribble   D

South Ribble Borough Council, Civic Centre, West Paddock, Leyland PR25 1DH
☎ 01772 421491 🖷 01772 622287 🖂 info@southribble.gov.uk
🖥 www.southribble.gov.uk

FACTS AND FIGURES
Parliamentary Constituencies: South Ribble
EU Constituencies: North West
Election Frequency: Elections are by thirds

PRINCIPAL OFFICERS

Chief Executive: Mr Mike Nuttall, Chief Executive & Chief Finance Officer, Civic Centre, West Paddock, Leyland PR25 1DH
☎ 01772 421491 🖂 mnuttall@southribble.gov.uk

Senior Management: Mr Garry Barclay, Head of Shared Assurance Services, Civic Centre, West Paddock, Leyland PR25 1DH ☎ 01772 625272 🖂 gbarclay@southribble.gov.uk

Senior Management: Mr Mark Gaffney, Director - Neighbourhoods, Environmental Health & Assets, Civic Centre, West Paddock, Leyland PR25 1DH ☎ 01772 625671 🖂 mgaffney@southribble.gov.uk

Senior Management: Mrs Susan Guinness, Head of Shared Financial Services, Civic Centre, West Paddock, Leyland PR25 1DH
☎ 01772 421491 🖂 sguinness@southribble.gov.uk

Senior Management: Ms Denise Johnson, Director - Development, Enterprise & Communities, Civic Centre, West Paddock, Leyland PR25 1DH ☎ 01772 625558 🖂 djohnson@southribble.gov.uk

Senior Management: Mr Steve Nugent, Head of HR, Civic Centre, West Paddock, Leyland PR25 1DH ☎ 01772 421491 🖂 snugent@southribble.gov.uk

Senior Management: Mr Ian Parker, Director - Corporate Governance & Business Transformation, Civic Centre, West Paddock, Leyland PR25 1DH ☎ 01772 625550 🖂 iparker@southribble.gov.uk

Architect, Building / Property Services: Ms Mandy Catterall, Property Services Manager, Civic Centre, West Paddock, Leyland PR25 1DH ☎ 01772 421491 🖂 mcatterall@southribble.gov.uk

PR / Communications: Mrs Caroline Taylor, Senior Public Relations Officer, Civic Centre, West Paddock, Leyland PR25 1DH
☎ 01772 421491 🖂 ctaylor@southribble.gov.uk

Community Planning: Mr Jonathan Noad, Planning Manager, Civic Centre, West Paddock, Leyland PR25 1DH ☎ 01772 421491 ⌁ jnoad@southribble.gov.uk

Computer Management: Mr John Healey, ICT Manager, Civic Centre, West Paddock, Leyland PR25 1DH ☎ 01772 421491 ⌁ jhealey@southribble.gov.uk

Corporate Services: Mr Ian Parker, Director - Corporate Governance & Business Transformation, Civic Centre, West Paddock, Leyland PR25 1DH ☎ 01772 625550 ⌁ iparker@southribble.gov.uk

Customer Service: Mr Kevin Conway, Gateway Manager, Civic Centre, West Paddock, Leyland PR25 1DH ☎ 01772 627112 ⌁ kconway@southribble.gov.uk

Direct Labour: Mr Mark Gaffney, Director - Neighbourhoods, Environmental Health & Assets, Civic Centre, West Paddock, Leyland PR25 1DH ☎ 01772 625671 ⌁ mgaffney@southribble.gov.uk

Electoral Registration: Mr Martin O'Loughlin, Democratic Services Manager, Civic Centre, West Paddock, Leyland PR25 1DH ☎ 01772 625307 ⌁ moloughlin@southribble.gov.uk

Emergency Planning: Ms Kerry Maguire, Senior Risk & Insurance Officer, Civic Centre, West Paddock, Leyland PR25 1DH ☎ 01772 625256 ⌁ kmaguire@southribble.gov.uk

Environmental Health: Mrs Jennifer Mullin, Public Health Manager, Civic Centre, West Paddock, Leyland PR25 1DH ☎ 01772 625329 ⌁ jmullin@southribble.gov.uk

Estates, Property & Valuation: Ms Mandy Catterall, Property Services Manager, Civic Centre, West Paddock, Leyland PR25 1DH ☎ 01772 421491 ⌁ mcatterall@southribble.gov.uk

Finance: Ms Susan Guinness, Head of Shared Financial Services, Town Hall, Market Street, Chorley PR7 1DP ☎ 01257 515151 ⌁ susan.guinness@chorley.gov.uk

Fleet Management: Mr Roger Ashcroft, Waste, Transport & Neighbourhoods Manager, Civic Centre, West Paddock, Leyland PR25 1DH ☎ 01772 625612 ⌁ rashcroft@southribble.gov.uk

Grounds Maintenance: Mr Andrew Richardson, Parks & Neighbourhoods Manager, Civic Centre, West Paddock, Leyland PR25 1DH ☎ 01772 625674 ⌁ arichardson@southribble.gov.uk

Health and Safety: Mr Jeff Lambert, Health & Safety Officer, Civic Centre, West Paddock, Leyland PR25 1DH ☎ 01772 625331 ⌁ jlambertl@southribble.gov.uk

Home Energy Conservation: Mr Pradip Patel, Private Sector Officer, Civic Centre, West Paddock, Leyland PR25 1DH ☎ 01772 421491 Extn 5365 ⌁ dppatel@southribble.gov.uk

Legal: Mr David Whelan, Legal Services Manager, Civic Centre, West Paddock, Leyland PR25 1DH ☎ 01772 421491 ⌁ dwhelan@southribble.gov.uk

Licensing: Mrs Jennifer Mullin, Public Health Manager, Civic Centre, West Paddock, Leyland PR25 1DH ☎ 01772 625329 ⌁ jmullin@southribble.gov.uk

Member Services: Mr Martin O'Loughlin, Democratic Services Manager, Civic Centre, West Paddock, Leyland PR25 1DH ☎ 01772 625307 ⌁ moloughlin@southribble.gov.uk

Parking: Mr Andrew Richardson, Parks & Neighbourhoods Manager, Civic Centre, West Paddock, Leyland PR25 1DH ☎ 01772 625674 ⌁ arichardson@southribble.gov.uk

Partnerships: Mr Howard Anthony, Temporary Partnership Manager, Civic Centre, West Paddock, Leyland PR25 1DH ☎ 01772 421491 ⌁ hanthony@southribble.gov.uk

Personnel / HR: Mr Steve Nugent, Head of HR, Civic Centre, West Paddock, Leyland PR25 1DH ☎ 01772 421491 ⌁ snugent@southribble.gov.uk

Planning: Mr Jonathan Noad, Planning Manager, Civic Centre, West Paddock, Leyland PR25 1DH ☎ 01772 421491 ⌁ jnoad@southribble.gov.uk

Procurement: Ms Janet Hinds, Procurement & Partnerships Manager, Civic Centre, West Paddock, Leyland PR25 1DH ☎ 01257 575622 ⌁ janet.hinds@chorley.gov.uk

Recycling & Waste Minimisation: Miss Laura Wright, Recycling Officer, Civic Centre, West Paddock, Leyland PR25 1DH ☎ 01772 421491 Extn 5606 ⌁ lwright@southribble.gov.uk

Regeneration: Mr Howerd Booth, Community Works Manager, Civic Centre, West Paddock, Leyland PR25 1DH ☎ 01772 421491 ⌁ hbooth@southribble.gov.uk

Staff Training: Mr Steve Nugent, Head of HR, Civic Centre, West Paddock, Leyland PR25 1DH ☎ 01772 421491 ⌁ snugent@southribble.gov.uk

Street Scene: Mr Mark Gaffney, Director, Civic Centre, West Paddock, Leyland PR25 1DH ☎ 01772 625671 ⌁ mgaffney@southribble.gov.uk

Tourism: Miss Jennifer Clough, Principal Economic Development Officer, Civic Centre, West Paddock, Leyland PR25 1DH ☎ 01772 421491 ⌁ jclough@southribble.gov.uk

Waste Collection and Disposal: Mr Roger Ashcroft, Waste, Transport & Neighbourhoods Manager, Civic Centre, West Paddock, Leyland PR25 1DH ☎ 01772 421491

Waste Collection and Disposal: Mr Mark Gaffney, Director - Neighbourhoods, Environmental Health & Assets, Civic Centre, West Paddock, Leyland PR25 1DH ☎ 01772 625671 ⌁ mgaffney@southribble.gov.uk

Waste Management: Mr Roger Ashcroft, Waste, Transport & Neighbourhoods Manager, Civic Centre, West Paddock, Leyland PR25 1DH ☎ 01772 625612 ⌁ rashcroft@southribble.gov.uk

SOUTH RIBBLE

Waste Management: Mr Mark Gaffney, Director - Neighbourhoods, Environmental Health & Assets, Civic Centre, West Paddock, Leyland PR25 1DH ☎ 01772 625671
✎ mgaffney@southribble.gov.uk

COUNCILLORS

Mayor: Woollard, Linda (CON - Broad Oak)
cllr.lwoollard@southribble.gov.uk

Deputy Mayor: Titherington, Michael (LAB - Broadfield)
cllr.mtitherington@southribble.gov.uk

Leader of the Council: Mullineaux, Peter (CON - Samlesbury & Walton)
cllr.pmullineaux@southribble.gov.uk

Deputy Leader of the Council: Clark, Colin (CON - Longton & Hutton West)
cllr.cclark@southribble.gov.uk

Ball, Andrea (CON - Walton-le-Dale East)
cllr.aball@southribble.gov.uk

Bell, Jane (LAB - Seven Stars)
cllr.jbell@southribble.gov.uk

Bennett, Warren (CON - Coupe Green & Gregson Lane)
cllr.wbennett@southribble.gov.uk

Bird, David (CON - Howick & Priory)

Blow, Renee (CON - Lostock Hall)

Coulton, Colin (CON - Longton & Hutton West)
cllr.ccoulton@southribble.gov.uk

Donoghue, Mall (LAB - Seven Stars)

Evans, William (LAB - Earnshaw Bridge)
cllr.wevans@southribble.gov.uk

Forrest, Derek (LAB - Leyland Central)
cllr.dforrest@southribble.gov.uk

Foster, Paul (LAB - Bamber Bridge West)
cllr.pfoster@southribble.gov.uk

Green, Mary (CON - Moss Side)
cllr.mary.green@southribble.gov.uk

Green, Michael (CON - Moss Side)
cllr.michael.green@southribble.gov.uk

Hamilton, Claire (LAB - Leyland Central)

Hancock, Harold (LD - Broad Oak)

Hesketh, Jon (CON - Longton & Hutton West)
cllr.jhesketh@southribble.gov.uk

Higgins, Mick (LAB - Bamber Bridge East)
cllr.mhiggins@southribble.gov.uk

Howarth, David (LD - Howick & Priory)
cllr.dhowarth@southribble.gov.uk

Hughes, Cliff (CON - Lostock Hall)
cllr.chughes@southribble.gov.uk

Jones, Susan (LAB - Leyland St Ambrose)
cllr.sjones@southribble.gov.uk

Jones, Kenneth (LAB - St Ambrose)
cllr.kjones@southribble.gov.uk

Marsh, James (CON - Coupe Green & Gregson Lane)
cllr.jmarsh@southribble.gov.uk

Martin, Keith (LAB - Middleforth)
cllr.kmartin@southribble.gov.uk

Mawson, Elizabeth (LAB - Charnock)

Moon, Caroline (CON - Buckshaw & Worden)
cllr.cmoon@southribble.gov.uk

Mort, Jacqueline (CON - Lostock Hall)
cllr.jmort@southribble.gov.uk

Nathan, Barbara (IND - Walton-le-Dale East)

Nathan, Michael (CON - Walton-le-Dale West)

Nelson, Michael (CON - Walton-le-Dale West)
cllr.mnelson@southribble.gov.uk

Noblet, Rebecca (CON - Howick & Priory)
cllr.rnoblet@southribble.gov.uk

Ogilvie, Alan (CON - Buckshaw & Worden)
cllr.aogilvie@southribble.gov.uk

Patten, James (LAB - Middleforth)
cllr.jpatten@southribble.gov.uk

Rainsbury, John (CON - Hoole)
cllr.jrainsbury@southribble.gov.uk

Smith, Phil (CON - New Longton & Hutton East)
cllr.psmith@southribble.gov.uk

Smith, Margaret (CON - New Longton & Hutton East)
cllr.msmith@southribble.gov.uk

Snape, Susan (CON - Earnshaw Bridge)

Suthers, David (CON - Hoole)
cllr.dsuthers@southribble.gov.uk

Tomlinson, Caleb (LAB - Bamber Bridge West)
cllr.ctomlinson@southribble.gov.uk

Tomlinson, Matthew (LAB - Broadfield)
cllr.mtomlinson@southribble.gov.uk

Walton, Karen (CON - Farington West)

Walton, Graham (CON - Farington West)
cllr.gwalton@southribble.gov.uk

Watkinson, Ian
(LAB - Charnock)

Watts, David (LAB - Bamber Bridge East)
cllr.dwatts@southribble.gov.uk

Wharton, Paul
(CON - Farington East)

Woodcock, Jonathan
(LAB - Farington East)

Wooldridge, David
(LAB - Middleforth)

Yates, Barrie (CON - Samlesbury & Walton)
cllr.byates@southribble.gov.uk

POLITICAL COMPOSITION
CON: 28, LAB: 19, LD: 2, IND: 1

COMMITTEE CHAIRS

Licensing: Mr John Rainsbury

Planning: Mr Jon Hesketh

South Somerset   **D**

South Somerset District Council, Council Offices, Brympton Way, Yeovil BA20 2HT
☎ 01935 462462 🖷 01935 462188 ⌨ ssdc@southsomerset.gov.uk
🖥 www.southsomerset.gov.uk

FACTS AND FIGURES
Parliamentary Constituencies: Somerton and Frome, Yeovil
EU Constituencies: South West
Election Frequency: Elections are of whole council

PRINCIPAL OFFICERS

Chief Executive: Mr Alex Parmley, Chief Executive, Council Offices, Brympton Way, Yeovil BA20 2HT
⌨ alex.parmley@southsomerset.gov.uk

Senior Management: Mrs Rina Singh, Strategic Director - Place & Performance, Council Offices, Brympton Way, Yeovil BA20 2HT
☎ 01935 462462 ⌨ rina.singh@southsomerset.gov.uk

Senior Management: Ms Vega Sturgess, Strategic Director - Operations & Customer Focus, Council Offices, Brympton Way, Yeovil BA20 2HT ☎ 01935 462462
⌨ vega.sturgess@southsomerset.gov.uk

Architect, Building / Property Services: Mr Garry Green, Engineering & Property Services Manager, Council Offices, Brympton Way, Yeovil BA20 2HT ☎ 01935 462462
⌨ garry.green@southsomerset.gov.uk

Best Value: Mrs Rina Singh, Strategic Director - Place & Performance, Council Offices, Brympton Way, Yeovil BA20 2HT
☎ 01935 462462 ⌨ rina.singh@southsomerset.gov.uk

Building Control: Mr David Durrant, Building Control Manager, Houndstone Close, Abbey Manor Park, Taunton BA20 1AS
☎ 01935 462462 ⌨ david.durrant@southsomerset.gov.uk

PR / Communications: Mr Martin Hacker, Communications Officer, Council Offices, Brympton Way, Yeovil BA20 2HT
☎ 01935 462462 ⌨ martin.hacker@southsomerset.gov.uk

PR / Communications: Mrs Mary Ostler, Media & Communications Officer, Council Offices, Brympton Way, Yeovil BA20 2HT ☎ 01935 462462 ⌨ mary.ostler@southsomerset.gov.uk

Community Planning: Mrs Helen Rutter, Assistant Director - Communities, Church Field, Wincanton BA9 9AG ☎ 01963 435012
⌨ helen.rutter@southsomerset.gov.uk

Community Safety: Mr Steve Brewer, Community Safety Co-ordinator, Council Offices, Brympton Way, Yeovil BA20 2HT
☎ 01935 462462 ⌨ steve.brewer@southsomerset.gov.uk

Computer Management: Mr Roger Brown, ICT Manager, Council Offices, Brympton Way, Yeovil BA20 2HT ☎ 01935 462462
⌨ roger.brown@southsomerset.gov.uk

Corporate Services: Mr Ian Clarke, Assistant Director - Legal & Corporate Services, Council Offices, Brympton Way, Yeovil BA20 2HT ☎ 01935 462462 ⌨ ian.clarke@southsomerset.gov.uk

Customer Service: Mr Jason Toogood, Customer Services Manager, Council Offices, Brympton Way, Yeovil BA20 2HT
☎ 01935 462462 ⌨ jason.toogood@southsomerset.gov.uk

Direct Labour: Mr Chris Cooper, Streetscene Manager, South Somerset Direct Services, 7 Artillery Road, Luton Trading Estate, Yeovil BA22 8RP ☎ 01935 462462
⌨ chris.cooper@southsomerset.gov.uk

Economic Development: Mr David Julian, Economic Development Manager, Council Offices, Brympton Way, Yeovil BA20 2HT ☎ 01935 462462 ⌨ david.julian@southsomerset.gov.uk

Economic Development: Mr Martin Woods, Assistant Director - Economy, Council Offices, Brympton Way, Yeovil BA20 2HT
☎ 01935 462462 ⌨ martin.woods@southsomerset.gov.uk

E-Government: Mr Roger Brown, ICT Manager, Council Offices, Brympton Way, Yeovil BA20 2HT ☎ 01935 462462
⌨ roger.brown@southsomerset.gov.uk

Electoral Registration: Mr Roger Quantock, Senior Democractic Services Officer, Council Offices, Brympton Way, Yeovil BA20 2HT
☎ 01935 462462 ⌨ roger.quantock@southsomerset.gov.uk

Emergency Planning: Ms Pam Harvey, Emergency Planning Officer, Council Offices, Brympton Way, Yeovil BA20 2HT
☎ 01935 462462 ⌨ pharvey@eastdevon.gov.uk

Energy Management: Mr Keith Wheaton-Green, Environmental Performance Manager, Council Offices, Brympton Way, Yeovil BA20 2HT ☎ 01935 462462
⌨ keith.wheaton-green@southsomerset.gov.uk

Environmental Health: Mr Alasdair Bell, Environmental Health Manager, Council Offices, Brympton Way, Yeovil BA20 2HT
☎ 01935 462462 ⌨ alasdair.bell@southsomerset.gov.uk

Estates, Property & Valuation: Mr Garry Green, Engineering & Property Services Manager, Council Offices, Brympton Way, Yeovil BA20 2HT ☎ 01935 462462 ⌨ garry.green@southsomerset.gov.uk

Facilities: Mr Garry Green, Engineering & Property Services Manager, Council Offices, Brympton Way, Yeovil BA20 2HT
☎ 01935 462462 ⌨ garry.green@southsomerset.gov.uk

Finance: Ms Donna Parham, Assistant Director - Financial & Corporate Services, Council Offices, Brympton Way, Yeovil BA20 2HT ☎ 01935 462462 ⌨ donna.parham@southsomerset.gov.uk

Fleet Management: Ms Niki Atkins, Fleet Service Supervisor, Lufton Depot, 7 Artillery Road, Yeovil BA22 8RP ☎ 01935 462462
⌨ niki.atkins@southsomerset.gov.uk

Grounds Maintenance: Mr Chris Cooper, Streetscene Manager, South Somerset Direct Services, 7 Artillery Road, Luton Trading Estate, Yeovil BA22 8RP ☎ 01935 462462
⌨ chris.cooper@southsomerset.gov.uk

Health and Safety: Ms Pam Harvey, Emergency Planning Officer, Council Offices, Brympton Way, Yeovil BA20 2HT ☎ 01935 462462
⌨ pharvey@eastdevon.gov.uk

SOUTH SOMERSET

Home Energy Conservation: Mr Martin Chapman, Principal Housing Standards Officer, Unit 10 Bridge Barns, Long Sutton TA10 9PZ ☎ 01935 462462 ⌨ martin.chapman@southsomerset.gov.uk

Housing: Mr Colin McDonald, Strategic Housing Manager, Council Offices, Brympton Way, Yeovil BA20 2HT ☎ 01935 462462 ⌨ colin.mcdonald@southsomerset.gov.uk

Legal: Mr Ian Clarke, Assistant Director - Legal & Corporate Services, Council Offices, Brympton Way, Yeovil BA20 2HT ☎ 01935 462462 ⌨ ian.clarke@southsomerset.gov.uk

Legal: Ms Lynda Creek, Head of Legal Services, Council Offices, Brympton Way, Yeovil BA20 2HT ⌨ lynda.creek@southsomerset.gov.uk

Leisure and Cultural Services: Ms Lynda Pincombe, Community Health & Leisure Manager, Council Offices, Brympton Way, Yeovil BA20 2HT ☎ 01935 462462 ⌨ lynda.pincombe@southsomerset.gov.uk

Licensing: Mr Nigel Marston, Licensing Manager, Council Offices, Brympton Way, Yeovil BA20 2HT ☎ 01935 462462 ⌨ nigel.marston@southsomerset.gov.uk

Lottery Funding, Charity and Voluntary: Mr David Crisfield, Third Sector & Partnership Co-ordinator, Council Offices, Brympton Way, Yeovil BA20 2HT ☎ 01935 462462 ⌨ david.crisfield@southsomerset.gov.uk

Member Services: Ms Angela Cox, Democratic Services Manager, Council Offices, Brympton Way, Yeovil BA20 2HT ☎ 01935 462462 ⌨ angela.cox@southsomerset.gov.uk

Parking: Mr Garry Green, Engineering & Property Services Manager, Council Offices, Brympton Way, Yeovil BA20 2HT ☎ 01935 462462 ⌨ garry.green@southsomerset.gov.uk

Partnerships: Mr David Crisfield, Third Sector & Partnership Co-ordinator, Council Offices, Brympton Way, Yeovil BA20 2HT ☎ 01935 462462 ⌨ david.crisfield@southsomerset.gov.uk

Personnel / HR: Mr Mike Holliday, Human Resources & Performance Manager, Council Offices, Brympton Way, Yeovil BA20 2HT ☎ 01935 462462 ⌨ mike.holliday@southsomerset.gov.uk

Planning: Mr David Norris, Development Control Manager, Council Offices, Brympton Way, Yeovil BA20 2HT ☎ 01935 462462 ⌨ david.norris@southsomerset.gov.uk

Procurement: Mr Gary Russ, Procurement & Risk Manager, Council Offices, Brympton Way, Yeovil BA20 2HT ☎ 01935 462462 ⌨ gary.russ@southsomerset.gov.uk

Recycling & Waste Minimisation: Mr Dave Mansell, Recycling Development Officer, Somerset County Council, County Hall, Taunton TA1 4DY ☎ 01823 356013 ⌨ dgmansell@somerset.gov.uk

Regeneration: Mr David Julian, Economic Development Manager, Council Offices, Brympton Way, Yeovil BA20 2HT ☎ 01935 462462 ⌨ david.julian@southsomerset.gov.uk

Staff Training: Mr Mike Holliday, Human Resources & Performance Manager, Council Offices, Brympton Way, Yeovil BA20 2HT ☎ 01935 462462 ⌨ mike.holliday@southsomerset.gov.uk

Street Scene: Mr Chris Cooper, Streetscene Manager, South Somerset Direct Services, 7 Artillery Road, Luton Trading Estate, Yeovil BA22 8RP ☎ 01935 462462 ⌨ chris.cooper@southsomerset.gov.uk

Sustainable Communities: Mr Paul Wheatley, Spatial Policy Manager, Council Offices, Brympton Way, Yeovil BA20 2HT ☎ 01935 462462 ⌨ paul.wheatley@southsomerset.gov.uk

Tourism: Mr David Julian, Economic Development Manager, Council Offices, Brympton Way, Yeovil BA20 2HT ☎ 01935 462462 ⌨ david.julian@southsomerset.gov.uk

Transport: Mr Nigel Collins, Transport Strategy Officer, Council Offices, Brympton Way, Yeovil BA20 2HT ☎ 01935 462462 ⌨ nigel.collins@southsomerset.gov.uk

Transport Planner: Mr Nigel Collins, Transport Strategy Officer, Council Offices, Brympton Way, Yeovil BA20 2HT ☎ 01935 462462 ⌨ nigel.collins@southsomerset.gov.uk

Children's Play Areas: Mr Rob Parr, Senior Play & Youth Facilities Officer, Council Offices, Brympton Way, Yeovil BA20 2HT ☎ 01935 462462 ⌨ rob.parr@southsomerset.gov.uk

COUNCILLORS

Chair: Best, Mike (LD - Crewkerne)
mike.best@southsomerset.gov.uk

Leader of the Council: Pallister, Ric (LD - Parrett)
ric.pallister@southsomerset.gov.uk

Deputy Leader of the Council: Roundell Greene, Jo (LD - St Michael's)
jo.roundellgreene@southsomerset.gov.uk

Aparicio Paul, Clare (CON - Langport & Huish)
clare.apariciopaul@southsomerset.gov.uk

Baker, Jason (LD - Holyrood (Chard))
jason.baker@southsomerset.gov.uk

Bakewell, Cathy (LD - Coker)
cathy.bakewell@southsomerset.gov.uk

Barrett, Marcus (CON - Crewkerne)
marcus.barrett@southsomerset.gov.uk

Beech, Mike (CON - Tower)
mike.beech@southsomerset.gov.uk

Bloomfield, Neil (CON - Martock)
neil.bloomfield@southsomerset.gov.uk

Broom, Amanda (CON - Combe (Chard))
amanda.broom@southsomerset.gov.uk

Bulmer, Dave (IND - Jocelyn (Chard))
dave.bulmer@southsomerset.gov.uk

Capozzoli, Tony (IND - Ivelchester)
tony.capozzoli@southsomerset.gov.uk

Clark, John (LD - Yeovil (West))
john.clark@southsomerset.gov.uk

Colbert, Nick (CON - Wincanton)
nick.colbert@southsomerset.gov.uk

Dance, Adam (LD - South Petherton)
adam.dance@southsomerset.gov.uk

Dibben, Gye (CON - Yeovil Without)
gye.dibben@southsomerset.gov.uk

Dyke-Bracher, Sarah (LD - Milborne Port)
sarah.dyke-bracher@southsomerset.gov.uk

Field, John (CON - Yeovil (South))
john.field@southsomerset.gov.uk

Gage, Nigel (CON - Yeovil (South))
nigel.gage@southsomerset.gov.uk

Goodall, Carol (LD - Ilminster)
carol.goodall@southsomerset.gov.uk

Groskop, Anna (CON - Bruton)
anna.groskop@southsomerset.gov.uk

Gubbins, Peter (LD - Yeovil (Central))
peter.gubbins@southsomerset.gov.uk

Hobhouse, Henry (LD - Cary)
henry.hobhouse@southsomerset.gov.uk

Hussain, Kaysar (LD - Yeovil (Central))
kaysar.hussain@southsomerset.gov.uk

Inglefield, Tim (CON - Blackmoor Vale)
tim.inglefield@southsomerset.gov.uk

Keitch, Val (LD - Ilminster Town)
val.keitch@southsomerset.gov.uk

Kendall, Andy (LD - Yeovil (Central))
andy.kendall@southsomerset.gov.uk

Kenton, Jenny (LD - Crimchard (Chard))
jenny.kenton@southsomerset.gov.uk

Lewis, Mike (CON - Camelot)
michael.lewis@southsomerset.gov.uk

Lindsay, Sarah (CON - Brympton)
sarah.lindsay@southsomerset.gov.uk

Lock, Mike (LD - Yeovil Without)
mike.lock@southsomerset.gov.uk

Lock, Tony (LD - Yeovil (East))
tony.lock@southsomerset.gov.uk

Maxwell, Paul (LD - Eggwood)
paul.maxwell@southsomerset.gov.uk

McAllister, Sam (CON - Yeovil (South))
sam.mcallister@southsomerset.gov.uk

Middleton, Graham (CON - Martock)
graham.middleton@southsomerset.gov.uk

Norris, David (CON - Wessex)
david.norriscllr@southsomerset.gov.uk

Oakes, Graham (LD - Yeovil Without)
graham.oakes@southsomerset.gov.uk

Osborne, Sue (CON - Windwhistle)
sue.osborne@southsomerset.gov.uk

Osborne, Tiffany (CON - Curry Rivel)
tiffany.osborne@southsomerset.gov.uk

Page, Stephen (LD - Wessex)
stephen.page@southsomerset.gov.uk

Raikes, Crispin (LD - South Petherton)
crispin.raikes@southsomerset.gov.uk

Read, Wes (CON - Yeovil (West))
wes.read@southsomerset.gov.uk

Recardo, David (LD - Yeovil (East))
david.recardo@southsomerset.gov.uk

Ruddle, Dean (CON - Wessex)
dean.ruddle@southsomerset.gov.uk

Seal, Sylvia (LD - Hamdon)
sylvia.seal@southsomerset.gov.uk

Seaton, Gina (CON - Coker)
gina.seaton@southsomerset.gov.uk

Seib, Peter (LD - Brympton)
peter.seib@southsomerset.gov.uk

Shortland, Garry (LD - Avishayes (Chard))
garry.shortland@southsomerset.gov.uk

Singleton, Angie (LD - Crewkerne Town)
angie.singleton@southsomerset.gov.uk

Smith, Alan (LD - Yeovil (West))
alan.smith@southsomerset.gov.uk

Steele, Sue (CON - Islemoor)
sue.steele@southsomerset.gov.uk

Stickland, Rob (LD - Yeovil (East))
rob.stickland@southsomerset.gov.uk

Turpin, Andrew (LD - Tatworth & Forton)
andrew.turpin@southsomerset.gov.uk

Vijeh, Linda (CON - Neroche)
linda.vijeh@southsomerset.gov.uk

Wale, Martin (CON - Combe (Chard))
martin.wale@southsomerset.gov.uk

Wallace, William (CON - Blackmoor Vale)
william.wallace@southsomerset.gov.uk

Weeks, Nick (CON - Cary)
nick.weeks@southsomerset.gov.uk

Winder, Colin (CON - Wincanton)
colin.winder@southsomerset.gov.uk

Yeomans, Derek (CON - Burrow Hill)
derek.yeomans@southsomerset.gov.uk

POLITICAL COMPOSITION
LD: 29, CON: 28, IND: 2

COMMITTEE CHAIRS

Audit: Mr Derek Yeomans

Licensing: Mr Martin Wale

South Staffordshire   D

South Staffordshire District Council, Council Offices, Codsall
WV8 1PX
☎ 01902 696000 🖨 01902 696800 ✆ info@sstaffs.gov.uk
🖥 www.sstaffs.gov.uk

FACTS AND FIGURES
Parliamentary Constituencies: Staffordshire South
EU Constituencies: West Midlands

SOUTH STAFFORDSHIRE

Election Frequency: Elections are of whole council

PRINCIPAL OFFICERS

Chief Executive: Mr Dave Heywood, Chief Executive, Council Offices, Codsall WV8 1PX ☎ 01902 696700 ✆ d.heywood@sstaffs.gov.uk

Senior Management: Ms Frankie Cartwright, Director - Financial & Welfare Services, Council Offices, Codsall WV8 1PX ☎ 01902 696640 ✆ f.cartwright@sstaffs.gov.uk

Senior Management: Mr Andrew Johnson, Director - Planning & Strategic Services, Council Offices, Codsall WV8 1PX ☎ 01902 696457 ✆ a.johnson@sstaffs.gov.uk

Senior Management: Mr David Pattison, Director - Legal & Public Health Protection, Council Offices, Codsall WV8 1PX ☎ 01902 696132 ✆ d.pattison@sstaffs.gov.uk

Senior Management: Mrs Jackie Smith, Director - Environmental & Customer Services, Council Offices, Codsall WV8 1PX ☎ 01902 696463 ✆ j.smith@sstaffs.gov.uk

Architect, Building / Property Services: Mr Adam Hale, Facilities Management Team Leader, Council Offices, Codsall WV8 1PX ☎ 01902 696114 ✆ a.hale@sstaffs.gov.uk

Best Value: Ms Clodagh Peterson, Policy & Partnership Manager, Council Offices, Codsall WV8 1PX ☎ 01902 696424 ✆ c.peterson@sstaffs.gov.uk

Best Value: Mr Steve Winterflood, Chief Executive, Council Offices, Codsall WV8 1PX ☎ 01902 696700 ✆ s.winterflood@sstaffs.gov.uk

Building Control: Mrs Jackie Smith, Director - Environmental Services, Council Offices, Codsall WV8 1PX ☎ 01902 696463 ✆ j.smith@sstaffs.gov.uk

PR / Communications: Mr Dave Heywood, Chief Executive, Council Offices, Codsall WV8 1PX ☎ 01902 696700 ✆ d.heywood@sstaffs.gov.uk

PR / Communications: Mr Steve Winterflood, Chief Executive, Council Offices, Codsall WV8 1PX ☎ 01902 696700 ✆ s.winterflood@sstaffs.gov.uk

Community Planning: Mr Dave Heywood, Chief Executive, Council Offices, Codsall WV8 1PX ☎ 01902 696700 ✆ d.heywood@sstaffs.gov.uk

Community Safety: Mrs Maggie Quinn, Partnership & Locality Manager, Council Offices, Codsall WV8 1PX ☎ 01902 696530 ✆ m.quinn@sstaffs.gov.uk

Corporate Services: Ms Clodagh Peterson, Policy & Partnership Manager, Council Offices, Codsall WV8 1PX ☎ 01902 696424 ✆ c.peterson@sstaffs.gov.uk

Customer Service: Mrs Jackie Smith, Director - Environmental & Customer Services, Council Offices, Codsall WV8 1PX ☎ 01902 696463 ✆ j.smith@sstaffs.gov.uk

Economic Development: Mr Andrew Johnson, Director - Planning & Strategic Services, Council Offices, Codsall WV8 1PX ☎ 01902 696457 ✆ a.johnson@sstaffs.gov.uk

Economic Development: Mr Grant Mitchell, Strategic Development & Planning Manager, Council Offices, Codsall WV8 1PX ☎ 01902 696438 ✆ g.mitchell@sstaffs.gov.uk

Electoral Registration: Ms Clodagh Peterson, Policy & Partnership Manager, Council Offices, Codsall WV8 1PX ☎ 01902 696424 ✆ c.peterson@sstaffs.gov.uk

Emergency Planning: Mrs Jackie Smith, Director - Environmental & Customer Services, Council Offices, Codsall WV8 1PX ☎ 01902 696463 ✆ j.smith@sstaffs.gov.uk

Environmental / Technical Services: Mrs Jackie Smith, Director - Environmental & Customer Services, Council Offices, Codsall WV8 1PX ☎ 01902 696463 ✆ j.smith@sstaffs.gov.uk

Environmental Health: Mr John Gerring, Environmental Health Manager, Council Offices, Codsall WV8 1PX ☎ 01902 696205 ✆ j.gerring@sstaffs.gov.uk

Environmental Health: Ms Jenny Rhodes, Environmental Health Manager, Council Offices, Codsall WV8 1PX ☎ 01902 696205 ✆ j.rhodes@sstaffs.gov.uk

Finance: Mrs Helen Ogram, Chief Finance Officer, Council Offices, Codsall WV8 1PX ☎ 01902 696608 ✆ h.ogram@sstaffs.gov.uk

Grounds Maintenance: Mrs Jackie Smith, Director - Environmental & Customer Services, Council Offices, Codsall WV8 1PX ☎ 01902 696463 ✆ j.smith@sstaffs.gov.uk

Health and Safety: Mr David Pattison, Director - Legal & Public Health Protection, Council Offices, Codsall WV8 1PX ☎ 01902 696132 ✆ d.pattison@sstaffs.gov.uk

Home Energy Conservation: Mrs Jackie Smith, Director - Environmental & Customer Services, Council Offices, Codsall WV8 1PX ☎ 01902 696463 ✆ j.smith@sstaffs.gov.uk

Housing: Mr Grant Mitchell, Strategic Development & Planning Manager, Council Offices, Codsall WV8 1PX ☎ 01902 696438 ✆ g.mitchell@sstaffs.gov.uk

Legal: Mr David Pattison, Director - Legal & Public Health Protection, Council Offices, Codsall WV8 1PX ☎ 01902 696132 ✆ d.pattison@sstaffs.gov.uk

Leisure and Cultural Services: Mrs Jackie Smith, Director - Environmental & Customer Services, Council Offices, Codsall WV8 1PX ☎ 01902 696463 ✆ j.smith@sstaffs.gov.uk

Licensing: Mr David Pattison, Director - Legal & Public Health Protection, Council Offices, Codsall WV8 1PX ☎ 01902 696132 ✆ d.pattison@sstaffs.gov.uk

Lighting: Mrs Jackie Smith, Director - Environmental & Customer Services, Council Offices, Codsall WV8 1PX ☎ 01902 696463 ✆ j.smith@sstaffs.gov.uk

Lighting: Mrs Jackie Smith, Director - Environmental & Customer Services, Council Offices, Codsall WV8 1PX ☎ 01902 696463 ⏴ j.smith@sstaffs.gov.uk

Member Services: Mr Dave Heywood, Chief Executive, Council Offices, Codsall WV8 1PX ☎ 01902 696700 ⏴ d.heywood@sstaffs.gov.uk

Parking: Mrs Jackie Smith, Director - Environmental & Customer Services, Council Offices, Codsall WV8 1PX ☎ 01902 696463 ⏴ j.smith@sstaffs.gov.uk

Partnerships: Mr Dave Heywood, Chief Executive, Council Offices, Codsall WV8 1PX ☎ 01902 696700 ⏴ d.heywood@sstaffs.gov.uk

Partnerships: Ms Clodagh Peterson, Policy & Partnership Manager, Council Offices, Codsall WV8 1PX ☎ 01902 696424 ⏴ c.peterson@sstaffs.gov.uk

Personnel / HR: Mrs Wendy Bridgwater, Human Resources Manager, Council Offices, Codsall WV8 1PX ☎ 01902 696103 ⏴ w.bridgwater@sstaffs.gov.uk

Planning: Mr Andrew Johnson, Director - Planning & Strategic Services, Council Offices, Codsall WV8 1PX ☎ 01902 696457 ⏴ a.johnson@sstaffs.gov.uk

Procurement: Mr David Pattison, Director - Legal & Public Health Protection, Council Offices, Codsall WV8 1PX ☎ 01902 696132 ⏴ d.pattison@sstaffs.gov.uk

Recycling & Waste Minimisation: Mrs Jackie Smith, Director - Environmental & Customer Services, Council Offices, Codsall WV8 1PX ☎ 01902 696463 ⏴ j.smith@sstaffs.gov.uk

Recycling & Waste Minimisation: Mr Gary Withington, Environmental Services Manager, Council Offices, Codsall WV8 1PX ☎ 01902 696406 ⏴ g.withington@sstaffs.gov.uk

Regeneration: Mr Andrew Johnson, Director - Planning & Strategic Services, Council Offices, Codsall WV8 1PX ☎ 01902 696457 ⏴ a.johnson@sstaffs.gov.uk

Regeneration: Mr Grant Mitchell, Strategic Development & Planning Manager, Council Offices, Codsall WV8 1PX ☎ 01902 696438 ⏴ g.mitchell@sstaffs.gov.uk

Staff Training: Mrs Wendy Bridgwater, Human Resources Manager, Council Offices, Codsall WV8 1PX ☎ 01902 696103 ⏴ w.bridgwater@sstaffs.gov.uk

Street Scene: Mrs Jackie Smith, Director - Environmental & Customer Services, Council Offices, Codsall WV8 1PX ☎ 01902 696463 ⏴ j.smith@sstaffs.gov.uk

Sustainable Communities: Mr Andrew Johnson, Director - Planning & Strategic Services, Council Offices, Codsall WV8 1PX ☎ 01902 696457 ⏴ a.johnson@sstaffs.gov.uk

Tourism: Mr Andrew Johnson, Director - Planning & Strategic Services, Council Offices, Codsall WV8 1PX ☎ 01902 696457 ⏴ a.johnson@sstaffs.gov.uk

Tourism: Mr Grant Mitchell, Strategic Development & Planning Manager, Council Offices, Codsall WV8 1PX ☎ 01902 696438 ⏴ g.mitchell@sstaffs.gov.uk

Waste Management: Mr Gary Withington, Environmental Services Manager, Council Offices, Codsall WV8 1PX ☎ 01902 696406 ⏴ g.withington@sstaffs.gov.uk

COUNCILLORS

Chair: Williams, Bernard (CON - Cheslyn Hay South) b.williams@sstaffs.gov.uk

Vice-Chair: Chapman, Val (CON - Bilbrook) v.chapman@sstaffs.gov.uk

Leader of the Council: Edwards, Brian (CON - Kinver) b.edwards@sstaffs.gov.uk

Deputy Leader of the Council: Lees, Roger (CON - Himley & Swindon) r.lees@sstaffs.gov.uk

Ashley, Jeff (LAB - Huntington & Hatherton) j.ashley@sstaffs.gov.uk

Barrow, Meg (CON - Codsall North) m.barrow@sstaffs.gov.uk

Bates, Leonard (CON - Penkridge North East & Acton Trussell) l.bates@sstaffs.gov.uk

Bolton, Joyce (CON - Brewood & Coven)

Bond, Mary (CON - Wombourne South West) m.bond@sstaffs.gov.uk

Bond, Barry (CON - Wombourne North & Lower Penn) b.bond@sstaffs.gov.uk

Bourke, Anthony (IND - Perton East) a.bourke@sstaffs.gov.uk

Caine, Nigel (CON - Perton Lakeside) n.caine@sstaffs.gov.uk

Cartwright, Donald (CON - Penkridge West) d.cartwright@sstaffs.gov.uk

Clifft, David (IND - Essington) d.clifft@sstaffs.gov.uk

Cope, Robert (IND - Featherstone & Shareshill) r.cope@sstaffs.gov.uk

Cox, Brian (CON - Wheaton Aston, Bishopswood & Lapley) b.cox@sstaffs.gov.uk

Davies, Michael (CON - Wombourne South West) m.davies@sstaffs.gov.uk

Emery, Lisa (CON - Cheslyn Hay North & Saredon) l.emery@sstaffs.gov.uk

Ewart, Matthew (CON - Codsall North) m.ewart@sstaffs.gov.uk

Fieldhouse, Paul (CON - Bilbrook) p.fieldhouse@sstaffs.gov.uk

Ford, Isabel (CON - Penkridge North East & Acton Trussell) i.ford@sstaffs.gov.uk

Heseltine, Rita (CON - Perton Lakeside) r.heseltine@sstaffs.gov.uk

Hingley, Lin (CON - Kinver) l.hingley@sstaffs.gov.uk

SOUTH STAFFORDSHIRE

Hinton, Alan (CON - Wombourne North & Lower Penn)
a.hinton@sstaffs.gov.uk

Hollis, Steve (UKIP - Cheslyn Hay North & Saredon)
s.hollis@sstaffs.gov.uk

Holmes, Diane (CON - Brewood & Coven)
d.holmes@sstaffs.gov.uk

James, Keith (CON - Perton Dippons)
k.james@sstaffs.gov.uk

Johnson, Janet (CON - Great Wyrley Town)
j.johnson@sstaffs.gov.uk

Lawrence, Michael (CON - Great Wyrley Town)
m.lawrence@sstaffs.gov.uk

Lever, Peter (IND - Essington)
p.lever@sstaffs.gov.uk

Lobuczek, Henryk (CON - Featherstone & Shareshill)
h.lobuczek@sstaffs.gov.uk

Lockley, Dave (CON - Cheslyn Hay South)
d.lockley@sstaffs.gov.uk

Marshall, Robert (CON - Codsall South)
r.marshall@sstaffs.gov.uk

Mason, Terry (CON - Pattingham & Patshull)
t.mason@sstaffs.gov.uk

McCardle, Robert (CON - Trysull & Seisdon)
r.mccardle@sstaffs.gov.uk

Michell, John (CON - Codsall South)
j.michell@sstaffs.gov.uk

Moreton, Roy (CON - Perton Lakeside)
r.moreton@sstaffs.gov.uk

Perry, Raymond (CON - Great Wyrley Landywood)
r.perry@sstaffs.gov.uk

Perry, Kathleen (CON - Great Wyrley Town)
k.perry@sstaffs.gov.uk

Raven, Christine (CON - Penkridge South East)
c.raven@sstaffs.gov.uk

Raven, John (CON - Penkridge South East)
j.raven@sstaffs.gov.uk

Reade, Robert (CON - Wombourne North & Lower Penn)

Sutton, Wendy (CON - Brewood & Coven)
w.sutton@sstaffs.gov.uk

Upton, Ken (CON - Wombourne South East)
k.upton@sstaffs.gov.uk

Williams, Reginald (CON - Wombourne South East)
r.williams@sstaffs.gov.uk

Williams, Kathleen (CON - Great Wyrley Landywood)
k.williams@sstaffs.gov.uk

Williams, Henry (CON - Kinver)
h.williams@sstaffs.gov.uk

Williams, David (CON - Huntington & Hatherton)
d.williams@sstaffs.gov.uk

Wright, Royston (CON - Wheaton Aston, Bishopswood & Lapley)
r.wright@sstaffs.gov.uk

POLITICAL COMPOSITION
CON: 43, IND: 4, LAB: 1, UKIP: 1

COMMITTEE CHAIRS

Audit: Mr John Michell

Licensing: Mr Roy Moreton

Planning: Mr Brian Cox

South Tyneside   M

South Tyneside Council, Town Hall and Civic Offices, Westoe Road, South Shields NE33 2RL
☎ 0191 427 7000 🖳 www.southtyneside.gov.uk

FACTS AND FIGURES
Parliamentary Constituencies: Jarrow, South Shields
EU Constituencies: North East
Election Frequency: Elections are by thirds

PRINCIPAL OFFICERS

Chief Executive: Mr Martin Swales, Chief Executive, Town Hall and Civic Offices, Westoe Road, South Shields NE33 2RL
🖰 martin.swales@southtyneside.gov.uk

Senior Management: Mr David Cramond, Corporate Director - Economic Regeneration, Town Hall and Civic Offices, Westoe Road, South Shields NE33 2RL ☎ 0191 424 7969
🖰 david.cramond@southtyneside.gov.uk

Senior Management: Ms Amanda Healy, Director - Public Health, Town Hall and Civic Offices, Westoe Road, South Shields NE33 2RL
☎ 0191 424 6678 🖰 amanda.healy@southtyneside.gov.uk

Senior Management: Mr John Pearce, Corporate Director - Children, Adults & Health, Town Hall and Civic Offices, Westoe Road, South Shields NE33 2RL ☎ 0191 424 7765
🖰 john.pearce@southtyneside.gov.uk

Architect, Building / Property Services: Mr Paul Scrafton, Head of Asset Management, Town Hall and Civic Offices, Westoe Road, South Shields NE33 2RL ☎ 0191 424 7235
🖰 paul.scrafton@southtyneside.gov.uk

Best Value: Ms Rachel Davison, Performance & Information Manager, Town Hall and Civic Offices, Westoe Road, South Shields NE33 2RL ☎ 0191 424 7546 🖰 rachel.davison@southtyneside.gov.uk

Building Control: Mr George Mansbridge, Head of Development Services, Town Hall and Civic Offices, Westoe Road, South Shields NE33 2RL ☎ 0191 424 7566
🖰 george.mansbridge@southtyneside.gov.uk

Catering Services: Ms Elizabeth Luke, Catering Services Manager, Town Hall and Civic Offices, Westoe Road, South Shields NE33 2RL ☎ 0191 424 6710 🖰 elizabeth.luke@southtyneside.gov.uk

Children / Youth Services: Mrs Karen Davison, Strategic Lead - Early Help & SEN, Town Hall and Civic Offices, Westoe Road, South Shields NE33 2RL ☎ 0191 424 6597
🖰 karen.davison@southtynside.gov.uk

Children / Youth Services: Mr John Pearce, Corporate Director - Children, Adults & Health, Town Hall and Civic Offices, Westoe Road, South Shields NE33 2RL ☎ 0191 424 7765 ✆ john.pearce@southtyneside.gov.uk

Civil Registration: Mr Mike Harding, Head of Legal Services, Town Hall & Civic Offices, Westoe Road, South Shields NE33 2RL ☎ 0191 424 7009 ✆ mike.harding@southtyneside.gov.uk

Civil Registration: Mrs Jacqueline Todd, Superintendent Registrar, Town Hall and Civic Offices, Westoe Road, South Shields NE33 2RL ☎ 0191 424 6352 ✆ jacqueline.todd@southtyneside.gov.uk

PR / Communications: Ms Tania Robinson, Head of Marketing & Communications, Town Hall and Civic Offices, Westoe Road, South Shields NE33 2RL ☎ 0191 424 7817 ✆ tania.robinson@southtyneside.gov.uk

Community Planning: Mr Peter Mennell, Housing & Planning Growth Manager, Town Hall and Civic Offices, Westoe Road, South Shields NE33 2RL ☎ 0191 424 7646 ✆ peter.mennell@southtyneside.gov.uk

Community Safety: Mr Dave Owen, Area Crime & Justice Co-ordinator, Town Hall and Civic Offices, Westoe Road, South Shields NE33 2RL ☎ 0191 424 7938 ✆ dave.owen@southtyneside.gov.uk

Computer Management: Mr Stuart Reid, Head of Finance, South Tyneside Council, Town Hall & Civic Offices, Westoe Road, South Shields NE33 2RL ☎ 0191 424 7765 ✆ stuart.reid@southtyneside.gov.uk

Consumer Protection and Trading Standards: Mr Stuart Wright, Regulatory Services Manager, Town Hall and Civic Offices, Westoe Road, South Shields NE33 2RL ☎ 0191 424 7869 ✆ stuart.wright@southtyneside.gov.uk

Contracts: Mr Mike Conlon, Head of Corporate & Commercial Services, Town Hall and Civic Offices, Westoe Road, South Shields NE33 2RL ☎ 0191 424 7765 ✆ mike.conlon@southtyneside.gov.uk

Corporate Services: Mrs Hayley Johnson, Corporate Lead - Strategy & Performance, Town Hall and Civic Offices, Westoe Road, South Shields NE33 2RL ☎ 0191 4271717 ✆ hayley.johnson@southtyneside.gov.uk

Customer Service: Ms Gillian Harrison, Customer Services Team Manager, Town Hall and Civic Offices, Westoe Road, South Shields NE33 2RL ☎ 0191 424 1201 ✆ gillian.harrison@southtyneside.gov.uk

Economic Development: Mr David Cramond, Corporate Director - Economic Regeneration, Town Hall and Civic Offices, Westoe Road, South Shields NE33 2RL ☎ 0191 424 7969 ✆ david.cramond@southtyneside.gov.uk

Economic Development: Mr John Scott, Corporate Lead - Business, Employment & Skills, Town Hall and Civic Offices, Westoe Road, South Shields NE33 2RL ☎ 0191 424 6250 ✆ john.scott@southtyneside.gov.uk

Education: Mr Peter Cutts, Head of Education, Learning & Skills, Town Hall and Civic Offices, Westoe Road, South Shields NE33 2RL ☎ 0191 424 7697 ✆ peter.cutts@southtyneside.gov.uk

Electoral Registration: Ms Joanne Gelson, Elections Manager, Town Hall and Civic Offices, Westoe Road, South Shields NE33 2RL ☎ 0191 4247169 ✆ joanne.gelson@southtyneside.gov.uk

Emergency Planning: Mr Tony Hanson, Environmental Health Manager, Town Hall and Civic Offices, Westoe Road, South Shields NE33 2RL ☎ 0191 424 7901 ✆ tony.hanson@southtyneside.gov.uk

Energy Management: Mr Paul Scrafton, Head of Asset Management, Town Hall and Civic Offices, Westoe Road, South Shields NE33 2RL ☎ 0191 424 7235 ✆ paul.scrafton@southtyneside.gov.uk

Environmental / Technical Services: Mr George Mansbridge, Head of Development Services, Town Hall and Civic Offices, Westoe Road, South Shields NE33 2RL ☎ 0191 424 7566 ✆ george.mansbridge@southtyneside.gov.uk

Environmental Health: Mr George Mansbridge, Head of Development Services, Town Hall and Civic Offices, Westoe Road, South Shields NE33 2RL ☎ 0191 424 7566 ✆ george.mansbridge@southtyneside.gov.uk

Estates, Property & Valuation: Mr Paul Scrafton, Head of Asset Management, Town Hall and Civic Offices, Westoe Road, South Shields NE33 2RL ☎ 0191 424 7235 ✆ paul.scrafton@southtyneside.gov.uk

Events Manager: Mr Richard Jago, Culture & Libraries Manager, Town Hall and Civic Offices, Westoe Road, South Shields NE33 2RL ☎ 0191 424 7984 ✆ rich.jago@southtyneside.gov.uk

Facilities: Mr Paul Mossa, Corporate Facilities Manager, Town Hall and Civic Offices, Westoe Road, South Shields NE33 2RL ☎ 0191 424 7241 ✆ paul.mossa@southtyneside.gov.uk

Finance: Mr Ian Bainbridge, Head of Pensions, Town Hall and Civic Offices, Westoe Road, South Shields NE33 2RL ☎ 0191 427 4112 ✆ ian.bainbridge@southtyneside.gov.uk

Finance: Mr Stuart Reid, Head of Finance, South Tyneside Council, Town Hall & Civic Offices, Westoe Road, South Shields NE33 2RL ☎ 0191 424 7765 ✆ stuart.reid@southtyneside.gov.uk

Pensions: Mr Ian Bainbridge, Head of Pensions, Town Hall and Civic Offices, Westoe Road, South Shields NE33 2RL ☎ 0191 427 4112 ✆ ian.bainbridge@southtyneside.gov.uk

Grounds Maintenance: Mr Gary Kirsop, Director - Housing & Area Management, Strathmore, Jarrow NE32 3DP ☎ 0191 427 2557 ✆ Gary.kirsop@southtynesidehomes.org.uk

Health and Safety: Mr Graham Fells, HR Corporate Lead, Town Hall and Civic Offices, Westoe Road, South Shields NE33 2RL ☎ 0191 424 7323 ✆ graham.fells@southtyneside.gov.uk

SOUTH TYNESIDE

Highways: Mr Dave Carr, Highways & Infrastructure Manager, Town Hall and Civic Offices, Westoe Road, South Shields NE33 2RL ☎ 0191 427 2553 ◌ dave.carr@southtyneside.gov.uk

Home Energy Conservation: Mrs Debra Ralph, Home Energy Officer, Strathmore, Jarrow NE32 3DP ☎ 0191 424 7902 ◌ debra.ralph@southtyneside.gov.uk

Housing: Mr Gary Kirsop, Director - Housing & Area Management, Middlefields, South Shields NE34 0NT ☎ 0191 427 2557 ◌ gary.kirsop@southtynesidehomes.org.uk

Housing Maintenance: Mr Jason Crews, Head of Property Services, Middlefields, South Shields NE34 0NT ☎ 0191 427 2624 ◌ jason.crews@southtyneside.gov.uk

Legal: Mr Mike Harding, Head of Legal Services, Town Hall & Civic Offices, Westoe Road, South Shields NE33 2RL ☎ 0191 424 7009 ◌ mike.harding@southtyneside.gov.uk

Leisure and Cultural Services: Mr David Brooks, Corporate Lead - Culture & Leisure Services, Town Hall and Civic Offices, Westoe Road, South Shields NE33 2RL ☎ 0191 424 7570 ◌ david.brooks@southtyneside.gov.uk

Licensing: Mr George Mansbridge, Head of Development Services, Town Hall and Civic Offices, Westoe Road, South Shields NE33 2RL ☎ 0191 424 7566 ◌ george.mansbridge@southtyneside.gov.uk

Lifelong Learning: Mr Peter Cutts, Head of Education, Learning & Skills, Town Hall and Civic Offices, Westoe Road, South Shields NE33 2RL ☎ 0191 424 7697 ◌ peter.cutts@southtyneside.gov.uk

Lighting: Mr Paul Scrafton, Head of Asset Management, Town Hall and Civic Offices, Westoe Road, South Shields NE33 2RL ☎ 0191 424 7235 ◌ paul.scrafton@southtyneside.gov.uk

Member Services: Mrs Hayley Johnson, Corporate Lead - Strategy & Performance, Town Hall & Civic Offices, Westoe Road, South Shields NE33 2RL ☎ 0191 4271717 ◌ hayley.johnson@southtyneside.gov.uk

Parking: Mr Dave Pentland, Parking & Utilities Manager, Town Hall and Civic Offices, Westoe Road, South Shields NE33 2RL ☎ 0191 424 7617 ◌ dave.pentland@southtyneside.gov.uk

Partnerships: Mrs Hayley Johnson, Corporate Lead - Strategy & Performance, Town Hall & Civic Offices, Westoe Road, South Shields NE33 2RL ☎ 0191 4271717 ◌ hayley.johnson@southtyneside.gov.uk

Personnel / HR: Mr Graham Fells, HR Corporate Lead, Town Hall and Civic Offices, Westoe Road, South Shields NE33 2RL ☎ 0191 424 7323 ◌ graham.fells@southtyneside.gov.uk

Planning: Mr George Mansbridge, Head of Development Services, Town Hall and Civic Offices, Westoe Road, South Shields NE33 2RL ☎ 0191 424 7566 ◌ george.mansbridge@southtyneside.gov.uk

Procurement: Mr Stuart Reid, Head of Finance, South Tyneside Council, Town Hall & Civic Offices, Westoe Road, South Shields NE33 2RL ☎ 0191 424 7765 ◌ stuart.reid@southtyneside.gov.uk

Public Libraries: Mr Richard Jago, Culture & Libraries Manager, Town Hall and Civic Offices, Westoe Road, South Shields NE33 2RL ☎ 0191 424 7984 ◌ rich.jago@southtyneside.gov.uk

Recycling & Waste Minimisation: Mr Bob Cummins, Waste & Recycling Team Leader, Town Hall and Civic Offices, Westoe Road, South Shields NE33 2RL ☎ 0191 427 2656 ◌ bob.cummins@southtyneside.gov.uk

Regeneration: Mr John Sparkes, Head of Regeneration, Town Hall and Civic Offices, Westoe Road, South Shields NE33 2RL ☎ 0191 424 7603 ◌ john.sparkes@southtyneside.gov.uk

Road Safety: Ms Kim Quest-Law, Road Safety Co-ordinator, Town Hall and Civic Offices, Westoe Road, South Shields NE33 2RL ☎ 0191 424 7613 ◌ kim.quest-law@southtyneside.gov.uk

Social Services: Mr Tony Dailide, Head of Adult Social Care, Town Hall and Civic Offices, Westoe Road, South Shields NE33 2RL ☎ 0191 424 7055 ◌ tony.dailide@southtyneside.gov.uk

Social Services: Mrs Shona Gallagher, Head of Children & Families Social Care, Town Hall and Civic Offices, Westoe Road, South Shields NE33 2RL ☎ 0191 424 4749 ◌ shona.gallagher@southtyneside.gov.uk

Social Services (Adult): Mr Tony Dailide, Head of Adult Social Care, Town Hall and Civic Offices, Westoe Road, South Shields NE33 2RL ☎ 0191 424 7055 ◌ tony.dailide@southtyneside.gov.uk

Social Services (Children): Mrs Shona Gallagher, Head of Children & Families Social Care, Town Hall and Civic Offices, Westoe Road, South Shields NE33 2RL ☎ 0191 424 4749 ◌ shona.gallagher@southtyneside.gov.uk

Public Health: Ms Amanda Healy, Director - Public Health, Town Hall and Civic Offices, Westoe Road, South Shields NE33 2RL ☎ 0191 424 6678 ◌ amanda.healy@southtyneside.gov.uk

Staff Training: Mr Graham Fells, HR Corporate Lead, Town Hall and Civic Offices, Westoe Road, South Shields NE33 2RL ☎ 0191 424 7323 ◌ graham.fells@southtyneside.gov.uk

Street Scene: Mr Bob Cummins, Waste & Recycling Team Leader, Town Hall and Civic Offices, Westoe Road, South Shields NE33 2RL ☎ 0191 427 2656 ◌ bob.cummins@southtyneside.gov.uk

Tourism: Ms Tania Robinson, Head of Marketing & Communications, Town Hall and Civic Offices, Westoe Road, South Shields NE33 2RL ☎ 0191 424 7817

Town Centre: Mr John Scott, Corporate Lead - Business, Employment & Skills, Town Hall and Civic Offices, Westoe Road, South Shields NE33 2RL ☎ 0191 424 6250 ◌ john.scott@southtyneside.gov.uk

Traffic Management: Mr Dave Carr, Highways & Infrastructure Manager, Town Hall and Civic Offices, Westoe Road, South Shields NE33 2RL ☎ 0191 427 2553 ◌ dave.carr@southtyneside.gov.uk

Transport: Mr Andrew Whittaker, Corporate Lead - Area Management, Town Hall and Civic Offices, Westoe Road, South Shields NE33 2RL ☎ 0191 427 2063
🖰 andrew.whittaker@southtyneside.gov.uk

Transport Planner: Mr Andrew Whittaker, Corporate Lead - Area Management, Town Hall and Civic Offices, Westoe Road, South Shields NE33 2RL ☎ 0191 427 2063
🖰 andrew.whittaker@southtyneside.gov.uk

Waste Collection and Disposal: Mr Bob Cummins, Waste & Recycling Team Leader, Town Hall and Civic Offices, Westoe Road, South Shields NE33 2RL ☎ 0191 427 2656
🖰 bob.cummins@southtyneside.gov.uk

Waste Collection and Disposal: Mr Andrew Whittaker, Corporate Lead - Area Management, Town Hall and Civic Offices, Westoe Road, South Shields NE33 2RL ☎ 0191 427 2063
🖰 andrew.whittaker@southtyneside.gov.uk

Waste Management: Mr Andrew Whittaker, Corporate Lead - Area Management, Town Hall and Civic Offices, Westoe Road, South Shields NE33 2RL ☎ 0191 427 2063
🖰 andrew.whittaker@southtyneside.gov.uk

COUNCILLORS

Leader of the Council: Malcolm, Iain (LAB - Horsley Hill)
cllr.iain.malcolm@southtyneside.co.uk

Deputy Leader of the Council: Kerr, Alan (LAB - Monkton)
cllr.alan.kerr@southtyneside.co.uk

Amar, Joe (LAB - Biddick & All Saints)
cllr.joe.amar@southtyneside.gov.uk

Anglin, John (LAB - Beacon & Bents)
cllr.john.anglin@southtyneside.gov.uk

Atkinson, Joan (LAB - Cleadon & East Boldon)
cllr.joan.atkinson@southtyneside.gov.uk

Bell, Joanne (LAB - Boldon Colliery)
cllr.joan.bell@southtyneside.co.uk

Boyack, Peter (LAB - Whitburn & Marsden)
cllr.peter.boyack@southtyneside.gov.uk

Brady, Bill (LAB - Whiteleas)
cllr.bill.brady@southtyneside.co.uk

Clare, Michael (LAB - Simonside & Rekendyke)
cllr.michael.clare@southtyneside.co.uk

Cunningham, Fay (LAB - Bede)
cllr.fay.cunningham@southtyneside.gov.uk

Dick, Norman (LAB - West Park)
cllr.norman.dick@southtyneside.gov.uk

Dix, Robert (LAB - Harton)
cllr.rob.dix@southtyneside.gov.uk

Dixon, Tracey (LAB - Whitburn & Marsden)
cllr.tracey.dixon@southtyneside.co.uk

Donaldson, Alexander (LAB - Cleadon Park)
cllr.alex.donaldson@southtyneside.gov.uk

Duncan, Sandra (LAB - Boldon Colliery)
cllr.sandra.duncan@southtyneside.gov.uk

Ellison, Adam (LAB - Hebburn North)
cllr.adam.ellison@southtyneside.gov.uk

Flynn, Wilf (LAB - Hebburn South)
cllr.wilf.flynn@southtyneside.gov.uk

Foreman, Jim (LAB - Cleadon Park)
cllr.jim.foreman@southtyneside.co.uk

Gibson, Ernest (LAB - Whiteleas)
cllr.ernest.gibson@southtyneside.co.uk

Hay, Pat (LAB - Harton)
cllr.pat.hay@southtyneside.gov.uk

Hetherington, Anne (LAB - West Park)
cllr.anne.hetherington@southtyneside.gov.uk

Hobson, Gladys (LAB - West Park)
cllr.gladys.hobson@southtyneside.gov.uk

Hughes, Lee (IND - Bede)
cllr.lee.hughes@southtyneside.gov.uk

Huntley, Audrey (LAB - Fellgate & Hedworth)
cllr.audrey.huntley@southtyneside.gov.uk

Keegan, Joan (LAB - Monkton)
cllr.joan.margaret.keegan@southtyneside.gov.uk

Kilgour, Geraldine (LAB - Fellgate & Hedworth)
cllr.geraldine.kilgour@southtyneside.gov.uk

Leask, Eileen (LAB - Horsley Hill)
cllr.eileen.leask@southtyneside.gov.uk

Malcolm, Edward (LAB - Simonside & Rekendyke)
cllr.ed.malcolm@southtyneside.co.uk

Maxwell, Katharine (LAB - Westoe)
cllr.katharine.maxwell@southtyneside.gov.uk

Maxwell, Neil (LAB - Harton)
cllr.neil.maxwell@southtyneside.gov.uk

Maxwell, Nancy (LAB - Hebburn South)
cllr.nancy.maxwell@southtyneside.co.uk

McCabe, John (LAB - Hebburn South)
cllr.john.mccabe@southtyneside.co.uk

McHugh, Liz (LAB - Hebburn North)
cllr.liz.mchugh@southtyneside.gov.uk

McMillan, Audrey (LAB - Beacon & Bents)
cllr.audrey.mcmillan@southtyneside.co.uk

Meling, Margaret (LAB - Cleadon & East Boldon)
cllr.margaret.meling@southtyneside.gov.uk

Peacock, Margaret (LAB - Bede)
cllr.margaret.peacock@southtyneside.gov.uk

Perry, Jim (LAB - Primrose)
cllr.jim.perry@southtyneside.co.uk

Porthouse, Richard (LAB - Hebburn North)
cllr.richard.porthouse@southtyneside.gov.uk

Proudlock, Lynne (LAB - Simonside & Rekendyke)
cllr.lynne.proudlock@southtyneside.gov.uk

Punchion, Olive (LAB - Biddick & All Saints)
cllr.olive.punchion@southtyneside.gov.uk

Purvis, Doreen (LAB - Whiteleas)
cllr.doreen.purvis@southtyneside.gov.uk

Sewell, Jim (LAB - Monkton)
cllr.jim.sewell@southtyneside.co.uk

SOUTH TYNESIDE

Smith, Moira (LAB - Primrose)
cllr.moira.smith@southtyneside.gov.uk

Smith, Alan (LAB - Fellgate & Hedworth)
cllr.alan.smith@southtyneside.gov.uk

Stephenson, Sheila (LAB - Westoe)
cllr.sheila.stephenson@southtyneside.gov.uk

Stephenson, Ken (LAB - Primrose)
cllr.ken.stephenson@southtyneside.gov.uk

Strike, Alison (LAB - Boldon Colliery)
cllr.alison.strike@southtyneside.co.uk

Townsley, David (LAB - Cleadon & East Boldon)
cllr.david.townsley@southtyneside.gov.uk

Traynor, Susan (LAB - Cleadon Park)
cllr.susan.traynor@southtyneside.gov.uk

Walsh, Mark (LAB - Horsley Hill)
cllr.mark.walsh@southtyneside.gov.uk

Walsh, Anne (LAB - Biddick & All Saints)
cllr.anne.walsh@southtyneside.gov.uk

Welsh, Joyce (LAB - Whitburn & Marsden)
cllr.joyce.welsh@southtyneside.gov.uk

West, Allan (LAB - Westoe)
cllr.allan.west@southtyneside.gov.uk

Wood, John (LAB - Beacon & Bents)
cllr.john.wood@southtyneside.gov.uk

POLITICAL COMPOSITION
LAB: 53, IND: 1

Southampton City   U

Southampton City Council, Civic Centre, Southampton
SO14 7LY
☎ 023 8083 3000 🖥 www.southampton.gov.uk

FACTS AND FIGURES
Parliamentary Constituencies: Romsey and Southampton North,
Southampton, Itchen, Southampton, Test
EU Constituencies: South East
Election Frequency: Elections are by thirds

PRINCIPAL OFFICERS

Chief Executive: Ms Dawn Baxendale, Chief Executive, Civic
Centre, Southampton SO14 7LY ☎ 023 8083 4428
 dawn.baxendale@southampton.gov.uk

Senior Management: Ms Carole Binns, Acting Service Director -
Adult Social Services, Civic Centre, Southampton SO14 7LY
 carole.binns@southampton.gov.uk

Senior Management: Ms Hilary Brooks, Service Director -
Children & Families, Civic Centre, Southampton SO14 7LY
☎ 023 8083 3021 hilary.brooks@southampton.gov.uk

Senior Management: Dr Bob Coates, Acting Director - Public
Health, Civic Centre, Southampton SO14 7LY ☎ 023 8022 3855
 bob.coates@southampton.gov.uk

Senior Management: Ms Mel Creighton, Service Director -
Strategic Finance & Commercialisation, Civic Centre, Southampton
SO14 7LY ☎ 020 8083 2049 mel.creighton@southampton.gov.uk

Senior Management: Mr Richard Crouch, Chief Operations
Officer, Civic Centre, Southampton SO14 7LY
 richard.crouch@southampton.gov.uk

Senior Management: Mr Stephen Giacchino, Transformation
Implementation Director, Civic Centre, Southampton SO14 7LY
☎ 023 8083 7713 stephen.giacchino@southampton.gov.uk

Senior Management: Mr Mike Harris, Service Director - Growth,
Civic Centre, Civic Centre Road, Southampton SO14 7LP
☎ 023 8083 2438 mike.harris@southampton.gov.uk

Senior Management: Mr Rob Harwood, Service Director - Digital
& Business Operations, Civic Centre, Southampton SO14 7LY
☎ 023 8083 3436 rob.harwood@southampton.gov.uk

Senior Management: Mr Richard Ivory, Service Director - Legal
& Governance, Civic Centre, Southampton SO14 7LY
☎ 023 8083 2794 richard.ivory@southampton.gov.uk

Senior Management: Mr Paul Juan, Acting Service Director -
Adults, Housing & Communities, Civic Centre, Southampton SO14
7LY paul.juan@southampton.gov.uk

Senior Management: Ms Janet King, Service Director - HR &
OD, Civic Centre, Southampton SO14 7LY
 janet.king@southampton.gov.uk

Senior Management: Ms Emma Lewis, Service Director -
Intelligence, Insight & Communications, Civic Centre, Southampton
SO14 7LY ☎ 023 8091 7984 emma.lewis@southampton.gov.uk

Senior Management: Mr Mitch Sanders, Service Director -
Transactions & Universal Services, Civic Centre, Southampton SO14
7LY ☎ 023 8022 3855 mitch.sanders@southampton.gov.uk

Senior Management: Ms Suki Sitaram, Chief Strategy Officer,
Civic Centre, Southampton SO14 7LY ☎ 023 8083 2060
 suki.sitaram@southampton.gov.uk

Building Control: Mr Neil Ferris, Building Control Partnership
Manager, Civic Centre, Southampton SO14 7LP ☎ 023 8083 2781
 neil.ferris@southampton.gov.uk

Children / Youth Services: Ms Jo Cassey, Principal Officer -
Education & Early Years, Civic Centre, Southampton SO14 7LY
☎ 023 8091 7503 jo.cassey@southampton.gov.uk

Civil Registration: Ms Linda Francis, Bereavement &
Registrations Manager, Civic Centre, Southampton SO14 7LY
☎ 023 8091 5325 linda.francis@southampton.gov.uk

Community Planning: Mr Paul Juan, Acting Service Director -
Adults, Housing & Communities, Civic Centre, Southampton
SO14 7LY paul.juan@southampton.gov.uk

Community Safety: Mr Mitch Sanders, Service Director - Transactions & Universal Services, Floor 5, 1 Guildhall Square, Southampton SO14 7FP ☎ 023 8022 3855 ⏚ mitch.sanders@southampton.gov.uk

Computer Management: Mr Kevin Foley, Head of IT Solutions, Civic Centre, Southampton SO14 7LY ☎ 023 8022 3855 ⏚ kevin.foley@southampton.gov.uk

Consumer Protection and Trading Standards: Mr Mitch Sanders, Service Director - Transactions & Universal Services, Floor 5, 1 Guildhall Square, Southampton SO14 7FP ☎ 023 8022 3855 ⏚ mitch.sanders@southampton.gov.uk

Contracts: Mr Rob Harwood, Service Director - Digital & Business Operations, Civic Centre, Southampton SO14 7LY ☎ 023 8083 3436 ⏚ rob.harwood@southampton.gov.uk

Customer Service: Mr Rob Harwood, Service Director - Digital & Business Operations, Civic Centre, Southampton SO14 7LY ☎ 023 8083 3436 ⏚ rob.harwood@southampton.gov.uk

Economic Development: Ms Denise Eghill, Head of Economic Development & Skills, Civic Centre, Southampton SO14 7LY ☎ 023 8083 4509 ⏚ denise.eghill@southampton.gov.uk

Economic Development: Mr Jeff Walters, Economic Development Manager, Civic Centre, Southampton SO14 7LY ☎ 023 8083 2256 ⏚ jeff.walters@southampton.gov.uk

Education: Ms Marijke Elst, Business Services Manager, Civic Centre, Southampton SO14 7LY ☎ 023 8083 2422 ⏚ marijke.elst@southampton.gov.uk

Emergency Planning: Mr Ian Collins, Emergency Planning Manager, City Depot, First Avenue, Millbrook, Southampton SO15 0LJ ☎ 023 8083 2089 ⏚ ian.collins@southampton.gov.uk

Energy Management: Mr Jason Taylor, Energy Manager, 45 Castle Way, Southampton SO14 2PD ☎ 023 8083 2641 ⏚ jason.taylor@southampton.gov.uk

Estates, Property & Valuation: Mr Mark Bradbury, Head of Capital Assets, Civic Centre, Southampton SO14 7LY ☎ 023 8083 2261 ⏚ mark.bradbury@southampton.gov.uk

Events Manager: Mr Craig Lintott, Events Manager, Civic Centre, Southampton SO14 7LY ☎ 023 8083 2077 ⏚ craig.lintott@southampton.gov.uk

Facilities: Mr Charles Stewart, Civic Buildings Manager, Civic Centre, Southampton SO14 7LY ☎ 023 8083 2877 ⏚ chez.stewart@southampton.gov.uk

Grounds Maintenance: Mr John Horton, Parks & Street Cleansing Manager, Civic Centre, Southampton SO14 7LY ☎ 023 8083 3561 ⏚ john.horton@southampton.gov.uk

Health and Safety: Mr Graham Armstrong, Head of Adult Housing & Community Care, Civic Centre, Southampton SO14 7LY ☎ 023 8083 4364 ⏚ graham.armstrong@southampton.gov.uk

Housing: Mr Paul Juan, Acting Service Director - Adults, Housing & Communities, Civic Centre, Southampton SO14 7LY ⏚ paul.juan@southampton.gov.uk

Housing: Mr Steve Smith, Housing Services Manager, Civic Centre, Southampton SO14 7LY ☎ 023 8091 5161 ⏚ steve.smith@southampton.gov.uk

Licensing: Mr Phil Bates, Licensing Manager, Civic Centre, Southampton SO14 7LY ☎ 023 8083 3523 ⏚ phil.bates@southampton.gov.uk

Lottery Funding, Charity and Voluntary: Mr John Connelly, Regeneration Manager, Civic Centre, Southampton SO14 7LY ☎ 023 8083 4402 ⏚ john.connelly@southampton.gov.uk

Personnel / HR: Ms Janet King, Service Director - HR & OD, Civic Centre, Southampton SO14 7LY ⏚ janet.king@southampton.gov.uk

Planning: Mr Samuel Fox, Planning & Development Manager, Civic Centre, Southampton SO14 7LY ☎ 023 8083 2044 ⏚ samuel.fox@southampton.gov.uk

Public Libraries: Mr David Baldwin, Libraries Manager, Civic Centre, Southampton SO14 7LY ☎ 023 8083 2219 ⏚ david.baldwin@southampton.gov.uk

Regeneration: Mr Paul Juan, Acting Service Director - Adults, Housing & Communities, Civic Centre, Southampton SO14 7LY ⏚ paul.juan@southampton.gov.uk

Social Services (Adult): Ms Carole Binns, Acting Service Director - Adult Social Services, Civic Centre, Southampton SO14 7LY ⏚ carole.binns@southampton.gov.uk

Social Services (Adult): Mr Paul Juan, Acting Service Director - Adults, Housing & Communities, Civic Centre, Southampton SO14 7LY ⏚ paul.juan@southampton.gov.uk

Social Services (Children): Ms Hilary Brooks, Service Director - Children & Families, Civic Centre, Southampton SO14 7LY ☎ 023 8083 3021 ⏚ hilary.brooks@southampton.gov.uk

Public Health: Dr Bob Coates, Acting Director - Public Health, Civic Centre, Southampton SO14 7LY ☎ 023 8022 3855 ⏚ bob.coates@southampton.gov.uk

Street Scene: Mr John Harvey, Highways Manager, 1 Guild Hall Sqaure, Southampton SO14 7FP ☎ 023 8083 3927 ⏚ john.harvery@southampton.gov.uk

Sustainable Communities: Ms Suki Sitaram, Chief Strategy Officer, Civic Centre, Southampton SO14 7LY ☎ 023 8083 2060 ⏚ suki.sitaram@southampton.gov.uk

Tourism: Mr Mike Harris, Service Director - Growth, Civic Centre, Civic Centre Road, Southampton SO14 7LP ☎ 023 8083 2438 ⏚ mike.harris@southampton.gov.uk

SOUTHAMPTON CITY

Traffic Management: Mr John Harvey, Highways Manager, 1 Guild Hall Sqaure, Southampton SO14 7FP ☎ 023 8083 3927
✆ john.harvery@southampton.gov.uk

COUNCILLORS

Mayor: McEwing, Catherine (LAB - Redbridge)
councillor.c.mcewing@southampton.gov.uk

Sheriff: Harris, Les (CON - Bassett)
councillor.l.harris@southampton.gov.uk

Leader of the Council: Letts, Simon (LAB - Bitterne)
councillor.s.letts@southampton.gov.uk

Deputy Leader of the Council: Rayment, Jacqui (LAB - Bevois)
councillor.j.rayment@southampton.gov.uk

Group Leader: Morrell, Keith (IND - Coxford)
councillor.k.morrell@southampton.gov.uk

Group Leader: Moulton, Jeremy (CON - Freemantle)
councillor.j.moulton@southampton.gov.uk

Baillie, Peter (CON - Harefield)
councillor.p.baillie@southampton.gov.uk

Baillie, James (CON - Sholing)
councillor.j.baillie@southampton.gov.uk

Barnes-Andrews, Stephen (LAB - Bevois)
councillor.s.barnes-andrews@southampton.gov.uk

Blatchford, Sue (LAB - Woolston)
councillor.s.blatchford@southampton.gov.uk

Bogle, Sarah (LAB - Bargate)
councillor.s.bogle@southampton.gov.uk

Burke, Derek (LAB - Bevois)
councillor.d.burke@southampton.gov.uk

Chaloner, Mark (LAB - Shirley)
councillor.m.chaloner@southampton.gov.uk

Claisse, Matthew (CON - Portswood)
councillor.m.claisse@southampton.gov.uk

Coombs, Hannah (LAB - Shirley)
councillor.h.coombs@southampton.gov.uk

Denness, Mike (LAB - Millbrook)
councillor.m.denness@southampton.gov.uk

Fitzhenry, Daniel (CON - Harefield)
councillor.d.fitzhenry@southampton.gov.uk

Fuller, David (CON - Bitterne Park)
councillor.d.fuller@southampton.gov.uk

Furnell, David (LAB - Millbrook)
councillor.d.furnell@southampton.gov.uk

Hammond, Christopher (LAB - Woolston)
councillor.c.hammond@southampton.gov.uk

Hannides, John (CON - Bassett)
councillor.j.hannides@southampton.gov.uk

Harris, Beryl (CON - Bassett)
councillor.b.harris@southampton.gov.uk

Hecks, Nigel (CON - Sholing)
councillor.n.hecks@southampton.gov.uk

Houghton, Alex (CON - Peartree)
councillor.a.houghton@southampton.gov.uk

Inglis, John (CON - Bitterne Park)
councillor.j.inglis@southampton.gov.uk

Jordan, John (LAB - Bitterne)
councillor.j.jordan@southampton.gov.uk

Kaur, Satvir (LAB - Shirley)
councillor.s.kaur@southampton.gov.uk

Keogh, Eamonn (LAB - Peartree)
councillor.e.keogh@southampton.gov.uk

Laurent, Valerie (CON - Harefield)
councillor.v.laurent@southampton.gov.uk

Lewzey, Paul (LAB - Peartree)
councillor.p.lewzey@southampton.gov.uk

Mintoff, Sharon (LAB - Swaythling)
councillor.s.mintoff@southamptong.gov.uk

Murphy, Frances (LAB - Bitterne)
councillor.f.murphy@southampton.gov.uk

Noon, John (LAB - Bargate)
councillor.j.noon@southampton.gov.uk

O'Neill, Paul (CON - Portswood)
councillor.p.o'neill@southampton.gov.uk

Paffey, Darren (LAB - Bargate)
councillor.d.paffey@southampton.gov.uk

Painton, Bob (CON - Swaythling)
councillor.b.painton@southampton.gov.uk

Parnell, Brian (CON - Freemantle)
councillor.b.parnell@southampton.gov.uk

Payne, Warwick (LAB - Woolston)
councillor.w.payne@southampton.gov.uk

Pope, Andrew (IND - Redbridge)
councillor.a.pope@southampton.gov.uk

Savage, John (LAB - Portswood)
councillor.j.savage@southampton.gov.uk

Shields, Dave (LAB - Freemantle)
councillor.d.shields@southampton.gov.uk

Taggart, Sarah (LAB - Millbrook)
councillor.s.taggart@southampton.gov.uk

Thomas, Don (IND - Coxford)
councillor.d.thomas@southampton.gov.uk

Thomas, Tammy (IND - Coxford)
councillor.t.thomas@southampton.gov.uk

Vassiliou, Spiros (CON - Swaythling)
councillor.s.vassiliou@southampton.gov.uk

Whitbread, Lee (LAB - Redbridge)
councillor.l.whitbread@southampton.gov.uk

White, Ivan (CON - Bitterne Park)
councillor.i.white@southampton.gov.uk

Wilkinson, Graham (CON - Sholing)
councillor.g.wilkinson@southampton.gov.uk

POLITICAL COMPOSITION
LAB: 25, CON: 19, IND: 4

COMMITTEE CHAIRS

Children & Families: Mr Eamonn Keogh

Licensing: Ms Sue Blatchford

Planning: Mr Mike Denness

Southend-on-Sea U

Southend-on-Sea Borough Council, Civic Centre, Southend-on-Sea SS2 6ER
☎ 01702 215000 ◌ council@southend.gov.uk
🖥 www.southend.gov.uk

FACTS AND FIGURES
Parliamentary Constituencies: Rochford and Southend East, Southend West
EU Constituencies: Eastern
Election Frequency: Elections are by thirds

PRINCIPAL OFFICERS

Chief Executive: Mr Robert Tinlin, Chief Executive & Town Clerk, PO Box 6, Civic Centre, Victoria Avenue, Southend-on-Sea SS2 6ER ☎ 01702 215101 ◌ robtinlin@southend.gov.uk

Senior Management: Dr Andrea Atherton, Director - Public Health, Civic Centre, Southend-on-Sea SS2 6ER ☎ 01702 212802 ◌ andrea.atherton@southend.gov.uk

Senior Management: Mr Simon Leftley, Deputy Chief Executive, Civic Centre, Victoria Avenue, Southend-on-Sea SS2 6ER ☎ 01702 214729 ◌ simonleftley@southend.gov.uk

Senior Management: Mr Andy Lewis, Deputy Chief Executive, PO Box 6, Civic Centre, Victoria Avenue, Southend-on-Sea SS2 6ER ☎ 01702 212214 ◌ andrewlewis@southend.gov.uk

Building Control: Dr Peter Geraghty, Head of Planning & Transport, Civic Centre, Southend-on-Sea SS2 6ER ☎ 01702 215339 ◌ petergeraghty@southend.gov.uk

Children / Youth Services: Mr Simon Leftley, Deputy Chief Executive, Civic Centre, Victoria Avenue, Southend-on-Sea SS2 6ER ☎ 01702 214729 ◌ simonleftley@southend.gov.uk

PR / Communications: Mr Adam Keating, Media & Communications Officer, Civic Centre, Southend-on-Sea SS2 6ER ☎ 01702 212057 ◌ adamkeating@southend.gov.uk

Community Safety: Mr Simon Ford, Community Safety Manager, Civic Centre, Victoria Avenue, Southend-on-Sea SS2 6ER ☎ 0300 333 4444 ◌ simonford@southend.gov.uk

Computer Management: Mr David Cummings, Group Manager - ICT, Civic Centre, Southend-on-Sea SS2 6ER ☎ 01702 215000 ◌ davidcummings@southend.gov.uk

Consumer Protection and Trading Standards: Ms Dipti Patel, Head of Public Protection, Civic Centre, Southend-on-Sea SS2 6ER ☎ 01702 215325 ◌ diptipatel@southend.gov.uk

Customer Service: Mr Nick Corrigan, Head of Customer Services, Civic Centre, Victoria Avenue, Southend-on-Sea SS2 6ER ☎ 01702 534612 ◌ nickcorrigan@southend.gov.uk

Economic Development: Mr Scott Dolling, Head of Services, Economy & Regeneration, Civic Centre, Southend-on-Sea SS2 6ER ◌ scottdolling@southend.gov.uk

Electoral Registration: Mr Colin Gamble, Group Manager - Democratic Services, Civic Centre, Southend-on-Sea SS2 6ER ☎ 01702 534820 ◌ colingamble@southend.gov.uk

Emergency Planning: Mr Keith Holden, Emergency Planning Officer, PO Box 6, Civic Centre, Victoria Avenue, Southend-on-Sea SS2 6ER ☎ 01702 215023 ◌ keithholden@southend.gov.uk

Energy Management: Mr Jeremy Martin, Energy Officer, Civic Centre, Southend-on-Sea SS2 6ER ☎ 01702 215190 ◌ jeremymartin@southend.gov.uk

Environmental / Technical Services: Mr Andy Lewis, Deputy Chief Executive, PO Box 6, Civic Centre, Victoria Avenue, Southend-on-Sea SS2 6ER ☎ 01702 212214 ◌ andrewlewis@southend.gov.uk

Environmental Health: Ms Dipti Patel, Head of Public Protection & Waste, Civic Centre, Victoria Avenue, Southend-on-Sea SS2 6ER ☎ 01702 215000 ◌ diptipatel@southend.gov.uk

European Liaison: Mr Mark Murphy, Regeneration Services Manager, Civic Centre, Southend-on-Sea SS2 6ER ☎ 01702 215429 ◌ markmurphy@southend.gov.uk

Facilities: Mr Gary Green, Group Manager - Facilities & Bereavement, Civic Centre, Southend-on-Sea SS2 6ER ☎ 0702 215603 ◌ garygreen@southend.gov.uk

Finance: Mr Joe Chesterton, Head of Finance & Resources, Civic Centre, Victoria Avenue, Southend-on-Sea SS2 6ER ☎ 01702 215393 ◌ joechesterton@southend.gov.uk

Finance: Ms Linda Everard, Head of Internal Audit, Civic Centre, Southend-on-Sea SS2 6ER ☎ 01702 215000 ◌ lindaeverard@southend.gov.uk

Grounds Maintenance: Mr Graham Owen, Health & Safety Officer, Civic Centre, Southend-on-Sea SS2 6ER ☎ 01702 215350 ◌ grahamowen@southend.gov.uk

Health and Safety: Mr Lee Colby, Regulatory Service Operator, Civic Centre, Southend-on-Sea SS2 6ER ☎ 01702 215814 ◌ leecolby@southend.gov.uk

Highways: Mr Zulfiqar Ali, Group Manager - Traffic & Highways, Civic Centre, Southend-on-Sea SS2 6ER ☎ 01702 215369 ◌ zulfiqarali@southend.gov.uk

Local Area Agreement: Mr Ade Butteriss, Strategy & Performance Manager, Civic Centre, Victoria Avenue, Southend-on-Sea SS2 6ER ☎ 01702 215187 ◌ adebutteriss@southend.gov.uk

Legal: Mr John Williams, Head of Legal & Democratic Services, Civic Centre, Southend-on-Sea SS2 6ER ☎ 01702 215102 ◌ johnwilliams@southend.gov.uk

Leisure and Cultural Services: Mr Nick Harris, Head of Culture, Civic Centre, Victoria Avenue, Southend-on-Sea SS2 6ER ☎ 01702 215619 ◌ nickharris@southend.gov.uk

SOUTHEND-ON-SEA

Licensing: Mr Carl Robinson, Group Manager - Regulatory Services, Civic Centre, Southend-on-Sea SS2 6ER ☎ 01702 215156 ✆ carlrobinson@southend.gov.uk

Lottery Funding, Charity and Voluntary: Ms Lysane Eddy, Partnerships Manager, Civic Centre, Southend-on-Sea SS2 6ER ☎ 01702 215111 ✆ lysanneeddy@southend.gov.uk

Member Services: Mr Colin Gamble, Group Manager - Democratic Services, Civic Centre, Southend-on-Sea SS2 6ER ☎ 01702 534820 ✆ colingamble@southend.gov.uk

Member Services: Mr John Williams, Head of Legal & Democratic Services, Civic Centre, Southend-on-Sea SS2 6ER ☎ 01702 215102 ✆ johnwilliams@southend.gov.uk

Partnerships: Ms Lysane Eddy, Partnerships Manager, Civic Centre, Southend-on-Sea SS2 6ER ☎ 01702 215111 ✆ lysanneeddy@southend.gov.uk

Personnel / HR: Ms Joanna Ruffle, Head of People & Policy, Civic Centre, Southend-on-Sea SS2 6ER ☎ 01702 215393; 01708 432181 ✆ joanna.ruffle@havering.gov.uk

Planning: Dr Peter Geraghty, Head of Planning & Transport, Civic Centre, Southend-on-Sea SS2 6ER ☎ 01702 215339 ✆ petergeraghty@southend.gov.uk

Public Libraries: Mr Simon May, Libraries Services Manager, Civic Centre, Southend-on-Sea SS2 6ER ☎ 01702 534101 ✆ simonmay@southend.gov.uk

Recycling & Waste Minimisation: Ms Dipti Patel, Head of Public Protection & Waste, Civic Centre, Victoria Avenue, Southend-on-Sea SS2 6ER ☎ 01702 215000 ✆ diptipatel@southend.gov.uk

Regeneration: Mr Scott Dolling, Head of Services, Economy & Regeneration, Civic Centre, Southend-on-Sea SS2 6ER ✆ scottdolling@southend.gov.uk

Social Services: Mr Simon Leftley, Deputy Chief Executive, Civic Centre, Victoria Avenue, Southend-on-Sea SS2 6ER ☎ 01702 214729 ✆ simonleftley@southend.gov.uk

Social Services (Adult): Ms Sharon Houlden, Head of Adult Services & Housing, Civic Centre, Southend-on-Sea SS2 6ER ☎ 01702 215000 ✆ sharonhoulden@southend.gov.uk

Public Health: Dr Andrea Atherton, Director - Public Health, Civic Centre, Southend-on-Sea SS2 6ER ☎ 01702 212802 ✆ andrea.atherton@southend.gov.uk

Staff Training: Ms Joanna Ruffle, Head of People & Policy, Civic Centre, Southend-on-Sea SS2 6ER ☎ 01702 215393; 01708 432181 ✆ joanna.ruffle@havering.gov.uk

Street Scene: Mrs Marzia Abel, Town Centre Manager, Civic Centre, Southend-on-Sea SS2 6ER ☎ 01702 212052 ✆ marziaabel@southend.gov.uk

Sustainable Communities: Mr Mark Murphy, Regeneration Services Manager, Civic Centre, Southend-on-Sea SS2 6ER ☎ 01702 215429 ✆ markmurphy@southend.gov.uk

Sustainable Development: Mr Chris Livemore, Sustainable Officer, Civic Centre, Southend-on-Sea SS2 6ER ☎ 01702 215832 ✆ chrislivemore@southend.gov.uk

Tourism: Mr Scott Dolling, Head of Services, Economy & Regeneration, Civic Centre, Southend-on-Sea SS2 6ER ✆ scottdolling@southend.gov.uk

Town Centre: Mrs Marzia Abel, Town Centre Manager, Civic Centre, Southend-on-Sea SS2 6ER ☎ 01702 212052 ✆ marziaabel@southend.gov.uk

Traffic Management: Dr Peter Geraghty, Head of Planning & Transport, Civic Centre, Southend-on-Sea SS2 6ER ☎ 01702 215339 ✆ petergeraghty@southend.gov.uk

Transport: Dr Peter Geraghty, Head of Planning & Transport, Civic Centre, Southend-on-Sea SS2 6ER ☎ 01702 215339 ✆ petergeraghty@southend.gov.uk

Transport Planner: Dr Peter Geraghty, Head of Planning & Transport, Civic Centre, Southend-on-Sea SS2 6ER ☎ 01702 215339 ✆ petergeraghty@southend.gov.uk

Total Place: Ms Lysane Eddy, Partnerships Manager, Civic Centre, Southend-on-Sea SS2 6ER ☎ 01702 215111 ✆ lysanneeddy@southend.gov.uk

Waste Collection and Disposal: Ms Dipti Patel, Head of Public Protection & Waste, Civic Centre, Victoria Avenue, Southend-on-Sea SS2 6ER ☎ 01702 215000 ✆ diptipatel@southend.gov.uk

COUNCILLORS

Mayor: McMahon, Judith (LAB - Kursaal)
cllrmcmahon@southend.gov.uk

Deputy Mayor: Evans, Margaret (CON - West Leigh)
cllrevans@southend.gov.uk

Leader of the Council: Lamb, John (CON - West Leigh)
cllrlamb@southend.gov.uk

Deputy Leader of the Council: Holland, Ann (CON - Southchurch)
cllrholland@southend.gov.uk

Arscott, Bernard (CON - Leigh)
cllrarscott@southend.gov.uk

Assenheim, Michael (IND - Shoeburyness)
cllrassenheim@southend.gov.uk

Aylen, Stephen (INDNA - Belfairs)
cllraylen@southend.gov.uk

Ayling, Brian (IND - St Luke's)
cllrayling@southend.gov.uk

Borton, Margaret (LAB - Victoria)
cllrborton@southend.gov.uk

Boyd, Helen (CON - Blenheim Park)
cllrboyd@southend.gov.uk

Bright, Alex (CON - Southchurch)
cllrbright@southend.gov.uk

Buckley, Steve (CON - St Laurence)
cllrbuckley@southend.gov.uk

Burzotta, David (CON - Chalkwell)
cllrburzotta@southend.gov.uk

Butler, Maureen (CON - Belfairs)
cllrbutler@southend.gov.uk

Byford, Trevor (CON - Eastwood Park)
cllrbyford@southend.gov.uk

Callaghan, Tino (IND - Prittlewell)
cllrcallaghan@southend.gov.uk

Courtenay, James (CON - Blenheim Park)
cllrcourtenay@southend.gov.uk

Cox, Tony (CON - West Shoebury)
cllrcox@southend.gov.uk

Crystall, Alan (LD - Leigh)
cllrcrystall@southend.gov.uk

Davidson, Margaret (CON - Prittlewell)
cllrdavidson@southend.gov.uk

Davies, Lawrence (IND - Kursaal)
cllrdavies@southend.gov.uk

Endersby, Caroline (IND - St Luke's)
cllrendersby@southend.gov.uk

Flewitt, Mark (CON - St Laurence)
cllrflewitt@southend.gov.uk

Folkard, Nigel (CON - Chalkwell)
cllrfolkard@southend.gov.uk

Garston, David (CON - Prittlewell)
cllrdgarston@southend.gov.uk

Garston, Jonathan (CON - Milton)
cllrjgartson@southend.gov.uk

Gilbert, Ian (LAB - Victoria)
cllrgilbert@southend.gov.uk

Habermel, Stephen (CON - Chalkwell)
cllrhabermel@southend.gov.uk

Hadley, Roger (CON - Shoeburyness)
cllrhadley@southend.gov.uk

Jarvis, Derek (CON - West Shoebury)
cllrjarvis@southend.gov.uk

Jones, Anne (LAB - Westborough)
cllrannejones@southend.gov.uk

Kenyon, Derek (IND - Southchurch)
cllrkenyon@southend.gov.uk

McDonald, Helen (LAB - Kursaal)
cllrmcdonald@southend.gov.uk

McGlone, David (UKIP - St Laurence)
cllrmcglone@southend.gov.uk

Moring, Andrew (CON - Eastwood Park)
cllrmoring@southend.gov.uk

Moyies, James (IND - West Shoebury)
cllrmoyies@southend.gov.uk

Nevin, Cheryl (LAB - Milton)
cllrnevin@southend.gov.uk

Norman, David (LAB - Victoria)
cllrdnorman@southend.gov.uk

Phillips, Georgina (CON - West Leigh)
cllrphillips@southend.gov.uk

Robinson, Kevin (LAB - Westborough)
cllrkrobinson@southend.gov.uk

Salter, Lesley (CON - Belfairs)
cllrsalter@southend.gov.uk

Stafford, Mike (IND - Thorpe)
cllrstafford@southend.gov.uk

Terry, Martin (IND - Thorpe)
cllrterry@southend.gov.uk

Van Looy, Paul (IND - St Luke's)
cllrvanlooy@southend.gov.uk

Walker, Christopher (CON - Eastwood Park)
cllrwalker@southend.gov.uk

Ward, Nick (IND - Shoeburyness)
cllrward@southend.gov.uk

Ware-Lane, Julian (LAB - Milton)
cllrware-lane@southend.gov.uk

Waterworth, Floyd (UKIP - Blenheim Park)
cllrwaterworth@southend.gov.uk

Wexham, Peter (LD - Leigh)
cllrwexham@southend.gov.uk

Willis, Charles (LAB - Westborough)
cllrwillis@southend.gov.uk

Woodley, Ronald (IND - Thorpe)
cllrwoodley@southend.gov.uk

POLITICAL COMPOSITION
CON: 24, IND: 12, LAB: 10, LD: 2, UKIP: 2, INDNA: 1

COMMITTEE CHAIRS

Audit: Mrs Margaret Davidson

Development Control: Mr Floyd Waterworth

Health & Wellbeing: Mrs Lesley Salter

Licensing: Mr Roger Hadley

Southwark　　　　　　　　　　L

Southwark London Borough Council, 160 Tooley Street, London SE1 2QH
☎ 020 7525 5000 🖳 www.southwark.gov.uk

FACTS AND FIGURES
Parliamentary Constituencies: Bermondsey and Old Southwark, Camberwell and Peckham, Dulwich and West Norwood
EU Constituencies: London
Election Frequency: Elections are of whole council

PRINCIPAL OFFICERS

Chief Executive: Mrs Eleanor Kelly, Chief Executive, 160 Tooley Street, London SE1 2QH ☎ 020 7525 7171
🖰 eleanor.kelly@southwark.gov.uk

SOUTHWARK

Senior Management: Ms Deborah Collins, Strategic Director - Environment & Leisure, 160 Tooley Street, London SE1 2QH
☎ 020 7525 7630 ⌨ deborah.collins@southwark.gov.uk

Senior Management: Mr David Quirke-Thornton, Strategic Director - Children's & Adults' Services, 160 Tooley Street, London SE1 2QH
☎ 020 7525 3289 ⌨ david.quirke-thornton@southwark.gov.uk

Senior Management: Ms Gerri Scott, Strategic Director - Housing & Modernisation, 160 Tooley Street, London SE1 2QH
☎ 020 7525 7464 ⌨ gerri.scott@southwark.gov.uk

Senior Management: Mr Duncan Whitfield, Strategic Director - Finance & Governance, 160 Tooley Street, London SE1 2QH
☎ 020 7525 7180 ⌨ duncan.whitfield@southwark.gov.uk

Access Officer / Social Services (Disability): Mr Stephen Douglass, Director - Communities, 160 Tooley Street, London SE1 2QH ☎ 020 7525 0886 ⌨ stephen.douglass@southwark.gov.uk

Architect, Building / Property Services: Mr Matthew Jackson, Head of Property, 5th Floor, 160 Tooley Street, London SE1 2QH
☎ 020 7525 1332 ⌨ matthew.jackson@southwark.gov.uk

Building Control: Mr Peter Card, Head of Building Control, 160 Tooley Street, London SE1 2QH ☎ 020 7525 5588
⌨ peter.card@southwark.gov.uk

PR / Communications: Ms Louise Neilan, Media Manager, 2nd Floor, 160 Tooley Street, London SE1 2QH ☎ 020 7525 7023
⌨ louise.neilan@southwark.gov.uk

Community Safety: Mr Jonathon Toy, Head of Community Safety & Enforcement, Southwark Council, 3rd Floor, 160 Tooley Street, London SE1 2QH ☎ 020 7525 1479
⌨ jonathon.toy@southwark.gov.uk

Computer Management: Mr Mark James-Compton, Head of IT, 2nd Floor, 160 Tooley Street, London SE1 2QH ☎ 020 7252 1651
⌨ mark.james-compton@southwark.gov.uk

Contracts: Ms Jan McMahon, Head of Corporate Contracts & Contract Management, Southwark Council, 2nd Floor, 160 Tooley Street, London SE1 2QH ☎ 020 7525 3620
⌨ jan.mcmahon@southwark.gov.uk

Corporate Services: Mr Stephen Gaskell, Head of Strategy & Partnerships, 160 Tooley Street, London SE1 2QH
☎ 020 7252 7293

Customer Service: Mr Dominic Cain, Director - Exchequer, Southwark Council, 1st Floor, 160 Tooley Street, London SE1 2QH
☎ 020 7525 0636 ⌨ dominic.cain@southwark.gov.uk

Customer Service: Mr Richard Selley, Director - Customer Experience, Southwark Council, 3rd Floor, 160 Tooley Street, London SE1 2QH ☎ 020 7525 7320 ⌨ richard.selley@southwark.gov.uk

Education: Ms Maggie Donnellan, Head of Primary Achievement, Southwark Council, 1st Floor, PCT, 160 Tooley Street, London SE1 2HZ ☎ 020 7525 5030 ⌨ maggie.donnellan@southwark.gov.uk

Education: Mr Glenn Garcia, Head of Pupil Access, Southwark Council, 4th Floor, 160 Tooley Street, London SE1 2QH
☎ 020 7525 2717 ⌨ glenn.garcia@southwark.gov.uk

Electoral Registration: Ms Frances Biggs, Head of Electoral Services, Southwark Council, 2nd Floor, 160 Tooley Street, London SE1 2QH ☎ 020 7525 7694 ⌨ frances.biggs@southwark.gov.uk

Emergency Planning: Mr Andy Snazell, Emergency Planning & Resilience Manager, 3rd Floor, 160 Tooley Street, London SE1 2QH
☎ 020 7525 3517 ⌨ andy.snazell@southwark.gov.uk

Energy Management: Mr Ian Smith, Director - Environment, Southwark Council, 3rd Floor, 160 Tooley Street, London SE1 2QH
☎ 020 7525 2484 ⌨ ian.smith@southwark.gov.uk

Environmental Health: Mr David Littleton, Head of Regulatory Services, 3rd Floor, 160 Tooley Street, London SE1 2QH
☎ 020 7525 5727 ⌨ david.littleton@southwark.gov.uk

Estates, Property & Valuation: Mr Stephen Platts, Director - Regeneration, Southwark Council, 5th Floor, 160 Tooley Street, London SE1 2QH ☎ 020 7525 5640
⌨ stephen.platts@southwark.gov.uk

European Liaison: Ms Lisa Marie Bowles, European & Funding Officer, Southwark Council, 1st Floor, 160 Tooley Street, London SE1 2QH ☎ 020 7525 1022 ⌨ lisa-marie.bowles@southwark.gov.uk

Events Manager: Mr Paul Cowell, Events & Arts Manager, Southwark Council, 2nd Floor, 160 Tooley Street, London SE1 2QH
☎ 020 7525 0857 ⌨ paul.cowell@southwark.gov.uk

Facilities: Mr Keith Andrews, Building Manager (Corporate Facilities Management), 2nd Floor, 160 Tooley Street, London SE1 2QS ☎ 020 7525 2804 ⌨ keith.andrews@southwark.gov.uk

Finance: Mr Duncan Whitfield, Strategic Director - Finance & Governance, Southwark Council, 2nd Floor, 160 Tooley Street, London SE1 2QH ☎ 020 7525 7180
⌨ duncan.whitfield@southwark.gov.uk

Pensions: Mr Malcolm Laird, SAP Payroll & Pensions Manager, 160 Tooley Street, London SE1 2QH ☎ 020 7525 4915
⌨ malcolm.laird@southwark.gov.uk

Pensions: Ms Caroline Watson, Pension Fund Investment Manager, 160 Tooley Street, London SE1 2QH ☎ 020 7525 4379
⌨ caroline.watson@southwark.gov.uk

Fleet Management: Mr Ian Smith, Director - Environment, Southwark Council, 3rd Floor, 160 Tooley Street, London SE1 2QH
☎ 020 7525 2484 ⌨ ian.smith@southwark.gov.uk

Grounds Maintenance: Mr Matthew Hill, Head of Highways, 3rd Floor, 160 Tooley Street, London SE1 2QH ☎ 020 7525 3541
⌨ matthew.hill@southwark.gov.uk

Highways: Mr Matthew Hill, Head of Highways, 3rd Floor, 160 Tooley Street, London SE1 2QH ☎ 020 7525 3541
⌨ matthew.hill@southwark.gov.uk

Housing: Ms Gerri Scott, Strategic Director - Housing & Modernisation, Southwark Council, 2nd Floor, 160 Tooley Street, London SE1 2QH ☎ 020 7525 7464 ✆ gerri.scott@southwark.gov.uk

Housing Maintenance: Mr David Markham, Director - Asset Management, 3rd Floor, 160 Tooley Street, London SE1 2QH ☎ 020 7525 7201 ✆ david.markham@southwark.gov.uk

Legal: Ms Shelley Burke, Head of Overview & Scrutiny, Southwark Council, 2nd Floor, 160 Tooley Street, London SE1 2QH ☎ 020 7525 7344 ✆ shelley.burke@southwark.gov.uk

Legal: Ms Doreen Forrester-Brown, Director - Law & Democracy, Southwark Council, 2nd Floor, 160 Tooley Street, London SE1 2QH ☎ 020 7525 7502 ✆ doreen.forrester-brown@southwark.gov.uk

Leisure and Cultural Services: Ms Rebecca Towers, Head of Parks & Leisure, Southwark Council, 3rd Floor, 160 Tooley Street, London SE1 2QH ☎ 020 7525 0771 ✆ rebecca.towers@southwark.gov.uk

Licensing: Mr Richard Parkins, Health Safety Licensing & Environmental Protection Unit Manager, Southwark Council, 3rd Floor, 160 Tooley Street, London SE1 2QH ☎ 020 7525 5767 ✆ richard.parkins@southwark.gov.uk

Lottery Funding, Charity and Voluntary: Ms Bonnie Royal, Commissioning & Voluntary Sector Support Manager, Southwark Council, 2nd Floor, 160 Tooley Street, London SE1 2QH ☎ 020 7525 7389 ✆ bonnie.royal@southwark.gov.uk

Parking: Mr David Sole, Parking Service & Development Manager, Southwark Council, 3rd Floor, 160 Tooley Street, London SE1 2QH ☎ 020 7525 2037 ✆ david.sole@southwark.gov.uk

Personnel / HR: Ms Marie Rance, Human Resources Manager, 160 Tooley Street, London SE1 2QH ☎ 020 7525 0714 ✆ marie.rance@southwark.gov.uk

Planning: Mr Simon Bevan, Director - Planning, Southwark Council, 5th Floor, 160 Tooley Street, London SE1 2QH ☎ 020 7525 5655 ✆ simon.bevan@southwark.gov.uk

Procurement: Ms Elaine McLester, Head of Procurement, Southwark Council, 2nd Floor, 160 Tooley Street, London SE1 2QH ☎ 020 7525 7733 ✆ elaine.mclester@southwark.gov.uk

Regeneration: Mr Stephen Platts, Director - Regeneration, Southwark Council, 5th Floor, 160 Tooley Street, London SE1 2QH ☎ 020 7525 5640 ✆ stephen.platts@southwark.gov.uk

Road Safety: Mr Eamon Doran, Group Manager - Sustainable Travel & Road Safety, Southwark Council, 5th Floor, 160 Tooley Street, London SE1 2QH ☎ 020 7525 0513 ✆ eamon.doran@southwark.gov.uk

Social Services: Ms Sarah Desai, Director - Commissioning, Modernisation & Partners, Southwark Council, PCT, 1st Floor, PO Box 64529, London SE1P 5LX ☎ 020 7525 0446 ✆ sarah.desai@southwarkpct.nhs.uk

Social Services: Ms Gillian Holdsworth, Director - Public Health & Health Improvement, Southwark Council, 1st Floor, 160 Tooley Street, London SE1 2QH ☎ 020 7525 0298

Social Services: Ms Lesley Humber, Director - Operations & Locality, Southwark Council, 1st Floor, 160 Tooley Street, London SE1 2QH ☎ 020 7525 0407

Social Services (Children): Mr David Quirke-Thornton, Strategic Director - Children's & Adults' Services, 160 Tooley Street, London SE1 2QH ☎ 020 7525 3289 ✆ david.quirke-thornton@southwark.gov.uk

Public Health: Mr Jin Lim, Acting Director - Public Health, 160 Tooley Street, London SE1 2QH ☎ 020 7252 0281 ✆ jim.lim@southwark.gov.uk

Street Scene: Mr Qassim Kazaz, Principal Project Manager - Transport, PO Box 64529, HUB 1, 3rd Floor, London SE1P 5LX ☎ 020 7525 2091 ✆ qassim.kazaz@southwark.gov.uk

Town Centre: Mr Jon Abbott, Head of Regeneration (North), Southwark Council, 5th Floor, 160 Tooley Street, London SE1 2QH ☎ 020 7525 4902 ✆ jon.abbott@southwark.gov.uk

Town Centre: Mr David Strevens, Peckham Town Centre Manager, Peckham Partnership Project Team, Sumner House, Sumner Road, London SE15 5QS ☎ 020 7525 1001 ✆ david.strevens@southwark.gov.uk

Traffic Management: Miss Sally Crew, Transport Policy Manager, 5th Floor, 160 Tooley Street, London SE1 2QH ☎ 020 7525 5564 ✆ sally.crew@southwark.gov.uk

Transport: Mr Ian Smith, Director - Environment, Manor Place Depot, 30-34 Penrose Street, London SE17 3DW ☎ 020 7525 2484 ✆ ian.smith@southwark.gov.uk

Transport Planner: Mr Simon Bevan, Director - Planning, Southwark Council, 5th Floor, 160 Tooley Street, London SE1 2QH ☎ 020 7525 5655 ✆ simon.bevan@southwark.gov.uk

Waste Collection and Disposal: Mr Michael McNicholas, Head of Waste & Cleaning, 43 Devon Street, London SE15 1AL ☎ 020 7525 3449 ✆ michael.mcnicholas@southwark.gov.uk

Waste Management: Mr Michael McNicholas, Head of Waste & Cleaning, 43 Devon Street, London SE15 1AL ☎ 020 7525 3449 ✆ michael.mcnicholas@southwark.gov.uk

Children's Play Areas: Ms Rebecca Towers, Head of Parks & Leisure, Southwark Council, 3rd Floor, 160 Tooley Street, London SE1 2QH ☎ 020 7525 0771 ✆ rebecca.towers@southwark.gov.uk

COUNCILLORS

Mayor: Whittam, Kath (LAB - Rotherhithe) kath.whittam@southwark.gov.uk

Deputy Mayor: Smith, Charlie (LAB - East Dulwich) charlie.smith@southwark.gov.uk

Leader of the Council: John, Peter (LAB - South Camberwell) peter.john@southwark.gov.uk

SOUTHWARK

Deputy Leader of the Council: Cryan, Stephanie (LAB - Rotherhithe)
stephanie.cryan@southwark.gov.uk

Group Leader: Al-Samerai, Anood (LD - Riverside)
anood.al-samerai@southwark.gov.uk

Akoto, Evelyn (LAB - Livesey)
evelyn.akoto@southwark.gov.uk

Ali, Jasmine (LAB - The Lane)
jasmine.ali@southwark.gov.uk

Anderson, Maisie (LAB - Newington)
maisie.anderson@southwark.gov.uk

Barber, James (LD - East Dulwich)
james.barber@southwark.gov.uk

Burgess, Radha (LAB - Brunswick Park)
radha.burgess@southwark.gov.uk

Chopra, Sunil (LAB - Nunhead)
sunil.chopra@southwark.gov.uk

Coldwell, James (LAB - Newington)
james.coldwell@southwark.gov.uk

Colley, Fiona (LAB - Nunhead)
fiona.colley@southwark.gov.uk

Dale, Catherine (LAB - South Bermondsey)
catherine.dale@southwark.gov.uk

Dennis, Helen (LAB - Chaucer)
helen.dennis@southwark.gov.uk

Dixon-Fyle, Dora (LAB - Camberwell Green)
dora.dixon-fyle@southwark.gov.uk

Dolezal, Nick (LAB - The Lane)
nick.dolezal@southwark.gov.uk

Eastham, Karl (LAB - Chaucer)
karl.eastham@southwark.gov.uk

Edwards, Gavin (LAB - Peckham Rye)
gavin.edwards@southwark.gov.uk

Fleming, Paul (LAB - Faraday)
paul.fleming@southwark.gov.uk

Flynn, Tom (LAB - Camberwell Green)
tom.flynn@southwark.gov.uk

Green, Lucas (LAB - Grange)
lucas.green@southwark.gov.uk

Hamvas, Renata (LAB - Peckham Rye)
renata.hamvas@southwark.gov.uk

Hargrove, Barrie (LAB - Peckham)
barrie.hargrove@southwark.gov.uk

Hartley, Jon (LAB - College)
jon.hartley@southwark.gov.uk

Hubber, David (LD - Surrey Docks)
david.hubber@southwark.gov.uk

Johnson, Ben (LD - Grange)
ben.johnson@southwark.gov.uk

Jury-Dada, Samantha (LAB - Faraday)
samantha.jury-dada@southwark.gov.uk

Kerslake, Eleanor (LAB - Newington)
eleanor.kerslake@southwark.gov.uk

King, Sarah (LAB - South Camberwell)
sarah.king@southwark.gov.uk

Kirby, Anne (LAB - Village)
anne.kirby@southwark.gov.uk

Lamb, Octavia (LAB - South Camberwell)
octavia.lamb@southwark.gov.uk

Lambe, Sunny (LAB - South Bermondsey)
sunny.lambe@southwark.gov.uk

Lauder, Lorraine (LAB - Faraday)
lorraine.lauder@southwark.gov.uk

Linforth-Hall, Maria (LD - Cathedrals)
maria.linforthhall@southwark.gov.uk

Livingstone, Richard (LAB - Livesey)
richard.livingstone@southwark.gov.uk

Lury, Rebecca (LAB - East Walworth)
rebecca.lury@southwark.gov.uk

Luthra, Vijay (LAB - Chaucer)
vijay.luthra@southwark.gov.uk

Lyons, Jane (CON - Village)
jane.lyons@southwark.gov.uk

Mann, Eliza (LD - Riverside)
eliza.mann@southwark.gov.uk

McCallum, Hamish (LD - Riverside)
hamish.mccallum@southwark.gov.uk

Merrill, Darren (LAB - East Walworth)
darren.merrill@southwark.gov.uk

Mills, Victoria (LAB - Peckham Rye)
victoria.mills@southwark.gov.uk

Mitchell, Michael (CON - Village)
michael.mitchell@southwark.gov.uk

Mohammed, Jamille (LAB - The Lane)
jamille.mohammed@southwark.gov.uk

Morris, Adele (LD - Cathedrals)
adele.morris@southwark.gov.uk

Noakes, David (LD - Cathedrals)
david.noakes@southwark.gov.uk

O'Brien, Damian (LD - Grange)
damian.obrien@southwark.gov.uk

Okosun, James (LD - Surrey Docks)
james.okosun@southwark.gov.uk

Pollak, Leo (LAB - South Bermondsey)
leo.pollak@southwark.gov.uk

Rhule, Sandra (LAB - Nunhead)
sandra.rhule@southwark.gov.uk

Rose, Catherine (LAB - College)
catherine.rose@southwark.gov.uk

Seaton, Martin (LAB - East Walworth)
martin.seaton@southwark.gov.uk

Shimell, Rosie (LD - East Dulwich)
rosie.shimell@southwark.gov.uk

Simmons, Andy (LAB - College)
andy.simmons@southwark.gov.uk

Situ, Johnson (LAB - Peckham)
johnson.situ@southwark.gov.uk

Situ, Michael (LAB - Livesey)
michael.situ@southwark.gov.uk

Soanes, Cleo (LAB - Peckham)
cleo.soanes@southwark.gov.uk

Whitehead, Dan (LD - Surrey Docks)
dan.whitehead@southwark.gov.uk

Williams, Bill (LAB - Rotherhithe)
bill.williams@southwark.gov.uk

Williams, Kieron (LAB - Camberwell Green)
kieron.williams@southwark.gov.uk

Williams, Mark (LAB - Brunswick Park)
mark.williams@southwark.gov.uk

Wingfield, Ian (LAB - Brunswick Park)
ian.wingfield@southwark.gov.uk

POLITICAL COMPOSITION
LAB: 48, LD: 13, CON: 2

COMMITTEE CHAIRS

Audit: Mr Paul Fleming

Health & Wellbeing: Mr Peter John

Licensing: Ms Renata Hamvas

Planning: Mr Nick Dolezal

Spelthorne   D

Spelthorne Borough Council, Council Offices, Knowle Green,
Staines TW18 1XB
☎ 01784 451499 ✆ customer.services@spelthorne.gov.uk
🖥 www.spelthorne.gov.uk

FACTS AND FIGURES
Parliamentary Constituencies: Spelthorne
EU Constituencies: South East
Election Frequency: Elections are of whole council

PRINCIPAL OFFICERS

Chief Executive: Mr Roberto Tambini, Chief Executive, Council
Offices, Knowle Green, Staines TW18 1XB ☎ 01784 446250
✆ r.tambini@spelthorne.gov.uk

Deputy Chief Executive: Mr Terry Collier, Deputy Chief
Executive, Council Offices, Knowle Green, Staines TW18 1XB
☎ 01784 446296 ✆ t.collier@spelthorne.gov.uk

Deputy Chief Executive: Mr Lee O'Neil, Deputy Chief Executive,
Council Offices, Knowle Green, Staines TW18 1XB ☎ 01784 446377
✆ l.oneil@spelthorne.gov.uk

Senior Management: Mrs Deborah Ashman, Joint Group Head
- Community Wellbeing, Council Offices, Knowle Green, Staines
TW18 1XB ☎ 01784 446206 ✆ d.ashman@spelthorne.gov.uk

Senior Management: Ms Heather Morgan, Group Head -
Regeneration & Growth, Council Offices, Knowle Green, Staines
TW18 1XB ☎ 01784 446352 ✆ h.morgan@spelthorne.gov.uk

Senior Management: Dr Sandy Muirhead, Group Head -
Commissioning & Transformation, Council Offices, Knowle Green,
Staines TW18 1XB ☎ 01784 446318 ✆ s.muirhead@spelthorne.gov.uk

Senior Management: Mrs Linda Norman, Group Head - Finance
& Customer Relations, Council Offices, Knowle Green, Staines
TW18 1XB ☎ 01784 446375 ✆ l.norman@spelthorne.gov.uk

Senior Management: Ms Karen Sinclair, Joint Group Head -
Community Wellbeing, Council Offices, Knowle Green, Staines
TW18 1XB ☎ 01784 446206 ✆ k.sinclair@spelthorne.gov.uk

Senior Management: Ms Jackie Taylor, Group Head -
Neighbourhood Services, Council Offices, Knowle Green, Staines
TW18 1XB ☎ 01784 446412 ✆ j.taylor@spelthorne.gov.uk

Access Officer / Social Services (Disability): Mr Terry Collier,
Deputy Chief Executive, Council Offices, Knowle Green, Staines
TW18 1XB ☎ 01784 446296 ✆ t.collier@spelthorne.gov.uk

Architect, Building / Property Services: Mr Dave Phillips,
Asset Manager, Council Offices, Knowle Green, Staines TW18 1XB
☎ 01784 446424 ✆ d.phillips@spelthorne.gov.uk

Best Value: Mr Lee O'Neil, Deputy Chief Executive, Council
Offices, Knowle Green, Staines TW18 1XB ☎ 01784 446377
✆ l.oneil@spelthorne.gov.uk

Building Control: Mr Stephen Bowden, Building Control Manager,
Council Offices, Knowle Green, Staines TW18 1XB ☎ 01784 446365
✆ s.bowden@spelthorne.gov.uk

Children / Youth Services: Mr Lee O'Neil, Deputy Chief
Executive, Council Offices, Knowle Green, Staines TW18 1XB
☎ 01784 446377 ✆ l.oneil@spelthorne.gov.uk

PR / Communications: Ms Dawn Morrison, Head of
Communications, Council Offices, Knowle Green, Staines TW18 1XB
☎ 01784 446432 ✆ d.morrison@spelthorne.gov.uk

Community Safety: Mr Keith McGroary, Head of Community
Safety & Economic Development, Council Offices, Knowle Green,
Staines TW18 1XB ☎ 01784 444224
✆ k.mcgroary@spelthorne.gov.uk

Computer Management: Mrs Helen Dunn, Head of ICT, Council
Offices, Knowle Green, Staines TW18 1XB ☎ 01932 425550; 01748
451499 ✆ helen.dunn@runnymede.gov.uk

Corporate Services: Mr Terry Collier, Deputy Chief Executive,
Council Offices, Knowle Green, Staines TW18 1XB ☎ 01784 446296
✆ t.collier@spelthorne.gov.uk

Customer Service: Mrs Linda Norman, Group Head - Finance &
Customer Relations, Council Offices, Knowle Green, Staines TW18
1XB ☎ 01784 446375 ✆ l.norman@spelthorne.gov.uuk

Direct Labour: Ms Debbie O'Sullivan, Head of Human Resources,
Council Offices, Knowle Green, Staines TW18 1XB ☎ 01784 444289
✆ d.o'sullivan@spelthorne.gov.uk

Direct Labour: Ms Angela Tooth, Head of Human Resources,
Council Offices, Knowle Green, Staines TW18 1XB ☎ 01784 446289
✆ a.tooth@spelthorne.gov.uk

SPELTHORNE

Economic Development: Mr Keith McGroary, Head of Community Safety & Economic Development, Council Offices, Knowle Green, Staines TW18 1XB ☎ 01784 444224 ✆ k.mcgroary@spelthorne.gov.uk

E-Government: Mrs Helen Dunn, Head of ICT, Council Offices, Knowle Green, Staines TW18 1XB ☎ 01932 425550; 01748 451499 ✆ helen.dunn@runnymede.gov.uk

Electoral Registration: Ms Jayne McEwan, Electoral Services Officer, Council Offices, Knowle Green, Staines TW18 1XB ☎ 01784 446232 ✆ j.mcewan@spelthorne.gov.uk

Emergency Planning: Mr Nick Moon, Managing Director - Applied Resilience, Civic Centre, Station Road, Addlestone KT15 2AH ☎ 01932 425178 ✆ nick@appliedresilience.org

Emergency Planning: Mr Roberto Tambini, Chief Executive, Council Offices, Knowle Green, Staines TW18 1XB ☎ 01784 446250 ✆ r.tambini@spelthorne.gov.uk

Energy Management: Dr Sandy Muirhead, Group Head - Commissioning & Transformation, Council Offices, Knowle Green, Staines TW18 1XB ☎ 01784 446318 ✆ s.muirhead@spelthorne.gov.uk

Environmental / Technical Services: Ms Jackie Taylor, Group Head - Neighbourhood Services, Council Offices, Knowle Green, Staines TW18 1XB ☎ 01784 446412 ✆ j.taylor@spelthorne.gov.uk

Environmental Health: Ms Tracey Willmott-French, Senior Environmental Health Manager, Council Offices, Knowle Green, Staines TW18 1XB ☎ 01784 446271 ✆ t.willmott-french@spelthorne.gov.uk

Estates, Property & Valuation: Mr Dave Phillips, Asset Manager, Council Offices, Knowle Green, Staines TW18 1XB ☎ 01784 446424 ✆ d.phillips@spelthorne.gov.uk

Events Manager: Ms Lisa Stonehouse, Leisure Services Manager, Council Offices, Knowle Green, Staines TW18 1XB ☎ 01784 446431 ✆ l.stonehouse@spelthorne.gov.uk

Facilities: Mrs Linda Norman, Group Head - Finance & Customer Relations, Council Offices, Knowle Green, Staines TW18 1XB ☎ 01784 446375 ✆ l.norman@spelthorne.gov.uuk

Finance: Mr Terry Collier, Deputy Chief Executive, Council Offices, Knowle Green, Staines TW18 1XB ☎ 01784 446296 ✆ t.collier@spelthorne.gov.uk

Finance: Mrs Linda Norman, Group Head - Finance & Customer Relations, Council Offices, Knowle Green, Staines TW18 1XB ☎ 01784 446375 ✆ l.norman@spelthorne.gov.uuk

Grounds Maintenance: Ms Jackie Taylor, Group Head - Neighbourhood Services, Council Offices, Knowle Green, Staines TW18 1XB ☎ 01784 446412 ✆ j.taylor@spelthorne.gov.uk

Health and Safety: Mr Stuart Mann, Corporate Health & Safety Officer, Council Offices, Knowle Green, Staines TW18 1XB ☎ 01784 446270 ✆ s.mann@spelthorne.gov.uk

Health and Safety: Mr Stuart Mann, Corporate Health & Safety Officer, Council Offices, Knowle Green, Staines TW18 1XB ☎ 01784 446270 ✆ s.mann@spelthorne.gov.uk

Home Energy Conservation: Ms Jackie Taylor, Group Head - Neighbourhood Services, Council Offices, Knowle Green, Staines TW18 1XB ☎ 01784 446412 ✆ j.taylor@spelthorne.gov.uk

Housing: Mrs Deborah Ashman, Joint Group Head - Community Wellbeing, Council Offices, Knowle Green, Staines TW18 1XB ☎ 01784 446206 ✆ d.ashman@spelthorne.gov.uk

Housing: Ms Karen Sinclair, Joint Group Head - Community Wellbeing, Council Offices, Knowle Green, Staines TW18 1XB ☎ 01784 446206 ✆ k.sinclair@spelthorne.gov.uk

Legal: Mr Michael Graham, Head of Corporate Governance & Monitoring Officer, Council Offices, Knowle Green, Staines TW18 1XB ☎ 01784 446227 ✆ m.graham@spelthorne.gov.uk

Leisure and Cultural Services: Mr Lee O'Neil, Deputy Chief Executive, Council Offices, Knowle Green, Staines TW18 1XB ☎ 01784 446377 ✆ l.oneil@spelthorne.gov.uk

Licensing: Ms Dawn Morrison, Head of Communications, Council Offices, Knowle Green, Staines TW18 1XB ☎ 01784 446432 ✆ d.morrison@spelthorne.gov.uk

Lottery Funding, Charity and Voluntary: Mr Terry Collier, Deputy Chief Executive, Council Offices, Knowle Green, Staines TW18 1XB ☎ 01784 446296 ✆ t.collier@spelthorne.gov.uk

Member Services: Mr Michael Graham, Head of Corporate Governance & Monitoring Officer, Council Offices, Knowle Green, Staines TW18 1XB ☎ 01784 446227 ✆ m.graham@spelthorne.gov.uk

Member Services: Mr Greg Halliwell, Principal Committee Manager, Council Offices, Knowle Green, Staines TW18 1XB ☎ 01784 446267 ✆ g.halliwell@spelthorne.gov.uk

Parking: Ms Jackie Taylor, Group Head - Neighbourhood Services, Council Offices, Knowle Green, Staines TW18 1XB ☎ 01784 446412 ✆ j.taylor@spelthorne.gov.uk

Partnerships: Mr Roberto Tambini, Chief Executive, Council Offices, Knowle Green, Staines TW18 1XB ☎ 01784 446250 ✆ r.tambini@spelthorne.gov.uk

Personnel / HR: Ms Debbie O'Sullivan, Head of Human Resources, Council Offices, Knowle Green, Staines TW18 1XB ☎ 01784 444289 ✆ d.o'sullivan@spelthorne.gov.uk

Planning: Mr John Brooks, Head of Planning & Housing Strategy, Council Offices, Knowle Green, Staines TW18 1XB ☎ 01784 446346 ✆ j.brooks@spelthorne.gov.uk

Procurement: Mr Terry Collier, Deputy Chief Executive, Council Offices, Knowle Green, Staines TW18 1XB ☎ 01784 446296 ✆ t.collier@spelthorne.gov.uk

Recycling & Waste Minimisation: Ms Jackie Taylor, Group Head - Neighbourhood Services, Council Offices, Knowle Green, Staines TW18 1XB ☎ 01784 446412 ✐ j.taylor@spelthorne.gov.uk

Regeneration: Ms Heather Morgan, Group Head - Regeneration & Growth, Council Offices, Knowle Green, Staines TW18 1XB ☎ 01784 446352 ✐ h.morgan@spelthorne.gov.uk

Staff Training: Ms Debbie O'Sullivan, Head of Human Resources, Council Offices, Knowle Green, Staines TW18 1XB ☎ 01784 444289 ✐ d.o'sullivan@spelthorne.gov.uk

Staff Training: Ms Angela Tooth, Head of Human Resources, Council Offices, Knowle Green, Staines TW18 1XB ☎ 01784 446289 ✐ a.tooth@spelthorne.gov.uk

Street Scene: Ms Jackie Taylor, Group Head - Neighbourhood Services, Council Offices, Knowle Green, Staines TW18 1XB ☎ 01784 446412 ✐ j.taylor@spelthorne.gov.uk

Tourism: Mr Keith McGroary, Head of Community Safety & Economic Development, Council Offices, Knowle Green, Staines TW18 1XB ☎ 01784 444224 ✐ k.mcgroary@spelthorne.gov.uk

Town Centre: Mr Michael Graham, Head of Corporate Governance & Monitoring Officer, Council Offices, Knowle Green, Staines TW18 1XB ☎ 01784 446227 ✐ m.graham@spelthorne.gov.uk

Town Centre: Mr Keith McGroary, Head of Community Safety & Economic Development, Council Offices, Knowle Green, Staines TW18 1XB ☎ 01784 444224 ✐ k.mcgroary@spelthorne.gov.uk

Transport: Ms Jackie Taylor, Group Head - Neighbourhood Services, Council Offices, Knowle Green, Staines TW18 1XB ☎ 01784 446412 ✐ j.taylor@spelthorne.gov.uk

Transport Planner: Mr John Brooks, Head of Planning & Housing Strategy, Council Offices, Knowle Green, Staines TW18 1XB ☎ 01784 446346 ✐ j.brooks@spelthorne.gov.uk

Waste Collection and Disposal: Ms Jackie Taylor, Group Head - Neighbourhood Services, Council Offices, Knowle Green, Staines TW18 1XB ☎ 01784 446412 ✐ j.taylor@spelthorne.gov.uk

Waste Management: Ms Jackie Taylor, Group Head - Neighbourhood Services, Council Offices, Knowle Green, Staines TW18 1XB ☎ 01784 446412 ✐ j.taylor@spelthorne.gov.uk

Children's Play Areas: Ms Sabina Sims, Allotments Officer, Council Offices, Knowle Green, Staines TW18 1XB ☎ 01784 446327 ✐ s.sims@spelthorne.gov.uk

COUNCILLORS

Mayor: Friday, Alfred (CON - Sunbury East)
cllr.friday@spelthorne.gov.uk

Deputy Mayor: Leighton, Vivienne (CON - Shepperton Town)
cllr.leighton@spelthorne.gov.uk

Leader of the Council: Harvey, Ian (CON - Sunbury East)
cllr.harvey@spelthorne.gov.uk

Deputy Leader of the Council: Harman, Tony (CON - Riverside & Laleham)
cllr.harman@spelthorne.gov.uk

Group Leader: Beardsmore, Ian (LD - Sunbury Common)
cllr.beardsmore@spelthorne.gov.uk

Attewell, Maureen (CON - Laleham & Shepperton Green)
cllr.attewell@spelthorne.gov.uk

Barnard, Colin (CON - Shepperton Town)
cllr.barnard@spelthorne.gov.uk

Barratt, Richard (CON - Stanwell North)
cllr.barratt@spelthorne.gov.uk

Boughtflower, John (CON - Ashford North & Stanwell South)
cllr.boughtflower@spelthorne.gov.uk

Burkmar, Steven (INDNA - Staines South)
cllr.burkmar@spelthorne.gov.uk

Capes, Sabine (CON - Staines South)
cllr.capes@spelthorne.gov.uk

Chandler, Rose (CON - Ashford East)
cllr.chandler@spelthorne.gov.uk

Davis, Colin (CON - Staines)
cllr.davis@spelthorne.gov.uk

Doran, Susan (LAB - Stanwell North)
cllr.doran@spelthorne.gov.uk

Dunn, Sandra (LD - Halliford & Sunbury West)
cllr.dunn@spelthorne.gov.uk

Edgington, Quentin (R - Riverside & Laleham)
cllr.edgington@spelthorne.gov.uk

Evans, Tim (CON - Halliford & Sunbury West)
cllr.evans@spelthorne.gov.uk

Flurry, Kevin (CON - Stanwell North)
cllr.flurry@spelthorne.gov.uk

Forbes-Forsyth, Penny (R - Staines South)
cllr.forbes-forsyth@spelthorne.gov.uk

Francis, Mark (CON - Staines)
cllr.francis@spelthorne.gov.uk

Frazer, Chris (CON - Ashford East)
cllr.frazer@spelthorne.gov.uk

Gething, Nick (CON - Ashford Town)
cllr.gething@spelthorne.gov.uk

Griffiths, Alison (CON - Sunbury Common)
cllr.griffiths@spelthorne.gov.uk

Islam, Naz (CON - Ashford Town)
cllr.islam@spelthorne.gov.uk

Jones, Anthony (CON - Halliford & Sunbury West)
cllr.jones@spelthorne.gov.uk

Kavanagh, John (CON - Ashford Common)
cllr.kavanagh@spelthorne.gov.uk

Madams, Mary (CON - Laleham & Shepperton Green)
cllr.madams@spelthorne.gov.uk

Mitchell, Tony (CON - Ashford East)
cllr.mitchell@spelthorne.gov.uk

Mooney, Sinead (CON - Ashford North & Stanwell South)
cllr.mooney@spelthorne.gov.uk

Patel, Daxa (CON - Sunbury East)
cllr.patel@spelthorne.gov.uk

SPELTHORNE

Pinkerton, Jean (CON - Staines)
cllr.pinkerton@spelthorne.gov.uk

Rybinski, Olivia (CON - Ashford Town)
cllr.rybinski@spelthorne.gov.uk

Saliagopoulos, Denise (CON - Riverside & Laleham)
cllr.saliagopoulos@spelthorne.gov.uk

Sexton, Joanne (CON - Ashford North & Stanwell South)
cllr.sexton@spelthorne.gov.uk

Sider, Robin (CON - Shepperton Town)
cllr.sider@spelthorne.gov.uk

Smith-Ainsley, Richard (CON - Laleham & Shepperton Green)
cllr.smith-ainsley@spelthorne.gov.uk

Spoor, Bernie (LD - Sunbury Common)
cllr.spoor@spelthorne.gov.uk

Thomson, Howard (CON - Ashford Common)
cllr.thomson@spelthorne.gov.uk

Williams, Howard (CON - Ashford Common)
cllr.williams@spelthorne.gov.uk

POLITICAL COMPOSITION
CON: 32, LD: 3, R: 2, INDNA: 1, LAB: 1

COMMITTEE CHAIRS

Audit: Ms Mary Madams

Licensing: Mr Robin Sider

Planning: Mr Richard Smith-Ainsley

St. Albans City   D

St. Albans City & District Council, District Council Offices, St. Peter's Street, St. Albans AL1 3JE
☎ 01727 866100 ⌨ contactus@stalbans.gov.uk
🖥 www.stalbans.gov.uk

FACTS AND FIGURES
Parliamentary Constituencies: Hitchin and Harpenden, St. Albans
EU Constituencies: Eastern
Election Frequency: Elections are by thirds

PRINCIPAL OFFICERS

Chief Executive: Dr James Blake, Chief Executive, District Council Offices, St. Peter's Street, St. Albans AL1 3JE
☎ 01727 819264 ⌨ james.blake@stalbans.gov.uk

Deputy Chief Executive: Mr Colm O'Callaghan, Deputy Chief Executive (Finance), District Council Offices, St. Albans AL1 3JE ☎ 01727 819200
⌨ colm.o'callaghan@stalbans.gov.uk

Senior Management: Ms Karen Dragovic, Head of Housing, District Council Offices, St. Peter's Street, St. Albans AL1 3JE
☎ 01727 819400 ⌨ karen.dragovic@stalbans.gov.uk

Senior Management: Ms Amanda Foley, Head of Corporate Services, District Council Offices, St. Peter's Street, St. Albans AL1 3JE ☎ 01727 819308 ⌨ amanda.foley@stalbans.gov.uk

Senior Management: Ms Tracy Harvey, Head of Planning & Building Control, District Council Offices, St. Peter's Street, St. Albans AL1 3JE ☎ 01727 819300 ⌨ tracy.harvey@stalbans.gov.uk

Senior Management: Mr Mike Lovelady, Head of Legal, Democratic & Regulatory Services, District Council Offices, St. Peter's Street, St. Albans AL1 3JE ☎ 01727 819502
⌨ mike.lovelady@stalbans.gov.uk

Senior Management: Mr Richard Shwe, Head of Community Services, District Council Offices, St. Peter's Street, St. Albans AL1 3JE ☎ 01727 819365 ⌨ richard.shwe@stalbans.gov.uk

Best Value: Ms Helen Wright, Policy, Partnerships & Economic Development Manager, District Council Offices, St. Peter's Street, St. Albans AL1 3JE ☎ 01727 814546 ⌨ helen.wright@stalbans.gov.uk

Building Control: Ms Tracy Harvey, Head of Planning & Building Control, District Council Offices, St. Peter's Street, St. Albans AL1 3JE ☎ 01727 819300 ⌨ tracy.harvey@stalbans.gov.uk

Children / Youth Services: Mr Richard Shwe, Head of Community Services, District Council Offices, St. Peter's Street, St. Albans AL1 3JE ☎ 01727 819365 ⌨ richard.shwe@stalbans.gov.uk

PR / Communications: Ms Claire Wainwright, Executive & Communications Manager, District Council Offices, St. Peter's Street, St. Albans AL1 3JE ☎ 01727 819572
⌨ claire.wainwright@stalbans.gov.uk

Community Safety: Mr Neil Kieran, Principal Community Protection Officer, District Council Offices, St. Peter's Street, St. Albans AL1 3JE ☎ 01727 819416 ⌨ neil.kieran@stalbans.gov.uk

Computer Management: Ms Amanda Foley, Head of Corporate Services, District Council Offices, St. Peter's Street, St. Albans AL1 3JE ☎ 01727 819308 ⌨ amanda.foley@stalbans.gov.uk

Corporate Services: Dr James Blake, Chief Executive, District Council Offices, St. Peter's Street, St. Albans AL1 3JE
☎ 01727 819264 ⌨ james.blake@stalbans.gov.uk

Customer Service: Ms Amanda Foley, Head of Corporate Services, District Council Offices, St. Peter's Street, St. Albans AL1 3JE ☎ 01727 819308 ⌨ amanda.foley@stalbans.gov.uk

Economic Development: Ms Maria Cutler, Principal Policy & Economic Development Officer, District Council Offices, St. Peter's Street, St. Albans AL1 3JE ☎ 01727 819243
⌨ maria.cutler@stalbans.gov.uk

Electoral Registration: Mr Mike Lovelady, Head of Legal, Democratic & Regulatory Services, District Council Offices, St. Peter's Street, St. Albans AL1 3JE ☎ 01727 819502
⌨ mike.lovelady@stalbans.gov.uk

Emergency Planning: Mr Paul Blande, Emergency Planning & Community Resilience Officer, District Council Offices, St. Peter's Street, St. Albans AL1 3JE ☎ 01727 814612
⌨ paul.blande@stablans.gov.uk

Environmental Health: Ms Maria Stagg, Regulatory Services Manager, District Council Offices, St. Peter's Street, St. Albans AL1 3JE ☎ 01727 819436 ✆ maria.stagg@stalbans.gov.uk

Estates, Property & Valuation: Ms Debbi White, Property & Asset Manager, District Council Offices, St. Peter's Street, St. Albans AL1 3JE ☎ 01727 819515 ✆ debbi.white@stalbans.gov.uk

Facilities: Ms Debbi White, Property & Asset Manager, District Council Offices, St. Peter's Street, St. Albans AL1 3JE ☎ 01727 819515 ✆ debbi.white@stalbans.gov.uk

Finance: Mr Colm O'Callaghan, Deputy Chief Executive (Finance), District Council Offices, St. Peter's Street, St. Albans AL1 3JE ☎ 01727 819200 ✆ colm.o'callaghan@stalbans.gov.uk

Grounds Maintenance: Mr Jon Green, Parks & Green Spaces Manager, District Council Offices, St. Peter's Street, St. Albans AL1 3JE ☎ 01727 819233 ✆ jon.green@stalbans.gov.uk

Health and Safety: Ms Maria Stagg, Regulatory Services Manager, District Council Offices, St. Peter's Street, St. Albans AL1 3JE ☎ 01727 819436 ✆ maria.stagg@stalbans.gov.uk

Housing: Ms Karen Dragovic, Head of Housing, District Council Offices, St. Peter's Street, St. Albans AL1 3JE ☎ 01727 819400 ✆ karen.dragovic@stalbans.gov.uk

Housing Maintenance: Ms Karen Dragovic, Head of Housing, District Council Offices, St. Peter's Street, St. Albans AL1 3JE ☎ 01727 819400 ✆ karen.dragovic@stalbans.gov.uk

Legal: Mr Mike Lovelady, Head of Legal, Democratic & Regulatory Services, District Council Offices, St. Peter's Street, St. Albans AL1 3JE ☎ 01727 819502 ✆ mike.lovelady@stalbans.gov.uk

Leisure and Cultural Services: Mr Richard Shwe, Head of Community Services, District Council Offices, St. Peter's Street, St. Albans AL1 3JE ☎ 01727 819365 ✆ richard.shwe@stalbans.gov.uk

Licensing: Mrs Lesley Cameron, Business Compliance Manager, District Council Offices, St. Peter's Street, St. Albans AL1 3JE ☎ 01727 819454 ✆ lesley.cameron@stalbans.gov.uk

Lottery Funding, Charity and Voluntary: Mr Alan Partington, Financial Services Manager, District Council Offices, St. Peter's Street, St. Albans AL1 3JE ☎ 01727 819201 ✆ alan.partington@stalbans.gov.uk

Member Services: Ms Elizabeth Heath, Democratic Services Manager, District Council Offices, St. Peter's Street, St. Albans AL1 3JE ☎ 01727 819519 ✆ elizabeth.heath@stalbans.gov.uk

Parking: Ms Maria Stagg, Regulatory Services Manager, District Council Offices, St. Peter's Street, St. Albans AL1 3JE ☎ 01727 819436 ✆ maria.stagg@stalbans.gov.uk

Partnerships: Ms Helen Wright, Policy, Partnerships & Economic Development Manager, District Council Offices, St. Peter's Street, St. Albans AL1 3JE ☎ 01727 814546 ✆ helen.wright@stalbans.gov.uk

Personnel / HR: Ms Amanda Foley, Head of Corporate Services, District Council Offices, St. Peter's Street, St. Albans AL1 3JE ☎ 01727 819308 ✆ amanda.foley@stalbans.gov.uk

Planning: Ms Tracy Harvey, Head of Planning & Building Control, District Council Offices, St. Peter's Street, St. Albans AL1 3JE ☎ 01727 819300 ✆ tracy.harvey@stalbans.gov.uk

Procurement: Mr Richard Shwe, Head of Community Services, District Council Offices, St. Peter's Street, St. Albans AL1 3JE ☎ 01727 819365 ✆ richard.shwe@stalbans.gov.uk

Recycling & Waste Minimisation: Mr Richard Shwe, Head of Community Services, District Council Offices, St. Peter's Street, St. Albans AL1 3JE ☎ 01727 819365 ✆ richard.shwe@stalbans.gov.uk

Regeneration: Ms Maria Cutler, Principal Policy & Economic Development Officer, District Council Offices, St. Peter's Street, St. Albans AL1 3JE ☎ 01727 819243 ✆ maria.cutler@stalbans.gov.uk

Staff Training: Ms Amanda Foley, Head of Corporate Services, District Council Offices, St. Peter's Street, St. Albans AL1 3JE ☎ 01727 819308 ✆ amanda.foley@stalbans.gov.uk

Street Scene: Ms Tracy Harvey, Head of Planning & Building Control, District Council Offices, St. Peter's Street, St. Albans AL1 3JE ☎ 01727 819300 ✆ tracy.harvey@stalbans.gov.uk

Sustainable Communities: Ms Helen Wright, Policy, Partnerships & Economic Development Manager, District Council Offices, St. Peter's Street, St. Albans AL1 3JE ☎ 01727 814546 ✆ helen.wright@stalbans.gov.uk

Sustainable Development: Ms Candice Luper, Sustainability Projects Officer, District Council Offices, St. Peter's Street, St. Albans AL1 3JE ☎ 01727 819466 ✆ candice.luper@stalbans.gov.uk

Tourism: Ms Jenny Swatton, Policy Officer (Economic Development & Projects), District Council Offices, St. Peter's Street, St. Albans AL1 3JE ☎ 01727 819492 ✆ jenny.swatton@stalbans.gov.uk

Waste Collection and Disposal: Mr Richard Shwe, Head of Community Services, District Council Offices, St. Peter's Street, St. Albans AL1 3JE ☎ 01727 819365 ✆ richard.shwe@stalbans.gov.uk

Waste Management: Mr Richard Shwe, Head of Community Services, District Council Offices, St. Peter's Street, St. Albans AL1 3JE ☎ 01727 819365 ✆ richard.shwe@stalbans.gov.uk

COUNCILLORS

Mayor: Leonard, Frances (CON - Sandridge)
cllr.f.leonard@stalbans.gov.uk

Deputy Mayor: Clark, Gillian (CON - Wheathampstead)
cllr.g.clark@stalbans.gov.uk

Leader of the Council: Daly, Julian (CON - Harpenden West)
cllr.j.daly@stalbans.gov.uk

Deputy Leader of the Council: Campbell, Alec (CON - St Peters)
cllr.a.campbell@stalbans.gov.uk

Group Leader: Grover, Simon (GRN - St Peters)
cllr.s.grover@stalbans.gov.uk

ST. ALBANS CITY

Group Leader: Mills, Roma (LAB - Batchwood)
cllr.r.mills@stalbans.gov.uk

Group Leader: White, Chris (LD - Clarence)
cllr.c.white@stalbans.gov.uk

Bolton, Lyn (CON - Marshalswick North)
cllr.l.bolton@stalbans.gov.uk

Brazier, Chris (LD - Colney Heath)
cllr.c.brazier@stalbans.gov.uk

Brewster, Annie (CON - Wheathampstead)
cllr.a.brewster@stalbans.gov.uk

Calder, Simon (CON - London Colney)
cllr.s.calder@stalbans.gov.uk

Chichester-Miles, Daniel (CON - Harpenden West)
cllr.d.chichester-miles@stalbans.gov.uk

Chivers, Jessica (CON - Verulam)
cllr.j.chivers@stalbans.gov.uk

Churchard, Janet (LD - Marshalswick North)
cllr.j.churchard@stalbans.gov.uk

Clegg, Thomas (LD - Marshalswick North)
cllr.t.clegg@stalbans.gov.uk

Crawley, Maxine (IND - Redbourn)
cllr.m.crawley@stalbans.gov.uk

Curthoys, Richard (CON - Marshalswick South)
cllr.r.curthoys@stalbans.gov.uk

Davies, Alun (CON - St Peters)
cllr.a.davies@stalbans.gov.uk

Davies, Chris (LD - Verulam)
cllr.c.davies@stalbans.gov.uk

Day, Jamie (LD - Colney Heath)
cllr.j.day@stalbans.gov.uk

Donald, Robert (LD - Cunningham)
cllr.r.donald@stalbans.gov.uk

Ellis, Brian (CON - Harpenden South)
cllr.b.ellis@stalbans.gov.uk

Farmer, Rosemary (CON - Harpenden East)
cllr.r.farmer@stalbans.gov.uk

Farrell, Matthew (LD - Ashley)
cllr.m.farrell@stalbans.gov.uk

Featherstone, Sue (CON - St Stephen)
cllr.s.featherstone@stalbans.gov.uk

Gardner, Katherine (LAB - London Colney)
cllr.k.gardner@stalbans.gov.uk

Gaygusuz, Salih (CON - Marshalswick South)
cllr.m.salih@stalbans.gov.uk

Gibbard, Brian (CON - St Stephen)
cllr.b.gibbard@stalbans.gov.uk

Gordon, Dreda (LAB - London Colney)
cllr.d.gordon@stalbans.gov.uk

Grant, Iain (LAB - Sopwell)
cllr.i.grant@stalbans.gov.uk

Harris, Eileen (LAB - Sopwell)
cllr.e.harris@stalbans.gov.uk

Harrison, Geoffrey (LD - Cunningham)
cllr.g.harrison@stalbans.gov.uk

Heritage, David (CON - Harpenden South)
cllr.d.heritage@stalbans.gov.uk

Heritage, Teresa (CON - Harpenden South)
cllr.t.heritage@stalbans.gov.uk

Hill, Edgar (LD - Verulam)
cllr.e.hill@stalbans.gov.uk

Hodgson, Stephen (CON - Harpenden North)
cllr.s.hodgson@stalbans.gov.uk

Lee, Aislinn (LD - Park Street)
cllr.a.lee@stalbans.gov.uk

Maynard, Mary (CON - Harpenden East)
cllr.m.maynard@stalbans.gov.uk

McHale, Gerard (LD - Clarence)
cllr.g.mchale@stalbans.gov.uk

McKeown, Steve (CON - Marshalswick South)
cllr.s.mckeown@stalbans.gov.uk

Mead, Victoria (CON - Redbourn)

Pakenham, Malachy (LAB - Batchwood)
cllr.m.pakenham@stalbans.gov.uk

Pawle, Bert (CON - Harpenden North)
cllr.a.pawle@stalbans.gov.uk

Prowse, Robert (LD - Cunningham)
cllr.r.prowse@stalbans.gov.uk

Read, Beric (CON - Sandridge)
cllr.b.read@stalbans.gov.uk

Rowlands, Anthony (LD - Ashley)
cllr.a.rowlands@stalbans.gov.uk

Smith, Tim (CON - Batchwood)
cllr.t.smith@stalbans.gov.uk

Smith, Janet (LAB - Sopwell)
cllr.j.smith@stalbans.gov.uk

Stephens, Matt (CON - Harpenden West)
cllr.m.stephens@stalbans.gov.uk

Swendell, Tony (IND - Redbourn)
cllr.a.swendell@stalbans.gov.uk

Turner, Geoffrey (CON - Harpenden North)
cllr.g.turner@stalbans.gov.uk

Wakely, Mike (CON - Harpenden East)
cllr.m.wakely@stalbans.gov.uk

Winstone, David (CON - St Stephen)
cllr.d.winstone@stalbans.gov.uk

Wood, Sandra (CON - Wheathampstead)
cllr.s.wood@stalbans.gov.uk

Wright, Jock (CON - Park Street)
cllr.j.wright@stalbans.gov.uk

Yates, David (LD - Park Street)
cllr.d.yates@stalbans.gov.uk

Zia, Iqbal (LD - Ashley)
cllr.i.zia@stalbans.gov.uk

POLITICAL COMPOSITION
CON: 31, LD: 16, LAB: 7, IND: 2, GRN: 1, Vacant: 1

COMMITTEE CHAIRS

Audit: Mr Chris White

Community, Environment & Leisure: Mr Anthony Rowlands

Health & Wellbeing: Rev Robert Donald

Licensing: Mr Richard Curthoys

Planning, Resources & Housing: Ms Roma Mills

St. Edmundsbury   D

St. Edmundsbury Borough Council, West Suffolk House, Western Way, Bury St. Edmunds IP33 3YB
☎ 01284 763233 ◦ customer.services@westsuffolk.gov.uk
🖥 www.westsuffolk.gov.uk

FACTS AND FIGURES
Parliamentary Constituencies: Bury St. Edmunds
EU Constituencies: Eastern
Election Frequency: Elections are of whole council

PRINCIPAL OFFICERS

Chief Executive: Mr Ian Gallin, Joint Chief Executive, West Suffolk House, Western Way, Bury St. Edmunds IP33 3YB ☎ 01284 757001
◦ ian.gallin@westsuffolk.gov.uk

Senior Management: Ms Davina Howes, Head of Families & Communities, West Suffolk House, Western Way, Bury St. Edmunds IP33 3EY ☎ 01284 757070 ◦ davina.howes@westsuffolk.gov.uk

Senior Management: Ms Jill Korwin, Director, West Suffolk House, Western Way, Bury St. Edmunds IP33 3YB
☎ 01284 757252 ◦ jill.korwin@westsuffolk.gov.uk

Senior Management: Ms Rachael Mann, Head of Resources & Performance, West Suffolk House, Western Way, Bury St. Edmunds IP33 3EY ☎ 01638 719245 ◦ rachael.mann@westsuffolk.gov.uk

Senior Management: Mr Simon Phelan, Head of Housing, West Suffolk House, Western Way, Bury St. Edmunds IP33 3YB
☎ 01638 719440 ◦ simon.phelan@westsuffolk.gov.uk

Senior Management: Mrs Karen Points, Head of HR, Legal & Democratic Services, West Suffolk House, Western Way, Bury St. Edmunds IP33 3EY ☎ 01285 757015
◦ karen.points@westsuffolk.gov.uk

Senior Management: Mr Mark Walsh, Head of Operations, West Suffolk House, Western Way, Bury St. Edmunds IP33 3EY
☎ 01284 757300 ◦ mark.walsh@westsuffolk.gov.uk

Senior Management: Mr Alex Wilson, Director, West Suffolk House, Western Way, Bury St. Edmunds IP33 3YB
☎ 01284 757695 ◦ alex.wilson@westsuffolk.gov.uk

Senior Management: Mr Steven Wood, Head of Planning & Growth, West Suffolk House, Western Way, Bury St. Edmunds IP33 3EY ☎ 01284 757306 ◦ steven.wood@westsuffolk.gov.uk

Architect, Building / Property Services: Mr Michael Lindsell, Service Manager - Property Services, West Suffolk House, Western Way, Bury St. Edmunds IP33 3YB ☎ 01284 757385
◦ michael.lindsell@westsuffolk.gov.uk

Building Control: Mr Rob Fysh, Principal Building Control Surveyor, West Suffolk House, Western Way, Bury St. Edmunds IP33 3YB ☎ 01284 757379 ◦ rob.fysh@westsuffolk.gov.uk

PR / Communications: Ms Marianne Hulland, Service Manager - Corporate Communications, West Suffolk House, Western Way, Bury St. Edmunds IP33 3YU ☎ 01284 757034
◦ marrianna.hulland@westsuffolk.gov.uk

Computer Management: Mr James Wager, ICT Infrastructure Support Manager, West Suffolk House, Western Way, Bury St. Edmunds IP33 3EY ☎ 01284 757205
◦ james.wager@westsuffolk.gov.uk

Corporate Services: Ms Liz Barnard, Service Manager - Corporate Policy, Forest Heath District Council, College Heath Road, Mildenhall IP28 7EY ☎ 01638 719454
◦ liz.barnard@westsuffolk.gov.uk

Corporate Services: Ms Tanya Sturman, Service Manager - Corporate Policy, Forest Heath District Council, College Heath Road, Mildenhall IP28 7EY ☎ 01638 719473
◦ tanya.sturman@westsuffolk.gov.uk

Customer Service: Mr Chris Bolton, Service Manager - Customer Services & Transformation, Forest Heath District Council, College Heath Road, Mildenhall IP28 7EY ☎ 01638 719320
◦ chris.bolton@westsuffolk.gov.uk

Economic Development: Mrs Andrea Mayley, Service Manager - Economic Development & Growth, West Suffolk House, Western Way, Bury St. Edmunds IP33 3YU ☎ 01284 757343
◦ andrea.mayley@westsuffolk.gov.uk

Electoral Registration: Mrs Fiona Osman, Service Manager - Democratic Services & Elections, West Suffolk House, Western Way, Bury St. Edmunds IP33 3EY ☎ 01285 757105
◦ fiona.osman@westsuffolk.gov.uk

Emergency Planning: Mr Alan Points, District Emergency Planning Officer, West Suffolk House, Western Way, Bury St. Edmunds IP33 1YU ☎ 01284 758461
◦ alan.points@westsuffolk.gov.uk

Energy Management: Mr Andrew Oswald, Environment & Energy Team Leader, West Suffolk House, Western Way, Bury St. Edmunds IP33 3YB ☎ 01284 757622 ◦ andrew.oswald@westsuffolk.gov.uk

Environmental / Technical Services: Mr Peter Gudde, Service Manager - Environmental Health, West Suffolk House, Western Way, Bury St. Edmunds IP33 3YB ☎ 01284 757042
◦ peter.gudde@westsuffolk.gov.uk

Environmental Health: Mr Peter Gudde, Service Manager - Environmental Health, West Suffolk House, Western Way, Bury St. Edmunds IP33 3YB ☎ 01284 757042
◦ peter.gudde@westsuffolk.gov.uk

ST. EDMUNDSBURY

Estates, Property & Valuation: Ms Charlotte Squirrell, Senior Estates Surveyor, West Suffolk House, Western Way, Bury St. Edmunds IP33 3YB ☎ 01284 757361 ⌁ charlotte.squirrell@westsuffolk.gov.uk

Events Manager: Mr Nick Wells, Entertainment & Events Manager, West Suffolk House, Western Way, Bury St. Edmunds IP33 3YB ☎ 01284 758103 ⌁ nick.wells@westsuffolk.gov.uk

Facilities: Ms Teresa Claydon, Facilities & CCTV Manager, West Suffolk House, Western Way, Bury St. Edmunds IP33 3YB ☎ 01284 757398 ⌁ teresa.claydon@westsuffolk.gov.uk

Fleet Management: Mr Philip Clifford, Fleet & Technical Manager, West Suffolk House, Western Way, Bury St. Edmunds IP33 3YU ☎ 01284 757459 ⌁ philip.clifford@westsuffolk.gov.uk

Grounds Maintenance: Mr Chris Silverwood, Service Manager - Operations, Waste & Street Scene, West Suffolk House, Western Way, Bury St. Edmunds IP33 3YB ☎ 01284 757472 ⌁ chris.silverwood@westsuffolk.gov.uk

Health and Safety: Mr Martin Hosker, Health & Safety Manager, West Suffolk House, Western Way, Bury St. Edmunds IP33 3YU ☎ 01284 757010 ⌁ martin.hosker@westsuffolk.gov.uk

Housing: Mr Tony Hobby, Service Manager - Housing Operations, Forest Heath District Council, College Heath Road, Mildenhall IP28 7EY ☎ 01638 719348 ⌁ tony.hobby@westsuffolk.gov.uk

Housing: Mr Simon Phelan, Head of Housing, West Suffolk House, Western Way, Bury St. Edmunds IP33 3YB ☎ 01638 719440 ⌁ simon.phelan@westsuffolk.gov.uk

Housing Maintenance: Mr Andrew Newman, Service Manager - Housing Standards, Forest Heath District Council, College Heath Road, Mildenhall IP28 7EY ☎ 01638 719276 ⌁ andrew.newman@westsuffolk.gov.uk

Legal: Mr Steven Boyle, Interim Service Manager - Legal, West Suffolk House, Western Way, Bury St. Edmunds IP33 3YB ☎ 01285 757165 ⌁ steven.boyle@westsuffolk.gov.uk

Leisure and Cultural Services: Mr Damien Parker, Service Manager - Operations, Leisure & Culture, West Suffolk House, Western Way, Bury St. Edmunds IP33 3YB ☎ 01284 757090 ⌁ damien.parker@westsuffolk.gov.uk

Licensing: Mr Tom Wright, Business Regulation & Licensing Manager, West Suffolk House, Western Way, Bury St. Edmunds IP33 3YB ☎ 01638 719223 ⌁ tom.wright@westsuffolk.gov.uk

Member Services: Mrs Karen Points, Head of HR, Legal & Democratic Services, West Suffolk House, Western Way, Bury St. Edmunds IP33 3EY ☎ 01285 757015 ⌁ karen.points@westsuffolk.gov.uk

Parking: Mr Darren Dixon, Car Parks Manager, West Suffolk House, Western Way, Bury St. Edmunds IP33 3EY ☎ 01284 757413 ⌁ darren.dixon@westsuffolk.gov.uk

Personnel / HR: Ms Wendy Canham, Service Manager - HR & OD, West Suffolk House, Western Way, Bury St. Edmunds IP33 3YB ☎ 01284 757006 ⌁ wendy.canham@westsuffolk.gov.uk

Planning: Ms Rachel Almond, Service Manager - Planning & Development, Forest Heath District Council, College Heath Road, Mildenhall IP28 7EY ☎ 01638 719455 ⌁ rachel.almond@westsuffolk.gov.uk

Planning: Ms Marie Smith, Service Manager - Planning Strategy, Forest Heath District Council, College Heath Road, Mildenhall IP29 7EY ☎ 01638 719260 ⌁ marie.smith@westsuffolk.gov.uk

Procurement: Mr Zia Quader, Procurement Manager, West Suffolk House, Western Way, Bury St. Edmunds IP33 3YB ☎ 01284 757310 ⌁ zia.quader@westsuffolk.gov.uk

Recycling & Waste Minimisation: Mr Mark Christie, Service Manager - Business, West Suffolk House, Western Way, Bury St. Edmunds IP33 3YB ☎ 01638 719220 ⌁ mark.christie@westsuffolk.gov.uk

Regeneration: Mrs Andrea Mayley, Service Manager - Economic Development & Growth, West Suffolk House, Western Way, Bury St. Edmunds IP33 3YU ☎ 01284 757343 ⌁ andrea.mayley@westsuffolk.gov.uk

Staff Training: Ms Juliet Fulford, Learning & Development Advisor, Forest Heath District Council, College Heath Road, Mildenhall IP28 7EY ☎ 01284 757047 ⌁ juliet.fulford@westsuffolk.gov.uk

Street Scene: Mr Chris Silverwood, Service Manager - Operations, Waste & Street Scene, West Suffolk House, Western Way, Bury St. Edmunds IP33 3YB ☎ 01284 757472 ⌁ chris.silverwood@westsuffolk.gov.uk

Waste Collection and Disposal: Mr Chris Silverwood, Service Manager - Operations, Waste & Street Scene, West Suffolk House, Western Way, Bury St. Edmunds IP33 3YB ☎ 01284 757472 ⌁ chris.silverwood@westsuffolk.gov.uk

Waste Management: Mr Mark Walsh, Head of Operations, West Suffolk House, Western Way, Bury St. Edmunds IP33 3EY ☎ 01284 757300 ⌁ mark.walsh@westsuffolk.gov.uk

Children's Play Areas: Mr Timothy McGee, Playground Inspector, West Suffolk House, Western Way, Bury St. Edmunds IP33 3YB ☎ 01284 757063 ⌁ timothy.mcgee@westsuffolk.gov.uk

COUNCILLORS

Mayor: Wakelam, Julia (GRN - Risbygate) julia.wakelam@stedsbc.gov.uk

Deputy Mayor: Clements, Terry (CON - Horringer & Whelnetham) terry.clements@stedsbc.gov.uk

Leader of the Council: Griffiths, John (CON - Ixworth) john.griffiths@stedsbc.gov.uk

Deputy Leader of the Council: Mildmay-White, Sara (CON - Rougham) sara.mildmay-white@stedsbc.gov.uk

Group Leader: Brown, Anthony (UKIP - Haverhill East)
tony.brown@stedsbc.gov.uk

Group Leader: Nettleton, David (IND - Risbygate)
david.nettleton@stedsbc.gov.uk

Broughton, Sarah (CON - Great Barton)
sarah.broughton@stedsbc.gov.uk

Brown, Simon (CON - Pakenham)
simon.brown@stedsbc.gov.uk

Buckle, Terry (CON - Moreton Hall)
terry.buckle@stedsbc.gov.uk

Bull, Carol (CON - Barningham)
carol.bull@stedsbc.gov.uk

Burns, John (UKIP - Haverhill East)
john.burns@stedsbc.gov.uk

Chung, Patrick (CON - Southgate)
patrick.chung@stedsbc.gov.uk

Cockle, Bob (LAB - St Olaves)
bob.cockle@stedsbc.gov.uk

Crooks, Jason (UKIP - Haverhill South)
jason.crooks@stedsbc.gov.uk

Everitt, Robert (CON - MInden)
robert.everitt@stedsbc.gov.uk

Farthing, Jeremy (CON - Haverhill West)
jeremy.farthing@stedsbc.gov.uk

Fox, Paula (CON - Haverhill South)
paula.fox@stedsbc.gov.uk

Glossop, Susan (CON - Risby)
susan.glossop@stedsbc.gov.uk

Hailstone, Wayne (CON - Westgate)
wayne.hailstone@stedsbc.gov.uk

Hind, Diane (LAB - Northgate)
diane.hind@stedsbc.gov.uk

Hopfensperger, Rebecca (CON - Fornham)
rebecca.hopfensperger@stedsbc.gov.uk

Hopfensperger, Paul (IND - St Olaves)
paul.hopfensperger@stedsbc.gov.uk

Houlder, Ian (CON - Barrow)
ian.houlder@stedsbc.gov.uk

Marks, Margaret (CON - Haverhill West)
margaret.marks@stedsbc.gov.uk

McLatchy, Betty (CON - Haverhill North)
betty.mclatchy@stedsbc.gov.uk

McLatchy, Ivor (CON - Haverhill East)
ivor.mclatchy@stedsbc.gov.uk

Midwood, Jane (CON - Withersfield)
jane.midwood@stedsbc.gov.uk

Pollington, Clive (CON - Wickhambrook)
clive.pollington@stedsbc.gov.uk

Pugh, Alaric (CON - Clare)
alaric.pugh@stedsbc.gov.uk

Rayner, Joanna (CON - Abbeygate)
joanna.rayner@stedsbc.gov.uk

Richardson, Karen (CON - Haverhill East)
karen.richardson@stedsbc.gov.uk

Roach, David (CON - Haverhill West)
david.roach@stedsbc.gov.uk

Robbins, Barry (UKIP - Haverhill North)
barry.robbins@stedsbc.gov.uk

Rout, Richard (CON - Westgate)
richard.rout@stedsbc.gov.uk

Rushen, Angela (CON - Chedburgh)
angela.rushen@stedsbc.gov.uk

Speed, Andrew (CON - Abbeygate)
andrew.speed@stedsbc.gov.uk

Springett, Clive (CON - Minden)
clive.springett@stedsbc.gov.uk

Stamp, Sarah (CON - Southgate)
sarah.stamp@stedsbc.gov.uk

Stevens, Peter (CON - Cavendish)
peter.stevens@stedsbc.gov.uk

Thompson, Peter (CON - Moreton Hall)
peter.thompson@stedsbc.gov.uk

Thorndyke, Jim (CON - Stanton)
jim.thorndyke@stedsbc.gov.uk

Warby, Frank (CON - Moreton Hall)
frank.warby@stedsbc.gov.uk

Warby, Patricia (CON - Eastgate)
patricia.warby@stedsbc.gov.uk

Williams, Anthony (UKIP - Haverhill North)
anthony.williams@stedsbc.gov.uk

POLITICAL COMPOSITION
CON: 34, UKIP: 5, IND: 2, LAB: 2, GRN: 1

COMMITTEE CHAIRS

Audit: Ms Sarah Broughton

Development Control: Mr Jim Thorndyke

Licensing: Mr Frank Warby

St. Helens   M

St. Helens Metropolitan Borough Council, Town Hall, Victoria Square, Corporation Street, St. Helens WA10 1HP
☎ 01744 456789 🖨 01744 456895 🖳 www.sthelens.gov.uk

FACTS AND FIGURES
Parliamentary Constituencies: St. Helens North, St. Helens South and Whiston
EU Constituencies: North West
Election Frequency: Elections are by thirds

PRINCIPAL OFFICERS

Chief Executive: Mr Mike Palin, Chief Executive, Town Hall, Victoria Square, Corporation Street, St. Helens WA10 1HP
☎ 01744 676101 🖑 mikepalin@sthelens.gov.uk

Deputy Chief Executive: Mr Ian Roberts, Deputy Chief Executive & Strategic Director - Corporate Services, Town Hall, Victoria Square, Corporation Street, St. Helens WA10 1HP ☎ 01744 673201 🖑 ianroberts@sthelens.gov.uk

ST. HELENS

Senior Management: Mrs Jan Bakewell, Head of Legal Services, Town Hall, Victoria Square, Corporation Street, St. Helens WA10 1HP ☎ 01744 673263 ◌ janbakewell@sthelens.gov.uk

Senior Management: Mrs Cath Fogarty, Assistant Treasurer - Regulation & Compliance, Town Hall, Victoria Square, Corporation Street, St. Helens WA10 1HP ☎ 01744 676885 ◌ cathfogarty@sthelens.gov.uk

Senior Management: Mrs Sue Forster, Interim Director - Public Health, Atlas House, Corporation Street, St. Helens WA9 1LD ☎ 01744 673232 ◌ susanforster@sthelens.gov.uk

Senior Management: Mr Gordon Lee, Assistant Treasurer - Service Delivery, Town Hall, Victoria Square, Corporation Street, St. Helens WA10 1HP ☎ 01744 675230 ◌ gordonlee@sthelens.gov.uk

Senior Management: Mr Wayne Traynor, Assistant Treasurer - Accountancy & Financial Management, Town Hall, Victoria Square, Corporation Street, St. Helens WA10 1HP ☎ 01744 673230 ◌ waynetraynor@sthelens.gov.uk

Architect, Building / Property Services: Mr Stuart Rainbow, Manager - Architectural Services, Town Hall, Victoria Square, Corporation Street, St. Helens WA10 1HP ☎ 01744 676463 ◌ stuartrainbow@sthelens.gov.uk

Building Control: Mr John Murdock, Principal Building Control Officer, Town Hall, Victoria Square, Corporation Street, St. Helens WA10 1HP ☎ 01744 676241 ◌ johnmurdock@sthelens.gov.uk

Catering Services: Mrs Vikki Atherton, Licensing & Land Charges Officer, 3rd Floor, Wesley House, Corporation Street, St. Helens WA10 1HF ☎ 01744 675326 ◌ vikkiatherton@sthelens.gov.uk

Children / Youth Services: Mr Mike Wyatt, Strategic Director - People's Services, 2nd Floor, Gamble Building, Victoria Square, St. Helens WA10 1DY ☎ 01744 676309 ◌ mikewyatt@sthelens.gov.uk

Civil Registration: Mrs Anne Atherton, Registration Services Manager, Town Hall, Victoria Square, Corporation Street, St. Helens WA10 1HP ☎ 01744 677541 ◌ anneatherton@sthelens.gov.uk

PR / Communications: Mr Nick Cook, Press & Public Relations Manager, Town Hall, Victoria Square, Corporation Street, St. Helens WA10 1HP ☎ 01744 676165 ◌ nickcook@sthelens.gov.uk

Community Safety: Mr Stephen Tracey, Senior Assistant Director - Social Work & Community, Town Hall, Victoria Square, Corporation Street, St. Helens WA10 1HP ☎ 01744 676490 ◌ stephentracey@sthelens.gov.uk

Computer Management: Mr Ste Sharples, ICT Business Manager, Lincoln House, Corporation Street, St. Helens WA9 1LD ☎ 01744 676930 ◌ stesharples@sthelens.gov.uk

Consumer Protection and Trading Standards: Mr Darrell Wilson, Chief Trading Standards Officer, Wesley House, Corporation Street, St. Helens WA10 1HF ☎ 01744 676493 ◌ darrellwilson@sthelens.gov.uk

Corporate Services: Mr Peter Hughes, Governance & City Region Liason, Town Hall, Victoria Square, Corporation Street, St. Helens WA10 1HP ☎ 01744 673209 ◌ peterhughes@sthelens.gov.uk

Customer Service: Mrs Karen Gillis, Customer Relations Manager, Wesley House, Corporation Street, St. Helens WA10 1HF ☎ 01744 676917 ◌ karengillis@sthelens.gov.uk

Direct Labour: Mr Paul Sanderson, Strategic Director - Environmental & Trading Standards, Wesley House, Corporation Street, St. Helens WA10 1HF ☎ 01744 676383 ◌ paulsanderson@sthelens.gov.uk

Economic Development: Mr Steve Berlyne, Funding & Economic Intelligence Manager, Town Hall, Victoria Square, Corporation Street, St. Helens WA10 1HP ☎ 01744 671750 ◌ stevenberlyne@sthelens.gov.uk

Electoral Registration: Mrs Bev Kenrick, Electoral Services Manager, Town Hall, Victoria Square, Corporation Street, St. Helens WA10 1HP ☎ 01744 676140 ◌ bevkenrick@sthelens.gov.uk

Emergency Planning: Mrs Vicky Finch, Risk & Resilience Manager, Town Hall, Victoria Square, Corporation Street, St. Helens WA10 1HP ☎ 01744 674423 ◌ vickyfinch@sthelens.gov.uk

Environmental / Technical Services: Mr Paul Sanderson, Strategic Director - Environmental & Trading Standards, Wesley House, Corporation Street, St. Helens WA10 1HF ☎ 01744 676383 ◌ paulsanderson@sthelens.gov.uk

Environmental Health: Mr Anthony Smith, Chief Environmental Health Officer, Wesley House, Corporation Street, St. Helens WA10 1HF ☎ 01744 676339 ◌ anthonysmith@sthelens.gov.uk

Estates, Property & Valuation: Mr Stephen Littler, Estates Manager, Town Hall, Victoria Square, Corporation Street, St. Helens WA10 1HP ☎ 01744 676789 ◌ stevelittler@sthelens.gov.uk

European Liaison: Mr Steve Berlyne, Funding & Economic Intelligence Manager, Town Hall, Vistoria Square, Corporation Street, St. Helens WA10 1HP ☎ 01744 671750 ◌ stevenberlyne@sthelens.gov.uk

Events Manager: Mrs Suzanne Davies, Strategic Events Officer, Town Hall, Victoria Square, Corporation Street, St. Helens WA10 1HP ☎ 01744 676360 ◌ suzannedavies@sthelens.gov.uk

Facilities: Mr Chris Dove, Public Buildings & Support Services Manager, Town Hall, Victoria Square, Corporation Street, St. Helens WA10 1HP ☎ 01744 676133 ◌ chrisdove@sthelens.gov.uk

Finance: Mr Ian Roberts, Deputy Chief Executive & Strategic Director - Corporate Services, Town Hall, Victoria Square, Corporation Street, St. Helens WA10 1HP ☎ 01744 673201 ◌ ianroberts@sthelens.gov.uk

Finance: Mrs Anne Salisbury, Local Taxation Manager, Wesley House, Corporation Street, St. Helens WA10 1HF ☎ 01744 675249 ◌ annesalisbury@sthelens.gov.uk

Grounds Maintenance: Mr Tim Jones, Civic Pride & Community Spaces Manager, Hardshaw Brook Depot, Parr Street, St. Helens WA9 1JR ☎ 01744 676761 timjones@sthelens.gov.uk

Health and Safety: Mrs June Bracken, Health & Safety Manager, Town Hall, Victoria Square, Corporation Street, St. Helens WA10 1HP ☎ 01744 671722 junebracken@sthelens.gov.uk

Highways: Mr Rory Lingham, Assistant Director - Engineering, Wesley House, Corporation Street, St. Helens WA10 1HF ☎ 01744 676381 rorylingham@sthelens.gov.uk

Housing: Mr Keith Holland, Benefits Manager, Wesley House, Corporation Street, St. Helens WA10 1HF ☎ 01744 674339 keithholland@sthelens.gov.uk

Housing: Mr Stephen Tracey, Senior Assistant Director - Social Work & Community, Atlas House, 2 Corporation Street, St. Helens WA9 1LD ☎ 01744 676490 stephentracey@sthelens.gov.uk

Legal: Mrs Jan Bakewell, Head of Legal Services, Town Hall, Victoria Square, Corporation Street, St. Helens WA10 1HP ☎ 01744 673263 janbakewell@sthelens.gov.uk

Licensing: Mrs Lorraine Simpson, Licensing & Land Charges Officer, Wesley House, Corporation Street, St. Helens WA10 1HF ☎ 01744 675349 lorrainesimpson@sthelens.gov.uk

Lighting: Mr William May, Assistant Head - Asset Management, 4th Floor, Wesley House, Corporation Street, St. Helens WA10 1HP ☎ 01744 676650 williammay@sthelens.gov.uk

Lottery Funding, Charity and Voluntary: Mr Peter Hughes, Governance & City Region Liason, Town Hall, Victoria Square, Corporation Street, St. Helens WA10 1HP ☎ 01744 673209 peterhughes@sthelens.gov.uk

Lottery Funding, Charity and Voluntary: Mr Wayne Traynor, Assistant Treasurer - Accountancy & Financial Management, Town Hall, Victoria Square, Corporation Street, St. Helens WA10 1HP ☎ 01744 673230 waynetraynor@sthelens.gov.uk

Member Services: Mrs Joanne Griffiths, Democratic Services Manager, Town Hall, Victoria Square, Corporation Street, St. Helens WA10 1HP ☎ 01744 676789 joanne.griffiths@sthelens.gov.uk

Parking: Mr Robert McAllister, Parking Services Manager, Town Hall, Victoria Square, Corporation Street, St. Helens WA10 1HP ☎ 01744 676902 bobmcallister@sthelens.gov.uk

Partnerships: Mr Peter Hughes, Governance & City Region Liason, Town Hall, Victoria Square, Corporation Street, St. Helens WA10 1HP ☎ 01744 673209 peterhughes@sthelens.gov.uk

Personnel / HR: Mr Brendan Farrell, Head - Human Resources, Town Hall, Victoria Square, Corporation Street, St. Helens WA10 1HP ☎ 01744 673206 brendanfarrell@sthelens.gov.uk

Procurement: Mr Rob Banks, Corporate Procurement Manager, Town Hall Annexe, Corporation Street, St. Helens WA10 1HP ☎ 01744 676787 robbanks@sthelens.gov.uk

Public Libraries: Mrs Susan Williamson, Head - Library Service, Chester Lane Library, Four Acre Lane, St. Helens WA9 4DE ☎ 01744 677493 susanwilliamson@sthelens.gov.uk

Recycling & Waste Minimisation: Mr Brian Malcolm, Environmental Care Manager, Hardshaw Brook Depot, Parr Street, St. Helens WA9 1JR ☎ 01744 673317 brianmalcolm@sthelens.gov.uk

Regeneration: Mr Mark Dickens, Head - Regeneration, Town Hall, Victoria Square, Corporation Street, St. Helens WA10 1HP ☎ 01744 676606, : 01744 676154 markdickens@sthelens.gov.uk

Social Services (Adult): Mr Mike Wyatt, Strategic Director - People's Services, Gamble Building, Victoria Square, Corporation Street, St. Helens WA10 1DY ☎ 01744 676309 mikewyatt@sthelens.gov.uk

Social Services (Children): Mr Mike Wyatt, Strategic Director - People's Services, 2nd Floor, Gamble Building, Victoria Square, St. Helens WA10 1DY ☎ 01744 676309 mikewyatt@sthelens.gov.uk

Public Health: Mrs Sue Forster, Interim Director - Public Health, Atlas House, Corporation Street, St. Helens WA9 1LD ☎ 01744 673232 susanforster@sthelens.gov.uk

Staff Training: Mr David Broster, Training & Development Manager, Town Hall, Victoria Square, Corporation Street, St. Helens WA10 1HP ☎ 01744 674413 davidbroster@sthelens.gov.uk

Town Centre: Mr Gary Maddocks, Town Centre Manager, Town Hall, Victoria Square, Corporation Street, St. Helens WA10 1HP ☎ 01744 676731 garymaddocks@sthelens.gov.uk

Traffic Management: Mr George Houghton, Head - Traffic Engineering, Wesley House, Corporate Street, St. Helens WA10 1HF ☎ 01744 676380 georgehoughton@sthelens.gov.uk

Transport Planner: Mr David Brown, Transport Officer - Policy, Town Hall, Victoria Square, Corporation Street, St. Helens WA10 1HP ☎ 01744 676512 davidbrown@sthelens.gov.u

Waste Collection and Disposal: Mr Brian Malcolm, Environmental Care Manager, Hardshaw Brook Depot, Parr Street, St. Helens WA9 1JR ☎ 01744 673317 brianmalcolm@sthelens.gov.uk

Waste Management: Mr Brian Malcolm, Environmental Care Manager, Hardshaw Brook Depot, Parr Street, St. Helens WA9 1JR ☎ 01744 673317 brianmalcolm@sthelens.gov.uk

COUNCILLORS

Mayor: Banks, Charles (LAB - Earlestown) cllrcdbanks@sthelens.gov.uk

Leader of the Council: Grunewald, Barrie (LAB - Rainhill) cllrbgrunewald-leader@sthelens.gov.uk

Deputy Leader of the Council: Bowden, Andy (LAB - Parr) cllrabowden@sthelens.gov.uk

Group Leader: Jones, Allan (CON - Rainford) cllrajones@sthelens.gov.uk

Group Leader: Sims, Teresa (LD - Eccleston) cllrsims@sthelens.gov.uk

ST. HELENS

Baines, David (LAB - Windle)

Banks, Jeanette (LAB - Haydock)
cllrjbanks@sthelens.gov.uk

Bell, Jeanie (LAB - Newton-le-Willows)
cllrjbell@sthelens.gov.uk

Bond, Martin (LAB - Haydock)
cllrmbond@sthelens.gov.uk

Burns, Anthony (LAB - Haydock)
cllraburns@sthelens.gov.uk

Charlton, Nova (LAB - Thatto Heath)
cllrncharlton@sthelens.gov.uk

Clarke, Lynn (LAB - Town Centre)
cllrlclarke@sthelens.gov.uk

Cross, Gareth (LAB - Bold)
cllrgcross@sthelens.gov.uk

Cunliffe, Alan (LAB - Blackbrook)
cllracunliffe@sthelens.gov.uk

Deakin, Keith (LAB - Earlestown)
cllrkdeakin@sthelens.gov.uk

De'Asha, Joe (LAB - Rainhill)
cllrde'asha@sthelens.gov.uk

Dyer, Sandra (LAB - Newton-le-Willows)
cllrsdyer@sthelens.gov.uk

Fletcher, Jeffrey (LAB - Moss Bank)
cllrjfletcher@sthelens.gov.uk

Fulham, John (LAB - Moss Bank)
cllrjfulham@sthelens.gov.uk

Gill, Carole (LAB - Town Centre)
cllrcgill@sthelens.gov.uk

Glover, Stephen (LAB - Rainhill)
cllrsglover@sthelens.gov.uk

Glover, Lynn (LAB - Windle)
cllrlglover@sthelens.gov.uk

Gomez-Aspron, Seve (LAB - Newton-le-Willows)
cllrsgomez-aspron@sthelens.gov.uk

Haw, Michael (LD - Eccleston)
cllrmhaw@sthelens.gov.uk

Ireland, Pat (LAB - Thatto Heath)
cllrpireland@sthelens.gov.uk

Jackson, Patricia (LAB - Sutton)
cllrpjackson@sthelens.gov.uk

Jackson, Jimmy (LAB - Sutton)
cllrjjackson@sthelens.gov.uk

Johnson, Anthony (LAB - Bold)
cllrajohnson@sthelens.gov.uk

Johnson, Janet (LAB - Sutton)
cllrjjohnson@sthelens.gov.uk

Long, Derek (LAB - West Park)
cllrdlong@sthelens.gov.uk

Lynch, Paul (LAB - Moss Bank)
cllrplynch@sthelens.gov.uk

Maloney, Linda (LAB - Blackbrook)
cllrlmaloney@sthelens.gov.uk

McCauley, Richard (LAB - Thatto Heath)
cllrmccauley@sthelens.gov.uk

McDonnell, Dennis (LAB - Billinge & Seneley Green)
cllrdmcdonnell@sthelens.gov.uk

McQuade, Paul (LAB - Blackbrook)
cllrpmcquade@sthelens.gov.uk

Murphy, Susan (LAB - Billinge & Seneley Green)
cllrsemurphy@sthelens.gov.uk

Mussell, Linda (CON - Rainford)
cllrlmussell@sthelens.gov.uk

Neal, Gill (LAB - Windle)
cllrgneal@sthelens.gov.uk

Pearl, Geoff (LD - Eccleston)
cllrgpearl@sthelens.gov.uk

Pearson, Joe (LAB - Billinge & Seneley Green)
cllrjpearson@sthelens.gov.uk

Preston, Lisa (LAB - Town Centre)
cllrlpreston@sthelens.gov.uk

Preston, Charlie (LAB - Earlestown)
cllrcpreston@sthelens.gov.uk

Pritchard, Paul (LAB - West Park)
cllrppritchard@sthelens.gov.uk

Quinn, Marlene (LAB - West Park)
cllrmquinn@sthelens.gov.uk

Reynolds, Rob (CON - Rainford)
cllrrreynolds@sthelens.gov.uk

Roberts, Keith (LAB - Parr)
cllrkroberts@sthelens.gov.uk

Shields, Terry (LAB - Parr)
cllrtshields@sthelens.gov.uk

Wiseman, John (LAB -)
cllrjwiseman@sthelens.gov.uk

POLITICAL COMPOSITION
LAB: 42, LD: 3, CON: 3

COMMITTEE CHAIRS

Audit: Mr Barrie Grunewald

Children & Young People's Services: Mrs Lynn Glover

Health & Adult Social Care: Mr Joe Pearson

Licensing: Ms Jeanette Banks

Planning: Mr Stephen Glover

Stafford   D

Stafford Borough Council, Civic Centre, Riverside, Stafford
ST16 3AQ
☎ 01785 619000 ✆ info@staffordbc.gov.uk 🖵 www.staffordbc.gov.uk

FACTS AND FIGURES
Parliamentary Constituencies: Stafford, Stone
EU Constituencies: West Midlands
Election Frequency: Elections are of whole council

PRINCIPAL OFFICERS

Chief Executive: Mr Tim Clegg, Chief Executive, Civic Centre,
Riverside, Stafford ST16 3AQ ☎ 01785 619200
✆ timclegg@staffordbc.gov.uk

Senior Management: Ms Judith Aupers, Head of Governance, Civic Centre, Riverside, Stafford ST16 3AQ ☎ 01543 454411 ⏚ judithaupers@cannockchase.gov.uk

Senior Management: Mr Adam Hill, Head of Leisure & Culture, Civic Centre, Riverside, Stafford ST16 3AQ ☎ 01785 619299 ⏚ amhill@staffordbc.gov.uk

Senior Management: Mr Norman Jones, Head of Policy & Improvement, Civic Centre, Riverside, Stafford ST16 3AQ ☎ 01785 619199 ⏚ npjones@staffordbc.gov.uk

Senior Management: Mr Bob Kean, Deputy Managing Director & Head of Finance, Civic Centre, PO Box 28, Cannock WS11 1BG ☎ 01543 464334 ⏚ bobkeane@cannockchasedc.gov.uk

Senior Management: Mr Peter Kendrick, Head of Technology, Civic Centre, Riverside, Stafford ST16 3AQ ☎ 01785 619274 ⏚ pkendrick@staffordbc.gov.uk

Senior Management: Mr Richard Lawrence, Head of Development & Planning, Civic Centre, Riverside, Stafford ST16 3AQ ☎ 01785 619583 ⏚ rlawrence@staffordbc.gov.uk

Senior Management: Mr Neville Raby, Head of Human Resources & Property Services, Civic Centre, Riverside, Stafford ST16 3AQ ☎ 01785 619205 ⏚ nraby@staffordbc.gov.uk

Senior Management: Mr Howard Thomas, Head of Environment, Civic Centre, Riverside, Stafford ST16 3AQ ☎ 01785 619358 ⏚ hthomas@staffordbc.gov.uk

Senior Management: Mr Alistair Welch, Head of Law & Administration, Civic Centre, Riverside, Stafford ST16 3AQ ☎ 01785 619204 ⏚ awelch@staffordbc.gov.uk

Architect, Building / Property Services: Mr Jim Davis, Property Services Manager, Civic Centre, Riverside, Stafford ST16 3AQ ☎ 01785 619395 ⏚ jdavis@staffordbc.gov.uk

Best Value: Mr Norman Jones, Head of Policy & Improvement, Civic Centre, Riverside, Stafford ST16 3AQ ☎ 01785 619199 ⏚ npjones@staffordbc.gov.uk

Building Control: Mr Paul Beckley, Building Control Manager, Stafford Borough Council, Civic Centre, Riverside, Stafford ST16 3AQ ☎ 01785 619311 ⏚ paulbeckley@cannockchasedc.gov.uk

PR / Communications: Mr Will Conaghan, Press & Communications Manager, Civic Centre, Riverside, Stafford ST16 3AQ ☎ 01785 619230 ⏚ wjconghan@staffordbc.gov.uk

Community Planning: Mr Norman Jones, Head of Policy & Improvement, Civic Centre, Riverside, Stafford ST16 3AQ ☎ 01785 619199 ⏚ npjones@staffordbc.gov.uk

Community Safety: Mr Norman Jones, Head of Policy & Improvement, Civic Centre, Riverside, Stafford ST16 3AQ ☎ 01785 619199 ⏚ npjones@staffordbc.gov.uk

Computer Management: Mr Peter Kendrick, Head of Technology, Stafford Borough Council, Civic Centre, Riverside, Stafford ST16 3AQ ☎ 01785 619274 ⏚ pkendrick@stafford.gov.uk

Contracts: Mr Jim Davis, Property Services Manager, Civic Centre, Riverside, Stafford ST16 3AQ ☎ 01785 619395 ⏚ jdavis@staffordbc.gov.uk

Customer Service: Mr Norman Jones, Head of Policy & Improvement, Civic Centre, Riverside, Stafford ST16 3AQ ☎ 01785 619199 ⏚ npjones@staffordbc.gov.uk

Economic Development: Mr Ted Manders, Head of Planning & Regeneration, Civic Centre, Riverside, Stafford ST16 3AQ ☎ 01785 619583 ⏚ tmanders@staffordbc.gov.uk

E-Government: Mr Peter Kendrick, Head of Technology, Stafford Borough Council, Civic Centre, Riverside, Stafford ST16 3AQ ☎ 01785 619274 ⏚ pkendrick@stafford.gov.uk

Electoral Registration: Mrs Jane Peat, Electoral Services Manager, Civic Centre, Riverside, Stafford ST16 3AQ ☎ 01785 619424 ⏚ jpeat@staffordbc.gov.uk

Emergency Planning: Mr Ian Thompson, Chief Executive, Civic Centre, Riverside, Stafford ST16 3AQ ☎ 01785 619200 ⏚ ianthompson@staffordbc.gov.uk

Energy Management: Mr Ted Manders, Head of Planning & Regeneration, Civic Centre, Riverside, Stafford ST16 3AQ ☎ 01785 619583 ⏚ tmanders@staffordbc.gov.uk

Environmental / Technical Services: Mr Howard Thomas, Head of Environment, Civic Centre, Riverside, Stafford ST16 3AQ ☎ 01785 619358 ⏚ hthomas@staffordbc.gov.uk

Environmental Health: Mr Howard Thomas, Head of Environment, Civic Centre, Riverside, Stafford ST16 3AQ ☎ 01785 619358 ⏚ hthomas@staffordbc.gov.uk

Estates, Property & Valuation: Mr Jim Davis, Property Services Manager, Civic Centre, Riverside, Stafford ST16 3AQ ☎ 01785 619395 ⏚ jdavis@staffordbc.gov.uk

Events Manager: Ms Liz Hulse, Events Manager, Civic Centre, Riverside, Stafford ST16 3AQ ☎ 01785 619300 ⏚ lhulse@staffordbc.gov.uk

Facilities: Mr Jim Davis, Property Services Manager, Civic Centre, Riverside, Stafford ST16 3AQ ☎ 01785 619395 ⏚ jdavis@staffordbc.gov.uk

Finance: Mr Bob Kean, Deputy Managing Director & Head of Finance, Civic Centre, PO Box 28, Cannock WS11 1BG ☎ 01543 464334 ⏚ bobkeane@cannockchasedc.gov.uk

Grounds Maintenance: Mr Phil Gammon, Head of Operational Services, Civic Centre, Riverside, Stafford ST16 3AQ ☎ 01785 619108 ⏚ pgammon@staffordbc.gov.uk

STAFFORD

Health and Safety: Mr Neville Raby, Head of Human Resources & Property Services, Civic Centre, Riverside, Stafford ST16 3AQ ☎ 01785 619205 ~ nraby@staffordbc.gov.uk

Legal: Mr Alistair Welch, Head of Law & Administration, Civic Centre, Riverside, Stafford ST16 3AQ ☎ 01785 619204 ~ awelch@staffordbc.gov.uk

Leisure and Cultural Services: Mr Adam Hill, Head of Leisure & Culture, Civic Centre, Riverside, Stafford ST16 3AQ ☎ 01785 619299 ~ amhill@staffordbc.gov.uk

Lottery Funding, Charity and Voluntary: Mr Norman Jones, Head of Policy & Improvement, Civic Centre, Riverside, Stafford ST16 3AQ ☎ 01785 619199 ~ npjones@staffordbc.gov.uk

Member Services: Mr Alistair Welch, Head of Law & Administration, Civic Centre, Riverside, Stafford ST16 3AQ ☎ 01785 619204 ~ awelch@staffordbc.gov.uk

Parking: Mr Steve Allen, Car Parking Manager, Civic Centre, Riverside, Stafford ST16 3AQ ☎ 01785 619071 ~ sallen@staffordbc.gov.uk

Partnerships: Mr Norman Jones, Head of Policy & Improvement, Civic Centre, Riverside, Stafford ST16 3AQ ☎ 01785 619199 ~ npjones@staffordbc.gov.uk

Personnel / HR: Mr Neville Raby, Head of Human Resources & Property Services, Civic Centre, Riverside, Stafford ST16 3AQ ☎ 01785 619205 ~ nraby@staffordbc.gov.uk

Planning: Mr John Holmes, Development Control Manager, Civic Centre, Riverside, Stafford ST16 3AQ ☎ 01785 619302 ~ jholmes@staffordbc.gov.uk

Recycling & Waste Minimisation: Mr Mark Street, Environmental Health Manager, Civic Centre, Riverside, Stafford ST16 3AQ ☎ 01785 619390 ~ mstreet@staffordbc.gov.uk

Regeneration: Mr Ted Manders, Head of Planning & Regeneration, Civic Centre, Riverside, Stafford ST16 3AQ ☎ 01785 619583 ~ tmanders@staffordbc.gov.uk

Staff Training: Mr Neville Raby, Head of Human Resources & Property Services, Civic Centre, Riverside, Stafford ST16 3AQ ☎ 01785 619205 ~ nraby@staffordbc.gov.uk

Street Scene: Mr Phil Gammon, Head of Operational Services, Civic Centre, Riverside, Stafford ST16 3AQ ☎ 01785 619108 ~ pgammon@staffordbc.gov.uk

Sustainable Communities: Mr Ian Thompson, Chief Executive, Civic Centre, Riverside, Stafford ST16 3AQ ☎ 01785 619200 ~ ianthompson@staffordbc.gov.uk

Sustainable Development: Ms Karen Davies, Climate Change & Sustainable Development Co-ordinator, Civic Centre, Riverside, Stafford ST16 3AQ ☎ 01785 619408 ~ kdavies@staffordbc.gov.uk

Tourism: Ms Lisa Heaton, Tourism, Heritage & Visitor Services Manager, Civic Centre, Riverside, Stafford ST16 3AQ ☎ 01785 619348 ~ lheaton@staffordbc.gov.uk

Town Centre: Mr Ted Manders, Head of Planning & Regeneration, Civic Centre, Riverside, Stafford ST16 3AQ ☎ 01785 619583 ~ tmanders@staffordbc.gov.uk

Waste Collection and Disposal: Mr Mark Street, Environmental Health Manager, Civic Centre, Riverside, Stafford ST16 3AQ ☎ 01785 619390 ~ mstreet@staffordbc.gov.uk

Waste Collection and Disposal: Mr Howard Thomas, Head of Environment, Civic Centre, Riverside, Stafford ST16 3AQ ☎ 01785 619358 ~ hthomas@staffordbc.gov.uk

Waste Management: Mr Howard Thomas, Head of Environment, Civic Centre, Riverside, Stafford ST16 3AQ ☎ 01785 619358 ~ hthomas@staffordbc.gov.uk

COUNCILLORS

Mayor: Loughran, Angela (LAB - Manor)
aloughran@staffordbc.gov.uk

Leader of the Council: Farrington, Patrick (CON - Baswich)
pfarrington@staffordbc.gov.uk

Deputy Leader of the Council: Smith, Mike (CON - Gnosall & Woodseaves)
rmsmith@staffordbc.gov.uk

Bakker-Collier, Lynne (CON - St Michael's & Stonefield)
lbakker-collier@staffordbc.gov.uk

Baron, Christine (IND - Forebridge)
cabaron@staffordbc.gov.uk

Barron, Jenny (CON - Weeping Cross & Wildwood)
jbarron@staffordbc.gov.uk

Barron, Ray (CON - Weeping Cross & Wildwood)
rbarron@staffordbc.gov.uk

Beatty, Frances (CON - Milwich)
fbeatty@staffordbc.gov.uk

Bowen, Maureen (LAB - Highfields & Western Downs)
mbowen@staffordbc.gov.uk

Collier, Geoffrey (CON - St Michael's & Stonefield)
gcollier@staffordbc.gov.uk

Cooke, Ralph (LAB - Penkside)
rcooke@staffordbc.gov.uk

Cross, Bryan (CON - Holmcroft)
bcross@staffordbc.gov.uk

Davies, Isabella (CON - Doxey & Castletown)
iedavies@staffordbc.gov.uk

Dodson, Michael (CON - Fulford)
mdodson@staffordbc.gov.uk

Draper, Rowan (LAB - Littleworth)
rdraper@staffordbc.gov.uk

Edgeller, Ann (CON - Baswich)
aedgeller@staffordbc.gov.uk

Farnham, Joyce (CON - St Michael's & Stonefield)
jfarnham@staffordbc.gov.uk

STAFFORDSHIRE

Finlay, Francis (CON - Milford)
ffinlay@staffordbc.gov.uk

Godfrey, Aidan (LAB - Common)
agodfrey@staffordbc.gov.uk

Goodall, Margaret (CON - Walton)
mgoodall@staffordbc.gov.uk

Harp, Andrew (CON - Milwich)
aharp@staffordbc.gov.uk

Hood, Jill (IND - Walton)
jhood@staffordbc.gov.uk

James, Roy (CON - Swynnerton & Oulton)
rjames@staffordbc.gov.uk

Jennings, Mary (CON - Littleworth)
mjennings@staffordbc.gov.uk

Jones, Peter (CON - Eccleshall)
pjones@staffordbc.gov.uk

Jones, Gareth (CON - Barlaston)
ejones@staffordbc.gov.uk

Kemp, William (LAB - Coton)
jkemp@staffordbc.gov.uk

Learoyd, Stewart (CON - Haywood & Hixon)
slearoyd@staffordbc.gov.uk

Leighton, Stephen (CON - Seighford & Church Eaton)
sleighton@staffordbc.gov.uk

Nixon, Louise (LAB - Coton)
lnixon@staffordbc.gov.uk

O'Connor, Stephen (LAB - Highfields & Western Downs)
soconnor@staffordbc.gov.uk

Perkins, Alan (CON - Haywood & Hixon)
aperkins@staffordbc.gov.uk

Pert, Jeremy (CON - Eccleshall)
jpert@staffordbc.gov.uk

Price, Brian (CON - Swynnerton & Oulton)
dprice@staffordbc.gov.uk

Price, Jonathan (CON - Holmcroft)
jprice@staffordbc.gov.uk

Rowlands, Geoffrey (LAB - Manor)
growlands@staffordbc.gov.uk

Roycroft, Peter (CON - Fulford)
proycroft@staffordbc.gov.uk

Sutherland, Raymond (CON - Seighford & Church Eaton)
rsutherland@staffordbc.gov.uk

Trowbridge, Carolyn (CON - Rowley)
ctrowbridge@staffordbc.gov.uk

Williamson, Kenneth (CON - Gnosall & Woodseaves)
kwilliamson@staffordbc.gov.uk

POLITICAL COMPOSITION
CON: 29, LAB: 9, IND: 2

COMMITTEE CHAIRS
Audit: Mrs Angela Loughran

Licensing: Mr Alan Perkins

Planning: Mr Bryan Cross

Staffordshire   C

Staffordshire County Council, Number 1, Staffordshire Place, Stafford ST16 2LP
☎ 0300 111 8000 ⏁ contactus@staffordshire.gov.uk
🖥 www.staffordshire.gov.uk

FACTS AND FIGURES
Parliamentary Constituencies: Cannock Chase, Lichfield, Staffordshire South
EU Constituencies: West Midlands
Election Frequency: Elections are of whole council

PRINCIPAL OFFICERS

Chief Executive: Mr John Henderson, Chief Executive, Number 1, Staffordshire Place, Stafford ST16 2LP ☎ 01785 276100
⏁ john.henderson@staffordshire.gov.uk

Deputy Chief Executive: Mrs Helen Riley, Deputy Chief Executive & Director - Families & Communities, Number 1, Staffordshire Place, Stafford ST16 2LP ☎ 01785 277000
⏁ helen.riley@staffordshire.gov.uk

Senior Management: Mr Andrew Burns, Director - Finance & Resources, Number 1, Staffordshire Place, Stafford ST16 2LP
☎ 01785 276302 ⏁ andrew.burns@staffordshire.gov.uk

Senior Management: Mr Darryl Eyers, Director - Economy, Infrastructure & Skills, Number 1, Staffordshire Place, Stafford ST16 2LP ☎ 01785 378580 ⏁ darryl.eyers@staffordshire.gov.uk

Senior Management: Dr Richard Harling, Director - Health & Care, Number 1, Staffordshire Place, Stafford ST16 2LP
☎ 01785 278700 ⏁ richard.harling@staffordshire.gov.uk

Senior Management: Mrs Helen Riley, Deputy Chief Executive & Director - Families & Communities, Number 1, Staffordshire Place, Stafford ST16 2LP ☎ 01785 277000
⏁ helen.riley@staffordshire.gov.uk

Senior Management: Mr John Tradewell, Director - Strategy, Governance & Change, Number 1, Staffordshire Place, Stafford ST16 2LP ☎ 01785 276102 ⏁ john.tradwell@staffordshire.gov.uk

Access Officer / Social Services (Disability): Ms Wendy Woodward, Accountable Lead - Independent Futures, Wedgewood Building, Tipping Street, Stafford ST16 2DH ☎ 01785 895428
⏁ wendy.woodward@staffordshire.gov.uk

Architect, Building / Property Services: Mr Jamie MacDonald, Head of Strategic Property, Number 1, Staffordshire Place, Stafford ST16 2LP ☎ 01785 277508 ⏁ jamie.macdonald@staffordshire.gov.uk

Catering Services: Ms Joanne Hand, Catering Manager, County Buildings, Martin Street, Stafford ST16 2LH ☎ 01785 276030
⏁ joanne.hand@staffordshire.gov.uk

Civil Registration: Ms Hannah Cotton-Diederich, Registration Service Manager, Number 2, Staffordshire Place, Tipping Street, Stafford ST16 2DH ☎ 01785 277245
⏁ hannah.cotton-diederich@staffordshire.gov.uk

STAFFORDSHIRE

Community Safety: Mr Michael Harrison, Commissioner for Safety, Wedgewood Building, Tipping Street, Stafford ST16 2DH
☎ 01785 278163 ⌨ michael.harrison@staffordshire.gov.uk

Computer Management: Mr Vic Falcus, Head of ICT Service Management, Number 1, Staffordshire Place, Stafford ST16 2LP
☎ 01785 278032 ⌨ vic.falcus@staffordshire.gov.uk

Consumer Protection and Trading Standards: Ms Trish Caldwell, Business Support Manager, Number 1, Staffordshire Place, Stafford ST16 2LP ☎ 01785 277804 ⌨ trish.caldwell@staffordshire.gov.uk

Contracts: Mr Jon Waller, Head of Financial Strategy & Support, Number 2, Staffordshire Place, Tipping Street, Stafford ST16 2DH
☎ 01785 276380 ⌨ jon.waller@staffordshire.gov.uk

Customer Service: Ms Dionne Lowndes, Head of Customer Services, Number 2, Staffordshire Place, Tipping Street, Stafford ST16 2DH ☎ 01785 854236 ⌨ dionne.lowndes@staffordshire.gov.uk

Economic Development: Mr Mark Parkinson, Economic Development & Planning Policy Manager, Number 1, Staffordshire Place, Stafford ST16 2LP ☎ 01785 276807
⌨ mark.parkinson@staffordshire.gov.uk

Education: Mr Chris Kiernan, Interim Commissioner for Education, Wedgewood Building, Tipping Street, Stafford ST16 2DH
☎ 01785 277828 ⌨ chris.kiernan@staffordshire.gov.uk

Emergency Planning: Ms Beth Morgan, Director - Staffordshire Civil Contingencies Unit, Staffordshire Fire Station, Beaconside, Stafford ST18 0DD ☎ 01785 898608 ⌨ ccu@staffordshirefire.gov.uk

Energy Management: Mr Lee Wells, Senior Land & Property Information Officer, Number 2, Staffordshire Place, Tipping Street, Stafford ST16 2DH ☎ 01785 277732
⌨ lee.wells@staffordshire.gov.uk

Estates, Property & Valuation: Mr Kevin Danks, Estates & Valuation Manager, Number 2, Staffordshire Place, Tipping Street, Stafford ST16 2DH ☎ 01785 277702
⌨ kevin.danks@staffordshire.gov.uk

European Liaison: Mr Nigel Senior, Group Manager - Economic Development, Number 1, Staffordshire Place, Stafford ST16 2LP
☎ 01785 277365 ⌨ nigel.senior@staffordshire.gov.uk

Facilities: Mr Craig Morris, FM & Business Manager, Number 1, Staffordshire Place, Stafford ST16 2LP ☎ 01785 277516
⌨ craig.morris@entrust-ed.co.uk

Finance: Mr Andrew Burns, Director - Finance & Resources, Number 1, Staffordshire Place, Stafford ST16 2LP ☎ 01785 276302
⌨ andrew.burns@staffordshire.gov.uk

Pensions: Ms Janet Caiazzo, Pensions Manager, Number 2, Staffordshire Place, Tipping Street, Stafford ST16 2DH
☎ 01785 276441 ⌨ janet.caiazzo@staffordshire.gov.uk

Pensions: Ms Melanie Stokes, Strategic Investment Manager, Number 2, Staffordshire Place, Tipping Street, Stafford ST16 2DH
☎ 01785 276330 ⌨ melanie.stokes@staffordshire.gov.uk

Fleet Management: Mr Michael Simmonds, Group Manager - Fleetcare & Print Commissioning, Beacon Business Park, Weston Road, Stafford ST18 0WL ☎ 01785 854821
⌨ michael.simmonds@staffordshire.gov.uk

Grounds Maintenance: Ms Michelle Ryan, Head of Operations - Cleaning & Grounds Services, Kingston Centre, Fairway, Stafford ST16 3TW ☎ 01785 277640 ⌨ michelle.ryan@entrust-ed.co.uk

Health and Safety: Mrs Becky Lee, Health, Safety & Wellbeing Manager, Number 1, Staffordshire Place, Stafford ST16 2LP
☎ 01785 276846 ⌨ becky.lee@staffordshire.gov.uk

Highways: Mr James Bailey, Commissioner for Highways & the Built Country, Number 1, Staffordshire Place, Stafford ST16 2LP
☎ 01785 276591 ⌨ james.bailey@staffordshire.gov.uk

Local Area Agreement: Mr Andrew Donaldson, Strategic Policy & Partnerships Manager, Number 1, Staffordshire Place, Stafford ST16 2LP ☎ 01785 278399
⌨ andrew.donaldson@staffordshire.gov.uk

Legal: Mr John Tradewell, Director - Strategy, Governance & Change, Number 1, Staffordshire Place, Stafford ST16 2LP
☎ 01785 276102 ⌨ john.tradwell@staffordshire.gov.uk

Leisure and Cultural Services: Mrs Janene Cox, Commissioner for Tourism & the Cultural County, Number 1, Staffordshire Place, Stafford ST16 2LP ☎ 01785 278368
⌨ janene.cox@staffordshire.gov.uk

Lifelong Learning: Mr Anthony Baines, County Commissioner for Skills & Employability, Wedgewood Building, Tipping Street, Stafford ST16 2DH ☎ 01785 278774
⌨ anthony.baines@staffordshire.gov.uk

Lighting: Mr Glynn Hook, Principal Lighting Engineer, Staffordshire Place, Tipping Street, Stafford ST16 2DH ☎ 01785 276561
⌨ glynn.hook@staffordshire.gov.uk

Member Services: Ms Ann-Marie Davidson, Head of Member & Democratic Services, County Buildings, Martin Street, Stafford ST16 2LH ☎ 01785 276131 ⌨ ann-marie.davidson@staffordshire.gov.uk

Parking: Mr David Walters, Regulation & Governance Manager, Number 1, Staffordshire Place, Stafford ST16 2LP ☎ 01785 854024
⌨ david.walters@staffordshire.gov.uk

Partnerships: Mr Andrew Donaldson, Strategic Policy & Partnerships Manager, Number 1, Staffordshire Place, Stafford ST16 2LP ☎ 01785 278399 ⌨ andrew.donaldson@staffordshire.gov.uk

Personnel / HR: Ms Lisa Cartwright, Head of Human Resources, Number 1, Staffordshire Place, Stafford ST16 2LP ☎ 01785 278188
⌨ lisa.cartwright@staffordshire.gov.uk

Planning: Mr Mike Grundy, Planning, Policy & Development Control Manager, Number 2, Staffordshire Place, Tipping Street, Stafford ST16 2DH ☎ 01785 277297
⌨ mike.grundy@staffordshire.gov.uk

Procurement: Mr Ian Turner, Head of Commercial, Number 2, Staffordshire Place, Tipping Street, Stafford ST16 2DH ☎ 01785 277228 ⌁ ian.turner@staffordshire.gov.uk

Public Libraries: Mrs Janene Cox, Commissioner for Tourism & the Cultural County, Number 1, Staffordshire Place, Stafford ST16 2LP ☎ 01785 278368 ⌁ janene.cox@staffordshire.gov.uk

Recycling & Waste Minimisation: Ms Sally Talbot, Group Manager - Waste Management & Environmental Projects, Number 1, Staffordshire Place, Stafford ST16 2LP ☎ 01785 276227 ⌁ sally.talbot@staffordshire.gov.uk

Regeneration: Mr John Flynn, Physical Regeneration Group Manager, Number 1, Staffordshire Place, Stafford ST16 2LP ☎ 01785 277707 ⌁ john.flynn@staffordshire.gov.uk

Road Safety: Ms Melanie Langdown, Performance & Operations Manager, 18 Garnet House, Wolseley Court, Staffordshire Technology Park, Stafford ST18 0GA ☎ 0300 111 8012 ⌁ melanie.langdown@staffordshire.gov.uk

Social Services (Adult): Dr Richard Harling, Director - Health & Care, Number 1, Staffordshire Place, Stafford ST16 2LP ☎ 01785 278700 ⌁ richard.harling@staffordshire.gov.uk

Social Services (Children): Mrs Helen Riley, Deputy Chief Executive & Director - Families & Communities, Number 1, Staffordshire Place, Stafford ST16 2LP ☎ 01785 277000 ⌁ helen.riley@staffordshire.gov.uk

Public Health: Dr Richard Harling, Director - Health & Care, Number 1, Staffordshire Place, Stafford ST16 2LP ☎ 01785 278700 ⌁ richard.harling@staffordshire.gov.uk

Staff Training: Ms Danielle Ware, Strategic Lead for Learning & Development, Number 1, Staffordshire Place, Stafford ST16 2LP ☎ 01785 895211 ⌁ danielle.ware@staffordshire.gov.uk

Sustainable Development: Mr Ian Benson, Commissioner for the Sustainable County, Number 1, Staffordshire Place, Stafford ST16 2LP ☎ 01785 276550 ⌁ ian.benson@staffordshire.gov.uk

Tourism: Mr Grame Whitehead, Tourism & Marketing Team Leader, Number 1, Staffordshire Place, Stafford ST16 2LP ☎ 01785 277335 ⌁ grame.whitehead@staffordshire.gov.uk

Traffic Management: Mr Nick Dawson, Connectivity Strategy Manager, Number 1, Staffordshire Place, Stafford ST16 2LP ☎ 01785 276629 ⌁ nick.dawson@staffordshire.gov.uk

Transport: Mr Clive Thomson, Commissioner for Transport & the Connected County, Number 1, Staffordshire Place, Stafford ST16 2LP ☎ 01785 276522 ⌁ clive.thomson@staffordshire.gov.uk

Transport Planner: Mr Nick Dawson, Connectivity Strategy Manager, Number 1, Staffordshire Place, Stafford ST16 2LP ☎ 01785 276629 ⌁ nick.dawson@staffordshire.gov.uk

Waste Management: Ms Sally Talbot, Group Manager - Waste Management & Environmental Projects, Number 1, Staffordshire Place, Stafford ST16 2LP ☎ 01785 276227 ⌁ sally.talbot@staffordshire.gov.uk

COUNCILLORS

Chair: Eagland, Janet (CON - Lichfield - Lichfield Rural North) janet.eagland@staffordshire.gov.uk

Vice-Chair: Fraser, Bob (CON - East Staffordshire - Dove) bob.fraser@staffordshire.gov.uk

Leader of the Council: Atkins, Philip (CON - East Staffordshire - Uttoxeter Rural) philip.atkins@staffordshire.gov.uk

Deputy Leader of the Council: Parry, Ian (CON - Stafford - Stone Rural) ian.parry@staffordshire.gov.uk

Group Leader: Cooke, Chris (IND - Tamworth - Stoneydelph) chris.cooke@staffordshire.gov.uk

Group Leader: Woodward, Susan (LAB - Lichfield - Burntwood North) susan.woodward@staffordshire.gov.uk

Adams, Ben (CON - Tamworth - Perrycrofts) ben.adams@staffordshire.gov.uk

Adamson, George (LAB - Cannock Chase - Hednesford & Rawnsley) george.adamson@staffordshire.gov.uk

Astle, Margaret (LAB - Newcastle - Kidsgrove) margaret.astle@staffordshire.gov.uk

Atkins, Charlotte (LAB - Staffordshire Moorlands - Leek South) charlotte.atkins@staffordshire.gov.uk

Beech, Ann (LAB - Newcastle - Audley & Chesterton) ann.beech@staffordshire.gov.uk

Bloomer, Len (CON - Stafford - Stafford Trent Valley) leonard.bloomer@staffordshire.gov.uk

Brookes, David (CON - East Staffordshire - Uttoxeter Town) david.brookes@staffordshire.gov.uk

Chapman, Frank (CON - Stafford - Eccleshall) frank.chapman@staffordshire.gov.uk

Clarke, Ron (LAB - East Staffordshire - Burton Town) ron.clarke@staffordshire.gov.uk

Compton, Maureen (LAB - Stafford - Stafford Central) maureen.compton@staffordshire.gov.uk

Corbett, Tim (CON - East Staffordshire - Needwood Forest) timothy.corbett@staffordshire.gov.uk

Davies, Mike (CON - South Staffordshire - Wombourne) mike.davies@staffordshire.gov.uk

Davies, Peter (LAB - East Staffordshire - Burton Trent) peter.davies@staffordshire.gov.uk

Davis, Derek (LAB - Cannock Chase - Chadsmoor) derek.davis@staffordshire.gov.uk

Day, William (IND - Staffordshire Moorlands - Caverswall) william.day@staffordshire.gov.uk

Dean, Carol (LAB - Tamworth - Bolebridge) carol.dean@staffordshire.gov.uk

Deaville, Mark (CON - Staffordshire Moorlands - Cheadle & Checkley) mark.deaville@staffordshire.gov.uk

Dudson, Alan (LAB - Cannock Chase - Brereton & Ravenhill) alan.dudson@staffordshire.gov.uk

Edwards, Brian (CON - South Staffordshire - Kinver) brian.edwards@staffordshire.gov.uk

STAFFORDSHIRE

Finn, Terry (CON - Lichfield - Lichfield City South)
terence.finn@staffordshire.gov.uk

Francis, John (CON - Stafford - Stafford South East)
john.francis@staffordshire.gov.uk

Greatorex, Michaeal (CON - Tamworth - Watling South)
michael.greatorex@staffordshire.gov.uk

Hambleton, Sandra (LAB - Newcastle - Bradwell, Porthill & Wolstanton)
sandra.hambleton@staffordshire.gov.uk

Heath, Gill (CON - Staffordshire Moorlands - Leek Rural)
gill.heath@staffordshire.gov.uk

Hollinshead, Ian (IND - Stafford - Stafford North)
ian.hollinshead@staffordshire.gov.uk

Huckfield, Derrick (IND - Newcastle - Keele, Knutton & Silverdale)
derrick.huckfield@staffordshire.gov.uk

Jackson, Kevin (LAB - Staffordshire Moorlands - Biddulph South & Endon)
kevin.jackson@staffordshire.gov.uk

James, Keith (CON - South Staffordshire - Perton)
keith.james@staffordshire.gov.uk

Jenkins, Brian (LAB - Tamworth - Watling North)
brian.jenkins@staffordshire.gov.uk

Jones, Philip (CON - Stafford - Stone Urban)
philip.e.jones@staffordshire.gov.uk

Lawrence, Mike (CON - South Staffordshire - Cheslyn Hay, Essington & Great Wyrley)
michael.lawrence@staffordshire.gov.uk

Lawson, Ian (CON - Staffordshire Moorlands - Biddulph North)
ian.lawson@staffordshire.gov.uk

Loades, David (CON - Newcastle - Newcastle Rural)
david.loades@staffordshire.gov.uk

Marshall, Robert (CON - South Staffordshire - Codsall)
robert.marshall@staffordshire.gov.uk

Martin, Geoffrey (CON - Cannock Chase - Etchinghill & Heath)
geoffrey.martin@staffordshire.gov.uk

McKiernan, Shelagh (LAB - East Staffordshire - Horninglow & Stretton)
shelagh.mckiernan@staffordshire.gov.uk

Mitchell, Christine (LAB - Cannock Chase - Hednesford & Rawnsley)
christine.mitchell@staffordshire.gov.uk

Olszweski, Mark (LAB - Newcastle - May Bank & Cross Heath)
mark.olszweski@staffordshire.gov.uk

Peaple, Sheree (LAB - Tamworth - Amington)
sheree.peaple@staffordshire.gov.uk

Perry, Kath (CON - South Staffordshire - Cheslyn Hay, Essington & Great Wyrley)
kathleen.perry@staffordshire.gov.uk

Rowlands, Trish (LAB - Stafford - Stafford West)
trish.rowlands@staffordshire.gov.uk

Sheriff, Jeff (UKIP - Lichfield - Burntwood South)
jeffrey.sheriff@staffordshire.gov.uk

Smith, David (CON - Lichfield - Lichfield Rural South)
david.smith@staffordshire.gov.uk

Spicer, Alison (LAB - Cannock Chase - Cannock Town Centre)
alison.spicer@staffordshire.gov.uk

Sutton, Mark (CON - South Staffordshire - Brewood)
mark.sutton@staffordshire.gov.uk

Sweeney, Stephen (CON - Newcastle - Newcastle South)
stephen.sweeney@staffordshire.gov.uk

Tagg, Simon (CON - Newcastle - Westlands & Thistleberry)
simon.tagg@staffordshire.gov.uk

Taylor, John (LAB - Newcastle - Talke & Red Street)
john.taylor@staffordshire.gov.uk

Tittley, Martyn (CON - Lichfield - Lichfield Rural West)
martyn.tittley@staffordshire.gov.uk

Todd, Dianne (LAB - Cannock Chase - Cannock Villages)
dianne.todd@staffordshire.gov.uk

White, Alan (CON - Lichfield - Lichfield Rural East)
alan.white@staffordshire.gov.uk

Wileman, Conor (CON - East Staffordshire - Burton Tower)
conor.wileman@staffordshire.gov.uk

Williams, David (CON - South Staffordshire - Penkridge)
david.williams2@staffordshire.gov.uk

Winnington, Mark (CON - Stafford - Gnosall & Doxey)
mark.winnington@staffordshire.gov.uk

Wood, Caroline (LAB - Lichfield - Lichfield City North)
caroline.wood@staffordshire.gov.uk

Worthington, Mike (CON - Staffordshire Moorlands - Churnet Valley)
mike.worthington@staffordshire.gov.uk

POLITICAL COMPOSITION
CON: 34, LAB: 23, IND: 4, UKIP: 1

COMMITTEE CHAIRS

Audit: Mr Martyn Tittley

Pensions: Mr Mike Lawrence

Planning: Mr Tim Corbett

Staffordshire Moorlands   D

Staffordshire Moorlands District Council, Moorlands House, Stockwell Street, Leek ST13 6HQ
☎ 01538 395400 🖷 01538 395474 ◌ info@staffsmoorlands.gov.uk
🖳 www.staffsmoorlands.gov.uk

FACTS AND FIGURES
Parliamentary Constituencies: Staffordshire Moorlands, Stoke-on-Trent North, Stone
EU Constituencies: West Midlands
Election Frequency: Elections are of whole council

PRINCIPAL OFFICERS

Chief Executive: Mr Simon Baker, Chief Executive, Moorlands House, Stockwell Street, Leek ST13 6HQ ☎ 01538 395400
◌ simon.baker@staffsmoorlands.gov.uk;
simon.baker@highpeak.gov.uk

Senior Management: Mr Dai Larner, Executive Director - Place, Moorlands House, Stockwell Street, Leek ST13 6HQ
☎ 01538 395400 ◌ dai.larner@highpeak.gov.uk

Senior Management: Mr Andrew Stokes, Executive Director - Transformation, Moorlands House, Stockwell Street, Leek ST13 6HQ ☎ 01538 395622 🖰 andrew.stokes@staffsmoorlands.gov.uk

Senior Management: Mr Mark Trillo, Executive Director - People, Moorlands House, Stockwell Street, Leek ST13 6HQ ☎ 01538 395623 🖰 mark.trillo@staffsmoorlands.gov.uk

Access Officer / Social Services (Disability): Mr Mike Green, Planning Applications Manager, Moorlands House, Stockwell Street, Leek ST13 6HQ ☎ 01538 395400 🖰 mike.green@staffsmoorlands.gov.uk

Architect, Building / Property Services: Ms Joanne Higgins, Property Services Manager, Moorlands House, Stockwell Street, Leek ST13 6HQ ☎ 01538 395400 🖰 joanne.higgins@staffsmoorlands.gov.uk

Best Value: Mr Chris Elliott, Transformation Manager, Moorlands House, Stockwell Street, Leek ST13 6HQ ☎ 01538 395400 🖰 chris.elliott@staffsmoorlands.gov.uk

Building Control: Mr Mike Green, Planning Applications Manager, Moorlands House, Stockwell Street, Leek ST13 6HQ ☎ 01538 395400 🖰 mike.green@staffsmoorlands.gov.uk

Building Control: Mr Robert Weaver, Head of Regulatory Services, Moorlands House, Stockwell Street, Leek ST13 6HQ ☎ 01538 395400 🖰 robert.weaver@highpeak.gov.uk

Catering Services: Mr Terry Crawford, Visitor Services Manager, Pavilion Gardens, Buxton SK17 6BE ☎ 01298 28400 Ext 4224 🖰 terry.crawford@highpeak.gov.uk

PR / Communications: Ms Carolyn Sanders, Communications Business Partner, Moorlands House, Stockwell Street, Leek ST13 6HQ ☎ 01538 395588 🖰 carolyn.sanders@staffsmoorlands.gov.uk

Community Planning: Mr Mark Forrester, Democratic & Community Services Manager, Moorlands House, Stockwell Street, Leek ST13 6HQ ☎ 01538 395768 🖰 mark.forrester@staffsmoorlands.gov.uk

Community Planning: Ms Alison Wheeldon, Environmental Policy Officer, Moorlands House, Stockwell Street, Leek ST13 6HQ ☎ 0845 129 7777 🖰 alison.wheeldon@staffsmoorlands.gov.uk

Community Safety: Mr Mark Forrester, Democratic & Community Services Manager, Moorlands House, Stockwell Street, Leek ST13 6HQ ☎ 01538 395768 🖰 mark.forrester@staffsmoorlands.gov.uk

Community Safety: Mr David Smith, Principal Officer - Community & Partnerships, Moorlands House, Stockwell Street, Leek ST13 6HQ ☎ 01538 395692 🖰 david.smith@staffsmoorlands.gov.uk

Computer Management: Mr Chris Elliott, Transformation Manager, Moorlands House, Stockwell Street, Leek ST13 6HQ ☎ 01538 395400 🖰 chris.elliott@staffsmoorlands.gov.uk

Computer Management: Ms Mary Walker, Organisational Development & Transformation Manager, Moorlands House, Stockwell Street, Leek ST13 6HQ 🖰 mary.walker@staffsmoorlands.gov.uk

Contracts: Mr Andrew Stokes, Executive Director - Transformation, Moorlands House, Stockwell Street, Leek ST13 6HQ ☎ 01538 395622 🖰 andrew.stokes@staffsmoorlands.gov.uk

Corporate Services: Mr Peter Dunkley, Customer Services Manager, Moorlands House, Stockwell Street, Leek ST13 6HQ ☎ 01538 395614 🖰 peter.dunkley@staffsmoorlands.gov.uk

Customer Service: Mr Terry Crawford, Visitor Services Manager, Pavilion Gardens, Buxton SK17 6BE ☎ 01298 28400 Ext 4224 🖰 terry.crawford@highpeak.gov.uk

Customer Service: Ms Lousie Pearce, Head of Customer Services, Moorlands House, Stockwell Street, Leek ST13 6HQ 🖰 louise.pearce@staffsmoorlands.gov.uk

Customer Service: Ms Tammy Towers, Environmental Health Manager, Moorlands House, Stockwell Street, Leek ST13 6HQ ☎ 0845 129 7777 🖰 tammy.towers@staffsmoorlands.gov.uk

Economic Development: Ms Pranali Parikh, Regeneration Manager, Moorlands House, Stockwell Street, Leek ST13 6HQ ☎ 01538 395582 🖰 pranali.parikh@staffsmoorlands.gov.uk

E-Government: Mr Chris Elliott, Transformation Manager, Moorlands House, Stockwell Street, Leek ST13 6HQ ☎ 01538 395400 🖰 chris.elliott@staffsmoorlands.gov.uk

Electoral Registration: Ms Caroline Cooke, Corporate Electoral Administration Manager, Moorlands House, Stockwell Street, Leek ST13 6HQ ☎ 01538 395400 🖰 caroline.cooke@staffsmoorlands.gov.uk

Electoral Registration: Ms Jeanette Marsh, Legal Services Manager, Moorlands House, Stockwell Street, Leek ST13 6HQ ☎ 01538 395400 🖰 jeanette.marsh@staffsmoorlands.gov.uk

Emergency Planning: Mr David Owen, Corporate Health & Safety Advisor, Moorlands House, Stockwell Street, Leek ST13 6HQ ☎ 01538 395595 🖰 david.owen@staffsmoorlands.gov.uk

Energy Management: Ms Joanne Higgins, Property Services Manager, Moorlands House, Stockwell Street, Leek ST13 6HQ ☎ 01538 395400 🖰 joanne.higgins@staffsmoorlands.gov.uk

Environmental / Technical Services: Mr Shaun Hollinshead, Street Cleansing Manager, Fowlchurch Depot, Fowlchurch Road, Leek ST13 6BH ☎ 01538 395798 🖰 shaun.hollinshead@staffsmoorlands.gov.uk

Environmental / Technical Services: Mr John Tildesley, Environmental Health Services Manager, Fowlchurch Depot, Fowlchurch Road, Leek ST13 6BH ☎ 01538 395400 🖰 john.tildesley@staffsmoorlands.gov.uk

STAFFORDSHIRE MOORLANDS

Environmental / Technical Services: Ms Tammy Towers, Environmental Health Manager, Moorlands House, Stockwell Street, Leek ST13 6HQ ☎ 0845 129 7777
🖂 tammy.towers@staffsmoorlands.gov.uk

Environmental Health: Ms Tammy Towers, Environmental Health Manager, Moorlands House, Stockwell Street, Leek ST13 6HQ
☎ 0845 129 7777 🖂 tammy.towers@staffsmoorlands.gov.uk

Environmental Health: Mr Robert Weaver, Head of Regulatory Services, Moorlands House, Stockwell Street, Leek ST13 6HQ
☎ 01538 395400 🖂 robert.weaver@highpeak.gov.uk

Estates, Property & Valuation: Ms Joanne Higgins, Property Services Manager, Moorlands House, Stockwell Street, Leek ST13 6HQ ☎ 01538 395400 🖂 joanne.higgins@staffsmoorlands.gov.uk

Facilities: Ms Joanne Higgins, Property Services Manager, Moorlands House, Stockwell Street, Leek ST13 6HQ
☎ 01538 395400 🖂 joanne.higgins@staffsmoorlands.gov.uk

Finance: Ms Claire Hazeldene, Finance & Procurement Manager, Moorlands House, Stockwell Street, Leek ST13 6HQ
☎ 01538 395400 🖂 claire.hazeldene@staffsmoorlands.gov.uk

Finance: Mr Rob Jones, Revenue & Benefits Manager, Town Hall, Buxton SK17 6EL ☎ 01538 395400 🖂 rob.jones@highpeak.gov.uk

Finance: Mr Andrew Stokes, Executive Director - Transformation, Moorlands House, Stockwell Street, Leek ST13 6HQ
☎ 01538 395622 🖂 andrew.stokes@staffsmoorlands.gov.uk

Fleet Management: Ms Joy Redfern, Street Scene Manager, Moorlands House, Stockwell Street, Leek ST13 6HQ
☎ 01298 28400 Ext 4411 🖂 joy.redfern@staffsmoorlands.gov.uk

Grounds Maintenance: Mr Keith Parker, Head of Operational Services, Moorlands House, Stockwell Street, Leek ST13 6HQ
☎ 01538 395400 🖂 keith.parker@staffsmoorlands.gov.uk

Grounds Maintenance: Mr Tony Wheat, Leisure Services Manager, Town Hall, Market Place, Buxton SK17 6EL
☎ 01538 395400 🖂 anthony.wheat@staffsmoorlands.gov.uk

Health and Safety: Mr David Owen, Emergency Planning, Health & Safety Advisor, Moorlands House, Stockwell Street, Leek ST13 6HQ ☎ 01538 395595 🖂 david.owen@staffsmoorlands.gov.uk

Home Energy Conservation: Mr Ian Young, Housing Strategy Manager, Moorlands House, Stockwell Street, Leek ST13 6HQ
☎ 01538 395400 🖂 ian.young@staffsmoorlands.gov.uk

Housing: Mr Ian Young, Housing Strategy Manager, Moorlands House, Stockwell Street, Leek ST13 6HQ ☎ 01538 395400
🖂 ian.young@staffsmoorlands.gov.uk

Legal: Ms Jeanette Marsh, Legal Services Manager, Moorlands House, Stockwell Street, Leek ST13 6HQ ☎ 01538 395400
🖂 jeanette.marsh@staffsmoorlands.gov.uk

Legal: Mr Mark Trillo, Executive Director - People, Moorlands House, Stockwell Street, Leek ST13 6HQ ☎ 01538 395623
🖂 mark.trillo@staffsmoorlands.gov.uk

Leisure and Cultural Services: Mr Keith Parker, Head of Operational Services, Moorlands House, Stockwell Street, Leek ST13 6HQ ☎ 01538 395400 🖂 keith.parker@staffsmoorlands.gov.uk

Leisure and Cultural Services: Mr Tony Wheat, Leisure Services Manager, Moorlands House, Stockwell Street, Leek ST13 6HQ ☎ 01538 395400 🖂 anthony.wheat@staffsmoorlands.gov.uk

Leisure and Cultural Services: Ms Alison Wheeldon, Environmental Policy Officer, Moorlands House, Stockwell Street, Leek ST13 6HQ ☎ 0845 129 7777
🖂 alison.wheeldon@staffsmoorlands.gov.uk

Licensing: Mr Peter Dunkley, Customer Services Manager, Moorlands House, Stockwell Street, Leek ST13 6HQ
☎ 01538 395614 🖂 peter.dunkley@staffsmoorlands.gov.uk

Licensing: Ms Tammy Towers, Environmental Health Manager, Town Hall, Market Place, Buxton SK17 6EL ☎ 0845 129 7777
🖂 tammy.towers@staffsmoorlands.gov.uk

Licensing: Mr Robert Weaver, Head of Regulatory Services, Moorlands House, Stockwell Street, Leek ST13 6HQ
☎ 01538 395400 🖂 robert.weaver@highpeak.gov.uk

Lottery Funding, Charity and Voluntary: Mr Mark Forrester, Democratic & Community Services Manager, Moorlands House, Stockwell Street, Leek ST13 6HQ ☎ 01538 395768
🖂 mark.forrester@staffsmoorlands.gov.uk

Member Services: Ms Jeanette Marsh, Legal Services Manager, Moorlands House, Stockwell Street, Leek ST13 6HQ
☎ 01538 395400 🖂 jeanette.marsh@staffsmoorlands.gov.uk

Member Services: Mr Mark Trillo, Executive Director - People, Moorlands House, Stockwell Street, Leek ST13 6HQ
☎ 01538 395623 🖂 mark.trillo@staffsmoorlands.gov.uk

Parking: Mr Mark Forrester, Democratic & Community Services Manager, Moorlands House, Stockwell Street, Leek ST13 6HQ
☎ 01538 395768 🖂 mark.forrester@staffsmoorlands.gov.uk

Parking: Ms Joanne Higgins, Property Services Manager, Moorlands House, Stockwell Street, Leek ST13 6HQ
☎ 01538 395400 🖂 joanne.higgins@staffsmoorlands.gov.uk

Partnerships: Mr Mark Forrester, Democratic & Community Services Manager, Moorlands House, Stockwell Street, Leek ST13 6HQ ☎ 01538 395768 🖂 mark.forrester@staffsmoorlands.gov.uk

Personnel / HR: Ms Julie Grime, Human Resources Manager, Moorlands House, Stockwell Street, Leek ST13 6HQ
☎ 01538 395400 🖂 julie.grime@staffsmoorlands.gov.uk

Personnel / HR: Ms Mary Walker, Organisational Development & Transformation Manager, Moorlands House, Stockwell Street, Leek ST13 6HQ 🖂 mary.walker@staffsmoorlands.gov.uk

Planning: Mr Mike Green, Planning Applications Manager, Moorlands House, Stockwell Street, Leek ST13 6HQ
☎ 01538 395400 ⌨ mike.green@staffsmoorlands.gov.uk

Planning: Mr Robert Weaver, Head of Regulatory Services, Moorlands House, Stockwell Street, Leek ST13 6HQ
☎ 01538 395400 ⌨ robert.weaver@highpeak.gov.uk

Procurement: Mr Chris Elliott, Transformation Manager, Moorlands House, Stockwell Street, Leek ST13 6HQ
☎ 01538 395400 ⌨ chris.elliott@staffsmoorlands.gov.uk

Recycling & Waste Minimisation: Ms Nicola Kemp, Operations Manager - Contract Management, Fowlchurch Depot, Fowlchurch Road, Leek ST13 6BH ☎ 01538 395794
⌨ nicola.kemp@staffsmoorlands.gov.uk

Recycling & Waste Minimisation: Ms Joy Redfern, Street Scene Manager, Moorlands House, Stockwell Street, Leek ST13 6HQ ☎ 01298 28400 Ext 4411
⌨ joy.redfern@staffsmoorlands.gov.uk

Regeneration: Ms Pranali Parikh, Regeneration Manager, Moorlands House, Stockwell Street, Leek ST13 6HQ
☎ 01538 395582 ⌨ pranali.parikh@staffsmoorlands.gov.uk

Social Services: Mr Rob Jones, Revenue & Benefits Manager, Town Hall, Market Place, Buxton SK17 6EL ☎ 01538 395400
⌨ rob.jones@highpeak.gov.uk

Staff Training: Ms Julie Grime, Human Resources Manager, Moorlands House, Stockwell Street, Leek ST13 6HQ
☎ 01538 395400 ⌨ julie.grime@staffsmoorlands.gov.uk

Street Scene: Mr Shaun Hollinshead, Environment Manager - Operations, Fowlchurch Depot, Fowlchurch Road, Leek ST13 6BH
☎ 01538 395798 ⌨ shaun.hollinshead@staffsmoorlands.gov.uk

Street Scene: Mr Keith Parker, Head of Operational Services, Moorlands House, Stockwell Street, Leek ST13 6HQ
☎ 01538 395400 ⌨ keith.parker@staffsmoorlands.gov.uk

Street Scene: Ms Joy Redfern, Street Scene Manager, Moorlands House, Stockwell Street, Leek ST13 6HQ ☎ 01298 28400 Ext 4411
⌨ joy.redfern@staffsmoorlands.gov.uk

Sustainable Communities: Mr Mark Forrester, Democratic & Community Services Manager, Moorlands House, Stockwell Street, Leek ST13 6HQ ☎ 01538 395768
⌨ mark.forrester@staffsmoorlands.gov.uk

Sustainable Development: Ms Alison Wheeldon, Environmental Policy Officer, Moorlands House, Stockwell Street, Leek ST13 6HQ
☎ 0845 129 7777 ⌨ alison.wheeldon@staffsmoorlands.gov.uk

Tourism: Mr Terry Crawford, Visitor Services Manager, Pavilion Gardens, Buxton SK17 6BE ☎ 01298 28400 Ext 4224
⌨ terry.crawford@highpeak.gov.uk

Tourism: Ms Pranali Parikh, Regeneration Manager, Moorlands House, Stockwell Street, Leek ST13 6HQ ☎ 01538 395582
⌨ pranali.parikh@staffsmoorlands.gov.uk

Town Centre: Ms Pranali Parikh, Regeneration Manager, Moorlands House, Stockwell Street, Leek ST13 6HQ
☎ 01538 395582 ⌨ pranali.parikh@staffsmoorlands.gov.uk

Waste Collection and Disposal: Mr Shaun Hollinshead, Environment Manager - Operations, Fowlchurch Depot, Fowlchurch Road, Leek ST13 6BH ☎ 01538 395798
⌨ shaun.hollinshead@staffsmoorlands.gov.uk

Waste Collection and Disposal: Mr Keith Parker, Head of Operational Services, Moorlands House, Stockwell Street, Leek ST13 6HQ ☎ 01538 395400 ⌨ keith.parker@staffsmoorlands.gov.uk

Waste Management: Ms Nicola Kemp, Operations Manager - Contract Management, Fowlchurch Depot, Fowlchurch Road, Leek ST13 6BH ☎ 01538 395794 ⌨ nicola.kemp@staffsmoorlands.gov.uk

COUNCILLORS

Chair: Pearce, Collin (CON - Checkley)
colin.pearce@staffsmoorlands.gov.uk

Vice-Chair: Shaw, David (CON - Werrington)
david.shaw@staffsmoorlands.gov.uk

Leader of the Council: Ralphs, Sybil (CON - Bagnall & Stanley)
sybil.ralphs@staffsmoorlands.gov.uk

Deputy Leader of the Council: Forrester, Arthur (CON - Alton)
arthur.forrester@staffsmoorlands.gov.uk

Group Leader: Malyon, Linda (R - Ipstones)
linda.maylon@staffsmoorlands.gov.uk

Aktins, Charlotte (LAB - Leek North)
charlotte.atkins@staffsmoorlands.gov.uk

Alcock, Richard (IND - Cheadle South East)
richard.alcock@staffsmoorlands.gov.uk

Banks, Alan (CON - Cheadle West)
alan.banks@staffsmoorlands.gov.uk

Bond, Geoff (CON - Brown Edge & Endon)
geof.bond@staffsmoorlands.gov.uk

Bowen, Michael (CON - Cheddleton)
michael.bowen@staffsmoorlands.gov.uk

Bull, Julie (CON - Cheadle North East)
julie.bull@staffsmoorlands.gov.uk

Davies, Jim (IND - Biddulph North)
jim.davies@staffsmoorlands.gov.uk

Deaville, Mark (CON - Checkley)
mark.deaville@staffsmoorlands.gov.uk

Done, Rebecca (CON - Leek East)
rebecca.done@staffsmoorlands.gov.uk

Ellis, Stephen (CON - Cheadle West)
stephen.ellis@staffsmoorlands.gov.uk

Emery, Ben (CON - Leek West)
ben.emery@staffsmoorlands.gov.uk

Fallows, Elsie (CON - Churnet)
elsie.fallows@staffsmoorlands.gov.uk

STAFFORDSHIRE MOORLANDS

Flunder, Keith (CON - Forsbrook)
keith.flunder@staffsmoorlands.gov.uk

Gledhill, Mike (LAB - Leek South)
mike.gledhill@staffsmoorlands.gov.uk

Grocott, Deborah (CON - Cheadle South East)
deborah.grocott@staffsmoorland.gov.uk

Hall, Tony (IND - Biddulph North)
tony.hall@staffsmoorlands.gov.uk

Harrison, Keith (IND - Leek South)
keith.harrison@staffsmoorlands.gov.uk

Hart, Andrew (IND - Biddulph North)
andrew.hart@staffsmoorlands.gov.uk

Hawkins, Norma (CON - Horton)
norma.hawkins@staffsmoorlands.gov.uk

Heath, Gill (CON - Dane)
gill.heath@staffsmoorlands.gov.uk

Herdman, Ian (CON - Forsbrook)
ian.herdman@staffsmoorlands.gov.uk

Hughes, Barbara (CON - Cellarhead)
barbara.hughes@staffsmoorlands.gov.uk

Jackson, Peter (CON - Cheadle West)
peter.jackson@staffsmoorlands.gov.uk

Jackson, Kevin (LAB - Biddulph East)
kevin.jackson@staffsmoorlands.gov.uk

Jebb, Christina (LD - Brown Edge & Endon)
christina.jebb@staffsmoorlands.gov.uk

Johnson, Brian (CON - Leek East)
brian.johnson@staffsmoorlands.gov.uk

Jones, John (IND - Biddulph Moor)
john.jones@staffsmoorlands.gov.uk

Lawson, Ian (IND - Biddulph West)
ian.lawson@staffsmoorlandlands.gov.uk

Lea, Linda (CON - Brown Edge & Endon)
linda.lea@staffsmoorlands.gov.uk

Lockett, Gail (CON - Leek South)
gail.lockett@staffsmoorlands.gov.uk

Lovatt, Madelaine (LAB - Biddulph East)
madelaine.lovatt@staffsmoorlands.gov.uk

Lovatt, Margaret (LAB - Leek North)
margaret.lovatt@staffsmoorlands.gov.uk

Lucas, Ivor (IND - Churnet)
ivor.lucas@staffsmoorlands.gov.uk

McNicol, Tony (CON - Cellarhead)
tony.mcnicol@staffsmoorlands.gov.uk

Ogden, Dani (CON - Leek North)
dani.ogden@staffsmoorlands.gov.uk

Plant, Robert (CON - Leek West)
robert.plant@staffsmoorlands.gov.uk

Podmore, Neal (CON - Leek West)
neal.podmore@staffsmoorlands.gov.uk

Redfern, John (LD - Biddulph South)
john.redfern@staffsmoorlands.gov.uk

Riley, Teresa (CON - Manifold)
teresa.riley@staffsmoorlands.gov.uk

Roberts, Paul (CON - Caverswall)
paul.roberts@staffsmoorlands.gov.uk

Scalise, Sav (CON - Cheddleton)
salvino.scalise@staffsmoorlands.gov.uk

Sheldon, Hilda (IND - Biddulph West)
hilda.sheldon@staffsmoorlands.gov.uk

Trigger, David (CON - Checkley)
david.trigger@staffsmoorlands.gov.uk

Wain, Edwin (CON - Hamps Valley)
edwin.wain@staffsmoorlands.gov.uk

Walley, Jeanette (LAB - Biddulph East)
jeanette.walley@staffsmoorlands.gov.uk

Ward, Ross (CON - Werrington)
ross.ward@staffsmoorlands.gov.uk

Wilkinson, Abigail (UKIP - Forsbrook)
abigail.wilkinson@staffsmoorlands.gov.uk

Wilkinson, Peter (UKIP - Cheadle North East)
peter.wilkinson@staffsmoorlands.gov.uk

Wood, Pamela (INDNA - Leek East)
pamela.wood@staffsmoorlands.gov.uk

Wood, Christopher (LAB - Biddulph West)
christopher.wood@staffsmoorlands.gov.uk

Worthington, Michael (CON - Cheddleton)
michael.worthington@staffsmoorlands.gov.uk

POLITICAL COMPOSITION
CON: 34, IND: 9, LAB: 7, LD: 2, UKIP: 2, R: 1, INDNA: 1

COMMITTEE CHAIRS

Audit: Mr Jim Davies

Licensing: Ms Julie Bull

Planning: Mr Stephen Ellis

Stevenage   D

Stevenage Borough Council, Daneshill House, Danestrete, Stevenage SG1 1HN
☎ 01438 242242 🖷 01438 242566 ✆ csc@stevenage.gov.uk
🖳 www.stevenage.gov.uk

FACTS AND FIGURES
Parliamentary Constituencies: Stevenage
EU Constituencies: Eastern
Election Frequency: Elections are by thirds

PRINCIPAL OFFICERS

Chief Executive: Mr Scott Crudgington, Chief Executive, Daneshill House, Danestrete, Stevenage SG1 1HN ☎ 01438 242185
✆ scott.crudgington@stevenage.gov.uk

Deputy Chief Executive: Mr Matthew Partridge, Strategic Director - Communities & Deputy Chief Executive, Daneshill House, Danestrete, Stevenage SG1 1HN ☎ 01438 242456
✆ matthew.partridge@stevenage.gov.uk

Senior Management: Mr Matthew Partridge, Strategic Director - Communities & Deputy Chief Executive, Daneshill House, Danestrete, Stevenage SG1 1HN ☎ 01438 242456
⌕ matthew.partridge@stevenage.gov.uk

Senior Management: Mr Thomas Pike, Strategic Director - Environment, Daneshill House, Danestrete, Stevenage SG1 1HN ☎ 01438 242288 ⌕ thomas.pike@stevenage.gov.uk

Building Control: Mr Steve Polfreman, Building Control Manager, Daneshill House, Danestrete, Stevenage SG1 1HN ☎ 01438 242256 ⌕ steve.polfreman@stevenage.gov.uk

Children / Youth Services: Mr Aidan Sanderson, Head of Leisure, Environmental Health & Children's Services, Daneshill House, Danesrete, Stevenage SG1 1HN ☎ 01438 242311 ⌕ aidan.sanderson@stevenage.gov.uk

PR / Communications: Ms Lucy Culkin, Communications Manager, Daneshill House, Danestrete, Stevenage SG1 1HN ☎ 01438 242168 ⌕ lucie.culkin@stevenage.gov.uk

Community Safety: Ms Debbie Barker, Senior Corporate Policy Officer (Community Safety & Strategic Partnerships), Daneshill House, Danestrete, Stevenage SG1 1HN ☎ 01438 242242 ⌕ debbie.barker@stevenage.gov.uk

Computer Management: Mr Henry Lewis, Head of Service - Share Business & Technology Services, Daneshill House, Danestrete, Stevenage SG1 1HN ☎ 01438 242496 ⌕ henry.lewis@stevenage.gov.uk

Contracts: Mr Lee Myers, Head of Environmental Services, Cavendish Road, Stevenage SG1 2ES ☎ 01438 248710 ⌕ lee.myers@stevenage.gov.uk

Customer Service: Mr Richard Protheroe, Head of Chief Executive's Unit, Daneshill House, Danestrete, Stevenage SG1 1HN ☎ 01438 242938 ⌕ richard.protheroe@stevenage.gov.uk

Direct Labour: Mr Lee Myers, Head of Environmental Services, Cavendish Road, Stevenage SG1 2ES ☎ 01438 248710 ⌕ lee.myers@stevenage.gov.uk

E-Government: Mr Henry Lewis, Head of Service - Share Business & Technology Services, Daneshill House, Danestrete, Stevenage SG1 1HN ☎ 01438 242496 ⌕ henry.lewis@stevenage.gov.uk

Electoral Registration: Ms Jacqui Hubbard, Electoral Services Manager, Daneshill House, Danestrete, Stevenage SG1 1HN ☎ 01438 242174 ⌕ jacqui.hubbard@stevenage.gov.uk

Emergency Planning: Ms Suzanne Brightwell, Senior Performance & Resilience Officer, Daneshill House, Danestrete, Stevenage SG1 1HN ☎ 01438 242966 ⌕ suzanne.brightwell@stevenage.gov.uk

Emergency Planning: Ms Sue Kingsley-Smith, Senior Performance & Resilience Officer, Daneshill House, Danestrete, Stevenage SG1 1HN ☎ 01438 242390 ⌕ sue.kingsley-smith@stevenage.gov.uk

Environmental Health: Mr Aidan Sanderson, Head of Leisure, Environmental Health & Children's Services, Daneshill House, Danesrete, Stevenage SG1 1HN ☎ 01438 242311 ⌕ aidan.sanderson@stevenage.gov.uk

European Liaison: Mrs Maureen Nicholson, Member Services Officer, Daneshill House, Danestrete, Stevenage SG1 1HN ☎ 01438 242278 ⌕ maureen.nicholson@stevenage.gov.uk

Events Manager: Ms Lucy Culkin, Communications Manager, Daneshill House, Danestrete, Stevenage SG1 1HN ☎ 01438 242168 ⌕ lucie.culkin@stevenage.gov.uk

Facilities: Mr Andy Cristophi, Facilities Manager, Daneshill House, Danestrete, Stevenage SG1 1HN ☎ 01438 242705 ⌕ andy.cristophi@stevenage.gov.uk

Finance: Ms Clare Fletcher, Assistant Director - Finance, Daneshill House, Danestrete, Stevenage SG1 1HN ☎ 01438 242933 ⌕ clare.fletcher@stevenage.gov.uk

Fleet Management: Mr Simon Martin, Contracts Manager, Cavendish Road, Stevenage SG1 2ES ☎ 01438 218800 ⌕ simon.martin@stevenage.gov.uk

Grounds Maintenance: Mr Paul Seaby, Contracts Manager, Cavendish Road, Stevenage SG1 2ES ☎ 01438 242772 ⌕ paul.seaby@stevenage.gov.uk

Health and Safety: Mr Tony Hughes, Corporate Health & Safety Advisor, Daneshill House, Danestrete, Stevenage SG1 1HN ☎ 01438 218033 ⌕ tony.hughes@stevenage.gov.uk

Housing: Mr Ash Ahmed, Assistant Director - Housing Development, Daneshill House, Danestrete, Stevenage SG1 1HN ☎ 01438 242242 ⌕ ash.ahmed@stevenage.gov.uk

Housing: Mrs Jaine Cresser, Head of Housing Management Services, Daneshill House, Danestrete, Stevenage SG1 1HN ☎ 01483 242455 ⌕ tony.campbell@stevenage.gov.uk

Housing Maintenance: Mr Brian Golton, Building Maintenance & Repairs Services, Daneshill House, Danestrete, Stevenage SG1 1HN ☎ 01438 242261 ⌕ brian.golton@stevenage.gov.uk

Legal: Mr Paul Froggatt, Borough Solicitor, Daneshill House, Danestrete, Stevenage SG1 1HN ☎ 01438 242212 ⌕ paul.froggatt@stevenage.gov.uk

Leisure and Cultural Services: Mr Aidan Sanderson, Head of Leisure, Environmental Health & Children's Services, Daneshill House, Danesrete, Stevenage SG1 1HN ☎ 01438 242311 ⌕ aidan.sanderson@stevenage.gov.uk

Licensing: Ms Heather Morris, Licensing Manager, Daneshill House, Danestrete, Stevenage SG1 1HN ☎ 01438 212175 ⌕ heather.morris@stevenage.gov.uk

Member Services: Ms Jackie Cansick, Constitutional Services Manager, Daneshill House, Danestrete, Stevenage SG1 1HN ☎ 01438 242216 ⌕ jackie.cansick@stevenage.gov.uk

STEVENAGE

Parking: Mr Keith Moore, Parking Services Manager, Daneshill House, Danestrete, Stevenage SG1 1HN ☎ 01438 242277 ⏚ keith.moore@stevenage.gov.uk

Partnerships: Mr Richard Protheroe, Head of Chief Executive's Unit, Daneshill House, Danestrete, Stevenage SG1 1HN ☎ 01438 242938 ⏚ richard.protheroe@stevenage.gov.uk

Planning: Mr Zayd Al-Jawad, Head of Planning & Engineering, Daneshill House, Danestrete, Stevenage SG1 1HN ☎ 01438 242242 ⏚ zayd.al-jawad@stevenage.gov.uk

Planning: Mr Paul Pinkney, Interim Head of Regeneration & Transport, Daneshill House, Danestrete, Stevenage SG1 1HN ☎ 01438 242547 ⏚ paul.pinkney@stevenage.gov.uk

Procurement: Ms Sharon Wallace, Corporate Procurement Manager, Daneshill House, Danestrete, Stevenage SG1 1HN ☎ 01438 242083 ⏚ sharon.wallace@stevenage.gov.uk

Recycling & Waste Minimisation: Mr Lee Myers, Head of Environmental Services, Cavendish Road, Stevenage SG1 2ES ☎ 01438 248710 ⏚ lee.myers@stevenage.gov.uk

Regeneration: Mr Noel O'Neill, Assistant Director - Regeneration, Daneshill House, Danestrete, Stevenage SG1 1HN ☎ 01438 242547 ⏚ noel.o'neill@stevenage.gov.uk

Staff Training: Ms Christina Hefferon, Head of Human Resources & Organisational Development, Daneshill House, Danestrete, Stevenage SG1 1HN ☎ 01438 242164 ⏚ christina.hefferon@stevenage.gov.uk

Street Scene: Ms Julia Knight, Environmental Performance & Development Manager, Daneshill House, Danestrete, Stevenage SG1 1HN ☎ 01438 242900 ⏚ julia.knight@stevenage.gov.uk

Sustainable Communities: Mr Paul Pinkney, Interim Head of Regeneration & Transport, Daneshill House, Danestrete, Stevenage SG1 1HN ☎ 01438 242547 ⏚ paul.pinkney@stevenage.gov.uk

Transport: Mr Rob Woodisse, Principal Engineer, Daneshill House, Danestrete, Stevenage SG1 1HN ☎ 01438 242272 ⏚ rob.woodisse@stevenage.gov.uk

Waste Collection and Disposal: Mr Lee Myers, Head of Environmental Services, Cavendish Road, Stevenage SG1 2ES ☎ 01438 248710 ⏚ lee.myers@stevenage.gov.uk

Waste Management: Mr Lee Myers, Head of Environmental Services, Cavendish Road, Stevenage SG1 2ES ☎ 01438 248710 ⏚ lee.myers@stevenage.gov.uk

Children's Play Areas: Mr Aidan Sanderson, Head of Leisure, Environmental Health & Children's Services, Daneshill House, Danesrete, Stevenage SG1 1HN ☎ 01438 242311 ⏚ aidan.sanderson@stevenage.gov.uk

COUNCILLORS

Leader of the Council: Taylor, Sharon (LAB - Symonds Green)
sharon.taylor@stevenage.gov.uk

Deputy Leader of the Council: Gardner, John (LAB - Roebuck)
john.gardner@stevenage.gov.uk

Group Leader: Bibby, Philip (CON - Woodfield)
philip.bibby@stevenage.gov.uk

Bainbridge, Doug (LAB - Longmeadow)
doug.bainbridge@stevenage.gov.uk

Batson, Sherma (LAB - Roebuck)
sherma.batson@stevenage.gov.uk

Briscoe, Lloyd (LAB - Martins Wood)
lloyd.briscoe@stevenage.gov.uk

Broom, Rob (LAB - Shephall)
rob.broom@stevenage.gov.uk

Brown, Jim (LAB - Old Town)
jim.brown@stevenage.gov.uk

Burrell, Howard (LAB - Chells)
howard.burrell@stevenage.gov.uk

Chester, Laurie (LAB - Symonds Green)
laurie.chester@stevenage.gov.uk

Connolly, Elaine (LAB - Bedwell)
elaine.connolly@stevenage.gov.uk

Cullen, David (LAB - Bedwell)
david.cullen@stevenage.gov.uk

Downing, Michael (LAB - Symonds Green)
michael.downing@stevenage.gov.uk

Fraser, James (CON - Old Town)
james.fraser@stevenage.gov.uk

Gardner, Michelle (LAB - Bandley Hill)
michelle.gardner@stevenage.gov.uk

Harrington, Liz (LAB - Bedwell)
liz.harrington@stevenage.gov.uk

Hearn, Sharon (CON - Bandley Hill)
sharon.hearn@stevenage.gov.uk

Henry, Richard (LAB - St Nicholas)
richard.henry@stevenage.gov.uk

Hollywell, Jackie (LAB - Chells)
jackie.hollywell@stevenage.gov.uk

Hurst, Matthew (CON - Longmeadow)
matthew.hurst@stevenage.gov.uk

Latif, Carol (LAB - St Nicholas)
carol.latif@stevenage.gov.uk

Lawrence, Graham (CON - Woodfield)
graham.lawrence@stevenage.gov.uk

Lloyd, Joan (LAB - Bandley Hill)
joan.lloyd@stevenage.gov.uk

Lloyd, John (LAB - Roebuck)
john.lloyd@stevenage.gov.uk

Martin-Haugh, Lin (LAB - Pin Green)
lin.martin-haugh@stevenage.gov.uk

McGuinness, Andy (LD - Manor)
andy.mcguiness@stevenage.gov.uk

McKay, Maureen (LAB - Martins Wood)
maureen.mckay@stevenage.gov.uk

Mead, John (LAB - Shephall)
john.mead@stevenage.gov.uk

Mead, Sarah (LAB - Martins Wood)
sarah.mead@stevenage.gov.uk

Mitchell, Adam (CON - Longmeadow)
adam.mitchell@stevenage.gov.uk

Notley, Margaret (CON - Woodfield)
margaret.notley@stevenage.gov.uk

Parker, Robin (LD - Manor)
robin.parker@stevenage.gov.uk

Raynor, Ralph (LAB - St Nicholas)
ralph.raynor@stevenage.gov.uk

Saunders, Chris (LAB - Old Town)
chris.saunders@stevenage.gov.uk

Snell, Graham (LD - Manor)
graham.snell@stevenage.gov.uk

Speller, Simon (LAB - Pin Green)
simon.speller@stevenage.gov.uk

Stuart, Pam (LAB - Chells)
pam.stuart@stevenage.gov.uk

Thomas, Jeanette (LAB - Pin Green)
jeanette.thomas@stevenage.gov.uk

Webb, Ann (LAB - Shephall)
ann.webb@stevenage.gov.uk

POLITICAL COMPOSITION
LAB: 29, CON: 7, LD: 3

Stirling   S

Stirling Council, Old Viewforth, Stirling FK8 2ET
☎ 01786 404040 ⌁ info@stirling.gov.uk 🖵 www.stirling.gov.uk

FACTS AND FIGURES
Parliamentary Constituencies: Stirling
EU Constituencies: Scotland
Election Frequency: Elections are of whole council

PRINCIPAL OFFICERS

Chief Executive: Mr Stewart Carruth, Chief Executive, Old Viewforth, Stirling FK8 2ET ☎ 01786 233047 ⌁ carruths@stirling.gov.uk

Senior Management: Ms Carol Beattie, Senior Manager - Economic Development & Regeneration, Old Viewforth, Stirling FK8 2ET ☎ 01786 233139 ⌁ beattiec@stirling.gov.uk

Senior Management: Mr Jim Boyle, Chief Finance Officer, Teith House, Kerse Road, Stirling FK7 7QA ☎ 01786 233362 ⌁ boylej@stirling.gov.uk

Senior Management: Mr Alastair Brown, Director - Localities & Infrastructure, Old Viewforth, Stirling FK8 2ET ⌁ browna@stirling.gov.uk

Senior Management: Dr Stacey Burlet, Director - Communities & Partnerships, Old Viewforth, Stirling FK8 2ET ☎ 01786 233013 ⌁ burlets@stirling.gov.uk

Senior Management: Ms Kristine Johnson, Chief Officer - HR & OD, Teith House, Kerse Road, Stirling FK7 7QA ☎ 01786 233294 ⌁ johnsonk@stirling.gov.uk

Senior Management: Mr Kevin Kelman, Senior Manager - Schools & Learning, Municipal Buildings, 8 - 10 Corn Exchange Road, Stirling FK8 2HU ☎ 01786 233224 ⌁ kelmank@stirling.gov.uk

Senior Management: Mr Alan Milliken, Senior Manager - Communities & People, Municipal Buildings, 8 - 10 Corn Exchange Road, Stirling FK8 2HU ☎ 01786 233225 ⌁ millikena@stirling.gov.uk

Senior Management: Ms Nicole Paterson, Senior Manager - Environment & Place, Endrick House, Stirling FK7 7SZ ☎ 01786 237794 ⌁ patersonn@stirling.gov.uk

Senior Management: Mr Brian Roberts, Senior Manager - Infrastructure Development, Teith House, Kerse Road, Stirling FK7 7QA ☎ 01786 233462 ⌁ robertsb@stirling.gov.uk

Senior Management: Mr Iain Strachan, Chief Governance Officer, Old Viewforth, Stirling FK8 2ET ☎ 01786 233108 ⌁ strachani@stirling.gov.uk

Senior Management: Ms Maria Valente, Senior Manager - Children & Families, Old Viewforth, Stirling FK8 2ET ☎ 01786 404040 ⌁ valentem@stirling.gov.uk

Architect, Building / Property Services: Mr Drew Leslie, Infrastructure Developments Manager, Teith House, Kerse Road, Stirling FK7 7QA ☎ 01786 233323 ⌁ leslied@stirling.gov.uk

Architect, Building / Property Services: Mr Brian Roberts, Senior Manager - Infrastructure Development, Teith House, Kerse Road, Stirling FK7 7QA ☎ 01786 233462 ⌁ robertsb@stirling.gov.uk

Best Value: Mr Paul Fleming, Senior Manager - Corporate Services, Teith House, Kerse Road, Stirling FK7 7QA ☎ 01786 233094 ⌁ flemingp@stirling.gov.uk

Building Control: Ms Linda Hill, Service Manager - Regulatory, Municipal Buildings, 8 - 10 Corn Exchange Road, Stirling FK8 2HU ☎ 01786 233631 ⌁ hillin@stirling.gov.uk

Catering Services: Ms Margaret Gilmour, FM Services Manager, Teith House, Kerse Road, Stirling FK7 7QA ☎ 01786 233263 ⌁ gilmourm@stirling.gov.uk

Children / Youth Services: Mr Bill Miller, Service Manager - Youth Services & Adult Learning, Teith House, Kerse Road, Stirling FK7 7QA ☎ 01786 233595 ⌁ millerb@stirling.gov.uk

Civil Registration: Ms Elizabeth Ferguson, District Registrar, Customer First, 1 - 5 Port Street, Stirling FK8 2EJ ☎ 01786 233962 ⌁ fergusone@stirling.gov.uk

PR / Communications: Ms Kirsty Scott, Manager - Communications, Marketing & Events, Old Viewforth, Stirling FK8 2ET ☎ 01786 233064 ⌁ scotta@stirling.gov.uk

STIRLING

Community Safety: Ms Margaret Wallace, Manager - City & Communities, Old Viewforth, Stirling FK8 2ET ☎ 01786 233540 ✆ wallacem@stirling.gov.uk

Computer Management: Ms Heather Robb, ICT & Information Management Manager, Teith House, Kerse Road, Stirling FK7 7QA ☎ 01786 233041 ✆ robbh@stirling.gov.uk

Consumer Protection and Trading Standards: Ms Lorraine MacGillivray, Team Leader - Regulatory Services, Municipal Buildings, Stirling FK8 2QU ☎ 01786 233637 ✆ macgillivrayl@stirling.gov.uk

Contracts: Mr Iain Strachan, Chief Governance Officer, Old Viewforth, Stirling FK8 2ET ☎ 01786 233108 ✆ strachani@stirling.gov.uk

Corporate Services: Mr Paul Fleming, Senior Manager - Corporate Services, Old Viewforth, Stirling FK8 2ET ☎ 01786 233094 ✆ flemingp@stirling.gov.uk

Customer Service: Mr John Muir, Senior Manager - Customers & Business Change, Library HQ, Borrowmeadow Road, Stirling FK7 7TN ☎ 01786 233062 ✆ muirj@stirling.gov.uk

Direct Labour: Mr John MacMillan, Manager - Housing Property, Allan Water House, Stirling FK7 7SG ☎ 01786 237718 ✆ macmillanj@stirling.gov.uk

Direct Labour: Mr Jamie Wright, Manager - Roads & Transport, Endrick House, Kerse Road, Stirling FK7 7SZ ☎ 01786 237647 ✆ wrightj@stirling.gov.uk

Economic Development: Ms Carol Beattie, Senior Manager - Economic Development & Regeneration, Old Viewforth, Stirling FK8 2ET ☎ 01786 233139 ✆ beattiec@stirling.gov.uk

Education: Ms Sharon Johnstone, Senior Manager - Education, Children, Young People & Families, Municipal Buildings, 8 - 10 Corn Exchange Road, Stirling FK8 2HU ☎ 01786 233202 ✆ johnstones2@stirling.gov.uk

Education: Mr Kevin Kelman, Senior Manager - Schools & Learning, Municipal Buildings, 8 - 10 Corn Exchange Road, Stirling FK8 2HU ☎ 01786 233224 ✆ kelmank@stirling.gov.uk

Education: Mr Alan Milliken, Senior Manager - Communities & People, Municipal Buildings, 8 - 10 Corn Exchange Road, Stirling FK8 2HU ☎ 01786 233225 ✆ millikena@stirling.gov.uk

E-Government: Mr David Laughlin, Strategy & Delivery Manager, Teith House, Kerse Road, Stirling FK7 7QA ☎ 01786 233509 ✆ laughlind@stirling.gov.uk

Emergency Planning: Mr David Bright, Resilience & Risk Manager, Teith House, Kerse Road, Stirling FK7 7QA ☎ 01786 233167 ✆ brightd@stirling.gov.uk

Energy Management: Mr Pierre Boinot, Energy Officer, Teith House, Kerse Road, Stirling FK7 7QA ☎ 01786 233228 ✆ bionotp@stirling.gov.uk

Energy Management: Mrs Grace Conner, Energy Officer, Teith House, Kerse Road, Stirling FK7 7QA ☎ 01786 233231 ✆ connerg@stirling.gov.uk

Environmental Health: Mr Leslie Fisher, Service Manager - Environmental Health & Trading Standards, Municipal Buildings, Stirling FK8 2QU ☎ 01786 432180 ✆ fisherl@stirling.gov.uk

Estates, Property & Valuation: Mr Drew Leslie, Infrastructure Developments Manager, Teith House, Kerse Road, Stirling FK7 7QA ☎ 01786 233323 ✆ leslied@stirling.gov.uk

European Liaison: Ms Margaret Wallace, Manager - City & Communities, Old Viewforth, Stirling FK8 2ET ☎ 01786 233540 ✆ wallacem@stirling.gov.uk

Events Manager: Ms Kirsty Scott, Manager - Communications, Marketing & Events, Old Viewforth, Stirling FK8 2ET ☎ 01786 233064 ✆ scotta@stirling.gov.uk

Facilities: Ms Margaret Gilmour, FM Services Manager, Teith House, Kerse Road, Stirling FK7 7QA ☎ 01786 233263 ✆ gilmourm@stirling.gov.uk

Facilities: Mr Jim McNeish, Office Facilities Manager, Teith House, Kerse Road, Stirling FK7 7QA ☎ 01786 233333 ✆ mcneishj@stirling.gov.uk

Finance: Mr Jim Boyle, Chief Finance Officer, Teith House, Kerse Road, Stirling FK7 7QA ☎ 01786 233362 ✆ boylej@stirling.gov.uk

Fleet Management: Mr Gavin Hutton, Manager - Business Strategy, Fleet Services, Springkerse Depot, Kerse Road, Stirling FK7 7TE ☎ 01786 237599 ✆ huttong@stirling.gov.uk

Grounds Maintenance: Ms Nicole Paterson, Senior Manager - Environment & Place, Endrick House, Stirling FK7 7SZ ☎ 01786 237794 ✆ patersonn@stirling.gov.uk

Health and Safety: Mr Nick Sabo, Health & Safety Adviser, Teith House, Kerse Road, Stirling FK7 7QA ☎ 01786 233288 ✆ sabon@stirling.gov.uk

Home Energy Conservation: Mr Brian Cree, Energy Officer, Viewforth, Stirling FK8 2ET ☎ 01786 442887 ✆ creeb@stirling.gov.uk

Housing: Ms Carol Hamilton, Manager - Housing Management, Endrick House, Stirling FK7 7SG ☎ 01786 237652 ✆ hamiltonc@stirling.gov.uk

Housing Maintenance: Mr John MacMillan, Manager - Housing Property, Allanwater House, Stirling FK7 7SG ☎ 01786 237718 ✆ macmillanj@stirling.gov.uk

Legal: Mr Iain Strachan, Chief Governance Officer, Old Viewforth, Stirling FK8 2ET ☎ 01786 233108 ✆ strachani@stirling.gov.uk

Leisure and Cultural Services: Mr Eddie White, Manager - Libraries, Archives & Culture, Old Viewforth, Stirling FK8 2ET ☎ 01789 233022 ✆ whitee@stirling.gov.uk

Licensing: Ms Linda Hill, Service Manager - Regulatory, Municipal Buildings, 8 - 10 Corn Exchange Road, Stirling FK8 2HU
☎ 01786 233631 ✆ hillin@stirling.gov.uk

Lifelong Learning: Mr Ed Gibbon, Team Leader - Adult Learning, Cowane Centre, Cowane Street, Stirling FK8 1JP ☎ 01786 237526 ✆ gibbone@stirling.gov.uk

Lighting: Mr Ian Young, Team Leader - Bridge, Flood & Street Lighting, Endrick House, Kerse Road, Stirling FK7 7SZ
☎ 01786 237645 ✆ youngi@stirling.gov.uk

Lottery Funding, Charity and Voluntary: Ms Jean Cowie, Funding Officer, Old Viewforth, Stirling FK8 2ET ☎ 01786 233143
✆ cowiej@stirling.gov.uk

Member Services: Ms Joyce Allen, Democratic Support Manager, Old Viewforth, Stirling FK8 2ET ☎ 01786 233095
✆ allenj@stirling.gov.uk

Parking: Mr Alan Ogilvie, Team Leader - Traffic Management, Endrick House, Stirling FK7 7SZ ☎ 01786 233449
✆ ogilvieaf@stirling.gov.uk

Partnerships: Dr Stacey Burlet, Director - Communities & Partnerships, Old Viewforth, Stirling FK8 2ET ☎ 01786 233013
✆ burlets@stirling.gov.uk

Personnel / HR: Ms Kristine Johnson, Chief Officer - HR & OD, Teith House, Kerse Road, Stirling FK7 7QA ☎ 01786 233294
✆ johnsonk@stirling.gov.uk

Planning: Mr Peter Morgan, Chief Planning Officer, Municipal Buildings, Corn Exchange Road, Stirling FK8 2HU ☎ 01786 233682
✆ morganp@stirling.gov.uk

Procurement: Ms Isabel McKnight, Strategic Procurement & Commissioning Manager, Old Viewforth, Stirling FK8 2ET
☎ 01786 233389 ✆ mcknighti@stirling.gov.uk

Public Libraries: Mr Eddie White, Manager - Libraries, Archives & Culture, Old Viewforth, Stirling FK8 2ET ☎ 01789 233022
✆ whitee@stirling.gov.uk

Recycling & Waste Minimisation: Mr David Hopper, Sustainable Development Manager, Teith House, Kerse Road, Stirling FK7 7QA ☎ 01786 237566 ✆ hopperd@stirling.gov.uk

Regeneration: Ms Carol Beattie, Senior Manager - Economic Development & Regeneration, Old Viewforth, Stirling FK8 2ET
☎ 01786 233139 ✆ beattiec@stirling.gov.uk

Road Safety: Mr Stuart Geddes, Road Safety Engineer, Teith House, Kerse Road, Stirling FK7 7QA ☎ 01786 233440
✆ geddess@stirling.gov.uk

Social Services: Ms Val de Souza, Head of Social Services / Chief Social Worker, Kilncraigs, Alloa FK10 1EB ☎ 01259 225017
✆ vdesouza@clacks.gov.uk

Social Services (Children): Ms Maria Valente, Senior Manager - Children & Families, Old Viewforth, Stirling FK8 2ET
☎ 01786 404040 ✆ valentem@stirling.gov.uk

Staff Training: Ms Jean Beagley, Learning & Development Advisor, Unit 12, Back O'Hill Industrial Estate, Stirling FK8 1SH
☎ 01786 233982 ✆ beagleyj@stirling.gov.uk

Street Scene: Ms Nicole Paterson, Senior Manager - Environment & Place, Endrick House, Stirling FK7 7SG ☎ 01786 237794
✆ patersonn@stirling.gov.uk

Tourism: Ms Carol Beattie, Senior Manager - Economic Development & Regeneration, Old Viewforth, Stirling FK8 2ET
☎ 01786 233139 ✆ beattiec@stirling.gov.uk

Town Centre: Ms Margaret Wallace, Manager - City & Communities, Old Viewforth, Stirling FK8 2ET ☎ 01786 233540
✆ wallacem@stirling.gov.uk

Traffic Management: Mr Alan Ogilvie, Team Leader - Traffic Management, Teith House, Kerse Road, Stirling FK7 7QA
☎ 01786 233449 ✆ ogilvieaf@stirling.gov.uk

Waste Collection and Disposal: Mr David Hopper, Sustainable Development Manager, Teith House, Kerse Road, Stirling FK7 7QA
☎ 01786 237566 ✆ hopperd@stirling.gov.uk

Waste Management: Mr David Hopper, Sustainable Development Manager, Teith House, Kerse Road, Stirling FK7 7QA
☎ 01786 237566 ✆ hopperd@stirling.gov.uk

COUNCILLORS

Provost: Robbins, Mike (LAB - Dunblane and Bridge of Allan)
robbinsm@stirling.gov.uk

Deputy Provost: Campbell, Callum (CON - Dunblaine and Bridge of Allan)
campbellc@stirling.gov.uk

Leader of the Council: Boyd, Johanna (LAB - Castle)
boydj@stirling.gov.uk

Deputy Leader of the Council: Benny, Neil (CON - Stirling West)
bennyn@stirling.gov.uk

Berrill, Alistair (CON - Forth and Endrick)
berrilla@stirling.gov.uk

Brisley, Margaret (LAB - BannockBurn)
brisleym@stirling.gov.uk

Earl, Martin (CON - Trossachs and Teith)
earlm@stirling.gov.uk

Farmer, Scott (SNP - Stirling West)
farmers@stirling.gov.uk

Gibson, Danny (LAB - Stirling East)
gibsond@stirling.gov.uk

Hayes, Alycia (SNP - Trossachs and Teith)
hayesa@stirling.gov.uk

Hendry, John (LAB - Castle)
hendryj@stirling.gov.uk

Houston, Graham (SNP - Dunblaine and Bridge of Allan)
houstong@stirling.gov.uk

STIRLING

Lambie, Graham (SNP - Forth and Endrick)
lambieg@stirling.gov.uk

MacPherson, Alasdair (SNP - BannockBurn)
macphersona@stirling.gov.uk

McChord, Corrie (LAB - Stirling East)
mcchordc@stirling.gov.uk

Muirhead, Ian (SNP - Forth and Endrick)
muirheadi@stirling.gov.uk

Paterson, Steven (SNP - Stirling East)
patersonst@stirling.gov.uk

Ruskell, Mark (SGP - Dunblane and Bridge of Allan)
ruskellm@stirling.gov.uk

Simpson, Christine (LAB - Stirling West)
simpsonc@stirling.gov.uk

Thomson, Jim (SNP - Castle)
thomsonjo3@stirling.gov.uk

Weir, Violet (LAB - BannockBurn)
weirv@stirling.gov.uk

Wood, Fergus (SNP - Trossachs and Teith)
woodf@stirling.gov.uk

POLITICAL COMPOSITION
SNP: 9, LAB: 8, CON: 4, SGP: 1

Stirling   M

Stockport Metropolitan Borough Council, Town Hall, Edward
Street, Stockport SK1 3XE
☎ 0161 480 4949 🖷 0161 477 9530 ⌨ www.stockport.gov.uk

FACTS AND FIGURES
Parliamentary Constituencies: Cheadle, Denton and Reddish,
Hazel Grove, Stockport
EU Constituencies: North West
Election Frequency: Elections are by thirds

PRINCIPAL OFFICERS

Chief Executive: Mr Eamonn Boylan, Chief Executive, Town Hall,
Edward Street, Stockport SK1 3XE ☎ 0161 474 3001
⌂ eamonn.boylan@stockport.gov.uk

Deputy Chief Executive: Mrs Laureen Donnan, Deputy Chief
Executive, Town Hall, Edward Street, Stockport SK1 3XE
☎ 0161 474 3180 ⌂ laureen.donnan@stockport.gov.uk

Senior Management: Ms Caroline Simpson, Corporate Director -
Services to Place Management & Regeneration, Fred Perry House,
Piccadilly, Stockport SK1 3XE ☎ 0161 218 1940
⌂ caroline.simpson@stockport.gov.uk

Senior Management: Dr Stephen Watkins, Director - Public
Health, Town Hall, Edward Street, Stockport SK1 3XE
☎ 0161 474 2436 ⌂ stephen.watkins@stockport.gov.uk

Senior Management: Mr Andrew Webb, Corporate Director -
Services to People, Stopford House, Piccadilly, Stockport SK1 3XE
☎ 0161 474 3808 ⌂ andrew.webb@stockport.gov.uk

Architect, Building / Property Services: Ms Julie Newbatt,
Operations Lead, Carillion Stockport Property Services, Stopford
House, Piccadilly, Stockport SK1 3XE ☎ 0161 217 6915
⌂ julie.newbatt@carillionplc.com

Building Control: Mr Ian O'Donnell, Head of Service - Public
Protection, Fred Perry House, Piccadilly, Stockport SK1 3XE
☎ 0161 474 4175 ⌂ ian.odonnell@stockport.gov.uk

Catering Services: Ms Joyce Rowe, Venue Catering Operations
Manager, Solutions SK Ltd, Venue Catering, Stopford House,
Piccadilly, Stockport SK1 3XE ☎ 0161 474 4575
⌂ joyce.rowe@solutionssk.co.uk

Children / Youth Services: Mr Phil Beswick, Director -
Education Services, Stopford House, Piccadilly, Stockport SK1 3XE
☎ 0161 474 3832 ⌂ phil.beswick@stockport.gov.uk

Children / Youth Services: Ms Chris McLoughlin, Service
Director - Children's Safeguarding & Prevention, Stopford House,
Piccadilly, Stockport SK1 3XE ☎ 0161 474 4624
⌂ chris.mcloughlin@stockport.gov.uk

Civil Registration: Mr Murray Carr, Head of Estate & Asset
Management, Stopford House, Stockport SK1 3XE ☎ 0161 474 3019
⌂ murray.carr@stockport.gov.uk

PR / Communications: Ms Sue Williams, Strategic Head of
Service, Town Hall, Edward Street, Stockport SK1 3XE
☎ 0161 474 2175 ⌂ sue.williams@stockport.gov.uk

Community Planning: Ms Emma Curle, Chief Planning Officer,
Fred Perry House, Piccadilly, Stockport SK1 3XE ☎ 0161 474 3542
⌂ emma.curle@stockport.gov.uk

Community Safety: Mr Ian O'Donnell, Head of Service - Public
Protection, Fred Perry House, Piccadilly, Stockport SK1 3XE
☎ 0161 474 4175 ⌂ ian.odonnell@stockport.gov.uk

Computer Management: Mr Paul James, Head of Information &
Communication, Town Hall, Edward Street, Stockport SK1 3XE
☎ 0161 474 5430 ⌂ paul.james@stockport.gov.uk

Consumer Protection and Trading Standards: Mr Ian
O'Donnell, Head of Service - Public Protection, Fred Perry House,
Piccadilly, Stockport SK1 3XE ☎ 0161 474 4175
⌂ ian.odonnell@stockport.gov.uk

Contracts: Mr Michael Cullen, Borough Treasurer, Stopford House,
Stockport SK1 3XE ☎ 0161 474 4631
⌂ michael.cullen@stockport.gov.uk

Corporate Services: Mrs Laureen Donnan, Deputy Chief
Executive, Town Hall, Edward Street, Stockport SK1 3XE
☎ 0161 474 3180 ⌂ laureen.donnan@stockport.gov.uk

Customer Service: Mrs Alison Blount, Head of Revenues &
Benefits, Stopford House, Piccadilly, Stockport SK1 3XE
☎ 0161 474 5107 ⌂ alison.blount@stockport.gov.uk

Direct Labour: Mr Stephen Morris, Managing Director - Solutions SK, Solutions SK Ltd, Enterprise House, Birdhall Lane, Cheadle Heath, Stockport SK3 0XT ☎ 0161 474 5566
⌀ stephen.morris@solutionssk.co.uk

Economic Development: Ms Nicola Turner, Head of Growth, Fred Perry House, Edward Street, Stockport SK1 3XE
☎ 0161 218 1635 ⌀ nicola.turner@stockport.gov.uk

Education: Mr Phil Beswick, Director - Education Services, Stopford House, Piccadilly, Stockport SK1 3XE ☎ 0161 474 3832
⌀ phil.beswick@stockport.gov.uk

Electoral Registration: Mrs Caroline Cooke, Electoral Services Manager, Town Hall, Edward Street, Stockport SK1 3XE
☎ 0161 474 3184 ⌀ caroline.e.cooke@stockport.gov.uk

Emergency Planning: Mrs Claire Grindlay, Head of Business Support (Place), Stopford House, Edward Street, Stockport SK1 3XE ☎ 0161 474 4191 ⌀ claire.grindlay@stockport.gov.uk

Energy Management: Mr John Millington, Energy Manager, Carillion Stockport Property Services, Stopford House, Piccadilly, Stockport SK1 3XE ☎ 0161 217 6919
⌀ john.millington@carillionplc.com

Environmental / Technical Services: Mr Ian O'Donnell, Head of Service - Public Protection, Fred Perry House, Piccadilly, Stockport SK1 3XE ☎ 0161 474 4175 ⌀ ian.odonnell@stockport.gov.uk

Environmental Health: Mr Ian O'Donnell, Head of Service - Public Protection, Fred Perry House, Piccadilly, Stockport SK1 3XE
☎ 0161 474 4175 ⌀ ian.odonnell@stockport.gov.uk

Estates, Property & Valuation: Mr Murray Carr, Head of Estate & Asset Management, Stopford House, Stockport SK1 3XE
☎ 0161 474 3019 ⌀ murray.carr@stockport.gov.uk

European Liaison: Ms Nicola Turner, Head of Growth, Fred Perry House, Edward Street, Stockport SK1 3XE ☎ 0161 218 1635
⌀ nicola.turner@stockport.gov.uk

Events Manager: Mr Jonathan Whittle, Events Manager, Town Hall, Edward Street, Stockport SK1 3XE ☎ 0161 474 3450
⌀ jonathan.whittle@stockport.gov.uk

Facilities: Ms Julie Newbatt, Operations Lead, Carillion Stockport Property Services, Stopford House, Piccadilly, Stockport SK1 3XE
☎ 0161 217 6915 ⌀ julie.newbatt@carillionplc.com

Finance: Mr Michael Cullen, Borough Treasurer, Stopford House, Stockport SK1 3XE ☎ 0161 474 4631
⌀ michael.cullen@stockport.gov.uk

Fleet Management: Ms Jennie Bannister, Transport Manager - Solutions SK, Solutions SK Ltd, Enterprise House, Bird Hall Lane, Cheadle Heath, Stockport SK3 0XS ☎ 0161 474 3753
⌀ jennie.bannister@solutionssk.co.uk

Health and Safety: Ms Ann-Marie McCullough, CSS Manager - Health, Safety & Wellbeing, Stopford House, Piccadilly, Stockport SK1 3XE ☎ 0161 474 3056
⌀ ann-marie.mccullough@stockport.gov.uk

Home Energy Conservation: Mr Andy Kippax, Strategic Housing Lead, Fred Perry House, Stockport SK1 3XE ☎ 0161 474 4319
⌀ andy.kippax@stockport.gov.uk

Housing: Ms Helen McHale, Chief Executive - Stockport Homes, Stockport Homes, 2nd Floor, 1 St. Peter's Square, Stockport SK1 1NZ ☎ 0161 474 2865 ⌀ helen.mchale@stockporthomes.org

Housing Maintenance: Mr Mark Hudson, Director - Technical Services - Stockport Homes, Stockport Homes, 2nd Floor, St Peter's Square, Stockport SK1 1NZ ☎ 0161 474 4508
⌀ mark.hudson@stockporthomes.org

Legal: Ms Celia Tierney, Head of Service - Legal & Governance, Town Hall, Edward Street, Stockport SK1 3XE ☎ 0161 474 3230
⌀ celia.tierney@stockport.gov.uk

Leisure and Cultural Services: Mr Peter Ashworth, Head of Culture & Leisure, Staircase House, 30 Market Place, Stockport SK1 1ES ☎ 0161 474 2392 ⌀ peter.ashworth@stockport.gov.uk

Licensing: Mr Ian O'Donnell, Head of Service - Public Protection, Fred Perry House, Piccadilly, Stockport SK1 3XE ☎ 0161 474 4175
⌀ ian.odonnell@stockport.gov.uk

Lifelong Learning: Mr Richard Mortimer, Head of Learning & Employment, Stopford House, Piccadilly, Stockport SK1 3XE
☎ 0161 474 3864 ⌀ richard.mortimer@stockport.gov.uk

Lighting: Mr Andrew Suggett, Network Assets Manager, Enterprise House, Oakhurst Drive, Cheadle Heath, Stockport SL3 0XT ☎ 0161 474 2425 ⌀ andrew.suggett@stockport.gov.uk

Member Services: Mr Craig Ainsworth, Democratic Services Manager, Town Hall, Edward Street, Stockport SK1 3XE
☎ 0161 474 3204 ⌀ craig.ainsworth@stockport.gov.uk

Parking: Mr Adam Forbes, Public Realm Manager - Parking, Patrols & Waste, Endeavor House, Bredbury Parkway, Bredbury, Stockport SK6 2SN ☎ 0161 474 3680 ⌀ adam.forbes@stockport.gov.uk

Personnel / HR: Ms Sue Williams, Strategic Head of Service, Town Hall, Edward Street, Stockport SK1 3XE ☎ 0161 474 2175
⌀ sue.williams@stockport.gov.uk

Planning: Ms Emma Curle, Chief Planning Officer, Fred Perry House, Piccadilly, Stockport SK1 3XE ☎ 0161 474 3542
⌀ emma.curle@stockport.gov.uk

Procurement: Mr Michael Cullen, Borough Treasurer, Stopford House, Stockport SK1 3XE ☎ 0161 474 4631
⌀ michael.cullen@stockport.gov.uk

Public Libraries: Ms Janet Wood, Head of Service & Customer Engagement, Fred Perry House, Edward Street, Stockport SK1 3XE
☎ 0161 474 4443 ⌀ janet.wood@stockport.gov.uk

STOCKPORT

Recycling & Waste Minimisation: Mr Adam Forbes, Public Realm Manager - Parking, Patrols & Waste, Endeavor House, Bredbury Parkway, Bredbury, Stockport SK6 2SN ☎ 0161 474 3680 ✆ adam.forbes@stockport.gov.uk

Regeneration: Ms Nicola Turner, Head of Growth, Fred Perry House, Edward Street, Stockport SK1 3XE ☎ 0161 218 1635 ✆ nicola.turner@stockport.gov.uk

Road Safety: Mr Pete Price, Interim Head of Highways & Transportation, Fred Perry House, Stockport SK1 3XE ☎ 0161 474 4901 ✆ pete.price@stockport.gov.uk

Social Services (Adult): Mr Mark Fitton, Director - Operational Social Care, Stopford House, Piccadilly, Stockport SK1 3XE ☎ 0161 474 3198 ✆ mark.fitton@stockport.gov.uk

Social Services (Children): Ms Chris McLoughlin, Service Director - Children's Safeguarding & Prevention, Stopford House, Piccadilly, Stockport SK1 3XE ☎ 0161 474 4624 ✆ chris.mcloughlin@stockport.gov.uk

Public Health: Dr Donna Sager, Deputy Director - Public Health, Stopford House, Edward Street, Stockport SK1 3XE ☎ 0161 474 3928 ✆ donna.sager@stockport.gov.uk

Staff Training: Ms Sue Williams, Strategic Head of Service, Town Hall, Edward Street, Stockport SK1 3XE ☎ 0161 474 2175 ✆ sue.williams@stockport.gov.uk

Sustainable Communities: Ms Nicola Turner, Head of Growth, Fred Perry House, Edward Street, Stockport SK1 3XE ☎ 0161 218 1635 ✆ nicola.turner@stockport.gov.uk

Sustainable Development: Ms Nicola Turner, Head of Growth, Fred Perry House, Edward Street, Stockport SK1 3XE ☎ 0161 218 1635 ✆ nicola.turner@stockport.gov.uk

Tourism: Mr Peter Ashworth, Head of Culture & Leisure, Staircase House, 30 Market Place, Stockport SK1 1ES ☎ 0161 474 2392 ✆ peter.ashworth@stockport.gov.uk

Town Centre: Ms Nicola Turner, Head of Growth, Fred Perry House, Edward Street, Stockport SK1 3XE ☎ 0161 218 1635 ✆ nicola.turner@stockport.gov.uk

Traffic Management: Mr Pete Price, Interim Head of Highways & Transportation, Fred Perry House, Stockport SK1 3XE ☎ 0161 474 4901 ✆ pete.price@stockport.gov.uk

Transport: Mr Pete Price, Interim Head of Highways & Transportation, Fred Perry House, Stockport SK1 3XE ☎ 0161 474 4901 ✆ pete.price@stockport.gov.uk

Transport Planner: Mr Pete Price, Interim Head of Highways & Transportation, Fred Perry House, Stockport SK1 3XE ☎ 0161 474 4901 ✆ pete.price@stockport.gov.uk

Waste Collection and Disposal: Mr Adam Forbes, Public Realm Manager - Parking, Patrols & Waste, Endeavor House, Bredbury Parkway, Bredbury, Stockport SK6 2SN ☎ 0161 474 3680 ✆ adam.forbes@stockport.gov.uk

Waste Management: Mr Adam Forbes, Public Realm Manager - Parking, Patrols & Waste, Endeavor House, Bredbury Parkway, Bredbury, Stockport SK6 2SN ☎ 0161 474 3680 ✆ adam.forbes@stockport.gov.uk

COUNCILLORS

Mayor: Gordon, Chris (LD - Bredbury & Woodley)
cllr.chris.gordon@stockport.gov.uk

Deputy Mayor: Walker, Lisa (CON - Bramhall North)
cllr.lisa.walker@stockport.gov.uk

Leader of the Council: Ganotis, Alexander (LAB - Heatons North)
cllr.a.ganotis@stockport.gov.uk

Deputy Leader of the Council: Wild, Wendy (LAB - Davenport & Cale Green)
cllr.wendy.wild@stockport.gov.uk

Group Leader: Kirkham, Mags (R - Bredbury Green & Romiley)
cllr.m.kirkham@stockport.gov.uk

Group Leader: Lloyd, Syd (CON - Bredbury Green & Romiley)
syd@sparkling-ice.com

Group Leader: Nottingham, Adrian (R - Heald Green)
cllr.a.nottingham@stockport.gov.uk

Group Leader: Roberts, Iain (LD - Cheadle & Gatley)
cllr.iain.roberts@stockport.gov.uk

Abell, Geoff (LD - Marple North)
cllr.geoff.abell@stockport.gov.uk

Allan, Malcolm (LD - Marple North)
cllr.malcolm.allan@stockport.gov.uk

Bagnall, Brian (CON - Bramhall South)
cllr.brian.bagnall@stockport.gov.uk

Bailey, Sheila (LAB - Edgeley & Cheadle Heath)
bailey.harding@ntlworld.com

Blair, Kenny (CON - Marple South)
cllr.kenny.blair@stockport.gov.uk

Bodsworth, Stuart (LD - Cheadle Hulme South)
cllr.stuart.bodsworth@stockport.gov.uk

Booth, Laura (LAB - Offerton)
cllr.laura.booth@stockport.gov.uk

Brett, Walter (LAB - Reddish South)
cllr.walter.brett@stockport.gov.uk

Butler, Kate (LAB - Reddish North)
cllr.kate.butler@stockport.gov.uk

Charles-Jones, Anna (R - Heald Green)
cllr.anna.charles-jones@stockport.gov.uk

Coaton, Richard (LAB - Edgeley & Cheadle Heath)
each.labour@ntlworld.com

Corris, Stuart (CON - Bredbury & Woodley)
cllr.stuart.corris@stockport.gov.uk

Corris, Christine (LD - Bredbury & Woodley)
cllr.christine.corris@stockport.gov.uk

Davies, Dickie (LAB - Davenport & Cale Green)
cllr.dickie.davies@stockport.gov.uk

Dowse, Tom (CON - Marple South)
cllr.tom.dowse@stockport.gov.uk

Driver, Roy (LAB - Reddish North)
cllr.roy.driver@stockport.gov.uk

Finnie, Annette (CON - Marple North)
cllr.annette.finnie@stockport.gov.uk

Fitzpatrick, Dean (LAB - Heatons South)
cllr.d.fitzpatrick@stockport.gov.uk

Foster, Colin (LAB - Heatons South)
colfoster@colfoster.demon.co.uk

Goddard, Dave (LD - Offerton)
cllr.dave.goddard@stockport.gov.uk

Greenhalgh, Graham (LD - Cheadle & Gatley)
cllr.graham.greenhalgh@stockport.gov.uk

Grundy, Tom (LAB - Reddish South)
cllr.tom.grundy@stockport.gov.uk

Guariento, Yvonne (LAB - Reddish South)
cllr.yvonne.guariento@stockport.gov.uk

Hadfield, Paul (CON - Stepping Hill)
cllr.paul.hadfield@stockport.gov.uk

Harding, Philip (LAB - Edgeley & Cheadle Heath)
bailey.harding@ntlworld.com

Hawthorne, Daniel (LD - Manor)
cllr.d.hawthorne@stockport.gov.uk

Holloway, Keith (LD - Cheadle & Gatley)
cllr.keith.holloway@stockport.gov.uk

Holt, Linda (CON - Bramhall North)
cllr.linda.holt@stockport.gov.uk

Humphreys, Sylvia (R - Heald Green)
cllr.sylvia.humphreys@stockport.gov.uk

Hunter, Mark (LD - Cheadle Hulme South)
cllr.mark.hunter@stockport.gov.uk

Hurleston, Mike (CON - Bramhall South)
cllr.mike.hurleston@stockport.gov.uk

Ingham, Susan (LD - Marple South)
cllr.susan.ingham@stockport.gov.uk

Johnstone, Oliver (CON - Hazel Grove)
cllr.oliver.johnstone@stockport.gov.uk

Lewis-Booth, Julian (CON - Hazel Grove)
cllr.julian.lewis-booth@stockport.gov.uk

McAuley, Patrick (IND - Manor)
cllr.patrick.mcauley@stockport.gov.uk

McGahan, John (CON - Bramhall South)
cllr.john.mcgahan@stockport.gov.uk

McGee, Tom (LAB - Heatons South)
tom.mcgee@btinternet.com

Meikle, Wendy (LD - Offerton)
cllr.wendy.meikle@stockport.gov.uk

Murphy, Christopher (LAB - Brinnington & Central)
chris.murf@btinternet.com

Pantall, John (LD - Cheadle Hulme North)
cllr.john.pantall@stockport.gov.uk

Porgess, Paul (LD - Cheadle Hulme North)
cllr.paul.porgess@stockport.gov.uk

Rowles, Maureen (LAB - Brinnington & Central)
cllr.maureen.rowles@stockport.gov.uk

Sedgwick, David (LAB - Heatons North)
cllr.david.sedgwick@stockport.gov.uk

Smart, Lisa (LD - Bredbury Green & Romiley)
cllr.lisa.smart@stockport.gov.uk

Somekh, June (LD - Cheadle Hulme North)
cllr.june.somekh@stockport.gov.uk

Sorton, Andy (LAB - Brinnington & Central)
cllr.andy.sorton@stockport.gov.uk

Stewart, Charlie (LAB - Manor)
cllr.charlie.stewart@stockport.gov.uk

Taylor, John (LAB - Heatons North)
cllr.john.taylor@stockport.gov.uk

Twigge, Jon (LD - Hazel Grove)
cllr.jon.twigge@stockport.gov.uk

Vine, Alanna (CON - Bramhall North)
cllr.alanna.vine@stockport.gov.uk

Weldon, Mark (LD - Stepping Hill)
cllr.mark.weldon@stockport.gov.uk

Wilson, David (LAB - Reddish North)
cllr.david.wilson@stockport.gov.uk

Wilson, Elise (LAB - Davenport & Cale Green)
cllr.elise.wilson@stockport.gov.uk

Wright, John (CON - Stepping Hill)
cllr.john.wright@stockport.gov.uk

Wyatt, Suzanne (LD - Cheadle Hulme South)
cllr.suzanne.wyatt@stockport.gov.uk

POLITICAL COMPOSITION
LAB: 23, LD: 20, CON: 15, R: 4, IND: 1

COMMITTEE CHAIRS

Adult Care Services & Housing: Mr Keith Holloway

Audit: Mr Stuart Corris

Children & Young People: Ms Linda Holt

Health & Wellbeing: Mr Tom McGee

Licensing, Environment & Housing: Mr Christopher Murphy

Planning & Highways: Mr Philip Harding

Stockton-on-Tees   U

Stockton-on-Tees Borough Council, PO Box 11, Municipal Buildings, Church Road, Stockton-on-Tees TS18 1LD
☎ 01642 393939 ∘ customer.comments@stockton.gov.uk
🖥 www.stockton.gov.uk

FACTS AND FIGURES
Parliamentary Constituencies: Stockton North, Stockton South
EU Constituencies: North East
Election Frequency: Elections are of whole council

PRINCIPAL OFFICERS

Chief Executive: Mr Neil Schneider, Chief Executive, PO Box 34, Municipal Buildings, Church Road, Stockton-on-Tees TS18 1LD
☎ 01642 527000 ∘ neil.schneider@stockton.gov.uk

STOCKTON-ON-TEES

Deputy Chief Executive: Mrs Julie Danks, Deputy Chief Executive, Municipal Buildings, Church Road, Stockton-on-Tees TS18 1LD ☎ 01642 527007 ◌ julie.danks@stockton.gov.uk

Senior Management: Mr David Bond, Director - Law & Democracy (Monitoring Officer), PO Box 11, Municipal Buildings, Church Road, Stockton-on-Tees TS18 1LD ☎ 01642 527060 ◌ david.bond@stockton.gov.uk

Senior Management: Ms Beccy Brown, Director - HR, Legal & Communications, Municipal Buildings, Church Road, Stockton-on-Tees TS18 1LD ☎ 01642 527003 ◌ beccy.brown@stockton.gov.uk

Senior Management: Mr Garry Cummings, Director - Finance & Business Services, PO Box 11, Municipal Buildings, Church Road, Stockton-on-Tees TS18 1LD ◌ garry.cummings@stockton.gov.uk

Senior Management: Mrs Julie Danks, Deputy Chief Executive, Municipal Buildings, Church Road, Stockton-on-Tees TS18 1LD ☎ 01642 527007 ◌ julie.danks@stockton.gov.uk

Senior Management: Mr Paul Dobson, Transformation Team Leader, Municipal Buildings, Church Road, Stockton-on-Tees TS18 1LD ☎ 01642 527068 ◌ paul.dobson@stockton.gov.uk

Senior Management: Ms Jane Humphreys, Corporate Director - Children's Services, PO Box 228, Municipal Buildings, Stockton-on-Tees TS18 1XE ☎ 01642 527053 ◌ jane.humphreys@stockton.gov.uk

Senior Management: Dr Peter Kelly, Director - Adults & Health, PO Box 11, Municipal Buildings, Church Road, Stockton-on-Tees TS18 1LD ☎ 01642 527052 ◌ peter.kelly@stockton.gov.uk

Senior Management: Mr Reuben Kench, Director - Culture, Leisure & Events, PO Box 228, Municipal Buildings, Church Road, Stockton-on-Tees TS18 1LD ☎ 01642 527039 ◌ reuben.kench@stockton.gov.uk

Senior Management: Ms Lesley King, Head of Performance & Partnerships, PO Box 11, Municipal Buildings, Church Road, Stockton-on-Tees TS18 1LD ☎ 01642 527004 ◌ lesley.king@stockton.gov.uk

Senior Management: Mr Jamie McCann, Director - Community Services, Stirling House, Tedder Avenue, Thornaby, Thornbury TS17 9JP ☎ 01642 527071 ◌ jamie.mccann@stockton.gov.uk

Senior Management: Mr Richard McGuckin, Director - Economic Growth & Development Services, PO Box 229, Kingsway House, West Precinct, Billingham TS23 2YS ☎ 01642 526765 ◌ richard.mcguckin@stockton.gov.uk

Architect, Building / Property Services: Mr Richard McGuckin, Director - Economic Growth & Development Services, PO Box 229, Kingsway House, West Precinct, Billingham TS23 2YS ☎ 01642 526765 ◌ richard.mcguckin@stockton.gov.uk

Building Control: Mr Raymond Sullivan, Building Control Manager, Gloucester House, Church Road, Stockton-on-Tees TS18 1TW ☎ 01642 526040 ◌ raymond.sullivan@stockton.gov.uk

Catering Services: Mr Jamie McCann, Director - Community Services, Stirling House, Tedder Avenue, Thornaby, Thornbury TS17 9JP ☎ 01642 527071 ◌ jamie.mccann@stockton.gov.uk

Children / Youth Services: Ms Jane Humphreys, Corporate Director - Children's Services, PO Box 228, Municipal Buildings, Stockton-on-Tees TS18 1XE ☎ 01642 527053 ◌ jane.humphreys@stockton.gov.uk

Children / Youth Services: Mr Shaun McLurg, Assistant Director - Safeguarding & Looked After Children, Municipal Buildings, Church Road, Stockton-on-Tees TS18 1LD ☎ 01642 527049 ◌ shaun.mclurg@stockton.gov.uk

Civil Registration: Ms Sue Daniels, Head of Performance & Business Services, Municipal Buildings, Church Road, Stockton-on-Tees TS18 1LE ☎ 01642 393939 ◌ sue.daniels@stockton.gov.uk

Civil Registration: Ms Jayne Robins, Registration & Bereavement Services Manager, Nightingale House, Balaclava Street, Stockton-on-Tees TS18 2AL ☎ 01642 527724 ◌ jayne.robins@stockton.gov.uk

PR / Communications: Ms Beccy Brown, Director - HR, Legal & Communications, Municipal Buildings, Church Road, Stockton-on-Tees TS18 1LD ☎ 01642 527003 ◌ beccy.brown@stockton.gov.uk

PR / Communications: Ms Kirsty Grundy, Senior Media Relations Officer, PO Box 117, Municipal Buildings, Church Road, Stockton-on-Tees TS18 1YD ☎ 01642 528804 ◌ kirsty.grundy@stockton.gov.uk

Community Planning: Mr Gregory Archer, Principal Planning Officer, PO Box 11, Municipal Buildings, Church Road, Stockton-on-Tees TS18 1LD ☎ 01642 526052 ◌ Gregory.Archer@stockton.gov.uk

Community Safety: Mr Mike Batty, Head of Community Protection, 16 Church Road, PO Box 323, Stockton-on-Tees TS18 1XD ☎ 01642 393939 ◌ mike.batty@stockton.gov.uk

Computer Management: Mr Ian Miles, Assistant Director - Xentrall Shared Services, Town Hall DBC, Feethams, Darlington DL1 5QT ☎ 01642 527012 ◌ ian.miles@xentrall.org.uk

Consumer Protection and Trading Standards: Mr David Kitching, Trading Standards & Licensing Manager, 16 Church Road, Stockton-on-Tees TS18 1XD ☎ 01642 526530 ◌ david.kitching@stockton.gov.uk

Contracts: Mr Jamie McCann, Director - Community Services, Stirling House, Tedder Avenue, Thornaby, Thornbury TS17 9JP ☎ 01642 527071 ◌ jamie.mccann@stockton.gov.uk

Corporate Services: Mrs Julie Danks, Deputy Chief Executive, Municipal Buildings, Church Road, Stockton-on-Tees TS18 1LD ☎ 01642 527007 ◌ julie.danks@stockton.gov.uk

Corporate Services: Ms Lesley King, Head of Performance & Partnerships, PO Box 11, Municipal Buildings, Church Road, Stockton-on-Tees TS18 1LD ☎ 01642 527004 ◌ lesley.king@stockton.gov.uk

Customer Service: Ms Kath Hornsey, Customer Services & Administration Manager, PO Box 11, Municipal Buildings, Church Road, Stockton-on-Tees TS18 1LD ☎ 01642 526283 ⌂ kath.hornsey@stockton.gov.uk

Direct Labour: Mr Jamie McCann, Director - Community Services, Stirling House, Tedder Avenue, Thornaby, Thornbury TS17 9JP ☎ 01642 527071 ⌂ jamie.mccann@stockton.gov.uk

Economic Development: Mr Mark Rowell, Business Enterprise Manager, PO Box 34, Municipal Buildings, Church Road, Stockton-on-Tees TS18 1LE ☎ 01642 526010 ⌂ mark.rowell@stockton.gov.uk

Education: Ms Jane Humphreys, Corporate Director - Children's Services, PO Box 228, Municipal Buildings, Stockton-on-Tees TS18 1XE ☎ 01642 527053 ⌂ jane.humphreys@stockton.gov.uk

Education: Ms Diane McConnell, Assistant Director - Schools & SEN, Municipal Buildings, Church Road, Stockton-on-Tees TS18 1LD ☎ 01642 527041 ⌂ diane.mcconnell@stockton.gov.uk

E-Government: Mr Ian Miles, Assistant Director - Xentrall Shared Services, Town Hall DBC, Feethams, Darlington DL1 5QT ☎ 01642 527012 ⌂ ian.miles@xentrall.org.uk

Electoral Registration: Mrs Margaret Waggott, Assistant Director - Administration, Democratic & Electoral Services, PO Box 11, Municipal Buildings, Church Road, Stockton-on-Tees TS18 1LD ☎ 01642 527064 ⌂ margaret.waggott@stockton.gov.uk

Emergency Planning: Mr Stuart Marshall, Emergency Planning Officer, Stirling House, Teddar Avenue, Thornaby, Stockton-on-Tees TS19 9JP ☎ 01642 393939

Energy Management: Mr Ian Hodgson, Maintenance & Facilities Manager, Kingsway House, West Precinct, Billingham TS18 2YS ☎ 01642 526889 ⌂ ian.hodgson@stockton.gov.uk

Environmental / Technical Services: Mr Mike Chicken, Built & Natural Environment Manager, Kingsway House, West Precinct, Billingham TS18 2YS ☎ 01642 528148 ⌂ mike.chicken@stockton.gov.uk

Environmental / Technical Services: Mr Paul Dobson, Transformation Team Leader, Municipal Buildings, Church Road, Stockton-on-Tees TS18 1LD ☎ 01642 527068 ⌂ paul.dobson@stockton.gov.uk

Environmental / Technical Services: Mr Neil Schneider, Chief Executive, PO Box 34, Municipal Buildings, Church Road, Stockton-on-Tees TS18 1LD ☎ 01642 527000 ⌂ neil.schneider@stockton.gov.uk

Environmental Health: Mr Colin Snowdon, Environmental Health Manager, 16 Church Road, Stockton-on-Tees TS18 1XD ☎ 01642 526555 ⌂ colin.snowdon@stockton.gov.uk

Estates, Property & Valuation: Mr Paul Hutchinson, Principal Building Control Surveyor, Queensway House, West Precinct, Billingham TS23 2YQ ☎ 01642 526043 ⌂ paul.hutchinson@stockton.gov.uk

European Liaison: Mr Mark Rowell, Business Enterprise Manager, PO Box 34, Municipal Buildings, Church Road, Stockton-on-Tees TS18 1LE ☎ 01642 526010 ⌂ mark.rowell@stockton.gov.uk

Events Manager: Mr Reuben Kench, Director - Culture, Leisure & Events, PO Box 228, Municipal Buildings, Church Road, Stockton-on-Tees TS18 1LD ☎ 01642 527039 ⌂ reuben.kench@stockton.gov.uk

Finance: Mr Garry Cummings, Director - Finance & Business Services, PO Box 11, Municipal Buildings, Church Road, Stockton-on-Tees TS18 1LD ⌂ garry.cummings@stockton.gov.uk

Finance: Mrs Julie Danks, Deputy Chief Executive, Municipal Buildings, Church Road, Stockton-on-Tees TS18 1LD ☎ 01642 527007 ⌂ julie.danks@stockton.gov.uk

Finance: Mrs Debbie Hurwood, Transformation Manager, Kingsway House, West Precinct, Billingham TS23 2YL ☎ 01642 527014 ⌂ debbie.hurwood@stockton.gov.uk

Fleet Management: Mr Jamie McCann, Director - Community Services, Stirling House, Tedder Avenue, Thornaby, Thornbury TS17 9JP ☎ 01642 527071 ⌂ jamie.mccann@stockton.gov.uk

Fleet Management: Mr John Thirling, Fleet Workshop Assistant, PO Box 11, Municipal Buildings, Church Road, Stockton-on-Tees TS18 1LD ☎ 01642 393939 ⌂ john.thirling@stockton.gov.uk

Grounds Maintenance: Mr Richard Bradley, Care For Your Area Service Manager, Cowpen Lane Depot, Billingham, Stockton-on-Tees TS23 4DD ☎ 01642 393939 ⌂ richard.bradley@stockton.gov.uk

Grounds Maintenance: Mr Jamie McCann, Director - Community Services, Stirling House, Tedder Avenue, Thornaby, Thornbury TS17 9JP ☎ 01642 527071 ⌂ jamie.mccann@stockton.gov.uk

Health and Safety: Mr Derek MacDonald, Health & Safety Manager, Bayhealth House, 5 Prince Regent Street, Stockton-on-Tees TS18 1DF ☎ 01642 528205 ⌂ derek.macdonald@stockton.gov.uk

Health and Safety: Mr Mark Stephenson, Community Services Manager, PO Box 11, Municipal Buildings, Church Road, Stockton-on-Tees TS18 1LD ☎ 01642 393939 ⌂ mark.stephenson@stockton.gov.uk

Highways: Mr Simon Milner, Highway Network Manager, PO Box 229, Kingsway House, West Precinct, Billingham TS23 2YS ☎ 01642 526703 ⌂ simon.milner@stockton.gov.uk

Home Energy Conservation: Mr Mike Chicken, Built & Natural Environment Manager, Kingsway House, West Precinct, Billingham TS23 2YL ☎ 01642 528148 ⌂ mike.chicken@stockton.gov.uk

Housing: Ms Julie Nixon, Transformation Manager, 16 Church Road, Stockton-on-Tees TS18 1TX ☎ 01642 527072 ⌂ julie.nixon@stockton.gov.uk

STOCKTON-ON-TEES

Local Area Agreement: Ms Lesley King, Head of Performance & Partnerships, PO Box 11, Municipal Buildings, Church Road, Stockton-on-Tees TS18 1LD ☎ 01642 527004 ✆ lesley.king@stockton.gov.uk

Legal: Mr David Bond, Director - Law & Democracy (Monitoring Officer), PO Box 11, Municipal Buildings, Church Road, Stockton-on-Tees TS18 1LD ☎ 01642 527060 ✆ david.bond@stockton.gov.uk

Leisure and Cultural Services: Mr Steve Chaytor, Managing Director - Tees Active Ltd, Redheugh House, Thornaby Place, Thornaby, Stockton-on-Tees TS17 6SG ☎ 01642 527322 ✆ steven.chaytor@teesactive.co.uk

Leisure and Cultural Services: Mr Reuben Kench, Director - Culture, Leisure & Events, PO Box 228, Municipal Buildings, Church Road, Stockton-on-Tees TS18 1XE ☎ 01642 527039 ✆ reuben.kench@stockton.gov.uk

Leisure and Cultural Services: Mr Neil Russell, Leisure & Sports Development Manager, Kingsway House, Billingham Town Centre, Billingham TS23 2YS ☎ 01642 526412 ✆ neil.russell@stockton.gov.uk

Licensing: Mr David Kitching, Trading Standards & Licensing Manager, 16 Church Road, Stockton-on-Tees TS18 1XD ☎ 01642 526530 ✆ david.kitching@stockton.gov.uk

Lifelong Learning: Mr Reuben Kench, Director - Culture, Leisure & Events, PO Box 228, Municipal Buildings, Church Road, Stockton-on-Tees TS18 1LD ☎ 01642 527039 ✆ reuben.kench@stockton.gov.uk

Lighting: Mr Simon Milner, Highway Network Manager, PO Box 229, Kingsway House, West Precinct, Billingham TS23 2YS ☎ 01642 526703 ✆ simon.milner@stockton.gov.uk

Lottery Funding, Charity and Voluntary: Ms Julie Nixon, Transformation Manager, 16 Church Road, Stockton-on-Tees TS18 1TX ☎ 01642 527072 ✆ julie.nixon@stockton.gov.uk

Member Services: Mrs Margaret Waggott, Assistant Director - Administration, Democratic & Electoral Services, PO Box 11, Municipal Buildings, Church Road, Stockton-on-Tees TS18 1LD ☎ 01642 527064 ✆ margaret.waggott@stockton.gov.uk

Parking: Ms Joanne Roberts, Traffic & Road Safety Manager, PO Box 11, Municipal Buildings, Church Road, Stockton-on-Tees TS18 1LD ☎ 01642 393939 ✆ joanne.roberts@stockton.gov.uk

Partnerships: Ms Liz Hanley, Assistant Director - Adult Social Care, PO Box 228, Municipal Buildings, Church Road, Stockton-on-Tees TS18 1XE ☎ 01642 527055 ✆ liz.hanley@stockton.gov.uk

Personnel / HR: Ms Beccy Brown, Director - HR, Legal & Communications, Municipal Buildings, Church Road, Stockton-on-Tees TS18 1LD ☎ 01642 527003 ✆ beccy.brown@stockton.gov.uk

Public Libraries: Mr Reuben Kench, Director - Culture, Leisure & Events, PO Box 228, Municipal Buildings, Church Road, Stockton-on-Tees TS18 1LD ☎ 01642 527039 ✆ reuben.kench@stockton.gov.uk

Recycling & Waste Minimisation: Mr Jamie McCann, Director - Community Services, Stirling House, Tedder Avenue, Thornaby, Thornbury TS17 9JP ☎ 01642 527071 ✆ jamie.mccann@stockton.gov.uk

Recycling & Waste Minimisation: Mr Dale Rowbotham, Waste Technical Officer, Stirling House, Tedder Avenue, Thornaby, Thornbury TS17 9JP ☎ 01642 527181 ✆ dale.rowbotham@stockton.gov.uk

Regeneration: Mr James Glancey, Principal Project Officer, PO Box 11, Municipal Buildings, Church Road, Stockton-on-Tees TS18 1LD ☎ 01642 393939 ✆ james.glancey@stockton.gov.uk

Road Safety: Mr Neil Ellison, Sustainability Manager, PO Box 229, Kingsway House, West Precinct, Billingham TS23 2YL ☎ 01642 526736 ✆ neil.ellison@stockton.gov.uk

Road Safety: Mr Simon Milner, Highway Network Manager, PO Box 229, Kingsway House, West Precinct, Billingham TS23 2YS ☎ 01642 526703 ✆ simon.milner@stockton.gov.uk

Road Safety: Ms Joanne Roberts, Traffic & Road Safety Manager, PO Box 11, Municipal Buildings, Church Road, Stockton-on-Tees TS18 1LD ☎ 01642 393939 ✆ joanne.roberts@stockton.gov.uk

Social Services: Ms Jane Humphreys, Corporate Director - Children's Services, PO Box 228, Municipal Buildings, Stockton-on-Tees TS18 1XE ☎ 01642 527053 ✆ jane.humphreys@stockton.gov.uk

Social Services: Ms Diane McConnell, Assistant Director - Schools & SEN, Municipal Buildings, Church Road, Stockton-on-Tees TS18 1LD ☎ 01642 527041 ✆ diane.mcconnell@stockton.gov.uk

Social Services (Adult): Mr Sean McEneany, Transformation Manager, Municipal Buildings, Church Road, Stockton-on-Tees TS18 1LD ☎ 01642 527045 ✆ sean.mceneany@stockton.gov.uk

Social Services (Children): Mr Shaun McLurg, Assistant Director - Safeguarding & Looked After Children, Municipal Buildings, Church Road, Stockton-on-Tees TS18 1LD ☎ 01642 527049 ✆ shaun.mclurg@stockton.gov.uk

Safeguarding: Mr Shaun McLurg, Assistant Director - Safeguarding & Looked After Children, Municipal Buildings, Church Road, Stockton-on-Tees TS18 1LD ☎ 01642 527049 ✆ shaun.mclurg@stockton.gov.uk

Public Health: Dr Peter Kelly, Director - Adults & Health, PO Box 11, Municipal Buildings, Church Road, Stockton-on-Tees TS18 1LD ☎ 01642 527052 ✆ peter.kelly@stockton.gov.uk

Staff Training: Ms Liz Purdy, Principal HR Business Partner, PO Box 11, Municipal Buildings, Church Road, Stockton-on-Tees TS18 1LD ☎ 01642 393939 ✆ liz.purdy@stockton.gov.uk

Street Scene: Mr Jamie McCann, Director - Community Services, Stirling House, Tedder Avenue, Thornaby, Thornbury TS17 9JP ☎ 01642 527071 ✆ jamie.mccann@stockton.gov.uk

Sustainable Communities: Mr Paul Dobson, Transformation Team Leader, Municipal Buildings, Church Road, Stockton-on-Tees TS18 1LD ☎ 01642 527068 ⌨ paul.dobson@stockton.gov.uk

Sustainable Communities: Mr Neil Ellison, Sustainability Manager, Kingsway House, West Precinct, Billingham TS23 2YL ☎ 01642 526736 ⌨ neil.ellison@stockton.gov.uk

Sustainable Communities: Mr Neil Schneider, Chief Executive, PO Box 34, Municipal Buildings, Church Road, Stockton-on-Tees TS18 1LD ☎ 01642 527000 ⌨ neil.schneider@stockton.gov.uk

Sustainable Development: Mr Mike Chicken, Built & Natural Environment Manager, Gloucester House, 70 Church Road, Stockton-on-Tees TS18 1TW ☎ 01642 528148 ⌨ mike.chicken@stockton.gov.uk

Sustainable Development: Mr Neil Ellison, Sustainability Manager, Kingsway House, Billingham Town Centre, Billingham TS23 2YS ☎ 01642 526736 ⌨ neil.ellison@stockton.gov.uk

Town Centre: Mr James Glancey, Principal Project Officer, PO Box 11, Municipal Buildings, Church Road, Stockton-on-Tees TS18 1LD ☎ 01642 393939 ⌨ james.glancey@stockton.gov.uk

Traffic Management: Mr Richard McGuckin, Director - Economic Growth & Development Services, PO Box 229, Kingsway House, West Precinct, Billingham TS23 2YS ☎ 01642 526765 ⌨ richard.mcguckin@stockton.gov.uk

Traffic Management: Mr Simon Milner, Highway Network Manager, PO Box 229, Kingsway House, West Precinct, Billingham TS23 2YS ☎ 01642 526703 ⌨ simon.milner@stockton.gov.uk

Transport: Mr Richard McGuckin, Director - Economic Growth & Development Services, PO Box 229, Kingsway House, West Precinct, Billingham TS23 2YS ☎ 01642 526765 ⌨ richard.mcguckin@stockton.gov.uk

Transport: Mr John Thirling, Fleet Workshop Assistant, PO Box 11, Municipal Buildings, Church Road, Stockton-on-Tees TS18 1LD ☎ 01642 393939 ⌨ john.thirling@stockton.gov.uk

Transport Planner: Mr Richard McGuckin, Director - Economic Growth & Development Services, PO Box 229, Kingsway House, West Precinct, Billingham TS23 2YS ☎ 01642 526765 ⌨ richard.mcguckin@stockton.gov.uk

Transport Planner: Ms Joanne Roberts, Traffic & Road Safety Manager, PO Box 11, Municipal Buildings, Church Road, Stockton-on-Tees TS18 1LD ☎ 01642 393939 ⌨ joanne.roberts@stockton.gov.uk

Waste Collection and Disposal: Mr Richard Bradley, Care For Your Area Service Manager, Cowpen Lane Depot, Billingham, Stockton-on-Tees TS23 4DD ☎ 01642 393939 ⌨ richard.bradley@stockton.gov.uk

Waste Collection and Disposal: Mr Jamie McCann, Director - Community Services, Stirling House, Tedder Avenue, Thornaby, Thornbury TS17 9JP ☎ 01642 527071 ⌨ jamie.mccann@stockton.gov.uk

Waste Management: Mr Jamie McCann, Director - Community Services, Stirling House, Tedder Avenue, Thornaby, Thornbury TS17 9JP ☎ 01642 527071 ⌨ jamie.mccann@stockton.gov.uk

COUNCILLORS

Mayor: Dixon, Kenneth (INDNA - Ingleby Barwick West)
kenneth.dixon@stockton.gov.uk

Deputy Mayor: Perry, Maurice (CON - Fairfield)
maurice.perry@stockton.gov.uk

Leader of the Council: Cook, Robert (LAB - Norton South)
robert.cook@stockton.gov.uk

Deputy Leader of the Council: Beall, Jim (LAB - Roseworth)
jim.beall@stockton.gov.uk

Group Leader: Houchen, Ben (CON - Yarm)
ben.houchen@stockton.gov.uk

Atkinson, Helen (IND - Billingham West)
helen.atkinson@stockton.gov.uk

Bailey, Sonia (LAB - Mandale & Victoria)
sonia.bailey@stockton.gov.uk

Baker, Paul (IND - Newtown)
paul.baker@stockton.gov.uk

Barlow, Chris (LAB - Billingham North)
chris.barlow@stockton.gov.uk

Brown, Derrick (LAB - Stainsby Hill)
derrick.brown@stockton.gov.uk

Cherrett, Julia (LD - Bishopsgarth & Elm Tree)
julia.roberts@stockton.gov.uk

Clark, Carol (LAB - Grangefield)
carol.clark@stockton.gov.uk

Clough, Chris (IND - Billingham West)
chris.clough@stockton.gov.uk

Cooke, Nigel (LAB - Hardwick & Salters Lane)
nigel.cooke@stockton.gov.uk

Corr, Gillian (IND - Ingleby Barwick East)
gillian.corr@stockton.gov.uk

Cunningham, Evaline (LAB - Billingham East)
evaline.cunningham@stockton.gov.uk

Dalgarno, Ian (IND - Village)
ian.dalgarno@stockton.gov.uk

Dennis, Phillip (CON - Eaglescliffe)
phil.dennis@stockton.gov.uk

Faulks, Kevin (INDNA - Ingleby Barwick East)
kevin.faulks@stockton.gov.uk

Gardner, Jonn (CON - Northern Parishes)
jonn.gardner@stockton.gov.uk

Grainge, Lisa (LAB - Bishopsgarth & Elm Tree)
lisa.grainge@stockton.gov.uk

Hall, Lynn (CON - Hartburn)
lynne.hall@stockton.gov.uk

Hampton, Elsi (CON - Yarm)
elsihampton@stockton.gov.uk

Harrington, David (IND - Ingleby Barwick West)
david.harrington@stockton.gov.uk

STOCKTON-ON-TEES

Hewitt, Di (LAB - Stockton Town Centre)
di.hewitt@stockton.gov.uk

Houghton, Stefan (CON - Eaglescliffe)
stefan.houghton@stockton.gov.uk

Inman, Barbara (LAB - Roseworth)
barbara.inman@stockton.gov.uk

Javed, Mohammed (LAB - Parkfield & Oxbridge)
mohammed.javed@stockton.gov.uk

Johnson, Eileen (LAB - Norton South)
eileen.johnson@stockton.gov.uk

Kirton, Paul (LAB - Stockton Town Centre)
paul.kirton@stockton.gov.uk

McCoy, Ann (LAB - Billingham Central)
ann.mccoy@stockton.gov.uk

Mitchell, Allan (LAB - Parkfield & Oxbridge)
allan.mitchell@stockton.gov.uk

Moore, Mick (IND - Village)
mick.moore@stockton.gov.uk

Nelson, Kath (LAB - Norton North)
kathryn.nelson@stockton.gov.uk

Nelson, Steve (LAB - Norton North)
steve.nelson@stockton.gov.uk

O'Donnell, Jean (LAB - Billingham South)
jean.odonnell@stockton.gov.uk

Parry, Stephen (LAB - Billingham North)
stephen.parry@stockton.gov.uk

Patterson, Ross (INDNA - Ingleby Barwick West)
ross.patterson@stockton.gov.uk

Povey, Lauriane (LAB - Billingham North)
lauriane.povey@stockton.gov.uk

Proud, Rachel (LAB - Newtown)
rachael.proud@stockton.gov.uk

Richardson, Stephen (CON - Grangefield)
stephenrichardson.stockton@yahoo.com

Rowling, Paul (LAB - Mandale & Victoria)
paul.rowling@stockton.gov.uk

Smith, Michael (LAB - Billingham South)
michael.smith@stockton.gov.uk

Stephenson, Norma (LAB - Hardwick & Salters Lane)
norma.stephenson@stockton.gov.uk

Stephenson, Andrew (IND - Western Parishes)
afsegg@hotmail.co.uk

Stoker, Mick (LAB - Billingham East)
mick.stoker@stockton.gov.uk

Stott, Tracey (LAB - Mandale & Victoria)
tracey.stott@stockton.gov.uk

Tunney, Laura (CON - Eaglescliffe)
laura.tunney@stockton.gov.uk

Vickers, Matthew (CON - Hartburn)
mathew.vickers@stockton.gov.uk

Walmsley, Sylvia (IND - Stainsby Hill)
sylvia.walmsley@stockton.gov.uk

Watson, Sally Ann (CON - Ingleby Barwick East)
sallyann.watson@stockton.gov.uk

Whitehill, Julia (CON - Yarm)
julia.whitehill@stockton.gov.uk

Wilburn, David (LAB - Norton West)
david.wilburn@stockton.gov.uk

Wilburn, Norma (LAB - Norton West)
norma.wilburn@stockton.gov.uk

Woodhead, Bill (CON - Fairfield)
william.woodhead@stockton.gov.uk

Woodhouse, Barry (LAB - Billingham Central)
barry.woodhouse@stockton.gov.uk

POLITICAL COMPOSITION
LAB: 30, CON: 13, IND: 9, INDNA: 3, LD: 1

COMMITTEE CHAIRS

Adult Services & Health: Mr Mohammed Javed

Audit: Mr Barry Woodhouse

Children & Young People: Ms Carol Clark

Health & Wellbeing: Mr Jim Beall

Licensing: Mr Paul Kirton

Planning: Ms Norma Stephenson

Stoke-on-Trent City   U

Stoke-on-Trent City Council, Civic Centre, Glebe Street,
Stoke-on-Trent ST4 1HH
☎ 01782 234234 ✆ enquiries@stoke.gov.uk 🖳 www.stoke.gov.uk

FACTS AND FIGURES
Parliamentary Constituencies: Stoke-on-Trent Central, Stoke-on-Trent North, Stoke-on-Trent South
EU Constituencies: West Midlands
Election Frequency: Elections are by thirds

PRINCIPAL OFFICERS

Chief Executive: Mr David Sidaway, City Director, Civic Centre, Glebe Street, Stoke-on-Trent ST4 1HH ☎ 01782 236426 ✆ david.sidaway@stoke.gov.uk

Senior Management: Ms Lesley Mountford, Director - Public Health, Civic Centre, Glebe Street, Stoke-on-Trent ST4 1HH

Senior Management: Ms Louise Rees, Director - Children, Adults & Family Services, Civic Centre, Glebe Street, Stoke-on-Trent ST4 1HH ☎ 01782 235988 ✆ louise.rees@stoke.gov.uk

Senior Management: Ms Laura Rowley, Director - Resources & Customer Services, Civic Centre, Glebe Street, Stoke-on-Trent ST4 1HH

Architect, Building / Property Services: Ms Julie Griffin, Assistant Director - Co-operative Working, Civic Centre, Glebe Street, Stoke-on-Trent ST4 1HH ☎ 01782 236365 ✆ julie.griffin@stoke.gov.uk

Building Control: Mr Harmesh Jassall, Strategic Manager - Planning & Building Regulations, Civic Centre, Glebe Street, Stoke-on-Trent ST4 1HH ☏ harmesh.jassall@stoke.gov.uk

Children / Youth Services: Mr Geoff Caterall, Strategic Manager - Inclusion, Civic Centre, Glebe Street, Stoke-on-Trent ST4 1HH ☎ 01782 238812 ☏ geoff.caterall@stoke.gov.uk

Children / Youth Services: Mr Paul Gerrard, Strategic Manager - School Support, Civic Centre, Glebe Street, Stoke-on-Trent ST4 1HH ☎ 01782 236860 ☏ paul.gerrard@stoke.gov.uk

Children / Youth Services: Mr Robert Johnstone, Strategic Manager - Pupil Achievement, Civic Centre, Glebe Street, Stoke-on-Trent ST4 1HH ☎ 01782 236855 ☏ robert.johnstone@stoke.gov.uk

Civil Registration: Mr Martyn Brindley, Strategic Manager - Public Protection, Civic Centre, Glebe Street, Stoke-on-Trent ST4 1HH ☏ martyn.brindley@stoke.gov.uk

PR / Communications: Ms Emma Rodgers, Strategic Manager - Communications & Marketing, Civic Centre, Glebe Street, Stoke-on-Trent ST4 1HH ☏ emma.rodgers@stoke.gov.uk

Computer Management: Mr Neil Mason, Assistant Director - ICT, Libraries & Business Support, Civic Centre, Glebe Street, Stoke-on-Trent ST4 1HH ☎ 01782 232779 ☏ neil.mason@stoke.gov.uk

Computer Management: Ms Janet Preece, Strategic Manager - ICT Operations, Swift House A, Glebe Street, Stoke-on-Trent ST4 1HH ☎ 01782 232899 ☏ janet.preece@stoke.gov.uk

Corporate Services: Mr John Bowler, Strategic Manager - ICT, Civic Centre, Glebe Street, Stoke-on-Trent ST4 1RN ☎ 01782 232553 ☏ john.bowler@stoke.gov.uk

Corporate Services: Ms Kerry Cartlidge, Financial & Commercial Manager, Civic Centre, Glebe Street, Stoke-on-Trent ST4 1HH ☎ 01782 232704 ☏ kerry.cartlidge@stoke.gov.uk

Corporate Services: Mr Neil Chadwick, Governance Manager, Civic Centre, Glebe Street, Stoke-on-Trent ST4 1HH ☎ 01782 233386 ☏ neil.chadwick@stoke.gov.uk

Corporate Services: Ms Helen Dos Santos, Business Services Manager, Civic Centre, Glebe Street, Stoke-on-Trent ST4 1HH ☎ 01782 232655 ☏ helen.dossantos@stoke.gov.uk

Corporate Services: Mr Chris Haines, Team Leader, Civic Centre, Glebe Street, Stoke-on-Trent ST4 1HH ☎ 01782 232666 ☏ chris.haines@stoke.gov.uk

Customer Service: Ms Emily Bagnal, Strategic Manager - Customer Services, Civic Centre, Glebe Street, Stoke-on-Trent ST4 1HH ☎ 01782 235346 ☏ emily.bagnal@stoke.gov.uk

Events Manager: Mr Christopher Austin, Events & Commercial Manager, Civic Centre, Glebe Street, Stoke-on-Trent ST4 1HH ☎ 01782 233222 ☏ christopher.austin@stoke.gov.uk

Finance: Ms Clare Potts, Finance & Commercial Manager - Place, Civic Centre, Glebe Street, Stoke-on-Trent ST4 1HH ☎ 01782 232696 ☏ clare.potts@stoke.gov.uk

Finance: Ms Sue Woodall, Audit Services Manager, Civic Centre, Glebe Street, Stoke-on-Trent ST4 1HH ☎ 01782 232689 ☏ sue.woodall@stoke.gov.uk

Pensions: Mr Neil Harvey, Pay & Conditions Compliance Manager, Civic Centre, Glebe Street, Stoke-on-Trent ST4 1HH ☎ 01782 232651 ☏ neil.harvey@stoke.gov.uk

Health and Safety: Mr Peter Burgess, Strategic Manager - Health, Safety & Emergency, Civic Centre, Glebe Street, Stoke-on-Trent ST4 1HH ☎ 01782 236842 ☏ peter.burgess@stoke.gov.uk

Housing: Mr Carl Brazier, Director - Housing Services, Civic Centre, Glebe Street, Stoke-on-Trent ST4 1HH ☎ 01782 233449 ☏ carl.brazier@stoke.gov.uk

Legal: Ms Fiona Ledden, Assistant Director - Legal, Civic Centre, Glebe Street, Stoke-on-Trent ST4 1HH ☎ 01782 232722 ☏ fiona.ledden@stoke.gov.uk

Leisure and Cultural Services: Ms Michelle Adams, Acting Head - Economic Development, Culture & Sport, Civic Centre, Glebe Street, Stoke-on-Trent ST4 1HH ☎ 01782 235029 ☏ michelle.adams@stoke.gov.uk

Member Services: Mr Paul Baddeley, Scrutiny Officer, Civic Centre, Glebe Street, Stoke-on-Trent ST4 1HH ☎ 01782 233451 ☏ paul.baddeley@stoke.gov.uk

Member Services: Ms Helen Barr, Team Leader - Democratic & Committee Support, Civic Centre, Glebe Street, Stoke-on-Trent ST4 1HH ☎ 01782 232784 ☏ helen.barr@stoke.gov.uk

Member Services: Ms Suzanne Hackley, Team Leader - Cabinet & Committee Support, Civic Centre, Glebe Street, Stoke-on-Trent ST4 1HH ☎ 01782 232622 ☏ suzanne.hackley@stoke.gov.uk

Member Services: Ms Julie Harvey, Team Leader - Democratic & Committee Support, Civic Centre, Glebe Street, Stoke-on-Trent ST4 1HH ☎ 01782 232617 ☏ julie.harvey@stoke.gov.uk

Member Services: Ms Michaleen Hilton, Council & Civil Support Team Leader, Civic Centre, Glebe Street, Stoke-on-Trent ST4 1HH ☎ 01782 232638 ☏ michaleen.hilton@stoke.gov.uk

Personnel / HR: Mr Ed Pilmore, Strategic Manager - Human Resources, Civic Centre, Glebe Street, Stoke-on-Trent ST4 1HH ☎ 01782 232754 ☏ ed.pilmore@stoke.gov.uk

Personnel / HR: Ms Naomi Wood, Strategic Manager - Human Resources, Civic Centre, Glebe Street, Stoke-on-Trent ST4 1HH ☏ naomi.wood@stoke.gov.uk

Procurement: Ms Carolyn Higgs, Specialist Commissioning Manager, Civic Centre, Glebe Street, Stoke-on-Trent ST4 1HH ☎ 01782 237791 ☏ carolyn.higgs@cotswold.gov.uk

STOKE-ON-TRENT CITY

Procurement: Mr Darren Pearce, Strategic Manager - Corporate Procurement, Civic Centre, Glebe Street, Stoke-on-Trent ST4 1HH
☎ 01782 232841 ⏍ darren.pearce@stoke.gov.uk

Public Libraries: Ms Janet Thursfield, Strategic Manager - Libraries & Archives, Civic Centre, Glebe Street, Stoke-on-Trent ST4 1HH ☎ 01782 238497 ⏍ janet.thursfield@stoke.gov.uk

Regeneration: Ms Jo Tyzzer, Assistant Director - Regeneration, Planning & Development, Civic Centre, Glebe Street, Stoke-on-Trent ST4 1HH ☎ 01782 236648 ⏍ jo.tyzzer@stoke.gov.uk

Social Services (Adult): Ms Christine Whitehead, Assistant Director - Adult Social Care, Civic Centre, Glebe Street, Stoke-on-Trent ST4 1HH ☎ 01782 232852
⏍ christine.whitehead@stoke.gov.uk

Social Services (Children): Mr Mark Warr, Assistant Director - Children's Social Care, Civic Centre, Glebe Street, Stoke-on-Trent ST4 1HH ☎ 01782 235903 ⏍ mark.warr@stoke.gov.uk

Public Health: Ms Lesley Mountford, Director - Public Health, Civic Centre, Glebe Street, Stoke-on-Trent ST4 1HH

Transport: Mr Austin Knott, Planning & Transportation Policy Manager, Civic Centre, Glebe Street, Stoke-on-Trent ST4 1HH
⏍ austin.knott@stoke.gov.uk

COUNCILLORS

The Lord Mayor: Munday, Anthony (IND - Baddeley, Milton & Norton)
anthony.munday@stoke.gov.uk

Deputy Lord Mayor: Irving, Ross (CON - Weston Coyney)
ross.irving@stoke.gov.uk

Leader of the Council: Conway, David (IND - Little Chell & Stanfield)
david.conway@stoke.gov.uk

Deputy Leader of the Council: Brown, Abi (CON - Meir Park)
abi.brown@stoke.gov.uk

Group Leader: Pervez, Mohammed (LAB - Moorcroft)
mohammed.pervez@stoke.gov.uk

Baddeley, Melanie (IND - Abbey Hulton & Townsend)
melanie.baddeley@stoke.gov.uk

Banks, Kath (LAB - Hollybush & Longton West)
kath.banks@stoke.gov.uk

Barnes, Jackie (IND - Springfields & Trent Vale)
jackie.barnes@stoke.gov.uk

Beardmore, Craig (CON - Meir Hay)
craig.beardmore@stoke.gov.uk

Bell, Joan (LAB - Blurton East)
joan.bell@stoke.gov.uk

Bell, Mick (UKIP - Fenton West & Mount Pleasant)
mick.bell@stoke.gov.uk

Bowers, Jean (IND - Birches Head & Central Forest Park)
jean.bowers@stoke.gov.uk

Bowers, Sabrina (IND - Birches Head & Central Forest Park)
sabrina.bowers@stoke.gov.uk

Brereton, Jack (CON - Baddeley, Milton & Norton)
jack.brereton@stoke.gov.uk

Bridges, Janine (IND - Great Chell & Packmoor)
janine.bridges@stoke.gov.uk

Broughan, Richard (IND - Abbey Hulton & Townsend)
richard.broughan@stoke.gov.uk

Brown, Lloyd (LAB - Blurton West & Newstead)
lloyd.brown@stoke.gov.uk

Chetwynd, Candi (LAB - Ford Green & Smallthorne)
candi.chetwynd@stoke.gov.uk

Conteh, Randolph (IND - Penkhull & Stoke)
randolph.conteh@stoke.gov.uk

Dale, Rita (IND - Eaton Park)
rita.dale@stoke.gov.uk

Dodd, Lilian (IND - Dresden & Florence)
lilianl.dodd@stoke.gov.uk

Dutton, Alan (LAB - Burslem Central)
alan.dutton@stoke.gov.uk

Evans, David (CON - Baddeley, Milton & Norton)
david.evans@stoke.gov.uk

Follows, Terence (IND - Hanford & Trentham)
terence.follows@stoke.gov.uk

Funnell, Stephen (LAB - Benilee & Ubberley)
stephen.funnell@stoke.gov.uk

Garner, Joy (LAB - Burslem Park)
joy.garner@stoke.gov.uk

Garner, Martin (LAB - Goldenhill & Sandyford)
martin.garner@stoke.gov.uk

Hamer, Olwen (LAB - Sandford Hill)
olwen.hamer@stoke.gov.uk

James, Ann (IND - Great Chell & Packmoor)
ann.james@stoke.gov.uk

Jellyman, Daniel (CON - Hanford & Trentham)
daniel.jellyman@stoke.gov.uk

Kallar, Gurmeet Singh (LAB - Bradeley & Chell Heath)
gurmeetsingh.kallar@stoke.gov.uk

Khan, Majid (LAB - Etruria & Hanley)
majid.khan@stoke.gov.uk

Maqsoom, Sadaqat (CON - Littlewood North & Normacot)
sadaqat.maqsoom@stoke.gov.uk

Pender, Shaun (LAB - Hartshill & Basford)
shaun.pender@stoke.gov.uk

Pitt, Sheila (LAB - Bentilee & Ubberley)
sheila.pitt@stoke.gov.uk

Platt, Andy (LAB - Boothen & Oakhill)
andy.platt@stoke.gov.uk

Powell-Beckett, Joanne (IND - Sneyd Green)
joanne.powell-beckett@stoke.gov.uk

Robinson, Chris (LAB - Broadway & Longton East)
chris.robinson@stoke.gov.uk

Rosenau, Ruth (LAB - Meir North)
ruth.rosenau@stoke.gov.uk

Shotton, Paul (LAB - Fenton East)
paul.shotton@stoke.gov.uk

Wagner, Lee (IND - Tunstall)
lee.wanger@stoke.gov.uk

Watson, Alastair (LAB - Joiners Square)
alastair.watson@stoke.gov.uk

Wazir, Amjid (LAB - Hanley Park & Shelton)
amjid.wazir@stoke.gov.uk

Wheeldon, Debbie (LAB - Meir South)
debbie.wheeldon@stoke.gov.uk

POLITICAL COMPOSITION
LAB: 21, IND: 15, CON: 7, UKIP: 1

COMMITTEE CHAIRS

Adults & Neighbourhoods: Ms Joan Bell

Audit: Ms Jean Bowers

Children & Young People: Mr Shaun Pender

Planning: Mr Ross Irving

Stratford-upon-Avon   D

Stratford-upon-Avon District Council, Elizabeth House, Church Street, Stratford-upon-Avon CV37 6HX
☎ 01789 267575 ▤ 01789 260007 ✆ info@stratford-dc.gov.uk
▣ www.stratford.gov.uk

FACTS AND FIGURES
Parliamentary Constituencies: Stratford-on-Avon
EU Constituencies: West Midlands
Election Frequency: Elections are by thirds

PRINCIPAL OFFICERS

Chief Executive: Mr Dave Webb, Executive Director & Head of Paid Service, Elizabeth House, Church Street, Stratford-upon-Avon CV37 6HX ☎ 01789 260101 ✆ dave.webb@stratford-dc.gov.uk

Assistant Chief Executive: Mr David Buckland, Executive Director, Elizabeth House, Church Street, Stratford-upon-Avon CV37 6HX ☎ 01789 260425 ✆ david.buckland@stratford-dc.gov.uk

Senior Management: Mr Phil Grafton, Head of Government & Democracy / Monitoring Officer, Elizabeth House, Church Street, Stratford-upon-Avon CV37 6HX ☎ 01789 260400 ✆ phil.grafton@stratford-dc.gov.uk

Senior Management: Mr Tony Perks, Head of Technical Services, Elizabeth House, Church Street, Stratford-upon-Avon CV37 6HX ☎ 01789 260620 ✆ tony.perks@stratford-dc.gov.uk

Senior Management: Mr David Platts, Head of ICT & Revenues, Elizabeth House, Church Street, Stratford-upon-Avon CV37 6HX ✆ david.platts@stratford-dc.gov.uk

Senior Management: Mr Robert Weeks, Head of Planning & Housing, Elizabeth House, Church Street, Stratford-upon-Avon CV37 6HX ☎ 01789 260810 ✆ robert.weeks@stratford-dc.gov.uk

Building Control: Mr Martin Bennett, Building Control Team Leader, Elizabeth House, Church Street, Stratford-upon-Avon CV37 6HX ☎ 01789 260684 ✆ martin.bennett@stratford-dc.gov.uk

PR / Communications: Ms Beverley Hemming, Corporate Communications Manager, Elizabeth House, Church Street, Stratford-upon-Avon CV37 6HX ☎ 01789 260105 ✆ beverley.hemming@stratford-dc.gov.uk

Community Safety: Ms Karin Stanley, Governance & Community Safety Manager, Elizabeth House, Church Street, Stratford-upon-Avon CV37 6HX ☎ 01786 260619 ✆ karin.stanley@stratford-dc.gov.uk

Computer Management: Mr Jason Lorenz, Business Development Manager, Elizabeth House, Church Street, Stratford-upon-Avon CV37 6HX ☎ 01789 260479 ✆ jason.lorenz@stratford-dc.gov.uk

Computer Management: Mr David Platts, Head of ICT & Revenues, Elizabeth House, Church Street, Stratford-upon-Avon CV37 6HX ✆ david.platts@stratford-dc.gov.uk

Consumer Protection and Trading Standards: Mr Geoff Turton, Environmental Health Manager, Elizabeth House, Church Street, Stratford-upon-Avon CV37 6HX ☎ 01789 260886 ✆ geoff.turton@stratford-dc.gov.uk

Customer Service: Mr Robert Weeks, Head of Planning & Housing, Elizabeth House, Church Street, Stratford-upon-Avon CV37 6HX ☎ 01789 260810 ✆ robert.weeks@stratford-dc.gov.uk

Economic Development: Mr Dave Webb, Executive Director & Head of Paid Service, Elizabeth House, Church Street, Stratford-upon-Avon CV37 6HX ☎ 01789 260101 ✆ dave.webb@stratford-dc.gov.uk

Electoral Registration: Mr David Dalby, Democratic Services Manager, Elizabeth House, Church Street, Stratford-upon-Avon CV37 6HX ☎ 01789 260210 ✆ david.dalby@stratford-dc.gov.uk

Emergency Planning: Mr Robert Weeks, Head of Planning & Housing, Elizabeth House, Church Street, Stratford-upon-Avon CV37 6HX ☎ 01789 260810 ✆ robert.weeks@stratford-dc.gov.uk

Energy Management: Mr Paul Chapman, Policy Officer, Elizabeth House, Church Street, Stratford-upon-Avon CV37 6HX ☎ 01789 267125 ✆ paul.chapman@stratford-dc.gov.uk

Environmental Health: Mr Tony Perks, Head of Technical Services, Elizabeth House, Church Street, Stratford-upon-Avon CV37 6HX ☎ 01789 260620 ✆ tony.perks@stratford-dc.gov.uk

Estates, Property & Valuation: Mr Tony Perks, Head of Technical Services, Elizabeth House, Church Street, Stratford-upon-Avon CV37 6HX ☎ 01789 260620 ✆ tony.perks@stratford-dc.gov.uk

Finance: Mr David Buckland, Executive Director, Elizabeth House, Church Street, Stratford-upon-Avon CV37 6HX ☎ 01789 260425 ✆ david.buckland@stratford-dc.gov.uk

Grounds Maintenance: Mr Tony Perks, Head of Technical Services, Elizabeth House, Church Street, Stratford-upon-Avon CV37 6HX ☎ 01789 260620 ✆ tony.perks@stratford-dc.gov.uk

STRATFORD-UPON-AVON

Health and Safety: Mr Mark Sainsbury, Premises & Safety Manager, Elizabeth House, Church Street, Stratford-upon-Avon CV37 6HX ☎ 01789 260708 📧 mark.sainsbury@stratford-dc.gov.uk

Home Energy Conservation: Mr Dave Webb, Executive Director & Head of Paid Service, Elizabeth House, Church Street, Stratford-upon-Avon CV37 6HX ☎ 01789 260101 📧 dave.webb@stratford-dc.gov.uk

Housing: Mr Robert Weeks, Head of Planning & Housing, Elizabeth House, Church Street, Stratford-upon-Avon CV37 6HX ☎ 01789 260810 📧 robert.weeks@stratford-dc.gov.uk

Legal: Mr Phil Grafton, Head of Government & Democracy / Monitoring Officer, Elizabeth House, Church Street, Stratford-upon-Avon CV37 6HX ☎ 01789 260400 📧 phil.grafton@stratford-dc.gov.uk

Leisure and Cultural Services: Mr Tony Perks, Head of Technical Services, Elizabeth House, Church Street, Stratford-upon-Avon CV37 6HX ☎ 01789 260620 📧 tony.perks@stratford-dc.gov.uk

Licensing: Mr Tony Perks, Head of Technical Services, Elizabeth House, Church Street, Stratford-upon-Avon CV37 6HX ☎ 01789 260620 📧 tony.perks@stratford-dc.gov.uk

Member Services: Mr David Dalby, Democratic Services Manager, Elizabeth House, Church Street, Stratford-upon-Avon CV37 6HX ☎ 01789 260210 📧 david.dalby@stratford-dc.gov.uk

Partnerships: Mr Dave Webb, Executive Director & Head of Paid Service, Elizabeth House, Church Street, Stratford-upon-Avon CV37 6HX ☎ 01789 260101 📧 dave.webb@stratford-dc.gov.uk

Personnel / HR: Mr David Buckland, Executive Director, Elizabeth House, Church Street, Stratford-upon-Avon CV37 6HX ☎ 01789 260425 📧 david.buckland@stratford-dc.gov.uk

Planning: Mr Robert Weeks, Head of Planning & Housing, Elizabeth House, Church Street, Stratford-upon-Avon CV37 6HX ☎ 01789 260810 📧 robert.weeks@stratford-dc.gov.uk

Procurement: Ms Karin Stanley, Governance & Community Safety Manager, Elizabeth House, Church Street, Stratford-upon-Avon CV37 6HX ☎ 01786 260619 📧 karin.stanley@stratford-dc.gov.uk

Recycling & Waste Minimisation: Mr Tony Perks, Head of Technical Services, Elizabeth House, Church Street, Stratford-upon-Avon CV37 6HX ☎ 01789 260620 📧 tony.perks@stratford-dc.gov.uk

Staff Training: Ms Laila Doman, HR Manager, Elizabeth House, Church Street, Stratford-upon-Avon CV37 6HX ☎ 01789 260709 📧 laila.doman@stratford-dc.gov.uk

Street Scene: Mr Tony Perks, Head of Technical Services, Elizabeth House, Church Street, Stratford-upon-Avon CV37 6HX ☎ 01789 260620 📧 tony.perks@stratford-dc.gov.uk

Sustainable Communities: Mr Dave Webb, Executive Director & Head of Paid Service, Elizabeth House, Church Street, Stratford-upon-Avon CV37 6HX ☎ 01789 260101 📧 dave.webb@stratford-dc.gov.uk

Tourism: Mrs Nancy Singleton, Business Enterprise & Tourism Manager, Elizabeth House, Church Street, Stratford-upon-Avon CV37 6HX ☎ 01789 260803 📧 nancy.singleton@stratford-dc.gov.uk

Waste Collection and Disposal: Mr Tony Perks, Head of Technical Services, Elizabeth House, Church Street, Stratford-upon-Avon CV37 6HX ☎ 01789 260620 📧 tony.perks@stratford-dc.gov.uk

Waste Management: Mr Tony Perks, Head of Technical Services, Elizabeth House, Church Street, Stratford-upon-Avon CV37 6HX ☎ 01789 260620 📧 tony.perks@stratford-dc.gov.uk

Children's Play Areas: Ms Ann Hill, Community Leisure Services Manager, Elizabeth House, Church Street, Stratford-upon-Avon CV37 6HX ☎ 01789 260638 📧 ann.hill@stratford-dc.gov.uk

COUNCILLORS

Chair: Adams, Susan (CON - Alcester & Rural) susan.adams@stratford-dc.gov.uk

Vice-Chair: Atkinson, George (CON - Tanworth-in-Arden) george.atkinson@stratford-dc.gov.uk

Leader of the Council: Saint, Christopher (CON - Shipston North) chris.saint@stratford-dc.gov.uk

Deputy Leader of the Council: Thirlwell, Stephen (CON - Henley-in-Arden) stephen.thirlwell@stratford-dc.gov.uk

Group Leader: Moorse, Peter (LD - Hathaway) pmoorse@cix.co.uk

Barker, Jo (CON - Shipston South) jo.barker@stratford-dc.gov.uk

Barnes, Peter (IND - Welford-on-Avon) peter.barnes@stratford-dc.gov.uk

Brain, Mike (CON - Quinton) mike.brain@stratford-dc.gov.uk

Bromwich, Tony (CON - Southam North) tony.bromwich@stratford-dc.gov.uk

Cargill, Mark (CON - Bidford West & Salford) mark.cargill@stratford-dc.gov.uk

Crump, Andrew (CON - Southam South) andrew.crump@stratford-dc.gov.uk

Dalla Mura, Bart (CON - Red Horse) bart.dallamura@stratford-dc.gov.uk

Fojtik, Jason (LAB - Clopton) jason.fojtik@stratford-dc.gov.uk

Fradgley, Jennifer (LD - Guildhall) jenny.fradgley@stratford-dc.gov.uk

Giles, Molly (CON - Shottery) molly.giles@stratford-dc.gov.uk

Gittus, Mike (CON - Kinwarton) mike.gittus@stratford-dc.gov.uk

Gray, Stephen (CON - Brailes & Compton) stephen.gray@stratford-dc.gov.uk

Harris, Jacqui (CON - Harbury) jacqui.harris@stratford-dc.gov.uk

Howse, Maurice (CON - Avenue) maurice.howse@stratford-dc.gov.uk

Jefferson, Tony (CON - Welcombe)
tony.jefferson@stratford-dc.gov.uk

Kendall, Danny (CON - Wellesbourne West)
danny.kendall@stratford-dc.gov.uk

Kerridge, Justin (CON - Studley with Mappleborough Green)
justin.kerridge@stratford-dc.gov.uk

Kettle, Christopher (CON - Bishop's Itchington)
chris.kettle@stratford-dc.gov.uk

Lawton, Simon (CON - Wootton Wawen)
simon.lawton@stratford-dc.gov.uk

Mills, Christopher (CON - Kineton)
christopher.mills@stratford-dc.gov.uk

Organ, Lynda (CON - Bridgetown)
lynda.organ@stratford-dc.gov.uk

Parry, Anne (CON - Wellesbourne East)
anne.parry@stratford-dc.gov.uk

Payne, Eric (CON - Alcester Town)
eric.payne@stratford-dc.gov.uk

Pemberton, Daren (CON - Bidford East)
daren.pemberton@stratford-dc.gov.uk

Richards, Peter (CON - Snitterfield)
peter.richards@stratford-dc.gov.uk

Riches, Dave (CON - Long Itchington & Stockton)
dave.riches@stratford-dc.gov.uk

Rolfe, Kate (LD - Tiddington)
kate.rolfe@stratford-dc.gov.uk

Seccombe, Philip (CON - Ettington)
philip@seccombes.co.uk

Vaudry, Robert (CON - Bishopton)
robert.vaudy@stratford-dc.gov.uk

Williams, Chris (CON - Napton & Fenny Compton)
chris.williams@stratford-dc.gov.uk

Wright, Hazel (LD - Studley with Sambourne)
hazel.wright@stratford-dc.gov.uk

POLITICAL COMPOSITION
CON: 30, LD: 4, IND: 1, LAB: 1

COMMITTEE CHAIRS

Audit: Mr Maurice Howse

Licensing: Mr Christopher Mills

Licensing: Ms Anne Parry

Licensing: Ms Susan Adams

Stroud   D

Stroud District Council, Council Offices, Ebley Mill, Westward Road, Stroud GL5 4UB
☎ 01453 766321 🖷 01453 750932 ⏚ information@stroud.gov.uk
🖥 www.stroud.gov.uk

FACTS AND FIGURES
Parliamentary Constituencies: Cotswold, Stroud
EU Constituencies: South West
Election Frequency: Elections are by thirds

PRINCIPAL OFFICERS

Chief Executive: Mr David Hagg, Chief Executive, Council Offices, Ebley Mill, Westward Road, Stroud GL5 4UB ☎ 01453 754290
⏚ david.hagg@stroud.gov.uk

Senior Management: Mrs Sandra Cowley, Strategic Head of Finance & Business Services, Council Offices, Ebley Mill, Westward Road, Stroud GL5 4UB ☎ 01453 754340
⏚ sandra.cowley@stroud.gov.uk

Senior Management: Mrs Joanne Jordan, Strategic Head of Customer Services, Council Offices, Ebley Mill, Westward Road, Stroud GL5 4UB ☎ 01453 754005 ⏚ joanne.jordan@stroud.gov.uk

Senior Management: Mrs Allison Richards, Strategic Head of Tenant & Corporate Services, Council Offices, Ebley Mill, Westward Road, Stroud GL5 4UB ☎ 01453 754272
⏚ allison.richards@stroud.gov.uk

Senior Management: Mr Barry Wyatt, Strategic Head of Development Services, Council Offices, Ebley Mill, Westward Road, Stroud GL5 4UB ☎ 01453 754210 ⏚ barry.wyatt@stroud.gov.uk

Architect, Building / Property Services: Ms Alison Fisk, Head of Asset Management, Council Offices, Ebley Mill, Westward Road, Stroud GL5 4UB ☎ 01453 754430 ⏚ alison.fisk@stroud.gov.uk

Architect, Building / Property Services: Mr Andy Nash, Head of Asset Management, Council Offices, Ebley Mill, Westward Road, Stroud GL5 4UB ☎ 01453 754430 ⏚ andy.nash@stroud.gov.uk

Building Control: Mr Paul Bowley, Building Control Manager, Council Offices, Ebley Mill, Westward Road, Stroud GL5 4UB
☎ 01453 754520 ⏚ paul.bowley@stroud.gov.uk

Children / Youth Services: Mrs Joanne Jordan, Strategic Head of Customer Services, Council Offices, Ebley Mill, Westward Road, Stroud GL5 4UB ☎ 01453 754005 ⏚ joanne.jordan@stroud.gov.uk

PR / Communications: Mrs Allison Richards, Strategic Head of Tenant & Corporate Services, Council Offices, Ebley Mill, Westward Road, Stroud GL5 4UB ☎ 01453 754272
⏚ allison.richards@stroud.gov.uk

Community Planning: Mr Barry Wyatt, Strategic Head of Development Services, Council Offices, Ebley Mill, Westward Road, Stroud GL5 4UB ☎ 01453 754210 ⏚ barry.wyatt@stroud.gov.uk

Community Safety: Mr Mike Hammond, Community & Facilities Manager, Council Offices, Ebley Mill, Westward Road, Stroud GL5 4UB ☎ 01453 754447 ⏚ mike.hammond@stroud.gov.uk

Computer Management: Mrs Sandra Cowley, Strategic Head of Finance & Business Services, Council Offices, Ebley Mill, Westward Road, Stroud GL5 4UB ☎ 01453 754340
⏚ sandra.cowley@stroud.gov.uk

Corporate Services: Mrs Allison Richards, Strategic Head of Tenant & Corporate Services, Council Offices, Ebley Mill, Westward Road, Stroud GL5 4UB ☎ 01453 754272
⏚ allison.richards@stroud.gov.uk

STROUD

Customer Service: Mrs Joanne Jordan, Strategic Head of Customer Services, Council Offices, Ebley Mill, Westward Road, Stroud GL5 4UB ☎ 01453 754005 ⊕ joanne.jordan@stroud.gov.uk

Economic Development: Mr Barry Wyatt, Strategic Head of Development Services, Council Offices, Ebley Mill, Westward Road, Stroud GL5 4UB ☎ 01453 754210 ⊕ barry.wyatt@stroud.gov.uk

E-Government: Mrs Sandra Cowley, Strategic Head of Finance & Business Services, Council Offices, Ebley Mill, Westward Road, Stroud GL5 4UB ☎ 01453 754340 ⊕ sandra.cowley@stroud.gov.uk

Electoral Registration: Mrs Allison Richards, Strategic Head of Tenant & Corporate Services, Council Offices, Ebley Mill, Westward Road, Stroud GL5 4UB ☎ 01453 754272 ⊕ allison.richards@stroud.gov.uk

Emergency Planning: Mr Mike Hammond, Community & Facilities Manager, Council Offices, Ebley Mill, Westward Road, Stroud GL5 4UB ☎ 01453 754447 ⊕ mike.hammond@stroud.gov.uk

Energy Management: Mr Jon Beckett, Head of Environmental Health, Council Offices, Ebley Mill, Westward Road, Stroud GL5 4UB ☎ 01453 754443 ⊕ jon.beckett@stroud.gov.uk

Environmental / Technical Services: Mr Jon Beckett, Head of Environmental Health, Council Offices, Ebley Mill, Westward Road, Stroud GL5 4UB ☎ 01453 754443 ⊕ jon.beckett@stroud.gov.uk

Environmental Health: Mr Jon Beckett, Head of Environmental Health, Council Offices, Ebley Mill, Westward Road, Stroud GL5 4UB ☎ 01453 754443 ⊕ jon.beckett@stroud.gov.uk

Estates, Property & Valuation: Ms Jill Fallows, Property Investment Manager, Council Offices, Ebley Mill, Westward Road, Stroud GL5 4UB ☎ 01453 754433 ⊕ jill.fallows@stroud.gov.uk

Facilities: Mr Mike Hammond, Community & Facilities Manager, Council Offices, Ebley Mill, Westward Road, Stroud GL5 4UB ☎ 01453 754447 ⊕ mike.hammond@stroud.gov.uk

Finance: Mrs Sandra Cowley, Strategic Head of Finance & Business Services, Council Offices, Ebley Mill, Westward Road, Stroud GL5 4UB ☎ 01453 754340 ⊕ sandra.cowley@stroud.gov.uk

Grounds Maintenance: Mr Carlos Novoth, Public Spaces Manager, Council Offices, Ebley Mill, Westward Road, Stroud GL5 4UB ☎ 01453 754406 ⊕ carlos.novoth@stroud.gov.uk

Health and Safety: Mr Phil Park, Commercial Services Manager, Council Offices, Ebley Mill, Westward Road, Stroud GL5 4UB ☎ 01453 754471 ⊕ phil.park@stroud.gov.uk

Home Energy Conservation: Mr Jon Beckett, Head of Environmental Health, Council Offices, Ebley Mill, Westward Road, Stroud GL5 4UB ☎ 01453 754443 ⊕ jon.beckett@stroud.gov.uk

Housing: Mr Tim Power, Head of Housing Management, Council Offices, Ebley Mill, Westward Road, Stroud GL5 4UB ☎ 01453 754155 ⊕ tim.power@stroud.gov.uk

Housing Maintenance: Mr Tim Power, Head of Housing Management, Council Offices, Ebley Mill, Westward Road, Stroud GL5 4UB ☎ 01453 754155 ⊕ tim.power@stroud.gov.uk

Legal: Ms Karen Trickey, Legal Services Manager & Monitoring Officer, Council Offices, Ebley Mill, Westward Road, Stroud GL5 4UB ☎ 01453 754396 ⊕ karen.trickey@stroud.gov.uk

Leisure and Cultural Services: Mrs Joanne Jordan, Strategic Head of Customer Services, Council Offices, Ebley Mill, Westward Road, Stroud GL5 4UB ☎ 01453 754005 ⊕ joanne.jordan@stroud.gov.uk

Licensing: Mr Jon Beckett, Head of Environmental Health, Council Offices, Ebley Mill, Westward Road, Stroud GL5 4UB ☎ 01453 754443 ⊕ jon.beckett@stroud.gov.uk

Lottery Funding, Charity and Voluntary: Mrs Joanne Jordan, Strategic Head of Customer Services, Council Offices, Ebley Mill, Westward Road, Stroud GL5 4UB ☎ 01453 754005 ⊕ joanne.jordan@stroud.gov.uk

Member Services: Mrs Allison Richards, Strategic Head of Tenant & Corporate Services, Council Offices, Ebley Mill, Westward Road, Stroud GL5 4UB ☎ 01453 754272 ⊕ allison.richards@stroud.gov.uk

Personnel / HR: Mrs Allison Richards, Strategic Head of Tenant & Corporate Services, Council Offices, Ebley Mill, Westward Road, Stroud GL5 4UB ☎ 01453 754272 ⊕ allison.richards@stroud.gov.uk

Planning: Ms Geraldine LeCointe, Planning Manager, Council Offices, Ebley Mill, Westward Road, Stroud GL5 4UB ☎ 01453 754233 ⊕ geraldine.lecointe@stroud.gov.uk

Procurement: Miss Sarah Turner, Principal Procurement Officer, Council Offices, Ebley Mill, Westward Road, Stroud GL5 4UB ☎ 01453 754346 ⊕ sarah.turner@stroud.gov.uk

Recycling & Waste Minimisation: Mr Carlos Novoth, Public Spaces Manager, Council Offices, Ebley Mill, Westward Road, Stroud GL5 4UB ☎ 01453 754406 ⊕ carlos.novoth@stroud.gov.uk

Regeneration: Mr Mark Russell, Planning Strategy Manager, Council Offices, Ebley Mill, Westward Road, Stroud GL5 4UB ☎ 01453 754305 ⊕ mark.russell@stroud.gov.uk

Staff Training: Mrs Allison Richards, Strategic Head of Tenant & Corporate Services, Council Offices, Ebley Mill, Westward Road, Stroud GL5 4UB ☎ 01453 754272 ⊕ allison.richards@stroud.gov.uk

Street Scene: Mr Carlos Novoth, Public Spaces Manager, Council Offices, Ebley Mill, Westward Road, Stroud GL5 4UB ☎ 01453 754406 ⊕ carlos.novoth@stroud.gov.uk

Sustainable Communities: Mr Barry Wyatt, Strategic Head of Development Services, Council Offices, Ebley Mill, Westward Road, Stroud GL5 4UB ☎ 01453 754210 ⊕ barry.wyatt@stroud.gov.uk

Sustainable Development: Mr Barry Wyatt, Strategic Head of Development Services, Council Offices, Ebley Mill, Westward Road, Stroud GL5 4UB ☎ 01453 754210 ⊕ barry.wyatt@stroud.gov.uk

Tourism: Mrs Joanne Jordan, Strategic Head of Customer Services, Council Offices, Ebley Mill, Westward Road, Stroud GL5 4UB ☎ 01453 754005 ⌨ joanne.jordan@stroud.gov.uk

Total Place: Mrs Joanne Jordan, Strategic Head of Customer Services, Council Offices, Ebley Mill, Westward Road, Stroud GL5 4UB ☎ 01453 754005 ⌨ joanne.jordan@stroud.gov.uk

Waste Collection and Disposal: Mr Carlos Novoth, Public Spaces Manager, Council Offices, Ebley Mill, Westward Road, Stroud GL5 4UB ☎ 01453 754406 ⌨ carlos.novoth@stroud.gov.uk

Waste Management: Mr Carlos Novoth, Public Spaces Manager, Council Offices, Ebley Mill, Westward Road, Stroud GL5 4UB ☎ 01453 754406 ⌨ carlos.novoth@stroud.gov.uk

Children's Play Areas: Mrs Joanne Jordan, Strategic Head of Customer Services, Council Offices, Ebley Mill, Westward Road, Stroud GL5 4UB ☎ 01453 754005 ⌨ joanne.jordan@stroud.gov.uk

COUNCILLORS

Chair: Kay, Norman (GRN - Nailsworth)
cllr.norman.kay@stroud.gov.uk

Vice-Chair: Powell, Gary (LAB - Stonehouse)
cllr.gary.powell@stroud.gov.uk

Baxendale, Martin (GRN - Stroud Valley)
cllr.martin.baxendale@stroud.gov.uk

Binns, Dorcas (CON - Minchinhampton)
cllr.dorcas.binns@stroud.gov.uk

Braun, Catherine (GRN - Wootton-under-Edge)
cllr.catherine.braun@stroud.gov.uk

Brine, Chrisopher (LAB - Stonehouse)
cllr.chris.brine@stroud.gov.uk

Butcher, George (LD - Wootton-under-Edge)
cllr.george.butcher@stroud.gov.uk

Clifton, Miranda (LAB - Cam East)
cllr.miranda.clifton@stroud.gov.uk

Cooper, Nigel (CON - Painswick & Upton)
cllr.nigel.cooper@stroud.gov.uk

Cornell, Doina (LAB - Dursley)
cllr.doina.cornell@stroud.gov.uk

Craig, Gordon (CON - Berkeley Vale)
cllr.gordon.craig@stroud.gov.uk

Curley, Rachel (LAB - Cainscross)
cllr.rachel.curley@stroud.gov.uk

Davies, Stephen (CON - Severn)

Denney, Paul (LAB - Cam West)
cllr.paul.denney@stroud.gov.uk

Dewey, Jim (GRN - Coaley & Uley)
cllr.jim.dewey@stroud.gov.uk

Edmunds, Jonathan (GRN - Randwick, Whiteshill & Ruscombe)
cllr.jonathan.edmunds@stroud.gov.uk

Fellows, Chas (CON - Chalford)
cllr.chas.fellows@stroud.gov.uk

Fryer, Colin (LAB - Dursley)
cllr.colin.fryer@stroud.gov.uk

Hayward, Alison (LAB - Dursley)
cllr.alison.hayward@stroud.gov.uk

Hurst, Nicholas (CON - Minchinhampton)
cllr.nick.hurst@stroud.gov.uk

Job, Julie (CON - Painswick & Upton)
cllr.julie.job@stroud.gov.uk

Jones, Haydn (CON - Berkeley Vale)
cllr.haydn.jones@stoud.gov.uk

Jones, John (CON - Severn)
cllr.john.jones@stroud.gov.uk

Lydon, Stephen (LAB - The Stanleys)
cllr.stephen.lydon@stroud.gov.uk

Marjoram, John (GRN - Stroud Trinity)
cllr.john.marjoram@stroud.gov.uk

McAsey, Phil (CON - Amberley & Woodchester)
cllr.phlip.mcasey@stroud.gov.uk

McKeown, Karen (LAB - Rodborough)
cllr.karen.mckeown@stroud.gov.uk

Miles, Jenny (LAB - Cainscross)
cllr.jenny.miles@stroud.gov.uk

Mossman, Dave (CON - Hardwicke)
cllr.dave.mossman@stroud.gov.uk

Oxley, Gill (CON - Hardwicke)
cllr.gill.oxley@stroud.gov.uk

Pearson, Keith (CON - Painswick & Upton)
cllr.keith.pearson@stroud.gov.uk

Peters, Elizabeth (CON - Chalford)
cllr.elizabeth.peters@stroud.gov.uk

Pickering, Simon (GRN - Stroud Slade)
cllr.simon.pickering@stroud.gov.uk

Prenter, Nigel (LAB - Rodborough)
cllr.nigel.prenter@stroud.gov.uk

Rathor, Skeena (LAB - Stroud Central)
cllr.skeena.rathor@stroud.gov.uk

Reed, Sue (LAB - Nailsworth)
cllr.sue.reed@stroud.gov.uk

Reeves, Mark (CON - Kingswood)

Robinson, Stephen (LAB - Nailsworth)
cllr.steve.robinson@stroud.gov.uk

Ross, Mattie (LAB - Stonehouse)
cllr.mattie.ross@stroud.gov.uk

Studdert-Kennedy, Nigel (IND - The Stanleys)
cllr.nigel.studdert-kennedy@stroud.gov.uk

Sutton, Haydn (CON - Stroud Farmhill & Paganhill)

Tipper, Brian (CON - Cam East)
cllr.brian.tipper@stroud.gov.uk

Tomblin, Jessica (CON - Cam West)
cllr.jessica.tomblin@stroud.gov.uk

Townley, Chas (LAB - Stroud Uplands)

Tucker, Ken (LD - Wootton-under-Edge)
cllr.ken.tucker@stroud.gov.uk

Whiteside, Martin (GRN - Thrupp)
cllr.martin.whiteside@stroud.gov.uk

STROUD

Williams, Thomas (LAB - Cainscross)
cllr.tom.williams@stroud.gov.uk

Williams, Timothy (CON - Bisley)
cllr.tim.williams@stroud.gov.uk

Wride, Penny (CON - Berkley Vale)
cllr.penelope.wride@stoud.gov.uk

Young, Deborah (CON - Chalford)
cllr.debbie.young@stroud.gov.uk

POLITICAL COMPOSITION
CON: 21, LAB: 18, GRN: 8, LD: 2, IND: 1

COMMITTEE CHAIRS

Audit: Mr Nigel Studdert-Kennedy

Community Services & Licensing: Mr Stephen Robinson

Housing: Ms Mattie Ross

Suffolk   C

Suffolk County Council, Endeavour House, 8 Russell Road,
Ipswich IP1 2BX
☎ 0845 606 6067 🖶 01473 214549 🖥 www.suffolk.gov.uk

FACTS AND FIGURES
Parliamentary Constituencies: Suffolk Central and Ipswich North,
Suffolk South, Suffolk West
EU Constituencies: Eastern
Election Frequency: Elections are of whole council

PRINCIPAL OFFICERS

Chief Executive: Ms Deborah Cadman, Chief Executive,
Endeavour House, 8 Russell Road, Ipswich IP1 2BX
☎ 01473 264000 🖑 deborah.cadman@suffolkcc.gov.uk

Assistant Chief Executive: Mr Chris Bally, Assistant Chief
Executive, Endeavour House, 8 Russell Road, Ipswich IP1 2BX
☎ 01473 264000 🖑 chris.bally@suffolk.gov.uk

Senior Management: Ms Sue Cook, Director - Children & Adults,
Endeavour House, 8 Russell Road, Ipswich IP1 2BX
☎ 01473 264000 🖑 sue.cook@suffolk.gov.uk

Senior Management: Mr Geoff Dobson, Director - Resource
Management, Endeavour House, 8 Russell Road, Ipswich IP1 2BX
☎ 01473 264000 🖑 geoff.dobson@suffolk.gov.uk

Senior Management: Mr Abdul Razzaq, Director - Public Health
& Protection, Endeavour House, 8 Russell Road, Ipswich IP1 2BX
🖑 abdul.razzaq@suffolk.gov.uk

Architect, Building / Property Services: Mr Duncan Johnson,
Assistant Director - Corporate Property, Endeavour House, 8
Russell Road, Ipswich IP1 2BX ☎ 01473 264180
🖑 duncan.johnson@suffolk.gov.uk

PR / Communications: Mr Simon Higgins, Head of Communications
& Customer Service, Endeavour House, 8 Russell Road, Ipswich
IP1 2BX ☎ 01473 264000 🖑 simon.higgins@suffolk.gov.uk

Computer Management: Mr Chris Bally, Assistant Chief
Executive, Endeavour House, 8 Russell Road, Ipswich IP1 2BX
☎ 01473 264000 🖑 chris.bally@suffolk.gov.uk

Consumer Protection and Trading Standards: Mr Matt West,
Assistant Director - Trading Standards, Endeavour House, 8 Russell
Road, Ipswich IP1 2BX ☎ 01473 264866 🖑 matt.west@suffolk.gov.uk

Contracts: Mr Aidan Dunn, Assistant Director - Procurement &
Contract Management, Endeavour House, 8 Russell Road, Ipswich
IP1 2BX ☎ 01473 264000 🖑 aidan.dunn@suffolk.gov.uk

Customer Service: Mr Simon Higgins, Head of Communications
& Customer Service, Endeavour House, 8 Russell Road, Ipswich
IP1 2BX ☎ 01473 264000 🖑 simon.higgins@suffolk.gov.uk

Economic Development: Ms Sue Roper, Assistant Director -
Strategic Development, Endeavour House, 8 Russell Road, Ipswich
IP1 2BX ☎ 01473 264000 🖑 sue.roper@sufolk.gov.uk

Electoral Registration: Ms Sue Morgan, Head of Democratic
Services, Endeavour House, 8 Russell Road, Ipswich IP1 2BX
☎ 01473 264512 🖑 sue.morgan@suffolk.gov.uk

Emergency Planning: Mr Andrew Osman, Head of Emergency
Planning, Suffolk Joint Emergency Planning Unit, GFB3 Endeavour
House, 8 Russell Road, Ipswich IP1 2BX ☎ 01473 265332
🖑 andrew.osman@suffolk.gov.uk

Facilities: Mr James Carrick, Corporate Facilities Co-ordinator,
Endeavour House, 8 Russell Road, Ipswich IP1 2BX
☎ 01473 264000 🖑 james.carrick@suffolk.gov.uk

Finance: Mr Geoff Dobson, Director - Resource Management,
Endeavour House, 8 Russell Road, Ipswich IP1 2BX
☎ 01473 264000 🖑 geoff.dobson@suffolk.gov.uk

Health and Safety: Mr Paul Butcher, Head of Health & Safety,
Endeavour House, 8 Russell Road, Ipswich IP1 2BX
☎ 01473 264000 🖑 paul.butcher@suffolk.gov.uk

Highways: Mr Mark Stevens, Assistant Director - Operational
Highways, Endeavour House, 8 Russell Road, Ipswich IP1 2BX
☎ 01473 264000 🖑 mark.stevens@suffolk.gov.uk

Local Area Agreement: Ms Clair Harvey, Business Development
Specialist, Endeavour House, 8 Russell Road, Ipswich IP1 2BX
☎ 01473 265304 🖑 clair.harvey@suffolk.gov.uk

Legal: Mr Tim Earl, Head of Legal Services, Endeavour House, 8
Russell Road, Ipswich IP1 2BX ☎ 01473 260860
🖑 tim.earl@suffolk.gov.uk

Legal: Mr Tim Ryder, Assistant Director & Monitoring Officer,
Endeavour House, 8 Russell Road, Ipswich IP1 2BX
☎ 01473 583000 🖑 tim.ryder@suffolk.gov.uk

Member Services: Ms Sue Morgan, Head of Democratic Services,
Endeavour House, 8 Russell Road, Ipswich IP1 2BX
☎ 01473 264512 🖑 sue.morgan@suffolk.gov.uk

Personnel / HR: Ms Sally Marlow, Head of Strategic Human Resources, Endeavour House, 8 Russell Road, Ipswich IP1 2BX
☎ 01473 264000 ◌ sally.marlow@suffolk.gov.uk

Planning: Ms Sue Roper, Assistant Director - Strategic Development, Endeavour House, 8 Russell Road, Ipswich IP1 2BX
☎ 01473 264000 ◌ sue.roper@sufolk.gov.uk

Recycling & Waste Minimisation: Mr Steve Palfrey, Head - Waste, Endeavour House, 8 Russell Road, Ipswich IP1 2BX
☎ 01473 264787 ◌ steve.palfrey@suffolk.gov.uk

Road Safety: Mr Mike Motteram, Road Safety Manager, Endeavour House, 8 Russell Road, Ipswich IP1 2BX
☎ 01743 264996 ◌ mike.motteram@suffolk.gov.uk

Public Health: Mr Abdul Razzaq, Director - Public Health & Protection, Endeavour House, 8 Russell Road, Ipswich IP1 2BX
◌ abdul.razzaq@suffolk.gov.uk

Waste Collection and Disposal: Mr Steve Palfrey, Head - Waste, Endeavour House, 8 Russell Road, Ipswich IP1 2BX
☎ 01473 264787 ◌ steve.palfrey@suffolk.gov.uk

Waste Management: Mr Steve Palfrey, Head - Waste, Endeavour House, 8 Russell Road, Ipswich IP1 2BX ☎ 01473 264787
◌ steve.palfrey@suffolk.gov.uk

COUNCILLORS

Leader of the Council: Noble, Colin (CON - Row Heath)
colin.noble@suffolk.gov.uk

Deputy Leader of the Council: Storey, Jane (CON - Thedwastre North)
jane.storey@suffolk.gov.uk

Group Leader: Ereira, Mark (GRN - Tower)
mark.ereira@suffolk.gov.uk

Group Leader: Martin, Sandy (LAB - St John's)
sandy.martin@suffolk.gov.uk

Group Leader: Mountford, Bill (UKIP - Lowestoft South)
bill.mountford@suffolk.gov.uk

Group Leader: Wood, David (LD - Peninsula)
david.wood@suffolk.gov.uk

Adams, Sarah (LAB - St Margaret's & Westgate)
sarah.adams@suffolk.gov.uk

Antill, Jenny (CON - Cosford)
jenny.antill@suffolk.gov.uk

Armitage, Helen (LAB - Chantry)
helen.armitage@suffolk.gov.uk

Barber, Nick (CON - Felixstowe Coastal)
nick.barber@suffolk.gov.uk

Barker, Sonia (LAB - Pakefield)
sonia.barker@suffolk.gov.uk

Beckwith, Trevor (IND - Eastgate & Moreton Hall)
trevor.beckwith@suffolk.gov.uk

Bee, Mark (CON - Beccles)
mark.bee@suffolk.gov.uk

Beer, Peter (CON - Great Cornard)
peter.beer@suffolk.gov.uk

Bole, Kathy (LAB - Whitehouse & Whitton)
kathy.bole@suffolk.gov.uk

Bond, Michael (CON - Wickham)
michael.bond@suffolk.gov.uk

Brown, Tony (UKIP - Haverhill East & Kedington)
tony.brown@suffolk.gov.uk

Burns, John (UKIP - Haverhill Cangle)
john.burns@suffolk.gov.uk

Burroughes, Stephen (CON - Framlingham)
stephen.burroughes@suffolk.gov.uk

Busby, David (LD - Belstead Brook)
david.busby@suffolk.gov.uk

Byatt, Peter (LAB - Pakefield)
peter.byatt@suffolk.gov.uk

Clements, Kim (LAB - Gainsborough)
kim.clements@suffolk.gov.uk

Clements, Terry (CON - Thingoe South)
terry.clements@suffolk.gov.uk

Craig, Janet (LAB - Gunton)
janet.craig@suffolk.gov.uk

Crossley, James (UKIP - Whitehouse & Whitton)
james.crossley@suffolk.gov.uk

Evans, Mary (CON - Clare)
mary.evans@suffolk.gov.uk

Field, John (LD - Gipping Valley)
john.field@suffolk.gov.uk

Finch, James (CON - Stour Valley)
james.finch@suffolk.gov.uk

Fleming, Jessica (CON - Hartismere)
jessica.fleming@suffolk.gov.uk

Flood, Julian (UKIP - Haverhill Cangle)
julian.flood@suffolk.gov.uk

Gage, Sandra (LAB - Rushmere)
sandra.gage@suffolk.gov.uk

Gardiner, Peter (LAB - Chantry)
peter.gardiner@suffolk.gov.uk

Gaylard, Mandy (LAB - St Helen's)
mandy.gaylard@suffolk.gov.uk

Goldson, Tony (CON - Halesworth)
tony.goldson@suffolk.gov.uk

Goodwin, John (CON - Felixstowe North & Trimley)
john.goodwin@suffolk.gov.uk

Gower, Michael (CON - Blything)
michael.gower@suffolk.gov.uk

Green, Gary (CON - Stowmarket North & Stowupland)
gary.green@suffolk.gov.uk

Hackett, Derek (UKIP - Lowestoft South)
derek.hackett@suffolk.gov.uk

Hicks, Matthew (CON - Thredling)
matthew.hicks@suffolk.gov.uk

Hopfensperger, Rebecca (CON - Thingoe North)
rebecca.hopfensperger@suffolk.gov.uk

Hudson, Christopher (CON - Kesgrave & Rushmere St Andrew)
christopher.hudson@suffolk.gov.uk

SUFFOLK

Hudson, David (UKIP - Exning & Newmarket)
david.hudson@suffolk.gov.uk

Jacklin, Leonard (LAB - Oulton)
leonard.jacklin@suffolk.gov.uk

Jones, Gordon (CON - Samford)
gordon.jones@suffolk.gov.uk

Kemp, Richard (IND - Melford)

Ladd, Michael (CON - Kessingland & Southwold)
michael.ladd@suffolk.gov.uk

Lockington, Inga (LD - St Margaret's & Westgate)
inga.lockington@suffolk.gov.uk

McGregor, Guy (CON - Hoxne & Eye)
guy.mcgregor@suffolk.gov.uk

Millar, Robin (CON - Newmarket & Red Lodge)
robin.millar@suffolk.gov.uk

Nettleton, David (IND - Tower)
david.nettleton@suffolk.gov.uk

Newman, Graham (CON - Felixstowe Coastal)
graham.newman@.suffolk.gov.uk

O'Brien, Patricia (CON - Martlesham)
patricia.obrien@suffolk.gov.uk

Otton, Penny (LD - Thedwastre South)
penny.otton@.suffolk.gov.uk

Page, Caroline (LD - Woodbridge)
caroline.page@suffolk.gov.uk

Patience, Keith (LAB - Gunton)
keith.patience@suffolk.gov.uk

Poole, Bert (UKIP - Oulton)
bert.poole@suffolk.gov.uk

Punt, Chris (CON - Beccles)
chris.punt@suffolk.gov.uk

Quinton, Bill (LAB - Priory Heath)
bill.quinton@suffolk.gov.uk

Reid, Andrew (CON - Wilford)
andrew.reid@suffolk.gov.uk

Ritchie, David (CON - Bungay)
david.ritchie@suffolk.gov.uk

Rudkin, Bryony (LAB - Bridge)
bryony.rudkin@suffolkcc.gov.uk

Sayers, John (CON - Sudbury)
john.sayers@suffolk.gov.uk

Searle, Stephen (UKIP - Stowmarket South)
stephen.searle@suffolk.gov.uk

Sheldrick, Trevor (LD - Hadleigh)
trevor.sheldrick@suffolk.gov.uk

Silvester, Reg (UKIP - Brandon)
reg.silvester@suffolk.gov.uk

Smith, Richard (CON - Aldeburgh & Leiston)
richard.smith@suffolk.gov.uk

Spence, Colin (CON - Sudbury East & Waldingfield)
colin.spence@suffolk.gov.uk

Spicer, Joanna (CON - Blackbourn)
joanna.spicer@suffolk.gov.uk

Stamp, Sarah (CON - Hardwick)
sarah.stamp@suffolk.gov.uk

Stringer, Andrew (GRN - Upper Gipping)
andrew.stringer@suffolk.gov.uk

Truelove, Julia (LD - Bosmere)
julia.truelove@suffolk.gov.uk

Vickery, Robin (CON - Carlford)
robin.vickery@suffolk.gov.uk

Waters, James (CON - Mildenhall)
james.waters@suffolk.gov.uk

West, Paul (CON - Bixley)
paul.west@suffolk.gov.uk

Whiting, Robert (CON - Kesgrave & Rushmere St Andrew)
robert.whiting@suffolk.gov.uk

POLITICAL COMPOSITION
CON: 37, LAB: 15, UKIP: 10, LD: 8, IND: 3, GRN: 2

COMMITTEE CHAIRS

Audit: Mr Michael Bond

Development Control: Mr Peter Beer

Education & Children's Services: Mr Graham Newman

Health & Wellbeing: Mr Tony Goldson

Pensions: Mr Andrew Reid

Suffolk Coastal   D

Suffolk Coastal District Council, Council Offices, Melton Hill, Woodbridge IP12 1AU
☎ 01394 383789 📠 01394 385100 🖳 www.suffolkcoastal.gov.uk

FACTS AND FIGURES
Parliamentary Constituencies: Suffolk Coastal
EU Constituencies: Eastern
Election Frequency: Elections are of whole council

PRINCIPAL OFFICERS

Chief Executive: Mr Stephen Baker, Chief Executive, Council Offices, Melton Hill, Woodbridge IP12 1AU ☎ 01394 444348 ⎷ chiefexecutive@eastsuffolk.gov.uk

Senior Management: Mr Arthur Charvonia, Strategic Director, Council Offices, Melton Hill, Woodbridge IP12 1AU ☎ 01502 523606 ⎷ arthur.charvonia@eastsuffolk.gov.uk

Senior Management: Mr Andrew Jarvis, Strategic Director, Council Offices, Melton Hill, Woodbridge IP12 1AU ☎ 01394 444323 ⎷ andrew.jarvis@eastsuffolk.gov.uk

Building Control: Mr Philip Ridley, Head of Planning Services, Council Offices, Melton Hill, Woodbridge IP12 1AU ☎ 01502 562111 ⎷ philip.ridley@eastsuffolk.gov.uk

PR / Communications: Mr Steve Henry, Communications Manager, Council Offices, Melton Hill, Woodbridge IP12 1AU ☎ 01394 444361 ⎷ steve.henry@eastsuffolk.gov.uk

Community Planning: Mr Philip Ridley, Head of Planning Services, Council Offices, Melton Hill, Woodbridge IP12 1AU ☎ 01502 562111 ⏱ philip.ridley@eastsuffolk.gov.uk

Community Safety: Mr Richard Best, Active Communities Manager, Council Offices, Melton Hill, Woodbridge IP12 1AU ☎ 01502 562111 ⏱ richard.best@eastsuffolk.gov.uk

Computer Management: Ms Sandra Lewis, ICT & Programme Manager, Council Offices, Melton Hill, Woodbridge IP12 1AU ☎ 01394 444205 ⏱ sandra.lewis@eastsuffolk.gov.uk

Contracts: Mr Ian Purdom, Principal Service Manager, Council Offices, Melton Hill, Woodbridge IP12 1AU ☎ 01502 523507 ⏱ ian.purdom@eastsuffolk.gov.uk

Customer Service: Mr Darren Knight, Head of Customer Services, Council Offices, Melton Hill, Woodbridge IP12 1AU ☎ 01502 523330 ⏱ darren.knight@eastsuffolk.gov.uk

Economic Development: Mrs Catherine Thornber, Economic Services Manager, Council Offices, Melton Hill, Woodbridge IP12 1AU ☎ 01394 652111 ⏱ catherine.thornber@eastsuffolk.gov.uk

Electoral Registration: Mrs Karen Last, Electoral Services Manager, Council Offices, Melton Hill, Woodbridge IP12 1AU ☎ 01394 444324 ⏱ karen.last@eastsuffolk.gov.uk

Environmental Health: Mr Phil Gore, Head of Environmental Services & Port Health, Council Offices, Melton Hill, Woodbridge IP12 1AU ☎ 01502 652111 ⏱ phil.gore@eastsuffolk.gov.uk

Estates, Property & Valuation: Mr Andrew Jarvis, Strategic Director, Council Offices, Melton Hill, Woodbridge IP12 1AU ☎ 01394 444323 ⏱ andrew.jarvis@eastsuffolk.gov.uk

Finance: Ms Homira Javadi, Chief Finance Officer, Council Offices, Melton Hill, Woodbridge IP12 1AU ☎ 01502 562111 ⏱ homira.javadi@eastsuffolk.gov.uk

Health and Safety: Mr Phil Gore, Head of Environmental Services & Port Health, Council Offices, Melton Hill, Woodbridge IP12 1AU ☎ 01502 652111 ⏱ phil.gore@eastsuffolk.gov.uk

Health and Safety: Mr Mark Sims, Food & Safety Manager, Council Offices, Melton Hill, Woodbridge IP12 1AU ☎ 01394 444356 ⏱ mark.sims@suffolkcoastal.gov.uk

Home Energy Conservation: Mrs Teresa Howarth, Environmental Health Officer, Council Offices, Melton Hill, Woodbridge IP12 1AU ☎ 01394 444206 ⏱ teresa.howarth@suffolkcoastal.gov.uk

Housing: Mr Justin Hunt, Head of Housing Services, Council Offices, Melton Hill, Woodbridge IP12 1AU ☎ 01502 523144 ⏱ justin.hunt@eastsuffolk.gov.uk

Legal: Mrs Hilary Slater, Head of Legal & Democratic Services, Council Offices, Melton Hill, Woodbridge IP12 1AU ☎ 01502 562111 ⏱ hilary.slater@eastsuffolk.gov.uk

Leisure and Cultural Services: Mr Andrew Jarvis, Strategic Director, Council Offices, Melton Hill, Woodbridge IP12 1AU ☎ 01394 444323 ⏱ andrew.jarvis@eastsuffolk.gov.uk

Lifelong Learning: Mrs Heather Shilling, Human Resources Officer, Council Offices, Melton Hill, Woodbridge IP12 1AU ☎ 01502 523221 ⏱ heather.shilling@eastsuffolk.gov.uk

Lottery Funding, Charity and Voluntary: Mr Richard Best, Active Communities Manager, Council Offices, Melton Hill, Woodbridge IP12 1AU ☎ 01502 562111 ⏱ richard.best@eastsuffolk.gov.uk

Member Services: Mrs Karen Cook, Cabinet Business Manager, Council Offices, Melton Hill, Woodbridge IP12 1AU ☎ 01394 444326 ⏱ Karen.cook@suffolkcoastal.gov.uk

Personnel / HR: Mrs Carol Lower, Human Resources & Workforce Development Manager, Council Offices, Melton Hill, Woodbridge IP12 1AU ☎ 01502 523228 ⏱ carol.lower@eastsuffolk.gov.uk

Planning: Mr Philip Ridley, Head of Planning Services, Council Offices, Melton Hill, Woodbridge IP12 1AU ☎ 01502 562111 ⏱ philip.ridley@eastsuffolk.gov.uk

Procurement: Mr Ian Purdom, Principal Service Manager, Council Offices, Melton Hill, Woodbridge IP12 1AU ☎ 01502 523507 ⏱ ian.purdom@eastsuffolk.gov.uk

Regeneration: Mr Paul Wood, Head of Economic Development & Regeneration, Council Offices, Melton Hill, Woodbridge IP12 1AU ☎ 01508 562111 ⏱ paul.wood@eastsuffolk.gov.uk

Staff Training: Mrs Heather Shilling, Human Resources Officer, Council Offices, Melton Hill, Woodbridge IP12 1AU ☎ 01502 523221 ⏱ heather.shilling@eastsuffolk.gov.uk

Sustainable Development: Mr Philip Ridley, Head of Planning Services, Council Offices, Melton Hill, Woodbridge IP12 1AU ☎ 01502 562111 ⏱ philip.ridley@eastsuffolk.gov.uk

Tourism: Mrs Catherine Thornber, Economic Services Manager, Council Offices, Melton Hill, Woodbridge IP12 1AU ☎ 01394 652111 ⏱ catherine.thornber@eastsuffolk.gov.uk

COUNCILLORS

Leader of the Council: Herring, Ray (CON - Orford & Eyke) ray.herring@suffolkcoastal.gov.uk

Deputy Leader of the Council: Holdcroft, Geoff (CON - Woodbridge) geoff.holdcroft@suffolkcoastal.gov.uk

Amoss, Mark (CON - Wickham Market) mark.amoss@suffolkcoastal.gov.uk

Bidwell, Jim (CON - Melton) james.bidwell@suffolkcoastal.gov.uk

Bird, Stuart (CON - Felixstowe West) stuart.bird@suffolkcoastal.gov.uk

Block, Christine (LD - Deben) christine.block@suffolkcoastal.gov.uk

SUFFOLK COASTAL

Bloomfield, Stephen (CON - Felixstowe North)
stephen.bloomfield@suffolkcoastal.gov.uk

Blundell, Chris (CON - Martlesham)
chris.blundell@suffolkcoastal.gov.uk

Bond, Michael (CON - Rendlesham)
michael.bond@suffolkcoastal.gov.uk

Burroughes, Stephen (CON - Peasenhall & Yoxford)
stephen.burroughes@suffolkcoastal.gov.uk

Catchpole, Raymond (CON - Wenhaston & Westleton)
raymond.catchpole@suffolkcoastal.gov.uk

Coleman, Peter (CON - Felixstowe South)
peter.coleman@suffolkcoastal.gov.uk

Cooper, Tony (IND - Leiston)
tony.cooper@suffolkcoastal.gov.uk

Day, Jane (CON - Melton)
jane.day@suffolkcoastal.gov.uk

Deacon, Mike (LAB - Felixstowe North)
michael.deacon@suffolkcoastal.gov.uk

Dean, Deborah (CON - Tower)
deborah.dean@suffolkcoastal.gov.uk

Dunnett, Phillip (CON - Saxmundham)
phillip.dunnett@suffolkcoastal.gov.uk

Fisher, John (IND - Saxmundham)
john.fisher@suffolkcoastal.gov.uk

Fryatt, Tony (CON - Grundisburgh)
tony.fryatt@suffolkcoastal.gov.uk

Gallant, Steve (CON - Felixstowe East)
steve.gallant@suffolkcoastal.gov.uk

Green, Tracey (CON - Felixstowe West)
tracey.green@suffolkcoastal.gov.uk

Harding, Graham (CON - The Trimleys)
graham.harding@suffolkcoastal.gov.uk

Harvey, Susan (CON - Kirton)
susan.harvey@suffolkcoastal.gov.uk

Haworth, Terry-Jill (CON - Aldeburgh)
terry-jill.haworth@suffolkcoastal.gov.uk

Hedgley, Colin (CON - Woodbridge)
colin.hedgley@suffolkcoastal.gov.uk

Hudson, Christopher (CON - Framlingham)
christopher.hudson@suffolkcoastal.gov.uk

Jones, Maureen (CON - Aldeburgh)
maureen.jones@suffolkcoastal.gov.uk

Kelso, John (LD - Martlesham)
john.kelso@suffolkcoastal.gov.uk

Kerry, Richard (CON - The Trimleys)
richard.kerry@suffolkcoastal.gov.uk

Lawson, Stuart (CON - Kesgrave West)
stuart.lawson@suffolkcoastal.gov.uk

Lynch, Geoff (CON - Kesgrave East)
geoff.lynch@suffolkcoastal.gov.uk

McCallum, Debbie (CON - Kesgrave West)
debbie.mccallum@suffolkcoastal.gov.uk

Mower, Sue (CON - Kesgrave East)
susan.mower@suffolkcoastal.gov.uk

Mulcahy, Patti (CON - Woodbridge)
patricia.mulcahy@suffolkcoastal.gov.uk

Newton, Mark (CON - Tower)
mark.newton@suffolkcoastal.gov.uk

Poulter, Carol (CON - Hacheston)
carol.poulter@suffolkcoastal.gov.uk

Pratt, Ian (CON - Leiston)
ian.pratt@suffolkcoastal.gov.uk

Rous, Paul (CON - Framlingham)
paul.rous@suffolkcoastal.gov.uk

Savage, Doreen (CON - Felixstowe East)
doreen.savage@suffolkcoastal.gov.uk

Smith, Andy (CON - Felixstowe South)
andy.smith@suffolkcoastal.gov.uk

Whiting, Robert (CON - Fynn Valley)
robert.whiting@suffolkcoastal.gov.uk

Yeo, Nicky (CON - Nacton & Purdis Farm)
nicola.yeo@suffolkcoastal.gov.uk

POLITICAL COMPOSITION
CON: 37, IND: 2, LD: 2, LAB: 1

COMMITTEE CHAIRS

Audit: Mr Geoff Lynch

Licensing & Health: Mr Colin Hedgley

Planning: Ms Debbie McCallum

Sunderland   M

Sunderland City Council, Civic Centre, Sunderland SR2 7DN
☎ 0191 520 5555 ⌁ enquiries@sunderland.gov.uk
🖥 www.sunderland.gov.uk

FACTS AND FIGURES
Parliamentary Constituencies: Houghton and Sunderland South, Sunderland Central, Washington and Sunderland West
EU Constituencies: North East
Election Frequency: Elections are by thirds

PRINCIPAL OFFICERS

Chief Executive: Mrs Sonia Tognarelli, Interim Head of Paid Service (Head of Financial Resources), Civic Centre, Sunderland SR2 7DN ☎ 0191 561 1851 ⌁ sonia.tognarelli@sunderland.gov.uk

Assistant Chief Executive: Ms Sarah Reed, Assistant Chief Executive, Civic Centre, Sunderland SR2 7DN ☎ 0191 561 1114 or 1134 ⌁ sarah.reed@sunderland.gov.uk

Senior Management: Ms Fiona Brown, Director - People Services, Civic Centre, Sunderland SR2 7DN ☎ 0191 520 5555 ⌁ fiona.brown@sunderland.gov.uk

Senior Management: Mr Lee Cranston, Executive Director - Economy & Place, Civic Centre, Sunderland SR2 7DN ⌁ lee.cranston@sunderland.gov.uk

Senior Management: Mr Bob Donaldson, Director - Strategy, Partnerships & Transformation, Jack Crawford House, Commercial Road, Sunderland SR2 8QR ☎ 0191 561 1517
⌂ bob.donaldson@sunderland.gov.uk

Senior Management: Ms Gillian Gibson, Director - Public Health, Civic Centre, Sunderland SR2 7DN
⌂ gillian.gibson@sunderland.gov.uk

Senior Management: Mr Barry Scarr, Executive Director - Corporate Services, Civic Centre, Sunderland SR2 7DN
⌂ barry.scarr@sunderland.gov.uk

Access Officer / Social Services (Disability): Ms Fiona Brown, Director - People Services, Civic Centre, Sunderland SR2 7DN
☎ 0191 520 5555 ⌂ fiona.brown@sunderland.gov.uk

Catering Services: Mr Andrew Cummings, Catering Support Officer, South Hylton House, Sunderland SR4 0JL
☎ 0191 520 5555 ⌂ andrew.cummings@sunderland.gov.uk

Children / Youth Services: Mr Simon Marshall, Director - Education, Civic Centre, Sunderland SR2 7DN ☎ 0191 520 5555
⌂ simon.marshall@sunderland.gov.uk

Children / Youth Services: Miss Sandra Mitchell, Head of Community & Family Wellbeing, Civic Centre, Sunderland SR2 7DN
☎ 0191 561 1438 ⌂ sandra.mitchell@sunderland.gov.uk

Civil Registration: Ms Karen Lounton, Bereavement & Registration Services Manager, Civic Centre, Sunderland SR2 7DN
☎ 0191 561 7931 ⌂ karen.lounton@sunderland.gov.uk

Community Planning: Mr Lee Cranston, Executive Director - Economy & Place, Civic Centre, Sunderland SR2 7DN
⌂ lee.cranston@sunderland.gov.uk

Community Safety: Mrs Julie Smith, Associate Policy Lead for Community Safety, Civic Centre, Sunderland SR2 7DN
☎ 0191 561 1591 ⌂ julie.smith@sunderland.gov.uk

Computer Management: Ms Liz St Louis, Head of Customer Service & Development, Civic Centre, Sunderland SR2 7DN
☎ 0191 561 4902 ⌂ liz.stlouis@sunderland.gov.uk

Consumer Protection and Trading Standards: Mr Richard Reading, Trading Standards & Licensing Manager, Jack Crawford House, Sunderland SR2 8QR ☎ 0191 561 1710
⌂ richard.reading@sunderland.gov.uk

Contracts: Mr Jonathan Rowson, Assistant Head of Law & Governance - Commercial Team, Civic Centre, Sunderland SR2 7DN ☎ 0191 561 1034 ⌂ jonathan.rowson@sunderland.gov.uk

Corporate Services: Ms Charlotte Burnham, Head of Scrutiny & Area Arrangements, Civic Centre, Sunderland SR2 7DN
☎ 0191 561 1147 ⌂ charlotte.burnham@sunderland.gov.uk

Corporate Services: Ms Rhiannon Hood, Assistant Head of Law & Governance, Civic Centre, Sunderland SR2 7DN ☎ 0191 561 1005
⌂ rhiannon.hood@sunderland.gov.uk

Corporate Services: Mr John Rawling, Deputy Director - HR & OD, Civic Centre, Sunderland SR2 7DN ☎ 0191 520 5555
⌂ john.rawling@sunderland.gov.uk

Corporate Services: Mr Barry Scarr, Executive Director - Corporate Services, Civic Centre, Sunderland SR2 7DN
⌂ barry.scarr@sunderland.gov.uk

Corporate Services: Mr Phil Spooner, Community Leadership Programmes, Civic Centre, Sunderland SR2 7DN ☎ 0191 520 5555
⌂ phil.spooner@sunderland.gov.uk

Customer Service: Ms Margaret Douglas, Complaints & Feedback Team Manager, Civic Centre, Sunderland SR2 7DN
☎ 0191 561 1065 ⌂ margaret.douglas@sunderland.gov.uk

Customer Service: Ms Liz St Louis, Head of Customer Service & Development, Civic Centre, Sunderland SR2 7DN ☎ 0191 561 4902
⌂ liz.stlouis@sunderland.gov.uk

Economic Development: Mr Lee Cranston, Executive Director - Economy & Place, Civic Centre, Sunderland SR2 7DN
⌂ lee.cranston@sunderland.gov.uk

Economic Development: Mr Taylor Vince, Head of Strategic Economic Development, Civic Centre, Sunderland SR2 7DN
☎ 0191 561 1113 ⌂ vince.taylor@sunderland.gov.uk

Education: Mr Simon Marshall, Director - Education, Civic Centre, Sunderland SR2 7DN ☎ 0191 520 5555
⌂ simon.marshall@sunderland.gov.uk

Education: Miss Sandra Mitchell, Head of Community & Family Wellbeing, Civic Centre, Sunderland SR2 7DN ☎ 0191 561 1438
⌂ sandra.mitchell@sunderland.gov.uk

Education: Mrs Annette Parr, Lead Support & Intervention Officer - Vulnerable Groups, Sandhill Centre, Sunderland SR2 7DN
☎ 0191 561 1584 ⌂ annette.parr@sunderland.gov.uk

E-Government: Ms Debbie Ross, E-Neighbourhood Programme Manager, Moorside, Sunderland SR3 3XN ☎ 0191 561 4216
⌂ debbie.ross@sunderland.gov.uk

Electoral Registration: Ms Lindsay Dixon, Head of Electoral Services, Civic Centre, Sunderland SR2 7DN ☎ 0191 561 1142
⌂ bill.crawford@sunderland.gov.uk

Emergency Planning: Mr Stephen Eagling, Security Services & Emergency Planning Manager, Civic Centre, Sunderland SR2 7DN
☎ 0191 520 5555 ⌂ stephen.eagling@sunderland.gov.uk

Energy Management: Mr Andrew Atkinson, Energy Conservation Team Leader, Civic Centre, Sunderland SR2 7DN ☎ 0191 561 2728
⌂ andrew.atkinson@sunderland.gov.uk

Estates, Property & Valuation: Mr Nick Wood, Head of Property, Civic Centre, Sunderland SR2 7DN ☎ 0191 561 2631
⌂ nick.wood@sunderland.gov.uk

SUNDERLAND

European Liaison: Ms Catherine Auld, Head of Business Investment, Civic Centre, Sunderland SR2 7DN ☎ 0191 561 1156 ✉ catherine.auld@sunderland.gov.uk

Facilities: Ms Jill Rose, Relationship Manager - Corporate Affairs, Civic Centre, Sunderland SR2 7DN ☎ 0191 561 1101 ✉ jill.rose@sunderland.gov.uk

Finance: Mrs Sonia Tognarelli, Interim Head of Paid Service (Head of Financial Resources), Civic Centre, Sunderland SR2 7DN ☎ 0191 561 1851 ✉ sonia.tognarelli@sunderland.gov.uk

Fleet Management: Mr Ian Bell, Fleet & Transport Manager, Civic Centre, Sunderland SR2 7DN ☎ 0191 561 4531 ✉ sonia.tognarelli@sunderland.gov.uk

Health and Safety: Mr John Rawling, Deputy Director - HR & OD, Civic Centre, Sunderland SR2 7DN ☎ 0191 520 5555 ✉ john.rawling@sunderland.gov.uk

Health and Safety: Mr Geoff Scrafton, Interim Health & Safety Manager, Civic Centre, Sunderland SR2 7DN ☎ 0191 520 5555 ✉ geoff.scrafton@sunderland.gov.uk

Highways: Mr Mark Jackson, Head of Infrastructure & Transportation, Civic Centre, Sunderland SR2 7DN ☎ 0191 520 5555 ✉ mark.jackson@sunderland.gov.uk

Home Energy Conservation: Mr Andrew Atkinson, Energy Conservation Team Leader, Civic Centre, Sunderland SR2 7DN ☎ 0191 561 2728 ✉ andrew.atkinson@sunderland.gov.uk

Housing: Mr Alan Caddick, Head of Housing, Leechmere Centre, Leechmere Industrial Estate, Carrmere Road, Sunderland SR2 9TQ ☎ 0191 520 5555 ✉ alan.caddick@sunderland.gov.uk

Housing: Ms Liz McEvoy, Team Leader - Housing Strategy, Civic Centre, Sunderland SR2 7DN ☎ 0191 561 1240 ✉ liz.mcevoy@sunderland.gov.uk

Housing: Mr Peter Smith, Access to Housing Manager, City Library, 1st Floor, Fawcett Street, Sunderland SR2 7DN ☎ 0191 520 5555 ✉ peter.j.smith@sunderland.gov.uk

Legal: Mrs Elaine Waugh, Head of Law & Governance, Civic Centre, Sunderland SR2 7DN ☎ 0191 561 1053 ✉ elaine.waugh@sunderland.gov.uk

Leisure and Cultural Services: Ms Fiona Brown, Director - People Services, Civic Centre, Sunderland SR2 7DN ☎ 0191 520 5555 ✉ fiona.brown@sunderland.gov.uk

Licensing: Mr Richard Reading, Trading Standards & Licensing Manager, Civic Centre, Sunderland SR2 7DN ☎ 0191 561 1710 ✉ richard.reading@sunderland.gov.uk

Lifelong Learning: Mr Simon Marshall, Director - Education, Civic Centre, Sunderland SR2 7DN ☎ 0191 520 5555 ✉ simon.marshall@sunderland.gov.uk

Member Services: Ms Rhiannon Hood, Assistant Head of Law & Governance, Civic Centre, Sunderland SR2 7DN ☎ 0191 561 1005 ✉ rhiannon.hood@sunderland.gov.uk

Parking: Ms Julie Tunstall, Deputy Parking Services Manager, Jack Crawford House, Commercial Road, Sunderland SR2 8QR ☎ 01915611582 ✉

Partnerships: Mr Bob Donaldson, Director - Strategy, Partnerships & Transformation, Jack Crawford House, Commercial Road, Sunderland SR2 8QR ☎ 0191 561 1517 ✉ bob.donaldson@sunderland.gov.uk

Partnerships: Ms Jessica May, Partnership Manager, Civic Centre, Sunderland SR2 7DN ☎ 0191 561 1476 ✉ jessica.may@sunderland.gov.uk

Personnel / HR: Ms Tracy Palmer, Head of Human Resources Management, Civic Centre, Sunderland SR2 7DN ☎ 0191 561 1722 ✉ tracy.palmer@sunderland.gov.uk

Procurement: Mr Paul Davies, Assistant City Treasurer (Audit & Procurement), Corporate Services, PO Box 100, Civic Centre, Sunderland SR2 7DN ☎ 0191 561 2825 ✉ paul.davies@sunderland.gov.uk

Public Libraries: Ms Victoria French, Assistant Head of Community Services, Civic Centre, Sunderland SR2 7DN ☎ 0191 561 4588 ✉ victoria.french@sunderland.gov.uk

Recycling & Waste Minimisation: Mr Les Clark, Chief Operating Officer - Place, Civic Centre, Sunderland SR2 7DN ☎ 0191 561 4501 ✉ les.clark@sunderland.gov.uk

Social Services: Ms Fiona Brown, Director - People Services, Civic Centre, Sunderland SR2 7DN ☎ 0191 520 5555 ✉ fiona.brown@sunderland.gov.uk

Social Services: Ms Gill Lawson, Service Development Manager - Care & Support, Community Equipment Service, Sunderland SR2 7DN ☎ 0191 5614432

Social Services (Adult): Ms Ann Dingwall, Commissioning Lead, Civic Centre, Sunderland SR2 7DN ☎ 0191 520 5555 ✉ ann.dingwall@sunderland.gov.uk

Social Services (Adult): Mr Phil Hounsell, Service Development Manager, Civic Centre, Sunderland SR2 7DN ☎ 0191 5612877

Social Services (Adult): Ms Lynden Langman, Service Development Manager - Long Term Specialist Care, Dock Street,, Sunderland, Sunderland SR2 7DN ☎ 0191 5618075 ✉ lynden.langman@sunderland.gov.uk

Social Services (Adult): Ms Anne Prentice, Service Development Lead, Civic Centre, Sunderland SR2 7DN ☎ 0191 5618987 ✉ anne.prentice@sunderland.gov.uk

Social Services (Children): Mr Keith Moore, Deputy Director of Children's Services, Civic Centre, Sunderland SR2 7DN ☎ 0191 561 1397 ✉ keith.moore@sunderland.gov.uk

Public Health: Ms Gillian Gibson, Director - Public Health, Civic Centre, Sunderland SR2 7DN ☏ gillian.gibson@sunderland.gov.uk

Street Scene: Mr Les Clark, Chief Operating Officer - Place, Civic Centre, Sunderland SR2 7DN ☎ 0191 561 4501 ☏ les.clark@sunderland.gov.uk

Street Scene: Mr James Newell, Assistant Head of Streetscene, Jack Crawford House, Commercial Road, Sunderland SR2 8QR ☎ 01915611607 ☏ james.newell@sunderland.gov.uk

Street Scene: Mr Bill Seymour, Refuse & Recycling Manager, South Hylton House, Sunderland SR2 7DN ☎ 0191 5614546 ☏ bill.seymour@sunderland.gov.uk

Traffic Management: Mr Mark Jackson, Head of Infrastructure & Transportation, Civic Centre, Sunderland SR2 7DN ☎ 0191 520 5555 ☏ mark.jackson@sunderland.gov.uk

Transport: Mr Bob Donaldson, Director - Strategy, Partnerships & Transformation, Jack Crawford House, Commercial Road, Sunderland SR2 8QR ☎ 0191 561 1517 ☏ bob.donaldson@sunderland.gov.uk

Transport: Mr Mark Jackson, Head of Infrastructure & Transportation, Civic Centre, Sunderland SR2 7DN ☎ 0191 520 5555 ☏ mark.jackson@sunderland.gov.uk

Transport Planner: Mr Mark Jackson, Head of Infrastructure & Transportation, Civic Centre, Sunderland SR2 7DN ☎ 0191 520 5555 ☏ mark.jackson@sunderland.gov.uk

Total Place: Mr Taylor Vince, Head of Strategic Economic Development, Civic Centre, Sunderland SR2 7DN ☎ 0191 561 1113 ☏ vince.taylor@sunderland.gov.uk

Waste Collection and Disposal: Mr Les Clark, Chief Operating Officer - Place, Civic Centre, Sunderland SR2 7DN ☎ 0191 561 4501 ☏ les.clark@sunderland.gov.uk

Waste Management: Mr Les Clark, Chief Operating Officer - Place, Civic Centre, Sunderland SR2 7DN ☎ 0191 561 4501 ☏ les.clark@sunderland.gov.uk

COUNCILLORS

Mayor: Emmerson, Alan (LAB - Ryhope)
cllr.alan.emerson@sunderland.gov.uk

Deputy Mayor: MacKnight, Doris (LAB - Castle)
cllr.doris.macknight@sunderland.gov.uk

Leader of the Council: Watson, Paul (LAB - Pallion)
cllr.paul.watson@sunderland.gov.uk

Deputy Leader of the Council: Trueman, Henry (LAB - Washington West)
cllr.henry.trueman@sunderland.gov.uk

Allan, David (LAB - Sandhill)
cllr.dave.allan@sunderland.gov.uk

Allen, Anthony (IND - Copt Hill)
cllr.anthony.allen@sunderland.gov.uk

Atkinson, Rebecca (LAB - Barnes)
cllr.rebecca.atkinson@sunderland.gov.uk

Ball, Ellen (LAB - Ryhope)
cllr.ellen.ball@sunderland.gov.uk

Beck, Margaret (LAB - Fulwell)
cllr.margaret.beck@sunderland.gov.uk

Bell, Richard (LAB - Redhill)
cllr.richard.bell@sunderland.gov.uk

Blackburn, James (LAB - Hetton)
cllr.james.blackburn@sunderland.gov.uk

Copeland, Rosalind (LAB - Southwick)
cllr.rosalind.copeland@sunderland.gov.uk

Cummings, John (LAB - Hetton)
cllr.john.cummings@sunderland.gov.uk

Curran, Barry (LAB - St. Peter's)
cllr.barry.curran@sunderland.gov.uk

Davison, Ronny (LAB - Redhill)
cllr.ronny.davison@sunderland.gov.uk

Dixon, Darryl (LAB - St. Chad's)
cllr.darryl.dixon@sunderland.gov.uk

Dixon, Michael (CON - St. Michael's)
cllr.michael.dixon@sunderland.gov.uk

Elliott, Miles (LAB - Southwick)
cllr.miles.elliott@sunderland.gov.uk

Ellis, Sheila (IND - Houghton)
cllr.sheila.ellis@sunderland.gov.uk

English, Colin (LAB - Doxford)
cllr.colin.english@sunderland.gov.uk

Essl, Michael (LAB - Barnes)
cllr.michael.essl@sunderland.gov.uk

Farr, Anthony (LAB - Ryhope)
cllr.anthony.farr@sunderland.gov.uk

Farthing, Louise (LAB - Washington South)
cllr.louise.farthing@sunderland.gov.uk

Fletcher, Jill (LAB - Washington North)
cllr.jill.fletcher@sunderland.gov.uk

Forbes, Margaret (CON - St. Michael's)
cllr.margaret.forbes@sunderland.gov.uk

Foster, Stephen (LAB - Castle)
cllr.stephen.foster@sunderland.gov.uk

Francis, Bob (CON - Fulwell)
cllr.bob.francis@sunderland.gov.uk

Galbraith, Gillian (LAB - St. Chad's)
cllr.gillian.galbraith@sunderland.gov.uk

Galbraith, Ian (LAB - Barnes)
cllr.ian.galbraith@sunderland.gov.uk

Gallagher, Jacqui (LAB - Sandhill)
cllr.jacqui.gallagher@sunderland.gov.uk

Gibson, Elizabeth (LAB - Doxford)
cllr.elizabeth.gibson@sunderland.gov.uk

Gibson, Peter (LAB - Silksworth)
cllr.peter.gibson@sunderland.gov.uk

Gofton, Cecilia (LAB - Pallion)
cllr.cecilia.gofton@sunderland.gov.uk

Heron, Juliana (LAB - Houghton)
cllr.juliana.heron@sunderland.gov.uk

SUNDERLAND

Howe, George (CON - Fulwell)
cllr.george.howe@sunderland.gov.uk

Jackson, Julia (LAB - St. Peter's)
cllr.julia.jackson@sunderland.gov.uk

Kay, Ian (LAB - Millfield)
cllr.iain.kay@sunderland.gov.uk

Kelly, John (LAB - Washington North)
cllr.john.kelly@sunderland.gov.uk

Lauchlan, Len (LAB - Washington Central)
cllr.len.lauchlan@sunderland.gov.uk

Lawson, Anne (LAB - Shiney Row)
cllr.anne.lawson@sunderland.gov.uk

Leadbitter, Shirley (CON - St. Peter's)
cllr.shirley.leadbitter@sunderland.gov.uk

Marshall, Christine (LAB - Doxford)
cllr.christine.marshall@sunderland.gov.uk

McClennan, Barbara (LAB - Hendon)
cllr.barbara.mcclennan@sunderland.gov.uk

Middleton, Paul (LAB - Washington South)
cllr.paul.middleton@sunderland.gov.uk

Miller, Fiona (LAB - Washington East)
cllr.fiona.miller@sunderland.gov.uk

Miller, Graeme (LAB - Washington South)
cllr.graeme.miller@sunderland.gov.uk

Mordey, Michael (LAB - Hendon)
cllr.michael.mordey@sunderland.gov.uk

O'Neil, Victoria (LAB - Hendon)
cllr.victoria.oneil@sunderland.gov.uk

Porthouse, Stuart (LAB - St. Chad's)
cllr.stuart.porthouse@sunderland.gov.uk

Price, Bob (LAB - Millfield)
cllr.bob.price@sunderland.gov.uk

Scanlan, Lynda (LAB - Millfield)
cllr.lynda.scanlan@sunderland.gov.uk

Scaplehorn, Bernard (LAB - Washington West)
cllr.bernard.scaplehorn@sunderland.gov.uk

Smith, Patricia (LAB - Silksworth)
cllr.patricia.smith@sunderland.gov.uk

Smith, Derrick (IND - Copt Hill)
cllr.derrick.smith@sunderland.gov.uk

Snowdon, Dianne (LAB - Washington Central)
cllr.derrick.snowdon@sunderland.gov.uk

Snowdon, David (LAB - Washington East)
cllr.david.snowdon@sunderland.gov.uk

Speding, Melville (LAB - Shiney Row)
cllr.melville.speding@sunderland.gov.uk

Stewart, Paul (LAB - Redhill)
cllr.paul.stewart@sunderland.gov.uk

Taylor, Tony (LAB - Washington East)
cllr.tony.taylor@sunderland.gov.uk

Trueman, Dorothy (LAB - Washington West)
cllr.dorothy.trueman@sunderland.gov.uk

Turner, Doris (LAB - Hetton)
cllr.doris.turner@sunderland.gov.uk

Turton, William (LAB - Houghton)
cllr.billy.turton@sunderland.gov.uk

Turton, Mary (LAB - Copt Hill)
cllr.mary.turton@sunderland.gov.uk

Tye, Philip (LAB - Silksworth)
cllr.philip.tye@sunderland.gov.uk

Walker, Geoff (LAB - Shiney Row)
cllr.geoffrey.walker@sunderland.gov.uk

Walker, Peter (LAB - Washington North)
cllr.peter.walker@sunderland.gov.uk

Waller, Debra (LAB - Sandhill)
cllr.debra.waller@sunderland.gov.uk

Waters, Karen (LAB - St. Anne's)
cllr.karen.waters@sunderland.gov.uk

Watson, Susan (LAB - St. Anne's)
cllr.thomas.wright@sunderland.gov.uk

Williams, Linda (LAB - Washington Central)
cllr.linda.williams@sunderland.gov.uk

Wilson, Denny (LAB - Castle)
cllr.denny.wilson@sunderland.gov.uk

Wilson, Amy (LAB - Pallion)
cllr.amy.wilson@sunderland.gov.uk

Wood, Peter (CON - St. Michael's)
cllr.peter.wood@sunderland.gov.uk

Wright, Norma (LAB - Southwick)
cllr.norma.wright@sunderland.gov.uk

Wright, Thomas (LAB - St. Anne's)
cllr.thomas.wright@sunderland.gov.uk

POLITICAL COMPOSITION
LAB: 66, CON: 6, IND: 3

Surrey   C

Surrey County Council, County Hall, Penrhyn Road, Kingston upon Thames KT1 2DN
☎ 0345 600 9009 🖨 020 8541 9004 ✆ contact.centre@surreycc.gov.uk
💻 www.surreycc.gov.uk

FACTS AND FIGURES
Parliamentary Constituencies: Surrey East
EU Constituencies: South East
Election Frequency: Elections are of whole council

PRINCIPAL OFFICERS

Chief Executive: Mr David McNulty, Chief Executive, County Hall, Penrhyn Road, Kingston upon Thames KT1 2DN ☎ 020 8541 8018 ✆ david.mcnulty@surreycc.gov.uk

Deputy Chief Executive: Mrs Julie Fisher, Deputy Chief Executive & Strategic Director - Children, Schools & Families, County Hall, Penrhyn Road, Kingston upon Thames KT1 2DN ☎ 020 8541 9550 ✆ julie.fisher@surreycc.gov.uk

Assistant Chief Executive: Ms Susie Kemp, Assistant Chief Executive, County Hall, Penrhyn Road, Kingston upon Thames KT1 2DN ☎ 020 8541 7043 ✆ susie.kemp@surreycc.gov.uk

Senior Management: Ms Helen Atkinson, Strategic Director - Adult Social Care & Public Health, County Hall, Penrhyn Road, Kingston upon Thames KT1 2DN ✆ helen.atkinson@surreycc.gov.uk

Senior Management: Mrs Julie Fisher, Deputy Chief Executive & Strategic Director - Children, Schools & Families, County Hall, Penrhyn Road, Kingston upon Thames KT1 2DN ☎ 020 8541 9550 ✆ julie.fisher@surreycc.gov.uk

Senior Management: Mr Trevor Pugh, Strategic Director - Environment & Infrastructure, County Hall, Penrhyn Road, Kingston upon Thames KT1 2DN ☎ 020 8541 9628 ✆ trevor.pugh@surreycc.gov.uk

Senior Management: Ms Yvonne Rees, Chief Executive (Mole Valley) & Strategic Director - Customers & Communities (Surrey CC), County Hall, Penrhyn Road, Kingston upon Thames KT1 2DN ☎ 01306 879101 ✆ yvonne.rees@molevalley.gov.uk

Access Officer / Social Services (Disability): Ms Helen Atkinson, Strategic Director - Adult Social Care & Public Health, County Hall, Penrhyn Road, Kingston upon Thames KT1 2DN ✆ helen.atkinson@surreycc.gov.uk

Architect, Building / Property Services: Mr John Stebbings, Acting Chief Property Officer, County Hall, Penrhyn Road, Kingston upon Thames KT1 2DN ☎ 020 8213 2554 ✆ john.stebbings@surreycc.gov.uk

Building Control: Mr Peter Hopkins, Lead Asset Manager, County Hall, Penrhyn Road, Kingston upon Thames KT1 2DN ☎ 07817 404110 ✆ peter.hopkins@surreycc.gov.uk

Catering Services: Ms Beverley Baker, Head of Commercial Services, Epsom Local Office, The Parade, Epsom KT18 5BY ☎ 01372 832370 ✆ beverley.baker@surreycc.gov.uk

Children / Youth Services: Ms Caroline Budden, Assistant Director - Children's Services & Safeguarding, Fairmont House, Bull Hill, Leatherhead KT22 7AH ☎ 01372 833400 ✆ caroline.budden@surreycc.gov.uk

Children / Youth Services: Mrs Julie Fisher, Deputy Chief Executive & Strategic Director - Children, Schools & Families, County Hall, Penrhyn Road, Kingston upon Thames KT1 2DN ☎ 020 8541 9550 ✆ julie.fisher@surreycc.gov.uk

Children / Youth Services: Mr Garath Symonds, Assistant Director - Commissioning & Prevention, County Hall, Penrhyn Road, Kingston upon Thames KT1 2DN ☎ 01372 833543 ✆ garath.symonds@surreycc.gov.uk

Civil Registration: Mrs Linda Aboe, Registration & Nationality Service Member, Rylston, 81 Oatlands Drive, Weybridge KT13 9LN ☎ 01932 794704 ✆ linda.aboe@surreycc.gov.uk

PR / Communications: Ms Louise Footner, Head of Communications, County Hall, Room G29, Penrhyn Road, Kingston upon Thames KT1 2DN ☎ 020 8541 9624 ✆ louise.footner@surreycc.gov.uk

Community Safety: Mr Gordon Falconer, Senior Manager - Community Safety, County Hall, Penrhyn Road, Kingston upon Thames KT1 2DN ☎ 020 8541 7296 ✆ gordon.falconer@surreycc.gov.uk

Computer Management: Mr Matt Scott, Chief Information Officer, County Hall, Penrhyn Road, Kingston upon Thames KT1 2DN ☎ 0345 600 9009 ✆ matt.scott@surreycc.gov.uk

Consumer Protection and Trading Standards: Mr Steve Ruddy, Head of Trading Standards, County Hall, Penrhyn Road, Kingston upon Thames KT1 2DN ☎ 01372 371730 ✆ steve.ruddy@surreycc.gov.uk

Contracts: Ms Laura Langstaff, Head of Procurement & Commissioning, County Hall, Penrhyn Road, Kingston upon Thames KT1 2DN ☎ 020 8541 9233 ✆ laura.langstaff@surreycc.gov.uk

Customer Service: Mr Mark Irons, Head of Service, County Hall, Penrhyn Road, Kingston upon Thames KT1 2DN ☎ 020 8541 7848 ✆ mark.irons@surreycc.gov.uk

Economic Development: Ms Rachel Ford, Senior Manager - Economic Growth, County Hall, Penrhyn Road, Kingston upon Thames KT1 2DN ✆ rachel.ford@surreycc.gov.uk

Education: Mrs Julie Fisher, Deputy Chief Executive & Strategic Director - Children, Schools & Families, County Hall, Penrhyn Road, Kingston upon Thames KT1 2DN ☎ 020 8541 9550 ✆ julie.fisher@surreycc.gov.uk

Emergency Planning: Mr Ian Good, Head of Emergency Management, Room 194, County Hall, Penrhyn Road, Kingston upon Thames KT1 2DN ☎ 020 8541 9168 ✆ ian.good@surreycc.gov.uk

Energy Management: Mr Steve Ruddy, Corporate Head of Service, Pippbrook, Dorking RH4 1SJ ☎ 01306 879225 ✆ steve.ruddy@molevalley.gov.uk

Environmental Health: Mr Ian Boast, Assistant Director - Environment, County Hall, Penrhyn Road, Kingston upon Thames KT1 2DN ☎ 020 8541 9479 ✆ ian.boast@surreycc.gov.uk

Estates, Property & Valuation: Mr Keith Brown, Schools & Programme Manager, County Hall, Penrhyn Road, Kingston upon Thames KT1 2DN ☎ 020 8541 8651 ✆ keith.brown@surreycc.gov.uk

Finance: Ms Sheila Little, Director - Finance, County Hall, Penrhyn Road, Kingston upon Thames KT1 2DN ☎ 020 8541 7012 ✆ sheila.little@surreycc.gov.uk

Pensions: Mr Jason Bailey, Pensions Manager, County Hall, Penrhyn Road, Kingston upon Thames KT1 2DN ☎ 0345 600 9009 ✆ jason.bailey@surreycc.gov.uk

Fleet Management: Ms Tracey Coventry, Transport Co-ordination Centre Manager, County Hall, Penrhyn Road, Kingston upon Thames KT1 2DN ☎ 020 8541 9592 ✆ tracey.coventry@surreycc.gov.uk

Grounds Maintenance: Ms Morag Turner, Workplace Delivery Manager, County Hall, Penrhyn Road, Kingston upon Thames KT1 2DN ☎ 020 8541 9863 ✆ morag.turner@surreycc.gov.uk

SURREY

Health and Safety: Mr Dave Blane, Senior Health & Safety Manager, County Hall, Penrhyn Road, Kingston upon Thames KT1 2DN ☎ 020 8541 8736 ⁓ dave.blane@surreycc.gov.uk

Highways: Mr Jason Russell, Assistant Director - Highways, Merrow Complex, Merrow Lane, Merrow, Guildford GU4 7BQ ☎ 020 8541 7102 ⁓ jason.russell@surreycc.gov.uk

Legal: Mrs Ann Charlton, Director - Legal, Democratic & Cultural Services, County Hall, Room 129, Penrhyn Road, Kingston upon Thames KT1 2DN ☎ 020 8541 9001 ⁓ ann.charlton@surreycc.gov.uk

Leisure and Cultural Services: Mr Peter Milton, Head of Cultural Services, Room 353, County Hall, Penrhyn Road, Kingston upon Thames KT1 2DN ☎ 020 8541 7679 ⁓ peter.milton@surreycc.gov.uk

Lottery Funding, Charity and Voluntary: Mrs Mary Burguieres, Lead Manager - Policy & Strategy Partnership, Room 318, County Hall, Penrhyn Road, Kingston upon Thames KT1 2DN

Member Services: Ms Rachel Crossley, Lead Manager - Democratic Services, County Hall, Penrhyn Road, Kingston upon Thames KT1 2DN ☎ 020 8541 9993 ⁓ rachel.crossley@surreycc.gov.uk

Partnerships: Mr James Painter, Community Partnership Manager, East Surrey Area Office A02, Lesbourne Road, Reigate RH2 7JP ⁓ james.painter@surreycc.gov.uk

Personnel / HR: Mrs Carmel Millar, Head of HR & Organisational Development, County Hall, Penrhyn Road, Kingston upon Thames KT1 2DN ☎ 020 8541 9824 ⁓ carmel.millar@surreycc.gov.uk

Planning: Mr Dominic Forbes, Planning & Development Group Manager, County Hall, Penrhyn Road, Kingston upon Thames KT1 2DN ☎ 020 8541 9312 ⁓ dominic.forbes@surreycc.gov.uk

Procurement: Ms Laura Langstaff, Head of Procurement & Commissioning, County Hall, Penrhyn Road, Kingston upon Thames KT1 2DN ☎ 020 8541 9233 ⁓ laura.langstaff@surreycc.gov.uk

Public Libraries: Mrs Rose Wilson, Library Operations Manager of Cultural Services, Runnymede Centre, Chertsey Road, Addlestone KT15 2EP ☎ 01932 794178 ⁓ rose.wilson@surreycc.gov.uk

Recycling & Waste Minimisation: Mr Ian Boast, Assistant Director - Environment, County Hall, Penrhyn Road, Kingston upon Thames KT1 2DN ☎ 020 8541 9479 ⁓ ian.boast@surreycc.gov.uk

Recycling & Waste Minimisation: Ms Lesley Harding, Place & Sustainability Group Manager, County Hall, Penrhyn Road, Kingston upon Thames KT1 2DN ⁓ lesley.harding@surreycc.gov.uk

Recycling & Waste Minimisation: Mr Richard Parkinson, Head of Waste, County Hall, Penrhyn Road, Kingston upon Thames KT1 2DN ☎ 0345 600 9009 ⁓ richard.parkinson@surreycc.gov.uk

Regeneration: Mr Tony Samuels, Cabinet Associate - Assets & Regeneration, County Hall, Penrhyn Road, Kingston upon Thames KT1 2DN ☎ 020 8541 7595 ⁓ tony.samuels@surreycc.gov.uk

Road Safety: Mr Duncan Knox, Road Safety Team Manager, Surrey Safety Camera Partnership, PO Box 930, Guildford GU4 8WU ☎ 020 8541 7443 ⁓ duncan.knox@surreycc.gov.uk

Social Services: Ms Helen Atkinson, Strategic Director - Adult Social Care & Public Health, County Hall, Penrhyn Road, Kingston upon Thames KT1 2DN ⁓ helen.atkinson@surreycc.gov.uk

Social Services (Adult): Ms Helen Atkinson, Strategic Director - Adult Social Care & Public Health, County Hall, Penrhyn Road, Kingston upon Thames KT1 2DN ⁓ helen.atkinson@surreycc.gov.uk

Social Services (Children): Mr Garath Symonds, Assistant Director - Commissioning & Prevention, County Hall, Penrhyn Road, Kingston upon Thames KT1 2DN ☎ 01372 833543 ⁓ garath.symonds@surreycc.gov.uk

Families: Mrs Julie Fisher, Deputy Chief Executive & Strategic Director - Children, Schools & Families, County Hall, Penrhyn Road, Kingston upon Thames KT1 2DN ☎ 020 8541 9550 ⁓ julie.fisher@surreycc.gov.uk

Public Health: Ms Helen Atkinson, Strategic Director - Adult Social Care & Public Health, County Hall, Penrhyn Road, Kingston upon Thames KT1 2DN ⁓ helen.atkinson@surreycc.gov.uk

Staff Training: Mrs Carmel Millar, Head of HR & Organisational Development, County Hall, Penrhyn Road, Kingston upon Thames KT1 2DN ☎ 020 8541 9824 ⁓ carmel.millar@surreycc.gov.uk

Traffic Management: Mr Iain Reeve, Assistant Director - Strategy Transport & Planning, County Hall, Penrhyn Road, Kingston upon Thames KT1 2DN ☎ 0845 600 9375 ⁓ iain.reeve@surreycc.gov.uk

Transport: Mr Iain Reeve, Assistant Director - Strategy Transport & Planning, County Hall, Penrhyn Road, Kingston upon Thames KT1 2DN ☎ 0845 600 9375 ⁓ iain.reeve@surreycc.gov.uk

Transport Planner: Mr Iain Reeve, Assistant Director - Strategy Transport & Planning, County Hall, Penrhyn Road, Kingston upon Thames KT1 2DN ☎ 0845 600 9375 ⁓ iain.reeve@surreycc.gov.uk

Waste Management: Mr Ian Boast, Assistant Director - Environment, County Hall, Penrhyn Road, Kingston upon Thames KT1 2DN ☎ 020 8541 9479 ⁓ ian.boast@surreycc.gov.uk

Waste Management: Mr Richard Parkinson, Head of Waste, County Hall, Penrhyn Road, Kingston upon Thames KT1 2DN ☎ 0345 600 9009 ⁓ richard.parkinson@surreycc.gov.uk

COUNCILLORS

Chair: Marks, Sally (CON - Caterham Valley) sally.marks@surreycc.gov.uk

Vice-Chair: Skellett, Nick (CON - Oxted) n.skellett@surreycc.gov.uk

Leader of the Council: Hodge, David (CON - Warlingham) david.hodge@surreycc.gov.uk

Deputy Leader of the Council: Martin, Peter (CON - Godalming South, Milford & Witley) peterj.martin@surreycc.gov.uk

Group Leader: Harrison, Nick (R - Nork & Tattenhams)
nicholas.harrison@surreycc.gov.uk

Group Leader: Windsor, Helena (UKIP - Godstone)
helena.windsor@surreycc.gov.uk

Angell, Mary (CON - Woodham & New Haw)
mary.angell@surreycc.gov.uk

Barker, William (CON - Horsleys)
b.barker@surreycc.gov.uk

Barton, Nikki (R - Haslemere)
nikki.barton@surreycc.gov.uk

Beardsmore, Ian (IND - Sunbury Common & Ashford Common)
ian.beardsmore@btinternet.com

Beckett, John (R - Ewell)
jbeckett@epsom-ewell.gov.uk

Bennison, Mike (CON - Hinchley Wood, Claygate & Oxshott)
michael.bennison@surreycc.gov.uk

Bowes, Liz (CON - Woking South East)
liz.bowes@surreycc.gov.uk

Bramhall, Natalie (CON - Redhill West & Meadvale)
natalie.bramhall@surreycc.gov.uk

Brett-Warburton, Mark (CON - Guildford South East)
mark.brett-warburton@surreycc.gov.uk

Carasco, Ben (CON - Woking North)
ben.carasco@surreycc.gov.uk

Chapman, Bill (CON - Camberley East)
bill.chapman@surreycc.gov.uk

Clack, Helyn (CON - Dorking Rural)
helyn.clack@surreycc.gov.uk

Coleman, Carol (CON - Ashford)
carol.coleman@surreycc.gov.uk

Cooksey, Stephen (IND - Dorking South & the Holmwoods)
stephen.cooksey@surreycc.gov.uk

Cosser, Steve (CON - Godalming North)
steve.cosser@surreycc.gov.uk

Curran, Clare (CON - Bookham & Fetcham West)
clare.curran@surreycc.gov.uk

Ellwood, Graham (CON - Guildford East)
graham.ellwood@surreycc.gov.uk

Essex, Jonathan (IND - Redhill East)
jonathan.essex@surreycc.gov.uk

Evans, Tim (CON - Lower Sunbury & Halliford)
tim.evans@surreycc.gov.uk

Evans, Robert (LAB - Stanwell & Stanwell Moor)
robert.evans@surreycc.gov.uk

Few, Mel (CON - Foxhills, Thorpe & Virginia Water)
mel.few@surreycc.gov.uk

Forster, Will (IND - Woking South)
will.forster@surreycc.gov.uk

Frost, Pat (CON - Farnham Central)
pat.frost@surreycc.gov.uk

Fuller, Denis (CON - Camberley West)
denis.fuller@surreycc.gov.uk

Furey, John (CON - Addlestone)
john.furey@surreycc.gov.uk

Gardner, Bob (CON - Merstham & Banstead South)
bob.gardner@surreycc.gov.uk

Goodman, Mike (CON - Bagshot, Windlesham & Chobham)
mike.goodman@surreycc.gov.uk

Goodwin, David (IND - Guildford South West)
goodwind@guildford.gov.uk

Gosling, Michael (CON - Tadworth, Walton & Kingswood)
michael.gosling@surreycc.gov.uk

Grant-Duff, Zully (CON - Reigate)
zully.grantduff@surreycc.gov.uk

Gray, Ramon (CON - Weybridge)
ramon.gray@surreycc.gov.uk

Gulati, Ken (CON - Banstead, Woodmansterne & Chipstead)
ken.gulati@surreycc.gov.uk

Hall, Tim (CON - Leatherhead & Fetcham East)
tim.hall@surreycc.gov.uk

Hammond, Kay (CON - Horley West, Salfords & Sidlow)
k.hammond@surreycc.gov.uk

Harmer, David (CON - Waverley Western Villages)
david.harmer@surreycc.gov.uk

Heath, Marisa (CON - Englefield Green)
marisa.heath@surreycc.gov.uk

Hickman, Peter (R - The Dittons)
peter.hickman@surreycc.gov.uk

Hicks, Margaret (CON - Hersham)
margaret.hicks@surreycc.gov.uk

Hussain, Saj (CON - Knaphill & Goldsworth West)
saj.hussain@surreycc.gov.uk

Ivison, David (CON - Heatherside & Parkside)
david.ivison@surreycc.gov.uk

Johnson, George (UKIP - Shalford)
gtj@8210guy.com

Kemeny, Linda (CON - Woking South West)
linda.kemeny@surreycc.gov.uk

Kemp, Colin (CON - Goldsworth East & Horsell Village)
colin.kemp@surreycc.gov.uk

Kington, Eber (R - Ewell Court, Auriol & Cuddington)
ekington@epsom-ewell.gov.uk

Lake, Rachael (CON - Walton)
r.lake@surreycc.gov.uk

Lay, Yvonna (CON - Egham)
yvonna.lay@surreycc.gov.uk

Le Gal, Denise (CON - Farnham North)
denise.legal@surreycc.gov.uk

Lewis, Mary (CON - Cobham)
mary.lewis@surreycc.gov.uk

Mallett, Ernest (R - West Molesey)
ernest.mallett@surreycc.gov.uk

Mason, Jan (R - West Ewell)
jmason@epsom-ewell.gov.uk

Moseley, Marsha (CON - Ash)
marsha.moseley@guildford.gov.uk

Mountain, Tina (CON - Epsom Town & Downs)
tina.mountain@surreycc.gov.uk

SURREY

Norman, Chris (CON - Chertsey)
chris.norman@surreycc.gov.uk

Orrick, John (IND - Caterham Hill)
john.orrick@surreycc.gov.uk

Page, Adrian (CON - Lightwater, West End & Bisley)
adrian.page@surreycc.gov.uk

Persand, Karan (CON - Epsom West)
karan.persand@surreycc.gov.uk

Pitt, Chris (CON - Frimley Green and Mytchett)
chris.pitt@surreycc.gov.uk

Ramsdale, Wyatt (CON - Farnham South)
wyatt.ramsdale@surreycc.gov.uk

Ross-Tomlin, Dorothy (CON - Horley East)
dorothy.rosstomlin@surreycc.gov.uk

Saliagopoulos, Denise (CON - Staines upon Thames)
denise.saliagopoulos@surreycc.gov.uk

Samuels, Tony (CON - Walton South & Oatlands)
tony.samuels@surreycc.gov.uk

Searle, Pauline (IND - Guildford North)
pauline.searle@surreycc.gov.uk

Selleck, Stuart (R - East Molesey & Esher)
stuart.selleck@surreycc.gov.uk

Sydney, Michael (CON - Lingfield)
michael.sydney@surreycc.gov.uk

Taylor, Keith (CON - Shere)
keith.taylor@surreycc.gov.uk

Thomson, Barbara (CON - Earlswood & Reigate South)
barbara.thomson@surreycc.gov.uk

Townsend, Chris (R - Ashtead)
cllr.townsend@molevalley.gov.uk

Turner-Stewart, Denise (CON - Staines South & Ashford West)
denise.turnerstewart@surreycc.gov.uk

Walsh, Richard (CON - Laleham & Shepperton)
richard.walsh@surreycc.gov.uk

Watson, Hazel (IND - Dorking Hills)
h.watson@surreycc.gov.uk

White, Fiona (IND - Guildford West)
fiona.white@surreycc.gov.uk

Wilson, Richard (CON - The Byfleets)
richard.wilson@surreycc.gov.uk

Witham, Keith (CON - Worplesdon)
keithwitham1@hotmail.co.uk

Young, Victoria (CON - Waverley Eastern Villages)
victoria.young@surreycc.gov.uk

Young, Alan (CON - Cranleigh & Ewhurst)
ayoung500@yahoo.co.uk

POLITICAL COMPOSITION
CON: 60, IND: 9, R: 9, UKIP: 2, LAB: 1

COMMITTEE CHAIRS

Audit: Mr Stuart Selleck

Pensions: Mr Nick Harrison

Planning: Mr Tim Hall

Surrey Heath D

Surrey Heath Borough Council, Surrey Heath House, Knoll Road, Camberley GU15 3HD
☎ 01276 707100 🖷 01276 707177 🖑 enquiries@surreyheath.gov.uk
🖳 www.surreyheath.gov.uk

FACTS AND FIGURES
Parliamentary Constituencies: Surrey Heath
EU Constituencies: South East
Election Frequency: Elections are of whole council

PRINCIPAL OFFICERS

Chief Executive: Mrs Karen Whelan, Chief Executive, Surrey Heath House, Knoll Road, Camberley GU15 3HD ☎ 01276 707100 🖑 karen.whelan@surreyheath.gov.uk

Senior Management: Mr Daniel Harrison, Executive Head - Business, Surrey Heath House, Knoll Road, Camberley GU15 3HD ☎ 01276 707100 🖑 daniel.harrison@surreyheath.gov.uk

Senior Management: Mrs Karen Limmer, Head of Legal, Surrey Heath House, Knoll Road, Camberley GU15 3HD ☎ 01276 707100 🖑 karen.limmer@surreyheath.gov.uk

Senior Management: Mrs Louise Livingston, Executive Head - Transformation, Surrey Heath House, Knoll Road, Camberley GU15 3HD ☎ 01276 707100 🖑 louise.livingstone@surreyheath.gov.uk

Senior Management: Mr Kelvin Menon, Executive Head - Finance, Surrey Heath House, Knoll Road, Camberley GU15 3HD ☎ 01276 707100 🖑 kelvin.menon@surreyheath.gov.uk

Senior Management: Mr Tim Pashen, Executive Head - Community, Surrey Heath House, Knoll Road, Camberley GU15 3HD ☎ 01276 707100 🖑 tim.pashen@surreyheath.gov.uk

Senior Management: Mr Richard Payne, Executive Head - Corporate, Surrey Heath House, Knoll Road, Camberley GU15 3HD ☎ 01276 707100 🖑 richard.payne@surreyheath.gov.uk

Senior Management: Mrs Jenny Rickard, Executive Head - Regulatory, Surrey Heath House, Knoll Road, Camberley GU15 3HD ☎ 01276 707100 🖑 jenny.rickard@surreyheath.gov.uk

Best Value: Mr Kelvin Menon, Executive Head - Finance, Surrey Heath House, Knoll Road, Camberley GU15 3HD ☎ 01276 707100 🖑 kelvin.menon@surreyheath.gov.uk

Building Control: Mrs Karen Limmer, Head of Legal, Surrey Heath House, Knoll Road, Camberley GU15 3HD ☎ 01276 707100 🖑 karen.limmer@surreyheath.gov.uk

PR / Communications: Ms Joanne Atkinson, Media & Consultation Officer, Surrey Heath House, Knoll Road, Camberley GU15 3HD ☎ 01276 707100 🖑 joanne.atkinson@surreyheath.gov.uk

PR / Communications: Ms Kate Noviss, Media & Marketing Manager, Surrey Heath House, Knoll Road, Camberley GU15 3HD ☎ 01276 707100 🖑 kate.noviss@surreyheath.gov.uk

Community Safety: Mr Kevin Cantlon, Business & Community Development Manager, Surrey Heath House, Knoll Road, Camberley GU15 3HD ☎ 01276 707100 ⏚ kevin.cantlon@surreyheath.gov.uk

Computer Management: Mrs Janet Jones, ICT Manager, Surrey Heath House, Knoll Road, Camberley GU15 3HD ☎ 01276 707100 ⏚ janet.jones@surreyheath.gov.uk

Contracts: Mrs Karan Jassi, Contracts Monitoring Officer, Surrey Heath House, Knoll Road, Camberley GU15 3HD ☎ 01276 707100 ⏚ louise.livingston@surreyheath.gov.uk

Corporate Services: Mr Richard Payne, Executive Head - Corporate, Surrey Heath House, Knoll Road, Camberley GU15 3HD ☎ 01276 707100 ⏚ richard.payne@surreyheath.gov.uk

Customer Service: Ms Lynn Smith, Customer Relations Manager, Surrey Heath House, Knoll Road, Camberley GU15 3HD ☎ 01276 707100 ⏚ lynn.smith@surreyheath.gov.uk

Economic Development: Mr Kevin Cantlon, Business & Community Development Manager, Surrey Heath House, Knoll Road, Camberley GU15 3HD ☎ 01276 707100 ⏚ kevin.cantlon@surreyheath.gov.uk

E-Government: Mrs Janet Jones, ICT Manager, Surrey Heath House, Knoll Road, Camberley GU15 3HD ☎ 01276 707100 ⏚ janet.jones@surreyheath.gov.uk

Electoral Registration: Ms Rachel Whillis, Democratic & Electoral Services Manager, Surrey Heath House, Knoll Road, Camberley GU15 3HD ☎ 01276 707100 ⏚ rachel.whillis@surreyheath.gov.uk

Emergency Planning: Mr Tim Pashen, Executive Head - Community, Surrey Heath House, Knoll Road, Camberley GU15 3HD ☎ 01276 707100 ⏚ tim.pashen@surreyheath.gov.uk

Environmental / Technical Services: Mr Tim Pashen, Executive Head - Community, Surrey Heath House, Knoll Road, Camberley GU15 3HD ☎ 01276 707100 ⏚ tim.pashen@surreyheath.gov.uk

Environmental Health: Mr Tim Pashen, Executive Head - Community, Surrey Heath House, Knoll Road, Camberley GU15 3HD ☎ 01276 707100 ⏚ tim.pashen@surreyheath.gov.uk

Estates, Property & Valuation: Mr Jonathan Gregory, Estates & Asset Manager, Surrey Heath House, Knoll Road, Camberley GU15 3HD ☎ 01276 707100 ⏚ jonathan.gregory@surreyheath.gov.uk

Facilities: Mrs Sarah Packham, Corporate Property Officer, Surrey Heath House, Knoll Road, Camberley GU15 3HD ☎ 01276 707100 ⏚ sarah.packham@surreyheath.gov.uk

Finance: Mr Kelvin Menon, Executive Head - Finance, Surrey Heath House, Knoll Road, Camberley GU15 3HD ☎ 01276 707100 ⏚ kelvin.menon@surreyheath.gov.uk

Fleet Management: Mrs Sarah Packham, Corporate Property Officer, Surrey Heath House, Knoll Road, Camberley GU15 3HD ☎ 01276 707100 ⏚ sarah.packham@surreyheath.gov.uk

Grounds Maintenance: Ms Sue McCubbin, Recreation & Business Services Manager, Surrey Heath House, Knoll Road, Camberley GU15 3HD ☎ 01276 707100 ⏚ sue.mccubbin@surreyheath.gov.uk

Health and Safety: Mr Tim Pashen, Executive Head - Community, Surrey Heath House, Knoll Road, Camberley GU15 3HD ☎ 01276 707100 ⏚ tim.pashen@surreyheath.gov.uk

Housing: Mr Clive Jinman, Housing Services Manager, Surrey Heath House, Knoll Road, Camberley GU15 3HD ☎ 01276 707100 ⏚ clive.jinman@surreyheath.gov.uk

Legal: Mrs Karen Limmer, Head of Legal, Surrey Heath House, Knoll Road, Camberley GU15 3HD ☎ 01276 707100 ⏚ karen.limmer@surreyheath.gov.uk

Leisure and Cultural Services: Mr Daniel Harrison, Executive Head - Business, Surrey Heath House, Knoll Road, Camberley GU15 3HD ☎ 01276 707100 ⏚ daniel.harrison@surreyheath.gov.uk

Licensing: Mr Derek Seekings, Licensing Officer, Surrey Heath House, Knoll Road, Camberley GU15 3HD ☎ 01276 707100 ⏚ derek.seekings@surreyheath.gov.uk

Member Services: Ms Rachel Whillis, Democratic & Electoral Services Manager, Surrey Heath House, Knoll Road, Camberley GU15 3HD ☎ 01276 707100 ⏚ rachel.whillis@surreyheath.gov.uk

Parking: Mr Eugene Leal, Parking Services Manager, Surrey Heath House, Knoll Road, Camberley GU15 3HD ☎ 01276 707100 ⏚ eugene.leal@surreyheath.gov.uk

Personnel / HR: Mrs Louise Livingston, Executive Head - Transformation, Surrey Heath House, Knoll Road, Camberley GU15 3HD ☎ 01276 707100 ⏚ louise.livingstone@surreyheath.gov.uk

Planning: Mrs Jenny Rickard, Executive Head - Regulatory, Surrey Heath House, Knoll Road, Camberley GU15 3HD ☎ 01276 707100 ⏚ jenny.rickard@surreyheath.gov.uk

Procurement: Mr Kelvin Menon, Executive Head - Finance, Surrey Heath House, Knoll Road, Camberley GU15 3HD ☎ 01276 707100 ⏚ kelvin.menon@surreyheath.gov.uk

Recycling & Waste Minimisation: Mr Tim Pashen, Executive Head - Community, Surrey Heath House, Knoll Road, Camberley GU15 3HD ☎ 01276 707100 ⏚ tim.pashen@surreyheath.gov.uk

Regeneration: Mrs Louise Livingston, Executive Head - Transformation, Surrey Heath House, Knoll Road, Camberley GU15 3HD ☎ 01276 707100 ⏚ louise.livingstone@surreyheath.gov.uk

Staff Training: Mrs Louise Livingston, Executive Head - Transformation, Surrey Heath House, Knoll Road, Camberley GU15 3HD ☎ 01276 707100 ⏚ louise.livingstone@surreyheath.gov.uk

Street Scene: Mr Steve Burrows, Street Scene Officer, Surrey Heath House, Knoll Road, Camberley GU15 3HD ☎ 01276 707100 ⏚ steve.burrows@surreyheath.gov.uk

SURREY HEATH

Sustainable Development: Mrs Jenny Rickard, Executive Head - Regulatory, Surrey Heath House, Knoll Road, Camberley GU15 3HD ☎ 01276 707100 ◌ jenny.rickard@surreyheath.gov.uk

Waste Collection and Disposal: Mr Tim Pashen, Executive Head - Community, Surrey Heath House, Knoll Road, Camberley GU15 3HD ☎ 01276 707100 ◌ tim.pashen@surreyheath.gov.uk

Waste Management: Mr Tim Pashen, Executive Head - Community, Surrey Heath House, Knoll Road, Camberley GU15 3HD ☎ 01276 707100 ◌ tim.pashen@surreyheath.gov.uk

Children's Play Areas: Ms Sue McCubbin, Recreation & Business Services Manager, Surrey Heath House, Knoll Road, Camberley GU15 3HD ☎ 01276 707100 ◌ sue.mccubbin@surreyheath.gov.uk

COUNCILLORS

Mayor: Winterton, John (CON - Lightwater)
john.winterton@surreyheath.gov.uk

Deputy Mayor: White, Valerie (CON - Bagshot)
valerie.white@surreyheath.gov.uk

Leader of the Council: Gibson, Moira (CON - Windlesham)
moira.gibson@surreyheath.gov..uk

Deputy Leader of the Council: Brooks, Richard (CON - Town)
richard.brooks@surreyheath.gov..uk

Group Leader: Bates, Rodney (LAB - Old Dean)
rodney.bates@surreyheath.gov..uk

Adams, Dan (CON - St. Pauls)
dan.adams@surreyheath.gov.uk

Allen, David (CON - Frimley)
dra01@btconnect.com

Chambers, Nick (CON - Old Dean)
nick.chambers@surreyheath.gov.uk

Chapman, Bill (CON - St. Pauls)
bill.chapman@surreyheath.gov..uk

Chapman, Vivienne (CON - St. Pauls)
vivienne.chapman@surreyheath.gov..uk

Cullen, Ian (CON - Heatherside)
ian.cullen@surreyheath.gov.uk

Deach, Paul (CON - Mytchett & Deepcut)
paul.deach@surreyheath.gov.uk

Dougan, Colin (CON - St. Michaels)
colin.dougan@surreyheath.gov..uk

Fennell, Craig (CON - Mytchett & Deepcut)
craig.fennell@surreyheath.gov.uk

Gandhum, Surinder (CON - Lightwater)
surinder.gandhum@surreyheath.gov.uk

Hawkins, Josephine (CON - Parkside)
josephine.hawkins@surreyheath.gov..uk

Hawkins, Edward (CON - Parkside)
edward.hawkins@surreyheath.gov..uk

Hutchinson, Ruth (LD - Bagshot)
ruth.hutchinson@surreyheath.gov.uk

Ilnicki, Paul (CON - Heatherside)
paul.ilnicki@surreyheath.gov..uk

Jennings-Evans, Rebecca (CON - Lightwater)
rebecca.jennings-evans@surreyheath.gov.uk

Lewis, Oliver (CON - Frimley Green)
oliver.lewis@surreyheath.gov.uk

Lewis, David (CON - Watchetts)
david.lewis@surreyheath.gov.uk

Lytle, Jonathan (CON - Heatherside)
johnathan.lytle@surreyheath.gov.uk

Malcaus Cooper, Katie (CON - Bagshot)
katie.malcauscooper@surreyheath.gov.uk

Mansell, Bruce (CON - Frimley)
bruce.mansell@surreyheath.gov..uk

Mansfield, David (CON - Bisley)
david.mansfield@surreyheath.gov.uk

McClafferty, Alan (CON - St. Michaels)

Morley, Charlotte (CON - Watchetts)
charlotte.morley@surreyheath.gov.uk

Nelson, Max (CON - Frimley Green)
max.nelson@surreyheath.gov.uk

Page, Adrian (CON - West End)
adrian.page@surreyheath.gov.uk

Perry, Robin (CON - Town)
robin.perry@surryheath.gov.uk

Pitt, Chris (CON - Frimley Green)
chris.pitt@surreyheath.gov.uk

Potter, Joanne (CON - Mytchett & Deepcut)
joanne.potter@surreyheath.gov.uk

Price, Wynne (CON - Bisley)
wynne.price@surreyheath.gov..uk

Price, Nic (CON - West End)
nic.price@surreyheath.gov.uk

Ratiram, Darryl (CON - Parkside)
darryl.ratiram@surreyheath.gov.uk

Sams, Ian (CON - Frimley) ian.sams@surreyheath.gov.uk

Sturt, Conrad (CON - Windlesham)
conrad.sturt@surreyheath.gov.uk

Tedder, Pat (IND - Chobham) pat.tedder@surreyheath.gov.uk

Wheeler, Victoria (IND - Chobham)
victoria.wheeler@surreyheath.gov.uk

POLITICAL COMPOSITION
CON: 36, IND: 2, LAB: 1, LD: 1

COMMITTEE CHAIRS

Audit: Ms Rebecca Jennings-Evans

Licensing: Mr Bill Chapman

Planning: Mr Edward Hawkins

Sutton L

Sutton London Borough Council, Civic Offices, St. Nicholas Way, Sutton SM1 1EA
☎ 020 8770 5000 🖶 020 8770 5404 ◌ contactcentre@sutton.gov.uk
🖥 www.sutton.gov.uk

FACTS AND FIGURES
Parliamentary Constituencies: Carshalton and Wallington, Sutton and Cheam
EU Constituencies: London
Election Frequency: Elections are of whole council

PRINCIPAL OFFICERS

Chief Executive: Mr Niall Bolger, Chief Executive, Civic Offices, St. Nicholas Way, Sutton SM1 1EA ☎ 020 8770 5000 ⌖ niall.bolger@sutton.gov.uk

Senior Management: Dr Nicola Lang, Director - Public Health, Civic Offices, St. Nicholas Way, Sutton SM1 1EA ⌖ nicola.lang@sutton.gov.uk

Senior Management: Ms Jan Underhill, Executive Head of Wellbeing, Civic Offices, St. Nicholas Way, Sutton SM1 1EA ☎ 020 8770 4359 ⌖ jan.underhill@sutton.gov.uk

Access Officer / Social Services (Disability): Mr Simon Latham, Executive Head of Environment, Housing & Regeneration, 24 Denmark Road, Carshalton SM5 2JG ☎ 020 8770 4005 ⌖ simon.latham@sutton.gov.uk

Architect, Building / Property Services: Mr Ade Adebayo, Executive Head of Asset Planning, Management & Capital Delivery, Civic Offices, St. Nicholas Way, Sutton SM1 1EA ☎ 020 8770 6109 ⌖ ade.adebayo@sutton.gov.uk

Architect, Building / Property Services: Mr Alex Fitzgerald, Head of Asset Management, 24 Denmark Road, Carshalton SM5 2JG ☎ 020 8770 6154 ⌖ alex.fitzgerald@sutton.gov.uk

Children / Youth Services: Mr Richard Nash, Executive Head of Children's Social Care & Safeguarding, Civic Offices, St. Nicholas Way, Sutton SM1 1EA ☎ 020 8770 4502 ⌖ richard.nash@sutton.gov.uk

PR / Communications: Mr Andreas Christophorou, Head of Communications, Civic Offices, St. Nicholas Way, Sutton SM1 1EA ☎ 020 8770 4048 ⌖ andreas.christophorou@sutton.gov.uk

Community Safety: Mr Warren Shadbolt, Executive Head of Safer & Stronger Communities, Sutton Police Station, 🖳 Carshalton Road, Sutton SM1 4RF ☎ 020 8649 0601 ⌖ warren.shadbolt@met.pnn.police.uk

Computer Management: Mr Rob Miller, Head of Shared ICT Service, Guildhall 1, High Street, Kingston upon Thames KT1 1EU ☎ 07920 590018 ⌖ rob.miller@kingston.gov.uk

Contracts: Mr Mark Brewer, Head of Procurement, Civic Offices, St. Nicholas Way, Sutton SM1 1EA ☎ 020 8770 5300 ⌖ mark.brewer@sutton.gov.uk

Customer Service: Ms Jessica Crowe, Executive Head of Customers, Commissioning & Governance, Civic Offices, St. Nicholas Way, Sutton SM1 1EA ☎ 020 8770 6519 ⌖ jessica.crowe@sutton.gov.uk

Economic Development: Mr Greg MacDonald, Executive Head of Economic Development, Planning & Sustainability, 24 Denmark Road, Carshalton SM5 2JG ☎ 020 8770 5000 ⌖ greg.macdonald@sutton.gov.uk

Education: Mr Colin Stewart, Executive Head of Education & Early Intervention, Civic Offices, St. Nicholas Way, Sutton SM1 1EA ☎ 020 8770 5000 ⌖ colin.stewart@sutton.gov.uk

Electoral Registration: Ms Martha Matheou, Head of Electoral Services, Civic Offices, St. Nicholas Way, Sutton SM1 1EA ☎ 020 8770 5000 ⌖ martha.matheou@sutton.gov.uk

Emergency Planning: Mr Glenn Phillips, Head of Community Safety Services, Old Police Station, 🖳 Carshalton Road, Carshalton SM1 4RF ☎ 020 8649 0607 ⌖ glenn.phillips@sutton.gov.uk

Environmental / Technical Services: Ms Mary Morrissey, Strategic Director - Environment, Housing & Regeneration, 24 Denmark Road, Carshalton SM5 2JG ☎ 020 8770 6401 ⌖ mary.morrissey@sutton.gov.uk

Environmental Health: Mrs Jan Gransden, Group Manager - Enforcement Services, 24 Denmark Road, Carshalton SM5 2JG ☎ 020 8770 5550 ⌖ jan.gransden@sutton.gov.uk

Estates, Property & Valuation: Mr Ade Adebayo, Executive Head of Asset Planning, Management & Capital Delivery, Civic Offices, St. Nicholas Way, Sutton SM1 1EA ☎ 020 8770 6109 ⌖ ade.adebayo@sutton.gov.uk

Finance: Mr Gerald Almeroth, Strategic Director - Resources, Civic Offices, St. Nicholas Way, Sutton SM1 1EA ☎ 020 8770 5501 ⌖ gerald.almeroth@sutton.gov.uk

Finance: Mr Phil Butlin, Executive Head of Finance, Civic Offices, St. Nicholas Way, Sutton SM1 1EA ☎ 020 8770 5000 ⌖ phil.butlin@sutton.gov.uk

Pensions: Mr Andy Banham, Head of Pensions, Civic Offices, St. Nicholas Way, Sutton SM1 1EA ☎ 020 8770 5000 ⌖ andy.banham@sutton.gov.uk

Fleet Management: Mr Matt Clubb, Executive Head of Environment Commissioning, 24 Denmark Road, Carshalton SM5 2JG ☎ 020 8770 6116 ⌖ matt.clubb@sutton.gov.uk

Grounds Maintenance: Mr Mark Dalzell, Head of Parks, Biodiversity & Street Cleansing, 24 Denmark Road, Carshalton SM5 2JG ☎ 020 8770 4695 ⌖ mark.dalzell@sutton.gov.uk

Health and Safety: Mr David Garioch, Corporate Health & Safety Manager, 24 Denmark Road, Carshalton SM5 2JG ☎ 020 8770 5070 ⌖ david.garioch@surreycc.gov.uk

Highways: Mr Mehmet Mazhar, Interim Service Manager - Traffic Management & Design, Guildhall 1, High Street, Kingston upon Thames KT1 1EU ☎ 020 8547 5943 ⌖ mehmet.mazhar@kingston.gov.uk

SUTTON

Home Energy Conservation: Mrs Jan Gransden, Group Manager - Enforcement Services, 24 Denmark Road, Carshalton SM1 2JG ☎ 020 8770 5550 ⑪ jan.gransden@sutton.gov.uk

Licensing: Mr Richard Winch, Senior Principal Licensing Officer, 24 Denmark Road, Carshalton SM5 2JG ☎ 020 8770 5622 ⑪ richard.winch@sutton.gov.uk

Member Services: Ms Alexa Coates, Committee & Management Services Support Manager, Civic Offices, St. Nicholas Way, Sutton SM1 1EA ☎ 020 8770 5094 ⑪ alexa.coates@sutton.gov.uk

Parking: Mr Glenn Phillips, Head of Community Safety Services, Old Police Station, ⚍ Carshalton Road, Carshalton SM1 4RF ☎ 020 8649 0607 ⑪ glenn.phillips@sutton.gov.uk

Personnel / HR: Ms Kate Enver, Joint Head of HR Business Partnership, Civic Offices, St. Nicholas Way, Sutton SM1 1EA ☎ 020 8770 4148 ⑪ kate.enver@sutton.gov.uk

Planning: Mr Greg MacDonald, Executive Head of Economic Development, Planning & Sustainability, 24 Denmark Road, Carshalton SM5 2JG ☎ 020 8770 5000 ⑪ greg.macdonald@sutton.gov.uk

Procurement: Mr Mark Brewer, Head of Procurement, Civic Offices, St. Nicholas Way, Sutton SM1 1EA ☎ 020 8770 5300 ⑪ mark.brewer@sutton.gov.uk

Social Services: Mr Tolis Vouyioukas, Strategic Director - People Services, Civic Offices, St. Nicholas Way, Sutton SM1 1EA ☎ 020 8770 4502 ⑪ tolis.vouyiokas@sutton.gov.uk

Social Services (Adult): Mr Nick Ireland, Executive Head of Adult Social Care, Civic Offices, St. Nicholas Way, Sutton SM1 1EA ☎ 020 8770 4506 ⑪ nick.ireland@sutton.gov.uk

Social Services (Adult): Mr Tolis Vouyioukas, Strategic Director - People Services, Civic Offices, St. Nicholas Way, Sutton SM1 1EA ☎ 020 8770 4502 ⑪ tolis.vouyiokas@sutton.gov.uk

Social Services (Children): Mr Richard Nash, Executive Head of Children's Social Care & Safeguarding, Civic Offices, St. Nicholas Way, Sutton SM1 1EA ☎ 020 8770 4502 ⑪ richard.nash@sutton.gov.uk

Social Services (Children): Mr Tolis Vouyioukas, Strategic Director - People Services, Civic Offices, St. Nicholas Way, Sutton SM1 1EA ☎ 020 8770 4502 ⑪ tolis.vouyiokas@sutton.gov.uk

Public Health: Dr Nicola Lang, Director - Public Health, Civic Offices, St. Nicholas Way, Sutton SM1 1EA ⑪ nicola.lang@sutton.gov.uk

Staff Training: Mr James Taylor, Lead Consultant - Planning & Development, Council Chamber, Royal Borough of Kingston, 1st Floor, Guildhall, High Street, Kingston upon Thames KT1 1EU ☎ 020 8547 5174 ⑪ james.taylor@kingston.gov.uk

Street Scene: Ms Mary Morrissey, Strategic Director - Environment, Housing & Regeneration, 24 Denmark Road, Carshalton SM1 2JG ☎ 020 8770 6401 ⑪ mary.morrissey@sutton.gov.uk

Sustainable Development: Ms Mary Morrissey, Strategic Director - Environment, Housing & Regeneration, 24 Denmark Road, Carshalton SM1 2JG ☎ 020 8770 6401 ⑪ mary.morrissey@sutton.gov.uk

Town Centre: Mr Martin Furtauer-Hayes, Town Centre Manager, Civic Offices, St. Nicholas Way, Sutton SM1 1EA ☎ 020 8770 5125 ⑪ martin.furtauer-hayes@sutton.gov.uk

COUNCILLORS

Mayor: Clifton, Richard (LD - Sutton South)
richard.clifton@sutton.gov.uk

Deputy Mayor: Patel, Nali (LD - The Wrythe)
nali.patel@sutton.gov.uk

Leader of the Council: Dombey, Ruth (LD - Sutton North)
ruth.dombey@sutton.gov.uk

Deputy Leader of the Council: Wales, Simon (LD - Sutton West)
simon.wales@sutton.gov.uk

Group Leader: Crowley, Tim (CON - Carshalton South & Clockhouse)
timcrowley@blueyonder.co.uk

Abellan, Manuel (LD - Beddington South)
manuel.abellan@sutton.gov.uk

Ali, Pathumal (LD - Beddington North)
pathumal.ali@sutton.gov.uk

Bartolucci, David (LD - Sutton Central)
david.bartolucci@sutton.gov.uk

Bourne, Samantha (LD - Nonsuch)
samantha.bourne@sutton.gov.uk

Broadbent, Richard (LD - Nonsuch)
richard.broadbent@sutton.gov.uk

Burke, Kevin (LD - Sutton West)
kevin.burke@sutton.gov.uk

Burstow, Mary (LD - Cheam)
mary.burstow@sutton.gov.uk

Butt, Moira (CON - Carshalton South & Clockhouse)
moira.butt@sutton.gov.uk

Cook, Steve (LD - Wallington South)
steve.cook@sutton.gov.uk

Court, Margaret (LD - Wandle Valley)
mpcourt@hotmail.com

Crossby, Jean (LD - St Helier)
jean.crossby@sutton.gov.uk

Davey, Adrian (LD - Stonecot)
adrian.davey@sutton.gov.uk

Emmerson, Nick (LD - Stonecot)
nick.emmerson@sutton.gov.uk

Fivey, Trish (LD - Sutton South)
trish.fivey@sutton.gov.uk

Galligan, Vincent (LD - Sutton Central)
vincent.galligan@sutton.gov.uk

Garratt, Neil (CON - Beddington South)
neil.garratt@sutton.gov.uk

Gonzalez, Martin (LD - St Helier)
martin.gonzalez@sutton.gov.uk

Gordon, Sunita (LD - Wallington North)
sunita.gordon@sutton.gov.uk

Haldane, Amy (LD - Carshalton South & Clockhouse)
amy.haldane@sutton.gov.uk

Heron, Marlene (LD - Sutton North)
marlene.heron@sutton.gov.uk

Hicks, David (CON - Belmont)
david.hicks@sutton.gov.uk

Hookway, Arthur (LD - Worcester Park)
arthur.hookway@sutton.gov.uk

Hunt, Doug (LD - St Helier)
doug.hunt@sutton.gov.uk

Javelot, Miquel (LD - Stonecot)
miquel.javelot@sutton.gov.uk

Joyce, Edward (LD - Beddington South)
edward.joyce@sutton.gov.uk

Marston, Richard (LD - Worcester Park)
richard.marston@sutton.gov.uk

Mathys, Wendy (LD - Sutton West)
wendy.mathys@sutton.gov.uk

Mattey, Nick (IND - Beddington North)
nick.mattey@sutton.gov.uk

McCoy, Jayne (LD - Wallington South)
jayne.mccoy@sutton.gov.uk

McManus, Patrick (CON - Belmont)
patrick.mcmanus@sutton.gov.uk

Melican, Joyce (LD - Wallington North)
joyce.melican@sutton.gov.uk

Mirhashem, Ali (LD - Sutton Central)
ali.mirhashem@sutton.gov.uk

Morton, Callum (LD - The Wrythe)
callum.morton@sutton.gov.uk

Pascoe, Jane (CON - Belmont)
jane.pascoe@sutton.gov.uk

Penneck, Steve (LD - Sutton North)
steve.penneck@sutton.gov.uk

Piracha, Nighat (LD - Beddington North)
nighat.piracha@sutton.gov.uk

Pollock, Hamish (LD - Carshalton Central)
hamish.pollock@sutton.gov.uk

Radford, Marian (LD - Wallington North)
marian.radford@sutton.gov.uk

Ramsey, Holly (CON - Cheam)
holly.ramsey@sutton.gov.uk

Reynolds, Jason (LD - Wandle Valley)
jason.reynolds@sutton.gov.uk

Sadiq, Muhammed (LD - Wallington South)
muhammed.sadiq@sutton.gov.uk

Sangster, Daniel (LD - Nonsuch)
daniel.sangster@sutton.gov.uk

Shields, Tony (CON - Sutton South)
tony.shields@sutton.gov.uk

Stears, Colin (LD - The Wrythe)
colin.stears@sutton.gov.uk

Whitehead, Jill (LD - Carshalton Central)
jill.whitehead@sutton.gov.uk

Witham, Graham (IND - Cheam)
graham.witham@sutton.gov.uk

Williams, Chris (LD - Carshalton Central)
chris.williams@sutton.gov.uk

Wingfield, Paul (LD - Worcester Park)
paul.wingfield@sutton.gov.uk

Zuchowska, Hanna (LD - Wandle Valley)
hanna.zuchowska@sutton.gov.uk

POLITICAL COMPOSITION
LD: 44, CON: 8, IND: 2

COMMITTEE CHAIRS

Adult Social Services & Health: Mr Colin Stears

Audit: Mr David Hicks

Children, Family & Education: Ms Wendy Mathys

Environment & Neighbourhood: Ms Jill Whitehead

Licensing: Ms Mary Burstow

Pensions: Ms Sunita Gordon

Planning: Ms Samantha Bourne

Swale   D

Swale Borough Council, Swale House, East Street,
Sittingbourne ME10 3HT
☎ 01795 417850 ⎙ 01795 417217 ✆ csc@swale.gov.uk
🖳 www.swale.gov.uk

FACTS AND FIGURES
Parliamentary Constituencies: Faversham & Mid Kent,
Sittingbourne and Sheppey
EU Constituencies: South East
Election Frequency: Elections are by thirds

PRINCIPAL OFFICERS

Chief Executive: Mr Abdool Kara, Chief Executive, Swale House,
East Street, Sittingbourne ME10 3HT ☎ 01795 417394
✆ abdoolkara@swale.gov.uk

Senior Management: Mr Mark Radford, Director - Corporate
Services, Swale House, East Street, Sittingbourne ME10 3HT
☎ 01795 417269 ✆ markradford@swale.gov.uk

Senior Management: Ms Emma Wiggins, Interim Director -
Regeneration, Swale House, East Street, Sittingbourne ME10 3HT
☎ 01795 417396 ✆ emmawiggins@swale.gov.uk

Architect, Building / Property Services: Mr James Freeman,
Head of Development, Swale House, East Street, Sittingbourne
ME10 3HT ☎ 01795 417309 ✆ jamesfreeman@swale.gov.uk

PR / Communications: Ms Sara Toal, Head of Communications,
Swale House, East Street, Sittingbourne ME10 3HT
☎ 01795 417066 ✆ saratoal@swale.gov.uk

SWALE

Community Planning: Ms Emma Wiggins, Interim Director - Regeneration, Swale House, East Street, Sittingbourne ME10 3HT ☎ 01795 417396 ⌁ emmawiggins@swale.gov.uk

Community Safety: Mrs Charlotte Hudson, Head of Community Safety, Swale House, East Street, Sittingbourne ME10 3HT ☎ 01795 417196 ⌁ charlottehudson@swale.gov.uk

Computer Management: Mr Tony Bullock, ICT Services Manager, Swale House, East Street, Sittingbourne ME10 3HT ☎ 01795 417264 ⌁ tonybullock@swale.gov.uk

Computer Management: Mr Andrew Cole, Head of ICT Shared Services, Maidstone House, King Street, Maidstone ME15 6JQ ☎ 01622 602662 ⌁ andrew.cole@tunbridgewells.gov.uk

Contracts: Mr Dave Thomas, Head of Commissioning & Customer Contact, Swale House, East Street, Sittingbourne ME10 3HT ☎ 01795 417263 ⌁ davethomas@swale.gov.uk

Corporate Services: Mr Mark Radford, Director - Corporate Services, Swale House, East Street, Sittingbourne ME10 3HT ☎ 01795 417269 ⌁ markradford@swale.gov.uk

Customer Service: Mrs Carol Sargeant, Customer Services Manager, Swale House, East Street, Sittingbourne ME10 3HT ☎ 01795 417055 ⌁ carolsargeant@swale.gov.uk

Customer Service: Mr Dave Thomas, Head of Commissioning & Customer Contact, Swale House, East Street, Sittingbourne ME10 3HT ☎ 01795 417263 ⌁ davethomas@swale.gov.uk

Economic Development: Mr Kieren Mansfield, Economic Development Officer, Swale House, East Street, Sittingbourne ME10 3HT ☎ 01795 417262 ⌁ kierenmansfield@swale.gov.uk

Economic Development: Ms Emma Wiggins, Interim Director - Regeneration, Swale House, East Street, Sittingbourne ME10 3HT ☎ 01795 417396 ⌁ emmawiggins@swale.gov.uk

Electoral Registration: Ms Katherine Bescoby, Democratic & Electoral Services Officer, Swale House, East Street, Sittingbourne ME10 3HT ☎ 01795 417330 ⌁ katherinebescoby@swale.gov.uk

Emergency Planning: Ms Della Fackrell, Emergency Planning Officer, Swale House, East Street, Sittingbourne ME10 3HT ☎ 01795 417430 ⌁ dellafackrell@swale.gov.uk

Energy Management: Mr Phil Garland, Lead Officer - Home Energy Conservation Act, Swale House, East Street, Sittingbourne ME10 3HT ☎ 01795 417231 ⌁ philgarland@swale.gov.uk

Energy Management: Ms Janet Hill, Cimate Change Officer, Swale House, East Street, Sittingbourne ME10 3HT ☎ 01795 417341 ⌁ janethill@swale.gov.uk

Environmental Health: Mr Phil Garland, Lead Officer - Home Energy Conservation Act, Swale House, East Street, Sittingbourne ME10 3HT ☎ 01795 417231 ⌁ philgarland@swale.gov.uk

Estates, Property & Valuation: Mr Kent Parker, Estates Surveyor, Swale House, East Street, Sittingbourne ME10 3HT ☎ 01795 417349 ⌁ kentparker@swale.gov.uk

Facilities: Mrs Anne Adams, Head of Property Services, Swale House, East Street, Sittingbourne ME10 3HT ☎ 01795 417311 ⌁ anneadams@swale.gov.uk

Finance: Mr Nick Vickers, Head of Finance & S151 Officer, Swale House, East Street, Sittingbourne ME10 3HT ☎ 01795 417396 ⌁ nickvickers@swale.gov.uk

Grounds Maintenance: Mr Graeme Tuff, Landscape Officer, Swale House, East Street, Sittingbourne ME10 3HT ☎ 01795 417127 ⌁ graemetuff@swale.gov.uk

Health and Safety: Ms Emma Larkins, Health & Safety & Risk Officer, Swale House, East Street, Sittingbourne ME10 3HT ☎ 01795 417078

Home Energy Conservation: Mr Phil Garland, Lead Officer - Home Energy Conservation Act, Swale House, East Street, Sittingbourne ME10 3HT ☎ 01795 417231 ⌁ philgarland@swale.gov.uk

Housing: Ms Amber Christou, Head of Resident Services, Swale House, East Street, Sittingbourne ME10 3HT ☎ 01795 417237 ⌁ amberchristou@swale.gov.uk

Local Area Agreement: Ms Gill Harris, Spatial Planning Manager, Swale House, East Street, Sittingbourne ME10 3HT ☎ 01795 417118 ⌁ gillharris@swale.gov.uk

Leisure and Cultural Services: Mr Martyn Cassell, Leisure & Technical Services Manager, Swale House, East Street, Sittingbourne ME10 3HT ☎ 01795 417155 ⌁ martyncassell@swale.gov.uk

Licensing: Ms Angela Seaward, Licensing Officer, Swale House, East Street, Sittingbourne ME10 3HT ☎ 01795 417364 ⌁ angelaseaward@swale.gov.uk

Member Services: Ms Katherine Bescoby, Democratic & Electoral Services Officer, Swale House, East Street, Sittingbourne ME10 3HT ☎ 01795 417330 ⌁ katherinebescoby@swale.gov.uk

Personnel / HR: Ms Dena Smart, Head of HR Shared Services, Swale House, East Street, Sittingbourne ME10 3HT ☎ 01795 417391 ⌁ denasmart@swale.gov.uk

Planning: Mr James Freeman, Head of Development, Swale House, East Street, Sittingbourne ME10 3HT ☎ 01795 417309 ⌁ jamesfreeman@swale.gov.uk

Procurement: Mr Dave Thomas, Head of Commissioning & Customer Contact, Swale House, East Street, Sittingbourne ME10 3HT ☎ 01795 417263 ⌁ davethomas@swale.gov.uk

Recycling & Waste Minimisation: Mr Dave Thomas, Head of Commissioning & Customer Contact, Swale House, East Street, Sittingbourne ME10 3HT ☎ 01795 417263 ⌁ davethomas@swale.gov.uk

Recycling & Waste Minimisation: Mr Alan Turner, Cleansing Services Manager, Swale House, East Street, Sittingbourne ME10 3HT ☎ 01795 417285 📧 alanturner@swale.gov.uk

Regeneration: Ms Kathryn Carr, Director - Regeneration, Swale House, East Street, Sittingbourne ME10 3HT ☎ 01795 417321 📧 kathryncarr@swale.gov.uk

Regeneration: Ms Emma Wiggins, Interim Director - Regeneration, Swale House, East Street, Sittingbourne ME10 3HT ☎ 01795 417396 📧 emmawiggins@swale.gov.uk

Staff Training: Mrs Catherine Harrison, Training & Development Manager, Swale House, East Street, Sittingbourne ME10 3HT ☎ 01795 417381 📧 catherineharrison@swale.gov.uk

Tourism: Ms Lyn Newton, Economy & Community Services Manager, Swale House, East Street, Sittingbourne ME10 3HT ☎ 01795 417420 📧 lynnewton@swale.gov.uk

Tourism: Ms Emma Wiggins, Interim Director - Regeneration, Swale House, East Street, Sittingbourne ME10 3HT ☎ 01795 417396 📧 emmawiggins@swale.gov.uk

Total Place: Mr Abdool Kara, Chief Executive, Swale House, East Street, Sittingbourne ME10 3HT ☎ 01795 417394 📧 abdoolkara@swale.gov.uk

Waste Collection and Disposal: Mr Alan Turner, Cleansing Services Manager, Swale House, East Street, Sittingbourne ME10 3HT ☎ 01795 417285 📧 alanturner@swale.gov.uk

Waste Management: Mr Dave Thomas, Head of Commissioning & Customer Contact, Swale House, East Street, Sittingbourne ME10 3HT ☎ 01795 417263 📧 davethomas@swale.gov.uk

Waste Management: Mr Alan Turner, Cleansing Services Manager, Swale House, East Street, Sittingbourne ME10 3HT ☎ 01795 417285 📧 alanturner@swale.gov.uk

Children's Play Areas: Mr Graeme Tuff, Landscape Officer, Swale House, East Street, Sittingbourne ME10 3HT ☎ 01795 417127 📧 graemetuff@swale.gov.uk

COUNCILLORS

Mayor: Ingham, Lesley (CON - Sheppey East)
lesleyingham57@yahoo.co.uk

Deputy Mayor: Prescott, Colin (CON - East Downs)
colinprescott@swale.gov.uk

Leader of the Council: Bowles, Andrew (CON - Boughton & Courtenay)
leader@swale.gov.uk

Deputy Leader of the Council: Lewin, Gerald (CON - Hartlip, Newington & Upchurch)
cllrlewin@swale.gov.uk

Group Leader: Henderson, Mike (IND - Priory)
mikeshenderson@outlook.com

Aldridge, Sarah (CON - Roman)
sarahaldridge@swale.gov.uk

Baldock, Mike (UKIP - Borden & Grove Park)
mikebaldock@swale.gov.uk

Beart, Cameron (CON - Queenborough & Halfway)
cameronbeart@swale.gov.uk

Bobbin, George (CON - Boughton & Courtenay)
george.bobbin@btinternet.com

Bonney, Monique (IND - West Downs)
montybon1@aol.com

Booth, Andy (CON - Minster Cliffs)
andybooth@swale.gov.uk

Booth, Tina (CON - Sheppey Central)
tinabooth@swale.gov.uk

Bowen, Lloyd (CON - Teynham & Lynsted)
lloydbowen@swale.gov.uk

Clark, Roger (CON - Milton Regis)
clark.miltonregis@gmail.com

Coleman, Katy (UKIP - Milton Regis)
katycolman@swale.gov.uk

Conway, Derek (CON - Woodstock)
derekconway@swale.gov.uk

Cosgrove, Mike (CON - St. Ann's)
cllrcosgrove@swale.gov.uk

Crowther, Adrian (UKIP - Minster Cliffs)
adrian.crowther@kent.gov.uk

Darby, Richard (UKIP - Queenborough & Halfway)
rdarbypax@aol.com

Dendor, Mike (CON - Kemsley)
mikedendor@swale.gov.uk

Dewar-Whalley, Duncan (CON - Bobbing, Iwade & Lower Halstow)
duncandewar-whalley@swale.gov.uk

Ellen, Mark (LAB - Sheerness)
cllr.markellen@yahoo.co.uk

Fleming, Paul (UKIP - Roman)
paulfleming104@googlemail.com

Galvin, Mick (UKIP - Sheerness)
mickgalvin@swale.gov.uk

Garrad, June (UKIP - Sheppey Central)
jvgarrad@aol.com

Gent, Sue (CON - Kemsley)
gentmiss@blueyonder.co.uk

Hall, James (UKIP - Murston)
jameshall@swale.gov.uk

Hampshire, Nicholas (CON - Borden & Grove Park)
nicholashampshire@hotmail.com

Harrison, Angela (LAB - Sheerness)
angelaharrison@swale.gov.uk

Horton, Alan (CON - Homewood)
alanhorton@swale.gov.uk

Hunt, James (CON - The Meads)
jameshunt@swale.gov.uk

Ingleton, Ken (CON - Sheppey Central)
kjingleton@aol.com

Kay, Nigel (CON - St. Ann's)
nigelkay@swale.gov.uk

SWALE

Koffie-Williams, Samuel (CON - Murston)
samuelkwilliams@swale.gov.uk

Marchington, Peter (CON - Queenborough & Halfway)
petermarchington@hotmail.co.uk

Mulhern, Bryan (CON - Abbey)
bryanmulhern@swale.gov.uk

Nissanga, Padmini (UKIP - Sheppey East)
mininissanga@swale.gov.uk

Pugh, Ken (CON - Minster Cliffs)
kenpugh@uwclub.net

Samuel, George (CON - Woodstock)
georgesamuel@swale.gov.uk

Simmons, David (CON - Watling)
davidsimmons@swale.gov.uk

Stokes, Ben (CON - Bobbing, Iwade & Lower Halstow)
benstokes@swale.gov.uk

Truelove, Roger (LAB - Homewood)
rtruelove12@gmail.com

Walker, Anita (CON - Abbey)
anitajwalker@yahoo.co.uk

Whelan, Ghlin (LAB - Chalkwell)
ghlinwhelan@gmail.com

Whiting, Mike (CON - Teynham & Lynsted)
mikewhiting@swale.gov.uk

Wilcox, Ted (CON - Watling)
tedwilcox@swale.gov.uk

Wright, John (CON - Hartlip, Newington & Upchurch)
johnwright@swale.gov.uk

POLITICAL COMPOSITION
CON: 32, UKIP: 9, LAB: 4, IND: 2

COMMITTEE CHAIRS

Audit: Mr Nicholas Hampshire

Licensing: Ms Lesley Ingham

Planning: Mr Bryan Mulhern

Swansea, City of   W

City and County of Swansea Council, Civic Centre,
Oystermouth Road, Swansea SA1 3SN
☎ 01792 636000 ⌁ contact@swansea.gov.uk 🖥 www.swansea.gov.uk

FACTS AND FIGURES
Parliamentary Constituencies: Gower, Swansea East, Swansea
West
EU Constituencies: Wales
Election Frequency: Elections are of whole council

PRINCIPAL OFFICERS

Chief Executive: Mr Phil Roberts, Chief Executive, Civic Centre,
Oystermouth Road, Swansea SA1 3SN ☎ 01792 637500
⌁ phil.roberts@swansea.gov.uk

Senior Management: Mr Mike Hawes, Head - Financial Services,
Civic Centre, Oystermouth Road, Swansea SA1 3SN
☎ 01792 636423 ⌁ mike.hawes@swansea.gov.uk

Senior Management: Mr Martin Nicholls, Director - Place, Heol y
gors, Cwmbwrla, Swansea SA5 8LD ☎ 01792 511002
⌁ martin.nicholls@swansea.gov.uk

Senior Management: Mr Chris Sivers, Director - People, The
Guildhall, Swansea SA1 4PE ☎ 01792 637521
⌁ chris.sivers@swansea.gov.uk

Senior Management: Mr Dean Taylor, Director - Corporate
Services, The Guildhall, Swansea SA1 4PE ☎ 01792 637521
⌁ dean.taylor@swansea.gov.uk

Architect, Building / Property Services: Mr Martin Nicholls,
Director - Place, Heol y gors, Cwmbwrla, Swansea SA5 8LD
☎ 01792 511002 ⌁ martin.nicholls@swansea.gov.uk

Building Control: Mr Peter Richards, Divisional Officer, Civic
Centre, Oystermouth Road, Swansea SA1 3SN ☎ 01792 635622
⌁ peter.richards@swansea.gov.uk

Catering Services: Ms Anne-Marie Evans, Catering & Cleaning
Facilities Manager, Civic Centre, Oystermouth Road, Swansea
SA1 3SN ☎ 01792 636097 ⌁ anne.marie.evans@swansea.gov.uk

Children / Youth Services: Mr David Howes, Head - Children &
Family Services, Oldway Centre, High Street, Swansea SA1 1LT
☎ 01792 636248 ⌁ david.howes@swansea.gov.uk

Civil Registration: Mr Noel Evans, Registration & Bereavement
Services Manager, Civic Centre, Oystermouth Road, Swansea
SA1 3SN ☎ 01792 636275 ⌁ noel.evans@swansea.gov.uk

PR / Communications: Mr Lee Wenham, Head -
Communications, Marketing, Overview & Scrutiny, Civic Centre,
Oystermouth Road, Swansea SA1 3SN ☎ 01792 637158
⌁ lee.wenham@swansea.gov.uk

Community Safety: Mr Jeff Davison, Community Safety Co-
ordinator, Cockett Police Station, John Street, Cockett, Swansea
SA2 0FR ☎ 01792 456999 Extn 52757
⌁ jeff.davison@swansea.gov.uk

Computer Management: Ms Sarah Caulkin, Head - Information
& Business Change, Civic Centre, Oystermouth Road, Swansea
SA1 3SN ☎ 01792 636849 ⌁ sarah.caulkin@swansea.gov.uk

Consumer Protection and Trading Standards: Mr Lee
Morgan, Head - Housing & Public Protection, Civic Centre,
Oystermouth Road, Swansea SA1 3SN ☎ 01792 635017
⌁ lee.morgan@swansea.gov.uk

Economic Development: Mr Phillip Holmes, Head - Economic
Regeneration & Planning, Civic Centre, Oystermouth Road,
Swansea SA1 3SN ☎ 01792 636979
⌁ phillip.holmes@swansea.gov.uk

Education: Mr Lindsay Harvey, Chief Education Officer, Civic
Centre, Oystermouth Road, Swansea SA1 3SN ☎ 01792 637166
⌁ lindsay.harvey@swansea.gov.uk

Education: Mr Brian Roles, Head - Planning & Resources, Oldway
Centre, 36 Orchard Street, Swansea SA1 5AQ ☎ 01792 636357
⌁ brian.roles@swansea.gov.uk

Electoral Registration: Mr Patrick Arran, Head - Legal, Democratic Services & Procurement, Civic Centre, Oystermouth Road, Swansea SA1 3SN ☎ 01792 636699 ✆ patrick.arran@swansea.gov.uk

Energy Management: Mr John Llewellyn, Energy Manager, Civic Centre, Oystermouth Road, Swansea SA1 3SN ☎ 01792 636359 ✆ john.llewellyn@swansea.gov.uk

Estates, Property & Valuation: Mr Martin Nicholls, Director - Place, Heol y gors, Cwmbwrla, Swansea SA5 8LD ☎ 01792 511002 ✆ martin.nicholls@swansea.gov.uk

European Liaison: Mr Paul Relf, European Officer, Civic Centre, Oystermouth Road, Swansea SA1 3SN ☎ 01792 636858 ✆ paul.relf@swansea.gov.uk

Events Manager: Mr Nigel Jones, Special Events Manager, Penllergaer Offices, Swansea SA4 9GJ ☎ 01792 635413 ✆ nigel.jones@swansea.gov.uk

Facilities: Ms Rebecca Jones, Facilities Manager, Civic Centre, Oystermouth Road, Swansea SA1 3SN ☎ 01792 636030 ✆ rebecca.jones@swansea.gov.uk

Finance: Mr Mike Hawes, Head - Financial Services, Civic Centre, Oystermouth Road, Swansea SA1 3SN ☎ 01792 636423 ✆ mike.hawes@swansea.gov.uk

Treasury: Mr Jeffrey Dong, Chief Treasury Officer, Civic Centre, Oystermouth Road, Swansea SA1 3SN ☎ 01792 636934 ✆ jeffrey.dong@swansea.gov.uk

Pensions: Ms Lynne Miller, Senior Pensions Officer, Civic Centre, Oystermouth Road, Swansea SA1 3SN ☎ 01792 636460 ✆ lynne.miller@swansea.gov.uk

Fleet Management: Mr Mark Barrow, Fleet Manager, The Central Transport Unit, Morfa Road, Swansea SA1 2EN ☎ 01792 511909 ✆ mark.barrow@swansea.gov.uk

Health and Safety: Mr Craig Gimblett, Health, Safety & Wellbeing Manager, Guildhall, Swansea SA1 4PE ☎ 01792 636620 ✆ craig.gimblett@swansea.gov.uk

Highways: Mr Chris Howell, Head - Waste Management, City and County of Swansea, Environment Department, Clydach Depot, Clydach SA1 5BJ ☎ 01792 761759 ✆ chris.howell@swansea.gov.uk

Housing: Mr Lee Morgan, Head - Housing & Public Protection, Civic Centre, Oystermouth Road, Swansea SA1 3SN ☎ 01792 635017 ✆ lee.morgan@swansea.gov.uk

Legal: Mr Patrick Arran, Head - Legal, Democratic Services & Procurement, Civic Centre, Oystermouth Road, Swansea SA1 3SN ☎ 01792 636699 ✆ patrick.arran@swansea.gov.uk

Leisure and Cultural Services: Mr Steve Hardman, Library & Service Manager, Civic Centre, Oystermouth Road, Swansea SA1 3SN ☎ 01792 636610 ✆ steve.hardman@swansea.gov.uk

Leisure and Cultural Services: Ms Tracey McNulty, Head - Cultural Services, Guildhall, Swansea SA1 4PE ☎ 01792 635403 ✆ tracey.mcnulty@swansea.gov.uk

Licensing: Mrs Lynda Williams, Divisional Officer, Civic Centre, Oystermouth Road, Swansea SA1 3SN ☎ 01792 635600 ✆ lynda.williams@swansea.gov.uk

Lifelong Learning: Mr Mike Hughes, Lifelong Learning Services Manager, Dynevor Information Centre, Dynevor Place, Swansea SA1 3ET ☎ 01792 648081 ✆ mike.hughes@swansea.gov.uk

Lighting: Mr Jonathan Hurley, Principal Lighting Manager of Design, Civic Centre, Oystermouth Road, Swansea SA1 3SN ☎ 01792 841666 ✆ jonathan.hurley@swansea.gov.uk

Lottery Funding, Charity and Voluntary: Mr Spencer Martin, Voluntary Sector Relationship Co-ordinator, Civic Centre, Oystermouth Road, Swansea SA1 3SN ☎ 01792 636734 ✆ spencer.martin@swansea.gov.uk

Member Services: Mr Patrick Arran, Head - Legal, Democratic Services & Procurement, Civic Centre, Oystermouth Road, Swansea SA1 3SN ☎ 01792 636699 ✆ patrick.arran@swansea.gov.uk

Member Services: Mr Huw Evans, Democratic Services & Complaints Manager, Civic Centre, Oystermouth Road, Swansea SA1 3SN ☎ 01792 637347 ✆ huw.evans@swansea.gov.uk

Parking: Mr Gary Newman, Parking Manager, Guildhall, Swansea SA1 3SN ☎ 01792 635987 ✆ gary.newman@swansea.gov.uk

Personnel / HR: Mr Steve Rees, Head - Human Resources, Guildhall, Swansea SA1 4PE ☎ 01792 636067 ✆ steve.rees@swansea.gov.uk

Planning: Mr Phillip Holmes, Head - Economic Regeneration & Planning, Civic Centre, Oystermouth Road, Swansea SA1 3SN ☎ 01792 636979 ✆ phillip.holmes@swansea.gov.uk

Procurement: Mr Andrew Williams, Principal Procurement Officer, Civic Centre, Oystermouth Road, Swansea SA1 3SN ☎ 01792 637322 ✆ andrew.williams@swansea.gov.uk

Public Libraries: Mr Steve Hardman, Library & Service Manager, Civic Centre, Oystermouth Road, Swansea SA1 3SN ☎ 01792 636610 ✆ steve.hardman@swansea.gov.uk

Recycling & Waste Minimisation: Ms Trish Flint, Recycling Leader, Pipehouse Wharf, Off Morta Road, Swansea SA1 2EN ☎ 01792 511924 ✆ trish.flint@swansea.gov.uk

Regeneration: Mr Martin Nicholls, Director - Place, Heol y gors, Cwmbwrla, Swansea SA5 8LD ☎ 01792 511002 ✆ martin.nicholls@swansea.gov.uk

Road Safety: Mr Mark Thomas, Team Leader - Traffic Management, Penllergaer Offices, Swansea SA4 9GJ ☎ 01792 636233 ✆ mark.thomas@swansea.gov.uk

SWANSEA, CITY OF

Social Services: Ms Deborah Driffield, Chief Social Services Officer, Oldway Centre, High Street, Swansea SA1 1LT
☎ 01792 636245 ⏴ deborah.driffield@swansea.gov.uk

Social Services (Adult): Ms Alex Williams, Head - Adult Services, Civic Centre, Oystermouth Road, Swansea SA1 3SN
☎ 01792 636245 ⏴ alex.williams2@swansea.gov.uk

Social Services (Children): Ms Julie Thomas, Head - Child & Family Services, Civic Centre, Oystermouth Road, Swansea SA1 3SN ☎ 01792 636248 ⏴ julie.thomas5@swansea.gov.uk

Families: Ms Julie Thomas, Head - Child & Family Services, Civic Centre, Oystermouth Road, Swansea SA1 3SN ☎ 01792 636248 ⏴ julie.thomas5@swansea.gov.uk

Staff Training: Mr Khan Prince, Senior Organisational Development Officer, Guildhall, Swansea SA1 4PE ☎ 01792 636742 ⏴ khan.prince@swansea.gov.uk

Street Scene: Mr Chris Howell, Head - Waste Management, City and County of Swansea, Environment Department, Clydach Depot, Clydach SA1 5BJ ☎ 01792 761759 ⏴ chris.howell@swansea.gov.uk

Sustainable Development: Ms Tanya Nash, Sustainable Development Manager, Civic Centre, Oystermouth Road, Swansea SA1 3SN ☎ 01792 635198 ⏴ tanya.nash@swansea.gov.uk

Tourism: Mrs Frances Jenkins, Strategic Manager, Tourism, Marketing & Events, Penllergaer Offices, Swansea SA4 9GJ
☎ 01792 635201 ⏴ frances.jenkins@swansea.gov.uk

Town Centre: Ms Lisa Wells, City Centre Manager, Civic Centre, Oystermouth Road, Swansea SA1 3SN ☎ 01792 476370 ⏴ lisa.wells@swansea.gov.uk

Traffic Management: Mr Mark Thomas, Team Leader - Traffic Management, Penllergaer Offices, Swansea SA4 9GJ
☎ 01792 636233 ⏴ mark.thomas@swansea.gov.uk

Transport: Mr Mark Thomas, Team Leader - Traffic Management, Penllergaer Offices, Swansea SA4 9GJ ☎ 01792 636233 ⏴ mark.thomas@swansea.gov.uk

Waste Collection and Disposal: Mr Ian Whettleton, Divisional Officer - Waste Management, Guildhall, Swansea SA1 4PE
☎ 01792 635600 ⏴ ian.whettleton@swansea.gov.uk

Waste Management: Mr Ian Whettleton, Divisional Officer - Waste Management, Guildhall, Swansea SA1 4PE ☎ 01792 635600 ⏴ ian.whettleton@swansea.gov.uk

COUNCILLORS

Leader of the Council: Stewart, Rob (LAB - Morriston)
rob.stewart@swansea.gov.uk

Deputy Leader of the Council: Richards, Christine (LAB - Lower Loughor)
christine.richards@swansea.gov.uk

Anderson, Cyril (LAB - Townhill)
cllr.cyril.anderson@swansea.gov.uk

Bayliss, John (LAB - Uplands)
john.bayliss@swansea.gov.uk

Black, Peter (LD - Cwmbwrla)
peter.black@swansea.gov.uk

Burtonshaw, June (LAB - Penderry)

Child, Mark (LAB - West Cross)
mark.child@swansea.gov.uk

Clay, Bob (LAB - Llansamlet)
bob.clay@swansea.gov.uk

Clay, Uta (LAB - Llansamlet)
uta.clay@swansea.gov.uk

Colburn, Anthony (CON - Oystermouth)
tony.colburn@swansea.gov.uk

Cole, David (LAB - Penyrheol)
david.cole@swansea.gov.uk

Cook, Ann (LAB - Cockett)
ann.cook@swansea.gov.uk

Crouch, Sybil (LAB - Castle)
sybil.crouch@swansea.gov.uk

Curtice, Jan (LAB - Penyrheol)
jan.curtice@swansea.gov.uk

Davies, Nick (LAB - Uplands)
nick.davies2@swansea.gov.uk

Day, Mike (LD - Sketty)
mike.day@swansea.gov.uk

Downing, Philip (LAB - Pontarddulais)
philip.downing@swansea.gov.uk

Doyle, Ryland (LAB - Llansamlet)
ryland.doyle@swansea.gov.uk

Evans, William (LAB - Kingsbridge)
william.evans@swansea.gov.uk

Evans, Ceri (LAB - Morriston)
cllr.ceri.evans@swansea.gov.uk

Evans, Mandy (LAB - Bonymaen)
mandy.evans2@swansea.gov.uk

Fitzgerald, Wendy (IND - Penllergaer)
wendy.fitzgerald@swansea.gov.uk

Francis-Davies, Robert (LAB - Morriston)
robert.davies@swansea.gov.uk

Gordon, Fiona (LAB - Castle)
fiona.gordon@swansea.gov.uk

Hale, Joe (LAB - St Thomas)
joe.hale@swansea.gov.uk

Harris, Jane (LAB - Pontarddulais)
jane.harris@swansea.gov.uk

Hennegan, Terry (LAB - Penderry)
terry.hennegan@swansea.gov.uk

Holley, Chris (LD - Cwmbwrla)
chris.holley@swansea.gov.uk

Hood-Williams, Paxton (CON - Fairwood)
paxton.hood-williams@swansea.gov.uk

Hopkins, Beverley (LAB - Landore)
beverley.hopkins@swansea.gov.uk

Hopkins, David (LAB - Townhill)
david.hopkins@swansea.gov.uk

James, Lynda (IND - Pennard)
lynda.james@swansea.gov.uk

Jardine, Yvonne (LAB - Morriston)
yvonne.jardine@swansea.gov.uk

Jones, Andrew (LAB - Cockett)
andrew.jones@swansea.gov.uk

Jones, Susan (IND - Gowerton)
susan.jones3@swansea.gov.uk

Jones, Jeffrey (LD - Killay South)
jeff.w.jones@swansea.gov.uk

Jones, Mary (LD - Killay North)
mary.jones@swansea.gov.uk

King, Elliott (LAB - Cockett)
cllr.elliott.king@swansea.gov.uk

Kirchner, Erika (LAB - Castle)
erika.kirchner@swansea.gov.uk

Lewis, Richard (LD - Gower)
richard.lewis@swansea.gov.uk

Lewis, David (LAB - Gorseinon)
david.lewis2@swansea.gov.uk

Lewis, Andrea (LAB - Morriston)
andrea.s.lewis@swansea.gov.uk

Lloyd, Clive (LAB - St Thomas)
clive.lloyd@swansea.gov.uk

Lloyd, Paul (LAB - Bonymaen)
paul.lloyd@swansea.gov.uk

Marsh, Keith (IND - Bishopston)
keith.marsh@swansea.gov.uk

Matthews, Penny (LAB - Llansamlet)
penny.matthews@swansea.gov.uk

May, Peter (IND - Uplands)
cllr.peter.may@swansea.gov.uk

Meara, Paul (LD - Sketty)
paul.meara@swansea.gov.uk

Morris, Hazel (LAB - Penderry)
hazel.morris@swansea.gov.uk

Newbury, John (LD - Dunvant)
john.newbury@swansea.gov.uk

Owen, Byron (LAB - Mynyddbach)
byron.g.owen@swansea.gov.uk

Owens, Geraint (LAB - Cockett)
geraint.owens@swansea.gov.uk

Phillips, David (LAB - Castle)
david.philips@swansea.gov.uk

Philpott, Cheryl (LD - Sketty)
cheryl.philpott@swansea.gov.uk

Raynor, Jennifer (LAB - Dunvant)
jennifer.raynor@swansea.gov.uk

Rees, Huw (LD - Sketty)
huw.rees2@swansea.gov.uk

Richard, Ioan (O - Mawr)
ioan.richard@swansea.gov.uk

Smith, Paulette (LAB - Clydach)
paulette.smith@swansea.gov.uk

Smith, Robert (LAB - Upper Loughor)
robert.smith@swansea.gov.uk

Stanton, June (LD - Sketty)
june.stanton@swansea.gov.uk

Sullivan, Gareth (IND - Llangyfelach)
gareth.sullivan@swansea.gov.uk

Tanner, Gloria (LAB - Mynyddbach)
gloria.tanner@swansea.gov.uk

Thomas, Graham (LD - Cwmbwrla)
graham.thomas@swansea.gov.uk

Thomas, Miles (CON - Newton)
miles.thomas2@swansea.gov.uk

Thomas, Ceinwen (LAB - Mynyddbach)
ceinwen.thomas@swansea.gov.uk

Thomas, Des (LAB - West Cross)
des.thomas@swansea.gov.uk

Thomas, Mark (LAB - Penclawdd)
mark.thomas2@swansea.gov.uk

Tyler-Lloyd, Linda (CON - Mayals)
linda.tyler-lloyd@swansea.gov.uk

Walker, Gordon (INDNA - Clydach)
gordon.walker@swansea.gov.uk

Walton, Lesley (LAB - Townhill)
lesley.walton@swansea.gov.uk

White, Mike (LAB - Landore)
mike.white@swansea.gov.uk

Woollard, Neil (LAB - Uplands)
cllr.neil.woollard@swansea.gov.uk

POLITICAL COMPOSITION
LAB: 48, LD: 12, IND: 6, CON: 4, INDNA: 1, O: 1

COMMITTEE CHAIRS

Licensing: Ms Penny Matthews

Planning: Mr Paul Lloyd

Swindon U

Swindon Borough Council, Civic Offices, Euclid Street,
Swindon SN1 2JH
☎ 01793 463000 ✆ customerservices@swindon.gov.uk
🖥 www.swindon.gov.uk

FACTS AND FIGURES
EU Constituencies: South West
Election Frequency: Elections are by thirds

PRINCIPAL OFFICERS

Chief Executive: Mr John Gilbert, Chief Executive, Civic Offices,
Euclid Street, Swindon SN1 2JH ☎ 01793 463068
✆ jgilbert@swindon.gov.uk

Senior Management: Mr Bernie Brannan, Corporate Director
- Service Delivery, Wat Tyler House West, Beckhampton Street,
Swindon SN1 2JG ☎ 01793 464376 ✆ bbrannan@swindon.gov.uk

SWINDON

Senior Management: Mr Andy Evans, Corporate Director - Economy, Regeneration & Skills, Wat Tyler House West, Beckhampton Street, Swindon SN1 2JG ☎ 01793 463201 ⌁ aevans@swindon.gov.uk

Senior Management: Mr Stuart McKellar, Corporate Director - Resources, Wat Tyler House West, Beckhampton Street, Swindon SN1 2JG ☎ 01793 463300 ⌁ smckellar@swindon.gov.uk

Senior Management: Ms Samantha Mowbray, Head of Performance, People & Engagement, Wat Tyler House West, Beckhampton Streen, Swindon SN1 2JG ☎ 07823 525337 ⌁ smowbray@swindon.gov.uk

Senior Management: Ms Karen Reeve, Director - Children's Services, Civic Offices, Euclid Street, Swindon SN1 2JH ☎ 01793 463200 ⌁ kreeve@swindon.gov.uk

Senior Management: Mr Stephen Taylor, Director - Law & Democratic Services, Civic Offices, Euclid Street, Swindon SN1 2JH ☎ 01793 463012 ⌁ staylor@swindon.gov.uk

Senior Management: Ms Sue Wald, Director - Adult Social Services, Wat Tyler House West, Beckhampton Street, Swindon SN1 2JG ☎ 01793 465713 ⌁ swald@swindon.gov.uk

Architect, Building / Property Services: Mr Nic Newland, Head of Design & Architecture, Wat Tyler West House, Beckhampton Street, Swindon SN1 1JG ☎ 01793 463620 ⌁ nnewland@swindon.gov.uk

Architect, Building / Property Services: Mr Rob Richards, Head of Property Assets, Wat Tyler House West, Beckhampton Street, Swindon SN1 2JG ☎ 01793 463521 ⌁ rrichards@swindon.gov.uk

Building Control: Mr David Dewart, Service Manager - Building Control & Special Projects, Wat Tyler House West, Beckhampton Street, Swindon SN1 2JG ☎ 01793 466445 ⌁ ddewart@swindon.gov.uk

Children / Youth Services: Ms Karen Reeve, Director - Children's Services, Civic Offices, Euclid Street, Swindon SN1 2JH ☎ 01793 463200 ⌁ kreeve@swindon.gov.uk

Civil Registration: Ms Mamie Beasant, Superintendent Registrar, Civic Offices, Euclid Street, Swindon SN1 2JH ☎ 01793 522738 ⌁ mbeasant@swindon.gov.uk

PR / Communications: Mr Galvin Calthrop, Head of Communications & Insight, Civic Offices, Euclid Street, Swindon SN1 2JH ☎ 01793 463176 ⌁ gcalthrop@swindon.gov.uk

Computer Management: Mr Glyn Peach, Head of Information & Technology Strategy, Wat Tyler House West, 1st Floor, Beckhampton Street, Swindon SN1 2JG ☎ 01793 465848 ⌁ gpeach@swindon.gov.uk

Consumer Protection and Trading Standards: Mr Paul Simmonds, Environmental Services Manager, Wat Tyler House West, Beckhampton Street, Swindon SN1 2JG ☎ 01793 466097 ⌁ psimmonds@swindon.gov.uk

Corporate Services: Ms Kirsty Cole, Head of Finance & Change, Wat Tyler House West, Beckhampton Street, Swindon SN1 2JG ☎ 01793 464610 ⌁ kcole@swindon.gov.uk

Customer Service: Mrs Karen McMahon, Head of Customer & Business Services, Wat Tyler West, Beckhampton Street, Swindon SN1 1JG ☎ 01793 464935 ⌁ kmcmahon@swindon.gov.uk

Direct Labour: Mr Bernie Brannan, Corporate Director - Service Delivery, Wat Tyler House West, Beckhampton Street, Swindon SN1 2JG ☎ 01793 464376 ⌁ bbrannan@swindon.gov.uk

Economic Development: Mr Andy Evans, Corporate Director - Economy, Regeneration & Skills, Wat Tyler House West, Beckhampton Street, Swindon SN1 2JG ☎ 01793 463201 ⌁ aevans@swindon.gov.uk

Education: Mr Peter Nathan, Head of Education, Wat Tyler House West, Beckhampton Street, Swindon SN1 2JG ⌁ pnathan@swindon.gov.uk

Electoral Registration: Ms Sally Sprason, Electoral Services Manager, Civic Offices, Euclid Street, Swindon SN1 2JH ☎ 01793 463999 ⌁ ssprason@swindon.gov.uk

Emergency Planning: Mr Sam Weller, Head of Civic Protection Unit, Wat Tyler House West, Beckhampton Street, Swindon SN1 2JG ☎ 01793 464871 ⌁ sweller@swindon.gov.uk

Environmental Health: Ms Cherry Jones, Director - Public Health, Wat Tyler House West, Beckhampton Street, Swindon SN1 2JG ☎ 01793 444681 ⌁ cherryjones@swindon.gov.uk

Facilities: Mr Darren Priddle, Senior Facilities Management Co-ordinator, Wat Tyler House West, Beckhampton Street, Swindon SN1 2JG ☎ 01793 469952 ⌁ dpriddle@swindon.gov.uk

Finance: Ms Kirsty Cole, Head of Finance & Change, Wat Tyler House West, Beckhampton Street, Swindon SN1 2JG ☎ 01793 464610 ⌁ kcole@swindon.gov.uk

Finance: Mr Stuart McKellar, Corporate Director - Resources, Wat Tyler House West, Beckhampton Street, Swindon SN1 2JG ☎ 01793 463300 ⌁ smckellar@swindon.gov.uk

Fleet Management: Mr Steve Kemble, Fleet Manager, Waterside, Derby Close, Swindon SN1 1TZ ☎ 01793 464187 ⌁ skemble@swindon.gov.uk

Health and Safety: Mrs Karen McMahon, Head of Customer & Business Services, Wat Tyler West, Beckhampton Street, Swindon SN1 1JG ☎ 01793 464935 ⌁ kmcmahon@swindon.gov.uk

Highways: Mr Jason Humm, Head of Highway Maintenance, Wat Tyler House West, Beckhampton Street, Swindon SN1 2JG ☎ 01793 463201 ⌁ jhumm@swindon.gov.uk

Housing: Mr Mike Ash, Head of Housing & Community Safety, Wat Tyler West House, Beckhampton Street, Swindon SN1 2JG ☎ 01793 466146 ⌁ mash@swindon.gov.uk

Housing Maintenance: Mr Gerry O'Connor, Head of Property Maintenance, Wat Tyler House, Beckhampton Street, Swindon SN2 2JG ☎ 01796 463452 ⌨ go'connor@swindon.gov.uk

Legal: Mr Stephen Taylor, Director - Law & Democratic Services, Civic Offices, Euclid Street, Swindon SN1 2JH ☎ 01793 463012 ⌨ staylor@swindon.gov.uk

Leisure and Cultural Services: Mr Richard Bell, Head of Planning, Regulatory Services & Heritage, Wat Tyler West House, Beckhampton Street, Swindon SN1 2JG ☎ 01793 465724 ⌨ rbell@swindon.gov.uk

Licensing: Mr Richard Bell, Head of Planning, Regulatory Services & Heritage, Wat Tyler West House, Beckhampton Street, Swindon SN1 2JG ☎ 01793 465724 ⌨ rbell@swindon.gov.uk

Lottery Funding, Charity and Voluntary: Mr Patrick Weir, Head of Localities, Volunteering & Community Involvement, Wat Tyler House West, Beckhampton Street, Swindon SN1 2JG ☎ 07946 595852 ⌨ pweir@swindon.gov.uk

Member Services: Mr Steve Jones, Committee & Member Services Manager, Civic Offices, Euclid Street, Swindon SN1 2JH ☎ 01793 463602 ⌨ stevejones@swindon.gov.uk

Parking: Ms Dawn Woollard, Head of Parking, Wat Tyler West House, Beckhampton Street, Swindon SN1 2JG ☎ 01793 463000 ⌨ dwoollard@swindon.gov.uk

Personnel / HR: Ms Sonia Grewal, Head of People Development, Wat Tyler West House, Beckhampton Street, Swindon SN1 2JG ⌨ sgrewal@swindon.gov.uk

Planning: Mr Richard Bell, Head of Planning, Regulatory Services & Heritage, Wat Tyler West House, Beckhampton Street, Swindon SN1 2JG ☎ 01793 465724 ⌨ rbell@swindon.gov.uk

Regeneration: Mr Andy Evans, Corporate Director - Economy, Regeneration & Skills, Wat Tyler House West, Beckhampton Street, Swindon SN1 2JG ☎ 01793 463201 ⌨ aevans@swindon.gov.uk

Road Safety: Ms Margaret Tester, Road Safety Manager, Wat Tyler West House, Beckhampton Street, Swindon SN1 2JG ☎ 01793 466399 ⌨ mtester@swindon.gov.uk

Social Services (Adult): Ms Angela Plummer, Interim Head of Commissioning - Adult Social Services, Wat Tyler House West, Beckhampton Street, Swindon SN1 2JG ☎ 01793 465713 ⌨ aplummer@swindon.gov.uk

Social Services (Children): Mrs Maria Young, Head of Children's Social Care, Community Health & Family, Civic Offices, Euclid Street, Swindon SN1 2JH ☎ 01793 463268 ⌨ myoung@swindon.gov.uk

Public Health: Ms Cherry Jones, Director - Public Health, Civic Offices, Euclid Street, Swindon SN1 2JH ☎ 01793 444681 ⌨ cherryjones@swindon.gov.uk

Street Scene: Mr Leon Barrett, Head of Street Smart, Wat Tyler West House, Beckhampton Street, Swindon SN1 2JG ⌨ lbarrett@swindon.gov.uk

Town Centre: Mr Mark Walker, Community Programme Lead, Civic Offices, Euclid Street, Swindon SN1 2JH ☎ 01793 464605 ⌨ mwalker@swindon.gov.uk

Transport: Mr Nigel Hale, Passenger Transport Manager, Wat Tyler West House, Beckhampton Street, Swindon SN1 2JG ☎ 01793 466211 ⌨ nhale@swindon.gov.uk

Waste Management: Mr Leon Barrett, Head of Street Smart, Wat Tyler West House, Beckhampton Street, Swindon SN1 2JG ⌨ lbarrett@swindon.gov.uk

COUNCILLORS

Mayor: Shaw, Eric (CON - Chiseldon & Lawn)
ericshaw1937@btinternet.com

Deputy Mayor: Penny, Maureen (CON - Blunsdon & Highworth)
maureen.penny2@btinternet.com

Leader of the Council: Renard, David (CON - Haydon Wick)
drenard@swindon.gov.uk

Deputy Leader of the Council: Holland, Russell (CON - St Margaret & South Marston)
rholland@swindon.gov.uk

Group Leader: Grant, James (LAB - Rodbourne Cheney)
grant4gt@btinternet.com

Group Leader: Pajak, Stan (LD - Eastcott)
stanpajak@ymail.com

Ali, Junab (LAB - Central)
junab@hotmail.co.uk

Allsopp, Steve (LAB - Walcot & Park North)
jean.norris1@ntlworld.com

Amin, Abdul (LAB - Walcot & Park North)
abdulamin22@gmail.com

Ballman, Ray (LAB - Gorsehill & Pinehurst)
jbswin@yahoo.co.uk

Ballman, John (LAB - Gorsehill & Pinehurst)
jbswin@yahoo.co.uk

Bishop, Alan (CON - Blunsdon & Highworth)
alanandjulie@live.com

Bushell, Emma (LAB - Walcot & Park North)
emmabushell@yahoo.co.uk

Courtliff, Matthew (LAB - Lydiard & Freshbrook)
cllrmatthew@outlook.com

Crabbe, Wayne (CON - Wroughton & Wichelstowe)

Davies, Malcolm (CON - Priory Vale)
cllrmalcolmdavies@gmail.com

Dempsey, Mark (LAB - Penhill & Upper Stratton)
mark@markdempsey.org.uk

Dixon, Paul (LAB - Eastcott)
p.dixon8@ntlworld.com

Donachie, Oliver (CON - Haydon Wick)
oliver.donachie@gmail.com

Elliott, Toby (CON - Priory Vale)
cllrtoby@outlook.com

Ellis, Claire (CON - Old Town)
claireellis@hotmail.co.uk

SWINDON

Exell, Stephanie (LAB - Mannington & Western)
steph.exell@sky.com

Faramarzi, Emma (CON - Priory Vale)
efaramarzi@swindon.gov.uk

Foley, Fionuala (CON - Chiseldon & Lawn)
ffoley@swindon.gov.uk

Ford, Brian (CON - Wroughton & Wichelstowe)
brian.ford@absolutely-independent.co.uk

Friend, Mary (CON - St Andrews)
mry4441@gmail.com

Haines, John (CON - St Margaret & South Marston)
cllrjhaines@hotmail.co.uk

Heenan, Dale (CON - Covingham & Dorcan)
dale@covinghamandnytheintouch.com

Howard, Fay (LAB - Liden, Eldene & Park South)
fayhoward@live.co.uk

Lovell, Colin (CON - St Margaret & South Marston)
colin.lovell2@ntlworld.com

Martin, Nick (CON - Shaw)
nmartin@swindon.gov.uk

Martin, Mary (CON - Shaw)
marymartin@swindon.gov.uk

Martyn, Cathy (CON - Wroughton & Wichelstowe)
cathy@themartynfamily.co.uk

McCracken, Gemma (CON - St Andrews)
gemmaleroy@btinternet.com

Milner-Barry, Jane (LAB - Old Town)
janemilnerbarry@gmail.com

Moffatt, Des (LAB - Rodbourne Cheney)
fendessy@yahoo.co.uk

Montaut, Derique (LAB - Liden, Eldene & Park South)
derique.montaut@ntlworld.com

Page, Teresa (LAB - Penhill & Upper Stratton)
teresapageswindon@yahoo.co.uk

Parry, Kevin (CON - Covingham & Dorcan)
cllrkevin.parry@ntlworld.com

Parry, Barbara (CON - Covingham & Dorcan)
barbara.parry5@gmail.com

Perkins, Garry (CON - Haydon Wick)
ecp@swindon1.fsnet.co.uk

Robbins, James (LAB - Mannington & Western)
robbins.james@gmail.com

Shelley, Carol (LAB - Gorsehill & Pinehurst)
cshelleyswindon@gmail.com

Small, Kevin (LAB - Mannington & Western)
kevinsmall@hotmail.com

Sumner, Gary (CON - Ridgeway)
gary@ridgewayvillages.co.uk

Swinyard, Timothy (CON - Lydiard & Freshbrook)
timswin@hotmail.com

Sydney-Smith, Caryl (CON - Lydiard & Freshbrook)
carylss@hotmail.com

Tomlinson, Vera (CON - St Andrews)
vtomlinson@swindon.gov.uk

Tray, Joe (LAB - Penhill & Upper Stratton)
j.tray@ntlworld.com

Watts, Nadine (LAB - Old Town)
nadine.watts@live.co.uk

Watts, Peter (LAB - Rodbourne Cheney)
peterwattsrodbournecheney@live.co.uk

Watts, Chris (LAB - Liden, Eldene & Park South)
cllrchriswatts@outlook.com

Weisinger, Steve (CON - Blunsdon & Highworth)
sweisinger@swindon.gov.uk

Williams, Keith (CON - Shaw)
krwilliams@swindon.gov.uk

Wood, David (LD - Eastcott)
dave@swindonlibdems.org

Wright, Julie (LAB - Central)
juliecaseworker@hotmail.co.uk

Wright, Robert (LAB - Central)
bob.wright.gov@ntlworld.com

POLITICAL COMPOSITION
CON: 30, LAB: 25, LD: 2

COMMITTEE CHAIRS

Audit: Mr Steve Weisinger

Children's Health, Social Care & Education: Ms Gemma McCracken

Licensing: Mrs Vera Tomlinson

Planning: Mr Kevin Parry

Tameside   M

Tameside Metropolitan Borough Council, Council Offices, Wellington Road, Ashton-under-Lyne OL6 6DL
☎ 0161 342 8355 🖷 0161 342 3070 ✆ general@tameside.gov.uk
🖳 www.tameside.gov.uk

FACTS AND FIGURES
Parliamentary Constituencies: Ashton under Lyne, Denton and Reddish, Stalybridge and Hyde
EU Constituencies: North West
Election Frequency: Elections are by thirds

PRINCIPAL OFFICERS

Chief Executive: Mr Steven Pleasant, Chief Executive, Dukinfield Town Hall, King Street, Dukinfield SK16 4LA ☎ 0161 342 3500 ✆ steven.pleasant@tameside.gov.uk

Senior Management: Mrs Stephanie Butterworth, Executive Director - People, Dukinfield Town Hall, King Street, Dukinfield SK16 4LA ☎ 0161 342 8355

Senior Management: Ms Angela Hardman, Director - Public Health, Dukinfield Town Hall, King Street, Dukinfield SK16 4LA ☎ 0161 342 2908 ✆ angela.hardman@tameside.gov.uk

Senior Management: Mr Robin Monk, Executive Director - Place, Dukinfield Town Hall, King Street, Dukinfield SK16 4LA ☎ 0161 342 3340 ✆ robin.monk@tameside.gov.uk

Senior Management: Ms Sandra Stewart, Executive Director - Governance, Resources & Pensions, Dukinfield Town Hall, King Street, Dukinfield SK16 4LA ☎ 0161 342 3028 ⌁ sandra.stewart@tameside.gov.uk

Access Officer / Social Services (Disability): Mrs Stephanie Butterworth, Executive Director - People, Dukinfield Town Hall, King Street, Dukinfield SK16 4LA ☎ 0161 342 8355

Architect, Building / Property Services: Mr Robin Monk, Executive Director - Place, Dukinfield Town Hall, King Street, Dukinfield SK16 4LA ☎ 0161 342 3340 ⌁ robin.monk@tameside.gov.uk

Building Control: Mr Robin Monk, Executive Director - Place, Dukinfield Town Hall, King Street, Dukinfield SK16 4LA ☎ 0161 342 3340 ⌁ robin.monk@tameside.gov.uk

Building Control: Mr Ian Saxon, Assistant Executive Director - Environmental Services, Dukinfield Town Hall, King Street, Dukinfield SK16 4LA ☎ 0161 342 3470 ⌁ ian.saxon@tameside.gov.uk

Children / Youth Services: Mrs Stephanie Butterworth, Executive Director - People, Dukinfield Town Hall, King Street, Dukinfield SK16 4LA ☎ 0161 342 8355

Civil Registration: Ms Sandra Stewart, Executive Director - Governance, Resources & Pensions, Dukinfield Town Hall, King Street, Dukinfield SK16 4LA ☎ 0161 342 3028 ⌁ sandra.stewart@tameside.gov.uk

PR / Communications: Ms Sarah Dobson, Head of Policy & Communications, Dukinfield Town Hall, King Street, Dukinfield SK16 4LA ☎ 0161 342 4417 ⌁ sarah.dobson@tameside.gov.uk

Community Planning: Mr Robin Monk, Executive Director - Place, Dukinfield Town Hall, King Street, Dukinfield SK16 4LA ☎ 0161 342 3340 ⌁ robin.monk@tameside.gov.uk

Community Safety: Mrs Emma Varnam, Head of Stronger Communities, Hyde Town Hall, Market Street, Hyde SK14 1AL ☎ 0161 342 3337 ⌁ emma.varnam@tameside.gov.uk

Computer Management: Mr Tim Rainey, Assistant Chief Executive - Digital Tameside, Dukinfield Town Hall, King Street, Dukinfield SK16 4LA ☎ 0161 342 3299 ⌁ tim.rainey@tameside.gov.uk

Consumer Protection and Trading Standards: Mr Robin Monk, Executive Director - Place, Dukinfield Town Hall, King Street, Dukinfield SK16 4LA ☎ 0161 342 3340 ⌁ robin.monk@tameside.gov.uk

Consumer Protection and Trading Standards: Mr Ian Saxon, Assistant Executive Director - Environmental Services, Dukinfield Town Hall, King Street, Dukinfield SK16 4LA ☎ 0161 342 3470 ⌁ ian.saxon@tameside.gov.uk

Contracts: Mr Ian Duncan, Section 151 Officer, Dukinfield Town Hall, King Street, Dukinfield SK16 4LA ☎ 0161 342 3864 ⌁ ian.duncan@tameside.gov.uk

Customer Service: Mrs Stephanie Butterworth, Executive Director - People, Dukinfield Town Hall, King Street, Dukinfield SK16 4LA ☎ 0161 342 8355

Economic Development: Mr Damien Bourke, Executive Director - Development & Investment, Dukinfield Town Hall, King Street, Dukinfield SK16 4LA ☎ 0161 342 3544 ⌁ damien.bourke@tameside.gov.uk

Economic Development: Mr Robin Monk, Executive Director - Place, Dukinfield Town Hall, King Street, Dukinfield SK16 4LA ☎ 0161 342 3340 ⌁ robin.monk@tameside.gov.uk

Education: Mr Bob Berry, Interim Assistant Executive Director - Education, Dukinfield Town Hall, King Street, Dukinfield SK16 4LA ☎ 0161 342 2050 ⌁ bob.berry@tameside.gov.uk

Education: Mrs Stephanie Butterworth, Executive Director - People, Dukinfield Town Hall, King Street, Dukinfield SK16 4LA ☎ 0161 342 8355 ⌁

E-Government: Mr Tim Rainey, Assistant Chief Executive - Digital Tameside, Dukinfield Town Hall, King Street, Dukinfield SK16 4LA ☎ 0161 342 3299 ⌁ tim.rainey@tameside.gov.uk

Electoral Registration: Mr Robert Landon, Head - Democratic Services, Dukinfield Town Hall, King Street, Dukinfield SK16 4LA ☎ 0161 342 8355 ⌁ robert.landon@tameside.gov.uk

Emergency Planning: Mr Michael Gurney, Emergency Planning Manager, Dukinfield Town Hall, King Street, Dukinfield SK16 4LA ☎ 0161 342 3705 ⌁ michael.gurney@tameside.gov.uk

Emergency Planning: Mr Ian Saxon, Assistant Executive Director - Environmental Services, Dukinfield Town Hall, King Street, Dukinfield SK16 4LA ☎ 0161 342 3470 ⌁ ian.saxon@tameside.gov.uk

Energy Management: Mr Ian Saxon, Assistant Executive Director - Environmental Services, Dukinfield Town Hall, King Street, Dukinfield SK16 4LA ☎ 0161 342 3470 ⌁ ian.saxon@tameside.gov.uk

Environmental / Technical Services: Mr Robin Monk, Executive Director - Place, Dukinfield Town Hall, King Street, Dukinfield SK16 4LA ☎ 0161 342 3340 ⌁ robin.monk@tameside.gov.uk

Environmental / Technical Services: Mr Ian Saxon, Assistant Executive Director - Environmental Services, Dukinfield Town Hall, King Street, Dukinfield SK16 4LA ☎ 0161 342 3470 ⌁ ian.saxon@tameside.gov.uk

Environmental Health: Mr Robin Monk, Executive Director - Place, Dukinfield Town Hall, King Street, Dukinfield SK16 4LA ☎ 0161 342 3340 ⌁ robin.monk@tameside.gov.uk

Environmental Health: Mr Ian Saxon, Assistant Executive Director - Environmental Services, Dukinfield Town Hall, King Street, Dukinfield SK16 4LA ☎ 0161 342 3470 ⌁ ian.saxon@tameside.gov.uk

TAMESIDE

Estates, Property & Valuation: Mr Robin Monk, Executive Director - Place, Dukinfield Town Hall, King Street, Dukinfield SK16 4LA ☎ 0161 342 3340 ♨ robin.monk@tameside.gov.uk

Estates, Property & Valuation: Mrs Elaine Todd, Assistant Executive Director - Asset & Investment Partnership, Dukinfield Town Hall, King Street, Dukinfield SK16 4LA ☎ 0161 342 8355

Events Manager: Mrs Emma Varnam, Head of Stronger Communities, Hyde Town Hall, Market Street, Hyde SK14 1AL ☎ 0161 342 3337 ♨ emma.varnam@tameside.gov.uk

Finance: Mr Ian Duncan, Section 151 Officer, Dukinfield Town Hall, King Street, Dukinfield SK16 4LA ☎ 0161 342 3864 ♨ ian.duncan@tameside.gov.uk

Pensions: Ms Sandra Stewart, Executive Director - Governance, Resources & Pensions, Dukinfield Town Hall, King Street, Dukinfield SK16 4LA ☎ 0161 342 3028 ♨ sandra.stewart@tameside.gov.uk

Fleet Management: Mr Ian Saxon, Assistant Executive Director - Environmental Services, Dukinfield Town Hall, King Street, Dukinfield SK16 4LA ☎ 0161 342 3470 ♨ ian.saxon@tameside.gov.uk

Health and Safety: Mr Robin Monk, Executive Director - Place, Dukinfield Town Hall, King Street, Dukinfield SK16 4LA ☎ 0161 342 3340 ♨ robin.monk@tameside.gov.uk

Health and Safety: Mr Ian Saxon, Assistant Executive Director - Environmental Services, Dukinfield Town Hall, King Street, Dukinfield SK16 4LA ☎ 0161 342 3470 ♨ ian.saxon@tameside.gov.uk

Highways: Mr Robin Monk, Executive Director - Place, Dukinfield Town Hall, King Street, Dukinfield SK16 4LA ☎ 0161 342 3340 ♨ robin.monk@tameside.gov.uk

Home Energy Conservation: Mr Ian Saxon, Assistant Executive Director - Environmental Services, Dukinfield Town Hall, King Street, Dukinfield SK16 4LA ☎ 0161 342 3470 ♨ ian.saxon@tameside.gov.uk

Legal: Ms Sandra Stewart, Executive Director - Governance, Resources & Pensions, Dukinfield Town Hall, King Street, Dukinfield SK16 4LA ☎ 0161 342 3028 ♨ sandra.stewart@tameside.gov.uk

Leisure and Cultural Services: Mrs Emma Varnam, Head of Stronger Communities, Hyde Town Hall, Market Street, Hyde SK14 1AL ☎ 0161 342 3337 ♨ emma.varnam@tameside.gov.uk

Licensing: Mr Robin Monk, Executive Director - Place, Dukinfield Town Hall, King Street, Dukinfield SK16 4LA ☎ 0161 342 3340 ♨ robin.monk@tameside.gov.uk

Licensing: Mr Ian Saxon, Assistant Executive Director - Environmental Services, Dukinfield Town Hall, King Street, Dukinfield SK16 4LA ☎ 0161 342 3470 ♨ ian.saxon@tameside.gov.uk

Lifelong Learning: Mrs Stephanie Butterworth, Executive Director - People, Dukinfield Town Hall, King Street, Dukinfield SK16 4LA ☎ 0161 342 8355 ♨

Member Services: Mr Robert Landon, Head - Democratic Services, Dukinfield Town Hall, King Street, Dukinfield SK16 4LA ☎ 0161 342 8355 ♨ robert.landon@tameside.gov.uk

Parking: Mr Robin Monk, Executive Director - Place, Dukinfield Town Hall, King Street, Dukinfield SK16 4LA ☎ 0161 342 3340 ♨ robin.monk@tameside.gov.uk

Parking: Mr Ian Saxon, Assistant Executive Director - Environmental Services, Dukinfield Town Hall, King Street, Dukinfield SK16 4LA ☎ 0161 342 3470 ♨ ian.saxon@tameside.gov.uk

Personnel / HR: Ms Tracy Brennand, Assistant Executive Director - People & Workforce Development, Dukinfield Town Hall, King Street, Dukinfield SK16 4LA ☎ 0161 342 3279 ♨ tracy.brennand@tameside.gov.uk

Personnel / HR: Ms Sandra Stewart, Executive Director - Governance, Resources & Pensions, Dukinfield Town Hall, King Street, Dukinfield SK16 4LA ☎ 0161 342 3028 ♨ sandra.stewart@tameside.gov.uk

Planning: Mr Robin Monk, Executive Director - Place, Dukinfield Town Hall, King Street, Dukinfield SK16 4LA ☎ 0161 342 3340 ♨ robin.monk@tameside.gov.uk

Planning: Mr Ian Saxon, Assistant Executive Director - Environmental Services, Dukinfield Town Hall, King Street, Dukinfield SK16 4LA ☎ 0161 342 3470 ♨ ian.saxon@tameside.gov.uk

Procurement: Mr Ian Duncan, Section 151 Officer, Dukinfield Town Hall, King Street, Dukinfield SK16 4LA ☎ 0161 342 3864 ♨ ian.duncan@tameside.gov.uk

Public Libraries: Mrs Stephanie Butterworth, Executive Director - People, Dukinfield Town Hall, King Street, Dukinfield SK16 4LA ☎ 0161 342 8355 ♨

Recycling & Waste Minimisation: Mr Robin Monk, Executive Director - Place, Dukinfield Town Hall, King Street, Dukinfield SK16 4LA ☎ 0161 342 3340 ♨ robin.monk@tameside.gov.uk

Recycling & Waste Minimisation: Mr Ian Saxon, Assistant Executive Director - Environmental Services, Dukinfield Town Hall, King Street, Dukinfield SK16 4LA ☎ 0161 342 3470 ♨ ian.saxon@tameside.gov.uk

Regeneration: Mr Robin Monk, Executive Director - Place, Dukinfield Town Hall, King Street, Dukinfield SK16 4LA ☎ 0161 342 3340 ♨ robin.monk@tameside.gov.uk

Road Safety: Mr Damien Bourke, Executive Director - Development & Investment, Dukinfield Town Hall, King Street, Dukinfield SK16 4LA ☎ 0161 342 3544 ♨ damien.bourke@tameside.gov.uk

Road Safety: Mr Robin Monk, Executive Director - Place, Dukinfield Town Hall, King Street, Dukinfield SK16 4LA ☎ 0161 342 3340 ⌂ robin.monk@tameside.gov.uk

Road Safety: Mr Ian Saxon, Assistant Executive Director - Environmental Services, Dukinfield Town Hall, King Street, Dukinfield SK16 4LA ☎ 0161 342 3470 ⌂ ian.saxon@tameside.gov.uk

Social Services: Mrs Stephanie Butterworth, Executive Director - People, Dukinfield Town Hall, King Street, Dukinfield SK16 4LA ☎ 0161 342 8355

Social Services (Adult): Mrs Stephanie Butterworth, Executive Director - People, Dukinfield Town Hall, King Street, Dukinfield SK16 4LA ☎ 0161 342 8355

Social Services (Children): Mrs Stephanie Butterworth, Executive Director - People, Dukinfield Town Hall, King Street, Dukinfield SK16 4LA ☎ 0161 342 8355

Public Health: Ms Angela Hardman, Director - Public Health, Dukinfield Town Hall, King Street, Dukinfield SK16 4LA ☎ 0161 342 2908 ⌂ angela.hardman@tameside.gov.uk

Sustainable Communities: Mr Robin Monk, Executive Director - Place, Dukinfield Town Hall, King Street, Dukinfield SK16 4LA ☎ 0161 342 3340 ⌂ robin.monk@tameside.gov.uk

Sustainable Development: Mr Robin Monk, Executive Director - Place, Dukinfield Town Hall, King Street, Dukinfield SK16 4LA ☎ 0161 342 3340 ⌂ robin.monk@tameside.gov.uk

Town Centre: Mr Damien Bourke, Executive Director - Development & Investment, Dukinfield Town Hall, King Street, Dukinfield SK16 4LA ☎ 0161 342 3544 ⌂ damien.bourke@tameside.gov.uk

Town Centre: Mr Robin Monk, Executive Director - Place, Dukinfield Town Hall, King Street, Dukinfield SK16 4LA ☎ 0161 342 3340 ⌂ robin.monk@tameside.gov.uk

Traffic Management: Mr Robin Monk, Executive Director - Place, Dukinfield Town Hall, King Street, Dukinfield SK16 4LA ☎ 0161 342 3340 ⌂ robin.monk@tameside.gov.uk

Traffic Management: Mr Ian Saxon, Assistant Executive Director - Environmental Services, Dukinfield Town Hall, King Street, Dukinfield SK16 4LA ☎ 0161 342 3470 ⌂ ian.saxon@tameside.gov.uk

Transport: Mr Robin Monk, Executive Director - Place, Dukinfield Town Hall, King Street, Dukinfield SK16 4LA ☎ 0161 342 3340 ⌂ robin.monk@tameside.gov.uk

Transport Planner: Mr Robin Monk, Executive Director - Place, Dukinfield Town Hall, King Street, Dukinfield SK16 4LA ☎ 0161 342 3340 ⌂ robin.monk@tameside.gov.uk

Waste Collection and Disposal: Mr Robin Monk, Executive Director - Place, Dukinfield Town Hall, King Street, Dukinfield SK16 4LA ☎ 0161 342 3340 ⌂ robin.monk@tameside.gov.uk

Waste Collection and Disposal: Mr Ian Saxon, Assistant Executive Director - Environmental Services, Dukinfield Town Hall, King Street, Dukinfield SK16 4LA ☎ 0161 342 3470 ⌂ ian.saxon@tameside.gov.uk

Waste Management: Mr Robin Monk, Executive Director - Place, Dukinfield Town Hall, King Street, Dukinfield SK16 4LA ☎ 0161 342 3340 ⌂ robin.monk@tameside.gov.uk

Waste Management: Mr Ian Saxon, Assistant Executive Director - Environmental Services, Dukinfield Town Hall, King Street, Dukinfield SK16 4LA ☎ 0161 342 3470 ⌂ ian.saxon@tameside.gov.uk

COUNCILLORS

Leader of the Council: Quinn, Kieran (LAB - Droylsden East)

Deputy Leader of the Council: Taylor, John (LAB - Dukinfield)

Affleck, Betty (LAB - Hyde Godley) betty.affleck@tameside.gov.uk

Bailey, Maria (LAB - Audenshaw)

Beeley, Basil (CON - Stalybridge South)

Bell, John (CON - Hyde Werneth)

Bowden, Helen (LAB - Hyde Newton)

Bowerman, Joyce (LAB - Ashton St. Peters)

Bray, Warren (LAB - Ashton St. Peters)

Buckley, Paul (CON - Ashton Hurst) paul.buckley@tameside.gov.uk

Buglass, Chris (LAB - Longdendale)

Cartey, Yvonne (LAB - Ashton St. Michaels)

Cooney, Gerald (LAB - Droylsden West)

Cooper, Janet (LAB - Longdendale)

Dickinson, Doreen (CON - Stalybridge South)

Drennan, Leigh (LAB - Ashton Hurst)

Fairfoull, Bill (LAB - Ashton St. Michaels)

Feeley, Leanne (LAB - Dukinfield & Stalybridge)

Fitzpatrick, Philip (LAB - Hyde Newton)

Fitzpatrick, Jim (LAB - Hyde Godley)

Fowler, Mike (LAB - Denton South)

Glover, Mike (LAB - Ashton Hurst) mike.glover@tameside.gov.uk

Gwynne, Allison (LAB - Denton North East)

Holland, Barrie (LAB - Droylsden West)

Holland, Ann (LAB - Droylsden West)

Homer, Jack (LAB - Mossley)

Jackson, Jan (LAB - Stalybridge North)

Kinsey, Andy (LAB - Hyde Werneth) andy.kinsey@tameside.gov.uk

Kitchen, Joseph (LAB - Hyde Godley)

Lane, Jacqueline (LAB - Dukinfield)

TAMESIDE

Lane, Dawson (LAB - Denton West)

McNally, David (LAB - Ashton St. Peters)

Middleton, Jim (LAB - Droylsden East)

Newton, George (LAB - Denton South)

Patrick, Clive (CON - Stalybridge South)
clive.patrick1@tameside.gov.uk

Pearce, Adrian (LAB - Stalybridge North)
adrian.pearce@tameside.gov.uk

Peet, Gillian (LAB - Longdendale)

Piddington, Catherine (LAB - Ashton Waterloo)

Quinn, Susan (LAB - Droylsden East)

Reid, Claire (LAB - Denton South)

Ricci, Vincent (LAB - Denton North East)

Robinson, Peter (LAB - Hyde Newton)

Ryan, Oliver (LAB - Audenshaw)
oliver.ryan@tameside.gov.uk

Sharif, Tafheen (LAB - Mossley)

Sidebottom, Margaret (LAB - Ashton St. Michaels)

Smith, Michael (LAB - Denton West)

Smith, Teresa (LAB - Audenshaw)

Sweeton, David (LAB - Dukinfield & Stalybridge)

Travis, Lynn (LAB - Ashton Waterloo)

Travis, Frank (LAB - Mossley)
frank.travis@tameside.gov.uk

Ward, Denise (LAB - Denton North East)

Warrington, Brenda (LAB - Denton West)

Welsh, Kevin (LAB - Stalybridge North)

Welsh, Ruth (CON - Hyde Werneth)

Whitehead, Lorraine (LAB - Ashton Waterloo)
lorraine.whitehead@tameside.gov.uk

Wild, Brian (LAB - Dukinfield)

Willis, Eleanor (LAB - Dukinfield & Stalybridge)

POLITICAL COMPOSITION
LAB: 51, CON: 6

Tamworth   D

Tamworth Borough Council, Marmion House, Lichfield Street, Tamworth B79 7BZ
☎ 01827 709709 🖶 01827 709271 ✆ enquiries@tamworth.gov.uk
🖳 www.tamworth.gov.uk

FACTS AND FIGURES
Parliamentary Constituencies: Tamworth
EU Constituencies: West Midlands
Election Frequency: Elections are by thirds

PRINCIPAL OFFICERS
Chief Executive: Mr Tony Goodwin, Chief Executive, Marmion House, Lichfield Street, Tamworth B79 7BZ ☎ 01827 709313 ✆ tony-goodwin@tamworth.gov.uk

Senior Management: Mr John Wheatley, Executive Director - Corporate Services & S151 Officer, Marmion House, Lichfield Street, Tamworth B79 7BZ ☎ 01827 709252 ✆ john-wheatley@tamworth.gov.uk

Architect, Building / Property Services: Mr Paul Weston, Head of Asset Management, Marmion House, Lichfield Street, Tamworth B79 7BZ ☎ 01827 709377 ✆ paul-weston@tamworth.gov.uk

PR / Communications: Ms Anica Goodwin, Director - Transformation & Corporate Performance, Marmion House, Lichfield Street, Tamworth B79 7BZ ☎ 01827 709225 ✆ anica-goodwin@tamworth.gov.uk

Community Safety: Mrs Joanne Sands, Head of Community Safety, Sandy Way Depot, Amington, Tamworth B77 4ED ☎ 01827 709585 ✆ joanne-sands@tamworth.gov.uk

Computer Management: Mrs Nicki Burton, Director - Technology & Corporate Programmes, Marmion House, Lichfield Street, Tamworth B79 7BZ ☎ 01827 709420 ✆ nicki-burton@tamworth.gov.uk

Contracts: Mr David Onion, Corporate Procurement Officer, Marmion House, Lichfield Street, Tamworth B79 7BZ ☎ 01827 709371 ✆ david-onion@tamworth.gov.uk

Customer Service: Mrs Tracey Tudor, Head of Customer Services, Marmion House, Lichfield Street, Tamworth B79 7BZ ☎ 01827 709709 ✆ tracey-tudor@tamworth.gov.uk

Economic Development: Mr Matthew Bowers, Head of Planning & Regeneration, Marmion House, Lichfield Street, Tamworth B79 7BZ ☎ 01827 709276 ✆ matthew-bowers@tamworth.gov.uk

E-Government: Mrs Nicki Burton, Director - Technology & Corporate Programmes, Marmion House, Lichfield Street, Tamworth B79 7BZ ☎ 01827 709420 ✆ nicki-burton@tamworth.gov.uk

Electoral Registration: Mr John Wheatley, Executive Director - Corporate Services & S151 Officer, Marmion House, Lichfield Street, Tamworth B79 7BZ ☎ 01827 709252 ✆ john-wheatley@tamworth.gov.uk

Emergency Planning: Mrs Nicki Burton, Director - Technology & Corporate Programmes, Marmion House, Lichfield Street, Tamworth B79 7BZ ☎ 01827 709420 ✆ nicki-burton@tamworth.gov.uk

Energy Management: Mr Paul Weston, Head of Asset Management, Marmion House, Lichfield Street, Tamworth B79 7BZ ☎ 01827 709377 ✆ paul-weston@tamworth.gov.uk

Environmental Health: Mr Stephen Lewis, Head of Environmental Health, Marmion House, Lichfield Street, Tamworth B79 7BZ ☎ 01827 709428 ✆ stephen-lewis@tamworth.gov.uk

Estates, Property & Valuation: Mr Paul Weston, Head of Asset Management, Marmion House, Lichfield Street, Tamworth B79 7BZ ☎ 01827 709377 ✆ paul-weston@tamworth.gov.uk

Facilities: Mr Andrew Barratt, Director - Assets & Environment, Marmion House, Lichfield Street, Tamworth B79 7BZ ☎ 01827 709453 ✆ andrew-barratt@tamworth.gov.uk

Finance: Mr Stefan Garner, Director - Finance, Marmion House, Lichfield Street, Tamworth B79 7BZ ☎ 01827 709242 ⌨ stefan-garner@tamworth.gov.uk

Fleet Management: Mr Andrew Barratt, Director - Assets & Environment, Marmion House, Lichfield Street, Tamworth B79 7BZ ☎ 01827 709453 ⌨ andrew-barratt@tamworth.gov.uk

Grounds Maintenance: Mrs Sarah McGrandle, Head of Environmental Management, Sandy Way Depot, Amington, Tamworth B77 4ED ☎ 01827 709349 ⌨ sarah-mcgrandle@tamworth.gov.uk

Health and Safety: Mr Steve Langston, Health & Safety Manager, Marmion House, Lichfield Street, Tamworth B79 7BZ ☎ 01543 308107; 01827 709224 ⌨ steven.langston@lichfielddc.gov.uk

Housing: Mr Robert Barnes, Director - Housing & Health, Marmion House, Lichfield Street, Tamworth B79 7BZ ☎ 01827 709447 ⌨ robert-barnes@tamworth.gov.uk

Housing Maintenance: Mr John Murden, Repairs Manager, Marmion House, Lichfield Street, Tamworth B79 7BZ ☎ 01827 709406 ⌨ john-murden@tamworth.gov.uk

Legal: Mrs Jane Hackett, Solicitor to the Council & Monitoring Officer, Marmion House, Lichfield Street, Tamworth B79 7BZ ☎ 01827 709258 ⌨ jane-hackett@tamworth.gov.uk

Licensing: Mr Andrew Barratt, Director - Assets & Environment, Marmion House, Lichfield Street, Tamworth B79 7BZ ☎ 01827 709453 ⌨ andrew-barratt@tamworth.gov.uk

Lottery Funding, Charity and Voluntary: Mrs Karen Clancy, Partnership Funding Officer, Marmion House, Lichfield Street, Tamworth B79 7BZ ☎ 01827 709565 ⌨ karen-clancy@tamworth.gov.uk

Member Services: Mrs Jane Hackett, Solicitor to the Council & Monitoring Officer, Marmion House, Lichfield Street, Tamworth B79 7BZ ☎ 01827 709258 ⌨ jane-hackett@tamworth.gov.uk

Parking: Mr Andrew Barratt, Director - Assets & Environment, Marmion House, Lichfield Street, Tamworth B79 7BZ ☎ 01827 709453 ⌨ andrew-barratt@tamworth.gov.uk

Partnerships: Mrs Karen Adderley, Head of Partnerships & Commissioning, Marmion House, Lichfield Street, Tamworth B79 7BZ ☎ 01827 709569 ⌨ karen-adderley@tamworth.gov.uk

Personnel / HR: Mrs Christie Tims, Head of Organisational Development, Marmion House, Lichfield Street, Tamworth B79 7BZ ☎ 01827 709215 ⌨ christie-tims@tamworth.gov.uk

Planning: Mr Matthew Bowers, Head of Planning & Regeneration, Marmion House, Lichfield Street, Tamworth B79 7BZ ☎ 01827 709276 ⌨ matthew-bowers@tamworth.gov.uk

Procurement: Mr David Onion, Corporate Procurement Officer, Marmion House, Lichfield Street, Tamworth B79 7BZ ☎ 01827 709371 ⌨ david-onion@tamworth.gov.uk

Recycling & Waste Minimisation: Mr Andrew Barratt, Director - Assets & Environment, Marmion House, Lichfield Street, Tamworth B79 7BZ ☎ 01827 709453 ⌨ andrew-barratt@tamworth.gov.uk

Regeneration: Mr Matthew Fletcher, Senior Economic Development & Regeneration Officer, Marmion House, Lichfield Street, Tamworth B79 7BZ ☎ 01827 709382 ⌨ matthew-fletcher@tamworth.gov.uk

Staff Training: Mrs Zoe-Louise Wolicki, Human Resources Advisor/Training, Marmion House, Lichfield Street, Tamworth B79 7BZ ☎ 01827 709223 ⌨ zoe-wolicki@tamworth.gov.uk

Street Scene: Mrs Sarah McGrandle, Head of Environmental Management, Marmion House, Lichfield Street, Tamworth B79 7BZ ☎ 01827 709349 ⌨ sarah-mcgrandle@tamworth.gov.uk

Sustainable Communities: Mr Robert Barnes, Director - Housing & Health, Marmion House, Lichfield Street, Tamworth B79 7BZ ☎ 01827 709447 ⌨ robert-barnes@tamworth.gov.uk

Tourism: Ms Stacy Birt, Tourism & Town Centre Development Manager, Marmion House, Lichfield Street, Tamworth B79 7BZ ☎ 01827 709583 ⌨ stacy-birt@tamworth.gov.uk

Town Centre: Mrs Joanne Sands, Head of Community Safety, Sandy Way Depot, Amington, Tamworth B77 4ED ☎ 01827 709585 ⌨ joanne-sands@tamworth.gov.uk

Waste Collection and Disposal: Mr Andrew Barratt, Director - Assets & Environment, Marmion House, Lichfield Street, Tamworth B79 7BZ ☎ 01827 709453 ⌨ andrew-barratt@tamworth.gov.uk

Waste Management: Mr Andrew Barratt, Director - Assets & Environment, Marmion House, Lichfield Street, Tamworth B79 7BZ ☎ 01827 709453 ⌨ andrew-barratt@tamworth.gov.uk

Children's Play Areas: Mrs Sarah McGrandle, Head of Environmental Management, Marmion House, Lichfield Street, Tamworth B79 7BZ ☎ 01827 709349 ⌨ sarah-mcgrandle@tamworth.gov.uk

COUNCILLORS

Deputy Mayor: Chesworth, John (CON - Spital) john-chesworth@tamworth.gov.uk

Leader of the Council: Cook, Daniel (CON - Trinity) daniel-cook@tamworh.gov.uk

Deputy Leader of the Council: Pritchard, Robert (CON - Spital) robert-pritchard@tamworth.gov.uk

Group Leader: Madge, Tony (UKIP - Stonydelph) tony-madge@tamworth.gov.uk

Group Leader: Peaple, Simon (LAB - Glascote) simon.peaple@tamworth.gov.uk

Bilcliff, Robert (UKIP - Stonydelph) robertbilcliff@aol.com

Claymore, Steven (CON - Castle) steven-claymore@tamworth.gov.uk

Clements, Tina (CON - Wilnecote) tina-clements@tamworth.gov.uk

TAMWORTH

Cooke, Chris (UKIP - Glascote)
chris-cooke@tamworth.gov.uk

Couchman, Alice (LAB - Glascote)
alice_couchman@yahoo.co.uk

Doyle, Stephen (CON - Stonydelph)
stephen-doyle@tamworth.gov.uk

Faulkner, John (LAB - Bolehall)
john-faulkner@tamworth.gov.uk

Ford, Richard (CON - Belgrave)
richard-ford@tamworth.gov.uk

Gant, Maureen (CON - Spital)
maureen-gant@tamworth.gov.uk

Goodall, Joy (CON - Belgrave)
joy-goodall@tamworth.gov.uk

Goodall, Simon (CON - Belgrave)
simon-goodall@tamworth.gov.uk

Greatorex, Michael (CON - Mercian)
michael-greatorex@tamworth.gov.uk

James, Andrew (CON - Mercian)
andrew-james@tamworth.gov.uk

Kingstone, Richard (CON - Mercian)
Richard-Kingstone@tamworth.gov.uk

Lunn, Allan (CON - Castle)
allan-lunn@tamworth.gov.uk

Norchi, Ken (LAB - Bolehall)
kenneth-norchi@tamworth.gov.uk

Oates, Michael (CON - Trinity)
michael-oates@tamworth.gov.uk

Oates, Jeremy (CON - Trinity)
jeremy-oates@tamworth.gov.uk

Peaple, Tom (LAB - Amington)
tom-peaple@tamworth.gov.uk

Rogers, Roy (CON - Wilnecote)
roy-rogers@tamworth.gov.uk

Seekings, Peter (LAB - Bolehall)
peter-seekings@tamworth.gov.uk

Standen, Patrick (LAB - Wilnecote)
Patrick-Standen@tamworth.gov.uk

Summers, Martin (CON - Amington)
martin-summers@tamworth.gov.uk

Thurgood, Peter (CON - Castle)
peter-thurgood@tamworth.gov.uk

Thurgood, Michelle (CON - Amington)
michelle-thurgood@tamworth.gov.uk

POLITICAL COMPOSITION
CON: 20, LAB: 7, UKIP: 3

COMMITTEE CHAIRS

Audit: Mr John Chesworth

Licensing: Mr Michael Oates

Planning: Mr Michael Greatorex

Tandridge D

Tandridge District Council, Council Offices, Station Road East, Oxted RH8 0BT
☎ 03456 009009 ✆ customerservices@tandridge.gov.uk
🖥 www.tandridge.gov.uk

FACTS AND FIGURES
Parliamentary Constituencies:
EU Constituencies: South East
Election Frequency: Elections are by thirds

PRINCIPAL OFFICERS

Chief Executive: Ms Louise Round, Chief Executive, Council Offices, Station Road East, Oxted RH8 0BT ☎ 01883 732999 ✆ lround@tandridge.gov.uk

Assistant Chief Executive: Mr Clive Moore, Assistant Chief Executive of Legal, Council Offices, Station Road East, Oxted RH8 0BT ☎ 01883 732740 ✆ cmoore@tandridge.gov.uk

Senior Management: Miss Seanne Giddy, Head of Personnel & Training Services, Council Offices, Station Road East, Oxted RH8 0BT ☎ 01883 732979 ✆ sgiddy@tandridge.gov.uk

Senior Management: Mr Stuart Mitchenall, Head of Business Support Services, Council Offices, Station Road East, Oxted RH8 0BT ☎ 01883 732724 ✆ smitchenall@tandridge.gov.uk

Senior Management: Mr Alistair Montgomery, Chief Finance Officer, Council Offices, Station Road East, Oxted RH8 0BT ☎ 01883 732902 ✆ amontgomery@tandridge.gov.uk

Senior Management: Ms Hazel Oakley, Electoral Services Manager, Council Offices, Station Road East, Oxted RH8 0BT ☎ 01883 732976 ✆ hoakley@tandridge.gov.uk

Senior Management: Mr Vince Sharp, Committee Services Manager, Council Offices, Station Road East, Oxted RH8 0BT ☎ 01883 732776 ✆ vsharp@tandridge.gov.uk

Senior Management: Ms Giuseppina Valenza, Head of Communications & Customer Services, Council Offices, Station Road East, Oxted RH8 0BT ☎ 01883 732704 ✆ gvalenza@tandridge.gov.uk

PR / Communications: Ms Giuseppina Valenza, Head of Communications & Customer Services, Council Offices, Station Road East, Oxted RH8 0BT ☎ 01883 732704 ✆ gvalenza@tandridge.gov.uk

Community Safety: Ms Hilary New, Community Safety Manager, Council Offices, Station Road East, Oxted RH8 0BT ☎ 01883 732703 ✆ hnew@tandridge.gov.uk

Computer Management: Mr Stuart Mitchenall, Head of Business Support Services, Council Offices, Station Road East, Oxted RH8 0BT ☎ 01883 732724 ✆ smitchenall@tandridge.gov.uk

Contracts: Mr Simon Mander, Waste & Recycling Contract Manager, Council Offices, Station Road East, Oxted RH8 0BT ☎ 01883 732955 ✆ smander@tandridge.gov.uk

Customer Service: Ms Giuseppina Valenza, Head of Communications & Customer Services, Council Offices, Station Road East, Oxted RH8 oBT ☎ 01883 732704 ✒ gvalenza@tandridge.gov.uk

Direct Labour: Mr Nic Martlew, Depot Manager, Tandridge Commercial Services, Warren Lane Depot, Hurst Green, Oxted RH8 9DB ☎ 01883 732774

Economic Development: Ms Belinda Purcell, Policy Manager, Council Offices, Station Road East, Oxted RH8 oBT ☎ 01883 732705 ✒ bpurcell@tandridge.gov.uk

E-Government: Mr Stuart Mitchenall, Head of Business Support Services, Council Offices, Station Road East, Oxted RH8 oBT ☎ 01883 732724 ✒ smitchenall@tandridge.gov.uk

Electoral Registration: Ms Hazel Oakley, Electoral Services Manager, Council Offices, Station Road East, Oxted RH8 oBT ☎ 01883 732976 ✒ hoakley@tandridge.gov.uk

Emergency Planning: Mr Clive Moore, Assistant Chief Executive of Legal, Council Offices, Station Road East, Oxted RH8 oBT ☎ 01883 732740 ✒ cmoore@tandridge.gov.uk

Environmental Health: Mr Paul Barton, Chief Community Services Officer, Council Offices, Station Road East, Oxted RH8 oBT ☎ 01883 732840 ✒ pbarton@tandridge.gov.uk

Finance: Mr Alistair Montgomery, Chief Finance Officer, Council Offices, Station Road East, Oxted RH8 oBT ☎ 01883 732902 ✒ amontgomery@tandridge.gov.uk

Grounds Maintenance: Mr Steve Hyder, Contracts & Services Manager, Council Offices, Station Road East, Oxted RH8 oBT ☎ 01883 732967 ✒ shyder@tandridge.gov.uk

Home Energy Conservation: Mr Clifford Darby, Private Sector Housing Manager, Council Offices, Station Road East, Oxted RH8 oBT ☎ 01883 732838 ✒ cdarby@tandridge.gov.uk

Housing: Ms Jayne Godden-Miller, Chief Housing Officer, Council Offices, Station Road East, Oxted RH8 oBT ☎ 01883 732828 ✒ jgodden-miller@tandridge.gov.uk

Housing Maintenance: Mr Robert Preedy, Technical Manager, Council Offices, Station Road East, Oxted RH8 oBT ☎ 01883 732805 ✒ rpreedy@tandridge.gov.uk

Legal: Mr Clive Moore, Assistant Chief Executive of Legal, Council Offices, Station Road East, Oxted RH8 oBT ☎ 01883 732740 ✒ cmoore@tandridge.gov.uk

Licensing: Mr Paul Barton, Chief Community Services Officer, Council Offices, Station Road East, Oxted RH8 oBT ☎ 01883 732840 ✒ pbarton@tandridge.gov.uk

Lottery Funding, Charity and Voluntary: Mr Vince Sharp, Committee Services Manager, Council Offices, Station Road East, Oxted RH8 oBT ☎ 01883 732776 ✒ vsharp@tandridge.gov.uk

Member Services: Mr Vince Sharp, Committee Services Manager, Council Offices, Station Road East, Oxted RH8 oBT ☎ 01883 732776 ✒ vsharp@tandridge.gov.uk

Parking: Mr Paul Barton, Chief Community Services Officer, Council Offices, Station Road East, Oxted RH8 oBT ☎ 01883 732840 ✒ pbarton@tandridge.gov.uk

Personnel / HR: Miss Seanne Giddy, Head of Personnel & Training Services, Council Offices, Station Road East, Oxted RH8 oBT ☎ 01883 732979 ✒ sgiddy@tandridge.gov.uk

Planning: Mr Piers Mason, Chief Planning Officer, Council Offices, Station Road East, Oxted RH8 oBT ☎ 01883 732893 ✒ pmason@tandridge.gov.uk

Planning: Ms Sarah Thompson, Head of Strategic Planning Policy, Council Offices, Station Road East, Oxted RH8 oBT ☎ 01883 732887 ✒ sthompson@tandridge.gov.uk

Procurement: Mr Alistair Montgomery, Chief Finance Officer, Council Offices, Station Road East, Oxted RH8 oBT ☎ 01883 732902 ✒ amontgomery@tandridge.gov.uk

Recycling & Waste Minimisation: Mr Paul Barton, Chief Community Services Officer, Council Offices, Station Road East, Oxted RH8 oBT ☎ 01883 732840 ✒ pbarton@tandridge.gov.uk

Staff Training: Miss Seanne Giddy, Head of Personnel & Training Services, Council Offices, Station Road East, Oxted RH8 oBT ☎ 01883 732979 ✒ sgiddy@tandridge.gov.uk

Street Scene: Mr Paul Barton, Chief Community Services Officer, Council Offices, Station Road East, Oxted RH8 oBT ☎ 01883 732840 ✒ pbarton@tandridge.gov.uk

Sustainable Development: Mr Matt Chapman, Planning Policy & Trees Officer, Council Offices, Station Road East, Oxted RH8 oBT ☎ 01883 732764 ✒ mchapman@tandridge.gov.uk

Waste Collection and Disposal: Mr Paul Barton, Chief Community Services Officer, Council Offices, Station Road East, Oxted RH8 oBT ☎ 01883 732840 ✒ pbarton@tandridge.gov.uk

Waste Management: Mr Paul Barton, Chief Community Services Officer, Council Offices, Station Road East, Oxted RH8 oBT ☎ 01883 732840 ✒ pbarton@tandridge.gov.uk

Children's Play Areas: Mr Paul Barton, Chief Community Services Officer, Council Offices, Station Road East, Oxted RH8 oBT ☎ 01883 732840 ✒ pbarton@tandridge.gov.uk

COUNCILLORS

Chair: Cannon, Patrick (CON - Chaldon)
cllr.patrick.cannon@tandridgedc.gov.uk

Leader of the Council: Fisher, Martin (CON - Oxted North & Tandridge)
cllr.martin.fisher@tandridgedc.gov.uk

Ainsworth, Simon (CON - Oxted South)
cllr.simon.ainsworth@tandridgedc.gov.uk

TANDRIDGE

Allen, Martin (IND - Tatsfield & Titsey)
cllr.martin.allen@tandridgedc.gov.uk

Black, Gill (CON - Bletchingley & Nutfield)
cllr.gill.black@tandridgedc.gov.uk

Blake-Thomas, Eileen (CON - Godstone)
cllr.eileen.blake-thomas@tandridgedc.gov.uk

Bond, Peter (CON - Burstow, Horne & Outwood)
cllr.peter.bond@tandridgedc.gov.uk

Botten, Christopher (LD - Portley)
chris.botten@outlook.com

Bradbury, Sakina (CON - Whyteleafe)
cllr.sakina.bradbury@tandridgedc.gov.uk

Childs, Nick (CON - Godstone)
cllr.nick.childs@tandridgedc.gov.uk

Compton, Barry (CON - Oxted South)
cllr.barry.compton@tandridgedc.gov.uk

Connolly, Beverley (CON - Harestone)
cllr.beverley.connolly@tandridgedc.gov.uk

Cooley, David (CON - Warlingham West)
cllr.david.cooley@tandridgedc.gov.uk

Cooper, Michael (CON - Harestone)
cllr.michael.cooper@tandridgedc.gov.uk

Davies, Philip (R - Limpsfield)
phildavies713@gmail.com

Duck, Geoffrey (CON - Queens Park)
cllr.geoffrey.duck@tandridgedc.gov.uk

Dunbar, Lindsey (CON - Limpsfield)
cllr.lindsey.dunbar@tandridgedc.gov.uk

Elias, Tony (CON - Bletchingley & Nutfield)
cllr.tony.elias@tandridgedc.gov.uk

Fitzgerald, Harry (CON - Burstow, Horne & Outwood)
cllr.harry.fitzgerald@tandridgedc.gov.uk

Harwood, Ken (CON - Felbridge)
cllr.ken.harwood@tandridgedc.gov.uk

Jecks, Keith (CON - Woldingham)
cllr.keith.jecks@tandridgedc.gov.uk

Jones, Alun (LD - Valley)
cllr.alun.jones@tandridgedc.gov.uk

Lee, David (LD - Whyteleafe)
cllr.david.lee@tandridgedc.gov.uk

Lockwood, Liz (CON - Lingfield & Crowhurst)
cllr.liz.lockwood@tandridgedc.gov.uk

Manley, Clive (CON - Portley)
cllr.clive.manley@tandridgedc.gov.uk

Morrow, Simon (LD - Warlingham East, Chelsham & Farleigh)
cllr.simon.morrow@tandridgedc.gov.uk

Parker, Elizabeth (CON - Oxted South)
cllr.elizabeth.parker@tandridgedc.gov.uk

Perkins, Brian (CON - Lingfield & Crowhurst)
cllr.brian.perkins@tandridgedc.gov.uk

Prew, Keith (CON - Warlingham West)
cllr.keith.prew@tandridgedc.gov.uk

Pursehouse, Jeremy (LD - Warlingham East, Chelsham & Farleigh)
cllr.j.pursehouse@tandridgedc.gov.uk

Stead, Rod (CON - Queens Park)
cllr.rod.stead@tandridgedc.gov.uk

Steeds, Lesley (CON - Dormansland & Felcourt)
cllr.lesley.steeds@tandridgedc.gov.uk

Steer, Cindy (CON - Warlingham East, Chelsham & Farleigh)

Thorn, Rosemary (CON - Godstone)
cllr.rosemary.thorn@tandridgedc.gov.uk

Vickers, Debbie (CON - Bletchingley & Nutfield)
cllr.debbie.vickers@tandridgedc.gov.uk

Warner, Caroline (LD - Westway)
cllr.caroline.warner@tandridgedc.gov.uk

Wates, Guy (CON - Burstow, Horne & Outwood)
cllr.guy.waters@tandridge.gov.uk

Webster, Eithne (CON - Westway)
cllr.eithne.webster@tandridgedc.gov.uk

Weightman, David (CON - Oxted North & Tandridge)
cllr.david.weightman@tandridgedc.gov.uk

Wren, Jackie (R - Oxted North & Tandridge)
cllr.jackie.wren@tandridgedc.gov.uk

Young, Maureen (CON - Dormansland & Felcourt)
cllr.maureen.young@tandridgedc.gov.uk

POLITICAL COMPOSITION
CON: 32, LD: 6, R: 2, IND: 1

Taunton Deane   D

Taunton Deane Borough Council, The Deane House, Belvedere Road, Taunton TA1 1HE
☎ 01823 356356 📠 01823 356329 📧 enquiries@tauntondeane.gov.uk
🖥 www.tauntondeane.gov.uk

FACTS AND FIGURES
Parliamentary Constituencies: Taunton Deane
EU Constituencies: South West
Election Frequency: Elections are of whole council

PRINCIPAL OFFICERS

Chief Executive: Mrs Penny James, Chief Executive, The Deane House, Belvedere Road, Taunton TA1 1HE ☎ 01823 356401
📧 p.james@tauntondeane.gov.uk

Deputy Chief Executive: Ms Shirlene Adam, Director - Operations, Deputy CEO & S151 Officer, The Deane House, Belvedere Road, Taunton TA1 1HE ☎ 01823 356310
📧 s.adam@tauntondeane.gov.uk

Assistant Chief Executive: Mr Bruce Lang, Assistant Chief Executive & Monitoring Officer, The Deane House, Belvedere Road, Taunton TA1 1HE ☎ 01823 356403; 01984 635200
📧 bdlang@westsomerset.gov.uk; b.lang@tauntondeane.gov.uk

Senior Management: Ms Shirlene Adam, Director - Operations, Deputy CEO & S151 Officer, The Deane House, Belvedere Road, Taunton TA1 1HE ☎ 01823 356310 📧 s.adam@tauntondeane.gov.uk

Senior Management: Mr James Barrah, Director - Housing & Communities, The Deane House, Belvedere Road, Taunton TA1 1HE
☎ 01823 358699 📧 j.barrah@tauntondeane.gov.uk

Senior Management: Mr Brendon Cleere, Director - Growth & Development, The Deane House, Belvedere Road, Taunton TA1 1HE ☎ 01823 356350 ⁂ b.cleere@tauntondeane.gov.uk

Access Officer / Social Services (Disability): Mr Edwin Norton, Senior Building Control, Surveyor & Access Officer, The Deane House, Belvedere Road, Taunton TA1 1HE ☎ 01823 356476 ⁂ e.norton@tauntondeane.gov.uk

Architect, Building / Property Services: Mr Tim Child, Divisional Manager - Property Estates Team, The Deane House, Belvedere Road, Taunton TA1 1HE ☎ 01823 356356 ⁂ t.child@tauntondeane.gov.uk

Building Control: Mr Nigel Hunt, Somerset Building Control Partnership Manager, Bridgwater House, Kings Square, Bridgwater TA6 9ZY ☎ 01823 356473 ⁂ nigel.hunt@mendip.gov.uk

PR / Communications: Mrs Debbie Rundle, Media & PR Officer, The Deane House, Belvedere Road, Taunton TA1 1HE ☎ 01823 356407 ⁂ d.rundle@tauntondeane.gov.uk

Community Planning: Mr Tim Burton, Assistant Director - Planning & Environment, The Deane House, Belvedere Road, Taunton TA1 1HE ☎ 01823 358403 ⁂ t.burton@tauntondeane.gov.uk

Community Safety: Ms Tracey-Ann Biss, Parking & Civil Contingencies Manager, The Deane House, Belvedere Road, Taunton TA1 1HE ☎ 01823 356455 ⁂ t.biss@tauntondeane.gov.uk

Computer Management: Ms Fiona Kirkham, ICT & Information Manager, The Deane House, Belvedere Road, Taunton TA1 1HE ☎ 01823 356522 ⁂ f.kirkham@tauntondeane.gov.uk

Corporate Services: Mr Richard Sealy, Assistant Director - Corporate Services, The Deane House, Belvedere Road, Taunton TA1 1HE ☎ 01823 658690 ⁂ r.sealy@tauntondeane.gov.uk

Customer Service: Mr Rob Liddell, Head of Customer Contact, The Deane House, Belvedere Road, Taunton TA1 1HE ☎ 01823 356356 ⁂ r.liddell@tauntondeane.gov.uk

Direct Labour: Mr Chris Hall, Assistant Director - Operational Delivery, The Deane House, Belvedere Road, Taunton TA1 1HE ☎ 01823 356403 ⁂ c.hall@tauntondeane.gov.uk

Economic Development: Mr David Evans, Economic Development Manager, The Deane House, Belvedere Road, Taunton TA1 1HE ☎ 01823 356545 ⁂ d.evans@tauntondeane.gov.uk

Economic Development: Mr Ian Timms, Assistant Director - Business Development, The Deane House, Belvedere Road, Taunton TA1 1HE ☎ 01823 356577 ⁂ itimms@westsomerset.gov.uk

Electoral Registration: Mrs Elisa Day, Electoral Services Manager, West Somerset House, Killick Way, Williton, Taunton TA4 4QA ☎ 01984 635272 ⁂ eday@westsomerset.gov.uk

Emergency Planning: Ms Tracey-Ann Biss, Parking & Civil Contingencies Manager, The Deane House, Belvedere Road, Taunton TA1 1HE ☎ 01823 356455 ⁂ t.biss@tauntondeane.gov.uk

Environmental Health: Mr Scott Weetch, Community & Client Services Manager, The Deane House, Belvedere Road, Taunton TA1 1HE ☎ 01823 356317 ⁂ s.weetch@tauntondeane.gov.uk

Estates, Property & Valuation: Mr Tim Child, Divisional Manager - Property Estates Team, The Deane House, Belvedere Road, Taunton TA1 1HE ☎ 01823 356356 ⁂ t.child@tauntondeane.gov.uk

Facilities: Ms Angela Hill, Facilities & Corporate Administration Manager, The Deane House, Belvedere Road, Taunton TA1 1HE ☎ 01823 356597 ⁂ a.hill@tauntondeane.gov.uk

Finance: Mr Paul Fitzgerald, Assistant Director - Resources, West Somerset House, Killick Way, Williton, Taunton TA4 4QA ⁂ pfitzgerald@westsomerset.gov.uk

Grounds Maintenance: Mr Richard Hopkins, Open Spaces Area Manager, Priory Way Depot, Taunton TA1 2BB ☎ 01823 356360 ⁂ r.hopkins@tauntondeane.gov.uk

Health and Safety: Ms Catrin Brown, Health & Safety Manager, The Deane House, Belvedere Road, Taunton TA1 1HE ☎ 01823 356578 ⁂ c.brown@tauntondeane.gov.uk

Home Energy Conservation: Ms Barbara Wells, Energy Efficiency Officer, Sedgemoor Council, Bridgwater House, King's Square, Bridgwater TA6 3AR ☎ 01278 436426 ⁂ b.wells@sedgemoor.gov.uk

Housing: Mr Steve Boland, Housing Services Lead, The Deane House, Belvedere Road, Taunton TA1 1HE ☎ 01823 356446 ⁂ s.boland@tauntondeane.gov.uk

Housing: Mr Simon Lewis, Assistant Director - Housing & Community Development, The Deane House, Belvedere Road, Taunton TA1 1HE ☎ 01823 356397 ⁂ s.lewis@tauntondeane.gov.uk

Housing: Mr Terry May, Assitant Director - Property & Development, The Deane House, Belvedere Road, Taunton TA1 1HE ☎ 01823 358400 ⁂ t.may@tauntondeane.gov.uk

Housing Maintenance: Mr Phil Webb, Housing Manager - Property Services, The Deane House, Belvedere Road, Taunton TA1 1HE ☎ 01823 356505 ⁂ p.webb@tauntondeane.gov.uk

Legal: Mrs Lesley Dolan, SHAPE Business Services Manager, The Deane House, Belvedere Road, Taunton TA1 1HE ☎ 0300 303 8588 ⁂ lesley.dolan@mendip.gov.uk

Leisure and Cultural Services: Ms Alison North, Community Leisure Manager, Priory Depot, Priory Way, Taunton TA1 1HE ☎ 01823 356576 ⁂ a.north@tauntondeane.gov.uk

Licensing: Mr John Rendell, Licensing Manager, The Deane House, Belvedere Road, Taunton TA1 1HE ☎ 01823 358343 ⁂ j.rendell@tauntondeane.gov.uk

Member Services: Mr Richard Bryant, Democratic Services Manager, The Deane House, Belvedere Road, Taunton TA1 1HE ☎ 01823 356414 ⁂ r.bryant@tauntondeane.gov.uk

TAUNTON DEANE

Parking: Ms Tracey-Ann Biss, Parking & Civil Contingencies Manager, The Deane House, Belvedere Road, Taunton TA1 1HE
☎ 01823 356455 ⌂ t.biss@tauntondeane.gov.uk

Personnel / HR: Ms Fiona Wills, Human Resources Manager, The Deane House, Belvedere Road, Taunton TA1 1HE ☎ 01823 356450 ⌂ f.wills@tauntondeane.gov.uk

Planning: Mr Tim Burton, Assistant Director - Planning & Environment, The Deane House, Belvedere Road, Taunton TA1 1HE
☎ 01823 358403 ⌂ t.burton@tauntondeane.gov.uk

Planning: Mr Bryn Kitching, Area Planning Manager, The Deane House, Belvedere Road, Taunton TA1 1HE

Procurement: Mr Jon Batstone, Procurement Manager, The Deane House, Belvedere Road, Taunton TA1 1HE ☎ 01823 358286 ⌂ j.batstone@tauntondeane.gov.uk

Staff Training: Ms Fiona Wills, Human Resources Manager, The Deane House, Belvedere Road, Taunton TA1 1HE ☎ 01823 356450 ⌂ f.wills@tauntondeane.gov.uk

Tourism: Ms Corinne Matthews, Economic Regeneration Manager, West Somerset House, Killick Way, Williton, Taunton TA4 4QA
☎ 01823 356356 ⌂ c.matthews@tauntondeane.gov.uk

Children's Play Areas: Mr Josep Galicia, Open Spaces Supervisor, Deane DLO, Priory Depot, Priory Way, Taunton TA1 2BB
☎ 01823 356360 ⌂ j.galicia@tauntondeane.gov.uk

COUNCILLORS

Leader of the Council: Williams, John (CON - Neroche)
cllr.j.williams@tauntondeane.gov.uk

Deputy Leader of the Council: Edwards, Mark (CON - Trull)
cllr.m.edwards@tauntondeane.gov.uk

Adkins, Jean (IND - Norton Fitzwarren)
cllr.j.adkins@tauntondeane.gov.uk

Adkins, Michael (CON - Lyngford)
cllr.m.adkins@tauntondeane.gov.uk

Aldridge, Thomas (UKIP - Lyngford)
cllr.t.aldridge@tauntondeane.gov.uk

Beale, Terry (CON - Killams & Mountfield)
cllr.t.beale@tauntondeane.gov.uk

Berry, Patrick (CON - Manor & Wilton)
cllr.p.berry@tauntondeane.gov.uk

Blatchford, Julia (CON - Bishops Hull)
cllr.j.blatchford@tauntondeane.gov.uk

Booth, Christopher (LD - Halcon)
cllr.c.booth@tauntondeane.gov.uk

Bowrah, Robert (CON - Wellington, Rockwell Green & West)
cllr.r.bowrah@tauntondeane.gov.uk

Brown, William (CON - Wellington North)
cllr.w.brown@tauntondeane.gov.uk

Cavill, Norman (CON - West Monkton)
cllr.n.cavill@tauntondeane.gov.uk

Coles, Simon (LD - Eastgate)
cllr.s.coles@tauntondeane.gov.uk

Coombes, William (CON - Blackbrook & Holway)
cllr.w.coombes@tauntondeane.gov.uk

Cossey, Duncan (CON - North Curry & Stoke St Gregory)
cllr.d.cossey@tauntondeane.gov.uk

Davies, Thomas (CON - Pyrland & Rowbarton)
cllr.t.davies@tauntondeane.gov.uk

Durdan, Kelly (CON - Ruishton & Creech)
cllr.k.durdan@tauntondeane.gov.uk

Durdan, David (CON - Ruishton & Creech)
cllr.d.durdan@tauntondeane.gov.uk

Edwards, Charlotte (CON - Blackdown)
cllr.c.edwards@tauntondeane.gov.uk

Farbahi, Habib (LD - Comeytrowe)
cllr.h.farbahi@tauntondeane.gov.uk

Floyd, Mollie (LD - Comeytrowe)
cllr.m.floyd@tauntondeane.gov.uk

Gage, John (CON - Pyrland & Rowbarton)
cllr.j.gage@tauntondeane.gov.uk

Gaines, Edward (IND - Wiveliscombe & West Deane)
cllr.e.gaines@tauntondeane.gov.uk

Govier, Andrew (LAB - Wellington North)
cllr.a.govier@tauntondeane.gov.uk

Gunner, Alison (CON - Bishops Lydeard)
cllr.a.gunner@tauntondeane.gov.uk

Habgood, Roger (CON - Bradford on Tone)
cllr.r.habgood@tauntondeane.gov.uk

Hall, Terence (CON - Manor & Wilton)
cllr.t.hall@tauntondeane.gov.uk

Herbert, Catherine (CON - Killams & Mountfield)
cllr.c.herbert@tauntondeane.gov.uk

Hill, Chris (CON - Monument)
cllr.c.hill@tauntondeane.gov.uk

Hill, Marcia (LD - Pyrland & Rowbarton)
cllr.m.hill@tauntondeane.gov.uk

Horsley, Jefferson (LD - Fairwater)
cllr.j.horsley@tauntondeane.gov.uk

Hunt, James (CON - Wellington East)
cllr.j.hunt@tauntondeane.gov.uk

James, Gary (CON - Wellington East)
cllr.g.james@tauntondeane.gov.uk

Lees, Sue (LD - Fairwater)
cllr.s.lees@tauntondeane.gov.uk

Lees, Richard (LD - Eastgate)
cllr.r.lees@tauntondeane.gov.uk

Lisgo, Libby (LAB - Lyngford)
cllr.l.lisgo@tauntondeane.gov.uk

Martin-Scott, Stephen (CON - Manor & Wilton)
cllr.s.martin-scott@tauntondeane.gov.uk

Morrell, Ian (IND - Bishops Hull)
cllr.i.morrell@tauntondeane.gov.uk

Nicholls, Simon (LD - Comeytrowe)
cllr.s.nicholls@tauntondeane.gov.uk

Parrish, Richard (CON - West Monkton)
cllr.r.parrish@tauntondeane.gov.uk

Priory-Sankey, Hazel (LD - Blackbrook & Holway)
cllr.h.prior-sankey@tauntondeane.gov.uk

Reed, Janet (CON - Wellington, Rockwell Green & West)
cllr.j.reed@tauntondeane.gov.uk

Ross, Steve (IND - Wiveliscombs & West Deane)
cllr.s.ross@tauntondeane.gov.uk

Ryan, Roger (CON - Halcon)
cllr.r.ryan@tauntondeane.gov.uk

Smith, Frederica (LD - Halcon)
cllr.frederica.smith@tauntondeane.gov.uk

Smith, Francesca (LD - Blackbrook & Holway)
cllr.f.smith@tauntondeane.gov.uk

Stock-Williams, Vivienne (IND - Wellington, Rockwell Green & West)
cllr.v.stock-williams@tauntondeane.gov.uk

Stone, Philip (LD - North Curry & Stoke St Gregory)
cllr.p.stone@tauntondeane.gov.uk

Sully, Andrew (CON - Norton Fitzwarren)
cllr.a.sully@tauntondeane.gov.uk

Townsend, Nicolas (CON - Staplegrove)
cllr.n.townsend@tauntondeane.gov.uk

Tucker, Caroline (CON - Staplegrove)
cllr.c.tucker@tauntondeane.gov.uk

Warmington, Jane (CON - Bishops Lydeard)
cllr.j.warmington@tauntondeane.gov.uk

Watson, Peter (CON - Bishops Lydeard)
cllr.p.watson@tauntondeane.gov.uk

Webber, Denise (CON - West Monkton)
cllr.d.webber@tauntondeane.gov.uk

Wedderkopp, Danny (LD - Fairwater)
cllr.d.wedderkopp@tauntondeane.gov.uk

Wren, Gwilyn (CON - Milverton & North Deane)
cllr.g.wren@tauntondeane.gov.uk

POLITICAL COMPOSITION
CON: 34, LD: 14, IND: 5, LAB: 2, UKIP: 1

Teignbridge   D

Teignbridge District Council, Forde House, Brunel Road, Newton Abbot TQ12 4XX
☎ 01626 361101 ✆ info@teignbridge.gov.uk
🖥 www.teignbridge.gov.uk

FACTS AND FIGURES
Parliamentary Constituencies:
EU Constituencies: South West
Election Frequency: Elections are of whole council

PRINCIPAL OFFICERS

Chief Executive: Ms Nicola Bulbeck, Chief Executive, Forde House, Brunel Road, Newton Abbot TQ12 4XX ☎ 01626 361101 ✆ nicola.bulbeck@teignbridge.gov.uk

Deputy Chief Executive: Mr Phil Shears, Deputy Chief Executive, Forde House, Brunel Road, Newton Abbot TQ12 4XX ☎ 01626 361101 ✆ phil.shears@teignbridge.gov.uk

Senior Management: Mrs Sue Aggett, Business Lead - Environment, Health & Wellbeing, Forde House, Brunel Road, Newton Abbot TQ12 4XX ☎ 01626 215163 ✆ sue.aggett@teignbridge.gov.uk

Architect, Building / Property Services: Mr Tony Watson, Business Manager - Economy & Assets, Forde House, Brunel Road, Newton Abbot TQ12 4XX ☎ 01626 215828 ✆ tony.watson@teignbridge.gov.uk

Best Value: Ms Nicola Bulbeck, Chief Executive, Forde House, Brunel Road, Newton Abbot TQ12 4XX ☎ 01626 361101 ✆ nicola.bulbeck@teignbridge.gov.uk

Building Control: Mr Andy Carpenter, Head - Building Control Partnership, Forde House, Brunel Road, Newton Abbot TQ12 4XX ☎ 01626 215721 ✆ andrew.carpenter@devonbuildingcontrol.gov.uk

PR / Communications: Ms Emma Pearcy, Communications Officer, Forde House, Brunel Road, Newton Abbot TQ12 4XX ☎ 01626 215164 ✆ emma.pearcy@teignbridge.gov.uk

Community Planning: Mr Simon Thornley, Business Manager - Strategic Place, Forde House, Brunel Road, Newton Abbot TQ12 4XX ☎ 01626 215706 ✆ simon.thornley@teignbridge.gov.uk

Community Safety: Mrs Rebecca Hewitt, Senior Community Safety Officer, Forde House, Brunel Road, Newton Abbot TQ12 4XX ☎ 01626 215873 ✆ rebecca.hewitt@teignbridge.gov.uk

Computer Management: Mr Chris Powell, Strata Chief Operating Officer, Forde House, Brunel Road, Newton Abbot TQ12 4XX ☎ 01392 265050 ✆ chris.powell@strata.solutions

Contracts: Mrs Carly Wedderburn, Corporate Procurement Officer, Forde House, Brunel Road, Newton Abbot TQ12 4XX ☎ 01626 215120 ✆ carly.wedderburn@teignbridge.gov.uk

Customer Service: Mrs Elizabeth Guy, Customer Services Manager, Forde House, Brunel Road, Newton Abbot TQ12 4XX ☎ 01626 215510 ✆ liz.guy@teignbridge.gov.uk

Economic Development: Mr Tony Watson, Business Manager - Economy & Assets, Forde House, Brunel Road, Newton Abbot TQ12 4XX ☎ 01626 215828 ✆ tony.watson@teignbridge.gov.uk

Electoral Registration: Mrs Cathy Ruelens, Electoral Services Co-ordinator, Forde House, Brunel Road, Newton Abbot TQ12 4XX ☎ 01626 215103 ✆ cathy.ruelens@teignbridge.gov.uk

Emergency Planning: Mr David Eaton, Environmental Protection Manager, Forde House, Brunel Road, Newton Abbot TQ12 4XX ☎ 01626 215064 ✆ david.eaton@teignbridge.gov.uk

Energy Management: Mrs Sue Aggett, Business Lead - Environment, Health & Wellbeing, Forde House, Brunel Road, Newton Abbot TQ12 4XX ☎ 01626 215163 ✆ sue.aggett@teignbridge.gov.uk

TEIGNBRIDGE

Environmental Health: Mrs Sue Aggett, Business Lead - Environment, Health & Wellbeing, Forde House, Brunel Road, Newton Abbot TQ12 4XX ☎ 01626 215163 🖰 sue.aggett@teignbridge.gov.uk

Estates, Property & Valuation: Mr Tony Watson, Business Manager - Economy & Assets, Forde House, Brunel Road, Newton Abbot TQ12 4XX ☎ 01626 215828 🖰 tony.watson@teignbridge.gov.uk

European Liaison: Mr Neil Blaney, Economy Manager, Forde House, Brunel Road, Newton Abbot TQ12 4XX ☎ 01626 215233 🖰 neil.blaney@teignbridge.gov.uk

Facilities: Mr Tony Watson, Business Manager - Economy & Assets, Forde House, Brunel Road, Newton Abbot TQ12 4XX ☎ 01626 215828 🖰 tony.watson@teignbridge.gov.uk

Finance: Mrs Lesley Tucker, Section 151 Officer, Forde House, Brunel Road, Newton Abbot TQ12 4XX ☎ 01626 215203 🖰 lesley.tucker@teignbridge.gov.uk

Grounds Maintenance: Ms Lorraine Montgomery, Business Manager - Environment & Leisure, Forde House, Brunel Road, Newton Abbot TQ12 4XX ☎ 01626 215852 🖰 lorraine.montgomery@teignbridge.gov.uk

Health and Safety: Mr Peter Wilson, Health & Safety Officer, Forde House, Brunel Road, Newton Abbot TQ12 4XX ☎ 01626 215155 🖰 peter.wilson@teignbridge.gov.uk

Home Energy Conservation: Ms Zoe Farmer, Affordable Warmth & Home Energy Officer, Forde House, Brunel Road, Newton Abbot TQ12 4XX ☎ 01626 215764 🖰 zoe.farmer@teignbridge.gov.uk

Housing: Mrs Amanda Pujol, Business Manager - Housing & Revenue Benefits, Forde House, Brunel Road, Newton Abbot TQ12 4XX ☎ 01626 215301 🖰 amanda.pujol@teignbridge.gov.uk

Legal: Mrs Kate Davies, Solicitor to the Council, Forde House, Brunel Road, Newton Abbot TQ12 4XX ☎ 01626 215119 🖰 kate.davies@teignbridge.gov.uk

Leisure and Cultural Services: Ms Lorraine Montgomery, Business Manager - Environment & Leisure, Forde House, Brunel Road, Newton Abbot TQ12 4XX ☎ 01626 215852 🖰 lorraine.montgomery@teignbridge.gov.uk

Licensing: Mrs Andrea Furness, Licensing Officer, Forde House, Brunel Road, Newton Abbot TQ12 4XX ☎ 01626 215108 🖰 andrea.furness@teignbridge.gov.uk

Member Services: Mr Neil Aggett, Democratic Services Manager, Forde House, Brunel Road, Newton Abbot TQ12 4XX ☎ 01626 215113 🖰 neil.aggett@teignbridge.gov.uk

Parking: Mr Neil Blaney, Economy Manager, Forde House, Brunel Road, Newton Abbot TQ12 4XX ☎ 01626 215233 🖰 neil.blaney@teignbridge.gov.uk

Personnel / HR: Ms Nicola Bulbeck, Chief Executive, Forde House, Brunel Road, Newton Abbot TQ12 4XX ☎ 01626 361101 🖰 nicola.bulbeck@teignbridge.gov.uk

Planning: Mr Nick Davies, Business Manager - Strategic Place, Forde House, Brunel Road, Newton Abbot TQ12 4XX ☎ 01626 215745 🖰 nick.davies@teignbridge.gov.uk

Procurement: Mrs Carly Wedderburn, Corporate Procurement Officer, Forde House, Brunel Road, Newton Abbot TQ12 4XX ☎ 01626 215120 🖰 carly.wedderburn@teignbridge.gov.uk

Recycling & Waste Minimisation: Mr Chris Braines, Waste Management Officer, Forde House, Brunel Road, Newton Abbot TQ12 4XX ☎ 01626 215841 🖰 chris.braines@teignbridge.gov.uk

Regeneration: Mr Tony Watson, Business Manager - Economy & Assets, Forde House, Brunel Road, Newton Abbot TQ12 4XX ☎ 01626 215828 🖰 tony.watson@teignbridge.gov.uk

Staff Training: Mrs Debbie Hutchings, Training & Development Manager, Forde House, Brunel Road, Newton Abbot TQ12 4XX ☎ 01626 215138 🖰 debbie.hutchings@teignbridge.gov.uk

Sustainable Communities: Mr Gary Powell, Community Projects Officer, Forde House, Brunel Road, Newton Abbot TQ12 4XX ☎ 01626 215169 🖰 gary.powell@teignbridge.gov.uk

Tourism: Mrs Michelle Taylor, Tourism & Marketing Officer, Forde House, Brunel Road, Newton Abbot TQ12 4XX ☎ 01626 215614 🖰 michelle.taylor@teignbridge.gov.uk

Town Centre: Mr Tony Watson, Business Manager - Economy & Assets, Forde House, Brunel Road, Newton Abbot TQ12 4XX ☎ 01626 215828 🖰 tony.watson@teignbridge.gov.uk

Waste Collection and Disposal: Mr Chris Braines, Waste Management Officer, Forde House, Brunel Road, Newton Abbot TQ12 4XX ☎ 01626 215841 🖰 chris.braines@teignbridge.gov.uk

Waste Management: Mr Chris Braines, Waste Management Officer, Forde House, Brunel Road, Newton Abbot TQ12 4XX ☎ 01626 215841 🖰 chris.braines@teignbridge.gov.uk

COUNCILLORS

Chair: Price, Graham (CON - Dawlish Central & North East) graham.price@teignbridge.gov.uk

Leader of the Council: Christophers, Jeremy (CON - Haytor) jeremy.christophers@teignbridge.gov.uk

Deputy Leader of the Council: Gribble, George (CON - Bovey) george.gribble@teignbridge.gov.uk

Austen, Beryl (IND - Kingsteignton East) beryl.austen@teignbridge.gov.uk

Barker, Stuart (CON - Ashburton & Buckfastleigh) stuart.barker@teignbridge.gov.uk

Brodie, Jackie (LD - Newton Abbot Bushell) jackie.brodie@teignbridge.gov.uk

Bromell, Peter (IND - Teignbridge North) peter.bromell@teignbridge.gov.uk

Bullivant, Phil (CON - Newton Abbot Bradley)
philip.bullivant@teignbridge.gov.uk

Clarance, Chris (CON - Shaldon & Stokeinteignhead)
christopher.clarance@teignbridge.gov.uk

Clemens, Humphrey (CON - Dawlish South West)
humphrey.clemens@teignbridge.gov.uk

Colclough, Mary (IND - Ambrook)
mary.colclough@teignbridge.gov.uk

Connett, Alan (LD - Kenton with Starcross)
alan.connett@teignbridge.gov.uk

Cook, Sheila (LD - Kerswell with Combe)
sheila.cook@teignbridge.gov.uk

Cox, David (LD - Teignmouth West)
david.cox@teignbridge.gov.uk

Dennis, Charlie (CON - Ashburton & Buckfastleigh)
charlie.dennis@teignbridge.gov.uk

Dewhurst, Alistair (LD - Ipplepen)
alistair.dewhirst@teignbridge.gov.uk

Ford, Amanda (CON - Teign Valley)
amanda.ford@teignbridge.gov.uk

Fusco, Vince (CON - Teignmouth East)
vince.fusco@teignbridge.gov.uk

Golder, Timothy (CON - Bishopsteignton)
timothy.golder@teignbridge.gov.uk

Goodey, John (CON - Kenn Valley)
john.goodey@teignbridge.gov.uk

Grainger, Judy (CON - Newton Abbot Bushell)
judy.grainger@teignbridge.gov.uk

Haines, Mike (IND - Kerswell with Combe)
mike.haines@teignbridge.gov.uk

Hellier-Lang, Doug (CON - Chudleigh)
doug.hellierlang@teignbridge.gov.uk

Hockin, Ted (CON - Dawlish Central & North East)
edward.hockin@teignbridge.gov.uk

Hocking, Michael (LD - Newton Abbot Bradley)
michael.hocking@teignbridge.gov.uk

Hook, Gordon (LD - Newton Abbot Buckland & Milber)
gordon.hook@teignbridge.gov.uk

Jeffery, Mike (CON - Moorland)
mike.jeffery@teignbridge.gov.uk

Jones, Ann (LD - Newton Abbot College)
ann.jones@teignbridge.gov.uk

Kerswell, Avril (CON - Bovey)
avril.kerswell@teignbridge.gov.uk

Lake, Kevin (CON - Kenn Valley)
kevin.lake@teignbridge.gov.uk

Matthews, Dave (CON - Teignmouth West)
dave.matthews@teignbridge.gov.uk

Mayne, Lisa (CON - Dawlish Central & North East)
lisa.mayne@teignbridge.gov.uk

Nutley, John (LD - Ashburton & Buckfastleigh)
john.nutley@teignbridge.gov.uk

Parker, Colin (LD - Newton Abbot Buckland & Milber)
colin.parker@teignbridge.gov.uk

Pilkington, Mike (LD - Newton Abbot College)
mike.pilkington@teignbridge.gov.uk

Prowse, Rosalind (CON - Dawlish South West)
rosalind.prowse@teignbridge.gov.uk

Rollason, David (LD - Kingsteignton West)
dave.rollason@teignbridge.gov.uk

Russell, Sylvia (CON - Teignmouth East)
sylvia.russell@teignbridge.gov.uk

Smith, Dennis (CON - Ambrook)
dennis.smith@teignbridge.gov.uk

Thorne, Bill (CON - Kingsteignton West)
bill.thorne@teignbridge.gov.uk

Walters, Mike (CON - Kingsteignton East)
mike.walters@teignbridge.gov.uk

Winsor, Reg (CAP - Newton Abbot Buckland & Milber)
reg.winsor@teignbridge.gov.uk

POLITICAL COMPOSITION
CON: 25, LD: 12, IND: 4, Vacant: 2, CAP: 1

COMMITTEE CHAIRS

Audit: Mr Chris Clarance

Licensing: Mr Ted Hockin

Planning: Mr Dennis Smith

Telford & Wrekin   U

Telford & Wrekin Council, Civic Offices, Telford TF3 4LD
☎ 01952 380000 ✆ contact@telford.gov.uk 🖳 www.telford.gov.uk

FACTS AND FIGURES
Parliamentary Constituencies: Telford, Wrekin, The
EU Constituencies: West Midlands
Election Frequency: Elections are of whole council

PRINCIPAL OFFICERS

Chief Executive: Mr Richard Partington, Managing Director,
Addenbrooke House, Ironmasters Way, Telford TF3 4NT
☎ 01952 380130 ✆ richard.partington@telford.gov.uk

Senior Management: Mr Clive Jones, Director - Children & Adult
Services, Civic Offices, Telford TF3 4LD ☎ 01952 380000
✆ clive.jones@telford.gov.uk

Senior Management: Mr Jonathan Rowe, Director -
Neighbourhood, Customer & Cultural Services, Addenbrooke
House, Ironmasters Way, Telford TF3 4NT ☎ 01952 382900
✆ jonathan.rowe@telford.gov.uk

Architect, Building / Property Services: Mr Chris Goulson,
Service Delivery Manager, 2nd Floor, Wellington Civic & Leisure
Centre, Wellington, Telford TF1 1LX ☎ 01952 384302
✆ chris.goulson@telford.gov.uk

Building Control: Mr Keith Harris, Group Manager - Development
Team Manager, Civic Offices, Telford TF3 4LD ☎ 01952 384601
✆ keith.harris@telford.gov.uk

TELFORD & WREKIN

Catering Services: Ms Kate Sumner, Cleaning Group Manager, 2nd Floor, Wellington Civic & Leisure Centre, Wellington, Telford TF1 1LX ☎ 01952 380917 ⏚ kate.sumner@telford.gov.uk

Civil Registration: Ms Kerry Caitlin, Superintendent Registrar / Registration Services Manager, Wellington Civic & Leisure Centre, Wellington, Telford TF1 1LX ☎ 01952 382444 ⏚ kerry.caitlin@telford.gov.uk

PR / Communications: Mr Nigel Newman, Corporate Communications Manager, Addenbrooke House, Ironmasters Way, Telford TF3 4NT ☎ 01952 382403 ⏚ nigel.newman@telford.gov.uk

Community Safety: Mr Jas Bedesha, Cohesion Service Delivery Manager, Darby House, 5th Floor Wing C, Telford TF3 4LD ☎ 01952 382101 ⏚ jas.bedesha@telford.gov.uk

Computer Management: Miss Kirsty King, ICT Service Delivery Manager, 1st Floor, Whitechapel House, Telford TF2 9SP ☎ 01952 383480 ⏚ kirsty.king@telford.gov.uk

Consumer Protection and Trading Standards: Ms Nicky Minshall, Public Protection Service Delivery Manager, Darby House, 7th Floor, Wing A, Telford TF3 4LD ☎ 01952 381820 ⏚ nicky.minshall@telford.gov.uk

Contracts: Mr Ken Clarke, Assistant Director - Finance, Team & Resources, Addenbrooke House, Ironmasters Way, Telford TF3 4NT ☎ 01952 383100 ⏚ ken.clarke@telford.gov.uk

Customer Service: Ms Angie Astley, Assistant Director - Neighbourhood & Customer Services, Addenbrooke House, Ironmasters Way, Telford TF3 4NT ☎ 01952 382400 ⏚ angie.astley@telford.gov.uk

Economic Development: Ms Katherine Kynaston, Assistant Director - Development & Employment, Wellington Civic & Leisure Centre, Wellington, Telford TF1 1LX ☎ 01952 384201 ⏚ katherine.kynaston@telford.gov.uk

Education: Mr Jim Collins, Assistant Director - Education & Corporate Parenting, Addenbrooke House, Ironmasters Way, Telford TF3 4NT ☎ 01952 380800 ⏚ jim.collins@telford.gov.uk

Emergency Planning: Ms Heather Gumsley, Civil Resilience Manager, Unit B4B, Stafford Park 11, Telford TF3 3AY ☎ 01952 381957 ⏚ heather.gumsley@telford.gov.uk

Facilities: Mr Clive Barton, Facilities Management Group Manager, Wellington Civic & Leisure Centre, Wellington, Telford TF1 1LX ☎ 01952 380000 ⏚ clive.barton@telford.gov.uk

Fleet Management: Ms Viv McKay, Commissioning - Vulnerable People, Darby House, 2nd Floor, Wing C, Telford TF3 4LD ☎ 01952 380000 ⏚ vivianne.mckay2@telford.gov.uk

Grounds Maintenance: Mr Danny Chetwood, Neighbourhood & Environment Manager, Granville House, Telford TF3 4LL ☎ 01952 384384 ⏚ danny.chetwood@telford.gov.uk

Health and Safety: Ms Nicky Minshall, Public Protection Service Delivery Manager, Darby House, 7th Floor, Wing A, Telford TF3 4LD ☎ 01952 381820 ⏚ nicky.minshall@telford.gov.uk

Highways: Mr Dominic Proud, Service Delivery Manager - Transport & Highway Development, Civic Offices, Telford TF3 4LD ☎ 01952 380000 ⏚ dominic.proud@telford.gov.uk

Housing: Ms Katherine Kynaston, Assistant Director - Development & Employment, Wellington Civic & Leisure Centre, Wellington, Telford TF1 1LX ☎ 01952 384201 ⏚ katherine.kynaston@telford.gov.uk

Housing Maintenance: Ms Katherine Kynaston, Assistant Director - Development & Employment, Wellington Civic & Leisure Centre, Wellington, Telford TF1 1LX ☎ 01952 384201 ⏚ katherine.kynaston@telford.gov.uk

Local Area Agreement: Mr Jon Power, Organisational & Delivery Development Manager, Addenbrooke House, Ironmaster Way, Telford TF3 4NT ☎ 01952 380141 ⏚ jon.power@telford.gov.uk

Legal: Mr Jonathan Eatough, Assistant Director - Governance, Procurement & Commission, Addenbrooke House, Ironmasters Way, Telford TF3 4NT ☎ 01952 383200 ⏚ jonathon.eatough@telford.gov.uk

Licensing: Ms Nicky Minshall, Public Protection Service Delivery Manager, Darby House, 7th Floor, Wing A, Telford TF3 4LD ☎ 01952 381820 ⏚ nicky.minshall@telford.gov.uk

Lifelong Learning: Ms Sue Marston, Skills Manager, Addenbrooke House, Ironmasters Way, Telford TF3 4NT ☎ 01952 380897 ⏚ sue.marston@telford.gov.uk

Lighting: Ms Amanda Roberts, Highways Capital Programme Group Manager, Whitechapel House, Ground Floor, Telford TF2 9SP ☎ 01952 384659 ⏚ amanda.roberts@telford.gov.uk

Member Services: Ms Emma Price, PA to the Members, Civic Offices, Telford TF3 4LD ☎ 01952 380000 ⏚ emma.price@telford.gov.uk

Parking: Mr Adam Brookes, Development Control Officer, Civic Offices, Telford TF3 4LD ☎ 01952 380000 ⏚ adam.brookes@telford.gov.uk

Partnerships: Mr Jon Power, Organisational & Delivery Development Manager, Addenbrooke House, Ironmaster Way, Telford TF3 4NT ☎ 01952 380141 ⏚ jon.power@telford.gov.uk

Personnel / HR: Mr John Harris, People Services Manager, Addenbrooke House, Ironmasters Way, Telford TF3 4NT ☎ 01952 383520 ⏚ john.harris@telford.gov.uk

Planning: Mr David Fletcher, Development Management Manager, Wellington Civic & Leisure Centre, Wellington, Telford TF1 1LX ⏚ dave.fletcher@telford.gov.uk

Procurement: Ms Sarah Bass, Procurement & Broker Service Delivery Specialist, Wellington Civic & Leisure Centre, Wellington, Telford TF1 1LX ☎ 01952 382470 ⏚ sarah.bass@telford.gov.uk

Public Libraries: Mr Andrew Meredith, Service Delivery Manager - Customer & Registrars Services, Addenbrooke House, Ironmasters Way, Telford TF3 4NT ☎ 01952 382560 ⏚ andrew.meredith@telford.gov.uk

Recycling & Waste Minimisation: Mr Dave Hanley, Highways & Neighbourhood Management Manager, Granville House, St George's Road, Donnington Wood, Telford TF2 7RA
☎ 01952 384855 ◦⊕ dave.hanley@telford.gov.uk

Regeneration: Mr James Dunn, Regeneration & Investment Manager, Wellington Civic & Leisure Centre, Wellington, Telford TF1 1LX ☎ 01952 384591 ◦⊕ james.dunn@telford.gov.uk

Road Safety: Ms Amanda Roberts, Highways Capital Programme Group Manager, PO Box 212, Darby House, Lawn Central, Telford TF3 4LB ☎ 01952 384659 ◦⊕ amanda.roberts@telford.gov.uk

Social Services (Adult): Mr Richard Smith, Director - Health & Wellbeing, Addenbrooke House, Ironmasters Way, Telford TN3 4NT
☎ 01952 381011 ◦⊕ richard.smith@telford.gov.uk

Social Services (Children): Ms Jo Britton, Assistant Director - Children's Safeguarding, Civic Offices, Telford TF3 4LD
☎ 01952 380000 ◦⊕ jo.britton@telford.gov.uk

Public Health: Ms Liz Noakes, Assistant Director - Health & Wellbeing, Addenbrooke House, Ironmasters Way, Telford TF3 4NT
☎ 01952 383003 ◦⊕ liz.noakes@telford.gov.uk

Street Scene: Mr Dominic Proud, Service Delivery Manager - Transport & Highway Development, Civic Offices, Telford TF3 4LD
☎ 01952 380000 ◦⊕ dominic.proud@telford.gov.uk

Sustainable Communities: Ms Katherine Kynaston, Assistant Director - Development & Employment, PO Box 212, Darby House, Lawn Central, Telford TF3 4LB ☎ 01952 384201 ◦⊕ katherine.kynaston@telford.gov.uk

Sustainable Development: Ms Katherine Kynaston, Assistant Director - Development & Employment, PO Box 212, Darby House, Lawn Central, Telford TF3 4LB ☎ 01952 384201 ◦⊕ katherine.kynaston@telford.gov.uk

Town Centre: Mr James Dunn, Regeneration & Investment Manager, Wellington Civic & Leisure Centre, Wellington, Telford TF1 1LX ☎ 01952 384591 ◦⊕ james.dunn@telford.gov.uk

Transport: Mr Dominic Proud, Service Delivery Manager - Transport & Highway Development, Civic Offices, Telford TF3 4LD
☎ 01952 380000 ◦⊕ dominic.proud@telford.gov.uk

Transport Planner: Ms Viv McKay, Commissioning - Vulnerable People, Civic Offices, Telford TF3 4LD ☎ 01952 380000
◦⊕ vivianne.mckay2@telford.gov.uk

Waste Collection and Disposal: Mr Dave Hanley, Highways & Neighbourhood Management Manager, Granville House, St George's Road, Donnington Wood, Telford TF2 7RA
☎ 01952 384855 ◦⊕ dave.hanley@telford.gov.uk

Waste Management: Ms Debbie Germany, Strategic Waste & Neighbourhood Service Performance Delivery Manager, Granville House, St George's Road, Donnington Wood, Telford TF2 7RA
☎ 01952 384712 ◦⊕ debbie.germany@telford.gov.uk

COUNCILLORS

Leader of the Council: Davies, Shaun (LAB - Malinslee & Dawley Bank)
shaun.davies@telford.gov.uk

Deputy Leader of the Council: Overton, Richard (LAB - St Georges)
richard.overton@telford.gov.uk

Ashford, John (CON - Ketley & Overdale)
john.ashford@telford.gov.uk

Barnes, Steve (CON - Dawley & Aqueduct)
steve.barnes@telford.gov.uk

Bentley, Stephen (CON - Edgmond & Ercall Magna)
stephen.bentley@telford.gov.uk

Blundell, Karen (LD - Apley Castle)
karen.blundell@telford.gov.uk

Boylan, Mark (CON - Ketley & Overdale)
mark.boylan@telford.gov.uk

Burford, Andy (LAB - Dawley & Aqueduct)
andy.burford@telford.gov.uk

Burrell, Stephen (CON - Edgmond & Ercall Magna)
stephen.burrell@telford.gov.uk

Carter, Lee (LAB - College)
lee.carter@telford.gov.uk

Carter, Eric (CON - Newport South & East)
eric.carter@telford.gov.uk

Clare, Elizabeth (LAB - Donnington)
elizabeth.clare@telford.gov.uk

Cook, Graham (LAB - Haygate)
graham.cook@telford.gov.uk

Dugmore, Nigel (CON - Muxton)
nigel.dugmore@telford.gov.uk

Eade, Andrew (CON - Church Aston & Lilleshall)
andrew.eade@telford.gov.uk

England, Nathan (LAB - The Nedge)
nathan.england@telford.gov.uk

England, Arnold (LAB - Brookside)
arnold.england@telford.gov.uk

Evans, Rae (LAB - Woodside)
rae.evans@telford.gov.uk

Fletcher, Ian (CON - Priorslee)
ian.fletcher@telford.gov.uk

Fletcher, Veronica (CON - Priorslee)
veronica.fletcher@telford.gov.uk

Francis, Joy (CON - Ketley & Overdale)
joy.francis@telford.gov.uk

Furnival, Connor (IND - The Nedge)
connor.furnival@telford.gov.uk

Greenaway, Jayne (CON - Horsehay & Lightmoor)
jayne.greenaway@telford.gov.uk

Guy, Kevin (LAB - Woodside)
kevin.guy@telford.gov.uk

Hosken, Miles (CON - Ercall)
miles.hosken@telford.gov.uk

Jones, Janice (LAB - Madeley & Sutton Hill)
janice.jones@telford.gov.uk

TELFORD & WREKIN

Kiernan, Terry (CON - Admaston & Bratton)
terry.kiernan@telford.gov.uk

Lawrence, Adrian (CON - Muxton)
adrian.lawrence@telford.gov.uk

Loveridge, Jackie (LAB - Brookside)
jackie.loveridge@telford.gov.uk

Lowery, Nicola (CON - Ironbridge Gorge)
nicola.lowery@telford.gov.uk

Mason, Clive (LAB - Donnington)
clive.mason@telford.gov.uk

McClements, Angela (LAB - Arleston)
angela.mcclements@telford.gov.uk

Meredith, Adrian (CON - Newport South & East)
adrian.meredith@telford.gov.uk

Minor, John (LAB - St Georges)
john.minor@telford.gov.uk

Murray, Leon (LAB - Hadley & Leegomery)
leon.murray@telford.gov.uk

Nelson, Tim (CON - Newport North & West)
tim.nelson@telford.gov.uk

Pinter, Jane (LAB - Dawley & Aqueduct)
jane.pinter@telford.gov.uk

Reynolds, Gilly (LAB - Oakengates & Ketley Bank)
gilly.reynolds@telford.gov.uk

Reynolds, Stephen (LAB - Oakengates & Ketley Bank)
stephen.reynolds@telford.gov.uk

Reynolds, Shirley (LAB - Wrockwardine Wood & Trench)
shirley.reynolds@telford.gov.uk

Rhodes, Hilda (LAB - Oakengates & Ketley Bank)
hilda.rhodes@telford.gov.uk

Sahota, Kuldip Singh (LAB - Malinslee & Dawley Bank)
kuldip.sahota@telford.gov.uk

Scott, Peter (IND - Newport North & West)
peter.scott@telford.gov.uk

Seymour, Jacqui (CON - Wrockwardine)
jacqui.seymour@telford.gov.uk

Sloan, Robert (LAB - Hadley & Leegomery)
rob.sloan@telford.gov.uk

Smith, Malcolm (LAB - Hadley & Leegomery)
malcolm.smith@telford.gov.uk

Smith, Charles (LAB - Wrockwardine Wood & Trench)
charles.smith@telford.gov.uk

Tillotson, Barry (CON - Park)
barry.tillotson@telford.gov.uk

Tomlinson, Karen (LD - Dothill)
karen.tomlinson@telford.gov.uk

Tomlinson, Bill (LD - Shawbirch)
bill.tomlinson@telford.gov.uk

Turley, Chris (LAB - The Nedge)
chris.turley@telford.gov.uk

Watling, Paul (LAB - Madeley & Sutton Hill)
paul.watling@telford.gov.uk

Wright, David (CON - Madeley & Sutton Hill)
dave.wright@telford.gov.uk

POLITICAL COMPOSITION
LAB: 27, CON: 21, LD: 3, IND: 2, Vacant: 1

COMMITTEE CHAIRS

Audit: Mr Robert Sloan

Children & Young People: Mr Kevin Guy

Health & Adult Care: Mr Andy Burford

Health & Wellbeing: Mr Richard Overton

Licensing: Mr Clive Mason

Planning: Mr John Minor

Tendring   D

Tendring District Council, Town Hall, Station Road, Clacton-on-Sea CO15 1SE
☎ 01255 686868 🖳 www.tendringdc.gov.uk

FACTS AND FIGURES
Parliamentary Constituencies: Clacton, Harwich and Essex North
EU Constituencies: Eastern
Election Frequency: Elections are of whole council

PRINCIPAL OFFICERS

Chief Executive: Mr Ian Davidson, Chief Executive, Town Hall, Station Road, Clacton-on-Sea CO15 1SE ☎ 01255 686007 ✐ idavidson@tendringdc.gov.uk

Senior Management: Mr Martyn Knappett, Head of Corporate Services, Town Hall, Station Road, Clacton-on-Sea CO15 1SE ☎ 01255 686501 ✐ mknappett@tendringdc.gov.uk

Senior Management: Mr Paul Price, Head of Operational Services, Town Hall, Station Road, Clacton-on-Sea CO15 1SE ☎ 01255 686430 ✐ pprice@tendringdc.gov.uk

Building Control: Mr Alan Corbyn, Building Control Manager, Council Offices, Thorpe Road, Weeley, Clacton-on-Sea CO16 9AJ ☎ 01255 686160 ✐ acorbyn@tendringdc.gov.uk

PR / Communications: Mr Nigel Brown, Communications Manager, Town Hall, Station Road, Clacton-on-Sea CO15 1SE ☎ 01255 686338 ✐ nbrown@tendringdc.gov.uk

Community Safety: Mrs Leanne Thornton, Community Safety Manager, Town Hall, Station Road, Clacton-on-Sea CO15 1SE ☎ 01225 686353 ✐ lthornton@tendringdc.gov.uk

Contracts: Mr Ian Taylor, Head of Public Realm, Northbourne Depot, Vista Road, Clacton-on-Sea CO15 6AY ☎ 01255 686982 ✐ itaylor@tendring.gov.uk

Corporate Services: Mr Martyn Knappett, Head of Corporate Services, Town Hall, Station Road, Clacton-on-Sea CO15 1SE ☎ 01255 686501 ✐ mknappett@tendringdc.gov.uk

Customer Service: Mrs Anastasia Simpson, Head of People, Performance & Projects, Town Hall, Station Road, Clacton-on-Sea CO15 1SE ☎ 01255 686324 ✐ asimpson@tendringdc.gov.uk

E-Government: Miss Karen Neath, Management & Members' Support Manager, Town Hall, Station Road, Clacton-on-Sea CO15 1SE ☎ 01255 686520 ◌ kneath@tendringdc.gov.uk

Electoral Registration: Mrs Alison Rowlands, Elections Operations Manager, Town Hall, Station Road, Clacton-on-Sea CO16 1SE ☎ 01255 686586 ◌ arowlands@tendringdc.gov.uk

Emergency Planning: Mr Damian Williams, Head of Building & Engineering Services, Town Hall, Station Road, Clacton-on-Sea CO15 1SE ☎ 01255 686319 ◌ dwilliams@tendringdc.gov.uk

Estates, Property & Valuation: Mr Andrew White, Head of Property Services, Town Hall, Station Road, Clacton-on-Sea CO15 1SE ☎ 01255 686933 ◌ awhite@tendringdc.gov.uk

Events Manager: Mr Michael Carran, Head of Sports & Leisure, Town Hall, Station Road, Clacton-on-Sea CO15 1SE ☎ 01255 686689 ◌ mcarran@tendringdc.gov.uk

Facilities: Mr Damian Williams, Head of Building & Engineering Services, Town Hall, Station Road, Clacton-on-Sea CO15 1SE ☎ 01255 686319 ◌ dwilliams@tendringdc.gov.uk

Finance: Mr Richard Barrett, Head of Finance, Revenues & Benefits Services, Town Hall, Station Road, Clacton-on-Sea CO16 9RG ☎ 01255 686521 ◌ rbarrett@tendring.gov.uk

Fleet Management: Mr Trevor Mills, Open Space & Transport Manager, Northbourne Depot, Vista Road, Clacton-on-Sea CO15 6AY ☎ 01255 686643 ◌ tmills@tendringdc.gov.uk

Grounds Maintenance: Mr Trevor Mills, Open Space & Transport Manager, Northbourne Depot, Vista Road, Clacton-on-Sea CO15 6AY ☎ 01255 686643 ◌ tmills@tendringdc.gov.uk

Health and Safety: Mr John Fox, Head of Environmental Services, Council Offices, Thorpe Road, Weeley, Clacton-on-Sea CO16 9AJ ☎ 01255 686746 ◌ jfox@tendringdc.gov.uk

Highways: Mr Mike Badger, Head of Coastal Protection, Town Hall, Station Road, Clacton-on-Sea CO15 1SE ☎ 01255 686975 ◌ mbadger@tendringdc.gov.uk

Housing: Mr Paul Price, Head of Operational Services, Town Hall, Station Road, Clacton-on-Sea CO15 1SE ☎ 01255 686430 ◌ pprice@tendringdc.gov.uk

Housing Maintenance: Mr Damian Williams, Head of Building & Engineering Services, Town Hall, Station Road, Clacton-on-Sea CO15 1SE ☎ 01255 686319 ◌ dwilliams@tendringdc.gov.uk

Legal: Ms Lisa Hastings, Head of Governance & Legal Services, Town Hall, Station Road, Clacton-on-Sea CO15 1SE ☎ 01255 868561 ◌ lhastings@tendringdc.gov.uk

Leisure and Cultural Services: Mr Michael Carran, Head of Sports & Leisure, Town Hall, Station Road, Clacton-on-Sea CO15 1SE ☎ 01255 686689 ◌ mcarran@tendringdc.gov.uk

Licensing: Mr Ian Taylor, Head of Public Realm, Northbourne Depot, Vista Road, Clacton-on-Sea CO15 6AY ☎ 01255 686982 ◌ itaylor@tendring.gov.uk

Lighting: Mr Mike Badger, Head of Coastal Protection, Town Hall, Station Road, Clacton-on-Sea CO15 1SE ☎ 01255 686975 ◌ mbadger@tendringdc.gov.uk

Member Services: Miss Ashley Wood, Management & Members' Support Officer, Town Hall, Station Road, Clacton-on-Sea CO15 1SE ☎ 01255 686583 ◌ awood@tendringdc.gov.uk

Parking: Mr Ian Taylor, Head of Public Realm, Northbourne Depot, Vista Road, Clacton-on-Sea CO15 6AY ☎ 01255 686982 ◌ itaylor@tendring.gov.uk

Personnel / HR: Mrs Anastasia Simpson, Head of People, Performance & Projects, Town Hall, Station Road, Clacton-on-Sea CO15 1SE ☎ 01255 686324 ◌ asimpson@tendringdc.gov.uk

Planning: Mrs Catherine Bicknell, Head of Planning, Council Offices, Thorpe Road, Weeley, Clacton-on-Sea CO16 9AJ ☎ 01255 686101 ◌ cbicknell@tendringdc.gov.uk

Procurement: Mrs Jane Taylor, Procurement Officer, Town Hall, Station Road, Clacton-on-Sea CO15 1SE ☎ 01255 686955 ◌ jtaylor@tendringdc.gov.uk

Regeneration: Mr Tom Gardiner, Head of Regeneration, Town Hall, Station Road, Clacton-on-Sea CO15 1SE ☎ 01255 686102 ◌ tgardiner@tendringdc.gov.uk

Street Scene: Mr Mike Badger, Head of Coastal Protection, Town Hall, Station Road, Clacton-on-Sea CO15 1SE ☎ 01255 686975 ◌ mbadger@tendringdc.gov.uk

Tourism: Mr Michael Carran, Head of Sports & Leisure, Town Hall, Station Road, Clacton-on-Sea CO15 1SE ☎ 01255 686689 ◌ mcarran@tendringdc.gov.uk

Town Centre: Mrs Rachel Fryer, Town Centre Co-ordinator, Council Offices, Thorpe Road, Weeley, Clacton-on-Sea CO16 9AJ ☎ 01255 686149 ◌ rfryer@tendringdc.gov.uk

Total Place: Mr Martyn Knappett, Head of Corporate Services, Town Hall, Station Road, Clacton-on-Sea CO15 1SE ☎ 01255 686501 ◌ mknappett@tendringdc.gov.uk

Children's Play Areas: Mr Ian Taylor, Head of Public Realm, Northbourne Depot, Vista Road, Clacton-on-Sea CO15 6AY ☎ 01255 686982 ◌ itaylor@tendring.gov.uk

COUNCILLORS

Chair: Chapman, Jayne (IND - Brightlingsea) cllr.jchapman@tendringdc.gov.uk

Vice-Chair: Platt, Mark (CON - Hamford) cllr.mplatt@tendringdc.gov.uk

Leader of the Council: Stock, Neil (CON - Ardleigh & Little Bromley) cllr.nstock@tendringdc.gov.uk

TENDRING

Deputy Leader of the Council: Guglielmi, Giancarlo (CON - Manningtree, Mistley, Little Bentley & Tendring)
cllr.gguglielmi@tendringdc.gov.uk

Amos, Chris (CON - St. John's)
cllr.camos@tendringdc.gov.uk

Baker, Andy (CON - Lawford)
cllr.abaker@tendringdc.gov.uk

Bennison, Lisbeth (UKIP - Peter Bruff)
cllr.lbennison@tendringdc.gov.uk

Bray, Jeffrey (UKIP - Little Clacton & Weeley)
cllr.jbray@tendringdc.gov.uk

Broderick, Joy (R - Haven)
cllr.jbroderick@tendringdc.gov.uk

Brown, John (UKIP - Harwich West)
cllr.jabrown@tendringdc.gov.uk

Brown, Barry (CON - Harwich East Central)
cllr.bbrown@tendringdc.gov.uk

Brown, Mike (CON - Little Clacton & Weeley)
cllr.mbrown@tendringdc.gov.uk

Bucke, Robert (INDNA - Holland & Kirby)
cllr.rbucke@tendringdc.gov.uk

Callender, Ricky (CON - Harwich West)
cllr.rcallender@tendringdc.gov.uk

Calver, Garry (LAB - Harwich East Central)
cllr.gcalver@tendringdc.gov.uk

Cawthorn, Peter (UKIP - Alton Park)
cllr.pcawthorn@tendringdc.gov.uk

Chittock, John (UKIP - Bockings Elm)
cllr.jchittock@tendringdc.gov.uk

Coley, Alan (CON - Manningtree, Mistley, Little Bentley & Tendring)
cllr.acoley@tendringdc.gov.uk

Cossens, Mark (CON - Holland & Kirby)
cllr.mcossens@tendringdc.gov.uk

Davis, Anne (UKIP - Hamford)
cllr.adavis@tendringdc.gov.uk

Everett, Richard (UKIP - Rush Green)
cllr.reverett@tendringdc.gov.uk

Fairley, Zoe (CON - Bradfield, Wrabness & Wix)
cllr.zfairley@tendringdc.gov.uk

Ferguson, Tanya (CON - Ramsey & Parkeston)
cllr.tferguson@tendringdc.gov.uk

Fowler, Maria (LAB - Harwich West Central)
cllr.mfowler@tendringdc.gov.uk

Gray, Laurie (UKIP - Homelands)
cllr.lagray@tendringdc.gov.uk

Griffiths, Christopher (CON - St. James)
cllr.cgriffiths@tendringdc.gov.uk

Guglielmi, Valerie (CON - Lawford)
cllr.vguglielmi@tendringdc.gov.uk

Heaney, Rosemary (CON - Thorrington, Frating, Elmstead & Great Bromley)
cllr.rheaney@tendringdc.gov.uk

Henderson, Ivan (LAB - Harwich East)
cllr.ihenderson@tendringdc.gov.uk

Henderson, Jo (LAB - Harwich West Central)
cllr.jhenderson@tendringdc.gov.uk

Hones, John (UKIP - St. Mary's)
cllr.jhones@tendringdc.gov.uk

Honeywood, Paul (CON - Pier)
cllr.phoneywood@tendringdc.gov.uk

Howard, Tom (IND - Great & Little Oakley)
cllr.thoward@tendringdc.gov.uk

Hughes, John (UKIP - St. James)
cllr.jhughes@tendringdc.gov.uk

Khan, Mohammed (UKIP - Pier)
cllr.mkhan@tendringdc.gov.uk

King, Kanagasundaram (R - St. Bartholomew's)
cllr.kking@tendringdc.gov.uk

Land, Daniel (CON - Beaumont & Thorpe)
cllr.dland@tendringdc.gov.uk

Massey, Andy (CON - St. Paul's)
cllr.amassey@tendringdc.gov.uk

McWilliams, Lynda (CON - Great Bentley)
cllr.lmcwilliams@tendringdc.gov.uk

Miles, Delyth (CON - Walton)
cll.dmiles@tendringdc.gov.uk

Newton, Mary (UKIP - Rush Green)
cllr.mnewton@tendringdc.gov.uk

Nicholls, Fred (CON - Thorrington, Frating, Elmstead & Great Bromley)
cllr.fnicholls@tendringdc.gov.uk

Parsons, Jack (UKIP - Not Specified)
cllr.jparsons@tendringdc.gov.uk

Pemberton, Andrew (UKIP - Peter Bruff)
cllr.apemberton@tendringdc.gov.uk

Poonian, Anne (UKIP - Walton)
cllr.apoonian@tendringdc.gov.uk

Porter, Alex (UKIP - Alton Park)
cllr.aporter@tendringdc.gov.uk

Raby, Roy (UKIP - Golf Green)
cllr.rraby@tendringdc.gov.uk

Scott, Gary (LD - Alresford)
cllr.gscott@tendringdc.gov.uk

Skeels, Mick (UKIP - Burrsville)
cllr.mjskeels@tendringdc.gov.uk

Skeels, Michael (UKIP - St. John's)
cllr.mskeels@tendringdc.gov.uk

Steady, Graham (IND - Brightlingsea)
cllr.gsteady@tendringdc.gov.uk

Stephenson, Mark (UKIP - St. Mary's)
cllr.mstephenson@tendringdc.gov.uk

Talbot, Michael (IND - St. Osyth & Point Clear)
cllr.mtalbot@tendringdc.gov.uk

Turner, Nicholas (CON - Frinton)
cllr.nturner@tendringdc.gov.uk

Watling, Giles (CON - Frinton)
cllr.gwatling@tendringdc.gov.uk

Watson, Kevin (UKIP - Golf Green)
cllr.kwatson@tendringdc.gov.uk

White, John (IND - St. Osyth & Point Clear)
cllr.jwhite@tendringdc.gov.uk

Whitmore, Edward (UKIP - Bockings Elm)
cllr.twhitmore@tendringdc.gov.uk

Winfield, Colin (R - St. Bartholomew's)
cllr.cwinfield@tendringdc.gov.uk

Yallop, Karen (IND - Brightlingsea)
cllr.kyallop@tendringdc.gov.uk

POLITICAL COMPOSITION
CON: 23, UKIP: 22, IND: 6, LAB: 4, R: 3, LD: 1, INDNA: 1

COMMITTEE CHAIRS

Audit: Mr Alan Coley

Licensing: Mr Mark Cossens

Planning: Mr John White

Test Valley   D

Test Valley Borough Council, Beech Hurst, Weyhill Road, Andover SP10 3AJ
☎ 01264 368000 ▭ www.testvalley.gov.uk

FACTS AND FIGURES
Parliamentary Constituencies: Hampshire North West, Romsey and Southampton North
EU Constituencies: South East
Election Frequency: Elections are of whole council

PRINCIPAL OFFICERS

Chief Executive: Mr Roger Tetstall, Chief Executive, Beech Hurst, Weyhill Road, Andover SP10 3AJ ☎ 01264 368000
⌁ rtetstall@testvalley.gov.uk

Senior Management: Mr Andrew Ferrier, Corporate Director, Beech Hurst, Weyhill Road, Andover SP10 3AJ ☎ 01264 368000
⌁ aferrier@testvalley.gov.uk

Senior Management: Mrs Carol Moore, Corporate Director, Beech Hurst, Weyhill Road, Andover SP10 3AJ ☎ 01264 368000
⌁ cmoore@testvalley.gov.uk

Architect, Building / Property Services: Mr Stuart Bacon, Principal Building Surveyor, Beech Hurst, Weyhill Road, Andover SP10 3AJ ☎ 01264 368000 ⌁ sbacon@testvalley.gov.uk

Building Control: Mr Graham Murrell, Building Control Manager, Beech Hurst, Weyhill Road, Andover SP10 3AJ ☎ 01264 368000
⌁ gmurrell@testvalley.gov.uk

PR / Communications: Mrs Kathryn Binfield, Communications Manager, Beech Hurst, Weyhill Road, Andover SP10 3AJ
☎ 01264 368000 ⌁ kbinfield@testvalley.gov.uk

Community Planning: Mr Andrew Ferrier, Corporate Director, Beech Hurst, Weyhill Road, Andover SP10 3AJ ☎ 01264 368000
⌁ aferrier@testvalley.gov.uk

Community Safety: Ms Verna Brown, Communities Manager, Beech Hurst, Weyhill Road, Andover SP10 3AJ ☎ 01264 368606
⌁ vbrown@testvalley.gov.uk

Computer Management: Mr Tony Fawcett, Head of IT Services, Beech Hurst, Weyhill Road, Andover SP10 3AJ ☎ 01962 848262; 01264 368901 ⌁ tfawcett@winchester.gov.uk; tfacwett@testvalley.gov.uk

Corporate Services: Mrs Carol Moore, Corporate Director, Beech Hurst, Weyhill Road, Andover SP10 3AJ ☎ 01264 368000
⌁ cmoore@testvalley.gov.uk

Customer Service: Mrs Paula Staff, Customer Relationship Manager, Beech Hurst, Weyhill Road, Andover SP10 3AJ
☎ 01264 368938 ⌁ pstaff@testvalley.gov.uk

Economic Development: Mr David Gleave, Economic Development Officer, Beech Hurst, Weyhill Road, Andover SP10 3AJ ☎ 01264 368309 ⌁ dgleave@testvalley.gov.uk

E-Government: Mr Tony Fawcett, Head of IT Services, Beech Hurst, Weyhill Road, Andover SP10 3AJ ☎ 01264 368901
⌁ tfawcett@testvalley.gov.uk

Electoral Registration: Mrs Francis Cleland, Electoral Services Manager, Beech Hurst, Weyhill Road, Andover SP10 3AJ
☎ 01264 368000 ⌁ fcleland@testvalley.gov.uk

Emergency Planning: Mr Michael White, Licensing Manager, Beech Hurst, Weyhill Road, Andover SP10 3AJ ☎ 01264 368000
⌁ mwhite@testvalley.gov.uk

Environmental / Technical Services: Mr Paul Wykes, Head of Environmental Services, Portway Depot, Macadam Way, West Portway, Andover SP10 3XW ☎ 01264 368000
⌁ pwykes@testvalley.gov.uk

Environmental Health: Mr Brian Cowcher, Head of Housing & Environmental Health Services, Beech Hurst, Weyhill Road, Andover SP10 3AJ ☎ 01264 368601 ⌁ bcowcher@testvalley.gov.uk

Environmental Health: Ms Carol Ruddle, Environmental Health Manager, Beech Hurst, Weyhill Road, Andover SP10 3AJ
☎ 01264 368000 ⌁ cruddle@testvalley.gov.uk

Estates, Property & Valuation: Mr Simon Ellis, Head of Estates & Economic Development Services, Beech Hurst, Weyhill Road, Andover SP10 3AJ ☎ 01264 368301 ⌁ sellis@testvalley.gov.uk

Facilities: Mr Stuart Bacon, Principal Building Surveyor, Beech Hurst, Weyhill Road, Andover SP10 3AJ ☎ 01264 368000
⌁ sbacon@testvalley.gov.uk

Finance: Mr William Fullbrook, Head of Finance, Beech Hurst, Weyhill Road, Andover SP10 3AJ ☎ 01264 368201
⌁ wfullbrook@testvalley.gov.uk

Grounds Maintenance: Mr Paul Wykes, Head of Environmental Services, Portway Depot, Macadam Way, West Portway, Andover SP10 3XW ☎ 01264 368000 ⌁ pwykes@testvalley.gov.uk

TEST VALLEY

Health and Safety: Ms Carol Ruddle, Environmental Health Manager, Beech Hurst, Weyhill Road, Andover SP10 3AJ
☎ 01264 368000 ✆ cruddle@testvalley.gov.uk

Housing: Mr Brian Cowcher, Head of Housing & Environmental Health Services, Beech Hurst, Weyhill Road, Andover SP10 3AJ
☎ 01264 368601 ✆ bcowcher@testvalley.gov.uk

Legal: Mr Bill Lynds, Head of Legal & Democratic Services, Beech Hurst, Weyhill Road, Andover SP10 3AJ ☎ 01264 368000
✆ wlynds@testvalley.gov.uk

Leisure and Cultural Services: Mr David Tasker, Head of Community & Leisure Services, Beech Hurst, Weyhill Road, Andover SP10 3AJ ☎ 01264 368801 ✆ dtasker@testvalley.gov.uk

Licensing: Mr Michael White, Licensing Manager, Beech Hurst, Weyhill Road, Andover SP10 3AJ ☎ 01264 368000
✆ mwhite@testvalley.gov.uk

Member Services: Mrs Emma Horbury, Democratic Services Manager, Beech Hurst, Weyhill Road, Andover SP10 3AJ
☎ 01264 368000 ✆ ehorbury@testvalley.gov.uk

Parking: Mr Steve Raw, Engineering & Transport Manager, Beech Hurst, Weyhill Road, Andover SP10 3AJ ☎ 01264 368000
✆ sraw@testvalley.gov.uk

Personnel / HR: Ms Alexandra Rowland, HR Manager, Beech Hurst, Weyhill Road, Andover SP10 3AJ ☎ 01264 368251
✆ arowland@testvalley.gov.uk

Planning: Mr Paul Jackson, Head of Planning & Building Services, Beech Hurst, Weyhill Road, Andover SP10 3AJ ☎ 01264 368000
✆ pjackson@testvalley.gov.uk

Procurement: Mr David Owers, Procurement Officer, Beech Hurst, Weyhill Road, Andover SP10 3AJ ☎ 01264 368000
✆ dowers@testvalley.gov.uk

Recycling & Waste Minimisation: Mr Paul Wykes, Head of Environmental Services, Portway Depot, Macadam Way, West Portway, Andover SP10 3XW ☎ 01264 368000
✆ pwykes@testvalley.gov.uk

Regeneration: Mr Simon Ellis, Head of Estates & Economic Development Services, Beech Hurst, Weyhill Road, Andover SP10 3AJ ☎ 01264 368301 ✆ sellis@testvalley.gov.uk

Staff Training: Mrs Penny Billingham, HR Adviser, Beech Hurst, Weyhill Road, Andover SP10 3AJ ☎ 01264 368000
✆ pbillingham@testvalley.gov.uk

Street Scene: Mr Vince Taylor, Street Scene Manager, Portway Depot, Macadam Way, West Portway, Andover SP10 3XW
☎ 01264 368000 ✆ vtaylor@testvalley.gov.uk

Tourism: Mr David Gleave, Economic Development Officer, Beech Hurst, Weyhill Road, Andover SP10 3AJ ☎ 01264 368309
✆ dgleave@testvalley.gov.uk

Town Centre: Mr Chris Gregory, Town Centre Manager, Beech Hurst, Weyhill Road, Andover SP10 3AJ ☎ 07854 027080
✆ chris@heartflood.co.uk

Traffic Management: Mr Steve Raw, Engineering & Transport Manager, Beech Hurst, Weyhill Road, Andover SP10 3AJ
☎ 01264 368000 ✆ sraw@testvalley.gov.uk

Transport Planner: Ms Vivien Messenger, Transport Planner, Beech Hurst, Weyhill Road, Andover SP10 3AJ ☎ 01264 368000
✆ vmessenger@testvalley.gov.uk

Transport Planner: Mrs Anne Tomlinson, Transport Planner, Beech, Weyhill Road, Andover SP10 3AJ ☎ 01264 368000
✆ atomlinson@testvalley.gov.uk

Waste Collection and Disposal: Mr Paul Wykes, Head of Environmental Services, Portway Depot, Macadam Way, West Portway, Andover SP10 3XW ☎ 01264 368000
✆ pwykes@testvalley.gov.uk

Waste Management: Mr Paul Wykes, Head of Environmental Services, Portway Depot, Macadam Way, West Portway, Andover SP10 3XW ☎ 01264 368000 ✆ pwykes@testvalley.gov.uk

COUNCILLORS

Mayor: Hamilton, Karen (CON - Andover - Harroway)
cllrkhamilton@testvalley.gov.uk

Deputy Mayor: Borg-Neal, Carl (CON - Andover - Harroway)
cllrcborg-neal@testvalley.gov.uk

Leader of the Council: Carr, Ian (CON - Charlton)
cllricarr@testvalley.gov.uk

Deputy Leader of the Council: Hatley, Martin (CON - Ampfield & Braishfield)
cllrmhatley@testvalley.gov.uk

Adams-King, Nick (CON - Blackwater)
cllrmadams-king@testvalley.gov.uk

Anderdon, Nigel (CON - Chilworth, Nursling & Rownhams)
cllrnanderdon@testvalley.gov.uk

Andersen, Iris (CON - Andover - St Mary's)
cllriandersen@testvalley.gov.uk

Bailey, Gordon (CON - Blackwater)
cllrgbailey@testvalley.gov.uk

Baverstock, Dorothy (LD - Romsey - Cupernham)
cllrdbaverstock@testvalley.gov.uk

Beesley, Andrew (LD - Valley Park)
cllrabeesley@testvalley.gov.uk

Boulton, Peter (CON - Broughton & Stockbridge)
cllrpboulton@testvalley.gov.uk

Brook, Alexander (CON - Andover - Alamein)
CllrABrook@testvalley.gov.uk

Brookes, Zilliah (CON - Andover - Millway)
cllrzbrooks@testvalley.gov.uk

Budzynski, Jan (CON - Andover - Winton)
cllrjbudzynski@testvalley.gov.uk

Bundy, Philip (CON - Chilworth, Nursling & Rownhams)
cllrpbundy@testvalley.gov.uk

Busk, Daniel (CON - Broughton & Stockbridge)
cllrdbusk@testvalley.gov.uk

Cockaday, John (CON - Andover - St. Mary's)
cllrjcockaday@testvalley.gov.uk

Collier, Clive (CON - Romsey - Abbey)
cllrccollier@testvalley.gov.uk

Cooper, Mark (LD - Romsey - Tadburn)
cllrmcooper@testvalley.gov.uk

Cosier, Stephen (LD - North Baddesley)
cllrscosier@testvalley.gov.uk

Denny, David (CON - Andover - St. Mary's)
cllrddenny@testvalley.gov.uk

Dowden, Alan (LD - Valley Park)
cllradowden@testvalley.gov.uk

Dowden, Celia (LD - North Baddesley)
cllrcdowden@testvalley.gov.uk

Drew, David (CON - Harewood)
cllrddrew@testvalley.gov.uk

Few Brown, Benjamin (IND - Amport)
cllrbfewbrown@testvalley.gov.uk

Finlay, Alison (CON - Chilworth, Nursling & Rownhams)
cllrafinlay@testvalley.gov.uk

Flood, Maureen (CON - Anna)
cllrmflood@testvalley.gov.uk

Giddings, Peter (CON - Bourne Valley)
cllrpgiddings@testvalley.gov.uk

Hawke, Sandra (CON - Andover - Millway)
cllrshawke@testvalley.gov.uk

Hibberd, Ian (CON - Romsey Extra)
cllrihibberd@testvalley.gov.uk

Hope, Anthony (CON - Over Wallop)
cllrahope@testvalley.gov.uk

Hurst, Peter (LD - Romsey - Tadburn)
cllrphurst@testvalley.gov.uk

Jeffrey, Ian (CON - Dun Valley)

Johnston, Alison (CON - Romsey Extra)
cllrajohnston@testvalley.gov.uk

Lashbrook, Philip (CON - Penton Bellinger)
cllrplashbrook@testvalley.gov.uk

Lovell, Jan (CON - Andover - Winton)
cllrjlovell@testvalley.gov.uk

Lynn, Christopher (CON - Andover - Winton)
cllrclynn@testvalley.gov.uk

Mutton, Pam (CON - Penton Bellinger)
cllrpmutton@testvalley.gov.uk

Neal, James (CON - Andover - Millway)
cllrjneal@testvalley.gov.uk

North, Phil (CON - Andover - Alamein)
cllrpnorth@testvalley.gov.uk

Page, Brian (CON - Andover - Harroway)
cllrbpage@testvalley.gov.uk

Preston, Tracey (CON - Andover - Alamein)
cllrtpreston@testvalley.gov.uk

Ray, John (CON - Romsey - Cupernham)

Richards, Ian (CON - Romsey - Abbey)
cllririchards@testvalley.gov.uk

Stallard, Graham (CON - Anna)
cllrgstallard@testvalley.gov.uk

Tilling, Katherine (LD - Valley Park)
cllrktilling@testvalley.gov.uk

Tupper, Ann (LD - North Baddesley)
cllratupper@testvalley.gov.uk

Ward, Anthony (CON - King's Somborne & Michelmersh)
cllrtward@testvalley.gov.uk

POLITICAL COMPOSITION
CON: 38, LD: 9, IND: 1

COMMITTEE CHAIRS
Licensing: Mr Jan Budzynski

Planning: Mr Clive Collier

Tewkesbury   D

Tewkesbury Borough Council, Council Offices, Gloucester Road, Tewkesbury GL20 5TT
☎ 01684 295010 🖷 01684 272040
🖰 democraticservices@tewkesbury.gov.uk 🖳 www.tewkesbury.gov.uk

FACTS AND FIGURES
Parliamentary Constituencies: Tewkesbury
EU Constituencies: South West
Election Frequency: Elections are of whole council

PRINCIPAL OFFICERS

Chief Executive: Mr Mike Dawson, Chief Executive, Council Offices, Gloucester Road, Tewkesbury GL20 5TT ☎ 01684 272001
🖰 chiefexecutive@tewkesbury.gov.uk

Deputy Chief Executive: Ms Rachel North, Deputy Chief Executive, Council Offices, Gloucester Road, Tewkesbury GL20 5TT
🖰 rachel.north@tewkesbury.gov.uk

Senior Management: Ms Sara Freckleton, Borough Solicitor & Monitoring Officer, Council Offices, Gloucester Road, Tewkesbury GL20 5TT ☎ 01684 272010 🖰 sara.freckleton@tewkesbury.gov.uk

Best Value: Mr Graeme Simpson, Corporate Services Group Manager, Council Offices, Gloucester Road, Tewkesbury GL20 5TT
☎ 01684 272002 🖰 graeme.simpson@tewkesbury.gov.uk

Building Control: Mr Iain Houston, Building Control Manager, Municipal Offices, The Promenade, Cheltenham GL50 9SA
☎ 01242 264293 🖰 iain.houston@cheltenham.gov.uk

Children / Youth Services: Mr Andy Sanders, Economic & Community Development Manager, Council Offices, Gloucester Road, Tewkesbury GL20 5TT ☎ 01684 272094
🖰 andy.sanders@tewkesbury.gov.uk

PR / Communications: Ms Clare Davies, Communications & Policy Manager, Council Offices, Gloucester Road, Tewkesbury GL20 5TT ☎ 01684 272291 🖰 clare.davies@tewkesbury.gov.uk

TEWKESBURY

Community Planning: Mrs Julie Wood, Development Services Group Manager, Council Offices, Gloucester Road, Tewkesbury GL20 5TT ☎ 01684 272095 ⌂ julie.wood@tewkesbury.gov.uk

Community Safety: Mr Richard Kirk, Interim Environmental & Housing Services Group Manager, Council Offices, Gloucester Road, Tewkesbury GL20 5TT ☎ 01684 272259 ⌂ richard.kirk@tewkesbury.gov.uk

Computer Management: Mr Graeme Simpson, Corporate Services Group Manager, Council Offices, Gloucester Road, Tewkesbury GL20 5TT ☎ 01684 272002 ⌂ graeme.simpson@tewkesbury.gov.uk

Contracts: Mrs Shirin Wotherspoon, Principal Solicitor (Commercial), Tewkesbury Borough Council, Council Offices, Gloucester Road, Tewkesbury GL20 5TT ☎ 01684 272017 ⌂ shirin.wotherspoon@tewkesbury.gov.uk

Corporate Services: Mr Graeme Simpson, Corporate Services Group Manager, Council Offices, Gloucester Road, Tewkesbury GL20 5TT ☎ 01684 272002 ⌂ graeme.simpson@tewkesbury.gov.uk

Customer Service: Mr Graeme Simpson, Corporate Services Group Manager, Council Offices, Gloucester Road, Tewkesbury GL20 5TT ☎ 01684 272002 ⌂ graeme.simpson@tewkesbury.gov.uk

Economic Development: Mrs Julie Wood, Development Services Group Manager, Council Offices, Gloucester Road, Tewkesbury GL20 5TT ☎ 01684 272095 ⌂ julie.wood@tewkesbury.gov.uk

E-Government: Mr Graeme Simpson, Corporate Services Group Manager, Council Offices, Gloucester Road, Tewkesbury GL20 5TT ☎ 01684 272002 ⌂ graeme.simpson@tewkesbury.gov.uk

Electoral Registration: Mrs Lin O'Brien, Democratic Group Services Manager, Council Offices, Gloucester Road, Tewkesbury GL20 5TT ☎ 01684 272020 ⌂ lin.o'brien@tewkesbury.gov.uk

Emergency Planning: Mr Richard Kirk, Interim Environmental & Housing Services Group Manager, Council Offices, Gloucester Road, Tewkesbury GL20 5TT ☎ 01684 272259 ⌂ richard.kirk@tewkesbury.gov.uk

Environmental Health: Mr David Steels, Environmental Health Manager, Council Offices, Gloucester Road, Tewkesbury GL20 5TT ☎ 01684 272172 ⌂ david.steels@tewkesbury.gov.uk

Estates, Property & Valuation: Mr Andy Noble, Asset Manager, Council Offices, Gloucester Road, Tewkesbury GL20 5TT ☎ 01684 272023 ⌂ andy.noble@tewkesbury.gov.uk

Facilities: Mr Andy Noble, Asset Manager, Council Offices, Gloucester Road, Tewkesbury GL20 5TT ☎ 01684 272023 ⌂ andy.noble@tewkesbury.gov.uk

Finance: Mr Simon Dix, Finance & Asset Management Group Manager, Council Offices, Gloucester Road, Tewkesbury GL20 5TT ☎ 01684 272005 ⌂ simon.dix@tewkesbury.gov.uk

Health and Safety: Mr Richard Kirk, Interim Environmental & Housing Services Group Manager, Council Offices, Gloucester Road, Tewkesbury GL20 5TT ☎ 01684 272259 ⌂ richard.kirk@tewkesbury.gov.uk

Housing: Mr Richard Kirk, Interim Environmental & Housing Services Group Manager, Council Offices, Gloucester Road, Tewkesbury GL20 5TT ☎ 01684 272259 ⌂ richard.kirk@tewkesbury.gov.uk

Legal: Mr Peter Lewis, Head of Legal Services, Council Offices, Gloucester Road, Tewkesbury GL20 5TT ☎ 01684 272012 ⌂ peter.lewis@tewkesbury.gov.uk

Leisure and Cultural Services: Mr Andy Sanders, Economic & Community Development Manager, Council Offices, Gloucester Road, Tewkesbury GL20 5TT ☎ 01684 272094 ⌂ andy.sanders@tewkesbury.gov.uk

Licensing: Mr Richard Kirk, Interim Environmental & Housing Services Group Manager, Council Offices, Gloucester Road, Tewkesbury GL20 5TT ☎ 01684 272259 ⌂ richard.kirk@tewkesbury.gov.uk

Member Services: Mrs Lin O'Brien, Democratic Group Services Manager, Council Offices, Gloucester Road, Tewkesbury GL20 5TT ☎ 01684 272020 ⌂ lin.o'brien@tewkesbury.gov.uk

Personnel / HR: Ms Janet Martin, HR Advisor, Council Offices, Gloucester Road, Tewkesbury GL20 5TT ☎ 01684 272057 ⌂ janet.martin@tewkesbury.gov.uk

Planning: Mr Paul Skelton, Development Control Manager, Council Offices, Gloucester Road, Tewkesbury GL20 5TT ☎ 01684 272102 ⌂ paul.skelton@tewkesbury.gov.uk

Regeneration: Mrs Julie Wood, Development Services Group Manager, Council Offices, Gloucester Road, Tewkesbury GL20 5TT ☎ 01684 272095 ⌂ julie.wood@tewkesbury.gov.uk

Staff Training: Ms Janet Martin, HR Advisor, Council Offices, Gloucester Road, Tewkesbury GL20 5TT ☎ 01684 272057 ⌂ janet.martin@tewkesbury.gov.uk

Tourism: Mrs Julie Wood, Development Services Group Manager, Council Offices, Gloucester Road, Tewkesbury GL20 5TT ☎ 01684 272095 ⌂ julie.wood@tewkesbury.gov.uk

COUNCILLORS

Mayor: Blackwell, Gillian (CON - Hucclecote) councillor.blackwell@tewkesbury.gov.uk

Deputy Mayor: Turbyfield, Harry (CON - Brockworth) councillor.turbyfield@tewkesbury.gov.uk

Leader of the Council: Vines, Robert (CON - Badgeworth) councillor.vines@tewkesbury.gov.uk

Deputy Leader of the Council: Waters, David (CON - Coombe Hill) councillor.waters@tewkesbury.gov.uk

Group Leader: Berry, Kay (LD - Churchdown St John's) councillor.berry@tewkesbury.gov.uk

Group Leader: Sztymiak, Mike (IND - Tewkesbury Town with Mitton)
councillor.sztymiak@tewkesbury.gov.uk

Allen, Ron (CON - Winchcombe)
councillor.allen@tewkesbury.gov.uk

Awford, Philip (CON - Highnam with Hawbridge)
councillor.awford@tewkesbury.gov.uk

Bird, Robert (CON - Cleeve West)
councillor.bird@tewkesbury.gov.uk

Bishop, Richard (CON - Churchdown Brookfield)
councillor.bishop@tewkesbury.gov.uk

Bocking, Graham (CON - Innsworth with Down Hatherley)
councillor.bocking@tewkesbury.gov.uk

Cromwell, Kevin (CON - Tewkesbury Prior's Park)
councillor.cromwell@tewkesbury.gov.uk

Davies, Derek (CON - Highnam with Hawbridge)
councillor.davies@tewkesbury.gov.uk

Day, Janet (CON - Winchcombe)
councillor.day@tewkesbury.gov.uk

Dean, Mike (CON - Cleeve Hill)
councillor.dean@tewkesbury.gov.uk

East, Bob (CON - Cleeve St Michael's)
councillor.east@tewkesbury.gov.uk

Evans, Alexander (CON - Churchdown St John's)
councillor.evans@tewkesbury.gov.uk

Evetts, John (CON - Isbourne)
councillor.evetts@tewkesbury.gov, uk

Foyle, David (CON - Churchdown Brookfield)
councillor.foyle@tewkesbury.gov.uk

Furolo, Ron (CON - Brockworth)
councillor.furolo@tewkesbury.gov.uk

Garnham, Rob (CON - Cleeve West)
councillor.garnham@tewkesbury.gov.uk

Godwin, Pauline (CON - Northway)
councillor.godwin@tewkesbury.gov.uk

Gore, Melanie (CON - Oxenton Hill)
councillor.gore@tewkesbury.gov.uk

Greening, Julie (CON - Tewkesbury Prior's Park)
councillor.greening@tewkesbury.gov.uk

Hatton, Ruth (CON - Brockworth)
councillor.hatton@tewkesbury.gov.uk

Hesketh, John (CON - Ashchurch with Walton Cardiff)
councillor.hesketh@tewkesbury.gov.uk

Hillier-Richardson, Sue (INDNA - Cleeve Grange)
councillor.hillier-richardson@tewkesbury.gov.uk

Hollaway, Anna (CON - Cleeve Hill)
councillor.hollaway@tewkesbury.gov.uk

MacTiernan, Elaine (CON - Northway)
councillor.mactiernan@tewkesbury.gov.uk

Mason, Jim (CON - Winchcombe)
councillor.mason@tewkesbury.gov.uk

McLain, Heather (CON - Ashchurch with Walton Cardiff)
hmclain@hotmail.co.uk

Reece, Andrew (CON - Cleeve St Michael's)
councillor.reece@tewkesburyb.gov.uk

Smith, Vernon (CON - Tewkesbury Newtown)
councillor.smithv@tewkesbury.gov.uk

Spencer, Terrance (CON - Twyning)
councillor.spencer@tewkesbury.gov.uk

Stokes, Pearl (LD - Churchdown St John's)
councillor.stokes@tewkesbury.gov.uk

Surman, Philip (CON - Shurdington)
councillor.surman@tewkesbury.gov.uk

Williams, Mark (CON - Coombe Hill)
councillor.williams@tewkesbury.gov.uk

Workman, Philip (IND - Tewkesbury Town With Mitton)
councillor.workman@tewkesbury.gov.uk

POLITICAL COMPOSITION
CON: 33, IND: 2, LD: 2, INDNA: 1

COMMITTEE CHAIRS

Audit: Mr Ron Furolo

Licensing: Mr Rob Garnham

Planning: Mr John Evetts

Thanet   D

Thanet District Council, Thanet Council Offices, Cecil Street, Margate CT9 1XZ
☎ 01843 577000 📠 01843 290906 ✆ customer.services@thanet.gov.uk
🖳 www.thanet.gov.uk

FACTS AND FIGURES
Parliamentary Constituencies:
EU Constituencies: South East
Election Frequency: Elections are biennial

PRINCIPAL OFFICERS

Chief Executive: Ms Madeline Homer, Chief Executive, Thanet Council Offices, Cecil Street, Margate CT9 1XZ ☎ 01843 577123 ✆ madeline.homer@thanet.gov.uk

Senior Management: Mr Tim Howes, Director - Corporate Governance & Monitoring Officer, Thanet Council Offices, Cecil Street, Margate CT9 1XZ ☎ 01843 577906 ✆ tim.howes@thanet.gov.uk

Senior Management: Mr Robert Kenyon, Director - Community Services, Thanet Council Offices, Cecil Street, Margate CT9 1XZ ☎ 01843 577008 ✆ rob.kenyon@thanet.gov.uk

Senior Management: Mr Gavin Waite, Director - Operational Services, Thanet Council Offices, Cecil Street, Margate CT9 1XZ ☎ 01843 577742 ✆ gavin.waite@thanet.gov.uk

Senior Management: Mr Tim Willis, Director - Corporate Resources, Thanet Council Offices, Cecil Street, Margate CT9 1XZ ☎ 01843 577617 ✆ tim.willis@thanet.gov.uk

Building Control: Mr Chris Weller, Building Control Manager, Thanet Council Offices, Cecil Street, Margate CT9 1XZ ☎ 01843 577156 ✆ chris.weller@thanet.gov.uk

THANET

PR / Communications: Miss Hannah Thorpe, Head of Communications, Thanet Council Offices, Cecil Street, Margate CT9 1XZ ☎ 01843 577120 ⏚ hannah.thorpe@thanet.gov.uk

Community Planning: Mr Robert Kenyon, Director - Community Services, Thanet Council Offices, Cecil Street, Margate CT9 1XZ ☎ 01843 577008 ⏚ rob.kenyon@thanet.gov.uk

Community Safety: Ms Penny Button, Head of Safer Neighbourhoods, Thanet Council Offices, Cecil Street, Margate CT9 1XZ ☎ 01843 577425 ⏚ penny.button@thanet.gov.uk

Computer Management: Mr Sean Hale, Head of ICT, EK Services, Military Road, Canterbury CT1 1YW ☎ 01227 862341 ⏚ sean.hale@ekservices.org

Contracts: Ms Karen Paton, Strategic Procurement Manager, Council Offices, Cecil Street, Margate CT9 1XZ ☎ 01843 577112 ⏚ karen.paton@thanet.gov.uk

Customer Service: Mr Dominic Whelan, Shared Services Director, EK Services, Military Road, Canterbury CT1 1YW ☎ 01227 862073 ⏚ dominic.whelan@ekservices.org

Economic Development: Ms Abigail Raymond, Head of Built Environment, Thanet Council Offices, Cecil Street, Margate CT9 1XZ ☎ 01843 577137 ⏚ abigail.raymond@thanet.gov.uk

E-Government: Mrs Roz Edridge, Business Systems Manager, East Kent Services, Council Offices, Cecil Street, Margate CT9 1XZ ☎ 01843 577033 ⏚ roz.edridge@ekservices.org

Electoral Registration: Miss Claire Hawken, Electoral Services Manager, Thanet Council Offices, Cecil Street, Margate CT9 1XZ ☎ 01843 577021 ⏚ claire.l.hawken@thanet.gov.uk

Emergency Planning: Mr Mike Humber, Technical Services Manager, Thanet Council Offices, Cecil Street, Margate CT9 1XZ ☎ 01843 577083 ⏚ mike.humber@thanet.gov.uk

Environmental / Technical Services: Mr Mike Humber, Technical Services Manager, Thanet Council Offices, Cecil Street, Margate CT9 1XZ ☎ 01843 577083 ⏚ mike.humber@thanet.gov.uk

Environmental Health: Ms Penny Button, Head of Safer Neighbourhoods, Thanet Council Offices, Cecil Street, Margate CT9 1XZ ☎ 01843 577425 ⏚ penny.button@thanet.gov.uk

Estates, Property & Valuation: Mr Chris Rolle, Interim Head of Asset Management, Thanet Council Offices, Cecil Street, Margate CT9 1XZ ☎ 01843 577646 ⏚ chris.rolle@thanet.gov.uk

Events Manager: Mrs Suzie Hooper, Events & Community Projects Officer, Thanet Council Offices, Cecil Street, Margate CT9 1XZ ☎ 01843 577409 ⏚ suzie.hooper@thanet.gov.uk

Facilities: Mr Paul Holebrook, Facilities Manager, Thanet Council Offices, Cecil Street, Margate CT9 1XZ ☎ 01843 577291 ⏚ paul.holebrook@thanet.gov.uk

Finance: Mrs Joanna Miller, Head of Finance, Thanet Council Offices, Cecil Street, Margate CT9 1XZ ☎ 01843 577722 ⏚ joanna.miller@thanet.gov.uk

Grounds Maintenance: Mr Roger Wragg, Open Spaces Manager, Thanet Council Offices, Cecil Street, Margate CT9 1XZ ☎ 01843 57788 ⏚ roger.wragg@thanet.gov.uk

Health and Safety: Mr Stewart Bundy, Health & Safety Compliance Officer, Thanet Council Offices, Cecil Street, Margate CT9 1XZ ☎ 01304 872799 ⏚ stewart.bundy@thanet.gov.uk

Home Energy Conservation: Mr Bob Porter, Head of Housing, Thanet Council Offices, Cecil Street, Margate CT9 1XZ ☎ 01843 577006 ⏚ bob.porter@thanet.gov.uk

Housing: Mr Bob Porter, Head of Housing, Thanet Council Offices, Cecil Street, Margate CT9 1XZ ☎ 01843 577006 ⏚ bob.porter@thanet.gov.uk

Housing Maintenance: Mr Paul Bridge, Director - Operations & Business Transformation, EK Housing, East Kent Housing Ltd, Garrity House, Miners Way, Aylesham CT3 3BF ☎ 01304 853749 ⏚ paul.bridge@eastkenthousing.org.uk

Legal: Miss Ciara Feeney, Head of Legal Service & Monitoring Officer, Thanet Council Offices, Cecil Street, Margate CT9 1XZ ☎ 01843 577455 ⏚ ciara.feeney@thanet.gov.uk

Leisure and Cultural Services: Ms Penny Button, Head of Safer Neighbourhoods, Thanet Council Offices, Cecil Street, Margate CT9 1XZ ☎ 01843 577425 ⏚ penny.button@thanet.gov.uk

Licensing: Mr Philip Bensted, Regulatory Services Manager, Council Offices, Cecil Street, Margate CT9 1XZ ☎ 01843 577630 ⏚ philip.bensted@thanet.gov.uk

Member Services: Mr Nicholas Hughes, Committee Services Manager, Thanet Council Offices, Cecil Street, Margate CT9 1XZ ☎ 01843 577208 ⏚ nicholas.hughes@thanet.gov.ul

Parking: Mr Robin Chantrill-Smith, Civil Enforcement Manager, Thanet Council Offices, Cecil Street, Margate CT9 1XZ ☎ 01843 577472 ⏚ robin.chantrill-smith@thanet.gov.uk

Partnerships: Ms Penny Button, Head of Safer Neighbourhoods, Thanet Council Offices, Cecil Street, Margate CT9 1XZ ☎ 01843 577425 ⏚ penny.button@thanet.gov.uk

Personnel / HR: Ms Juli Oliver-Smith, Head of EK Human Resources, East Kent HR Partnership, Dover District Council, White Cliffs Business Park, Whitfield, Dover CT16 3PJ ☎ 07917 473616 ⏚ hrpartnership@dover.gov.uk

Planning: Ms Abigail Raymond, Head of Built Environment, Thanet Council Offices, Cecil Street, Margate CT9 1XZ ☎ 01843 577137 ⏚ abigail.raymond@thanet.gov.uk

Procurement: Ms Karen Paton, Strategic Procurement Manager, Council Offices, Cecil Street, Margate CT9 1XZ ☎ 01843 577112 ⏚ karen.paton@thanet.gov.uk

Recycling & Waste Minimisation: Mr Geoff Dunne, Head of Operational Services, Thanet Council Offices, Cecil Street, Margate CT9 1XZ ☎ 01843 577840 ✍ geoff.dunne@thanet.gov.uk

Regeneration: Mr Robert Kenyon, Director - Community Services, Thanet Council Offices, Cecil Street, Margate CT9 1XZ ☎ 01843 577008 ✍ rob.kenyon@thanet.gov.uk

Staff Training: Mrs Janette Gates, HR Business Manager, East Kent HR Partnership, Dover District Council, White Cliffs Business Park, Whitfield, Dover CT16 3PJ ☎ 01304 872799 ✍ janette.gates@ekhr.org

Street Scene: Mr Phil Snook, Street Scene Enforcement Manager, Thanet Council Offices, Cecil Street, Margate CT9 1XZ ☎ 01843 577658 ✍ phil.snook@thanet.gov.uk

Sustainable Communities: Ms Penny Button, Head of Safer Neighbourhoods, Thanet Council Offices, Cecil Street, Margate CT9 1XZ ☎ 01843 577425 ✍ penny.button@thanet.gov.uk

Tourism: Ms Paula Harbridge, Tourism Manager, Thanet Council Offices, Cecil Street, Margate CT9 1XZ ☎ 01843 577644 ✍ paula.harbridge@thanet.gov.uk

Town Centre: Ms Louise Askew, Economic Development Manager, Thanet Council Offices, Cecil Street, Margate CT9 1XZ ☎ 01843 577178 ✍ lousie.askew@thanet.gov.uk

Waste Collection and Disposal: Mr Geoff Dunne, Head of Operational Services, Thanet Council Offices, Cecil Street, Margate CT9 1XZ ☎ 01843 577840 ✍ geoff.dunne@thanet.gov.uk

Waste Management: Mr Geoff Dunne, Head of Operational Services, Thanet Council Offices, Cecil Street, Margate CT9 1XZ ☎ 01843 577840 ✍ geoff.dunne@thanet.gov.uk

COUNCILLORS

Chair: Piper, Stuart (UKIP - Northwood)
cllr-stuart.piper@thanet.gov.uk

Leader of the Council: Well, Christopher (UKIP - Cliftonville East)
cllr-chris.wells@thanet.gov.uk

Deputy Leader of the Council: Fairbrass, Lin (UKIP - Nethercourt)
cllr-lin.fairbrass@thanet.gov.uk

Group Leader: Bayford, Robert (CON - Kingsgate)
cllr-robert.bayford@thanet.gov.uk

Ashbee, Ash (IND - Westbrook)
cllr-ash.ashbee@thanet.gov.uk

Bambridge, Sam (CON - Westgate-on-Sea)
cllr-sam.bambridge@thanet.gov.uk

Braidwood, Bertie (UKIP - Westgate-on-Sea)
cllr-bertie.braidwood@thanet.gov.uk

Brimm, Suzanne (UKIP - Birchington South)
cllr-suzanne.brimm@thanet.gov.uk

Buckley, John (UKIP - Beacon Road)
cllr-john.buckley@thanet.gov.uk

Campbell, Peter (LAB - Central Harbour)
cllr-peter.campbell@thanet.gov.uk

Coleman-Cooke, Keith (CON - Birchington North)
cllr-keith.coleman-cooke@thanet.gov.uk

Coleman-Cooke, Glenn (UKIP - Birchington South)
cllr-glenn.coleman-cooke@thanet.gov.uk

Connor, Terry (UKIP - Sir Moses Montefiore)
cllr-terry.connor@thanet.gov.uk

Constantine, Karen (LAB - Newington)
cllr-karen.constantine@thanet.gov.uk

Crow-Brown, Derek (UKIP - Thanet Villages)
cllr-derek.crow-brown@thanet.gov.uk

Curran, Jonathan (CON - Garlinge)
cllr-jonathan.curran@thanet.gov.uk

Dawson, Emma (CON - Cliftonville West)
cllr-emma.dawson@thanet.gov.uk

Day, Simon (CON - Birchington North)
cllr-simon.day@thanet.gov.uk

Dellar, Julie (UKIP - Cliftonville West)
cllr-julie.dellar@thanet.gov.uk

Dennis, John (UKIP - Garlinge)
cllr-john.dennis@thanet.gov.uk

Dexter, Roy (CON - St Peters)
cllr-roy.dexter@thanet.gov.uk

Dixon, Rosamund (UKIP - Dane Valley)
cllr-rosamund.dixon@thanet.gov.uk

Edwards, Robin (UKIP - Salmestone)
cllr-robin.edwards@thanet.gov.uk

Elenor, Jeffrey (IND - Margate Central)
cllr-jeffrey.elenor@thanet.gov.uk

Evans, Peter (UKIP - Salmestone)
cllr-peter.evans@thanet.gov.uk

Fairbrass, Jeremy (UKIP - Nethercourt)
cllr-jeremy.fairbrass@thanet.gov.uk

Falcon, Janet (UKIP - Eastcliff)
cllr-janet.falcon@thanet.gov.uk

Fenner, Michelle (LAB - Sir Moses Montefiore)
cllr-michelle.fenner@thanet.gov.uk

Game, Lesley Ann (CON - Cliftonville East)
cllr-lesley.game@thanet.gov.uk

Gregory, Ian (CON - St Peters)
cllr-ian.gregory@thanet.gov.uk

Gregory, Ken (CON - Thanet Villages)
cllr-ken.gregory@thanet.gov.uk

Grove, Bob (IND - Thanet Villages)
cllr-bob.grove@thanet.gov.uk

Hayton, William (IND - Bradstowe)
cllr-bill.hayton@thanet.gov.uk

Hillman, Gary (UKIP - Dane Valley)
cllr-gary.hillman.@thanet.gov.uk

Howes, Alan (UKIP - Birchington South)
cllr-alan.howes@thanet.gov.uk

Jaye-Jones, Edward (UKIP - Cliftonville East)
cllr-edward.jaye-jones@thanet.gov.uk

Johnston, Iris (LAB - Margate Central)
cllr-iris.johnston@thanet.gov.uk

THANET

Larkins, Sarah (UKIP - Eastcliff)
cllr-sarah.larkins@thanet.gov.uk

Martin, Beverly (UKIP - Central Harbour)
cllr-beverly.martin@thanet.gov.uk

Matterface, Jennifer (LAB - Beacon Road)
cllr-jennifer.matterface@thanet.gov.uk

Parson, David (CON - Bradstowe)
cllr-david.parsons@thanet.gov.uk

Partington, Carol (CON - Westgate-on-sea)
cllr-carol.partington@thanet.gov.uk

Piper, Lynda (UKIP - Northwood)
cllr-lynda.piper@thanet.gov.uk

Potts, Roy (UKIP - Newington)
cllr-roy.potts@thanet.gov.uk

Potts, Linda (UKIP - Cliftonville West)
cllr-linda.potts@thanet.gov.uk

Rogers, Brenda (CON - Cliffsend & Pegwell)
cllr-brenda.rogers@thanet.gov.uk

Rusiecki, George (UKIP - Northwood)
cllr-george.rusiecki@thanet.gov.uk

Saunders, Mave (CON - Viking)
cllr-mave.saunders@thanet.gov.uk

Saunders, David (CON - Viking)
cllr-david.saunders@thanet.gov.uk

Savage, Jason (CON - St Peters)
cllr-jason.savage@thanet.gov.uk

Shonk, Trevor (UKIP - Central Harbour)
cllr-trevor.shonk@thanet.gov.uk

Stummer-Schmertzing, Hunter (UKIP - Eastcliff)
cllr-hunter.stummer-schmertzing@thanet.gov.uk

Taylor, Gary (UKIP - Dane Valley)
cllr-gary.taylor@thanet.gov.uk

Taylor-Smith, Rosanna (CON - Viking)
cllr-rosanna.taylor-smith@thanet.gov.uk

Tomlinson, Michael (CON - Westbrook)
cllr-mick.tomlinson@thanet.gov.uk

Townsend, John (UKIP - Cliffsend & Pegwell)
cllr-john.townsend@thanet.gov.uk

POLITICAL COMPOSITION
UKIP: 29, CON: 18, LAB: 5, IND: 4

COMMITTEE CHAIRS

Audit: Mr John Buckley

Licensing: Ms Linda Potts

Planning: Mr Peter Evans

Three Rivers   D

Three Rivers District Council, Three Rivers House, Northway, Rickmansworth WD3 1RL
☎ 01923 776611
✆ enquiries@threerivers.gov.uk
🖥 www.threerivers.gov.uk

FACTS AND FIGURES
Parliamentary Constituencies: South West Hertfordshire, St. Albans, Watford
EU Constituencies: Eastern
Election Frequency: Elections are by thirds

PRINCIPAL OFFICERS

Chief Executive: Dr Steven Halls, Chief Executive, Three Rivers House, Northway, Rickmansworth WD3 1RL ☎ 01923 727281
✆ steven.halls@threerivers.gov.uk

Senior Management: Mr Geof Muggeridge, Director - Community & Environment, Three Rivers House, Northway, Rickmansworth WD3 1RL ☎ 01923 776611
✆ geof.muggeridge@threerivers.gov.uk

Senior Management: Ms Joanne Wagstaffe, Director - Finance, Town Hall, Watford WD17 3EX ☎ 01923 776611
✆ joanne.wagstaffe@watford.gov.uk

Architect, Building / Property Services: Mrs Kimberley Rowley, Interim Head of Regulatory Services, Three Rivers House, Northway, Rickmansworth WD3 1RL ☎ 01923 776611
✆ kimberley.rowley@threerivers.gov.uk

Building Control: Mr Geof Muggeridge, Director - Community & Environment, Three Rivers House, Northway, Rickmansworth WD3 1RL ☎ 01923 776611 ✆ geof.muggeridge@threerivers.gov.uk

PR / Communications: Mr Kevin Snow, Communications Manager, Three Rivers House, Northway, Rickmansworth WD3 1RL ☎ 01923 776611 ✆ kevin.snow@threerivers.gov.uk

Community Planning: Mr Renato Messere, Head of Economic & Sustainable Development, Three Rivers House, Northway, Rickmansworth WD3 1RL ☎ 01923 776611
✆ renato.messere@threerivers.gov.uk

Community Safety: Mr Andy Stovold, Community Partnerships Manager, Three Rivers House, Northway, Rickmansworth WD3 1RL ☎ 01923 776611 ✆ andy.stovold@threerivers.gov.uk

Computer Management: Mrs Emma Tiernan, ICT Client Manager, Town Hall, Watford WD17 3EX ☎ 01923 776611
✆ emma.tiernan@watford.gov.uk

Corporate Services: Mr Phil King, Emergency Planning & Risk Manager, Three Rivers House, Northway, Rickmansworth WD3 1RL ☎ 01923 727260 ✆ phil.king@threerivers.gov.uk

Customer Service: Mr William Hall, Customer Services Manager, Three Rivers House, Northway, Rickmansworth WD3 1RL ☎ 01923 776611 ✆ billy.hall@threerivers.gov.uk

Economic Development: Mr Renato Messere, Head of Economic & Sustainable Development, Three Rivers House, Northway, Rickmansworth WD3 1RL ☎ 01923 776611
✆ renato.messere@threerivers.gov.uk

E-Government: Mrs Emma Tiernan, ICT Client Manager, Town Hall, Watford WD17 3EX ☎ 01923 776611
✆ emma.tiernan@watford.gov.uk

Electoral Registration: Mr Tim Revell, Interim Elections Manager, Three Rivers House, Northway, Rickmansworth WD3 1RL
☎ 01923 776611 ◌ tim.revell@threerivers.gov.uk

Emergency Planning: Mr Phil King, Emergency Planning & Risk Manager, Three Rivers House, Northway, Rickmansworth WD3 1RL
☎ 01923 727260 ◌ phil.king@threerivers.gov.uk

Energy Management: Mr Renato Messere, Head of Economic & Sustainable Development, Three Rivers House, Northway, Rickmansworth WD3 1RL ☎ 01923 776611
◌ renato.messere@threerivers.gov.uk

Environmental / Technical Services: Mr Malcolm Clarke, Environmental Services Manager, Batchwood Depot, Harefield Road, Rickmansworth WD3 1RL ☎ 01923 776611
◌ malcolm.clarke@threerivers.gov.uk

Environmental Health: Ms Kimberley Grout, Housing Services Manager, Three Rivers House, Northway, Rickmansworth WD3 1RL
☎ 01923 776611 ◌ kimberley.grout@threerivers.gov.uk

Estates, Property & Valuation: Ms Lyn Ware, Interim Head of Property Services, Three Rivers House, Northway, Rickmansworth WD3 1RL ☎ 01923 776611 ◌ lyn.ware@threerivers.gov.uk

Facilities: Ms Tracy Langley, Facilities Manager, Three Rivers House, Northway, Rickmansworth WD3 1RL ☎ 01923 776611
◌ tracy.langley@threerivers.gov.uk

Finance: Ms Joanne Wagstaffe, Director - Finance, Town Hall, Watford WD17 3EX ☎ 01923 776611
◌ joanne.wagstaffe@watford.gov.uk

Treasury: Mr Bob Watson, Head of Finance - Shared Services, Town Hall, Watford WD17 3EX ☎ 01923 727188
◌ bob.watson@watford.gov.uk

Grounds Maintenance: Mr Malcolm Clarke, Environmental Services Manager, Batchwood Depot, Harefield Road, Rickmansworth WD3 1RL ☎ 01923 776611
◌ malcolm.clarke@threerivers.gov.uk

Health and Safety: Mr Gary Neville, Corporate Health & Safety Advisor, Three Rivers House, Northway, Rickmansworth WD3 1RL
☎ 01923 776611 ◌ gary.neville@threerivers.gov.uk

Housing: Ms Kimberley Grout, Housing Services Manager, Three Rivers House, Northway, Rickmansworth WD3 1RL ☎ 01923 776611
◌ kimberley.grout@threerivers.gov.uk

Legal: Mrs Anne Morgan, Solicitor to the Council, Three Rivers House, Northway, Rickmansworth WD3 1RL ☎ 01923 776611
◌ anne.morgan@threerivers.gov.uk

Leisure and Cultural Services: Mr Chris Hope, Head of Community Services, Three Rivers House, Northway, Rickmansworth WD3 1RL ☎ 01923 776611
◌ chris.hope@threerivers.gov.uk

Licensing: Mrs Kimberley Rowley, Interim Head of Regulatory Services, Three Rivers House, Northway, Rickmansworth WD3 1RL
☎ 01923 776611 ◌ kimberley.rowley@threerivers.gov.uk

Lottery Funding, Charity and Voluntary: Mr Karl Stonebank, Voluntary Sector Officer, Three Rivers House, Northway, Rickmansworth WD3 1RL ☎ 01923 776611
◌ karl.stonebank@threerivers.gov.uk

Member Services: Ms Sarah Haythorpe, Principal Committee Manager, Three Rivers House, Northway, Rickmansworth WD3 1RL
☎ 01923 776611 ◌ sarah.haythorpe@threeriver.gov.uk

Parking: Mrs Kimberley Rowley, Interim Head of Regulatory Services, Three Rivers House, Northway, Rickmansworth WD3 1RL
☎ 01923 776611 ◌ kimberley.rowley@threerivers.gov.uk

Partnerships: Mr Andy Stovold, Community Partnerships Manager, Three Rivers House, Northway, Rickmansworth WD3 1RL
☎ 01923 776611 ◌ andy.stovold@threerivers.gov.uk

Personnel / HR: Mrs Cathy Watson, Head of Human Resources, Three Rivers House, Northway, Rickmansworth WD3 1RL
☎ 01923 776611 ◌ cathy.watson@watford.gov.uk

Planning: Mrs Kimberley Rowley, Interim Head of Regulatory Services, Three Rivers House, Northway, Rickmansworth WD3 1RL
☎ 01923 776611 ◌ kimberley.rowley@threerivers.gov.uk

Recycling & Waste Minimisation: Mrs Alison Page, Head of Environmental Protection, Three Rivers House, Northway, Rickmansworth WD3 1RL ☎ 01923 776611
◌ alison.page@threerivers.gov.uk

Staff Training: Ms Sherrie Ralton, Learning & Development Officer, Three Rivers House, Northway, Rickmansworth WD3 1RL
☎ 01923 776611 ◌ sherrie.ralton@threerivers.gov.uk

Street Scene: Mrs Alison Page, Head of Environmental Protection, Three Rivers House, Northway, Rickmansworth WD3 1RL
☎ 01923 776611 ◌ alison.page@threerivers.gov.uk

Sustainable Communities: Dr Steven Halls, Chief Executive, Three Rivers House, Northway, Rickmansworth WD3 1RL
☎ 01923 727281 ◌ steven.halls@threerivers.gov.uk

Sustainable Development: Mr Renato Messere, Head of Economic & Sustainable Development, Three Rivers House, Northway, Rickmansworth WD3 1RL ☎ 01923 776611
◌ renato.messere@threerivers.gov.uk

Town Centre: Mr Renato Messere, Head of Economic & Sustainable Development, Three Rivers House, Northway, Rickmansworth WD3 1RL ☎ 01923 776611
◌ renato.messere@threerivers.gov.uk

Transport Planner: Mr Renato Messere, Head of Economic & Sustainable Development, Three Rivers House, Northway, Rickmansworth WD3 1RL ☎ 01923 776611
◌ renato.messere@threerivers.gov.uk

THREE RIVERS

Waste Collection and Disposal: Mr Malcolm Clarke, Environmental Services Manager, Batchwood Depot, Harefield Road, Rickmansworth WD3 1RL ☎ 01923 776611 ⁅ malcolm.clarke@threerivers.gov.uk

Waste Management: Mr Malcolm Clarke, Environmental Services Manager, Batchwood Depot, Harefield Road, Rickmansworth WD3 1RL ☎ 01923 776611 ⁅ malcolm.clarke@threerivers.gov.uk

Children's Play Areas: Mr Chris Hope, Head of Community Services, Three Rivers House, Northway, Rickmansworth WD3 1RL ☎ 01923 776611 ⁅ chris.hope@threerivers.gov.uk

COUNCILLORS

Chair: Scarth, Andrew (LD - Oxhey Hall & Hayling)

Vice-Chair: Barber, Diana (CON - Penn & Mill End)
diana.barber@threerivers.gov.uk

Leader of the Council: Bedford, Sara (LD - Abbots Langley & Bedmond)
sara.bedford@threerivers.gov.uk

Deputy Leader of the Council: Shaw, Ann (LD - Chorleywood South & Maple Cross)
ann.shaw@threerivers.gov.uk

Group Leader: Cox, Stephen (LAB - South Oxhey)
stephen.oxhey@threerivers.gov.uk

Group Leader: Sangster, Ralph (CON - Rickmansworth Town)
ralph.sangster@threerivers.gov.uk

Barnes, Rupert (CON - Dickinsons)
rupert.barnes@threerivers.gov.uk

Bedford, Matthew (LD - Abbots Langley & Bedmond)
matthew.bedford@threerivers.gov.uk

Bishop, Eric (CON - Carpenders Park)
eric.bishop@threerivers.gov.uk

Brading, Phil (LD - Dickinsons)
phil.brading@threerivers.gov.uk

Brooks, Martin (LD - Leavesden)
martin.brooks2@threerivers.gov.uk

Butler, Marilyn (CON - Chorleywood North & Sarratt)
marilyn.butler@threerivers.gov.uk

Butt, Kemal (LD - Moor Park & Eastbury)
kemal.butt@threerivers.gov.uk

Coltman, Valerie (CON - Carpenders Park)

Coltman, David (CON - Carpenders Park)

Drury, Steve (LD - Durrants)
steve.drury@threerivers.gov.uk

Getkahn, Peter (LD - Dickinsons)
peter.getkahn@threerivers.gov.uk

Giles-Medhurst, Stephen (LD - Leavesden)
sgm@cix.co.uk

Harris, Ty (CON - Oxhey Hall & Hayling)
ty.harris@threerivers.gov.uk

Hayward, Alex (CON - Chorleywood North & Sarratt)
alex.hayward@threerivers.gov.uk

Hiscocks, Paula (CON - Rickmansworth Town)
paula.hiscocks@threerivers.gov.uk

Kenison, Heather (CON - Chorleywood North & Sarratt)
heather.kennison@threerivers.gov.uk

Killick, Angela (CON - Chorleywood South & Maple Cross)
angela.killick@threerivers.gov.uk

King, Joan (LAB - South Oxhey)
joan.king@threerivers.gov.uk

King, Stephen (LAB - South Oxhey)

Lloyd, Chris (LD - Durrants)
chris.lloyd@threerivers.gov.uk

Major, David (LD - Abbots Langley & Bedmond)
david.major@threerivers.gov.uk

Mann, Joy (LD - Gade Valley)
joy.mann@threerivers.gov.uk

Morris, Debbie (CON - Moor Park & Eastbury)
debbie.morris@threerivers.gov.uk

Nelmes, Sarah (LD - Penn & Mill End)
sarah.nelmes@threerivers.gov.uk

Proctor, Leslie (CON - Gade Valley)
leslie.proctor@threerivers.gov.uk

Ranger, Reena (CON - Moor Park & Eastbury)
reena.ranger@threerivers.gov.uk

Sansom, David (CON - Rickmansworth Town)
david.sansom@threerivers.gov.uk

Scarth, Alison (LD - Oxhey Hall & Hayling)
alison.scarth@threerivers.gov.uk

Seabourne, Roger (LD - Penn & Mill End)
roger.seabourne@threerivers.gov.uk

Trevett, Martin (LD - Chorleywood South & Maple Cross)
martin.trevett@threerivers.gov.uk

Turner, Kate (LD - Leavesden)
kate.turner@threerivers.gov.uk

Wall, Alison (LD - Durrants)
alison.wall@threerivers.gov.uk

Whately-Smith, Chris (LD - Gade Valley)
chris.whately-smith@threerivers.gov.uk

POLITICAL COMPOSITION
LD: 20, CON: 16, LAB: 3

Thurrock U

Thurrock Council, Civic Offices, New Road, Grays RM17 6SL ☎ 01375 652652 🖷 01375 652359 ⁅ initialsurname@thurrock.gov.uk 🖳 www.thurrock.gov.uk

FACTS AND FIGURES
Parliamentary Constituencies: Thurrock
EU Constituencies: Eastern
Election Frequency: Elections are by thirds

PRINCIPAL OFFICERS

Chief Executive: Ms Lyn Carpenter, Chief Executive, Civic Offices, New Road, Grays RM17 6SL ☎ 01375 652390 ⁅ lcarpenter@thurrock.gov.uk

Senior Management: Mrs Sharon Bayliss, Director - Commercial Services, Civic Offices, New Road, Grays RM17 6SL
☎ 01375 659840 ◦ sbayliss@thurrock.gov.uk

Senior Management: Mr Sean Clark, Director - Finance & IT / Section 151 Officer, Civic Offices, New Road, Grays RM17 6SL
☎ 01375 652010 ◦ sclark@thurrock.gov.uk

Senior Management: Mr Steve Cox, Corporate Director - Environment & Place, Civic Offices, New Road, Grays RM17 6SL
☎ 01375 652581 ◦ scox@thurrock.gov.uk

Senior Management: Mr Roger Harris, Corporate Director - Adults, Housing & Health, Civic Offices, New Road, Grays RM17 6SL ☎ 01375 652561 ◦ r.harris@thurrock.gov.uk

Senior Management: Ms Jackie Hinchliffe, Director - Human Resources, Organisational Development & Transformation, Civic Offices, New Road, Grays RM17 6SL ☎ 01375 652016
◦ jhinchliffe@thurrock.gov.uk

Senior Management: Mr Rory Patterson, Corporate Director - Children's Services, Civic Offices, New Road, Grays RM17 6SL
☎ 01375 652077 ◦ rpatterson@thurrock.gov.uk

Senior Management: Mrs Fiona Taylor, Director - Law & Governance, Civic Centre, Dagenham RM10 7BN ☎ 020 8227 2114
◦ fiona.taylor@bdtlegal.org.uk

Architect, Building / Property Services: Mr Matthew Essex, Head of Regeneration & Assets, Civic Offices, New Road, Grays RM17 6SL ☎ 01375 652581 ◦ messex@thurrock.gov.uk

Building Control: Mr Stuart Fyffe, Senior Building Control Surveyor, Civic Offices, New Road, Grays RM17 6SL
☎ 01375 652165 ◦ sfyffe@thurrock.gov.uk

Civil Registration: Ms Lynn Whipps, Superintendent Registrar, Civic Offices, New Road, Grays RM17 6SL ☎ 01375 375245
◦ lwhipps@thurrock.gov.uk

PR / Communications: Ms Karen Wheeler, Head of Strategy, Communications & Customer Services, Civic Offices, New Road, Grays RM17 6SL ☎ 01375 659688 ◦ kwheeler@thurrock.gov.uk

Community Safety: Ms Natalie Warren, Community Development & Equalities Manager, Civic Offices, New Road, Grays RM17 6SL
☎ 01375 652186 ◦ nwarren@thurrock.gov.uk

Computer Management: Mr Murray James, Operational Lead of ICT, Civic Offices, New Road, Grays RM17 6SL ☎ 01375 652951
◦ murray.james@serco.com

Consumer Protection and Trading Standards: Mr Gavin Dennett, Environmental Health & Trading Standards Manager, Civic Offices, New Road, Grays RM17 6SL ☎ 01375 652581
◦ gdennett@thurrock.gov.uk

Customer Service: Ms Tracie Heiser, Head of Customer Services & Business Administration, Serco, Civic Offices, New Road, Grays RM17 6SL ☎ 01375 366243 ◦ theiser@thurrock.gov.uk

Education: Mr Roger Edwardson, Interim Strategic Lead of School Improvement, Learning & Skills, Civic Offices, New Road, Grays RM17 6SL ☎ 01375 652973 ◦ redwardson@thurrock.gov.uk

E-Government: Mr Lee Henley, Information Manager, Civic Offices, New Road, Grays RM17 6SL ☎ 01375 652500

E-Government: Mr Steve Rigden, Web Manager, Civic Offices, New Road, Grays RM17 6SL ☎ 01375 652038
◦ srigden@thurrock.gov.uk

Electoral Registration: Ms Elaine Sheridan, Electoral Services Manager, Civic Offices, New Road, Grays RM17 6SL
☎ 01375 652580 ◦ esheridan@thurrock.gov.uk

Emergency Planning: Mrs Toni Barlow, Emergency Planning Principal Officer, Civic Offices, New Road, Grays RM17 6SL
☎ 01375 413768 ◦ tbarlow@thurrock.gov.uk

Facilities: Mr Paul Danskin, Facilities Manager, Civic Offices, New Road, Grays RM17 6SL ☎ 01375 652467
◦ pdanskin@thurrock.gov.uk

Finance: Mr Sean Clark, Director - Finance & IT / Section 151 Officer, Civic Offices, New Road, Grays RM17 6SL ☎ 01375 652010
◦ sclark@thurrock.gov.uk

Grounds Maintenance: Mr Daren Spring, Street Services Manager, Civic Offices, New Road, Grays RM17 6SL
☎ 01375 413612 ◦ dspring@thurrock.gov.uk

Health and Safety: Mr Tony Sprackling, Principal Officer - Health & Safety, Civic Offices, New Road, Grays RM17 6SL
◦ asprackling@thurrock.gov.uk

Highways: Ms Ann Osola, Head of Highways & Transport, Civic Offices, New Road, Grays RM17 6SL ☎ 01375 652393
◦ aosola@thurrock.gov.uk

Housing: Mr Roger Harris, Corporate Director - Adults, Housing & Health, Civic Offices, New Road, Grays RM17 6SL ☎ 01375 652561
◦ r.harris@thurrock.gov.uk

Housing: Mr Richard Parkin, Head of Housing, Civic Offices, New Road, Grays RM17 6SL ☎ 01375 652625 ◦ rparkin@thurrock.gov.uk

Legal: Mrs Fiona Taylor, Director - Law & Governance, Civic Centre, Dagenham RM10 7BN ☎ 020 8227 2114
◦ fiona.taylor@bdtlegal.org.uk

Leisure and Cultural Services: Mr Grant Greatrex, Sport, Leisure & Policy Development Manager, Civic Offices, New Road, Grays RM17 6SL ☎ 01375 413940 ◦ ggreatrex@thurrock.gov.uk

Licensing: Mr Paul Adams, Principal Licensing Officer, Civic Offices, New Road, Grays RM17 6SL ◦ padams@thurrock.gov.uk

Lifelong Learning: Mr Rory Patterson, Corporate Director - Children's Services, Civic Offices, New Road, Grays RM17 6SL
☎ 01375 652077 ◦ rpatterson@thurrock.gov.uk

THURROCK

Lighting: Mr Dave Parish, Street Lighting Engineer, Civic Offices, New Road, Grays RM17 6SL ☎ 01375 387430 ✆ dparish@thurrock.gov.uk

Lottery Funding, Charity and Voluntary: Ms Natalie Warren, Community Development & Equalities Manager, Civic Offices, New Road, Grays RM17 6SL ☎ 01375 652186 ✆ nwarren@thurrock.gov.uk

Member Services: Ms Cara Smith, Office Manager, Civic Offices, New Road, Grays RM17 6SL ☎ 01375 633622 ✆ csmith@thurrock.gov.uk

Parking: Ms Marie Buckley, Parking Services Co-ordinator, Civic Offices, New Road, Grays RM17 6SL ☎ 01375 652968 ✆ mbuckley@thurrock.gov.uk

Personnel / HR: Ms Jackie Hinchliffe, Director - Human Resources, Organisational Development & Transformation, Civic Offices, New Road, Grays RM17 6SL ☎ 01375 652016 ✆ jhinchliffe@thurrock.gov.uk

Planning: Mr Andrew Millard, Head of Planning & Growth, Civic Offices, New Road, Grays RM17 6SL ☎ 01375 652710 ✆ amillard@thurrock.gov.uk

Procurement: Mr Sean Clark, Director - Finance & IT / Section 151 Officer, Civic Offices, New Road, Grays RM17 6SL ☎ 01375 652010 ✆ sclark@thurrock.gov.uk

Public Libraries: Ms Jenny Meads, Operations & Data Manager, Thameside Theatre Complex, Orsett Road, Grays RM17 5DX ☎ 01375 413970 ✆ jmeads@thurrock.gov.uk

Recycling & Waste Minimisation: Mr Daren Spring, Street Services Manager, Civic Offices, New Road, Grays RM17 6SL ☎ 01375 413612 ✆ dspring@thurrock.gov.uk

Regeneration: Mr Matthew Essex, Head of Regeneration & Assets, Civic Offices, New Road, Grays RM17 6SL ☎ 01375 652581 ✆ messex@thurrock.gov.uk

Road Safety: Ms Julie Cooper, Active Travel Co-ordinator, Civic Offices, New Road, Grays RM17 6SL ☎ 01375 652574 ✆ jcooper@thurrock.gov.uk

Social Services: Mr Andrew Carter, Head of Children's Social Care, Civic Offices, New Road, Grays RM17 6SL ☎ 01375 659676 ✆ acarter@thurrock.gov.uk

Social Services (Adult): Mr Les Billingham, Head of Adult Services, Civic Offices, New Road, Grays RM17 6SL ☎ 01375 652294 ✆ l.billingham@thurrock.gov.uk

Social Services (Adult): Mr Roger Harris, Corporate Director - Adults, Housing & Health, Civic Offices, New Road, Grays RM17 6SL ☎ 01375 652561 ✆ r.harris@thurrock.gov.uk

Social Services (Children): Mr Andrew Carter, Head of Children's Social Care, Civic Offices, New Road, Grays RM17 6SL ☎ 01375 659676 ✆ acarter@thurrock.gov.uk

Public Health: Mr Ian Wake, Director - Public Health, Civic Offices, New Road, Grays RM17 6SL ☎ 01375 652561 ✆ iwake@thurrock.gov.uk

Staff Training: Ms Wendy Allen, Workforce Planning & Development Manager, Civic Offices, New Road, Grays RM17 6SL ☎ 01375 652674 ✆ wallen@thurrock.gov.uk

Street Scene: Mr Richard Parkin, Head of Housing, Civic Offices, New Road, Grays RM17 6SL ☎ 01375 652625 ✆ rparkin@thurrock.gov.uk

Sustainable Development: Ms Lisa Ricketts, Business Support Officer, Civic Offices, New Road, Grays RM17 6SL ☎ 01375 652271 ✆ lricketts@thurrock.gov.uk

Transport: Ms Tracey Ashwell, Highways & Transportation Services Manager, Civic Offices, New Road, Grays RM17 6SL ☎ 01375 413883 ✆ tashwell@thurrock.gov.uk

Waste Management: Mr Daren Spring, Street Services Manager, Civic Offices, New Road, Grays RM17 6SL ☎ 01375 413612 ✆ dspring@thurrock.gov.uk

COUNCILLORS

Mayor: Kent, Cathy (LAB - Grays Thurrock)
ckent@thurrock.gov.uk

Deputy Mayor: Ojetola, Tunde (CON - South Chafford)
tojetola@thurrock.gov.uk

Leader of the Council: Gledhill, Robert (CON - Little Thurrock Rectory)
rgledhill@thurrock.gov.uk

Deputy Leader of the Council: Hebb, Shane (CON - Stanford-le-Hope West)
shebb@thurrock.gov.uk

Aker, Tim (UKIP - Aveley & Uplands)
tim.aker@ukip.org

Allen, John (UKIP - Tilbury St. Chads)
jaallen@thurrock.gov.uk

Baker, Chris (UKIP - Belhus)
cbaker@thurrock.gov.uk

Baker, Jan (UKIP - Ockendon)
jabaker@thurrock.gov.uk

Baker, James (UKIP - East Tilbury)
jxbaker@thurrock.gov.uk

Baldwin, Clare (LAB - Tilbury Riverside & Thurrock Park)
cbaldwin@thurrock.gov.uk

Cherry, Russell (UKIP - Chadwell St. Mary)
rcherry@thurrock.gov.uk

Churchman, Colin (IND - Stanford East & Corringham Town)
cchurchman@thurrock.gov.uk

Collins, Gary (CON - The Homesteads)
gcollins@thurrock.gov.uk

Coxshall, Mark (CON - Chafford & North Stifford)
mcoxshall@thurrock.gov.uk

Duffin, Jack (UKIP - Stanford East & Corringham Town)
jduffin@thurrock.gov.uk

Fish, Tony (LAB - Grays Riverside)
txfish2@thurrock.gov.uk

Gamester, Leslie (UKIP - Stifford Clays)
lgamester@thurrock.gov.uk

Gerrish, Oliver (LAB - West Thurrock & South Stifford)
ogerrish@thurrock.gov.uk

Hague, Garry (CON - Chafford & North Stifford)
ghague@thurrock.gov.uk

Halden, James (CON - The Homesteads)
jhalden@thurrock.gov.uk

Hamilton, Graham (UKIP - Belhus)
ghamilton@thurrock.gov.uk

Holloway, Clifford (LAB - West Thurrock & South Stifford)
cholloway@thurrock.gov.uk

Holloway, Victoria (LAB - West Thurrock & South Stifford)
vholloway@thurrock.gov.uk

Jones, Roy (UKIP - Stanford East & Corringham Town)
rojones@thurrock.gov.uk

Kelly, Tom (CON - Little Thurrock Rectory)
tkelly@thurrock.gov.uk

Kent, John (LAB - Grays Thurrock)
jkent@thurrock.gov.uk

Kerin, Martin (LAB - Grays Riverside)
mkerin@thurrock.gov.uk

Liddiard, Steve (LAB - Tilbury St. Chads)
sliddiard@thurrock.gov.uk

Little, Brian (CON - Orsett)
blittle@thurrock.gov.uk

Little, Susan (CON - Orsett)
slittle@thurrock.gov.uk

MacPherson, Suzanne (CON - South Chafford)
smacpherson@thurrock.gov.uk

Maney, Benjamin (CON - Little Thurrock Blackshots)
bmaney@thurrock.gov.uk

Okunade, Bukky (LAB - Tilbury Riverside & Thurrock Park)
bokunade@thurrock.gov.uk

Piccolo, Terry (CON - Stanford-le-Hope West)
tpiccolo@thurrock.gov.uk

Pothecary, Jane (LAB - Grays Riverside)
jpothecary@thurrock.gov.uk

Potter, David (UKIP - Ockendon)
dpotter@thurrock.gov.uk

Redsell, Joycelyn (CON - Little Thurrock Blackshots)
jredsell@thurrock.gov.uk

Rice, Gerard (LAB - Chadwell St. Mary)
grice@thurrock.gov.uk

Rice, Barbara (LAB - Chadwell St. Mary)
brice@thurrock.gov.uk

Sammons, Sue (UKIP - East Tilbury)
ssammons@thurrock.gov.uk

Sheridan, Angela (UKIP - Belhus)
asheridan@thurrock.gov.uk

Smith, Peter (UKIP - Aveley & Uplands)

Snell, Graham (UKIP - Stifford Clays)
gsnell@thurrock.gov.uk

Spillman, Luke (UKIP - Aveley & Uplands)
lspillman@thurrock.gov.uk

Stewart, Deborah (CON - Corringham & Fobbing)
dstewart@thurrock.gov.uk

Stone, Michael (LAB - Grays Thurrock)
mstone@thurrock.gov.uk

Tolson, Pauline (CON - The Homesteads)
ptolson@thurrock.gov.uk

Watkins, Aaron (CON - Corringham & Fobbing)
awatkins@thurrock.gov.uk

Wheeler, Kevin (UKIP - Ockendon)
kxwheeler@thurrock.gov.uk

POLITICAL COMPOSITION
CON: 17, UKIP: 17, LAB: 14, IND: 1

COMMITTEE CHAIRS

Audit: Mr John Kent

Children's Services: Ms Bukky Okunade

Health & Wellbeing: Mr James Halden

Licensing: Mr Michael Stone

Planning: Mr Tom Kelly

Tonbridge & Malling   D

Tonbridge & Malling Borough Council, Gibson Building,
Gibson Drive, Kings Hill, West Malling ME19 4LZ
☎ 01732 844522 ᐧ᷇ customer.services@tmbc.gov.uk
🖳 www.tmbc.gov.uk

FACTS AND FIGURES
Parliamentary Constituencies: Tonbridge and Malling
EU Constituencies: South East
Election Frequency: Elections are of whole council

PRINCIPAL OFFICERS

Chief Executive: Miss Julie Beilby, Chief Executive, Gibson
Building, Gibson Drive, Kings Hill, West Malling ME19 4LZ
☎ 01732 876382 ᐧ᷇ central.services@tmbc.gov.uk

Senior Management: Mr Steve Humphrey, Director - Planning,
Housing & Environmental Health, Gibson Building, Gibson Drive,
Kings Hill, West Malling ME19 4LZ ☎ 01732 876256
ᐧ᷇ steve.humphrey@tmbc.gov.uk

Senior Management: Mr Mark Raymond, Chief Corporate Policy
Officer, Gibson Building, Gibson Drive, Kings Hill, West Malling
ME19 4LZ ☎ 01732 876267 ᐧ᷇ mark.raymond@tmbc.gov.uk

Senior Management: Mrs Sharon Shelton, Director - Finance
& Transformation, Gibson Building, Gibson Drive, Kings Hill, West
Malling ME19 4LZ ☎ 01732 876092 ᐧ᷇ sharon.shelton@tmbc.gov.uk

Senior Management: Mr Adrian Stanfield, Director - Central
Services, Gibson Building, Gibson Drive, Kings Hill, West Malling
ME19 4LZ ☎ 01732 876346 ᐧ᷇ legal.services@tmbc.gov.uk

TONBRIDGE & MALLING

Senior Management: Mr Robert Styles, Director - Street Scene, Leisure & Technical Services, Gibson Building, Gibson Drive, Kings Hill, West Malling ME19 4LZ ☎ 01732 876160
⌨ robert.styles@tmbc.gov.uk

Architect, Building / Property Services: Mr John DeKnop, Buildings & Facilities Manager, Gibson Building, Gibson Drive, Kings Hill, West Malling ME19 4LZ ☎ 01732 876028
⌨ property.services@tmbc.gov.uk

Building Control: Mr Kevin Tomsett, Head of Parking & Surveying, Council Offices, Argyle Road, Sevenoaks TN13 1HG
☎ 01732 227000 ⌨ kevin.tomsett@sevenoaks.gov.uk

Children / Youth Services: Mr Robert Styles, Director - Street Scene, Leisure & Technical Services, Gibson Building, Gibson Drive, Kings Hill, West Malling ME19 4LZ ☎ 01732 876160
⌨ robert.styles@tmbc.gov.uk

PR / Communications: Mrs Linda Moreau, Media & Communications Manager, Gibson Building, Gibson Drive, Kings Hill, West Malling ME19 4LZ ☎ 01732 876009
⌨ linda.moreau@tmbc.gov.uk

Community Planning: Mr Mark Raymond, Chief Corporate Policy Officer, Gibson Building, Gibson Drive, Kings Hill, West Malling ME19 4LZ ☎ 01732 876267 ⌨ mark.raymond@tmbc.gov.uk

Community Safety: Mr Anthony Garnett, Licensing & Community Safety Manager, Gibson Building, Gibson Drive, Kings Hill, West Malling ME19 4LZ ☎ 01732 876346 ⌨ anthony.garnett@tmbc.gov.uk

Computer Management: Mr Darren Everden, Information Technology Manager, Gibson Building, Gibson Drive, Kings Hill, West Malling ME19 4LZ ☎ 01732 876117
⌨ darren.everden@tmbc.gov.uk

Contracts: Mrs Lynn Francis, Principal Solicitor, Gibson Building, Gibson Drive, Kings Hill, West Malling ME19 4LZ
☎ 01732 876030 ⌨ lynn.francis@tmbc.gov.uk

Corporate Services: Mr Mark Raymond, Chief Corporate Policy Officer, Gibson Building, Gibson Drive, Kings Hill, West Malling ME19 4LZ ☎ 01732 876267 ⌨ mark.raymond@tmbc.gov.uk

Customer Service: Mr Charlie Steel, Personnel & Customer Services Manager, Gibson Building, Gibson Drive, Kings Hill, West Malling ME19 4LZ ☎ 01732 876015 ⌨ charlie.steel@tmbc.gov.uk

Economic Development: Mr Mark Raymond, Chief Corporate Policy Officer, Gibson Building, Gibson Drive, Kings Hill, West Malling ME19 4LZ ☎ 01732 876267 ⌨ mark.raymond@tmbc.gov.uk

E-Government: Mr Darren Everden, Information Technology Manager, Gibson Building, Gibson Drive, Kings Hill, West Malling ME19 4LZ ☎ 01732 876117 ⌨ darren.everden@tmbc.gov.uk

Electoral Registration: Mr Richard Beesley, Elections & Special Projects Manager, Gibson Building, Gibson Drive, Kings Hill, West Malling ME19 4LZ ☎ 01732 876229 ⌨ richard.beesley@tmbc.gov.uk

Energy Management: Mr John DeKnop, Buildings & Facilities Manager, Gibson Building, Gibson Drive, Kings Hill, West Malling ME19 4LZ ☎ 01732 876028 ⌨ property.services@tmbc.gov.uk

Environmental Health: Mrs Jane Heeley, Chief Environmental Health Officer, Gibson Building, Gibson Drive, Kings Hill, West Malling ME19 4LZ ☎ 01732 876189 ⌨ jane.heeley@tmbc.gov.uk

Estates, Property & Valuation: Mrs Katie Exon, Estates Manager, Gibson Building, Gibson Drive, Kings Hill, West Malling ME19 4LZ ☎ 01732 876364 ⌨ property.services@tmbc.gov.uk

Events Manager: Mr Darren Lanes, Head of Leisure Services, Gibson Building, Gibson Drive, Kings Hill, West Malling ME19 4LZ ☎ 01732 876171 ⌨ darren.lanes@tmbc.gov.uk

Facilities: Mr John DeKnop, Buildings & Facilities Manager, Gibson Building, Gibson Drive, Kings Hill, West Malling ME19 4LZ ☎ 01732 876028 ⌨ property.services@tmbc.gov.uk

Finance: Mrs Sharon Shelton, Director - Finance & Transformation, Gibson Building, Gibson Drive, Kings Hill, West Malling ME19 4LZ ☎ 01732 876092 ⌨ sharon.shelton@tmbc.gov.uk

Grounds Maintenance: Mr John Dicker, Senior Parks Officer, Gibson Building, Gibson Drive, Kings Hill, West Malling ME19 4LZ ☎ 01732 876162 ⌨ john.dicker@tmbc.gov.uk

Health and Safety: Mrs Jane Heeley, Chief Environmental Health Officer, Gibson Building, Gibson Drive, Kings Hill, West Malling ME19 4LZ ☎ 01732 876189 ⌨ jane.heeley@tmbc.gov.uk

Home Energy Conservation: Mrs Hazel Skinner, Environmental Health Officer, Gibson Building, Gibson Drive, Kings Hill, West Malling ME19 4LZ ☎ 01732 876199 ⌨ hazel.skinner@tmbc.gov.uk

Housing: Mr Steve Humphrey, Director - Planning, Housing & Environmental Health, Gibson Building, Gibson Drive, Kings Hill, West Malling ME19 4LZ ☎ 01732 876256
⌨ steve.humphrey@tmbc.gov.uk

Legal: Mr Adrian Stanfield, Director - Central Services, Gibson Building, Gibson Drive, Kings Hill, West Malling ME19 4LZ
☎ 01732 876346 ⌨ legal.services@tmbc.gov.uk

Leisure and Cultural Services: Mr Robert Styles, Director - Street Scene, Leisure & Technical Services, Gibson Building, Gibson Drive, Kings Hill, West Malling ME19 4LZ ☎ 01732 876160
⌨ robert.styles@tmbc.gov.uk

Licensing: Mr Anthony Garnett, Licensing & Community Safety Manager, Gibson Building, Gibson Drive, Kings Hill, West Malling ME19 4LZ ☎ 01732 876346 ⌨ anthony.garnett@tmbc.gov.uk

Lottery Funding, Charity and Voluntary: Mr Mark Raymond, Chief Corporate Policy Officer, Gibson Building, Gibson Drive, Kings Hill, West Malling ME19 4LZ ☎ 01732 876267
⌨ mark.raymond@tmbc.gov.uk

Member Services: Miss Claire Fox, Principal Administrator, Gibson Building, Gibson Drive, Kings Hill, West Malling ME19 4LZ
☎ 01732 876045 ⌨ committee.services@tmbc.gov.uk

Parking: Mr Steve Humphrey, Director - Planning, Housing & Environmental Health, Gibson Building, Gibson Drive, Kings Hill, West Malling ME19 4LZ ☎ 01732 876256
✆ steve.humphrey@tmbc.gov.uk

Partnerships: Mr Mark Raymond, Chief Corporate Policy Officer, Gibson Building, Gibson Drive, Kings Hill, West Malling ME19 4LZ
☎ 01732 876267 ✆ mark.raymond@tmbc.gov.uk

Personnel / HR: Ms Delia Gordon, Personnel & Development Manager, Gibson Building, Gibson Drive, Kings Hill, West Malling ME19 4LZ ☎ 01732 876019 ✆ delia.gordon@tmbc.gov.uk

Personnel / HR: Mr Charlie Steel, Personnel & Customer Services Manager, Gibson Building, Gibson Drive, Kings Hill, West Malling ME19 4LZ ☎ 01732 876015
✆ personnel.services@tmbc.gov.uk

Planning: Mr Steve Humphrey, Director - Planning, Housing & Environmental Health, Gibson Building, Gibson Drive, Kings Hill, West Malling ME19 4LZ ☎ 01732 876256
✆ steve.humphrey@tmbc.gov.uk

Procurement: Mr Neil Lawley, Chief Financial Services Officer, Gibson Building, Gibson Drive, Kings Hill, West Malling ME19 4LZ ☎ 01732 876095 ✆ neil.lawley@tmbc.gov.uk

Recycling & Waste Minimisation: Mr Dennis Gardner, Head of Waste & Street Scene, Gibson Building, Gibson Drive, Kings Hill, West Malling ME19 4LZ ☎ 01732 876204
✆ dennis.gardner@tmbc.gov.uk

Staff Training: Ms Delia Gordon, Personnel & Development Manager, Gibson Building, Gibson Drive, Kings Hill, West Malling ME19 4LZ ☎ 01732 876019 ✆ delia.gordon@tmbc.gov.uk

Street Scene: Mr Dennis Gardner, Head of Waste & Street Scene, Gibson Building, Gibson Drive, Kings Hill, West Malling ME19 4LZ
☎ 01732 876204 ✆ dennis.gardner@tmbc.gov.uk

Sustainable Communities: Mr Mark Raymond, Chief Corporate Policy Officer, Gibson Building, Gibson Drive, Kings Hill, West Malling ME19 4LZ ☎ 01732 876267 ✆ mark.raymond@tmbc.gov.uk

Waste Collection and Disposal: Mr Dennis Gardner, Head of Waste & Street Scene, Gibson Building, Gibson Drive, Kings Hill, West Malling ME19 4LZ ☎ 01732 876204
✆ dennis.gardner@tmbc.gov.uk

Waste Management: Mr Dennis Gardner, Head of Waste & Street Scene, Gibson Building, Gibson Drive, Kings Hill, West Malling ME19 4LZ ☎ 01732 876204 ✆ dennis.gardner@tmbc.gov.uk

COUNCILLORS

Mayor: Rhodes, Mark (CON - Hildenborough)
mark.rhodes@tmbc.gov.uk

Deputy Mayor: Dalton, Roger (CON - Burham & Wouldham)
roger.dalton@tmbc.gov.uk

Leader of the Council: Heslop, Nicolas (CON - Cage Green)
nicolas.heslop@tmbc.gov.uk

Deputy Leader of the Council: Coffin, Martin (CON - Wrotham, Ightham & Stansted)
martin.coffin@tmbc.gov.uk

Group Leader: Oakley, Anita (LD - Larkfield South)
anita.oakley@tmbc.gov.uk

Anderson, Jill (CON - Hadlow & East Peckham)
jill.anderson@tmbc.gov.uk

Baldock, Owen (CON - Castle)
owen.baldock@tmbc.gov.uk

Balfour, Matthew (CON - Downs & Mereworth)
matthew.balfour@tmbc.gov.uk

Barker, Sarah (CON - Kings Hill)
sarah.barker@tmbc.gov.uk

Base, Michael (CON - Aylesford North & Walderslade)
michael.base@tmbc.gov.uk

Bates, Pam (CON - Trench)
pam.bates@tmbc.gov.uk

Bell, Sue (CON - Snodland East & Ham Hill)
sue.bell@tmbc.gov.uk

Betts, Robin (CON - Wrotham, Ightham & Stansted)
robin.betts@tmbc.gov.uk

Bishop, Timothy (LD - Larkfield South)
timothy.bishop@tmbc.gov.uk

Bolt, Peter (CON - Judd)
peter.bolt@tmbc.gov.uk

Botten, Jon (CON - Medway)
jon.botten@tmbc.gov.uk

Branson, Vivian (CON - Castle)
vivian.branson@tmbc.gov.uk

Brown, Barbara (CON - Snodland West & Holborough Lakes)
barbara.brown@tmbc.gov.uk

Cannon, Tom (CON - Ditton)
tom.cannon@tmbc.gov.uk

Cure, David (CON - Judd)
david.cure@tmbc.gov.uk

Davis, Dave (CON - Burham & Wouldham)
dave.davis@tmbc.gov.uk

Davis, Mark (CON - Cage Green)
mark.davis@tmbc.gov.uk

Dean, Trudy (LD - Larkfield North)
trudy.dean@tmbc.gov.uk

Edmondston-Low, Tom (CON - Higham)
tom.edmondston-low@tmbc.gov.uk

Elks, Benjamin (CON - Medway)
benjamin.elks@tmbc.gov.uk

Hall, Sandra (CON - Aylesford North & Walderslade)
sandra.hall@tmbc.gov.uk

Hammond, Steve (CON - Aylesford South)
steve.hammond@tmbc.gov.uk

Heslep, Maria (CON - Vauxhall)
maria.heslep@tmbc.gov.uk

Jessel, Simon (CON - Wateringbury)
simon.jessel@tmbc.gov.uk

Keeley, David (CON - Snodland West & Holborough Lakes)
david.keeley@tmbc.gov.uk

TONBRIDGE & MALLING

Kemp, Ann (CON - Downs & Mereworth)
ann.kemp@tmbc.gov.uk

King, Steven (CON - Snodland West & Holborough Lakes)
steven.king@tmbc.gov.uk

Lancaster, Russell (CON - Medway)
russell.lancaster@tmbc.gov.uk

Lettington, David (CON - Snodland East & Ham Hill)
david.lettington@tmbc.gov.uk

Luck, Sasha (CON - West Malling & Leybourne)
sasha.luck@tmbc.gov.uk

Luker, Brian (CON - West Malling & Leybourne)
brian.luker@tmbc.gov.uk

Markham, Daniel (CON - East Malling)
daniel.markham@tmbc.gov.uk

Montague, Piers (CON - Kings Hill)
piers.montague@tmbc.gov.uk

O'Toole, Lee (CON - Kings Hill)
lee.otoole@tmbc.gov.uk

Parry-Waller, Mike (CON - Larkfield North)
mike.parry-waller@tmbc.gov.uk

Perry, Steve (CON - Borough Green & Long Mill)
steve.perry@tmbc.gov.uk

Rogers, Howard (CON - Hadlow & East Peckham)
howard.rogers@tmbc.gov.uk

Roud, Roger (LD - East Malling)
roger.roud@tmbc.gov.uk

Sergison, Janet (CON - Hadlow & East Peckham)
janet.sergison@tmbc.gov.uk

Shaw, Tim (IND - Borough Green & Long Mill)
tim.shaw@tmbc.gov.uk

Shrubsole, Sophie (CON - West Malling & Leybourne)
sophie.shrubsole@tmbc.gov.uk

Smith, Christopher (CON - Hildenborough)
christoper.smith@tmbc.gov.uk

Spence, Sarah (CON - Vauxhall)
sarah.spence@tmbc.gov.uk

Sullivan, Allan (CON - Aylesford North & Walderslade)
allan.sullivan@tmbc.gov.uk

Taylor, Mike (IND - Borough Green & Long Mill)
mike.taylor@tmbc.gov.uk

Tombolis, Frixos (CON - Higham)
frixos.tombolis@tmbc.gov.uk

Walker, Trevor (CON - Aylesford South)
trevor.c.walker@tmbc.gov.uk

Walker, Ben (CON - Ditton)
ben.walker@tmbc.gov.uk

POLITICAL COMPOSITION
CON: 47, LD: 4, IND: 2, Vacant: 1

COMMITTEE CHAIRS
Audit: Ms Vivian Branson

Licensing: Mrs Jill Anderson

Planning: Mr Dave Davis

Torbay U

Torbay Council, Town Hall, Castle Circus, Torquay TQ1 3DR
☎ 01803 201201 🖷 01803 292866 ✆ fss@torbay.gov.uk
🖳 www.torbay.gov.uk

FACTS AND FIGURES
Parliamentary Constituencies: Torbay
EU Constituencies: South West
Election Frequency: Elections are of whole council

PRINCIPAL OFFICERS

Chief Executive: Mr Steve Parrock, Executive Director, Tor Hill House, Union Street, Torquay TQ2 5QW ☎ 01803 208973 ✆ steve.parrock@torbay.gov.uk

Senior Management: Mr Andy Dempsey, Director - Children's Services, Town Hall, Castle Circus, Torquay TQ1 3DR ✆ andy.dempsey@torbay.gov.uk

Senior Management: Dr Caroline Dimond, Director - Public Health, Town Hall, Castle Circus, Torquay TQ1 3DR ✆ caroline.dimond@torbay.gov.uk

Senior Management: Ms Caroline Taylor, Director - Adult Services, Town Hall, Castle Circus, Torquay TQ1 3DR ☎ 01803 207116 ✆ caroline.taylor@torbay.gov.uk

Architect, Building / Property Services: Mr Robert Mason, Property Records & Estates Assistant, Tor Hill House, Union Street, Torquay TQ2 5QW ☎ 01803 207925 ✆ robert.mason@torbay.gov.uk

Building Control: Mr Colin Edgecombe, Senior Service Manager, Town Hall, Castle Circus, Torquay TQ1 3DR ☎ 01803 208085 ✆ colin.edgecombe@torbay.gov.uk

Children / Youth Services: Mr Andy Dempsey, Director - Children's Services, Town Hall, Castle Circus, Torquay TQ1 3DR ✆ andy.dempsey@torbay.gov.uk

Civil Registration: Mr Stephen Lemming, Superintendent Registrar, Oldway Mansion, Paignton, Torquay TQ3 2TE ☎ 01803 207130 ✆ stephen.lemming@torbay.gov.uk

PR / Communications: Mrs Michelle Pierce, Head of Communications, Tor Hill House, Union Street, Torquay TQ2 5QW ☎ 01803 208832 ✆ michelle.pierce@torbay.gov.uk

Community Safety: Ms Frances Hughes, Assistant Director - Community & Customer Services, Roebuck House, Abbey Road, Torquay TQ2 5TF ☎ 01803 208002 ✆ frances.hughes@torbay.gov.uk

Computer Management: Mr Bob Clark, Executive Head of Information Services, Town Hall, Castle Circus, Torquay TQ1 3DR ☎ 01803 207420 ✆ bob.clark@torbay.gov.uk

Consumer Protection and Trading Standards: Ms Frances Hughes, Assistant Director - Community & Customer Services, Roebuck House, Abbey Road, Torquay TQ2 5TF ☎ 01803 208002 ✆ frances.hughes@torbay.gov.uk

Contracts: Ms Tracey Field, Senior Procurement Officer, Town Hall, Castle Circus, Torquay TQ1 3DR ☎ 01803 208391 ✆ tracey.field@torbay.gov.uk

Corporate Services: Ms Anne-Marie Bond, Assistant Director - Corporate & Business Services, Town Hall, Castle Circus, Torquay TQ1 3DR ☎ 01803 207160 ✆ anne-marie.bond@torbay.gov.uk

Customer Service: Ms Alison Whittaker, Customer First Service Manager, Town Hall, Castle Circus, Torquay TQ1 3DR ☎ 01803 207221 ✆ alison.whittaker@torbay.gov.uk

Economic Development: Mr Steve Parrock, Executive Director, Tor Hill House, Union Street, Torquay TQ2 5QW ☎ 01803 208973 ✆ steve.parrock@torbay.gov.uk

Education: Mr Andy Dempsey, Director - Children's Services, Town Hall, Castle Circus, Torquay TQ1 3DR ✆ andy.dempsey@torbay.gov.uk

Electoral Registration: Ms Cathrine Haydn, Electoral Services Manager, Town Hall, Castle Circus, Torquay TQ1 3DR ☎ 01803 207076 ✆ catherine.haydn@torbay.gov.uk

Emergency Planning: Mr Chris Packer, Emergency Planning Officer, Town Hall, Castle Circus, Torquay TQ1 3DR ☎ 01803 207045 ✆ chris.packer@torbay.gov.uk

Environmental Health: Ms Frances Hughes, Assistant Director - Community & Customer Services, Town Hall, Castle Circus, Torquay TQ1 3DR ☎ 01803 208002 ✆ frances.hughes@torbay.gov.uk

European Liaison: Mr Alan Denby, Director - Economic Strategy, Tor Hill House, Torquay TQ2 5QW ☎ 01803 208671 ✆ alan.denby@torbay.gov.uk

Events Manager: Mr Phil Black, Culture & Events Service Manager, Town Hall, Castle Circus, Torquay TQ1 3DR ☎ 01803 207923 ✆ phil.black@torbay.gov.uk

Facilities: Mr Stuart Left, Facilities Management Officer, Tor Hill House, Union Street, Torquay TQ2 5QW ☎ 01803 208979 ✆ stuart.left@torbay.gov.uk

Health and Safety: Mr Colin de Jongh, Health & Safety Manager, Town Hall, Castle Circus, Torquay TQ1 3DR ☎ 01803 207161 ✆ colin.dejongh@torbay.gov.uk

Highways: Mr Ian Jones, Highways & Transport Services Manager, Town Hall, Castle Circus, Torquay TQ1 3DR ☎ 01803 207835 ✆ ian.jones@torbay.gov.uk

Housing: Ms Tara Fowler, Environmental Health Manager, Town Hall, Castle Circus, Torquay TQ1 3DR ☎ 01803 208074 ✆ tara.fowler@torbay.gov.uk

Legal: Ms Anne-Marie Bond, Assistant Director - Corporate & Business Services, Town Hall, Castle Circus, Torquay TQ1 3DR ☎ 01803 207160 ✆ anne-marie.bond@torbay.gov.uk

Leisure and Cultural Services: Mr Phil Black, Culture & Events Service Manager, Town Hall, Castle Circus, Torquay TQ1 3DR ☎ 01803 207923 ✆ phil.black@torbay.gov.uk

Licensing: Mr Steve Cox, Principal Safety & Licensing Officer, Town Hall, Castle Circus, Torquay TQ1 3DR ☎ 01803 208034 ✆ steve.cox@torbay.gov.uk

Lighting: Mr Dave Simmons, Street Lighting Engineer, Town Hall, Castle Circus, Torquay TQ1 3DR ☎ 01803 207718 ✆ dave.simmons@torbay.gov.uk

Member Services: Mrs June Gurry, Democratic Services Manager, Town Hall, Castle Circus, Torquay TQ1 3DR ☎ 01803 207012 ✆ june.gurry@torbay.gov.uk

Parking: Ms Susie Hayman, Service Manager, Town Hall, Castle Circus, Torquay TQ1 3DR ☎ 01803 207690 ✆ susie.hayman@torbay.gov.uk

Personnel / HR: Ms Susan Wiltshire, HR Manager, Town Hall, Castle Circus, Torquay TQ1 3DR ☎ 01803 207361 ✆ susan.wilson@torbay.gov.uk

Planning: Mr Pat Steward, Senior Service Manager, Town Hall, Castle Circus, Torquay TQ1 3DR ☎ 01803 208811 ✆ pat.steward@torbay.gov.uk

Procurement: Ms Tracey Field, Senior Procurement Officer, Town Hall, Castle Circus, Torquay TQ1 3DR ☎ 01803 208391 ✆ tracey.field@torbay.gov.uk

Recycling & Waste Minimisation: Ms Carol Arthur, Recycling Officer, Town Hall, Castle Circus, Torquay TQ1 3DR ☎ 01803 207744 ✆ carol.arthur@torbay.gov.uk

Regeneration: Mr Alan Denby, Director - Economic Strategy, Tor Hill House, Torquay TQ2 5QW ☎ 01803 208671 ✆ alan.denby@torbay.gov.uk

Road Safety: Ms Bev Hannah, Road Safety Officer, Town Hall, Castle Circus, Torquay TQ1 3DR ☎ 01803 207677 ✆ beverley.hannah@torbay.gov.uk

Public Health: Dr Caroline Dimond, Director - Public Health, Town Hall, Castle Circus, Torquay TQ1 3DR ✆ caroline.dimond@torbay.gov.uk

Sustainable Communities: Ms Frances Hughes, Assistant Director - Community & Customer Services, Town Hall, Castle Circus, Torquay TQ1 3DR ☎ 01803 208002 ✆ frances.hughes@torbay.gov.uk

Tourism: Ms Carolyn Custerton, Chief Executive Officer, 5 Vaughan Parade, Torquay TQ2 5JG ☎ 01803 296296 ✆ carolyn.custer@englishriviera.co.uk

Traffic Management: Mr Ian Jones, Highways & Transport Services Manager, Town Hall, Castle Circus, Torquay TQ1 3DR ☎ 01803 207835 ✆ ian.jones@torbay.gov.uk

TORBAY

Transport: Mr Ian Jones, Highways & Transport Services Manager, Town Hall, Castle Circus, Torquay TQ1 3DR ☎ 01803 207835 ⊕ ian.jones@torbay.gov.uk

Transport Planner: Mr Adam Luscombe, Transport Planning Officer, Town Hall, Castle Circus, Torquay TQ1 3DR ☎ 01803 207693 ⊕ adam.luscombe@torbay.gov.uk

Waste Collection and Disposal: Mr Ian Hartley, Waste Client Manager, Town Hall, Castle Circus, Torquay TQ1 3DR ☎ 01803 208695 ⊕ ian.hartley@torbay.gov.uk

Waste Management: Mr Ian Hartley, Waste Client Manager, Town Hall, Castle Circus, Torquay TQ1 3DR ☎ 01803 208695 ⊕ ian.hartley@torbay.gov.uk

COUNCILLORS

Chair: Hill, Ray (CON - St Marychurch)
ray.hill@torbay.gov.uk

Vice-Chair: Brooks, Anne (CON - St Marychurch)
anne.brooks@torbay.gov.uk

Mayor: Oliver, Gordon (CON - No Ward)
mayor@torbay.gov.uk

Deputy Mayor: Mills, Derek (CON - Churston with Galmpton)
derek.mills@torbay.gov.uk

Group Leader: Morey, Mike (IND - Berry Head with Furzeham)
mike.morey@torbay.gov.uk

Group Leader: Thomas, David (CON - Blatchcombe)
david.thomas@torbay.gov.uk

Amil, Nicole (CON - Cockington with Chelston)
nicole.amil@torbay.gov.uk

Barnby, Jane (CON - Goodrington with Roselands)
jane.barnby@torbay.gov.uk

Bent, Neil (CON - St Marychurch)
neil.bent@torbay.gov.uk

Bye, Nick (CON - Wellswood)
nick.bye@torbay.gov.uk

Carter, Christine (LD - Roundham with Hyde)
christine.carter@torbay.gov.uk

Cunningham, Barbara (CON - Roundham with Hyde)
barbara.cunningham@torbay.gov.uk

Darling, Mandy (LD - Tormohun)
mandy.darling@torbay.gov.uk

Darling, Steve (LD - Watcombe)
steve.darling@torbay.gov.uk

Doggett, Ian (LD - Clifton with Maidenway)
ian.doggett@torbay.gov.uk

Ellery, Vic (IND - Berry Head with Furzeham)
vic.ellery@torbay.gov.uk

Excell, Robert (CON - Tormohun)
Robert.Excell@torbay.gov.uk

Haddock, Richard (CON - St Marys with Summercombe)
richard.haddock@torbay.gov.uk

King, Mark (CON - Cockington with Chelston)
mark.king@torbay.gov.uk

Kingscote, Mark (CON - Shiphay with the Willows)
mark.kingscote@torbay.gov.uk

Lang, Andy (CON - Tormohun)
andy.lang@torbay.gov.uk

Lewis, Chris (CON - Preston)
chris.lewis@torbay.gov.uk

Manning, Terry (CON - St Marys with Summercombe)
terry.manning@torbay.gov.uk

Morris, Dave (CON - Shiphay with the Willows)
dave.morris@torbay.gov.uk

O'Dwyer, James (CON - Wellswood)
james.o'dwyer@torbay.gov.uk

Parrott, Julien (UKIP - Ellacombe)
julien.parrott@torbay.gov.uk

Robson, Chris (CON - Blatchcombe)
chris.robson@torbay.gov.uk

Sanders, Adrian (LD - Clifton with Maidenway)
adrian.sanders@torbay.gov.uk

Stockman, Jackie (IND - Berry Head with Furzeham)
jackie.stockman@torbay.gov.uk

Stocks, Cindy (LD - Ellacombe)
cindy.stocks@torbay.gov.uk

Stringer, Roger (LD - Watcombe)
roger.stringer@torbay.gov.uk

Stubley, Di (CON - Churston with Galmpton)
di.stubley@torbay.gov.uk

Sykes, Lynn (CON - Preston)
lynn.sykes@torbay.gov.uk

Thomas, John (CON - Blatchcombe)
john.thomas@torbay.gov.uk

Tolchard, Anna (CON - Preston)
anna.tolchard@torbay.gov.uk

Tyerman, Alan (CON - Goodrington with Roselands)
alan.tyerman@torbay.gov.uk

Winfield, Thomas (CON - Cockington with Chelston)
thomas.winfield@torbay.gov.uk

POLITICAL COMPOSITION
CON: 26, LD: 7, IND: 3, UKIP: 1

COMMITTEE CHAIRS

Audit: Mr Alan Tyerman

Development Management: Mr Mark Kingscote

Health & Wellbeing: Mr Derek Mills

Licensing: Mr Terry Manning

Torfaen   W

Torfaen County Borough Council, Civic Centre, Pontypool NP4 6YB
☎ 01495 762200 ⊠ 01495 755513 🖳 www.torfaen.gov.uk

FACTS AND FIGURES
Parliamentary Constituencies: Torfaen
EU Constituencies: Wales

Election Frequency: Elections are of whole council

PRINCIPAL OFFICERS

Chief Executive: Ms Alison Ward, Chief Executive, Civic Centre, Pontypool NP4 6YB ☎ 01495 742603 ⌂ alison.ward@torfaen.gov.uk

Assistant Chief Executive: Mr Nigel Aurelius, Assistant Chief Executive (Resources), Civic Centre, Pontypool NP4 6YB ☎ 01495 742623 ⌂ nigel.aurelius@torfaen.gov.uk

Assistant Chief Executive: Mr Dave Congreve, Assistant Chief Executive (Communities), Civic Centre, Pontypool NP4 6YB ☎ 01495 742606 ⌂ david.congreve@torfaen.gov.uk

Access Officer / Social Services (Disability): Ms Sue Evans, Chief Officer - Social Care & Housing, Police HQ, Croesyceiliog, Cwmbran NP44 2XJ ☎ 01495 762200 ⌂ sue.evans@torfaen.gov.uk

Best Value: Mrs Lynne Williams, Head of Business Support & Intelligence, Civic Centre, Pontypool NP4 6YB ☎ 01495 742158 ⌂ lynne.williams@torfaen.gov.uk

Building Control: Mr Dean Harris, Premises Manager, Civic Centre, Pontypool NP4 6YB ☎ 01495 762200 ⌂ dean.harris@torfaen.gov.uk

Catering Services: Ms Toni Edwards, Catering & Cleaning Manager, Croesyceiliog CEC, The Highway, Croesyceiliog, Cwmbran NP44 2HF ☎ 01495 762200 ⌂ toni.edwards@torfaen.gov.uk

Children / Youth Services: Mr Keith Rutherford, Head of Children's Services, Civic Centre, Pontypool NP4 6YB ☎ 01633 648622 ⌂ keith.rutherford@torfaen.gov.uk

Civil Registration: Ms Lisa Dando-Ellis, Head of Customer Care Services & Registration, Civic Centre, Pontypool NP4 6YB ☎ 01495 762200 ⌂ lisa.dando-ellis@torfaen.gov.uk

PR / Communications: Mr Neil Jones, Head of Communication & Civil Contingencies, Civic Centre, Pontypool NP4 6YB ☎ 01495 742151 ⌂ neil.jones@torfaen.gov.uk

Community Planning: Mr Mark Sharwood, Public Services Development Manager, Civic Centre, Pontypool NP4 6YB ☎ 01495 742157 ⌂ mark.sharwood@torfaen.gov.uk

Community Safety: Ms Karen Kerslake, Information & Communications Team Manager, Civic Centre, Pontypool NP4 6YB ☎ 01633 628971 ⌂ karen.kerslake@torfaen.gov.uk

Computer Management: Mr Stephen Jeynes, Service & Technical Manager, SRS, Gilchrist Thomas Industrial Estate, Blaenavon NP4 9RL ☎ 01495 762200 ⌂ stephen.jeynes@torfaen.gov.uk

Corporate Services: Mr Richard Edmunds, Head of Strategic Services & Democratic Support, Civic Centre, Pontypool NP4 6YB ☎ 01495 742163 ⌂ richard.edmunds@torfaen.gov.uk

Customer Service: Ms Lisa Dando-Ellis, Head of Customer Care Services & Registration, Civic Centre, Pontypool NP4 6YB ☎ 01495 762200 ⌂ lisa.dando-ellis@torfaen.gov.uk

Customer Service: Ms Linda King, Customer Services Manager, Civic Centre, Pontypool NP4 6YB ☎ 01495 766363 ⌂ linda.king@torfaen.gov.uk

Education: Mr Dermot McChrystal, Interim Head of Education Services, Pearl House, Hanbury Road, Pontypool NP4 6JL ☎ 01495 762200 ⌂ dermot.mcchrystal@torfaen.gov.uk

E-Government: Mr Matt Lewis, Chief Operating Officer, SRS, Gilchrist Thomas Industrial Estate, Blaenavon NP4 9RL ☎ 01495 762200 ⌂ matt.lewis@torfaen.gov.uk

Electoral Registration: Ms Caroline Jenever-Jones, Elections & Business Manager, Civic Centre, Pontypool NP4 6YB ☎ 01495 762200 ⌂

Emergency Planning: Mr Neil Jones, Head of Communication & Civil Contingencies, Civic Centre, Pontypool NP4 6YB ☎ 01495 742151 ⌂ neil.jones@torfaen.gov.uk

Energy Management: Mr Allan Jones, Energy Manager, Ty Blaen, New Inn, Pontypool NP4 0LS ☎ 01495 742898 ⌂ allan.jones@torfaen.gov.uk

Environmental Health: Ms Kim Pugh, Head of Public Protection, Pearl House, Hanbury Road, Pontypool NP4 6JL ☎ 01495 762200 ⌂ kim.pugh@torfaen.gov.uk

Estates, Property & Valuation: Mr Robert Flower, Estates & Valuation Manager, Civic Centre, Pontypool NP4 6YB ☎ 01495 742897 ⌂ robert.flower@torfaen.gov.uk

European Liaison: Mr Rob Wellington, Head of European Policy & External Funding, Civic Centre, Pontypool NP4 6YB ☎ 01495 742143 ⌂ rob.wellington@torfaen.gov.uk

Events Manager: Ms Verity Hiscocks, Arts Development Manager, Ty Blaen, New Inn, Pontypool NP4 0LS ☎ 01495 762200 ⌂ verity.hiscocks@torfaen.gov.uk

Finance: Mr David Lilly, Head of Financial Services, Civic Centre, Pontypool NP4 6YB ☎ 01495 742624 ⌂ david.lilly@torfaen.gov.uk

Pensions: Ms Mary Rollin, Pensions Manager, Civic Centre, Pontypool NP4 6YB ☎ 01495 762200 ⌂ mary.rollin@torfaen.gov.uk

Fleet Management: Mr Rico Cottrell, Transport & Depot Manager, Ty Blaen, New Inn, Pontypool NP4 0LS ☎ 01495 766798 ⌂ rico.cottrell@torfaen.gov.uk

Grounds Maintenance: Mr Steve Horseman, Streetscene Co-ordinator, Ty Blaen, New Inn, Pontypool NP4 0LS ☎ 01495 762200 ⌂ steve.horsham@torfaen.gov.uk

Health and Safety: Ms Claire Burt, Corporate Health & Safety Manager, Civic Centre, Pontypool NP4 6YB ☎ 01495 762200 ⌂ claire.burt@torfaen.gov.uk

Highways: Mr Steve Jarrett, Head of Highways & Transportation, County Hall, Cwmbran NP44 2WN ☎ 01495 742426 ⌂ steve.jarrett@torfaen.gov.uk

TORFAEN

Home Energy Conservation: Mr Allan Jones, Energy Manager, County Hall, Cwmbran NP44 2WN ☎ 01495 742898 ⏚ allan.jones@torfaen.gov.uk

Housing: Mr Neil Howell, Head of Housing & Business Support, Ty'r Efail, Lower Mill Field, Pontypool NP4 0RH ☎ 01495 762200 ⏚ neil.howell@torfaen.gov.uk

Legal: Ms Lynda Willis, Chief Legal Officer & Monitoring Officer, Civic Centre, Pontypool NP4 6YB ☎ 01495 762660 ⏚ lynda.willis@torfaen.gov.uk

Licensing: Mr Steve Bendell, Team Leader - Licensing, Ty Blaen, New Inn, Pontypool NP4 0LS ☎ 01495 747279 ⏚ steve.bendell@torfaen.gov.uk

Lifelong Learning: Ms Ann Brain, Adult Education Officer, Croesyceiliog CEC, The Highway, Croesyceiliog, Cwmbran NP44 2HF ☎ 01633 648154 ⏚ ann.brain@torfaen.gov.uk

Lighting: Mr Steve Jarrett, Head of Highways & Transportation, County Hall, Cwmbran NP44 2WN ☎ 01495 742426 ⏚ steve.jarrett@torfaen.gov.uk

Lottery Funding, Charity and Voluntary: Mr Rob Wellington, Head of European Policy & External Funding, Civic Centre, Pontypool NP4 6YB ☎ 01495 742143 ⏚ rob.wellington@tofaen.gov.uk

Member Services: Mrs Lynne Williams, Head of Business Support & Intelligence, Civic Centre, Pontypool NP4 6YB ☎ 01495 742158 ⏚ lynne.williams@torfaen.gov.uk

Parking: Mr Steve Horseman, Streetscene Co-ordinator, Ty Blaen, New Inn, Pontypool NP4 0LS ☎ 01495 762200 ⏚ steve.horsham@torfaen.gov.uk

Partnerships: Mr Lyndon Puddy, Head of Public Service Support Unit, Civic Centre, Pontypool NP4 6YB ⏚ lyndon.puddy@torfaen.gov.uk

Personnel / HR: Mr Graeme Russell, Head of Human Resources & Pension, Civic Centre, Pontypool NP4 6YB ☎ 01495 742568 ⏚ graeme.russell@torfaen.gov.uk

Planning: Mr Duncan Smith, Chief Planning & Public Protection Officer, Ty Blaen, New Inn, Pontypool NP4 0LS ☎ 01495 742568 ⏚ duncan.smith@torfaen.gov.uk

Procurement: Mr Andrew Maisey, Head of Procurement, Civic Centre, Pontypool NP4 6YB ☎ 01495 742380 ⏚ andrew.maisey@torfaen.gov.uk

Public Libraries: Ms Christine George, Torfaen Library & Information Manager, Ty Blaen, Torfaen, Panteg Way, New Inn, Pontypool NP4 0LS ☎ 01633 628943 ⏚ christine.george@torfaen.gov.uk

Recycling & Waste Minimisation: Mr Cynon Edwards, Waste Management Group Leader, Ty Blaen, New Inn, Pontypool NP4 0LS ☎ 01495 766789 ⏚ cynon.edwards@torfaen.gov.uk

Regeneration: Ms Cath Thomas, Head of Economy, Enterprise & Environment, Civic Centre, Pontypool NP4 6YB ☎ 01495 762200 ⏚ cath.thomas@torfaen.gov.uk

Road Safety: Mr Pat Bates, Road Safety Strategy Officer, Ty Blaen, New Inn, Pontypool NP4 0LS ☎ 01495 762200 ⏚ patrick.bates@torfaen.gov.uk

Social Services: Ms Sue Evans, Chief Officer - Social Care & Housing, Police HQ, Croesyceiliog, Cwmbran NP44 2XJ ☎ 01495 762200 ⏚ sue.evans@torfaen.gov.uk

Social Services (Adult): Ms Sue Evans, Chief Officer - Social Care & Housing, Police HQ, Croesyceiliog, Cwmbran NP44 2XJ ☎ 01495 762200 ⏚ sue.evans@torfaen.gov.uk

Social Services (Children): Ms Sue Evans, Chief Officer - Social Care & Housing, Police HQ, Croesyceiliog, Cwmbran NP44 2XJ ☎ 01495 762200 ⏚ sue.evans@torfaen.gov.uk

Street Scene: Mr Steve Horseman, Streetscene Co-ordinator, Ty Blaen, New Inn, Pontypool NP4 0LS ☎ 01495 762200 ⏚ steve.horsham@torfaen.gov.uk

Sustainable Communities: Ms Rachael O'Shaughnessy, Environmental & Sustainability Manager, Ty Blaen, New Inn, Pontypool NP4 0LS ☎ 01633 648018 ⏚ rachael.o'shaughnessy@torfaen.gov.uk

Sustainable Development: Ms Rachael O'Shaughnessy, Environmental & Sustainability Manager, Ty Blaen, New Inn, Pontypool NP4 0LS ☎ 01633 648018 ⏚ rachael.o'shaughnessy@torfaen.gov.uk

Tourism: Mrs Katie Gates, Team Leader - Economy & Heritage Tourism, Civic Centre, Pontypool NP4 6YB ☎ 01495 762200 ⏚ katie.gates@torfaen.gov.uk

Town Centre: Mr David Evans, Team Leader - Pontypool Regeneration, Pearl House, Hanbury Road, Pontypool NP4 6JL ☎ 01495 762200 ⏚ david.evans@torfaen.gov.uk

Traffic Management: Mr Andrew Williams, Group Leader - Highways, Traffic & Engineering, Ty Blaen, New Inn, Pontypool NP4 0LS ☎ 01495 742426 ⏚ andrew.williams@torfaen.gov.uk

Transport: Mr Andrew Williams, Group Leader - Highways, Traffic & Engineering, Ty Blaen, New Inn, Pontypool NP4 0LS ☎ 01495 742426 ⏚ andrew.williams@torfaen.gov.uk

Transport Planner: Mr Andrew Williams, Group Leader - Highways, Traffic & Engineering, Ty Blaen, New Inn, Pontypool NP4 0LS ☎ 01495 742426 ⏚ andrew.williams@torfaen.gov.uk

Waste Collection and Disposal: Mr Cynon Edwards, Waste Management Group Leader, Ty Blaen, New Inn, Pontypool NP4 0LS ☎ 01495 766789 ⏚ cynon.edwards@torfaen.gov.uk

Waste Management: Mr Cynon Edwards, Waste Management Group Leader, Ty Blaen, New Inn, Pontypool NP4 0LS ☎ 01495 766789 ⏚ cynon.edwards@torfaen.gov.uk

Children's Play Areas: Mr Steve Horseman, Streetscene Co-ordinator, Ty Blaen, New Inn, Pontypool NP4 0LS ☎ 01495 762200 ✆ steve.horsham@torfaen.gov.uk

COUNCILLORS

Mayor: Crick, Veronica (LAB - Croesyceiliog South)
veronica.crick@torfaen.gov.uk

Deputy Mayor: Powell, Jessica (LAB - Pontnewydd)
jessica.powell@torfaen.gov.uk

Leader of the Council: Wellington, Robert (LAB - Greenmeadow)
leader@torfaen.gov.uk

Deputy Leader of the Council: Hunt, Anthony (LAB - Panteg)
anthony.hunt@torfaen.gov.uk

Ashley, Stuart (LAB - Pontnewydd)
stuart.ashley@torfaen.gov.uk

Barnett, Mary (LAB - Upper Cwmbran)
mary.barnett@torfaen.gov.uk

Bevan, Huw (CON - Llanyravon South)
huw.bevan@torfaen.gov.uk

Brooks, Stephen (LAB - St Dials)
stephen.brooks@torfaen.gov.uk

Burnett, Ronald (IND - Two Locks & Henllys)
ronald.burnett@torfaen.gov.uk

Cameron, Pamela (LAB - Two Locks & Henllys)
pamela.cameron@torfaen.gov.uk

Caron, Glyn (LAB - Llanyravon North)
glyn.caron@torfaen.gov.uk

Clark, Gwyneira (LAB - Abersychan)
gwyneira.clark@torfaen.gov.uk

Clark, Richard (LAB - Croesyceiliog North)
richard.clark@torfaen.gov.uk

Constance, Leonard (LAB - Brynwern)
leonard.constance@torfaen.gov.uk

Cross, Fiona (PC - Coed Eva)
fiona.cross@torfaen.gov.uk

Cunningham, B John (LAB - Upper Cwmbran)
john.cunningham@torfaen.gov.uk

Daniels, David (LAB - Llantarnam)
david.daniels@torfaen.gov.uk

Davies, Nigel (LAB - Croesyceiliog North)
nigel.davies@torfaen.gov.uk

Davies, Giles (LAB - Abersychan)
giles.davies@torfaen.gov.uk

Evans, Stuart (IND - Blaenavon)
stuart.evans@torfaen.gov.uk

Furzer, Alun (LAB - Blaenavon)
alun.furzer@torfaen.gov.uk

Graham, Maria (IND - Llantarnam)
maria.graham@torfaen.gov.uk

Harnett, Kelvin (IND - Pontnewynydd)
kelvin.harnett@torfaen.gov.uk

Harris, Michael (IND - Pontypool)
michael.harris@torfaen.gov.uk

Haynes, Elizabeth (IND - St Dials)
elizabeth.haynes@torfaen.gov.uk

James, Keith (CON - New Inn)
keith.james@torfaen.gov.uk

Jeremiah, Mike (IND - Wainfelin)
mike.jeremiah@torfaen.gov.uk

Jones, Alan (LAB - Blaenavon)
alan.s.jones@torfaen.gov.uk

Jones, Lewis (LAB - Trevethin)
deputyleader@torfaen.gov.uk

Kemp, Robert (IND - Upper Cwmbran)
robert.kemp@torfaen.gov.uk

Marshall, John (LAB - Trevethin)
john.marshal@torfaen.gov.uk

Mason, Neil (LAB - St Cadocs & Penygarn)
neil.mason@torfaen.gov.uk

Mawby, Brian (LAB - Pontnewydd)
brian.mawby@torfaen.gov.uk

Mills, Raymond (CON - New Inn)
raymond.mills@torfaen.gov.uk

Owen, Amanda (LAB - Greenmeadow)
amanda.owen@torfaen.gov.uk

Parrish, Norma (LAB - Panteg)
norma.parrish@torfaen.gov.uk

Rees, Jeff (PC - Fairwater)
jeff.rees@torfaen.gov.uk

Seabourne, Philip (LAB - Fairwater)
phil.seabourne@torfaen.gov.uk

Smith, Graham (CON - New Inn)
graham.smith@torfaen.gov.uk

Taylor, Barry (LAB - Snatchwood)
barry.taylor@torfaen.gov.uk

Thomas, Colette (LAB - Two Locks & Henllys)
colette.thomas@torfaen.gov.uk

Tomlinson, Wayne (IND - Abersychan)
wayne.tomlinson@torfaen.gov.uk

Waite, Neil (LAB - Cwmynyscoy)
neil.waite@torfaen.gov.uk

Yeowell, David (LAB - Panteg)
david.yeowell@torfaen.gov.uk

POLITICAL COMPOSITION
LAB: 29, IND: 9, CON: 4, PC: 2

COMMITTEE CHAIRS

Audit: Mr Jeff Rees

Licensing: Mr Neil Waite

Pensions: Ms Mary Barnett

Planning: Mr Brian Mawby

Torridge   D

Torridge District Council, Riverbank House, Bideford
EX39 2QG
☎ 01237 428700 🖷 01237 479164 ✆ customer.services@torridge.gov.uk
🖥 www.torridge.gov.uk

TORRIDGE

FACTS AND FIGURES
Parliamentary Constituencies: Devon West and Torridge
EU Constituencies: South West
Election Frequency: Elections are of whole council

PRINCIPAL OFFICERS

Chief Executive: Mrs Jenny Wallace, Head of Paid Service, Riverbank House, Bideford EX39 2QG ☎ 01237 428700 ✆ jenny.wallace@torridge.gov.uk

Senior Management: Mr Steve Hearse, Strategic Manager - Resources (& S151 Officer), Riverbank House, Bideford EX39 2QG ☎ 01237 428700 ✆ steve.hearse@torridge.gov.uk

Senior Management: Mr Jamie Hollis, Senior Solicitor & Monitoring Officer, Riverbank House, Bideford EX39 2QG ☎ 01237 428700 ✆ jamie.hollis@torridge.gov.uk

Architect, Building / Property Services: Mr David Green, Planning Manager, Riverbank House, Bideford EX39 2QG ☎ 01237 428721 ✆ david.green@torridge.gov.uk

Community Planning: Mr David Green, Planning Manager, Riverbank House, Bideford EX39 2QG ☎ 01237 428721 ✆ david.green@torridge.gov.uk

Computer Management: Mr Roger Bonaparte, Business Transformation Manager, Bridge Buildings, Bideford EX39 2HT ☎ 01237 428700 ✆ roger.bonaparte@torridge.gov.uk

Contracts: Mr Andrew Waite, Property Manager, Riverbank House, Bideford EX39 2QG ☎ 01237 428752 ✆ andrew.waite@torridge.gov.uk

Contracts: Mr Andrew Waite, Property Manager, Riverbank House, Bideford EX39 2QG ☎ 01237 428752 ✆ andrew.waite@torridge.gov.uk

Corporate Services: Mr Jon Walter, Governance Manager, Riverbank House, Bideford EX39 2QG ☎ 01237 428700 ✆ jon.walter@torridge.gov.uk

Customer Service: Mr Simon Toon, Customer Support Manager, Riverbank House, Bideford EX39 2QG ☎ 01237 428980 ✆ simon.toon@torridge.gov.uk

Direct Labour: Mr Richard Haste, Waste & Recycling Manager, Riverbank House, Bideford EX39 2QG ☎ 01237 428963 ✆ richard.haste@torridge.gov.uk

Electoral Registration: Ms Charlotte Gordon, Senior Electoral & Democratic Services Officer, Riverbank House, Bideford EX39 2QG ☎ 01237 428701 ✆ charlotte.gordon@torridge.gov.uk

Energy Management: Mr Andrew Waite, Property Manager, Riverbank House, Bideford EX39 2QG ☎ 01237 428752 ✆ andrew.waite@torridge.gov.uk

Estates, Property & Valuation: Mr Andrew Waite, Property Manager, Riverbank House, Bideford EX39 2QG ☎ 01237 428752 ✆ andrew.waite@torridge.gov.uk

Finance: Mr Steve Hearse, Strategic Manager - Resources (& S151 Officer), Riverbank House, Bideford EX39 2QG ☎ 01237 428700 ✆ steve.hearse@torridge.gov.uk

Health and Safety: Mr Christopher Parkhouse, Corporate Health & Safety Advisor, Riverbank House, Bideford EX39 2QG ☎ 01237 428820 ✆ christopher.parkhouse@torridge.gov.uk

Legal: Mr Jamie Hollis, Senior Solicitor & Monitoring Officer, Riverbank House, Bideford EX39 2QG ☎ 01237 428700 ✆ jamie.hollis@torridge.gov.uk

Leisure and Cultural Services: Mr Sean Kearney, Commercial & Leisure Services Manager, Riverbank House, Bideford EX39 2QG ☎ 01237 428700 ✆ sean.kearney@torridge.gov.uk

Member Services: Mr Jon Walter, Governance Manager, Riverbank House, Bideford EX39 2QG ☎ 01237 428700 ✆ jon.walter@torridge.gov.uk

Personnel / HR: Mrs Sarah Ayres, Human Resources Manager, Riverbank House, Bideford EX39 2QG ☎ 01237 428700 ✆ sarah.ayres@torridge.gov.uk

Planning: Mr David Green, Planning Manager, Riverbank House, Bideford EX39 2QG ☎ 01237 428721 ✆ david.green@torridge.gov.uk

Recycling & Waste Minimisation: Mr Richard Haste, Waste & Recycling Manager, Westcombe Depot, Westcombe, Bideford EX39 3JQ ☎ 01237 428963 ✆ richard.haste@torridge.gov.uk

Recycling & Waste Minimisation: Mr Richard Haste, Waste & Recycling Manager, Riverbank House, Bideford EX39 2QG ☎ 01237 428963 ✆ richard.haste@torridge.gov.uk

Staff Training: Mrs Sarah Ayres, Human Resources Manager, Riverbank House, Bideford EX39 2QG ☎ 01237 428700 ✆ sarah.ayres@torridge.gov.uk

Street Scene: Mr Richard Haste, Waste & Recycling Manager, Riverbank House, Bideford EX39 2QG ☎ 01237 428963 ✆ richard.haste@torridge.gov.uk

Waste Collection and Disposal: Mr Richard Haste, Waste & Recycling Manager, Riverbank House, Bideford EX39 2QG ☎ 01237 428963 ✆ richard.haste@torridge.gov.uk

Waste Collection and Disposal: Mr Richard Haste, Waste & Recycling Manager, Riverbank House, Bideford EX39 2QG ☎ 01237 428963 ✆ richard.haste@torridge.gov.uk

Waste Management: Mr Richard Haste, Waste & Recycling Manager, Riverbank House, Bideford EX39 2QG ☎ 01237 428963 ✆ richard.haste@torridge.gov.uk

COUNCILLORS

Chair: Langmead, Mervyn (CON - Bideford East)
councillor.langmead@torridge.gov.uk

Vice-Chair: Himan, John (CON - Northam)
councillor.himan@torridge.gov.uk

Leader of the Council: Whittaker, Jane (CON - Northam)
councillor.whittaker@torridge.gov.uk

Boundy, Betty (CON - Winkleigh)
councillor.boundy@torridge.gov.uk

Boyle, Alison (CON - Kenwith)
councillor.boyle@torridge.gov.uk

Brenton, David (LAB - Bideford South)
councillor.brenton@torridge.gov.uk

Brown, Margaret (IND - Torrington)
councillor.brown@torridge.gov.uk

Carroll, Ken (CON - Holsworthy)
councillor.carroll@torridge.gov.uk

Christie, Peter (GRN - Bideford North)
councillor.christie@torridge.gov.uk

Darch, Roger (UKIP - Torrington)
councillor.darch@torridge.gov.uk

Dart, Anna (IND - Hartland & Bradworthy)
councillor.dart@torridge.gov.uk

Davis, Kenny (UKIP - Appledore)
councillor.davis@torridge.gov.uk

Dezart, Gaston (UKIP - Bideford East)
councillor.dezart@torridge.gov.uk

Eastman, Andrew (CON - Appledore)
councillor.eastman@torridge.gov.uk

Gregorek, Zyg (CON - Forest)
councillor.gregorek@torridge.gov.uk

Hackett, Philip (CON - Coham Bridge)
councillor.hackett@torridge.gov.uk

Hancock, Richard (UKIP - Northam)
councillor.hancock@torridge.gov.uk

Hicks, Robert (IND - Waldon)
councillor.hicks@torridge.gov.uk

Hurley, David (CON - Shebbear & Langtree)
councillor.hurley@torridge.gov.uk

Inch, Simon (CON - Bideford South)
councillor.simoninch@torridge.gov.uk

Inch, Anthony (CON - Bideford South)
councillor.tonyinch@torridge.gov.uk

James, Kenneth (IND - Tamarside)
councillor.james@torridge.gov.uk

Johns, Trevor (LD - Bideford North)
councillor.tjohns@torridge.gov.uk

Julian, Robin (UKIP - Clovelly Bay)
councillor.julian@torridge.gov.uk

Langton-Lockton, John (CON - Orchard Hill)
cllr.langton-lockton@torridge.gov.uk

Le Maistre, Peter (CON - Westward Ho!)
councillor.lemaistre@torridge.gov.uk

Lock, Rosemary (CON - Three Moors)
councillor.lock@torridge.gov.uk

McGeough, Dermot (CON - Bideford North)
councillor.mcgeough@torridge.gov.uk

Morrish, James (CON - Two Rivers)
councillor.morrish@torridge.gov.uk

Parker, Ian (CON - Holsworthy)
councillor.parker@torridge.gov.uk

Pennington, Philip (IND - Monkleigh & Littleham)
councillor.pennington@torridge.gov.uk

Robinson, Sam (CON - Bideford East)
councillor.robinson@torridge.gov.uk

Simmons, Catherine (INDNA - Torrington)
councillor.simmons@torridge.gov.uk

Watson, Peter (CON - Broadheath)
councillor.watson@torridge.gov.uk

Whittle, Alan (UKIP - Hartland & Bradworthy)
councillor.whittle@torridge.gov.uk

Wiseman, Richard (IND - Clinton)
councillor.wiseman@torridge.gov.uk

POLITICAL COMPOSITION
CON: 20, IND: 6, UKIP: 6, INDNA: 1, LAB: 1, LD: 1, GRN: 1

COMMITTEE CHAIRS

Audit: Mr Philip Hackett

Licensing: Mr Anthony Inch

Planning: Mrs Rosemary Lock

Tower Hamlets   L

Tower Hamlets London Borough Council, Town Hall, Mulberry Place, 5 Clove Crescent, London E14 2BG
☎ 020 7364 5000 🖨 020 7364 4296
⌨ forename.surname@towerhamlets.gov.uk
🖥 www.towerhamlets.gov.uk

FACTS AND FIGURES
Parliamentary Constituencies: Bethnal Green and Bow, Poplar and Limehouse
EU Constituencies: London
Election Frequency: Elections are of whole council

PRINCIPAL OFFICERS

Chief Executive: Mr Will Tuckley, Chief Executive, Town Hall, Mulberry Place, 5 Clove Crescent, London E14 2BG
☎ 020 7364 5000 ⌨ will.tuckley@towerhamlets.gov.uk

Senior Management: Ms Melanie Clay, Corporate Director - Law, Probity, Governance & Monitoring Officer, Town Hall, Mulberry Place, 5 Clove Crescent, London E14 2BG ☎ 020 7364 4801
⌨ melanie.clay@towerhamlets.gov.uk

Senior Management: Ms Zena Cooke, Corporate Director - Resources, Town Hall, Mulberry Place, 5 Clove Crescent, London E14 2BG ⌨ zeena.cooke@towerhamlets.gov.uk

Senior Management: Mr Aman Dalvi, Corporate Director - Development & Renewal, Town Hall, Mulberry Place, 5 Clove Crescent, London E14 2BG ☎ 020 7634 4247
⌨ aman.dalvi@towerhamlets.gov.uk

Senior Management: Ms Debbie Jones, Corporate Director - Children's Services, Town Hall, Mulberry Place, 5 Clove Crescent, London E14 2BG ⌨ debbie.jones@towerhamlets.gov.uk

TOWER HAMLETS

Senior Management: Mrs Denise Radley, Director - Adults' Services, Town Hall, Mulberry Place, 5 Clove Crescent, London E14 2BG ☏ denise.radley@towerhamlets.gov.uk

Architect, Building / Property Services: Ms Ann Sutcliffe, Service Head - Corporate Property & Capital Delivery, Town Hall, Mulberry Place, 5 Clove Crescent, London E14 2BG ☎ 020 7364 4077 ☏ ann.sutcliffe@towerhamlets.gov.uk

Building Control: Mr John McGeary, Building Control Manager, Town Hall, Mulberry Place, 5 Clove Crescent, London E14 2BG ☎ 020 7364 5242 ☏ john.mcgeary@towerhamlets.gov.uk

Children / Youth Services: Mr Terry Parkin, Interim Service Head - Learning & Achievement, Town Hall, Mulberry Place, 5 Clove Crescent, London E14 2BG ☎ 020 7364 4056 ☏ terry.parkin@towerhamlets.gov.uk

Civil Registration: Ms Catherine Sutton, Superintendent Registrar, Bromley Public Hall, Bow Road, London E3 3AA ☎ 020 7364 7983 ☏ catherine.sutton@towerhamlets.gov.uk

PR / Communications: Mr Andreas Christophorou, Head of Communications & Marketing, Town Hall, Mulberry Place, 5 Clove Crescent, London E14 2BG ☏ andreas.christophorou@towerhamlets.gov.uk

Community Safety: Mr Andy Bamber, Service Head - Safer Communities, Town Hall, Mulberry Place, 5 Clove Crescent, London E14 2BG ☎ 020 7364 0764 ☏ andy.bamber@towerhamlets.gov.uk

Computer Management: Mr Sean Green, Service Head - Customer Access, Transformation & ICT, Town Hall, Mulberry Place, 5 Clove Crescent, London E14 2BG ☎ 020 7364 4672 ☏ sean.green@towerhamlets.gov.uk

Consumer Protection and Trading Standards: Mr Dave Tolley, Head of Trading Standards & Environmental Health, Toby Club, Vawdrey Close, London E1 4UA ☎ 020 7364 6724 ☏ david.tolley@towerhamlets.gov.uk

Contracts: Mr Zamil Ahmed, Head of Procurment & Programme Management, Town Hall, Mulberry Place, 5 Clove Crescent, London E14 2BG ☎ 020 7364 4385 ☏ zamil.ahmed@towerhamlets.gov.uk

Contracts: Ms Philippa Terry, Head - Contracts Services, Ground Floor, Council Offices, Toby Lane, London E1 4DN ☎ 020 7364 5161 ☏ philippa.terry@towerhamlets.gov.uk

Customer Service: Mr Keith Paulin, Head of Customer Services, Town Hall, Mulberry Place, 5 Clove Crescent, London E14 2BG ☎ 020 7364 3118 ☏ keith.paulin@towerhamlets.gov.uk

Economic Development: Mr Aman Dalvi, Corporate Director - Development & Renewal, Town Hall, Mulberry Place, 5 Clove Crescent, London E14 2BG ☎ 020 7634 4247 ☏ aman.dalvi@towerhamlets.gov.uk

Education: Ms Debbie Jones, Corporate Director - Children's Services, Town Hall, Mulberry Place, 5 Clove Crescent, London E14 2BG ☏ debbie.jones@towerhamlets.gov.uk

Electoral Registration: Ms Louise Stamp, Head of Electoral Services, Town Hall, Mulberry Place, 5 Clove Crescent, London E14 2BG ☎ 020 7364 3139 ☏ louise.stamp@towerhamlets.gov.uk

Emergency Planning: Mr Steve Crawley, Civil Protection & Business Continuity Co-ordinator, 3rd Floor, Mulberry Place, 5 Clove Crescent, London E14 2BE ☎ 020 7364 4181 ☏ steve.crawley@towerhamlets.gov.uk

Energy Management: Ms Sian Pipe, Energy Manager, Energy Efficiency Unit, Gladstone Place, Roman Road, London E3 5ES ☎ 020 7364 2523 ☏ sian.pipe@towerhamlets.gov.uk

Environmental / Technical Services: Mr Andy Bamber, Service Head - Safer Communities, Town Hall, Mulberry Place, 5 Clove Crescent, London E14 2BG ☎ 020 7364 0764 ☏ andy.bamber@towerhamlets.gov.uk

Environmental / Technical Services: Mr Dave Tolley, Head of Trading Standards & Environmental Health, Toby Club, Vawdrey Close, London E1 4UA ☎ 020 7364 6724 ☏ david.tolley@towerhamlets.gov.uk

Estates, Property & Valuation: Ms Ann Sutcliffe, Service Head - Corporate Property & Capital Delivery, Town Hall, Mulberry Place, 5 Clove Crescent, London E14 2BG ☎ 020 7364 4077 ☏ ann.sutcliffe@towerhamlets.gov.uk

Events Manager: Mr Steve Murray, Head - Arts & Events, 192 - 196 Hanbury Street, London E1 5HU ☎ 020 7364 7910 ☏ stephen.murray@towerhamlets.gov.uk

Facilities: Ms Ann Sutcliffe, Service Head - Corporate Property & Capital Delivery, Town Hall, Mulberry Place, 5 Clove Crescent, London E14 2BG ☎ 020 7364 4077 ☏ ann.sutcliffe@towerhamlets.gov.uk

Finance: Ms Zena Cook, Corporate Director - Resources, Town Hall, Mulberry Place, 5 Clove Crescent, London E14 2BG ☎ 020 7364 4700 ☏ zena.cook@towerhamlets.gov.uk

Pensions: Mr Anant Dodia, Pensions Manager, Town Hall, Mulberry Place, 5 Clove Crescent, London E14 2BG ☎ 020 7364 4248 ☏ anant.dodia@towerhamlets.gov.uk

Fleet Management: Mr Lee Perry, Passenger Services Operations Manager, 1 Silvocea Way, Blackwall, London E14 0JJ ☎ 020 7364 4977 ☏ lee.perry@towerhamlets.gov.uk

Grounds Maintenance: Ms Ann Sutcliffe, Service Head - Corporate Property & Capital Delivery, Town Hall, Mulberry Place, 5 Clove Crescent, London E14 2BG ☎ 020 7364 4077 ☏ ann.sutcliffe@towerhamlets.gov.uk

Health and Safety: Mr Dave Tolley, Head of Trading Standards & Environmental Health, Toby Club, Vawdrey Close, London E1 4UA ☎ 020 7364 6724 ☏ david.tolley@towerhamlets.gov.uk

Highways: Mr Roy Ormsby, Service Head - Public Realm, Town Hall, Mulberry Place, 5 Clove Crescent, London E14 2BG ☎ 020 7364 6769 ☏ roy.ormsby@towerhamlets.gov.uk

Home Energy Conservation: Ms Sian Pipe, Energy Manager, Energy Efficiency Unit, Gladstone Place, Roman Road, London E3 5ES ☎ 020 7364 2523 ✆ sian.pipe@towerhamlets.gov.uk

Housing: Ms Susmita Sen, Chief Executive - Tower Hamlets Homes, 1st Floor, 2 Lawn House Close, London E14 9YQ ☎ 020 7364 7134 ✆ susmita.sen@thh.gov.uk

Local Area Agreement: Mr Kevin Kewin, Interim Service Head - Corporate Strategy & Equality, Town Hall, Mulberry Place, 5 Clove Crescent, London E14 2BG ☎ 020 7296 6880 ✆ kevin.kewin@towerhamlets.gov.uk

Legal: Mr Graham White, Interim Service Head - Legal Services, Town Hall, Mulberry Place, 5 Clove Crescent, London E14 2BG ☎ 020 7364 4348 ✆ graham.white@towerhamlets.gov.uk

Leisure and Cultural Services: Ms Shazia Hussain, Service Head - Culture, Learning & Leisure, Town Hall, Mulberry Place, 5 Clove Crescent, London E14 2BG ☎ 020 7364 4470 ✆ shazia.hussain@towerhamlets.gov.uk

Licensing: Mr Dave Tolley, Head of Trading Standards & Environmental Health, Toby Club, Vawdrey Close, London E1 4UA ☎ 020 7364 6724 ✆ david.tolley@towerhamlets.gov.uk

Lifelong Learning: Ms Judith St John, Head of Idea Store, 3rd Floor, 1 Gladstone Place, London E3 5EG ☎ 020 7364 5630 ✆ judith.stjohn@towerhamlets.gov.uk

Lighting: Mr Stanley Perpie, Street Lighting Engineer, Anchorage House, 4th Floor, 5 Clove Crescent, London E14 2BE ☎ 020 7364 6802 ✆ stanley.perpie@towerhamlets.gov.uk

Lottery Funding, Charity and Voluntary: Mr Everett Haughton, Third Sector Programmes Manager, Mulberry Place, Anchorage House, 2 Clove Crescent, London E14 2BG ☎ 020 7364 4639 ✆ everett.haughton@towerhamlets.gov.uk

Lottery Funding, Charity and Voluntary: Ms Louise Russell, Service Head - Corporate Strategy & Equality, Town Hall, Mulberry Place, 5 Clove Crescent, London E14 2BG ☎ 020 7364 3267 ✆ louise.russell@towerhamlets.gov.uk

Member Services: Ms Beverley McKenzie, Head of Members' Service, Town Hall, Mulberry Place, 5 Clove Crescent, London E14 2BG ☎ 020 7364 4872 ✆ beverley.mckenzie@towerhamlets.gov.uk

Parking: Mr Misrad Bakalovic, Head of Parking Services, Blackwall Depot, 1 Silvocea Way, London E14 0JT ☎ 020 7364 6999 ✆ misrad.bakalovic@towerhamlets.gov.uk

Partnerships: Ms Shazia Hussain, Service Head - Culture, Learning & Leisure, 4th Floor, Mulberry Place, 5 Clove Crescent, London E14 2BE ☎ 020 7364 4470 ✆ shazia.hussain@towerhamlets.gov.uk

Personnel / HR: Mr Stuart Young, Interim HR & OD Transformation Manager, Town Hall, Mulberry Place, 5 Clove Crescent, London E14 2BG ☎ 020 7364 4922 ✆ stuart.young@towerhamlets.gov.uk

Planning: Mr Owen Whalley, Service Head - Development Control & Building Control, Anchorage House, 2 Clove Crescent, London E14 2BE ☎ 020 7364 5314 ✆ owen.whalley@towerhamlets.gov.uk

Procurement: Mr Zamil Ahmed, Head of Procurment & Programme Management, Town Hall, Mulberry Place, 5 Clove Crescent, London E14 2BG ☎ 020 7364 4385 ✆ zamil.ahmed@towerhamlets.gov.uk

Public Libraries: Ms Judith St John, Head of Idea Store, 3rd Floor, 1 Gladstone Place, London E3 5EG ☎ 020 7364 5630 ✆ judith.stjohn@towerhamlets.gov.uk

Recycling & Waste Minimisation: Mr Roy Ormsby, Service Head - Public Realm, Town Hall, Mulberry Place, 5 Clove Crescent, London E14 2BG ☎ 020 7364 6769 ✆ roy.ormsby@towerhamlets.gov.uk

Regeneration: Ms Jackie Odunoye, Service Head - Strategy, Regeneration & Sustainability, Town Hall, Mulberry Place, 5 Clove Crescent, London E14 2BG ☎ 020 7364 7522 ✆ jackie.odunoye@towerhamlets.gov.uk

Road Safety: Ms Margaret Cooper, Head of Transport & Highways, Town Hall, Mulberry Place, 5 Clove Crescent, London E14 2BG ☎ 020 7364 6851 ✆ margaret.cooper@towerhamlets.gov.uk

Social Services (Adult): Mrs Denise Radley, Director - Adults' Services, Town Hall, Mulberry Place, 5 Clove Crescent, London E14 2BG ✆ denise.radley@towerhamlets.gov.uk

Social Services (Children): Ms Debbie Jones, Corporate Director - Children's Services, Town Hall, Mulberry Place, 5 Clove Crescent, London E14 2BG ✆ debbie.jones@towerhamlets.gov.uk

Social Services (Children): Ms Nasima Patel, Service Head - Children's Social Care, Town Hall, Mulberry Place, 5 Clove Crescent, London E14 2BG ☎ 020 7364 2213 ✆ nasima.patel@towerhamlets.gov.uk

Public Health: Dr Somen Banerjee, Director - Public Health, Town Hall, Mulberry Place, 5 Clove Crescent, London E14 2BG ✆ somen.banerjee@towerhamlets.gov.uk

Staff Training: Mr Stuart Young, Interim HR & OD Transformation Manager, Town Hall, Mulberry Place, 5 Clove Crescent, London E14 2BG ☎ 020 7364 4922 ✆ stuart.young@towerhamlets.gov.uk

Street Scene: Mr Roy Ormsby, Service Head - Public Realm, Town Hall, Mulberry Place, 5 Clove Crescent, London E14 2BG ☎ 020 7364 6769 ✆ roy.ormsby@towerhamlets.gov.uk

Sustainable Communities: Ms Jackie Odunoye, Service Head - Strategy, Regeneration & Sustainability, Town Hall, Mulberry Place, 5 Clove Crescent, London E14 2BG ☎ 020 7364 7522 ✆ jackie.odunoye@towerhamlets.gov.uk

Sustainable Development: Ms Jackie Odunoye, Service Head - Strategy, Regeneration & Sustainability, Town Hall, Mulberry Place, 5 Clove Crescent, London E14 2BG ☎ 020 7364 7522 ✆ jackie.odunoye@towerhamlets.gov.uk

TOWER HAMLETS

Tourism: Mr Aman Dalvi, Corporate Director - Development & Renewal, Town Hall, Mulberry Place, 5 Clove Crescent, London E14 2BG ☎ 020 7634 4247 ⏚ aman.dalvi@towerhamlets.gov.uk

Traffic Management: Ms Margaret Cooper, Head of Transport & Highways, Town Hall, Mulberry Place, 5 Clove Crescent, London E14 2BG ☎ 020 7364 6851 ⏚ margaret.cooper@towerhamlets.gov.uk

Transport Planner: Ms Margaret Cooper, Head of Transport & Highways, Anchorage House, 5 Clove Crescent, London E14 2BE ☎ 020 7364 6851 ⏚ margaret.cooper@towerhamlets.gov.uk

Waste Collection and Disposal: Mr Roy Ormsby, Service Head - Public Realm, Town Hall, Mulberry Place, 5 Clove Crescent, London E14 2BG ☎ 020 7364 6769 ⏚ roy.ormsby@towerhamlets.gov.uk

Waste Management: Mr Roy Ormsby, Service Head - Public Realm, Town Hall, Mulberry Place, 5 Clove Crescent, London E14 2BG ☎ 020 7364 6769 ⏚ roy.ormsby@towerhamlets.gov.uk

COUNCILLORS

Mayor: Biggs, John (LAB - No Ward)
mayor@towerhamlets.gov.uk

Deputy Mayor: Islam, Sirajul (LAB - Bethnal Green)
cllr.sirajul.islam@towerhamlets.gov.uk

Deputy Mayor: Khatun, Shiria (LAB - Lansbury)
shiria.khatan@towerhamlets.gov.uk

Deputy Mayor: Saunders, Rachael (LAB - Mile End)
cllr.rachael.saunders@towerhamlets.gov.uk

Group Leader: Golds, Peter (CON - Island Gardens)
cllrpetergolds@aol.com

Group Leader: Rahman, Oliur (IND - Stepney Green)
cllr.oliur.rahman@towerhamlets.gov.uk

Ahmed, Ohid (IND - Lansbury)
cllr.ohid.ahmed@towerhamlets.gov.uk

Ahmed, Suluk (IND - Spitalfields & Banglatown)
cllr.suluk.ahmed@towerhamlets.gov.uk

Ahmed, Rajib (LAB - Lansbury)
cllr.rajib.ahmed@towerhamlets.gov.uk

Akhtar, Sabina (LAB - Stepney Green)
sabina.akhtar@towerhamlets.gov.uk

Alam, Mahbub (IND - St Dunstan's)
mahbubm.alam@towerhamlets.gov.uk

Alam, Shah (IND - Mile End)
cllr.shah.alam@towerhamlets.gov.uk

Ali, Shahed (IND - Whitechapel)
shahed.ali@towerhamlets.gov.uk

Ali, Amina (LAB - Bow East)
cllr.amina.ali@towerhamlets.gov.uk

Asad, Abdul (IND - Whitechapel)
cllr.abdul.asad@towerhamlets.gov.uk

Aston, Craig (CON - Limehouse)
cllrcraigaston@gmail.com

Begum, Asma (LAB - Bow West)
cllr.asmak.begum@towerhamlets.gov.uk

Blake, Rachel (LAB - Bow East)
cllr.rachel.blake@towerhamlets.gov.uk

Chapman, Chris (CON - Blackwall & Cubitt Town)
cllrchrischapman@gmail.com

Chesterton, Dave (LAB - Blackwall & Cubitt Town)
cllr.dave.chesterton@towerhamlets.gov.uk

Choudhury, Gulam Kibria (IND - Poplar)
cllr.kibria.choudhury@toerhamlets.gov.uk

Cregan, Andrew (LAB - Island Gardens)
cllr.andrew.cregan@towerhamlets.gov.uk

Dockerill, Julia (CON - St Katharine's & Wapping)
cllr.julia.dockerill@towerhamlets.gov.uk

Edgar, David (LAB - Mile End)
cllr.david.edgar@towerhamlets.gov.uk

Francis, Marc (LAB - Bow East)
cllr.marc.francis@towerhamlets.gov.uk

Haque, Shafiqul (IND - Bethnal Green)
cllr.shafiqul.haque@towerhamlets.gov.uk

Harrisson, Clare (LAB - St Peter's)
cllr.clare.harrisson@towerhamlets.gov.uk

Hassell, Danny (LAB - Bromley South)
cllr.danny.hassell@towerhamlets.gov.uk

Jones, Denise (LAB - St Katharine's & Wapping)
cllr.denise.jones@towerhamlets.gov.uk

Khan, Rabina (IND - Shadwell)
cllr.rabina.khan@towerhamlets.gov.uk

Khan, Aminur (IND - Whitechapel)
cllr.aminur.khan@towerhamlets.gov.uk

Miah, Abjol (IND - St Peter's)
cllr.abjol.miah@towerhamlets.gov.uk

Miah, Harun (IND - Shadwell)
harun.miah579@o2.co.uk

Miah, Md. Maium (IND - Canary Wharf)
cllr.maium.miah@towerhamlets.gov.uk

Miah, Ayas (LAB - St Dunstan's)
cllr.ayas.miah@towerhamlets.gov.uk

Mufti Miah, Mohammed (IND - Bromley North)
cllr.mohammed.muftimiah@towerhamlets.gov.uk

Mukit, Abdul (LAB - Weavers)
cllr.abdulc.mukit@towerhamlets.gov.uk

Mustaquim, Muhammad (IND - St Peter's)
cllr.muhammad.mustaquim@towerhamlets.gov.uk

Peck, Joshua (LAB - Bow West)
cllr.joshua.peck@towerhamlets.gov.uk

Pierce, John (LAB - Weavers)
cllr.john.pierce@towerhamlets.gov.uk

Robbani, Gulam (IND - Spitalfields & Banglatown)
cllr.gulam.robbani@towerhamlets.gov.uk

Ronald, Candida (LAB - Blackwall & Cubitt Town)
cllr.candida.ronald@towerhamlets.gov.uk

Uddin, Helal (LAB - Bromley South)
cllr.helal.uddin@towerhamlets.gov.uk

Uddin Ahmed, Khales (LAB - Bromley North)
cllr.khales.uddinahmed@towerhamlets.gov.uk

Whitelock Gibbs, Amy (LAB - Bethnal Green)
cllr.amy.whitelockgibbs@towerhamlets.gov.uk

Wood, Andrew (CON - Canary Wharf)
cllrandrewwood@gmail.com

POLITICAL COMPOSITION
LAB: 24, IND: 17, CON: 5

COMMITTEE CHAIRS

Audit: Ms Candida Ronald

Development: Mr Marc Francis

Health & Wellbeing: Ms Amy Whitelock Gibbs

Licensing: Mr Rajib Ahmed

Pensions: Mr Andrew Cregan

Trafford   M

Trafford Metropolitan Borough Council, Trafford Town Hall, Talbot Road, Stretford, Manchester M32 0TH
☎ 0161 912 2000 ⏚ access.trafford@trafford.gov.uk
🖥 www.trafford.gov.uk

FACTS AND FIGURES
Parliamentary Constituencies: Altrincham and Sale West, Stretford and Urmston, Wythenshawe and Sale East
EU Constituencies: North West
Election Frequency: Elections are by thirds

PRINCIPAL OFFICERS

Chief Executive: Ms Theresa Grant, Chief Executive, Trafford Town Hall, Talbot Road, Stretford, Manchester M32 0TH
☎ 0161 912 1900 ⏚ theresa.grant@trafford.gov.uk

Deputy Chief Executive: Ms Helen Jones, Deputy Chief Executive, Trafford Town Hall, Talbot Road, Stretford, Manchester M32 0TH ☎ 0161 912 1915 ⏚ helen.jones@trafford.gov.uk

Senior Management: Ms Jill Colbert, Interim Corporate Director - Children, Families & Wellbeing, Trafford Town Hall, Talbot Road, Stretford, Manchester M32 0TH ☎ 0161 912 1901 ⏚ jill.colbert@trafford.gov.uk

Senior Management: Ms Joanne Hyde, Corporate Director - Resources, Trafford Town Hall, Talbot Road, Stretford, Manchester M32 0TH ☎ 0161 912 1586 ⏚ joanne.hyde@trafford.gov.uk

Senior Management: Ms Helen Jones, Deputy Chief Executive, Trafford Town Hall, Talbot Road, Stretford, Manchester M32 0TH
☎ 0161 912 1915 ⏚ helen.jones@trafford.gov.uk

Architect, Building / Property Services: Mr Simon Davis, Head of Property, Trafford Town Hall, Talbot Road, Stretford, Manchester M32 0TH ☎ 07773 073207 ⏚ simon.davis1@trafford.gov.uk

Building Control: Mr Iain Veitch, Head of Regulatory Services, Trafford Town Hall, Talbot Road, Stretford, Manchester M32 0TH
☎ 0161 912 4174 ⏚ iain.veitch@trafford.gov.uk

Catering Services: Mr Phil Valentine, Environment Strategic Business Manager, Trafford Town Hall, Talbot Road, Stretford, Manchester M32 0TH ☎ 0161 912 4301
⏚ phil.valentine@trafford.gov.uk

Children / Youth Services: Ms Jill Colbert, Interim Corporate Director - Children, Families & Wellbeing, Trafford Town Hall, Talbot Road, Stretford, Manchester M32 0TH ☎ 0161 912 1901
⏚ jill.colbert@trafford.gov.uk

Children / Youth Services: Mr Ken McDonald, Head of South Area Team: YOS & CAHMS, Trafford Town Hall, Talbot Road, Stretford, Manchester M32 0TH ☎ 0161 911 8223
⏚ ken.mcdonald@trafford.gov.uk

Civil Registration: Ms Jane Le Fevre, Director - Legal & Democratic Services, Trafford Town Hall, Talbot Road, Stretford, Manchester M32 0TH ☎ 0161 912 4215 ⏚ jane.lefevre@trafford.gov.uk

PR / Communications: Ms Kelly Dooley, Public Relations Manager, Trafford Town Hall, Talbot Road, Stretford, Manchester M32 0TH ☎ 0161 912 1262 ⏚ kelly.dooley@trafford.gov.uk

Community Safety: Ms Liz Baxter, Strategic Manager - Crime & Anti-social Behaviour, Trafford Town Hall, Talbot Road, Stretford, Manchester M32 0TH ☎ 0161 912 1231 ⏚ liz.baxter@trafford.gov.uk

Computer Management: Mr John Callan, Head of ICT, Trafford Town Hall, Talbot Road, Stretford, Manchester M32 0TH
☎ 0161 912 2138 ⏚ john.callan@trafford.gov.uk

Consumer Protection and Trading Standards: Mr Iain Veitch, Head of Regulatory Services, Trafford Town Hall, Talbot Road, Stretford, Manchester M32 0TH ☎ 0161 912 4174
⏚ iain.veitch@trafford.gov.uk

Contracts: Ms Sharon Robson, Director of STaR, Trafford Town Hall, Talbot Road, Stretford, Manchester M32 0TH ☎ 0161 912 2823 ⏚ sharon.robson@star-procurement.gov.uk

Customer Service: Ms Sarah Curran, Head of Customer Service, Waterside House, Sale Waterside, Sale, Manchester M33 7ZF
☎ 0121 912 2823 ⏚ sarah.curran@trafford.gov.uk

Economic Development: Mr Stephen James, Head of Strategic Growth, Trafford Town Hall, Talbot Road, Stretford, Manchester M32 0TH ☎ 0161 912 4430 ⏚ stephen.james@carrington.gov.uk

Education: Mr Adrian Hallett, Head of Education, Sale Waterside, Waterside House, Sale M33 7ZF ☎ 0161 912 8685
⏚ adrian.hallett@trafford.gov.uk

Education: Ms Alison Milne, Head of Service - Access & Inclusion, Trafford Town Hall, Talbot Road, Stretford, Manchester M32 0TH
☎ 0161 912 3233 ⏚ alison.milne@trafford.gov.uk

E-Government: Mr John Callan, Head of ICT, Trafford Town Hall, Talbot Road, Stretford, Manchester M32 0TH ☎ 0161 912 2138
⏚ john.callan@trafford.gov.uk

TRAFFORD

Electoral Registration: Mr Peter Forrester, Democratic Services Manager, Trafford Town Hall, Talbot Road, Stretford, Manchester M32 0TH ☎ 0161 912 1815 ☏ peter.forrester@trafford.gov.uk

Emergency Planning: Mr David Hooley, Emergency Planning Manager, Trafford Town Hall, Talbot Road, Stretford, Manchester M32 0TH ☎ 0161 912 3425 ☏ david.hooley@trafford.gov.uk

Energy Management: Mr Andrew Hunt, Sustainability Manager, Carrington Depot, 148 Manchester Road, Carrington, Manchester M31 4QN ☎ 0161 912 4691 ☏ andrew.hunt@trafford.gov.uk

Environmental Health: Mr Iain Veitch, Head of Regulatory Services, Trafford Town Hall, Talbot Road, Stretford, Manchester M32 0TH ☎ 0161 912 4174 ☏ iain.veitch@trafford.gov.uk

Estates, Property & Valuation: Mr Simon Davis, Head of Property, Trafford Town Hall, Talbot Road, Stretford, Manchester M32 0TH ☎ 07773 073207 ☏ simon.davis1@trafford.gov.uk

Facilities: Mr John Holmes, Account Manager, Trafford Town Hall, Talbot Road, Stretford, Manchester M32 0TH ☎ 0161 912 6597 ☏ john.holmes@amey.co.uk

Grounds Maintenance: Ms Tara Dumas, Head of Environmental Services, Trafford Town Hall, Talbot Road, Stretford, Manchester M32 0TH ☎ 0161 912 2835 ☏ tara.dumas@trafford.gov.uk

Health and Safety: Mr Richard Fontana, Health & Safety Manager, Trafford Town Hall, Talbot Road, Stretford, Manchester M32 0TH ☎ 0161 912 4919 ☏ richard.fontana@trafford.gov.uk

Highways: Mr Mark Pickering, Contracts Director, Trafford Town Hall, Talbot Road, Stretford, Manchester M32 0TH ☏ mark.pickering2@amey.co.uk

Housing: Mr Richard Roe, Director - Economic Growth & Regulatory Services, Trafford Town Hall, Talbot Road, Stretford, Manchester M32 0TH ☎ 0161 912 4265 ☏ richard.roe@trafford.gov.uk

Legal: Ms Jane Le Fevre, Director - Legal & Democratic Services, Trafford Town Hall, Talbot Road, Stretford, Manchester M32 0TH ☎ 0161 912 4215 ☏ jane.lefevre@trafford.gov.uk

Leisure and Cultural Services: Ms Debbie Cowley, Strategic Manager - Culture & Sport, Waterside House, Sale Waterside, Sale, Manchester M33 6FZ ☎ 0161 912 3110 ☏ debbie.cowley@trafford.gov.uk

Licensing: Mr Iain Veitch, Head of Regulatory Services, Trafford Town Hall, Talbot Road, Stretford, Manchester M32 0TH ☎ 0161 912 4174 ☏ iain.veitch@trafford.gov.uk

Lighting: Mr Trevor Chester, Street Lighting Manager, Carrington Depot, 148 Manchester Road, Carrington, Manchester M31 4QN ☎ 0161 672 6497 ☏ trevor.chester@amey.co.uk

Member Services: Mr Peter Forrester, Democratic Services Manager, Trafford Town Hall, Talbot Road, Stretford, Manchester M32 0TH ☎ 0161 912 1815 ☏ peter.forrester@trafford.gov.uk

Parking: Ms Nicola Henry, Parking Services Manager, Waterside House, Sale Waterside, Sale, Manchester M33 6FZ ☎ 0161 912 4046 ☏ nicola.henry@trafford.gov.uk

Partnerships: Ms Kerry Purnell, Head of Partnerships & Performance, Trafford Town Hall, Talbot Road, Stretford, Manchester M32 0TH ☎ 0161 912 1231 ☏ kerry.purnell@trafford.gov.uk

Personnel / HR: Ms Lisa Hooley, Acting Director - HR, Trafford Town Hall, Talbot Road, Stretford, Manchester M32 0TH ☎ 0161 912 4670 ☏ lisa.hooley@trafford.gov.uk

Planning: Ms Rebecca Coley, Head of Planning & Development, Waterside House, Sale Waterside, Sale M33 6FZ ☎ 0161 912 4788 ☏ rebecca.coley@trafford.gov.uk

Procurement: Ms Sharon Robson, Director of STaR, Trafford Town Hall, Talbot Road, Stretford, Manchester M32 0TH ☎ 0161 912 2823 ☏ sharon.robson@star-procurement.gov.uk

Public Libraries: Ms Sarah Curran, Head of Customer Service, Waterside House, Sale Waterside, Sale, Manchester M33 7ZF ☎ 0121 912 2823 ☏ sarah.curran@trafford.gov.uk

Recycling & Waste Minimisation: Mr Gary Taylor, Waste Manager, Carrington Depot, 148 Manchester Road, Carrington, Manchester M31 4QN ☎ 07752 667458 ☏ gary.taylor@trafford.gov.uk

Regeneration: Mr Stephen James, Head of Strategic Growth, Trafford Town Hall, Talbot Road, Stretford, Manchester M32 0TH ☎ 0161 912 4430 ☏ stephen.james@carrington.gov.uk

Road Safety: Mr Steve Tilby, Traffic & Road Safety Manager, Waterside House, Sale M33 7ZF ☎ 0161 912 4312 ☏ steve.tilby@amey.co.uk

Social Services (Adult): Ms Diane Eaton, Director - Integrated Services, Trafford Town Hall, Talbot Road, Stretford, Manchester M32 0TH ☎ 0161 912 2705 ☏ diane.eaton@trafford.gov.uk

Social Services (Children): Ms Cathy Rooney, Director - Safeguarding & Professional Development, Trafford Town Hall, Talbot Road, Stretford, Manchester M32 0TH ☎ 0161 911 8650 ☏ cathy.rooney@trafford.gov.uk

Staff Training: Ms Lisa Hooley, Acting Director - HR, Trafford Town Hall, Talbot Road, Stretford, Manchester M32 0TH ☎ 0161 912 4670 ☏ lisa.hooley@trafford.gov.uk

Town Centre: Mr Martin Ledson, Altrincham Town Centre Interim Manager, Trafford Town Hall, Talbot Road, Stretford, Manchester M32 0TH ☎ 0161 912 4137 ☏ martin.ledson@trafford.gov.uk

Transport: Mr Colin Maycroft, Service Operations Manager, Moss View Centre, Moss View Road, Partington, Manchester M31 4DX ☎ 0161 912 2926 ☏ colin.maycroft@trafford.gov.uk

Waste Collection and Disposal: Mr Gary Taylor, Waste Manager, Carrington Depot, 148 Manchester Road, Carrington, Manchester M31 4QN ☎ 07752 667458 ☏ gary.taylor@trafford.gov.uk

Waste Management: Mr Gary Taylor, Waste Manager, Carrington Depot, 148 Manchester Road, Carrington, Manchester M31 4QN
☎ 07752 667458 ⊕ gary.taylor@trafford.gov.uk

COUNCILLORS

Mayor: Lloyd, Judith (LAB - Longford)
judith.lloyd@trafford.gov.uk

Deputy Mayor: Coupe, Jonathan (CON - Flixton)
jonathan.coupe@trafford.gov.uk

Leader of the Council: Anstee, Sean (CON - Bowdon)
sean.anstee@trafford.gov.uk

Deputy Leader of the Council: Williams, Alex (CON - Altrincham)
alex.williams@trafford.gov.uk

Group Leader: Bowker, Ray (LD - Village)
ray.bowker@trafford.gov.uk

Group Leader: Western, Andrew (LAB - Priory)
andrew.western@trafford.gov.uk

Acton, David (LAB - Gorse Hill)
david.acton@trafford.gov.uk

Adshead, Stephen (LAB - Stretford)
stephen.adshead@trafford.gov.uk

Anstee, Stephen (CON - Broadheath)
stephen.anstee@trafford.gov.uk

Barclay, Karen (CON - Bowdon)
karen.barclay@trafford.gov.uk

Baugh, Jane (LAB - Priory)
jane.baugh@trafford.gov.uk

Bennett, Joanne (LAB - Sale Moor)
joanne.bennett@trafford.gov.uk

Blackburn, Linda (CON - Davyhulme East)
linda.blackburn@trafford.gov.uk

Boyes, Chris (CON - Brooklands)
chris.boyes@trafford.gov.uk

Brophy, Jane (LD - Timperley)
jane.brophy@trafford.gov.uk

Brotherton, Barry (LAB - Priory)
barry.brotherton@trafford.gov.uk

Bruer-Morris, Angela (CON - Timperley)
angela.bruer-morris@trafford.gov.uk

Bunting, Daniel (CON - St. Mary's)
dan.bunting@trafford.gov.uk

Butt, Dylan (CON - Hale Barns)
dylan.butt@trafford.gov.uk

Carter, Karina (LAB - Bucklow St. Martins)
karina.carter@trafford.gov.uk

Cawdrey, Mark (CON - Davyhulme East)
mark.cawdrey@trafford.gov.uk

Chilton, Rob (CON - St. Mary's)
robert.chilton@trafford.gov.uk

Cordingley, Mike (LAB - Gorse Hill)
michael.cordingley@trafford.gov.uk

Cornes, Michael (CON - Davyhulme East)
michael.cornes@trafford.gov.uk

Dagnall, Louise (LAB - Broadheath)
louise.dagnall@trafford.gov.uk

Dixon, Pamela (CON - Brooklands)
pamela.dixon@trafford.gov.uk

Duffield, Anne (LAB - Longford)
anne.duffield@trafford.gov.uk

Evans, Nathan (CON - Timperley)
nathan.evans@trafford.gov.uk

Evans, Laura (CON - Village)
laura.evans@trafford.gov.uk

Fishwick, Tony (LD - Village)
tony.fishwick@trafford.gov.uk

Freeman, Mike (LAB - Sale Moor)
mike.freeman@trafford.gov.uk

Gratix, Philip (LAB - Sale Moor)
philip.gratix@trafford.gov.uk

Haddad, Denise (CON - Hale Central)
denise.haddad@trafford.gov.uk

Harding, Joanne (LAB - Urmston)
joanne.harding@trafford.gov.uk

Holden, John (CON - St. Mary's)
john.holden@trafford.gov.uk

Hopps, David (CON - Brooklands)
david.hopps@trafford.gov.uk

Hyman, Michael (CON - Bowdon)
michael.hyman@trafford.gov.uk

Hynes, Catherine (LAB - Urmston)
catherine.hynes@trafford.gov.uk

Jarman, David (LAB - Longford)
david.jarman@trafford.gov.uk

Lally, Paul (CON - Flixton)
paul.lally@trafford.gov.uk

Lamb, John (CON - Ashton upon Mersey)
john.lamb@trafford.gov.uk

Malik, Ejaz (LAB - Clifford)
ejaz.malik@trafford.gov.uk

Mitchell, Alan (CON - Hale Central)
alan.mitchell@trafford.gov.uk

Myers, Patrick (CON - Hale Barns)
patrick.myers@trafford.gov.uk

O'Sullivan, Dolores (LAB - Stretford)
dolores.osullivan@trafford.gov.uk

Procter, Kevin (LAB - Urmston)
kevin.procter@trafford.gov.uk

Reilly, June (CON - Davyhulme West)
june.reilly@trafford.gov.uk

Reilly, John (CON - Davyhulme West)
john.reilly@trafford.gov.uk

Rigby, Brian (CON - Ashton upon Mersey)
brian.rigby@trafford.gov.uk

Ross, Tom (LAB - Stretford)
tom.ross@trafford.gov.uk

Sephton, Matthew (CON - Altrincham)
matthew.sephton@trafford.gov.uk

TRAFFORD

Sharp, Bernard (CON - Hale Barns)
bernard.sharp@trafford.gov.uk

Shaw, Brian (CON - Davyhulme West)
brian.shaw@trafford.gov.uk

Smith, John (LAB - Bucklow St. Martins)
john.smith@trafford.gov.uk

Stennett, Whit (LAB - Clifford)
whit.stennett@trafford.gov.uk

Taylor, Sophie (LAB - Clifford)
sophie.taylor@trafford.gov.uk

Walsh, Laurence (LAB - Gorse Hill)
laurence.walsh@trafford.gov.uk

Ward, Vivienne (CON - Flixton)
viv.ward@trafford.gov.uk

Western, Denise (LAB - Broadheath)
denise.western@trafford.gov.uk

Whetton, Michael (CON - Ashton upon Mersey)
michael.whetton@trafford.gov.uk

Wright, James (LAB - Bucklow St. Martins)
james.wright@trafford.gov.uk

Young, Michael (CON - Altrincham)
michael.young@trafford.gov.uk

Young, Patricia (CON - Hale Central)
patricia.young@trafford.gov.uk

POLITICAL COMPOSITION
CON: 34, LAB: 26, LD: 3

COMMITTEE CHAIRS

Audit: Mr Jonathan Coupe

Health & Wellbeing: Mr Alex Williams

Licensing: Mr Michael Whetton

Planning & Development Management: Mrs Vivienne Ward

Tunbridge Wells   D

Tunbridge Wells Borough Council, Town Hall, Tunbridge Wells TN1 1RS
☎ 01892 526121 📠 01892 534227 ⟁ info@tunbridgewells.gov.uk
🖳 www.tunbridgewells.gov.uk

FACTS AND FIGURES
Parliamentary Constituencies: Tunbridge Wells
EU Constituencies: South East
Election Frequency: Elections are by thirds

PRINCIPAL OFFICERS

Chief Executive: Mr William Benson, Chief Executive, Town Hall, Tunbridge Wells TN1 1RS ☎ 01892 554227
⟁ william.benson@tunbridgewells.gov.uk

Senior Management: Mr Lee Colyer, Director - Finance & Corporate Services (S151 Officer), Town Hall, Tunbridge Wells TN1 1RS ☎ 01892 554132 ⟁ lee.colyer@tunbridgewells.gov.uk

Senior Management: Mr Jonathan MacDonald, Director - Planning & Development, Town Hall, Tunbridge Wells TN1 1RS
☎ 01892 554293 ⟁ jonathan.macdonald@tunbridgewells.gov.uk

Senior Management: Mr Paul Taylor, Director - Change & Communities, Town Hall, Tunbridge Wells TN1 1RS ☎ 01892 526121 ⟁ paul.taylor@tunbridgewells.gov.uk

Architect, Building / Property Services: Mr Keith Delves, Facilities Management Surveyor, Town Hall, Tunbridge Wells TN1 1RS ☎ 01892 554011 ⟁ keith.delves@tunbridgewells.gov.uk

Building Control: Mr Glenn Cooper, Building Control Team Leader, Town Hall, Tunbridge Wells TN1 1RS ☎ 01892 554015 ⟁ glenn.cooper@tunbridgewells.gov.uk

PR / Communications: Ms Lizzie Goodwin, Communications Manager, Town Hall, Tunbridge Wells TN1 1RS ☎ 01892 554273 ⟁ lizzie.goodwin@tunbridgewells.gov.uk

Community Safety: Mr Terry Hughes, Community Safety Manager, Town Hall, Tunbridge Wells TN1 1RS ☎ 01892 554224 ⟁ terry.hughes@tunbridgewells.gov.uk

Computer Management: Mr Andrew Cole, Head of ICT Shared Services, Maidstone House, King Street, Maidstone ME15 6JQ
☎ 01622 602662 ⟁ andrew.cole@tunbridgewells.gov.uk

Customer Service: Mrs Denise Shortall, Customer Service & Gateway Manager, Town Hall, Tunbridge Wells TN1 1RS
☎ 01892 554218 ⟁ denise.shortall@tunbridgewells.gov.uk

Customer Service: Mrs Ingrid Weatherup, Corporate Complaints & FOI Officer, Town Hall, Tunbridge Wells TN1 1RS
☎ 01895 554077 ⟁ ingrid.weatherup@tunbridgewells.gov.uk

Economic Development: Mrs Hilary Smith, Economic Development Manager, Town Hall, Tunbridge Wells TN1 1RS
☎ 01454 554433 ⟁ hilary.smith@tunbridgewells.gov.uk

E-Government: Mr Andrew Cole, Head of ICT Shared Services, Maidstone House, King Street, Maidstone ME15 6JQ
☎ 01622 602662 ⟁ andrew.cole@tunbridgewells.gov.uk

Electoral Registration: Mr Mat Jefferys, Acting Democratic & Legal Services Manager, Town Hall, Tunbridge Wells TN1 1RS
☎ 01892 554403 ⟁ mat.jefferys@tunbridgewells.gov.uk

Environmental / Technical Services: Mr Gary Stevenson, Head of Environment & Street Scene, Town Hall, Tunbridge Wells TN1 1RS ☎ 01892 554014 ⟁ gary.stevenson@tunbridgewells.gov.uk

Environmental Health: Mr Gary Stevenson, Head of Environment & Street Scene, Town Hall, Tunbridge Wells TN1 1RS
☎ 01892 554014 ⟁ gary.stevenson@tunbridgewells.gov.uk

Estates, Property & Valuation: Mrs Diane Brady, Property & Development Manager, Town Hall, Tunbridge Wells TN1 1RS
☎ 01892 526121 ⟁ diana.brady@tunbridgewells.gov.uk

Finance: Mr Lee Colyer, Director - Finance & Corporate Services (S151 Officer), Town Hall, Tunbridge Wells TN1 1RS ☎ 01892 554132 ✎ lee.colyer@tunbridgewells.gov.uk

Grounds Maintenance: Mr Peter Every, Parks & Sports Team Leader, Town Hall, Tunbridge Wells TN1 1RS ☎ 01892 526121 ✎ peter.every@tunbridgewells.gov.uk

Health and Safety: Mr Mike Catling, Corporate Health & Safety Advisor, Town Hall, Tunbridge Wells TN1 1RS ☎ 07968 475934 ✎ mike.catling@tunbridgewells.gov.uk

Home Energy Conservation: Ms Karin Grey, Sustainability Manager, Town Hall, Tunbridge Wells TN1 1RS ☎ 01892 554240 ✎ karin.grey@tunbridgewells.gov.uk

Housing: Mrs Jane Lang, Housing Services Manager, Town Hall, Tunbridge Wells TN1 1RS ☎ 01892 554157 ✎ jane.lang@tunbridgewells.gov.uk

Leisure and Cultural Services: Mr Kevin Hetherington, Head of Communities & Wellbeing, Town Hall, Tunbridge Wells TN1 1RS ☎ 01892 526121 ✎ kevin.hetherington@tunbridgewells.gov.uk

Licensing: Mrs Claire Perry, Licensing Partnership Manager, Council Offices, Argyle Road, Sevenoaks TN13 1HG ☎ 01732 227325; 07970 731616 ✎ claire.perry@tunbridgewells.gov.uk

Member Services: Mr Mat Jefferys, Acting Democratic & Legal Services Manager, Town Hall, Tunbridge Wells TN1 1RS ☎ 01892 554403 ✎ mat.jefferys@tunbridgewells.gov.uk

Parking: Ms Rosemarie Bennett, Parking Manager, Town Hall, Tunbridge Wells TN1 1RS ☎ 01892 554082 ✎ rosemarie.bennett@tunbridgewells.gov.uk

Personnel / HR: Mrs Nicky Carter, Head of HR, Town Hall, Tunbridge Wells TN1 1RS ☎ 01892 526121 ✎ nicky.carter@tunbridgewells.gov.uk

Planning: Ms Karen Fossett, Head of Planning Services, Town Hall, Tunbridge Wells TN1 1RS ☎ 01892 526121 ✎ karen.fossett@tunbridgewells.gov.uk

Recycling & Waste Minimisation: Mr Edwin Burgess, Waste & Street Care Manager, Town Hall, Tunbridge Wells TN1 1RS ☎ 01892 526121 ✎ edwin.burgess@tunbridgwells.gov.uk

Regeneration: Mr David Candlin, Head of Economic Development, Town Hall, Tunbridge Wells TN1 1RS ☎ 01892 554038 ✎ david.candlin@tunbridgewells.gov.uk

Staff Training: Mrs Nicky Carter, Head of HR, Town Hall, Tunbridge Wells TN1 1RS ☎ 01892 526121 ✎ nicky.carter@tunbridgewells.gov.uk

Street Scene: Mr Gary Stevenson, Head of Environment & Street Scene, Town Hall, Tunbridge Wells TN1 1RS ☎ 01892 554014 ✎ gary.stevenson@tunbridgewells.gov.uk

Tourism: Mrs Stephanie Covey, Tourist Information Centre Supervisor, Town Hall, Tunbridge Wells TN1 1RS ☎ 01892 526121 ✎ stephanie.covey@tunbridgewells.gov.uk

Transport Planner: Mr Bartholomew Wren, Economic Development Officer, Town Hall, Tunbridge Wells TN1 1RS ☎ 01892 526121 ✎ bartholomew.wren@tunbridgewells.gov.uk

Waste Collection and Disposal: Mr Edwin Burgess, Waste & Street Care Manager, Town Hall, Tunbridge Wells TN1 1RS ☎ 01892 526121 ✎ edwin.burgess@tunbridgwells.gov.uk

COUNCILLORS

Mayor: Neve, David (LD - St James')
david.neve@tunbridgewells.gov.uk

Deputy Mayor: Soyke, Julia (CON - Speldhurst & Bidborough)
julia.soyke@tunbridgewells.gov.uk

Leader of the Council: Jukes, David (CON - Speldhurst & Bidborough)
david.jukes@tunbridgewells.gov.uk

Deputy Leader of the Council: McDermott, Alan (CON - Brenchley & Horsmonden)
alan.mcdermott@tunbridgewells.gov.uk

Backhouse, Bob (CON - Sherwood)
bob.backhouse@tunbridgewells.gov.uk

Barrington-King, Paul (CON - Pembury)
paul.barrington-king@tunbridgewells.gov.uk

Basu, Ronen (CON - Culverden)
ronen.basu@tunbridgewells.gov.uk

Bland, Godfrey (CON - Hawkhurst & Sandhurst)
godfrey.bland@tunbridgewells.gov.uk

Bulman, Peter (CON - Park)
peter.bulman@tunbridgewells.gov.uk

Chapelard, Ben (LD - St James')
ben.chapelard@tunbridgewells.gov.uk

Cob, Barbara (CON - Broadwater)
barbara.cob**@tunbridgewells.gov.uk**

Dawlings, Tom (CON - Benenden & Cranbrook)
tom.dawlings@tunbridgewells.gov.uk

Elliot, David (CON - Southborough North)
david.elliott@tunbridgewells.gov.uk

Gray, Nathan (CON - Hawkhurst & Sandhurst)
nathan.gray@tunbridgewells.gov.uk

Hall, Linda (CON - Benenden & Cranbrook)
linda.hall@tunbridgewells.gov.uk

Hamilton, Sarah (CON - Paddock Wood (East))
sarah.hamilton@tunbridgewells.gov.uk

Hannam, James (CON - Frittenden & Sissinghurst)
james.hannam@tunbridgewells.gov.uk

Hastie, Edmund (CON - Goudhurst & Lamberhurst)
edmund.hastie@tunbridgewells.gov.uk

Heasman, Lawrence (CON - Pantiles & St Mark's)
lawrence.heasman@tunbridgewells.gov.uk

Hill, Dianne (LAB - Southborough & High Brooms)
dianne.hill@tunbridgewells.gov.uk

TUNBRIDGE WELLS

Hills, Bill (CON - Paddock Wood (East))
bill.hills@tunbridgewells.gov.uk

Holden, Sean (CON - Benenden & Cranbrook)
sean.holden@tunbridgewells.gov.uk

Horwood, Len (CON - Pantiles & St Mark's)
len.horwood@tunbridgewells.gov.uk

Huggett, Thelma (CON - Rusthall)
thelma.huggett@tunbrigewells.gov.uk

Jamil, Nasir (CON - St John's)
nasir.jamil@tunbridgewells.gov.uk

Lewis-Grey, Alex (CON - Culverden)
alex.lewis-gray@tunbridgewells.gov.uk

Lidstone, Peter (LD - St John's)
peter.lidstone@tunbridgewells.gov.uk

Mackonochie, Carol (CAP - Capel)
carol.mackonochie@tunbridgewells.gov.uk

March, Jane (CON - Brenchley & Horsmonden)
jane.march@tunbridgewells.gov.uk

Moore, Tracy (CON - Park)
tracy.moore@tunbridgewells.gov.uk

Munn, Graham (LAB - Southborough & High Brooms)
graham.munn@tunbridgewells.gov.uk

Noakes, Barry (CON - Goudhurst & Lamberhurst)
barry.noakes@tunbridgewells.gov.uk

Nuttall, Sue (CON - Pembury)
sue.nuttall@tumbridgewells.gov.uk

Oakford, Peter (CON - St John's)
peter.oakford@tunbridgewells.gov.uk

Palmer, Beverley (CON - Hawkhurst & Sandhurst)
beverley.palmer@tunbridgewells.gov.uk

Podbury, Joy (CON - Rusthall)
joy.podbury@tunbridgewells.gov.uk

Rankin, Catherine (CON - Park)
catherine.rankin@tunbrigewells.gov.uk

Reilly, David (CON - Pembury)
david.reilly@tunbridgewells.gov.uk

Scholes, James (CON - Pantiles & St Mark's)
james.scholes@tunbridgewells.gov.uk

Simmons, Joe (CON - Southborough North)
joe.simmons@tunbridgewells.gov.uk

Sloan, Don (CON - Culverden)
don.sloan@tunbridgewells.gv.uk

Stanyer, Julian (CON - Speldhurst & Bidborough)
julian.stanyer@tunbridgewells.gov.uk

Stewart, Claire (CON - Paddock Wood (West))
claire.stewart@tunbridgewells.gov.uk

Thomas, Elizabeth (CON - Paddock Wood (West))
elizabeth.thomas@tunbridgewells.gov.uk

Uddin, Zulhash (CON - Southborough & High Brooms)
zulhash.uddin@tunbridgewells.gov.uk

Weatherly, Lynne (CON - Sherwood)
lynne.weatherly@tunbridgewells.gov.uk

Williams, Frank (CON - Sherwood)
frank.williams@tunbridgewells.gov.uk

Woodward, Chris (CON - Broadwater)
chris.woodward@tunbridgewells.gov.uk

POLITICAL COMPOSITION
CON: 42, LD: 3, LAB: 2, CAP: 1

COMMITTEE CHAIRS

Audit & Governance: Mr Len Horwood

Licensing: Mr Bob Backhouse

Planning: Mrs Julia Soyke

Uttlesford   D

Uttlesford District Council, Council Offices, London Road, Saffron Walden CB11 4ER
☎ 01799 510510 🖷 01799 510550 📧 uconnect@uttlesford.gov.uk
🖥 www.uttlesford.gov.uk

FACTS AND FIGURES
Parliamentary Constituencies: Saffron Walden
EU Constituencies: Eastern
Election Frequency: Elections are of whole council

PRINCIPAL OFFICERS

Chief Executive: Ms Dawn French, Chief Executive, Council Offices, London Road, Saffron Walden CB11 4ER
📧 dfrench@uttlesford.gov.uk

Assistant Chief Executive: Mr Michael Perry, Assistant Chief Executive, Council Offices, London Road, Saffron Walden CB11 4ER
☎ 01799 510416 📧 mperry@uttlesford.gov.uk

Senior Management: Mr Roger Harborough, Director - Public Services, Council Offices, London Road, Saffron Walden CB11 4ER
☎ 01799 510457 📧 rharborough@uttlesford.gov.uk

Senior Management: Mr Adrian Webb, Director - Finance & Corporate Services, Council Offices, London Road, Saffron Walden CB11 4ER ☎ 01799 510421 📧 awebb@uttlesford.gov.uk

Access Officer / Social Services (Disability): Ms Sue Locke, Health Improvement Senior Officer, Council Offices, London Road, Saffron Walden CB11 4ER ☎ 01799 510537
📧 slocke@uttlesford.gov.uk

Building Control: Mr John Farnell, Building Control Team Leader, Council Offices, London Road, Saffron Walden CB11 4ER
☎ 01799 510538 📧 jfarnell@uttlesford.gov.uk

PR / Communications: Mr Richard Auty, Assistant Director - Corporate Services, Council Offices, London Road, Saffron Walden CB11 4ER ☎ 01799 510500 📧 rauty@uttlesford.gov.uk

Community Safety: Mr Martin Ford, Community Safety Officer, Council Offices, London Road, Saffron Walden CB11 4ER
☎ 01799 510555 📧 mford@uttlesford.gov.uk

Computer Management: Mr Alan Mose, ICT Service Delivery Manager, Council Offices, London Road, Saffron Walden CB11 4ER
☎ 01799 510520 📧 amose@uttlesford.gov.uk

Corporate Services: Mr Richard Auty, Assistant Director - Corporate Services, Council Offices, London Road, Saffron Walden CB11 4ER ☎ 01799 510500 ◌ rauty@uttlesford.gov.uk

Customer Service: Mr Richard Auty, Assistant Director - Corporate Services, Council Offices, London Road, Saffron Walden CB11 4ER ☎ 01799 510500 ◌ rauty@uttlesford.gov.uk

Economic Development: Mr Simon Jackson, Economic Development Officer, Council Offices, London Road, Saffron Walden CB11 4ER ☎ 01799 510512 ◌ sjackson@uttlesford.gov.uk

E-Government: Mr Adrian Webb, Director - Finance & Corporate Services, Council Offices, London Road, Saffron Walden CB11 4ER ☎ 01799 510421 ◌ awebb@uttlesford.gov.uk

Electoral Registration: Mr Peter Snow, Democratic & Electoral Services Manager, Council Offices, London Road, Saffron Walden CB11 4ER ☎ 01799 510431 ◌ psnow@uttlesford.gov.uk

Emergency Planning: Mrs Lisa Lipscombe, Emergency Planning Officer, Council Offices, London Road, Saffron Walden CB11 4ER ☎ 01799 510624 ◌ llipscombe@uttlesford.gov.uk

Environmental / Technical Services: Mr Roger Harborough, Director - Public Services, Council Offices, London Road, Saffron Walden CB11 4ER ☎ 01799 510457 ◌ rharborough@uttlesford.gov.uk

Environmental / Technical Services: Mr Geoff Smith, Head of Environmental Health, Council Offices, London Road, Saffron Walden CB11 4ER ☎ 01799 510582 ◌ gsmith@uttlesford.gov.uk

Environmental Health: Mr Roger Harborough, Director - Public Services, Council Offices, London Road, Saffron Walden CB11 4ER ☎ 01799 510457 ◌ rharborough@uttlesford.gov.uk

Environmental Health: Mrs Roz Millership, Assistant Director - Housing & Environmental Services, Council Offices, London Road, Saffron Walden CB11 4ER ☎ 01799 510516 ◌ rmillership@uttlesford.gov.uk

Environmental Health: Mr Geoff Smith, Head of Environmental Health, Council Offices, London Road, Saffron Walden CB11 4ER ☎ 01799 510582 ◌ gsmith@uttlesford.gov.uk

Finance: Ms Angela Knight, Assistant Director - Finance, Council Offices, London Road, Saffron Walden CB11 4ER ☎ 01799 510446 ◌ aknight@uttlesford.gov.uk

Fleet Management: Mrs Catherine Chapman, Street Services Operations Manager, Council Offices, London Road, Saffron Walden CB11 4ER ☎ 01799 510557 ◌ cchapman@uttlesford.gov.uk

Grounds Maintenance: Mrs Catherine Chapman, Street Services Operations Manager, Council Offices, London Road, Saffron Walden CB11 4ER ☎ 01799 510557 ◌ cchapman@uttlesford.gov.uk

Health and Safety: Mr Geoff Smith, Head of Environmental Health, Council Offices, London Road, Saffron Walden CB11 4ER ☎ 01799 510582 ◌ gsmith@uttlesford.gov.uk

Home Energy Conservation: Mr John Farnell, Building Control Team Leader, Council Offices, London Road, Saffron Walden CB11 4ER ☎ 01799 510538 ◌ jfarnell@uttlesford.gov.uk

Housing: Mrs Roz Millership, Assistant Director - Housing & Environmental Services, Council Offices, London Road, Saffron Walden CB11 4ER ☎ 01799 510516 ◌ rmillership@uttlesford.gov.uk

Housing Maintenance: Mrs Roz Millership, Assistant Director - Housing & Environmental Services, Council Offices, London Road, Saffron Walden CB11 4ER ☎ 01799 510516 ◌ rmillership@uttlesford.gov.uk

Legal: Mr Michael Perry, Assistant Chief Executive - Legal, Council Offices, London Road, Saffron Walden CB11 4ER ☎ 01799 510416 ◌ mperry@uttlesford.gov.uk

Licensing: Mrs Amanda Turner, Licensing Officer, Council Offices, London Road, Saffron Walden CB11 4ER ☎ 01779 510613 ◌ aturner@uttlesford.gov.uk

Member Services: Mr Peter Snow, Democratic & Electoral Services Manager, Council Offices, London Road, Saffron Walden CB11 4ER ☎ 01799 510431 ◌ psnow@uttlesford.gov.uk

Partnerships: Mr Adrian Webb, Director - Finance & Corporate Services, Council Offices, London Road, Saffron Walden CB11 4ER ☎ 01799 510421 ◌ awebb@uttlesford.gov.uk

Personnel / HR: Mr Richard Auty, Assistant Director - Corporate Services, Council Offices, London Road, Saffron Walden CB11 4ER ☎ 01799 510500 ◌ rauty@uttlesford.gov.uk

Planning: Mr Nigel Brown, Development Control Manager, Council Offices, London Road, Saffron Walden CB11 4ER ☎ 01799 510476 ◌ nbrown@uttlesford.gov.uk

Planning: Mr Roger Harborough, Director - Public Services, Council Offices, London Road, Saffron Walden CB11 4ER ☎ 01799 510457 ◌ rharborough@uttlesford.gov.uk

Procurement: Ms Christine Oakey, Procurement Manager, Council Offices, London Road, Saffron Walden CB11 4ER ☎ 01799 510451 ◌ coakey@uttlesford.gov.uk

Recycling & Waste Minimisation: Mrs Catherine Chapman, Street Services Operations Manager, Council Offices, London Road, Saffron Walden CB11 4ER ☎ 01799 510557 ◌ cchapman@uttlesford.gov.uk

Street Scene: Mrs Catherine Chapman, Street Services Operations Manager, Council Offices, London Road, Saffron Walden CB11 4ER ☎ 01799 510557 ◌ cchapman@uttlesford.gov.uk

Sustainable Communities: Mr Roger Harborough, Director - Public Services, Council Offices, London Road, Saffron Walden CB11 4ER ☎ 01799 510457 ◌ rharborough@uttlesford.gov.uk

Sustainable Development: Mr Roger Harborough, Director - Public Services, Council Offices, London Road, Saffron Walden CB11 4ER ☎ 01799 510457 ◌ rharborough@uttlesford.gov.uk

UTTLESFORD

Waste Collection and Disposal: Mrs Catherine Chapman, Street Services Operations Manager, Council Offices, London Road, Saffron Walden CB11 4ER ☎ 01799 510557
✒ cchapman@uttlesford.gov.uk

Waste Management: Mrs Catherine Chapman, Street Services Operations Manager, Council Offices, London Road, Saffron Walden CB11 4ER ☎ 01799 510557 ✒ cchapman@uttlesford.gov.uk

COUNCILLORS

Leader of the Council: Rolfe, Howard (CON - Ashdon)
cllrrolfe@uttlesford.gov.uk

Deputy Leader of the Council: Barker, Susan (CON - High Easter & The Rodings)
cllrbarker@uttlesford.gov.uk

Anjum, Aisha (R - Saffron Walden (Shire))
cllranjum@uttlesford.gov.uk

Artus, Keith (CON - Broad Oak & the Hallingburys)
cllrartus@uttlesford.gov.uk

Asker, Heather (R - Saffron Walden (Castle))
cllrasker@uttlesford.gov.uk

Barker, Graham (CON - Great Dunmow South & Barnston)
cllrgbarker@uttlesford.gov.uk

Chambers, Robert (CON - Littlebury, Chesterford & Wendon Lofts)
cllrchambers@uttlesford.gov.uk

Davey, John (CON - Great Dunmow North)
cllrdavey@uttlesford.gov.uk

Davies, Paul (CON - Great Dunmow North)
cllrdavies@uttlesford.gov.uk

Dean, Alan (LD - Stansted North)
cllrdean@uttlesford.gov.uk

Fairhurst, Paul (R - Saffron Walden (Shire))
cllrfairhurst@uttlesford.gov.uk

Farthing, Terry (CON - Stansted South & Birchanger)
cllrfarthing@uttlesford.gov.uk

Felton, Marie (CON - Felsted & Stebbing)
cllrfelton@uttlesford.gov.uk

Foley, Martin (LD - Thaxted & The Eastons)
cllrfoley@uttlesford.gov.uk

Freeman, John (CON - Thaxted & The Eastons)
cllrjfreeman@uttlesford.gov.uk

Freeman, Richard (R - Saffron Walden (Castle))
cllrfreeman@uttlesford.gov.uk

Gleeson, Rory (LD - Elsenham & Henham)
cllrgleeson@uttlesford.gov.uk

Goddard, Thom (CON - Stansted South & Birchanger)
cllrgoddard@uttlesford.gov.uk

Gordon, Jim (CON - Takeley)
cllrgordon@uttlesford.gov.uk

Hargreaves, Neil (R - Newport)
cllrhargreaves@uttlesford.gov.uk

Harris, Stephanie (CON - Fitch Green & Little Dunmow)
cllrharris@uttlesford.gov.uk

Hicks, Eric (CON - Great Dunmow South & Barnston)
cllrhicks@uttlesford.gov.uk

Howell, Simon (CON - The Sampfords)
cllrhowell@uttlesford.gov.uk

Jones, Derek (CON - Takeley)
cllrdjones@uttlesford.gov.uk

Knight, Tina (CON - Debden & Wimbish)
cllrknight@uttlesford.gov.uk

Lemon, Mark (IND - Hatfield)
cllrlemon@uttlesford.gov.uk

Light, Barbara (R - Saffron Walden (Audley))
cllrlight@uttlesford.gov.uk

Lodge, John (R - Saffron Walden (Shire))
cllrlodge@uttlesford.gov.uk

Loughlin, Janice (LD - Stort Valley)
cllrloughlin@uttlesford.gov.uk

Mills, Alan (CON - Felsted & Stebbing)
cllrmills@uttlesford.gov.uk

Morris, Sharon (R - Saffron Walden (Audley))
cllrmorris@uttlesford.gov.uk

Oliver, Edward (CON - Clavering)
cllroliver@uttlesford.gov.uk

Parr, Elizabeth (LD - Elsenham & Henham)
cllrparr@uttlesford.gov.uk

Parry, Joanna (R - Newport)
cllrparry@uttlesford.gov.uk

Ranger, Vic (CON - Great Dunmow South & Barnston)
cllrranger@uttlesford.gov.uk

Redfern, Julie (CON - Littlebury, Chesterford & Wendon Lofts)
cllrredfern@uttlesford.gov.uk

Ryles, Howard (CON - Takeley)
cllrryles@uttlesford.gov.uk

Snell, Geoffrey (LD - Stansted North)
cllrsnell@uttlesford.gov.uk

Wells, Lesley (CON - Broad Oak & the Hallingburys)
cllrwells@uttlesford.gov.uk

POLITICAL COMPOSITION
CON: 23, R: 9, LD: 6, IND: 1

COMMITTEE CHAIRS

Audit: Mr Edward Oliver

Licensing: Mr Robert Chambers

Planning: Mr Vic Ranger

Vale of Glamorgan   W

Vale of Glamorgan Council, Civic Offices, Holton Road, Barry CF63 4RU
☎ 01446 700111 ✒ c1v@valeofglamorgan.gov.uk
🖥 www.valeofglamorgan.gov.uk

FACTS AND FIGURES
Parliamentary Constituencies: Cardiff South and Penarth, Vale of Glamorgan
EU Constituencies: Wales
Election Frequency: Elections are of whole council

PRINCIPAL OFFICERS

Chief Executive: Mr Rob Thomas, Managing Director, Civic Offices, Holton Road, Barry CF63 4RU ☎ 01446 704630
⌁ drthomas@valeofglamorgan.gov.uk

Senior Management: Mr Phil Evans, Director - Social Services, Dock Offices, Subway Road, Barry CF63 4RT ☎ 01446 704676
⌁ pjevans@valeofglamorgan.gov.uk

Senior Management: Mr Miles Punter, Director - Environment & Housing Services, The Alps, Quarry Road, Wenvoe CF5 6AA
☎ 029 2067 3101 ⌁ mepunter@valeofglamorgan.gov.uk

Access Officer / Social Services (Disability): Mrs Linda Brown, Joint Corporate Equality Officer, Civic Offices, Holton Road, Barry CF63 4RU ☎ 01446 709362 ⌁ ljbrown@valeofglamorgan.gov.uk

Access Officer / Social Services (Disability): Ms Nicola Hinton, Joint Corporate Equality Officer, Civic Offices, Holton Road, Barry CF63 4RU ☎ 01446 709362
⌁ nhinton@valeofglamorgan.gov.uk

Architect, Building / Property Services: Mrs Jane O'Leary, Operational Manager - Property Services, Civic Offices, Holton Road, Barry CF63 4RU ☎ 01446 709270
⌁ jo'leary@valeofglamorgan.gov.uk

Best Value: Mr Huw Isaac, Head of Performance & Development, Civic Offices, Holton Road, Barry CF63 4RU ☎ 01446 709760
⌁ hisaac@valeofglamorgan.gov.uk

Catering Services: Mrs Carole Tyley, Catering Manager, Provincial House, Kendrick Road, Barry CF62 8BF
☎ 029 2067 3037 ⌁ ctyley@valeofglamorgan.gov.uk

Children / Youth Services: Ms Rachel Evans, Head of Children & Young People's Services, Dock Offices, Subway Road, Barry CF63 4RT ☎ 01446 704792 ⌁ rjevans@valeofglamorgan.gov.uk

Civil Registration: Mrs Tania Carter, Registration Manager / Superintendent Registrar, Civic Offices, Holton Road, Barry CF63 4RU ☎ 01446 709166 ⌁ tcarter@valeofglamorgan.gov.uk

PR / Communications: Mr Rob Jones, Senior Media Officer, Civic Offices, Holton Road, Barry CF63 4RU ☎ 01446 709530
⌁ rajones@valeofglamorgan.gov.uk

Community Planning: Mr Huw Isaac, Head of Performance & Development, Civic Offices, Holton Road, Barry CF63 4RU
☎ 01446 709760 ⌁ hisaac@valeofglamorgan.gov.uk

Community Safety: Mr Dave Holland, Head of Shared Regulatory Services, Civic Offices, Holton Road, Barry CF63 4RU
☎ 01446 709720 ⌁ dholland@valeofglamorgan.gov.uk

Computer Management: Mr David Vining, Head of Strategic ICT, Civic Offices, Holton Road, Barry CF63 4RU ☎ 01446 709382
⌁ djvining@valeofglamorgan.gov.uk

Consumer Protection and Trading Standards: Ms Christina Hill, Operational Manager - Commercial Services, Civic Offices, Holton Road, Barry CF63 4RU ☎ 01446 709344
⌁ chill@valeofglamorgan.gov.uk

Customer Service: Mr Tony Curliss, Operational Manager - Customer Relations, C1V, Barry Leisure Centre, Greenwood Street, Barry CF63 4JJ ☎ 01446 729500
⌁ tcurliss@valeofglamorgan.gov.uk

Direct Labour: Mr Miles Punter, Director - Environment & Housing Services, The Alps, Quarry Road, Wenvoe CF5 6AA ☎ 029 2067 3101 ⌁ mepunter@valeofglamorgan.gov.uk

E-Government: Mr Huw Isaac, Head of Performance & Development, Civic Offices, Holton Road, Barry CF63 4RU
☎ 01446 709760 ⌁ hisaac@valeofglamorgan.gov.uk

Electoral Registration: Miss Rebecca Light, Electoral & Members' Services Team Leader, Civic Offices, Holton Road, Barry CF63 4RU ☎ 01446 709304 ⌁ rmlight@valeofglamorgan.gov.uk

Emergency Planning: Ms Debbie Spargo, Principal Civic Protection Officer, The Alps, Quarry Road, Wenvoe, Barry CF5 6AA
☎ 029 2067 3041 ⌁ daspargo@valeofglamorgan.gov.uk

Energy Management: Mr David Powell, Energy Manager, Civic Offices, Holton Road, Barry CF63 4RU ☎ 01446 709576
⌁ dpowell@valeofglamorgan.gov.uk

Environmental / Technical Services: Mr Miles Punter, Director - Environment & Housing Services, The Alps, Quarry Road, Wenvoe CF5 6AA ☎ 029 2067 3101 ⌁ mepunter@valeofglamorgan.gov.uk

Environmental Health: Mr Dave Holland, Head of Shared Regulatory Services, Civic Offices, Holton Road, Barry CF63 4RU
☎ 01446 709720 ⌁ dholland@valeofglamorgan.gov.uk

Environmental Health: Mr Philip Stanton, Service Manager - Environmental Health, Raven's Court, Brewery Lane, Bridgend CF31 4AP ☎ 01656 643141 ⌁ philip.stanton@bridgend.gov.uk

Estates, Property & Valuation: Mrs Jane O'Leary, Operational Manager - Property Services, Civic Offices, Holton Road, Barry CF63 4RU ☎ 01446 709270 ⌁ jo'leary@valeofglamorgan.gov.uk

Events Manager: Ms Sarah Jones, Events Officer, Dock Office, Subway Road, Barry CF63 4RT ☎ 01446 704737
⌁ sejones@valeofglamorgan.gov.uk

Facilities: Ms Rachel Slee, Facilities Co-ordinator, Civic Offices, Holton Road, Barry CF63 4RU ☎ 01446 709243
⌁ rhslee@valeofglamorgan.gov.uk

Fleet Management: Mr Miles Punter, Director - Environment & Housing Services, The Alps, Quarry Road, Wenvoe CF5 6AA
☎ 029 2067 3101 ⌁ mepunter@valeofglamorgan.gov.uk

Health and Safety: Mr Richard Stopgate, Principal Corporate Health & Safety Officer, The Alps, Quarry Road, Wenvoe, Cardiff CF5 6AA ☎ 029 2067 3263 ⌁ rdstopgate@valeofglamorgan.gov.uk

Home Energy Conservation: Mr David Powell, Energy Manager, Civic Offices, Holton Road, Barry CF63 4RU ☎ 01446 709576
⌁ dpowell@valeofglamorgan.gov.uk

VALE OF GLAMORGAN

Legal: Ms Debbie Marles, Head of Legal Services, Civic Offices, Holton Road, Barry CF63 4RU ☎ 01446 709402 ✉ dmarles@valeofglamorgan.gov.uk

Leisure and Cultural Services: Mr David Knevett, Operational Manager - Leisure, Civic Offices, Holton Road, Barry CF63 4RU ☎ 01446 704817 ✉ dpknevett@valeofglamorgan.gov.uk

Licensing: Ms Yvonne Witchell, Licensing Team Leader, Civic Offices, Angel Street, Bridgend CF31 4WB ☎ 01656 643105 ✉ yvonne.witchell@bridgend.gov.uk

Member Services: Mr Jeff Rees, Team Leader - Principal Democratic & Scrutiny Services Officer, Civic Offices, Holton Road, Barry CF63 4RU ☎ 01446 709413 ✉ jerees@valeofglamorgan.gov.uk

Partnerships: Mrs Helen Moses, Strategy & Sustainability Manager, Barry Fire Station, Port Road West, Barry CF62 3AZ ☎ 01446 450205 ✉ hmoses@valeofglamorgan.gov.uk

Personnel / HR: Mr Reuben Bergman, Head of Human Resources, Provincial House, Kendrick Road, Barry CF62 8BF ☎ 01446 709357 ✉ rbergman@valeofglamorgan.gov.uk

Planning: Mr Miles Punter, Director - Environment & Housing Services, The Alps, Quarry Road, Wenvoe CF5 6AA ☎ 029 2067 3101 ✉ mepunter@valeofglamorgan.gov.uk

Procurement: Mrs Carys Lord, Head of Finance, Civic Offices, Holton Road, Barry CF63 4RU ☎ 01446 709254 ✉ cllord@valeofglamorgan.gov.uk

Public Libraries: Mr Andrew Borsden, Lead Officer - Youth & Community Learning, Provincial House, Kendrick Road, Barry CF62 8BF ☎ 01446 709148 ✉ amborsden@valeofglamorgan.gov.uk

Regeneration: Mr Miles Punter, Director - Environment & Housing Services, The Alps, Quarry Road, Wenvoe CF5 6AA ☎ 029 2067 3101 ✉ mepunter@valeofglamorgan.gov.uk

Road Safety: Ms Clare Cameron, Principal Transport & Road Safety Officer, Dock Office, Barry Docks, Barry CF63 4RT ☎ 01446 704768 ✉ ccameron@valeofglamorgan.gov.uk

Social Services: Mr Phil Evans, Director - Social Services, Dock Offices, Subway Road, Barry CF63 4RT ☎ 01446 704676 ✉ pjevans@valeofglamorgan.gov.uk

Social Services (Adult): Mr Lance Carver, Head of Adult Services & Locality Manager, Dock Offices, Subway Road, Barry CF63 4RT ☎ 01446 704678 ✉ lcarver@valeofglamorgan.gov.uk

Social Services (Children): Ms Rachel Evans, Head of Children & Young People's Services, Dock Offices, Subway Road, Barry CF63 4RT ☎ 01446 704792 ✉ rjevans@valeofglamorgan.gov.uk

Street Scene: Mr Miles Punter, Director - Environment & Housing Services, The Alps, Quarry Road, Wenvoe CF5 6AA ☎ 029 2067 3101 ✉ mepunter@valeofglamorgan.gov.uk

Sustainable Communities: Mr Miles Punter, Director - Environment & Housing Services, The Alps, Quarry Road, Wenvoe CF5 6AA ☎ 029 2067 3101 ✉ mepunter@valeofglamorgan.gov.uk

COUNCILLORS

Mayor: Egan, Stuart (LAB - Buttrills)
scegan@valeofglamorgan.gov.uk

Deputy Mayor: Williams, Edward (IND - Llantwit Major)
edwilliams@valeofglamorgan.gov.uk

Leader of the Council: Moore, Neil (LAB - Cadoc)
nmoore@valeofglamorgan.gov.uk

Deputy Leader of the Council: Burnett, Lis (LAB - St. Augustines)
lburnett@valeofglamorgan.gov.uk

Group Leader: Thomas, John (CON - St. Athan)
jwthomas@valeofglamorgan.gov.uk

Bennett, Anthony (CON - Llantwit Major)
agbennett@valeofglamorgan.gov.uk

Bertin, Richard (IND - Court)
rjbertin@valeofglamorgan.gov.uk

Birch, Rhiannon (LAB - Cornerswell)
rbirch@valeofglamorgan.gov.uk

Birch, Janice (LAB - Stanwell)
jbirch@valeofglamorgan.gov.uk

Bird, Jonathan (CON - Wenvoe)
jbird@valeofglamorgan.gov.uk

Brooks, Bronwen (LAB - Court)
bbrooks@valeofglamorgan.gov.uk

Cox, Geoffrey (CON - Cowbridge)
gacox@valeofglamorgan.gov.uk

Curtis, Claire (LAB - Dyfan)
ccurtis@valeofglamorgan.gov.uk

Drake, Pamela (LAB - Castleland)
pdrake@valeofglamorgan.gov.uk

Drysdale, John (LAB - Illtyd)
jdrysdale@valeofglamorgan.gov.uk

Edmunds, Kate (LAB - Llandough)
kedmunds@valeofglamorgan.gov.uk

Elmore, Christopher (LAB - Castleland)
celmore@valeofglamorgan.gov.uk

Franks, Christopher (PC - Dinas Powys)
familyfranks@btinternet.com

Hacker, Eric (IND - Llantwit Major)
ehacker@valeofglamorgan.gov.uk

Hamilton, Howard (LAB - Illtyd)
hhamilton@valeofglamorgan.gov.uk

Hartrey, Val (PC - Dinas Powys)
vmhartrey@valeofglamorgan.gov.uk

Hatton, Keith (PC - Dinas Powys)
khatton@valeofglamorgan.gov.uk

Hodges, Nic (PC - Baruc)
nphodges@valeofglamorgan.gov.uk

James, Jeff (CON - Rhoose)
hjwjames@valeofglamorgan.gov.uk

Jarvie, Hunter (CON - Cowbridge)
hjarvie@valeofglamorgan.gov.uk

John, Gwyn (IND - Llantwit Major)
gjohn@valeofglamorgan.gov.uk

Johnson, Frederick (LAB - Cadoc)
ftjohnson@valeofglamorgan.gov.uk

Johnson, Ian James (PC - Buttrills)
ljohnson@valeofglamorgan.gov.uk

Kelly- Owen, Maureen (CON - Plymouth)
mkellyowen@valeofglamorgan.gov.uk

King, Peter (LAB - Cornerswell)
pking@valeofglamorgan.gov.uk

Mahoney, Kevin (UKIP - Sully)
kpmahoney@valeofglamorgan.gov.uk

Moore, Anne (LAB - Cadoc)
ajmoore@valeofglamorgan.gov.uk

Parker, Andrew (CON - Cowbridge)
aparker@valeofglamorgan.gov.uk

Penrose, Bob (IND - Sully)
bpenrose@valeofglamorgan.gov.uk

Powell, Anthony (LAB - Dyfan)
agpowell@valeofglamorgan.gov.uk

Preston, Audrey (CON - St. Brides Major)

Probert, Rhona (LAB - Illtyd)
rprobert@valeofglamorgan.gov.uk

Riley, Adam (IND - Rhoose)
apriley@valeofglamorgan.gov.uk

Roberts, Gwyn (LAB - St. Augustines)
groberts@valeofglamorgan.gov.uk

Thomas, Ray (CON - Llandow / Ewenny)
rathomas@valeofglamorgan.gov.uk

Traherne, Rhodri (CON - Peterston-Super-Ely)
rtraherne@valeofglamorgan.gov.uk

Wiliam, Steffan (PC - Baruc)
stwiliam@valeofglamorgan.gov.uk

Wilkinson, Margaret (LAB - Gibbonsdown)
mrwilkinson@valeofglamorgan.gov.uk

Williams, A Clive (CON - Plymouth)
cwilliams@valeofglamorgan.gov.uk

Williams, Christopher (IND - Dinas Powys)
cjwilliams@valeofglamorgan.gov.uk

Wilson, Mark (LAB - Stanwell)
mrwilson@valeofglamorgan.gov.uk

POLITICAL COMPOSITION
LAB: 20, CON: 12, IND: 7, PC: 6, UKIP: 1

COMMITTEE CHAIRS
Licensing: Mr Anthony Powell

Planning: Mr Frederick Johnson

Vale of White Horse   D

Vale of White Horse District Council, 135 Eastern Avenue,
Milton Park, Milton
OX14 4SB
☎ 01235 520202 ✆ comments@whitehorsedc.gov.uk
💻 www.whitehorsedc.gov.uk

VALE OF WHITE HORSE

FACTS AND FIGURES
Parliamentary Constituencies: Oxford West and Abingdon,
Wantage
EU Constituencies: South East
Election Frequency: Elections are of whole council

PRINCIPAL OFFICERS

Chief Executive: Mr David Hill, Chief Executive, 135 Eastern
Avenue, Milton Park, Milton OX14 4SB ☎ 01235 547612
✆ david.hill@southandvale.gov.uk

Deputy Chief Executive: Mr Steve Bishop, Strategic Director, 135
Eastern Avenue, Milton Park, Milton, Abingdon OX14 4SB
☎ 01235 540332 ✆ steve.bishop@southandvale.gov.uk

Senior Management: Mr Andrew Down, Head of HR, IT &
Technical Services, 135 Eastern Avenue, Milton Park, Milton,
Abingdon OX14 4SB ☎ 01235 540372
✆ andrew.down@southandvale.gov.uk

Senior Management: Mr Adrian Duffield, Head of Planning, 135
Eastern Avenue, Milton Park, Milton, Abingdon OX14 4SB
☎ 01235 540340 ✆ adrian.duffield@southandvale.gov.uk

Senior Management: Mr William Jacobs, Head of Finance, 135
Eastern Avenue, Milton Park, Milton, Abingdon OX14 4SB
☎ 01235 540526 ✆ william.jacobs@southandvale.gov.uk

Senior Management: Mrs Clare Kingston, Head of Corporate
Strategy, 135 Eastern Avenue, Milton Park, Milton, Abingdon OX14
4SB ☎ 01235 540356 ✆ clare.kingston@southandvale.gov.uk

Senior Management: Mrs Margaret Reed, Head of Legal &
Democratic Services, 135 Eastern Avenue, Milton Park, Milton,
Abingdon OX14 4SB ☎ 01235 540407
✆ margaret.reed@southandvale.gov.uk

Building Control: Mr Adrian Duffield, Head of Planning, 135
Eastern Avenue, Milton Park, Milton, Abingdon OX14 4SB
☎ 01235 540340 ✆ adrian.duffield@southandvale.gov.uk

PR / Communications: Mrs Clare Kingston, Head of Corporate
Strategy, 135 Eastern Avenue, Milton Park, Milton, Abingdon OX14
4SB ☎ 01235 540356 ✆ clare.kingston@southandvale.gov.uk

PR / Communications: Mrs Shona Ware, Communications &
Grants Manager, 135 Eastern Avenue, Milton Park, Milton, Abingdon
OX14 4SB ☎ 01235 540406 ✆ shona.ware@southandvale.gov.uk

Community Safety: Mrs Liz Hayden, Legal, Licensing &
Community Safety Manager, 135 Eastern Avenue, Milton Park,
Milton, Abingdon OX14 4SB ☎ 01491 823705
✆ liz.hayden@southandvale.gov.uk

Community Safety: Mrs Margaret Reed, Head of Legal &
Democratic Services, 135 Eastern Avenue, Milton Park, Milton,
Abingdon OX14 4SB ☎ 01235 540407
✆ margaret.reed@southandvale.gov.uk

Computer Management: Mr Andrew Down, Head of HR, IT
& Technical Services, 135 Eastern Avenue, Milton Park, Milton,
Abingdon OX14 4SB ☎ 01235 540372
~✆ andrew.down@southandvale.gov.uk

VALE OF WHITE HORSE

Computer Management: Mr Simon Turner, IT Operations Manager, 135 Eastern Avenue, Milton Park, Milton, Abingdon OX14 4SB ☎ 01235 540400 ⌇ simon.turner@southandvale.gov.uk

Contracts: Mrs Margaret Reed, Head of Legal & Democratic Services, 135 Eastern Avenue, Milton Park, Milton, Abingdon OX14 4SB ☎ 01235 540407 ⌇ margaret.reed@southandvale.gov.uk

Economic Development: Mrs Suzanne Malcolm, Economic Development Manager, 135 Eastern Avenue, Milton Park, Milton, Abingdon OX14 4SB ☎ 01235 547619 ⌇ suzanne.malcolm@southandvale.gov.uk

E-Government: Mr Andrew Down, Head of HR, IT & Technical Services, 135 Eastern Avenue, Milton Park, Milton, Abingdon OX14 4SB ☎ 01235 540372 ⌇ andrew.down@southandvale.gov.uk

Electoral Registration: Mr Steven Corrigan, Democratic Services Manager, 135 Eastern Avenue, Milton Park, Milton, Abingdon OX14 4SB ☎ 01235 547675 ⌇ steven.corrigan@southandvale.gov.uk

Electoral Registration: Mrs Margaret Reed, Head of Legal & Democratic Services, 135 Eastern Avenue, Milton Park, Milton, Abingdon OX14 4SB ☎ 01235 540407 ⌇ margaret.reed@southandvale.gov.uk

Emergency Planning: Mr John Backley, Technical & Facilities Manager, 135 Eastern Avenue, Milton Park, Milton, Abingdon OX14 4SB ☎ 01235 540443 ⌇ john.backley@southandvale.gov.uk

Emergency Planning: Mr Andrew Down, Head of HR, IT & Technical Services, 135 Eastern Avenue, Milton Park, Milton, Abingdon OX14 4SB ☎ 01235 540372 ⌇ andrew.down@southandvale.gov.uk

Environmental / Technical Services: Mr John Backley, Technical & Facilities Manager, 135 Eastern Avenue, Milton Park, Milton, Abingdon OX14 4SB ☎ 01235 540443 ⌇ john.backley@southandvale.gov.uk

Environmental / Technical Services: Mr Andrew Down, Head of HR, IT & Technical Services, 135 Eastern Avenue, Milton Park, Milton, Abingdon OX14 4SB ☎ 01235 540372 ⌇ andrew.down@southandvale.gov.uk

Environmental / Technical Services: Mrs Clare Kingston, Head of Corporate Strategy, 135 Eastern Avenue, Milton Park, Milton, Abingdon OX14 4SB ☎ 01235 540356 ⌇ clare.kingston@southandvale.gov.uk

Environmental / Technical Services: Ms Diane Moore, Food & Safety Manager, 135 Eastern Avenue, Milton Park, Milton, Abingdon OX14 4SB ☎ 01235 540382 ⌇ diane.moore@southandvale.gov.uk

Environmental Health: Mr Paul Holland, Environmental Protection Manager, 135 Eastern Avenue, Milton Park, Milton, Abingdon OX14 4SB ☎ 01235 540454 ⌇ paul.hollans@southandvale.gov.uk

Estates, Property & Valuation: Mrs Suzanne Malcolm, Economic Development Manager, 135 Eastern Avenue, Milton Park, Milton, Abingdon OX14 4SB ☎ 01235 547619 ⌇ suzanne.malcolm@southandvale.gov.uk

Facilities: Mr John Backley, Technical & Facilities Manager, 135 Eastern Avenue, Milton Park, Milton, Abingdon OX14 4SB ☎ 01235 540443 ⌇ john.backley@southandvale.gov.uk

Facilities: Mr Andrew Down, Head of HR, IT & Technical Services, 135 Eastern Avenue, Milton Park, Milton, Abingdon OX14 4SB ☎ 01235 540372 ⌇ andrew.down@southandvale.gov.uk

Finance: Mr Steve Bishop, Strategic Director, 135 Eastern Avenue, Milton Park, Milton, Abingdon OX14 4SB ☎ 01235 540332 ⌇ steve.bishop@southandvale.gov.uk

Finance: Mr William Jacobs, Head of Finance, 135 Eastern Avenue, Milton Park, Milton, Abingdon OX14 4SB ☎ 01235 540526 ⌇ william.jacobs@southandvale.gov.uk

Grounds Maintenance: Mrs Clare Kingston, Head of Corporate Strategy, 135 Eastern Avenue, Milton Park, Milton, Abingdon OX14 4SB ☎ 01235 540356 ⌇ clare.kingston@southandvale.gov.uk

Grounds Maintenance: Mr Ian Matten, Waste & Parks Manager, 135 Eastern Avenue, Milton Park, Milton, Abingdon OX14 4SB ☎ 01235 540373 ⌇ ian.matten@southandvale.gov.uk

Health and Safety: Mrs Clare Kingston, Head of Corporate Strategy, 135 Eastern Avenue, Milton Park, Milton, Abingdon OX14 4SB ☎ 01235 540356 ⌇ clare.kingston@southandvale.gov.uk

Health and Safety: Ms Sally Truman, Policy, Partnership & Engagement Manager, 135 Eastern Avenue, Milton Park, Milton, Abingdon OX14 4SB ☎ 01235 450408 ⌇ sally.truman@southandvale.gov.uk

Housing: Mr Phil Ealey, Housing Needs Manager, 135 Milton Avenue, Milton Park, Milton, Abingdon OX14 4SB ☎ 01235 547623 ⌇ phil.ealey@southandvale.gov.uk

Legal: Mrs Liz Hayden, Legal, Licensing & Community Safety Manager, 135 Eastern Avenue, Milton Park, Milton, Abingdon OX14 4SB ☎ 01491 823705 ⌇ liz.hayden@southandvale.gov.uk

Legal: Mrs Margaret Reed, Head of Legal & Democratic Services, 135 Eastern Avenue, Milton Park, Milton, Abingdon OX14 4SB ☎ 01235 540407 ⌇ margaret.reed@southandvale.gov.uk

Leisure and Cultural Services: Miss Kate Arnold, Leisure Manager, 135 Eastern Avenue, Milton Park, Milton, Abingdon OX14 4SB ☎ 01235 547632 ⌇ kate.arnold@southandvale.gov.uk

Leisure and Cultural Services: Miss Emma Dolman, Arts Manager, Cornerstone, 25 Station Road, Didcot OX11 7NE ☎ 01235 515131 ⌇ emma.dolman@southandvale.gov.uk

Licensing: Mrs Liz Hayden, Legal, Licensing & Community Safety Manager, 135 Eastern Avenue, Milton Park, Milton, Abingdon OX14 4SB ☎ 01491 823705 ⌇ liz.hayden@southandvale.gov.uk

Licensing: Mrs Margaret Reed, Head of Legal & Democratic Services, 135 Eastern Avenue, Milton Park, Milton, Abingdon OX14 4SB ☎ 01235 540407 ⌇ margaret.reed@southandvale.gov.uk

Member Services: Mr Steven Corrigan, Democratic Services Manager, 135 Eastern Avenue, Milton Park, Milton, Abingdon OX14 4SB ☎ 01235 547675 ◌ steven.corrigan@southandvale.gov.uk

Member Services: Mrs Margaret Reed, Head of Legal & Democratic Services, 135 Eastern Avenue, Milton Park, Milton, Abingdon OX14 4SB ☎ 01235 540407 ◌ margaret.reed@southandvale.gov.uk

Parking: Mr John Backley, Technical & Facilities Manager, 135 Eastern Avenue, Milton Park, Milton, Abingdon OX14 4SB ☎ 01235 540443 ◌ john.backley@southandvale.gov.uk

Parking: Mr Andrew Down, Head of HR, IT & Technical Services, 135 Eastern Avenue, Milton Park, Milton, Abingdon OX14 4SB ☎ 01235 540372 ◌ andrew.down@southandvale.gov.uk

Partnerships: Mrs Clare Kingston, Head of Corporate Strategy, 135 Eastern Avenue, Milton Park, Milton, Abingdon OX14 4SB ☎ 01235 540356 ◌ clare.kingston@southandvale.gov.uk

Partnerships: Ms Sally Truman, Policy, Partnership & Engagement Manager, 135 Eastern Avenue, Milton Park, Milton, Abingdon OX14 4SB ☎ 01235 450408 ◌ sally.truman@southandvale.gov.uk

Personnel / HR: Mr Andrew Down, Head of HR, IT & Technical Services, 135 Eastern Avenue, Milton Park, Milton, Abingdon OX14 4SB ☎ 01235 540372 ◌ andrew.down@southandvale.gov.uk

Personnel / HR: Mr Mark Gibbons, Human Resources Manager, 135 Eastern Avenue, Milton Park, Milton, Abingdon OX14 4SB ☎ 01491 823412 ◌ mark.gibbons@southandvale.gov.uk

Planning: Mr Adrian Duffield, Head of Planning, 135 Eastern Avenue, Milton Park, Milton, Abingdon OX14 4SB ☎ 01235 540340 ◌ adrian.duffield@southandvale.gov.uk

Planning: Miss Paula Fox, Development Manager (South), 135 Eastern Avenue, Milton Park, Milton, Abingdon OX14 4SB ☎ 01235 540361 ◌ paula.fox@southandvale.gov.uk

Planning: Ms Emily Hamerton, Development Manager (Vale), 135 Eastern Avenue, Milton Park, Milton OX14 4SB ◌ emily.hamerton@southandvale.gov.uk

Recycling & Waste Minimisation: Mrs Clare Kingston, Head of Corporate Strategy, 135 Eastern Avenue, Milton Park, Milton, Abingdon OX14 4SB ☎ 01235 540356 ◌ clare.kingston@southandvale.gov.uk

Recycling & Waste Minimisation: Mr Ian Matten, Waste & Parks Manager, 135 Eastern Avenue, Milton Park, Milton, Abingdon OX14 4SB ☎ 01235 540373 ◌ ian.matten@southandvale.gov.uk

Regeneration: Mr Gerry Brough, Interim Head of Development & Regeneration, 135 Eastern Avenue, Milton Park, Milton OX14 4SB ◌ gerry.brough@southandvale.gov.uk

Staff Training: Mr Andrew Down, Head of HR, IT & Technical Services, 135 Eastern Avenue, Milton Park, Milton, Abingdon OX14 4SB ☎ 01235 540372 ◌ andrew.down@southandvale.gov.uk

Staff Training: Mr Mark Gibbons, Human Resources Manager, 135 Eastern Avenue, Milton Park, Milton, Abingdon OX14 4SB ☎ 01491 823412 ◌ mark.gibbons@southandvale.gov.uk

Sustainable Communities: Mr Adrian Duffield, Head of Planning, 135 Eastern Avenue, Milton Park, Milton, Abingdon OX14 4SB ☎ 01235 540340 ◌ adrian.duffield@southandvale.gov.uk

Sustainable Development: Mrs Clare Kingston, Head of Corporate Strategy, 135 Eastern Avenue, Milton Park, Milton, Abingdon OX14 4SB ☎ 01235 540356 ◌ clare.kingston@southandvale.gov.uk

Sustainable Development: Ms Sally Truman, Policy, Partnership & Engagement Manager, 135 Eastern Avenue, Milton Park, Milton, Abingdon OX14 4SB ☎ 01235 450408 ◌ sally.truman@southandvale.gov.uk

Town Centre: Mrs Suzanne Malcolm, Economic Development Manager, 135 Eastern Avenue, Milton Park, Milton, Abingdon OX14 4SB ☎ 01235 547619 ◌ suzanne.malcolm@southandvale.gov.uk

Waste Collection and Disposal: Mrs Clare Kingston, Head of Corporate Strategy, 135 Eastern Avenue, Milton Park, Milton, Abingdon OX14 4SB ☎ 01235 540356 ◌ clare.kingston@southandvale.gov.uk

Waste Collection and Disposal: Mr Ian Matten, Waste & Parks Manager, 135 Eastern Avenue, Milton Park, Milton, Abingdon OX14 4SB ☎ 01235 540373 ◌ ian.matten@southandvale.gov.uk

Waste Management: Mrs Clare Kingston, Head of Corporate Strategy, 135 Eastern Avenue, Milton Park, Milton, Abingdon OX14 4SB ☎ 01235 540356 ◌ clare.kingston@southandvale.gov.uk

Waste Management: Mr Ian Matten, Waste & Parks Manager, 135 Eastern Avenue, Milton Park, Milton, Abingdon OX14 4SB ☎ 01235 540373 ◌ ian.matten@southandvale.gov.uk

COUNCILLORS

Chair: Badcock, Mike (CON - Abingdon Caldecott) mike.badcock@whitehorsedc.gov.uk

Vice-Chair: Waite, Reg (CON - Blewbury & Harwell) reg.waite@whitehorsedc.gov.uk

Leader of the Council: Barber, Matthew (CON - Steventon & the Hanneys) matthew.barber@whitehorsedc.gov.uk

Deputy Leader of the Council: Cox, Roger (CON - Faringdon) roger.cox@whitehorsedc.gov.uk

Group Leader: Hallett, Debby (LD - Botley & Sunningwell) cllr.debby.hallett@gmail.com

Badcock, Alice (CON - Abingdon Caldecott) alice.badcock@whitehorsedc.gov.uk

Batts, Eric (CON - Kingston Bagpuize) cllrericbatts@gmail.com

Blagrove, Edward (CON - Kennington & Radley) edward.blagrove@whitehorsedc.gov.uk

Constance, Yvonne (CON - Ridgeway) yvonne.constance@whitehorsedc.gov.uk

VALE OF WHITE HORSE

Crick, Margaret (LD - Abingdon Dunmore)

Davenport, Stuart (CON - Drayton)
stuart.davenport@whitehorsedc.gov.uk

Dickson, Charlotte (CON - Wantage Charlton)
charlotte@leahouse.com

Dickson, St John (CON - Wantage Charlton)
stjohn.dickson@whitehorsedc.gov.uk

Duffield, Gervase (CON - Sutton Courtenay)
gervase.duffield@whitehorsedc.gov.uk

Finch, Katie (CON - Abingdon Abbey Northcourt)
katie.finch@whitehorsedc.gov.uk

Hall, Robert (CON - Abingdon Peachcroft)
robert.hall@whitehorsedc.gov.uk

Hannaby, Jenny (LD - Wantage & Grove Brook)
jenny@yeomanryhouse.co.uk

Hayward, Anthony (CON - Thames)
anthony.hayward@whitehorsedc.gov.uk

Hoddinott, Dudley (LD - Cumnor)
dhoddinott@clara.co.uk

Howell, Simon (CON - Watchfield & Shrivenham)
simon.p.howell@btinternet.com

Jenkins, Vicky (CON - Abingdon Peachcroft)
vicky.jenkins@whitehorsedc.gov.uk

Johnston, Bob (LD - Kennington & Radley)
bobtjohnston@googlemail.com

Kanith, Mohinder (CON - Faringdon)
mohinder.kainth@gmail.com

Lovatt, Sandy (CON - Abingdon Dunmore)
sandy.lovatt@whitehorsedc.gov.uk

Lovatt, Monica (CON - Abingdon Fitzharris)
monica.lovatt@whitehorsedc.gov.uk

Mabbett, Ben (CON - Grove North)
ben.mabbett@whitehorsedc.gov.uk

McCarthy, Chris (CON - Grove North)
chris.mccarthy@whitehorsedc.gov.uk

Murray, Michael (CON - Hendreds)
mike.murray@causewayland.com

Palmer, Chris (CON - Abingdon Fitzharris)
chris.palmer@whitehorsedc.gov.uk

Pighills, Helen (LD - Abingdon Abbey Northcourt)
helen.pighills@whitehorsedc.gov.uk

Reynolds, Julia (CON - Wantage & Grove Brook)
julia.reynolds3@btinternet.com

Roberts, Judy (LD - Cumnor)
judy.roberts@whitehorsedc.gov.uk

Sharp, Robert (CON - Stanford)
robert.sharp@whitehorsedc.gov.uk

Shelley, Janet (CON - Blewbury & Harwell)
janet.shelley@whitehorsedc.gov.uk

Smith, Emily (LD - Botley & Sunningwell)
emily.smith@whitehorsedc.gov.uk

Spencer, Henry (CON - Wootton)
henry.spencer@whitehorsedc.gov.uk

Ware, Elaine (CON - Watchfield & Shrivenham)
elaine.ware@whitehorsedc.gov.uk

Webber, Catherine (LD - Marcham)
catherine.webber@whitehorsedc.gov.uk

POLITICAL COMPOSITION
CON: 29, LD: 9

COMMITTEE CHAIRS

Licensing: Ms Charlotte Dickson

Planning: Mr Sandy Lovatt

Wakefield City   M

Wakefield City Council, Town Hall, Wood Street, Wakefield WF1 2HQ
☎ 03458 506506 ⏂ customerservices@wakefield.gov.uk
🖥 www.wakefield.gov.uk

FACTS AND FIGURES
Parliamentary Constituencies: Hemsworth, Morley and Outwood, Normanton, Pontefract and Castleford, Wakefield
EU Constituencies: Yorkshire and the Humber
Election Frequency: Elections are by thirds

PRINCIPAL OFFICERS

Chief Executive: Ms Joanne Roney, Chief Executive, Town Hall, Wakefield WF1 2HQ ☎ 01924 305101 ⏂ jroney@wakefield.gov.uk

Assistant Chief Executive: Mr Michael Clements, Assistant Chief Executive - Resources & Governance, Town Hall, Wood Street, Wakefield WF1 2HQ ☎ 01924 306535
⏂ mclements@wakefield.gov.uk

Assistant Chief Executive: Ms Helen Grantham, Assistant Chief Executive - Organisational Development, County Hall, Bond Street, Wakefield WF1 2QW ☎ 01924 306700
⏂ hgrantham@wakefield.gov.uk

Senior Management: Mr Andrew Balchin, Corporate Director - Adults, Health & Communities, Wakefield One, Burton Street, Wakefield WF1 2DA ☎ 01924 306634 ⏂ abalchin@wakefield.gov.uk

Senior Management: Dr Andrew Furber, Director - Public Health, Town Hall, Wood Street, Wakefield WF1 2HQ ☎ 01942 305347
⏂ afurber@wakefield.gov.uk

Senior Management: Mr Andrew Wallhead, Corporate Director - Regeneration & Economic Growth, Wakefield One, Burton Street, Wakefield WF1 2DA ☎ 01924 306950
⏂ awallhead@wakefield.gov.uk

Senior Management: Mr John Wilson, Corporate Director - Children & Young People, Town Hall, Wood Street, Wakefield WF1 2HQ ☎ 01924 307725 ⏂ jwilson@wakefield.gov.uk

Architect, Building / Property Services: Mr Kevin Fisher, Service Manager - Property & Facilities Management, Wakefield One, Burton Street, Wakefield WF1 2DA ☎ 01924 306490
⏂ kevinfisher@wakefield.gov.uk

Building Control: Mr Neil Rodgers, Service Director - Planning Transportation & Highways, Wakefield One, Burton Street, Wakefield WF1 2DA ☎ 01924 305858 ⌂ nrodgers@wakefield.gov.uk

Catering Services: Mr Kevin Fisher, Service Manager - Property & Facilities Management, Wakefield One, Burton Street, Wakefield WF1 2DA ☎ 01924 306490 ⌂ kevinfisher@wakefield.gov.uk

Children / Youth Services: Mr Stephen Crofts, Service Manager - Localities, Youth & Youth Justice, Manygates Education Centre, Manygates Lane, Sandal, Wakefield WF2 7DQ ☎ 01924 303335 ⌂ scrofts@wakefield.gov.uk

Civil Registration: Ms Bernadette Livesey, Service Director - Legal & Governance, County Hall, Bond Street, Wakefield WF1 2QW ☎ 01924 305177 ⌂ blivesey@wakefield.gov.uk

PR / Communications: Ms Lucinda Jackson, Service Manager - Communications, Customers & Policy, County Hall, Bond Street, Wakefield WF1 2QW ☎ 01924 303454 ⌂ lucindajackson@wakefield.gov.uk

Community Planning: Mr Andrew Balchin, Corporate Director - Adults, Health & Communities, Wakefield One, Burton Street, Wakefield WF1 2DA ☎ 01924 306634 ⌂ abalchin@wakefield.gov.uk

Community Safety: Mr Andrew Balchin, Corporate Director - Adults, Health & Communities, Wakefield One, Burton Street, Wakefield WF1 2DA ☎ 01924 306634 ⌂ abalchin@wakefield.gov.uk

Computer Management: Mr Mick O'Malley, Systems & Technical Services Manager, Town Hall, Wood Street, Wakefield WF1 2HQ ☎ 01977 727641 ⌂ mo'malley@wakefield.gov.uk

Customer Service: Ms Lucinda Jackson, Service Manager - Communications, Customers & Policy, County Hall, Bond Street, Wakefield WF1 2QW ☎ 01924 303454 ⌂ lucindajackson@wakefield.gov.uk

Economic Development: Ms Sarah Pearson, Service Director - Economic Growth & Strategic Housing, Wakefield One, Burton Street, Wakefield WF1 2DA ☎ 01924 305461 ⌂ spearson@wakefield.gov.uk

Electoral Registration: Ms Sandra Hardy, Electoral Services Manager, Town Hall, Wood Street, Wakefield WF1 2HQ ☎ 01924 605020 ⌂ shardy@wakefield.gov.uk

Emergency Planning: Mr Neil Favager, Emergency Planning & Business Continuity Manager, Wakefield One, Burton Street, Wakefield WF1 2DA ☎ 01924 305048 ⌂ nfavager@wakefield.gov.uk

Environmental / Technical Services: Mr Glynn Humphries, Service Director - Environment & Streetscene, Wakefield One, Burton Street, Wakefield WF1 2DA ☎ 01924 306518 ⌂ ghumphries@wakefield.gov.uk

Estates, Property & Valuation: Mr Kevin Fisher, Service Manager - Property & Facilities Management, Wakefield One, Burton Street, Wakefield WF1 2DA ☎ 01924 306490 ⌂ kevinfisher@wakefield.gov.uk

Events Manager: Mr Ben Cook, Service Manager - Markets, Major Events & Tourism, Wakefield One, Burton Street, Wakefield WF1 2DA ☎ 01924 305136 ⌂ bcook@wakefield.gov.uk

Facilities: Mr Kevin Fisher, Service Manager - Property & Facilities Management, Wakefield One, Burton Street, Wakefield WF1 2DA ☎ 01924 306490 ⌂ kevinfisher@wakefield.gov.uk

Finance: Mr Graham Saxton, Chief Finance Manager, Wakfield One, Burton Street, Wakefield WF1 2DA ☎ 01924 306433 ⌂ gsaxton@wakefield.gov.uk

Fleet Management: Mr Peter Johnson, Service Manager - Transport, Environment & Streetscene, Newton Bar, Wakefield WF1 2TX ☎ 01924 306300 ⌂ pjohnson@wakefield.gov.uk

Grounds Maintenance: Mr Charles Tindill, Streetscene Manager - Service Development, Normanton Depot Complex, Block C, Normanton WF6 2DZ ☎ 01924 304929 ⌂ ctindill@wakefield.gov.uk

Health and Safety: Mr Neil Favager, Emergency Planning & Business Continuity Manager, Wakefield One, Burton Street, Wakefield WF1 2DA ☎ 01924 305048 ⌂ nfavager@wakefield.gov.uk

Highways: Mr Neil Rodgers, Service Director - Planning Transportation & Highways, Wakefield One, Burton Street, Wakefield WF1 2DA ☎ 01924 305858 ⌂ nrodgers@wakefield.gov.uk

Housing: Ms Sarah Pearson, Service Director - Economic Growth & Strategic Housing, Wakefield One, Burton Street, Wakefield WF1 2DA ☎ 01924 305461 ⌂ spearson@wakefield.gov.uk

Legal: Ms Bernadette Livesey, Service Director - Legal & Governance, County Hall, Bond Street, Wakefield WF1 2QW ☎ 01924 305177 ⌂ blivesey@wakefield.gov.uk

Leisure and Cultural Services: Ms Karen Collins, Service Director - Sport & Culture, Town Hall, Wood Street, Wakefield WF1 2HQ ☎ 01924 306931 ⌂ karencollins@wakefield.gov.uk

Licensing: Ms Pam Taylor, Licensing Officer, Town Hall, Wood Street, Wakefield WF1 2HQ ☎ 01924 302916 ⌂ ptaylor@wakefield.gov.uk

Member Services: Ms Bernadette Livesey, Service Director - Legal & Governance, County Hall, Bond Street, Wakefield WF1 2QW ☎ 01924 305177 ⌂ blivesey@wakefield.gov.uk

Parking: Mr Graham West, Service Manager - Highways Network Planning, Transportation & Highways, Wakefield One, Burton Street, Wakefield WF1 2DA ☎ 01924 306057 ⌂ gwest@wakefield.gov.uk

Personnel / HR: Ms Jill Clayton, Service Manager - Human Resources & Organisational Development, Town Hall, Wood Street, Wakefield WF1 2HQ ☎ 01924 305854 ⌂ jillclayton@wakefield.gov.uk

WAKEFIELD CITY

Planning: Mr Neil Rodgers, Service Director - Planning Transportation & Highways, Wakefield One, Burton Street, Wakefield WF1 2DA ☎ 01924 305858 ◌ nrodgers@wakefield.gov.uk

Procurement: Mr Graham Saxton, Chief Finance Manager, Wakfield One, Burton Street, Wakefield WF1 2DA ☎ 01924 306433 ◌ gsaxton@wakefield.gov.uk

Public Libraries: Ms Karen Collins, Service Director - Sport & Culture, Town Hall, Wood Street, Wakefield WF1 2HQ ☎ 01924 306931 ◌ karencollins@wakefield.gov.uk

Recycling & Waste Minimisation: Mr John Allen, Streetscene Manager - Waste, Sterling Industrial Park, Carr Wood Road, Castleford WF10 4PJ ☎ 01977 722101 ◌ jallen@wakefield.gov.uk

Regeneration: Mr Andrew Wallhead, Corporate Director - Regeneration & Economic Growth, Wakefield One, Burton Street, Wakefield WF1 2DA ☎ 01924 306950 ◌ awallhead@wakefield.gov.uk

Road Safety: Mr Graham West, Service Manager - Highways Network Planning, Transportation & Highways, Wakefield One, Burton Street, Wakefield WF1 2DA ☎ 01924 306057 ◌ gwest@wakefield.gov.uk

Social Services (Adult): Mr Rob Hurren, Director - Integrated Care, Town Hall, Wood Street, Wakefield WF1 2HQ ☎ 01924 307760 ◌ rhurren@wakefield.gov.uk

Social Services (Children): Mr John Wilson, Corporate Director - Children & Young People, Town Hall, Wood Street, Wakefield WF1 2HQ ☎ 01924 307725 ◌ johnwilson@wakefield.gov.uk

Safeguarding: Mr Mark Barratt, Service Director - Safeguarding & Family Support, County Hall, Bond Street, Wakefield WF1 2QW ☎ 01924 305670 ◌ mbarratt@wakefield.gov.uk

Public Health: Dr Andrew Furber, Director - Public Health, Town Hall, Wood Street, Wakefield WF1 2HQ ☎ 01942 305347 ◌ afurber@wakefield.gov.uk

Staff Training: Ms Jill Clayton, Service Manager - Human Resources & Organisational Development, Town Hall, Wood Street, Wakefield WF1 2HQ ☎ 01924 305854 ◌ jillclayton@wakefield.gov.uk

Street Scene: Mr Glynn Humphries, Service Director - Environment & Streetscene, Wakefield One, Burton Street, Wakefield WF1 2DA ☎ 01924 306518 ◌ ghumphries@wakefield.gov.uk

Sustainable Development: Ms Sarah Pearson, Service Director - Economic Growth & Strategic Housing, Wakefield One, Burton Street, Wakefield WF1 2DA ☎ 01924 305461 ◌ spearson@wakefield.gov.uk

Tourism: Mr Ben Cook, Service Manager - Markets, Major Events & Tourism, Wakefield One, Burton Street, Wakefield WF1 2DA ☎ 01924 305136 ◌ bcook@wakefield.gov.uk

Town Centre: Ms Sarah Pearson, Service Director - Economic Growth & Strategic Housing, Wakefield One, Burton Street, Wakefield WF1 2DA ☎ 01924 305461 ◌ spearson@wakefield.gov.uk

Traffic Management: Mr Graham West, Service Manager - Highways Network Planning, Transportation & Highways, Wakefield One, Burton Street, Wakefield WF1 2DA ☎ 01924 306057 ◌ gwest@wakefield.gov.uk

Waste Collection and Disposal: Mr Glynn Humphries, Service Director - Environment & Streetscene, Wakefield One, Burton Street, Wakefield WF1 2DA ☎ 01924 306518 ◌ ghumphries@wakefield.gov.uk

Waste Management: Mr Glynn Humphries, Service Director - Environment & Streetscene, Wakefield One, Burton Street, Wakefield WF1 2DA ☎ 01924 306518 ◌ ghumphries@wakefield.gov.uk

COUNCILLORS

Mayor: Ellis, Harry (LAB - Knottingley) hellis@wakefield.gov.uk

Deputy Mayor: Barker, Kevin (LAB - Wakefield Rural) kevinbarker@wakefield.gov.uk

Leader of the Council: Box, Peter (LAB - Altofts & Whitwood) pbox@wakefield.gov.uk

Deputy Leader of the Council: Jeffery, Denise (LAB - Castleford Central & Glasshoughton) djeffery@wakefield.gov.uk

Ahmed, Nadeem (CON - Wakefield South) cllrnahmed@wakefield.gov.uk

Austin, Tracey (LAB - Wakefield North) taustin@wakefield.gov.uk

Ayre, George (LAB - Pontefract South) gayre@wakefield.gov.uk

Benson, Wilf (IND - South Emsall & South Kirkby) wbenson@wakefield.gov.uk

Binns, Cynthia (CON - Wakefield Rural) cynthiabinns@wakefield.gov.uk

Blezard, Elaine (LAB - Normanton) eblezard@wakefield.gov.uk

Burton, Glenn (LAB - Knottingley) gburton@wakefield.gov.uk

Byford, Darren (LAB - Horbury & South Ossett) dbyford@wakefield.gov.uk

Carrington, Jessica (LAB - Ackworth, North Elmsall & Upton) jcarrington@wakefield.gov.uk

Case, Ryan (LAB - Wakefield West) rcase@wakefield.gov.uk

Collins, Michelle (LAB - South Emsall & South Kirkby) michellecollins@wakefield.gov.uk

Crewe, Yvonne (LAB - Airedale & Ferry Fryston) ycrewe@wakefield.gov.uk

Cummings, Maureen (LAB - Crofton, Ryhill & Walton) mcummings@wakefield.gov.uk

Dagger, David (LAB - Normanton) ddagger@wakefield.gov.uk

Dews, David (UKIP - Wrenthorpe & Outwood West)
ddews@wakefield.gov.uk

Farmer, Nick (UKIP - Ossett)
nfarmer@wakefield.gov.uk

Forster, Richard (LAB - Castleford Central & Glasshoughton)
rforster@wakefield.gov.uk

Garbutt, Alan (LAB - Ackworth, North Elmsall & Upton)
agarbutt@wakefield.gov.uk

Garbutt, Patricia (LAB - Pontefract North)
pgarbutt@wakefield.gov.uk

Graham, Monica (CON - Wakefield South)
mgraham@wakefield.gov.uk

Heptinstall, Faith (LAB - Crofton, Ryhill & Walton)
fheptinstall@wakefield.gov.uk

Heptinstall, Stuart (LAB - Wakefield East)
sheptinstall@wakefield.gov.uk

Hepworth, Jo (LAB - Altofts & Whitwood)
johepworth@wakefield.gov.uk

Holmes, Janet (LAB - Horbury & South Ossett)
jholmes@wakefield.gov.uk

Holwell, Margaret (CON - Horbury & South Ossett)
mholwell@wakefield.gov.uk

Hudson, Clive (LAB - Stanley & Outwood East)
chudson@wakefield.gov.uk

Hunt, Richard (CON - Wakefield South)
rhunt@wakefield.gov.uk

Isherwood, Margaret (LAB - Wakefield North)
margaretisherwood@wakefield.gov.uk

Isherwood, Graham (LAB - Featherstone)
gisherwood@wakefield.gov.uk

Johnson, Martyn (LAB - Wrenthorpe & Outwood West)
martynjohnson@wakefield.gov.uk

Jones, David (LAB - Pontefract South)
davidjones@wakefield.gov.uk

Keith, Charlie (LAB - Wrenthorpe & Outwood West)
ckeith@wakefield.gov.uk

Kitching, Pauline (LAB - Hemsworth)
pkitching@wakefield.gov.uk

Lloyd, Glyn (LAB - Hemsworth)
glynlloyd@wakefield.gov.uk

Loughran, Celia (LAB - Pontefract South)
cloughran@wakefield.gov.uk

Lund, Ros (LAB - Wakefield East)
rlund@wakefield.gov.uk

Malkin, Lorna (LAB - Pontefract North)
lmalkin@wakefield.gov.uk

Manifield, Albert (LAB - Crofton, Ryhill & Walton)
amanifield@wakefield.gov.uk

Masterman, Lynn (LAB - Ossett)
lmasterman@wakefield.gov.uk

Mitchell, Hilary (LAB - Wakefield West)
hilarymitchell@wakefield.gov.uk

Morley, Matthew (LAB - Stanley & Outwood East)
mmorley@wakefield.gov.uk

Pickin, Sandra (LAB - Hemsworth)
spickin@wakefield.gov.uk

Rhodes, Elizabeth (LAB - Wakefield North)
brhodes@wakefield.gov.uk

Rowley, Olivia (LAB - Wakefield East)
orowley@wakefield.gov.uk

Sanders, Ian (CON - Wakefield Rural)
isanders@wakefield.gov.uk

Scott, Kathryn (LAB - Airedale & Ferry Fryston)
kathrynscott@wakefield.gov.uk

Shaw, Les (LAB - Airedale & Ferry Fryston)
lesshaw@wakefield.gov.uk

Speight, Jacquie (LAB - Altofts & Whitwood)
jspeight@wakefield.gov.uk

Stokes, Graham (LAB - Knottingley)
gstokes@wakefield.gov.uk

Swift, Kevin (LAB - Wakefield West)
kswift@wakefield.gov.uk

Taylor, Richard (LAB - Featherstone)
dicktaylor@wakefield.gov.uk

Taylor, Angela (CON - Ossett)
actaylor@wakefield.gov.uk

Tennant, Clive (LAB - Pontefract North)
clivetennant@wakefield.gov.uk

Tennant-King, Maureen (LAB - Featherstone)
mtennantking@wakefield.gov.uk

Tulley, Steve (LAB - South Emsall & South Kirkby)
stulley@wakefield.gov.uk

Wallis, Anthony (LAB - Castleford Central & Glasshoughton)
awallis@wakefield.gov.uk

Ward, Martyn (LAB - Ackworth, North Elmsall & Upton)
martynward@wakefield.gov.uk

Wassell, Alan (LAB - Normanton)
alanwassel@wakefield.gov.uk

Williams, Jacqueline (LAB - Stanley & Outwood East)
jacquelinewilliams@wakefield.gov.uk

POLITICAL COMPOSITION
LAB: 53, CON: 7, UKIP: 2, IND: 1

COMMITTEE CHAIRS

Adults & Health: Mrs Elizabeth Rhodes

Audit: Mr Glenn Burton

Licensing: Miss Jacqueline Williams

Planning & Highways: Miss Sandra Pickin

Walsall   M

Walsall Metropolitan Borough Council, Civic Centre, Darwall Street, Walsall WS1 1TP

☎ 01922 650000 ✆ info@walsall.gov.uk ⌨ www.walsall.gov.uk

FACTS AND FIGURES
Parliamentary Constituencies: Aldridge-Brownhills, Walsall North, Walsall South
EU Constituencies: West Midlands
Election Frequency: Elections are by thirds

WALSALL

PRINCIPAL OFFICERS

Chief Executive: Mr Paul Sheehan, Chief Executive, Civic Centre, Darwall Street, Walsall WS1 1TP ☎ 01922 652006 ◌ sheehanp@walsall.gov.uk

Senior Management: Ms Julie Alderson, Interim Executive Director - Change & Governance, Civic Centre, Darwall Street, Walsall WS1 1TP ◌ julie.alderson@walsall.gov.uk

Senior Management: Ms Paula Furnival, Executive Director - Adult Social Care, Civic Centre, Darwall Street, Walsall WS1 1TP ☎ 01922 654710 ◌ paula.furnival@walsall.gov.uk

Senior Management: Mr David Haley, Executive Director - Children's Services, Civic Centre, Darwall Street, Walsall WS1 1TP ☎ 01922 652035 ◌ haleyd@walsall.gov.uk

Senior Management: Mr Simon Neilson, Executive Director - Economy & Environment, Civic Centre, Darwall Street, Walsall WS1 1TP ◌ neilsons@walsall.gov.uk

Access Officer / Social Services (Disability): Ms Sue Fox, Access Officer - Policy Unit, Civic Centre, Dawall Street, Walsall WS1 1TP ☎ 01922 652010 ◌ foxs@walsall.gov.uk

Catering Services: Mrs Carol Tipper, Catering Manager, Catering Public Service Enterprise, Darwall Street, Walsall WS1 1TP ☎ 01922 653120 ◌ carol.tipper@walsall.gov.uk

Children / Youth Services: Mr David Haley, Executive Director - Children's Services, Civic Centre, Darwall Street, Walsall WS1 1TP ☎ 01922 652035 ◌ haleyd@walsall.gov.uk

Civil Registration: Ms Holly Holdsworth, Superintendent Registrar, Civic Centre, Darwall Street, Walsall WS1 1TP ☎ 01922 654607 ◌ holdsworthh@walsall.gov.uk

Community Safety: Ms Lynne Hughes, Area Manager Community Safety, Civic Centre, Darwall Street, Walsall WS1 1TP ☎ 01922 654289 ◌ hughesl@walsall.gov.uk

Computer Management: Mr Paul Gordon, Head of Shared Services & Procurement, Civic Centre, Darwall Street, Walsall WS1 1TP ☎ 07792 920257 ◌ paul.gordon@walsall.gov.uk

Customer Service: Ms Helen Dudson, Corporate Performance Manager, Civic Centre, Darwall Street, Walsall WS1 1TP ☎ 01922 653732 ◌ dudsonh@walsall.gov.uk

Education: Mr David Haley, Executive Director - Children's Services, Civic Centre, Darwall Street, Walsall WS1 1TP ☎ 01922 652035 ◌ haleyd@walsall.gov.uk

E-Government: Mr Paul Gordon, Head of Shared Services & Procurement, Civic Centre, Darwall Street, Walsall WS1 1TP ☎ 07792 920257 ◌ paul.gordon@walsall.gov.uk

Emergency Planning: Mr Alan Boyd, Resilience Manager, Sandwell Council House, Oldbury B69 3DE ☎ 0121 569 3060; 0121 569 3983 ◌ alan_boyd@sandwell.gov.uk

Environmental Health: Mr David Elrington, Area Manager, Civic Centre, Darwall Street, Walsall WS1 1TP ☎ 01922 653023 ◌ david.elrington@walsall.gov.uk

Events Manager: Ms Sunita Lal Kooner, Venue Hire & Development, Civic Centre, Darwall Street, Walsall WS1 1TP ☎ 01922 650302 ◌ lalkooners@walsall.gov.uk

Facilities: Ms Sarah Hart, Head of Property Services, Civic Centre, Darwall Street, Walsall WS1 1TP ☎ 01922 471275 ◌ sarah.hart@walsall.gov.uk

Finance: Mr James Walsh, Chief Finance Officer, Civic Centre, Darwall Street, Walsall WS1 1TP ☎ 01922 653554 ◌ walshj@walsall.gov.uk

Grounds Maintenance: Mr Mark Holden, Head of Street Pride, Environmental Depot, 200 Pelsall Road, Brownhills WS8 7EN ☎ 01922 654201 ◌ holdenmi@walsall.gov.uk

Health and Safety: Ms Irena Hergottova, Corporate Consultation Equalities Lead, Civic Centre, Darwall Street, Walsall WS1 1TP ☎ 01922 655751 ◌ hergottovai@walsall.gov.uk

Legal: Mr Tony Cox, Head of Legal & Democratic Services, The Council House, Lichfield Street, Walsall WS1 1JX ☎ 01992 654822 ◌ tcox@walsall.gov.uk

Leisure and Cultural Services: Mr Chris Holliday, Head of Leisure & Culture, 12th Floor, Tameway Tower, 48 Bridge Street, Walsall WS1 1JZ ☎ 01922 650339 ◌ hollidayc@walsall.gov.uk

Lighting: Mr Steve Pretty, Divisional Manager - Transportation Services, Civic Centre, Darwall Street, Walsall WS1 1TP ☎ 01922 652598 ◌ prettys@walsall.gov.uk

Member Services: Mr John Garner, Head of Democratic Services, Civic Centre, Darwall Street, Walsall WS1 1TP ☎ 01922 654366 ◌ garnerj@walsall.gov.uk

Parking: Ms Glynnis Jeavons, Car Park Manager, Civic Centre, Darwall Street, Walsall WS1 1TP ☎ 01922 652493 ◌ jeavonsg@walsall.gov.uk

Personnel / HR: Mr Steve McGowan, Head of Human Resources, Civic Centre, Darwall Street, Walsall WS1 1TP ☎ 01922 655601 ◌ mcgow@walsall.gov.uk

Recycling & Waste Minimisation: Mr David Roberts, Service Manager - Operations, Environmental Depot, 200 Pelsall Road, Brownhills WS8 7EN ☎ 01922 654236 ◌ robertsd@walsall.gov.uk

Regeneration: Mr Mark Lavender, Head of Strategic Regeneration, Civic Centre, Darwall Street, Walsall WS1 1TP ☎ 01922 654772 ◌ lavenderm@walsall.gov.uk

Social Services: Ms Paula Furnival, Executive Director - Adult Social Care, Civic Centre, Darwall Street, Walsall WS1 1TP ☎ 01922 654710 ◌ paula.furnival@walsall.gov.uk

Social Services (Children): Mr David Haley, Executive Director - Children's Services, Civic Centre, Darwall Street, Walsall WS1 1TP ☎ 01922 652035 ⌨ haleyd@walsall.gov.uk

Town Centre: Ms Helen Kindon, Town Centre Manager, Civic Centre, Darwall Street, Walsall WS1 1TP ☎ 01922 652095 ⌨ kindonh@walsall.gov.uk

Traffic Management: Mr Steve Griffiths, Team Leader, Civic Centre, Darwall Street, Walsall WS1 1TP ☎ 01922 654645 ⌨ griffithss@walsall.gov.uk

Waste Collection and Disposal: Mr David Roberts, Service Manager - Operations, Environmental Depot, 200 Pelsall Road, Brownhills WS8 7EN ☎ 01922 654236 ⌨ robertsd@walsall.gov.uk

Waste Management: Mr David Roberts, Service Manager - Operations, Environmental Depot, 200 Pelsall Road, Brownhills WS8 7EN ☎ 01922 654236 ⌨ robertsd@walsall.gov.uk

COUNCILLORS

Mayor: Phillips, Kath (LAB - Bloxwich East)
cllr.kath.phillips@walsall.gov.uk

Deputy Mayor: Longhi, Marco (CON - Pelsall)
cllr.marco.longhi@walsall.gov.uk

Leader of the Council: Coughlan, Sean (LAB - Willenhall South)
cllr.sean.coughlan@walsall.gov.uk

Deputy Leader of the Council: Jeavons, Lee (LAB - Birchills Leamore)
cllr.lee.jeavsons@walsall.gov.uk

Allen, Bradley (CON - Bloxwich West)
cllr.bradley.allen@walsall.gov.uk

Andrew, Adrian (CON - Pheasey Park Farm)
cllr.adrian.andrew@walsall.gov.uk

Barker, Daniel (LD - Short Heath)
cllr.daniel.barker@walsall.gov.uk

Bennett, Oliver (CON - Pelsall)
cllr.oliver.bennett@walsall.gov.uk

Bird, Mike (CON - Pheasey Park Farm)
cllr.mike.bird@walsall.gov.uk

Bott, Paul (IND - Darlaston South)
cllr.paul.bott@walsall.gov.uk

Bott, Chris (IND - Darlaston South)
cllr.chris.bott@walsall.gov.uk

Burley, Rose (LAB - Bentley & Darlaston North)
cllr.rose.burley@walsall.gov.uk

Chambers, Keith (LAB - Bentley & Darlaston North)
cllr.keith.chambers@walsall.gov.uk

Clarke, Gary (CON - Aldridge North & Walsall Wood)
cllr.gary.clarke@walsall.gov.uk

Clews, Claire (LAB - Rushall Shelfield)
cllr.claire.clews@walsall.gov.uk

Cooper, Sarah Jane (CON - Short Heath)
cllr.sarah.jane.cooper@walsall.gov.uk

Coughlan, Diane (LAB - Willenhall South)
cllr.diane.coughlan@walsall.gov.uk

Craddock, Stephen (UKIP - Brownhills)
cllr.stephen.craddock@walsall.gov.uk

Creaney, Carl (LAB - Willenhall South)
cllr.carl.creaney@walsall.gov.uk

Ditta, Allah (LAB - Palfrey)
cllr.a.ditta@walsall.gov.uk

Ditta, Sabina (LAB - Palfrey)
cllr.sabina.ditta@walsall.gov.uk

Douglas-Maul, Brian (CON - Streetly)
cllr.brian.douglas-maul@walsall.gov.uk

Ferguson, Kenneth (CON - Brownhills)
cllr.ken.ferguson@walsall.gov.uk

Fitzpatrick, Shaun (LAB - Bloxwich East)
cllr.shaun.fitzpatrick@walsall.gov.uk

Fitzpatrick, Julie (LAB - Bloxwich East)
cllr.julie.fitzpatrick@walsall.gov.uk

Follows, Matthew (CON - Bloxwich West)
cllr.matthew.follows@walsall.gov.uk

Gultasib, Naheed (LAB - Pleck)
cllr.naheed.gultasib@walsall.gov.uk

Harris, Anthony (CON - Aldridge North & Walsall Wood)
cllr.anthony.harris@walsall.gov.uk

Harrison, Louise (CON - Bloxwich West)
cllr.louise.harrison@walsall.gov.uk

Hazell, Liz (UKIP - Willenhall North)
cllr.liz.hazell@walsall.gov.uk

Hazell, Darren (UKIP - Short Heath)
cllr.darren.hazell@walsall.gov.uk

Hicken, Adam (CON - Willenhall North)
cllr.adam.hicken@walsall.gov.uk

Hughes, Eddie (CON - Streetly)
cllr.eddie.hughes@walsall.gov.uk

Hussain, Khizar (LAB - Pleck)
cllr.khizar.hussain@walsall.gov.uk

James, Douglas (LAB - Darlaston South)
cllr.douglas.james@walsall.gov.uk

Jones, Christopher (LAB - Birchills Leamore)
cllr.chris.jones@walsall.gov.uk

Jukes, Tina (LAB - Birchills Leamore)
cllr.tina.jukes@walsall.gov.uk

Kudhail, Amers (CON - Streetly)
cllr.amers.kudhail@walsall.gov.uk

Martin, Rose (CON - Paddock)
cllr.rose.martin@walsall.gov.uk

Murray, John (CON - Aldridge Central & South)
cllr.john.murray@walsall.gov.uk

Nawaz, Aftab (LAB - St. Matthew's)
cllr.aftab.nawaz@walsall.gov.uk

Nazir, Abdus (LAB - St. Matthew's)
cllr.abdus.nazir@walsall.gov.uk

Perry, Garry (CON - Pelsall)
cllr.garry.perry@walsall.gov.uk

Rattigan, Lorna (CON - Rushall Shelfield)
cllr.lorna.rattigan@walsall.gov.uk

WALSALL

Robertson, Ian (LAB - Blakenall)
cllr.ian.robertson@walsall.gov.uk

Rochelle, John (CON - Aldridge Central & South)
cllr.john.rochelle@walsall.gov.uk

Russell, Eileen (LAB - St. Matthew's)
cllr.eileen.russell@walsall.gov.uk

Sarohi, Harbans (LAB - Pleck)
cllr.harbans.sarohi@walsall.gov.uk

Sears, Keith (CON - Aldridge North & Walsall Wood)
cllr.keith.sears@walsall.gov.uk

Shires, Ian (LD - Willenhall North)
cllr.ian.shires@walsall.gov.uk

Sohal, Gurmeet (CON - Paddock)
cllr.gurmeet.sohal@walsall.gov.uk

Towe, Christopher (CON - Pheasey Park Farm)
cllr.crhis.towe@walsall.gov.uk

Underhill, Angela (LAB - Bentley & Darlaston North)
cllr.angela.underhill@walsall.gov.uk

Wade, Stephen (LAB - Brownhills)
cllr.stephen.wade@walsall.gov.uk

Ward, Matthew (LAB - Blakenall)
cllr.matt.ward@walsall.gov.uk

Washbrook, Peter (CON - Paddock)
cllr.peter.washbrook@walsall.gov.uk

Whyte, Victoria (LAB - Palfrey)
cllr.victoria.whyte@walsall.gov.uk

Wilson, Timothy (CON - Aldridge Central & South)
cllr.timothy.wilson@walsall.gov.uk

Worrall, Richard (LAB - Rushall-Shelfield)
cllr.richard.worrall@walsall.gov.uk

Young, Ann (LAB - Blakenall)
cllr.ann.young@walsall.gov.uk

POLITICAL COMPOSITION
LAB: 28, CON: 25, UKIP: 3, IND: 2, LD: 2

COMMITTEE CHAIRS

Education & Children's Services: Mr Christopher Towe

Licensing: Mr Shaun Fitzpatrick

Planning: Ms Victoria Whyte

Social Care & Health: Mr Marco Longhi

Waltham Forest   L

Waltham Forest London Borough Council, Town Hall, Forest Road, London E17 4JF
☎ 020 8496 3000 ⌂ wfdirect@walthamforest.gov.uk
🖥 www.walthamforest.gov.uk

FACTS AND FIGURES
Parliamentary Constituencies: Chingford and Woodford, Leyton and Wanstead, Walthamstow
EU Constituencies: London
Election Frequency: Elections are of whole council

PRINCIPAL OFFICERS

Chief Executive: Mr Martin Esom, Chief Executive, Town Hall, Forest Road, London E17 4JF ☎ 020 8496 3000
⌂ martin.esom@walthamforest.gov.uk

Deputy Chief Executive: Ms Linzi Roberts-Egan, Deputy Chief Executive, Town Hall, Forest Road, London E17 4JF
☎ 020 8496 3500 ⌂ linzi.roberts-egan@walthamforest.gov.uk

Assistant Chief Executive: Ms Rhona Cadenhead, Chief Executive - Corporate Development, Town Hall, Forest Road, London E17 4JF ☎ 020 8496 3000
⌂ rhoda.cadenhead@walthamforest.gov.uk

Senior Management: Mr Ken Jones, Director - Housing & Growth, Town Hall, Forest Road, London E17 4JF ☎ 020 8496 3000
⌂ ken.jones@walthamforest.gov.uk

Senior Management: Ms Michele Moloney, Director - Neighbourhoods & Commissioning, Town Hall, Forest Road, London E17 4JF ☎ 020 8496 3000
⌂ michele.moloney@walthamforest.gov.uk

Senior Management: Ms Lucy Shomali, Director - Regeneration & Growth, Town Hall, Forest Road, London E17 4JF
☎ 020 8496 6734 ⌂ lucy.shomali@walthamforest.gov.uk

Senior Management: Mr John Turnbull, Director - Finance & Chief Finance Officer, Town Hall, Forest Road, London E17 4JF
☎ 020 8496 3000 ⌂ john.turnbull@walthamforest.gov.uk

Access Officer / Social Services (Disability): Ms Bernice Solvey, Interim Divisional Director - Adult Social Care, Town Hall, Forest Road, London E17 4JF ☎ 020 8496 3477
⌂ bernice.solvey@walthamforest.gov.uk

Architect, Building / Property Services: Mr Steve Sprayson, Interim Head of Corporate Asset Management, Town Hall, Forest Road, London E17 4JF ☎ 020 8496 8079
⌂ steven.sprayson@walthamforest.gov.uk

Building Control: Mr Julian Ruaux, Head of Building Control, Sycamore House, Waltham Forest Town Hall, Forest Road, London E17 4JF ☎ 020 8496 3000 ⌂ julian.ruaux@walthamforest.gov.uk

Building Control: Ms Lucy Shomali, Director - Regeneration & Growth, Town Hall, Forest Road, London E17 4JF ☎ 020 8496 6734
⌂ lucy.shomali@walthamforest.gov.uk

Catering Services: Ms Christine Cornall, Catering Manager, Town Hall, Forest Road, London E17 4JF ☎ 020 8496 8264
⌂ christine.cornall@walthamforest.gov.uk

Children / Youth Services: Ms Heather Flinders, Divisional Director - Children & Families, Town Hall, Forest Road, London E17 4JF ☎ 020 8496 3206 ⌂ heather.flinders@walthamforest.gov.uk

Children / Youth Services: Ms Denise Humphrey, Group Manager of Early Help 11 - 18, Outset Centre, 1a Grange Road, London E17 8AH ☎ 020 8496 1534
⌂ denise.humphrey@walthamforest.gov.uk

PR / Communications: Ms Rhona Cadenhead, Chief Executive - Corporate Development, Town Hall, Forest Road, London E17 4JF ☎ 020 8496 3000 ✆ rhoda.cadenhead@walthamforest.gov.uk

Computer Management: Mr Paul Golland, Head of ICT, Town Hall, Forest Road, London E17 4JF ☎ 020 8496 3629 ✆ paul.golland@walthamforest.gov.uk

Consumer Protection and Trading Standards: Ms Kellie Hopkins, Head of Neighbourhood Management, Sycamore House, Town Hall, Forest Road, London E17 4JF ☎ 020 8496 2201 ✆ kellie.hopkins@walthamforest.gov.uk

Contracts: Mr David Levy, Director - Supply Chain & Procurement, PO Box 54, Civic Centre, Silver Street, Enfield EN1 3XF ☎ 020 8496 3000 ✆ dave.levy@walthamforest.gov.uk

Customer Service: Ms Eshe Dow, Interim Director - Customer Service & Business Operations, Town Hall, Forest Road, London E17 4JF ☎ 020 8496 3000 ✆ eshe.dow@walthamforest.gov.uk

Customer Service: Ms Michele Moloney, Director - Neighbourhoods & Commissioning, Town Hall, Forest Road, London E17 4JF ☎ 020 8496 3000 ✆ michele.moloney@walthamforest.gov.uk

Education: Ms Rosalind Turner, Director - Learning & System Leadership, Town Hall, Forest Road, London E17 4JF ☎ 020 8496 3000 ✆ rosalind.turner@walthamforest.gov.uk

E-Government: Mr Paul Golland, Head of ICT, Town Hall, Forest Road, London E17 4JF ☎ 020 8496 3629 ✆ paul.golland@walthamforest.gov.uk

Emergency Planning: Mr Ron Presswell, Design & Conservation Manager, Sycamore House, Waltham Forest Town Hall Complex, Forest Road, London E17 4JF ☎ 020 8496 6736 ✆ ron.presswell@walthamforest.gov.uk

Environmental / Technical Services: Ms Kellie Hopkins, Head of Neighbourhood Management, Sycamore House, Town Hall, Forest Road, London E17 4JF ☎ 020 8496 2201 ✆ kellie.hopkins@walthamforest.gov.uk

Environmental Health: Ms Kellie Hopkins, Head of Neighbourhood Management, Sycamore House, Town Hall, Forest Road, London E17 4JF ☎ 020 8496 2201 ✆ kellie.hopkins@walthamforest.gov.uk

Events Manager: Ms Corinne Hurn, Events Manager, Town Hall, Forest Road, London E17 4JF ☎ 020 8496 6793 ✆ corrine.hurn@walthamforest.gov.uk

Finance: Mr John Turnbull, Director - Finance & Chief Finance Officer, Town Hall, Forest Road, London E17 4JF ☎ 020 8496 3000 ✆ john.turnbull@walthamforest.gov.uk

Treasury: Ms Debbie Drew, Treasury & Pensions Manager, Town Hall, Forest Road, London E17 4JF ☎ 020 8496 8165 ✆ debbie.drew@walthamforest.gov.uk

Pensions: Ms Debbie Drew, Treasury & Pensions Manager, Town Hall, Forest Road, London E17 4JF ☎ 020 8496 8165 ✆ debbie.drew@walthamforest.gov.uk

Fleet Management: Ms Kellie Hopkins, Head of Neighbourhood Management, Sycamore House, Town Hall, Forest Road, London E17 4JF ☎ 020 8496 2201 ✆ kellie.hopkins@walthamforest.gov.uk

Grounds Maintenance: Mr Ben Frearson, Project Engineer - Parks & Play, Town Hall, Forest Road, London E17 4JF ☎ 020 8496 2606 ✆ ben.frearson@walthamforest.gov.uk

Health and Safety: Ms Ann Whalley, Health & Safety Manager, Town Hall, Forest Road, London E17 4JF ☎ 020 8496 6931 ✆ ann.whalley@walthamforest.gov.uk

Highways: Ms Kellie Hopkins, Head of Neighbourhood Management, Sycamore House, Town Hall, Forest Road, London E17 4JF ☎ 020 8496 2201 ✆ kellie.hopkins@walthamforest.gov.uk

Highways: Mr Kathiraval Valavan, Head of Highways, Low Hall, Argall Avenue, London E10 7AS ☎ 020 8496 2525 ✆ velu.valavan@walthamforest.gov.uk

Housing: Ms Lucy Shomali, Director - Regeneration & Growth, Town Hall, Forest Road, London E17 4JF ☎ 020 8496 6734 ✆ lucy.shomali@walthamforest.gov.uk

Leisure and Cultural Services: Ms Lorna Lee, Head of Cultural & Heritage Services, Town Hall, Forest Road, London E17 4JF ☎ 020 8496 3203 ✆ lorna.lee@walthamforest.gov.uk

Licensing: Mr Adrian Simpson, Food, Safety & Trading Standards Manager, Town Hall, Forest Road, London E17 4JF ☎ 020 8496 2202 ✆ adrian.simpson@walthamforest.gov.uk

Lighting: Ms Kellie Hopkins, Head of Neighbourhood Management, Sycamore House, Town Hall, Forest Road, London E17 4JF ☎ 020 8496 2201 ✆ kellie.hopkins@walthamforest.gov.uk

Lighting: Mr Chris Warner, Street Lighting & Responsive Maintenance Manager, Low Hall, Argall Avenue, London E10 7AS ☎ 020 8496 2515 ✆ chris.warner@walthamforest.gov.uk

Lottery Funding, Charity and Voluntary: Ms Ellen Amorina, Community Engagement & Funding Officer, Town Hall, Forest Road, London E17 4JF ☎ 020 8496 3000 ✆ ellen.amorina@walthamforest.gov.uk

Member Services: Ms Angela Cater, Deputy Head - Councillor Services, Town Hall, Forest Road, London E17 4JF ☎ 020 8496 4611 ✆ angela.cater@walthamforest.gov.uk

Parking: Ms Karen Naylor, Head of Parking, Transport & CCTV, Low Hall Depot, Argall Avenue, London E10 7AS ☎ 020 8496 3000 ✆ Karen.naylor@walthamforest.gov.uk

Partnerships: Mr Alastair Macorkindale, Early Help Group Manager, Sycamore House, Waltham Forest Town Hall Complex, Forest Road, London E17 4JF ☎ 020 8496 6827 ✆ alastair.macorkindale@walthamforest.gov.uk

WALTHAM FOREST

Personnel / HR: Mr Gerry Kemble, Head of Schools Traded Services, Town Hall, Forest Road, London E17 4JF ☎ 020 8496 4300 ⏚ gerry.kemble@walthamforest.gov.uk

Personnel / HR: Mr Stuart Petrie, Head of Human Resources, Town Hall, Forest Road, London E17 4JF ☎ 020 8496 8076 ⏚ stuart.petrie@walthamforest.gov.uk

Planning: Ms Lucy Shomali, Director - Regeneration & Growth, Town Hall, Forest Road, London E17 4JF ☎ 020 8496 6734 ⏚ lucy.shomali@walthamforest.gov.uk

Procurement: Mr David Levy, Director - Supply Chain & Procurement, Town Hall, Forest Road, London E17 4JF ☎ 020 8496 3000 ⏚ dave.levy@walthamforest.gov.uk

Public Libraries: Ms Lorna Lee, Head of Cultural & Heritage Services, Town Hall, Forest Road, London E17 4JF ☎ 020 8496 3203 ⏚ lorna.lee@walthamforest.gov.uk

Recycling & Waste Minimisation: Ms Kellie Hopkins, Head of Neighbourhood Management, Sycamore House, Town Hall, Forest Road, London E17 4JF ☎ 020 8496 2201 ⏚ kellie.hopkins@walthamforest.gov.uk

Regeneration: Ms Lucy Shomali, Director - Regeneration & Growth, Town Hall, Forest Road, London E17 4JF ☎ 020 8496 6734 ⏚ lucy.shomali@walthamforest.gov.uk

Social Services: Ms Heather Flinders, Divisional Director - Children & Families, Town Hall, Forest Road, London E17 4JF ☎ 020 8496 3206 ⏚ heather.flinders@walthamforest.gov.uk

Social Services: Mr Daniel Phelps, Divisional Director - Early Help, Town Hall, Forest Road, London E17 4JF ☎ 020 8496 5050 ⏚ daniel.phelps@walthamforest.gov.uk

Social Services: Ms Linzi Roberts-Egan, Deputy Chief Executive, Town Hall, Forest Road, London E17 4JF ☎ 020 8496 3500 ⏚ linzi.roberts-egan@walthamforest.gov.uk

Social Services (Adult): Ms Bernice Solvey, Interim Divisional Director - Adult Social Care, Town Hall, Forest Road, London E17 4JF ☎ 020 8496 3477 ⏚ bernice.solvey@walthamforest.gov.uk

Social Services (Adult): Ms Bernice Solvey, Interim Divisional Director - Adult Social Care, Town Hall, Forest Road, London E17 4JF ☎ 020 8496 3477 ⏚ bernice.solvey@walthamforest.gov.uk

Social Services (Children): Ms Denise Humphrey, Group Manager of Early Help 11 - 18, Town Hall, Forest Road, London E17 4JF ☎ 020 8496 1534 ⏚ denise.humphrey@walthamforest.gov.uk

Safeguarding: Ms Bernice Solvey, Interim Divisional Director - Adult Social Care, Town Hall, Forest Road, London E17 4JF ☎ 020 8496 3477 ⏚ bernice.solvey@walthamforest.gov.uk

Families: Ms Heather Flinders, Divisional Director - Children & Families, Town Hall, Forest Road, London E17 4JF ☎ 020 8496 3206 ⏚ heather.flinders@walthamforest.gov.uk

Families: Mr Daniel Phelps, Divisional Director - Early Help, Town Hall, Forest Road, London E17 4JF ☎ 020 8496 5050 ⏚ daniel.phelps@walthamforest.gov.uk

Families: Ms Linzi Roberts-Egan, Deputy Chief Executive, Town Hall, Forest Road, London E17 4JF ☎ 020 8496 3500 ⏚ linzi.roberts-egan@walthamforest.gov.uk

Public Health: Dr Andrew Taylor, Director - Public Health, Town Hall, Forest Road, London E17 4JF ☎ 020 8496 3000 ⏚ andrew.taylor@walthamforest.gov.uk

Street Scene: Ms Kellie Hopkins, Head of Neighbourhood Management, Sycamore House, Town Hall, Forest Road, London E17 4JF ☎ 020 8496 2201 ⏚ kellie.hopkins@walthamforest.gov.uk

Tourism: Ms Lorna Lee, Head of Cultural & Heritage Services, Silverbirch House, Uplands Business Park, Blackhorse Lane, Walthamstow, London E17 5SN ☎ 020 8496 3203 ⏚ lorna.lee@walthamforest.gov.uk

Traffic Management: Ms Kellie Hopkins, Head of Neighbourhood Management, Sycamore House, Town Hall, Forest Road, London E17 4JF ☎ 020 8496 2201 ⏚ kellie.hopkins@walthamforest.gov.uk

Transport: Mr Kathiraval Valavan, Head of Highways, Low Hall, Argall Avenue, London E10 7AS ☎ 020 8496 2525 ⏚ velu.valavan@walthamforest.gov.uk

Transport Planner: Mr Neil Bullen, Regeneration & Growth Manager, Sycamore House, Town Hall, Forest Road, London E17 4JF ☎ 020 8496 3000 ⏚ neil.bullen@walthamforest.gov.uk

Waste Collection and Disposal: Ms Kellie Hopkins, Head of Neighbourhood Management, Sycamore House, Town Hall, Forest Road, London E17 4JF ☎ 020 8496 2201 ⏚ kellie.hopkins@walthamforest.gov.uk

Waste Management: Ms Kellie Hopkins, Head of Neighbourhood Management, Sycamore House, Town Hall, Forest Road, London E17 4JF ☎ 020 8496 2201 ⏚ kellie.hopkins@walthamforest.gov.uk

Children's Play Areas: Ms Margaret Burke, Group Manager of Early Help 0 - 11, Town Hall, Forest Road, London E17 4JF ☎ 020 8496 3557 ⏚ Margaret.burke@walthamforest.gov.uk

COUNCILLORS

Mayor: Herrington, Peter (CON - Endlebury) cllr.peter.herrington@walthamforest.gov.uk

Leader of the Council: Robbins, Chris (LAB - Grove Green) leader@walthamforest.gov.uk

Deputy Leader of the Council: Loakes, Clyde (LAB - Leytonstone) cllr.clyde.loakes@walthamforest.gov.uk

Group Leader: Davis, Matt (CON - Chingford Green) cllr.matt.davis@walthamforest.gov.uk

Ahmad, Masood (LAB - Lea Bridge) Cllr_m_ahmad@hotmail.com

Ali, Nadeem (LAB - William Morris) cllr.nadeem.ali@walthamforest.gov.uk

Ali, Liaquat (LAB - High Street)
cllr.liaquat.ali@walthamforest.gov.uk

Anwar, Raja (LAB - High Street)
cllr.raja.anwar@walthamforest.gov.uk

Asghar, Mohammad (LAB - Lea Bridge)
cllr.mohammad.asghar@walthamforest.gov.uk

Asghar, Naheed (LAB - Cathall)
cllr.naheed.asghar@walthamforest.gov.uk

Balkan, Millie (CON - Larkswood)
cllr.millie.balkan@walthamforest.gov.uk

Barnett, Peter (LAB - Wood Street)
cllr.peter.barnett@walthamforest.gov.uk

Bean, Angie (LAB - Wood Street)
cllr.angie.bean@walthamforest.gov.uk

Beg, Aktar (LAB - Valley)
cllr.aktar.beg@walthamforest.gov.uk

Bell, Tony (LAB - Hale End & Highams Park)
cllr.tony.bell@walthamforest.gov.uk

Bellamy, Karen (LAB - Higham Hill)
cllr.karen.bellamy@walthamforest.gov.uk

Bennett-Goodman, Tim (IND - Higham Hill)
cllr.tim.bennett-goodman@walthamforest.gov.uk

Berberi, Kastriot (LAB - Forest)
cllr.kastriot.berberi@walthamforest.gov.uk

Berg, Roy (CON - Endlebury)
cllr.roy.berg@walthamforest.gov.uk

Braham, Paul (CON - Hale End & Highams Park)
cllr.paul.braham@walthamforest.gov.uk

Coghill, Clare (LAB - High Street)
cllr.clare.coghill@walthamforest.gov.uk

Dhedi, Shabana (LAB - Forest)
cllr.shabana.dhedhi@walthamforest.gov.uk

Douglas, Paul (LAB - Chapel End)
cllr.paul.douglas@walthamforest.gov.uk

Edwards, Patrick (LAB - Cann Hall)
cllr.patrick.edwards@walthamforest.gov.uk

Edwards, Jacob (LAB - Leyton)
cllr.jacob.edwards@walthamforest.gov.uk

Emmerson, Stuart (LAB - William Morris)
cllr.stuart.emmerson@walthamforest.gov.uk

Erics, Caroline (CON - Endlebury)
cllr.caroline.erics@walthamforest.gov.uk

Fitzgerald, Marion (CON - Hatch Lane)
cllr.marion.fitzgerald@walthamforest.gov.uk

Gray, Jenny (LAB - Leytonstone)
cllr.jenny.gray@walthamforest.gov.uk

Halebi, Nick (CON - Chingford Green)
cllr.nick.halebi@walthamforest.gov.uk

Hemsted, Jemma (CON - Valley)
cllr.jemma.hemsted@walthamforest.gov.uk

Hemsted, Andy (CON - Chingford Green)
Andyhemsted1066@gmail.com

Highfield, Shameem (LAB - Cathall)
cllr.ska.highfield@walthamforest.gov.uk

Ihenachor, Whitney (LAB - Leyton)
cllr.whitney.ihenachor@walthamforest.gov.uk

James, Tim (CON - Hatch Lane)
cllr.tim.james@walthamforest.gov.uk

Khan, Johar (LAB - Markhouse)
cllr.johar.khan@walthamforest.gov.uk

Khan, Ahsan (LAB - Hoe Street)
cllr.ahsan.khan@walthamforest.gov.uk

Limbajee, Khevyn (LAB - Grove Green)
cllr.khevyn.limbajee@walthamforest.gov.uk

Littlejohn, Sally (LAB - Cann Hall)
cllr.sally.littlejohn@walthamforest.gov.uk

Lyons, Gerry (LAB - Forest)
cllr.gerry.lyons@walthamforest.gov.uk

Mahmood, Asim (LAB - Markhouse)
cllr.asim.mahmood@walthamforest.gov.uk

Mahmud, Saima (LAB - Hoe Street)
cllr.saima.mahmud@walthamforest.gov.uk

Mbachu, Anna (LAB - Grove Green)
cllr.anna.mbachu@walthamforest.gov.uk

Mill, Bernadette (CON - Larkswood)
cllr.bernadette.mill@walthamforest.gov.uk

Miller, Simon (LAB - Leyton)
cllr.simon.miller@walthamforest.gov.uk

Mitchell, Louise (LAB - Chapel End)
cllr.louise.mitchell@walthamforest.gov.uk

Moss, John (CON - Larkswood)
cllr.john.jc.moss@walthamforest.gov.uk

Osho, Yemi (LAB - Lea Bridge)
cllr.yemi.osho@walthamforest.gov.uk

Pye, Marie (LAB - Leytonstone)
cllr.marie.pye@walthamforest.gov.uk

Rackham, Sheree (CON - Hale End & Highams Park)
cllr.sheree.rackham@walthamforest.gov.uk

Rayner, Keith (LAB - Cann Hall)
cllr.keith.rayner@walthamforest.gov.uk

Rusling, Mark (LAB - Hoe Street)
cllr.mark.rusling@walthamforest.gov.uk

Siggers, Alan (CON - Valley)

Strathern, Alistair (LAB - Higham Hill)
cllr.alistair.strathern@walthamforest.gov.uk

Sweden, Richard (LAB - Wood Street)
cllr.richard.sweden@walthamforest.gov.uk

Terry, Steve (LAB - Chapel End)
cllr.steve.terry@walthamforest.gov.uk

Waldron, Sharon (LAB - Markhouse)
cllr.sharon.waldron@walthamforest.gov.uk

Walker, Geoffrey (CON - Hatch Lane)
cllr.geoff.walker@ntlworld.com

Wheeler, Terry (LAB - Cathall)
cllr.terry.wheeler@walthamforest.gov.uk

Williams, Grace (LAB - William Morris)
cllr.grace.williams@walthamforest.gov.uk

WALTHAM FOREST

POLITICAL COMPOSITION
LAB: 43, CON: 16, IND: 1

COMMITTEE CHAIRS

Adult Social Care: Mr Richard Sweden

Audit: Mr Paul Douglas

Children & Families: Ms Marie Pye

Health & Wellbeing: Mr Ahsan Khan

Licensing: Mr Nadeem Ali

Pensions: Mr Simon Miller

Planning: Ms Jenny Gray

Wandsworth   L

Wandsworth London Borough Council, Town Hall, Wandsworth High Street, London SW18 2PU
☎ 020 8871 6000 ▨ www.wandsworth.gov.uk

FACTS AND FIGURES
Parliamentary Constituencies: Battersea, Putney, Tooting
EU Constituencies: London
Election Frequency: Elections are of whole council

PRINCIPAL OFFICERS

Chief Executive: Mr Paul Martin, Chief Executive & Director - Administration, Town Hall, Wandsworth High Street, London SW18 2PU ☎ 020 8871 6001 ⁀ pmartin@wandsworth.gov.uk

Deputy Chief Executive: Mr Chris Buss, Director - Finance & Deputy Chief Executive, Town Hall, Wandsworth High Street, London SW18 2PU ☎ 020 8871 8300 ⁀ cbuss@wandsworth.gov.uk

Senior Management: Mr Chris Buss, Director - Finance & Deputy Chief Executive, Town Hall, Wandsworth High Street, London SW18 2PU ☎ 020 8871 8300 ⁀ cbuss@wandsworth.gov.uk

Senior Management: Ms Cathy Kerr, Director - Adult Social Services, Town Hall, Wandsworth High Street, London SW18 2PU ☎ 020 8891 7360 ⁀ ckerr@wandsworth.gov.uk

Senior Management: Mr Brian Reilly, Director - Housing & Regeneration, Reed House, Frogmore Complex, Frogmore, Wandsworth, London SW18 9AQ ☎ 020 8871 6591 ⁀ hrdirectorate@wandsworth.gov.uk

Senior Management: Ms Dawn Warwick, Director - Children's Services, Town Hall, Wandsworth High Street, London SW18 2PU ☎ 020 8871 6291 ⁀ dwarwick@wandsworth.gov.uk

Access Officer / Social Services (Disability): Toni Symonds, Access Team Manager, Town Hall Extension, 2nd Floor, Wandsworth High Street, London SW18 2PU ☎ 020 8871 8811 ⁀ tsymonds@wandsworth.gov.uk

Architect, Building / Property Services: Mr Andy Algar, Head of Property Services, Town Hall, Wandsworth High Street, London SW18 2PU ☎ 020 8871 6075 ⁀ aalgar@wandsworth.gov.uk

Best Value: Mr Jon Evans, Head of Policy & Communications, Town Hall, Wandsworth High Street, London SW18 2PU
☎ 020 8871 7815 ⁀ jevans@wandsworth.gov.uk

Catering Services: Mr John Dutton, Head of Facilities Management, Town Hall, Wandsworth High Street, London SW18 2PU ☎ 020 8871 7645 ⁀ jdutton@wandsworth.gov.uk

Children / Youth Services: Ms Dawn Warwick, Director - Children's Services, Town Hall, Wandsworth High Street, London SW18 2PU ☎ 020 8871 6291 ⁀ dwarwick@wandsworth.gov.uk

Civil Registration: Mr Martin Walker, Borough Solicitor & Assistant Director - Administration, Town Hall, Wandsworth High Street, London SW18 2PU ☎ 020 8871 6110
⁀ mwalker@wandsworth.gov.uk

PR / Communications: Mr Jon Evans, Head of Policy & Communications, Town Hall, Wandsworth High Street, London SW18 2PU ☎ 020 8871 7815 ⁀ jevans@wandsworth.gov.uk

Community Planning: Mr Jon Evans, Head of Policy & Communications, Town Hall, Wandsworth High Street, London SW18 2PU ☎ 020 8871 7815 ⁀ jevans@wandsworth.gov.uk

Community Safety: Mr Stewart Low, Head of Community Safety, Town Hall, Wandsworth High Street, London SW18 2PU
☎ 020 8871 6588 ⁀ slow@wandsworth.gov.uk

Computer Management: Mr D Tidey, Head of IT & Business Communications, Town Hall, Wandsworth High Street, London SW18 2PU ☎ 020 8871 6080 ⁀ dtidey@wandsworth.gov.uk

Consumer Protection and Trading Standards: Mr Paul Browne, Team Leader & Chief Inspector of Weights & Measures, Town Hall, Wandsworth High Street, London SW18 2PU
☎ 020 8871 7383 ⁀ pbrowne@wandsworth.gov.uk

Contracts: Mr Mark Glaister, Head of Procurement, Town Hall, Wandsworth High Street, London SW18 2PU ☎ 020 8871 5828
⁀ mglaister@wandsworth.gov.uk

Customer Service: Mrs Kristina Watson, Assistant Director - Customer Services & Service Transformation, Town Hall, Wandsworth High Street, London SW18 2PU ☎ 020 8871 7061
⁀ kwatson@wandsworth.gov.uk

Direct Labour: Mr Kevin Power, Assistant Director - Operational Services, Reed House, Frogmore Complex, Frogmore, Wandsworth, London SW18 9AQ ☎ 020 8871 6704 ⁀ kpower@wandsworth.gov.uk

Economic Development: Mr Nick Smales, Economic Development Officer, Town Hall, Wandsworth High Street, London SW18 2PU ☎ 020 8871 6202 ⁀ nsmales@wandsworth.gov.uk

Education: Mr John Johnson, Deputy Director - Children's Services, Town Hall, Wandsworth High Street, London SW18 2PU
☎ 020 8871 7891 ⁀ jjohnson@wandsworth.gov.uk

E-Government: Mr D Tidey, Head of IT & Business Communications, Town Hall, Wandsworth High Street, London SW18 2PU ☎ 020 8871 6080 ⁀ dtidey@wandsworth.gov.uk

Electoral Registration: Mr Martin Walker, Borough Solicitor & Assistant Director - Administration, Town Hall, Wandsworth High Street, London SW18 2PU ☎ 020 8871 6110 ⏚ mwalker@wandsworth.gov.uk

Emergency Planning: Mrs Debbie Western, Emergency Planning Officer, Frogmore House, Dormay Street, London SW18 1EY
☎ 020 8871 5747 ⏚ dwestern@wandsworth.gov.uk

Energy Management: Mr Andy Algar, Head of Property Services, Town Hall, Wandsworth High Street, London SW18 2PU
☎ 020 8871 6075 ⏚ aalgar@wandsworth.gov.uk

Environmental Health: Mrs Sue Kelleher, Head of Environmental Services & Strategic Business Management, Town Hall, Wandsworth High Street, London SW18 2PU ☎ 020 8871 8164 ⏚ skelleher@wandsworth.gov.uk

Estates, Property & Valuation: Mr Andy Algar, Head of Property Services, Town Hall, Wandsworth High Street, London SW18 2PU
☎ 020 8871 6075 ⏚ aalgar@wandsworth.gov.uk

European Liaison: Mr Nick Smales, Economic Development Officer, Town Hall, Wandsworth High Street, London SW18 2PU
☎ 020 8871 6202 ⏚ nsmales@wandsworth.gov.uk

Events Manager: Mr Jack Adam, Security, Arts, Events & Filming, The Park Office, Battersea Park, London SW11 4NJ
☎ 020 8871 7636 ⏚ jadam@wandsworth.gov.uk

Facilities: Mr John Dutton, Head of Facilities Management, Town Hall, Wandsworth High Street, London SW18 2PU
☎ 020 8871 7645 ⏚ jdutton@wandsworth.gov.uk

Finance: Mr Chris Buss, Director - Finance & Deputy Chief Executive, Town Hall, Wandsworth High Street, London SW18 2PU
☎ 020 8871 8300 ⏚ cbuss@wandsworth.gov.uk

Pensions: Ms Colette Hollands, Pensions Manager, Town Hall, Wandsworth High Street, London SW18 2PU ☎ 020 8871 6522
⏚ chollands@wandsworth.gov.uk

Fleet Management: Mr Ricky Cousins, Transport & Fleet Manager, Mechanical Workshops, Frogmore Complex, Dormay Street, London SW18 1EY ☎ 020 8871 6762
⏚ rcousins@wandsworth.gov.uk

Grounds Maintenance: Mr Simon Cooper-Grundy, Chief Parks Officer, Park Services, Battersea Park, London SW11 4NJ
☎ 020 8871 8117 ⏚ scooper-grundy@wandsworth.gov.uk

Health and Safety: Mr John Throssell, Health & Safety Manager, Town Hall, Wandsworth High Street, London SW18 2PU
☎ 020 8871 6220 ⏚ jthrossell@wandsworth.gov.uk

Highways: Mr Wale Adeyoyin, Head of Parking & Road Safety, Town Hall, Wandsworth High Street, London SW18 2PU
☎ 020 8871 6970 ⏚ wadeyoyin@wandsworth.gov.uk

Housing: Mr Brian Reilly, Director - Housing & Regeneration, Reed House, Frogmore Complex, Frogmore, Wandsworth, London SW18 9AQ ☎ 020 8871 6591 ⏚ hrdirectorate@wandsworth.gov.uk

Housing: Mr Dave Worth, Head of Housing Services, Reed House, Frogmore Complex, Frogmore, Wandsworth, London SW18 9AQ
☎ 020 8871 6837 ⏚ hcs@wandsworth.gov.uk

Housing Maintenance: Mr Ian Stewart, Head of Housing Management, Reed House, Frogmore Complex, Frogmore, Wandsworth, London SW18 9AQ ☎ 020 8871 6831
⏚ hcs@wandsworth.gov.uk

Legal: Mr Martin Walker, Borough Solicitor & Assistant Director - Administration, Town Hall, Wandsworth High Street, London SW18 2PU ☎ 020 8871 6110 ⏚ mwalker@wandsworth.gov.uk

Leisure and Cultural Services: Mr Paul McCue, Chief Executive - Enable Leisure & Culture, Town Hall, Wandsworth High Street, London SW18 2PU ☎ 020 8871 6868
⏚ pmccue@wandsworth.gov.uk

Lifelong Learning: Mr Santino Fragola, Head of Lifelong Learning, Professional Centre, Franciscan Road, Tooting, London SW17 8HE ☎ 020 8871 8491 ⏚ sfragola@wandsworth.gov.uk

Lighting: Mr Steve Kempster, Assistant Head of Operational Services, Frogmore Complex, Dormay Street, London SW18 1HA
☎ 020 8871 6570 ⏚ skempster@wandsworth.gov.uk

Lottery Funding, Charity and Voluntary: Mr Nick Smales, Economic Development Officer, Town Hall, Wandsworth High Street, London SW18 2PU ☎ 020 8871 6202
⏚ nsmales@wandsworth.gov.uk

Member Services: Mr Martin Walker, Borough Solicitor & Assistant Director - Administration, Town Hall, Wandsworth High Street, London SW18 2PU ☎ 020 8871 6110
⏚ mwalker@wandsworth.gov.uk

Parking: Mr Wale Adeyoyin, Head of Parking & Road Safety, Town Hall, Wandsworth High Street, London SW18 2PU
☎ 020 8871 6970 ⏚ wadeyoyin@wandsworth.gov.uk

Partnerships: Mr Jon Evans, Head of Policy & Communications, Town Hall, Wandsworth High Street, London SW18 2PU
☎ 020 8871 7815 ⏚ jevans@wandsworth.gov.uk

Personnel / HR: Mrs Catherine Parsons, Acting Head of HR, Town Hall, Wandsworth High Street, London SW18 2PU
☎ 020 8871 6190 ⏚ cparsons@wandsworth.gov.uk

Planning: Mr Tim Cronin, Head of Planning & Development, Reed House, Frogmore Complex, Frogmore, Wandsworth, London SW18 9AQ ☎ 020 8871 6627 ⏚ tcronin@wandsworth.gov.uk

Procurement: Mr Mark Glaister, Head of Procurement, Town Hall, Wandsworth High Street, London SW18 2PU ☎ 020 8871 5828
⏚ mglaister@wandsworth.gov.uk

Public Libraries: Mr Paul McCue, Chief Executive - Enable Leisure & Culture, Town Hall, Wandsworth High Street, London SW18 2PU ☎ 020 8871 6868 ⏚ pmccue@wandsworth.gov.uk

WANDSWORTH

Recycling & Waste Minimisation: Mr Shaun Morley, Head of Waste Management, Tadmore House, Frogmore Complex, Dormay Street, London SW18 1HA ☎ 020 8871 6938 ✉ smorley@wandsworth.gov.uk

Road Safety: Mr Wale Adeyoyin, Head of Parking & Road Safety, Town Hall, Wandsworth High Street, London SW18 2PU ☎ 020 8871 6970 ✉ wadeyoyin@wandsworth.gov.uk

Social Services: Ms Dawn Warwick, Director - Children's Services, Town Hall, Wandsworth High Street, London SW18 2PU ☎ 020 8871 6291 ✉ dwarwick@wandsworth.gov.uk

Social Services (Adult): Ms Cathy Kerr, Director - Adult Social Services, Town Hall, Wandsworth High Street, London SW18 2PU ☎ 020 8891 7360 ✉ ckerr@wandsworth.gov.uk

Social Services (Adult): Mr Alistair Rush, Assistant Director - Business Resources, Town Hall, Wandsworth High Street, London SW18 2PU ☎ 020 8871 6216 ✉ arush@wandsworth.gov.uk

Social Services (Adult): Mr Kerry Stevens, Assistant Director - Operations (Adults), Town Hall, Wandsworth High Street, London SW18 2PU ☎ 020 8871 8423 ✉ kstevens1@wandsworth.gov.uk

Social Services (Children): Ms Linda Webber, WSCB Business Manager, Town Hall, Wandsworth High Street, London SW18 2PU ☎ 020 8871 8610 ✉ lwebber@wandsworth.gov.uk

Public Health: Dr Houda Al-Sharifi, Director - Public Health, Town Hall, Wandsworth High Street, London SW18 2PU ✉ houda.al-sharifi@wandsworth.gov.uk

Staff Training: Mrs Catherine Parsons, Acting Head of HR, Town Hall, Wandsworth High Street, London SW18 2PU ☎ 020 8871 6190 ✉ cparsons@wandsworth.gov.uk

Street Scene: Mr David Tidley, Group Leader - Transformation, Town Hall, Wandsworth High Street, London SW18 2PU ☎ 020 8871 6970 ✉ dtidley@wandsworth.gov.uk

Sustainable Communities: Mr Jon Evans, Head of Policy & Communications, Town Hall, Wandsworth High Street, London SW18 2PU ☎ 020 8871 7815 ✉ jevans@wandsworth.gov.uk

Sustainable Development: Mr Jon Evans, Head of Policy & Communications, Town Hall, Wandsworth High Street, London SW18 2PU ☎ 020 8871 7815 ✉ jevans@wandsworth.gov.uk

Tourism: Mr Paul McCue, Chief Executive - Enable Leisure & Culture, Town Hall, Wandsworth High Street, London SW18 2PU ☎ 020 8871 6868 ✉ pmccue@wandsworth.gov.uk

Town Centre: Mr Nick Smales, Economic Development Officer, Town Hall, Wandsworth High Street, London SW18 2PU ☎ 020 8871 6202 ✉ nsmales@wandsworth.gov.uk

Traffic Management: Mr Wale Adeyoyin, Head of Parking & Road Safety, Town Hall, Wandsworth High Street, London SW18 2PU ☎ 020 8871 6970 ✉ wadeyoyin@wandsworth.gov.uk

Transport: Mr Ricky Cousins, Transport & Fleet Manager, Mechanical Workshops, Frogmore Complex, Dormay Street, London SW18 1EY ☎ 020 8871 6762 ✉ rcousins@wandsworth.gov.uk

Transport Planner: Mr John Stone, Head of Forward Planning & Transportation, Town Hall Extension, Wandsworth High Street, London SW18 2PU ☎ 020 8871 6628 ✉ jstone@wandsworth.gov.uk

Waste Collection and Disposal: Mr Shaun Morley, Head of Waste Management, Tadmore House, Frogmore Complex, Dormay Street, London SW18 1HA ☎ 020 8871 6938 ✉ smorley@wandsworth.gov.uk

Waste Management: Mr Shaun Morley, Head of Waste Management, Tadmore House, Frogmore Complex, Dormay Street, London SW18 1HA ☎ 020 8871 6938 ✉ smorley@wandsworth.gov.uk

COUNCILLORS

Mayor: Field, Richard (CON - Nightingale) rfield@wandsworth.gov.uk

Deputy Mayor: Speck, Wendy (LAB - Latchmere) wspeck@wandsworth.gov.uk

Leader of the Council: Govindia, Ravi (CON - East Putney) rgovindia@wandsworth.gov.uk

Deputy Leader of the Council: Cook, Jonathan (CON - Shaftesbury) jonathancook@wandsworth.gov.uk

Group Leader: Hogg, Simon (LAB - Latchmere) shogg@wandsworth.gov.uk

Allin-Khan, Rosena (LAB - Bedford) rallin-khan@wandsworth.gov.uk

Ambache, Jeremy (LAB - Roehampton & Putney Heath) jambache@wandsworth.gov.uk

Anderson, Fleur (LAB - Bedford) fanderson@wandsworth.gov.uk

Belton, Tony (LAB - Latchmere) tbelton@wandsworth.gov.uk

Caddy, Kim (CON - Southfields) kcaddy@wandsworth.gov.uk

Carpenter, Peter (LAB - Roehampton & Putney Heath) pcarpenter@wandsworth.gov.uk

Clay, Claire (CON - Wandsworth Common) cclay@wandsworth.gov.uk

Cooper, Leonie (LAB - Furzedown) leoniecooper@wandsworth.gov.uk

Cooper, Jane (CON - West Putney) janecooper@wandsworth.gov.uk

Cousins, James (IND - Shaftesbury) jcousins@wandsworth.gov.uk

Critchard, Annamarie (LAB - Tooting) acritchard@wandsworth.gov.uk

Crivelli, George (CON - East Putney) gcrivelli@wandsworth.gov.uk

Cuff, Nick (CON - West Hill) ncuff@wandsworth.gov.uk

Daley, James (LAB - Tooting) jamesdaley@wandsworth.gov.uk

Dawson, Peter (CON - Northcote)
pdawson@wandsworth.gov.uk

Dodd, Jane (CON - Northcote)
jdodd@wandsworth.gov.uk

Dunn, Antonia (CON - Bedford)
adunn@wandsworth.gov.uk

Ellis, Paul (CON - Balham)
pellis@wandsworth.gov.uk

Gibbons, Andy (LAB - Graveney)
agibbons@wandsworth.gov.uk

Graham, Angela (CON - Earlsfield)
agraham@wandsworth.gov.uk

Grimston, Malcolm (IND - West Hill)
mgrimston@wandsworth.gov.uk

Hampton, Melanie (CON - St Mary's Park)
mhampton@wandsworth.gov.uk

Hanson, Marie (CON - Queenstown)
mhanson@wandsworth.gov.uk

Hart, Ian (CON - Nightingale)
ihart@wandsworth.gov.uk

Heaster, Maurice (CON - Wandsworth Common)
mheaster@wandsworth.gov.uk

Humphries, Guy (CON - Southfields)
ghumphries@wandsworth.gov.uk

Johnson, Martin (CON - Northcote)
martinjohnson@wandsworth.gov.uk

Jones, Candida (LAB - Furzedown)
cjones1@wandsworth.gov.uk

Lescott, Charles (CON - Earlsfield)
clescott@wandsworth.gov.uk

Lewer, Ian (CON - West Putney)
ilewer@wandsworth.gov.uk

Macdonald, Alaina (LAB - Graveney)
amacdonald1@wandsworth.gov.uk

Maddan, James (CON - Thamesfield)
jmaddan@wandsworth.gov.uk

McCausland, Piers (CON - Fairfield)
pmccausland@wandsworth.gov.uk

McDermott, Sarah (CON - Nightingale)
smcdermott@wandsworth.gov.uk

McDonnell, Leslie (CON - East Putney)
lmcdonnell@wandsworth.gov.uk

McKinney, Sue (LAB - Roehampton & Putney Heath)
smckinney@wandsworth.gov.uk

Nardelli, Nicola (CON - Queenstown)
nnardelli@wandsworth.gov.uk

O'Broin, Rory (CON - St Mary's Park)
ro'broin@wandsworth.gov.uk

Osborn, Rex (LAB - Graveney)
rosborn@wandsworth.gov.uk

Peterkin, Andrew (CON - West Hill)
apeterkin@wandsworth.gov.uk

Ryder, Michael (CON - Thamesfield)
mryder@wandsworth.gov.uk

Salier, Clare (CON - Balham)
csalier@wandsworth.gov.uk

Senior, Guy (CON - Shaftesbury)
gsenior@wandsworth.gov.uk

Stokes, Rachael (LAB - Earlsfield)
rstokes@wandsworth.gov.uk

Strickland, Tessa (CON - St Mary's Park)
tstrickland@wandsworth.gov.uk

Sutters, Steffi (CON - West Putney)
ssutters@wandsworth.gov.uk

Sweet, Will (CON - Fairfield)
wsweet@wandsworth.gov.uk

Thom, Stuart (CON - Fairfield)
sthom@wandsworth.gov.uk

Thomas, Mark (LAB - Furzedown)
markthomas@wandsworth.gov.uk

Torrington, Rosemary (CON - Thamesfield)
rtorrington@wandsworth.gov.uk

Tracey, Kathy (CON - Wandsworth Common)
ktracey@wandworth.gov.uk

Usher, Caroline (CON - Balham)
cusher@wandsworth.gov.uk

Walsh, Terence (CON - Southfields)
twalsh@wandsworth.gov.uk

White, Paul (LAB - Tooting)
pwhite@wandsworth.gov.uk

POLITICAL COMPOSITION
CON: 39, LAB: 18, IND: 2

COMMITTEE CHAIRS

Adult Care & Health: Mrs Claire Clay

Audit: Mr Maurice Heaster

Education & Children's Services: Ms Clare Salier

Education & Children's Services: Mr Peter Dawson

Health & Wellbeing: Mr James Maddan

Housing & Regeneration: Mrs Jane Cooper

Licensing: Mrs Caroline Usher

Pensions: Mr Maurice Heaster

Planning: Mrs Sarah McDermott

Warrington   U

Warrington Borough Council, Town Hall, Sankey Street,
Warrington WA1 1UH
☎ 01925 443322 contact@warrington.gov.uk
 www.warrington.gov.uk

FACTS AND FIGURES
Parliamentary Constituencies: Warrington North, Warrington South
EU Constituencies: North West
Election Frequency: Elections are by thirds

WARRINGTON

PRINCIPAL OFFICERS

Chief Executive: Prof Steven Broomhead, Chief Executive, Town Hall, Sankey Street, Warrington WA1 1UH ☎ 01925 442101 ⌨ sbroomhead@warrington.gov.uk

Deputy Chief Executive: Ms Katherine Fairclough, Deputy Chief Executive, Town Hall, Sankey Street, Warrington WA1 1UH ☎ 01925 442311 ⌨ kfairclough@warrington.gov.uk

Senior Management: Dr Muna Abdel Aziz, Director - Public Health, Town Hall, Sankey Street, Warrington WA1 1UH ☎ 01925 443967 ⌨ mabdelaziz@warrington.gov.uk

Senior Management: Mr Andy Farrall, Executive Director - Economic Regeneration, Growth & Environment, Town Hall, Sankey Street, Warrington WA1 1UH ☎ 01925 442701 ⌨ afarrall@warrington.gov.uk

Senior Management: Mr Steve Reddy, Executive Director - Families & Wellbeing, Town Hall, Sankey Street, Warrington WA1 1UH ☎ 01925 442900 ⌨ sreddy@warrington.gov.uk

Access Officer / Social Services (Disability): Mr Steve Peddie, Operational Director - Adult Services, New Town House, Buttermarket Street, Warrington WA1 2NJ ☎ 01925 444251 ⌨ speddie@warrington.gov.uk

Architect, Building / Property Services: Mr Stewart Brown, Service Manager - Property & Estates, New Town House, Buttermarket Street, Warrington WA1 2NJ ☎ 01925 442850 ⌨ s_brown@warrington.gov.uk

Building Control: Mr Tony Gartside, Service Manager - Building Control, New Town House, Buttermarket Street, Warrington WA1 2NJ ☎ 01925 442547 ⌨ tgartside@warrington.gov.uk

Children / Youth Services: Ms Fiona Waddington, Assistant Director - Children & Young People's Targeted Services, 2nd Floor, New Town House, Buttermarket Street, Warrington WA1 1NJ ☎ 01925 443900 ⌨ fwaddington@warrington.gov.uk

Civil Registration: Ms Jane Briscall, Superintendent Registrar - Births, Death & Marriages, The Registry Office, Museum Street, Warrington WA1 1JX ☎ 01925 442706 ⌨ jbriscall1@warrington.gov.uk

PR / Communications: Ms Kate Lindley, Head of Customer Strategy & Communications, Town Hall, Sankey Street, Warrington WA1 1UH ☎ 01925 443322 ⌨ klindley@warrington.gov.uk

Community Safety: Mr Doug Ryan, Crime & Disorder Reduction Manager, Charles Stewart House, 55 Museum Street, Warrington WA1 1NE ☎ 01606 364850 ⌨ Douglas.Ryan@cheshire.pnn.police.uk

Computer Management: Mr Keith Traverse, Head of IT & Print Service, New Town House, Buttermarket Street, Warrington WA1 1NJ ☎ 01925 443949 ⌨ ktraverse@warrington.gov.uk

Consumer Protection and Trading Standards: Mr Peter Astley, Assistant Director - Regulation & Public Protection, New Town House, Buttermarket Street, Warrington WA1 1NJ ☎ 01925 442672 ⌨ pastley@warrington.gov.uk

Customer Service: Mr Adrian Webster, Head of Benefits, Contact Warrington & Exchequer Services, Town Hall, Sankey Street, Warrington WA1 1UH ☎ 01925 442266 ⌨ awebster@warrington.gov.uk

Economic Development: Mr Andy Farrall, Executive Director - Economic Regeneration, Growth & Environment, Town Hall, Sankey Street, Warrington WA1 1UH ☎ 01925 442700 ⌨ afarrall@warrington.gov.uk

Education: Mrs Hilary Smith, Interim Operational Director - Children & Young People's Universal Services, Town Hall, Sankey Street, Warrington WA1 1UH ☎ 01925 442940 ⌨ hsmith@warrington.gov.uk

E-Government: Mr Lynton Green, Director - Finance & Information Services, Quattro Building, Buttermarket Street, Warrington WA1 1BN ☎ 01925 443925 ⌨ lgreen@warrington.gov.uk

Electoral Registration: Mrs Alison McDonald, Electoral Services Manager, Town Hall, Sankey Street, Warrington WA1 1UH ☎ 01925 442041 ⌨ amcdonald@warrington.gov.uk

Emergency Planning: Mrs Theresa Whitfield, Risk & Resilience Manager, Quattro, Buttermarket Street, Warrington WA1 1NJ ☎ 01925 442657 ⌨ twhitfield@warrington.gov.uk

Energy Management: Mrs Rachel Waggett, Special Projects / Low Carbon Manager, New Town House, Buttermarket Street, Warrington WA1 1NJ ☎ 01925 442630 ⌨ rwaggett@warrington.gov.uk

Environmental / Technical Services: Mr Andy Farrall, Executive Director - Economic Regeneration, Growth & Environment, Town Hall, Sankey Street, Warrington WA1 1UH ☎ 01925 442701 ⌨ afarrall@warrington.gov.uk

Environmental Health: Mr Peter Astley, Assistant Director - Regulation & Public Protection, New Town House, Buttermarket Street, Warrington WA1 1NJ ☎ 01925 442672 ⌨ pastley@warrington.gov.uk

Estates, Property & Valuation: Mr Stewart Brown, Service Manager - Property & Estates, 3rd Floor, Quattro, Buttermarket Street, Warrington WA1 1NJ ☎ 01925 442850 ⌨ s_brown@warrington.gov.uk

Events Manager: Ms Kate Lindley, Head of Customer Strategy & Communications, Town Hall, Sankey Street, Warrington WA1 1UH ☎ 01925 443322 ⌨ klindley@warrington.gov.uk

Finance: Mr Lynton Green, Director - Finance & Information Services, Quattro Building, Buttermarket Street, Warrington WA1 1BN ☎ 01925 443925 ⌨ lgreen@warrington.gov.uk

Fleet Management: Mr David Boyer, Assistant Director - Transport & Environment, New Town House, Buttermarket Street, Warrington WA1 1NJ ☎ 01925 442530 ⌨ dboyer@warrington.gov.uk

Grounds Maintenance: Mr David Boyer, Assistant Director - Transport & Environment, New Town House, Buttermarket Street, Warrington WA1 1NJ ☎ 01925 442530 ⌨ dboyer@warrington.gov.uk

Health and Safety: Mrs Theresa Whitfield, Risk & Resilience Manager, Quattro, Buttermarket Street, Warrington WA1 1NJ
☎ 01925 442657 ⌨ twhitfield@warrington.gov.uk

Highways: Mr David Boyer, Assistant Director - Transport & Environment, New Town House, Buttermarket Street, Warrington WA1 1NJ ☎ 01925 442530 ⌨ dboyer@warrington.gov.uk

Home Energy Conservation: Mrs Rachel Waggett, Special Projects / Low Carbon Manager, New Town House, Buttermarket Street, Warrington WA1 1NJ ☎ 01925 442630 ⌨ rwaggett@warrington.gov.uk

Housing: Mr David Cowley, Head of Housing Services, The Gateway, 85 - 89 Sankey Street, Warrington WA1 1SR
☎ 01925 246890 ⌨ dcowley@warrington.gov.uk

Local Area Agreement: Mrs Kathryn Griffiths, Assistant Director - Partnerships & Performance, Quattro, Buttermarket Street, Warrington WA1 1NJ ☎ 01925 442797
⌨ kgriffiths@warrington.gov.uk

Legal: Mr Tim Date, Solicitor to the Council & Assistant Director - Corporate Governance, Quattro, Buttermarket Street, Warrington WA1 2NH ☎ 01925 442150 ⌨ tdate@warrington.gov.uk

Leisure and Cultural Services: Ms Emma Hutchinson, Managing Director - Livewire & Culture Warrington, Orford Jubilee Neighbourhood Hub, Jubilee Way, Warrington WA2 8HE
☎ 01925 625973 ⌨ ehutchinson@livewirewarrington.org

Licensing: Mr Peter Astley, Assistant Director - Regulation & Public Protection, New Town House, Buttermarket Street, Warrington WA1 1NJ ☎ 01925 442672 ⌨ pastley@warrington.gov.uk

Lifelong Learning: Mrs Penny Owen, Employment, Learning & Skills Manager, St Werbergh's, Irwell Road, Warrington WA4 6QR
☎ 01925 442696 ⌨ powen@warrington.gov.uk

Lighting: Mr Dave Vasey, Asset Maintenance & Street Works Manager, Hawthorne Avenue, Woolston, Warrington WA1 4AL
☎ 01925 442573 ⌨ dvasey@warrington.gov.uk

Lottery Funding, Charity and Voluntary: Ms Stephanie Duerden, Commissioning & Third Sector Partnership Manager, New Town House, Buttermarket Street, Warrington WA1 1NJ
☎ 01925 248462 ⌨ sduerden@warrington.gov.uk

Member Services: Mr Bryan Magan, Head - Democratic & Member Services, West Annexe, Town Hall, Sankey Street, Warrington WA1 1UH ☎ 01925 442112 ⌨ bmagan@warrington.gov.uk

Parking: Mr David Boyer, Assistant Director - Transport, Engineering & Operations, New Town House, Buttermarket Street, Warrington WA1 1NJ ☎ 01925 442530 ⌨ dboyer@warrington.gov.uk

Partnerships: Mrs Kathryn Griffiths, Assistant Director - Partnerships & Performance, 4th Floor, Quattro, Buttermarket Street, Warrington WA1 1NJ ☎ 01925 442797
⌨ kgriffiths@warrington.gov.uk

Personnel / HR: Mr Gareth Hopkins, Assistant Director - Human Resources, Quattro Building, Buttermarket Street, Warrington WA1 2NH ☎ 01925 443932 ⌨ ghopkins1@warrington.gov.uk

Planning: Mr Michael Bell, Service Manager - Planning Policy & Programmes, New Town House, Buttermarket Street, Warrington WA1 2NJ ☎ 01925 442795 ⌨ mbell@warrington.gov.uk

Procurement: Mr Chris Luke, Commissioning & Procurement Manager, Quattro Building, Buttermarket Street, Warrington WA1 1NJ ☎ 01925 442879 ⌨ cluke@warrington.gov.uk

Public Libraries: Ms Emma Hutchinson, Managing Director - Livewire & Culture Warrington, Orford Jubilee Neighbourhood Hub, Jubilee Way, Warrington WA2 8HE ☎ 01925 625973
⌨ ehutchinson@livewirewarrington.org

Recycling & Waste Minimisation: Mr David Boyer, Assistant Director - Transport & Environment, New Town House, Buttermarket Street, Warrington WA1 1NJ ☎ 01925 442530 ⌨ dboyer@warrington.gov.uk

Regeneration: Mr Andy Farrall, Executive Director - Economic Regeneration, Growth & Environment, Town Hall, Sankey Street, Warrington WA1 1UH ☎ 01925 442701 ⌨ afarrall@warrington.gov.uk

Road Safety: Mr Mark Tune, Traffic Management & Road Safety Manager, New Town House, Buttermarket Street, Warrington WA1 1NJ ☎ 01925 442695 ⌨ mtune@warrington.gov.uk

Social Services (Adult): Mr Steve Peddie, Operational Director - Adult Services, Town Hall, Sankey Street, Warrington WA1 1UH
☎ 01925 444251 ⌨ speddie@warrington.gov.uk

Social Services (Children): Ms Fiona Waddington, Assistant Director - Children & Young People's Targeted Services, 2nd Floor, New Town House, Buttermarket Street, Warrington WA1 1NJ
☎ 01925 443900 ⌨ fwaddington@warrington.gov.uk

Public Health: Dr Muna Abdel Aziz, Director - Public Health, Town Hall, Sankey Street, Warrington WA1 1UH ☎ 01925 443967
⌨ mabdelaziz@warrington.gov.uk

Staff Training: Mrs Penny Owen, Employment, Learning & Skills Manager, St Werberghs, Irwell Road, Warrington WA4 6QR
☎ 01925 442696 ⌨ powen@warrington.gov.uk

Street Scene: Mr David Boyer, Assistant Director - Transport & Environment, New Town House, Buttermarket Street, Warrington WA1 1NJ ☎ 01925 442530 ⌨ dboyer@warrington.gov.uk

Sustainable Communities: Mrs Kathryn Griffiths, Assistant Director - Partnerships & Performance, 4th Floor, Quattro, Buttermarket Street, Warrington WA1 1NJ ☎ 01925 442797
⌨ kgriffiths@warrington.gov.uk

Town Centre: Mr Barry McGorry, Town Centre Manager, Quattro, Buttermarket Street, Warrington WA1 1NJ ☎ 01925 443313
⌨ bmcgorry@warrington.gov.uk

WARRINGTON

Traffic Management: Mr David Boyer, Assistant Director - Transport & Environment, New Town House, Buttermarket Street, Warrington WA1 1NJ ☎ 01925 442530 🖑 dboyer@warrington.gov.uk

Transport: Mr Stephen Hunter, Service Manager - Transport for Warrington, New Town House, Buttermarket Street, Warrington WA1 1NJ ☎ 01925 442684 🖑 shunter@warrington.gov.uk

Transport Planner: Mr David Boyer, Assistant Director - Transport & Environment, New Town House, Buttermarket Street, Warrington WA1 1NJ ☎ 01925 442530 🖑 dboyer@warrington.gov.uk

Waste Collection and Disposal: Mr David Boyer, Assistant Director - Transport & Environment, New Town House, Buttermarket Street, Warrington WA1 1NJ ☎ 01925 442530 🖑 dboyer@warrington.gov.uk

Waste Management: Mr David Boyer, Assistant Director - Transport & Environment, New Town House, Buttermarket Street, Warrington WA1 1NJ ☎ 01925 442530 🖑 dboyer@warrington.gov.uk

Children's Play Areas: Mr David Boyer, Assistant Director - Transport & Environment, New Town House, Buttermarket Street, Warrington WA1 1NJ ☎ 01925 442530 🖑 dboyer@warrington.gov.uk

COUNCILLORS

Leader of the Council: O'Neill, Terry (LAB - Burtonwood & Winwick)
toneill@warrington.gov.uk

Deputy Leader of the Council: Friend, Graham (LAB - Poulton North)
gfriend@warrington.gov.uk

Axcell, Brian (LD - Appleton)
baxcell@warrington.gov.uk

Barr, Bob (LD - Lymm North & Thelwall)
bbarr@warrington.gov.uk

Bate, Ryan (LD - Grappenhall)
rbate@warrington.gov.uk

Bennett, Diana (LAB - Poulton North)
dbennett@warrington.gov.uk

Biggin, Mike (LD - Grappenhall)
mbiggin@warrington.gov.uk

Bowden, Russ (LAB - Birchwood)
rbowden@warrington.gov.uk

Buckley, Kath (CON - Lymm South)
kbuckley@warrington.gov.uk

Carey, Peter (LAB - Fairfield & Howley)
petercarey@warrington.gov.uk

Carter, Jean (LAB - Great Sankey South)
jcarter1@warrington.gov.uk

Cooksey, Hilary (LAB - Poplars & Hulme)
hcooksey@warrington.gov.uk

Creaghan, Maureen (LAB - Poulton South)
mcreaghan2@warrington.gov.uk

Davidson, Jan (LAB - Culcheth, Glazebury & Croft)
jdavidson@warrington.gov.uk

Dirir, Allin (LAB - Penketh & Cuerdley)
adirir@warrington.gov.uk

Dirir, Linda (LAB - Penketh & Cuerdley)
ldirir@warrington.gov.uk

Fitzsimmons, Chris (LAB - Birchwood)
cfitzsimmons@warrington.gov.uk

Flaherty, Jean (LAB - Fairfield & Howley)
jflaherty@warrington.gov.uk

Froggatt, Colin (LAB - Poulton South)
cfroggatt@warrington.gov.uk

Grime, Joan (LAB - Culcheth, Glazebury & Croft)
jgrime@warrington.gov.uk

Guthrie, Judith (LAB - Wesbrook)
jguthrie@warrington.gov.uk

Hall, Sarah (LAB - Bewsey & Whitecross)
shall@warrington.gov.uk

Hannon, Mike (LAB - Orford)
mhannon@warrington.gov.uk

Harris, Sharon (LD - Appleton)
sharris@warrington.gov.uk

Hart, Jan (LAB - Great Sankey North & Whittle Hall)
jhart@warrington.gov.uk

Higgins, Tony (LAB - Fairfield & Howley)
thiggins@warrington.gov.uk

Hill, Andrew (LAB - Rixton & Woolston)
ahill@warrington.gov.uk

Jennings, Tom (LAB - Bewsey & Whitecross)
tjennings@warrington.gov.uk

Johnson, Wendy (LD - Lymm North & Thelwall)
wjohnson@warrington.gov.uk

Keane, David (LAB - Penketh & Cuerdley)
dkeane@warrington.gov.uk

Kerr-Brown, John (LAB - Poplars & Hulme)
jkerrbrown@warrington.gov.uk

King, Amanda (LAB - Great Sankey South)
aking@warrington.gov.uk

Knowles, Rebecca (LAB - Chapelford & Old Hall)
rknowles@warrington.gov.uk

Krizanac, Stefan (LD - Westbrook)

Maher, Brian (LAB - Poplars & Hulme)
bmaher@warrington.gov.uk

Marks, Ian (LD - Lymm North & Thelwall)
imarks2@warrington.gov.uk

McCarthy, Tony (LAB - Rixton & Woolston)
tmccarthy@warrington.gov.uk

McLaughlin, Maureen (LAB - Latchford West)
mmclaughlin@warrington.gov.uk

Mitchell, Cathy (LAB - Burtonwood & Winwick)
cmitchell@warrington.gov.uk

Morgan, Les (LAB - Latchford West)

Morris, Kerri (LAB - Orford)
kmorris@warrington.gov.uk

Mundry, Hans (LAB - Latchford East)
hmundry@warrington.gov.uk

Mundry, Karen (LAB - Latchford East)
kmundry@warrington.gov.uk

Nelson, Pauline (LAB - Birchwood)
pnelson@warrington.gov.uk

Parish, Steve (LAB - Chapelford & Old Hall)
sparish@warrington.gov.uk

Patel, Hitesh (LAB - Great Sankey South)
hpatel@warrington.gov.uk

Price, Dan (LAB - Great Sankey North & Whittle Hall)
dprice1@warrington.gov.uk

Purnell, Russell (LAB - Poulton North)

Rashid, Faisal (LAB - Chapelford & Old Hall)
frashid@warrington.gov.uk

Smith, Matt (LAB - Culcheth, Glazebury & Croft)
msmith4@warrington.gov.uk

Tarr, Morgan (LAB - Orford)
mtarr@warrington.gov.uk

Walker, Peter (LD - Stockton Heath)
pwalker1@warrington.gov.uk

Welborn, Graham (LD - Stockton Heath)
gwelborn@warrington.gov.uk

Wheeler, Judith (LD - Appleton)
jwheeler1@warrington.gov.uk

Williams, Tony (LAB - Great Sankey North & Whittle Hall)
twilliams2@warrington.gov.uk

Woodyatt, Sheila (CON - Lymm South)
swoodyatt@warrington.gov.uk

Wright, Steve (LAB - Bewsey & Whitecross)
stevewright@warrington.gov.uk

Wright, Pat (LAB - Rixton & Woolston)
pwright@warrington.gov.uk

POLITICAL COMPOSITION
LAB: 45, LD: 11, CON: 2

COMMITTEE CHAIRS

Audit: Mr Chris Fitzsimmons

Development Management: Mr Tony McCarthy

Health & Wellbeing: Mr Terry O'Neill

Licensing: Mr Brian Maher

Warwick   D

Warwick District Council, Riverside House, Milverton Hill, Leamington Spa CV32 5HZ
☎ 01926 410410 ✆ contactus@warwickdc.gov.uk
🖳 www.warwickdc.gov.uk

FACTS AND FIGURES
Parliamentary Constituencies: Kenilworth and Southam, Warwick and Leamington
EU Constituencies: West Midlands
Election Frequency: Elections are of whole council

PRINCIPAL OFFICERS

Chief Executive: Mr Chris Elliott, Chief Executive, Riverside House, Milverton Hill, Leamington Spa CV32 5HZ ☎ 01926 456000
✆ chris.elliott@warwickdc.gov.uk

Deputy Chief Executive: Mr Bill Hunt, Deputy Chief Executive, Riverside House, Milverton Hill, Leamington Spa CV32 5HZ
☎ 01926 456014 ✆ bill.hunt@warwickdc.gov.uk

Deputy Chief Executive: Mr Andrew Jones, Deputy Chief Executive & Monitoring Officer, Riverside House, Milverton Hill, Leamington Spa CV32 5HZ ☎ 01926 456830
✆ andrew.jones@warwickdc.gov.uk

Senior Management: Ms Tracy Darke, Head of Development Services, Riverside House, Milverton Hill, Leamington Spa CV32 5HZ ☎ 01926 456501 ✆ tracy.darke@warwickdc.gov.uk

Senior Management: Mr Robert Hoof, Head of Neighbourhood Services, Riverside House, Milverton Hill, Leamington Spa CV32 5HZ ☎ 01926 456302 ✆ robert.hoof@warwickdc.gov.uk

Senior Management: Ms Marianne Rolfe, Head of Health & Community Protection, Riverside House, Milverton Hill, Leamington Spa CV32 5HZ ☎ 01926 456700
✆ marianne.rolfe@warwickdc.gov.uk

Senior Management: Mr Mike Snow, Head of Finance, Riverside House, Milverton Hill, Leamington Spa CV32 5HZ ☎ 01926 456800
✆ mike.snow@warwickdc.gov.uk

Senior Management: Mr Andy Thompson, Head of Housing & Property Services, Riverside House, Milverton Hill, Leamington Spa CV32 5HZ ☎ 01926 456403 ✆ andy.thompson@warwickdc.gov.uk

Senior Management: Ms Rose Winship, Head of Cultural Services, Riverside House, Milverton Hill, Leamington Spa CV32 5HZ ☎ 01926 456223 ✆ rose.winship@warwickdc.gov.uk

Architect, Building / Property Services: Mr Andy Thompson, Head of Housing & Property Services, Riverside House, Milverton Hill, Leamington Spa CV32 5HZ ☎ 01926 456403
✆ andy.thompson@warwickdc.gov.uk

Building Control: Mr Dennis Maddy, Chief Building Control Officer, Riverside House, Milverton Hill, Leamington Spa CV32 5HZ ☎ 01926 456511 ✆ dennis.maddy@warwickdc.gov.uk

PR / Communications: Ms Sam Ingram, Media & Communications Manager, Riverside House, Milverton Hill, Leamington Spa CV32 5HZ ☎ 01926 456069
✆ sam.ingram@warwickdc.gov.uk

Community Planning: Ms Jenny Murray, Manager - Joint Community Partnership, Riverside House, Milverton Hill, Leamington Spa CV32 5HZ ☎ 01926 413641
✆ jennymurray@warwickshire.gov.uk

Community Safety: Mr Peter Cutts, Community Safety Manager, Riverside House, Milverton Hill, Leamington Spa CV32 5HZ
☎ 01926 456021 ✆ pete.cutts@warwickdc.gov.uk

Community Safety: Mr Richard Hall, Head of Health & Community Protection, Riverside House, Milverton Hill, Leamington Spa CV32 5QH ☎ 01926 456700 ✆ richard.hall@warwickdc.gov.uk

WARWICK

Computer Management: Mr Ty Walter, Systems Development Manager, Riverside House, Milverton Hill, Leamington Spa CV32 5HZ ☎ 01926 456651 ⏚ ty.walters@warwickdc.gov.uk

Corporate Services: Mr Chris Elliott, Chief Executive, Riverside House, Milverton Hill, Leamington Spa CV32 5HZ ☎ 01926 456000 ⏚ chris.elliott@warwickdc.gov.uk

Customer Service: Ms Fiona Clark, Customer Contact Manager, Riverside House, Milverton Hill, Leamington Spa CV32 5HZ ☎ 01926 456237 ⏚ fiona.clark@warwickdc.gov.uk

Economic Development: Mr David Barber, Policy & Projects Manager, Riverside House, Milverton Hill, Leamington Spa CV32 5HZ ☎ 01926 456065 ⏚ david.barber@warwickdc.gov.uk

Electoral Registration: Mrs Gillian Friar, Electoral & Administration Officer, Deputy Chief Executive's Office, Riverside House, Milverton Hill, Leamington Spa CV32 5HZ ☎ 01926 456111 ⏚ gillian.friar@warwickdc.gov.uk

Energy Management: Mr Mark Perkins, Energy Manager, Riverside House, Milverton Hill, Leamington Spa CV32 5HZ ☎ 01926 456037 ⏚ mark.perkins@warwickdc.gov.uk

Environmental Health: Ms Marianne Rolfe, Head of Health & Community Protection, Riverside House, Milverton Hill, Leamington Spa CV32 5HZ ☎ 01926 456700 ⏚ marianne.rolfe@warwickdc.gov.uk

Estates, Property & Valuation: Mr Chris Makasis, Estates Manager, Riverside House, Milverton Hill, Leamington Spa CV32 5HZ ☎ 01926 546040 ⏚ chris.makasis@warwickdc.gov.uk

Finance: Mr Mike Snow, Head of Finance, Riverside House, Milverton Hill, Leamington Spa CV32 5HZ ☎ 01926 456800 ⏚ mike.snow@warwickdc.gov.uk

Health and Safety: Mr Ian Carden, Corporate Health & Safety Manager, Riverside House, Milverton Hill, Leamington Spa CV32 5HZ ☎ 01926 456716 ⏚ ian.carden@warwickdc.gov.uk

Home Energy Conservation: Mr Mark Perkins, Energy Manager, Riverside House, Milverton Hill, Leamington Spa CV32 5HZ ☎ 01926 456037 ⏚ mark.perkins@warwickdc.gov.uk

Housing: Mr Andy Thompson, Head of Housing & Property Services, Riverside House, Milverton Hill, Leamington Spa CV32 5HZ ☎ 01926 456403 ⏚ andy.thompson@warwickdc.gov.uk

Housing Maintenance: Mr Andy Thompson, Head of Housing & Property Services, Riverside House, Milverton Hill, Leamington Spa CV32 5HZ ☎ 01926 456403 ⏚ andy.thompson@warwickdc.gov.uk

Leisure and Cultural Services: Ms Rose Winship, Head of Cultural Services, Riverside House, Milverton Hill, Leamington Spa CV32 5HZ ☎ 01926 456223 ⏚ rose.winship@warwickdc.gov.uk

Licensing: Ms Marianne Rolfe, Head of Health & Community Protection, Riverside House, Milverton Hill, Leamington Spa CV32 5HZ ☎ 01926 456700 ⏚ marianne.rolfe@warwickdc.gov.uk

Member Services: Mr Graham Leach, Democratic Services Manager & Deputy Monitoring Officer, Riverside House, Milverton Hill, Leamington Spa CV32 5HZ ☎ 01926 456114 ⏚ graham.leach@warwickdc.gov.uk

Parking: Mr Gary Charlton, Contract Services Manager, Riverside House, Milverton Hill, Leamington Spa CV32 5HZ ☎ 01926 456315 ⏚ gary.charlton@warwickdc.gov.uk

Personnel / HR: Ms Tracy Dolphin, HR Manager, Riverside House, Milverton Hill, Leamington Spa CV32 5HZ ☎ 01926 456350 ⏚ tracy.dolphin@warwickdc.gov.uk

Planning: Ms Tracy Darke, Head of Development Services, Riverside House, Milverton Hill, Leamington Spa CV32 5HZ ☎ 01926 456501 ⏚ tracy.darke@warwickdc.gov.uk

Procurement: Mr John Roberts, Procurement Manager, Riverside House, Milverton Hill, Leamington Spa CV32 5HZ ☎ 01926 456201 ⏚ john.roberts@warwickdc.gov.uk

Regeneration: Mr Joe Baconnet, Economic Development & Regeneration Manager, Riverside House, Milverton Hill, Leamington Spa CV32 5HZ ☎ 01926 456011 ⏚ joseph.baconnet@warwickdc.gov.uk

Staff Training: Mrs Karen Weatherburn, Learning & Development Officer, Riverside House, Milverton Hill, Leamington Spa CV32 5HZ ☎ 01926 456307 ⏚ karen.weatherburn@warwickdc.gov.uk

Street Scene: Mr Robert Hoof, Head of Neighbourhood Services, Riverside House, Milverton Hill, Leamington Spa CV32 5HZ ☎ 01926 456302 ⏚ robert.hoof@warwickdc.gov.uk

Tourism: Mr Joe Baconnet, Economic Development & Regeneration Manager, Riverside House, Milverton Hill, Leamington Spa CV32 5HZ ☎ 01926 456011 ⏚ joseph.baconnet@warwickdc.gov.uk

Town Centre: Mr David Butler, Town Centre Development Officer, Riverside House, Milverton Hill, Leamington Spa CV32 5HZ ☎ 01926 456012 ⏚ david.butler@warwickdc.gov.uk

Waste Collection and Disposal: Mr Robert Hoof, Head of Neighbourhood Services, Riverside House, Milverton Hill, Leamington Spa CV32 5HZ ☎ 01926 456302 ⏚ robert.hoof@warwickdc.gov.uk

Waste Management: Mr Robert Hoof, Head of Neighbourhood Services, Riverside House, Milverton Hill, Leamington Spa CV32 5HZ ☎ 01926 456302 ⏚ robert.hoof@warwickdc.gov.uk

COUNCILLORS

Leader of the Council: Mobbs, Andrew (CON - Park Hill) andrew.mobbs@warwickdc.gov.uk

Deputy Leader of the Council: Coker, Michael (CON - Abbey) michael.coker@warwickdc.gov.uk

Ashford, Martyn (CON - Aylesford) martyn.ashford@warwickdc.gov.uk

Barrott, John (LAB - Sydenham)
john.barrott@warwickdc.gov.uk

Boad, Alan (LD - Crown)
alan.boad@warwickdc.gov.uk

Bromley, John-Paul (LAB - Saltisford)
john-paul.bromley@warwickdc.gov.uk

Bunker, Felicity (CON - Park Hill)
felicity.bunker@warwickdc.gov.uk

Butler, Noel (CON - Aylesford)
noel.butler@warwickdc.gov.uk

Cain, Gordon (CON - Manor)
gordon.cain@warwickdc.gov.uk

Cain, Patricia (CON - St. John's)
pat.cain@warwickdc.gov.uk

Cooke, John (CON - St. John's)
john.cooke@warwickdc.gov.uk

Cross, Stephen (CON - Woodloes)
stephen.cross@warwickdc.gov.uk

D'Arcy, Jacqueline (LAB - Emscote)
jackie.darcy@warwickdc.gov.uk

Davies, Richard (CON - St. John's)
richard.davies@warwickdc.gov.uk

Davison, Ian (GRN - Brunswick)
ian.davison@warwickdc.gov.uk

Day, Andrew (CON - Bishop's Tachbrook)
andrew.day@warwickdc.gov.uk

Doody, Michael (CON - Radford Semele)
michael.doody@warwickdc.gov.uk

Edgington, Richard (CON - Emscote)
richard.edgington@warwickdc.gov.uk

Evetts, Caroline (CON - Clarendon)
caroline.evetts@warwickdc.gov.uk

Falp, Judith (R - Whitnash)
judith.falp@warwickdc.gov.uk

Gallagher, Sue (CON - Arden)
susan.gallagher@warwickdc.gov.uk

Gifford, William (LD - Milverton)
bill.gifford@warwickdc.gov.uk

Gill, Balvinder (LAB - Sydenham)
balvinder.gill@warwickdc.gov.uk

Grainger, Moira-Ann (CON - Woodloes)
moira-ann.grainger@warwickdc.gov.uk

Grainger, Hayley (CON - Milverton)
hayley.grainger@warwickdc.gov.uk

Harrington, Nick (CON - Stoneleigh & Cubbington)
nick.harrington@warwickdc.gov.uk

Heath, Tony (R - Whitnash)
tony.heath@warwickdc.gov.uk

Hill, Rowena (CON - Abbey)
rowena.hill@warwickdc.gov.uk

Howe, Daniel (CON - Newbold)
daniel.howe@warwickdc.gov.uk

Illingworth, George (CON - Abbey)
george.illingworth@warwickdc.gov.uk

Knight, Jane (LAB - Clarendon)
jane.knight@warwickdc.gov.uk

Margrave, Robert (R - Whitnash)
rob.margrave@warwickdc.gov.uk

Morris, Terry (CON - Saltisford)
terry.morris@warwickdc.gov.uk

Murphy, Neale (CON - Myton & Heathcote)
neale.murphy@warwickdc.gov.uk

Naimo, Kristie (LAB - Brunswick)
kristie.naimo@warwickdc.gov.uk

Parkins, Stef (LAB - Crown)
stef.parkins@warwickdc.gov.uk

Phillips, Peter (CON - Budbrooke)
peter.phillips@warwickdc.gov.uk

Quinney, Colin (LAB - Leam)
colin.quinney@warwickdc.gov.uk

Redford, Pamela (CON - Stoneleigh & Cubbington)
pam.redford@warwickdc.gov.uk

Rhead, Alan (CON - Budbrooke)
alan.rhead@warwickdc.gov.uk

Shilton, David (CON - Park Hill)
david.shilton@warwickdc.gov.uk

Stevens, Amanda (CON - Manor)
amanda.stevens@warwickdc.gov.uk

Thompson, Andrew (CON - Newbold)
andrew.thompson@warwickdc.gov.uk

Weed, Barbara (LAB - Leam)
barbara.weed@warwickdc.gov.uk

Whiting, Peter (CON - Arden)
peter.whiting@warwickdc.gov.uk

POLITICAL COMPOSITION
CON: 30, LAB: 9, R: 3, LD: 2, GRN: 1

COMMITTEE CHAIRS

Audit: Mr Colin Quinney

Licensing: Mr George Illingworth

Planning: Mr John Cooke

Warwickshire   C

Warwickshire County Council, PO Box 9, Shire Hall, Warwick CV34 4RR
☎ 01926 410410 ⌨ www.warwickshire.gov.uk

FACTS AND FIGURES
Parliamentary Constituencies: Nuneaton, Stratford-on-Avon, Warwick and Leamington, Warwickshire North
EU Constituencies: West Midlands
Election Frequency: Elections are by thirds

PRINCIPAL OFFICERS

Chief Executive: Mr Jim Graham, Chief Executive, PO Box 9, Shire Hall, Warwick CV34 4RR ☎ 01926 410410
⌨ jimgraham@warwickshire.gov.uk

WARWICKSHIRE

Senior Management: Mr David Carter, Strategic Director - Resources Group, PO Box 9, Shire Hall, Warwick CV34 4RR
☎ 01926 412564 ⌂ davidcarter@warwickshire.gov.uk

Senior Management: Mr John Dixon, Interim Strategic Director - People, PO Box 9, Shire Hall, Warwick CV34 4RR ☎ 01926 742665 ⌂ johndixon@warwickshire.gov.uk

Senior Management: Ms Monica Fogarty, Strategic Director - Communities, PO Box 9, Shire Hall, Warwick CV34 4RR
☎ 01926 412514 ⌂ monicafogarty@warwickshire.gov.uk

Access Officer / Social Services (Disability): Ms Jenny Wood, Head of Social Care & Support Services, Saltisford Office Park, Ansell Way, Warwick CV34 4UL ☎ 01926 742977
⌂ jennywood@warwickshire.gov.uk

Architect, Building / Property Services: Mr Steve Smith, Head of Physical Assets, PO Box 3, Shire Hall, Warwick CV34 4RH
☎ 01926 412352 ⌂ stevesmith@warwickshire.gov.uk

Building Control: Mr Geoff Taylor, Estates & Smallholdings Service Manager, Shire Hall, Warwick CV34 4RR ☎ 01926 412521
⌂ geofftaylor@warwickshire.gov.uk

Catering Services: Ms Susan Hodson, Catering & Cleaning Services Manager, Unit 1 Montague Road, Warwick CV34 5LW
☎ 01926 413451 ⌂

Children / Youth Services: Ms Beate Wagner, Head of Service - Children's Social Care & Safeguarding, Saltisford Office Park, Ansell Way, Warwick CV34 4UL ☎ 01926 742577
⌂ beatewagner@warwickshire.gov.uk

Civil Registration: Mrs Alison John, Communications Manager, PO Box 9, Shire Hall, Warwick CV34 4RR ☎ 01926 412482
⌂ alison.john@warwickshire.gov.uk

PR / Communications: Ms Jayne Surman, Communication for Press & PR, PO Box 9, Shire Hall, Warwick CV34 4RR
☎ 01926 412757 ⌂ jaynesurman@warwickshire.gov.uk

Community Planning: Ms Jenny Murray, Manager - Joint Community Partnership, Riverside House, Milverton Hill, Leamington Spa CV32 5HZ ☎ 01926 413641
⌂ jennymurray@warwickshire.gov.uk

Community Safety: Mr Phil Evans, Head of Community Services, PO Box 43, Barrack Street, Warwick CV34 4SX ☎ 01926 412422
⌂ philevans@warwickshire.gov.uk

Computer Management: Mr Tonino Ciuffini, Head of ICT, PO Box 2, Shire Hall, Warwick CV34 4UB ☎ 01926 412879
⌂ toninociuffini@warwickshire.gov.uk

Consumer Protection and Trading Standards: Mr Phil Evans, Head of Community Services, PO Box 43, Barrack Street, Warwick CV34 4SX ☎ 01926 412422 ⌂ philevans@warwickshire.gov.uk

Customer Service: Ms Kushal Birla, Head of Customer Service & Communications, PO Box 9, Shire Hall, Warwick CV34 4RR
☎ 01926 412013 ⌂ kushalbirla@warwickshire.gov.uk

Economic Development: Mr Mark Ryder, Head of Transport & Economy, PO Box 43, Barrack Street, Warwick CV34 4UL
☎ 01926 412811 ⌂ markryder@warwickshire.gov.uk

Education: Mr Nigel Minns, Head of Education & Learning, Saltisford Office Park, Ansell Way, Warwick CV34 4UL
☎ 01926 742588 ⌂ nigelminns@warwickshire.gov.uk

E-Government: Mr Tonino Ciuffini, Head of ICT, PO Box 2, Shire Hall, Warwick CV34 4UB ☎ 01926 412879
⌂ toninociuffini@warwickshire.gov.uk

Emergency Planning: Mr Inderjit Dial, Emergency Planning Officer, PO Box 43, Barrack Street, Warwick CV34 4SX
☎ 024 7683 4948 ⌂ inderjitdial@warwickshire.gov.uk

Energy Management: Ms Jacky Lawrence, Energy Manager, Shire Hall, Warwick CV34 4RL ☎ 01926 476623
⌂ jackylawrence@warwickshire.gov.uk

Estates, Property & Valuation: Mr Julian Humphreys, Programme Manager, Shire Hall, Warwick CV34 4SA
☎ 01926 738636 ⌂ julianhumphreys@warwickshire.gov.uk

Events Manager: Mrs Alison John, Communications Manager, PO Box 9, Shire Hall, Warwick CV34 4RR ☎ 01926 412482
⌂ alison.john@warwickshire.gov.uk

Facilities: Mr John Findlay, Facilities Service Manager, PO Box 9, Shire Hall, Warwick CV34 4RR ☎ 01926 418642
⌂ johnfindlay@warwickshire.gov.uk

Finance: Mr John Betts, Head of Corporate Finance, PO Box 9, Shire Hall, Warwick CV34 4RR ☎ 01926 412441
⌂ johnbetts@warwickshire.gov.uk

Treasury: Mr John Betts, Head of Corporate Finance, PO Box 9, Shire Hall, Warwick CV34 4RR ☎ 01926 412441
⌂ johnbetts@warwickshire.gov.uk

Treasury: Mr Phil McGaffin, Exchequer Services Manager, PO Box 9, Shire Hall, Warwick CV34 4RR ☎ 01926 410410
⌂ philmcgaffin@warwickshire.gov.uk

Pensions: Mr Neil Buxton, Pensions Manager, PO Box 9, Shire Hall, Warwick CV34 4RR ☎ 01926 412195
⌂ neilbuxton@warwickshire.gov.uk

Fleet Management: Mr Alec Would, General Manager, PO Box 43, Barrack Street, Warwick CV34 4SX ☎ 01926 413489
⌂ alecwould@warwickshire.gov.uk

Health and Safety: Ms Ruth Pickering, County Health, Safety & Wellbeing Manager, PO Box 9, Shire Hall, Warwick CV34 4RR
☎ 01926 412316 ⌂ ruthpickering@warwickshire.gov.uk

Highways: Mr Mark Ryder, Head of Transport & Economy, PO Box 43, Barrack Street, Warwick CV34 4UL ☎ 01926 412811
⌂ markryder@warwickshire.gov.uk

Legal: Ms Sarah Duxbury, Head of Law & Governance, PO Box 9, Shire Hall, Warwick CV34 4RR ☎ 01926 412090 ⌁ sarahduxbury@warwickshire.gov.uk

Lighting: Mr Mike Cunningham, Principal Lighting Engineer, Budbrooke Depot, Old Budbrooke Road, Warwick CV35 7DP ☎ 01926 736548 ⌁ mikecunningham@warwickshire.gov.uk

Member Services: Mrs Jane Pollard, Democratic Services Manager, PO Box 9, Shire Hall, Warwick CV34 4RR ☎ 01926 412565 ⌁ janepollard@warwickshire.gov.uk

Parking: Mr Adrian Purchase, Contract Manager - Civil Parking Enforcement, PO Box 43, Barack Street, Warwick CV34 4SX ☎ 01926 412292 ⌁ adrianpurchase@warwickshire.gov.uk

Partnerships: Mr Dan Green, Localities Manager, PO Box 9, Shire Hall, Warwick CV34 4RR ☎ 01926 412491 ⌁ dangreen@warwickshire.gov.uk

Personnel / HR: Mrs Sue Evans, Head of HR & OD, PO Box 9, Shire Hall, Warwick CV34 4RR ☎ 01926 412314 ⌁ sueevans@warwickshire.gov.uk

Planning: Ms Jasbir Kaur, Strategic Plannig & Development Manager, PO Box 43, Barrack Street, Warwick CV34 4SX ☎ 01926 412170 ⌁ jasbirkaur@warwickshire.gov.uk

Procurement: Mr Paul White, County Procurement Manager, PO Box 9, Shire Hall, Warwick CV34 4RR ☎ 01926 736146 ⌁ paulwhite@warwickshire.gov.uk

Public Libraries: Mr Ayub Khan, Head of Libraries & Strategy, Barrack Street, Warwick CV34 4TH ☎ 01926 412657 ⌁ ayubkhan@warwickshire.gov.uk

Recycling & Waste Minimisation: Mr Glenn Fleet, Waste Management Manager, PO Box 43, Barrack Street, Warwick CV34 4SX ☎ 01926 418106 ⌁ glennfleet@warwickshire.gov.uk

Regeneration: Ms Mandy Walker, Group Manager - Regeneration Projects & Funding, PO Box 43, Barrack Street, Warwick CV34 4SX ☎ 01926 412843 ⌁ mandywalker@warwickshire.gov.uk

Road Safety: Ms Philippa Young, Group Manager - Road Safety Unit, PO Box 43, Shire Hall, Warwick CV34 4RR ☎ 01926 412842 ⌁ philippayoung@warwickshire.gov.uk

Social Services: Ms Jenny Wood, Head of Social Care & Support Services, Saltisford Office Park, Ansell Way, Warwick CV34 4UL ☎ 01926 742977 ⌁ jennywood@warwickshire.gov.uk

Social Services (Adult): Ms Jenny Wood, Head of Social Care & Support Services, Saltisford Office Park, Ansell Way, Warwick CV34 4UL ☎ 01926 742977 ⌁ jennywood@warwickshire.gov.uk

Social Services (Children): Ms Jenny Wood, Head of Social Care & Support Services, Saltisford Office Park, Ansell Way, Warwick CV34 4UL ☎ 01926 742977 ⌁ jennywood@warwickshire.gov.uk

Safeguarding: Ms Beate Wagner, Head of Service - Children's Social Care & Safeguarding, Saltisford Office Park, Ansell Way, Warwick CV34 4UL ☎ 01926 742577 ⌁ beatewagner@warwickshire.gov.uk

Public Health: Dr John Linnane, Director - Public Health, PO Box 9, Shire Hall, Warwick CV34 4RR ⌁ johnlinnane@warwickshire.gov.uk

Staff Training: Ms Allison Lehky, Business Partnership Manager, PO Box 43, Barrack Street, Warwick CV34 4SX ☎ 01926 412160 ⌁ allisonlehky@warwickshire.gov.uk

Sustainable Communities: Mr Phil Evans, Head of Community Services, PO Box 43, Barrack Street, Warwick CV34 4SX ☎ 01926 412422 ⌁ philevans@warwickshire.gov.uk

Sustainable Development: Mr Phil Evans, Head of Community Services, PO Box 43, Barrack Street, Warwick CV34 4SX ☎ 01926 412422 ⌁ philevans@warwickshire.gov.uk

Town Centre: Ms Mandy Walker, Group Manager - Regeneration Projects & Funding, PO Box 43, Barrack Street, Warwick CV34 4SX ☎ 01926 412843 ⌁ mandywalker@warwickshire.gov.uk

Traffic Management: Mr Mark Ryder, Head of Transport & Economy, PO Box 43, Barrack Street, Warwick CV34 4UL ☎ 01926 412811 ⌁ markryder@warwickshire.gov.uk

Transport: Mr Kevin McGovern, Group Manager, PO Box 43, Barrack Street, Warwick CV34 4SX ☎ 01926 412930 ⌁ kevinmcgovern@warwickshire.gov.uk

Transport Planner: Mr Kevin McGovern, Group Manager, PO Box 43, Barrack Street, Warwick CV34 4SX ☎ 01926 412930 ⌁ kevinmcgovern@warwickshire.gov.uk

Waste Collection and Disposal: Mr Christopher Moreton, Operation Manager - Waste Management, PO Box 43, Barrack Street, Warwick CV34 4SX ☎ 01926 412103 ⌁ christophermoreton@warwickshire.gov.uk

Waste Management: Mr Glenn Fleet, Waste Management Manager, PO Box 43, Barrack Street, Warwick CV34 4SX ☎ 01926 418106 ⌁ glennfleet@warwickshire.gov.uk

COUNCILLORS

Chair: Hicks, Bob (LAB - Nuneaton Abbey) cllrhicks@warwickshire.gov.uk

Vice-Chair: Fowler, Peter (CON - Coleshill) cllrfowler@warwickshire.gov.uk

Leader of the Council: Seccombe, Izzi (CON - Stour & the Vale) cllrmrsseccombe@warwickshire.gov.uk

Deputy Leader of the Council: Butlin, Peter (CON - Admirals) cllrbutlin@warwickshire.gov.uk

Appleton, John (CON - Southam) cllrappleton@warwickshire.gov.uk

Beaumont, John (LAB - Bulkington) cllrbeaumont@warwickshire.gov.uk

WARWICKSHIRE

Boad, Sarah (LD - Leamington North)
cllrboad@warwickshire.gov.uk

Brain, Mike (CON - Bidford-on-Avon)
cllrbrain@warwickshire.gov.uk

Caborn, Les (CON - Bishops Tachbrook)
cllrcaborn@warwickshire.gov.uk

Chattaway, Richard (LAB - Bede)
cllrchattaway@warwickshire.gov.uk

Chilvers, Jonathan (GRN - Leamington Brunswick)
cllrchilvers@warwickshire.gov.uk

Clark, Chris (LAB - Hartshill)
cllrclark@warwickshire.gov.uk

Clarke, Jeff (CON - Nuneaton St. Nicholas)
cllrclarke@warwickshire.gov.uk

Cockburn, Alan (CON - Kenilworth St. Johns)
cllrcockburn@warwickshire.gov.uk

Compton, Jose (CON - Leek Wootton)
cllrcompton@warwickshire.gov.uk

Dahmash, Yousef (CON - Caldecott)
cllrdahmash@warwickshire.gov.uk

Davies, Nicola (LD - Leamington North)
cllrndavies@warwickshire.gov.uk

Davies, Corinne (LAB - Nuneaton Camp Hill)
cllrcdavies@warwickshire.gov.uk

Dirveiks, Neil (LAB - Atherstone)
cllrdirveiks@warwickshire.gov.uk

Dodd, Richard (LD - Eastlands & Hillmorton)
cllrdodd@warwickshire.gov.uk

Doughty, Sara (LAB - Bedworth North)
cllrdoughty@warwickshire.gov.uk

Fradgley, Jenny (LD - Stratford South)
cllrfradgley@warwickshire.gov.uk

Gifford, Bill (LD - Leamington Milverton)
cllrgifford@warwickshire.gov.uk

Gittus, Mike (CON - Alcester)
cllrgittus@warwickshire.gov.uk

Hawkes, Brian (LAB - Bedworth West)
cllrhawkes@warwickshire.gov.uk

Hayfield, Colin (CON - Arley)
cllrhayfield@warwickshire.gov.uk

Holland, John (LAB - Warwick West)
cllrholland@warwickshire.gov.uk

Horner, John (CON - Aston Cantlow)
cllrhorner@warwickshire.gov.uk

Jackson, Julie (LAB - Poplar)
cllrjackson@warwickshire.gov.uk

Johnson, Philip (LAB - Nuneaton Galley Common)
cllrjohnson@warwickshire.gov.uk

Kaur, Kam (CON - Caldecott)
cllrkaur@warwickshire.gov.uk

Kendall, Danny (CON - Wellesbourne)
cllrkendall@warwickshire.gov.uk

Kirton, Bernard (IND - Whitnash)
cllrkirton@warwickshire.gov.uk

Kondaker, Keith (GRN - Nuneaton Weddington)
cllrkondakor@warwickshire.gov.uk

Lea, Joan (CON - Water Orton)
cllrmrslea@warwickshire.gov.uk

Lloyd, Keith (IND - Stratford Avenue & New Town)
cllrlloyd@warwickshire.gov.uk

Morgan, Jeff (CON - Nuneaton Whitestone)
cllrmorgan@warwickshire.gov.uk

Morris-Jones, Phillip (CON - Fosse)
cllrmorris-jones@warwickshire.gov.uk

Morson, Peter (LAB - Baddesley Ensor)
cllrmorson@warwickshire.gov.uk

Moss, Brian (LAB - Kingsbury)
cllrmoss@warwickshire.gov.uk

Olner, Bill (LAB - Arbury & Stockingford)
cllrolner@warwickshire.gov.uk

O'Rourke, Maggie (LAB - Lawford & New Bilton)
cllrorourke@warwickshire.gov.uk

Parsons, Dave (LAB - Polesworth)
cllrparsons@warwickshire.gov.uk

Perry, Mike (CON - Henley-in-Arden)
cllrperry@warwickshire.gov.uk

Phillips, Caroline (LAB - Arbury & Stockingford)
cllrphillips@warwickshire.gov.uk

Redford, Wallace (CON - Cubbington)
cllrredford@warwickshire.gov.uk

Rickhards, Clive (LD - Studley)
cllrrickhards@warwickshire.gov.uk

Roberts, Howard (IND - Dunchurch)
cllrroberts@warwickshire.gov.uk

Rolfe, Kate (LD - Stratford South)
cllrrolfe@warwickshire.gov.uk

Roodhouse, Jeremy (LD - Eastlands & Hillmorton)
cllrroodhouse@warwickshire.gov.uk

Saint, Chris (CON - Shipston-on-Stour)
cllrsaint@warwickshire.gov.uk

Shilton, Dave (CON - Kenilworth Park Hill)
cllrshilton@warwickshire.gov.uk

St. John, Jenny (LAB - Warwick North)
cllrstjohn@warwickshire.gov.uk

Stevens, Bob (CON - Feldon)
cllrstevens@warwickshire.gov.uk

Tandy, June (LAB - Nuneaton Wem Brook)
cllrtandy@warwickshire.gov.uk

Timms, Heather (CON - Earl Craven)
cllrtimms@warwickshire.gov.uk

Warner, Angela (CON - Warwick South)
cllrwarner@warwickshire.gov.uk

Webb, Mary (LAB - Brownsover)
cllrmwebb@warwickshire.gov.uk

Webb, Alan (LAB - Brownsover)
cllrawebb@warwickshire.gov.uk

Western, Matt (LAB - Leamington Willes)
cllrwestern@warwickshire.gov.uk

Whitehouse, John (LD - Kenilworth Abbey)
cllrwhitehouse@warwickshire.gov.uk

Williams, Chris (CON - Kineton)
cllrwilliams@warwickshire.gov.uk

POLITICAL COMPOSITION
CON: 26, LAB: 22, LD: 9, IND: 3, GRN: 2

COMMITTEE CHAIRS

Adult Social Care & Health: Mr Alan Webb

Children & Young People: Mr Dave Parsons

Health & Wellbeing: Mrs Izzi Seccombe

Pensions: Mrs Izzi Seccombe

Watford   D

Watford Borough Council, Town Hall, Watford WD17 3EX
☎ 01923 226400 🖷 01923 278100 ⌁ enquiries@watford.gov.uk
🖳 www.watford.gov.uk

FACTS AND FIGURES
Parliamentary Constituencies: Watford
EU Constituencies: Eastern
Election Frequency: Elections are by thirds

PRINCIPAL OFFICERS

Chief Executive: Mr Manny Lewis, Managing Director, Town Hall,
Watford WD17 3EX ☎ 01923 278186 ⌁ manny.lewis@watford.gov.uk

Architect, Building / Property Services: Mrs Linda Newell,
Property Manager, Town Hall, Watford WD17 3EX ☎ 01923 278216
⌁ linda.newell@watford.gov.uk

Best Value: Mrs Kathryn Robson, Partnerships & Performance
Section Head, Town Hall, Watford WD17 3EX ☎ 01923 278077
⌁ kathryn.robson@watford.gov.uk

Building Control: Mr Sean Peschiera, Building Control Team
Leader, Town Hall, Watford WD17 3EX ☎ 01923 727125
⌁ sean.peschiera@watford.gov.uk

Children / Youth Services: Mr Gary Oliver, Culture & Play
Section Head, Town Hall, Watford WD17 3EX ☎ 01923 278251
⌁ gary.oliver@watford.gov.uk

PR / Communications: Ms Liz Aelberry, Communications &
Engagement Section Head, Town Hall, Watford WD17 3EX
☎ 01923 278388 ⌁ liz.aelberry@watford.gov.uk

Community Safety: Ms Jane Taylor, Community Safety Manager,
Town Hall, Watford WD17 3EX ☎ 01923 278405
⌁ jane.taylor@watford.gov.uk

Computer Management: Mrs Emma Tiernan, ICT Client
Manager, Town Hall, Watford WD17 3EX ☎ 01923 776611
⌁ emma.tiernan@watford.gov.uk

Contracts: Mr Howard Hughes, Procurement Manager, Town Hall,
Watford WD17 3EX ☎ 01923 278370
⌁ howard.hughes@watford.gov.uk

Corporate Services: Ms Lesley Palumbo, Head of Corporate
Strategy & Client Services, Town Hall, Watford WD17 3EX
☎ 01923 278561 ⌁ lesley.palumbo@watford.gov.uk

Customer Service: Ms Danielle Negrello, Customer Service
Section Head, Town Hall, Watford WD17 3EX ☎ 01923 278927
⌁ danielle.negrello@watford.gov.uk

Economic Development: Mr Andrew Gibson, Economic
Development Officer, Town Hall, Watford WD17 3EX
☎ 01923 278286 ⌁ andrew.gibson@watford.gov.uk

Electoral Registration: Mr Gordon Amos, Elections Manager,
Town Hall, Watford WD17 3EX ☎ 01923 278339
⌁ gordon.amos@watford.gov.uk

Emergency Planning: Mr Clive Goodchild, Facilities & Emergency
Planning Manager, Town Hall, Watford WD17 3EX ☎ 01923 278378
⌁ clive.goodchild@watford.gov.uk

Energy Management: Mr Neil Walker, Energy & Renewal
Surveyor, Wiggenhall Depot, Wiggenhall Road, Watford WD18 0FB
☎ 01923 278149 ⌁ neil.walker@watford.gov.uk

Environmental / Technical Services: Ms Lesley Palumbo, Head
of Corporate Strategy & Client Services, Town Hall, Watford WD17
3EX ☎ 01923 278561 ⌁ lesley.palumbo@watford.gov.uk

Environmental Health: Ms Justine Hoy, Environmental Health
& Licensing Section Head, Wiggenhall Depot, Wiggenhall Road,
Watford WD18 0FB ☎ 01923 278449 ⌁ justine.hoy@watford.gov.uk

Estates, Property & Valuation: Mr David Lewis, Property
Manager, Town Hall, Watford WD17 3EX ☎ 01923 278216
⌁ david.lewis@watford.gov.uk

Facilities: Mr Clive Goodchild, Facilities & Emergency Planning
Manager, Town Hall, Watford WD17 3EX ☎ 01923 278378
⌁ clive.goodchild@watford.gov.uk

Finance: Ms Joanne Wagstaffe, Director - Finance, Town Hall,
Watford WD17 3EX ☎ 01923 776611
⌁ joanne.wagstaffe@watford.gov.uk

Treasury: Mr Bob Watson, Head of Finance - Shared Services,
Town Hall, Watford WD17 3EX ☎ 01923 727188
⌁ bob.watson@watford.gov.uk

Fleet Management: Mr Jamie Sells, ES Client Manager (Waste,
Recycling & Street Care), Town Hall, Watford WD17 3EX
☎ 01923 278496 ⌁ jamie.sells@watford.gov.uk

Grounds Maintenance: Mr Paul Rabbitts, ES Client Manager
(Parks & Projects), Town Hall, Watford WD17 3EX ☎ 01923 278250
⌁ paul.rabbitts@watford.gov.uk

WATFORD

Health and Safety: Mr James Ottery, Corporate Health & Safety Manager, Town Hall, Watford WD17 3EX ✆ james.ottery@hcc.org.uk

Home Energy Conservation: Mr Neil Walker, Energy & Renewal Surveyor, Wiggenhall Depot, Wiggenhall Road, Watford WD18 0FB ☎ 01923 278149 ✆ neil.walker@watford.gov.uk

Housing: Mr Avaz Magsood, Head of Housing, Town Hall, Watford WD17 3EX ☎ 01923 278902 ✆ avez.magsood@watford.gov.uk

Legal: Mrs Carol Chen, Head of Democracy & Governance, Town Hall, Watford WD17 3EX ☎ 01923 278350 ✆ carol.chen@watford.gov.uk

Leisure and Cultural Services: Mr Chris Fennell, Corporate Lesiure & Community Client Section Head, Town Hall, Watford WD17 3EX ☎ 01923 278251 ✆ chris.fennell@watford.gov.uk

Licensing: Mr Richard Brown, Environmental Health Manager (Business), Wiggenhall Depot, Wiggenhall Road, Watford WD18 0FB ☎ 01923 278440 ✆ richard.brown@watford.gov.uk

Member Services: Ms Caroline Harris, Member Development & Civic Events Officer, Town Hall, Watford WD17 3EX ☎ 01923 278374 ✆ caroline.harris@watford.gov.uk

Parking: Ms Jane Custance, Head of Regeneration & Development, Town Hall, Watford WD17 3EX ☎ 01923 278044 ✆ jane.custance@watford.gov.uk

Partnerships: Mrs Kathryn Robson, Partnerships & Performance Section Head, Town Hall, Watford WD17 3EX ☎ 01923 278077 ✆ kathryn.robson@watford.gov.uk

Personnel / HR: Mrs Cathy Watson, Head of Human Resources, Town Hall, Watford WD17 3EX ☎ 01923 776611 ✆ cathy.watson@watford.gov.uk

Planning: Ms Jane Custance, Head of Regeneration & Development, Town Hall, Watford WD17 3EX ☎ 01923 278044 ✆ jane.custance@watford.gov.uk

Procurement: Mr Howard Hughes, Procurement Manager, Town Hall, Watford WD17 3EX ☎ 01923 278370 ✆ howard.hughes@watford.gov.uk

Recycling & Waste Minimisation: Mr Jamie Sells, ES Client Manager (Waste, Recycling & Street Care), Town Hall, Watford WD17 3EX ☎ 01923 278496 ✆ jamie.sells@watford.gov.uk

Regeneration: Ms Jane Custance, Head of Regeneration & Development, Town Hall, Watford WD17 3EX ☎ 01923 278044 ✆ jane.custance@watford.gov.uk

Staff Training: Mrs Cathy Watson, Head of Human Resources, Town Hall, Watford WD17 3EX ☎ 01923 776611 ✆ cathy.watson@watford.gov.uk

Street Scene: Mr Jamie Sells, ES Client Manager (Waste, Recycling & Street Care), Town Hall, Watford WD17 3EX ☎ 01923 278496 ✆ jamie.sells@watford.gov.uk

Town Centre: Ms Maria Manion, Town Centre Manager, 5 Kings Court, 153 High Street, Watford WD17 2ER ☎ 01923 278260 ✆ maria.manion@watford.gov.uk

Waste Collection and Disposal: Mr Jamie Sells, ES Client Manager (Waste, Recycling & Street Care), Town Hall, Watford WD17 3EX ☎ 01923 278496 ✆ jamie.sells@watford.gov.uk

Waste Management: Mr Jamie Sells, ES Client Manager (Waste, Recycling & Street Care), Town Hall, Watford WD17 3EX ☎ 01923 278496 ✆ jamie.sells@watford.gov.uk

Children's Play Areas: Mr Paul Rabbitts, ES Client Manager (Parks & Projects), Town Hall, Watford WD17 3EX ☎ 01923 278250 ✆ paul.rabbitts@watford.gov.uk

COUNCILLORS

Directly Elected Mayor: Thornhill, Dorothy (LD - No Ward)
themayor@watford.gov.uk

Chair: Walford, Darren (LD - Tudor)
darren.walford@watford.gov.uk

Vice-Chair: Dhindsa, Jagtar Singh (LAB - Vicarage)
jagtar.dhindsa@watford.gov.uk

Deputy Mayor: Taylor, Peter (LD - Oxhey)
peter.taylor@watford.gov.uk

Group Leader: Bell, Nigel (LAB - Holywell)
nigel.bell@watford.gov.uk

Barks, David (LD - Park)
david.barks@watford.gov.uk

Bashir, Sohail (LAB - Callowland)
sohail.bashir@watford.gov.uk

Bolton, Stephen (LD - Central)
stephen.bolton@watford.gov.uk

Cavinder, Stephen (LD - Woodside)
stephen.cavinder@watford.gov.uk

Collett, Karen (LD - Woodside)
karen.collett@watford.gov.uk

Connal, Jackie (LAB - Holywell)
jackie.connal@watford.gov.uk

Crout, Keith (LD - Stanborough)
keith.crout@watford.gov.uk

Dychton, Aga (LD - Central)
aga.dychton@watford.gov.uk

Fahmy, Joe (LD - Tudor)
joe.fahmy@watford.gov.uk

Grimston, Amanda (LD - Meriden)
amanda.grimston@watford.gov.uk

Hastrick, Kareen (LD - Meriden)
kareen.hastrick@watford.gov.uk

Hofman, Mark (LD - Nascot)
mark.hofman@watford.gov.uk

Johnson, Jane (LD - Nascot)
jane.johnson@watford.gov.uk

Johnson, Stephen (LD - Tudor)
stephen.johnson@watford.gov.uk

Joynes, Anne (LAB - Leggatts)
anne.joynes@watford.gov.uk

Kent, Paddy (LD - Meriden)
paddy.kent@watford.gov.uk

Khan, Ahsan (LAB - Callowland)
ahsan.khan@watford.gov.uk

Khan, Asif (LAB - Leggatts)
asif.khan@watford.gov.uk

Laird, Robbie (LD - Callowland)
robbie.laird@watford.gov.uk

Maestas, Joanna (LD - Oxhey)
joanna.maestas@watford.gov.uk

Martins, Rabi (LD - Central)
rabi.martins@watford.gov.uk

Mauthoor, Bilqees (LAB - Leggatts)
bilqees.mauthoor@watford.gov.uk

Mills, Mo (LAB - Vicarage)
mo.mills@watford.gov.uk

Rindl, Anne (LD - Park)
anne.rindl@watford.gov.uk

Saffery, Glen (LD - Woodside)
glen.saffery@watford.gov.uk

Scudder, Derek (LD - Stanborough)
derek.scudder@watford.gov.uk

Shah, Nasreen (LAB - Vicarage)
nasreen.shah@watford.gov.uk

Sharpe, Iain (LD - Oxhey)
iain.sharpe@watford.gov.uk

Steele, Nikki (LD - Park)
nikki.steele@watford.gov.uk

Turmaine, Matt (LAB - Holywell)
matt.turmaine@watford.gov.uk

Watkin, Mark (LD - Nascot)
mark.watkin@watford.gov.uk

Williams, Tim (LD - Stanborough)
tim.williams@watford.gov.uk

POLITICAL COMPOSITION
LD: 26, LAB: 11

COMMITTEE CHAIRS

Audit: Mr Derek Scudder

Development Management: Mr Rabi Martins

Licensing: Mr Keith Crout

Waveney   D

Waveney District Council, Town Hall, High Street, Lowestoft NR32 1HS
☎ 01502 562111 ⏚ customer.services@wdc.eastsuffolk.gov.uk
🖥 www.waveney.gov.uk

FACTS AND FIGURES
Parliamentary Constituencies: Suffolk Coastal, Waveney
EU Constituencies: Eastern
Election Frequency: Elections are by thirds

PRINCIPAL OFFICERS

Chief Executive: Mr Stephen Baker, Chief Executive, Riverside, 4 Canning Road, Lowestoft NR33 0EQ ☎ 01394 444348
⏚ chiefexecutive@eastsuffolk.gov.uk

Senior Management: Mr Arthur Charvonia, Strategic Director, Riverside, 4 Canning Road, Lowestoft NR33 0EQ ☎ 01502 523606
⏚ arthur.charvonia@eastsuffolk.gov.uk

Senior Management: Mr Andrew Jarvis, Strategic Director, Riverside, 4 Canning Road, Lowestoft NR33 0EQ ☎ 01394 444323
⏚ andrew.jarvis@eastsuffolk.gov.uk

Architect, Building / Property Services: Mrs Gayle Hart, Manager, Riverside, 4 Canning Road, Lowestoft NR33 0EQ
☎ 01502 562111 ⏚ gayle.hart@eastsuffolk.gov.uk

Building Control: Mr Philip Ridley, Head of Planning, Riverside, 4 Canning Road, Lowestoft NR33 0EQ ☎ 01502 562111
⏚ philip.ridley@waveney.gov.uk

PR / Communications: Mr Phil Harris, Communications Officer, Riverside, Canning Road, Lowestoft NR33 0EQ ☎ 01502 523637
⏚ phil.harris@eastsuffolk.gov.uk

Community Planning: Mr Philip Ridley, Head of Planning Services, Riverside, Canning Road, Lowestoft NR33 0EQ
☎ 01502 562111 ⏚ philip.ridley@eastsuffolk.gov.uk

Community Safety: Mr Richard Best, Active Communities Manager, Riverside, Canning Road, Lowestoft NR33 0EQ
☎ 01502 562111 ⏚ richard.best@eastsuffolk.gov.uk

Community Safety: Ms Karen Hubbard, Community Safety Officer, Riverside, 4 Canning Town, Lowestoft NR33 0EQ
☎ 01502 562111 ⏚ karen.hubbard@eastsuffolk.gov.uk

Computer Management: Ms Ann Carey, Head of ICT, Riverside, 4 Canning Town, Lowestoft NR33 0EQ ☎ 01502 523215
⏚ ann.carey@eastsuffolk.gov.uk

Contracts: Mr Ian Purdom, Principal Service Manager, Riverside, 4 Canning Road, Lowestoft NR33 0EQ ☎ 01502 523507
⏚ ian.purdom@eastsuffolk.gov.uk

Customer Service: Mr Darren Knight, Head of Customer Service, Riverside, Canning Road, Lowestoft NR33 0EQ ☎ 01502 526111
⏚ darren.knight@eastsuffolk.gov.uk

Economic Development: Mr Paul Wood, Head of Economic Development & Regeneration, Riverside, 4 Canning Town, Lowestoft NR33 0EQ ☎ 01508 562111 ⏚ paul.wood@eastsuffolk.gov.uk

Electoral Registration: Mrs Sharon Shand, Service Manager - Electoral Services, Riverside, Canning Street, Lowestoft NR33 0EQ
☎ 01502 523253 ⏚ sharon.shand@eastsuffolk.gov.uk

Emergency Planning: Mr Phil Gore, Head of Environmental Services & Port Health, Riverside, Canning Road, Lowestoft NR33 0EQ ☎ 01502 652111 ⏚ phil.gore@eastsuffolk.gov.uk

WAVENEY

Energy Management: Mr Phil Gore, Head of Environmental Services & Port Health, Riverside, Canning Road, Lowestoft NR33 0EQ ☎ 01502 652111 ⌂ phil.gore@eastsuffolk.gov.uk

Environmental / Technical Services: Mr Phil Gore, Head of Environmental Services & Port Health, Riverside, Canning Road, Lowestoft NR33 0EQ ☎ 01502 652111 ⌂ phil.gore@eastsuffolk.gov.uk

Environmental Health: Mr Phil Gore, Head of Environmental Services & Port Health, Riverside, Canning Road, Lowestoft NR33 0EQ ☎ 01502 652111 ⌂ phil.gore@eastsuffolk.gov.uk

Estates, Property & Valuation: Mrs Gayle Hart, Manager, Riverside, 4 Canning Road, Lowestoft NR33 0EQ ☎ 01502 562111 ⌂ gayle.hart@eastsuffolk.gov.uk

Events Manager: Mrs Catherine Thornber, Economic Services Manager, Council Offices, Melton Hill, Woodbridge IP12 1AU ☎ 01394 652111 ⌂ catherine.thornber@eastsuffolk.gov.uk

Facilities: Mrs Sue Bowyer, Shared Estate Manager, Riverside, 4 Canning Road, Lowestoft NR33 0EQ ☎ 01502 562111 ⌂ sue.bowyer@eastsuffolk.gov.uk

Finance: Ms Homira Javadi, Chief Finance Officer, Riverside, 4 Canning Road, Lowestoft NR33 0EQ ☎ 01502 562111 ⌂ homira.javadi@eastsuffolk.gov.uk

Health and Safety: Ms Sheila Warnes, Health & Safety Advisor, Riverside, 4 Canning Street, Lowestoft NR33 0EQ ☎ 01502 523154 ⌂ sheila.warnes@eastsuffolk.gov.uk

Home Energy Conservation: Mrs Teresa Howarth, Environmental Health Officer, Council Offices, Melton Hill, Woodbridge IP12 1AU ☎ 01394 444206 ⌂ teresa.howarth@suffolkcoastal.gov.uk

Housing: Mr Justin Hunt, Head of Housing Services, Riverside, 4 Canning Road, Lowestoft NR33 0EQ ☎ 01502 562111 ⌂ justin.hunt@eastsuffolk.gov.uk

Housing Maintenance: Mr John Brown, Principal Service Manager - Building & Housing, Riverside, 4 Canning Road, Lowestoft NR33 0EQ ☎ 01502 562111 ⌂ john.brown@waveney.gov.uk

Legal: Mrs Hilary Slater, Head of Legal & Democratic Services, Riverside, 4 Canning Road, Lowestoft NR33 0EQ ☎ 01502 562111 ⌂ hilary.slater@eastsuffolk.gov.uk

Leisure and Cultural Services: Mrs Catherine Thornber, Economic Services Manager, Council Offices, Melton Hill, Woodbridge IP12 1AU ☎ 01394 652111 ⌂ catherine.thornber@eastsuffolk.gov.uk

Licensing: Mrs Caroline Evans, Licensing Service Manager, Melton Hill, Woodbridge IP12 1AU ☎ 01394 444678 ⌂ caroline.evans@eastsuffolk.gov.uk

Lifelong Learning: Mrs Heather Shilling, Human Resources Officer, Riverside, 4 Canning Road, Lowestoft NR33 0EQ ☎ 01502 523221 ⌂ heather.shilling@eastsuffolk.gov.uk

Lottery Funding, Charity and Voluntary: Mr Richard Best, Active Communities Manager, Riverside, 4 Canning Town, Lowestoft NR33 0EQ ☎ 01502 562111 ⌂ richard.best@eastsuffolk.gov.uk

Member Services: Mrs Nicola Wotton, Principal Service Manager - Democratic Services, Riverside, 4 Canning Road, Lowestoft NR33 0EQ ☎ 01502 562111 ⌂ nicola.wotton@eastsuffolk.gov.uk

Personnel / HR: Mrs Carol Lower, Human Resources & Workforce Development Manager, Riverside, 4 Canning Town, Lowestoft NR33 0EQ ☎ 01502 523228 ⌂ carol.lower@eastsuffolk.gov.uk

Planning: Mr Philip Ridley, Head of Planning Services, Riverside, 4 Canning Road, Lowestoft NR33 0EQ ☎ 01502 562111 ⌂ philip.ridley@eastsuffolk.gov.uk

Procurement: Mr Ian Purdom, Principal Service Manager, Riverside, 4 Canning Road, Lowestoft NR33 0EQ ☎ 01502 523507 ⌂ ian.purdom@eastsuffolk.gov.uk

Recycling & Waste Minimisation: Mr Kerry Blair, Head of Operations, Riverside, 4 Canning Road, Lowestoft NR33 0EQ ☎ 01502 523007 ⌂ kerry.blair@eastsuffolk.gov.uk

Regeneration: Mr Paul Wood, Head of Economic Development & Regeneration, Riverside, 4 Canning Town, Lowestoft NR33 0EQ ☎ 01508 562111 ⌂ paul.wood@eastsuffolk.gov.uk

Staff Training: Mrs Heather Shilling, Human Resources Officer, Riverside, 4 Canning Town, Lowestoft NR33 0EQ ☎ 01502 523221 ⌂ heather.shilling@eastsuffolk.gov.uk

Sustainable Communities: Mr Philip Ridley, Head of Planning Services, Riverside, 4 Canning Road, Lowestoft NR33 0EQ ☎ 01502 562111 ⌂ philip.ridley@eastsuffolk.gov.uk

Sustainable Development: Mr Philip Ridley, Head of Planning Services, Riverside, 4 Canning Road, Lowestoft NR33 0EQ ☎ 01502 562111 ⌂ philip.ridley@eastsuffolk.gov.uk

Tourism: Mrs Catherine Thornber, Economic Services Manager, Council Offices, Melton Hill, Woodbridge IP12 1AU ☎ 01394 652111 ⌂ catherine.thornber@eastsuffolk.gov.uk

Waste Management: Mr Kerry Blair, Head of Operations, Riverside, 4 Canning Road, Lowestoft NR33 0EQ ☎ 01502 523007 ⌂ kerry.blair@eastsuffolk.gov.uk

COUNCILLORS

Leader of the Council: Law, Colin (CON - Oulton Broad) colin.law@waveney.gov.uk

Deputy Leader of the Council: Ritchie, David (CON - The Saints) david.ritchie@waveney.gov.uk

Allen, Sue (CON - Southwold & Reydon) sue.allen@waveney.gov.uk

Ardley, Stephen (CON - Gunton & Corton) stephen.ardley@waveney.gov.uk

Ashdown, Paul (CON - Lothingland) paul.ashdown@waveney.gov.uk

Back, Edward (CON - Oulton)
edward.back@waveney.gov.uk

Barker, Sonia (LAB - Pakefield)
sonia.barker@waveney.gov.uk

Barnard, Mike (CON - Oulton Broad)
mike.barnard@waveney.gov.uk

Bee, Mark (CON - Worlingham)
mark.bee@waveney.gov.uk

Brooks, Norman (CON - Worlingham)
norman.brooks@waveney.gov.uk

Cackett, Alison (CON - Blything)
alison.cackett@waveney.gov.uk

Catchpole, Graham (CON - Beccles South)
graham.cole@waveney.gov.uk

Ceresa, Jenny (CON - Carlton Colville)
jenny.ceresa@waveney.gov.uk

Cherry, Malcolm (LAB - St Margarets)
malcolm.cherry@waveney.gov.uk

Cherry, Yvonne (LAB - Whitton)
yvonne.cherry@waveney.gov.uk

Craig, Janet (LAB - Harbour)
janet.craig@waveney.gov.uk

Elliott, Graham (GRN - Beccles North)
graham.elliott@waveney.gov.uk

Ford, June (LAB - Kirkley)
june.ford@waveney.gov.uk

Gandy, Tess (LAB - Normanston)
tess.gandy@waveney.gov.uk

Goldson, Tony (CON - Halesworth)
tony.goldson@waveney.gov.uk

Gooch, Louise (LAB - Pakefield)
louise.gooch@waveney.gov.uk

Graham, Ian (LAB - Pakefield)
ian.graham@waveney.gov.uk

Grant, Kathleen (CON - Carlton Colville)
kathleen.grant@waveney.gov.uk

Green, Alan (LAB - Kessingland)
alan.green@waveney.gov.uk

Groom, John (CON - Bungay)
john.groom@waveney.gov.uk

Harris-Logan, Louisa (LAB - St. Margarets)
louise.harris-loga@waveney.gov.uk

Ladd, Michael (CON - Southwold & Reydon)
michael.ladd@waveney.gov.uk

Light, Paul (CON - Carlton Colville)
paul.light@waveney.gov.uk

Logan, Steve (LAB - Kirkley)
steve.logan@waveney.gov.uk

Mortimer, Frank (CON - Carlton)
frank.mortimer@waveney.gov.uk

Mortimer, Trish (CON - Carlton)
trish.mortimer@waveney.gov.uk

Murray, Jane (LAB - Oulton)
jane.murray@waveney.gov.uk

Neil, Rob (IND - Normanston)
rob.neil@waveney.gov.uk

Nicholls, Lewis (LAB - St. Margarets)
lewis.nicholls@waveney.gov.uk

Patience, Keith (LAB - Normanston)
keith.patience@waveney.gov.uk

Pitchers, Malcolm (LAB - Kirkley)
malcolm.pitchers@waveney.gov.uk

Provan, Bruce (CON - Kessingland)
bruce.provan@waveney.gov.uk

Punt, Chris (CON - Beccles North)
chris.punt@waveney.gov.uk

Reynolds, Tom (LAB - Harbour)
tom.reynolds@waveney.gov.uk

Rivett, Craig (CON - Wrentham)
craig.rivett@waveney.gov.uk

Rudd, Mary (CON - Gunton & Corton)
mary.rudd@waveney.gov.uk

Smith, Letitia (CON - Halesworth)
letitia.smith@waveney.gov.uk

Smith, Jedda (LAB - Harbour)
jedda.smith@waveney.gov.uk

Springall, Kevin (CON - Wainford)
kevin.springall@waveney.gov.uk

Topping, Caroline (CON - Beccles South)
caroline.topping@waveney.gov.uk

Webb, Sarah (LAB - Whitton)
sarah.webb@waveney.gov.uk

Webb, Nick (LAB - Whitton)
nick.webb@waveney.gov.uk

Woods, Simon (CON - Bungay)
simon.woods@waveney.gov.uk

POLITICAL COMPOSITION
CON: 27, LAB: 19, GRN: 1, IND: 1

COMMITTEE CHAIRS

Licensing: Mr Norman Brooks

Planning: Mr Paul Ashdown

Waverley   D

Waverley Borough Council, Council Offices, The Burys,
Godalming GU7 1HR
☎ 01483 523333 ┄ enquiries@waverley.gov.uk
🖥 www.waverley.gov.uk

FACTS AND FIGURES
Parliamentary Constituencies: South West Surrey
EU Constituencies: South East
Election Frequency: Elections are of whole council

PRINCIPAL OFFICERS

Chief Executive: Mr Paul Wenham, Executive Director & Head of
Paid Service, Council Offices, The Burys, Godalming GU7 1HR
☎ 01483 523238 ┄ paul.wenham@waverley.gov.uk

WAVERLEY

Senior Management: Mr Graeme Clark, Director - Finance & Resources & Chief Finance Officer, Council Offices, The Burys, Godalming GU7 1HR ☎ 01483 523099
📧 graeme.clark@waverley.gov.uk

Senior Management: Mr Damian Roberts, Director - Operations, Council Offices, The Burys, Godalming GU7 1HR ☎ 01483 523398
📧 damian.roberts@waverley.gov.uk

Building Control: Mrs Elizabeth Sims, Head of Planning, Council Offices, The Burys, Godalming GU7 1HR ☎ 01483 523193
📧 elizabeth.sims@waverley.gov.uk

Catering Services: Mr David Allum, Head of Customer & Corporate Services, Council Offices, The Burys, Godalming GU7 1HR ☎ 01483 523338 📧 david.allum@waverley.gov.uk

Children / Youth Services: Mrs Katie Webb, Community Services Manager, Council Offices, The Burys, Godalming GU7 1HR ☎ 01483 523340 📧 katie.webb@waverley.gov.uk

PR / Communications: Mr Robin Taylor, Head of Policy & Governance, Council Offices, The Burys, Godalming GU7 1HR ☎ 01483 523108 📧 robin.taylor@waverley.gov.uk

Community Safety: Mr Kelvin Mills, Head of Community Services, Council Offices, The Burys, Godalming GU7 1HR ☎ 01483 523432
📧 kelvin.mills@waverley.gov.uk

Customer Service: Mr David Allum, Head of Customer & Corporate Services, Council Offices, The Burys, Godalming GU7 1HR ☎ 01483 523338 📧 david.allum@waverley.gov.uk

Economic Development: Mr Kelvin Mills, Head of Community Services, Council Offices, The Burys, Godalming GU7 1HR ☎ 01483 523432 📧 kelvin.mills@waverley.gov.uk

E-Government: Mr David Allum, Head of Customer & Corporate Services, Council Offices, The Burys, Godalming GU7 1HR ☎ 01483 523338 📧 david.allum@waverley.gov.uk

Electoral Registration: Mrs Tracey Stanbridge, Electoral Services Manager, Council Offices, The Burys, Godalming GU7 1HR ☎ 01483 523413 📧 tracey.stanbridge@waverley.gov.uk

Energy Management: Ms Fotini Kallipoliti, Sustainability Manager, Council Offices, The Burys, Godalming GU7 1HR ☎ 01483 523448 📧 fotini.kallipoliti@waverley.gov.uk

Environmental / Technical Services: Mr Richard Homewood, Head of Environmental Services, Council Offices, The Burys, Godalming GU7 1HR ☎ 01483 523411
📧 richard.homewood@waverley.gov.uk

Environmental Health: Miss Victoria Buckroyd, Environmental Health Manager, Council Offices, The Burys, Godalming GU7 1HR ☎ 01483 523436 📧 victoria.buckroyd@waverley.gov.uk

Facilities: Mr David Allum, Head of Customer & Corporate Services, Council Offices, The Burys, Godalming GU7 1HR ☎ 01483 523338 📧 david.allum@waverley.gov.uk

Finance: Mr Graeme Clark, Director - Finance & Resources & Chief Finance Officer, Council Offices, The Burys, Godalming GU7 1HR ☎ 01483 523099 📧 graeme.clark@waverley.gov.uk

Grounds Maintenance: Mr Kelvin Mills, Head of Community Services, Council Offices, The Burys, Godalming GU7 1HR ☎ 01483 523432 📧 kelvin.mills@waverley.gov.uk

Home Energy Conservation: Ms Fotini Kallipoliti, Sustainability Manager, Council Offices, The Burys, Godalming GU7 1HR ☎ 01483 523448 📧 fotini.kallipoliti@waverley.gov.uk

Housing: Mr Andrew Smith, Head of Strategic Housing & Delivery, Council Offices, The Burys, Godalming GU7 1HR ☎ 01483 523096 📧 andrew.smith@waverley.gov.uk

Housing Maintenance: Mr Hugh Wagstaff, Head of Housing Operations, Council Offices, The Burys, Godalming GU7 1HR ☎ 01483 523361 📧 hugh.wagstaff@waverley.gov.uk

Legal: Mr Daniel Bainbridge, Borough Solicitor, Council Offices, The Burys, Godalming GU7 1HR ☎ 01483 523235
📧 daniel.bainbridge@waverley.gov.uk

Leisure and Cultural Services: Mr Kelvin Mills, Head of Community Services, Council Offices, The Burys, Godalming GU7 1HR ☎ 01483 523432 📧 kelvin.mills@waverley.gov.uk

Licensing: Mr Robin Taylor, Head of Policy & Governance, Council Offices, The Burys, Godalming GU7 1HR ☎ 01483 523108 📧 robin.taylor@waverley.gov.uk

Member Services: Ms Emma McQuillan, Democratic Services Manager, Council Offices, The Burys, Godalming GU7 1HR ☎ 01483 523351 📧 emma.mcquillan@waverley.gov.uk

Parking: Mr Richard Homewood, Head of Environmental Services, Council Offices, The Burys, Godalming GU7 1HR ☎ 01483 523411 📧 richard.homewood@waverley.gov.uk

Personnel / HR: Mr Peter Vickers, Head of Finance, Council Offices, The Burys, Godalming GU7 1HR ☎ 01483 523539 📧 peter.vickers@waverley.gov.uk

Planning: Mrs Elizabeth Sims, Head of Planning, Council Offices, The Burys, Godalming GU7 1HR ☎ 01483 523193 📧 elizabeth.sims@waverley.gov.uk

Recycling & Waste Minimisation: Mr Richard Homewood, Head of Environmental Services, Council Offices, The Burys, Godalming GU7 1HR ☎ 01483 523411 📧 richard.homewood@waverley.gov.uk

Sustainable Development: Ms Fotini Kallipoliti, Sustainability Manager, Council Offices, The Burys, Godalming GU7 1HR ☎ 01483 523448 📧 fotini.kallipoliti@waverley.gov.uk

Waste Collection and Disposal: Mr Richard Homewood, Head of Environmental Services, Council Offices, The Burys, Godalming GU7 1HR ☎ 01483 523411 📧 richard.homewood@waverley.gov.uk

Waste Management: Mr Richard Homewood, Head of Environmental Services, Council Offices, The Burys, Godalming GU7 1HR ☎ 01483 523411 ✎ richard.homewood@waverley.gov.uk

Children's Play Areas: Mr Matt Lank, Parks Manager, Council Offices, The Burys, Godalming GU7 1HR ☎ 01483 523190 ✎ matt.lank@waverley.gov.uk

COUNCILLORS

Mayor: Storey, Christopher (CON - Farnham Weybourne & Badshot Lea)
christopher.storey@waverley.gov.uk

Deputy Mayor: Inchbald, Simon (CON - Chiddingfold & Dunsfold)
simon.inchbald@waverley.gov.uk

Leader of the Council: Potts, Julia (CON - Farnham Upper Hale)
julia.potts@waverley.gov.uk

Deputy Leader of the Council: Martin, Tom (CON - Godalming Holloway)
tom.martin@waverley.gov.uk

Adams, Brian (CON - Frensham Dockenfield & Tilford)
brian.adams@waverley.gov.uk

Band, Mike (CON - Shamley Green & Cranleigh North)
mike.band@waverley.gov.uk

Bolton, Andrew (CON - Godalming Central & Ockford)
andrew.bolton@waverley.gov.uk

Byham, Maurice (CON - Bramley, Busbridge & Hascombe)
maurice.byham@waverley.gov.uk

Cockburn, Carole (CON - Farnham Bourne)
carole.cockburn@waverley.gov.uk

Deanus, Kevin (CON - Alfold, Cranleigh Rural & Ellens Green)
kevin.deanus@waverley.gov.uk

Edwards, Jim (CON - Haslemere Critchmere & Shottermill)
james.edwards@waverley.gov.uk

Ellis, Patricia (CON - Cranleigh West)
patricia.ellis@waverley.gov.uk

Else, David (CON - Elstead & Thursley)
david.else@waverley.gov.uk

Else, Jenny (CON - Elstead & Thursley)
jenny.else@waverley.gov.uk

Foryszewski, Mary (CON - Cranleigh East)
mary.foryszewski@waverley.gov.uk

Fraser, John (R - Farnham Upper Hale)
john.fraser@waverley.gov.uk

Frost, Pat (CON - Farnham Wrecclesham & Rowledge)
pat.frost@waverley.gov.uk

Goodridge, Michael (CON - Blackheath & Wonersh)
michael.goodridge@waverley.gov.uk

Gordon-Smith, Tony (CON - Godalming Charterhouse)
tony.gordon-smith@waverley.gov.uk

Gray, John (CON - Chiddingfold & Dunsfold)
john.gray@waverley.gov.uk

Hall, Ged (CON - Frensham, Dockenfield & Tilford)
ged.hall@waverley.gov.uk

Hargreaves, Jill (CON - Farnham Firgrove)
jill.hargreaves@waverley.gov.uk

Henry, Val (CON - Ewhurst)
val.henry@waverley.gov.uk

Hesse, Christiaan (CON - Hindhead)
christiaan.hesse@waverley.gov.uk

Hill, Stephen (CON - Farnham Moor Park)
stephen.hill@waverley.gov.uk

Hodge, Mike (CON - Farnham Hale & Heath End)
mike.hodge@waverley.gov.uk

Holder, Nicholas (CON - Witley & Hambledon)
nicholas.holder@waverley.gov.uk

Hunter, David (CON - Godalming Binscombe)
david.hunter@waverley.gov.uk

Hyman, Jerry (R - Farnham Castle)
jerry.hyman@waverley.gov.uk

Isherwood, Peter (CON - Hindhead)
peter.isherwood@waverley.gov.uk

James, Anna (CON - Witley & Hambledon)
anna.james@waverley.gov.uk

King, Carole (CON - Haslemere Critchmere & Shottermill)
carole.king@waverley.gov.uk

Knowles, Robert (CON - Haslemere East & Grayswood)
robert.knowles@waverley.gov.uk

Le Gal, Denise (CON - Farnham Hale & Heath End)
deniselegal@waverley.gov.uk

Lear, Martin (CON - Farnham Bourne)
martin.lear@waverley.gov.uk

Leigh, Denis (CON - Milford)
denis.leigh@waverley.gov.uk

MacLeoad, Andy (IND - Farnham Moor Park)
andy.macleod@waverley.gov.uk

Martin, Peter (CON - Godalming Holloway)
peter.martin@waverley.gov.uk

Mirylees, Kika (R - Farnham Shortheath & Boundstone)
kika.mirylees@waverley.gov.uk

Mulliner, Stephen (CON - Haslemere East & Grayswood)
stephen.mulliner@waverley.gov.uk

Nasir, Nabeel (CON - Farnham Weybourne & Badshot Lea)
nabeel.nasir@waverley.gov.uk

Piper, Libby (CON - Haslemere Critchmere & Shottermill)
libby.piper@waverley.gov.uk

Pritchard, Sam (CON - Farnham Firgrove)
sam.pritchard@waverley.gov.uk

Ramsdale, Wyatt (CON - Farnham Wrecclesham & Rowledge)
wyatt.ramsdale@waverley.gov.uk

Reynolds, Stefan (CON - Godalming Charterhouse)
stefan.reynolds@waverley.gov.uk

Round, David (CON - Haslemere East & Grayswood)
david.round@waverley.gov.uk

Seaborne, Richard (CON - Bramley, Busbridge & Hascombe)
richard.seaborne@waverley.gov.uk

Stennett, Jeanette (CON - Cranleigh East)

Stennett, Stewart (CON - Cranleigh East)
stewart.stennett@waverley.gov.uk

Thornton, Simon (CON - Godalming Central & Ockford)
simon.thornton@waverley.gov.uk

WAVERLEY

Upton, Bob (CON - Milford)
bob.upton@waverley.gov.uk

Ward, John (R - Farnham Shortheath & Boundstone)
john.ward@waverley.gov.uk

Welland, Ross (CON - Godalming Farncombe & Catteshall)
ross.welland@waverley.gov.uk

Wheatley, Liz (CON - Godalming Binscombe)
liz.wheatley@waverley.gov.uk

Williams, Nick (CON - Godalming Farncombe & Catteshall)
nick.williams@waverley.gov.uk

Williamson, John (R - Farnham Castle)
john.williamson@waverley.gov.uk

POLITICAL COMPOSITION
CON: 50, R: 5, IND: 1

COMMITTEE CHAIRS

Audit: Mr John Gray

Licensing: Mr Simon Inchbald

Planning: Mr Peter Isherwood

Wealden   D

Wealden District Council, Council Offices, Vicarage Lane,
Hailsham BN27 2AX
☎ 01323 443322 ⌂ info@wealden.gov.uk 🖥 www.wealden.gov.uk

FACTS AND FIGURES
Parliamentary Constituencies: Wealden
EU Constituencies: South East
Election Frequency: Elections are of whole council

PRINCIPAL OFFICERS

Chief Executive: Mr Charles Lant, Chief Executive, Council
Offices, Vicarage Lane, Hailsham BN27 2AX ☎ 01323 443300
⌂ chiefexec@wealden.gov.uk

Senior Management: Mrs Isabel Garden, Director - Environment
& Community Services, Council Offices, Vicarage Lane, Hailsham
BN27 2AX ☎ 01892 602404 ⌂ isabel.garden@wealden.gov.uk

Senior Management: Mr Nigel Hannam, Director - Planning
Policy & Economic Development, Council Offices, Vicarage Lane,
Hailsham BN27 2AX ☎ 01323 443230
⌂ nigel.hannam@wealden.gov.uk

Senior Management: Mr Trevor Scott, Director - Governance &
Corporate Services, Council Offices, Pine Grove, Crowborough
TN6 1DH ☎ 01892 602524 ⌂ trevor.scott@wealden.gov.uk

Architect, Building / Property Services: Ms Amanda Hodge,
Head of Policy & Community Services, Council Offices, Vicarage
Lane, Hailsham BN27 2AX ☎ 01323 443364
⌂ amanda.hodge@wealden.gov.uk

Best Value: Mr Malcolm Harris, Policy Officer, Council Offices,
Vicarage Lane, Hailsham BN27 2AX ☎ 01323 443744
⌂ malcolm.harris@wealden.gov.uk

Building Control: Mr Kelvin Williams, Head of Planning &
Environmental Services, Council Offices, Vicarage Lane, Hailsham
BN27 2AX ☎ 01892 602484 ⌂ kelvin.williams@wealden.gov.uk

PR / Communications: Mr Jim Van den Bos, Communications
Officer, Council Offices, Vicarage Lane, Hailsham BN27 2AX
☎ 01892 602745 ⌂ jim.vandenbos@wealden.gov.uk

Computer Management: Mr David Palmer, Head of Business
Services, Council Offices, Vicarage Lane, Hailsham BN27 2AX
☎ 01323 443229 ⌂ david.palmer@wealden.gov.uk

Contracts: Mr Gerry Palmer, Corporate Procurement Manager,
Council Offices, Vicarage Lane, Hailsham BN27 2AX
☎ 01323 443350 ⌂ gerry.palmer@wealden.gov.uk

Corporate Services: Mr Trevor Scott, Director - Governance &
Corporate Services, Council Offices, Vicarage Lane, Hailsham BN27
2AX ☎ 01892 602524 ⌂ trevor.scott@wealden.gov.uk

Customer Service: Mr Alex White, Head of Customer Services,
Revenues & Benefits, Council Offices, Vicarage Lane, Hailsham
BN27 2AX ☎ 01323 443171 ⌂ alex.white@wealden.gov.uk

Economic Development: Mr Nigel Hannam, Director - Planning
Policy & Economic Development, Council Offices, Vicarage Lane,
Hailsham BN27 2AX ☎ 01323 443230
⌂ nigel.hannam@wealden.gov.uk

E-Government: Mr David Palmer, Head of Business Services,
Council Offices, Vicarage Lane, Hailsham BN27 2AX
☎ 01323 443229 ⌂ david.palmer@wealden.gov.uk

Electoral Registration: Mrs Heather Blanshard, Electoral
Services Manager, Council Offices, Vicarage Lane, Hailsham
BN27 2AX ☎ 01892 602416 ⌂ heather.blanshard@wealden.gov.uk

Emergency Planning: Mr John Wood, Emergency Planning
Officer, Council Offices, Vicarage Lane, Hailsham BN27 2AX
☎ 01323 443552 ⌂ john.wood@wealden.gov.uk

Energy Management: Ms Amanda Hodge, Head of Policy &
Community Services, Council Offices, Vicarage Lane, Hailsham
BN27 2AX ☎ 01323 443364 ⌂ amanda.hodge@wealden.gov.uk

Environmental Health: Mr Richard Parker-Harding, Head of
Environmental Health, Council Offices, Vicarage Lane, Hailsham
BN27 2AX ⌂ richard.parker-harding@rother.gov.uk

Estates, Property & Valuation: Ms Amanda Hodge, Head of
Policy & Community Services, Council Offices, Vicarage Lane,
Hailsham BN27 2AX ☎ 01323 443364
⌂ amanda.hodge@wealden.gov.uk

Facilities: Ms Amanda Hodge, Head of Policy & Community
Services, Council Offices, Vicarage Lane, Hailsham BN27 2AX
☎ 01323 443364 ⌂ amanda.hodge@wealden.gov.uk

Finance: Mr Steve Linnett, Chief Finance Officer, Council Offices,
Vicarage Lane, Hailsham BN27 2AX ☎ 01323 443234
⌂ steve.linnett@wealden.gov.uk

Finance: Mr Trevor Scott, Director - Governance & Corporate Services, Council Offices, Vicarage Lane, Hailsham BN27 2AX ☎ 01892 602524 ◌ trevor.scott@wealden.gov.uk

Grounds Maintenance: Ms Amanda Hodge, Head of Policy & Community Services, Council Offices, Vicarage Lane, Hailsham BN27 2AX ☎ 01323 443364 ◌ amanda.hodge@wealden.gov.uk

Home Energy Conservation: Mrs Julie Wilkins, Property Services Manager, Council Offices, Vicarage Lane, Hailsham BN27 2AX ☎ 01323 443312 ◌ julie.wilkins@wealden.gov.uk

Housing: Mrs Isabel Garden, Director - Environment & Community Services, Council Offices, Pine Grove, Crowborough TN6 1DH ☎ 01892 602404 ◌ isabel.garden@wealden.gov.uk

Housing: Ms Amanda Hodge, Head of Policy & Community Services, Council Offices, Vicarage Lane, Hailsham BN27 2AX ☎ 01323 443364 ◌ amanda.hodge@wealden.gov.uk

Housing Maintenance: Ms Amanda Hodge, Head of Policy & Community Services, Council Offices, Vicarage Lane, Hailsham BN27 2AX ☎ 01323 443364 ◌ amanda.hodge@wealden.gov.uk

Legal: Mrs Kristina Shaw-Hamilton, Legal Services Manager, Council Offices, Vicarage Lane, Hailsham BN27 2AX ☎ 01892 602574 ◌ kristina-shawhamilton@wealden.gov.uk

Leisure and Cultural Services: Mrs Helen Markwick, Community & Regeneration Manager, Council Offices, Vicarage Lane, Hailsham BN27 2AX ☎ 01323 442756 ◌ helen.markwick@wealden.gov.uk

Licensing: Mr Richard Parker-Harding, Head of Environmental Health, Council Offices, Vicarage Lane, Hailsham BN27 2AX ◌ richard.parker-harding@rother.gov.uk

Member Services: Mrs Gabriella Paterson-Griggs, Democratic Services Manager, Council Offices, Vicarage Lane, Hailsham BN27 2AX ☎ 01892 602433 ◌ gabriella.paterson@wealden.gov.uk

Parking: Ms Tina Ford, Car Parks & Office Manager, Council Offices, Vicarage Lane, Hailsham BN27 2AX ☎ 01323 443346 ◌ tina.ford@wealden.gov.uk

Personnel / HR: Mr David Palmer, Head of Business Services, Council Offices, Vicarage Lane, Hailsham BN27 2AX ☎ 01323 443229 ◌ david.palmer@wealden.gov.uk

Planning: Mrs Isabel Garden, Director - Environment & Community Services, Council Offices, Pine Grove, Crowborough TN6 1DH ☎ 01892 602404 ◌ isabel.garden@wealden.gov.uk

Planning: Mr Kelvin Williams, Head of Planning & Building Control, Council Offices, Vicarage Lane, Hailsham BN27 2AX ☎ 01892 602484 ◌ kelvin.williams@wealden.gov.uk

Procurement: Mr Gerry Palmer, Corporate Procurement Manager, Council Offices, Vicarage Lane, Hailsham BN27 2AX ☎ 01323 443350 ◌ gerry.palmer@wealden.gov.uk

Recycling & Waste Minimisation: Mrs Isabel Garden, Director - Environment & Community Services, Council Offices, Vicarage Lane, Hailsham BN27 2AX ☎ 01892 602404 ◌ isabel.garden@wealden.gov.uk

Regeneration: Mr Nigel Hannam, Director - Planning Policy & Economic Development, Council Offices, Vicarage Lane, Hailsham BN27 2AX ☎ 01323 443230 ◌ nigel.hannam@wealden.gov.uk

Staff Training: Mr David Palmer, Head of Business Services, Council Offices, Vicarage Lane, Hailsham BN27 2AX ☎ 01323 443229 ◌ david.palmer@wealden.gov.uk

Sustainable Communities: Mr Nigel Hannam, Director - Planning Policy & Economic Development, Council Offices, Vicarage Lane, Hailsham BN27 2AX ☎ 01323 443230 ◌ nigel.hannam@wealden.gov.uk

Tourism: Mrs Helen Markwick, Community & Regeneration Manager, Council Offices, Vicarage Lane, Hailsham BN27 2AX ☎ 01323 442756 ◌ helen.markwick@wealden.gov.uk

Waste Collection and Disposal: Mrs Isabel Garden, Director - Environment & Community Services, Council Offices, Vicarage Lane, Hailsham BN27 2AX ☎ 01892 602404 ◌ isabel.garden@wealden.gov.uk

Waste Management: Mrs Isabel Garden, Director - Environment & Community Services, Council Offices, Vicarage Lane, Hailsham BN27 2AX ☎ 01892 602404 ◌ isabel.garden@wealden.gov.uk

COUNCILLORS

Chair: Hardy, Chris (CON - Hartfield)
cllr.chris.hardy@wealden.gov.uk

Vice-Chair: Doodes, Pam (CON - Ninfield & Hooe with Wartling)
cllr.pam.doodes@wealden.gov.uk

Leader of the Council: Standley, Robert (CON - Wadhurst)
cllr.robert.standley@wealden.gov.uk

Deputy Leader of the Council: Dowling, Claire (CON - Uckfield Central)
cllr.claire.dowling@wealden.gov.uk

Angel, Dick (CON - Heathfield North & Central)
cllr.dick.angel@wealden.gov.uk

Balsdon, Kevin (CON - Pevensey & Westham)
cllr.kevin.balsdon@wealden.gov.uk

Bentley, Jo (CON - Hailsham South & West)
cllr.jo.bentley@wealden.gov.uk

Bowlder, Bob (CON - Heathfield East)
cllr.bob.bowdler@wealden.gov.uk

Clark, Lin (CON - Pevensey & Westham)
cllr.lin.clark@wealden.gov.uk

Collinson, Nicholas (CON - Hailsham Central & North)
cllr.nicholas.collinson@wealden.gov.uk

Coltman, Nigel (CON - Hailsham Central & North)
cllr.nigel.coltman@wealden.gov.uk

Dashwood-Morris, Barby (CON - Chiddingly & East Hoathly)
cllr.barby.dashwood-morris@wealden.gov.uk

WEALDEN

Dear, Dianne (CON - Pevensey & Westham)
cllr.dianne.dear@wealden.gov.uk

Dixon, Phil (CON - Rotherfield)
cllr.phil.dixon@wealden.gov.uk

Dunk, Jan (CON - Heathfield North & Central)
cllr.jan.dunk@wealden.gov.uk

Ede, Philip (CON - Alfriston)
cllr.philip.ede@wealden.gov.uk

Firth, Helen (CON - Uckfield New Town)
cllr.helen.firth@wealden.gov.uk

Fox, Jonica (CON - Cross-in-Hand / Five Ashes)
cllr.jonica.fox@wealden.gov.uk

Galley, Roy (CON - Danehill / Fletching / Nutley)
cllr.roy.galley@wealden.gov.uk

Grocock, Richard (CON - Hailsham South & West)
cllr.richard.grocock@wealden.gov.uk

Hollins, Jim (CON - Crowborough West)
cllr.jim.hollins@wealden.gov.uk

Holloway, Peter (CON - Forest Row)
cllr.peter.holloway@wealden.gov.uk

Howell, Johanna (CON - Frant / Withyham)
cllr.johanna.howell@wealden.gov.uk

Illingworth, Toby (CON - Buxted & Maresfield)
cllr.toby.illingworth@wealden.gov.uk

Isted, Stephen (IND - Crowborough Jarvis Brook)
cllr.stephen.isted@wealden.gov.uk

Long, Andy (CON - Herstmonceux)

Lunn, Michael (CON - Buxted & Maresfield)
cllr.michael.lunn@wealden.gov.uk

Lunn, Philip (CON - Crowborough East)
cllr.philip.lunn@wealden.gov.uk

Marlowe, Barry (CON - Uckfield Ridgewood)
cllr.barry.marlow@wealden.gov.uk

Moore, Rowena (CON - Forest Row)
cllr.rowena.moore@wealden.gov.uk

Moss, Kay (CON - Crowborough St Johns)
cllr.kay.moss@wealden.gov.uk

Murray, Douglas (CON - Willingdon)
cllr.douglas.murray@wealdon.gov.uk

Newton, Ann (CON - Framfield)
cllr.ann.newton@wealden.gov.uk

O'Rawe, Amanda (CON - Hailsham East)
cllr.amanda.orawe@wealden.gov.uk

Pinkney, Mark (CON - Hellingly)
cllr.mark.pinkney@wealden.gov.uk

Redman, Brian (CON - Mayfield)
cllr.brian.redman@wealden.gov.uk

Reed, Ronald (CON - Crowborough North)
cllr.ronald.reed@wealden.gov.uk

Reynolds, Carol (CON - Uckfield North)
cllr.carol.reynolds@wealden.gov.uk

Rose, Greg (CON - Crowborough East)
cllr.greg.rose@wealden.gov.uk

Roundell, Peter (CON - Danehill / Fletching / Nutley)
cllr.peter.roundell@wealden.gov.uk

Rutherford, William (CON - Frant / Withyham)
william.rutherford@wealden.gov.uk

Shing, Daniel (IND - Polegate South)
daniel.shing@wealden.gov.uk

Shing, Stephen (IND - Willingdon)
cllr.stephen.shing@wealden.gov.uk

Shing, Raymond (IND - Willingdon)
cllr.raymond.shing@wealden.gov.uk

Shing, Oi Lin (IND - Polegate North)
cllr.oilin.shing@wealden.gov.uk

Snell, Angela (CON - Polegate North)
cllr.angela.snell@wealden.gov.uk

Stedman, Susan (CON - Horam)
cllr.susan.stedman@wealden.gov.uk

Thomas, Roger (CON - Heathfield North & Central)
cllr.roger.thomas@wealden.gov.uk

Towey, Jeanette (CON - Crowborough West)
cllr.jeanette.towey@wealden.gov.uk

Triandafyllou, Chriss (CON - Halisham South & West)
cllr.chriss.triandafyllou@wealden.gov.uk

Waldock, Peter (CON - Uckfield North)
cllr.peter.waldock@wealden.gov.uk

Waller, Neil (CON - Crowborough North)
cllr.neil.waller@wealden.gov.uk

Wells, Graham (CON - Wadhurst)
cllr.graham.wells@wealden.gov.uk

White, David (LD - Hellingly)
cllr.david.white@wealden.gov.uk

Wilton, John (CON - East Dean)
cllr.john.wilton@wealden.gov.uk

POLITICAL COMPOSITION
CON: 49, IND: 5, LD: 1

COMMITTEE CHAIRS

Audit: Mr Peter Roundell

Licensing: Mr Nigel Coltman

Planning: Mr Kevin Balsdon

Wellingborough   D

Wellingborough Borough Council, Council Offices, Swanspool House, Wellingborough NN8 1BP
☎ 01933 229777 ✆ generalenquiries@wellingborough.gov.uk
🖥 www.wellingborough.gov.uk

FACTS AND FIGURES
Parliamentary Constituencies: Wellingborough
EU Constituencies: East Midlands
Election Frequency: Elections are of whole council

PRINCIPAL OFFICERS

Chief Executive: Mr John Campbell, Chief Executive & Head of Paid Service, Council Offices, Swanspool House, Wellingborough NN8 1BP ☎ 01933 231500 ✆ jcampbell@wellingborough.gov.uk

Senior Management: Ms Elizabeth Elliott, Head of Finance & S151 Officer, Council Offices, Swanspool House, Wellingborough NN8 1BP ☎ 01933 231679 ⏱ lelliott@wellingborough.gov.uk

Senior Management: Mrs Bridget Gamble, Head of Resources, Council Offices, Swanspool House, Wellingborough NN8 1BP ☎ 01933 231512 ⏱ bgamble@wellingborough.gov.uk

Senior Management: Mr Phil Grimley, Head of ICT Services, East Northamptonshire Council, Cedar Drive, Thrapston NN14 4LZ ☎ 01832 742076 ⏱ pgrimley@east_northamptonshire.gov.uk

Senior Management: Ms Julie Thomas, Head - Planning & Local Development, Council Offices, Swanspool House, Wellingborough NN8 1BP ☎ 01933 231924 ⏱ jthomas@wellingborough.gov.uk

Architect, Building / Property Services: Mr Paul Burnett, Property Services Manager, Council Offices, Swanspool House, Wellingborough NN8 1BP ☎ 01933 231586 ⏱ pburnett@wellingborough.gov.uk

Building Control: Ms Maxine Simmons, Principal Planning & Local Development Manager, Council Offices, Swanspool House, Wellingborough NN8 1BP ☎ 01933 231935 ⏱ msimmons@wellingborough.gov.uk

Community Planning: Ms Gill Chapman, Principal Community Support Manager, Council Offices, Swanspool House, Wellingborough NN8 1BP ☎ 01933 231839 ⏱ gchapman@wellingborough.gov.uk

Community Safety: Ms Gill Chapman, Principal Community Support Manager, Council Offices, Swanspool House, Wellingborough NN8 1BP ☎ 01933 231839 ⏱ gchapman@wellingborough.gov.uk

Computer Management: Mr Phil Grimley, Head of ICT Services, East Northamptonshire Council, Cedar Drive, Thrapston NN14 4LZ ☎ 01832 742076 ⏱ pgrimley@east_northamptonshire.gov.uk

Economic Development: Ms Victoria Phillipson, Principal Planning Policy & Regeneration Manager, Council Offices, Swanspool House, Wellingborough NN8 1BP ☎ 01933 231985 ⏱ vphillipson@wellingborough.gov.uk

Electoral Registration: Mr Samuel Whiteley, Electoral Services Team Leader, Council Offices, Swanspool House, Wellingborough NN8 1BP ☎ 01933 231513 ⏱ swhiteley@wellingborough.gov.uk

Emergency Planning: Ms Jo Adams, Emergency Planning Officer, Council Offices, Swanspool House, Wellingborough NN8 1BP ☎ 01933 231724 ⏱ jadams@northamptonshire.gov.uk

Environmental / Technical Services: Mr Bernard Gallyot, Managing Director - Wellingborough Norse, Wellingborough Norse, Trafalgar House, Sanders Park, Sanders Road, Finedon Road Industrial Estate, Wellingborough NN8 4FR ☎ 01933 234523 ⏱ bernard.gallyot@wellingborough.gov.uk

Environmental Health: Ms Amanda Wilcox, Principal Environmental Health Manager, Council Offices, Swanspool House, Wellingborough NN8 1BP ☎ 01933 231954 ⏱ awilcox@wellingborough.gov.uk

Estates, Property & Valuation: Mr Paul Burnett, Property Services Manager, Council Offices, Swanspool House, Wellingborough NN8 1BP ☎ 01933 231586 ⏱ pburnett@wellingborough.gov.uk

Events Manager: Ms Julia Wells, Events Officer, Council Offices, Swanspool House, Wellingborough NN8 1BP ☎ 01933 231986 ⏱ jwells@wellingborough.gov.uk

Facilities: Mr Tony Dagley, Facilities Manager, Wellingborough Norse, Trafalgar House, Sanders Road, Wellingborough NN8 4PP ☎ 01933 234538 ⏱ tony.dagley@ncsgrp.co.uk

Finance: Ms Elizabeth Elliott, Head of Finance & S151 Officer, Council Offices, Swanspool House, Wellingborough NN8 1BP ☎ 01933 231679 ⏱ lelliott@wellingborough.gov.uk

Fleet Management: Mr Bernard Gallyot, Managing Director - Wellingborough Norse, Wellingborough Norse, Trafalgar House, Sanders Park, Sanders Road, Finedon Road Industrial Estate, Wellingborough NN8 4FR ☎ 01933 234523 ⏱ bernard.gallyot@wellingborough.gov.uk

Grounds Maintenance: Mr Bernard Gallyot, Managing Director - Wellingborough Norse, Wellingborough Norse, Trafalgar House, Sanders Park, Sanders Road, Finedon Road Industrial Estate, Wellingborough NN8 4FR ☎ 01933 234523 ⏱ bernard.gallyot@wellingborough.gov.uk

Health and Safety: Ms Amanda Wilcox, Principal Environmental Health Manager, Council Offices, Swanspool House, Wellingborough NN8 1BP ☎ 01933 231954 ⏱ awilcox@wellingborough.gov.uk

Home Energy Conservation: Mr Clive Culling, Assistant Principal Housing Officer (Renewal), Council Offices, Swanspool House, Wellingborough NN8 1BP ☎ 01933 231854 ⏱ cculling@wellingborough.gov.uk

Housing: Ms Vicki Jessop, Prinicpal Housing Manager, Council Offices, Swanspool House, Wellingborough NN8 1BP ☎ 01933 231720 ⏱ vjessop@wellinborough.gov.uk

Legal: Ms Sue Lyons, Head - Democratic & Legal Services, Council Offices, Swanspool House, Wellingborough NN8 1BP ☎ 01536 534209; 01536 543209 ⏱ suelyons@kettering.gov.uk

Leisure and Cultural Services: Ms Gill Chapman, Principal Community Support Manager, Council Offices, Swanspool House, Wellingborough NN8 1BP ☎ 01933 231839 ⏱ gchapman@wellingborough.gov.uk

Licensing: Ms Amanda Wilcox, Principal Environmental Health Manager, Council Offices, Swanspool House, Wellingborough NN8 1BP ☎ 01933 231954 ⏱ awilcox@wellingborough.gov.uk

Lottery Funding, Charity and Voluntary: Ms Gill Chapman, Principal Community Support Manager, Council Offices, Swanspool House, Wellingborough NN8 1BP ☎ 01933 231839 ⏱ gchapman@wellingborough.gov.uk

WELLINGBOROUGH

Member Services: Mrs Karen Denton, Principal Corporate Support Manager, Council Offices, Swanspool House, Wellingborough NN8 1BP ☎ 01933 231601
🖑 kdenton@wellingborough.gov.uk

Personnel / HR: Mrs Karen Denton, Principal Corporate Support Manager, Council Offices, Swanspool House, Wellingborough NN8 1BP ☎ 01933 231601 🖑 kdenton@wellingborough.gov.uk

Planning: Ms Maxine Simmons, Principal Planning & Local Development Manager, Council Offices, Swanspool House, Wellingborough NN8 1BP ☎ 01933 231935
🖑 msimmons@wellingborough.gov.uk

Recycling & Waste Minimisation: Mr Bernard Gallyot, Managing Director - Wellingborough Norse, Wellingborough Norse, Trafalgar House, Sanders Park, Sanders Road, Finedon Road Industrial Estate, Wellingborough NN8 4FR ☎ 01933 234523
🖑 bernard.gallyot@wellingborough.gov.uk

Regeneration: Ms Victoria Phillipson, Principal Planning Policy & Regeneration Manager, Council Offices, Swanspool House, Wellingborough NN8 1BP ☎ 01933 231985
🖑 vphillipson@wellingborough.gov.uk

Staff Training: Mrs Karen Denton, Principal Corporate Support Manager, Council Offices, Swanspool House, Wellingborough NN8 1BP ☎ 01933 231601 🖑 kdenton@wellingborough.gov.uk

Street Scene: Mr Bernard Gallyot, Managing Director - Wellingborough Norse, Wellingborough Norse, Trafalgar House, Sanders Park, Sanders Road, Finedon Road Industrial Estate, Wellingborough NN8 4FR ☎ 01933 234523
🖑 bernard.gallyot@wellingborough.gov.uk

Sustainable Communities: Ms Victoria Phillipson, Principal Planning Policy & Regeneration Manager, Council Offices, Swanspool House, Wellingborough NN8 1BP ☎ 01933 231985
🖑 vphillipson@wellingborough.gov.uk

Sustainable Development: Ms Victoria Phillipson, Principal Planning Policy & Regeneration Manager, Council Offices, Swanspool House, Wellingborough NN8 1BP ☎ 01933 231985
🖑 vphillipson@wellingborough.gov.uk

Town Centre: Mr John Cable, Business Improvement District Manager, c/o The Management Suite, 18 Spring Lane, Wellingborough NN8 1EY ☎ 01933 270795
🖑 manager@wellingboroughtowncentre.co.uk

Waste Collection and Disposal: Mr Bernard Gallyot, Managing Director - Wellingborough Norse, Wellingborough Norse, Trafalgar House, Sanders Park, Sanders Road, Finedon Road Industrial Estate, Wellingborough NN8 4FR ☎ 01933 234523
🖑 bernard.gallyot@wellingborough.gov.uk

Waste Management: Mr Bernard Gallyot, Managing Director - Wellingborough Norse, Wellingborough Norse, Trafalgar House, Sanders Park, Sanders Road, Finedon Road Industrial Estate, Wellingborough NN8 4FR ☎ 01933 234523
🖑 bernard.gallyot@wellingborough.gov.uk

Children's Play Areas: Mr Bernard Gallyot, Managing Director - Wellingborough Norse, Wellingborough Norse, Trafalgar House, Sanders Park, Sanders Road, Finedon Road Industrial Estate, Wellingborough NN8 4FR ☎ 01933 234523
🖑 bernard.gallyot@wellingborough.gov.uk

COUNCILLORS

Mayor: Waters, Malcolm (CON - Redwell)
mwaters@wellingborough.gov.uk

Deputy Mayor: Graves, Barry (CON - Great Doddington & Wilby)
bgraves@wellingborough.gov.uk

Leader of the Council: Griffiths, Martin (CON - Brickhill)
mgriffiths@wellingborough.gov.uk

Deputy Leader of the Council: Partridge-Underwood, Tom (CON - Bozeat)
tpartridge-underwood@wellingborough.gov.uk

Group Leader: Scarborough, Andrew (LAB - Queensway)
ascarborough@wellingborough.gov.uk

Abram, Rosemary (LAB - Hatton)
rabram@wellingborough.gov.uk

Allebone, Timothy (CON - Brickhill)
tim.allebone@virgin.net

Anslow, Valerie (LAB - Swanspool)
vanslow@wellingborough.gov.uk

Aslam, Tony (LAB - Victoria)
taslam@wellingborough.gov.uk

Bailey, Barbara (CON - Finedon)

Beirne, Jo (CON - Wollaston)
jbeirne@wellingborough.gov.uk

Bell, Paul (CON - Redwell)
paul.bell@wellingborough.gov.uk

Bone, Jennie (CON - Harrowden & Sywell)
jbone@wellinborough.gov.uk

Carr, Jon-Paul (CON - Irchester)
jpcarr@wellingborough.gov.uk

Ekins, Jonathan (CON - Swanspool)
jekins@wellingborough.gov.uk

Emerson, Brian (LAB - Victoria)
bemerson@wellingborough.gov.uk

Francis, Elayne (LAB - Victoria)
efrancis@wellingborough.gov.uk

Gough, Robert (CON - Earls Barton)
rgough@wellinbrough.gov.uk

Hallam, Clive (CON - Harrowden & Sywell)
challam@wellingborough.gov.uk

Harrington, Ken (CON - Hatton)
kharrington@wellingborough.gov.uk

Henley, Adam (LAB - Queensway)
ahenley@wellingborough.gov.uk

Lawman, Graham (CON - Rixon)
glawman@wellingborough.gov.uk

Lawman, Lora (CON - Rixon)
lora.lawman@wellingborough.gov.uk

Lloyd, Thomas (CON - Irchester)
tlloyd@wellingborough.gov.uk

Maguire, Timothy (LAB - Irchester)
tmaguire@wellingborough.gov.uk

Morrall, Peter (CON - Earls Barton)
pmorrall@wellingborough.gov.uk

Patel, Umesh (CON - Rixon)
upatel@wellingborough.gov.uk

Scanlon, Sarah (CON - Croyland)
sscanlon@wellingborough.gov.uk

Simmons, Geoff (CON - Wollaston)
gsimmons@wellingborough.gov.uk

Skittral, Brian (CON - Croyland)
bskittrall@wellingborough.gov.uk

Stevenson, Laura (CON - Earls Barton)
lstevenson@wellingborough.gov.uk

Walia, Jay (CON - Isebrook)
jwalia@wellingborough.gov.uk

Ward, Malcolm (CON - Finedon)
mward@wellingborough.gov.uk

Waters, Veronica (CON - Redwll)
vwaters@wellingborough.gov.uk

Watts, Andrea (LAB - Queensway)
awatts@wellingborough.gov.uk

York, Martyn (CON - Croyland)
myork@wellingborough.gov.uk

POLITICAL COMPOSITION
CON: 27, LAB: 9

COMMITTEE CHAIRS

Audit: Mr Ken Harrington

Development: Mr Jon-Paul Carr

Licensing: Mr Geoff Simmons

Planning: Mr Malcolm Ward

Welwyn Hatfield   D

Welwyn Hatfield Borough Council, Council Offices, The Campus, Welwyn Garden City AL8 6AE
☎ 01707 357000 ⏚ contact-whc@welhat.gov.uk
🖥 www.welhat.gov.uk

FACTS AND FIGURES
Parliamentary Constituencies: Broxbourne, Welwyn Hatfield
EU Constituencies: Eastern
Election Frequency: Elections are by thirds

PRINCIPAL OFFICERS

Chief Executive: Dr Michel Saminaden, Chief Executive, Council Offices, The Campus, Welwyn Garden City AL8 6AE
☎ 01707 357327 ⏚ m.saminaden@welhat.gov.uk

Senior Management: Mr Robert Baldock, Director - Governance, Council Offices, The Campus, Welwyn Garden City AL8 6AE
☎ 01707 357277 ⏚

Senior Management: Mrs Pam Kettle, Director - Finance & Operations, Council Offices, The Campus, Welwyn Garden City AL8 6AE ☎ 01707 357275 ⏚ p.kettle@welhat.gov.uk

Architect, Building / Property Services: Mr Mike Storey, Corporate Property Manager, Council Offices, The Campus, Welwyn Garden City AL8 6AE ☎ 01707 357457 ⏚ m.storey@welhat.gov.uk

Best Value: Mr Paul Underwood, Head of Policy & Culture, Council Offices, The Campus, Welwyn Garden City AL8 6AE
☎ 01707 357220 ⏚ p.underwood@welhat.gov.uk

Building Control: Mr Mark Harvey, Building Control Manager, Council Offices, The Campus, Welwyn Garden City AL8 6AE
☎ 01707 357246 ⏚ m.harvey@welhat.gov.uk

Children / Youth Services: Mr Matt Rayner, Youth & Sport Partnership Manager, Council Offices, The Campus, Welwyn Garden City AL8 6AE ☎ 01707 357174 ⏚ m.rayner@welhat.gov.uk

PR / Communications: Mr Thom Burn, Policy & Communications Manager, Council Offices, The Campus, Welwyn Garden City AL8 6AE ☎ 01707 357271 ⏚ t.burn@welhat.gov.uk

Community Safety: Mrs Sian Chambers, Head of Housing & Community Services, Council Offices, The Campus, Welwyn Garden City AL8 6AE ☎ 01707 357640 ⏚ s.chambers@welhat.gov.uk

Computer Management: Mr David Houghton, IT Client Manager, Council Offices, The Campus, Welwyn Garden City AL8 6AE
☎ 01707 357260 ⏚ d.houghton@welhat.gov.uk

Contracts: Mr Andrew Harper, Procurement Manager, Council Offices, The Campus, Welwyn Garden City AL8 6AE
☎ 020 8207 2277; 01707 357371 ⏚ a.harper@welhat.gov.uk

Customer Service: Ms Sue Kiernan, Customer Service Manager, Council Offices, The Campus, Welwyn Garden City AL8 6AE
☎ 01707 357201 ⏚ s.kiernan@welhat.gov.uk

Economic Development: Ms Lisa Devayya, Economic Development Officer, Council Offices, The Campus, Welwyn Garden City AL8 6AE ☎ 01707 357269 ⏚ l.devayya@welhat.gov.uk

E-Government: Mrs Pam Kettle, Director - Finance & Operations, Council Offices, The Campus, Welwyn Garden City AL8 6AE
☎ 01707 357275 ⏚ p.kettle@welhat.gov.uk

Electoral Registration: Mr John Merron, Electoral Services Manager, Council Offices, The Campus, Welwyn Garden City AL8 6AE ☎ 01707 357354 ⏚ j.merron@welhat.gov.uk

Emergency Planning: Mr Andy Cremer, Risk & Resilience Manager, Council Offices, The Campus, Welwyn Garden City AL8 6AE ☎ 01707 357169 ⏚ a.cremer@welhat.gov.uk

Energy Management: Mr Vin Appasawmy, Energy Efficiency Officer, Council Offices, The Campus, Welwyn Garden City AL8 6AE ☎ 01707 357399 ⏚ v.appasawmy@welhat.gov.uk

WELWYN HATFIELD

Environmental / Technical Services: Mrs Pam Kettle, Director - Finance & Operations, Council Offices, The Campus, Welwyn Garden City AL8 6AE ☎ 01707 357275 ⌨ p.kettle@welhat.gov.uk

Environmental / Technical Services: Mr Durk Reyner, Head of Environment, Council Offices, The Campus, Welwyn Garden City AL8 6AE ☎ 01707 357160 ⌨ d.reyner@welhat.gov.uk

Environmental Health: Mr Nick Long, Head of Public Health & Protection, Council Offices, The Campus, Welwyn Garden City AL8 6AE ☎ 01707 357401 ⌨ n.long@welhat.gov.uk

Estates, Property & Valuation: Mr Mike Storey, Corporate Property Manager, Council Offices, The Campus, Welwyn Garden City AL8 6AE ☎ 01707 357457 ⌨ m.storey@welhat.gov.uk

Finance: Mrs Pam Kettle, Director - Finance & Operations, Council Offices, The Campus, Welwyn Garden City AL8 6AE ☎ 01707 357275 ⌨ p.kettle@welhat.gov.uk

Grounds Maintenance: Mr Durk Reyner, Head of Environment, Council Offices, The Campus, Welwyn Garden City AL8 6AE ☎ 01707 357160 ⌨ d.reyner@welhat.gov.uk

Health and Safety: Mr Andy Cremer, Risk & Resilience Manager, Council Offices, The Campus, Welwyn Garden City AL8 6AE ☎ 01707 357169 ⌨ a.cremer@welhat.gov.uk

Home Energy Conservation: Mr Vin Appasawmy, Energy Efficiency Officer, Council Offices, The Campus, Welwyn Garden City AL8 6AE ☎ 01707 357399 ⌨ v.appasawmy@welhat.gov.uk

Housing: Mrs Sian Chambers, Head of Housing & Community Services, Council Offices, The Campus, Welwyn Garden City AL8 6AE ☎ 01707 357640 ⌨ s.chambers@welhat.gov.uk

Legal: Ms Margaret Martinus, Head of Law & Administration, Council Offices, The Campus, Welwyn Garden City AL8 6AE ☎ 01707 357575 ⌨ m.martinus@welhat.gov.uk

Leisure and Cultural Services: Mr Paul Underwood, Head of Policy & Culture, Council Offices, The Campus, Welwyn Garden City AL8 6AE ☎ 01707 357220 ⌨ p.underwood@welhat.gov.uk

Licensing: Mr Nick Long, Head of Public Health & Protection, Council Offices, The Campus, Welwyn Garden City AL8 6AE ☎ 01707 357401 ⌨ n.long@welhat.gov.uk

Member Services: Mr Graham Seal, Governance Services Manager, Council Offices, The Campus, Welwyn Garden City AL8 6AE ☎ 01707 357444 ⌨ g.seal@welhat.gov.uk

Parking: Ms Vikki Hatfield, Parking Services Team Leader, Council Offices, The Campus, Welwyn Garden City AL8 6AE ☎ 01707 357555 ⌨ v.hatfield@welhat.gov.uk

Partnerships: Mrs Sian Chambers, Head of Housing & Community Services, Council Offices, The Campus, Welwyn Garden City AL8 6AE ☎ 01707 357640 ⌨ s.chambers@welhat.gov.uk

Personnel / HR: Ms Janet Pilbeam, Human Resources Manager, Council Offices, The Campus, Welwyn Garden City AL8 6AE ⌨ j.pilbeam@welhat.gov.uk

Planning: Mr Colin Haigh, Head of Planning, Council Offices, The Campus, Welwyn Garden City AL8 6AE ☎ 01707 357239 ⌨ c.haigh@welhat.gov.uk

Procurement: Mr Andrew Harper, Procurement Manager, Council Offices, The Campus, Welwyn Garden City AL8 6AE ☎ 020 8207 2277; 01707 357371 ⌨ a.harper@welhat.gov.uk

Recycling & Waste Minimisation: Ms Kirsten Roberts, Recycling & Environment Team Leader, Council Offices, The Campus, Welwyn Garden City AL8 6AE ☎ 01707 357177 ⌨ k.roberts@welhat.gov.uk

Staff Training: Ms Janet Pilbeam, Human Resources Manager, Council Offices, The Campus, Welwyn Garden City AL8 6AE ⌨ j.pilbeam@welhat.gov.uk

Street Scene: Mr Durk Reyner, Head of Environment, Council Offices, The Campus, Welwyn Garden City AL8 6AE ☎ 01707 357160 ⌨ d.reyner@welhat.gov.uk

Sustainable Communities: Mrs Sue Tiley, Planning Policy & Implementation Manager, Council Offices, The Campus, Welwyn Garden City AL8 6AE ☎ 01707 357268 ⌨ s.tiley@welhat.gov.uk

Town Centre: Ms Tina Benson, Town Centre Co-ordinator, Council Offices, The Campus, Welwyn Garden City AL8 6AE ☎ 01707 357567 ⌨ t.benson@welhat.gov.uk

Waste Collection and Disposal: Mr Durk Reyner, Head of Environment, Council Offices, The Campus, Welwyn Garden City AL8 6AE ☎ 01707 357160 ⌨ d.reyner@welhat.gov.uk

Waste Management: Ms Kirsten Roberts, Recycling & Environment Team Leader, Council Offices, The Campus, Welwyn Garden City AL8 6AE ☎ 01707 357177 ⌨ k.roberts@welhat.gov.uk

Children's Play Areas: Mr Durk Reyner, Head of Environment, Council Offices, The Campus, Welwyn Garden City AL8 6AE ☎ 01707 357160 ⌨ d.reyner@welhat.gov.uk

COUNCILLORS

Mayor: Mabbott, Patricia (CON - Sherrards) patricia.mabbott@welhat.gov.uk

Deputy Mayor: Sparks, Lynne (CON - Hatfield Villages) lynne.sparks@welhat.gov.uk

Leader of the Council: Dean, John (CON - Brookmans Park & Little Heath) john.dean@welhat.gov.uk

Deputy Leader of the Council: Perkins, Mandy (CON - Welwyn West) mandy.perkins@welhat.gov.uk

Bailey, Tom (LD - Welham Green & Hatfield South) tom.bailey@welhat.gov.uk

Basch, Rachel (LD - Handside) rachel.basch@welhat.gov.uk

Beckerman, Jon (CON - Sherrards)
jon.beckerman@welhat.gov.uk

Beckett, Helen (LAB - Peartree)
helen.beckett@welhat.gov.uk

Bell, Duncan (CON - Hatfield Villages)
duncan.bell@welhat.gov.uk

Bennett, Darren (CON - Panshanger)
darren.bennett@welhat.gov.uk

Birleson, Margaret (LAB - Hollybush)
margaret.birleson@welhat.gov.uk

Boulton, Stephen (CON - Brookmans Park & Little Heath)
stephen.boulton@welhat.gov.uk

Boulton, Jonathan (CON - Brookmans Park & Little Heath)
jonathan.boulton@welhat.gov.uk

Bower, Harry (CON - Sherrards)
harry.bower@welhat.gov.uk

Brandon, Lenny (LAB - Hatfield East)
lenny.brandon@welhat.gov.uk

Broach, James (LAB - Hatfield South West)
j.broach@welhat.gov.uk

Bromley, Helen (CON - Handside)
helen.bromley@welhat.gov.uk

Chesterman, Alan (LAB - Howlands)
alan.chesterman@welhat.gov.uk

Chesterman, Lynn (LAB - Hollybush)
lynn.chesterman@welhat.gov.uk

Cook, Maureen (LAB - Hatfield Central)
maureen.cook@welhat.gov.uk

Cowan, Malcolm (LD - Peartree)
malcolm.cowen@welhat.gov.uk

Cragg, Julie (CON - Welwyn East)
julie.cragg@welhat.gov.uk

Dean, Irene (CON - Northaw & Cuffley)
irene.dean@welhat.gov.uk

Fitzpatrick, John (LAB - Hatfield South West)
john.fitzpatrick@welhat.gov.uk

Fitzsimon, Barbara (CON - Haldens)
barbara.fitzsimon@welhat.gov.uk

Gillett, Caroline (CON - Hatfield East)
caroline.gillett@welhat.gov.uk

Hayes, Glyn (LAB - Hatfield Central)
glyn.hayes@welhat.gov.uk

Holloway, Max (LAB - Howlands)
max.holloway@welhat.gov.uk

Holman, Kerstin (CON - Hatfield East)
kerstin.holman@welhat.gov.uk

Johnston, Sara (CON - Panshanger)
sara.johnston@welhat.gov.uk

Kingsbury, Tony (CON - Welwyn West)
tony.kingsbury@welhat.gov.uk

Larkins, Mike (LAB - Haldens)
mike.larkins@welhat.gov.uk

Levitt, Martyn (CON - Panshanger)
martyn.levitt@welhat.gov.uk

Markiewicz, Steven (CON - Welwyn East)
steven.markiewicz@welhat.gov.uk

Michaelides, George (CON - Northaw & Cuffley)
george.michaelides@welhat.gov.uk

Morgan, Howard (CON - Hatfield Villages)
howard.morgan@welhat.gov.uk

Pace, Nick (CON - Hollybush)
nick.pace@welhat.gov.uk

Quenet, Helen (LD - Welham Green & Hatfield South)
helen.quenet@welhat.gov.uk

Roberts, Steve (LAB - Peartree)
steve.roberts@welhat.gov.uk

Sarson, Bernard (CON - Northaw & Cuffley)
bernard.sarson@welhat.gov.uk

Shah, Pankit (LAB - Hatfield Central)
pankit.shah@welhat.gov.uk

Spinks, Malcolm (CON - Haldens)
malcolm.spinks@welhat.gov.uk

Taylor, Nick (CON - Welwyn West)
nick.taylor@welhat.gov.uk

Thomson, Fiona (CON - Handside)
fiona.thomson@welhat.gov.uk

Thorpe, Kieran (LAB - Hatfield South West)
kieran.thorpe@welhat.gov.uk

Trigg, Roger (CON - Welwyn East)
roger.trigg@welhat.gov.uk

Weston, Pauline (LAB - Howlands)
pauline.weston@welhat.gov.uk

Zukowskyj, Paul (LD - Welham Green & Hatfield South)
paul.zukowskyj@welhat.gov.uk

POLITICAL COMPOSITION
CON: 28, LAB: 15, LD: 5

COMMITTEE CHAIRS

Audit: Mr George Michaelides

Development Management: Mr Stephen Boulton

Licensing: Mr Jon Beckerman

West Berkshire   U

West Berkshire Council, Council Offices, Market Street, Newbury RG14 5LD
☎ 01635 42400 📠 01635 519431 ✆ info@westberks.gov.uk 🖥 www.westberks.gov.uk

FACTS AND FIGURES
Parliamentary Constituencies: Newbury, Reading West, Wokingham
EU Constituencies: South East
Election Frequency: Elections are of whole council

PRINCIPAL OFFICERS

Chief Executive: Mr Nick Carter, Chief Executive, Council Offices, Market Street, Newbury RG14 5LD ☎ 01635 519104 ✆ ncarter@westberks.gov.uk

WEST BERKSHIRE

Senior Management: Mr John Ashworth, Corporate Director - Environment, Council Offices, Market Street, Newbury RG14 5LD
☎ 01635 519587 ⁋ jashworth@westberks.gov.uk

Senior Management: Ms Rachael Wardell, Corporate Director - Communities, West Street House, West Street, Newbury RG14 1BD
☎ 01635 519723 ⁋ rwardell@westberks.gov.uk

Access Officer / Social Services (Disability): Ms Valerie Witton, Access Officer, Council Offices, Market Street, Newbury RG14 5LD ☎ 01635 519489 ⁋ vwitton@westberks.gov.uk

Building Control: Mr Roger Paine, Building Control Manager, Council Offices, Market Street, Newbury RG14 5LD
☎ 01635 519694 ⁋ rpaine@westberks.gov.uk

Children / Youth Services: Mr Mac Heath, Head of Children's Services, Council Offices, Market Street, Newbury RG14 5LD
☎ 01635 519735 ⁋ mheath@westberks.gov.uk

Civil Registration: Mr David Holling, Head of Legal Services, Council Offices, Market Street, Newbury RG14 5LD
☎ 01635 519422 ⁋ dholling@westberks.gov.uk

PR / Communications: Mr Martin Dunscombe, Communications Manager, Council Offices, Market Street, Newbury RG14 5LD
☎ 01635 519122 ⁋ martin.dunscombe@westberks.gov.uk

Community Safety: Mrs Susan Powell, Safer Communities Partnership Team Manager, 20 Mill Lane, Newbury RG14 5LE
☎ 01635 264703 ⁋ spowell@westberks.gov.uk

Computer Management: Mr Kevin Griffin, Head of ICT & Corporate Support, Council Offices, Market Street, Newbury RG14 5LD ☎ 01635 519292 ⁋ kgriffin@westberks.gov.uk

Consumer Protection and Trading Standards: Mr Sean Murphy, Trading Standards & Licensing Manager - Public Protection, Council Offices, Market Street, Newbury RG14 5LD
☎ 01635 519840 ⁋ smurphy@westberks.gov.uk

Customer Service: Mr Sean Anderson, Head of Customer Services, Council Offices, Market Street, Newbury RG14 5LD
☎ 01635 519149 ⁋ sanderson@westberks.gov.uk

Economic Development: Ms Janet Duffield, Economic Development Officer, Council Offices, Market Street, Newbury RG14 5LD ☎ 01635 519475 ⁋ janet.duffield@westberks.gov.uk

Education: Mr Ian Pearson, Deputy Corporate Director - Communites & Head of Education, West Street House, West Street, Newbury RG14 1BD ☎ 01635 519729 ⁋ ipearson@westberks.gov.uk

E-Government: Mr David Lowe, Information Manager, Council Offices, Market Street, Newbury RG14 5LD ☎ 01635 42400 ⁋ dlowe@westberks.gov.uk

Electoral Registration: Mr Phil Runacres, Elections & Registration Manager, Council Offices, Market Street, Newbury RG14 5LD ☎ 01635 519463 ⁋ prunacres@westberks.gov.uk

Emergency Planning: Mrs Carolyn Richardson, Emergency Planning Officer, Council Offices, Market Street, Newbury RG14 5LD ☎ 01635 503265 ⁋ crichardson@westberks.gov.uk

Energy Management: Mr Adrian Slaughter, Principal Energy Efficiency Officer, Council Offices, Market Street, Newbury RG14 5LD ☎ 01635 503265 ⁋ aslaughter@westberks.gov.uk

Environmental / Technical Services: Mr Paul Hendry, Countryside Manager, Council Offices, Market Street, Newbury RG14 5LD ☎ 01635 519858 ⁋ phendry@westberks.gov.uk

Environmental Health: Mr Paul Hendry, Countryside Manager, Council Offices, Market Street, Newbury RG14 5LD
☎ 01635 519858 ⁋ phendry@westberks.gov.uk

Estates, Property & Valuation: Mr Stephen Broughton, Head of Culture & Environment Protection, Council Offices, Market Street, Newbury RG14 5LD ☎ 01635 519837
⁋ slbroughton@westberks.gov.uk

Facilities: Mr Stephen Broughton, Head of Culture & Environment Protection, Council Offices, Market Street, Newbury RG14 5LD ☎ 01635 519837 ⁋ slbroughton@westberks.gov.uk

Finance: Mr Andy Walker, Head of Finance, Council Offices, Market Street, Newbury RG14 5LD ☎ 01635 519433
⁋ awalker@westberks.gov.uk

Fleet Management: Mrs Jacquie Chambers, Benefit & Expenses Assistant, Council Offices, Market Street, Newbury RG14 5LD
☎ 01635 519272 ⁋ jchambers@westberks.gov.uk

Grounds Maintenance: Mr Stewart Souden, Grounds Maintenance Manager, Council Offices, Market Street, Newbury RG14 5LD ☎ 01635 519553

Health and Safety: Mr Mike Lindenburn, Health & Safety Manager, Council Offices, Market Street, Newbury RG14 5LD
☎ 01635 519253 ⁋ mlindenburn@westberks.gov.uk

Highways: Mr Mark Edwards, Head of Highways & Transport, Council Offices, Market Street, Newbury RG14 5LD
☎ 01635 519208 ⁋ medwards@westberks.gov.uk

Housing: Mrs June Graves, Head of Care Commissioning, Housing & Safeguarding, West Street House, West Street, Newbury RG14 1BD ☎ 01635 519733 ⁋ jgraves@westberks.gov.uk

Legal: Mr David Holling, Head of Legal Services, Council Offices, Market Street, Newbury RG14 5LD ☎ 01635 519422
⁋ dholling@westberks.gov.uk

Licensing: Mr Paul Anstey, Principal Environment Health Officer, Council Offices, Market Street, Newbury RG14 5LD
☎ 01635 519002 ⁋ panstey@westberks.gov.uk

Lighting: Mr Mark Edwards, Head of Highways & Transport, Council Offices, Market Street, Newbury RG14 5LD
☎ 01635 519208 ⁋ medwards@westberks.gov.uk

Member Services: Mrs Jo Watt, Members' Services Officer, Council Offices, Market Street, Newbury RG14 5LD
☎ 01635 519242 ✆ jwatt@westberks.gov.uk

Parking: Mr Mark Edwards, Head of Highways & Transport, Council Offices, Market Street, Newbury RG14 5LD
☎ 01635 519208 ✆ medwards@westberks.gov.uk

Personnel / HR: Mr Rob O'Reilly, Head of Human Resources, Council Offices, Market Street, Newbury RG14 5LD
☎ 01635 519575 ✆ roreilly@westberks.gov.uk

Planning: Mr Gary Lugg, Head of Planning & Countryside, Council Offices, Market Street, Newbury RG14 5LD ☎ 01635 519617
✆ glugg@westberks.gov.uk

Procurement: Mr David Holling, Head of Legal Services, Council Offices, Market Street, Newbury RG14 5LD ☎ 01635 519422
✆ dholling@westberks.gov.uk

Recycling & Waste Minimisation: Mr Paul Hendry, Countryside Manager, Council Offices, Market Street, Newbury RG14 5LD
☎ 01635 519858 ✆ phendry@westberks.gov.uk

Road Safety: Mr Mark Edwards, Head of Highways & Transport, Council Offices, Market Street, Newbury RG14 5LD
☎ 01635 519208 ✆ medwards@westberks.gov.uk

Social Services (Adult): Ms Tandra Forster, Head of Adult Social Care, West Street House, West Street, Newbury RG14 1BD
☎ 01635 519736 ✆ tforster@westberks.gov.uk

Social Services (Children): Ms Rachael Wardell, Corporate Director - Communities, West Street House, West Street, Newbury RG14 1BD ☎ 01635 519723 ✆ rwardell@westberks.gov.uk

Public Health: Dr Lise Llewellyn, Director - Public Health, Easthampstead House, Town Square, Bracknell RG12 1AQ
☎ 01344 352000 ✆ lise.llewellyn@bracknell-forest.gov.uk

Staff Training: Mr Rob O'Reilly, Head of Human Resources, Council Offices, Market Street, Newbury RG14 5LD
☎ 01635 519575 ✆ roreilly@westberks.gov.uk

Street Scene: Mr Mark Edwards, Head of Highways & Transport, Council Offices, Market Street, Newbury RG14 5LD
☎ 01635 519208 ✆ medwards@westberks.gov.uk

Traffic Management: Mr Mark Edwards, Head of Highways & Transport, Council Offices, Market Street, Newbury RG14 5LD
☎ 01635 519208 ✆ medwards@westberks.gov.uk

Transport: Mr Mark Edwards, Head of Highways & Transport, Council Offices, Market Street, Newbury RG14 5LD
☎ 01635 519208 ✆ medwards@westberks.gov.uk

Transport Planner: Mr Gary Lugg, Head of Planning & Countryside, Council Offices, Market Street, Newbury RG14 5LD
☎ 01635 519617 ✆ glugg@westberks.gov.uk

Waste Collection and Disposal: Mr Paul Hendry, Countryside Manager, Council Offices, Faraday Road, Newbury RG14 2AF
☎ 01635 519858 ✆ phendry@westberks.gov.uk

Waste Collection and Disposal: Ms Jackie Ward, Waste Manager, Council Offices, Market Street, Newbury RG14 5LD
☎ 01635 519216 ✆ jward@westberks.gov.uk

Waste Management: Mr Paul Hendry, Countryside Manager, Council Offices, Faraday Road, Newbury RG14 2AF
☎ 01635 519858 ✆ phendry@westberks.gov.uk

COUNCILLORS

Chair: Webb, Quentin (CON - Bucklebury)
qwebb@westberks.gov.uk

Vice-Chair: Jackson-Doerge, Carol (CON - Burghfield)
cjacksondoerge@westberks.gov.uk

Leader of the Council: Croft, Roger (CON - Thatcham South & Crookham)
rcroft@westberks.gov.uk

Deputy Leader of the Council: Jones, Graham (CON - Lambourn Valley)
gjones@westberks.gov.uk

Group Leader: Macro, Alan (LD - Theale)
amacro@westberks.gov.uk

Ardagh-Walter, Steve (CON - Thatcham West)
sardaghwalter@westberks.gov.uk

Argyle, Peter (CON - Calcot)
pargyle@westberks.gov.uk

Bairstow, Howard (CON - Falkland)
hbairstow@westberks.gov.uk

Bale, Pamela (CON - Pangbourne)
pbale@westberks.gov.uk

Bartlett, Jeremy (CON - Greenham)
jbartlett@westberks.gov.uk

Beck, Jeff (CON - Clay Hill)
jbeck@westberks.gov.uk

Benneyworth, Dennis (CON - Victoria)
dbenneyworth@westberks.gov.uk

Boeck, Dominic (CON - Aldermaston)
dboeck@westberks.gov.uk

Bridgman, Graham (CON - Mortimer)
gbridgman@westberks.gov.uk

Bryant, Paul (CON - Speen)
pbryant@westberks.gov.uk

Chadley, Anthony (CON - Birch Copse)
achadley@westberks.gov.uk

Chopping, Keith (CON - Sulhamstead)
kchopping@westberks.gov.uk

Clifford, Jeanette (CON - Northcroft)
jclifford@westberks.gov.uk

Cole, James (CON - Kintbury)
jcole@westberks.gov.uk

Cole, Hilary (CON - Chieveley)
hcole@westberks.gov.uk

WEST BERKSHIRE

Crumly, Richard (CON - Thatcham Central)
rcrumly@westberks.gov.uk

Denton-Powell, Rob (CON - Thatcham South & Crookham)
rdentonpowell@westberks.gov.uk

Dillon, Lee (LD - Thatcham North)
ldillon@westberks.gov.uk

Doherty, Lynne (CON - Northcroft)
ldoherty@westberks.gov.uk

Drummond, Billy (LD - Greenham)
bdrummond@westberks.gov.uk

Edwards, Adrian (CON - Falkland)
adrian.edwards@westberks.gov.uk

Ellison, Sheila (CON - Thatcham North)
sellison@westberks.gov.uk

Franks, Marcus (CON - Speen)
mfranks@westberks.gov.uk

Fredrickson, James (CON - Victoria)
jfredrickson@westberks.gov.uk

Goff, Dave (CON - Clay Hill)
dgoff@westberks.gov.uk

Goodes, Nick (CON - Thatcham West)
ngoodes@westberks.gov.uk

Gopal, Manohar (CON - Calcot)
mgopal@westberks.gov.uk

Hewer, Paul (CON - Hungerford)
phewer@westberks.gov.uk

Hooker, Clive (CON - Downlands)
chooker@westberks.gov.uk

Jaques, Marigold (CON - Thatcham Central)
mjaques@westberks.gov.uk

Johnston, Mike (CON - St Johns)
mjohnston@westberks.gov.uk

Jones, Rick (CON - Purley on Thames)
rjones@westberks.gov.uk

Law, Alan (CON - Basildon)
alaw@westberks.gov.uk

Linden, Tony (CON - Birch Copse)
tlinden@westberks.gov.uk

Lock, Mollie (LD - Mortimer)
mlock@westberks.gov.uk

Lundie, Gordon (CON - Lambourn Valley)
glundie@westberks.gov.uk

Metcalfe, Tim (CON - Purley on Thames)
tmetcalfe@westberks.gov.uk

Morrin, Ian (CON - Burghfield)
imorrin@westberks.gov.uk

Pask, Graham (CON - Bucklebury)
gpask@westberks.gov.uk

Pick, Anthony (CON - St Johns)
apick@westberks.gov.uk

Podger, James (CON - Hungerford)
jpodger@westberks.gov.uk

Simpson, Garth (CON - Cold Ash)
gsimpson@westberks.gov.uk

Somner, Richard (CON - Calcot)
rsomner@westberks.gov.uk

Stansfeld, Anthony (CON - Kintbury)
astansfeld@westberks.gov.uk

von Celsing, Virginia (CON - Compton)
vvoncelsing@westberks.gov.uk

Webster, Emma (CON - Birch Copse)
ewebster@westberks.gov.uk

Zverko, Laszlo (CON - Westwood)
lzverko@westberks.gov.uk

POLITICAL COMPOSITION
CON: 48, LD: 4

COMMITTEE CHAIRS

Health & Wellbeing: Mr Graham Jones

Licensing: Mr Graham Bridgman

Planning: Ms Hilary Cole

West Devon   D

West Devon Borough Council, Kilworthy Park, Drake Road, Tavistock PL19 0BZ
☎ 01822 813600 ✆ services@westdevon.gov.uk
🖥 www.westdevon.gov.uk

FACTS AND FIGURES
Parliamentary Constituencies: Devon Central, Devon West and Torridge
EU Constituencies: South West
Election Frequency: Elections are of whole council

PRINCIPAL OFFICERS

Chief Executive: Mr Steve Jorden, Executive Director - Strategy & Commissioning & Head of Paid Service, Kilworthy Park, Drake Road, Tavistock PL19 0BZ ☎ 01803 861105 ✆ steve.jorden@swdevon.gov.uk

Deputy Chief Executive: Ms Sophie Hosking, Executive Director - Service Delivery & Commercial Development, Follaton House, Plymouth Road, Totnes TQ9 5NE ☎ 01803 861105 ✆ sophie.hosking@swdevon.gov.uk

Senior Management: Mr Darren Arulvasagam, Group Manager - Business Development, Kilworthy Park, Drake Road, Tavistock PL19 0BZ ☎ 01803 861234 ✆ darren.arulvasagam@swdevon.gov.uk

Senior Management: Mrs Helen Dobby, Group Manager - Commercial Services, Kilworthy Park, Drake Road, Tavistock PL19 0BZ ☎ 01822 813600 ✆ helen.dobby@swdevon.gov.uk

Senior Management: Mr Steve Mullineaux, Group Manager - Support Services, Kilworthy Park, Drake Road, Tavistock PL19 0BZ ☎ 01822 813600 ✆ steve.mullineaux@swdevon.gov.uk

Community Planning: Mr Ross Kennerley, Lead Specialist - Place Strategy, Kilworthy Park, Drake Road, Tavistock PL19 0BZ ☎ 01822 813647 ✆ ross.kennerley@swdevon.gov.uk

Computer Management: Mr Mike Ward, ICT Community of Practice Lead, Kilworthy Park, Drake Road, Tavistock PL19 0BZ ☎ 01803 861234 ◌ mike.ward@swdevon.gov.uk

Economic Development: Ms Nadine Trout, Tourism Officer, Kilworthy Park, Drake Road, Tavistock PL19 0BZ ☎ 01822 813600 ◌ nadine.trout@swdevon.gov.uk

Electoral Registration: Ms Clare Chapman, Electoral Services Officer, Kilworthy Park, Drake Road, Tavistock PL19 0BZ ☎ 01822 813664 ◌ clare.chapman@westdevon.gov.uk

Emergency Planning: Mr James Kershaw, Head of Emergency Planning, Kilworthy Park, Drake Road, Tavistock PL19 0BZ ☎ 01822 813600 ◌ james.kershaw@swdevon.gov.uk

Estates, Property & Valuation: Mr Chris Brook, Community of Practice - Assets, Kilworthy Park, Drake Road, Tavistock PL19 0BZ ☎ 01822 813600 ◌ chris.brook@swdevon.gov.uk

Finance: Miss Lisa Buckle, Head of Finance & Audit, Kilworthy Park, Drake Road, Tavistock PL19 0BZ ☎ 01822 813644 ◌ lisa.buckle@westdevon.gov.uk

Grounds Maintenance: Mrs Helen Dobby, Group Manager - Commercial Services, Kilworthy Park, Drake Road, Tavistock PL19 0BZ ☎ 01822 813600 ◌ helen.dobby@swdevon.gov.uk

Housing: Ms Isabel Blake, Head of Housing, Kilworthy Park, Drake Road, Tavistock PL19 0BZ ☎ 01822 813600 ◌ isabel.blake@swdevon.gov.uk

Legal: Mrs Catherine Bowen, Borough Solicitor, Kilworthy Park, Drake Road, Tavistock PL19 0BZ ☎ 01822 813666 ◌ cbowen@westdevon.gov.uk

Leisure and Cultural Services: Mr Jon Parkinson, Leisure & Recreation Officer, Kilworthy Park, Drake Road, Tavistock PL19 0BZ ☎ 01822 813698 ◌ jon.parkinson@southhams.gov.uk

Member Services: Mr Darryl White, Democratic Services Manager, Kilworthy Park, Drake Road, Tavistock PL19 0BZ ☎ 01822 813662 ◌ darryl.white@swdevon.gov.uk

Parking: Mrs Catherine Aubertin, Car Parking & Contracts Performance Manager, Kilworthy Park, Drake Road, Tavistock PL19 0BZ ☎ 01822 813650 ◌ caubertin@westdevon.gov.uk

Personnel / HR: Mr Andy Wilson, Head of Corporate Services, Kilworthy Park, Drake Road, Tavistock PL19 0BZ ☎ 01822 813600 ◌ andy.wilson@swdevon.gov.uk

Street Scene: Mrs Catherine Aubertin, Car Parking & Contracts Performance Manager, Kilworthy Park, Drake Road, Tavistock PL19 0BZ ☎ 01822 813650 ◌ caubertin@westdevon.gov.uk

Waste Collection and Disposal: Mrs Jane Savage, Waste Reduction & Recycling Officer, Kilworthy Park, Drake Road, Tavistock PL19 0BZ ☎ 01822 813655 ◌ jsavage@westdevon.gov.uk

Waste Management: Mrs Helen Dobby, Group Manager - Commercial Services, Kilworthy Park, Drake Road, Tavistock PL19 0BZ ☎ 01822 813600 ◌ helen.dobby@swdevon.gov.uk

COUNCILLORS

Mayor: Sheldon, John (CON - Tavistock North) cllr.john.sheldon@westdevon.gov.uk

Deputy Mayor: Moody, Jeffrey (IND - Tavistock North) cllr.jeffrey.moody@westdevon.gov.uk

Leader of the Council: Sanders, Philip (CON - Buckland Manochorum) cllr.philip.sanders@westdevon.gov.uk

Deputy Leader of the Council: Baldwin, Bob (CON - Milton Ford) clr.bob.baldwin@westdevon.gov.uk

Ball, Kevin (CON - Okehampton North) cllr.kevin.ball@westdevon.gov.uk

Benson, Mike (CON - Bere Ferrers) cllr.mike.benson@westdevon.gov.uk

Cann, William (IND - South Tawton) cllr.william.cann@westdevon.gov.uk

Cheadle, Ric (IND - Buckland Monachorum) cllr.ric.cheadle@westdevon.gov.uk

Cloke, David (IND - Burrator) cllr.david.cloke@westdevon.gov.uk

Davies, Mike (CON - Okehampton North) cllr.mike.davies@westdevon.gov.uk

Edmonds, Chris (IND - Tamarside) cllr.chris.edmonds@westevon.gov.uk

Evans, Jess (CON - Tavistock South West) cllr.jess.evans@westdevon.gov.uk

Hockridge, John (IND - Bridestowe) cllr.john.hockridge@westdevon.gov.uk

Jory, Neil (CON - Tavistock North) cllr.neil.jory@westdevon.gov.uk

Kimber, Patrick (CON - Hatherleigh) cllr.patrick.kimber@westdevon.gov.uk

Leech, Tony (IND - Okehampton East) cllr.tony.leech@westdevon.gov.uk

McInnes, James (CON - Lew Valley) cllr.james.mcinnes@westdevon.gov.uk

Mott, Caroline (CON - Bridestowe) cllr.caroline.mott@westdevon.gov.uk

Moyse, Diana (CON - Burrator) cllr.diana.moyse@westdevon.gov.uk

Musgrave, Robin (LD - Bere Ferrers) cllr.robin.musgrave@westdevon.gov.uk

Oxborough, Robert (CON - Tavistock South) cllr.robert.oxborough@westdevon.gov.uk

Parker, Graham (CON - Tavistock South West) cllr.graham.parker@westdevon.gov.uk

Pearce, Terry (IND - Mary Tavy) cllr.terry.pearce@westdevon.gov.uk

Ridgers, Paul (CON - Drewsteignton) cllr.paul.ridgers@westdevon.gov.uk

WEST DEVON

Roberts, Annabel (CON - Dartmoor)
cllr.annabel.roberts@westdevon.gov.uk

Sampson, Robert (IND - Chagford)
cllr.robert.sampson@westdevon.gov.uk

Samuel, Lois (CON - Exbourne)
cllr.lois.samuel@westdevon.gov.uk

Sellis, Debo (CON - Walkham)
cllr.debo.sellis@westdevon.gov.uk

Stephens, Ben (CON - Okehampton South)
cllr.ben.stephens@westdevon.gov.uk

Watts, Louise (CON - Exbourne)
cllr.louise.watts@westdevon.gov.uk

Yelland, Julie (CON - Okehampton South)
cllr.julie.yelland@westdevon.gov.uk

POLITICAL COMPOSITION
CON: 21, IND: 9, LD: 1

West Dorset   D

West Dorset District Council, Stratton House, 58-60 High
West Street, Dorchester DT1 1UZ
☎ 01305 251010 🖷 01305 251481 🖳 www.dorsetforyou.com

FACTS AND FIGURES
Parliamentary Constituencies: Dorset West
EU Constituencies: South West
Election Frequency: Elections are of whole council

PRINCIPAL OFFICERS

Chief Executive: Mr Matt Prosser, Chief Executive, South Walks
House, South Walks Road, Dorchester DT1 1UZ ☎ 01305 251010

Assistant Chief Executive: Mr Stuart Caundle, Assistant Chief
Executive, South Walks House, South Walks Road, Dorchester
DT1 1UZ ☎ 01258 484010 ✆ scaundle@north-dorset.co.uk

Senior Management: Mr Martin Hamilton, Strategic Director,
South Walks House, South Walks Road, Dorchester DT1 1UZ
☎ 01305 838086 ✆ m.hamilton@westdorset-weymouth.gov.uk

Senior Management: Mr Stephen Hill, Strategic Director, South
Walks House, South Walks Road, Dorchester DT1 1UZ
☎ 01258 484034 ✆ shill@north-dorset.gov.uk

Senior Management: Mr Jason Vaughan, Strategic Director,
South Walks House, South Walks Road, Dorchester DT1 1UZ
☎ 01305 838233; 01305 251010
✆ j.vaughan@westdorset-weymouth.gov.uk

Architect, Building / Property Services: Mr David Brown, Head
of Assets & Infrastructure, South Walks House, South Walks Road,
Dorchester DT1 1UZ ☎ 01305 252297
✆ d.brown@westdorset-weymouth.gov.uk

Best Value: Ms Julie Strange, Head of Financial Services, Council
Offices, North Quay, Weymouth DT4 8TA ☎ 01305 838252; 01305
251010 ✆ j.strange@westdorset-weymouth.gov.uk

Building Control: Mr David Potter, Building Control Manager,
South Walks House, South Walks Road, Dorchester DT1 1UZ
☎ 01305 252258 ✆ d.potter@westdorset-weymouth.gov.uk

PR / Communications: Ms Penny Mell, Head of Business
Improvement, South Walks House, South Walks Road, Dorchester
DT1 1UZ ☎ 01305 838371 ✆ p.mell@westdorset-weymouth.gov.uk

Community Planning: Ms Hilary Jordan, Head of Planning,
Community & Policy Development, South Walks House, South
Walks Road, Dorchester DT1 1UZ ☎ 01305 252303
✆ h.jordan@westdorset-weymouth.gov.uk

Community Safety: Mr Graham Duggan, Head of Community
Protection, South Walks House, South Walks Road, Dorchester DT1
1UZ ☎ 01305 252285; 01305 251010
✆ g.duggan@westdorset-weymouth.gov.uk

Computer Management: Ms Penny Mell, Head of Business
Improvement, South Walks House, South Walks Road, Dorchester
DT1 1UZ ☎ 01305 838371 ✆ p.mell@westdorset-weymouth.gov.uk

Customer Service: Ms Penny Mell, Head of Business
Improvement, South Walks House, South Walks Road, Dorchester
DT1 1UZ ☎ 01305 838371 ✆ p.mell@westdorset-weymouth.gov.uk

Economic Development: Mr Trevor Hedger, Senior Economic
Regeneration Officer, South Walks House, South Walks Road,
Dorchester DT1 1UZ ☎ 01305 252378
✆ t.hedger@westdorset-weymouth.gov.uk

Electoral Registration: Ms Sue Bonham-Lovett, Electoral
Services Manager, South Walks House, South Walks Road,
Dorchester DT1 1UZ ☎ 01305 838477; 01305 251010
✆ s.bonham-lovett@westdorset-weymouth.gov.uk

Emergency Planning: Mr Grant Armfield, Engineering, Asset &
Emergency Planning Manager, South Walks House, South Walks
Road, Dorchester DT1 1UZ ☎ 01305 838213
✆ grantarmfield@weymouth.gov.uk

Energy Management: Mr Bob Savage, Senior Building Services
Engineer, South Walks House, South Walks Road, Dorchester
DT1 1UZ ☎ 01305 838318 ✆ bobsavage@weymouth.gov.uk

Environmental / Technical Services: Mr David Brown, Head
of Assets & Infrastructure, South Walks House, South Walks Road,
Dorchester DT1 1UZ ☎ 01305 252297
✆ d.brown@westdorset-weymouth.gov.uk

Environmental Health: Mr Graham Duggan, Head of Community
Protection, Stratton House, 58-60 High West Street, Dorchester
DT1 1UZ ☎ 01305 252285; 01305 251010
✆ g.duggan@westdorset-weymouth.gov.uk

Estates, Property & Valuation: Mr Greg Northcote, Head of
Estates, South Walks House, South Walks Road, Dorchester DT1
1UZ ☎ 01305 838268 ✆ g.northcote@westdorset-weymouth.gov.uk

Events Manager: Mr Nick Thornley, Head of Economy, Leisure & Tourism, South Walks House, South Walks Road, Dorchester DT1 1UZ ☎ 01305 252474; 01305 251010 ✆ n.thornley@westdorset-weymouth.gov.uk

Finance: Mr Jason Vaughan, Strategic Director, West Dorset District Council, 58/60 High West Street, Dorchester DT1 1UZ ☎ 01305 838233; 01305 251010 ✆ j.vaughan@westdorset-weymouth.gov.uk

Fleet Management: Ms Sally-Ann Arden-Nixon, Fleet Transport Co-ordinator, South Walks House, South Walks Road, Dorchester DT1 1UZ ☎ 01305 838447 ✆ sa.arden-nixon@westdorset-weymouth.gov.uk

Health and Safety: Mr Richard Noakes, Health, Safety & Welfare Officer, South Walks House, South Walks Road, Dorchester DT1 1UZ ☎ 01305 838356 ✆ r.noakes@westdorset-weymouth.gov.uk

Home Energy Conservation: Mr Clive Milone, Head of Housing, South Walks House, South Walks Road, Dorchester DT1 1UZ ☎ 01305 252313 ✆ c.milone@westdorset-weymouth.gov.uk

Housing: Mr Chris Branch, Housing Solutions Manager, South Walks House, South Walks Road, Dorchester DT1 1UZ ☎ 01305 838460 ✆ c.branch@westdorset-weymouth.gov.uk

Housing Maintenance: Mr Geoff Joy, Housing Improvement Manager, South Walks House, South Walks Road, Dorchester DT1 1UZ ☎ 01305 252286 ✆ g.joy@westdorset-weymouth.gov.uk

Legal: Mr Roger Greene, Legal Services Manager (Property & Litigation), South Walks House, South Walks Road, Dorchester DT1 1UZ ☎ 01305 252253 ✆ r.greene@westdorset-weymouth.gov.uk

Leisure and Cultural Services: Mr Nick Thornley, Head of Economy, Leisure & Tourism, South Walks House, South Walks Road, Dorchester DT1 1UZ ☎ 01305 252474; 01305 251010 ✆ n.thornley@westdorset-weymouth.gov.uk

Licensing: Ms Sue Moore, Business Licensing Manager, South Walks House, South Walks Road, Dorchester DT1 1UZ ☎ 01305 838205; 01305 252474 ✆ s.moore@westdorset-weymouth.gov.uk

Lottery Funding, Charity and Voluntary: Ms Jane Nicklen, Community Planning & Development Manager, South Walks House, South Walks Road, Dorchester DT1 1UZ ☎ 01305 252358 ✆ j.nicklen@westdorset-weymouth.gov.uk

Member Services: Ms Susan Carne, Democratic Services Manager, South Walks House, South Waks Road, Dorchester DT1 1UZ ☎ 01305 252216 ✆ s.carne@westdorset-weymouth.gov.uk

Parking: Mr Jack Creeber, Parking & Transport Manager, South Walks House, South Walks Road, Dorchester DT1 1UZ ☎ 01305 838349 ✆ j.creeber@westdorset-weymouth.gov.uk

Partnerships: Ms Caron Starkey, Business Change Manager, South Walks House, South Walks Road, Dorchester DT1 1UZ ☎ 01305 838277 ✆ c.starkey@westdorset-weymouth.gov.uk

Personnel / HR: Ms Mel Horton, Corporate Mangaer - Planning, Community & Policy Development, South Walks House, South Walks Road, Dorchester DT1 1UZ ☎ 01305 252473 ✆ m.horton@westdorset-weymouth.gov.uk

Planning: Ms Jean Marshall, Head of Planning, Development Management & Building Control, South Walks House, South Walks Road, Dorchester DT1 1UZ ☎ 01305 252230 ✆ j.marshall@westdorset-weymouth.gov.uk

Procurement: Ms Julia Long, Procurement Officer, South Walks House, South Walks Road, Dorchester DT1 1UZ ☎ 01305 838543 ✆ j.long@westdorset-weymouth.gov.uk

Regeneration: Mr Trevor Hedger, Senior Economic Regeneration Officer, South Walks House, South Walks Road, Dorchester DT1 1UZ ☎ 01305 252378 ✆ t.hedger@westdorset-weymouth.gov.uk

Sustainable Development: Ms Jean Marshall, Head of Planning, Development Management & Building Control, South Walks House, South Walks Road, Dorchester DT1 1UZ ☎ 01305 252230 ✆ j.marshall@westdorset-weymouth.gov.uk

Tourism: Mr Nick Thornley, Head of Economy, Leisure & Tourism, Stratton House, 58-60 High West Street, Dorchester DT1 1UZ ☎ 01305 252474; 01305 251010 ✆ n.thornley@westdorset-weymouth.gov.uk

Children's Play Areas: Mrs Tara Williams, Parks Surpervisor, Stratton House, 58-60 High West Street, Dorchester DT1 1UZ ☎ 01305 838297 ✆ t.williams@westdorset-weymouth.gov.uk

COUNCILLORS

Chair: Shorland, Peter (CON - Sherborne West)
cllrp.shorland@westdorset-dc.gov.uk

Vice-Chair: Dunseith, Jean (CON - Chickerell)
cllrj.dunseith@westdorset-dc.gov.uk

Leader of the Council: Alford, Anthony (CON - Netherbury)
cllra.alford@westdorset-dc.gov.uk

Deputy Leader of the Council: Thacker, Alan (CON - Broadmayne)
cllra.thacker@westdorset-dc.gov.uk

Barrowcliff, Peter (CON - Beaminster)
cllrp.barrowcliff@westdorset-dc.gov.uk

Bartlett, Thomas (CON - Chesil Bank)
cllrt.bartlett@westdorset-dc.gov.uk

Brown, Sandra (CON - Bridport South & Bothenhampton)
cllrs.brown@westdorset-dc.gov.uk

Bundy, Nigel (CON - Broadmayne & Crossways)
nigelbundy8@btinternet.com

Canning, Andy (LD - Dorchester North)
cllra.canning@westdorset-dc.gov.uk

Christopher, Simon (CON - Chideock & Symondsbury)
cllrs.christopher@westdorset-dc.gov.uk

Coatsworth, Ronald (CON - Bradpole)
cllrr.coatsworth@westdorset-dc.gov.uk

Cooke, Patrick (CON - Puddletown)
cllrp.cooke@westdorset-dc.gov.uk

WEST DORSET

Day, Keith (CON - Bridport North)
keithaday@aol.com

Duke, Gerald (CON - Dorchester West)
cllrg.duke@westdorset-dc.gov.uk

Elliott, Dominic (CON - Sherborne East)
cllrd.elliott@westdorset-dc.gov.uk

Farmer, Terry (CON - Sherborne East)
cllrt.farmer@westdorset-dc.gov.uk

Freeman, Robert (CON - Winterborne St Martin)
cllrr.freeman@westdorset-dc.gov.uk

Gardner, Ian (CON - Chickerell)
ian_c_gardner@talk21.com

Gould, Robert (CON - Queen Thorne)
cllrr.gould@westdorset-dc.gov.uk

Hall, Matthew (LD - Sherborne West)
mnwh1976@sky.com

Harries, Tim (LD - Dorchester East)
tim.harries49@gmail.com

Haynes, Jill (CON - Maiden Newton)
jill.haynes@dorsetcc.gov.uk

Hiscock, Peter (CON - Piddle Valley)
cllrp.hiscock@westdorest-dc.gov.uk

Horsington, Fred (CON - Cerne Valley)
cllrf.horsington@westdorset-dc.gov.uk

Hosford, Susie (LD - Dorchester North)
shosford@btinternet.com

Jones, Stella (LD - Dorchester East)
stella@sywardcottage.co.uk

Jones, Trevor (LD - Dorchester West)
trevor@sywardcottage.co.uk

Kayes, Ros (LD - Bridport North)
roskayes@gmail.com

Lawrence, Margaret (CON - Yetminster & Cam Vale)
cllrm.lawrence@westdorset-dc.gov.uk

Legg, Robin (LD - Bradford Abbas)
robin.legg@btinternet.com

McKenzie, Frances (CON - Bridport South & Bothenhampton)
fmfkmckenzie28@gmail.com

Penfold, Mary (CON - Frome Valley)
cllrm.penfold@westdorset-dc.gov.uk

Potter, Robin (LD - Dorchester South)
cllrr.potter@westdorset-dc.gov.uk

Rennie, Molly (LD - Dorchester South)
mollymadgerennie@hotmail.co.uk

Rickard, David (LD - Bridport South West)
cllrd.rickard@westdorset-dc.gov.uk

Roberts, Mark (CON - Loders)
lucullas.luccas@virgin.net

Russell, John (CON - Burton Bradstock)
cllrj.russell@westdorset-dc.gov.uk

Sewell, Jacqui (CON - Broadwindsor)
cllrj.sewell@westdorset-dc.gov.uk

Symonds, George (CON - Lyme Regis & Charmouth)
cllrg.symonds@westdorset-dc.gov.uk

Taylor, David (LD - Dorchester North)
cllrd.taylor@westdorset-dc.gov.uk

Turner, Daryl (CON - Lyme Regis)
cllrd.turner@westdorset-dc.gov.uk

Yarker, Timothy (CON - Cerne Valley)
cllrt.yarker@westdorset-dc.gov.uk

POLITICAL COMPOSITION
CON: 30, LD: 12

COMMITTEE CHAIRS

Audit: Mr Andy Canning

Licensing: Mr Ronald Coatsworth

Planning: Mr Fred Horsington

West Dunbartonshire   S

West Dunbartonshire Council, Council Offices, Garshake
Road, Dumbarton G82 3PU
☎ 01389 737000 ⌨ www.west-dunbarton.gov.uk

FACTS AND FIGURES
Parliamentary Constituencies: Dunbartonshire West
EU Constituencies: Scotland
Election Frequency: Elections are of whole council

PRINCIPAL OFFICERS

Chief Executive: Mrs Joyce White, Chief Executive, Council
Offices, Garshake Road, Dumbarton G82 3PU ☎ 01389 737667
⌁ joyce.white@west-dunbarton.gov.uk

Senior Management: Mr Richard Cairns, Strategic Director -
Regeneration, Environment & Growth, Council Offices, Garshake
Road, Dumbarton G82 3PU ☎ 01389 737603
⌁ richard.cairns@west-dunbarton.gov.uk

Senior Management: Mr Keith Redpath, Chief Officer - Health &
Care Partnership, Council Offices, Garshake Road, Dumbarton
G82 3PU ☎ 01389 737526 ⌁ keith.redpath@ggc.scot.nhs.uk

Senior Management: Mrs Angela Wilson, Strategic Director -
Transformation & Public Sector Reform, Council Offices, Garshake
Road, Dumbarton G82 3PU ☎ 01389 737607
⌁ am.wilson@west-dunbarton.gov.uk

Access Officer / Social Services (Disability): Mr Ricardo Rea,
Equalities Officer, Council Offices, Garshake Road, Dumbarton
G82 3PU ☎ 03189 737198 ⌁ ricardo.rea@west-dunbarton.gov.uk

Architect, Building / Property Services: Mr Jim McAloon,
Strategic Lead - Regeneration, Council Offices, Garshake Road,
Dumbarton G82 3PU ☎ 01389 737401
⌁ jim.mcaloon@west-dunbarton.gov.uk

Best Value: Mrs Angela Wilson, Strategic Director -
Transformation & Public Sector Reform, Council Offices, Garshake
Road, Dumbarton G82 3PU ☎ 01389 737607 ⌁ am.wilson@west-
dunbarton.gov.uk

Building Control: Ms Pamela Clifford, Planning & Building Standards Manager, Aurora House, Queens Quay, Clydebank G81 1BF ☎ 01389 738656 📧 pamela.clifford@west-dunbarton.gov.uk

Catering Services: Mrs Lynda McLaughlin, Leisure & Facilities Manager, Elm Road, Dumbarton G82 1NR ☎ 01389 602097 📧 lynda.mclaughlin@west-dunbarton.gov.uk

Children / Youth Services: Ms Jackie Irvine, Head of Children's Health, Care & Criminal Justice Services, Council Offices, Garshake Road, Dumbarton G82 3PU ☎ 01389 737709 📧 jackie.irvine@ggc.scot.nhs.uk

Children / Youth Services: Ms Laura Mason, Chief Education Officer, Council Offices, Garshake Road, Dumbarton G82 3PU ☎ 01389 737000 📧 laura.mason@west-dunbarton.gov.uk

Civil Registration: Mr George Hawthorn, Manager - Administration & Democratic Services, Council Offices, Garshake Road, Dumbarton G82 3PU ☎ 01389 737204 📧 george.hawthorn@west-dunbarton.gov.uk

PR / Communications: Mr Malcolm Bennie, Strategic Lead - Communications, Culture & Communities, Council Offices, Garshake Road, Dumbarton G82 3PU ☎ 01389 737187 📧 malcolm.bennie@west-dunbarton.gov.uk

Community Planning: Mr Peter Barry, Strategic Lead - Housing & Employability, Council Offices, Garshake Road, Dumbarton G82 3PU ☎ 01389 737573 📧 peter.barry@west-dunbarton.gov.uk

Community Safety: Ms Janice Winder, Partnership Officer, Levenvalley Enterprise Centre, Castlehill Road, Dumbarton G82 5BN ☎ 01389 772127 📧 janice.winder@west-dunbarton.gov.uk

Computer Management: Ms Vicki Rogers, Strategic Lead - People & Technology, Council Offices, Garshake Road, Dumbarton G82 3PU ☎ 01389 737534 📧 vicki.rogers@west-dunbarton.gov.uk

Consumer Protection and Trading Standards: Mr Graham Pollock, Manager - Regulatory Services, Aurora House, Queens Quay, Clydebank G81 1BF ☎ 0141 951 7972 📧 graham.pollock@west-dunbarton.gov.uk

Corporate Services: Mrs Angela Wilson, Strategic Director - Transformation & Public Sector Reform, Council Offices, Garshake Road, Dumbarton G82 3PU ☎ 01389 737607 📧 am.wilson@west-dunbarton.gov.uk

Customer Service: Mr Stephen Daly, Customer Services Manager, Council Offices, Garshake Road, Dumbarton G82 3PU ☎ 01389 737263 📧 stephen.daly@west-dunbarton.gov.uk

Direct Labour: Mr Martin Feeney, Building Services Manager, Whitecrook, Concho Street, Clydebank G81 1RQ ☎ 01389 737000 📧 martin.feeney@west-dunbarton.gov.uk

Economic Development: Mr Michael McGuinness, Economic Development Manager, Council Offices, Garshake Road, Dumbarton G82 3PU ☎ 01389 737415 📧 michael.mcguinness@west-dunbarton.gov.uk

Education: Ms Laura Mason, Chief Education Officer, Council Offices, Garshake Road, Dumbarton G82 3PU ☎ 01389 737000 📧 laura.mason@west-dunbarton.gov.uk

E-Government: Mr Peter Hessett, Strategic Lead - Regulatory, Council Offices, Garshake Road, Dumbarton G82 3PU ☎ 01389 737801 📧 peter.hessett@west-dunbarton.gov.uk

Electoral Registration: Mr David Thomson, Assessor & Electoral Registration Officer, 235 Dumbarton Road, Clydebank G81 4XJ ☎ 0141 562 1200

Emergency Planning: Mr John Duffy, Section Head of Risk, Health & Safety, Council Offices, Garshake Road, Dumbarton G82 3PU ☎ 01389 737897 📧 john.duffy2@west-dunbarton.gov.uk

Energy Management: Mr Craig Jardine, Corporate Asset Manager, Council Offices, Garshake Road, Dumbarton G82 3PU ☎ 01389 737829 📧 craig.jardine@west-dunbarton.gov.uk

Environmental / Technical Services: Mr Graham Pollock, Manager - Regulatory Services, Aurora House, Queens Quay, Clydebank G81 1BF ☎ 0141 951 7972 📧 graham.pollock@west-dunbarton.gov.uk

Environmental Health: Mr Graham Pollock, Manager - Regulatory Services, Aurora House, Queens Quay, Clydebank G81 1BF ☎ 0141 951 7972 📧 graham.pollock@west-dunbarton.gov.uk

Estates, Property & Valuation: Mr Stuart Gibson, Assets Co-ordinator, Council Offices, Garshake Road, Dumbarton G82 3PU ☎ 01389 737157 📧 stuart.gibson@west-dunbarton.gov.uk

European Liaison: Mr Michael McGuinness, Economic Development Manager, Council Offices, Garshake Road, Dumbarton G82 3PU ☎ 01389 737415 📧 michael.mcguinness@west-dunbarton.gov.uk

Events Manager: Mrs Lynda McLaughlin, Leisure & Facilities Manager, Elm Road, Dumbarton G82 1NR ☎ 01389 602097 📧 lynda.mclaughlin@west-dunbarton.gov.uk

Facilities: Mrs Lynda McLaughlin, Leisure & Facilities Manager, Elm Road, Dumbarton G82 1NR ☎ 01389 602097 📧 lynda.mclaughlin@west-dunbarton.gov.uk

Finance: Mr Stephen West, Strategic Lead - Resources, Council Offices, Garshake Road, Dumbarton G82 3PU ☎ 01389 737000 📧 stephen.west@west-dunbarton.gov.uk

Fleet Management: Mr Rodney Thornton, Fleet & Waste Services Manager, Council Offices, Richmond Street, Clydebank G82 1RF ☎ 01389 738731 📧 rodney.thornton@west-dunbarton.gov.uk

Grounds Maintenance: Mr Ian Bain, Greenspace Manager, Elm Road, Dumbarton G82 1NR ☎ 01389 608405 📧 ian.bain@west-dunbarton.gov.uk

Health and Safety: Mr John Duffy, Section Head of Risk, Health & Safety, Council Offices, Garshake Road, Dumbarton G82 3PU ☎ 01389 737897 📧 john.duffy2@west-dunbarton.gov.uk

WEST DUNBARTONSHIRE

Highways: Mr Jack McAulay, Roads & Transportation Manager, Council Offices, Garshake Road, Dumbarton G82 3PU
☎ 01389 737612 ⊗ jack.mcaulay@west-dunbarton.gov.uk

Housing: Mr Peter Barry, Strategic Lead - Housing & Employability, Council Offices, Garshake Road, Dumbarton G82 3PU ☎ 01389 737573 ⊗ peter.barry@west-dunbarton.gov.uk

Housing Maintenance: Mr Peter Barry, Strategic Lead - Housing & Employability, Council Offices, Garshake Road, Dumbarton G82 3PU ☎ 01389 737573 ⊗ peter.barry@west-dunbarton.gov.uk

Legal: Mr Peter Hessett, Strategic Lead - Regulatory, Council Offices, Garshake Road, Dumbarton G82 3PU ☎ 01389 737801 ⊗ peter.hessett@west-dunbarton.gov.uk

Licensing: Mr Peter Hessett, Strategic Lead - Regulatory, Council Offices, Garshake Road, Dumbarton G82 3PU ☎ 01389 737801 ⊗ peter.hessett@west-dunbarton.gov.uk

Lifelong Learning: Ms Lorna Campbell, Section Head of Community, Learning & Development, Aurora House, Queens Quay, Clydebank G81 1BF ☎ 0141 562 871 ⊗ lorna.campbell@west-dunbarton.gov.uk

Lighting: Mr Jack McAulay, Roads & Transportation Manager, Council Offices, Garshake Road, Dumbarton G82 3PU
☎ 01389 737612 ⊗ jack.mcaulay@west-dunbarton.gov.uk

Member Services: Mr George Hawthorn, Manager - Administration & Democratic Services, Council Offices, Garshake Road, Dumbarton G82 3PU ☎ 01389 737204 ⊗ george.hawthorn@west-dunbarton.gov.uk

Parking: Mr Jack McAulay, Roads & Transportation Manager, Council Offices, Garshake Road, Dumbarton G82 3PU
☎ 01389 737612 ⊗ jack.mcaulay@west-dunbarton.gov.uk

Personnel / HR: Ms Vicki Rogers, Strategic Lead - People & Technology, Council Offices, Garshake Road, Dumbarton G82 3PU ☎ 01389 737584 ⊗ vicki.rogers@west-dunbarton.gov.uk

Planning: Ms Pamela Clifford, Planning & Building Standards Manager, 3 Aurora House, Aurora Avenue, Clydebank C81 1BF ☎ 01389 738656 ⊗ pamela.clifford@west-dunbarton.gov.uk

Procurement: Mr Ian Hutchinson, Senior Procurement Officer, Council Offices, Garshake Road, Dumbarton G82 3PU
☎ 01389 737664 ⊗ ian.hutchinson@west-dunbarton.gov.uk

Public Libraries: Ms Gill Graham, Manager - Libraries & Culture, 19 Poplar Road, Dumbarton G82 2RJ ☎ 01389 737000 ⊗ gill.graham@west-dunbarton.gov.uk

Recycling & Waste Minimisation: Mr Rodney Thornton, Fleet & Waste Services Manager, Council Offices, Richmond Street, Clydebank G82 1RF ☎ 01389 738731 ⊗ rodney.thornton@west-dunbarton.gov.uk

Regeneration: Mr Jim McAloon, Strategic Lead - Regeneration, Council Offices, Garshake Road, Dumbarton G82 3PU
☎ 01389 737401 ⊗ jim.mcaloon@west-dunbarton.gov.uk

Road Safety: Mr Jack McAulay, Roads & Transportation Manager, Council Offices, Garshake Road, Dumbarton G82 3PU
☎ 01389 737612 ⊗ jack.mcaulay@west-dunbarton.gov.uk

Social Services: Ms Jackie Irvine, Head of Children's Health, Care & Criminal Justice Services, Council Offices, Garshake Road, Dumbarton G82 3PU ☎ 01389 737709 ⊗ jackie.irvine@ggc.scot.nhs.uk

Social Services (Adult): Ms Chris McNeill, Head of Community Health & Care Services, Council Offices, Garshake Road, Dumbarton G82 3PU ☎ 01389 737000 ⊗ chris.mcneill@west-dunbarton.gov.uk

Social Services (Children): Ms Chris McNeill, Head of Community Health & Care Services, Council Offices, Garshake Road, Dumbarton G82 3PU ☎ 01389 737000 ⊗ chris.mcneill@west-dunbarton.gov.uk

Tourism: Mr Michael McGuinness, Economic Development Manager, Council Offices, Garshake Road, Dumbarton G82 3PU
☎ 01389 737415 ⊗ michael.mcguinness@west-dunbarton.gov.uk

Town Centre: Mr Michael McGuinness, Economic Development Manager, Council Offices, Garshake Road, Dumbarton G82 3PU
☎ 01389 737415 ⊗ michael.mcguinness@west-dunbarton.gov.uk

Traffic Management: Mr Jack McAulay, Roads & Transportation Manager, Council Offices, Garshake Road, Dumbarton G82 3PU ☎ 01389 737612 ⊗ jack.mcaulay@west-dunbarton.gov.uk

Transport: Mr Jack McAulay, Roads & Transportation Manager, Council Offices, Garshake Road, Dumbarton G82 3PU
☎ 01389 737612 ⊗ jack.mcaulay@west-dunbarton.gov.uk

Transport Planner: Mr Ronald Dinnie, Strategic Lead - Environment & Neighbourhood, Council Offices, Garshake Road, Dumbarton G82 3PU ☎ 01389 737601 ⊗ ronald.dinnie@west-dunbarton.gov.uk

Waste Collection and Disposal: Mr Rodney Thornton, Fleet & Waste Services Manager, Council Offices, Richmond Street, Clydebank G82 1RF ☎ 01389 738731 ⊗ rodney.thornton@west-dunbarton.gov.uk

Children's Play Areas: Mr Ian Bain, Greenspace Manager, Elm Road, Dumbarton G82 1NR ☎ 01389 608405 ⊗ ian.bain@west-dunbarton.gov.uk

COUNCILLORS

ProvostMcAllister, Douglas (LAB - Kilpatrick) douglas.mcallister@west-dunbarton.gov.uk

Leader of the Council: Rooney, Martin (LAB - Lomond) martin.rooney@west-dunbarton.gov.uk

Agnew, Denis (IND - Clydebank Central) denis.agnew@west-dunbarton.gov.uk

Black, George (IND - Dumbarton) george.black@west-dunbarton.gov.uk

Bollan, James (SSP - Leven) james.bollan@west-dunbarton.gov.uk

Brown, Jim (SNP - Clydebank Central)
jim.brown@west-dunbarton.gov.uk

Casey, Gail (LAB - Clydebank Waterfront)
gail.casey@west-dunbarton.gov.uk

Finn, Jim (SNP - Kilpatrick)
jim.finn@west-dunbarton.gov.uk

Hendrie, William (SNP - Clydebank Waterfront)
william.hendrie@west-dunbarton.gov.uk

McBride, David (LAB - Dumbarton)
david.mcbride@west-dunbarton.gov.uk

McColl, Jonathan (SNP - Lomond)
jonathan.mccoll@west-dunbarton.gov.uk

McGinty, Michelle (LAB - Leven)
michelle.mcginty@west-dunbarton.gov.uk

McGlinchey, Patrick (LAB - Clydebank Central)
patrick.mcglinchey@west-dunbarton.gov.uk

McNair, Marie (IND - Clydebank Waterfront)
marie.mcnair@west-dunbarton.gov.uk

Millar, John (LAB - Leven)
john.millar@west-dunbarton.gov.uk

Mooney, John (LAB - Clydebank Central)
john.mooney@west-dunbarton.gov.uk

Murray, Ian (SNP - Dumbarton)
ian.murray@west-dunbarton.gov.uk

O'Neill, Lawrence (LAB - Kilpatrick)
lawrence.oneill@west-dunbarton.gov.uk

Rainey, Tommy (LAB - Dumbarton)
thomas.rainey@west-dunbarton.gov.uk

Robertson, Gail (SNP - Leven)

Ryall, Kath (LAB - Clydebank Waterfront)
kath.ryall@west-dunbarton.gov.uk

Sorrell, Hazel (LAB - Lomond)
hazel.sorrell@west-dunbarton.gov.uk

POLITICAL COMPOSITION
LAB: 12, SNP: 6, IND: 3, SSP: 1

West Lancashire   D

West Lancashire Borough Council, 52 Derby Street, Ormskirk L39 2DF
☎ 01695 577177 ⁂ customer.services@westlancs.gov.uk
🖥 www.westlancs.gov.uk

FACTS AND FIGURES
Parliamentary Constituencies: Lancashire West
EU Constituencies: North West
Election Frequency: Elections are by thirds

PRINCIPAL OFFICERS

Chief Executive: Ms Kim Webber, Chief Executive, 52 Derby Street, Ormskirk L39 2DF ☎ 01695 585005 ⁂ kim.webber@westlancs.gov.uk

Senior Management: Mr Terry Broderick, Borough Solicitor, 52 Derby Street, Ormskirk L39 2DF ☎ 01695 585001 ⁂ terry.broderick@westlancs.gov.uk

Senior Management: Mr John Harrison, Director - Development & Regeneration, 52 Derby Street, Ormskirk L39 2DF
☎ 01695 585132 ⁂ john.harrison@westlancs.gov.uk

Senior Management: Mr Bob Livermore, Director - Housing & Inclusion, 49 Westgate, Sandy Lane Centre, Skelmersdale WN8 8LP ☎ 01695 585200 ⁂ bob.livermore@westlancs.gov.uk

Senior Management: Mr Marc Taylor, Borough Treasurer, 52 Derby Street, Ormskirk L39 2DF ☎ 01695 585092 ⁂ marc.taylor@westlancs.gov.uk

Senior Management: Mr David Tilleray, Director - Leisure & Wellbeing, Robert Hodge Centre, Stanley Industrial Estate, Stanley Way, Skelmersdale WN8 8EE ☎ 01695 585202 ⁂ david.tilleray@westlancs.gov.uk

Senior Management: Mr Shaun Walsh, Borough Transformation Manager & Deputy Director - Housing & Inclusion, 49 Westgate, Sandy Lane Centre, Skelmersdale WN8 8LP ☎ 01695 585262 ⁂ shaun.walsh@westlancs.gov.uk

Architect, Building / Property Services: Mr Phil Holland, Property Services Manager, Sandy Lane Centre, 61 Westgate, Skelmersdale WN8 8LP ☎ 01695 585226 ⁂ phil.holland@westlancs.gov.uk

Best Value: Ms Alison Grimes, Partnership & Performance Officer, 52 Derby Street, Ormskirk L39 2DF ☎ 01695 585409 ⁂ alison.grimes@westlancs.gov.uk

Best Value: Ms Kim Webber, Chief Executive, 52 Derby Street, Ormskirk L39 2DF ☎ 01695 585005 ⁂ kim.webber@westlancs.gov.uk

Building Control: Mr John Harrison, Director - Development & Regeneration, 52 Derby Street, Ormskirk L39 2DF ☎ 01695 585132 ⁂ john.harrison@westlancs.gov.uk

Children / Youth Services: Mr John Nelson, Deputy Director - Leisure & Wellbeing, Robert Hodge Centre, Stanley Industrial Estate, Stanley Way, Skelmersdale WN8 8EE ☎ 01695 585157 ⁂ john.nelson@westlancs.gov.uk

PR / Communications: Ms Edwina Leigh, Consultation & Communications Manager, 52 Derby Street, Ormskirk L39 2DF ☎ 01695 577177 Extn 5433 ⁂ edwina.leigh@westlancs.gov.uk

Community Planning: Mr John Harrison, Director - Development & Regeneration, 52 Derby Street, Ormskirk L39 2DF ☎ 01695 585132 ⁂ john.harrison@westlancs.gov.uk

Community Safety: Mr Andrew Hill, Environmental Protection & Community Safety Manager, Robert Hodge Centre, Stanley Industrial Estate, Stanley Way, Skelmersdale WN8 8EE ☎ 01695 585243 (585242) ⁂ andrew.hill@westlancs.gov.uk

Computer Management: Mr Shaun Walsh, Borough Transformation Manager & Deputy Director - Housing & Inclusion, 52 Derby Street, Ormskirk L39 2DF ☎ 01695 585262 ⁂ shaun.walsh@westlancs.gov.uk

WEST LANCASHIRE

Contracts: Mr Phil Holland, Property Services Manager, Sandy Lane Centre, 61 Westgate, Skelmersdale WN8 8LP
☎ 01695 585226 ✆ phil.holland@westlancs.gov.uk

Customer Service: Mr Shaun Walsh, Borough Transformation Manager & Deputy Director - Housing & Inclusion, 52 Derby Street, Ormskirk L39 2DF ☎ 01695 585262
✆ shaun.walsh@westlancs.gov.uk

Economic Development: Mrs Paula Huber, Economic Regeneration Manager, 52 Derby Street, Ormskirk L39 2DF
☎ 01695 585359 ✆ paula.huber@westlancs.gov.uk

E-Government: Mr Shaun Walsh, Borough Transformation Manager & Deputy Director - Housing & Inclusion, 52 Derby Street, Ormskirk L39 2DF ☎ 01695 585262 ✆ shaun.walsh@westlancs.gov.uk

Electoral Registration: Mr Thomas Lynan, Electoral & Administration Services Manager, 52 Derby Street, Ormskirk L39 2DF ☎ 01695 585013 ✆ thomas.lynan@westlancs.gov.uk

Emergency Planning: Mr David Tilleray, Director - Leisure & Wellbeing, Robert Hodge Centre, Stanley Industrial Estate, Stanley Way, Skelmersdale WN8 8EE ☎ 01695 585202
✆ david.tilleray@westlancs.gov.uk

Energy Management: Mr Phil Holland, Property Services Manager, Sandy Lane Centre, 61 Westgate, Skelmersdale WN8 8LP
☎ 01695 585226 ✆ phil.holland@westlancs.gov.uk

Environmental Health: Mr Paul Charlson, Commercial Safety & Licensing Manager, Robert Hodge Centre, Stanley Industrial Estate, Stanley Way, Skelmersdale WN8 8EE ☎ 01695 585246
✆ paul.charlson@westlancs.gov.uk

Environmental Health: Mr Andrew Hill, Environmental Protection & Community Safety Manager, Robert Hodge Centre, Stanley Industrial Estate, Stanley Way, Skelmersdale WN8 8EE
☎ 01695 585243 (585242) ✆ andrew.hill@westlancs.gov.uk

Environmental Health: Mr David Tilleray, Director - Leisure & Wellbeing, Robert Hodge Centre, Stanley Industrial Estate, Stanley Way, Skelmersdale WN8 8EE ☎ 01695 585202
✆ david.tilleray@westlancs.gov.uk

Estates, Property & Valuation: Mrs Rachel Kneale, Estates & Valuations Manager, 52 Derby Street, Ormskirk L39 2DF
☎ 01695 712611 ✆ rachel.kneale@westlancs.gov.uk

European Liaison: Ms Kim Webber, Chief Executive, 52 Derby Street, Ormskirk L39 2DF ☎ 01695 585005
✆ kim.webber@westlancs.gov.uk

Facilities: Ms Kim Webber, Chief Executive, 52 Derby Street, Ormskirk L39 2DF ☎ 01695 585005 ✆ kim.webber@westlancs.gov.uk

Finance: Mr Marc Taylor, Borough Treasurer, 52 Derby Street, Ormskirk L39 2DF ☎ 01695 585092
✆ marc.taylor@westlancs.gov.uk

Fleet Management: Mr Jimmy Cummins, Fleet Maintenance Manager, Robert Hodge Centre, Stanley Industrial Estate, Stanley Way, Skelmersdale WN8 8EE ☎ 01695 577177 Extn: 5448
✆ jimmy.cummins@westlancs.gov.uk

Health and Safety: Mr Paul Adamson, Health & Safety Manager, Sandy Lane Centre, 61 Westgate, Skelmersdale WN8 8LP
☎ 01695 585241 ✆ paul.adamson@westlancs.gov.uk

Housing: Mr Bob Livermore, Director - Housing & Inclusion, 49 Westgate, Sandy Lane Centre, Skelmersdale WN8 8LP
☎ 01695 585200 ✆ bob.livermore@westlancs.gov.uk

Housing Maintenance: Mr Phil Holland, Property Services Manager, Sandy Lane Centre, 61 Westgate, Skelmersdale WN8 8LP
☎ 01695 585226 ✆ phil.holland@westlancs.gov.uk

Legal: Mr Terry Broderick, Borough Solicitor, 52 Derby Street, Ormskirk L39 2DF ☎ 01695 585001 ✆ terry.broderick@westlancs.gov.uk

Leisure and Cultural Services: Mr John Nelson, Deputy Director - Leisure & Wellbeing, 52 Derby Street, Ormskirk L39 2DF
☎ 01695 585157 ✆ john.nelson@westlancs.gov.uk

Licensing: Mr Paul Charlson, Commercial Safety & Licensing Manager, Robert Hodge Centre, Stanley Industrial Estate, Stanley Way, Skelmersdale WN8 8EE ☎ 01695 585246
✆ paul.charlson@westlancs.gov.uk

Lottery Funding, Charity and Voluntary: Ms Kim Webber, Chief Executive, 52 Derby Street, Ormskirk L39 2DF
☎ 01695 585005 ✆ kim.webber@westlancs.gov.uk

Member Services: Mr Mathew Jones, Legal & Member Services Manager, 52 Derby Street, Ormskirk L39 2DF ☎ 01695 585025
✆ mathew.jones@westlancs.gov.uk

Parking: Mr Steven Wilson, Markets & Parking Officer, 52 Derby Street, Ormskirk L39 2DF ☎ 01695 585105
✆ steven.wilson@westlancs.gov.uk

Personnel / HR: Mr Shaun Walsh, Borough Transformation Manager & Deputy Director - Housing & Inclusion, 52 Derby Street, Ormskirk L39 2DF ☎ 01695 585262
✆ shaun.walsh@westlancs.gov.uk

Planning: Mr John Harrison, Director - Development & Regeneration, 52 Derby Street, Ormskirk L39 2DF ☎ 01695 585132
✆ john.harrison@westlancs.gov.uk

Procurement: Mr Stephen Tinsley, Purchasing & Land Charges Manager, 52 Derby Street, Ormskirk L39 2DF ☎ 01695 577177 Extn: 5426 ✆ stephen.tinsley@westlancs.gov.uk

Regeneration: Mr Bob Livermore, Director - Housing & Inclusion, 49 Westgate, Sandy Lane Centre, Skelmersdale WN8 8LP
☎ 01695 585200 ✆ bob.livermore@westlancs.gov.uk

Staff Training: Mr Shaun Walsh, Borough Transformation Manager & Deputy Director - Housing & Inclusion, 52 Derby Street, Ormskirk L39 2DF ☎ 01695 585262 ✆ shaun.walsh@westlancs.gov.uk

Sustainable Communities: Ms Kim Webber, Chief Executive, 52 Derby Street, Ormskirk L39 2DF ☎ 01695 585005
✆ kim.webber@westlancs.gov.uk

Sustainable Development: Ms Tina Iball, Environmental Strategy Officer, Robert Hodge Centre, Stanley Industrial Estate, Stanley Way, Skelmersdale WN8 8EE ☎ 01695 585197
✆ tina.iball@westlancs.gov.uk

Tourism: Mrs Paula Huber, Economic Regeneration Manager, 52 Derby Street, Ormskirk L39 2DF ☎ 01695 585359
✆ paula.huber@westlancs.gov.uk

Town Centre: Mr Colin Brady, Technical Services Manager, 52 Derby Street, Ormskirk L39 2DF ☎ 01695 585125
✆ colin.brady@westlancs.gov.uk

COUNCILLORS

Mayor: Savage, Liz (LAB - Ashurst)
cllr.savage@westlancs.gov.uk

Leader of the Council: Moran, Ian (LAB - Up Holland)
cllr.moran@westlancs.gov.uk

Deputy Leader of the Council: Gagen, Yvonne (LAB - Ashurst)
cllr.gagen@westlancs.gov.uk

Group Leader: Westley, David (CON - Aughton & Downholland)
cllr.westley@westlancs.gov.uk

Aldridge, Terry (LAB - Moorside)
cllr.aldridge@westlancs.gov.uk

Ashcroft, Iain (CON - Hesketh-with-Becconsall)
cllr.ashcroft@westlancs.gov.uk

Bailey, Susan (CON - Aughton Park)
cllr.sbailey@westlancs.gov.uk

Barron, Malcolm (CON - North Meols)
cllr.barron@westlancs.gov.uk

Baybutt, Pam (CON - Wrightington)
cllr.baybutt@westlancs.gov.uk

Blake, May (CON - Parbold)
cllr.blake@westlancs.gov.uk

Blane, Thomas (CON - North Meols)
cllr.tblane@westlancs.gov.uk

Bullock, John (LAB - Up Holland)
cllr.bullock@westlancs.gov.uk

Cairns, John (CON - Tarleton)
cllr.cairns@westlancs.gov.uk

Cooper, Claire (LAB - Birch Green)
cllr.cooper@westlancs.gov.uk

Cotterill, Paul (LAB - Bickerstaffe)
cllr.cotterill@westlancs.gov.uk

Currie, Samuel (CON - Aughton & Downholland)
cllr.currie@westlancs.gov.uk

Davis, John (LAB - Burscough West)
cllr.davis@westlancs.gov.uk

Delaney, Noel (LAB - Scott)
cllr.delaney@westlancs.gov.uk

Devine, Terence (LAB - Moorside)
cllr.devine@westlancs.gov.uk

Dowling, Gareth (LAB - Knowsley)
cllr.dowling@westlancs.gov.uk

Evans, David (LAB - Burscough East)
cllr.d.evans@westlancs.gov.uk

Evans, Carolyn (CON - Wrightington)
cllr.cevans@westlancs.gov.uk

Furey, Neil (LAB - Skelmersdale North)
cllr.furey@westlancs.gov.uk

Gordon, John (CON - Rufford)
cllr.gordon@westlancs.gov.uk

Greenall, Paul (CON - Derby)
cllr.greenall@westlancs.gov.uk

Hennessy, Nikki (LAB - Knowsley)
cllr.hennessy@westlancs.gov.uk

Hodson, John (LAB - Scott)
cllr.hodson@westlancs.gov.uk

Hodson, Gail (LAB - Ashurst)
cllr.ghodson@westlancs.gov.uk

Hudson, Phil (LAB - Derby)
cllr.phudson@westlancs.gov.uk

Kay, James (CON - Tarleton)
cllr.kay@westlancs.gov.uk

Marshall, Charles (CON - Scarisbrick)
cllr.cmarshall@westlancs.gov.uk

Marshall, Jane (CON - Scarisbrick)
cllr.marshall@westlancs.gov.uk

McKay, David (LAB - Skelmersdale South)
cllr.mckay@westlancs.gov.uk

McKenna, Frank (LAB - Birch Green)
cllr.mckenna@westlancs.gov.uk

Mee, John (CON - Tarleton)
cllr.mee@westlancs.gov.uk

Melling, Ruth (CON - Burscough East)
cllr.melling@westlancs.gov.uk

Mills, Maureen (LAB - Halsall)
cllr.mills@westlancs.gov.uk

Moon, Paul (CON - Hesketh-with-Becconsall)
cllr.moon@westlancs.gov.uk

Nixon, Maureen (LAB - Tanhouse)
cllr.nixon@wetlancs.gov.uk

O'Toole, David (CON - Aughton & Downholland)
cllr.otoole@westlancs.gov.uk

Owen, Gaynar (LAB - Up Holland)
cllr.owen@westlancs.gov.uk

Owens, Adrian (IND - Derby)
cllr.owens@westlancs.gov.uk

Patterson, Jenny (LAB - Skelmersdale North)
cllr.patterson@westlancs.gov.uk

Pendleton, Robert (LAB - Tanhouse)
cllr.bpendleton@westlancs.gov.uk

Pope, Edward (CON - Newburgh)
cllr.pope@westlancs.gov.uk

Pritchard, Andrew (LAB - Burscough West)
cllr.pritchard@westlancs.gov.uk

WEST LANCASHIRE

Pryce-Roberts, Nicola (LAB - Skelmersdale South)
cllr.pryce-roberts@westlancs.gov.uk

West, Donna (LAB - Skelmersdale South)
cllr.west@westlancs.gov.uk

Westley, Marilyn (CON - Aughton Park)
cllr.mwestley@westlancs.gov.uk

Whittington, David (CON - Parbold)
cllr.whittington@westlancs.gov.uk

Wilkie, Kevin (LAB - Digmoor)
cllr.wilkie@westlancs.gov.uk

Wright, Kevin (LAB - Scott)
cllr.wright@westlancs.gov.uk

Wynn, Chris (LAB - Digmoor)
cllr.wynn@westlancs.gov.uk

Yates, Adam (LAB - Knowsley)
cllr.yates@westlancs.gov.uk

POLITICAL COMPOSITION
LAB: 31, CON: 22, IND: 1

COMMITTEE CHAIRS

Audit: Mr John Bullock

Licensing: Mr Terence Devine

Planning: Mr Gareth Dowling

West Lindsey   D

West Lindsey District Council, The Guildhall, Marshall's Yard,
Gainsborough DN21 2NA
☎ 01427 676676 ✆ customer.services@west-lindsey.gov.uk
🖥 www.west-lindsey.gov.uk

FACTS AND FIGURES
Parliamentary Constituencies: Gainsborough
EU Constituencies: Eastern
Election Frequency: Elections are by thirds

PRINCIPAL OFFICERS

Chief Executive: Mrs Manjeet Gill, Chief Executive, The Guildhall,
Marshall's Yard, Gainsborough DN21 2NA ☎ 01427 676676
✆ manjeet.gill@west-lindsey.gov.uk

Deputy Chief Executive: Mr Mark Sturgess, Chief Operating
Officer, The Guildhall, Marshall's Yard, Gainsborough DN21 2NA
☎ 01427 676687 ✆ mark.sturgess@west-lindsey.gov.uk

Senior Management: Mrs Penny Sharp, Commercial Director,
The Guildhall, Marshall's Yard, Gainsborough DN21 2NA
☎ 01427 675185 ✆ penny.sharp@west-lindsey.gov.uk

Building Control: Ms Rachael Hughes, Team Manager - Area
Development Team, The Guildhall, Marshall's Yard, Gainsborough
DN21 2NA ☎ 01427 676548 ✆ rachael.hughes@west-lindsey.gov.uk

PR / Communications: Ms Julie Heath, Senior Communications
Officer, The Guildhall, Marshall's Yard, Gainsborough DN21 2NA
☎ 01427 676502 ✆ julie.heath@west-lindsey.gov.uk

Community Planning: Mr Oliver Fytche-Taylor, Team Manager -
Spatial Planning, The Guildhall, Marshall's Yard, Gainsborough DN21
2NA ☎ 01427 646564 ✆ oliver.fytche-taylor@west-lindsey.gov.uk

Contracts: Ms Anna Grieve, Business Development Officer C&P,
The Guildhall, Marshall's Yard, Gainsborough DN21 2NA
☎ 01427 676620 ✆ anna.grieve@west-lindsey.gov.uk

Customer Service: Mrs Michelle Carrington, Strategic Lead -
Customer First, The Guildhall, Marshall's Yard, Gainsborough DN21
2NA ☎ 01427 675134 ✆ michelle.carrington@west-lindsey.gov.uk

Customer Service: Ms Lyn Marlow, Customer Relations Manager,
The Guildhall, Marshalls Yard, Gainsborough DN21 2NA
☎ 01427 676684 ✆ lyn.marlow@west-lindsey.gov.uk

Electoral Registration: Mrs Celia Chapman, Electoral
Registration Officer, The Guildhall, Marshall's Yard, Gainsborough
DN21 2NA ☎ 01427 676576 ✆ celia.chapman@west-lindsey.gov.uk

Finance: Mr Ian Knowles, Director - Resources, The Guildhall,
Marshall's Yard, Gainsborough DN21 2NA
✆ ian.knowles@west-lindsey.gov.uk

Health and Safety: Mrs Kim Leith, Health & Safety Co-ordinator,
The Guildhall, Marshall's Yard, Gainsborough DN21 2NA
☎ 01427 675110 ✆ kim.leith@west-lindsey.gov.uk

Home Energy Conservation: Ms Karen Lond, Energy &
Efficiency Adviser, The Guildhall, Marshall's Tard, Gainsborough
DN24 2NA ☎ 01427 676618 ✆ karen.lond@west-lindsey.gov.uk

Housing: Ms Sarah Troman, Strategic Lead - Housing &
Regeneration, The Guildhall, Marshall's Yard, Gainsborough DN21
2NA ☎ 01427 675190 ✆ sarah.troman@west-lindsey.gov.uk

Licensing: Mr Phil Hinch, Licensing & Support Team Leader, The
Guildhall, Marshall's Yard, Gainsborough DN21 2NA
☎ 01427 676610 ✆ phil.hinch@west-lindsey.gov.uk

Lottery Funding, Charity and Voluntary: Mr Grant White,
Enterprising Communities Officer, The Guildhall, Marshall's Yard,
Gainsborough DN21 2NA ☎ 01427 675145
✆ grant.white@west-lindsey.gov.uk

Member Services: Mr Alan Robinson, Monitoring Officer, The
Guildhall, Marshall's Yard, Gainsborough DN21 2NA
☎ 01427 676509 ✆ alan.robinson@wwest-lindsey.gov.uk

Parking: Mr David Kirkup, Senior Property Strategy Project Officer,
The Guildhall, Marshall's Yard, Gainsborough DN21 2NA
☎ 01427 676554 ✆ david.kirkup@west-lindsey.gov.uk

Personnel / HR: Mrs Emma Redwood, Team Manager, The
Guildhall, Marshall's Yard, Gainsborough DN21 2NA
☎ 01427 676591 ✆ emma.redwood@west-lindsey.gov.uk

Recycling & Waste Minimisation: Mr Ady Selby, Team Manager
- Operational Services, The Guildhall, Marshall's Yard, Gainsborough
DN21 2NA ☎ 01427 675154 ✆ ady.selby@west-lindsey.gov.uk

Tourism: Ms Marion Thomas, Arts & Tourism Manager, The Guildhall, Marshall's Yard, Gainsborough DN21 2NA
☎ 01427 675162 ◌ marion.thomas@west-lindsey.gov.uk

Waste Collection and Disposal: Mr Ady Selby, Team Manager - Operational Services, The Guildhall, Marshall's Yard, Gainsborough DN21 2NA ☎ 01427 675154 ◌ ady.selby@west-lindsey.gov.uk

Waste Management: Mr Ady Selby, Team Manager - Operational Services, The Guildhall, Marshall's Yard, Gainsborough DN21 2NA
☎ 01427 675154 ◌ ady.selby@west-lindsey.gov.uk

COUNCILLORS

Bardsley, Gillian (CON - Gainsborough North)
cllr.g.bardsley@west-lindsey.gov.uk

Bibb, Sheila (CON - Gainsborough North)
cllr.s.bibb@west-lindsey.gov.uk

Bierley, Owen (CON - Caistor & Yarborough)
owen@bierley.com

Boles, Matthew (LD - Gainsborough North)
cllr.m.boles@west-lindsey.gov.uk

Bond, David (LAB - Gainsborough East)
cllr.d.bond@west-lindsey.gov.uk

Brockway, Jackie (CON - Saxilby)
jackiebrockway@gmail.com

Cotton, David (LD - Saxilby)
david.cotton500@ntlworld.com

Curtis, Stuart (CON - Sudbrooke)
stuartlyncurtis@aol.com

Darcel, Christopher (IND - Cherry Willingham)
chris@darcel.entadsl.com

Devine, Michael (LAB - Gainsborough East)
cllr.m.devine@west-lindsey.gov.uk

Duguid, Adam (CON - Scotter & Blyton)
cllr.a.duguid@west-lindsey.gov.uk

England, Steve (CON - Dunholme & Welton)
cllr.s.england@west-lindsey.gov.uk

Fleetwood, Ian (CON - Bardney)
ifleet@barlings.demon.co.uk

Howitt-Cowan, Paul (CON - Hemswell)
cllr.p.howitt-cowan@west-lindsey.gov.uk

Kinch, Stuart (CON - Torksey)
stuart@thejohnkinchgroup.co.uk

Lawrence, Angela (CON - Caistor)
atlcaistor@gmail.com

Marfleet, Hugo (CON - Market Rasen)
cllr.h.marfleet@west-lindsey.gov.uk

McNeill, John (CON - Market Rasen)
cllr.j.mcneill@west-lindsey.gov.uk

McNeill, Giles (CON - Nettleham)
cllr.g.mcneill@west-lindsey.gov.uk

Mewis, Patricia (CON - Scotter & Blyton)
cllr.p.mewis@west-lindsey.gov.uk

Milne, Jessie (CON - Lea)
jessie.milne393@btinternet.com

Oaks, Richard (LAB - Gainsborough East)
cllr.r.oaks@west-lindsey.gov.uk

Palmer, Maureen (CON - Cherry Willingham)
cllr.m.palmer@west-lindsey.gov.uk

Parish, Malcolm (CON - Dunholme & Welton)
cllr.parish@btinternet.com

Patterson, Roger (CON - Scampton)
rogermpatterson@aol.com

Rainsforth, Judy (LD - Gainsborough South-West)
judyrainsforth@talktalk.net

Regis, Thomas (CON - Wold View)
tom@tomregis.com

Rodgers, Diana (IND - Dunholme & Welton)
cllr.d.rodgers@west-lindsey.gov.uk

Rollings, Lesley (LD - Scotter & Blyton)
lrollings@btinternet.com

Shore, Reg (LD - Stow)
regshore@mac.com

Smith, Thomas (CON - Market Rasen)
cllr.t.smith@west-lindsey.gov.uk

Strange, Lewis (CON - Kelsey)
cllrc.strange@lincolnshire.gov.uk

Summers, Jeff (CON - Waddingham & Spital)
cllr.j.summers@west-lindsey.gov.uk

Welburn, Anne (CON - Cherry Willingham)
anne.welburn@btinternet.com

White, Angela (LD - Nettleham)
cllr.a.white@west-lindsey.gov.uk

Young, Trevor (LD - Gainsborough South-West)
t.young91@btinternet.com

POLITICAL COMPOSITION
CON: 24, LD: 7, LAB: 3, IND: 2

COMMITTEE CHAIRS

Licensing: Ms Jessie Milne

Planning: Mr Stuart Curtis

West Lothian   S

West Lothian Council, West Lothian Civic Centre, Howden South Road, Livingston EH54 6FF
☎ 01506 280000 ◌ customer.service@westlothian.gov.uk
🖳 www.westlothian.gov.uk

FACTS AND FIGURES
Parliamentary Constituencies: Linlithgow and Falkirk East, Livingston
EU Constituencies: Scotland
Election Frequency: Elections are of whole council

PRINCIPAL OFFICERS

Chief Executive: Mr Graham Hope, Chief Executive, West Lothian Civic Centre, Howden South Road, Livingston EH54 6FF
☎ 01506 281679 ◌ graham.hope@westlothian.gov.uk

WEST LOTHIAN

Deputy Chief Executive: Dr Elaine Cook, Depute Chief Executive, West Lothian Civic Centre, Howden South Road, Livingston EH54 6FF ☎ 01506 283050 ⌂ elaine.cook@westlothian.gov.uk

Deputy Chief Executive: Mr Jim Forrest, Depute Chief Executive, West Lothian Civic Centre, Howden South Road, Livingston EH54 6FF ☎ 01506 281679 ⌂ jim.forrest@westlothian.gov.uk

Deputy Chief Executive: Mr Graeme Struthers, Depute Chief Executive, West Lothian Civic Centre, Howden South Road, Livingston EH54 6FF ☎ 01506 281679 ⌂ graeme.struthers@westlothian.gov.uk

Access Officer / Social Services (Disability): Ms Jane Kellock, Acting Head of Social Policy, West Lothian Civic Centre, Howden South Road, Livingston EH54 6FF ☎ 01506 281920 ⌂ jane.kellock@westlothian.gov.uk

Best Value: Mr Graeme Struthers, Depute Chief Executive, West Lothian Civic Centre, Howden South Road, Livingston EH54 6FF ☎ 01506 281679 ⌂ graeme.struthers@westlothian.gov.uk

Building Control: Mr Jim McGinley, Building Standards Manager, West Lothian Civic Centre, Howden South Road, Livingston EH54 6FF ☎ 01506 282395 ⌂ jim.mcginley@westlothian.gov.uk

Catering Services: Mr Jamie Fisher, Service Manager, Whitehill House, 7 Whitestone Place, Whitehill Industrial Estate, Bathgate EH48 2HA ☎ 01506 776672 ⌂ jamie.fisher@westlothian.gov.uk

Children / Youth Services: Ms Marion Barton, Head of Health Services, West Lothian Civic Centre, Howden South Road, Livingston EH54 6FF ⌂ marion.barton@westlothian.gov.uk

Children / Youth Services: Ms Jo MacPherson, Head of Children & Families, West Lothian Civic Centre, Howden South Road, Livingston EH54 6FF ☎ 01506 282194 ⌂ jo.macpherson@westlothian.gov.uk

Civil Registration: Ms Wendy Thomas, Chief Registrar, Bathgate Partnership Centre, South Bridge Street, Bathgate EH48 1TS ☎ 01506 282916 ⌂ wendy1.thomas@westlothian.gov.uk

PR / Communications: Mr Garry Heron, Corporate Communications Manager, West Lothian Civic Centre, Howden South Road, Livingston EH54 6FF ☎ 01506 282006 ⌂ garry.heron@westlothian.gov.uk

Community Safety: Mr Alistair Shaw, Head of Housing, Construction & Building, West Lothian Civic Centre, Howden South Road, Livingston EH54 6FF ☎ 01506 281754 ⌂ alistair.shaw@westlothian.gov.uk

Computer Management: Ms Jennifer Milne, IT Manager, West Lothian Civic Centre, Howden South Road, Livingston EH54 6FF ☎ 01506 281521 ⌂ jennifer.milne@westlothian.gov.uk

Consumer Protection and Trading Standards: Mr Andrew Blake, Environmental Health & Trading Standards Manager, County Buildings, High Street, Linlithgow EH49 7EZ ☎ 01506 282381 ⌂ andrew.blake@westlothian.gov.uk

Corporate Services: Mrs Julie Whitelaw, Head of Service - Corporate Services, West Lothian Civic Centre, Howden South Road, Livingston EH54 6FF ☎ 01506 281626 ⌂ julie.whitelaw@westlothian.gov.uk

Customer Service: Ms Karen Cawte, Customer Services Development Manager, West Lothian Civic Centre, Howden South Road, Livingston EH54 6FF ☎ 01506 821082 ⌂ karen.cawte@westlothian.gov.uk

Economic Development: Ms Alice Mitchell, Economic Development Manager, West Lothian Civic Centre, Howden South Road, Livingston EH54 6FF ☎ 01506 283079 ⌂ alice.mitchell@westlothian.gov.uk

Education: Mr James Cameron, Depute Chief Executive - Education, Planning & Area Services, West Lothian Civic Centre, Howden South Road, Livingston EH54 6FF ☎ 01506 281679 ⌂ james.cameron@westlothian.gov.uk

Education: Ms Donna McMaster, Head of Service for Education, West Lothian Civic Centre, Howden South Road, Livingston EH54 6FF ☎ 01506 283050 ⌂ donna.mcmaster@westlothian.gov.uk

Electoral Registration: Mr James Millar, Chief Legal Officer, West Lothian Civic Centre, Howden South Road, Livingston EH54 6FF ☎ 01506 281613 ⌂ james.millar@westlothian.gov.uk

Emergency Planning: Ms Caroline Burton, Emergency Planning Officer, West Lothian Civic Centre, Howden South Road, Livingston EH54 6FF ☎ 01506 281651 ⌂ caroline.burton@westlothian.gov.uk

Environmental Health: Mr Andrew Blake, Environmental Health & Trading Standards Manager, County Buildings, High Street, Linlithgow EH49 7EZ ☎ 01506 282381 ⌂ andrew.blake@westlothian.gov.uk

Estates, Property & Valuation: Mr Donald Forrest, Head of Service - Finance & Property Services, West Lothian Civic Centre, Howden South Road, Livingston EH54 6FF ☎ 01506 281679 ⌂ donald.forrest@westlothian.gov.uk

European Liaison: Mr David Greaves, Policy Manager, West Lothian Civic Centre, Howden South Road, Livingston EH54 6FF ☎ 01506 283097 ⌂ david.greaves@westlothian.gov.uk

Events Manager: Ms Amanda Lamb, Business Information Officer, West Lothian Civic Centre, Howden South Road, Livingston EH54 6FF ☎ 01506 283285 ⌂ amanda.lamb@westlothian.gov.uk

Facilities: Mr Jamie Fisher, Service Manager, Whitehill House, 7 Whitestone Place, Whitehill Industrial Estate, Bathgate EH48 2HA ☎ 01506 776672 ⌂ jamie.fisher@westlothian.gov.uk

Finance: Mr Donald Forrest, Head of Service - Finance & Property Services, West Lothian Civic Centre, Howden South Road, Livingston EH54 6FF ☎ 01506 281679 ⌂ donald.forrest@westlothian.gov.uk

Fleet Management: Mr Joe Drew, Fleet Co-ordinator, Fleet & Cleansing Depot, Nairn Road, Deans Industrial Estate, Livingston EH54 8AY ☎ 01506 777822 ⌂ joe.drew@westlothian.gov.uk

Grounds Maintenance: Mr Jim Jack, Head of Operational Services, Whitehill House, Whitehill Industrial Estate, Bathgate EH48 2HA ☎ 01506 776601 ⏚ jim.jack@westlothian.gov.uk

Health and Safety: Ms Kim Hardie, Health & Safety Manager, West Lothian Civic Centre, Howden South Road, Livingston EH54 6FF ☎ 01506 281414 ⏚ kim.hardie@westlothian.gov.uk

Highways: Mr David Wilson, Service Manager, West Lothian Civic Centre, Howden South Road, Livingston EH54 6FF ☎ 01506 776651 ⏚ david.wilson@westlothian.gov.uk

Housing: Mr Alistair Shaw, Head of Housing, Construction & Building, West Lothian Civic Centre, Howden South Road, Livingston EH54 6FF ☎ 01506 281754 ⏚ alistair.shaw@westlothian.gov.uk

Housing Maintenance: Mr Alistair Shaw, Head of Housing, Construction & Building, West Lothian Civic Centre, Howden South Road, Livingston EH54 6FF ☎ 01506 281754 ⏚ alistair.shaw@westlothian.gov.uk

Local Area Agreement: Mr Steve Field, Head of Area Services, County Buildings, High Street, Linlithgow EH49 7EZ ☎ 01506 282386 ⏚ steve.field@westlothian.gov.uk

Legal: Ms Carol Johnston, Chief Solicitor, West Lothian Civic Centre, Howden South Road, Livingston EH54 6FF ☎ 01506 281605 ⏚ carol.johnston@westlothian.gov.uk

Leisure and Cultural Services: Ms Laura Tyrell, Interim Manager - Culture & Sport, West Lothian Civic Centre, Howden South Road, Livingston EH54 6FF ☎ 01506 773847 ⏚ laura.tyrell@westlothian.gov.uk

Licensing: Legal Services, West Lothian Civic Centre, Howden South Road, Livingston EH54 6FF ☎ 01506 281632 ⏚ licensingservices@westlothian.gov.uk

Lighting: Mr David Wilson, Service Manager, West Lothian Civic Centre, Howden South Road, Livingston EH54 6FF ☎ 01506 776651 ⏚ david.wilson@westlothian.gov.uk

Lottery Funding, Charity and Voluntary: Mr Ian Hepburn, Community Regeneration Manager, West Lothian Civic Centre, Howden South Road, Livingston EH54 6FF ☎ 01506 281089 ⏚ ian.hepburn@westlothian.gov.uk

Member Services: Mr Lesley Henderson, HR Services Manager, West Lothian Civic Centre, Howden South Road, Livingston EH54 6FF ☎ 01506 281408 ⏚ lesley.henderson@westlothian.gov.uk

Personnel / HR: Mr Lesley Henderson, HR Services Manager, West Lothian Civic Centre, Howden South Road, Livingston EH54 6FF ☎ 01506 281408 ⏚ lesley.henderson@westlothian.gov.uk

Planning: Mr Graeme Malcolm, Raods & Transportation Manager, West Lothian Civic Centre, Howden South Road, Livingston EH54 6FF ☎ 01506 776633 ⏚ graeme.malcolm@westlothian.gov.uk

Planning: Mr Craig McCorriston, Head of Planning, Economic Development & Regeneration, West Lothian Civic Centre, Howden South Road, Livingston EH54 6FF ☎ 01506 282443 ⏚ craig.mccorriston@westlothian.gov.uk

Planning: Mr Chris Norman, Development Control Manager, County Buildings, High Street, Linlithgow EH49 7EZ ☎ 01506 282412 ⏚ chris.norman@westlothian.gov.uk

Procurement: Ms Christine Leese-Young, Procurement Manager, West Lothian Civic Centre, Howden South Road, Livingston EH54 6FF ☎ 01506 283259 ⏚ christine.leeseyoung@westlothian.gov.uk

Public Libraries: Ms Karen Cawte, Customer Services Development Manager, West Lothian Civic Centre, Howden South Road, Livingston EH54 6FF ☎ 01506 821082 ⏚ karen.cawte@westlothian.gov.uk

Recycling & Waste Minimisation: Mr David Goodenough, Operations Manager, Unit 3, Nairn Road, Deans Industrial Estate, Livingston EH54 8AY ☎ 01506 777607 ⏚ david.goodenough@westlothian.gov.uk

Regeneration: Ms Alice Mitchell, Economic Development Manager, West Lothian Civic Centre, Howden South Road, Livingston EH54 6FF ☎ 01506 283079 ⏚ alice.mitchell@westlothian.gov.uk

Road Safety: Mr Kevin Hamilton, Team Leader, County Buildings, High Street, Linlithgow EH49 7EZ ☎ 01506 282341 ⏚ kevin.hamilton@westlothian.gov.uk

Social Services: Ms Jane Kellock, Acting Head of Social Policy, West Lothian Civic Centre, Howden South Road, Livingston EH54 6FF ☎ 01506 281920 ⏚ jane.kellock@westlothian.gov.uk

Social Services (Adult): Ms Jane Kellock, Acting Head of Social Policy, West Lothian Civic Centre, Howden South Road, Livingston EH54 6FF ☎ 01506 281920 ⏚ jane.kellock@westlothian.gov.uk

Social Services (Children): Ms Jane Kellock, Acting Head of Social Policy, West Lothian Civic Centre, Howden South Road, Livingston EH54 6FF ☎ 01506 281920 ⏚ jane.kellock@westlothian.gov.uk

Public Health: Ms Marion Barton, Head of Health Services, West Lothian Civic Centre, Howden South Road, Livingston EH54 6FF ⏚ marion.barton@westlothian.gov.uk

Staff Training: Mr Lesley Henderson, HR Services Manager, West Lothian Civic Centre, Howden South Road, Livingston EH54 6FF ☎ 01506 281408 ⏚ lesley.henderson@westlothian.gov.uk

Sustainable Communities: Mr Ian Hepburn, Community Regeneration Manager, West Lothian Civic Centre, Howden South Road, Livingston EH54 6FF ☎ 01506 281089 ⏚ ian.hepburn@westlothian.gov.uk

Sustainable Development: Mr Craig McCorriston, Head of Planning, Economic Development & Regeneration, County Buildings, High Street, Linlithgow EH49 7EZ ☎ 01506 282443 ⏚ craig.mccorriston@westlothian.gov.uk

WEST LOTHIAN

Tourism: Ms Anna Young, Tourism Executive, West Lothian Civic Centre, Howden South Road, Livingston EH54 6FF
☎ 01506 283093 ⌨ anna.young@westlothian.gov.uk

Town Centre: Ms Alice Mitchell, Economic Development Manager, West Lothian Civic Centre, Howden South Road, Livingston EH54 6FF ☎ 01506 283079 ⌨ alice.mitchell@westlothian.gov.uk

Traffic Management: Mr Kevin Hamilton, Team Leader, County Buildings, High Street, Linlithgow EH49 7EZ ☎ 01506 282341 ⌨ kevin.hamilton@westlothian.gov.uk

Transport: Mr Ian Forbes, Public Transport Manager, County Buildings, High Street, Linlithgow EH49 7EZ ☎ 01506 282317 ⌨ ian.forbes@westlothian.gov.uk

COUNCILLORS

Provost: Kerr, Tom (CON - Linlithgow)
tom.kerr@westlothian.gov.uk

Leader of the Council: McGinty, John (LAB - Bathgate)
john.mcginty@westlothian.gov.uk

Anderson, Frank (SNP - East Livingston and East Calder)
frank.anderson@westlothian.gov.uk

Borrowman, Stuart (IND - Armadale and Blackridge)
stuart.borrowman@westlothian.gov.uk

Boyle, Tony (LAB - Broxburn, Uphall and Winchburgh)
tony.boyle@westlothian.gov.uk

Boyle, William (SNP - Bathgate)
william.boyle@westlothian.gov.uk

Calder, Diane (SNP - Broxburn, Uphall and Winchburgh)
diane.calder@westlothian.gov.uk

Campbell, Janet (SNP - Broxburn, Uphall and Winchburgh)
janet.campbell@westlothian.gov.uk

Cartmill, Harry (LAB - Bathgate)
harry.cartmill@westlothian.gov.uk

Conn, Tom (LAB - Linlithgow)
tom.conn@westlothian.gov.uk

Davidson, Alex (LAB - Broxburn, Uphall and Winchburgh)
alex.davidson@westlothian.gov.uk

De, Robert (SNP - Livingston North)
robert.de**@westlothian.gov.uk**

Dickson, Mary (SNP - Whitburn and Blackburn)
mary.dickson@westlothian.gov.uk

Dickson, Jim (SNP - Whitburn and Blackburn)
jim.dickson3@westlothian.gov.uk

Dixon, Jim (LAB - Armadale and Blackridge)
jim.dixon@westlothian.gov.uk

Dodds, David (LAB - Fauldhouse and The Breich Valley)
david.dodds@westlothian.gov.uk

Fitzpatrick, Lawrence (LAB - Livingston South)
lawrence.fitzpatrick@westlothian.gov.uk

John, Carl (SNP - East Livingston and East Calder)
carl.john@westlothian.gov.uk

Johnston, Peter (SNP - Livingston South)
peter.johnston@westlothian.gov.uk

King, Sarah (SNP - Armadale and Blackridge)

King, Dave (LAB - East Livingston and East Calder)
dave.king@westlothian.gov.uk

Logue, Danny (LAB - Livingston South)
danny.logue@westlothian.gov.uk

McCarra, Greg (SNP - Fauldhouse and the Briech Valley)
greg.mccarra@westlothian.gov.uk

McMillan, Anne (LAB - Livingston North)
anne.mcmillan@westlothian.gov.uk

Miller, Andrew (SNP - Livingston North)
andrew.miller@westlothian.gov.uk

Moohan, Angela (LAB - Livingston North)
angela.moohan@westlothian.gov.uk

Muir, John (SNP - Livingston South)
john.muir@westlothian.gov.uk

Muldoon, Cathy (LAB - Fauldhouse and the Briech Valley)
cathy.muldoon@westlothian.gov.uk

Paul, George (LAB - Whitburn and Blackburn)
george.paul@westlothian.gov.uk

Robertson, Barry (LAB - Whitburn and Blackburn)
barry.robertson@westlothian.gov.uk

Tait, David (SNP - Linlithgow)

Toner, Frank (LAB - East Livingstone and East Calder)
frank.toner@westlothian.gov.uk

Walker, Jim (SNP - Bathgate)
jim.walker@westlothian.gov.uk

POLITICAL COMPOSITION
LAB: 16, SNP: 15, CON: 1, IND: 1

COMMITTEE CHAIRS

Audit & Governance: Mr Harry Cartmill

Licensing: Mr Tony Boyle

Planning: Mr Tom Kerr

West Oxfordshire   D

West Oxfordshire District Council, Council Offices, Woodgreen, Witney OX28 1NB
☎ 01993 861000 🖷 01993 861050 ⌨ enquiries@westoxon.gov.uk
🖳 www.westoxon.gov.uk

FACTS AND FIGURES
Parliamentary Constituencies: Witney
EU Constituencies: South East
Election Frequency: Elections are by thirds

PRINCIPAL OFFICERS

Chief Executive: Mr David Neudegg, Managing Director, Council Offices, Trinity Road, Cirencester GL7 1PX ☎ 01285 623101 ⌨ david.neudegg@2020partnership.uk

Senior Management: Ms Christine Gore, Strategic Director - Communities & Planning, Council Offices, Trinity Road, Cirencester GL7 1PX ☎ 01285 623500 ⌨ christine.gore@cotswold.gov.uk

Senior Management: Mr Frank Wilson, Shared Strategic Director - Resources, Council Offices, Woodgreen, Witney OX28 1NB
☎ 01993 861291 ✆ frank.wilson@westoxon.gov.uk

Building Control: Mr Andrew Jones, Building Control Manager, Council Offices, Elmfield, New Yatt Road, Witney OX28 1PB
☎ 01285 623633 ✆ andrew.jones@cotswold.gov.uk

PR / Communications: Ms Carys Davis, Publicity & Information Officer, Council Offices, Woodgreen, Witney OX28 1NB
☎ 01993 861615 ✆ communications@westoxon.gov.uk

Community Planning: Mr Mike Clark, Corporate Planning Manager, Council Offices, Woodgreen, Witney OX28 1NB
☎ 01285 623565 ✆ mike.clark@cotswold.gov.uk

Community Safety: Mr Tony Dix, Community Safety Officer, Council Offices, Woodgreen, Witney OX28 1NB
✆ tony.dix@westoxon.gov.uk

Contracts: Mr Phil Martin, Head of Business Information & Change, Council Offices, Woodgreen, Witney OX28 1NB
☎ 01993 861201 ✆ phil.martin@westoxon.gov.uk

Corporate Services: Mr Phil Martin, Head of Business Information & Change, Council Offices, Woodgreen, Witney OX28 1NB ☎ 01993 861201 ✆ phil.martin@westoxon.gov.uk

Corporate Services: Mr Paul Stuart, Go Shared Services Head of Corporate Resources, Council Offices, Woodgreen, Witney OX28 1NB ☎ 01993 861171 ✆ paul.stuart@westoxon.gov.uk

Customer Service: Ms Clare Martin, Customer Services Manager, Council Offices, Woodgreen, Witney OX28 1NB ☎ 01993 861000 ✆ clare.martin@westoxon.gov.uk

Customer Service: Mr Phil Martin, Head of Business Information & Change, Council Offices, Woodgreen, Witney OX28 1NB
☎ 01993 861201 ✆ phil.martin@westoxon.gov.uk

Economic Development: Mr Dene Robson, Community Development Manager, Council Offices, Woodgreen, Witney OX28 1NB ☎ 01993 861481 ✆ dene.robson@westoxon.gov.uk

E-Government: Mr John Chorlton, ICT Operations Manager, Council Offices, Woodgreen, Witney OX28 1NB ☎ 01285 623000 ✆ john.chorlton@cotswold.gov.uk

Electoral Registration: Mr Keith Butler, Head of Democratic Services, Council Offices, Woodgreen, Witney OX28 1NB
☎ 01993 861521 ✆ keith.butler@westoxon.gov.uk

Emergency Planning: Mrs Claire Locke, Head of Environmental Services, Council Offices, Woodgreen, Witney OX28 1NB
☎ 01285 623427 ✆ claire.locke@cotswold.gov.uk

Environmental Health: Mr Phil Measures, Environmental Health Manager, Council Offices, Woodgreen, Witney OX28 1NB
☎ 01993 861376 ✆ phil.measures@westoxon.gov.uk

Estates, Property & Valuation: Mr David Thurlow, Estates Manager, Council Offices, Woodgreen, Witney OX28 1NB
☎ 01993 861583 ✆ david.thurlow@westoxon.gov.uk

Finance: Mr Frank Wilson, Shared Strategic Director - Resources, Council Offices, Woodgreen, Witney OX28 1NB ☎ 01993 861291 ✆ frank.wilson@westoxon.gov.uk

Health and Safety: Mr Mark Lane, Health & Safety Advisor, Council Offices, Woodgreen, Witney OX28 1NB
✆ mark.lane@westoxon.gov.uk

Housing: Mr Jon Dearing, Head of Revenues & Housing Support, Council Offices, Woodgreen, Witney OX28 1NB ☎ 01993 861221

Legal: Ms Bhavna Patel, Head of Legal & Property Services, Council Offices, Woodgreen, Witney OX28 1NB

Leisure and Cultural Services: Ms Diane Shelton, Head of Leisure & Communities, Council Offices, Woodgreen, Witney OX28 1NB ☎ 01285 623560 ✆ diana.shelton@westoxfordshire.gov.uk

Licensing: Ms Diane Shelton, Head of Leisure & Communities, Council Offices, Woodgreen, Witney OX28 1NB ☎ 01285 623560 ✆ diana.shelton@westoxfordshire.gov.uk

Member Services: Mr Keith Butler, Head of Democratic Services, Council Offices, Woodgreen, Witney OX28 1NB ☎ 01993 861521 ✆ keith.butler@westoxon.gov.uk

Personnel / HR: Ms Deborah Bainbridge, Head of Human Resources, Council Offices, Woodgreen, Witney OX28 1NB
☎ 01285 623148 ✆ deborah.bainbridge@cotswold.gov.uk

Planning: Mr Giles Hughes, Head of Planning & Strategic Housing, Council Offices, Woodgreen, Witney OX28 1NB
☎ 01993 861658 ✆ giles.hughes@westoxon.gov.uk

Procurement: Mr Phil Martin, Head of Business Information & Change, Council Offices, Woodgreen, Witney OX28 1NB
☎ 01993 861201 ✆ phil.martin@westoxon.gov.uk

Staff Training: Mrs Jan Bridges, Learning & Organisational Development Manager, Municipal Offices, Promenade, Cheltenham GL50 9SA ☎ 01242 775189 ✆ jan.bridges@cheltenham.gov.uk

Sustainable Communities: Mr Giles Hughes, Head of Planning & Strategic Housing, Council Offices, Woodgreen, Witney OX28 1NB ☎ 01993 861658 ✆ giles.hughes@westoxon.gov.uk

Sustainable Development: Mr Giles Hughes, Head of Planning & Strategic Housing, Council Offices, Woodgreen, Witney OX28 1NB ☎ 01993 861658 ✆ giles.hughes@westoxon.gov.uk

Tourism: Ms Diane Shelton, Head of Leisure & Communities, Council Offices, Woodgreen, Witney OX28 1NB ☎ 01285 623560 ✆ diana.shelton@westoxfordshire.gov.uk

Waste Management: Mrs Claire Locke, Head of Environmental Services, Council Offices, Woodgreen, Witney OX28 1NB ☎ 01285 623427 ✆ claire.locke@cotswold.gov.uk

WEST OXFORDSHIRE

COUNCILLORS

Chair: MacRae, Norman (CON - Carterton North East)
norman.macrae@westoxon.gov.uk

Vice-Chair: Crossland, Maxine (CON - Carterton North West)
maxine.crossland@westoxon.gov.uk

Leader of the Council: Mills, James (CON - Witney East)
james.mills@westoxon.gov.uk

Deputy Leader of the Council: Courts, Robert (CON - The Bartons)
robert.courts@westoxon.gov.uk

Group Leader: Cooper, Julian (LD - Woodstock & Bladon)
julian.cooper@westoxon.gov.uk

Group Leader: Enright, Duncan (LAB - Witney East)
duncan.enright@westoxon.gov.uk

Adams, Alvin (CON - Witney South)
alvin.adams@westoxon.gov.uk

Baker, Jeanette (CON - Witney East)
jeanette.baker@westoxon.gov.uk

Barrett, Martin (CON - Bampton & Clanfield)
martin.barrett@westoxon.gov.uk

Beaney, Andrew (CON - Kingham, Rollright & Enstone)
andrew.beaney@westoxon.gov.uk

Bishop, Richard (CON - Stonesfield & Tackley)
richard.bishop@westoxon.gov.uk

Brennan, Mick (CON - Carterton South)
michael.brennan@westoxon.gov.uk

Carter, Laetisia (LAB - Chipping Norton)
laetisis.carter@westoxon.gov.uk

Chapman, Louise (CON - Witney West)
louise.chapman@westoxon.gov.uk

Coles, Andrew (LAB - Witney Central)
andrew.coles@westoxon.gov.uk

Colston, Nigel (CON - Kingham, Rollright & Enstone)
nigel.colston@westoxon.gov.uk

Cotterill, Derek (CON - Burford)
derek.cotterill@westoxon.gov.uk

Cottrell-Dormer, Charles (CON - Stonesfield & Tackley)
charles.cottrell-dormer@westoxon.gov.uk

Dingwall, Colin (CON - Freeland & Hanborough)
colin.dingwall@westoxon.gov.uk

Dorward, Pete (CON - Witney Central)
pete.dorward@westoxon.gov.uk

Doughty, Jane (CON - Witney South)
jane.doughty@westoxon.gov.uk

Eaglestone, Harry (CON - Witney West)
harry.eaglestone@westoxon.gov.uk

Emery, Peter (CON - Eynsham & Cassington)
peter.emery@westoxon.gov.uk

Fenton, Hilary (CON - Standlake, Aston & Stanton Harcourt)
hilary.fenton@westoxon.gov.uk

Fenton, Ted (CON - Bampton & Clanfield)
ted.fenton@westoxon.gov.uk

Good, Steve (CON - Standlake, Aston & Stanton Harcourt)
steve.good@westoxon.gov.uk

Graham, Andy (LD - Charlbury & Finstock)
andy.graham@westoxon.gov.uk

Haine, Jeff (CON - Milton under Wychwood)
jeff.haine@westoxon.gov.uk

Handley, Peter (CON - Carterton North West)
peter.handley@westoxon.gov.uk

Harvey, David (CON - Witney South)
david.harvey@westoxon.gov.uk

Hill, Gill (CON - Hailey, Minster Lovell & Leafield)
gill.hill@westoxon.gov.uk

Howard, Henry (CON - Carterton North East)
henry.howard@westoxon.gov.uk

James, Edward (CON - Eynsham & Cassington)
edward.james@westoxon.gov.uk

Kelland, Peter (CON - Eynsham & Cassington)
peter.kelland@westoxon.gov.uk

Langridge, Richard (CON - Witney North)
richard.langridge@westoxon.gov.uk

Leffman, Liz (LD - Charlbury & Finstock)
liz.leffman@westoxon.gov.uk

Little, Lynn (CON - Carterton South)
lynn.little@westoxon.gov.uk

McFarlane, David (CON - Alvescot & Filkins)
david.mcfarlane@westoxon.gov.uk

Morris, Toby (CON - Witney North)
toby.morris@westoxon.gov.uk

Owen, Neil (CON - Chadlington & Churchill)
neil.owen@westoxon.gov.uk

Poskitt, Elizabeth (LD - Woodstock & Bladon)
elizabeth.poskitt@westoxon.gov.uk

Postan, Alex (CON - Brize Norton & Shilton)
alex.postan@westoxon.gov.uk

Reynolds, Carol (CON - Freeland & Hanborough)
carol.reynolds@westoxon.gov.uk

Saul, Geoff (LAB - Chipping Norton)
geoff.saul@westoxon.gov.uk

Simcox, Tom (CON - Ascott & Shipton)
tom.simcox@westoxon.gov.uk

St John, Harry (CON - North Leigh)
harry.stjohn@westoxon.gov.uk

Wall, Guy (CON - Chipping Norton)
guy.wall@westoxon.gov.uk

Woodruff, Ben (CON - Ducklington)
ben.woodruff@westoxon.gov.uk

POLITICAL COMPOSITION
CON: 40, LAB: 4, LD: 4, Vacant: 1

COMMITTEE CHAIRS

Audit: Mr Alvin Adams

Development Control: Mr Jeff Haine

Licensing: Mr Norman MacRae

West Somerset   **D**

West Somerset District Council, West Somerset House, Killick Way, Williton, Taunton TA4 4QA
☎ 01643 703704 ⬩ customerservices@westsomerset.gov.uk
🖥 www.westsomersetonline.gov.uk

FACTS AND FIGURES
Parliamentary Constituencies: Bridgwater and Somerset West
EU Constituencies: South West
Election Frequency: Elections are of whole council

PRINCIPAL OFFICERS

Chief Executive: Mrs Penny James, Chief Executive, West Somerset House, Killick Way, Williton, Taunton TA4 4QA
☎ 01823 356401 ⬩ p.james@tauntondeane.gov.uk

Deputy Chief Executive: Ms Shirlene Adam, Director - Operations, Deputy CEO & S151 Officer, West Somerset House, Killick Way, Williton, Taunton TA4 4QA ☎ 01823 356310
⬩ s.adam@tauntondeane.gov.uk

Assistant Chief Executive: Mr Bruce Lang, Assistant Chief Executive & Monitoring Officer, West Somerset House, Killick Way, Williton, Taunton TA4 4QA ☎ 01823 356403; 01984 635200
⬩ bdlang@westsomerset.gov.uk; b.lang@tauntondeane.gov.uk

Senior Management: Ms Shirlene Adam, Director - Operations, Deputy CEO & S151 Officer, West Somerset House, Killick Way, Williton, Taunton TA4 4QA ☎ 01823 356310
⬩ s.adam@tauntondeane.gov.uk

Senior Management: Mr James Barrah, Director - Housing & Communities, The Deane House, Belvedere Road, Taunton TA1 1HE
☎ 01823 358699 ⬩ j.barrah@tauntondeane.gov.uk

Senior Management: Mr Brendon Cleere, Director - Growth & Development, The Deane House, Belvedere Road, Taunton TA1 1HE
☎ 01823 356350 ⬩ b.cleere@tauntondeane.gov.uk

Access Officer / Social Services (Disability): Mr Edwin Norton, Senior Building Control, Surveyor & Access Officer, The Deane House, Belvedere Road, Taunton TA1 1HE ☎ 01823 356476
⬩ e.norton@tauntondeane.gov.uk

Architect, Building / Property Services: Mr Tim Child, Divisional Manager - Property Estates Team, The Deane House, Belvedere Road, Taunton TA1 1HE ☎ 01823 356356
⬩ t.child@tauntondeane.gov.uk

Building Control: Mr Nigel Hunt, Somerset Building Control Partnership Manager, Bridgwater House, Kings Square, Bridgwater TA6 9ZY ☎ 01823 356473 ⬩ nigel.hunt@mendip.gov.uk

PR / Communications: Mrs Debbie Rundle, Media & PR Officer, The Deane House, Belvedere Road, Taunton TA1 1HE
☎ 01823 356407 ⬩ d.rundle@tauntondeane.gov.uk

Community Planning: Mr Tim Burton, Assistant Director - Planning & Environment, The Deane House, Belvedere Road, Taunton TA1 1HE ☎ 01823 358403 ⬩ t.burton@tauntondeane.gov.uk

Community Safety: Ms Tracey-Ann Biss, Parking & Civil Contingencies Manager, West Somerset House, Killick Way, Williton, Taunton TA4 4QA ☎ 01823 356455
⬩ t.biss@tauntondeane.gov.uk

Computer Management: Ms Fiona Kirkham, ICT & Information Manager, The Deane House, Belvedere Road, Taunton TA1 1HE
☎ 01823 356522 ⬩ f.kirkham@tauntondeane.gov.uk

Corporate Services: Mr Richard Sealy, Assistant Director - Corporate Services, The Deane House, Belvedere Road, Taunton TA1 1HE ☎ 01823 658690 ⬩ r.sealy@tauntondeane.gov.uk

Customer Service: Mr Rob Liddell, Head of Customer Contact, The Deane House, Belvedere Road, Taunton TA1 1HE
☎ 01823 356356 ⬩ r.liddell@tauntondeane.gov.uk

Direct Labour: Mr Chris Hall, Assistant Director - Operational Delivery, The Deane House, Belvedere Road, Taunton TA1 1HE
☎ 01823 356403 ⬩ c.hall@tauntondeane.gov.uk

Economic Development: Mr David Evans, Economic Development Manager, The Deane House, Belvedere Road, Taunton TA1 1HE ☎ 01823 356545 ⬩ d.evans@tauntondeane.gov.uk

Economic Development: Mr Ian Timms, Assistant Director - Business Development, West Somerset House, Killick Way, Williton, Taunton TA4 4QA ☎ 01823 356577 ⬩ itimms@westsomerset.gov.uk

Electoral Registration: Mrs Elisa Day, Electoral Services Manager, West Somerset House, Killick Way, Williton, Taunton TA4 4QA ☎ 01984 635272 ⬩ eday@westsomerset.gov.uk

Emergency Planning: Ms Tracey-Ann Biss, Parking & Civil Contingencies Manager, West Somerset House, Killick Way, Williton, Taunton TA4 4QA ☎ 01823 356455
⬩ t.biss@tauntondeane.gov.uk

Environmental Health: Mr Scott Weetch, Community & Client Services Manager, The Deane House, Belvedere Road, Taunton TA1 1HE ☎ 01823 356317 ⬩ s.weetch@tauntondeane.gov.uk

Estates, Property & Valuation: Mr Tim Child, Divisional Manager - Property Estates Team, The Deane House, Belvedere Road, Taunton TA1 1HE ☎ 01823 356356 ⬩ t.child@tauntondeane.gov.uk

Facilities: Ms Angela Hill, Facilities & Corporate Administration Manager, The Deane House, Belvedere Road, Taunton TA1 1HE
☎ 01823 356597 ⬩ a.hill@tauntondeane.gov.uk

Finance: Mr Paul Fitzgerald, Assistant Director - Resources, West Somerset House, Killick Way, Williton, Taunton TA4 4QA
⬩ pfitzgerald@westsomerset.gov.uk

Grounds Maintenance: Mr Richard Hopkins, Open Spaces Area Manager, Priory Way Depot, Taunton TA1 2BB ☎ 01823 356360
⬩ r.hopkins@tauntondeane.gov.uk

Health and Safety: Ms Catrin Brown, Health & Safety Manager, The Deane House, Belvedere Road, Taunton TA1 1HE
☎ 01823 356578 ⬩ c.brown@tauntondeane.gov.uk

WEST SOMERSET

Home Energy Conservation: Ms Barbara Wells, Energy Efficiency Officer, Sedgemoor Council, Bridgwater House, King's Square, Bridgwater TA6 3AR ☎ 01278 436426 ✆ b.wells@sedgemoor.gov.uk

Housing: Mr Simon Lewis, Assistant Director – Housing & Community Development, The Deane House, Belvedere Road, Taunton TA1 1HE ☎ 01823 356397 ✆ s.lewis@tauntondeane.gov.uk

Housing Maintenance: Mr Phil Webb, Housing Manager – Property Services, The Deane House, Belvedere Road, Taunton TA1 1HE ☎ 01823 356505 ✆ p.webb@tauntondeane.gov.uk

Legal: Mrs Lesley Dolan, SHAPE Business Services Manager, The Deane House, Belvedere Road, Taunton TA1 1HE ☎ 0300 303 8588 ✆ lesley.dolan@mendip.gov.uk

Leisure and Cultural Services: Ms Alison North, Community Leisure Manager, Priory Depot, Priory Way, Taunton TA1 1HE ☎ 01823 356576 ✆ a.north@tauntondeane.gov.uk

Licensing: Mr John Rendell, Licensing Manager, The Deane House, Belvedere Road, Taunton TA1 1HE ☎ 01823 358343 ✆ j.rendell@tauntondeane.gov.uk

Member Services: Mr Richard Bryant, Democratic Services Manager, The Deane House, Belvedere Road, Taunton TA1 1HE ☎ 01823 356414 ✆ r.bryant@tauntondeane.gov.uk

Parking: Ms Tracey-Ann Biss, Parking & Civil Contingencies Manager, West Somerset House, Killick Way, Williton, Taunton TA4 4QA ☎ 01823 356455 ✆ t.biss@tauntondeane.gov.uk

Personnel / HR: Ms Fiona Wills, Human Resources Manager, The Deane House, Belvedere Road, Taunton TA1 1HE ☎ 01823 356450 ✆ f.wills@tauntondeane.gov.uk

Planning: Mr Tim Burton, Assistant Director – Planning & Environment, The Deane House, Belvedere Road, Taunton TA1 1HE ☎ 01823 358403 ✆ t.burton@tauntondeane.gov.uk

Planning: Mr Bryn Kitching, Area Planning Manager, The Deane House, Belvedere Road, Taunton TA1 1HE

Procurement: Mr Jon Batstone, Procurement Manager, The Deane House, Belvedere Road, Taunton TA1 1HE ☎ 01823 358286 ✆ j.batstone@tauntondeane.gov.uk

Regeneration: Ms Corinne Matthews, Economic Regeneration Manager, West Somerset House, Killick Way, Williton, Taunton TA4 4QA ☎ 01823 356356 ✆ c.matthews@tauntondeane.gov.uk

Staff Training: Ms Fiona Wills, Human Resources Manager, The Deane House, Belvedere Road, Taunton TA1 1HE ☎ 01823 356450 ✆ f.wills@tauntondeane.gov.uk

Tourism: Ms Corinne Matthews, Economic Regeneration Manager, West Somerset House, Killick Way, Williton, Taunton TA4 4QA ☎ 01823 356356 ✆ c.matthews@tauntondeane.gov.uk

Waste Collection and Disposal: Mr Chris Hall, Assistant Director - Operational Delivery, The Deane House, Belvedere Road, Taunton TA1 1HE ☎ 01823 356403 ✆ c.hall@tauntondeane.gov.uk

Children's Play Areas: Mr Josep Galicia, Open Spaces Supervisor, Deane DLO, Priory Depot, Priory Way, Taunton TA1 2BB ☎ 01823 356360 ✆ j.galicia@tauntondeane.gov.uk

COUNCILLORS

Chair: Heywood, Bruce (CON - Dulverton & District) bheywood@westsomerset.gov.uk

Vice-Chair: Woods, Rosemary (CON - Watchet) rwoods@westsomerset.gov.uk

Leader of the Council: Trollope-Bellew, Anthony (CON - Crowcombe & Stogumber) atrollope-bellew@westsomerset.gov.uk

Aldridge, Ian (IND - Williton) laldridge@westsomerset.gov.uk

Archer, David (CON - Minehead North) darcher@westsomerset.gov.uk

Behan, Adrian (UKIP - Alcombe) abehan@westsomerset.gov.uk

Chilcott, Mandy (CON - Minehead Central) mchilcott@westsomerset.gov.uk

Clifford, Rollo (CON - Porlock & District) rclifford@westsomerset.gov.uk

Davies, Hugh (IND - Williton) hdavies@westsomerset.gov.uk

Dewdney, Martin (CON - Old Cleeve) mdewdney@westsomerset.gov.uk

Dowding, Stuart (CON - West Quantock) sdowding@westsomerset.gov.uk

Goss, Susan (CON - Quantock Vale) sgoss@westsomerset.gov.uk

Hadley, Andrew (IND - Minehead Central) ahadley@westsomerset.gov.uk

Hall, Thomas (UKIP - Minehead South) thall@westsomerset.gov.uk

Jones, Ivor (UKIP - Minehead Central) ljones@westsomerset.gov.uk

Leaker, Bryan (CON - Dunster & Timbercombe) bleaker@westsomerset.gov.uk

Lillis, Richard (CON - Old Cleeve) rlillis@westsomerset.gov.uk

Maitland-Walker, Brenda (CON - Carhampton & Withycombe) bmaitland-walker@westsomerset.gov.uk

Mills, Karen (CON - Porlock & District) kmills@westsomerset.gov.uk

Morgan, Chris (IND - Quantock Vale) cmorgan@westsomerset.gov.uk

Murphy, Peter (LAB - Watchet) pmurphy@westsomerset.gov.uk

Parbrook, Jean (CON - Minehead South) jparbrook@westsomerset.gov.uk

Pugsley, Steven (CON - Greater Exmoor)
sjpugsley@westsomerset.gov.uk

Thomas, Roger (CON - Alcombe)
rthomas@westsomerset.gov.uk

Thwaites, Nicholas (CON - Dulverton & District)
nthwaites@westsomerset.gov.uk

Turner, Keith (CON - Brendon Hills)
kturner@westsomerset.gov.uk

Venner, Terry (UKIP - Minehead North)
tvenner@westsomerset.gov.uk

Westcott, David (CON - Watchet)
dwestcott@westsomerset.gov.uk

POLITICAL COMPOSITION
CON: 19, IND: 4, UKIP: 4, LAB: 1

West Sussex   C

West Sussex County Council, County Hall, Chichester
PO19 1RQ
☎ 01243 777100 ✆ customer.service@westsussex.gov.uk
🖥 www.westsussex.gov.uk

FACTS AND FIGURES
Parliamentary Constituencies: Arundel and South Downs, Bognor
Regis and Littlehampton, Chichester, Crawley, Horsham, Sussex Mid,
Worthing East and Shoreham, Worthing West
EU Constituencies: South East
Election Frequency: Elections are of whole council

PRINCIPAL OFFICERS

Chief Executive: Mr Nathan Elvery, Chief Executive, County Hall,
Chichester PO19 1RQ ☎ 03302 224268
✆ nathan.elvery@westsussex.gov.uk

Deputy Chief Executive: Mr Sean Ruth, Deputy Chief Executive,
County Hall, Chichester PO19 1RQ ☎ 03302 224991
✆ sean.ruth@westsussex.gov.uk

Senior Management: Dr Nike Arowobusoye, Director - Public
Health, County Hall, Chichester PO19 1RQ ☎ 03302 224984
✆ nike.arowobusoye@westsussex.gov.uk

Senior Management: Mrs Natasha Edmunds, Director -
Workforce, Organisational Development & Delivery Support, County
Hall, Chichester PO19 1RQ ☎ 033022 25342
✆ natasha.edmunds@westsussex.gov.uk

Senior Management: Mr Mark Howell, Director - Adults'
Operation, County Hall, Chichester PO19 1RQ ☎ 03302 222132
✆ mark.howell@westsussex.gov.uk

Senior Management: Mr Tony Kershaw, Director - Law,
Assurance & Strategy, County Hall, Chichester PO19 1RQ
☎ 033022 22662 ✆ tony.kershaw@westsussex.gov.uk

Senior Management: Ms Annie MacIver, Director - Family
Operations, County Hall, Chichester PO19 1RQ ☎ 03302 226486
✆ annie.maciver@westsussex.gov.uk

Senior Management: Ms Bernadette Marjoram, Executive
Director - Residents' Services, County Hall, Chichester PO19 1RQ
☎ 03302 227956 ✆ bernadette.marjoram@westsussex.gov.uk

Senior Management: Ms Deborah Myers, Director - Education &
Skills, County Hall, Chichester PO19 1RQ
✆ deborah.myers@westsussex.gov.uk

Senior Management: Ms Rachel North, Director - Communities,
County Hall, Chichester PO19 1RQ
✆ rachel.north@westsussex.gov.uk

Senior Management: Mr Nick Smales, Director - Economy,
Planning & Place, County Hall, Chichester PO19 1RQ
✆ nick.smales@westsussex.gov.uk

Senior Management: Ms Avril Wilson, Executive Director - Care,
Wellbeing & Education, County Hall, Chichester PO19 1RQ
☎ 03302 228185 ✆ avril.wilson@westsussex.gov.uk

Children / Youth Services: Ms Annie MacIver, Director - Family
Operations, County Hall, Chichester PO19 1RQ ☎ 03302 226486
✆ annie.maciver@westsussex.gov.uk

Civil Registration: Mrs Margaret Butler, Service Manager -
Registration & Coroner, County Hall, Chartway, Horsham
RH12 1XH ☎ 033022 27657 ✆ margaret.butler@westsussex.gov.uk

Civil Registration: Mr Sean Ruth, Deputy Chief Executive, County
Hall, Chichester PO19 1RQ ☎ 03302 224991
✆ sean.ruth@westsussex.gov.uk

PR / Communications: Ms Harriet Shelley, Head of
Communications, County Hall, Chichester PO19 1RQ
☎ 07850 537293 ✆ harriet.shelley@westsussex.gov.uk

Community Safety: Mrs Emily King, Principal Manager -
Community Safety & Wellbeing, County Hall, Chichester PO19 1RQ
☎ 033022 23876 ✆ emily.king@westsussex.gov.uk

Computer Management: Mrs Natasha Edmunds, Director -
Workforce, Organisational Development & Delivery Support, County
Hall, Chichester PO19 1RQ ☎ 033022 25342
✆ natasha.edmunds@westsussex.gov.uk

Consumer Protection and Trading Standards: Mr Sean Ruth,
Deputy Chief Executive, County Hall, Chichester PO19 1RQ
☎ 03302 224991 ✆ sean.ruth@westsussex.gov.uk

Corporate Services: Mr Peter Lewis, Interim Executive Director -
Corporate Resources & Services, County Hall, Chichester PO19 1RQ
☎ 03302 227125 ✆ peter.lewis@westsussex.gov.uk

Customer Service: Ms Amanda Anderson, Director - Customer
Service, County Hall, Chichester PO19 1RQ ☎ 03302 222267
✆ amanda.anderson@westsussex.gov.uk

Economic Development: Mr Nick Smales, Director - Economy,
Planning & Place, County Hall, Chichester PO19 1RQ
✆ nick.smales@westsussex.gov.uk

WEST SUSSEX

Electoral Registration: Mr Tony Kershaw, Director - Law, Assurance & Strategy, County Hall, Chichester PO19 1RQ ☎ 033022 22662 ✆ tony.kershaw@westsussex.gov.uk

Finance: Mr Peter Lewis, Interim Executive Director - Corporate Resources & Services, County Hall, Chichester PO19 1RQ ☎ 03302 227125 ✆ peter.lewis@westsussex.gov.uk

Pensions: Mrs Jo Jennings, HR Shared Services Manager, County Hall, Chichester PO19 1RQ ☎ 01243 777867 ✆ jo.jennings@westsussex.gov.uk

Fleet Management: Mr Paul Mace, Transport Provision Manager, Northleigh, County Hall, Chichester PO19 1RH ☎ 033022 25443 ✆ paul.mace@westsussex.gov.uk

Health and Safety: Mr David Ramsbottom, Health & Safety Lead Professional, County Hall, Chichester PO19 1RQ ☎ 033022 22463 ✆ david.ramsbottom@westsussex.gov.uk

Highways: Mr Matt Davey, Director - Highways & Transport, County Hall, Chichester PO19 1RQ ☎ 03302 225622 ✆ matt.davey@westsussex.gov.uk

Legal: Mr Tony Kershaw, Director - Law, Assurance & Strategy, County Hall, Chichester PO19 1RQ ☎ 033022 22662 ✆ tony.kershaw@westsussex.gov.uk

Lifelong Learning: Ms Annie MacIver, Director - Family Operations, County Hall, Chichester PO19 1RQ ☎ 03302 226486 ✆ annie.maciver@westsussex.gov.uk

Lighting: Mr Kevin Moss, Street Lighting Team Leader, Northleigh, County Hall, Chichester PO19 1RH ☎ 03302 226930 ✆ kevin.moss@westsussex.gov.uk

Member Services: Mr Charles Gauntlett, Senior Advisor - Democratic Services, Democratic Services Unit, County Hall, Chichester PO19 1RQ ☎ 03302 222524 ✆ charles.gauntlett@westsussex.gov.uk

Member Services: Mr Tony Kershaw, Director - Law, Assurance & Strategy, County Hall, Chichester PO19 1RQ ☎ 033022 22662 ✆ tony.kershaw@westsussex.gov.uk

Personnel / HR: Mrs Natasha Edmunds, Director - Workforce, Organisational Development & Delivery Support, County Hall, Chichester PO19 1RQ ☎ 033022 25342 ✆ natasha.edmunds@westsussex.gov.uk

Planning: Mr Nick Smales, Director - Economy, Planning & Place, County Hall, Chichester PO19 1RQ ✆ nick.smales@westsussex.gov.uk

Public Libraries: Mrs Lesley Sim, Information Services Manager, Willow Park, 4B Terminus Road, Chichester PO19 8EG ☎ 033022 24786 ✆ lesley.sim@westsussex.gov.uk

Recycling & Waste Minimisation: Ms Bernadette Marjoram, Executive Director - Residents' Services, County Hall, Chichester PO19 1RQ ☎ 03302 227956 ✆ bernadette.marjoram@westsussex.gov.uk

Road Safety: Mr Ron Paterson, Team Manager - Safe & Sustainable Transport Group, County Hall, Chichester PO19 1RQ ☎ 033022 26712 ✆ ron.paterson@westsussex.gov.uk

Social Services (Adult): Mr Mark Howell, Director - Adults' Operation, County Hall, Chichester PO19 1RQ ☎ 03302 222132 ✆ mark.howell@westsussex.gov.uk

Social Services (Children): Ms Annie MacIver, Director - Family Operations, County Hall, Chichester PO19 1RQ ☎ 03302 226486 ✆ annie.maciver@westsussex.gov.uk

Public Health: Dr Nike Arowobusoye, Director - Public Health, County Hall, Chichester PO19 1RQ ☎ 03302 224984 ✆ nike.arowobusoye@westsussex.gov.uk

Staff Training: Ms Julie Ferroni, Learning & Development Operations Manager, County Hall, Chichester PO19 1RQ ☎ 033022 22318 ✆ julie.ferroni@westsussex.gov.uk

Sustainable Development: Mrs Siobhan Walker, Partnership Manager - Sussex Energy Saving Department, Communities & Infrastructure, County Hall, Chichester PO19 1RQ ☎ 033022 26456 ✆ siobhan.walker@westsussex.gov.uk

Traffic Management: Mr Peter Bradley, Service Manager - Safety & Traffic Management, County Hall, Chichester PO19 1RQ ☎ 03302 222104 ✆ peter.bradley@westsussex.gov.uk

Transport: Mr Ian Patrick, Team Manager - Travelwise & Behavioural Change, Northleigh, Tower Street, Chichester PO19 1RH ☎ 033022 26715 ✆ ian.patrick@westsussex.gov.uk

Transport Planner: Mr Ian Patrick, Team Manager - Travelwise & Behavioural Change, Northleigh, Tower Street, Chichester PO19 1RH ☎ 033022 26715 ✆ ian.patrick@westsussex.gov.uk

Waste Collection and Disposal: Mr Andy Thorne, Waste Commissioner, County Hall, Chichester PO19 1RQ ☎ 033022 23349 ✆ andy.thorne@westsussex.gov.uk

Waste Management: Ms Bernadette Marjoram, Executive Director - Residents' Services, County Hall, Chichester PO19 1RQ ☎ 03302 227956 ✆ bernadette.marjoram@westsussex.gov.uk

COUNCILLORS

Chair: Arculus, Patricia (CON - Pulborough)
patricia.arculus@westsussex.gov.uk

Vice-Chair: Barnard, Lionel (CON - Henfield)
lionel.barnard@westsussex.gov.uk

Leader of the Council: Goldsmith, Louise (CON - Chichester West)
louise.goldsmith@westsussex.gov.uk

Deputy Leader of the Council: Field, Christine (CON - Lindfield & High Weald)
christine.field@westsussex.gov.uk

Acraman, William (CON - Worth Forest)
bill.acraman@westsussex.gov.uk

Barling, David (CON - Bramber Castle)
david.barling@westsussex.gov.uk

Barrett-Miles, Andrew (CON - Burgess Hill Town)
andrew.barrett-miles@westsussex.gov.uk

Bennett, Elizabeth (CON - East Grinstead Meridian)
liz.bennett@westsussex.gov.uk

Bradbury, Peter (CON - Cuckfield & Lucastes)
pete.bradbury@westsussex.gov.uk

Brown, Michael (CON - Fernhurst)
michael.brown@westsussex.gov.uk

Brunsdon, Heidi (CON - Imberdown)
heidi.brunsdon@westsussex.gov.uk

Buckland, Ian (LD - Littlehampton Town)
ian.buckland@westsussex.gov.uk

Burrett, Richard (CON - Pound Hill & Worth)
richard.burrett@westsussex.gov.uk

Catchpole, Peter (CON - Holbrook)
peter.catchpole@westsussex.gov.uk

Circus, Philip (CON - Storrington)
philip.circus@westsussex.gov.uk

Clark, Michael (UKIP - Saltings)
mick.clark@westsussex.gov.uk

Cloake, Michael (CON - Worthing Pier)
michael.cloake@westsussex.gov.uk

Crow, Duncan (CON - Tilgate & Furnace Green)
duncan.crow@westsussex.gov.uk

Dennis, Nigel (LD - Horsham Hurst)
nigel.dennis@westsussex.gov.uk

Duncton, Janet (CON - Petworth)
janet.duncton@westsussex.gov.uk

Evans, Peter (CON - East Preston & Ferring)
peter.evans@westsussex.gov.uk

Evans, Margaret (CON - Chichester South)
margaret.evans@westsussex.gov.uk

Glennon, Michael (UKIP - Lancing)
michael.glennon@westsussex.gov.uk

Griffiths, Peter (CON - Hurstpierpoint & Bolney)
peter.griffiths@westsussex.gov.uk

Hall, Patricia (UKIP - Durrington & Savlington)
trixie.hall@westsussex.gov.uk

High, Paul (CON - Worthing West)
paul.high@westsussex.gov.uk

Hillier, Stephen (CON - Haywards Heath East)
stephen.hillier@westsussex.gov.uk

Hunt, Jeremy (CON - Chichester North)
jeremy.hunt@westsussex.gov.uk

James, Sandra (UKIP - Bourne)
sandra.james@westsussex.gov.uk

Jones, Graham (UKIP - Felpham)
graham.jones@westsussex.gov.uk

Jones, Anne (CON - Burgess Hill East)
anne.jones@westsussex.gov.uk

Jones, Michael (LAB - Southgate & Crawley Central)
michael.jones@westsussex.gov.uk

Jupp, Amanda (CON - Billingshurst)
amanda.jupp@westsussex.gov.uk

Kennard, Debra (CON - Shoreham)
debbie.kennard@westsussex.gov.uk

Kitchen, Liz (CON - Warnham and Rusper)
liz.kitchen@westsussex.gov.uk

Lamb, Peter (LAB - Northgate & Three Bridges)
peter.lamb@westsussex.gov.uk

Lanzer, Robert (CON - Maidenbower)
bob.lanzer@westsussex.gov.uk

McAra, Gordon (IND - Midhurst)
gordon.mcara@westsussex.gov.uk

Metcalfe, Peter (CON - Kingston Buci)
peter.metcalfe@westsussex.gov.uk

Millson, Morwen (LD - Horsham Riverside)
morwen.millson@westsussex.gov.uk

Mockbridge, Janet (CON - Southwick)
janet.mockridge@westsussex.gov.uk

Montyn, Pieter (CON - The Witterings)
pieter.montyn@westsussex.gov.uk

Mullins, Susan (LAB - Gossops Green & Ifield East)
sue.mullins@westsussex.gov.uk

Oakley, Roger (CON - Worthing East)
roger.oakley@westsussex.gov.uk

Oakley, Simon (CON - Chichester East)
simon.oakley@westsussex.gov.uk

Oppler, Francis (LD - Bognor Regis East)
francis.oppler@westsussex.gov.uk

Oxlade, Christopher (LAB - Bewbush & Ifield West)
chris.oxlade@westsussex.gov.uk

Parsons, Lionel (UKIP - Sompting & North Lancing)
lionel.parsons@westsussex.gov.uk

Patel, Ashvin (CON - Bognor Regis West & Aldwick)
ashvin.patel@westsussex.gov.uk

Petch, Andrew (CON - Hassocks & Victoria)
andy.petch@westsussex.gov.uk

Peters, Nigel (CON - Arundel & Wick)
nigel.peters@westsussex.gov.uk

Phillips, Joan (UKIP - Middleton)
joan.phillips@westsussex.gov.uk

Quinn, Brian (LAB - Broadfield)
brian.quinn@westsussex.gov.uk

Rae, James (CON - Roffey)
jim.rae@westsussex.gov.uk

Rapnik, Ann (UKIP - Bersted)
ann.rapnik@westsussex.gov.uk

Rogers, Robin (LD - Northbrook)
robin.rogers@westsussex.gov.uk

Rogers, John (CON - Cissbury)
john.rogers@westsussex.gov.uk

Sheldon, David (LD - Horsham Tanbridge & Broadbridge Heath)
david.sheldon@westsussex.gov.uk

Smith, Bernard (UKIP - Selsey)
bernard.smith@westsussex.gov.uk

Smith, Brenda (LAB - Langley Green & West Green)
brenda.smith@westsussex.gov.uk

WEST SUSSEX

Smytherman, Robert (LD - Tarring)
bob.smytherman@westsussex.gov.uk

Sutcliffe, Anthony (UKIP - Nyetimber)
tony.sutcliffe@westsussex.gov.uk

Turner, Bryan (CON - Broadwater)
bryan.turner@westsussex.gov.uk

Tyler, Graham (CON - Rustington)
graham.tyler@westsussex.gov.uk

Urquhart, Deborah (CON - Angmering & Findon)
deborah.urquhart@westsussex.gov.uk

Waight, Steven (CON - Goring)
steve.waight@westsussex.gov.uk

Walsh, James (LD - Littlehampton East)
james.walsh@westsussex.gov.uk

Watson, Brad (CON - Southwater & Nuthurst)
brad.watson@westsussex.gov.uk

Whittington, Derek (CON - Fontwell)
derek.whittington@westsussex.gov.uk

Wickremaratchi, Sujan (CON - Haywards Heath Town)
sujan.wickremaratchi@westsussex.gov.uk

POLITICAL COMPOSITION
CON: 45, UKIP: 10, LD: 8, LAB: 6, IND: 1

COMMITTEE CHAIRS

Audit: Mrs Morwen Millson

Children & Young People: Mr Michael Cloake

Health & Adult Social Care: Mr Bryan Turner

Planning: Mrs Heidi Brunsdon

Western Isles   S

Western Isles Council, Council Offices, Sandwick Road,
Stornoway HS1 2BW
☎ 01851 703773 ✆ enquiries@cne-siar.gov.uk 🖥 www.cne-siar.gov.uk

FACTS AND FIGURES
Parliamentary Constituencies: Na h-Eileanan an Iar
EU Constituencies: Scotland
Election Frequency: Elections are of whole council

PRINCIPAL OFFICERS

Chief Executive: Mr Malcolm Burr, Chief Executive, Council
Offices, Sandwick Road, Stornoway HS1 2BW ☎ 01851 822602
✆ m.burr@cne-siar.gov.uk

Senior Management: Mr Ron Culley, Chief Officer, Council
Offices, Sandwick Road, Stornoway HS1 2BW ☎ 01851 822706
✆ ron.culley@cne-siar.gov.uk

Senior Management: Mr Robert Emmott, Director - Finance &
Corporate Resources, Council Offices, Sandwick Road, Stornoway
HS1 2BW ☎ 01851 822628 ✆ remmott@cne-siar.gov.uk

Senior Management: Mr Calum Iain Maciver, Director -
Development, Council Offices, Sandwick Road, Stornoway
HS1 2BW ☎ 01851 822685 ✆ calum.maciver@cne-siar.gov.uk

Senior Management: Mr Iain Mackinnon, Director - Technical
Services, Council Offices, Sandwick Road, Stornoway HS1 2BW
☎ 01851 822656 ✆ iain.mackinnon@cne-siar.gov.uk

Architect, Building / Property Services: Mr Iain Mackinnon,
Director - Technical Services, Council Offices, Sandwick Road,
Stornoway HS1 2BW ☎ 01851 822656
✆ iain.mackinnon@cne-siar.gov.uk

Best Value: Ms Norma Morrison, Organisational Development,
Council Offices, Sandwick Road, Stornoway HS1 2BW
☎ 01851 822614 ✆ norma.morrison@cne-siar.gov.uk

Building Control: Mr Keith Bray, Head of Development Services,
Council Offices, Sandwick Road, Stornoway HS1 2BW
☎ 01851 822686 ✆ kbray@cne-siar.gov.uk

Civil Registration: Mr Malcolm Macpherson, Customer Services
Manager, Council Offices, Sandwick Road, Stornoway HS1 2BW
☎ 01851 822360 ✆ mmacpherson@cne-siar.gov.uk

PR / Communications: Mr Nigel Scott, Communications Officer,
Council Offices, Sandwick Road, Stornoway HS1 2BW
☎ 01851 822622 ✆ nscott@cne-siar.gov.uk

Community Planning: Ms Gayle Findlay, Community Planning
Co-ordinator, Council Offices, Sandwick Road, Stornoway HS1 2BW
☎ 01851 822617 ✆ gayle.findlay@cne-siar.gov.uk

Community Safety: Mr Frank Creighton, Policy Officer, Council
Offices, Sandwick Road, Stornoway HS1 2BW ☎ 01870 604985
✆ fpcreighton@cne-siar.gov.uk

Computer Management: Mr Malcolm Nicol, Head of IT, Council
Offices, Sandwick Road, Stornoway HS1 2BW ☎ 01851 709573
✆ mnicol@cne-siar.gov.uk

Consumer Protection and Trading Standards: Ms Marina
MacSween, Trading Standards Officer, Council Offices, Sandwick
Road, Stornoway HS1 2BW ☎ 01851 822694
✆ mmacsween@cne-siar.gov.uk

Customer Service: Mr Robert Emmott, Director - Finance &
Corporate Resources, Council Offices, Sandwick Road, Stornoway
HS1 2BW ☎ 01851 822628 ✆ remmott@cne-siar.gov.uk

Economic Development: Mr Calum Iain Maciver, Director -
Development, Council Offices, Sandwick Road, Stornoway HS1
2BW ☎ 01851 822685 ✆ calum.maciver@cne-siar.gov.uk

Education: Mr Bernard Chisholm, Director - Education &
Children's Services, Council Offices, Sandwick Road, Stornoway
HS1 2BW ☎ 01851 822727 ✆ b.chisholm@cne-siar.gov.uk

E-Government: Mr Robert Emmott, Director - Finance &
Corporate Resources, Council Offices, Sandwick Road, Stornoway
HS1 2BW ☎ 01851 822628 ✆ remmott@cne-siar.gov.uk

Electoral Registration: Mr Derek Mackay, Head - Democratic
Services, Council Offices, Sandwick Road, Stornoway HS1 2BW
☎ 01851 822613 ✆ dmackay@cne-siar.gov.uk

Emergency Planning: Mr Andy MacDonald, Risk & Emergency Planning Manager, Council Offices, Sandwick Road, Stornoway HS1 2BW ☎ 01851 822612 ⌂ andy-macdonald@cne-siar.gov.uk

Energy Management: Mr Calum MacKenzie, Head of Estates, Council Offices, Sandwick Road, Stornoway HS1 2BW ☎ 01851 822659 ⌂ calum.mackenzie@cne-siar.gov.uk

Environmental / Technical Services: Mr Iain Mackinnon, Director - Technical Services, Council Offices, Sandwick Road, Stornoway HS1 2BW ☎ 01851 822656 ⌂ iain.mackinnon@cne-siar.gov.uk

Environmental Health: Mr Colm Fraser, Consumer & Environmental Health Services Manager, Council Offices, Sandwick Road, Stornoway HS1 2BW ☎ 01851 822688 ⌂ cfraser@cne-siar.gov.uk

Estates, Property & Valuation: Mr Calum MacKenzie, Head of Estates, Council Offices, Sandwick Road, Stornoway HS1 2BW ☎ 01851 822659 ⌂ calum.mackenzie@cne-siar.gov.uk

European Liaison: Miss Lesley McDonald, Head of Executive Office, Council Offices, Sandwick Road, Stornoway HS1 2BW ☎ 01851 822604 ⌂ lmcdonald@cne-siar.gov.uk

Events Manager: Miss Lesley McDonald, Head of Executive Office, Council Offices, Sandwick Road, Stornoway HS1 2BW ☎ 01851 822604 ⌂ lmcdonald@cne-siar.gov.uk

Facilities: Mr Calum MacKenzie, Head of Estates, Council Offices, Sandwick Road, Stornoway HS1 2BW ☎ 01851 822659 ⌂ calum.mackenzie@cne-siar.gov.uk

Finance: Mr Robert Emmott, Director - Finance & Corporate Resources, Council Offices, Sandwick Road, Stornoway HS1 2BW ☎ 01851 822628 ⌂ remmott@cne-siar.gov.uk

Fleet Management: Mr David Macleod, Head of Municipal Services, Council Offices, Sandwick Road, Stornoway HS1 2BW ☎ 01851 822663 ⌂ david-macleod@cne-siar.gov.uk

Grounds Maintenance: Mr Iain Mackinnon, Director - Technical Services, Council Offices, Sandwick Road, Stornoway HS1 2BW ☎ 01851 822656 ⌂ iain.mackinnon@cne-siar.gov.uk

Health and Safety: Mr Andy MacDonald, Risk & Emergency Planning Manager, Council Offices, Sandwick Road, Stornoway HS1 2BW ☎ 01851 822612 ⌂ andy-macdonald@cne-siar.gov.uk

Highways: Mr Iain Mackinnon, Director - Technical Services, Council Offices, Sandwick Road, Stornoway HS1 2BW ☎ 01851 822656 ⌂ iain.mackinnon@cne-siar.gov.uk

Housing: Mr Iain Watson, Housing Services Manager, Council Offices, Sandwick Road, Stornoway HS1 2BW ☎ 01851 822694 ⌂ iain.watson@cne-siar.gov.uk

Legal: Miss Lesley McDonald, Head of Executive Office, Council Offices, Sandwick Road, Stornoway HS1 2BW ☎ 01851 822604 ⌂ lmcdonald@cne-siar.gov.uk

Leisure and Cultural Services: Ms Emma MacSween, Head of Social & Partnership Services, Council Offices, Sandwick Road, Stornoway HS1 2BW ☎ 01851 822706 ⌂ emacsween@cne-siar.gov.uk

Licensing: Miss Lesley McDonald, Head of Executive Office, Council Offices, Sandwick Road, Stornoway HS1 2BW ☎ 01851 822604 ⌂ lmcdonald@cne-siar.gov.uk

Member Services: Miss Lesley McDonald, Head of Executive Office, Council Offices, Sandwick Road, Stornoway HS1 2BW ☎ 01851 822604 ⌂ lmcdonald@cne-siar.gov.uk

Parking: Mr Iain Mackinnon, Director - Technical Services, Council Offices, Sandwick Road, Stornoway HS1 2BW ☎ 01851 822656 ⌂ iain.mackinnon@cne-siar.gov.uk

Personnel / HR: Mrs Katherine MacKinnon, Head of Human Resources, Council Offices, Sandwick Road, Stornoway HS1 2BW ☎ 01851 822605 ⌂ kmackinnon@cne-siar.gov.uk

Planning: Mr Keith Bray, Head of Development Services, Council Offices, Sandwick Road, Stornoway HS1 2BW ☎ 01851 822686 ⌂ kbray@cne-siar.gov.uk

Planning: Mr John Cunningham, Policy Development Officer, Council Offices, Sandwick Road, Stornoway HS1 2BW ☎ 01851 822693 ⌂ jcunningham@cne-siar.gov.uk

Public Libraries: Ms Trish Campbell-Botten, Manager - Culture & Information Services, Council Offices, Sandwick Road, Stornoway HS1 2BW ☎ 01851 822746 ⌂ trish.campbell-botten@cne-siar.gov.uk

Recycling & Waste Minimisation: Mr David Macleod, Head of Municipal Services, Council Offices, Sandwick Road, Stornoway HS1 2BW ☎ 01851 822663 ⌂ david-macleod@cne-siar.gov.uk

Regeneration: Mr Joe Macpee, Head of Economic Development, Council Offices, Sandwick Road, Stornoway HS1 2BW ☎ 01851 822687 ⌂ jmacpee@cne-siar.gov.uk

Road Safety: Mr Donald Macrae, Principal Roads Maintenance Officer, Council Offices, Sandwick Road, Stornoway HS1 2BW ☎ 01851 822664

Staff Training: Mrs Katherine MacKinnon, Head of Human Resources, Council Offices, Sandwick Road, Stornoway HS1 2BW ☎ 01851 822605 ⌂ kmackinnon@cne-siar.gov.uk

Staff Training: Miss Marina Macleod, Personnel Officer (Training), Council Offices, Sandwick Road, Stornoway HS1 2BW ☎ 01851 822607 ⌂ marina.macleod@cne-siar.gov.uk

Sustainable Communities: Mr Calum Iain Maciver, Director - Development, Council Offices, Sandwick Road, Stornoway HS1 2BW ☎ 01851 822685 ⌂ calum.maciver@cne-siar.gov.uk

Sustainable Development: Mr Calum Iain Maciver, Director - Development, Council Offices, Sandwick Road, Stornoway HS1 2BW ☎ 01851 822685 ⌂ calum.maciver@cne-siar.gov.uk

WESTERN ISLES

Tourism: Mr Calum Iain Maciver, Director - Development, Council Offices, Sandwick Road, Stornoway HS1 2BW ☎ 01851 822685 ✆ calum.maciver@cne-siar.gov.uk

Traffic Management: Mr Iain Mackinnon, Director - Technical Services, Council Offices, Sandwick Road, Stornoway HS1 2BW ☎ 01851 822656 ✆ iain.mackinnon@cne-siar.gov.uk

Transport: Mr Iain Mackinnon, Director - Technical Services, Council Offices, Sandwick Road, Stornoway HS1 2BW ☎ 01851 822656 ✆ iain.mackinnon@cne-siar.gov.uk

Transport Planner: Mr Iain Mackinnon, Director - Technical Services, Council Offices, Sandwick Road, Stornoway HS1 2BW ☎ 01851 822656 ✆ iain.mackinnon@cne-siar.gov.uk

COUNCILLORS

Convener: Macdonald, Norman (IND - Sgir' Uige Agus Ceann A Tuath Nan Loch)
namacdonald@cne-siar.gov.uk

Leader of the Council: Campbell, Angus (IND - Steornabhagh a Deas)
angus.campbell@cne-siar.gov.uk

Blaney, David (IND - Barraigh, Bhatersaigh, Eiriosgeigh agus Uibhist a Deas)
d.blaney@cne-siar.gov.uk

Campbell, Archie (LAB - Beinn na Faoghla Agus Uibhist A Tuath)
akcampbell@cne-siar.gov.uk

Crichton, Donald (IND - Loch A Tuath)
donald.crichton@cne-siar.gov.uk

Macdonald, Catherine (IND - Na Hearadh agus Ceann a Deas nan Loch)
c.macdonald@cne-siar.gov.uk

MacDonald Beaton, Neil (IND - Beinn na Faoghla Agus Uibhist A Tuath)
neil.beaton@cne-siar.gov.uk

Maciver, John (IND - Loch a Tuath)
johna.maciver@cne-siar.gov.uk

Mackay, John (IND - An Taobh Siar agus Nis)
john.mackay@cne-siar.gov.uk

Mackay, Roddie (IND - Steornabhagh a Tuath)
roddie.mackay@cne-siar.gov.uk

Mackenzie, Iain (IND - Steornabhagh a Tuath)
iain.mackenzie@cne-siar.gov.uk

MacKenzie, Rae (SNP - Steornabhagh A Deas)
rae.mackenzie@cne-siar.gov.uk

MacKinnon, Ronald (LAB - Barraigh, Bhatersaigh, Eiriosgeigh agus Uibhist a Deas)
ronald.mackinnon@cne-siar.gov.uk

MacLean MacAulay, Iain (IND - Steornabhagh a Tuath)
iainm.macaulay@cne-siar.gov.uk

Maclennan, Alistair (IND - An Taobh Siar agus Nis)
a.maclennan@cne-siar.gov.uk

Macleod, Norman (IND - Sgire an Rubha)
nmmacleod@cne-siar.gov.uk

MacLeod, Kenneth (SNP - An Taobh Siar agus Nis)
kennethmacleod@cne-siar.gov.uk

MacLeod, Alasdair (IND - Sgire An Rubha)
alasdair.macleod@cne-siar.gov.uk

MacLeod, Cudig (IND - Sgir' Uige Agus Ceann A Tuath Nan Loch)
cudig.macleod@cne-siar.gov.uk

MacRae, Donald (LAB - Na Hearadh Agus Ceann A Deas Nan Loch)
djmacrae@cne-siar.gov.uk

Manford, Donald (SNP - Barraigh, Bhatersaigh, Eiriosgeigh agus Uibhist a Deas)
dmanford@cne-siar.gov.uk

Mccormack, Angus (IND - Steornabhagh a Deas)
a.mccormack@cne-siar.gov.uk

Mclean, Philip (SNP - Na Hearadh agus Ceann a Deas nan Loch)
p.mclean@cne-siar.gov.uk

Morrison, Angus (IND - Sgir' Uige Agus Ceann A Tuath Nan Loch)
angus.morrison@cne-siar.gov.uk

Murray, Gordon (SNP - Steornabhagh a Tuath)
gordon.murray@cne-siar.gov.uk

Nicolson, Charlie (IND - Steornabhagh a Deas)
charlie.nicolson@cne-siar.gov.uk

Steele, Donnie (IND - Barraigh, Bhatersaigh, Eiriosgaigh agus Uibhist a Deas)
donnie.steele@cne-siar.gov.uk

Stewart, Catriona (IND - Loch a Tuath)
catriona.stewart@cne-siar.gov.uk

Stewart, Zena (IND - Sgire An Rubha)
zena.stewart@cne-siar.gov.uk

Walker, Andrew (IND - Beinn na Faoghla Agus Uibhist A Tuath)
andrew.walker@cne-siar.gov.uk

POLITICAL COMPOSITION
IND: 22, SNP: 5, LAB: 3

COMMITTEE CHAIRS

Audit & Scrutiny: Mr Angus Mccormack

Education & Children's Services: Mrs Catriona Stewart

Westminster City L

Westminster City Council, Westminster City Hall, 64 Victoria Street, London SW1E 6QP
☎ 020 7641 6000 🖥 www.westminster.gov.uk

FACTS AND FIGURES
Parliamentary Constituencies: Cities of London and Westminster, Westminster North
EU Constituencies: London
Election Frequency: Elections are of whole council

PRINCIPAL OFFICERS

Chief Executive: Mr Charlie Parker, Chief Executive, Westminster City Hall, 64 Victoria Street, London SW1E 6QP ☎ 020 7641 2358 ✆ cparker@westminster.gov.uk

Senior Management: Ms Liz Bruce, Tri-Borough Executive Director - Adult Social Care, Town Hall, King Street, London W6 9JU ☎ 020 8753 5166 ✆ liz.bruce@lbhf.gov.uk

Senior Management: Mrs Clare Chamberlain, Tri-Borough Executive Director - Children's Services, Town Hall, Hornton Street, London W8 7NX ✆ clare.chamberlain@rbkc.gov.uk

Senior Management: Ms Julia Corkey, Director - Policy, Performance & Communications, Westminster City Hall, 64 Victoria Street, London SW1E 6QP ☎ 020 7641 2354 ✆ jcorkey@westminster.gov.uk

Senior Management: Mr Stuart Love, Executive Director - City Management & Communities, Westminster City Hall, 64 Victoria Street, London SW1E 6QP ☎ 020 7641 7940 ✆ slove@westminster.gov.uk

Senior Management: Dr Mike Robinson, Director - Public Health, Hammersmith Town Hall, 7 King Street, London W6 9JU ☎ 020 7641 4590 ✆ mrobinson4@westminster.gov.uk

Senior Management: Mr Greg Ward, Director - Economy, Westminster City Hall, 64 Victoria Street, London SW1E 6QP ☎ 020 7641 3025 ✆ gward@westminster.gov.uk

Senior Management: Mr Ed Watson, Executive Director - Growth, Planning & Housing, Westminster City Hall, 64 Victoria Street, London SW1E 6QP ✆ ewatson@westminster.gov.uk

Access Officer / Social Services (Disability): Mr Richard Holden, Tri-Borough Head of Children with Disabilities, Westminster City Hall, 64 Victoria Street, London SW1E 6QP ☎ 020 7361 3751 ✆ richard.holden@rbkc.gov.uk

Access Officer / Social Services (Disability): Mr Malcolm Rose, Team Leader, Westminster City Hall, 64 Victoria Street, London SW1E 6QP ☎ 020 7641 6617 ✆ mrose@westminster.gov.uk

Architect, Building / Property Services: Mr Guy Slocombe, Director - Property, Westminster City Hall, 64 Victoria Street, London SW1E 6QP ☎ 020 7641 5465 ✆ gslocombe@westminster.gov.uk

Building Control: Mr Tony Fenton, District Surveyor, Westminster City Hall, 64 Victoria Street, London SW1E 6QP ☎ 020 7641 7048 ✆ tfenton@westminster.gov.uk

Building Control: Mr John Walker, Operational Director - Development Planning, Westminster City Hall, 64 Victoria Street, London SW1E 6QP ☎ 020 7641 2519 ✆ jwalker@westminster.gov.uk

Children / Youth Services: Ms Melissa Caslake, Director - Family Services, Westminster City Hall, 64 Victoria Street, London SW1E 6QP ☎ 020 7641 2253 ✆ mcaslake@westminster.gov.uk

Children / Youth Services: Mrs Clare Chamberlain, Tri-Borough Executive Director - Children's Services, Town Hall, Hornton Street, London W8 7NX ✆ clare.chamberlain@rbkc.gov.uk

Children / Youth Services: Mr Ian Heggs, Tri-Borough Director - Schools, Westminster City Hall, 64 Victoria Street, London SW1E 6QP ☎ 020 7745 6465 ✆ ian.heggs@lbhf.gov.uk

Children / Youth Services: Ms Rachel Wright-Turner, Tri-Borough Director - Strategic Commissioning for Children & Families, Westminster City Hall, 64 Victoria Street, London SW1E 6QP ✆ rachel.wright-turner@rbkc.gov.uk

Civil Registration: Ms Christie Junor Sheppard, Registration & Nationality Superintendent Registrar, Westminster City Hall, 64 Victoria Street, London SW1E 6QP ☎ 020 7641 1790 ✆ cjsheppard@westminster.gov.uk

PR / Communications: Mr Robin Campbell, Head of Communications, Westminster City Hall, 64 Victoria Street, London SW1E 6QP ✆ robincampbell@westminster.gov.uk

PR / Communications: Ms Julia Corkey, Director - Policy, Performance & Communications, Westminster City Hall, 64 Victoria Street, London SW1E 6QP ☎ 020 7641 2354 ✆ jcorkey@westminster.gov.uk

Community Planning: Mr Richard Barker, Director - Community Services, Westminster City Hall, 64 Victoria Street, London SW1E 6QP ☎ 020 7641 2693 ✆ rbarker@westminster.gov.uk

Community Planning: Mrs Lisa Fairmaner, Spatial Planning Manager, Westminster City Hall, 64 Victoria Street, London SW1E 6QP ☎ 020 7641 4240 ✆ lfairmaner@westminster.gov.uk

Community Planning: Mr Stuart Reilly, Head of Major Projects, Westminster City Hall, 64 Victoria Street, London SW1E 6QP ☎ 020 7641 5949 ✆ sreilly@westminster.gov.uk

Community Planning: Mr Barry Smith, Operational Director - City Planning & Policy, Westminster City Hall, 64 Victoria Street, London SW1E 6QP ☎ 020 7641 2923 ✆ bsmith@westminster.gov.uk

Community Planning: Mr Martin Whittles, Head of Public Realm, Westminster City Hall, 64 Victoria Street, London SW1E 6QP ☎ 020 7641 3040 ✆ mwhittles@westminster.gov.uk

Community Safety: Mr Mick Smith, Head of Community Safety, Westminster City Hall, 64 Victoria Street, London SW1E 6QP ☎ 020 7641 4252 ✆ msmith@westminster.gov.uk

Computer Management: Mr Ed Garcez, Tri-Borough Chief Information Officer, Town Hall, King Street, London W6 9JU ☎ 020 8753 2900 ✆ ed.garcez@lbhf.gov.uk

Computer Management: Mr Ben Goward, Head of Digital, Westminster City Hall, 64 Victoria Street, London SW1E 6QP ☎ 020 7641 5504 ✆ bgoward@westminster.gov.uk

Computer Management: Ms Fatima Zohra, Corporate Information Manager, Westminster City Hall, 64 Victoria Street, London SW1E 6QP ☎ 020 7641 8578 ✆ fzohra@westminster.gov.uk

Consumer Protection and Trading Standards: Ms Sue Jones, Service Manager - Trading Standards, Westminster City Hall, 64 Victoria Street, London SW1E 6QP ☎ 020 7641 2721 ✆ sjones@westminster.gov.uk

WESTMINSTER CITY

Contracts: Mr Anthony Oliver, Chief Procurement Officer, Westminster City Hall, 64 Victoria Street, London SW1E 6QP ☎ 020 7641 2608 🖰 aoliver@westminster.gov.uk

Customer Service: Ms Julia Corkey, Director - Policy, Performance & Communications, Westminster City Hall, 64 Victoria Street, London SW1E 6QP ☎ 020 7641 2354 🖰 jcorkey@westminster.gov.uk

Economic Development: Mr Greg Ward, Director - Economy, Westminster City Hall, 64 Victoria Street, London SW1E 6QP ☎ 020 7641 3025 🖰 gward@westminster.gov.uk

Electoral Registration: Mr Martin Pyroyiannos, Legal & Electoral Services Manager, Westminster City Hall, 64 Victoria Street, London SW1E 6QP ☎ 020 7641 2732 🖰 mpyroyiannos@westminster.gov.uk

Emergency Planning: Mr Mick Smith, Head of Community Safety, Westminster City Hall, 64 Victoria Street, London SW1E 6QP ☎ 020 7641 4252 🖰 msmith@westminster.gov.uk

Energy Management: Ms Debbie Morris, Director - Human Resources, Town Hall, King Street, London W6 9JU ☎ 020 8753 3068 🖰 debbie.morris@lbhf.gov.uk

Environmental Health: Mr Andrew Ralph, Service Manager - Noise & Licensing Enforcement, Westminster City Hall, 64 Victoria Street, London SW1E 6QP ☎ 020 7641 2706 🖰 aralph@westminster.gov.uk

Environmental Health: Ms Sara Sutton, Director - Public Protection & Licensing, Westminster City Hall, 64 Victoria Street, London SW1E 6QP ☎ 020 7641 6916 🖰 ssutton@westminster.gov.uk

Estates, Property & Valuation: Mr Guy Slocombe, Director - Property, Westminster City Hall, 64 Victoria Street, London SW1E 6QP ☎ 020 7641 5465 🖰 gslocombe@westminster.gov.uk

Events Manager: Mr Ritchie Gibson, Commissioning Manager - Events, Filming & Contingencies, Westminster City Hall, 64 Victoria Street, London SW1E 6QP ☎ 020 7641 3256 🖰 rgibson@westminster.gov.uk

Facilities: Ms Debbie Morris, Director - Human Resources, Town Hall, King Street, London W6 9JU ☎ 020 8753 3068 🖰 debbie.morris@lbhf.gov.uk

Finance: Mr George Bruce, Tri-Borough Director - Pensions & Treasury, Westminster City Hall, 64 Victoria Street, London SW1E 6QP 🖰 g.bruce@westminster.gov.uk

Finance: Mr David Hodgkinson, Assistant City Treasurer, Westminster City Hall, 64 Victoria Street, London SW1E 6QP ☎ 020 7641 6000 🖰 dhodgkinson@westminster.gov.uk

Finance: Mr Steve Mair, City Treasurer, Westminster City Hall, 64 Victoria Street, London SW1E 6QP ☎ 020 7641 2831 🖰 smair@westminster.gov.uk

Finance: Mr Dave McNamara, Head of Finance for Children, Westminster City Hall, 64 Victoria Street, London SW1E 6QP ☎ 020 8753 3404 🖰 david.mcnamara@lbhf.gov.uk

Treasury: Mr Steve Mair, City Treasurer, Westminster City Hall, 64 Victoria Street, London SW1E 6QP ☎ 020 7641 2831 🖰 smair@westminster.gov.uk

Pensions: Mr George Bruce, Tri-Borough Director - Pensions & Treasury, Westminster City Hall, 64 Victoria Street, London SW1E 6QP 🖰 g.bruce@westminster.gov.uk

Grounds Maintenance: Mr Mark Banks, Head of Waste & Parks, Westminster City Hall, 64 Victoria Street, London SW1E 6QP ☎ 020 7641 3369 🖰 mbanks@westminster.gov.uk

Health and Safety: Mr James Armitage, Service Manager - Food, Health & Safety, Westminster City Hall, 64 Victoria Street, London SW1E 6QP ☎ 020 7641 3076 🖰 jarmitage@westminster.gov.uk

Highways: Mr Sean Dwyer, Highways Planning Manager, Westminster City Hall, 64 Victoria Street, London SW1E 6QP ☎ 020 7641 3326 🖰 sdwyer@westminster.gov.uk

Highways: Ms Sally Keiller, Head of Contracts (Highways, Infrastructure & Public Realm), Westminster City Hall, 64 Victoria Street, London SW1E 6QP ☎ 020 7641 2677 🖰 skeiller@westminster.gov.uk

Housing: Ms Barbara Brownlee, Director - Housing, Westminster City Hall, 64 Victoria Street, London SW1E 6QP ☎ 020 7641 3025 🖰 bbrownlee@westminster.gov.uk

Housing: Mr Fergus Coleman, Housing Supply Commissioning Manager, Westminster City Hall, 64 Victoria Street, London SW1E 6QP ☎ 020 7641 3211 🖰 fcoleman@westminster.gov.uk

Housing: Mr Dick Johnson, Head of Housing Finance, Westminster City Hall, 64 Victoria Street, London SW1E 6QP ☎ 020 7641 3029 🖰 djohnson1@westminster.gov.uk

Housing: Ms Victoria Midwinter, Head of Housing Needs, Westminster City Hall, 64 Victoria Street, London SW1E 6QP ☎ 020 7641 2029 🖰 vmidwinter@westminster.gov.uk

Housing: Mr Gregory Roberts, Head of Supporting People & Homelessness Commissioning, Westminster City Hall, 64 Victoria Street, London SW1E 6QP ☎ 020 7641 2834 🖰 groberts@westminster.gov.uk

Legal: Ms Rhian Davies, Chief Solicitor - Litigation & Social Care, Westminster City Hall, 64 Victoria Street, London SW1E 6QP ☎ 020 7641 2729 🖰 rdavies@westminster.gov.uk

Legal: Mrs Tasnim Shawkat, Tri-Borough Director - Law, Town Hall, Hornton Street, London W8 7NX ☎ 020 8753 2700 🖰 tasnim.shawkat@lbhf.gov.uk

Leisure and Cultural Services: Mr Richard Barker, Director - Community Services, Westminster City Hall, 64 Victoria Street, London SW1E 6QP ☎ 020 7641 2693 🖰 rbarker@westminster.gov.uk

Leisure and Cultural Services: Mr Andrew Durrant, Head of Westminster Sports Unit, Westminster City Hall, 64 Victoria Street, London SW1E 6QP ☎ 020 7641 5885 🖰 adurrant@westminster.gov.uk

Licensing: Ms Deirdre Hayes, Services Manager - EH Consultation & Licensing, Westminster City Hall, 64 Victoria Street, London SW1E 6QP ☎ 020 7641 3189 🖰 dhayes@westminster.gov.uk

Licensing: Mr Andrew Ralph, Service Manager - Noise & Licensing Enforcement, Westminster City Hall, 64 Victoria Street, London SW1E 6QP ☎ 020 7641 2706 🖰 aralph@westminster.gov.uk

Licensing: Mr Chris Wroe, Licensing Policy & Strategy Manager, Westminster City Hall, 64 Victoria Street, London SW1E 6QP ☎ 020 7641 5903 🖰 cwroe@westminster.gov.uk

Lottery Funding, Charity and Voluntary: Mr Richard Cressey, Senior Policy Officer, Westminster City Hall, 64 Victoria Street, London SW1E 6QP ☎ 020 7641 3403 🖰 rcressey@westminster.gov.uk

Member Services: Mr William Thavenot, Head of Cabinet Secretariat, Westminster City Hall, 64 Victoria Street, London SW1E 6QP ☎ 020 7641 5614 🖰 wthavenot@westminster.gov.uk

Partnerships: Mr Richard Cressey, Senior Policy Officer, Westminster City Hall, 64 Victoria Street, London SW1E 6QP ☎ 020 7641 3403 🖰 rcressey@westminster.gov.uk

Personnel / HR: Ms Rita Lawrence, Head of Organisational Development, Westminster City Hall, 64 Victoria Street, London SW1E 6QP ☎ 020 7641 2803 🖰 rlawrence@westminster.gov.uk

Personnel / HR: Ms Jo Meagher, Head of Operational People Service, Westminster City Hall, 64 Victoria Street, London SW1E 6QP ☎ 020 7641 5987 🖰 jmeagher@westminster.gov.uk

Personnel / HR: Mr Lee Witham, Director - People Services, Westminster City Hall, 64 Victoria Street, London SW1E 6QP ☎ 020 7641 3221 🖰 lwitham@westminster.gov.uk

Planning: Mr Graham King, Head of Strategic Planning & Transport, Westminster City Hall, 64 Victoria Street, London SW1E 6QP ☎ 020 7641 2749 🖰 gking@westminster.gov.uk

Planning: Mr John Walker, Operational Director - Development Planning, Westminster City Hall, 64 Victoria Street, London SW1E 6QP ☎ 020 7641 2519 🖰 jwalker@westminster.gov.uk

Procurement: Mr Anthony Oliver, Chief Procurement Officer, Westminster City Hall, 64 Victoria Street, London SW1E 6QP ☎ 020 7641 2608 🖰 aoliver@westminster.gov.uk

Public Libraries: Mr Mike Clarke, Tri-Borough Director - Libraries & Archives, Town Hall, Hornton Street, London W8 7NX ☎ 020 7641 2199 🖰 mclarke1@westminster.gov.uk

Recycling & Waste Minimisation: Mr Mark Banks, Head of Waste & Parks, 3rd Floor, Westminster City Hall, Victoria Street, London SW1E 6QP ☎ 020 7641 3369 🖰 mbanks@westminster.gov.uk

Regeneration: Mr Greg Ward, Director - Economy, Westminster City Hall, 64 Victoria Street, London SW1E 6QP ☎ 020 7641 3025 🖰 gward@westminster.gov.uk

Road Safety: Mr Peter Wilson, Commissioning Officer - Road Safety, Westminster City Hall, 64 Victoria Street, London SW1E 6QP ☎ 020 7641 2016 🖰 pwilson@westminster.gov.uk

Social Services: Ms Stella Baillie, Tri-Borough Director - Integrated Care, Town Hall, Hornton Street, London W8 7NX ☎ 020 7361 2398 🖰 stella.baillie2@lbhf.gov.uk

Social Services: Ms Gaynor Driscoll, Joint Commissioning Manager - Sexual Health, Westminster City Hall, 64 Victoria Street, London SW1E 6QP ☎ 020 7641 4000 🖰 gdriscoll@westminster.gov.uk

Social Services: Ms Sarah Thomas, Head of Family Recovery, Westminster City Hall, 64 Victoria Street, London SW1E 6QP ☎ 020 7641 4578 🖰 sarah.thomas@rbkc.gov.uk

Social Services: Ms Rachel Wright-Turner, Tri-Borough Director - Strategic Commissioning for Children & Families, Westminster City Hall, 64 Victoria Street, London SW1E 6QP 🖰 rachel.wright-turner@rbkc.gov.uk

Social Services (Adult): Ms Stella Baillie, Tri-Borough Director - Integrated Care, Town Hall, Hornton Street, London W8 7NX ☎ 020 7361 2398 🖰 stella.baillie2@lbhf.gov.uk

Social Services (Adult): Ms Helen Banham, Strategic Lead - Safeguarding & Professional Standards, Westminster City Hall, 64 Victoria Street, London SW1E 6QP ☎ 020 7641 4196 🖰 hbanham@westminster.gov.uk

Social Services (Adult): Mr Mike Boyle, Interim Director - Strategic Commissioning (Adults), Westminster City Hall, 64 Victoria Street, London SW1E 6QP ☎ 020 7641 3467 🖰 mboyle@westminster.gov.uk

Social Services (Adult): Ms Liz Bruce, Tri-Borough Executive Director - Adult Social Care, Town Hall, King Street, London W6 9JU ☎ 020 8753 5166 🖰 liz.bruce@lbhf.gov.uk

Social Services (Adult): Ms Mary Dalton, Head of Complex Needs Commissioning, Westminster City Hall, 64 Victoria Street, London SW1E 6QP ☎ 020 7641 6615 🖰 mdalton@westminster.gov.uk

Social Services (Children): Ms Melissa Caslake, Director - Family Services, Westminster City Hall, 64 Victoria Street, London SW1E 6QP ☎ 020 7641 2253 🖰 mcaslake@westminster.gov.uk

Social Services (Children): Mrs Clare Chamberlain, Tri-Borough Executive Director - Children's Services, Town Hall, Hornton Street, London W8 7NX 🖰 clare.chamberlain@rbkc.gov.uk

Social Services (Children): Ms H Farrell, Head of Child Protection, Westminster City Hall, 64 Victoria Street, London SW1E 6QP ☎ 020 7641 5341 🖰 hfarrell@westminster.gov.uk

Social Services (Children): Mr Glen Peache, Head of Looked After Children & Care Leavers, Westminster City Hall, 64 Victoria Street, London SW1E 6QP ☎ 020 7361 3317 🖰 glen.peache@rbkc.gov.uk

WESTMINSTER CITY

Social Services (Children): Ms Jayne Vertkin, Head of Early Intervention, Westminster City Hall, 64 Victoria Street, London SW1E 6QP ☎ 020 7641 5745 ⌨ jvertkin@westminster.gov.uk

Public Health: Dr Mike Robinson, Director - Public Health, Hammersmith Town Hall, 7 King Street, London W6 9JU ☎ 020 7641 4590 ⌨ mrobinson4@westminster.gov.uk

Staff Training: Ms Rita Lawrence, Head of Organisational Development, Westminster City Hall, 64 Victoria Street, London SW1E 6QP ☎ 020 7641 2803 ⌨ rlawrence@westminster.gov.uk

Street Scene: Mr Martin Whittles, Head of Public Realm, Westminster City Hall, 64 Victoria Street, London SW1E 6QP ☎ 020 7641 3040 ⌨ mwhittles@westminster.gov.uk

Sustainable Communities: Mr Stuart Love, Executive Director - City Management & Communities, Westminster City Hall, 64 Victoria Street, London SW1E 6QP ☎ 020 7641 7940 ⌨ slove@westminster.gov.uk

Town Centre: Mr Stuart Love, Executive Director - City Management & Communities, Westminster City Hall, 64 Victoria Street, London SW1E 6QP ☎ 020 7641 7940 ⌨ slove@westminster.gov.uk

Traffic Management: Mr Martin Low, City Commissioner - Transportation, Westminster City Hall, Victoria Street, London SW1E 6QP ☎ 020 7641 1981 ⌨ mlow@westminster.gov.uk

Transport: Mr Martin Low, City Commissioner - Transportation, Westminster City Hall, Victoria Street, London SW1E 6QP ☎ 020 7641 1981 ⌨ mlow@westminster.gov.uk

Transport: Mr John Taylor, Service Manager - Transportation Projects, Westminster City Hall, 64 Victoria Street, London SW1E 6QP ☎ 020 7641 2943 ⌨ jtaylor@westminster.gov.uk

Transport: Mr David Yeoell, Assistant City Commissioner - Transportation, Westminster City Hall, 64 Victoria Street, London SW1E 6QP ☎ 020 7641 2622 ⌨ dyeoell@westminster.gov.uk

Transport Planner: Mr Graham King, Head of Strategic Planning & Transport, Westminster City Hall, 64 Victoria Street, London SW1E 6QP ☎ 020 7641 2749 ⌨ gking@westminster.gov.uk

Transport Planner: Mr Martin Low, City Commissioner - Transportation, Westminster City Hall, Victoria Street, London SW1E 6QP ☎ 020 7641 1981 ⌨ mlow@westminster.gov.uk

Transport Planner: Mr David Yeoell, Assistant City Commissioner - Transportation, Westminster City Hall, 64 Victoria Street, London SW1E 6QP ☎ 020 7641 2622 ⌨ dyeoell@westminster.gov.uk

Waste Collection and Disposal: Mr Mark Banks, Head of Waste & Parks, Westminster City Hall, 64 Victoria Street, London SW1E 6QP ☎ 020 7641 3369 ⌨ mbanks@westminster.gov.uk

Waste Management: Mr Mark Banks, Head of Waste & Parks, Westminster City Hall, 64 Victoria Street, London SW1E 6QP ☎ 020 7641 3369 ⌨ mbanks@westminster.gov.uk

COUNCILLORS

Leader of the Council: Couttie, Philippa (CON - Knightsbridge & Belgravia)
leader@westminster.gov.uk

Deputy Leader of the Council: Davis, Robert (CON - Lancaster Gate)
rdavis@westminster.gov.uk

Group Leader: Hug, Adam (LAB - Westbourne)
ahug@westminster.gov.uk

Acton, Heather (CON - Hyde Park)
hacton@westminster.gov.uk

Adams, Ian (CON - Little Venice)
iadams@westminster.gov.uk

Aiken, Nicola (CON - Warwick)
naiken@westminster.gov.uk

Alexander, Julia (CON - Bryanston & Dorset Square)
jalexander@westminster.gov.uk

Arzymanow, Barbara (CON - Little Venice)
barzymanow@westminster.gov.uk

Astaire, Daniel (CON - Regent's Park)
dastaire@westminster.gov.uk

Beddoe, Richard (CON - Bryanston & Dorset Square)
rbeddoe@westminster.gov.uk

Begum, Rita (LAB - Maida Vale)
rbegum2@westminster.gov.uk

Boothroyd, David (LAB - Westbourne)
dboothroyd@westminster.gov.uk

Bott, Iain (CON - Marylebone High Street)
ibott@westminster.gov.uk

Burbridge, Susie (CON - Lancaster Gate)
sburbridge@westminster.gov.uk

Bush, Ruth (LAB - Harrow Road)
rbush@westminster.gov.uk

Caplan, Melvyn (CON - Little Venice)
mcaplan@westminster.gov.uk

Chalkley, Danny (CON - Vincent Square)
dchalkley@westminster.gov.uk

Church, Paul (CON - West End)
pchurch@westminster.gov.uk

Connell, Brian (CON - Bayswater)
bconnell@westminster.gov.uk

Cox, Antonia (CON - Hyde Park)
acox@westminster.gov.uk

Crockett, Thomas (CON - Maida Vale)
tcrockett@westminster.gov.uk

Cuthbertson, Peter (CON - Tachbrook)
pcuthbertson@westminster.gov.uk

Devenish, Antony (CON - Knightsbridge & Belgravia)
tdevenish@westminster.gov.uk

Dimoldenberg, Paul (LAB - Queen's Park)
pdimoldenberg@westminster.gov.uk

Evans, Nicholas (CON - Tachbrook)
nevans@westminster.gov.uk

Flight, Christabel (CON - Warwick)
cflight@westminster.gov.uk

Floru, Jean-Paul (CON - Hyde Park)
jfloru@westminster.gov.uk

Freeman, Peter (CON - Abbey Road)
pfreeman@westminster.gov.uk

Gassanly, Murad (IND - Churchill)
mgassanly@westminster.gov.uk

Glanz, Jonathan (CON - West End)
jglanz@westminster.gov.uk

Grahame, Barbara (LAB - Church Street)
bgrahame@westminster.gov.uk

Hall, Lindsey (CON - Abbey Road)
lhall@westminster.gov.uk

Harvey, David (CON - Vincent Square)
davidharvey@westminster.gov.uk

Harvey, Angela (CON - Tachbrook)
angelaharvery@westminster.gov.uk

Holloway, Richard (CON - Bayswater)
rholloway@westminster.gov.uk

Hyams, Louise (CON - St James's)
lhyams@westminster.gov.uk

Less, Aicha (LAB - Church Street)
aless@westminster.gov.uk

McAllister, Patricia (LAB - Queen's Park)
pmcallister@westminster.gov.uk

McKie, Guthrie (LAB - Harrow Road)
gmckie@westminster.gov.uk

Mitchell, Tim (CON - St James's)
tmitchell@westminster.gov.uk

Mohammed, Adnan (CON - Bryanston & Dorset Square)
amohammed@westminster.gov.uk

Mohindra, Gotz (CON - Regent's Park)
gmohindra@westminster.gov.uk

Prendergast, Jan (CON - Maida Vale)
jprendergast@westminster.gov.uk

Qureshi, Papya (LAB - Westbourne)
pqureshi1@westminster.gov.uk

Rahuja, Suhail (CON - Bayswater)
srahuja@westminster.gov.uk

Rigby, Robert (CON - Regent's Park)
rrigby@westminster.gov.uk

Robathan, Rachael (CON - Knightsbridge & Belgravia)
rrobathan@westminster.gov.uk

Roberts, Glenys (CON - West End)
groberts@westminster.gov.uk

Roca, Tim (LAB - Harrow Road)
troca@westminster.gov.uk

Rowley, Ian (CON - Marylebone High Street)
irowley@westminster.gov.uk

Scarborough, Karen (CON - Marylebone High Street)
kscarborough@westminster.gov.uk

Smith, Andrew (CON - Lancaster Gate)
asmith@westminster.gov.uk

Summers, Steven (CON - Vincent Square)
ssummers@westminster.gov.uk

Talukder, Shamim (LAB - Churchill)
stalukder@westminster.gov.uk

Taylor, Barrie (LAB - Queen's Park)
btaylor@westminster.gov.uk

Thomson, Cameron (CON - St James's)
cthomson@westminster.gov.uk

Toki, Aziz (LAB - Church Street)
atoki@westminster.gov.uk

Warner, Judith (CON - Abbey Road)
judithwarner@westminster.gov.uk

Wilkinson, Jacqui (CON - Warwick)
jwilkinson@westminster.gov.uk

Williams, Jason (LAB - Churchill)
jwilliams@westminster.gov.uk

POLITICAL COMPOSITION
CON: 44, LAB: 15, IND: 1

COMMITTEE CHAIRS

Adults, Health & Public Protection: Ms Antonia Cox

Audit: Mr Jonathan Glanz

Health & Wellbeing: Ms Rachael Robathan

Licensing: Mrs Nicola Aiken

Pensions: Mr Suhail Rahuja

Planning: Mr Richard Beddoe

Planning: Mr Antony Devenish

Planning: Mr Peter Freeman

Planning: Mr Robert Davis

Planning: Mr Andrew Smith

Weymouth & Portland D

Weymouth & Portland Borough Council, Council Offices, North Quay, Weymouth DT4 8TA
☎ 01305 838000 🖷 01305 760971 ✆ chiefexecutive@weymouth.gov.uk
💻 www.weymouth.gov.uk

FACTS AND FIGURES
Parliamentary Constituencies: Dorset South
EU Constituencies: South East
Election Frequency: Elections are by thirds

PRINCIPAL OFFICERS

Chief Executive: Mr Matt Prosser, Chief Executive, Council Offices, North Quay, Weymouth DT4 8TA ☎ 01305 251010

Assistant Chief Executive: Mr Stuart Caundle, Assistant Chief Executive, South Walks House, South Walks Road, Dorchester DT1 1UZ ☎ 01258 484010 ✆ scaundle@north-dorset.co.uk

Senior Management: Mr Martin Hamilton, Strategic Director, South Walks House, South Walks Road, Dorchester DT1 1UZ ☎ 01305 838086 ✆ m.hamilton@westdorset-weymouth.gov.uk

WEYMOUTH & PORTLAND

Senior Management: Mr Stephen Hill, Strategic Director, South Walks House, South Walks Road, Dorchester DT1 1UZ
☎ 01258 484034 ⌨ shill@north-dorset.gov.uk

Senior Management: Mr Jason Vaughan, Strategic Director, South Walks House, South Walks Road, Dorchester DT1 1UZ
☎ 01305 838233; 01305 251010
⌨ j.vaughan@westdorset-weymouth.gov.uk

Architect, Building / Property Services: Mr David Brown, Head of Assets & Infrastructure, South Walks House, South Walks Road, Dorchester DT1 1UZ ☎ 01305 252297
⌨ d.brown@westdorset-weymouth.gov.uk

Best Value: Ms Julie Strange, Head of Financial Services, South Walks House, South Walks Road, Dorchester DT1 1UZ ☎ 01305 838252; 01305 251010 ⌨ j.strange@westdorset-weymouth.gov.uk

Building Control: Mr David Potter, Building Control Manager, South Walks House, South Walks Road, Dorchester DT1 1UZ
☎ 01305 252258 ⌨ d.potter@westdorset-weymouth.gov.uk

PR / Communications: Ms Penny Mell, Head of Business Improvement, South Walks House, South Walks Road, Dorchester DT1 1UZ ☎ 01305 838371 ⌨ p.mell@westdorset-weymouth.gov.uk

Community Planning: Ms Hilary Jordan, Head of Planning, Community & Policy Development, South Walks House, South Walks Road, Dorchester DT1 1UZ ☎ 01305 252303
⌨ h.jordan@westdorset-weymouth.gov.uk

Community Safety: Mr Graham Duggan, Head of Community Protection, South Walks House, South Walks Road, Dorchester DT1 1UZ ☎ 01305 252285; 01305 251010
⌨ g.duggan@westdorset-weymouth.gov.uk

Computer Management: Ms Penny Mell, Head of Business Improvement, South Walks House, South Walks Road, Dorchester DT1 1UZ ☎ 01305 838371 ⌨ p.mell@westdorset-weymouth.gov.uk

Customer Service: Ms Penny Mell, Head of Business Improvement, South Walks House, South Walks Road, Dorchester DT1 1UZ ☎ 01305 838371 ⌨ p.mell@westdorset-weymouth.gov.uk

Economic Development: Mr Simon King, Senior Economic Regeneration Officer, South Walks House, South Walks Road, Dorchester DT1 1UZ ☎ 01305 838515
⌨ s.king@westdorset-weymouth.gov.uk

Electoral Registration: Ms Sue Bonham-Lovett, Electoral Services Manager, South Walks House, South Walks Road, Dorchester DT1 1UZ ☎ 01305 838477; 01305 251010
⌨ s.bonham-lovett@westdorset-weymouth.gov.uk

Emergency Planning: Mr Grant Armfield, Engineering, Asset & Emergency Planning Manager, South Walks House, South Walks Road, Dorchester DT1 1UZ ☎ 01305 838213
⌨ grantarmfield@weymouth.gov.uk

Energy Management: Mr Bob Savage, Senior Building Services Engineer, South Walks House, South Walks Road, Dorchester DT1 1UZ ☎ 01305 838318 ⌨ bobsavage@weymouth.gov.uk

Environmental / Technical Services: Mr David Brown, Head of Assets & Infrastructure, South Walks House, South Walks Road, Dorchester DT1 1UZ ☎ 01305 252297
⌨ d.brown@westdorset-weymouth.gov.uk

Environmental Health: Mr Graham Duggan, Head of Community Protection, South Walks House, South Walks Road, Dorchester DT1 1UZ ☎ 01305 252285; 01305 251010
⌨ g.duggan@westdorset-weymouth.gov.uk

Estates, Property & Valuation: Mr Greg Northcote, Head of Estates, South Walks House, South Walks Road, Dorchester DT1 1UZ ☎ 01305 838268 ⌨ g.northcote@westdorset-weymouth.gov.uk

Events Manager: Mr Nick Thornley, Head of Economy, Leisure & Tourism, South Walks House, South Walks Road, Dorchester DT1 1UZ ☎ 01305 252474; 01305 251010
⌨ n.thornley@westdorset-weymouth.gov.uk

Finance: Mr Jason Vaughan, Strategic Director, South Walks House, South Walks Road, Dorchester DT1 1UZ ☎ 01305 838233; 01305 251010 ⌨ j.vaughan@westdorset-weymouth.gov.uk

Fleet Management: Ms Sally-Ann Arden-Nixon, Fleet Transport Co-ordinator, South Walks House, South Walks Road, Dorchester DT1 1UZ ☎ 01305 838447
⌨ sa.arden-nixon@westdorset-weymouth.gov.uk

Health and Safety: Mr Richard Noakes, Health, Safety & Welfare Officer, South Walks House, South Walks Road, Dorchester DT1 1UZ ☎ 01305 838356 ⌨ r.noakes@westdorset-weymouth.gov.uk

Home Energy Conservation: Mr Clive Milone, Head of Housing, South Walks House, South Walks Road, Dorchester DT1 1UZ
☎ 01305 252313 ⌨ c.milone@westdorset-weymouth.gov.uk

Housing: Mr Chris Branch, Housing Solutions Manager, South Walks House, South Walks Road, Dorchester DT1 1UZ
☎ 01305 838460 ⌨ c.branch@westdorset-weymouth.gov.uk

Housing Maintenance: Mr Geoff Joy, Housing Improvement Manager, South Walks House, South Walks Road, Dorchester DT1 1UZ ☎ 01305 252286 ⌨ g.joy@westdorset-weymouth.gov.uk

Legal: Ms Lara Altree, Legal Services Manager (Planning & Environment), South Walks House, South Walks Road, Dorchester DT1 1UZ ☎ 01305 838219 ⌨ l.altree@westdorset-weymouth.gov.uk

Leisure and Cultural Services: Mr Nick Thornley, Head of Economy, Leisure & Tourism, South Walks House, South Walks Road, Dorchester DT1 1UZ ☎ 01305 252474; 01305 251010
⌨ n.thornley@westdorset-weymouth.gov.uk

Licensing: Ms Sue Moore, Business Licensing Manager, South Walks House, South Walks Road, Dorchester DT1 1UZ ☎ 01305 838205; 01305 252474 ⌨ s.moore@westdorset-weymouth.gov.uk

Lottery Funding, Charity and Voluntary: Ms Jane Nicklen, Community Planning & Development Manager, South Walks House, South Walks Road, Dorchester DT1 1UZ ☎ 01305 252358
⌨ j.nicklen@westdorset-weymouth.gov.uk

Member Services: Ms Susan Carne, Democratic Services Manager, South Walks House, South Walks Road, Dorchester DT1 1UZ ☎ 01305 252216 ✆ s.carne@westdorset-weymouth.gov.uk

Parking: Mr Jack Creeber, Parking & Transport Manager, South Walks House, South Walks Road, Dorchester DT1 1UZ ☎ 01305 838349 ✆ j.creeber@westdorset-weymouth.gov.uk

Partnerships: Ms Caron Starkey, Business Change Manager, South Walks House, South Walks Road, Dorchester DT1 1UZ ☎ 01305 838277 ✆ c.starkey@westdorset-weymouth.gov.uk

Personnel / HR: Mr Steve Barrett, HR Manager - Policy & Development, South Walks House, South Walks Road, Dorchester DT1 1UZ ☎ 01305 838319 ✆ s.barrett@westdorset-weymouth.gov.uk

Planning: Ms Jean Marshall, Head of Planning, Development Management & Building Control, South Walks House, South Walks Road, Dorchester DT1 1UZ ☎ 01305 252230 ✆ j.marshall@westdorset-weymouth.gov.uk

Procurement: Ms Julia Long, Procurement Officer, South Walks House, South Walks Road, Dorchester DT1 1UZ ☎ 01305 838543 ✆ j.long@westdorset-weymouth.gov.uk

Regeneration: Mr Simon King, Senior Economic Regeneration Officer, South Walks House, South Walks Road, Dorchester DT1 1UZ ☎ 01305 838515 ✆ s.king@westdorset-weymouth.gov.uk

Sustainable Development: Ms Jean Marshall, Head of Planning, Development Management & Building Control, South Walks House, South Walks Road, Dorchester DT1 1UZ ☎ 01305 252230 ✆ j.marshall@westdorset-weymouth.gov.uk

Tourism: Mr Nick Thornley, Head of Economy, Leisure & Tourism, South Walks House, South Walks Road, Dorchester DT1 1UZ ☎ 01305 252474; 01305 251010 ✆ n.thornley@westdorset-weymouth.gov.uk

Children's Play Areas: Ms Tara Williams, Parks Supervisor, Chickerell Road, Weymouth DT3 4DQ ☎ 01305 838297 ✆ t.williams@westdorset-weymouth.gov.uk

COUNCILLORS

Mayor: Kosior, Richard (CON - Weymouth West)
richardkosier@weymouth.gov.uk

Deputy Mayor: Brookes, Kevin (CON - Upwey & Broadwey)
kevinbrookes@weymouth.gov.uk

Leader of the Council: Cant, Jeff (CON - Wyke Regis)
jeffcant@weymouth.gov.uk

Blackwood, Andy (LAB - Westham West)
andyblackwood@weymouth.gov.uk

Bruce, Hazel (CON - Preston)
hazelbruce@weymouth.gov.uk

Bruce, Ian (CON - Preston)
ianbruce@weymouth.gov.uk

Drake, Francis (UKIP - Melcombe Regis)
francisgeorgedrake@gmail.com

Ellis, John (CON - Upwey & Broadwey)
johnellis@weymouth.gov.uk

Farquharson, James (CON - Preston)
jamesfarquharson@weymouth.gov.uk

Ferrari, Tony (CON - Wey Valley)
tonyferrari@weymouth.gov.uk

Hamilton, Lucy (LAB - Wyke Regis)
lucyhamilton@weymouth.gov.uk

Hawkins, David (IND - Tophill East)
davidhawkins@weymouth.gov.uk

Hope, Ryan (LD - Westham North)
ryanhope@weymouth.gov.uk

Huckle, Colin (LAB - Weymouth West)
colinhuckle@weymouth.gov.uk

James, Christine (LD - Westham North)
christinejames@weymouth.gov.uk

Kanji, Oz (LD - Westham North)
ozkanji@weymouth.gov.uk

Kimber, Paul (LAB - Underhill)
paulkimber@weymouth.gov.uk

Leicester, Margaret (IND - Tophill East)
mleicester7@gmail.com

Maslin, Sally (LD - Westham East)
sallymaslin@weymouth.gov.uk

McCartney, Penny (LAB - Tophill West)
pennymccartney@weymouth.gov.uk

Moore, Claudia (CON - Weymouth West)
claudiawebb300@yahoo.co.uk

Nixon, Pamela (CON - Wey Valley)
pamelanixon@weymouth.gov.uk

Nowak, Ray (LAB - Tophill West)
raynowak@weymouth.gov.uk

Orrell, Jon (GRN - Weymouth East)
jonorrell@weymouth.gov.uk

Osborne, Jason (CON - Melcombe Regis)
jasonosborne@weymouth.gov.uk

Page-Nash, Cathy (CON - Radipole)
cathypagenash@weymouth.gov.uk

Reed, Alison (CON - Weymouth East)
alisonreed@weymouth.gov.uk

Rockingham, Gareth (LAB - Westham East)
grockingham@outlook.com

Roebuck, Ian (LD - Radipole)
cllriroebuck@icloud.com

Roos, Tia (LAB - Melcolmbe Regis)
tiaroos@weymouth.gov.uk

Taylor, Gill (LD - Westham West)
gilltaylor@weymouth.gov.uk

Tewkesbury, Mark (LAB - Littlemoor)

Weaving, Ann (LAB - Littlemoor)
honeydog2013@hotmail.co.uk

Webb, Jason (CON - Tophill West)
jasonwebb@weymouth.gov.uk

West, Sandy (LAB - Underhill)
westsandra332@gmail.com

WEYMOUTH & PORTLAND

Wheller, Kate (LAB - Wyke Regis)
katewheller@weymouth.gov.uk

POLITICAL COMPOSITION
CON: 14, LAB: 12, LD: 6, IND: 2, GRN: 1, UKIP: 1

COMMITTEE CHAIRS

Audit: Ms Lucy Hamilton

Planning: Mr Mark Tewkesbury

Wigan   M

Wigan Metropolitan Borough Council, Town Hall, Library
Street, Wigan WN1 1YN
☎ 01942 244991 🖷 01942 827451 ✒ pr@wigan.gov.uk
🖳 www.wigan.gov.uk

FACTS AND FIGURES
Parliamentary Constituencies: Leigh, Makerfield, Wigan
EU Constituencies: North West
Election Frequency: Elections are by thirds

PRINCIPAL OFFICERS

Chief Executive: Ms Donna Hall, Chief Executive, Town Hall,
Library Street, Wigan WN1 1YN ☎ 01942 827148
✒ donna.hall@wigan.gov.uk

Deputy Chief Executive: Ms Alison McKenzie-Folan, Director
- Customer Transformation / Deputy Chief Executive, Town Hall,
Library Street, Wigan WN1 1YN ☎ 01942 827784
✒ a.mckenzie-folan@wigan.gov.uk

Deputy Chief Executive: Mr Paul McKevitt, Director - Resources
& Contracts / Deputy Chief Executive, Town Hall, Library Street,
Wigan WN1 1YN ☎ 01942 827235 ✒ p.mckevitt@wigan.gov.uk

Senior Management: Mr Karl Battersby, Director - Economy &
Environment, Town Hall, Library Street, Wigan WN1 1YN
☎ 01942 489101 ✒ karl.battersby@wigan.gov.uk

Senior Management: Mr Stuart Cowley, Director - Adult Social
Care & Health, Town Hall, Library Street, Wigan WN1 1YN
☎ 01942 489453 ✒ stuart.cowley@wigan.gov.uk

Senior Management: Mr James Winterbottom, Director -
Children & Families, Town Hall, Library Street, Wigan WN1 1YN
☎ 01942 486000 ✒ j.winterbottom@wigan.gov.uk

Building Control: Mr Mike Worden, Assistant Director - Planning
& Transport, Wigan Life Centre, Library Street, Wigan WN1 1YN
☎ 01942 489104 ✒ mike.worden@wigan.gov.uk

Children / Youth Services: Ms Jayne Ivory, Assistant Director
- Targeted Services, Wigan Life Centre, Library Street, Wigan WN1
1YN ☎ 01942 489452 ✒ jayne.ivory@wigan.gov.uk

Civil Registration: Mr Melvyn Jones, Superintendent Registrar,
Town Hall, Library Street, Wigan WN1 1YN ☎ 01942 489003
✒ g.greeson@wigan.gov.uk

PR / Communications: Ms Lucy Downham, Public Relations
Officer, Town Hall, Library Street, Wigan WN1 1YN ☎ 01942 827116
✒ l.downham@wigan.gov.uk

Community Safety: Ms Amanda Crane, Building Stronger
Communities Partnership Project Officer, Wigan Life Centre, Library
Street, Wigan WN1 1YN ☎ 01942 828377 ✒ a.crane@wigan.gov.uk

Computer Management: Mrs Alison Hughes, Assistant Director
- ICT Strategic Partnership, Town Hall, Library Street, Wigan WN1
1YN ☎ 01942 487356 ✒ alison.hughes@wigan.gov.uk

Consumer Protection and Trading Standards: Mr Mark Tilley,
Assistant Director - Infrastructure & Regulatory Services, Wigan
Life Centre, Library Street, Wigan WN1 1YN ☎ 01942 489108
✒ m.tilley@wigan.gov.uk

Contracts: Mr John Mitchell, Assistant Director - Contracts, Town
Hall, Library Street, Wigan WN1 1YN ☎ 01942 487355
✒ j.mitchell@wigan.gcsx.gov.uk

Corporate Services: Mr Paul McKevitt, Director - Resources
& Contracts / Deputy Chief Executive, Town Hall, Library Street,
Wigan WN1 1YN ☎ 01942 827235 ✒ p.mckevitt@wigan.gov.uk

Customer Service: Ms Alison McKenzie-Folan, Director -
Customer Transformation / Deputy Chief Executive, Town Hall,
Library Street, Wigan WN1 1YN ☎ 01942 827784
✒ a.mckenzie-folan@wigan.gov.uk

Customer Service: Ms Lesley O'Halloran, Assistant Director -
Customer Services, Town Hall, Library Street, Wigan WN1 1YN
☎ 01942 489455 ✒ l.o'halloran@wigan.gov.uk

Direct Labour: Mr Mark Tilley, Assistant Director - Infrastructure &
Regulatory Services, Wigan Life Centre, Library Street, Wigan WN1
1YN ☎ 01942 489108 ✒ m.tilley@wigan.gov.uk

Economic Development: Ms Emma Barton, Assistant Director -
Economic Development & Skills, Wigan Life Centre, Library Street,
Wigan WN1 1NY ☎ 01942 489105 ✒ e.barton@wigan.gov.uk

Economic Development: Mr Karl Battersby, Director - Economy
& Environment, Town Hall, Library Street, Wigan WN1 1YN
☎ 01942 489101 ✒ karl.battersby@wigan.gov.uk

Education: Mr Alan Lindsay, Assistant Director - Education, Wigan
Life Centre, Library Street, Wigan WN1 1YN ☎ 01942 486000
✒ a.lindsay@wigan.gov.uk

Electoral Registration: Ms Julie Baron, Principal Electoral
Services Officer, Town Hall, Library Street, Wigan WN1 1YN
☎ 01942 827170 ✒ j.baron@wigan.gov.uk

Emergency Planning: Dr Kate Ardern, Director - Public Health,
Wigan Life Centre, Library Street, Wigan WN1 1YN ☎ 01942 404245
✒ k.ardern@wigan.gov.uk

Emergency Planning: Mr Paul Turner, Public Health Consultant,
Wigan Life Centre, Library Street, Wigan WN1 1YN ☎ 01942 404904
✒ p.turner@wigan.gov.uk

Environmental / Technical Services: Mr Paul Barton, Assistant Director - Environmental Services, Wigan Life Centre, Library Street, Wigan WN1 1YN ☎ 01942 486955 ⊕ p.barton@wigan.gov.uk

Environmental Health: Mr Mark Tilley, Assistant Director - Infrastructure & Regulatory Services, Wigan Life Centre, Library Street, Wigan WN1 1YN ☎ 01942 489108 ⊕ m.tilley@wigan.gov.uk

Estates, Property & Valuation: Ms Linda Fisher, Assistant Director - Legal, Town Hall, Library Street, Wigan WN1 1YN ☎ 01942 827026 ⊕ linda.fisher@wigan.gov.uk

Facilities: Ms Heather Coombs, Facilities & Statutory Compliance Manager, Town Hall, Library Street, Wigan WN1 1YN ☎ 01942 827363 ⊕ h.coombs@wigan.gov.uk

Finance: Mr Tony Clarke, Assistant Director - Finance, Town Hall, Library Street, Wigan WN1 1YN ☎ 01942 827272 ⊕ t.clarke@wigan.gov.uk

Fleet Management: Mr Keith Simpson, Fleet Services Group Manager, Markerfield Way Depot, Makerfield Way, Ince, Wigan WN1 1YN ☎ 01942 705103 ⊕ k.simpson@wigan.gov.uk

Health and Safety: Mr Paul McKevitt, Director - Resources & Contracts / Deputy Chief Executive, Town Hall, Library Street, Wigan WN1 1YN ☎ 01942 827235 ⊕ p.mckevitt@wigan.gov.uk

Highways: Mr Mark Tilley, Assistant Director - Infrastructure & Regulatory Services, Wigan Life Centre, Library Street, Wigan WN1 1YN ☎ 01942 489108 ⊕ m.tilley@wigan.gov.uk

Housing: Ms Janice Barton, Chief Executive - Wigan & Leigh Housing, Unity House, Westwood Park Drive, Wigan WN3 4HE ☎ 01942 486507 ⊕ j.barton@wigan.gov.uk

Legal: Ms Linda Fisher, Assistant Director - Legal, Town Hall, Library Street, Wigan WN1 1YN ☎ 01942 827026 ⊕ linda.fisher@wigan.gov.uk

Leisure and Cultural Services: Ms Penny McGinty, Assistant Director - Leisure, Cultural & Property Services, Wigan Life Centre, Library Street, Wigan WN1 1YN ☎ 01942 489103 ⊕ p.mcginty@wigan.gov.uk

Licensing: Mr Steve Wearing, Licensing Manager, Town Hall, Library Street, Wigan WN1 1YN ☎ 01942 827114 ⊕ s.wearing@wigan.gov.uk

Lighting: Mr Keith Benson, Street Scene & Lighting Manager, Wigan Life Centre, Library Street, Wigan WN1 1YN ☎ 01942 488025 ⊕ k.benson@wigan.gov.uk

Member Services: Ms Christine Charnock-Jones, Principal Democratic Services Officer, Town Hall, Library Street, Wigan WN1 1YN ☎ 01942 827156 ⊕ c.charnock@wigan.gov.uk

Parking: Ms Sharon Brightcliffe, Car Parks Officer, Wigan Life Centre, Library Street, Wigan WN1 1YN ☎ 01942 489319 ⊕ s.brightcliffe@wigan.gov.uk

Partnerships: Mr Will Blandamer, Assistant Director - Reform & Transformation, Town Hall, Library Street, Wigan WN1 1YN ☎ 01942 827581 ⊕ will.blandamer@wigan.gov.uk

Personnel / HR: Ms Sonia Halliwell, Assistant Director - HR & OD, Town Hall, Library Street, Wigan WN1 1YN ☎ 01942 489455 ⊕ s.halliwell@wigan.gov.uk

Planning: Mr Mike Worden, Assistant Director - Planning & Transport, Wigan Life Centre, Library Street, Wigan WN1 1YN ☎ 01942 489104 ⊕ mike.worden@wigan.gov.uk

Procurement: Mr Jonathan Cliff, Corporate Procurement Manager, Town Hall, Library Street, Wigan WN1 1YN ☎ 01942 827671 ⊕ j.cliff@wigan.gov.uk

Public Libraries: Ms Lesley O'Halloran, Assistant Director - Customer Services, Town Hall, Library Street, Wigan WN1 1YN ☎ 01942 489455 ⊕ l.o'halloran@wigan.gov.uk

Recycling & Waste Minimisation: Ms Andrea Yates, Waste Manager, Makerfield Way Depot, Makerfield Way, Ince, Wigan WN2 2PR ☎ 01942 828333 ⊕ a.yates@wigan.gov.uk

Regeneration: Ms Emma Barton, Assistant Director - Economic Development & Skills, Wigan Life Centre, Library Street, Wigan WN1 1NY ☎ 01942 489105 ⊕ e.barton@wigan.gov.uk

Road Safety: Ms Carmel Foster-Devine, Transport Plan & Road Safety Manager, Wigan Life Centre, Library Street, Wigan WN1 1NY ☎ 01942 489358 ⊕ c.foster-devine@wigan.gov.uk

Social Services (Adult): Ms Sharon Barber, Assistant Director - Support & Safeguarding, Wigan Life Centre, Library Street, Wigan WN1 1NY ☎ 01942 489454 ⊕ sharon.barber@wigan.gov.uk

Social Services (Adult): Ms Jo Wilmott, Assistant Manager - Provider Management & Market Development, Town Hall, Library Street, Wigan WN1 1YN ☎ 01942 489454 ⊕ joanne.wilmott@wigan.gov.uk

Staff Training: Ms Sonia Halliwell, Assistant Director - HR & OD, Town Hall, Library Street, Wigan WN1 1YN ☎ 01942 489455 ⊕ s.halliwell@wigan.gov.uk

Street Scene: Mr Nick Burdekin, In Bloom Co-ordinator, Wigan Life Centre, Library Street, Wigan WN1 1YN ☎ 01942 489325 ⊕ n.burdekin@wigan.gov.uk

Sustainable Communities: Ms Kathryn Rees, Assistant Director - Transformation, Town Hall, Library Street, Wigan WN1 1YN ☎ 01942 487362 ⊕ k.rees@wigan.gov.uk

Tourism: Ms Emma Barton, Assistant Director - Economic Development & Skills, Wigan Life Centre, Library Street, Wigan WN1 1NY ☎ 01942 489105 ⊕ e.barton@wigan.gov.uk

Town Centre: Mr Lee Connor, Town Centre Manager, Wigan Life Centre, Library Street, Wigan WN1 1YN ☎ 01942 828347 ⊕ l.connor@wigan.gov.uk

WIGAN

Traffic Management: Mr Mark Tilley, Assistant Director - Infrastructure & Regulatory Services, Wigan Life Centre, Library Street, Wigan WN1 1YN ☎ 01942 489108 ✆ m.tilley@wigan.gov.uk

Transport: Mr Keith Simpson, Fleet Services Group Manager, Makerfield Way Depot, Makerfield Way, Ince, Wigan WN2 2PR ☎ 01942 705103 ✆ k.simpson@wigan.gov.uk

Transport Planner: Mr Rob Owen, Transport Strategy Manager, Wigan Life Centre, Library Street, Wigan WN1 1NY ☎ 01942 489310 ✆ r.owen@wigan.gov.uk

Transport Planner: Mr Mike Worden, Assistant Director - Planning & Transport, Wigan Life Centre, Library Street, Wigan WN1 1YN ☎ 01942 489104 ✆ mike.worden@wigan.gov.uk

Waste Collection and Disposal: Mr Paul Barton, Assistant Director - Environmental Services, Wigan Life Centre, Library Street, Wigan WN1 1YN ☎ 01942 486955 ✆ p.barton@wigan.gov.uk

Waste Management: Ms Andrea Yates, Waste Manager, Makerfield Way Depot, Makerfield Way, Ince, Wigan WN2 2PR ☎ 01942 828333 ✆ a.yates@wigan.gov.uk

COUNCILLORS

Mayor: Conway, Ronald (LAB - Aspull New Springs Whelley)
r.conway@wigan.gov.uk

Deputy Mayor: Clarke, Bill (LAB - Ashton)
b.clarke@wigan.gov.uk

Leader of the Council: Smith, Peter (LAB - Leigh West)
leader@wigan.gov.uk

Deputy Leader of the Council: Molyneux, David (LAB - Ince)
d.molyneux@wigan.gov.uk

Aldred, Martin (LAB - Atherton)
martin.aldred@wigan.gov.uk

Aldred, Mark (LAB - Atherleigh)
m.aldred@wigan.gov.uk

Aldred, Karen (LAB - Atherton)
k.aldred@wigan.gov.uk

Anderson, Kevin (LAB - Leigh South)
k.anderson@wigan.gov.uk

Arrowsmith, David (LAB - Orrell)
d.arrowsmith@wigan.gov.uk

Ash, Nigel (LAB - Ashton)
n.ash@wigan.gov.uk

Barber, Richard (LAB - Golborne & Lowton West)
r.barber@wigan.gov.uk

Blay, Paul (LAB - Hindley)
p.blay@wigan.gov.uk

Brierley, Robert (IND - Hindley Green)
r.brierley@wigan.gov.uk

Bullen, Jennifer (LAB - Ashton)
j.bullen@wigan.gov.uk

Carmichael, Francis (IND - Hindley Green)
f.carmichael@wigan.gov.uk

Churton, James (LAB - Hindley)
j.eccles-churton@wigan.gov.uk

Collins, Paul (LAB - Shevington with Lower Ground)
paul.collins@wigan.gov.uk

Crosby, Michael (LAB - Shevington with Lower Ground)
m.crosby@wigan.gov.uk

Cullen, Phyllis (LAB - Wigan West)
p.cullen@wigan.gov.uk

Cunliffe, Keith (LAB - Leigh East)
k.cunliffe@wigan.gov.uk

Davies, George (LAB - Wigan Central)
george.davies@wigan.gov.uk

Dawber, Stephen (LAB - Wigan West)
steve.dawber@wigan.gov.uk

Dewhurst, Michael (LAB - Douglas)
m.dewhurst@wigan.gov.uk

Dewhurst, Shirley (LAB - Douglas)
shirley.dewhurst@wigan.gov.uk

Draper, Pat (LAB - Douglas)
p.draper@wigan.gov.uk

Edwardson, Damian (LAB - Shevington with Lower Ground)
d.edwardson@wigan.gov.uk

Fairhurst, Debbie (IND - Standish with Langtree)
debbiefairhurst@wigan.gov.uk

Fairhurst, Gareth (IND - Standish with Langtree)
gareth.fairhurst@wigan.gov.uk

Greensmith, Susan (LAB - Leigh West)
s.greensmith@wigan.gov.uk

Grundy, James (CON - Lowton East)
james.grundy@wigan.gov.uk

Halliwell, Terence (LAB - Wigan West)
t.halliwell@wigan.gov.uk

Harding, John (LAB - Atherleigh)
j.harding@wigan.gov.uk

Hellier, Stephen (LAB - Tyldesley)
s.hellier@wigan.gov.uk

Hilton, John (LAB - Aspull New Springs Whelley)
j.hilton@wigan.gov.uk

Hodgkinson, Jamie (IND - Atherton)
jamie.hodgkinson@wigan.gov.uk

Holland, Patricia (LAB - Worsley Mesnes)
p.holland@wigan.gov.uk

Houlton, Kathleen (CON - Lowton East)
k.houlton@wigan.gov.uk

Houlton, Edward (CON - Lowton East)
edward.houlton@wigan.gov.uk

Hunt, Lawrence (LAB - Wigan Central)
i.hunt@wigan.gov.uk

Jones, Steve (IND - Bryn)
stephen.jones@wigan.gov.uk

Keane, Stuart (LAB - Golborne & Lowton West)
s.keane@wigan.gov.uk

Kelly, Phil (LAB - Worsley Mesnes)
p.kelly@wigan.gov.uk

Kenny, Paul (LAB - Winstanley)
p.kenny@wigan.gov.uk

Klieve, Yvonne (LAB - Golborne & Lowton West)
y.klieve@wigan.gov.uk

Marshall, Joanne (LAB - Tyldesley)
joanne.marshall@wigan.gov.uk

McLoughlin, Michael (LAB - Wigan Central)
m.mcLoughlin@wigan.gov.uk

Moodie, James (LAB - Ince)
j.moodie@wigan.gov.uk

Morgan, Marie (LAB - Winstanley)
marie.morgan@wigan.gov.uk

Morgan, Clive (LAB - Winstanley)
clive.morgan@wigan.gov.uk

Murphy, Stephen (LAB - Orrell)
stephen.murphy@wigan.gov.uk

Murphy, Sam (LAB - Pemberton)
sam.murphy@wigan.gov.uk

Murray, Nathan (LAB - Bryn)
n.murray@wigan.gov.uk

O'Brien, John (LAB - Leigh South)
j.o'brien@wigan.gov.uk

Platt, Joanne (LAB - Astley Mosley Common)
joanne.platt@wigan.gov.uk

Prescott, Jeanette (LAB - Pemberton)
j.prescott@wigan.gov.uk

Prescott, Paul (LAB - Pemberton)
paul.prescott@wigan.gov.uk

Rampling, Margaret (LAB - Bryn)
a.rampling@wigan.gov.uk

Ready, Christopher (LAB - Aspull New Springs Whelley)
c.ready@wigan.gov.uk

Rehman, Nazia (LAB - Tyldesley)
n.rehman@wigan.gov.uk

Rigby, Charles (LAB - Leigh South)
c.rigby@wigan.gov.uk

Roberts, Christtine (LAB - Astley Mosley Common)
christine.roberts@wigan.gov.uk

Rotherham, William (LAB - Worsley Mesnes)
w.rotherham@wigan.gov.uk

Sharratt, Janice (LAB - Ince)
j.sharratt@wigan.gov.uk

Smethurst, Eunice (LAB - Abram)
e.smethurst@wigan.gov.uk

Smethurst, Martyn (LAB - Abram)
m.smethurst@wigan.gov.uk

Stewart, Pamela (LAB - Atherleigh)
p.stewart@wigan.gov.uk

Stitt, David (LAB - Hindley Green)
k.stitt@wigan.gov.uk

Sweeney, Carl (LAB - Abram)
c.sweeney@wigan.gov.uk

Talbot, James (LAB - Hindley)
j.talbot@wigan.gov.uk

Taylor, Barry (LAB - Astley Mosley Common)
barry.taylor@wigan.gov.uk

Thorpe, Anita (LAB - Leigh East)
a.thorpe@wigan.gov.uk

Walker, Frederick (LAB - Leigh East)
f.walker@wigan.gov.uk

Whiteside, Myra (LAB - Leigh West)
m.whiteside@wigan.gov.uk

Whittingham, Raymond (CON - Standish with Langtree)
raymond.whittingham@wigan.gov.uk

Winstanley, Michael (CON - Orrell)
michael.winstanley@wigan.gov.uk

POLITICAL COMPOSITION
LAB: 64, IND: 6, CON: 5

COMMITTEE CHAIRS

Audit: Mr Carl Sweeney

Children & Young People: Mrs Myra Whiteside

Health & Social Care: Mr Nigel Ash

Licensing: Mr Paul Prescott

Planning: Mr Paul Prescott

Wiltshire Unitary   U

Wiltshire Council, County Hall, Trowbridge BA14 8JN
☎ 0300 456 0100 🖳 www.wiltshire.gov.uk

FACTS AND FIGURES
Parliamentary Constituencies: Chippenham, Devizes, Salisbury, Wiltshire North, Wiltshire South West

PRINCIPAL OFFICERS

Senior Management: Dr Carlton Brand, Corporate Director - ERO, SIRO, County Hall, Trowbridge BA14 8JN ☎ 01225 713001 ⌁ carltonbrand@wiltshire.gov.uk

Senior Management: Mrs Carolyn Godfrey, Corporate Director - Children's Services, County Hall, Bythesea Road, Trowbridge BA14 8JN ☎ 01225 713750 ⌁ carolyn.godfrey@wiltshire.gov.uk

Senior Management: Mrs Maggie Rae, Corporate Director - Public Health & Adults, County Hall, Bythesea Road, Trowbridge BA14 8JN ☎ 01225 718338 ⌁ maggie.rae@wiltshire.gov.uk

Building Control: Ms Sarah Ward, Head of Asset Management - Corporate Building Programme, County Hall, Trowbridge BA14 8JN ☎ 01225 713235 ⌁ sarah.ward@wiltshire.gov.uk

Children / Youth Services: Ms Julia Cramp, Joint Associate Director - Commissioning & Performance, County Hall, Trowbridge BA14 8JN ☎ 01225 718221 ⌁ julia.cramp@wiltshire.gov.uk

Children / Youth Services: Mrs Carolyn Godfrey, Corporate Director - Children's Services, County Hall, Bythesea Road, Trowbridge BA14 8JN ☎ 01225 713750 ⌁ carolyn.godfrey@wiltshire.gov.uk

WILTSHIRE UNITARY

Children / Youth Services: Mr Terrence Herbert, Associate Director - Operational Children's Services, County Hall, Trowbridge BA14 8JN ☎ 01225 713682 🖰 terrence.herbert@wiltshire.gov.uk

PR / Communications: Ms Laurie Bell, Associate Director - Communications & Communities, County Hall, Trowbridge BA14 8JN ☎ 0300 456 0100 🖰 laurie.bell@wiltshire.gov.uk

Community Planning: Dr Carlton Brand, Corporate Director - ERO, SIRO, County Hall, Trowbridge BA14 8JN ☎ 01225 713001 🖰 carltonbrand@wiltshire.gov.uk

Community Safety: Ms Mandy Bradley, Service Director - Public Protection, Court Mills Centre, Polebarn Road, Trowbridge BA14 7EG ☎ 0300 456 0100 🖰 mandy.bradley@wiltshire.gov.uk

Consumer Protection and Trading Standards: Ms Yvonne Bennett, Consumer Protection Manager, County Hall, Trowbridge BA14 8JN ☎ 0300 456 0100 🖰 yvonne.bennett@wiltshire.gov.uk

Contracts: Mr Michael Swabey, Strategy Manager, County Hall, Trowbridge BA14 8JD ☎ 01225 718662 🖰 mikeswabey@wiltshire.gov.uk

Contracts: Mr Arthur Williams, Principal Contracts Officer, County Hall, Trowbridge BA14 8JN ☎ 01225 713252 🖰 arthur.williams@wiltshire.gov.uk

Corporate Services: Dr Carlton Brand, Corporate Director - ERO, SIRO, County Hall, Trowbridge BA14 8JN ☎ 01225 713001 🖰 carltonbrand@wiltshire.gov.uk

Customer Service: Mrs Jacqui White, Service Director - Business Services, County Hall, Trowbridge BA14 8JN ☎ 0300 456 0100 🖰 jacquiwhite@wiltshire.gov.uk

Economic Development: Mr Alistair Cunningham, Associate Director - Economic Development & Planning Services, County Hall, Bythesea Road, Trowbridge BA14 8JN ☎ 01225 713203 🖰 alistair.cunningham@wiltshire.gov.uk

Education: Ms Julia Cramp, Joint Associate Director - Commissioning & Performance, County Hall, Trowbridge BA14 8JN ☎ 01225 718221 🖰 julia.cramp@wiltshire.gov.uk

Education: Mrs Stephanie Denovan, Service Director - Schools & Learning, County Hall, Bythesea Road, Trowbridge BA14 8JN ☎ 01225 713838 🖰 stephanie.denovan@wiltshire.gov.uk

Education: Ms Carolyn Godfrey, Corporate Director, County Hall, Trowbridge BA14 8JB ☎ 01225 713750 🖰 carolyn.godfrey@wiltshire.gov.uk

E-Government: Mr Ian Gibbons, Director - Legal & Democratic Services, County Hall, Bythesea Road, Trowbridge BA14 8JN ☎ 01225 713052 🖰 ian.gibbons@wiltshire.gov.uk

Environmental / Technical Services: Ms Tracy Carter, Associate Director - Waste & Environment, County Hall, Trowbridge BA14 8JN ☎ 01225 713258 🖰 tracy.carter@wiltshire.gov.uk

Environmental / Technical Services: Mr Parvis Khansari, Associate Director - Highways & Transport, County Hall, Bythesea Road, Trowbridge BA14 8JN ☎ 01225 713340 🖰 parvis.khansari@wiltshire.gov.uk

Events Manager: Ms Barbara Gray, Events & Sponsorship Manager, County Hall, Trowbridge BA14 8JN ☎ 0300 456 0100

Facilities: Mr Mark Smith, Service Director - Neighbourhood Services, County Hall, Trowbridge BA14 8JN ☎ 0300 456 0100 🖰 mark.smith@wiltshire.gov.uk

Finance: Mr Michael Hudson, Director - Finance, County Hall, Trowbridge BA14 8JN ☎ 0300 456 0100 🖰 michael.hudson@wiltshire.gov.uk

Treasury: Mr Keith Stephens, Business Analyst - Cash & Treasury, County Hall, Trowbridge BA14 8JN ☎ 01225 713603 🖰 keith.stephens@wiltshire.gov.uk

Pensions: Mr David Anthony, Head - Pensions, County Hall, Trowbridge BA14 8JN ☎ 01225 713613 🖰 david.anthony@wiltshire.gov.uk

Pensions: Ms Catherine Dix, Pension Investments Officer, County Hall, Trowbridge BA14 8JN ☎ 01225 713613 🖰 catherine.dix@wiltshire.gov.uk

Grounds Maintenance: Mr Mark Smith, Service Director - Neighbourhood Services, County Hall, Trowbridge BA14 8JN ☎ 0300 456 0100 🖰 mark.smith@wiltshire.gov.uk

Health and Safety: Mr Paul Collyer, Head of Occupational Health & Safety, County Hall, Trowbridge BA14 8JN ☎ 01225 713119 🖰 paulcollyer@wiltshire.gov.uk

Highways: Mr Parvis Khansari, Associate Director - Highways & Transport, County Hall, Bythesea Road, Trowbridge BA14 8JN ☎ 01225 713340 🖰 parvis.khansari@wiltshire.gov.uk

Legal: Mr Ian Gibbons, Associate Director - Legal & Governance (Monitoring Officer), County Hall, Bythesea Road, Trowbridge BA14 8JN ☎ 01225 713052 🖰 ian.gibbons@wiltshire.gov.uk

Leisure and Cultural Services: Mr Mark Smith, Service Director - Neighbourhood Services, County Hall, Trowbridge BA14 8JN ☎ 0300 456 0100 🖰 mark.smith@wiltshire.gov.uk

Lifelong Learning: Ms Joanne Pitt, Head of HR & OD, County Hall, Trowbridge BA14 8JN ☎ 0300 456 0100 🖰 joannapitt@wiltshire.gov.uk

Lottery Funding, Charity and Voluntary: Ms Sandie Lewis, Head - Community Strategy & Voluntary Sector Support, County Hall, Trowbridge BA14 8JN ☎ 01225 713150 🖰 sandie.lewis@wiltshire.gov.uk

Member Services: Mr Ian Gibbons, Director - Legal & Democratic Services, County Hall, Bythesea Road, Trowbridge BA14 8JN ☎ 01225 713052 🖰 ian.gibbons@wiltshire.gov.uk

Member Services: Mr John Quinton, Head - Democratic & Member Services & Cabinet Secretary, County Hall, Trowbridge BA14 8JN ☎ 01225 713054 ✆ johnquinton@wiltshire.gov.uk

Partnerships: Mrs Maggie Rae, Corporate Director - Public Health & Adults, County Hall, Bythesea Road, Trowbridge BA14 8JN ☎ 01225 718338 ✆ maggie.rae@wiltshire.gov.uk

Personnel / HR: Mr Barry Pirie, Director - Human Resources & Organisational Development, County Hall, Bythesea Road, Trowbridge BA14 8JN ☎ 0300 456 0100 ✆ barrie.pirie@wiltshire.gov.uk

Planning: Mr Brad Fleet, Service Director - Development Services, County Hall, Trowbridge BA14 8JN ☎ 0300 456 0100 ✆ brad.fleet@wiltshire.gov.uk

Procurement: Mr Robin Townsend, Associate Director - Corporate Function, Procurement & Programme Office, County Hall, Trowbridge BA14 8JN ✆ robin.townsend@wiltshire.gov.uk

Public Libraries: Ms Niki Lewis, Service Director - Community, Libraries, Heritage & Arts, County Hall, Bythesea Road, Trowbridge BA14 8JN ☎ 01225 713180 ✆ niki.lewis@wiltshire.gov.uk

Social Services: Ms Sue Geary, Head - Performance, Health & Workforce, County Hall, Trowbridge BA14 8JN ☎ 01225 713922 ✆ sue.geary@wiltshire.gov.uk

Social Services (Adult): Mr James Cawley, Associate Director - Adult Care Commissioning, Safeguarding & Housing, County Hall, Trowbridge BA14 8JN ☎ 0300 456 0100 ✆ james.cawley@wiltshire.gov.uk

Public Health: Mrs Maggie Rae, Corporate Director - Public Health & Adults, County Hall, Bythesea Road, Trowbridge BA14 8JN ☎ 01225 718338 ✆ maggie.rae@wiltshire.gov.uk

Staff Training: Ms Niki Lewis, Service Director - Community, Libraries, Heritage & Arts, County Hall, Trowbridge BA14 8JN ☎ 01225 713180 ✆ niki.lewis@wiltshire.gov.uk

Staff Training: Mr Barry Pirie, Director - Human Resources & Organisational Development, County Hall, Bythesea Road, Trowbridge BA14 8JN ☎ 01225 718226 ✆ barry.pirie@wiltshire.gov.uk

Sustainable Communities: Ms Niki Lewis, Service Director - Community, Libraries, Heritage & Arts, County Hall, Bythesea Road, Trowbridge BA14 8JN ☎ 01225 713180 ✆ niki.lewis@wiltshire.gov.uk

Transport: Mr Parvis Khansari, Associate Director - Highways & Transport, County Hall, Bythesea Road, Trowbridge BA14 8JN ☎ 01225 713340 ✆ parvis.khansari@wiltshire.gov.uk

Waste Collection and Disposal: Ms Tracy Carter, Associate Director - Waste & Environment, County Hall, Trowbridge BA14 8JN ☎ 01225 713258 ✆ tracy.carter@wiltshire.gov.uk

COUNCILLORS

Chair: Britton, Richard (CON - Alderbury & Whiteparish)
richard.britton@wiltshire.gov.uk

Vice-Chair: Bucknell, Allison (CON - Lyneham)
allison.bucknell@wiltshire.gov.uk

Leader of the Council: Scott, Jane (CON - By Brook)
jane.scott@wiltshire.gov.uk

Deputy Leader of the Council: Thomson, John (CON - Sherston)
john.thomson@wiltshire.gov.uk

Group Leader: Ansell, Glenis (LD - Calne North)
glenis.ansell@wiltshire.gov.uk

Group Leader: Clark, Ernie (IND - Hilperton)
ernie.clark@wiltshire.gov.uk

Group Leader: Rogers, Ricky (LAB - Salisbury Bemerton)
ricky.rogers@wiltshire.gov.uk

Allen, Desna (LD - Chippenham Queens & Sheldon)
desna.allen@wiltshire.gov.uk

Auckland, Chris (LD - Trowbridge Grove)
chris.auckland@wiltshire.gov.uk

Aves, Pat (LD - Melksham North)
pat.aves@wiltshire.gov.uk

Berry, Chuck (CON - Minety)
chuck.berry@wiltshire.gov.uk

Blakemore, Nick (LD - Trowbridge Adcroft)
nick.blakemore@wiltshire.gov.uk

Brown, Rosemary (LD - Bradford-on-Avon North)
rosemary.brown@wiltshire.gov.uk

Capp, Jamie (LD - Amesbury East)
jamie.capp@wiltshire.gov.uk

Carbin, Trevor (LD - Holt & Staverton)
trevor.carbin@wiltshire.gov.uk

Caswill, Chris (IND - Chippenham Monkton)
chris.caswill@wiltshire.gov.uk

Champion, Mary (CON - Royal Wootton Bassett North)
mary.champion@wiltshire.gov.uk

Chivers, Terry (IND - Melksham Without North)
terry.chivers@wiltshire.gov.uk

Clewer, Richard (CON - Salisbury St Pauls)
richard.clewer@wiltshire.gov.uk

Connolly, Mark (CON - Tidworth)
mark.connolly@wiltshire.gov.uk

Crisp, Christine (CON - Calne Rural)
christine.crisp@wiltshire.gov.uk

Cuthbert, Anna (CON - Bromham, Rowde & Potterne)
anna.cuthbert@wiltshire.gov.uk

Dalton, Brian (LD - Salisbury Harnham)
brian.dalton@wiltshire.gov.uk

Davis, Andrew (CON - Warminster East)
andrew.davis@wiltshire.gov.uk

Deane, Tony (CON - Tisbury)
tony.deane@wiltshire.gov.uk

Devine, Christopher (CON - Winterslow)
christopher.devine@wiltshire.gov.uk

Dobson, Stewart (CON - Marlborough East)
stewart.dobson@wiltshire.gov.uk

WILTSHIRE UNITARY

Douglas, Mary (CON - Salisbury St Francis & Stratford)
mary.douglas@wiltshire.gov.uk

Douglas, Bill (LD - Chippenham Hardens & England)
bill.douglas@wiltshire.gov.uk

Drewett, Dennis (IND - Trowbridge Park)
dennis.drewett@wiltshire.gov.uk

Edge, Peter (LD - Wilton & Lower Wylye Valley)
peter.edge@wiltshire.gov.uk

Evans, Peter (CON - Devizes East)
peterb.evans@wiltshire.gov.uk

Evans, Sue (CON - Devizes North)
sue.evans@wiltshire.gov.uk

Fogg, Nick (IND - Marlborough West)
nick.fogg@wiltshire.gov.uk

Gamble, Richard (CON - The Lavingtons & Erlestoke)
richard.gamble@wiltshire.gov.uk

Green, Jose (CON - Fovant & Chalke Valley)
jose.green@wiltshire.gov.uk

Greenman, Howard (CON - Kington)
howard.greenman@wiltshire.gov.uk

Groom, Mollie (CON - Royal Wootton Bassett East)
mollie.groom@wiltshire.gov.uk

Hawker, Russell (IND - Westbury West)
russell.hawker@wiltshire.gov.uk

Hewitt, Mike (CON - Bourne & Woodford Valley)
mike.hewitt@wiltshire.gov.uk

Hill, Alan (CON - Calne South & Cherhill)
alan.hill@wiltshire.gov.uk

Hoque, Atiqul (CON - Salisbury St Edmund & Milford)

Howard, Charles (CON - The Collingbournes & Netheravon)
charles.howard@wiltshire.gov.uk

Hubbard, Jon (LD - Melksham South)
jon.hubbard@wiltshire.gov.uk

Humphries, Keith (CON - Warminster Broadway)
keith.humphries@wiltshire.gov.uk

Hurst, Chris (LD - Royal Wootton Bassett South)
chris.hurst@wiltshire.gov.uk

Hutton, Peter (CON - Chippenham Cepen Park & Derriads)
peter.hutton@wiltshire.gov.uk

Jacobs, Simon (CON - Devizes & Roundway South)
simon.jacobs@wiltshire.gov.uk

Jeans, George (IND - Mere)
george.jeans@wiltshire.gov.uk

Jenkins, David (LD - Westbury North)
david.jenkins2@wiltshire.gov.uk

Johnson, Julian (CON - Downton & Ebble Valley)
julian.johnson@wiltshire.gov.uk

Jones, Bob (LD - Cricklade & Latton)
bob.jones@wiltshire.gov.uk

Killane, Simon (LD - Malmesbury)
simon.killane@wiltshire.gov.uk

King, Gordon (LD - Westbury East)
gordon.king@wiltshire.gov.uk

Knight, John (LD - Trowbridge Central)
john.knight@wiltshire.gov.uk

Kunkler, Jerry (CON - Pewsey)
jerry.kunkler@wiltshire.gov.uk

Lay, Jacqui (CON - Purton)
jacqui.lay@wiltshire.gov.uk

Macrae, Alan (CON - Corsham Pickwick)
alan.macrae@wiltshire.gov.uk

Madonald, Magnus (LD - Winsley & Westwood)
magnus.macdonald@wiltshire.gov.uk

Marshall, Howard (IND - Calne Central)
howard.marshall@wiltshire.gov.uk

Mayes, Laura (CON - Roundway)
laura.mayes@wiltshire.gov.uk

McLennan, Ian (LAB - Laverstock, Ford & Old Sarum)
ian.mclennan@wiltshire.gov.uk

Milton, Jemima (CON - West Selkley)
jemima.milton@wiltshire.gov.uk

Moss, Bill (CON - Salisbury St Marks & Bishopdown)
bill.moss@wiltshire.gov.uk

Newbury, Christopher (IND - Warminster Copheap & Wylye)
christopher.newbury@wiltshire.gov.uk

Oatway, Paul (CON - Pewsey Vale)
paul.oatway@wiltshire.gov.uk

Oldrieve, Stephen (LD - Trowbridge Paxcroft)
steve.oldrieve@wiltshire.gov.uk

Osborn, Helen (LD - Trowbridge Lambrok)
helen.osborn@wiltshire.gov.uk

Packard, Mark (LD - Chippenham Pewsham)
mark.packard@wiltshire.gov.uk

Packard, Linda (LD - Chippenham Lowden & Rowden)
linda.packard@wiltshire.gov.uk

Parker, Sheila (CON - Box & Colerne)
sheila.parker@wiltshire.gov.uk

Payne, Graham (CON - Trowbridge Drynham)
graham.payne@wiltshire.gov.uk

Phillips, Nina (CON - Chippenham Cepen Park & Redlands)
nina.phillips@wiltshire.gov.uk

Pollitt, David (UKIP - Melksham Central)
david.pollitt@wiltshire.gov.uk

Prickett, Horace (CON - Southwick)
horace.prickett@wiltshire.gov.uk

Randall, Leo (CON - Redlynch & Landford)
leo.randall@wiltshire.gov.uk

Rhe-Philipe, Fleur de (CON - Warminster Without)
fleur.derhephilipe@wiltshire.gov.uk

Ridout, Pip (CON - Warminster West)
pip.ridout@wiltshire.gov.uk

Seed, Jonathon (CON - Summerham & Seend)
jonathon.seed@wiltshire.gov.uk

Sheppard, James (CON - Aldbourne & Ramsbury)
james.sheppard@wiltshire.gov.uk

Smale, John (CON - Bulford, Allington & Figheldean)
johnf.smale@wiltshire.gov.uk

Sturgis, Toby (CON - Brinkworth)
toby.sturgis@wiltshire.gov.uk

Thompson, Melody (CON - Chippenham Hardenhuish)
melody.thompson@wiltshire.gov.uk

Thorn, Ian (LD - Bradford-on-Avon South)
ian.thorne@wiltshire.gov.uk

Tomes, Ian (LAB - Salisbury St Martins & Cathedral)
ian.tomes@wiltshire.gov.uk

Tonge, Dick (CON - Corsham Without & Box Hill)
richard.tonge@wiltshire.gov.uk

Trotman, Anthony (CON - Calne Chilvester & Abberd)
tony.trotman@wiltshire.gov.uk

Walsh, John (LAB - Salisbury Fisherton & Bemerton Village)
john.walsh@wiltshire.gov.uk

Wayman, Bridget (CON - Nadder & East Knoyle)
bridget.wayman@wiltshire.gov.uk

West, Ian (LD - Till & Wylye Valley)
ian.west@wiltshire.gov.uk

Westmoreland, Fred (CON - Amesbury West)
fred.westmoreland@wiltshire.gov.uk

Whalley, Philip (CON - Corsham Town)
philip.whalley@wiltshire.gov.uk

Wheeler, Stuart (CON - Burbage & The Bedwyns)
stuart.wheeler@wiltshire.gov.uk

While, Roy (CON - Melksham Without South)
roy.while@wiltshire.gov.uk

Whitehead, Philip (CON - Urchfont & The Cannings)
philip.whitehead@wiltshire.gov.uk

Wickham, Jerry (CON - Ethandune)
jerry.wickham@wiltshire.gov.uk

Williams, Christopher (CON - Ludgershall & Perham Down)
christopher.williams@wiltshire.gov.uk

Wright, Graham (IND - Durrington & Larkhill)
graham.wright@wiltshire.gov.uk

POLITICAL COMPOSITION
CON: 58, LD: 25, IND: 10, LAB: 4, UKIP: 1

COMMITTEE CHAIRS

Audit: Mr Tony Deane

Health & Wellbeing: Baroness Jane Scott

Licensing: Ms Pip Ridout

Pensions: Mr Tony Deane

Planning: Mr Andrew Davis

Winchester City   D

Winchester City Council, City Offices, Colebrook Street, Winchester SO23 9LJ
☎ 01962 840222 🖨 01962 841365 ✆ info@winchester.gov.uk
💻 www.winchester.gov.uk

FACTS AND FIGURES
Parliamentary Constituencies: Winchester
EU Constituencies: South East
Election Frequency: Elections are by thirds

PRINCIPAL OFFICERS

Deputy Chief Executive: Ms Laura Taylor, Chief Executive, City Offices, Colebrook Street, Winchester SO23 9LJ
✆ ltaylor@winchester.gov.uk

Senior Management: Mr Steve Tilbury, Corporate Director - Operations, City Offices, Colebrook Street, Winchester SO23 9LJ
☎ 01962 848256 ✆ stilbury@winchester.gov.uk

Architect, Building / Property Services: Mr Andrew Kingston, Property Services Manager, City Offices, Colebrook Street, Winchester SO23 9LJ ☎ 01962 848240
✆ akingston@winchester.gov.uk

Architect, Building / Property Services: Mr Kevin Warren, Head of Estates, City Offices, Colebrook Street, Winchester SO23 9LJ ☎ 01962 848528 ✆ kwarren@winchester.gov.uk

Best Value: Mr Simon Little, Head of Finance, City Offices, Colebrook Street, Winchester SO23 9LJ ☎ 01962 848224
✆ slittle@winchester.gov.uk

Building Control: Mr Chris Griffith-Jones, Head of Building Control, City Offices, Colebrook Street, Winchester SO23 9LJ
☎ 01962 840222 ✆ cgriffith-jones@winchester.gov.uk

Children / Youth Services: Mrs Lorraine Ronan, Head of Health & Wellbeing, City Offices, Colebrook Street, Winchester SO23 9LJ
☎ 01962 848369 ✆ lronan@winchester.gov.uk

PR / Communications: Mr Martin O'Neill, Head of Communications, City Offices, Colebrook Street, Winchester SO23 9LJ ☎ 01962 848504 ✆ moneill@winchester.gov.uk

Community Planning: Mr Steve Lincoln, Planning Manager, City Offices, Colebrook Street, Winchester SO23 9LJ ☎ 01962 848110
✆ slincoln@winchester.gov.uk

Community Safety: Mrs Sandra Tuddenham, Head of Community Safety & Neighbourhood Services, City Offices, Colebrook Street, Winchester SO23 9LJ ☎ 01962 848132
✆ studdenham@winchester.gov.uk

Computer Management: Mr Tony Fawcett, Head of IT Services, City Offices, Colebrook Street, Winchester SO23 9LJ ☎ 01962 848262; 01264 368901 ✆ tfawcett@winchester.gov.uk; tfacwett@testvalley.gov.uk

Contracts: Mr Andrew Kingston, Property Services Manager, City Offices, Colebrook Street, Winchester SO23 9LJ ☎ 01962 848240
✆ akingston@winchester.gov.uk

Economic Development: Ms Kate Cloud, Head of Economy & Arts, City Offices, Colebrook Street, Winchester SO23 9LJ
☎ 01962 848563 ✆ kcloud@winchester.gov.uk

Electoral Registration: Mrs Karen Vincent, Electoral Services Manager, City Offices, Colebrook Street, Winchester SO23 9LJ
☎ 01962 848125 ✆ kvincent@winchester.gov.uk

WINCHESTER CITY

Emergency Planning: Mr Simon Howson, Corporate Business Manager, City Offices, Colebrook Street, Winchester SO23 9LJ ☎ 01962 848104 ⏚ showson@winchester.gov.uk

Energy Management: Mr Paul Cooke, Energy Manager, City Offices, Colebrook Street, Winchester SO23 9LJ ☎ 01962 848325 ⏚ pcooke@winchester.gov.uk

Environmental / Technical Services: Mr Robert Heathcock, Joint Environmental Services Manager, City Offices, Colebrook Street, Winchester SO23 9LJ ☎ 01730 234383 ⏚ rob.heathcock@easthants.gov.uk

Environmental Health: Mr David Ingram, Head of Environment & Licensing, City Offices, Colebrook Street, Winchester SO23 9LJ ☎ 01962 848479 ⏚ dingram@winchester.gov.uk

Estates, Property & Valuation: Mr Kevin Warren, Head of Estates, City Offices, Colebrook Street, Winchester SO23 9LJ ☎ 01962 848528 ⏚ kwarren@winchester.gov.uk

Facilities: Ms Wendy Steele, Facilities Manager, City Offices, Colebrook Street, Winchester SO23 9LJ ☎ 01962 848397 ⏚ wsteele@winchester.gov.uk

Finance: Mr Simon Little, Head of Finance, City Offices, Colebrook Street, Winchester SO23 9LJ ☎ 01962 848224 ⏚ slittle@winchester.gov.uk

Fleet Management: Mr Dave Howarth, Payroll & Fleet Manager, City Offices, Colebrook Street, Winchester SO23 9LJ ☎ 01962 848157 ⏚ dhowarth@winchester.gov.uk

Grounds Maintenance: Ms Susan Croker, Head of Landscapes & Open Spaces, City Offices, Colebrook Street, Winchester SO23 9LJ ☎ 01962 848419 ⏚ scroker@winchester.gov.uk

Health and Safety: Mr Robert Cole, Corporate Health & Safety Adviser, City Offices, Colebrook Street, Winchester SO23 9LJ ☎ 01962 848164 ⏚ bcole@winchester.gov.uk

Housing: Mr Olu Fajuyitan, Senior Housing Needs Officer, City Offices, Colebrook Street, Winchester SO23 9LJ ☎ 01962 840222 ⏚ ofajuyitan@winchester.gov.uk

Housing: Mr Andy Palmer, Head of New Homes Delivery, City Offices, Colebrook Street, Winchester SO23 9LJ ☎ 01962 840152 ⏚ apalmer@winchester.gov.uk

Housing Maintenance: Mr Andrew Kingston, Property Services Manager, City Offices, Colebrook Street, Winchester SO23 9LJ ☎ 01962 848240 ⏚ akingston@winchester.gov.uk

Legal: Mr Howard Bone, Head of Legal & Democratic Services, City Offices, Colebrook Street, Winchester SO23 9LJ ☎ 01962 848310 ⏚ hbone@winchester.gov.uk

Legal: Ms Lisa Hall, Head of Legal Services, City Offices, Colebrook Street, Winchester SO23 9LJ ☎ 01962 840222 ⏚ lhall@winchester.gov.uk

Leisure and Cultural Services: Ms Eloise Appleby, Assistant Director, City Offices, Colebrook Street, Winchester SO23 9LJ ☎ 01962 848181 ⏚ eappleby@winchester.gov.uk

Licensing: Mr David Ingram, Head of Environment & Licensing, City Offices, Colebrook Street, Winchester SO23 9LJ ☎ 01962 848479 ⏚ dingram@winchester.gov.uk

Lifelong Learning: Mr Sakhumuzi Ngwenya, Training & Development Advisor, City Offices, Colebrook Street, Winchester SO23 9LJ ☎ 01962 840222 ⏚ sngwenya@winchester.gov.uk

Lottery Funding, Charity and Voluntary: Mrs Lorraine Ronan, Head of Health & Wellbeing, City Offices, Colebrook Street, Winchester SO23 9LJ ☎ 01962 848369 ⏚ lronan@winchester.gov.uk

Member Services: Mr David Blakemore, Democratic Services Manager, City Offices, Colebrook Street, Winchester SO23 9LJ ☎ 01962 848264 ⏚ dblakemore@winchester.gov.uk

Parking: Mr Richard Hein, Head of Parking & CCTV Manager, City Offices, Colebrook Street, Winchester SO23 9LJ ☎ 01962 848346 ⏚ rhein@winchester.gov.uk

Personnel / HR: Ms Alison Gavin, Head of Organisational Development, City Offices, Colebrook Street, Winchester SO23 9LJ ☎ 01962 840222 ⏚ agavin@winchester.gov.uk

Planning: Mr Steve Opacic, Head of Strategic Planning, City Offices, Colebrook Street, Winchester SO23 9LJ ☎ 01962 848101 ⏚ sopacic@winchester.gov.uk

Planning: Mrs Julie Pinnock, Head of Planning Management, City Offices, Colebrook Street, Winchester SO23 9LJ ☎ 01962 848439 ⏚ jpinnock@winchester.gov.uk

Recycling & Waste Minimisation: Mr Robert Heathcock, Joint Environmental Services Manager, City Offices, Colebrook Street, Winchester SO23 9LJ ☎ 01730 234383 ⏚ rob.heathcock@easthants.gov.uk

Staff Training: Ms Alison Gavin, Head of Organisational Development, City Offices, Colebrook Street, Winchester SO23 9LJ ☎ 01962 840222 ⏚ agavin@winchester.gov.uk

Street Scene: Mr Dave Brockway, Head of Streetcare & Drainage, City Offices, Colebrook Street, Winchester SO23 9LJ ☎ 01962 856412 ⏚ dbrockway@winchester.gov.uk

Tourism: Ms Ellen Simpson, Head of Tourism, City Offices, Colebrook Street, Winchester SO23 9LJ ☎ 01962 848219 ⏚ esimpson@winchester.gov.uk

Town Centre: Ms Heidi Isa, Market Towns Development Officer, City Offices, Colebrook Street, Winchester SO23 9LJ ☎ 01962 848069 ⏚ hisa@winchester.gov.uk

Traffic Management: Mr Simon Finch,, Assistant Director - Environment, City Offices, Colebrook Street, Winchester SO23 9LJ ☎ 01962 840222 ⏚ sfinch@winchester.gov.uk

Transport: Mr Simon Finch, Assistant Director - Environment, City Offices, Colebrook Street, Winchester SO23 9LJ ☎ 01962 840222 ✆ sfinch@winchester.gov.uk

Transport: Mr Dave Howarth, Payroll & Fleet Manager, City Offices, Colebrook Street, Winchester SO23 9LJ ☎ 01962 848157 ✆ dhowarth@winchester.gov.uk

Transport Planner: Mr Simon Finch, Assistant Director - Environment, City Offices, Colebrook Street, Winchester SO23 9LJ ☎ 01962 840222 ✆ sfinch@winchester.gov.uk

Waste Collection and Disposal: Mr Robert Heathcock, Joint Environmental Services Manager, City Offices, Colebrook Street, Winchester SO23 9LJ ☎ 01730 234383 ✆ rob.heathcock@easthants.gov.uk

Waste Management: Mr Robert Heathcock, Joint Environmental Services Manager, City Offices, Colebrook Street, Winchester SO23 9LJ ☎ 01730 234383 ✆ rob.heathcock@easthants.gov.uk

Children's Play Areas: Ms Susan Croker, Head of Landscapes & Open Spaces, City Offices, Colebrook Street, Winchester SO23 9LJ ☎ 01962 848419 ✆ scroker@winchester.gov.uk

COUNCILLORS

Mayor: Rutter, Jane (LD - The Worthys)
jrutter@winchester.gov.uk

Leader of the Council: Godfrey, Stephen (CON - Wonston & Micheldever)
sgodfrey@winchester.gov.uk

Deputy Leader of the Council: Weston, Victoria (CON - Central Meon Valley)
vweston@winchester.gov.uk

Achwal, Vivian (LD - Whiteley & Shedfield)
vachwal@winchester.gov.uk

Ashton, Guy (CON - St. Michael)
gashton@winchester.gov.uk

Bell, Eleanor (LD - Badger Farm & Olivers Battery)
ebell@winchester.gov.uk

Bentote, Roger (LD - Whiteley & Shedfield)
rbentote@winchester.gov.uk

Berry, Eileen (CON - St. Barnabas)
eberry@winchester.gov.uk

Brook, Caroline (CON - Denmead)
cbrook@winchester.gov.uk

Burns, Rosemary (CON - St. Bartholomew)
rburns@winchester.gov.uk

Byrnes, James (CON - Wonston & Micheldever)
jbyrnes@winchester.gov.uk

Clear, Angela (LD - Southwick & Wickham)
aclear@winchester.gov.uk

Cook, Susan (CON - Colden Common & Twyford)
sjcook@winchester.gov.uk

Cutler, Neil (LD - Southwick & Wickham)
ncutler@winchester.gov.uk

Elks, Nicki (LD - St. Bartholomew)
nelks@winchester.gov.uk

Evens, Therese (LD - Southwick & Wickham)
tevans@winchester.gov.uk

Gemmell, Linda (CON - Central Meon Valley)
lgemmell@winchester.gov.uk

Gottlieb, Kim (CON - Alresford & Itchen Valley)
kgottlieb@winchester.gov.uk

Green, Derek (LD - St. Luke)
dgreen@winchester.gov.uk

Griffiths, Lisa (CON - Alresford & Itchen Valley)
lgriffiths@winchester.gov.uk

Hiscock, Dominic (LD - St. Bartholomew)
dhiscock@winchester.gov.uk

Horrill, Caroline (CON - Wonston & Micheldever)
chorrill@winchester.gov.uk

Humby, Robert (CON - Bishops Waltham)
rhumby@winchester.gov.uk

Hutchinson, Liz (LD - St. Paul)
lhutchinson@winchester.gov.uk

Izard, Richard (LD - Colden Common & Twyford)
rizard@winchester.gov.uk

Jeffs, Ernest (CON - Alresford & Itchen Valley)
ejeffs@winchester.gov.uk

Laming, Brian (LD - Badger Farm & Olivers Battery)
blaming@winchester.gov.uk

Learney, Kelsie (LD - St. Barnabas)
klearney@winchester.gov.uk

Mather, Fiona (CON - St. Michael)
fmather@winchester.gov.uk

McLean, David (CON - Bishops Waltham)
dmclean@winchester.gov.uk

Miller, Steve (CON - Bishops Waltham)
smiller@winchester.gov.uk

Pearson, Frank (CON - Central Meon Valley)
fpearson@winchester.gov.uk

Porter, Jackie (LD - The Worthys)
jporter3@winchester.gov.uk

Prince, Malcolm (LD - The Worthys)
mprince@winchester.gov.uk

Read, Michael (CON - Denmead)
mread@winchester.gov.uk

Ruffell, Lawrence (CON - Upper Meon Valley)
lruffell@winchester.gov.uk

Scott, Jamie (LD - St. Luke)
jscott@winchester.gov.uk

Stallard, Patricia (CON - Denmead)
pstallard@winchester.gov.uk

Tait, Ian (CON - St. Michael)
itait@winchester.gov.uk

Thacker, Amber (CON - Upper Meon Valley)
athacker@winchester.gov.uk

Thompson, Lucille (LD - St. Paul)
lthompson@winchester.gov.uk

Tod, Martin (LD - St. Paul)
mtod@winchester.gov.uk

WINCHESTER CITY

Warwick, Jan (CON - Badger Farm & Olivers Battery)
jwarwick@winchester.gov.uk

Weir, Anne (LD - St. Barnabas)
aweir@winchester.gov.uk

POLITICAL COMPOSITION
CON: 24, LD: 20

Windsor & Maidenhead   U

The Royal Borough of Windsor & Maidenhead, Town Hall, St.
Ives Road, Maidenhead SL6 1RF
☎ 01628 798888 🖷 01628 796408 🖳 www.rbwm.gov.uk

FACTS AND FIGURES
Parliamentary Constituencies: Maidenhead, Windsor
EU Constituencies: South East
Election Frequency: Elections are of whole council

PRINCIPAL OFFICERS

Chief Executive: Ms Alison Alexander, Managing Director /
Strategic Director - Adults, Children & Health, Town Hall, St. Ives
Road, Maidenhead SL6 1RF ☎ 01628 796671
🕭 alison.alexander@rbwm.gov.uk

Senior Management: Mr Simon Fletcher, Strategic Director -
Operations, Town Hall, St. Ives Road, Maidenhead SL6 1RF
☎ 01628 796484 🕭 simon.fletcher@rbwm.gov.uk

Senior Management: Mr Russell O'Keefe, Strategic Director
- Corporate & Community Services, Town Hall, St. Ives Road,
Maidenhead SL6 1RF ☎ 01628 795521
🕭 russell.o'keefe@rbwm.gov.uk

Access Officer / Social Services (Disability): Mrs Debbie
Verity, Learning Difficulties & Disabilities Service Manager, York
House, Sheet Street, Windsor SL4 1DD ☎ 01628 683680
🕭 debbie.verity@rbwm.gov.uk

Best Value: Mr David Scott, Interim Strategic Director - Resources,
Town Hall, St. Ives Road, Maidenhead SL6 1RF ☎ 01628 796748
🕭 david.scott@rbwm.gov.uk

Children / Youth Services: Ms Alison Alexander, Strategic
Director - Children's Services, Town Hall, St. Ives Road, Maidenhead
SL6 1RF ☎ 01628 796671 🕭 alison.alexander@rbwm.gov.uk

Children / Youth Services: Mr Kevin McDaniel, Head of Schools
& Educational Services, Town Hall, St. Ives Road, Maidenhead
SL6 1RF 🕭 kevin.mcdaniel@rbwm.gov.uk

Civil Registration: Ms Clair Coe, Superintendent Registrar, Town
Hall, St. Ives Road, Maidenhead SL6 1RF ☎ 01628 796101
🕭 clair.williams@rbwm.gov.uk

PR / Communications: Ms Louisa Dean, Communications &
Marketing Manager, Town Hall, St. Ives Road, Maidenhead SL6 1RF
☎ 01628 796410 🕭 louisa.dean@rbwm.gov.uk

Community Planning: Ms Jenifer Jackson, Borough Planning
Manager, Town Hall, St. Ives Road, Maidenhead SL6 1RF
☎ 01628 796042 🕭 jenifer.jackson@rbwm.gov.uk

Community Safety: Mr Christopher Nash, Community Protection
Principal, Town Hall, St. Ives Road, Maidenhead SL6 1RF
☎ 01628 683645 🕭 christopher.nash@rbwm.gov.uk

Consumer Protection and Trading Standards: Mr Steve
Johnson, Trading Standards Manager, York House, Sheet Street,
Windsor SL4 1DD ☎ 01628 683555 🕭 steve.johnson@rbwm.gov.uk

Corporate Services: Mr Russell O'Keefe, Strategic Director
- Corporate & Community Services, Town Hall, St. Ives Road,
Maidenhead SL6 1RF ☎ 01628 795521
🕭 russell.o'keefe@rbwm.gov.uk

Customer Service: Ms Jacqui Hurd, Head of Customer Services,
Town Hall, St. Ives Road, Maidenhead SL6 1RF ☎ 01628 683969
🕭 jacqui.hurd@rbwm.gov.uk

Customer Service: Mr Andy Jeffs, Benefits & Business Service
Lead, Town Hall, St. Ives Road, Maidenhead SL6 1RF
🕭 andy.jeffs@rbwm.gov.uk

Economic Development: Mr Harjit Hunjan, Community &
Business Partnerships Manager, Town Hall, St. Ives Road,
Maidenhead SL6 1RF ☎ 01628 796947 🕭 harjit.hunjan@rbwm.gov.uk

Education: Ms Alison Alexander, Strategic Director - Children's
Services, Town Hall, St. Ives Road, Maidenhead SL6 1RF
☎ 01628 796671 🕭 alison.alexander@rbwm.gov.uk

Electoral Registration: Ms Suzanne Martin, Electoral Services
Manager, Town Hall, St. Ives Road, Maidenhead SL6 1RF
☎ 01628 682935 🕭 suzanne.martin@rbwm.gov.uk

Emergency Planning: Mr Craig Miller, Head of Community
Protection & Enforcement, York House, Sheet Street, Windsor
SL4 1DD ☎ 01628 683598 🕭 craig.miller@rbwm.gov.uk

Energy Management: Mr Craig Miller, Head of Community
Protection & Enforcement, York House, Sheet Street, Windsor
SL4 1DD ☎ 01628 683598 🕭 craig.miller@rbwm.gov.uk

Environmental Health: Ms Lisa Pigeon, Environmental Health
Lead, York House, Sheet Street, Windsor LS4 1DD
☎ 07970 446523 🕭 lisa.pigeon@rbwm.gov.uk

Estates, Property & Valuation: Mr Mark Shephard,
Regeneration & Property Service Lead, Town Hall, St. Ives Road,
Maidenhead SL6 1RF 🕭 mark.shephard@rbwm.gov.uk

Events Manager: Ms Julia White, Visitor Marketing Manager, York
House, Sheet Street, Windsor SL4 1DD ☎ 01753 743918
🕭 julia.white@rbwm.gov.uk

Facilities: Mr Dean Graham, Front of House Team Leader, Town
Hall, St. Ives Road, Maidenhead SL6 1RF ☎ 01628 796409
🕭 dean.graham@rbwm.gov.uk

Pensions: Mr Nick Greenwood, Pension Fund Manager, Town
Hall, St. Ives Road, Maidenhead SL6 1RF ☎ 01628 796701
🕭 nick.greenwood@rbwm.gov.uk

Pensions: Mr Pedro Pardo-Ecija, Investment Manager, Town Hall, St. Ives Road, Maidenhead SL6 1RF ☎ 01628 796704 ✆ pedro.pardo@rbwm.gov.uk

Pensions: Mr Kevin Taylor, Pensions Administrations Manager, Town Hall, St. Ives Road, Maidenhead SL6 1RF ☎ 01628 796747 ✆ kevin.taylor@rbwm.gov.uk

Fleet Management: Mr Mark Green, Fleet Management Officer, York House, Sheet Street, Windsor SL4 1DD ☎ 01628 796821 ✆ mark.green@rbwm.gov.uk

Health and Safety: Mr Terry Baldwin, Head of HR, Town Hall, St. Ives Road, Maidenhead SL6 1RF ☎ 01628 795622 ✆ terry.baldwin@rbwm.gov.uk

Highways: Mr Simon Fletcher, Strategic Director - Operations, Town Hall, St. Ives Road, Maidenhead SL6 1RF ☎ 01628 796484 ✆ simon.fletcher@rbwm.gov.uk

Highways: Mr Ben Smith, Head of Highways & Transport, Town Hall, St. Ives Road, Maidenhead SL6 1RF ☎ 01628 796147 ✆ ben.smith@rbwm.gov.uk

Home Energy Conservation: Mr Martyn Clemence, Housing Project Officer, York House, Sheet Street, Windsor SL4 1DD ☎ 01628 683596 ✆ martyn.clemence@rbwm.gov.uk

Housing: Ms Jacqui Hurd, Head of Customer Services, Town Hall, St. Ives Road, Maidenhead SL6 1RF ☎ 01628 683969 ✆ jacqui.hurd@rbwm.gov.uk

Local Area Agreement: Mr Harjit Hunjan, Community & Business Partnerships Manager, Town Hall, St. Ives Road, Maidenhead SL6 1RF ☎ 01628 796947 ✆ harjit.hunjan@rbwm.gov.uk

Lighting: Mr Ben Smith, Head of Highways & Transport, Town Hall, St. Ives Road, Maidenhead SL6 1RF ☎ 01628 796147 ✆ ben.smith@rbwm.gov.uk

Lottery Funding, Charity and Voluntary: Mr Harjit Hunjan, Community & Business Partnerships Manager, Town Hall, St. Ives Road, Maidenhead SL6 1RF ☎ 01628 796947 ✆ harjit.hunjan@rbwm.gov.uk

Member Services: Ms Karen Shepherd, Democratic Services Manager, Town Hall, St. Ives Road, Maidenhead SL6 1RF ☎ 01628 796529 ✆ karen.shepherd@rbwm.gov.uk

Parking: Mr Neil Walter, Parking Principal, Town Hall, St. Ives Road, Maidenhead SL6 1RF ☎ 01628 796485 ✆ neil.walter@rbwm.gov.uk

Partnerships: Mr Harjit Hunjan, Community & Business Partnerships Manager, Town Hall, St. Ives Road, Maidenhead SL6 1RF ☎ 01628 796947 ✆ harjit.hunjan@rbwm.gov.uk

Personnel / HR: Mr Terry Baldwin, Head of HR, Town Hall, St. Ives Road, Maidenhead SL6 1RF ☎ 01628 795622 ✆ terry.baldwin@rbwm.gov.uk

Planning: Mr Chris Hilton, Director - Development & Regeneration, Town Hall, St. Ives Road, Maidenhead SL6 1RF ☎ 01628 685712 ✆ chris.hilton@rbwm.gov.uk

Public Libraries: Mr Mark Taylor, Head of Library, Information Heritage & Arts Service, Maidenhead Library, St. Ives Road, Maidenhead SL6 1RF ☎ 01628 796989 ✆ mark.taylor@rbwm.gov.uk

Recycling & Waste Minimisation: Mr Craig Miller, Head of Community Protection & Enforcement, York House, Sheet Street, Windsor SL4 1DD ☎ 01628 683598 ✆ craig.miller@rbwm.gov.uk

Recycling & Waste Minimisation: Mr Steve Westbrooke, Service Development Team Leader, Town Hall, St. Ives Road, Maidenhead SL6 1RF ☎ 01628 683556 ✆ steve.westbrooke@rbwm.gov.uk

Regeneration: Mr Chris Hilton, Director - Development & Regeneration, Town Hall, St. Ives Road, Maidenhead SL6 1RF ☎ 01628 685712 ✆ chris.hilton@rbwm.gov.uk

Road Safety: Mr Anthony Carr, Traffic & Road Safety Manager, Town Hall, St. Ives Road, Maidenhead SL6 1RF ☎ 01628 796405 ✆ tony.carr@rbwm.gov.uk

Social Services (Adult): Mr Nick Davies, Service Leader - Commissioning Adults, Children & Health, York House, Sheet Street, Windsor SL4 1BY ☎ 01628 683614 ✆ nick.davies@rbwm.gov.uk

Social Services (Adult): Ms Angela Morris, Head of Adult Social Care & Health Partnerships, Town Hall, St. Ives Road, Maidenhead SL6 1RF ✆ angela.morris@rbwm.gov.uk

Social Services (Children): Ms Alison Alexander, Managing Director / Strategic Director - Adults, Children & Health, Town Hall, St. Ives Road, Maidenhead SL6 1RF ☎ 01628 796671 ✆ alison.alexander@rbwm.gov.uk

Staff Training: Mr Terry Baldwin, Head of HR, Town Hall, St. Ives Road, Maidenhead SL6 1RF ☎ 01628 795622 ✆ terry.baldwin@rbwm.gov.uk

Street Scene: Mr Ben Smith, Head of Highways & Transport, Town Hall, St. Ives Road, Maidenhead SL6 1RF ☎ 01628 796147 ✆ ben.smith@rbwm.gov.uk

Tourism: Ms Barbara Hunt, Accommodation & Information Manager, York House, Sheet Street, Windsor SL4 1DD ☎ 01753 743909 ✆ barbara.hunt@rbwm.gov.uk

Town Centre: Ms Steph James, Maidenhead Town Manager, Town Hall, St. Ives Road, Maidenhead SL6 1RF ☎ 01628 796128 ✆ steph.james@rbwm.gov.uk

Town Centre: Mr Kevin Mist, Head of Communications & Economic Development, Town Hall, St. Ives Road, Maidenhead SL6 1RF ☎ 01628 796443 ✆ kevin.mist@rbwm.gov.uk

Town Centre: Mr Paul Roach, Windsor Town Manager, York House, Sheet Street, Windsor SL4 1DD ☎ 01753 743921 ✆ paul.roach@rbwm.gov.uk

WINDSOR & MAIDENHEAD

Waste Collection and Disposal: Ms Naomi Markham, Waste Strategy Manager, York House, Sheet Street, Windsor SL4 1DD
📧 naomi.markham@rbwm.gov.uk

COUNCILLORS

Leader of the Council: Burbage, David (CON - Bray)
cllr.burbage@rbwm.gov.uk

Deputy Leader of the Council: Bicknell, Phillip (CON - Park)
cllr.bicknell@rbwm.gov.uk

Deputy Leader of the Council: Dudley, Simon (CON - Maidenhead Riverside)
cllr.dudley@rbwm.gov.uk

Airey, Natasha (CON - Park)
cllr.airey@rbwm.gov.uk

Airey, Michael (CON - Clewer South)
cllr.m.airey@rbwm.gov.uk

Alexander, Malcolm (CON - Eton & Castle)
cllr.alexander@rbwm.gov.uk

Bateson, Christine (CON - Sunningdale)
cllr.bateson@rbwm.gov.uk

Bathurst, George (CON - Sunninghill & South Ascot)
cllr.bathurst@rbwm.gov.uk

Beer, Malcolm (R - Old Windsor)
cllr.beer@rbwm.gov.uk

Bhatti, Hashim (CON - Clewer North)
cllr.bhatti@rbwm.gov.uk

Bowden, John (CON - Clewer East)
cllr.bowden@rbwm.gov.uk

Brimacombe, Paul (CON - Cox Green)
cllr.brimacombe@rbwm.gov.uk

Bullock, Clive (CON - Cox Green)
cllr.bullock@rbwm.gov.uk

Carroll, Stuart (CON - Boyn Hill)
cllr.carroll@rbwm.gov.uk

Clark, Gerry (CON - Bisham & Cookham)
cllr.clark@rbwm.gov.uk

Collins, John (CON - Clewer North)
cllr.collins@rbwm.gov.uk

Coppinger, David (CON - Bray)
cllr.coppinger@rbwm.gov.uk

Cox, Carwyn (CON - Hurley & Walthams)
cllr.cox@rbwm.gov.uk

Evans, David (CON - Hurley & Walthams)
cllr.d.evans@rbwm.gov.uk

Evans, Lilly (CON - Ascot & Cheapside)
cllr.l.evans@rbwm.gov.uk

Gilmore, Marius (CON - Pinkneys Green)
cllr.gilmore@rbwm.gov.uk

Grey, Jesse (CON - Datchet)
cllr.grey@rbwm.gov.uk

Hill, Geoffrey (CON - Oldfield)
cllr.hill@rbwm.gov.uk

Hilton, David (CON - Ascot & Cheapside)
cllr.hilton@rbwm.gov.uk

Hollingsworth, Charles (CON - Pinkneys Green)
cllr.hollingsworth@rbwm.gov.uk

Hunt, Maureen (CON - Hurley & Walthams)
cllr.hunt@rbwm.gov.uk

Ilyas, Mohammed (CON - Furze Platt)
cllr.ilyas@rbwm.gov.uk

Jenner, Andrew (CON - Maidenhead Riverside)
cllr.jenner@rbwm.gov.uk

Jones, Lynne (R - Old Windsor)
cllr.jones@rbwm.gov.uk

Kellaway, Richard (CON - Bisham & Cookham)
cllr.kellaway@rbwm.gov.uk

Lenton, John (CON - Horton & Wraysbury)
cllr.lenton@rbwm.gov.uk

Lion, Paul (CON - Boyn Hill)
cllr.lion@rbwm.gov.uk

Love, Philip (CON - Belmont)
cllr.love@rbwm.gov.uk

Luxton, Sayonara (CON - Sunningdale)
cllr.luxton@rbwm.gov.uk

Majeed, Ashgar (CON - Oldfield)
cllr.majeed@rbwm.gov.uk

McWilliams, Ross (CON - Cox Green)
cllr.mcwilliams@rbwm.gov.uk

Mills, Marion (CON - Belmont)
cllr.mills@rbwm.gov.uk

Muir, Gary (CON - Datchet)
cllr.muir@rbwm.gov.uk

Pryer, Nicola (CON - Clewer North)
cllr.pryer@rbwm.gov.uk

Quick, Eileen (CON - Clewer East)
cllr.quick@rbwm.gov.uk

Rankin, Jack (CON - Castle Without)
cllr.rankin@rbwm.gov.uk

Rayner, Samantha (CON - Eton Wick)
cllr.s.rayner@rbwm.gov.uk

Rayner, Colin (CON - Horton & Wraysbury)
cllr.rayner@rbwm.gov.uk

Richards, Wesley (CON - Castle Without)
cllr.richards@rbwm.gov.uk

Saunders, MJ (CON - Bisham & Cookham)
cllr.saunders@rbwm.gov.uk

Sharma, Hari (CON - Furze Platt)
cllr.sharma@rbwm.gov.uk

Sharp, Derek (CON - Furze Platt)
cllr.sharp@rbwm.gov.uk

Shelim, Shamsul (CON - Castle Without)
cllr.shelim@rbwm.gov.uk

Smith, Adam (CON - Maidenhead Riverside)
cllr.smith@rbwm.gov.uk

Story, John (CON - Sunninghill & South Ascot)
cllr.story@rbwm.gov.uk

Stretton, Claire (CON - Boyn Hill)
cllr.claire.stretton@rbwm.gov.uk

Targowska, Lisa (CON - Belmont)
cllr.targowska@rbwm.gov.uk

Walters, Leo (CON - Bray)
cllr.walters@rbwm.gov.uk

Werner, Simon (LD - Pinkneys Green)
cllr.werner@rbwm.gov.uk

Wilson, Derek (CON - Oldfield)
cllr.d.wilson@rbwm.gov.uk

Wilson, Edward (CON - Clewer South)
cllr.e.wilson@rbwm.gov.uk

Yong, Lynda (CON - Sunninghill & South Ascot)
cllr.yong@rbwm.gov.uk

POLITICAL COMPOSITION
CON: 54, R: 2, LD: 1

COMMITTEE CHAIRS

Audit & Performance: Mr Paul Brimacombe

Licensing: Mr Ashgar Majeed

Wirral   M

Wirral Metropolitan Borough Council, Wallasey Town Hall, Brighton Street, Wallasey, Wirral CH44 8ED
☎ 0151 606 2000 ▤ 0151 691 8468 ⏚ comments@wirral.gov.uk
🖥 www.wirral.gov.uk

FACTS AND FIGURES
Parliamentary Constituencies: Birkenhead, Wallasey, Wirral South, Wirral West
EU Constituencies: North West
Election Frequency: Elections are by thirds

PRINCIPAL OFFICERS

Chief Executive: Mr Eric Robinson, Chief Executive, Wallasey Town Hall, Brighton Street, Wallasey, Wirral CH44 8ED
☎ 0151 691 8589 ⏚ ericrobinson@wirral.gov.uk

Assistant Chief Executive: Mr David Armstrong, Assistant Chief Executive & Head of Asset Management, Hamilton Buildings, Conway Street, Birkenhead CH41 4FD ☎ 0151 666 4300
⏚ davidarmstrong@wirral.gov.uk

Senior Management: Mr Joe Blott, Strategic Director - Transformation & Resources, Wallasey Town Hall, Brighton Street, Wallasey, Wirral CH44 8ED ☎ 0151 606 2000
⏚ joeblott@wirral.gov.uk

Senior Management: Ms Clare Fish, Strategic Director - Families & Wellbeing, Wallasey Town Hall, Brighton Street, Wallasey, Wirral CH44 8ED ☎ 0151 666 2082 ⏚ clarefish@wirral.gov.uk

Access Officer / Social Services (Disability): Mr David Armstrong, Assistant Chief Executive & Head of Asset Management, Hamilton Buildings, Conway Street, Birkenhead CH41 4FD ☎ 0151 666 4300 ⏚ davidarmstrong@wirral.gov.uk

Architect, Building / Property Services: Mr David Armstrong, Assistant Chief Executive & Head of Asset Management, Hamilton Buildings, Conway Street, Birkenhead CH41 4FD ☎ 0151 666 4300 ⏚ davidarmstrong@wirral.gov.uk

Best Value: Mr Joe Blott, Strategic Director - Transformation & Resources, Wallasey Town Hall, Brighton Street, Wallasey, Wirral CH44 8ED ☎ 0151 606 2000 ⏚ joeblott@wirral.gov.uk

Building Control: Mr David Ball, Head of Regeneration & Environment, Wallasey Town Hall, North Annexe, Brighton Street, Wirral CH44 8ED ☎ 0151 691 8395 ⏚ davidball@wirral.gov.uk

Children / Youth Services: Ms Julia Hassall, Director - Children's Services, Hamilton Buildings, Conway Street, Birkenhead CH41 4FD ☎ 0151 666 4288 ⏚ juliahassall@wirral.gov.uk

Civil Registration: Ms Suzanne Johnston, Superintendent Registrar, Town Hall, Brighton Street, Wallasey CH44 8ED ☎ 0151 666 3679 ⏚ suzannejohnston@wirral.gov.uk

PR / Communications: Mr David Armstrong, Assistant Chief Executive & Head of Asset Management, Hamilton Buildings, Conway Street, Birkenhead CH41 4FD ☎ 0151 666 4300 ⏚ davidarmstrong@wirral.gov.uk

Community Planning: Mr David Armstrong, Assistant Chief Executive & Head of Asset Management, Hamilton Buildings, Conway Street, Birkenhead CH41 4FD ☎ 0151 666 4300 ⏚ davidarmstrong@wirral.gov.uk

Community Safety: Mr Mark Camborne, Head of Corporate & Community Safety, Cheshire Lines Building, Canning Street, Birkenhead CH41 8ED ☎ 0151 606 2071 ⏚ markcamborne@wirral.gov.uk

Computer Management: Mr Mike Zammit, Chief Information Officer, PO Box 2, Treasury Building, Cleveland Street, Birkenhead CH41 6BU ☎ 0151 666 3029 ⏚ mikezammit@wirral.gov.uk

Consumer Protection and Trading Standards: Mr Colin Clayton, Senior Manager - Environmental Health, South Annexe, Wallasey Town Hall, Brighton Street, Wallasey CH44 8ED ☎ 0151 691 8361 ⏚ colinclayton@wirral.gov.uk

Contracts: Mr Ray Williams, Head of Procurement, Town Hall, Brighton Street, Wallasey, Wirral CH44 8ED ☎ 0151 666 3377 ⏚ raywilliams@wirral.gov.uk

Corporate Services: Mr Joe Blott, Strategic Director - Transformation & Resources, Wallasey Town Hall, Brighton Street, Wallasey, Wirral CH44 8ED ☎ 0151 606 2000 ⏚ joeblott@wirral.gov.uk

Customer Service: Mr Mark Camborne, Head of Corporate & Community Safety, Cheshire Lines Building, Canning Street, Birkenhead CH41 8ED ☎ 0151 606 2071 ⏚ markcamborne@wirral.gov.uk

Economic Development: Mr David Ball, Head of Regeneration & Environment, Town Hall, Brighton Street, Wallasey CH44 8ED ☎ 0151 691 8395 ⏚ davidball@wirral.gov.uk

WIRRAL

Education: Ms Julia Hassall, Director - Children's Services, Social Services Headquarters, Westminster House, Hamilton Street, Birkenhead CH41 5FN ☎ 0151 666 4288 ⏱ juliahassall@wirral.gov.uk

Emergency Planning: Mr Mark Camborne, Head of Corporate & Community Safety, Cheshire Lines Building, Canning Street, Birkenhead CH41 8ED ☎ 0151 606 2071 ⏱ markcamborne@wirral.gov.uk

Energy Management: Mr David Armstrong, Assistant Chief Executive & Head of Asset Management, Hamilton Buildings, Conway Street, Birkenhead CH41 4FD ☎ 0151 666 4300 ⏱ davidarmstrong@wirral.gov.uk

Environmental / Technical Services: Mr Mark Smith, Head of Environment & Regulation, Cheshire Lines Building, Canning Street, Birkenhead CH41 8ED ☎ 0151 606 2103 ⏱ marksmith@wirral.gov.uk

Environmental Health: Mr Mark Smith, Head of Environment & Regulation, Cheshire Lines Building, Canning Street, Birkenhead CH41 8ED ☎ 0151 606 2103 ⏱ marksmith@wirral.gov.uk

Estates, Property & Valuation: Mr David Armstrong, Assistant Chief Executive & Head of Asset Management, Hamilton Buildings, Conway Street, Birkenhead CH41 4FD ☎ 0151 666 4300 ⏱ davidarmstrong@wirral.gov.uk

European Liaison: Mr David Ball, Head of Regeneration & Environment, Town Hall, Brighton Street, Wallasey CH44 8ED ☎ 0151 691 8395 ⏱ davidball@wirral.gov.uk

Events Manager: Mr David Armstrong, Assistant Chief Executive & Head of Asset Management, Hamilton Buildings, Conway Street, Birkenhead CH41 4FD ☎ 0151 666 4300 ⏱ davidarmstrong@wirral.gov.uk

Facilities: Mr David Armstrong, Assistant Chief Executive & Head of Asset Management, Hamilton Buildings, Conway Street, Birkenhead CH41 4FD ☎ 0151 666 4300 ⏱ davidarmstrong@wirral.gov.uk

Finance: Mr Tom Sault, Acting S151 Officer & Head of Financial Services, Wallasey Town Hall, Brighton Street, Wallasey, Wirral CH44 8ED ☎ 0151 666 3056 ⏱ tomsault@wirral.gov.uk

Pensions: Mr Peter Wallach, Head of Merseyside Pension Fund, 7th Floor, Castle Chambers, 43 Castle Street, Liverpool L69 2NW ☎ 0151 242 1390 ⏱ peterwallach@wirral.gov.uk

Grounds Maintenance: Ms Mary Worrall, Service Manager - Parks & Countryside Services, Cheshire Lines Building, Canning Street, Birkenhead CH41 1ND ☎ 0151 606 2210 ⏱ maryworrall@wirral.gov.uk

Health and Safety: Mr Andy McMillan, Health & Safety Manager, Cheshire Lines Building, Canning Street, Birkenhead CH41 1ND ☎ 0151 606 2364 ⏱ andymcmillan@wirral.gov.uk

Highways: Mr Mark Smith, Head of Environment & Regulation, Cheshire Lines Building, Canning Street, Birkenhead CH41 8ED ☎ 0151 606 2103 ⏱ marksmith@wirral.gov.uk

Home Energy Conservation: Mr David Armstrong, Assistant Chief Executive & Head of Asset Management, Hamilton Buildings, Conway Street, Birkenhead CH41 4FD ☎ 0151 666 4300 ⏱ davidarmstrong@wirral.gov.uk

Housing: Mr Ian Platt, Head of Housing, North Annexe, Town Hall, Brighton Street, Wallasey CH44 8ED ☎ 0151 691 8208 ⏱ ianplatt@wirral.gov.uk

Local Area Agreement: Ms Lucy Barrow, Senior Policy Manager, Wallasey Town Hall, Brighton Street, Wallasey CH44 8ED ☎ 0151 691 8006 ⏱ lucybarrow@wirral.gov.uk

Legal: Mr Surjit Tour, Head of Legal & Member Services / Monitoring Officer, Wallasey Town Hall, Brighton Street, Wallasey, Wirral CH44 8ED ☎ 0151 691 8569 ⏱ surjittour@wirral.gov.uk

Leisure and Cultural Services: Ms Clare Fish, Strategic Director - Families & Wellbeing, Wallasey Town Hall, Brighton Street, Wallasey, Wirral CH44 8ED ☎ 0151 666 2082 ⏱ clarefish@wirral.gov.uk

Licensing: Mrs Margaret O'Donnell, Licensing Manager, Town Hall, Brighton Street, Wallasey CH44 8ED ☎ 0151 691 8606 ⏱ margaretodonnell@wirral.gov.uk

Lifelong Learning: Ms Julia Hassall, Director - Children's Services, Social Services Headquarters, Westminster House, Hamilton Street, Birkenhead CH41 5FN ☎ 0151 666 4288 ⏱ juliahassall@wirral.gov.uk

Lighting: Mr Mark Smith, Head of Environment & Regulation, Cheshire Lines Building, Canning Street, Birkenhead CH41 8ED ☎ 0151 606 2103 ⏱ marksmith@wirral.gov.uk

Lottery Funding, Charity and Voluntary: Mr David Armstrong, Assistant Chief Executive & Head of Asset Management, Hamilton Buildings, Conway Street, Birkenhead CH41 4FD ☎ 0151 666 4300 ⏱ davidarmstrong@wirral.gov.uk

Member Services: Mr Surjit Tour, Head of Legal & Member Services / Monitoring Officer, Wallasey Town Hall, Brighton Street, Wallasey, Wirral CH44 8ED ☎ 0151 691 8569 ⏱ surjittour@wirral.gov.uk

Parking: Mr Mark Smith, Head of Environment & Regulation, Cheshire Lines Building, Canning Street, Birkenhead CH41 8ED ☎ 0151 606 2103 ⏱ marksmith@wirral.gov.uk

Personnel / HR: Mrs Chris Hyams, Head of Human Resources & Organisational Development, Wallasey Town Hall, Brighton Street, Wallasey, Wirral CH44 8ED ☎ 0151 691 8590 ⏱ chrishyams@wirral.gov.uk

Planning: Mr David Ball, Head of Regeneration & Environment, Town Hall, Brighton Street, Wallasey CH44 8ED ☎ 0151 691 8395 ⏱ davidball@wirral.gov.uk

Procurement: Mr Ray Williams, Head of Procurement, Town Hall, Brighton Street, Wallasey, Wirral CH44 8ED ☎ 0151 666 3377 ⏱ raywilliams@wirral.gov.uk

Public Libraries: Ms Julie Williams, Customer Services Manager, Town Hall, Brighton Street, Wallasey CH44 8ED ☎ 0151 691 8629 ✆ juliewilliams@wirral.gov.uk

Recycling & Waste Minimisation: Mr Mark Smith, Head of Environment & Regulation, Cheshire Lines Building, Canning Street, Birkenhead CH41 8ED ☎ 0151 606 2103 ✆ marksmith@wirral.gov.uk

Regeneration: Mr David Ball, Head of Regeneration & Environment, Town Hall, Brighton Street, Wallasey CH44 8ED ☎ 0151 691 8395 ✆ davidball@wirral.gov.uk

Road Safety: Mr Mark Smith, Head of Environment & Regulation, Cheshire Lines Building, Canning Street, Birkenhead CH41 8ED ☎ 0151 606 2103 ✆ marksmith@wirral.gov.uk

Social Services: Mr Graham Hodkinson, Director - Adult Social Services, PO Box 351, Social Services Headquarters, Birkenhead CH25 9EF ☎ 0151 666 3632 ✆ grahamhodkinson@wirral.gov.uk

Social Services (Adult): Mr Graham Hodkinson, Director - Adult Social Services, PO Box 351, Social Services Headquarters, Birkenhead CH25 9EF ☎ 0151 666 3632 ✆ grahamhodkinson@wirral.gov.uk

Social Services (Children): Ms Julia Hassall, Director - Children's Services, Social Services Headquarters, Westminster House, Hamilton Street, Birkenhead CH41 5FN ☎ 0151 666 4288 ✆ juliahassall@wirral.gov.uk

Staff Training: Mrs Chris Hyams, Head of Human Resources & Organisational Development, Wallasey Town Hall, Brighton Street, Wallasey, Wirral CH44 8ED ☎ 0151 691 8590 ✆ chrishyams@wirral.gov.uk

Street Scene: Mr Mark Smith, Head of Environment & Regulation, Cheshire Lines Building, Canning Street, Birkenhead CH41 8ED ☎ 0151 606 2103 ✆ marksmith@wirral.gov.uk

Sustainable Communities: Mr David Armstrong, Assistant Chief Executive & Head of Asset Management, Hamilton Buildings, Conway Street, Birkenhead CH41 4FD ☎ 0151 666 4300 ✆ davidarmstrong@wirral.gov.uk

Sustainable Development: Mr David Armstrong, Assistant Chief Executive & Head of Asset Management, Hamilton Buildings, Conway Street, Birkenhead CH41 4FD ☎ 0151 666 4300 ✆ davidarmstrong@wirral.gov.uk

Tourism: Mr David Armstrong, Assistant Chief Executive & Head of Asset Management, Hamilton Buildings, Conway Street, Birkenhead CH41 4FD ☎ 0151 666 4300 ✆ davidarmstrong@wirral.gov.uk

Town Centre: Mr David Ball, Head of Regeneration & Environment, Town Hall, Brighton Street, Wallasey CH44 8ED ☎ 0151 691 8395 ✆ davidball@wirral.gov.uk

Traffic Management: Mr Robert Clifford, Service Manager - Highway Management, Cheshire Lines, Canning Street, Birkenhead CH41 0ND ☎ 0151 606 2479 ✆ robertclifford@wirral.gov.uk

Transport: Mr David Armstrong, Assistant Chief Executive & Head of Asset Management, Hamilton Buildings, Conway Street, Birkenhead CH41 4FD ☎ 0151 666 4300 ✆ davidarmstrong@wirral.gov.uk

Transport Planner: Mr Mark Smith, Head of Environment & Regulation, Cheshire Lines Building, Canning Street, Birkenhead CH41 8ED ☎ 0151 606 2103 ✆ marksmith@wirral.gov.uk

Waste Collection and Disposal: Mr Mark Smith, Head of Environment & Regulation, Cheshire Lines Building, Canning Street, Birkenhead CH41 8ED ☎ 0151 606 2103 ✆ marksmith@wirral.gov.uk

Waste Management: Mr Mark Smith, Head of Environment & Regulation, Cheshire Lines Building, Canning Street, Birkenhead CH41 8ED ☎ 0151 606 2103 ✆ marksmith@wirral.gov.uk

Children's Play Areas: Ms Mary Worrall, Service Manager - Parks & Countryside Services, Cheshire Lines Building, Canning Street, Birkenhead CH41 1ND ☎ 0151 606 2210 ✆ maryworrall@wirral.gov.uk

COUNCILLORS

Mayor: Rowlands, Les (CON - Heswall)
lesrowlands@wirral.gov.uk

Deputy Mayor: Hackett, Pat (LAB - New Brighton)
pathackett@wirral.gov

Leader of the Council: Davies, Phil (LAB - Birkenhead and Tranmere)
phildavies@wirral.gov.uk

Deputy Leader of the Council: McLachlan, Ann (LAB - Bidston and St James)
annmclachlan@wirral.gov.uk

Group Leader: Gilchrist, Phil (LD - Eastham)
philgilchrist@wirral.gov.uk

Group Leader: Green, Jeff (CON - West Kirby and Thurstaston)
jeffgreen@wirral.gov.uk

Abbey, Ron (LAB - Leasowe and Moreton East)
ronabbey@wirral.gov.uk

Anderson, Tom (CON - Greasby, Frankby and Irby)
tomanderson@wirral.gov.uk

Berry, Bruce (CON - Moreton West and Saughall Massie)
bruceberry@wirral.gov.uk

Blakeley, Chris (CON - Moreton West and Saughall Massie)
chrisblakeley@wirral.gov.uk

Boult, Eddie (CON - Hoylake and Meols)
Eddieboult@wirral.gov.uk

Brighouse, Alan (LD - Oxton)
alanbrighouse@wirral.gov.uk

Brightmore, Phillip (LAB - Pensby and Thingwall)
phillipbrightmore@wirral.gov.uk

Burgess-Joyce, David (CON - Greasby, Frankby and Irby)

Carubia, Chris (LD - Eastham)
chriscarubia@wirral.gov.uk

Cleary, Pat (GRN - Birkenhead and Tranmere)
patcleary@wirral.gov.uk

Clements, Wendy (CON - Greasby, Frankby and Irby)
Wendyclements@wirral.gov.uk

WIRRAL

Crabtree, Jim (LAB - Bidston and St James)
jimcrabtree@wirral.gov.uk

Daniel, Matt (LAB - Liscard)
matthewdaniel@wirral.gov.uk

Davies, George (LAB - Claughton)
georgedavies@wirral.gov.uk

Davies, Bill (LAB - Rock Ferry)
billdavies@wirral.gov.uk

Davies, Angela (LAB - Prenton)
angeladavies@wirral.gov.uk

Doughty, Paul (LAB - Oxton)
pauldoughty@wirral.gov.uk

Elderton, David (CON - West Kirby and Thurstaston)
davidelderton@wirral.gov.uk

Ellis, Gerry (CON - Hoylake and Meols)

Foulkes, Steve (LAB - Claughton)
stevefoulkes@wirral.gov.uk

Fraser, Leah (CON - Wallasey)
leahfraser@wirral.gov.uk

Gregson, Robert (LAB - New Brighton)
robgregson@wirral.gov.uk

Hale, John (CON - Hoylake and Meols)
johnhale@wirral.gov.uk

Hayes, Paul (CON - Wallasey)
paulhayes@wirral.gov.uk

Hodson, Andrew (CON - Heswall)
andrewhodson@wirral.gov.uk

Hodson, Kathy (CON - Heswall)
kathyhodson@wirral.gov.uk

Johnson, Treena (LAB - Leasowe and Moreton East)

Jones, Adrian (LAB - Seacombe)
adrianjones@wirral.gov.uk

Jones, Chris (LAB - Seacombe)
christinejones@wirral.gov.uk

Kenny, Brian (LAB - Bidston and St James)

Leech, Anita (LAB - Leasowe and Moreton East)
anitaleech@wirral.gov.uk

McLaughlin, Moira (LAB - Rock Ferry)
moiramclaughlin@wirral.gov.uk

Meaden, Chris (LAB - Rock Ferry)
chrismeaden@wirral.gov.uk

Mitchell, Dave (LD - Eastham)
davemitchell@wirral.gov.uk

Mooney, Bernie (LAB - Liscard)
berniemooney@wirral.gov.uk

Muspratt, Christina (LAB - Bebington)
christinamuspratt@wirral.gov.uk

Niblock, Steve (LAB - Bromborough)
steveniblock@wirral.gov.uk

Norbury, Tony (LAB - Prenton)
tonynorbury@wirral.gov.uk

Patrick, Matthew (LAB - Upton)
matthewpatrick@wirral.gov.uk

Pilgrim, Tracey (CON - Clatterbridge)
traceysmith1@wirral.gov.uk

Povall, Cherry (CON - Clatterbridge)
cherrypovall@wirral.gov.uk

Realey, Denise (LAB - Prenton)
deniserealey@wirral.gov.uk

Reecejones, Louise (LAB - Pensby and Thingwall)
louisereecejones@wirral.gov.uk

Rennie, Lesley (CON - Wallasey)
lesleyrennie@wirral.gov.uk

Roberts, Denise (LAB - Claughton)
deniseroberts@wirral.gov.uk

Salter, John (LAB - Seacombe)
johnsalter@wirral.gov.uk

Smith, Walter (LAB - Bebington)
waltersmith@wirral.gov.uk

Smith, Tony (LAB - Upton)
tonysmith@wirral.gov.uk

Spriggs, Chris (LAB - New Brighton)
christinespriggs@wirral.gov.uk

Stapleton, Jean (LAB - Birkenhead and Tranmere)
jeanstapleton@wirral.gov.uk

Sullivan, Michael (LAB - Pensby and Thingwall)
mikesullivan@wirral.gov.uk

Sykes, Adam (CON - Clatterbridge)
adamsykes@wirral.gov.uk

Walsh, Joe (LAB - Bromborough)
joewalsh@wirral.gov.uk

Watt, Geoffrey (CON - West Kirby and Thurstaston)
geoffreywatt@wirral.gov.uk

Whittingham, Stuart (LAB - Upton)
stuartw@labour4wirral.gov.uk

Williams, Jerry (LAB - Bebington)
jerrywilliams@wirral.gov.uk

Williams, Irene (LAB - Bromborough)
irenewilliams@wirral.gov.uk

Williams, Steve (CON - Moreton West and Saughall Massie)
stevewilliams@wirral.gov.uk

Williams, Patricia (LD - Oxton)
patriciawilliams@wirral.gov.uk

Williamson, Janette (LAB - Liscard)
janwilliamson@wirral.gov.uk

POLITICAL COMPOSITION
LAB: 39, CON: 21, LD: 5, GRN: 1

COMMITTEE CHAIRS
Audit & Risk: Mr Jim Crabtree

Health & Wellbeing: Mr Phil Davies

Licensing: Mr Bill Davies

Pensions: Mr Paul Doughty

Planning: Ms Anita Leech

Woking   D

Woking Borough Council, Civic Offices, Gloucester Square, Woking GU21 6YL

☎ 01483 755855 🖰 customers@woking.gov.uk 🖳 www.woking.gov.uk

FACTS AND FIGURES
Parliamentary Constituencies: Woking
EU Constituencies: South East
Election Frequency: Elections are by thirds

PRINCIPAL OFFICERS

Chief Executive: Mr Ray Morgan, Chief Executive, Civic Offices, Gloucester Square, Woking GU21 6YL ☎ 01483 743051 🖰 ray.morgan@woking.gov.uk

Deputy Chief Executive: Mr Douglas Spinks, Deputy Chief Executive, Civic Offices, Gloucester Square, Woking GU21 6YL ☎ 01483 743783 🖰 douglas.spinks@woking.gov.uk

Senior Management: Ms Sue Barham, Strategic Director, Civic Offices, Gloucester Square, Woking GU21 6YL ☎ 01483 743810 🖰 sue.barham@woking.gov.uk

Senior Management: Mr Mark Rolt, Strategic Director, Civic Offices, Gloucester Square, Woking GU21 6YL ☎ 01483 743050 🖰 mark.rolt@woking.gov.uk

Access Officer / Social Services (Disability): Ms Rafeia Zaman, Equalities Officer, Civic Offices, Gloucester Square, Woking GU21 6YL ☎ 01483 743479 🖰 rafeia.zaman@woking.gov.uk

Architect, Building / Property Services: Mr David Loveless, Corporate Building Services & Design Team Leader, Civic Offices, Gloucester Square, Woking GU21 6YL ☎ 01483 743554 🖰 david.loveless@woking.gov.uk

Building Control: Mr David Edwards, Chief Building Control Surveyor, Civic Offices, Gloucester Square, Woking GU21 6YL ☎ 01483 743430 🖰 david.edwards@woking.gov.uk

Children / Youth Services: Ms Sue Barham, Strategic Director, Civic Offices, Gloucester Square, Woking GU21 6YL ☎ 01483 743810 🖰 sue.barham@woking.gov.uk

PR / Communications: Mr Andy Denner, Marketing Communications Manager, Civic Offices, Gloucester Square, Woking GU21 6YL ☎ 01483 743024 🖰 andy.denner@woking.gov.uk

Community Planning: Ms Sue Barham, Strategic Director, Civic Offices, Gloucester Square, Woking GU21 6YL ☎ 01483 743810 🖰 sue.barham@woking.gov.uk

Community Safety: Mrs Camilla Edmiston, Community Safety Officer, Civic Offices, Gloucester Square, Woking GU21 6YL ☎ 01483 743080 🖰 camilla.edmiston@woking.gov.uk

Computer Management: Mrs Adele Devon, ICT Manager, Civic Offices, Gloucester Square, Woking GU21 6YL ☎ 01483 743279 🖰 adele.devon@woking.gov.uk

Customer Service: Mr David Ripley, Revenue & Benefits Manager, Civic Offices, Gloucester Square, Woking GU21 6YL ☎ 01483 743630 🖰 david.ripley@woking.gov.uk

E-Government: Ms Adele Devon, IT Manager, Civic Offices, Gloucester Square, Woking GU21 6YL ☎ 01483 743279 🖰 adele.devon@woking.gov.uk

Electoral Registration: Mrs Charlotte Griffiths, Electoral & IS Manager, Civic Offices, Gloucester Square, Woking GU21 6YL ☎ 01483 743215 🖰 charlotte.griffiths@woking.gov.uk

Emergency Planning: Mr Geoff McManus, Neighbourhood Services Manager, Civic Offices, Gloucester Square, Woking GU21 6YL ☎ 01483 743707 🖰 geoff.mcmanus@woking.gov.uk

Environmental / Technical Services: Mr Geoff McManus, Neighbourhood Services Manager, Civic Offices, Gloucester Square, Woking GU21 6YL ☎ 01483 743707 🖰 geoff.mcmanus@woking.gov.uk

Environmental Health: Ms Emma Bourne, Environmental Health Manager, Civic Offices, Gloucester Square, Woking GU21 6YL ☎ 01483 743654 🖰 emma.bourne@woking.gov.uk

European Liaison: Mr Peter Bryant, Head of Democratic & Legal Services, Civic Offices, Gloucester Square, Woking GU21 6YL ☎ 01483 743030 🖰 peter.bryant@woking.gov.uk

Events Manager: Mr Andy Denner, Marketing Communications Manager, Civic Offices, Gloucester Square, Woking GU21 6YL ☎ 01483 743024 🖰 andy.denner@woking.gov.uk

Facilities: Mr David Jones, Temporary Senior Building Services Engineer, Civic Offices, Gloucester Square, Woking GU21 6YL ☎ 01483 768746 🖰 david.jones@woking.gov.uk

Finance: Mrs Leigh Clarke, Financial Services Manager & Chief Finance Officer, Civic Offices, Gloucester Square, Woking GU21 6YL ☎ 01483 743277 🖰 leigh.clarke@woking.gov.uk

Grounds Maintenance: Mr Geoff McManus, Neighbourhood Services Manager, Civic Offices, Gloucester Square, Woking GU21 6YL ☎ 01483 743707 🖰 geoff.mcmanus@woking.gov.uk

Health and Safety: Ms Lisa Harrington, Senior Health & Safety Officer, Civic Offices, Gloucester Square, Woking GU21 6YL ☎ 01483 743213 🖰 lisa.harrington@woking.gov.uk

Housing: Ms Sue Barham, Strategic Director, Civic Offices, Gloucester Square, Woking GU21 6YL ☎ 01483 743810 🖰 sue.barham@woking.gov.uk

Housing Maintenance: Mr Barry Montgomerie, Director - New Vision Homes, Civic Offices, Gloucester Square, Woking GU21 6YL ☎ 01483 743620 🖰 barry.montgomerie@nvhwoking.gov.uk

Legal: Mr Peter Bryant, Head of Democratic & Legal Services, Civic Offices, Gloucester Square, Woking GU21 6YL ☎ 01483 743030 🖰 peter.bryant@woking.gov.uk

WOKING

Leisure and Cultural Services: Ms Sue Barham, Strategic Director, Civic Offices, Gloucester Square, Woking GU21 6YL
☎ 01483 743810 ✆ sue.barham@woking.gov.uk

Licensing: Mrs Joanne McIntosh, Solicitor, Civic Offices, Gloucester Square, Woking GU21 6YL ☎ 01483 743038
✆ joanne.mcintosh@woking.gov.uk

Lottery Funding, Charity and Voluntary: Mr Frank Jeffrey, Democratic Services Manager, Civic Offices, Gloucester Square, Woking GU21 6YL ☎ 01483 743012 ✆ frank.jeffrey@woking.gov.uk

Member Services: Mr Frank Jeffrey, Democratic Services Manager, Civic Offices, Gloucester Square, Woking GU21 6YL
☎ 01483 743012 ✆ frank.jeffrey@woking.gov.uk

Parking: Mr Gavin Manger, Parking Services Manager, Civic Offices, Gloucester Square, Woking GU21 6YL ☎ 01483 743450
✆ gavin.manger@woking.gov.uk

Personnel / HR: Mrs Amanda Jeffrey, HR Manager, Civic Offices, Gloucester Square, Woking GU21 6YL ☎ 01483 743904
✆ amanda.jeffrey@woking.gov.uk

Planning: Mr Douglas Spinks, Deputy Chief Executive, Civic Offices, Gloucester Square, Woking GU21 6YL ☎ 01483 743783
✆ douglas.spinks@woking.gov.uk

Procurement: Mrs Sharon Eager, Corporate Client & Procurement Officer, Civic Offices, Gloucester Square, Woking GU21 6YL
☎ 01483 743711 ✆ sharon.eager@woking.gov.uk

Recycling & Waste Minimisation: Mr Geoff McManus, Neighbourhood Services Manager, Civic Offices, Gloucester Square, Woking GU21 6YL ☎ 01483 743707
✆ geoff.mcmanus@woking.gov.uk

Staff Training: Mrs Amanda Jeffrey, HR Manager, Civic Offices, Gloucester Square, Woking GU21 6YL ☎ 01483 743904
✆ amanda.jeffrey@woking.gov.uk

Sustainable Communities: Mr Tim Lowe, Senior Policy Officer - Sustainability, Civic Offices, Gloucester Square, Woking GU21 6YL
☎ 01483 743413 ✆ tim.lowe@woking.gov.uk

Sustainable Development: Mr Tim Lowe, Senior Policy Officer - Sustainability, Civic Offices, Gloucester Square, Woking GU21 6YL
☎ 01483 743413 ✆ tim.lowe@woking.gov.uk

Tourism: Mr Andy Denner, Marketing Communications Manager, Civic Offices, Gloucester Square, Woking GU21 6YL ☎ 01483 743024 ✆ andy.denner@woking.gov.uk

Waste Collection and Disposal: Mr Geoff McManus, Neighbourhood Services Manager, Civic Offices, Gloucester Square, Woking GU21 6YL ☎ 01483 743707 ✆ geoff.mcmanus@woking.gov.uk

Children's Play Areas: Mr Arran Henderson, Green Spaces Development Officer, Civic Offices, Gloucester Square, Woking GU21 6YL ☎ 01483 743669 ✆ arran.henderson@woking.gov.uk

COUNCILLORS

Mayor: Murray, Anne (CON - Horsell)
cllranne.murray@woking.gov.uk

Deputy Mayor: Cundy, Graham (CON - St Johns)
cllrgraham.cundy@woking.gov.uk

Leader of the Council: Kingsbury, John (CON - Heathlands)
cllrjohn.kingsbury@woking.gov.uk

Deputy Leader of the Council: Bittleston, David (CON - Mount Hermon)
cllrdavid.bittleston@woking.gov.uk

Addison, Hilary (CON - St Johns)
cllrhilary.addison@woking.gov.uk

Ali, Mohammad (LAB - Canalside)
cllrmohammad.ali@woking.gov.uk

Azad, Ayesha (CON - Healthlands)
cllrayesha.azad@woking.gov.uk

Aziz, Tahir (LAB - Canalside)
cllrtahir.aziz@woking.gov.uk

Barker, Ann-Marie (LD - Goldsworth Park)
cllrann-marie.barker@woking.gov.uk

Bond, John (IND - Byfleet & West Byfleet)
cllrjohn.bond@woking.gov.uk

Boote, Amanda (IND - Byfleet & West Byfleet)
cllramanda.boote@woking.gov.uk

Bowes, Ashley (CON - Pyrford)
cllrashley.bowes@woking.gov.uk

Bridgeman, Mary (IND - Byfleet & West Byfleet)
cllrmary.bridgeman@woking.gov.uk

Chrystie, Graham (CON - Pyrford)
cllrgraham.chrystie@woking.gov.uk

Davis, Kevin (CON - Heathlands)
cllrkevin.davis@woking.gov.uk

Eastwood, Ian (LD - Goldsworth Park)
cllrian.eastwood@woking.gov.uk

Forster, Will (LD - Hoe Valley)
cllrwill.forster@woking.gov.uk

Harlow, Debbie (CON - Knaphill)
cllrdebbie.harlow@woking.gov.uk

Howard, Ken (LD - St Johns)
cllrken.howard@woking.gov.uk

Hughes, Deborah (LD - Hoe Valley)
cllrdeborah.hughes@woking.gov.uk

Hunwicks, Beryl (CON - Horsell)
cllrberyl.hunwicks@woking.gov.uk

Hussain, Saj (CON - Knaphill)
cllrsaj.hussain@woking.gov.uk

Johnson, Ian (LD - Mount Hermon)
cllrian.johnson@woking.gov.uk

Kemp, Colin (CON - Horsell)
cllrcolin.kemp@woking.gov.uk

Mohammed, Rashid (CON - Pyrford)
cllrrashid.mohammed@woking.gov.uk

Morales, Louise (LD - Hoe Valley)
cllrlouise.morales@woking.gov.uk

Pengally, Mark (CON - Mount Herman)
cllrmark.pengelly@woking.gov.uk

Raja, Mohammed (LAB - Canalside)
cllrmilyas.raja@woking.gov.uk

Rana, Chitra (CON - Goldsworth Park)
cllrchitra.rana@woking.gov.uk

Whitehand, Melanie (CON - Knaphill)
cllrmelanie.whitehand@woking.gov.uk

POLITICAL COMPOSITION
CON: 17, LD: 7, IND: 3, LAB: 3

Wokingham   U

Wokingham Borough Council, Wokingham Borough Council, Shute End, Wokingham RG40 1BN
☎ 0118 974 6000 🖳 www.wokingham.gov.uk

FACTS AND FIGURES
Parliamentary Constituencies: Bracknell, Maidenhead, Reading East, Wokingham
EU Constituencies: South East
Election Frequency: Elections are by thirds

PRINCIPAL OFFICERS

Chief Executive: Mr Andy Couldrick, Chief Executive, Wokingham Borough Council, Shute End, Wokingham RG40 1BN
☎ 0118 974 6001 ✆ andy.couldrick@wokingham.gov.uk

Senior Management: Mr Graham Ebers, Director - Finance & Resources, PO Box 152, Council Offices, Shute End, Wokingham RG40 1WJ ☎ 0118 974 6557 ✆ graham.ebers@wokingham.gov.uk

Senior Management: Dr Lise Llewellyn, Director - Public Health, Easthampstead House, Town Square, Bracknell RG12 1AQ
☎ 01344 352000 ✆ lise.llewellyn@bracknell-forest.gov.uk

Senior Management: Ms Judith Ramsden, Director - Children's Services, PO Box 156, Civic Offices, 2nd Floor, Shute End, Wokingham RG40 1BN ☎ 0118 974 6203
✆ judith.ramsden@wokingham.gov.uk

Senior Management: Mr Stuart Rowbotham, Director - Health & Wellbeing, Wokingham Borough Council, Shute End, Wokingham RG40 1BN ☎ 0118 974 6762
✆ stuart.rowbotham@wokingham.gov.uk

Senior Management: Ms Heather Thwaites, Director - Environment, Wokingham Borough Council, Shute End, Wokingham RG40 1BN ☎ 0118 974 6425 ✆ heather.thwaites@wokingham.gov.uk

Architect, Building / Property Services: Mr Rodney Hing, Service Manager - Operational Property, Wokingham Borough Council, Shute End, Wokingham RG40 1BN ☎ 0118 974 6000
✆ rodney.hing@wokingham.gov.uk

Building Control: Mr Neil Badley, Head of Infrastructure Implementation, Civic Offices, Wokingham RG40 1WQ
☎ 0118 974 6366 ✆ neil.badley@wokingham.gov.uk

Children / Youth Services: Ms Lisa Humphrey, Head of Social Work & Early Intervention, Wokingham Borough Council, Shute End, Wokingham RG40 1BN ☎ 0300 456 0100
✆ lisa.humphrey@wokingham.gov.uk

Children / Youth Services: Ms Judith Ramsden, Director - Children's Services, PO Box 156, Civic Offices, 2nd Floor, Shute End, Wokingham RG40 1BN ☎ 0118 974 6203
✆ judith.ramsden@wokingham.gov.uk

Children / Youth Services: Mr Alan Stubberdfield, Interim Head of Learning & Achievement, Wokingham Borough Council, Shute End, Wokingham RG40 1BN ☎ 0118 974 6121
✆ alan.stubbersfield@wokingham.gov.uk

Civil Registration: Ms Liz Lepere, Superintendent Registrar, Council Offices, Shute End, Wokingham RG40 1BN
☎ 0118 974 6554 ✆ liz.lepere@wokingham.gov.uk

PR / Communications: Miss Andrea Jenkins, Service Manager - Communications, PO Box 150, Council Offices, Shute End, Wokingham RG40 1WQ ☎ 0118 974 6010
✆ andrea.jenkins@wokingham.gov.uk

Community Planning: Ms Sarah Hollamby, Head of Corporate Strategy & Performance, Wokingham Borough Council, Shute End, Wokingham RG40 1BN ☎ 0118 974 6817
✆ sarah.hollamby@wokingham.gov.uk

Community Planning: Ms Heather Thwaites, Director - Environment, Wokingham Borough Council, Shute End, Wokingham RG40 1BN ☎ 0118 974 6425 ✆ heather.thwaites@wokingham.gov.uk

Community Safety: Mr Stuart Rowbotham, Director - Health & Wellbeing, Council Offices, Shute End, Wokingham RG40 1BN
☎ 0118 974 6762 ✆ stuart.rowbotham@wokingham.gov.uk

Computer Management: Mr Mike Ibbitson, Head of Customer Services & IMT, Wokingham Borough Council, Shute End, Wokingham RG40 1BN ☎ 0118 974 6962
✆ mike.ibbitson@wokingham.gov.uk

Contracts: Mr Graham Ebers, Director - Finance & Resources, PO Box 152, Council Offices, Shute End, Wokingham RG40 1WJ
☎ 0118 974 6557 ✆ graham.ebers@wokingham.gov.uk

Corporate Services: Mr Neil Badley, Head of Infrastructure Implementation, Civic Offices, Wokingham RG40 1WQ
☎ 0118 974 6366 ✆ neil.badley@wokingham.gov.uk

Corporate Services: Mr Rob Stubbs, Head of Financial Services, PO Box 154, Civic Offices, 2nd Floor, Shute End, Wokingham RG40 1WN ☎ 0118 974 6973 ✆ rob.stubbs@wokingham.gov.uk

Customer Service: Ms Marion Wood, Senior Complaints Officer, Wokingham Borough Council, Shute End, Wokingham RG40 1BN
☎ 0118 974 6026 ✆ marion.wood@wokingham.gov.uk

Economic Development: Mr Andrew Nicholls, Economic Development Officer, PO Box 157, Council Offices, Shute End, Wokingham RG40 1WR ☎ 0118 974 6398
✆ andrew.nicholls@wokingham.gov.uk

E-Government: Mr Andrew Moulton, Head of Governance & Improvement Services, Wokingham Borough Council, Shute End, Wokingham RG40 1BN ☎ 0118 974 6677
✆ andrew.moulton@wokingham.gov.uk

WOKINGHAM

Electoral Registration: Ms Melanie Dark-Gale, Electoral Services Manager, Wokingham Borough Council, Shute End, Wokingham RG40 1BN ☎ 0300 456 0100
⌁ melanie.dark-gale@wokingham.gov.uk

Environmental / Technical Services: Mr Matt Davey, Head of Highways & Transport, PO Box 155, Civic Offices, Shute End, Wokingham RG40 1WW ☎ 0118 974 6000
⌁ matt.davey@wokingham.gov.uk

Estates, Property & Valuation: Mr Chris Gillett, Strategic Asset Manager, PO Box 151, Council Offices, Shute End, Wokingham RG40 1WH ☎ 0118 974 6700 ⌁ chris.gillett@wokingham.gov.uk

Facilities: Mr Rodney Hing, Service Manager - Operational Property, Wokingham Borough Council, Shute End, Wokingham RG40 1BN ☎ 0118 974 6000 ⌁ rodney.hing@wokingham.gov.uk

Finance: Mr Graham Ebers, Director - Finance & Resources, PO Box 152, Council Offices, Shute End, Wokingham RG40 1WJ ☎ 0118 974 6557 ⌁ graham.ebers@wokingham.gov.uk

Grounds Maintenance: Mrs Julia Woodbridge, Commissioning & Project Manager, Civic Offices, Shute End, Wokingham RG40 1BR ☎ 0118 974 6273 ⌁ julia.woodbridge@wokingham.gov.uk

Housing: Mr Simon Price, Head of Housing, Waterford House, Erfstadt Court, Wokingham RG40 2YF ☎ 0118 974 3775
⌁ simon.price@wokingham.gov.uk

Housing Maintenance: Mr Simon Price, Head of Housing, Waterford House, Erfstadt Court, Wokingham RG40 2YF
☎ 0118 974 3775 ⌁ simon.price@wokingham.gov.uk

Legal: Mr Andrew Moulton, Head of Governance & Improvement Services, Wokingham Borough Council, Shute End, Wokingham RG40 1BN ☎ 0118 974 6677 ⌁ andrew.moulton@wokingham.gov.uk

Member Services: Ms Anne Hunter, Democratic Services Manager, PO Box 150, Council Offices, Shute End, Wokingham RG40 1WQ ☎ 0118 974 6051 ⌁ anne.hunter@wokingham.gov.uk

Parking: Ms Alison Dray, Service Manager, Wokingham Borough Council, Shute End, Wokingham RG40 1BN ☎ 0118 974 6315
⌁ alison.dray@wokingham.gov.uk

Partnerships: Ms Josie Wragg, Head of Community Services, Wokingham Borough Council, Shute End, Wokingham RG40 1BN ☎ 0118 974 6002 ⌁ josie.wragg@wokingham.gov.uk

Personnel / HR: Ms Sarah Swindley, Service Manager - HR, Wokingham Borough Council, Shute End, Wokingham RG40 1BN ☎ 0118 974 6087 ⌁ jan.hale@wokingham.gov.uk

Planning: Ms Clare Lawrence, Head of Development Management & Regulatory Services, Wokingham Borough Council, Shute End, Wokingham RG40 1BN ☎ 0118 974 6444
⌁ clare.lawrence@wokingham.gov.uk

Procurement: Mr Kien Lac, Head of Commercial Services, Wokingham Borough Council, Shute End, Wokingham RG40 1BN ☎ 0118 974 6000 ⌁ kien.lac@wokingham.gov.uk

Recycling & Waste Minimisation: Mr Peter Baveystock, Waste & Recycling Manager, Civic Centre, Shute End, Wokingham RG40 1NL ☎ 0118 974 6338 ⌁ peter.baveystock@wokingham.gov.uk

Regeneration: Ms Heather Thwaites, Director - Environment, Wokingham Borough Council, Shute End, Wokingham RG40 1BN ☎ 0118 974 6425 ⌁ heather.thwaites@wokingham.gov.uk

Road Safety: Mr Matt Davey, Head of Highways & Transport, PO Box 155, Civic Offices, Shute End, Wokingham RG40 1WW ☎ 0118 974 6000 ⌁ matt.davey@wokingham.gov.uk

Social Services: Ms Lynne McFetridge, Head of Adult Social Care & Safeguarding, Wokingham Borough Council, Shute End, Wokingham RG40 1BN ☎ 0118 908 8196
⌁ lynne.mcfetridge@wokingham.gov.uk

Social Services: Mr Stuart Rowbotham, Director - Health & Wellbeing, Wokingham Borough Council, Shute End, Wokingham RG40 1BN ☎ 0118 974 6762
⌁ stuart.rowbotham@wokingham.gov.uk

Social Services (Adult): Mr Stuart Rowbotham, Director - Health & Wellbeing, Wokingham Borough Council, Shute End, Wokingham RG40 1BN ☎ 0118 974 6762
⌁ stuart.rowbotham@wokingham.gov.uk

Social Services (Children): Ms Judith Ramsden, Director - Children's Services, PO Box 156, Civic Offices, 2nd Floor, Shute End, Wokingham RG40 1BN ☎ 0118 974 6203
⌁ judith.ramsden@wokingham.gov.uk

Public Health: Dr Lise Llewellyn, Director - Public Health, Easthampstead House, Town Square, Bracknell RG12 1AQ ☎ 01344 352000 ⌁ lise.llewellyn@bracknell-forest.gov.uk

Staff Training: Ms Gillian Ward, Personnel Strategy & Organisation Development Manager, PO Box 150, Council Offices, Shute End, Wokingham RG40 1WQ ☎ 0118 974 6037
⌁ gillian.ward@wokingham.gov.uk

Town Centre: Mr Bernard Pich, Head of Regeneration, Wokingham Borough Council, Shute End, Wokingham RG40 1BN ☎ 0118 974 6700 ⌁ bernie.pich@wokingham.gov.uk

Traffic Management: Mr Matt Davey, Head of Highways & Transport, PO Box 155, Civic Offices, Shute End, Wokingham RG40 1WW ☎ 0118 974 6000 ⌁ matt.davey@wokingham.gov.uk

Waste Collection and Disposal: Mr Peter Baveystock, Waste & Recycling Manager, Civic Centre, Shute End, Wokingham RG40 1NL ☎ 0118 974 6338 ⌁ peter.baveystock@wokingham.gov.uk

Waste Management: Mr Peter Baveystock, Waste & Recycling Manager, Civic Centre, Shute End, Wokingham RG40 1NL ☎ 0118 974 6338 ⌁ peter.baveystock@wokingham.gov.uk

COUNCILLORS

Leader of the Council: Baker, Keith (CON - Coronation) keith.baker@wokingham.gov.uk

Deputy Leader of the Council: McGhee-Sumner, Julian (CON - Wescott)
julian.mcghee-sumner@wokingham.gov.uk

Ashwell, Mark (CON - Evendons)

Auty, Alistair (CON - Norreys)
alistair.auty@wokingham.gov.uk

Batth, Parry (CON - Shinfield North)
Parry.batth@wokingham.gov.uk

Blumenthal, Laura (CON - South Lake)
laura.blumenthal@wokingham.gov.uk

Bowring, Chris (CON - Evendons)
chris.bowring@wokingham.gov.uk

Bray, Prue (LD - Winnersh)
prue.bray@wokingham.gov.uk

Chopping, David (CON - Maiden Erlegh)
david.chopping@wokingham.gov.uk

Clark, UllaKarin (CON - Emmbrook)
ullakarin.clark@wokingham.gov.uk

Cowan, Gary (CON - Arborfield)
gary.cowan@wokingham.gov.uk

Croy, Andy (LAB - Bulmershe & Whitegates)

Dolinski, Richard (CON - Loddon)
richard.dolinski@wokingham.gov.uk

Ferris, Lindsay (LD - Twyford)
lindsay.ferris@wokingham.gov.uk

Firmager, Michael (CON - Hawkedon)
michael.firmager@wokingham.gov.uk

Haines, Kate (CON - Coronation)
kate.haines@wokingham.gov.uk

Haines, Mike (CON - Sonning)
mike.haines@wokingham.gov.uk

Haitham Taylor, Charlotte (CON - Shinfield South)
charlotte.haithamtaylor@wokingham.gov.uk

Halsall, John (CON - Remenham Wargrave & Ruscombe)
john.halsall@wokingham.gov.uk

Helliar-Symons, Pauline (CON - Wokingham Without)
pauline.helliar-symons@wokingham.gov.uk

Hobbs, Emma (CON - Charvil)
emma.hobbs@wokingham.gov.uk

Holton, Tim (CON - Hawkedon)
tim.holton@wokinghaam.gov.uk

Houldsworth, Philip (CON - Winnersh)
philip.houldsworth@wokingham.gov.uk

Jarvis, John (CON - Twyford)

Jones, Clive (CON - Hawkedon)
clive.jones@wokingham.gov.uk

Jorgensen, Norman (CON - Hillside)
norman.jorgensen@wokingham.gov.uk

Jorgensen, Pauline (CON - Hillside)
pauline.jorgensen@wokingham.gov.uk

Kaiser, John (CON - Barkham)
john.kaiser@wokingham.gov.uk

King, Dianne (CON - Evendons)
dianne.king@wokingham.gov.uk

Lee, David (CON - Norreys)
david.lee@wokingham.gov.uk

Loyes, Abdul (CON - Loddon)
abdul.loyes@wokingham.gov.uk

Margetts, Charles (CON - Finchampstead North)
charles.margetts@wokingham.gov.uk

Miall, Ken (CON - Maiden Erlegh)
ken.miall@wokingham.gov.uk

Mirfin, Philip (CON - Emmbrook)
philip.mirfin@wokingham.gov.uk

Munro, Stuart (CON - Swallowfield)
stuart.munro@wokingham.gov.uk

Patman, Barrie (CON - Shinfield South)
barrie.patman@wokingham.gov.uk

Pittock, Ian (CON - Finchampstead South)
ian.pittock@wokingham.gov.uk

Pitts, Bob (CON - Remenham Wargrave & Ruscombe)
bob.pitts@wokingham.gov.uk

Pollock, Anthony (CON - Shinfield South)
anthony.pollock@wokingham.gov.uk

Richards, Malcolm (CON - Norreys)
malcolm.richards@wokingham.gov.uk

Ross, Angus (CON - Wokingham Without)
angus.ross@wokingham.gov.uk

Rowland, Beth (LD - South Lake)
beth.rowland@wokingham.gov.uk

Shepherd-DuBey, Rachelle (LD - Winnersh)
rachelle.shepherd-dubey@wokingham.gov.uk

Singleton, Chris (CON - Emmbrook)
chris.singleton@wokingham.gov.uk

Sleight, David (CON - Wokingham Without)
david.sleight@wokingham.gov.uk

Smith, Wayne (CON - Hurst)
wayne.smith@wokingham.gov.uk

Smith, Chris (CON - Hillside)

Soane, Bill (CON - Loddon)

Stanton, Rob (CON - Finchampstead North)
rob.stanton@wokingham.gov.uk

Swaddle, Alison (CON - Bulmershe & Whitegates)

Swaddle, Paul (CON - Maiden Erlegh)
paul.swaddle@wokingham.gov.uk

Weeks, Simon (CON - Finchampstead South)
simon.weeks@wokingham.gov.uk

Whittle, Oliver (CON - Wescott)
oliver.whittle@wokingham.gov.uk

Younis, Shahid (CON - Bulmershe & Whitegates)
shahid.younis@wokingham.gov.uk

POLITICAL COMPOSITION
CON: 49, LD: 4, LAB: 1

COMMITTEE CHAIRS

Licensing: Mr Barrie Patman

Planning: Mr Tim Holton

WOLVERHAMPTON

Wolverhampton M

Wolverhampton City Council, Civic Centre, St. Peter's Square, Wolverhampton WV1 1SH
☎ 01902 556556 🖷 01902 554030 ⌃ citydirect@wolverhampton.gov.uk
🖳 www.wolverhampton.gov.uk

FACTS AND FIGURES
Parliamentary Constituencies: Wolverhampton North East, Wolverhampton South East, Wolverhampton South West
EU Constituencies: West Midlands
Election Frequency: Elections are by thirds

PRINCIPAL OFFICERS

Chief Executive: Mr Keith Ireland, Managing Director, Civic Centre, St. Peter's Square, Wolverhampton WV1 1SH
☎ 01902 554500 ⌃ keith.ireland@wolverhampton.gov.uk

Senior Management: Ms Geik Drever, Strategic Director - Pensions, Civic Centre, St. Peter's Square, Wolverhampton WV1 1SH
☎ 01902 552020 ⌃ geik.drever@wolverhampton.gov.uk

Senior Management: Ms Linda Sanders, Strategic Director - People, Civic Centre, St. Peter's Square, Wolverhampton WV1 1SH
☎ 01902 555300 ⌃ linda.sanders@wolverhampton.gov.uk

Senior Management: Mr Tim Johnson, Strategic Director - Place, Civic Centre, St. Peter's Square, Wolverhampton WV1 1SH
⌃ tim.johnson@wolverhampton.gov.uk

Senior Management: Ms Lesley Robers, Strategic Director - City Housing, Civic Centre, St. Peter's Square, Wolverhampton WV1 1SH
⌃ lesley.roberts@wolverhampton.gov.uk

Access Officer / Social Services (Disability): Ms Viv Griffin, Service Director - Disability & Mental Health, Civic Centre, St. Peter's Square, Wolverhampton WV1 1SH ☎ 01902 555370
⌃ vivienne.griffin@wolverhampton.gov.uk

Access Officer / Social Services (Disability): Ms Suzanne Smith, Head of All Age Disability, Civic Centre, St. Peter's Square, Wolverhampton WV1 1SH ☎ 01902 555377
⌃ suzanne.smith@wolverhampton.gov.uk

Architect, Building / Property Services: Mr Nick Edwards, Service Director - City Assets, Civic Centre, St. Peter's Square, Wolverhampton WV1 1SH ☎ 01902 554310
⌃ nick.edwards@wolverhampton.gov.uk

Building Control: Mr Stephen Alexander, Head of Planning, Civic Centre, St. Peter's Square, Wolverhampton WV1 1SH
☎ 01902 555610 ⌃ stephen.alexander@wolverhampton.gov.uk

Catering Services: Mr Chris East, Head of Facilities Management, Civic Centre, St. Peter's Square, Wolverhampton WV1 1SH
☎ 01902 555277 ⌃ chris.east@wolverhampton.gov.uk

Children / Youth Services: Ms Emma Bennett, Service Director - Children & Young People, Civic Centre, St. Peter's Square, Wolverhampton WV1 1SH ☎ 01902 551449
⌃ emma.bennett@wolverhampton.gov.uk

Civil Registration: Mr Martyn Sargeant, Group Manager - Corporate Adminstration, Civic Centre, St. Peter's Square, Wolverhampton WV1 1SH ☎ 01902 554286
⌃ martyn.sargeant@wolverhampton.gov.uk

PR / Communications: Mr Ian Fegan, Head of Communications, Civic Centre, St. Peter's Square, Wolverhampton WV1 1SH
☎ 01902 554286 ⌃ ian.fegan@wolverhampton.gov.uk

Community Safety: Ms Ros Jervis, Service Director - Wellbeing, Civic Centre, St. Peter's Square, Wolverhampton WV1 1SH
☎ 01902 550347 ⌃ ros.jervis@wolverhampton.gov.uk

Community Safety: Ms Karen Samuels, Head of Community Safety, Civic Centre, St. Peter's Square, Wolverhampton WV1 1SH
☎ 01902 551341 ⌃ karen.samuels@wolverhampton.gov.uk

Computer Management: Mr Andy Hoare, Head of ICT, Civic Centre, St. Peter's Square, Wolverhampton WV1 1SH
☎ 01902 554563 ⌃ andy.hoare@wolverhampton.gov.uk

Consumer Protection and Trading Standards: Mr Andy Jervis, Head of Regulatory Services, Civic Centre, St. Peter's Square, Wolverhampton WV1 1SH ☎ 01902 551261
⌃ andy.jervis@wolverhampton.gov.uk

Contracts: Mr Andy Moran, Head of Procurement, Civic Centre, St. Peter's Square, Wolverhampton WV1 1SH ☎ 01902 554132
⌃ andy.moran@wolverhampton.gov.uk

Corporate Services: Mr Kevin O'Keefe, Director - Governance, Civic Centre, St. Peter's Square, Wolverhampton WV1 1SH
☎ 01902 554910 ⌃ kevin.o'keefe@wolverhampton.gov.uk

Corporate Services: Mr Mark Taylor, Director - Finance, Civic Centre, St. Peter's Square, Wolverhampton WV1 1SH
☎ 01902 556609 ⌃ mark.taylor@wolverhampton.gov.uk

Customer Service: Ms Sue Handy, Head of Customer Services, Civic Centre, St. Peter's Square, Wolverhampton WV1 1SH
☎ 01902 554390 ⌃ sue.handy@wolverhampton.gov.uk

Economic Development: Ms Keren Jones, Service Director - City Economy, Civic Centre, St. Peter's Square, Wolverhampton WV1 1SH ☎ 01902 554739 ⌃ keren.jones@wolverhampton.gov.uk

Education: Mr Julien Kramer, Director - Education, Civic Centre, St. Peter's Square, Wolverhampton WV1 1SH ☎ 01902 554100
⌃ julien.kramer@wolverhampton.gov.uk

Electoral Registration: Mr Martyn Sargeant, Group Manager - Corporate Adminstration, Civic Centre, St. Peter's Square, Wolverhampton WV1 1SH ☎ 01902 554286
⌃ martyn.sargeant@wolverhampton.gov.uk

Emergency Planning: Mr Neil Rogerson, Resilience Manager, Civic Centre, St. Peter's Square, Wolverhampton WV1 1SH
☎ 01902 556560 ⌃ neil.rogerson@wolverhampton.gov.uk

Environmental Health: Mr Andy Jervis, Head of Regulatory Services, Civic Centre, St. Peter's Square, Wolverhampton WV1 1SH
☎ 01902 551261 ⌃ andy.jervis@wolverhampton.gov.uk

Events Manager: Mr Mark Blackstock, Head of Visitor Economy, Civic Centre, St. Peter's Square, Wolverhampton WV1 1SH
☎ 01902 556245 ⌃ mark.blackstock@wolverhampton.gov.uk

Facilities: Mr Chris East, Head of Facilities Management, Civic Centre, St. Peter's Square, Wolverhampton WV1 1SH
☎ 01902 555277 ⌁ chris.east@wolverhampton.gov.uk

Finance: Mr Mark Taylor, Director - Finance, Civic Centre, St. Peter's Square, Wolverhampton WV1 1SH ☎ 01902 556609 ⌁ mark.taylor@wolverhampton.gov.uk

Treasury: Mr Mark Taylor, Director - Finance, Civic Centre, St. Peter's Square, Wolverhampton WV1 1SH ☎ 01902 556609 ⌁ mark.taylor@wolverhampton.gov.uk

Pensions: Ms Geik Drever, Strategic Director - West Midlands Pension Fund, Civic Centre, St. Peter's Square, Wolverhampton WV1 1SH ☎ 01902 552020 ⌁ geik.drever@wolverhampton.gov.uk

Fleet Management: Mr Steve Wright, Head of Bereavement & Fleet Services, Civic Centre, St. Peter's Square, Wolverhampton WV1 1SH ☎ 01902 554866 ⌁ steve.wright@wolverhampton.gov.uk

Grounds Maintenance: Mr Steve Woodward, Head of Public Realm, Civic Centre, St. Peter's Square, Wolverhampton WV1 1SH ☎ 01902 554260 ⌁ steve.woodward@wolverhampton.gov.uk

Health and Safety: Ms Denise Pearce, Head of Human Resources, Civic Centre, St. Peter's Square, Wolverhampton WV1 1SH ☎ 01902 554515 ⌁ denise.pearce@wolverhampton.gov.uk

Highways: Ms Gwyn James, Transportation Manager, Civic Centre, St. Peter's Square, Wolverhampton WV1 1SH ☎ 01902 555755 ⌁ gwyn.james@wolverhampton.gov.uk

Housing: Mr Christopher Hale, Head of City Housing, Civic Centre, St. Peter's Square, Wolverhampton WV1 1SH ☎ 01902 551796 ⌁ christopher.hale@wolverhampton.gov.uk

Legal: Ms Tracey Christie, Head of Legal Services, Civic Centre, St. Peter's Square, Wolverhampton WV1 1SH ☎ 01902 554925 ⌁ tracey.christie@wolverhampton.gov.uk

Legal: Mr Kevin O'Keefe, Director - Governance, Civic Centre, St. Peter's Square, Wolverhampton WV1 1SH ☎ 01902 554910 ⌁ kevin.o'keefe@wolverhampton.gov.uk

Licensing: Mr Andy Jervis, Head of Regulatory Services, Civic Centre, St. Peter's Square, Wolverhampton WV1 1SH ☎ 01902 551261 ⌁ andy.jervis@wolverhampton.gov.uk

Member Services: Mr Martyn Sargeant, Group Manager - Corporate Adminstration, Civic Centre, St. Peter's Square, Wolverhampton WV1 1SH ☎ 01902 554286 ⌁ martyn.sargeant@wolverhampton.gov.uk

Parking: Mr Steve Woodward, Head of Public Realm, Civic Centre, St. Peter's Square, Wolverhampton WV1 1SH ☎ 01902 554260 ⌁ steve.woodward@wolverhampton.gov.uk

Partnerships: Ms Keren Jones, Service Director - City Economy, Civic Centre, St. Peter's Square, Wolverhampton WV1 1SH ☎ 01902 554739 ⌁ keren.jones@wolverhampton.gov.uk

Personnel / HR: Ms Charlotte Johns, Head of Transformation, Civic Centre, St. Peter's Square, Wolverhampton WV1 1SH ☎ 01902 554240 ⌁ charlotte.johns@wolverhampton.gov.uk

Personnel / HR: Ms Denise Pearce, Head of Human Resources, Civic Centre, St. Peter's Square, Wolverhampton WV1 1SH ☎ 01902 554515 ⌁ denise.pearce@wolverhampton.gov.uk

Planning: Mr Stephen Alexander, Head of Planning, Civic Centre, St. Peter's Square, Wolverhampton WV1 1SH ☎ 01902 555610 ⌁ stephen.alexander@wolverhampton.gov.uk

Procurement: Mr Andy Moran, Head of Procurement, Civic Centre, St. Peter's Square, Wolverhampton WV1 1SH ☎ 01902 554132 ⌁ andy.moran@wolverhampton.gov.uk

Regeneration: Ms Keren Jones, Service Director - City Economy, Civic Centre, St. Peter's Square, Wolverhampton WV1 1SH ☎ 01902 554739 ⌁ keren.jones@wolverhampton.gov.uk

Social Services: Ms Linda Sanders, Strategic Director - People, Civic Centre, St. Peter's Square, Wolverhampton WV1 1SH ☎ 01902 555300 ⌁ linda.sanders@wolverhampton.gov.uk

Social Services (Adult): Mr Tony Ivko, Service Director - Older People, Civic Centre, St. Peter's Square, Wolverhampton WV1 1SH ☎ 01902 555310 ⌁ anthony.ivko@wolverhampton.gov.uk

Social Services (Children): Ms Emma Bennett, Service Director - Children & Young People, Civic Centre, St. Peter's Square, Wolverhampton WV1 1SH ☎ 01902 551449 ⌁ emma.bennett@wolverhampton.gov.uk

Public Health: Ms Ros Jervis, Service Director - Wellbeing, Civic Centre, St. Peter's Square, Wolverhampton WV1 1SH ☎ 01902 550347 ⌁ ros.jervis@wolverhampton.gov.uk

Street Scene: Mr Steve Woodward, Head of Public Realm, Civic Centre, St. Peter's Square, Wolverhampton WV1 1SH ☎ 01902 554260 ⌁ steve.woodward@wolverhampton.gov.uk

Town Centre: Ms Cherry Shine, BID Director - Wolverhampton BID, 176 - 178 Stafford Street, Stafford Court, Wolverhampton WV1 1NA ☎ 01902 710903 ⌁ cherry@wolverhamptonbid.gov.uk

Transport: Ms Gwyn James, Transportation Manager, Civic Centre, St. Peter's Square, Wolverhampton WV1 1SH ☎ 01902 555755 ⌁ gwyn.james@wolverhampton.gov.uk

Waste Management: Mr Chris Huddart, Head of Commercial Services, Civic Centre, St. Peter's Square, Wolverhampton WV1 1SH ☎ 01902 556788 ⌁ chris.huddart@wolverhampton.gov.uk

COUNCILLORS

Leader of the Council: Lawrence, Roger (LAB - St. Peter's)
labourleadersoffice@wolverhampton.gov.uk

Deputy Leader of the Council: Bilson, Peter (LAB - Bushbury South and Low Hill)
peter.bilson@wolverhampton.gov.uk

WOLVERHAMPTON

Angus, Ian (LAB - Bushbury North)
ian.angus@wolverhampton.gov.uk

Bagri, Harbans (LAB - Blakenhall)
harbans.bagri@wolverhampton.gov.uk

Banger, Harman (LAB - East Park)
harman.banger@wolverhampton.gov.uk

Bateman, Philip (LAB - Wednesfield North)
phil.bateman@wolverhampton.gov.uk

Bateman, Mary (LAB - Wednesfield North)
mary.bateman@wolverhampton.gov.uk

Bedi-Chadha, Payal (LAB - Bilston East)
payal.bedi-chadha@wolverhampton.gov.uk

Bolshaw, Alan (LAB - Merry Hill)
alan.bolshaw@wolverhampton.gov.uk

Brackenridge, Greg (LAB - Wednesfield South)
greg.brackenridge@wolverhampton.gov.uk

Brookfield, Ian (LAB - Fallings Park)
ian.brookfield@wolverhampton.gov.uk

Brookfield, Paula (LAB - Wednesfield South)
paula.brookfield@wolverhampton.gov.uk

Claymore, Ian (LAB - Oxley)
ian.claymore@wolverhampton.gov.uk

Collingswood, Craig (LAB - Park)
craig.collingswood@wolverhampton.gov.uk

Darke, Claire (LAB - Park)
claire.darke@wolverhampton.gov.uk

Evans, Valerie (LAB - Fallings Park)
valerie.evans@wolverhampton.gov.uk

Evans, Steven (LAB - Fallings Park)
steve.evans4@wolverhampton.gov.uk

Findlay, Barry (CON - Tettenhall Regis)
barry.findlay@wolverhampton.gov.uk

Gakhal, Bhupinder (LAB - Wednesfield South)
bhupinder.gakhal@wolverhampton.gov.uk

Gibson, Val (LAB - Bilston East)
val.gibson@wolverhampton.gov.uk

Gwinnett, Malcolm (UKIP - Spring Vale)
malcolm.gwinnett@wolverhampton.gov.uk

Hardacre, Mike (LAB - Park)
mike.hardacre@wolverhampton.gov.uk

Haynes, Christopher (CON - Merry Hill)
christopher.haynes@wolverhampton.gov.uk

Hodgkiss, Julie (LAB - Oxley)
julie.hodgkiss@wolverhampton.gov.uk

Inston, Keith (LAB - East Park)
keith.inston@wolverhampton.gov.uk

Jaspal, Jasbir (LAB - Heath Town)
jasbir.jaspal@wolverhampton.gov.uk

Jaspal, Milkinderpal (LAB - Heath Town)
milkinder.jaspal@wolverhampton.gov.uk

Johnson, Andrew (LAB - Ettingshall)
cllra.johnson@wolverhampton.gov.uk

Kaur, Rupinderjit (LAB - Spring Vale)
rupinderjit.kaur@wolverhampton.gov.uk

Koussoukama, Welcome (LAB - Bilston North)
welcome.koussoukama@wolverhampton.gov.uk

Leach, Linda (LAB - Bilston North)
linda.leach@wolverhampton.gov.uk

Malcolm, Hazel (LAB - Bushbury North)
hazel.malcolm@wolverhampton.gov.uk

Mattu, Elias (LAB - Graiseley)
elias.mattu@wolverhampton.gov.uk

Miles, Louise (LAB - Oxley)
louise.miles@wolverhampton.gov.uk

Mills, Christine (CON - Merry Hill)
councillor.mills@wolverhampton.gov.uk

Moran, Lynne (LAB - St. Peter's)
lynne.moran@wolverhampton.gov.uk

Muston, Anwen (LAB - East Park)
anwen.muston@wolverhampton.gov.uk

O'Neill, Peter (LAB - Bushbury South and Low Hill)
peter.o'neill@wolverhampton.gov.uk

Page, Phillip (LAB - Bilston North)
phillip.page@wolverhampton.gov.uk

Patten, Patricia (CON - Penn)
patricia.patten@wolverhampton.gov.uk

Photay, Arun (CON - Tettenhall Wightwick)
arun.photay@wolverhampton.gov.uk

Potter, Rita (LAB - Wednesfield North)
rita.potter@wolverhampton.gov.uk

Reynolds, John (LAB - Graiseley)
john.reynolds@wolverhampton.gov.uk

Rowley, Judith (LAB - Blakenhall)
judith.rowley@wolverhampton.gov.uk

Rowley, John (LAB - Blakenhall)
john.rowley@wolverhampton.gov.uk

Russell, Zee (LAB - Ettingshall)
zee.russell@wolverhampton.gov.uk

Samuels, Sandra (LAB - Ettingshall)
councillorsandra.samuels@wolverhampton.gov.uk

Sarkiewicz, Caroline (LAB - Heath Town)
caroline.siarkiewicz@wolverhampton.gov.uk

Simkins, Stephen (LAB - Bilston East)
stephen.simkins@wolverhampton.gov.uk

Singh, Tersaim (LAB - St. Peter's)
tersaim.singh@wolverhampton.gov.uk

Singh, Gurmukh (LAB - Spring Vale)
gurmukh.singh@wolverhampton.gov.uk

Singh, Udey (CON - Tettenhall Regis)
udey.singh@wolverhampton.gov.uk

Singh, Paul (CON - Penn)
paul.singh@wolverhampton.gov.uk

Sweet, Paul (LAB - Bushbury South and Low Hill)
paul.sweet@wolverhampton.gov.uk

Sweetman, Jacqueline (LAB - Graiseley)
cllrsweetman@wolverhampton.gov.uk

Thompson, Wendy (CON - Tettenhall Wightwick)
wendy.thompson@wolverhampton.gov.uk

Waite, Martin (LAB - Penn)
martin.waite@wolverhampton.gov.uk

Warren, Daniel (LAB - Bushbury North)
daniel.warren@wolverhampton.gov.uk

Wynne, Andrew (CON - Tettenhall Wightwick)
andrew.wynne@wolverhampton.gov.uk

Yardley, Johnathan (CON - Tettenhall Regis)
jonathan.yardley@wolverhampton.gov.uk

POLITICAL COMPOSITION
LAB: 49, CON: 10, UKIP: 1

COMMITTEE CHAIRS

Licensing: Mr Alan Bolshaw

Planning: Ms Linda Leach

Worcester City	D

Worcester City Council, The Guildhall, High Street, Worcester WR1 2EY
☎ 01905 722233 🖷 01905 722059; 01905 722028
💻 www.worcester.gov.uk

FACTS AND FIGURES
Parliamentary Constituencies: Worcester
EU Constituencies: West Midlands
Election Frequency: Elections are by thirds

PRINCIPAL OFFICERS

Chief Executive: Ms Sheena Ramsey, Managing Director, The Guildhall, High Street, Worcester WR1 2EY ☎ 01905 722233 ⁌ sheena.ramsey@worcester.gov.uk

Senior Management: Mr David Blake, Corporate Director - Place, The Guildhall, High Street, Worcester WR1 2EY ☎ 01905 722233; 01905 722370 ⁌ david.blake@worcester.gov.uk

Senior Management: Mrs Lesley Meagher, Corporate Director - Resources, Guildhall, High Street, Worcester WR1 2EY ☎ 01905 722233, : 01905 722190 ⁌ lesley.meagher@worcester.gov.uk

Senior Management: Ms Rose Norris, Corporate Director - Commissioning & Delivery, The Guildhall, High Street, Worcester WR1 2EY ☎ 01905 722233 ⁌ rose.norris@worcester.gov.uk

Senior Management: Mr Timothy O'Gara, Legal Services Manager, The Guildhall, High Street, Worcester WR1 2EY ☎ 01905 722233, : 01905 722028 ⁌ timothy.o'gara@worcester.gov.uk

Senior Management: Mr David Sutton, Service Manager - Cleaner & Greener City, Orchard House, Worcester WR1 3BB ☎ 01905 722233, : 01905 722350 ⁌ david.sutton@worcester.gov.uk

PR / Communications: Mr Rob Byrne, Communications & PR Team Manager, Guildhall, High Street, Worcester WR1 2EY ☎ 01905 722233, : 01905 722350 ⁌ rob.byrne@worcester.gov.uk

Computer Management: Mr Mac Chivers, Information Technology Manager, Copenhagen Street, Worcester WR1 3EY ☎ 01905 722121 ⁌ SW2.ServiceDesk@worcester.gov.uk

Corporate Services: Mrs Helen Frances, Service Manager, Guildhall, High Street, Worcester WR1 2EY ☎ 01905 722233, 01905 722350 ⁌ helen.frances@worcester.gov.uk

Customer Service: Mrs Helen Frances, Service Manager, Guildhall, High Street, Worcester WR1 2EY ☎ 01905 722233, 01905 722350 ⁌ helen.frances@worcester.gov.uk

Economic Development: Mr David Blake, Corporate Director - Place, Guildhall, High Street, Worcester WR1 2EY ☎ 01905 722233, 01905 722370 ⁌ david.blake@worcester.gov.uk

E-Government: Mrs Helen Frances, Service Manager, Guildhall, High Street, Worcester WR1 2EY ☎ 01905 722233, 01905 722350 ⁌ helen.frances@worcester.gov.uk

Electoral Registration: Mrs Diane Thomas, Elections Officer, Guildhall, High Street, Worcester WR1 2EY ☎ 01905 722027, 01905 722028 ⁌ d.thomas@worcester.gov.uk

Emergency Planning: Ms Nina Warrington, Strategic Housing Services Manager, Guildhall, High Street, Worcester WR1 2EY ☎ 01905 722233, 01905 722211 ⁌ nina.warrington@worcester.gov.uk

Environmental / Technical Services: Mr David Sutton, Service Manager - Cleaner & Greener City, Guildhall, High Street, Worcester WR1 2EY ☎ 01905 722233, 01905 722350 ⁌ david.sutton@worcester.gov.uk

Environmental Health: Mr David Mellors, Team Leader - Environmental Health, The Guildhall, High Street, Worcester WR1 2EY ☎ 01905 722233 ⁌ david.mellors@worcester.gov.uk

Finance: Mr Andy Bromage, Internal Audit Shared Services Manager, The Guildhall, High Street, Worcester WR1 2EY ☎ 01905 722233, 01905 722168 ⁌ andy.bromage@worcester.gov.uk

Finance: Mrs Lesley Meagher, Corporate Director - Resources, The Guildhall, High Street, Worcester WR1 2EY ☎ 01905 722233, 01905 722190 ⁌ lesley.meagher@worcester.gov.uk

Grounds Maintenance: Mr David Sutton, Service Manager - Cleaner & Greener City, The Guildhall, High Street, Worcester WR1 2EY ☎ 01905 722233, 01905 722350 ⁌ david.sutton@worcester.gov.uk

Housing: Ms Nina Warrington, Strategic Housing Services Manager, The Guildhall, High Street, Worcester WR1 2EY ☎ 01905 722233, 01905 722211 ⁌ nina.warrington@worcester.gov.uk

Local Area Agreement: Mrs Helen Frances, Service Manager, Guildhall, High Street, Worcester WR1 2EY ☎ 01905 722233, 01905 722350 ⁌ helen.frances@worcester.gov.uk

Legal: Mr Timothy O'Gara, Legal Services Manager, The Guildhall, High Street, Worcester WR1 2EY ☎ 01905 722233, 01905 722028 ⁌ timothy.o'gara@worcester.gov.uk

Licensing: Mr Niall McMenamin, Senior Practitioner, Wyre Forest House, Finepoint Way, Kidderminster DY11 7WF ☎ 01905 822799 ⁌ wrsenquiries@worcsregservices.gov.uk

WORCESTER CITY

Member Services: Miss Claire Chaplin, Democratic & Electorial Services Manager, The Guildhall, High Street, Worcester WR1 2EY
☎ 01905 722233, 01905 722028 ✆ claire.chaplin@worcester.gov.uk

Member Services: Mrs Margaret Johnson, Democratic Services Administrator, The Guildhall, High Street, Worcester WR1 2EY
☎ 01905 722233, 01905 721120
✆ margaret.johnson@worcester.gov.uk

Member Services: Mr Julian Pugh, Democratic Services Administrator, The Guildhall, High Street, Worcester WR1 2EY
☎ 01905 722233, 01905 721120 ✆ julian.pugh@worcester.gov.uk

Parking: Mr David Sutton, Service Manager - Cleaner & Greener City, The Guildhall, High Street, Worcester WR1 2EY
☎ 01905 722233, 01905 722350 ✆ david.sutton@worcester.gov.uk

Personnel / HR: Mr Mark Edwards, Service Manager, The Guildhall, High Street, Worcester WR1 2EY ☎ 01905 722233, 01905 722304 ✆ mark.edwards@worcester.gov.uk

Planning: Mr Paul O'Conner, Service Manager, The Guildhall, High Street, Worcester WR1 2EY ☎ 01905 722233, 01905 722565 ✆ paul.o'conner@worcester.gov.uk

Procurement: Mrs Sheila Mari, Procurement Assistant, The Guildhall, High Street, Worcester WR1 2EY ☎ 01905 722233, 01905 722190 ✆ sheila.mari@worcester.gov.uk

Recycling & Waste Minimisation: Mr David Sutton, Service Manager - Cleaner & Greener City, The Guildhall, High Street, Worcester WR1 2EY ☎ 01905 722233, 01905 722350 ✆ david.sutton@worcester.gov.uk

Regeneration: Mr David Blake, Corporate Director - Place, The Guildhall, High Street, Worcester WR1 2EY ☎ 01905 722233, 01905 722370 ✆ david.blake@worcester.gov.uk

Staff Training: Mr Mark Edwards, Service Manager, The Guildhall, High Street, Worcester WR1 2EY ☎ 01905 722233, 01905 722304 ✆ mark.edwards@worcester.gov.uk

Street Scene: Mr David Sutton, Service Manager - Cleaner & Greener City, The Guildhall, High Street, Worcester WR1 2EY
☎ 01905 722233, : 01905 722350 ✆ david.sutton@worcester.gov.uk

Sustainable Communities: Mr David Blake, Corporate Director - Place, The Guildhall, High Street, Worcester WR1 2EY ☎ 01905 722233, : 01905 722370 ✆ david.blake@worcester.gov.uk

Sustainable Development: Mr David Blake, Corporate Director - Place, The Guildhall, High Street, Worcester WR1 2EY
☎ 01905 722233, 01905 722370 ✆ david.blake@worcester.gov.uk

Waste Collection and Disposal: Mr David Sutton, Service Manager - Cleaner & Greener City, The Guildhall, High Street, Worcester WR1 2EY ☎ 01905 722233, 01905 722350 ✆ david.sutton@worcester.gov.uk

Children's Play Areas: Mr David Sutton, Service Manager - Cleaner & Greener City, Orchard House, Worcester WR1 3BB
☎ 01905 722233, : 01905 722350 ✆ david.sutton@worcester.gov.uk

COUNCILLORS

Mayor: Denham, Paul (LAB - Rainbow Hill)
paul.denham@worcester.gov.uk

Deputy Mayor: Stephen, Louis (GRN - Battenhall)
louis.stephen@worcester.gov.uk

Leader of the Council: Gregson, Adrian (LAB - Rainbow Hill)
adrian.gregson@worcester.gov.uk

Deputy Leader of the Council: Squires, Joy (LAB - Arboretum)
joy.squires@worcester.gov.uk

Agar, Patricia (LAB - Nunnery)
pat.agar@worcester.gov.uk

Amos, Alan (CON - Bedwardine)
alan.amos@worcester.gov.uk

Bayliss, Marc (CON - Bedwardine)
mbayliss@worcester.gov.uk

Berry, Roger (LAB - Gorse Hill)
roger.berry@worcester.gov.uk

Biggs, Tracey (LAB - Nunnery)
tracey.biggs@worcester.gov.uk

Cawthorne, Chris (LAB - St. John)
christine.cawthorne@worcester.gov.uk

Cronin, Simon (LAB - Nunnery)
simon.cronin@worcester.gov.uk

Denham, Lynn (LAB - Cathedral)
lynn.denham@worcester.gov.uk

Ditta, Allah (CON - Cathedral)
allah.ditta@worcester.gov.uk

Feeney, Alan (CON - Warndon Parish North)
alan.feeney@worcester.gov.uk

Geraghty, Simon (CON - St. Clement)
simon.geraghty@worcester.gov.uk

Hodges, Jo (LAB - Warndon)
jo.hodges@worcester.gov.uk

Hodgson, Stephen (CON - Warndon Parish North)
stephen.hodgson@worcester.gov.uk

Hodgson, Lucy (CON - Warndon Parish South)
lucy.hodgson@worcester.gov.uk

Johnson, Mike (CON - St. Peter's Parish)
mandmjohnson@btinternet.com

Jones, Gareth (CON - St. Stephen)
gareth.jones@worcester.gov.uk

Knight, Roger (CON - St. Peter's Parish)
rogerdknight@tiscali.co.uk

Lacey, Matt (CON - Claines)
matthewlacey201@hotmail.com

Lamb, Matthew (LAB - St. John)
matthew.lamb@worcester.gov.uk

Laurenson, Neil (GRN - St. Stephen)
neil.laurenson@worcester.gov.uk

Mackay, Steve (CON - Battenhall)
stevemackay91@gmail.com

Mitchell, Chris (CON - St. Clement)
chris.mitchell@lmco.com

Riaz, Jabba (CON - Cathedral)
jabba.riaz@worcester.gov.uk

Roberts, Andrew (CON - Warndon Parish South)
andrew.roberts@worcester.gov.uk

Squires, George (LAB - Arboretum)
george.squires@worcester.gov.uk

Stafford, Andy (CON - Claines)

Stanley, James (CON - Claines)
james.stanley@worcester.gov.uk

Udall, Richard (LAB - St. John)
richard.udall@worcester.gov.uk

Wilkinson, David (CON - Bedwardine)
david.wilkinson@worcester.gov.uk

Williams, Elaine (LAB - Warndon)
elaine.williams@worcester.gov.uk

Williams, Geoffrey (LAB - Gorse Hill)
geoff.williams@worcester.gov.uk

POLITICAL COMPOSITION
CON: 18, LAB: 15, GRN: 2

COMMITTEE CHAIRS

Licensing: Mr Allah Ditta

Planning: Mr Chris Mitchell

Worcestershire   C

Worcestershire County Council, County Hall, Spetchley Road,
Worcester WR5 2NP
☎ 01905 763763 🖶 01905 763000 🖳 www.worcestershire.gov.uk

FACTS AND FIGURES
Parliamentary Constituencies: Bromsgrove, Redditch, Worcester,
Worcestershire Mid, Worcestershire West, Wyre Forest
EU Constituencies: West Midlands
Election Frequency: Elections are of whole council

PRINCIPAL OFFICERS

Chief Executive: Ms Clare Marchant, Chief Executive, County
Hall, Spetchley Road, Worcester WR5 2NP ☎ 01905 766100
cmarchant@worcestershire.gov.uk

Senior Management: Mr Sander Kristel, Interim Director - Adult
Social Services, County Hall, Spetchley Road, Worcester WR5 2NP
☎ 01905 766201 ⌨ skristel@worcestershire.gov.uk

Senior Management: Ms Catherine Driscoll, Director - Children,
Families & Communities, County Hall, Spetchley Road, Worcester
WR5 2NP ☎ 01905 766580 ⌨ cdriscoll@worcestershire.gov.uk

Senior Management: Mr John Hobbs, Director - Economy &
Infrastructure, County Hall, Spetchley Road, Worcester WR5 2NP
☎ 01905 844576 ⌨ jhobbs@worcestershire.gov.uk

Senior Management: Ms Frances Howie, Interim Director -
Public Health, County Hall, Spetchley Road, Worcester WR5 2NP
☎ 01905 845533 ⌨ fhowie@worcestershire.gov.uk

Senior Management: Mr Peter Bishop, Interim Director -
Commercial & Change, County Hall, Spetchley Road, Worcester
WR5 2NP ☎ 01905 766020 ⌨ pbishop@worcestershire.gov.uk

Senior Management: Mr Sean Pearce, Chief Financial Officer,
County Hall, Spetchley Road, Worcester WR5 2NP
☎ 01905 766268 ⌨ spearce@worcestershire.gov.uk

Architect, Building / Property Services: Mr Peter Bishop,
Strategic Commissioner - Service Transformation, County Hall,
Spetchley Road, Worcester WR5 2NP ☎ 01905 766020
⌨ pbishop@worcestershire.gov.uk

Children / Youth Services: Ms Catherine Driscoll, Director -
Children, Families & Communities, County Hall, Spetchley Road,
Worcester WR5 2NP ☎ 01905 766580
⌨ cdriscoll@worcestershire.gov.uk

Children / Youth Services: Mr Paul Finnemore, Commissioning
Manager (Young People), County Hall, Spetchley Road, Worcester
WR5 2NP ☎ 01905 765628 ⌨ pfinnemore@worcestershire.gov.uk

Civil Registration: Ms Sharon Duggan, Registration & Coroner's
Service Manager, County Hall, Spetchley Road, Worcester WR5
2NP ☎ 01905 728754 ⌨ sduggan@worcestershire.gov.uk

PR / Communications: Mr Jon Fraser, Community Engagement
Relationship Manager, County Hall, Spetchley Road, Worcester
WR5 2NP ☎ 01905 766478 ⌨ jfraser@worcestershire.gov.uk

Community Planning: Mr Neil Anderson, Head of Community
Services, County Hall, Spetchley Road, Worcester WR5 2NP
☎ 01905 766580 ⌨ nanderson@worcestershire.gov.uk

Computer Management: Mr Peter Bishop, Strategic
Commissioner - Service Transformation, County Hall, Spetchley
Road, Worcester WR5 2NP ☎ 01905 766020
⌨ pbishop@worcestershire.gov.uk

Customer Service: Ms Sarah Daniel, Programmes & Relationship
Manager, County Hall, Spetchley Road, Worcester WR5 2NP
☎ 01905 843224 ⌨ sdaniel@worcestershire.gov.uk

Customer Service: Ms Annette Stock, Complaints Manager,
County Hall, Spetchley Road, Worcester WR5 2NP
☎ 01905 766640 ⌨ astock@worcestershire.gov.uk

Economic Development: Mr Neil Anderson, Head of Community
Services, County Hall, Spetchley Road, Worcester WR5 2NP
☎ 01905 766580 ⌨ nanderson@worcestershire.gov.uk

Education: Mr Paul Finnemore, Commissioning Manager - Youth
Services, County Hall, Spetchley Road, Worcester WR5 2NP
☎ 01905 765628 ⌨ pfinnemore@worcestershire.gov.uk

Electoral Registration: Mr Simon Mallinson, Head of Legal &
Democratic Services, County Hall, Spetchley Road, Worcester
WR5 2NP ☎ 01905 766670 ⌨ smallinson@worcestershire.gov.uk

Emergency Planning: Mr Nick Riding, Emergency Planning
Manager, County Hall, Spetchley Road, Worcester WR5 2NP
☎ 01905 844511 ⌨ nriding@worcestershire.gov.uk

Energy Management: Mr John Hobbs, Director - Economy &
Infrastructure, County Hall, Spetchley Road, Worcester WR5 2NP
☎ 01905 844576 ⌨ jhobbs@worcestershire.gov.uk

WORCESTERSHIRE

Environmental / Technical Services: Mr John Hobbs, Director - Economy & Infrastructure, County Hall, Spetchley Road, Worcester WR5 2NP ☎ 01905 844576 ⏍ jhobbs@worcestershire.gov.uk

European Liaison: Mr Aamir Kayani, Skills & Investment Manager, County Hall, Spetchley Road, Worcester WR5 2NP ☎ 01905 766816 ⏍ akayani@worcestershire.gov.uk

Facilities: Mr David Harrison, Facilities Manager, 2 Kings Court, Charles Hastings Way, Worcester WR5 1JR ☎ 07734 777417 ⏍ david.harrison@worcestershire.gov.uk

Finance: Mrs Sue Alexander, Head of Financial Management, County Hall, Spetchley Road, Worcester WR5 2NP ☎ 01905 766942 ⏍ salexander@worcestershire.gov.uk

Finance: Mr Sean Pearce, Chief Financial Officer, County Hall, Spetchley Road, Worcester WR5 2NP ☎ 01905 766268 ⏍ spearce@worcestershire.gov.uk

Pensions: Mr Mark Forrester, Principal Pension Fund Accountant & Investment Officer, HR Service Centre, PO Box 374, County Hall, Spetchley Road, Worcester WR5 2XF ☎ 01905 766513 ⏍ mforrester@worcestershire.gov.uk

Pensions: Ms Linda Probin, Pensions Manager, HR Service Centre, PO Box 374, County Hall, Spetchley Road, Worcester WR5 2XF ☎ 01905 766511 ⏍ lprobin@worcestershire.gov.uk

Fleet Management: Mr Stuart Payton, Transport Network Development & Commissioning Manager, County Hall, Spetchley Road, Worcester WR5 2NP ☎ 01905 843092 ⏍ spayton@worcestershire.gov.uk

Health and Safety: Dr Clive Werrett, Corporate Health & Safety Manager, County Hall, Spetchley Road, Worcester WR5 2NP ☎ 01905 765920 ⏍ cwerrett@worcestershire.gov.uk

Highways: Mr Ian Bamforth, Highways Operations & PROW Manager, County Hall, Spetchley Road, Worcester WR5 2NP ☎ 01905 766845 ⏍ ibamforth@worcestershire.gov.uk

Legal: Mr Simon Mallinson, Head of Legal & Democratic Services, County Hall, Spetchley Road, Worcester WR5 2NP ☎ 01905 766670 ⏍ smallinson@worcestershire.gov.uk

Lifelong Learning: Ms Kathy Kirk, Strategic Libraries & Lifelong Learning Manager, County Hall, Spetchley Road, Worcester WR5 2NP ☎ 01905 766946 ⏍ kkirk@worcestershire.gov.uk

Member Services: Mr Jodie Townsend, Democratic Governance & Scrutiny Manager, County Hall, Spetchley Road, Worcester WR5 2NP ☎ 01905 844871 ⏍ jtownsend1@worcestershire.gov.uk

Personnel / HR: Ms Elaine Chandler, Head of Human Resources, County Hall, Spetchley Road, Worcester WR5 2NP ☎ 01905 844378 ⏍ echandler@worcestershire.gov.uk

Planning: Mr Neil Anderson, Head of Community Services, County Hall, Spetchley Road, Worcester WR5 2NP ☎ 01905 766580 ⏍ nanderson@worcestershire.gov.uk

Procurement: Mr David Griffiths, Procurement Manager, County Hall, Spetchley Road, Worcester WR5 2NP ⏍ dgriffiths@worcestershire.gov.uk

Public Libraries: Ms Kathy Kirk, Strategic Libraries & Lifelong Learning Manager, County Hall, Spetchley Road, Worcester WR5 2NP ☎ 01905 766946 ⏍ kkirk@worcestershire.gov.uk

Recycling & Waste Minimisation: Mr Richard Woodward, Waste Services Manager, County Hall, Spetchley Road, Worcester WR5 2NP ☎ 01905 843417 ⏍ rwoodward@worcestershire.gov.uk

Road Safety: Mr Ed Dursley, Streetworks Notification Manager, County Hall, Spetchley Road, Worcester WR5 2NP ☎ 01905 843515 ⏍ edursley@worcestershire.gov.uk

Social Services: Mr Sander Kristel, Interim Director - Adult Social Services, County Hall, Spetchley Road, Worcester WR5 2NP ☎ 01905 766201 ⏍ skristel@worcestershire.gov.uk

Social Services (Adult): Mr Sander Kristel, Interim Director - Adult Social Services, County Hall, Spetchley Road, Worcester WR5 2NP ☎ 01905 766201 ⏍ skristel@worcestershire.gov.uk

Social Services (Adult): Ms Frances Howie, Interim Director - Public Health, County Hall, Spetchley Road, Worcester WR5 2NP ☎ 01905 845533 ⏍ fhowie@worcestershire.gov.uk

Social Services (Children): Ms Diane Partridge, Assistant Director - Safeguarding, County Hall, Spetchley Road, Worcester WR5 2NP ☎ 01905 843498 ⏍ dpartridge2@worcestershire.gov.uk

Public Health: Ms Frances Howie, Interim Director - Public Health, County Hall, Spetchley Road, Worcester WR5 2NP ☎ 01905 845533 ⏍ fhowie@worcestershire.gov.uk

Sustainable Communities: Ms Liz Alston, Principal Sustainability Officer, County Hall, Spetchley Road, Worcester WR5 2NP ☎ 01905 766745 ⏍ ealston@worcestershire.gov.uk

Sustainable Development: Ms Liz Alston, Principal Sustainability Officer, County Hall, Spetchley Road, Worcester WR5 2NP ☎ 01905 766745 ⏍ ealston@worcestershire.gov.uk

Transport: Mr Andy Baker, Transport Planning & Commissioning Manager, County Hall, Spetchley Road, Worcester WR5 2NP ☎ 01905 843084 ⏍ acbaker@worcestershire.gov.uk

Total Place: Mr Sander Kristel, Director - Commercial & Change, County Hall, Spetchley Road, Worcester WR5 2NP ☎ 01905 766201 ⏍ skristel@worcestershire.gov.uk

Waste Collection and Disposal: Mr Richard Woodward, Waste Services Manager, County Hall, Spetchley Road, Worcester WR5 2NP ☎ 01905 843417 ⏍ rwoodward@worcestershire.gov.uk

COUNCILLORS

Chair: Hopwood, Ian (CON - Malvern Langland)

Vice-Chair: Miller, Tony (CON - Bowbrook)
a.miller880@btinternet.com

Leader of the Council: Hardman, Adrian (CON - Bredon)
aihardman@worcestershire.gov.uk

Deputy Leader of the Council: Geraghty, Simon (CON - Worcester - Riverside)
sgeraghty@worcestershire.gov.uk

Group Leader: McDonald, Peter (LAB - Beacon)
pmcdonald2@worcestershire.gov.uk

Group Leader: Parish, Jim (IND - Stourport-on-Severn)
jparish@worcestershire.gov.uk

Adams, Alastair (CON - Littletons)
aadams@worcestershire.gov.uk

Adams, Rob (CON - Upton Snodsbury)
radams@worcestershire.gov.uk

Agar, Pat (LAB - Nunnery)
pagar@worcestershire.gov.uk

Amos, Alan (LAB - Gorse Hill & Warndon)
alan.amos@worcester.gov.uk

Askin, Susan (LD - Claines)
saskin@worcestershire.gov.uk

Baker, Joseph (LAB - Arrow Valley East)
joebaker@worcestershire.gov.uk

Banks, Robert (CON - Evesham South)
rbanks@btconnect.com

Bayliss, Mark (CON - Worcester - St Peter)

Blagg, Anthony (CON - Bromsgrove Central)
a.blagg@worcestershire.gov.uk

Blagg, Sheila (CON - Woodvale)
sblagg@worcestershire.gov.uk

Bloore, Christopher (LAB - Bromsgrove South)
cbloore@worcestershire.gov.uk

Bridle, Peter (UKIP - Arrow Valley East)
pbridle@worcestershire.gov.uk

Broomfield, Maurice (CON - Ombersley)
mbroomfield2@worcestershire.gov.uk

Campion, John (CON - Bewdley)
jcampion@worcestershire.gov.uk

Clee, Stephen (CON - Chaddesley)
sjclee@worcestershire.gov.uk

Cross, Stuart (UKIP - Redditch South)
scross@worcestershire.gov.uk

Davey, Pamela (CON - Droitwich East)
pdavey@worcestershire.gov.uk

Denham, Paul (LAB - Rainbow Hill)
pdenham@worcestershire.gov.uk

Desmond, Nathan (CON - St Mary's)
ndesmond@worcestershire.gov.uk

Duffy, Lynne (CON - Droitwich West)
lduffy@worcestershire.gov.uk

Eyre, Liz (CON - Broadway)
eeyre@worcestershire.gov.uk

Fry, Andrew (LAB - Arrow Valley West)
andrewfry@worcestershire.gov.uk

Gretton, Philip (CON - Redditch South)
pgretton@worcestershire.gov.uk

Griffiths, June (CON - Alvechurch)
j.griffiths@bromsgrove.gov.uk

Grove, Phil (CON - Hallow)
pgrove@worcestershire.gov.uk

Hart, Marcus (CON - Kidderminster - St Johns)
marcushart78@yahoo.co.uk

Hill, Pattie (LAB - Arrow Valley West)
phill3@worcestershire.gov.uk

Hingley, Anne (CON - St Barnabas)
anne.hingley@wyreforestdc.gov.uk

Hodgson, Lucy (CON - Malvern Chase)
lhodgson@worcestershire.gov.uk

Holt, Clive (CON - Harvington)
cholt@worcestershire.gov.uk

Jenkins, Rachel (IND - Clent Hills)
rjenkins@worcestershire.gov.uk

Jenkins, Matthew (GRN - Worcester - St Stephen)
mjenkins3@worcestershire.gov.uk

Lunn, Robin (LAB - Redditch North)

Mallett, Luke (LAB - Bromsgrove West)
lmallett@worcestershire.gov.uk

Oborski, Fran (LIB - Kidderminster - St Chads)
franoborski@btinternet.com

Peters, Stephen (R - Wythall)
speters@worcestershire.gov.uk

Pollock, Ken (CON - Tenbury)
kpollock2@worcestershire.gov.uk

Prodger, Derek (CON - Bedwardine)
dprodger@worcestershire.gov.uk

Raine, John (GRN - Malvern Trinity)

Rayner, Mary (IND - St Georges & St Oswalds)
mrayner@worcestershire.gov.uk

Roberts, Andrew (CON - Warndon Parishes)
acroberts@worchester.gov.uk

Smith, John (CON - Evesham North West)
jhsmith@worcestershire.gov.uk

Sutton, Roger (IND - Croome)
rsutton@worcestershire.gov.uk

Taylor, Kit (CON - Bromsgrove East)
ktaylor3@worcestershire.gov.uk

Thomas, John (IND - Stourport-on-Severn)
jthomas2@worcestershire.gov.uk

Tucker, Liz (LD - Pershore)
ltucker@worcestershire.gov.uk

Tuthill, Paul (CON - Malvern Link)
ptuthill@worcestershire.gov.uk

Udall, Richard (LAB - Worcester - St John)
rudall2@worcestershire.gov.uk

Vickery, Graham (LAB - Redditch North)

Wells, Tom (LD - Powick)
talwells@btinternet.com

Yarranton, Gordon (CON - Cookley, Wolveryley & Wribbenhall)
gyarranton@worcestershire.gov.uk

WORCESTERSHIRE

POLITICAL COMPOSITION
CON: 31, LAB: 12, IND: 5, LD: 3, GRN: 2, UKIP: 2, R: 1, LIB: 1

Worthing D

Worthing Borough Council, Worthing Town Hall, Chapel Road, Worthing BN11 1HA
☎ 01903 239999 ✆ enquiries@adur-worthing.gov.uk
🖥 www.adur-worthing.gov.uk

FACTS AND FIGURES
Parliamentary Constituencies: Worthing West
EU Constituencies: South East
Election Frequency: Elections are by thirds

PRINCIPAL OFFICERS

Chief Executive: Mr Alex Bailey, Chief Executive, Civic Centre, Ham Road, Shoreham-by-Sea BN43 6PR ☎ 01903 221001 ✆ alex.bailey@adur-worthing.gov.uk

Senior Management: Mr Paul Brewer, Director - Digital & Resources, Worthing Town Hall, Chapel Road, Worthing BN11 1HA ☎ 01903 221302 ✆ paul.brewer@adur-worthing.gov.uk

Senior Management: Ms Mary D'Arcy, Director - Communities, Worthing Town Hall, Chapel Road, Worthing BN11 1HA ☎ 01903 221300 ✆ mary.d'arcy@adur-worthing.gov.uk

Senior Management: Ms Jane Eckford, Director - Customer Service, Worthing Town Hall, Chapel Road, Worthing BN11 1HA ☎ 01903 221059 ✆ jane.eckford@adur-worthing.gov.uk

Senior Management: Mr Martin Randall, Director - Economy, Civic Centre, Ham Road, Shoreham-by-Sea BN43 6PR ☎ 01903 221209 ✆ martin.randall@adur-worthing.gov.uk

Architect, Building / Property Services: Mr Steve Spinner, Head of Business & Technical Services, Portland House, Richmond Road, Worthing BN11 1LF ☎ 01903 221019 ✆ steve.spinner@adur-worthing.gov.uk

Building Control: Mr James Appleton, Head of Growth, Portland House, Richmond Road, Worthing BN11 1HS ☎ 01903 221333 ✆ james.appleton@adur-worthing.gov.uk

PR / Communications: Mr Neil Hopkins, Head of Communications, Worthing Town Hall, Chapel Road, Worthing BN11 1HA ✆ neil.hopkins@adur-worthing.gov.uk

Community Planning: Mr Paul Pennicott, Strategic Projects Officer, Worthing Town Hall, Chapel Road, Worthing BN11 1HA ☎ 01903 221347 ✆ paul.pennicott@adur-worthing.gov.uk

Community Safety: Mrs Jacqui Cooke, Safer Communities Manager, Worthing Town Hall, Chapel Road, Worthing BN11 1HA ☎ 08456 070999 ✆ jacqui.cooke@adur-worthing.gov.uk

Computer Management: Mr Simon Taylor, CenSus IT Operations Manager, Worthing Town Hall, Chapel Road, Worthing BN11 1HA ☎ 01903 221197 ✆ simon.taylor@adur-worthing.gov.uk

Contracts: Mr Steve Spinner, Head of Business & Technical Services, Portland House, Richmond Road, Worthing BN11 1LF ☎ 01903 221019 ✆ steve.spinner@adur-worthing.gov.uk

Corporate Services: Mr Paul Brewer, Director - Digital & Resources, Worthing Town Hall, Chapel Road, Worthing BN11 1HA ☎ 01903 221302 ✆ paul.brewer@adur-worthing.gov.uk

Customer Service: Ms Jane Eckford, Director - Customer Service, Worthing Town Hall, Chapel Road, Worthing BN11 1HA ☎ 01903 221059 ✆ jane.eckford@adur-worthing.gov.uk

Direct Labour: Mr Paul Brewer, Director - Digital & Resources, Worthing Town Hall, Chapel Road, Worthing BN11 1HA ☎ 01903 221302 ✆ paul.brewer@adur-worthing.gov.uk

Economic Development: Ms Tina Barker, Economic Development Officer, Commerce Way, Lancing BN15 8TA ☎ 01273 263206 ✆ tina.barker@adur-worthing.gov.uk

E-Government: Mr Paul Brewer, Director - Digital & Resources, Worthing Town Hall, Chapel Road, Worthing BN11 1HA ☎ 01903 221302 ✆ paul.brewer@adur-worthing.gov.uk

Electoral Registration: Ms Teresa Bryant, Electoral Services Manager, Worthing Town Hall, Chapel Road, Worthing BH11 1HA ☎ 01903 221474 ✆ teresa.bryant@adur-worthing.gov.uk

Emergency Planning: Mr Lloyd Harris, Emergency Planning Officer, Worthing Town Hall, Chapel Road, Worthing BN11 1HA ☎ 01903 221025 ✆ lloyd.harris@adur-worthing.gov.uk

Energy Management: Mr Paul Brewer, Director - Digital & Resources, Worthing Town Hall, Chapel Road, Worthing BN11 1HA ☎ 01903 221302 ✆ paul.brewer@adur-worthing.gov.uk

Environmental / Technical Services: Mr Paul Brewer, Director - Digital & Resources, Worthing Town Hall, Chapel Road, Worthing BN11 1HA ☎ 01903 221302 ✆ paul.brewer@adur-worthing.gov.uk

Environmental Health: Mr James Elliot, Senior Environmental Health Officer, Adur Civic Centre, Ham Road, Shoreham-by-Sea BN43 6PR ☎ 01273 263032 ✆ james.elliot@adur-worthing.gov.uk

Estates, Property & Valuation: Mr James Appleton, Head of Growth, Portland House, Richmond Road, Worthing BN11 1HS ☎ 01903 221333 ✆ james.appleton@adur-worthing.gov.uk

Facilities: Mr Steve Spinner, Head of Business & Technical Services, Portland House, Richmond Road, Worthing BN11 1LF ☎ 01903 221019 ✆ steve.spinner@adur-worthing.gov.uk

Finance: Mrs Sarah Gobey, Executive Head of Financial Services, Worthing Town Hall, Chapel Road, Worthing BN11 1HA ☎ 01903 221221 ✆ sarah.gobey@adur-worthing.gov.uk

Fleet Management: Ms Jane Eckford, Director - Customer Service, Worthing Town Hall, Chapel Road, Worthing BN11 1HA ☎ 01903 221059 ✆ jane.eckford@adur-worthing.gov.uk

Grounds Maintenance: Mr Andy Edwards, Head of Environment, Commerce Way, Lancing BN15 8TA ☎ 01273 263137 ✆ andy.edwards@adur-worthing.gov.uk

Health and Safety: Mrs Lesley Dexter, Senior Corporate Safety Officer, Portland House, Richmond Road, Worthing BN11 1LF ☎ 01273 263430 ✆ lesley.dexter@adur-worthing.gov.uk

Housing: Mr Paul Cooper, Head of Housing, Portland House, Richmond Road, Worthing BN11 1LF ☎ 01903 221190 ✆ paul.cooper@adur-worthing.gov.uk

Housing Maintenance: Mr Paul Cooper, Head of Housing, Portland House, Richmond Road, Worthing BN11 1LF ☎ 01903 221190 ✆ paul.cooper@adur-worthing.gov.uk

Legal: Ms Susan Sale, Solicitor to the Council, Worthing Town Hall, Chapel Road, Worthing BN11 1HA ☎ 01903 221119 ✆ susan.sale@adur-worthing.gov.uk

Leisure and Cultural Services: Ms Amanda O'Reilly, Head of Culture, Worthing Town Hall, Chapel Road, Worthing BN11 1HA ☎ 01903 221142 ✆ amanda.o'reilly@adur-worthing.gov.uk

Licensing: Mr Simon Jones, Licensing Officer, Commerce Way, Lancing BN15 8TA ☎ 01273 263191 ✆ simon.jones@adur-worthing.gov.uk

Member Services: Mrs Julia Smith, Democratic Services Manager, Worthing Town Hall, Chapel Road, Worthing BN11 1HA ☎ 01903 221150 ✆ julia.smith@adur-worthing.gov.uk

Parking: Mr Ashley Miles, Technical Assistant, Worthing Town Hall, Chapel Road, Worthing BN11 1HA ☎ 01903 221022 ✆ ashley.miles@adur-worthing.gov.uk

Partnerships: Mr Alex Bailey, Chief Executive, Civic Centre, Ham Road, Shoreham-by-Sea BN43 6PR ☎ 01903 221001 ✆ alex.bailey@adur-worthing.gov.uk

Personnel / HR: Mr Paul Brewer, Director - Digital & Resources, Worthing Town Hall, Chapel Road, Worthing BN11 1HA ☎ 01903 221302 ✆ paul.brewer@adur-worthing.gov.uk

Personnel / HR: Ms Heidi Christmas, Human Resources Manager, Worthing Town Hall, Chapel Road, Worthing BN11 1HA ✆ heidi.christmas@adur-worthing.gov.uk

Planning: Mr James Appleton, Head of Growth, Portland House, Richmond Road, Worthing BN11 1HS ☎ 01903 221333 ✆ james.appleton@adur-worthing.gov.uk

Procurement: Mr Bill Williamson, Procurement Officer, Portland House, Richmond Road, Worthing BN11 1HS ☎ 01903 221056 ✆ bill.williamson@adur-worthing.gov.uk

Recycling & Waste Minimisation: Ms Jane Eckford, Director - Customer Service, Worthing Town Hall, Chapel Road, Worthing BN11 1HA ☎ 01903 221059 ✆ jane.eckford@adur-worthing.gov.uk

Regeneration: Mr James Appleton, Head of Growth, Portland House, Richmond Road, Worthing BN11 1HS ☎ 01903 221333 ✆ james.appleton@adur-worthing.gov.uk

Staff Training: Ms Lois Ford, Learning & Development Co-ordinator, Worthing Town Hall, Chapel Road, Worthing BN11 1HA ☎ 01903 221043 ✆ lois.ford@adur-worthing.gov.uk

Street Scene: Mr David Steadman, Adur Town Centre & Street Scene Co-ordinator, Civic Centre, Ham Road, Shoreham-by-Sea BN43 6PR ☎ 01273 263152 ✆ david.steadman@adur-worthing.gov.uk

Sustainable Communities: Mr James Appleton, Head of Growth, Portland House, Richmond Road, Worthing BN11 1HS ☎ 01903 221333 ✆ james.appleton@adur-worthing.gov.uk

Sustainable Development: Mr James Appleton, Head of Growth, Portland House, Richmond Road, Worthing BN11 1HS ☎ 01903 221333 ✆ james.appleton@adur-worthing.gov.uk

Tourism: Ms Amanda O'Reilly, Head of Culture, Worthing Town Hall, Chapel Road, Worthing BN11 1HA ☎ 01903 221142 ✆ amanda.o'reilly@adur-worthing.gov.uk

Town Centre: Mr David Steadman, Adur Town Centre & Street Scene Co-ordinator, Civic Centre, Ham Road, Shoreham-by-Sea BN43 6PR ☎ 01273 263152 ✆ david.steadman@adur-worthing.gov.uk

Waste Collection and Disposal: Mr Tony Patching, Head of Waste & Cleansing, Worthing Town Hall, Chapel Road, Worthing BN11 1HA ☎ 01273 263049 ✆ tony.patching@adur-worthing.gov.uk

Waste Management: Mr Tony Patching, Head of Waste & Cleansing, Worthing Town Hall, Chapel Road, Worthing BN11 1HA ☎ 01273 263049 ✆ tony.patching@adur-worthing.gov.uk

COUNCILLORS

Mayor: McDonald, Sean (CON - Northbrook)
sean.mcdonald@worthing.gov.uk

Deputy Mayor: Vaughan, Vicky (CON - Broadwater)
vicky.vaughan@worthing.gov.uk

Leader of the Council: Humphreys, Daniel (CON - Offington)
daniel.humphreys@worthing.gov.uk

Deputy Leader of the Council: Turner, Bryan (CON - Gaisford)
bryan.turner@worthing.gov.uk

Atkins, Noel (CON - Salvington)
noel.atkins@worthing.gov.uk

Baker, Antony (IND - Salvington)
antony.baker@worthing.gov.uk

Barraclough, Roy (CON - Goring)
roy.barraclough@worthing.gov.uk

Bickers, Keith (CON - Selden)
keith.bickers@worthing.gov.uk

Bradley, Joan (CON - Marine)
joan.bradley@worthing.gov.uk

Buxton, Callum (CON - Selden)
callum.buxton@worthing.gov.uk

WORTHING

Crouch, Edward (CON - Marine)
edward.crouch@worthing.gov.uk

Doyle, James (GRN - Central)
james.doyle@worthing.gov.uk

Guest, Diane (CON - Heene)
diane.guest@worthing.gov.uk

Harman, Lionel (CON - Castle)
lionel.harman@worthing.gov.uk

Harman, Alex (CON - Selden)
alex.harman@worthing.gov.uk

High, Paul (CON - Heene)
paul.high@worthing.gov.uk

High, Joshua (CON - Heene)
joshua.high@worthing.gov.uk

Jelliss, Susan (UKIP - Durrington)
susan.jelliss@worthing.gov.uk

Jenkins, Kevin (CON - Gaisford)
kevin.jenkins@worthing.gov.uk

Mercer, Heather (CON - Salvington)
heather.mercer@worthing.gov.uk

Morgan, Nigel (CON - Broadwater)
nigel.morgan@worthing.gov.uk

Murphy, Louise (CON - Offington)
louise.murphy@worthing.gov.uk

Nolan, Mark (CON - Goring)
mark.nolan@worthing.gov.uk

Proudfoot, Luke (CON - Castle)
luke.proudfoot@worthing.gov.uk

Roberts, Clive (CON - Central)
clive.roberts@worthing.gov.uk

Sim, Jane (CON - Durrington)
jane.sim@worthing.gov.uk

Smytherman, Robert (LD - Tarring)
robert.smytherman@worthing.gov.uk

Sparkes, Elizabeth (CON - Offington)
elizabeth.sparkes@worthing.gov.uk

Thorpe, Hazel (LD - Tarring)
hazel.thorpe@worthing.gov.uk

Turner, Valerie (CON - Gaisford)
val.turner@worthing.gov.uk

Waight, Steve (CON - Goring)
steve.waight@worthing.gov.uk

Walker, Vic (CON - Broadwater)
vic.walker@worthing.gov.uk

Westover, Paul (CON - Central)
paul.westover@worthing.gov.uk

Wills, Steve (CON - Castle)
steve.wills@worthing.gov.uk

Withers, Mark (UKIP - Northbrook)
mark.withers@worthing.gov.uk

Wye, Tom (CON - Tarring)
tom.wye@worthing.gov.uk

Yallop, Paul (CON - Marine)
paul.yallop@worthing.gov.uk

POLITICAL COMPOSITION
CON: 31, LD: 2, UKIP: 2, GRN: 1, IND: 1

COMMITTEE CHAIRS

Licensing: Mr Paul High

Planning: Mr Kevin Jenkins

Wrexham   W

Wrexham County Borough Council, The Guildhall, Wrexham LL11 1AY

☎ 01978 292000 🖷 01978 292106 💻 www.wrexham.gov.uk

FACTS AND FIGURES
Parliamentary Constituencies: Clwyd South, Wrexham
EU Constituencies: Wales
Election Frequency: Elections are of whole council

PRINCIPAL OFFICERS

Chief Executive: Dr Helen Paterson, Chief Executive, The Guildhall, Wrexham LL11 1AY ☎ 01978 292101, 01978 292106 ⏚ helen.paterson@wrexham.gov.uk

Senior Management: Ms Clare Field, Executive Director, The Guildhall, Wrexham LL11 1AY ☎ 01978 297421, 01978 297422 ⏚ clare.field@wrexham.gov.uk

Senior Management: Mr Lee Robinson, Executive Director, The Guildhall, Wrexham LL11 1AY ☎ 01978 292401, 01978 292445 ⏚ lee.robinson@wrexham.gov.uk

Access Officer / Social Services (Disability): Ms Charlotte Walton, Head of Adult Social Care, 2nd Floor, Crown Buildings, 31 Chester Street, Wrexham LL13 8BG ☎ 01978 298010 ⏚ charlotte.walton@wrexham.gov.uk

Architect, Building / Property Services: Mr Simon Roberts, Facilities Management Manager, 3rd Floor, Crown Buildings, 31 Chester Street, Wrexham LL13 8BG ☎ 01978 297207, 01978 292207 ⏚ simon.roberts@wrexham.gov.uk

Best Value: Mr Mark Owen, Head of Finance, Lambpit Street, Wrexham LL11 1AR ☎ 01978 292701, 01978 292702 ⏚ mark.owen@wrexham.gov.uk

Building Control: Mr Dave Sharp, Principal Building Control Surveyor, Building Control Section, 2nd Floor, Crown Buildings, 31 Chester Street, Wrexham LL13 8BG ☎ 01978 298876, 01978 292502 ⏚ dave.sharp@wrexham.gov.uk

Catering Services: Mrs Vanessa Heritage-Smith, Catering Manager - Secondary Schools, 2nd Floor, Crown Buildings, 31 Chester Street, Wrexham LL13 8BG ☎ 01978 395538 ⏚ vanessa.heritage-smith@wrexham.gov.uk

Catering Services: Mrs Sue Williams, Catering Manager - Primary Schools, 2nd Floor, Crown Buildings, 31 Chester Street, Wrexham LL13 8BG ☎ 01978 295535 ⏚ sue.williams@wrexham.gov.uk

Children / Youth Services: Ms Susan Evans, Head of Children's Social Care, Crown Buildings, 31 Chester Street, Wrexham LL13 8BG ☎ 01978 295491 ✆ susan1.evans@wrexham.gov.uk

Civil Registration: Mrs Ruth Cooke, Superintendent Registrar, The Guildhall, Wrexham LL11 1AY ☎ 01978 292670 ✆ ruth.cooke@wrexham.gov.uk

PR / Communications: Ms Sue Wyn Jones, Communications & Social Media Manager, The Guildhall, Wrexham LL11 1AY ☎ 01978 292275 ✆ sue.wynjones@wrexham.gov.uk

Community Planning: Ms Gillian Grainger, Community Diversity Manager, 16 Lord Street, Wrexham LL11 1LG ☎ 01978 292261 ✆ gillian.grainger@wrexham.gov.uk

Community Safety: Ms Rhian Jones, Senior Performance, Improvements & Partnerships Officer, Lambpit Street, Wrexham LL11 1AR ☎ 01978 297043 ✆ rhian.jones@wrexham.gov.uk

Computer Management: Mrs Helen Gerrard, ICT, Customer Services & Communications Manager, 16 Lord Street, Wrexham LL11 1LG ☎ 01978 298951 ✆ helen.gerrard@wrexham.gov.uk

Consumer Protection and Trading Standards: Ms Toni Slater, Public Protection Service Manager, Public Protection Services, Ruthin Road, Wrexham LL13 7TU ☎ 01978 315710, 01978 315701 ✆ toni.slater@wrexham.gov.uk

Contracts: Mr Steve Bayley, Head of Housing & Economy, Lambpit Street, Wrexham LL11 1AR ☎ 01978 315501 ✆ steve.bayley@wrexham.gov.uk

Corporate Services: Mr Trevor Coxon, Head of Corporate & Customer Services, The Guildhall, Wrexham LL11 1AY ☎ 01978 292206, 01978 292207 ✆ trevor.coxon@wrexham.gov.uk

Customer Service: Mrs Helen Gerrard, ICT, Customer Services & Communications Manager, 16 Lord Street, Wrexham LL11 1LG ☎ 01978 298951 ✆ helen.gerrard@wrexham.gov.uk

Direct Labour: Mr Steve Bayley, Head of Housing & Economy, Lambpit Street, Wrexham LL11 1AR ☎ 01978 315501 ✆ steve.bayley@wrexham.gov.uk

Economic Development: Mr Steve Bayley, Head of Housing & Economy, Crown Buildings, 31 Chester Street, Wrexham LL13 8BG ☎ 01978 315501 ✆ steve.bayley@wrexham.gov.uk

Education: Mr John Davies, Head of Education, Lambpit Street, Wrexham LL11 1AR ☎ 01978 295401 ✆ john.davies@wrexham.gov.uk

E-Government: Mrs Helen Gerrard, ICT, Customer Services & Communications Manager, 16 Lord Street, Wrexham LL11 1LG ☎ 01978 298951 ✆ helen.gerrard@wrexham.gov.uk

Electoral Registration: Ms Gaynor Coventry, Electoral & Regeneration Services Manager, The Guildhall, Wrexham LL11 1AY ☎ 01978 292290, 01978 292293 ✆ gaynor.coventry@wrexham.gov.uk

Emergency Planning: Mr John Holland, Emergency Planning Manager, 16 Lord Street, Wrexham LL11 1LG ☎ 01978 298826 ✆ john.holland@wrexham.gov.uk

Energy Management: Mr Michael Cantwell, Senior Climate Change & Sustainability Officer, Crown Buildings, 31 Chester Street, Wrexham LL13 8BG ☎ 01978 298826 ✆ michael.cantwell@wrexham.gov.uk

Environmental / Technical Services: Mr Darren Williams, Service Manager - Environment, Abbey Road South, Industrial Estate, Wrexham LL13 9PW ☎ 01978 729629, : 01978 667155 ✆ darren.williams@wrexham.gov.uk

Environmental Health: Ms Toni Slater, Public Protection Service Manager, Ruthin Road, Wrexham LL13 7TU ☎ 01978 315710, 01978 315701 ✆ toni.slater@wrexham.gov.uk

Estates, Property & Valuation: Mrs Denise Garland, Strategic Assets Manager, Crown Buildings, 31 Chester Street, Wrexham LL13 8BG ☎ 01978 297214 ✆ denise.garland@wrexham.gov.uk

European Liaison: Mr Allan Forrest, Regeneration Project Manager, Lambpit Street, Wrexham LL11 1AR ☎ 01978 292446, 01978 292445 ✆ allan.forrest@wrexham.gov.uk

Events Manager: Mrs Amanda Davies, Town Centre Manager, 3rd Floor, Crown Buildings, 31 Chester Street, Wrexham LL13 8BG ☎ 01978 292544 ✆ amanda.davies@wrexham.gov.uk

Facilities: Mr Simon Roberts, Facilities Management Manager, 3rd Floor, Crown Buildings, 31 Chester Street, Wrexham LL13 8BG ☎ 01978 297207, : 01978 292207 ✆ simon.roberts@wrexham.gov.uk

Finance: Mr Mark Owen, Head of Finance, Lambpit Street, Wrexham LL11 1AR ☎ 01978 292701, 01978 292702 ✆ mark.owen@wrexham.gov.uk

Fleet Management: Mr David Bithell, Transport Planning Officer, Abbey Road South, Wrexham Industrial Estate, Wrexham LL13 9PW ☎ 01978 729770 ✆ david.bithell@wrexham.gov.uk

Grounds Maintenance: Mr Darren Williams, Service Manager - Environment, Abbey Road South, Industrial Estate, Wrexham LL13 9PW ☎ 01978 729629, 01978 667155 ✆ darren.williams@wrexham.gov.uk

Health and Safety: Mr Nigel Lawrence, Principal Health & Safety Officer, Ruthin Road, Wrexham LL13 7TU ☎ 01978 315562, 01978 292132 ✆ nigel.lawrence@wrexham.gov.uk

Highways: Mr Darren Williams, Service Manager - Environment, Abbey Road South, Industrial Estate, Wrexham LL13 9PW ☎ 01978 729629, 01978 667155 ✆ darren.williams@wrexham.gov.uk

Home Energy Conservation: Mr John Holland, Emergency Planning Manager, 16 Lord Street, Wrexham LL11 1LG ☎ 01978 298826 ✆ john.holland@wrexham.gov.uk

Housing: Mr Mike Jenkins, Service Manager - Housing, Ruthin Road, Wrexham LL13 7TU ☎ 01978 315401 ✆ mike.jenkins@wrexham.gov.uk

WREXHAM

Housing Maintenance: Mr Mike Jenkins, Service Manager - Housing, Ruthin Road, Wrexham LL13 7TU ☎ 01978 315401 ✆ mike.jenkins@wrexham.gov.uk

Legal: Mr Trevor Coxon, Head of Corporate & Customer Services, The Guildhall, Wrexham LL11 1AY ☎ 01978 292206, 01978 292207 ✆ trevor.coxon@wrexham.gov.uk

Licensing: Mr Lawrence Isted, Head of Community Wellbeing & Development, Lambpit Street, Wrexham LL1 1AR ☎ 01978 298801 ✆ lawrence.isted@wrexham.gov.uk

Lifelong Learning: Mr John Davies, Head of Education, Lambpit Street, Wrexham LL11 1AR ☎ 01978 295401 ✆ john.davies@wrexham.gov.uk

Lighting: Mr Darren Williams, Service Manager - Environment, Abbey Road South, Industrial Estate, Wrexham LL13 9PW ☎ 01978 729629, 01978 667155 ✆ darren.williams@wrexham.gov.uk

Member Services: Mr Trevor Coxon, Head of Corporate & Customer Services, The Guildhall, Wrexham LL11 1AY ☎ 01978 292206, : 01978 292207 ✆ trevor.coxon@wrexham.gov.uk

Parking: Ms Joanne Rodgers, Parking Services Co-ordinator, Abbey Road South, Industrial Estate, Wrexham LL13 9PW ☎ 01978 729697 ✆ joanne.rodgers@wrexham.gov.uk

Personnel / HR: Mr Trevor Coxon, Head of Corporate & Customer Services, The Guildhall, Wrexham LL11 1AY ☎ 01978 292206, : 01978 292207 ✆ trevor.coxon@wrexham.gov.uk

Planning: Mr Lawrence Isted, Head of Community Wellbeing & Development, Lambpit Street, Wrexham LL1 1AR ☎ 01978 298801 ✆ lawrence.isted@wrexham.gov.uk

Procurement: Mr Roger Barnett, Procurement Officer, Lambpit Street, Wrexham LL11 1AR ☎ 01978 292798, 01978 292702 ✆ roger.barnett@wrexham.gov.uk

Public Libraries: Mr Dylan Hughes, Leisure & Libraries Manager, 16 Lord Street, Wrexham LL11 1LG ☎ 01978 298855 ✆ dylan.hughes@wrexham.gov.uk

Recycling & Waste Minimisation: Mrs Maria Hughes, Waste Strategy Officer, Abbey Road South, Wrexham Industrial Estate, Wrexham LL13 8BG ☎ 01978 729692 ✆ maria.hughes@wrexham.gov.uk

Regeneration: Mrs Amanda Davies, Town Centre Manager, 3rd Floor, Crown Buildings, 31 Chester Street, Wrexham LL13 8BG ☎ 01978 292544 ✆ amanda.davies@wrexham.gov.uk

Road Safety: Ms Wendy Davies-Williams, Assistant Road Safety Officer, Abbey Road South, Industrial Estate, Wrexham LL13 9PW ☎ 01978 729605 ✆ wendy.davieswilliams@wrexham.gov.uk

Social Services: Mr Andrew Figiel, Head of Adult Social Care, 2nd Floor, Crown Buildings, 31 Chester Street, Wrexham LL13 8BG ☎ 01978 298010, : 01978 298029 ✆ andrew.figiel@wrexham.gov.uk

Social Services (Adult): Ms Charlotte Walton, Head of Adult Social Care, 2nd Floor, Crown Buildings, 31 Chester Street, Wrexham LL13 8BG ☎ 01978 298010 ✆ charlotte.walton@wrexham.gov.uk

Social Services (Children): Ms Susan Evans, Head of Children's Social Care, Crown Buildings, 31 Chester Street, Wrexham LL13 8BG ☎ 01978 295491 ✆ susan1.evans@wrexham.gov.uk

Staff Training: Ms Sue Pope, Training Manager, The Learning Centre, Wrexham LL1 1AY ☎ 01978 298366 ✆ sue.pope@wrexham.gov.uk

Street Scene: Mr Darren Williams, Service Manager - Environment, Abbey Road South, Industrial Estate, Wrexham LL13 9PW ☎ 01978 729629, 01978 667155 ✆ darren.williams@wrexham.gov.uk

Sustainable Development: Mr Lawrence Isted, Head of Community Wellbeing & Development, Lambpit Street, Wrexham LL1 1AR ☎ 01978 298801 ✆ lawrence.isted@wrexham.gov.uk

Tourism: Mr Peter Scott, Investment & Business Development Manager, 3rd Floor, Crown Buildings, 31 Chester Street, Wrexham LL13 8BG ☎ 01978 292405 ✆ peter.scott@wrexham.gov.uk

Town Centre: Mrs Amanda Davies, Town Centre Manager, 3rd Floor, Crown Buildings, 31 Chester Street, Wrexham LL13 8BG ☎ 01978 292544 ✆ amanda.davies@wrexham.gov.uk

Traffic Management: Mr Darren Williams, Service Manager - Environment, Abbey Road South, Industrial Estate, Wrexham LL13 9PW ☎ 01978 729629, 01978 667155 ✆ darren.williams@wrexham.gov.uk

Transport: Mr Darren Williams, Service Manager - Environment, Abbey Road South, Industrial Estate, Wrexham LL13 9PW ☎ 01978 729629, : 01978 667155 ✆ darren.williams@wrexham.gov.uk

Transport Planner: Mr Darren Williams, Service Manager - Environment, Abbey Road South, Industrial Estate, Wrexham LL13 9PW ☎ 01978 729629, 01978 667155 ✆ darren.williams@wrexham.gov.uk

Waste Collection and Disposal: Mr Darren Williams, Service Manager - Environment, Abbey Road South, Industrial Estate, Wrexham LL13 9PW ☎ 01978 729629, 01978 667155 ✆ darren.williams@wrexham.gov.uk

Waste Management: Mrs Maria Hughes, Waste Strategy Officer, Abbey Road South, Wrexham Industrial Estate, Wrexham LL13 8BG ☎ 01978 729692 ✆ maria.hughes@wrexham.gov.uk

Children's Play Areas: Mr Martin Howarth, Parks, Countryside & Public Rights of Way Manager, Abbey Road South, Industrial Estate, Wrexham LL13 9PW ☎ 01978 729630 ✆ martin.howarth@wrexham.gov.uk

COUNCILLORS

Mayor: Pritchard, John (IND - Marchwiel) john.pritchard@wrexham.gov.uk

Deputy Mayor: McCann, Bernie (IND - Gwersyllt East and South)
bernard.mccann@wrexham.gov.uk

Leader of the Council: Pritchard, Mark (INDNA - Esclusham)
mark.pritchard@wrexham.gov.uk

Deputy Leader of the Council: Roberts, Ian (IND - Chirk North)
ian1.roberts@wrexham.gov.uk

Bailey, Andrew (LAB - Gresford East and West)
andrew.bailey@wrexham.gov.uk

Baldwin, William (IND - Little Acton)
william.baldwin@wrexham.gov.uk

Bithell, David A (IND - Johnstown)
davida.bithell@wrexham.gov.uk

Bithell, David (IND - Stansty)
idavid.bithell@wrexham.gov.uk

Blackwell, Paul (LAB - Plas Madoc)
paul.blackwell@wrexham.gov.uk

Boland, Terry (IND - Llay)
terry.boland@wrexham.gov.uk

Cameron, Brian (LAB - Whitegate)
brian.cameron@wrexham.gov.uk

Childs, Krista (LAB - Coedpoeth)
krista.childs@wrexham.gov.uk

Davies, Dana (LAB - Ruabon)
dana.davies@wrexhams.gov.uk

Dutton, Robert (IND - Erddig)
bob.dutton@wrexham.gov.uk

Edwards, Michael (LD - Marford and Hoseley)
michael.edwards@wrexham.gov.uk

Edwards, Terence Alan (IND - New Broughton)
talan.edwards@wrexham.gov.uk

Evans, Terry (IND - Chirk South)
terry.evans@wrexham.gov.uk

Evans, Anne (LAB - Rhosnesni)
anne.evans@wrexham.gov.uk

Gregory, A Keith (PC - Smithfield)
keith.gregory@wrexham.gov.uk

Griffiths, Gareth (LAB - Coedpoeth)
gareth.wyngriffiths@wrexham.gov.uk

Griffiths, David (IND - Gwersyllt East and South)
david.griffiths@wrexham.gov.uk

Hughes, Kevin (LAB - Ponciau)
kevin1.hughes@wrexham.gov.uk

Jeffares, Pat (IND - Llangollen Rural)
pat.jeffares@wrexham.gov.uk

Jenkins, R Alun (LD - Offa)
alun.jenkins@wrexham.gov.uk

Jones, Hugh (CON - Rossett)
hugh.jones@wrexham.gov.uk

Jones, Arfon (PC - Gwersyllt West)
arfon.jones@wrexham.gov.uk

Kelly, James (LD - Borras Park)
james.kelly@wrexham.gov.uk

Kelly, David (IND - Minera)
david.kelly@wrexham.gov.uk

Kenyon, Lloyd (CON - Overton)
lloyd.kenyon@wrexham.gov.uk

King, Malcolm (LAB - Wynnstay)
malcolm.king@wrexham.gov.uk

Lowe, Geoffrey (IND - Acton)
geoff.lowe@wrexham.gov.uk

Lowe, Joan (IND - Penycae and Ruabon South)
joan.lowe@wrexham.gov.uk

Morris, Michael (CON - Holt)
michael.morris@wrexham.gov.uk

O'Toole, Carole (LD - Maesydre)
carole.otoole@wrexham.gov.uk

Owens, Mark (IND - Pant)
marka.owens@wrexham.gov.uk

Pemberton, Paul (IND - Ponciau)
paul.pemberton@wrexham.gov.uk

Phillips, John (IND - Penycae)
johnc.phillips@wrexham.gov.uk

Powell, Colin (LAB - Queensway)
colin.powell@wrexham.gov.uk

Prince, Ron (IND - Cartrefle)
ron.prince@wrexham.gov.uk

Roberts, J M Barbara (IND - Ceiriog Valley)
barbara.roberts@wrexham.gov.uk

Rogers, Neil (IND - Gwenfro)
neil.rogers@wrexham.gov.uk

Rogers, Paul (CON - Brymbo)
paul2.rogers@wrexham.gov.uk

Rogers, Graham (LAB - Hermitage)
graham1.rogers@wrexham.gov.uk

Roxburgh, Barbara (IND - Bryn Cefn)
barbara.roxburgh@wrexham.gov.uk

Skelland, Rodney (CON - Bronington)
rodney.skelland@wrexham.gov.uk

Taylor, David (IND - Cefn)
david.taylor@wrexham.gov.uk

Walsh, Robert (LD - Llay)
robert.walsh@wrexham.gov.uk

Williams, Michael (IND - Gwersyllt North)
michael.williams@wrexham.gov.uk

Williams, Andy (IND - Garden Village)
andy.williams@wrexham.gov.uk

Wilson, Steve (IND - Grosvenor)
steve.wilson@wrexham.gov.uk

Wright, Derek (LAB - Cefn)
derek.wright@wrexham.gov.uk

Wynn, Phil (IND - Brynyffynnon)
phil.wynn@wrexham.gov.uk

POLITICAL COMPOSITION
IND: 27, LAB: 12, LD: 5, CON: 5, PC: 2, INDNA: 1

COMMITTEE CHAIRS
Licensing: Mr David Griffiths

WREXHAM

Planning: Mr Michael Morris

Wychavon   D

Wychavon District Council, Civic Centre, Queen Elizabeth Drive, Pershore WR10 1PT
☎ 01386 565000 ⊕ service@wychavon.gov.uk 💻 www.wychavon.gov.uk

FACTS AND FIGURES
Parliamentary Constituencies: Redditch
EU Constituencies: West Midlands
Election Frequency: Elections are of whole council

PRINCIPAL OFFICERS

Chief Executive: Mr Jack Hegarty, Managing Director, Civic Centre, Queen Elizabeth Drive, Pershore WR10 1PT
☎ 01386 565401 ⊕ jack.hegarty@wychavon.gov.uk

Deputy Chief Executive: Mr Vic Allison, Deputy Managing Director, Civic Centre, Queen Elizabeth Drive, Pershore WR10 1PT
☎ 01386 565586 ⊕ vic.allison@wychavon.gov.uk

Senior Management: Mr Phil Merrick, Joint Head of Economy & Community Services, Civic Centre, Queen Elizabeth Drive, Pershore WR10 1PT ☎ 01386 565588 ⊕ phil.merrick@wychavon.gov.uk

Senior Management: Ms Fiona Narburgh, Joint Head of Strategy, Democratic & Customer Services, Civic Centre, Queen Elizabeth Drive, Pershore WR10 1PT ☎ 01386 565101 ⊕ fiona.narburgh@wychavon.gov.uk

Senior Management: Mr Gary Williams, Joint Head of Planning & Housing Services, Civic Centre, Queen Elizabeth Drive, Pershore WR10 1PT ☎ 01386 565279 ⊕ gary.williams@wychavon.gov.uk

Architect, Building / Property Services: Ms Kirsty May-Jones, Housing Development Officer, Civic Centre, Queen Elizabeth Drive, Pershore WR10 1PT ☎ 01386 565524 ⊕ kirsty.may-jones@wychavon.gov.uk

Architect, Building / Property Services: Mr Gary Williams, Joint Head of Planning & Housing Services, Civic Centre, Queen Elizabeth Drive, Pershore WR10 1PT ☎ 01386 565279 ⊕ gary.williams@wychavon.gov.uk

Best Value: Ms Cherrie Mansfield, Strategy & Performance Manager, Civic Centre, Queen Elizabeth Drive, Pershore WR10 1PT ☎ 01386 565508 ⊕ cherrie.mansfield@wychavon.gov.uk

PR / Communications: Ms Fiona Narburgh, Joint Head of Strategy, Democratic & Customer Services, Civic Centre, Queen Elizabeth Drive, Pershore WR10 1PT ☎ 01386 565101 ⊕ fiona.narburgh@wychavon.gov.uk

PR / Communications: Ms Emma Wild, Joint Marketing & Communications Manager, Civic Centre, Queen Elizabeth Drive, Pershore WR10 1PT ☎ 01386 565102 ⊕ emma.wild@wychavon.gov.uk

Community Planning: Ms Cherrie Mansfield, Strategy & Performance Manager, Civic Centre, Queen Elizabeth Drive, Pershore WR10 1PT ☎ 01386 565508 ⊕ cherrie.mansfield@wychavon.gov.uk

Community Safety: Mr David Hemming, Community Safety Manager, Civic Centre, Queen Elizabeth Drive, Pershore WR10 1PT ☎ 01386 565301 ⊕ david.hemming@wychavon.gov.uk

Computer Management: Mr Nigel Winters, ICT Development Manager, Civic Centre, Queen Elizabeth Drive, Pershore WR10 1PT ☎ 01386 565000 ⊕ nigel.winters@wychavon.gov.uk

Contracts: Mr Phil Merrick, Joint Head of Economy & Community Services, Civic Centre, Queen Elizabeth Drive, Pershore WR10 1PT ☎ 01386 565588 ⊕ phil.merrick@wychavon.gov.uk

Contracts: Mrs Caroline Smith, Procurement Officer, Civic Centre, Queen Elizabeth Drive, Pershore WR10 1PT ☎ 01386 565433 ⊕ caroline.smith@wychavon.gov.uk

Customer Service: Mrs Kath Smith, Customer & Support Services Manager, Civic Centre, Queen Elizabeth Drive, Pershore WR10 1PT ☎ 01386 565484 ⊕ kath.smith@wychavon.gov.uk

Economic Development: Mr Phil Merrick, Joint Head of Economy & Community Services, Civic Centre, Queen Elizabeth Drive, Pershore WR10 1PT ☎ 01386 565588 ⊕ phil.merrick@wychavon.gov.uk

Electoral Registration: Mrs Elaine Dicks, Electoral Services Officer, Civic Centre, Queen Elizabeth Drive, Pershore WR10 1PT ☎ 01386 565162, : 01386 565290 ⊕ elaine.dicks@wychavon.gov.uk

Emergency Planning: Mr Phil Merrick, Joint Head of Economy & Community Services, Civic Centre, Queen Elizabeth Drive, Pershore WR10 1PT ☎ 01386 565588 ⊕ phil.merrick@wychavon.gov.uk

Environmental Health: Mr Simon Wilkes, Head of Regulatory Services, Wyre Forest House, Finepoint Way, Kidderminster DY11 7FB ☎ 01562 738088 ⊕ simon.wilkes@worcsregservices.gov.uk

Estates, Property & Valuation: Mr Vic Allison, Deputy Managing Director, Civic Centre, Queen Elizabeth Drive, Pershore WR10 1PT ☎ 01386 565586 ⊕ vic.allison@wychavon.gov.uk

Events Manager: Ms Emma Wild, Joint Marketing & Communications Manager, Civic Centre, Queen Elizabeth Drive, Pershore WR10 1PT ☎ 01386 565102 ⊕ emma.wild@wychavon.gov.uk

Facilities: Mr Vic Allison, Deputy Managing Director, Civic Centre, Queen Elizabeth Drive, Pershore WR10 1PT ☎ 01386 565586 ⊕ vic.allison@wychavon.gov.uk

Finance: Mr Vic Allison, Deputy Managing Director, Civic Centre, Queen Elizabeth Drive, Pershore WR10 1PT ☎ 01386 565586 ⊕ vic.allison@wychavon.gov.uk

Finance: Ms Alison Williams, Financial Services Manager, Civic Centre, Queen Elizabeth Drive, Pershore WR10 1PT ☎ 01386 565501 ⊕ alison.williams@wychavon.gov.uk

Treasury: Ms Alison Williams, Financial Services Manager, Civic Centre, Queen Elizabeth Drive, Pershore WR10 1PT
☎ 01386 565501 ⌁ alison.williams@wychavon.gov.uk

Fleet Management: Mr Vic Allison, Deputy Managing Director, Civic Centre, Queen Elizabeth Drive, Pershore WR10 1PT
☎ 01386 565586 ⌁ vic.allison@wychavon.gov.uk

Grounds Maintenance: Ms Lynn Stevens, Parks Officer, Civic Centre, Queen Elizabeth Drive, Pershore WR10 1PT
☎ 01386 565407 ⌁ lynn.stevens@wychavon.gov.uk

Health and Safety: Mr Carl Wibberley, Safety Officer & Building Manager, Civic Centre, Queen Elizabeth Drive, Pershore WR10 1PT
☎ 01386 565493 ⌁ carl.wibberley@wychavon.gov.uk

Housing: Mrs Elaine Salter, Housing Services Manager, Civic Centre, Queen Elizabeth Drive, Pershore WR10 1PT
☎ 01386 565241 ⌁ elaine.salter@wychavon.gov.uk

Housing: Ms Mary Unwin, Senior Housing Needs Officer, Civic Centre, Queen Elizabeth Drive, Pershore WR10 1PT
☎ 01386 565352 ⌁ mary.unwin@wychavon.gov.uk

Legal: Mr Ian Marshall, Legal Services Manager, Civic Centre, Queen Elizabeth Drive, Pershore WR10 1PT ☎ 01386 565470, 01386 561089 ⌁ ian.marshall@wychavon.gov.uk

Leisure and Cultural Services: Mr Jem Teal, Community Development Manager, Civic Centre, Queen Elizabeth Drive, Pershore WR10 1PT ☎ 01386 565235 ⌁ jem.teal@wychavon.gov.uk

Licensing: Mr Simon Wilkes, Head of Regulatory Services, Wyre Forest House, Finepoint Way, Kidderminster DY11 7FB
☎ 01562 738088 ⌁ simon.wilkes@worcsregservices.gov.uk

Lottery Funding, Charity and Voluntary: Mr Jem Teal, Community Development Manager, Civic Centre, Queen Elizabeth Drive, Pershore WR10 1PT ☎ 01386 565235
⌁ jem.teal@wychavon.gov.uk

Member Services: Mrs Kath Smith, Customer & Support Services Manager, Civic Centre, Queen Elizabeth Drive, Pershore WR10 1PT
☎ 01386 565484 ⌁ kath.smith@wychavon.gov.uk

Parking: Mrs Christine Baxter, Parking Services Manager, Civic Centre, Queen Elizabeth Drive, Pershore WR10 1PT
☎ 01386 565226 ⌁ christine.baxter@wychavon.gov.uk

Partnerships: Mr Chris Brooks, Regeneration Manager, Civic Centre, Queen Elizabeth Drive, Pershore WR10 1PT
☎ 01386 565343 ⌁ chris.brooks@wychavon.gov.uk

Partnerships: Ms Cherrie Mansfield, Strategy & Performance Manager, Civic Centre, Queen Elizabeth Drive, Pershore WR10 1PT
☎ 01386 565508 ⌁ cherrie.mansfield@wychavon.gov.uk

Personnel / HR: Ms Vickie Lee, HR Services Manager, Civic Centre, Queen Elizabeth Drive, Pershore WR10 1PT
☎ 01386 565380 ⌁ vickie.lee@wychavon.gov.uk

Planning: Mr Gary Williams, Joint Head of Planning & Housing Services, Civic Centre, Queen Elizabeth Drive, Pershore WR10 1PT
☎ 01386 565279 ⌁ gary.williams@wychavon.gov.uk

Procurement: Mr Vic Allison, Deputy Managing Director, Civic Centre, Queen Elizabeth Drive, Pershore WR10 1PT
☎ 01386 565586 ⌁ vic.allison@wychavon.gov.uk

Recycling & Waste Minimisation: Mr Mark Edwards, Waste Management Officer, Civic Centre, Queen Elizabeth Drive, Pershore WR10 1PT ☎ 01386 565245 ⌁ mark.edwards@wychavon.gov.uk

Regeneration: Mr Chris Brooks, Regeneration Manager, Civic Centre, Queen Elizabeth Drive, Pershore WR10 1PT
☎ 01386 565343 ⌁ chris.brooks@wychavon.gov.uk

Staff Training: Ms Vickie Lee, HR Services Manager, Civic Centre, Queen Elizabeth Drive, Pershore WR10 1PT ☎ 01386 565380
⌁ vickie.lee@wychavon.gov.uk

Sustainable Communities: Ms Cherrie Mansfield, Strategy & Performance Manager, Civic Centre, Queen Elizabeth Drive, Pershore WR10 1PT ☎ 01386 565508
⌁ cherrie.mansfield@wychavon.gov.uk

Tourism: Ms Angela Tidmarsh, Tourism Officer, Civic Centre, Queen Elizabeth Drive, Pershore WR10 1PT ☎ 01386 565373
⌁ angela.tidmarsh@wychavon.gov.uk

Town Centre: Mr Chris Brooks, Regeneration Manager, Civic Centre, Queen Elizabeth Drive, Pershore WR10 1PT ☎ 01386 565343 ⌁ chris.brooks@wychavon.gov.uk

Transport Planner: Mr Fred Davies, Policy Manager, Civic Centre, Queen Elizabeth Drive, Pershore WR10 1PT ☎ 01386 565367
⌁ fred.davies@wychavon.gov.uk

Waste Collection and Disposal: Ms Sharon Casswell, Client Services Manager, Civic Centre, Queen Elizabeth Drive, Pershore WR10 1PT ☎ 01386 565203 ⌁ sharon.casswell@wychavon.gov.uk

Waste Management: Mr Mark Edwards, Waste Management Officer, Civic Centre, Queen Elizabeth Drive, Pershore WR10 1PT
☎ 01386 565245 ⌁ mark.edwards@wychavon.gov.uk

Children's Play Areas: Ms Lynn Stevens, Parks Officer, Civic Centre, Queen Elizabeth Drive, Pershore WR10 1PT
☎ 01386 565407 ⌁ lynn.stevens@wychavon.gov.uk

COUNCILLORS

Chair: Smith, F S (CON - Little Hampton)
jhsmith@jhsmith.plus.com

Leader of the Council: Robinson, Linda (CON - Upton Snodsbury)
linda.robinson@wychavon.gov.uk

Deputy Leader of the Council: Duffy, Lynne (CON - Lovett & North Claines)
lynne.duffy@live.com

Group Leader: Rowley, Margaret (LD - Bowbrook)
margaret.rowley@wychavon.gov.uk

WYCHAVON

Adams, Robert (CON - Norton and Whttington)
robert.adams@wychavon.gov.uk

Adams, Alastair (CON - Honeybourne and Pebworth)
adams.pebworth@gmail.com

Barclay, K (CON - Evesham South)
k.barclay101@btinternet.com

Beale, Graham (CON - Droitwich Spa South West)
graham.beale@wychavon.gov.uk

Bearcroft, Ged (UKIP - Great Hampton)
ged.bearcroft@wychavon.net

Bolton, Jan (CON - Droitwich Spa West)
jan.bolton6@btinternet.com

Brookes, Bob (CON - Droitwich Spa East)
bob@greenbox.uk.com

Bulman, James (CON - Evesham South)
james.bulman@wychavon.net

Darby, Adrian (LD - South Bredon Hill)
adrian.darby@wychavon.gov.uk

Davis, Ron (CON - Eckington)
alfa@rondavis.fsbusiness.co.uk

Dowty, Nigel (CON - Hartlebury)
nigel.dowty@wychavon.gov.uk

Duffy, George (CON - Droitwich Spa West)
george.duffy@wychavon.net

English, Michelle (CON - Fladbury)
michelle.english@wychavon.net

Eyre, Elizabeth (CON - Broadway & Wickhamford)
elizabeth.eyre@wychavon.gov.uk

Goodge, Mark (CON - Badsey)
mark.goodge@wychavon.net

Hamilton, Hugh (CON - Dodderhill)
hugh.hamilton@wychavon.net

Hardman, Adrian (CON - Bredon)
adrian.hardman@wychavon.gov.uk

Homer, Charles (CON - Harvington and Norton)
charles.homer@wychavon.gov.uk

King, Martin (CON - Bengeworth)
martin.king@wychavon.net

Lasota, Richard (CON - The Littletons)
richard.lasota@wychavon.gov.uk

Lawley, M (CON - Droitwich Spa South East)

Mackison, George (CON - Elmley Castle & Somerville)
georgegmconsulting@tesco.net

Middlebrough, Paul (CON - Drakes Broughton)
paul.middlebrough@wychavon.gov.uk

Miller, Tony (CON - Lovett & North Claines)
tony.miller@wychavon.gov.uk

Morris, Richard (CON - Droitwich Spa South East)
richard.morris@wychavon.gov.uk

Murphy, Roy (CON - Droitwich Spa Central)
roy.murphy@wychavon.net

Noyes, Thomas (CON - Droitwich Spa South West)
tom.noyes@wychavon.gov.uk

O'Donnell, Gerry (CON - Little Hampton)
gerry.donnell@sky.com

Raphael, Robert (CON - Evesham North)
robert@hamptonferry.co.uk

Rowley, Tony (CON - Pershore)
tonyrowley@btinternet.com

Sandalls, Josephine (CON - Evesham North)
josephine.sandalls@wychavon.gov.uk

Steel, Audrey (CON - Inkberrow)
panda@broadclosefarm.wanadoo.co.uk

Stokes, Emma (CON - Bengeworth)
stokes_e1@sky.com

Thomas, Bradley (CON - Broadway & Wickhamford)
bradley@bradleythomas.co.uk

Tomalin, K (CON - Droitwich Spa East)

Tomlinson, Peter (CON - Ombersley)
peter.tomlinson@wychavon.gov.uk

Tucker, Elizabeth (LD - Pinvin)
elizabeth.tucker@wychavon.gov.uk

Tucker, Charles (LD - Pershore)
charles.tucker@wychavon.gov.uk

Wilkinson, David (CON - Inkberrow)
david.wilkinson@e-railways.co.uk

Wood, Val (CON - Pershore)
val.wood@wychavon.gov.uk

Wright, Keith (LD - Bretforton and Offenhan)
keith.wright@wychavon.gov.uk

POLITICAL COMPOSITION
CON: 39, LD: 5, UKIP: 1

COMMITTEE CHAIRS

Licensing: Mr Thomas Noyes

Planning: Mr Tony Rowley

Wycombe   D

Wycombe District Council, District Council Offices, Queen Victoria Road, High Wycombe HP11 1BB
☎ 01494 461000 ✆ info@wycombe.gov.uk 🖳 www.wycombe.gov.uk

FACTS AND FIGURES
Parliamentary Constituencies: Aylesbury, Beaconsfield, Chesham and Amersham, Wycombe
EU Constituencies: South East
Election Frequency: Elections are of whole council

PRINCIPAL OFFICERS

Chief Executive: Ms Karen Satterford, Chief Executive, Council Offices, Queen Victoria Road, High Wycombe HP11 1BB
☎ 01494 421101 ✆ karen_satterford@wycombe.gov.uk

Senior Management: Ms Caroline Hughes, Head of Environment, Council Offices, Queen Victoria Road, High Wycombe HP11 1BB
☎ 01494 421701 ✆ caroline_hughes@wycombe.gov.uk

Senior Management: Ms Elaine Jewell, Head of Community Services, District Council Offices, Queen Victoria Road, High Wycombe HP11 1BB ☎ 01494 421800
⌗ elaine_jewell@wycombe.gov.uk

Senior Management: Mr John McMillan, Head of HR, ICT & Shared Support Services, Council Offices, Queen Victoria Road, High Wycombe HP11 1BB ☎ 01494 421127
⌗ john_mcmillan@wycombe.gov.uk

Senior Management: Mr Steve Richardson, Head of Financial & Commercial Services, District Council Offices, Queen Victoria Road, High Wycombe HP11 1BB ☎ 01494 421322
⌗ steve_richardson@wycombe.gov.uk

Senior Management: Mr Paul Shackley, Corporate Director - Growth & Regeneration, District Council Offices, Queen Victoria Road, High Wycombe HP11 1BB ☎ 01494 421401
⌗ paul_shackley@wycombe.gov.uk

Senior Management: Ms Penelope Tollitt, Head of Planning & Sustainability, District Council Offices, Queen Victoria Road, High Wycombe HP11 1BB ☎ 01494 421519
⌗ penelope_tollitt@wycombe.gov.uk

Senior Management: Ms Catherine Whitehead, Head of Democratic, Legal & Policy, District Council Offices, Queen Victoria Road, High Wycombe HP11 1BB ☎ 01494 421980
⌗ catherine.whitehead@wycombe.gov.uk

Access Officer / Social Services (Disability): Mr Alan Switalski, Access Officer, Council Offices, Queen Victoria Road, High Wycombe HP11 1BB ☎ 01494 421438
⌗ alan_switalski@wycombe.gov.uk

Architect, Building / Property Services: Mr Charles Brocklehurst, Major Projects & Property Executive, Council Offices, Queen Victoria Road, High Wycombe HP11 1BB ☎ 01494 421280
⌗ charles_brocklehurst@wycombe.gov.uk

Best Value: Miss Jacqueline Ford, Corporate Policy Team Leader, Council Offices, Queen Victoria Road, High Wycombe HP11 1BB ☎ 01494 421983 ⌗ jacqueline_ford@wycombe.gov.uk

Best Value: Ms Catherine Whitehead, Head of Democratic, Legal & Policy, District Council Offices, Queen Victoria Road, High Wycombe HP11 1BB ☎ 01494 421980
⌗ catherine.whitehead@wycombe.gov.uk

Building Control: Ms Alison Pipes, Building Control Manager, District Council Offices, Queen Victoria Road, High Wycombe HP11 1BB ☎ 01494 421425 ⌗ alison_pipes@wycombe.gov.uk

PR / Communications: Ms Catherine Spalton, Communications Team Leader, District Council Offices, Queen Victoria Road, High Wycombe HP11 1BB ☎ 01494 421230
⌗ catherine_spalton@wycombe.gov.uk

PR / Communications: Ms Catherine Whitehead, Head of Democratic, Legal & Policy, District Council Offices, Queen Victoria Road, High Wycombe HP11 1BB ☎ 01494 421980
⌗ catherine.whitehead@wycombe.gov.uk

Community Planning: Ms Catherine Whitehead, Head of Democratic, Legal & Policy, District Council Offices, Queen Victoria Road, High Wycombe HP11 1BB ☎ 01494 421980
⌗ catherine.whitehead@wycombe.gov.uk

Community Safety: Mr Daniel Sullivan, Strategic Prevent Co-ordinator, District Council Offices, Queen Victoria Road, High Wycombe HP11 1BB ☎ 01494 421371
⌗ daniel.sullivan@wycombe.gov.uk

Computer Management: Ms Mary Hayward-Ord, ICT Manager of Infrastructure, District Council Offices, Queen Victoria Road, High Wycombe HP11 1BB ☎ 01494 421179
⌗ mary_hayward-ord@wycombe.gov.uk

Computer Management: Mr Mark Lansbury, Business Systems Manager, District Council Offices, Queen Victoria Road, High Wycombe HP11 1BB ☎ 01494 421168
⌗ mark_lansbury@wycombe.gov.uk

Computer Management: Mr John McMillan, Head of HR, ICT & Shared Support Services, Council Offices, Queen Victoria Road, High Wycombe HP11 1BB ☎ 01494 421127
⌗ john_mcmillan@wycombe.gov.uk

Customer Service: Ms Karen Ashby, Customer Service Centre Manager, District Council Offices, Queen Victoria Road, High Wycombe HP11 1BB ☎ 01494 421111
⌗ karen.ashby@wycombe.gov.uk

Customer Service: Mr John McMillan, Head of HR, ICT & Shared Support Services, Council Offices, Queen Victoria Road, High Wycombe HP11 1BB ☎ 01494 421127
⌗ john_mcmillan@wycombe.gov.uk

Economic Development: Miss Jacqueline Ford, Corporate Policy Team Leader, Council Offices, Queen Victoria Road, High Wycombe HP11 1BB ☎ 01494 421983 ⌗ jacqueline_ford@wycombe.gov.uk

E-Government: Mr John McMillan, Head of HR, ICT & Shared Support Services, Council Offices, Queen Victoria Road, High Wycombe HP11 1BB ☎ 01494 421127
⌗ john_mcmillan@wycombe.gov.uk

Electoral Registration: Mr Rob Curtis, Statutory Services Manager, District Council Offices, Queen Victoria Road, High Wycombe HP11 1BB ☎ 01494 421242 ⌗ rob_curtis@wycombe.gov.uk

Emergency Planning: Mr Andrew Collinson, Policy Officer (Emergency Planning), District Council Offices, Queen Victoria Road, High Wycombe HP11 1BB ☎ 01494 421981
⌗ charles_meakings@wycombe.gov.uk

Emergency Planning: Ms Catherine Whitehead, Head of Democratic, Legal & Policy, District Council Offices, Queen Victoria Road, High Wycombe HP11 1BB ☎ 01494 421980
⌗ catherine.whitehead@wycombe.gov.uk

Energy Management: Mr Graham Weston, Energy Officer, Council Offices, Queen Victoria Road, High Wycombe HP11 1BB ☎ 01494 421565 ⌗ graham_weston@wycombe.gov.uk

WYCOMBE

Environmental / Technical Services: Ms Caroline Hughes, Head of Environment, Council Offices, Queen Victoria Road, High Wycombe HP11 1BB ☎ 01494 421701
◌ caroline_hughes@wycombe.gov.uk

Environmental Health: Mr Neil Stannett, Environmental Health Officer, District Council Offices, Queen Victoria Road, High Wycombe HP11 1BB ☎ 01494 421092
◌ neil_stannett@wycombe.gov.uk

Estates, Property & Valuation: Mr Charles Brocklehurst, Major Projects & Property Executive, Council Offices, Queen Victoria Road, High Wycombe HP11 1BB ☎ 01494 421280
◌ charles_brocklehurst@wycombe.gov.uk

Estates, Property & Valuation: Mr Robert Daniels, Estates Team Leader, District Council Offices, Queen Victoria Road, High Wycombe HP11 1BB ☎ 01494 421157
◌ robert.daniels@wycombe.gov.uk

Facilities: Mr John McMillan, Head of HR, ICT & Shared Support Services, Council Offices, Queen Victoria Road, High Wycombe HP11 1BB ☎ 01494 421127 ◌ john_mcmillan@wycombe.gov.uk

Finance: Mr Steve Richardson, Head of Financial & Commercial Services, District Council Offices, Queen Victoria Road, High Wycombe HP11 1BB ☎ 01494 421322
◌ steve_richardson@wycombe.gov.uk

Health and Safety: Mr Paul Spencer, Health & Safety Manager, District Council Offices, Queen Victoria Road, High Wycombe HP11 1BB ☎ 01494 421107 ◌ paul.spencer@wycombe.gov.uk

Housing: Mr Brian Daley, Housing Service Manager, Council Offices, Queen Victoria Road, High Wycombe HP11 1BB
☎ 01494 421601 ◌ brian_daley@wycombe.gov.uk

Housing: Ms Caroline Hughes, Head of Environment, Council Offices, Queen Victoria Road, High Wycombe HP11 1BB
☎ 01494 421701 ◌ caroline_hughes@wycombe.gov.uk

Legal: Ms Julie Openshaw, District Solicitor / Monitoring Officer, District Council Offices, Queen Victoria Road, High Wycombe HP11 1BB ☎ 01494 421252 ◌ julie_openshaw@wycombe.gov.uk

Leisure and Cultural Services: Ms Sarah Randall, Community Commissioning Manager, District Council Offices, Queen Victoria Road, High Wycombe HP11 1BB ☎ 01494 421888
◌ sarah_randall@wycombe.gov.uk

Licensing: Ms Caroline Steven, Licensing Team Leader, District Council Offices, Queen Victoria Road, High Wycombe HP11 1BB
☎ 01494 421222 ◌ caroline_steven@wycombe.gov.uk

Lifelong Learning: Ms Elaine Jewell, Head of Community Services, District Council Offices, Queen Victoria Road, High Wycombe HP11 1BB ☎ 01494 421800
◌ elaine_jewell@wycombe.gov.uk

Lottery Funding, Charity and Voluntary: Ms Elaine Jewell, Head of Community Services, District Council Offices, Queen Victoria Road, High Wycombe HP11 1BB ☎ 01494 421800
◌ elaine_jewell@wycombe.gov.uk

Member Services: Ms Catherine Whitehead, Head of Democratic, Legal & Policy, District Council Offices, Queen Victoria Road, High Wycombe HP11 1BB ☎ 01494 421980
◌ catherine.whitehead@wycombe.gov.uk

Parking: Mr Robin Evans, Parking Services Manager, District Council Offices, Queen Victoria Road, High Wycombe HP11 1BB
☎ 01494 421471 ◌ robin_evans@wycombe.gov.uk

Partnerships: Ms Catherine Whitehead, Head of Democratic, Legal & Policy, District Council Offices, Queen Victoria Road, High Wycombe HP11 1BB ☎ 01494 421980
◌ catherine.whitehead@wycombe.gov.uk

Personnel / HR: Mr John McMillan, Head of HR, ICT & Shared Support Services, Council Offices, Queen Victoria Road, High Wycombe HP11 1BB ☎ 01494 421127
◌ john_mcmillan@wycombe.gov.uk

Planning: Mr Alastair Nicholson, Development Manager, District Council Offices, Queen Victoria Road, High Wycombe HP11 1BB
☎ 01494 421510 ◌ alastair_nicholson@wycombe.gov.uk

Planning: Ms Penelope Tollitt, Head of Planning & Sustainability, District Council Offices, Queen Victoria Road, High Wycombe HP11 1BB ☎ 01494 421519 ◌ penelope_tollitt@wycombe.gov.uk

Procurement: Mr Steve Middleton, Procurement Manager, District Council Offices, Queen Victoria Road, High Wycombe HP11 1BB
☎ 01494 421315 ◌ steve_middleton@wycombe.gov.uk

Procurement: Mr Steve Richardson, Head of Financial & Commercial Services, District Council Offices, Queen Victoria Road, High Wycombe HP11 1BB ☎ 01494 421322
◌ steve_richardson@wycombe.gov.uk

Recycling & Waste Minimisation: Ms Caroline Hughes, Head of Environment, Council Offices, Queen Victoria Road, High Wycombe HP11 1BB ☎ 01494 421701 ◌ caroline_hughes@wycombe.gov.uk

Regeneration: Mr Charles Brocklehurst, Major Projects & Property Executive, Council Offices, Queen Victoria Road, High Wycombe HP11 1BB ☎ 01494 421280
◌ charles_brocklehurst@wycombe.gov.uk

Staff Training: Mr John McMillan, Head of HR, ICT & Shared Support Services, Council Offices, Queen Victoria Road, High Wycombe HP11 1BB ☎ 01494 421127
◌ john_mcmillan@wycombe.gov.uk

Staff Training: Ms Sarah Taylor, Training & Development Officer, Council Offices, Queen Victoria Road, High Wycombe HP11 1BB
☎ 01494 421139 ◌ sarah_taylor@wycombe.gov.uk

Street Scene: Ms Caroline Hughes, Head of Environment, Council Offices, Queen Victoria Road, High Wycombe HP11 1BB
☎ 01494 421701 ◌ caroline_hughes@wycombe.gov.uk

Sustainable Communities: Ms Elaine Jewell, Head of Community Services, District Council Offices, Queen Victoria Road, High Wycombe HP11 1BB ☎ 01494 421800 ✆ elaine_jewell@wycombe.gov.uk

Sustainable Development: Ms Penelope Tollitt, Head of Planning & Sustainability, District Council Offices, Queen Victoria Road, High Wycombe HP11 1BB ☎ 01494 421519 ✆ penelope_tollitt@wycombe.gov.uk

Tourism: Ms Elaine Jewell, Head of Community Services, District Council Offices, Queen Victoria Road, High Wycombe HP11 1BB ☎ 01494 421800 ✆ elaine_jewell@wycombe.gov.uk

Town Centre: Mr Oliver O'Dell, Chief Executive - High Wycombe BidCo, District Council Offices, Queen Victoria Road, High Wycombe HP11 1BB ☎ 01494 452705 ✆ oliver@hwtcp.co.uk

Total Place: Ms Catherine Whitehead, Head of Democratic, Legal & Policy, District Council Offices, Queen Victoria Road, High Wycombe HP11 1BB ☎ 01494 421980 ✆ catherine.whitehead@wycombe.gov.uk

Waste Collection and Disposal: Ms Caroline Hughes, Head of Environment, Council Offices, Queen Victoria Road, High Wycombe HP11 1BB ☎ 01494 421701 ✆ caroline_hughes@wycombe.gov.uk

Waste Management: Ms Caroline Hughes, Head of Environment, Council Offices, Queen Victoria Road, High Wycombe HP11 1BB ☎ 01494 421701 ✆ caroline_hughes@wycombe.gov.uk

COUNCILLORS

Leader of the Council: Wood, Katrina (CON - Tylers Green and Loudwater)
katrina.wood@wycombe.gov.uk

Deputy Leader of the Council: Barnes, Dominic (CON - Greater Marlow)
dominic.barnes@wycombe.gov.uk

Adey, Julia (CON - The Wooburns)
julia.adey@wycombe.gov.uk

Adoh, Shade (CON - Stokenchurch and Radnage)
shade.adoh@wycombe.gov.uk

Ahmed, Zia (CON - Sands)
zia.ahmed@wycombe.gov.uk

Ahmed, Khalil (LAB - Disraeli)
khalil.ahmed@wycombe.gov.uk

Appleyard, Mike (CON - Bourne End cum Hedsor)
michael.appleyard@wycombe.gov.uk

Asif, Mohammed (LAB - Oakridge and Castlefield)
mohammed.asif@wycombe.gov.uk

Baughan, Andrea (IND - Micklefield)
andrea.baughan@wycombe.gov.uk

Broadbent, Steve (CON - Greater Hughenden)
steve.broadbent@wycombe.gov.uk

Brown, Suzanne (CON - Marlow South East)
suzanne.brown@wycombe.gov.uk

Bull, Harry (CON - Totteridge)
harry.bull@wycombe.gov.uk

Carroll, David (CON - Greater Hughenden)
david.carroll@wycombe.gov.uk

Clarke, Marten (CON - Ryemead)
marten.clarke@wycombe.gov.uk

Clarke, Lesley (CON - Abbey)
lesley.clarke@wycombe.gov.uk

Collingwood, Alex (CON - Marlow North and West)
alex.collingwood@wycombe.gov.uk

Davy, Matthew (CON - Booker and Cressex)
matthew.davy@wycombe.gov.uk

Etholen, Carl (CON - Bledlow and Bradenham)
carl.etholen@wycombe.gov.uk

Farmer, Ray (LD - Ryemead)
ray.farmer@wycombe.gov.uk

Gaffney, Ron (CON - Hazlemere North)
ron.gaffney@wycombe.gov.uk

Graham, Sebert (LAB - Oakridge and Castlefield)
sebert.graham@wycombe.gov.uk

Green, Tony (CON - Terriers and Amersham Hill)
tony.green@wycombe.gov.uk

Hall, Gary (CON - The Risboroughs)
gary.hall@wycombe.gov.uk

Hanif, Mohammed (LAB - Oakridge and Castlefield)
mohammed.hanif@wycombe.gov.uk

Harris, Mark (CON - Greater Marlow)
mark.harris@wycombe.gov.uk

Harriss, Clive (CON - Icknield)
clive.harriss@wycombe.gov.uk

Hashmi, Muhammad Abdullah (LAB - Bowerdean)
abdullah.hashmi@wycombe.gov.uk

Hill, Alan (CON - Abbey)
alan.hill@wycombe.gov.uk

Hussain, Mahboob (CON - Abbey)
mahboob.hussain@wycombe.gov.uk

Hussain, Maz (CON - Disraeli)
maz.hussain@wycombe.gov.uk

Hussain, Arif (CON - Terriers and Amersham Hill)
arif.hussain@wycombe.gov.uk

Johncock, David (CON - Flackwell Heath and Little Marlow)
david.johncock@wycombe.gov.uk

Jones, Audrey (CON - Greater Hughenden)
audrey.jones@wycombe.gov.uk

Knight, Matt (IND - Micklefield)
matt.knight@wycombe.gov.uk

Knights, David (CON - The Risboroughs)
david.knights@wycombe.gov.uk

Langley, Julia (CON - The Wooburns)
julia.langley@wycombe.gov.uk

Lee, Tony (CON - Bourne End cum Hedsor)
tony.lee@wycombe.gov.uk

Mallen, Wendy (CON - Downley and Plomer Hill)
wendy.mallen@wycombe.gov.uk

Marshall, Neil (CON - Marlow North and West)
neil.marshall@wycombe.gov.uk

WYCOMBE

McCarthy, Hugh (CON - Hazlemere North)
hugh.mccarthy@wycombe.gov.uk

McEnnis, Ian (CON - Chiltern Rise)
ian.mcennis@wycombe.gov.uk

Newman, Richard (CON - Hazlemere South)
richard.newman@wycombe.gov.uk

Oliver, Catherine (CON - Hazlemere South)
catherine.oliver@wycombe.gov.uk

Pearce, Brian (IND - Booker and Cressex)
brian.pearce@wycombe.gov.uk

Peart, Graham (CON - Lacey Green, Speen and The Hampdens)
graham.peart@wycombe.gov.uk

Raja, Rafiq (LAB - Bowerdean)
rafiq.raja@wycombe.gov.uk

Raja, Sarfaraz (CON - Terriers and Amersham Hill)
sarfaraz.raja@wycombe.gov.uk

Saddique, Saeed (CON - Stokenchurch and Radnage)
saeed.saddique@wycombe.gov.uk

Savage, John (CON - Flackwell Heath and Little Marlow)
john.savage@wycombe.gov.uk

Scott, Richard (CON - Marlow South East)
richard.scott@wycombe.gov.uk

Shakespeare, David (CON - Tylers Green and Loudwater)
david.shakespeare@wycombe.gov.uk

Teesdale, Jean (CON - Chiltern Rise)
jean.teesdale@wycombe.gov.uk

Teesdale, Nigel (CON - Sands)
nigel.teesdale@wycombe.gov.uk

Turner, Paul (CON - Downley and Plomer Hill)
paul.turner@wycombe.gov.uk

Turner, Alan (CON - The Risboroughs)
alan.turner@wycombe.gov.uk

Wassell, Julia (IND - Totteridge)
julia.wassell@wycombe.gov.uk

Watson, David (CON - Flackwell Heath and Little Marlow)
david.watson@wycombe.gov.uk

Whitehead, Chris (CON - Hambleden Valley)
chris.whitehead@wycombe.gov.uk

Wilson, Roger (CON - Marlow North and West)
roger.wilson@wycombe.gov.uk

Wood, Lawrence (CON - Tylers Green and Loudwater)
lawrence.wood@wycombe.gov.uk

POLITICAL COMPOSITION
CON: 49, LAB: 6, IND: 4, LD: 1

COMMITTEE CHAIRS

Licensing: Mr Alan Hill

Planning: Mr Alan Hill

Wyre   D

Wyre Borough Council, Civic Centre, Breck Road, Poulton-le-Fylde FY6 7PU
☎ 01253 891000 ⬧ mailroom@wyrebc.gov.uk 🖥 www.wyrebc.gov.uk

FACTS AND FIGURES
Parliamentary Constituencies: Wyre and Preston North
EU Constituencies: North West
Election Frequency: Elections are of whole council

PRINCIPAL OFFICERS

Chief Executive: Mr Garry Payne, Chief Executive, Civic Centre, Breck Road, Poulton-le-Fylde FY6 7PU ☎ 01253 887500
⬧ garry.payne@wyre.gov.uk

Senior Management: Mr Mark Billington, Service Director - People & Places, Civic Centre, Breck Road, Poulton-le-Fylde FY6 7PU ☎ 01253 887508 ⬧ mark.billington@wyre.gov.uk

Senior Management: Mr Mark Broadhurst, Service Director - Health & Wellbeing, Civic Centre, Breck Road, Poulton-le-Fylde FY6 7PU ☎ 01253 887433 ⬧ mark.broadhurst@wyre.gov.uk

Senior Management: Mrs Marianne Hesketh, Service Director - Performance & Innovation, Civic Centre, Breck Road, Poulton-le-Fylde FY6 7PU ☎ 01253 887350; 01253 887350
⬧ marianne.hesketh@wyre.gov.uk; marianne.hesketh@wyre.gov.uk

Senior Management: Ms Clare James, Head of Finance, Civic Centre, Breck Road, Poulton-le-Fylde FY6 7PU ☎ 01253 887308
⬧ clare.james@wyre.gov.uk

Building Control: Ms Maria Blundy, Head of Built Environment, Civic Centre, Breck Road, Poulton-le-Fylde FY6 7PU
☎ 01253 887246 ⬧ maria.blundy@wyre.gov.uk

Community Safety: Ms Jane Murray, Community Safety Officer, Civic Centre, Breck Road, Poulton-le-Fylde FY6 7PU
☎ 01253 887292 ⬧ jane.murray@wyre.gov.uk

Corporate Services: Mr Corporate Support Team, Corporate Support, Civic Centre, Breck Road, Poulton-le-Fylde FY6 7PU
☎ 01253 887621 ⬧ corporatesupport@wyre.gov.uk

Customer Service: Mr Peter Mason, Head of Contact Centre, Civic Centre, Breck Road, Poulton-le-Fylde FY6 7PU
☎ 01253 887530 ⬧ peter.mason@wyre.gov.uk

Economic Development: Mrs Karen Stringer, Senior Economic Development Officer, Civic Centre, Breck Road, Poulton-le-Fylde FY6 7PU ☎ 01253 887532 ⬧ karen.stringer@wyre.gov.uk

E-Government: Ms Joanne Billington, Head of Governance, Civic Centre, Breck Road, Poulton-le-Fylde FY6 7PU ☎ 01253 887372
⬧ joanne.billington@wyre.gov.uk

Electoral Registration: Ms Joanne Porter, Electoral Services & Information Governance Manager, Civic Centre, Breck Road, Poulton-le-Fylde FY6 7PU ☎ 01253 887503
⬧ joanne.porter@wyre.gov.uk

Emergency Planning: Mr John Blundell, Depot Manager / Emergency Planning Officer, Civic Centre, Breck Road, Poulton-le-Fylde FY6 7PU ☎ 01253 887531 ⬧ john.blundell@wyre.gov.uk

Energy Management: Mr Mark Broadhurst, Service Director - Health & Wellbeing, Civic Centre, Breck Road, Poulton-le-Fylde FY6 7PU ☎ 01253 887433 ✆ mark.broadhurst@wyre.gov.uk

Environmental Health: Mrs Corinne Mason, Senior Environmental Health Officer, Civic Centre, Breck Road, Poulton-le-Fylde FY6 7PU ☎ 01253 887207 ✆ corinne.mason@wyre.gov.uk

European Liaison: Mrs Karen Stringer, Senior Economic Development Officer, Civic Centre, Breck Road, Poulton-le-Fylde FY6 7PU ☎ 01253 887532 ✆ karen.stringer@wyre.gov.uk

Finance: Ms Clare James, Head of Finance, Civic Centre, Breck Road, Poulton-le-Fylde FY6 7PU ☎ 01253 887308 ✆ clare.james@wyre.gov.uk

Fleet Management: Mr John Blundell, Depot Manager / Emergency Planning Officer, Civic Centre, Breck Road, Poulton-le-Fylde FY6 7PU ☎ 01253 887531 ✆ john.blundell@wyre.gov.uk

Grounds Maintenance: Mr Mark Billington, Service Director - People & Places, Civic Centre, Breck Road, Poulton-le-Fylde FY6 7PU ☎ 01253 887508 ✆ mark.billington@wyre.gov.uk

Health and Safety: Ms Kate Holmes, Health & Safety Advisor, Civic Centre, Breck Road, Poulton-le-Fylde FY6 7PU ☎ 01253 887508 ✆ kate.holmes@wyre.gov.uk

Home Energy Conservation: Mr Mark Broadhurst, Service Director - Health & Wellbeing, Civic Centre, Breck Road, Poulton-le-Fylde FY6 7PU ☎ 01253 887433 ✆ mark.broadhurst@wyre.gov.uk

Housing: Mr Mark Broadhurst, Service Director - Health & Wellbeing, Civic Centre, Breck Road, Poulton-le-Fylde FY6 7PU ☎ 01253 887433 ✆ mark.broadhurst@wyre.gov.uk

Housing Maintenance: Mr Mark Broadhurst, Service Director - Health & Wellbeing, Civic Centre, Breck Road, Poulton-le-Fylde FY6 7PU ☎ 01253 887433 ✆ mark.broadhurst@wyre.gov.uk

Legal: Ms Mary Grimshaw, Senior Solicitor, Civic Centre, Breck Road, Poulton-le-Fylde FY6 7PU ☎ 01253 887214 ✆ mary.grimshaw@wyre.gov.uk

Leisure and Cultural Services: Mr Ian Munro, Head of Culture, Leisure & Tourism, Civic Centre, Breck Road, Poulton-le-Fylde FY6 7PU ☎ 01253 887208 ✆ ian.munro@wyre.gov.uk

Licensing: Ms Christa Ferguson, Licensing Manager, Civic Centre, Breck Road, Poulton-le-Fylde FY6 7PU ☎ 01253 887476 ✆ christa.ferguson@wyre.gov.uk

Personnel / HR: Mrs Liesl Hadgraft, Head of Business Support, Civic Centre, Breck Road, Poulton-le-Fylde FY6 7PU ☎ 01253 887316 ✆ liesl.hadgraft@wyre.gov.uk

Planning: Mr David Thow, Head of Planning Services, Civic Centre, Breck Road, Poulton-le-Fylde FY6 7PU ☎ 01253 887287 ✆ david.thow@wyre.gov.uk

Procurement: Mr Allan Williams, Procurement Officer, Civic Centre, Breck Road, Poulton-le-Fylde FY6 7PU ☎ 01253 887440 ✆ allan.williams@wyre.gov.uk

Recycling & Waste Minimisation: Ms Ruth Hunter, Waste & Recycling Manager, Civic Centre, Breck Road, Poulton-le-Fylde FY6 7PU ☎ 01253 887478 ✆ ruth.hunter@wyre.gov.uk

Street Scene: Mr Mark Billington, Service Director - People & Places, Civic Centre, Breck Road, Poulton-le-Fylde FY6 7PU ☎ 01253 887508 ✆ mark.billington@wyre.gov.uk

Tourism: Ms Alexandra Holt, Tourism Development Officer, Civic Centre, Breck Road, Poulton-le-Fylde FY6 7PU ☎ 01253 887445 ✆ alexandra.holt@wyre.gov.uk

Waste Management: Ms Ruth Hunter, Waste & Recycling Manager, Civic Centre, Breck Road, Poulton-le-Fylde FY6 7PU ☎ 01253 887478 ✆ ruth.hunter@wyre.gov.uk

Children's Play Areas: Mr Mark Billington, Service Director - People & Places, Civic Centre, Breck Road, Poulton-le-Fylde FY6 7PU ☎ 01253 887508 ✆ mark.billington@wyre.gov.uk

COUNCILLORS

Mayor: Lees, Terry (LAB - Bourne)
terry.lees@wyre.gov.uk

Deputy Mayor: Anderton, Emma (LAB - Warren)
emma.anderton@wyre.gov.uk

Leader of the Council: Gibson, Peter (CON - Breck)
peter.gibson@wyre.gov.uk

Deputy Leader of the Council: Bowen, Lynne (CON - Hambleton and Stalmine)
lynne.bowen@wyre.gov.uk

Group Leader: Duffy, Ruth (LAB - Mount)

Amos, Ian (CON - Cleveleys Park)
ianl.amos@wyre.gov.uk

Amos, Rita (CON - Cleveleys Park)
rita.amos@wyre.gov.uk

Anderton, Marge (LAB - Warren)
marge.anderton@wyre.gov.uk

Atkins, Dulcie (CON - Garstang)
datkins@wyrebc.gov.uk

Ballard, Howard (CON - Bourne)
howard.ballard@wyre.gov.uk

Balmain, Tom (CON - Garstang)
tom.balmain@wyre.gov.uk

Barrowclough, Michael (LAB - Rossall)
michael.barrowclough@wyre.gov.uk

Beavers, Lorraine (LAB - Rossall)
lorraine.beavers@wyre.gov.uk

Berry, Roger (CON - Hardhorn with Highcross)
roger.berry@wyre.gov.uk

Birch, Colette (CON - Tithebarn)
colette.birch@wyre.gov.uk

Birch, Barry (CON - Hardhorn with Highcross)
barry.birch@wyre.gov.uk

WYRE

Bridge, Simon (CON - Hardhorn with Highcross)
simon.bridge@wyre.gov.uk

Catterall, Susan (CON - Great Eccleston)
sue.catterall@wyre.gov.uk

Collinson, Alice (CON - Garstang)
alice.collinson@wyre.gov.uk

Duffy, Ian (LAB - Mount)
ian.duffy@wyre.gov.uk

Fail, Rob (LAB - Jubilee)
rob.fail@wyre.gov.uk

Greenhough, Ron (CON - Carleton)
ron.greenhough@wyre.gov.uk

Henderson, David (CON - Breck)
david.henderson@wyre.gov.uk

Hodgkinson, John (CON - Jubilee)
john.hodgkinson@wyre.gov.uk

Holden, Graham (CON - Pilling)
graham.holden@wyre.gov.uk

Ibison, John (CON - Calder)
john.ibison@wyre.gov.uk

Ingham, Tom (CON - Marsh Mill)
tom.ingham@wyre.gov.uk

Jones, Kerry (CON - Stanah)
kerry.jones@wyre.gov.uk

Kay, Andrea (CON - Pheasant's Wood)
andrea.kay@wyre.gov.uk

McKay, Lesley (CON - Tithebarn)
lesley.mckay@wyre.gov.uk

Moon, Paul (CON - Preesall)
paul.moon@wyre.gov.uk

Murphy, Pete (CON - Brock with Catterall)
pete.murphy@wyre.gov.uk

Orme, Philip (CON - Preesall)
philip.orme@wyre.gov.uk

Ormrod, Patsy (CON - Victoria and Norcross)
patsy.ormrod@wyre.gov.uk

Pimbley, Sue (CON - Great Eccleston)
sue.pimbley@wyre.gov.uk

Reeves, Natalie (LAB - Bourne)
natalie.reeves@wyre.gov.uk

Robinson, Julie (CON - Hambleton and Stalmine)
julie.robinson@wyre.gov.uk

Shewan, Ronald (LAB - Pharos)
ron.shewan@wyre.gov.uk

Smith, Christine (LAB - Park)
christine.smith@wyre.gov.uk

Stephenson, Brian (LAB - Park)
brian.stephenson@wyre.gov.uk

Stephenson, Evelyn (LAB - Pharos)
evelyn.stephenson@wyre.gov.uk

Taylor, Ted (LAB - Rossall)
ted.taylor@wyre.gov.uk

Taylor, Vivien (CON - Preesall)
vivien.taylor@wyre.gov.uk

Turner, Ann (CON - Marsh Mill)
ann.turner@wyre.gov.uk

Turner, Shaun (CON - Brock with Catterall)
shaun.turner@wyre.gov.uk

Vincent, Matthew (CON - Stanah)
matthew.vincent@wyre.gov.uk

Vincent, Michael (CON - Carleton)
michael.vincent@wyre.gov.uk

Vincent, Alan (CON - Victoria and Norcross)
alanvincent@vslaw.co.uk

Walmsley, Lynn (CON - Marsh Mill)
lynn.walmsley@wyre.gov.uk

Wilson, Val (CON - Wyresdale)
val.wilson@wyre.gov.uk

POLITICAL COMPOSITION
CON: 36, LAB: 14

Wyre Forest   D

Wyre Forest District Council, Civic Centre, New Street,
Stourport-on-Severn DY13 8UJ
☎ 01562 732928 🖷 01562 67673
📧 communications@wyreforestdc.gov.uk 🖳 www.wyreforestdc.gov.uk

FACTS AND FIGURES
Parliamentary Constituencies: Wyre Forest
EU Constituencies: West Midlands
Election Frequency: Elections are by thirds

PRINCIPAL OFFICERS

Chief Executive: Mr Ian Miller, Chief Executive, Wyre Forest
House, Finepoint Way, Kidderminster DY11 7WF ☎ 01562 732700
📧 ian.miller@wyreforestdc.gov.uk

Senior Management: Ms Linda Collis, Director - Community
Wellbeing & Environment, Wyre Forest House, Finepoint Way,
Kidderminster DY11 7WF ☎ 01562 732900
📧 linda.collis@wyreforestdc.gov.uk

Senior Management: Mr Mike Parker, Director - Economic
Prosperity & Place, Wyre Forest House, Finepoint Way,
Kidderminster DY11 7WF ☎ 01562 732500
📧 mike.parker@wyreforestdc.gov.uk

Building Control: Mr Adrian Wyre, Principal Building Control
Surveyor, The Council House, Burcot Lane, Bromsgrove B60 1AA
☎ 01527 881350 📧 a.wyre@bromsgroveandredditch.gov.uk

PR / Communications: Mrs Jane Doyle, Communications Officer,
Wyre Forest House, Finepoint Way, Kidderminster DY11 7WF
☎ 01562 732928 📧 jane.doyle@wyreforestdc.gov.uk

PR / Communications: Mrs Suzanne Johnston-Hubbold,
Communications Officer, Wyre Forest House, Finepoint Way,
Kidderminster DY11 7WF ☎ 01562 73298 📧 suzanne.johnston-
hubbold@wyreforestdc.gov.uk

Community Planning: Ms Alison Braithwaite, Head of Transformation & Communications, Wyre Forest House, Finepoint Way, Kidderminster DY11 7WF ☎ 01562 732781, 01299 879688 ✆ alison.braithwaite@wyreforestdc.gov.uk

Community Safety: Mrs Kathryn Washington, Community Safety & Partnerships Officer, Wyre Forest House, Finepoint Way, Kidderminster DY11 7WF ☎ 01562 732956, 01562 879688 ✆ kathryn.washington@wyreforestdc.gov.uk

Computer Management: Mr Dave Johnson, ICT Manager, Wyre Forest House, Finepoint Way, Kidderminster DY11 7WF ☎ 01562 732138 ✆ dave.johnson@wyreforestdc.gov.uk

Contracts: Mrs Sally Tallon, Contracts & Freedom of Information Solicitor, Wyre Forest House, Finepoint Way, Kidderminster DY11 7WF ☎ 01562 732775 ✆ sally.tallon@wyreforestdc.gov.uk

Corporate Services: Mrs Caroline Newlands, Solicitor to the Council, Wyre Forest House, Finepoint Way, Kidderminster DY11 7WF ☎ 01562 732715 ✆ caroline.newlands@wyreforestdc.gov.uk

Customer Service: Mrs Lucy Wright, Corporate Customer Development Manager, Town Hall, Vicar Street, Kidderminster DY10 1DA ☎ 01562 732948 ✆ lucy.wright@wyreforestdc.gov.uk

Economic Development: Mr Dean Piper, Head of Economic Development & Regeneration - North Worcestershire, Wyre Forest House, Finepoint Way, Kidderminster DY11 7WF ☎ 01562 932192 ✆ dean.piper@nwedr.org.uk

Electoral Registration: Ms Alison Braithwaite, Head of Transformation & Communications, Wyre Forest House, Finepoint Way, Kidderminster DY11 7WF ☎ 01562 732781, 01299 879688 ✆ alison.braithwaite@wyreforestdc.gov.uk

Emergency Planning: Ms Rebecca Pritchett, North Worcestershire Civil Contingencies & Resilience Manager, Wyre Forest House, Finepoint Way, Kidderminster DY11 7WF ☎ 01562 732711 ✆ rebecca.pritchett@wyreforestdc.gov.uk

Environmental Health: Mr Simon Wilkes, Head of Regulatory Services, Wyatt House, Farrier Street, Worcester WR1 3BH ✆ simon.wilkes@worcsregservices.gov.uk

Estates, Property & Valuation: Ms Victoria Bendall, Estates Surveyor, Wyre Forest House, Finepoint Way, Kidderminster DY11 7WF ☎ 01562 732703 ✆ victoria.bendall@wyreforestdc.gov.uk

Estates, Property & Valuation: Ms Lucy Lomas, Estates Surveyor, Civic Centre, New Street, Stourport-on-Severn DY13 8UJ ☎ 01562 732706 ✆ lucy.lomas@wyreforestdc.gov.uk

Facilities: Mrs Elaine Brookes, Facilities & Asset Manager, Wyre Forest House, Finepoint Way, Kidderminster DY11 7WF ☎ 01562 732797 ✆ elaine.brookes@wyreforestdc.gov.uk

Finance: Mrs Tracey Southall, Chief Financial Officer, Wyre Forest House, Finepoint Way, Kidderminster DY11 7WF ☎ 01562 732100 ✆ tracey.southall@wyreforestdc.gov.uk

Fleet Management: Mr Steve Brant, Operations Manager, Green Street, Kidderminster DY10 1HA ☎ 01562 732922 ✆ steve.brant@wyreforestdc.gov.uk

Grounds Maintenance: Mr Joe Scully, Parks & Open Spaces Manager, Green Street, Kidderminster DY10 1HA ☎ 01562 732981 ✆ joe.scully@wyreforestdc.gov.uk

Health and Safety: Mr Steve Brant, Operations Manager, Green Street, Kidderminster DY10 1HA ☎ 01562 732922 ✆ steve.brant@wyreforestdc.gov.uk

Home Energy Conservation: Ms Jenny Moreton, Principal Health & Sustainability Officer, Wyre Forest House, Finepoint Way, Kidderminster DY11 7WF ☎ 01562 732569 ✆ jennifer.moreton@wyreforestdc.gov.uk

Housing: Mrs Kate Bailey, Strategic Housing Services Manager, Wyre Forest House, Finepoint Way, Kidderminster DY11 7WF ☎ 01562 732560 ✆ kate.bailey@wyreforestdc.gov.uk

Legal: Mrs Caroline Newlands, Solicitor to the Council, Wyre Forest House, Finepoint Way, Kidderminster DY11 7WF ☎ 01562 732715 ✆ caroline.newlands@wyreforestdc.gov.uk

Leisure and Cultural Services: Ms Linda Collis, Director - Community Wellbeing & Environment, Wyre Forest House, Finepoint Way, Kidderminster DY11 7WF ☎ 01562 732900 ✆ linda.collis@wyreforestdc.gov.uk

Leisure and Cultural Services: Ms Kay Higman, Cultural Services Manager, Wyre Forest House, Finepoint Way, Kidderminster DY11 7WF ☎ 01562 732902 ✆ kay.higman@wyreforestdc.gov.uk

Licensing: Mr Simon Wilkes, Head of Regulatory Services, Wyatt House, Farrier Street, Worcester WR1 3BH ✆ simon.wilkes@worcsregservices.gov.uk

Lottery Funding, Charity and Voluntary: Mrs Lesley Fox, Community Development Manager, Wyre Forest House, Finepoint Way, Kidderminster DY11 7WF ☎ 01562 732976 ✆ lesley.fox@wyreforestdc.gov.uk

Member Services: Ms Alison Braithwaite, Head of Transformation & Communications, Wyre Forest House, Finepoint Way, Kidderminster DY11 7WF ☎ 01562 732781, 01299 879688 ✆ alison.braithwaite@wyreforestdc.gov.uk

Parking: Mr Steve Brant, Operations Manager, Green Street, Kidderminster DY10 1HA ☎ 01562 732922 ✆ steve.brant@wyreforestdc.gov.uk

Personnel / HR: Ms Rachael Simpson, Senior HR Advisor, Civic Centre, New Street, Stourport-on-Severn DY13 8UJ ☎ 01562 732701 ✆ rachael.simpson@wyreforestdc.gov.uk

Planning: Mr John Baggott, Development Manager, Wyre Forest House, Finepoint Way, Kidderminster DY11 7WF ☎ 01562 732515 ✆ john.baggott@wyreforestdc.gov.uk

WYRE FOREST

Procurement: Ms Kathryn Pearsall, Principal Accountant, Wyre Forest House, Finepoint Way, Kidderminster DY11 7WF
⌀ kathryn.pearsall@wyreforestdc.gov.uk

Recycling & Waste Minimisation: Mr Steve Brant, Operations Manager, Wyre Forest House, Finepoint Way, Kidderminster DY11 7WF ☎ 01562 732922 ⌀ steve.brant@wyreforestdc.gov.uk

Regeneration: Mr Dean Piper, Head of Economic Development & Regeneration - North Worcestershire, Wyre Forest House, Finepoint Way, Kidderminster DY11 7WF ☎ 01562 932192
⌀ dean.piper@nwedr.org.uk

Street Scene: Mr Steve Brant, Operations Manager, Green Street, Kidderminster DY10 1HA ☎ 01562 732922
⌀ steve.brant@wyreforestdc.gov.uk

Sustainable Communities: Mr Mike Parker, Director - Economic Prosperity & Place, Wyre Forest House, Finepoint Way, Kidderminster DY11 7WF ☎ 01562 732500
⌀ mike.parker@wyreforestdc.gov.uk

Sustainable Development: Mr Mike Parker, Director - Economic Prosperity & Place, Wyre Forest House, Finepoint Way, Kidderminster DY11 7WF ☎ 01562 732500
⌀ mike.parker@wyreforestdc.gov.uk

Tourism: Mr Steve Singleton, Economic Development Manager - North Worcestershire, Wyre Forest House, Finepoint Way, Kidderminster DY11 7WF ☎ 01562 732168
⌀ steve.singleton@nwedr.org.uk

Town Centre: Mr Peter Michael, Town Centre Manager, Wyre Forest House, Finepoint Way, Kidderminster DY11 7WF
☎ 01562 732534 ⌀ peter.michael@wyreforestdc.gov.uk

Waste Collection and Disposal: Mr Steve Brant, Operations Manager, Green Street, Kidderminster DY10 1HA ☎ 01562 732922
⌀ steve.brant@wyreforestdc.gov.uk

Waste Management: Mr Steve Brant, Operations Manager, Green Street, Kidderminster DY10 1HA ☎ 01562 732922
⌀ steve.brant@wyreforestdc.gov.uk

Children's Play Areas: Ms Kay Higman, Cultural Services Manager, Wyre Forest House, Finepoint Way, Kidderminster DY11 7WF ☎ 01562 732902 ⌀ kay.higman@wyreforestdc.gov.uk

COUNCILLORS

Chair: Bishop, Rose (CON - Offmore & Comberton)
rose.bishop@wyreforestdc.gov.uk

Leader of the Council: Hart, Marcus (CON - Wyre Forest Rural)
stephen.williams@wyreforestdc.gov.uk

Deputy Leader of the Council: Hardiman, Ian (CON - Wyre Forest Rural)
ian.hardiman@wyreforestdc.gov.uk

Aston, John (IND - Aggborough & Spennells)
john.aston@wyreforestdc.gov.uk

Baker, Jeffrey (CON - Franche & Habberley North)
jeff.baker@wyreforestdc.gov.uk

Campion, John-Paul (CON - Bewdley & Rock)
john.campion@wyreforestdc.gov.uk

Chambers, Sally Jane (CON - Foley Park & Hoobrook)
sally.chambers@wyreforestdc.gov.uk

Clee, Stephen (CON - Bewdley & Rock)
sjclee@tinyonline.co.uk

Desmond, John (CON - Broadwaters)
john.desmond@wyreforestdc.gov.uk

Desmond, Nathan (CON - Foley Park & Hoobrook)
nathan.desmond@wyreforestdc.gov.uk

Dyke, Helen (IND - Aggborough & Spennells)
helen.dyke@wyreforestdc.gov.uk

Dyke, Peter (IND - Aggborough & Spennells)
peter.dyke@wyreforestdc.gov.uk

Fearn, Sara (CON - Mitton)
sara.fearn@wyreforest.gov.uk

Gale, Nicky (CON - Foley Park & Hoobrook)
nicky.gale@wyreforestdc.gov.uk

Hart, John (CON - Blakebrook & Habberley South)
john.hart@wyreforestdc.gov.uk

Henderson, Kenneth (CON - Areley Kings & Riverside)
ken.henderson@wyreforestdc.gov.uk

Higgs, Vi (LAB - Areley Kings & Riverside)

Hingley, Anne (CON - Franche & Habberley North)
anne.hingley@wyreforestdc.gov.uk

Knowles, Nigel (LAB - Franche & Habberley North)
nigelknowlesbewdley@hotmail.com

Little, David (CON - Lickhill)
david.little@wyreforestdc.gov.uk

Martin, Nicky (IND - Mitton)
nicky.martin@wyreforestdc.gov.uk

Miah, Shazu (LD - Offmore & Comberton)
shazu.miah@wyreforestdc.gov.uk

Oborski, Fran (LD - Offmore & Comberton)
fran.oborski@wyreforestdc.gov.uk

Onslow, Tracey (CON - Blakewood & Habberley South)
tracey.onslow@wyreforestdc.gov.uk

Rayner, Mary (IND - Broadwaters)
mary.rayner@wyreforestdc.gov.uk

Rogers, Chris (CON - Mitton)
chris.rogers@wyreforestdc.gov.uk

Shaw, James (LAB - Areley Kings & Riverside)
cllrjshaw@hotmail.com

Smith, Juliet (CON - Blakebrook & Habberley South)
juliet.smith@wyreforestdc.gov.uk

Vale, Rebecca (CON - Wribbenhall & Arley)
becky.vale@wyreforestdc.gov.uk

Walker, Steven (LAB - Broadwaters)
steven.walker@wyreforestdc.gov.uk

Williams, Stephen (CON - Wyre Forest Rural)
stephen.williams@wyreforestdc.gov.uk

Wilson, Rod (CON - Bewdley & Rock)
rod.wilson@wyreforestdc.gov.uk

Yarranton, Gordon (CON - Wribbenhall & Arley)
gordon.yarranton@wyreforestdc.gov.uk

POLITICAL COMPOSITION
CON: 22, IND: 5, LAB: 4, LD: 2

York, City of   U

City of York Council, West Offices, Station Rise, York YO1 6GA
☎ 01904 551550 ⁀ ycc@york.gov.uk ⌨ www.york.gov.uk

FACTS AND FIGURES
Parliamentary Constituencies: York Central, York Outer
EU Constituencies: Yorkshire and the Humber
Election Frequency: Elections are of whole council

PRINCIPAL OFFICERS

Chief Executive: Ms Mary Weastell, Chief Executive, West Offices, Station Rise, York YO1 6GA ☎ 01904 552000 ⁀ mary.weastell@york.gov.uk

Deputy Chief Executive: Mr Ian Floyd, Director - Customer & Business Support Services, West Offices, Station Rise, York YO1 6GA ☎ 01904 552909 ⁀ ian.floyd@york.gov.uk

Senior Management: Mr John Stonehouse, Corporate Director - Children's Services & Education, West Offices, Station Rise, York YO1 6GA ⁀ john.stonehouse@york.gov.uk

Senior Management: Mr Martin Farran, Director - Adult Care, West Offices, Station Rise, York YO1 6GA ☎ 01904 554045 ⁀ martin.farran@york.gov.uk

Senior Management: Ms Sharon Stolz, Director - Public Health, West Offices, Station Rise, York YO1 6GA ⁀ john.stonehouse@york.gov.uk

Senior Management: Mr John Stonehouse, Corporate Director - Children's Services & Education, West Offices, Station Rise, York YO1 6GA ⁀ john.stonehouse@york.gov.uk

Architect, Building / Property Services: Ms Tracey Carter, Assistant Director - Finance, Asset Management & Procurement, West Offices, Station Rise, York YO1 6GA ☎ 01904 553419 ⁀ tracey.carter@york.gov.uk

Building Control: Mr John Fowler, CYC Chief Building Control Officer, West Offices, Station Rise, York YO1 6GA ☎ 01423 500600 ext. 56597 ⁀ john.fowler@harrogate.gov.uk

Children / Youth Services: Mr Steve Flatley, Connexions Service Manager, West Offices, Station Rise, York YO1 6GA ☎ 01904 552367 ⁀ steve.flatley@york.gov.uk

Children / Youth Services: Mr Eoin Rush, Assistant Director - Children's Specialist Services, West Offices, Station Rise, York YO1 6GA ☎ 01904 554212 ⁀ eoin.rush@york.gov.uk

Civil Registration: Mr Robert Livesey, Registration Service Manager, Register Office, 56 Bootham, York YO30 7DA ☎ 01904 553194, 01904 638090 ⁀ robert.livesey@york.gov.uk

PR / Communications: Mrs Debbie Manson, Head of Communications, West Offices, Station Rise, York YO1 6GA ☎ 01904 552005 ⁀ debbie.manson@york.gov.uk

Community Planning: Mr Charlie Croft, Assistant Director - Communities, Culture & Public Realm, West Offices, Station Rise, York YO1 6GA ☎ 01904 553371 ⁀ charlie.croft@york.gov.uk

Community Safety: Ms Jane Mowat, Head of Community Safety, West Offices, Station Rise, York YO1 6GA ☎ 01904 555742, 01904 669077 ⁀ jane.mowat@york.gov.uk

Community Safety: Mr Steve Waddington, Assistant Director - Housing & Community Safety, West Offices, Station Rise, York YO1 6GA ☎ 01904 554016 ⁀ steve.waddington@york.gov.uk

Computer Management: Mr Roy Grant, Shared Head of ICT, West Offices, Station Rise, York YO1 6GA ☎ 01423 500600 ext. 58560 ⁀ roy.grant@harrogate.gov.uk

Consumer Protection and Trading Standards: Mr Matt Boxall, Trading Standards Manager, West Offices, Station Rise, York YO1 6GA ☎ 01904 551528 ⁀ matthew.boxall@york.gov.uk

Consumer Protection and Trading Standards: Mr Steve Waddington, Assistant Director - Housing & Community Safety, West Offices, Station Rise, York YO1 6GA ☎ 01904 554016 ⁀ steve.waddington@york.gov.uk

Contracts: Mr David Walker, Head of Customer, Resident & Exchequer Services, West Offices, Station Rise, York YO1 6GA ☎ 01904 552261 ⁀ david.walker@york.gov.uk

Customer Service: Ms Pauline Stuchfield, Assistant Director - Customers & Business Support Services, West Offices, Station Rise, York YO1 6GA ☎ 01904 551706 ⁀ pauline.stuchfield@york.gov.uk

Economic Development: Mr Neil Ferris, Corporate Director - Economy & Place, West Offices, Station Rise, York YO1 6GA ⁀ neil.ferris@york.gov.uk

Education: Ms Maxine Squire, Principal Advisor, West Offices, Station Rise, York YO1 6GA ☎ 01904 553007 ⁀ maxine.squire@york.gov.uk

Electoral Registration: Mr Andrew Flecknor, Electoral Services Manager, West Offices, Station Rise, York YO1 6GA ☎ 01904 552032, 01904 551052 ⁀ andrew.flecknor@york.gov.uk

Emergency Planning: Mr Jim Breen, Emergency Planning Co-ordinator, West Offices, Station Rise, York YO1 6GA ☎ 01904 551003, 01224 551001 ⁀ jim.breen@york.gov.uk

Energy Management: Ms Jacqui Warren, Head of Design Conservation & Sustainable Development, West Offices, Station Rise, York YO1 6GA ☎ 01904 551666 ⁀ jacqueline.warren@york.gov.uk

YORK, CITY OF

Environmental / Technical Services: Mr Mike Slater, Assistant Director - Development Services, Planning & Regeneration, West Offices, Station Rise, York YO1 6GA ☎ 01904 551300 ⌨ michael.slater@york.gov.uk

Environmental Health: Mr Matt Boxall, Trading Standards Manager, West Offices, Station Rise, York YO1 6GA ☎ 01904 551528 ⌨ matthew.boxall@york.gov.uk

Estates, Property & Valuation: Mr Philip Callow, Head of Asset & Property Management, West Offices, Station Rise, York YO1 6GA ☎ 01904 553360, : 01904 553314 ⌨ philip.callow@york.gov.uk

Facilities: Mr Ian Asher, Head of Commissioning & Design Services, West Offices, Station Rise, York YO1 6GA ☎ 01904 553379 ⌨ ian.asher@york.gov.uk

Finance: Ms Tracey Carter, Assistant Director - Finance, Asset Management & Procurement, West Offices, Station Rise, York YO1 6GA ☎ 01904 553419 ⌨ tracey.carter@york.gov.uk

Fleet Management: Mr Neil Ferris, Acting Director - City & Environmental Services, West Offices, Station Rise, York YO1 6GA ☎ 01904 551448 ⌨ neil.ferris@york.gov.uk

Grounds Maintenance: Mr Russell Stone, Head of Operations, West Offices, Station Rise, York YO1 6GA ☎ 01904 553108 ⌨ russell.stone@york.gov.uk

Health and Safety: Ms Lesley Sharp, Health, Safety & Wellbeing Deputy Manager, West Offices, Station Rise, York YO1 6GA ☎ 01904 554387 ⌨ lesley.sharp@york.gov.uk

Highways: Mr Neil Ferris, Acting Director - City & Environmental Services, West Offices, Station Rise, York YO1 6GA ☎ 01904 551448 ⌨ neil.ferris@york.gov.uk

Home Energy Conservation: Ms Jacqui Warren, Head of Design Conservation & Sustainable Development, West Offices, Station Rise, York YO1 6GA ☎ 01904 551666 ⌨ jacqueline.warren@york.gov.uk

Housing: Mr Steve Waddington, Assistant Director - Housing & Community Safety, West Offices, Station Rise, York YO1 6GA ☎ 01904 554016 ⌨ steve.waddington@york.gov.uk

Housing Maintenance: Mr Tom Brittain, Head of Housing Services, West Offices, Station Rise, York YO1 6GA ☎ 01904 551262 ⌨ tom.brittain@york.gov.uk

Legal: Mr Andrew Docherty, Assistant Director - Governance & ICT, West Offices, Station Rise, York YO1 6GA ☎ 01904 551004 ⌨ andrew.docherty@york.gov.uk

Legal: Ms Melanie Perara, Deputy Head of Legal Services, West Offices, Station Rise, York YO1 6GA ☎ 01904 551087 ⌨ melanie.perara@york.gov.uk

Leisure and Cultural Services: Mr Charlie Croft, Assistant Director - Communities, Culture & Public Realm, West Offices, Station Rise, York YO1 6GA ☎ 01904 553371 ⌨ charlie.croft@york.gov.uk

Licensing: Mr Matt Boxall, Trading Standards Manager, West Offices, Station Rise, York YO1 6GA ☎ 01904 551528 ⌨ matthew.boxall@york.gov.uk

Lifelong Learning: Mr Charlie Croft, Assistant Director - Communities, Culture & Public Realm, West Offices, Station Rise, York YO1 6GA ☎ 01904 553371 ⌨ charlie.croft@york.gov.uk

Lighting: Mr Neil Ferris, Acting Director - City & Environmental Services, West Offices, Station Road, York YO1 6GA ☎ 01904 551448 ⌨ neil.ferris@york.gov.uk

Member Services: Ms Dawn Steel, Head of Civic & Democratic Services, West Offices, Station Rise, York YO1 6GA ☎ 01904 551030 ⌨ dawn.steel@york.gov.uk

Parking: Mr Andrew Laslett, Operations Manager, West Offices, Station Rise, York YO1 6GA ☎ 01904 553370 ⌨ andy.laslett@york.gov.uk

Personnel / HR: Ms Pauline Stuchfield, Assistant Director - Customers & Business Support Services, West Offices, Station Rise, York YO1 6GA ☎ 01904 551706 ⌨ pauline.stuchfield@york.gov.uk

Planning: Mr Jonathan Carr, Head of Development Management, West Offices, Station Rise, York YO1 6GA ☎ 01904 551303 ⌨ jonathan.carr@york.gov.uk

Planning: Mr Mike Slater, Assistant Director - Development Services, Planning & Regeneration, West Offices, Station Rise, York YO1 6GA ☎ 01904 551300 ⌨ michael.slater@york.gov.uk

Procurement: Ms Tracey Carter, Assistant Director - Finance, Asset Management & Procurement, West Offices, Station Rise, York YO1 6GA ☎ 01904 553419 ⌨ tracey.carter@york.gov.uk

Public Libraries: Mr Charlie Croft, Assistant Director - Communities, Culture & Public Realm, West Offices, Station Rise, York YO1 6GA ☎ 01904 553371 ⌨ charlie.croft@york.gov.uk

Regeneration: Mr Mike Slater, Assistant Director - Development Services, Planning & Regeneration, West Offices, Station Rise, York YO1 6GA ☎ 01904 551300 ⌨ michael.slater@york.gov.uk

Road Safety: Mr Andrew Bradley, Sustainable Transport Operations Manager, West Offices, Station Rise, York YO1 6GA ☎ 01904 551404 ⌨ andrew.bradley@york.gov.uk

Social Services (Adult): Mr Martin Farran, Director - Adult Care, West Offices, Station Rise, York YO1 6GA ☎ 01904 554045 ⌨ martin.farran@york.gov.uk

Social Services (Children): Mr Eoin Rush, Assistant Director - Children's Specialist Services, West Offices, Station Rise, York YO1 6GA ☎ 01904 554212 ⌨ eoin.rush@york.gov.uk

Public Health: Ms Julie Hotchkiss, Director - Public Health, West Offices, Station Rise, York YO1 6GA ☎ 01904 553224 ⌨ julie.hotchkiss@york.gov.uk

Staff Training: Mr Mark Bennett, Head of Business HR, West Offices, Station Rise, York YO1 6GA ☎ 01904 554518
✆ mark.bennett@york.gov.uk

Street Scene: Mr Russell Stone, Head of Operations, West Offices, Station Rise, York YO1 6GA ☎ 01904 553108
✆ russell.stone@york.gov.uk

Sustainable Communities: Mr Mike Slater, Assistant Director - Development Services, Planning & Regeneration, West Offices, Station Rise, York YO1 6GA ☎ 01904 551300
✆ michael.slater@york.gov.uk

Sustainable Development: Ms Jacqui Warren, Head of Design Conservation & Sustainable Development, West Offices, Station Rise, York YO1 6GA ☎ 01904 551666
✆ jacqueline.warren@york.gov.uk

Traffic Management: Mr Richard Bogg, Highways Development Manager, West Offices, Station Rise, York YO1 6GA
☎ 01904 551426 ✆ richard.bogg@york.gov.uk

Transport: Mr Tony Clarke, Head of Transport, West Offices, Station Rise, York YO1 6GA ☎ 01904 551641
✆ tony.clarke@york.gov.uk

Waste Collection and Disposal: Mr Russell Stone, Head of Operations, West Offices, Station Rise, York YO1 6GA
☎ 01904 553108 ✆ russell.stone@york.gov.uk

Waste Management: Mr Russell Stone, Head of Operations, West Offices, Station Rise, York YO1 6GA ☎ 01904 553108
✆ russell.stone@york.gov.uk

Children's Play Areas: Mr Russell Stone, Head of Operations, West Offices, Station Rise, York YO1 6GA ☎ 01904 553108
✆ russell.stone@york.gov.uk

COUNCILLORS

The Lord Mayor: Taylor, Dave (GRN - Fishergate)
cllr.dtaylor@york.gov.uk

Leader of the Council: Carr, David (CON - Copmanthorpe)
cllr.dcarr@york.gov.uk

Group Leader: Aspden, Keith (LD - Fulford and Heslington)
cllr.kaspden@york.gov.uk

Group Leader: D'Agorne, Andrew (GRN - Fishergate)
cllr.adagorne@york.gov.uk

Group Leader: Looker, Janet (LAB - Guildhall)
cllr.jlooker@york.gov.uk

Ayre, Nigel (LD - Heworth Without)
cllr.nayre@york.gov.uk

Barnes, Stuart (LAB - Acomb)
cllr.sbarnes@york.gov.uk

Barnes, Neil (LAB - Hull Road)
cllr.nbarnes@york.gov.uk

Boyce, Barbara (LAB - Heworth)
cllr.bboyce@york.gov.uk

Brooks, Jenny (CON - Osbaldwick and Derwent)
cllr.jbrooks@york.gov.uk

Cannon, Mary (LAB - Holgate)
cllr.mcannon@york.gov.uk

Craghill, Denise (GRN - Guildhall)
cllr.dcraghill@york.gov.uk

Crisp, Sonja (LAB - Holgate)
cllr.scrisp@york.gov.uk

Cullwick, Chris (LD - Huntington and New Earswick)
cllr.ccullwick@york.gov.uk

Cuthbertson, Ian (LD - Haxby and Wigginton)
cllr.icuthbertson@york.gov.uk

Derbyshire, Fiona (LAB - Holgate)
cllr.fderbyshire@york.gov.uk

Dew, Peter (CON - Rawcliffe and Clifton Without)
cllr.pdew@york.gov.uk

Doughty, Paul (CON - Strensall)
cllr.pdoughty@york.gov.uk

Douglas, Helen (CON - Strensall)
cllr.hdouglas@york.gov.uk

Fenton, Stephen (LD - Dringhouses and Woodthorpe)
cllr.sfenton@york.gov.uk

Flinders, James (LAB - Guildhall)
cllr.jflinders@york.gov.uk

Funnell, Christina (LAB - Heworth)
cllr.cfunnell@york.gov.uk

Galvin, John (CON - Bishopthorpe)
cllr.jgalvin@york.gov.uk

Gates, John (CON - Haxby and Wigginton)
cllr.jgates@york.gov.uk

Gillies, Ian (CON - Rural West York)
cllr.igillies@york.gov.uk

Gunnell, Julie (LAB - Micklegate)
cllr.jgunnell@york.gov.uk

Hayes, Johnny (IND - Micklegate)
cllr.jhayes@york.gov.uk

Hunter, Susan (LD - Westfield)
cllr.shunter@york.gov.uk

Jackson, Sheena (LD - Westfield)
cllr.sjackson@york.gov.uk

Kramm, Lars (GRN - Micklegate)
cllr.lkramm@york.gov.uk

Levene, David (LAB - Hull Road)
cllr.dlevene@york.gov.uk

Lisle, Sam (CON - Rawcliffe and Clifton Without)
cllr.slisle@york.gov.uk

Mason, Ashley (LD - Dringhouses and Woodthorpe)
cllr.amason@york.gov.uk

Mercer, Suzie (CON - Wheldrake)
cllr.smercer@york.gov.uk

Myers, Keith (CON - Acomb)
cllr.kmyers@york.gov.uk

Myers, Danny (LAB - Clifton)
cllr.dmyers@york.gov.uk

Orrell, Keith (LD - Huntington and New Earswick)
cllr.korrell@york.gov.uk

YORK, CITY OF

Rawlings, Stuart (CON - Rawcliffe and Clifton Without)
cllr.srawlings@york.gov.uk

Reid, Ann (LD - Dringhouses and Woodthorpe)
cllr.areid@york.gov.uk

Richardson, Tony (CON - Haxby and Wigginton)
cllr.trichardson@york.gov.uk

Runciman, Carol (LD - Huntington and New Earswick)
cllr.crunciman@york.gov.uk

Shepherd, Hilary (LAB - Hull Road)
cllr.hshepherd@york.gov.uk

Steward, Chris (CON - Rural West York)
cllr.csteward@york.gov.uk

Waller, Andrew (LD - Westfield)
cllr.awaller@york.gov.uk

Warters, Mark (IND - Osbaldwick and Derwent)
cllr.mwarters@york.gov.uk

Wells, Margeret (LAB - Clifton)
cllr.mwells@york.gov.uk

Williams, Dafydd (LAB - Heworth)
cllr.dwilliams@york.gov.uk

POLITICAL COMPOSITION
LAB: 15, CON: 14, LD: 12, GRN: 4, IND: 2

COMMITTEE CHAIRS

Health & Wellbeing: Ms Carol Runciman

Licensing: Ms Helen Douglas

Planning: Ms Ann Reid

INDEX